# Instructor's Solutions Manual
## Single Variable

### William Ardis
*Collin County Community College*

# Thomas' Calculus
## Twelfth Edition

### Based on the Original Work by

# George B. Thomas, Jr.
*Massachusetts Institute of Technology*

### as Revised by

# Maurice D. Weir
*Naval Postgraduate School*

# Joel Hass
*University of California, Davis*

**Addison-Wesley**
is an imprint of

The author and publisher of this book have used their best efforts in preparing this book. These efforts include the development, research, and testing of the theories and programs to determine their effectiveness. The author and publisher make no warranty of any kind, expressed or implied, with regard to these programs or the documentation contained in this book. The author and publisher shall not be liable in any event for incidental or consequential damages in connection with, or arising out of, the furnishing, performance, or use of these programs.

Reproduced by Pearson Addison-Wesley from electronic files supplied by the author.

Copyright © 2010, 2005, 2001 Pearson Education, Inc.
Publishing as Pearson Addison-Wesley, 75 Arlington Street, Boston, MA 02116.

ISBN-13: 978-0-321-60807-9
ISBN-10: 0-321-60807-0

1 2 3 4 5 6 BB 12 11 10 09

**Addison-Wesley**
is an imprint of

www.pearsonhighered.com

# PREFACE TO THE INSTRUCTOR

This Instructor's Solutions Manual contains the solutions to every exercise in the 12th Edition of THOMAS' CALCULUS by Maurice Weir and Joel Hass, including the Computer Algebra System (CAS) exercises. The corresponding Student's Solutions Manual omits the solutions to the even-numbered exercises as well as the solutions to the CAS exercises (because the CAS command templates would give them all away).

In addition to including the solutions to all of the new exercises in this edition of Thomas, we have carefully revised or rewritten every solution which appeared in previous solutions manuals to ensure that each solution
- conforms exactly to the methods, procedures and steps presented in the text
- is mathematically correct
- includes all of the steps necessary so a typical calculus student can follow the logical argument and algebra
- includes a graph or figure whenever called for by the exercise, or if needed to help with the explanation
- is formatted in an appropriate style to aid in its understanding

Every CAS exercise is solved in both the MAPLE and *MATHEMATICA* computer algebra systems. A template showing an example of the CAS commands needed to execute the solution is provided for each exercise type. Similar exercises within the text grouping require a change only in the input function or other numerical input parameters associated with the problem (such as the interval endpoints or the number of iterations).

For more information about other resources available with Thomas' Calculus, visit http://pearsonhighered.com.

# TABLE OF CONTENTS

# 11 Parametric Equations and Polar Coordinates 647

# CHAPTER 1 FUNCTIONS

## 1.1 FUNCTIONS AND THEIR GRAPHS

1. domain $= (-\infty, \infty)$; range $= [1, \infty)$

2. domain $= [0, \infty)$; range $= (-\infty, 1]$

3. domain $= [-2, \infty)$; y in range and y $= \sqrt{5x + 10} \geq 0 \Rightarrow$ y can be any positive real number $\Rightarrow$ range $= [0, \infty)$.

4. domain $= (-\infty, 0] \cup [3, \infty)$; y in range and y $= \sqrt{x^2 - 3x} \geq 0 \Rightarrow$ y can be any positive real number $\Rightarrow$ range $= [0, \infty)$.

5. domain $= (-\infty, 3) \cup (3, \infty)$; y in range and y $= \frac{4}{3-t}$, now if t $< 3 \Rightarrow 3 - t > 0 \Rightarrow \frac{4}{3-t} > 0$, or if t $> 3$
   $\Rightarrow 3 - t < 0 \Rightarrow \frac{4}{3-t} < 0 \Rightarrow$ y can be any nonzero real number $\Rightarrow$ range $= (-\infty, 0) \cup (0, \infty)$.

6. domain $= (-\infty, -4) \cup (-4, 4) \cup (4, \infty)$; y in range and y $= \frac{2}{t^2 - 16}$, now if t $< -4 \Rightarrow t^2 - 16 > 0 \Rightarrow \frac{2}{t^2 - 16} > 0$, or if
   $-4 < t < 4 \Rightarrow -16 \leq t^2 - 16 < 0 \Rightarrow -\frac{2}{16} \leq \frac{2}{t^2 - 16} < 0$, or if t $> 4 \Rightarrow t^2 - 16 > 0 \Rightarrow \frac{2}{t^2 - 16} > 0 \Rightarrow$ y can be any
   nonzero real number $\Rightarrow$ range $= (-\infty, -\frac{1}{8}] \cup (0, \infty)$.

7. (a) Not the graph of a function of x since it fails the vertical line test.
   (b) Is the graph of a function of x since any vertical line intersects the graph at most once.

8. (a) Not the graph of a function of x since it fails the vertical line test.
   (b) Not the graph of a function of x since it fails the vertical line test.

9. base $= x$; (height)$^2 + \left(\frac{x}{2}\right)^2 = x^2 \Rightarrow$ height $= \frac{\sqrt{3}}{2} x$; area is a(x) $= \frac{1}{2}$ (base)(height) $= \frac{1}{2} (x) \left(\frac{\sqrt{3}}{2} x\right) = \frac{\sqrt{3}}{4} x^2$;
   perimeter is p(x) $= x + x + x = 3x$.

10. s $=$ side length $\Rightarrow s^2 + s^2 = d^2 \Rightarrow s = \frac{d}{\sqrt{2}}$; and area is a $= s^2 \Rightarrow$ a $= \frac{1}{2} d^2$

11. Let D $=$ diagonal length of a face of the cube and $\ell =$ the length of an edge. Then $\ell^2 + D^2 = d^2$ and
    $D^2 = 2\ell^2 \Rightarrow 3\ell^2 = d^2 \Rightarrow \ell = \frac{d}{\sqrt{3}}$. The surface area is $6\ell^2 = \frac{6d^2}{3} = 2d^2$ and the volume is $\ell^3 = \left(\frac{d^2}{3}\right)^{3/2} = \frac{d^3}{3\sqrt{3}}$.

12. The coordinates of P are $\left(x, \sqrt{x}\right)$ so the slope of the line joining P to the origin is m $= \frac{\sqrt{x}}{x} = \frac{1}{\sqrt{x}}$ (x $> 0$). Thus,
    $\left(x, \sqrt{x}\right) = \left(\frac{1}{m^2}, \frac{1}{m}\right)$.

13. $2x + 4y = 5 \Rightarrow y = -\frac{1}{2}x + \frac{5}{4}$; L $= \sqrt{(x - 0)^2 + (y - 0)^2} = \sqrt{x^2 + (-\frac{1}{2}x + \frac{5}{4})^2} = \sqrt{x^2 + \frac{1}{4}x^2 - \frac{5}{4}x + \frac{25}{16}}$
    $= \sqrt{\frac{5}{4}x^2 - \frac{5}{4}x + \frac{25}{16}} = \sqrt{\frac{20x^2 - 20x + 25}{16}} = \frac{\sqrt{20x^2 - 20x + 25}}{4}$

14. $y = \sqrt{x - 3} \Rightarrow y^2 + 3 = x$; L $= \sqrt{(x - 4)^2 + (y - 0)^2} = \sqrt{(y^2 + 3 - 4)^2 + y^2} = \sqrt{(y^2 - 1)^2 + y^2}$
    $= \sqrt{y^4 - 2y^2 + 1 + y^2} = \sqrt{y^4 - y^2 + 1}$

15. The domain is $(-\infty, \infty)$.

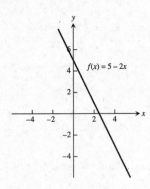

16. The domain is $(-\infty, \infty)$.

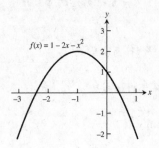

17. The domain is $(-\infty, \infty)$.

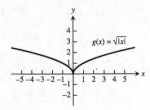

18. The domain is $(-\infty, 0]$.

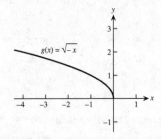

19. The domain is $(-\infty, 0) \cup (0, \infty)$.

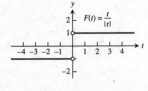

20. The domain is $(-\infty, 0) \cup (0, \infty)$.

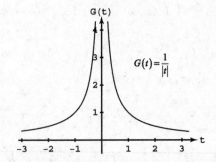

21. The domain is $(-\infty, -5) \cup (-5, -3] \cup [3, 5) \cup (5, \infty)$    22. The range is $[2, 3)$.

23. Neither graph passes the vertical line test

(a)

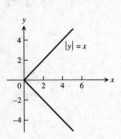

(b)

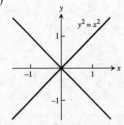

24. Neither graph passes the vertical line test

    (a)

    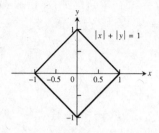

    (b)

    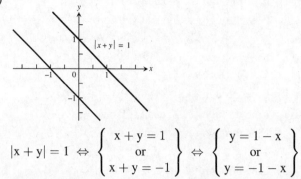

    $$|x + y| = 1 \Leftrightarrow \left\{ \begin{array}{c} x + y = 1 \\ \text{or} \\ x + y = -1 \end{array} \right\} \Leftrightarrow \left\{ \begin{array}{c} y = 1 - x \\ \text{or} \\ y = -1 - x \end{array} \right\}$$

25.

| x | 0 | 1 | 2 |
|---|---|---|---|
| y | 0 | 1 | 0 |

$f(x) = \begin{cases} x, & 0 \le x \le 1 \\ 2 - x, & 1 < x \le 2 \end{cases}$

26.

| x | 0 | 1 | 2 |
|---|---|---|---|
| y | 1 | 0 | 0 |

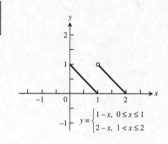

$y = \begin{cases} 1 - x, & 0 \le x \le 1 \\ 2 - x, & 1 < x \le 2 \end{cases}$

27. $F(x) = \begin{cases} 4 - x^2, & x \le 1 \\ x^2 + 2x, & x > 1 \end{cases}$

    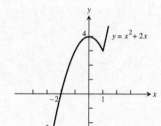

28. $G(x) = \begin{cases} \frac{1}{x}, & x < 0 \\ x, & 0 \le x \end{cases}$

    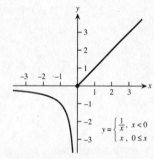

    $y = \begin{cases} \frac{1}{x}, & x < 0 \\ x, & 0 \le x \end{cases}$

29. (a) Line through $(0, 0)$ and $(1, 1)$: $y = x$; Line through $(1, 1)$ and $(2, 0)$: $y = -x + 2$

    $f(x) = \begin{cases} x, & 0 \le x \le 1 \\ -x + 2, & 1 < x \le 2 \end{cases}$

    (b) $f(x) = \begin{cases} 2, & 0 \le x < 1 \\ 0, & 1 \le x < 2 \\ 2, & 2 \le x < 3 \\ 0, & 3 \le x \le 4 \end{cases}$

30. (a) Line through $(0, 2)$ and $(2, 0)$: $y = -x + 2$

    Line through $(2, 1)$ and $(5, 0)$: $m = \frac{0 - 1}{5 - 2} = \frac{-1}{3} = -\frac{1}{3}$, so $y = -\frac{1}{3}(x - 2) + 1 = -\frac{1}{3}x + \frac{5}{3}$

    $f(x) = \begin{cases} -x + 2, & 0 < x \le 2 \\ -\frac{1}{3}x + \frac{5}{3}, & 2 < x \le 5 \end{cases}$

    (b) Line through $(-1, 0)$ and $(0, -3)$: $m = \frac{-3 - 0}{0 - (-1)} = -3$, so $y = -3x - 3$

    Line through $(0, 3)$ and $(2, -1)$: $m = \frac{-1 - 3}{2 - 0} = \frac{-4}{2} = -2$, so $y = -2x + 3$

    $f(x) = \begin{cases} -3x - 3, & -1 < x \le 0 \\ -2x + 3, & 0 < x \le 2 \end{cases}$

31. (a) Line through $(-1, 1)$ and $(0, 0)$: $y = -x$

Line through $(0, 1)$ and $(1, 1)$: $y = 1$

Line through $(1, 1)$ and $(3, 0)$: $m = \frac{0-1}{3-1} = \frac{-1}{2} = -\frac{1}{2}$, so $y = -\frac{1}{2}(x - 1) + 1 = -\frac{1}{2}x + \frac{3}{2}$

$$f(x) = \begin{cases} -x & -1 \le x < 0 \\ 1 & 0 < x \le 1 \\ -\frac{1}{2}x + \frac{3}{2} & 1 < x < 3 \end{cases}$$

(b) Line through $(-2, -1)$ and $(0, 0)$: $y = \frac{1}{2}x$

Line through $(0, 2)$ and $(1, 0)$: $y = -2x + 2$

Line through $(1, -1)$ and $(3, -1)$: $y = -1$

$$f(x) = \begin{cases} \frac{1}{2}x & -2 \le x \le 0 \\ -2x + 2 & 0 < x \le 1 \\ -1 & 1 < x \le 3 \end{cases}$$

32. (a) Line through $\left(\frac{T}{2}, 0\right)$ and $(T, 1)$: $m = \frac{1-0}{T-(T/2)} = \frac{2}{T}$, so $y = \frac{2}{T}\left(x - \frac{T}{2}\right) + 0 = \frac{2}{T}x - 1$

$$f(x) = \begin{cases} 0, & 0 \le x \le \frac{T}{2} \\ \frac{2}{T}x - 1, & \frac{T}{2} < x \le T \end{cases}$$

(b) $$f(x) = \begin{cases} A, & 0 \le x < \frac{T}{2} \\ -A, & \frac{T}{2} \le x < T \\ A, & T \le x < \frac{3T}{2} \\ -A, & \frac{3T}{2} \le x \le 2T \end{cases}$$

33. (a) $\lfloor x \rfloor = 0$ for $x \in [0, 1)$    (b) $\lceil x \rceil = 0$ for $x \in (-1, 0]$

34. $\lfloor x \rfloor = \lceil x \rceil$ only when x is an integer.

35. For any real number x, $n \le x \le n + 1$, where n is an integer. Now: $n \le x \le n + 1 \Rightarrow -(n + 1) \le -x \le -n$. By definition: $\lceil -x \rceil = -n$ and $\lfloor x \rfloor = n \Rightarrow -\lfloor x \rfloor = -n$. So $\lceil -x \rceil = -\lfloor x \rfloor$ for all $x \in \Re$.

36. To find f(x) you delete the decimal or fractional portion of x, leaving only the integer part.

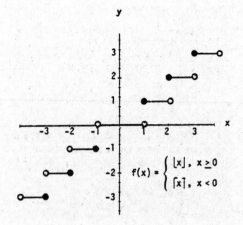

$$f(x) = \begin{cases} \lfloor x \rfloor, & x \ge 0 \\ \lceil x \rceil, & x < 0 \end{cases}$$

37.  Symmetric about the origin
     Dec: $-\infty < x < \infty$
     Inc: nowhere

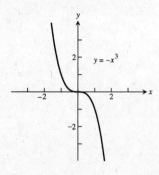

38.  Symmetric about the y-axis
     Dec: $-\infty < x < 0$
     Inc: $0 < x < \infty$

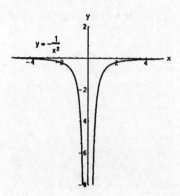

39.  Symmetric about the origin
     Dec: nowhere
     Inc: $-\infty < x < 0$
     $\quad\ \ 0 < x < \infty$

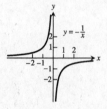

40.  Symmetric about the y-axis
     Dec: $0 < x < \infty$
     Inc: $-\infty < x < 0$

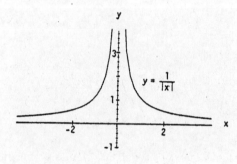

41.  Symmetric about the y-axis
     Dec: $-\infty < x \le 0$
     Inc: $0 < x < \infty$

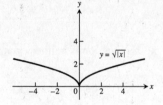

42.  No symmetry
     Dec: $-\infty < x \le 0$
     Inc: nowhere

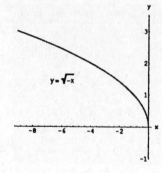

43. Symmetric about the origin

    Dec: nowhere

    Inc: $-\infty < x < \infty$

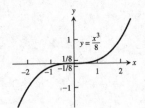

44. No symmetry

    Dec: $0 \le x < \infty$

    Inc: nowhere

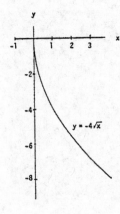

45. No symmetry

    Dec: $0 \le x < \infty$

    Inc: nowhere

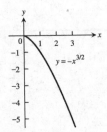

46. Symmetric about the y-axis

    Dec: $-\infty < x \le 0$

    Inc: $0 < x < \infty$

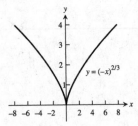

47. Since a horizontal line not through the origin is symmetric with respect to the y-axis, but not with respect to the origin, the function is even.

48. $f(x) = x^{-5} = \frac{1}{x^5}$ and $f(-x) = (-x)^{-5} = \frac{1}{(-x)^5} = -\left(\frac{1}{x^5}\right) = -f(x)$. Thus the function is odd.

49. Since $f(x) = x^2 + 1 = (-x)^2 + 1 = -f(x)$. The function is even.

50. Since $[f(x) = x^2 + x] \ne [f(-x) = (-x)^2 - x]$ and $[f(x) = x^2 + x] \ne [-f(x) = -(x)^2 - x]$ the function is neither even nor odd.

51. Since $g(x) = x^3 + x$, $g(-x) = -x^3 - x = -(x^3 + x) = -g(x)$. So the function is odd.

52. $g(x) = x^4 + 3x^2 - 1 = (-x)^4 + 3(-x)^2 - 1 = g(-x)$, thus the function is even.

53. $g(x) = \frac{1}{x^2 - 1} = \frac{1}{(-x)^2 - 1} = g(-x)$. Thus the function is even.

54. $g(x) = \frac{x}{x^2 - 1}$; $g(-x) = -\frac{x}{x^2 - 1} = -g(x)$. So the function is odd.

55. $h(t) = \frac{1}{t-1}$; $h(-t) = \frac{1}{-t-1}$; $-h(t) = \frac{1}{1-t}$. Since $h(t) \ne -h(t)$ and $h(t) \ne h(-t)$, the function is neither even nor odd.

56. Since $|t^3| = |(-t)^3|$, $h(t) = h(-t)$ and the function is even.

57. $h(t) = 2t + 1$, $h(-t) = -2t + 1$. So $h(t) \neq h(-t)$. $-h(t) = -2t - 1$, so $h(t) \neq -h(t)$. The function is neither even nor odd.

58. $h(t) = 2|t| + 1$ and $h(-t) = 2|-t| + 1 = 2|t| + 1$. So $h(t) = h(-t)$ and the function is even.

59. $s = kt \Rightarrow 25 = k(75) \Rightarrow k = \frac{1}{3} \Rightarrow s = \frac{1}{3}t$; $60 = \frac{1}{3}t \Rightarrow t = 180$

60. $K = c\,v^2 \Rightarrow 12960 = c(18)^2 \Rightarrow c = 40 \Rightarrow K = 40v^2$; $K = 40(10)^2 = 4000$ joules

61. $r = \frac{k}{s} \Rightarrow 6 = \frac{k}{4} \Rightarrow k = 24 \Rightarrow r = \frac{24}{s}$; $10 = \frac{24}{s} \Rightarrow s = \frac{12}{5}$

62. $P = \frac{k}{v} \Rightarrow 14.7 = \frac{k}{1000} \Rightarrow k = 14700 \Rightarrow P = \frac{14700}{v}$; $23.4 = \frac{14700}{v} \Rightarrow v = \frac{24500}{39} \approx 628.2$ in$^3$

63. $v = f(x) = x(14 - 2x)(22 - 2x) = 4x^3 - 72x^2 + 308x$; $0 < x < 7$.

64. (a)  Let h = height of the triangle. Since the triangle is isosceles, $\overline{AB}^2 + \overline{AB}^2 = 2^2 \Rightarrow \overline{AB} = \sqrt{2}$. So,
    $h^2 + 1^2 = \left(\sqrt{2}\right)^2 \Rightarrow h = 1 \Rightarrow B$ is at $(0, 1) \Rightarrow$ slope of AB $= -1 \Rightarrow$ The equation of AB is
    $y = f(x) = -x + 1$; $x \in [0, 1]$.
    (b)  $A(x) = 2x\,y = 2x(-x + 1) = -2x^2 + 2x$; $x \in [0, 1]$.

65. (a)  Graph h because it is an even function and rises less rapidly than does Graph g.
    (b)  Graph f because it is an odd function.
    (c)  Graph g because it is an even function and rises more rapidly than does Graph h.

66. (a)  Graph f because it is linear.
    (b)  Graph g because it contains $(0, 1)$.
    (c)  Graph h because it is a nonlinear odd function.

67. (a)  From the graph, $\frac{x}{2} > 1 + \frac{4}{x} \Rightarrow x \in (-2, 0) \cup (4, \infty)$
    (b)  $\frac{x}{2} > 1 + \frac{4}{x} \Rightarrow \frac{x}{2} - 1 - \frac{4}{x} > 0$
    $x > 0$: $\frac{x}{2} - 1 - \frac{4}{x} > 0 \Rightarrow \frac{x^2 - 2x - 8}{2x} > 0 \Rightarrow \frac{(x-4)(x+2)}{2x} > 0$
    $\Rightarrow x > 4$ since x is positive;
    $x < 0$: $\frac{x}{2} - 1 - \frac{4}{x} > 0 \Rightarrow \frac{x^2 - 2x - 8}{2x} < 0 \Rightarrow \frac{(x-4)(x+2)}{2x} < 0$
    $\Rightarrow x < -2$ since x is negative;
    sign of $(x - 4)(x + 2)$

    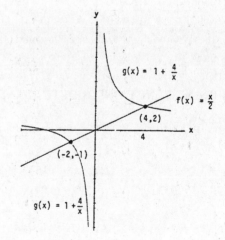

    Solution interval: $(-2, 0) \cup (4, \infty)$

68. (a) From the graph, $\frac{3}{x-1} < \frac{2}{x+1} \Rightarrow x \in (-\infty, -5) \cup (-1, 1)$

    (b) <u>Case</u> $x < -1$: $\frac{3}{x-1} < \frac{2}{x+1} \Rightarrow \frac{3(x+1)}{x-1} > 2$

    $\Rightarrow 3x + 3 < 2x - 2 \Rightarrow x < -5.$

    Thus, $x \in (-\infty, -5)$ solves the inequality.

    <u>Case</u> $-1 < x < 1$: $\frac{3}{x-1} < \frac{2}{x+1} \Rightarrow \frac{3(x+1)}{x-1} < 2$

    $\Rightarrow 3x + 3 > 2x - 2 \Rightarrow x > -5$ which is true

    if $x > -1$. Thus, $x \in (-1, 1)$ solves the

    inequality.

    <u>Case</u> $1 < x$: $\frac{3}{x-1} < \frac{2}{x+1} \Rightarrow 3x + 3 < 2x - 2 \Rightarrow x < -5$

    which is never true if $1 < x$, so no solution here.

    In conclusion, $x \in (-\infty, -5) \cup (-1, 1)$.

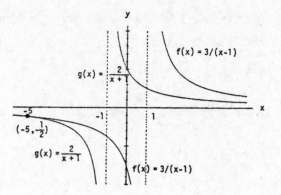

69. A curve symmetric about the x-axis will not pass the vertical line test because the points $(x, y)$ and $(x, -y)$ lie on the same vertical line. The graph of the function $y = f(x) = 0$ is the x-axis, a horizontal line for which there is a single y-value, 0, for any x.

70. price $= 40 + 5x$, quantity $= 300 - 25x \Rightarrow R(x) = (40 + 5x)(300 - 25x)$

71. $x^2 + x^2 = h^2 \Rightarrow x = \frac{h}{\sqrt{2}} = \frac{\sqrt{2}h}{2}$; cost $= 5(2x) + 10h \Rightarrow C(h) = 10\left(\frac{\sqrt{2}h}{2}\right) + 10h = 5h\left(\sqrt{2} + 2\right)$

72. (a) Note that 2 mi = 10,560 ft, so there are $\sqrt{800^2 + x^2}$ feet of river cable at \$180 per foot and $(10{,}560 - x)$ feet of land cable at \$100 per foot. The cost is $C(x) = 180\sqrt{800^2 + x^2} + 100(10{,}560 - x)$.

    (b) $C(0) = \$1{,}200{,}000$

    $C(500) \approx \$1{,}175{,}812$

    $C(1000) \approx \$1{,}186{,}512$

    $C(1500) \approx \$1{,}212{,}000$

    $C(2000) \approx \$1{,}243{,}732$

    $C(2500) \approx \$1{,}278{,}479$

    $C(3000) \approx \$1{,}314{,}870$

    Values beyond this are all larger. It would appear that the least expensive location is less than 2000 feet from the point P.

## 1.2 COMBINING FUNCTIONS; SHIFTING AND SCALING GRAPHS

1. $D_f: -\infty < x < \infty, D_g: x \geq 1 \Rightarrow D_{f+g} = D_{fg}: x \geq 1.$ $R_f: -\infty < y < \infty, R_g: y \geq 0, R_{f+g}: y \geq 1, R_{fg}: y \geq 0$

2. $D_f: x + 1 \geq 0 \Rightarrow x \geq -1, D_g: x - 1 \geq 0 \Rightarrow x \geq 1.$ Therefore $D_{f+g} = D_{fg}: x \geq 1.$
   $R_f = R_g: y \geq 0, R_{f+g}: y \geq \sqrt{2}, R_{fg}: y \geq 0$

3. $D_f: -\infty < x < \infty, D_g: -\infty < x < \infty, D_{f/g}: -\infty < x < \infty, D_{g/f}: -\infty < x < \infty, R_f: y = 2, R_g: y \geq 1,$
   $R_{f/g}: 0 < y \leq 2, R_{g/f}: \frac{1}{2} \leq y < \infty$

4. $D_f: -\infty < x < \infty, D_g: x \geq 0, D_{f/g}: x \geq 0, D_{g/f}: x \geq 0; R_f: y = 1, R_g: y \geq 1, R_{f/g}: 0 < y \leq 1, R_{g/f}: 1 \leq y < \infty$

5. (a) 2                               (b) 22                        (c) $x^2 + 2$
   (d) $(x + 5)^2 - 3 = x^2 + 10x + 22$   (e) 5                         (f) $-2$
   (g) $x + 10$                        (h) $(x^2 - 3)^2 - 3 = x^4 - 6x^2 + 6$

6.  (a)  $-\frac{1}{3}$                       (b)  2                                       (c)  $\frac{1}{x+1} - 1 = \frac{-x}{x+1}$

    (d)  $\frac{1}{x}$                          (e)  0                                       (f)  $\frac{3}{4}$

    (g)  $x - 2$                               (h)  $\frac{1}{\frac{1}{x+1}+1} = \frac{1}{\frac{x+2}{x+1}} = \frac{x+1}{x+2}$

7.  $(f \circ g \circ h)(x) = f(g(h(x))) = f(g(4-x)) = f(3(4-x)) = f(12-3x) = (12-3x) + 1 = 13 - 3x$

8.  $(f \circ g \circ h)(x) = f(g(h(x))) = f(g(x^2)) = f(2(x^2) - 1) = f(2x^2 - 1) = 3(2x^2 - 1) + 4 = 6x^2 + 1$

9.  $(f \circ g \circ h)(x) = f(g(h(x))) = f\left(g\left(\frac{1}{x}\right)\right) = f\left(\frac{1}{\frac{1}{x}+4}\right) = f\left(\frac{x}{1+4x}\right) = \sqrt{\frac{x}{1+4x} + 1} = \sqrt{\frac{5x+1}{1+4x}}$

10. $(f \circ g \circ h)(x) = f(g(h(x))) = f\left(g\left(\sqrt{2-x}\right)\right) = f\left(\frac{\left(\sqrt{2-x}\right)^2}{\left(\sqrt{2-x}\right)^2 + 1}\right) = f\left(\frac{2-x}{3-x}\right) = \frac{\frac{2-x}{3-x}+2}{3 - \frac{2-x}{3-x}} = \frac{8-3x}{7-2x}$

11. (a)  $(f \circ g)(x)$                     (b)  $(j \circ g)(x)$                     (c)  $(g \circ g)(x)$

    (d)  $(j \circ j)(x)$                      (e)  $(g \circ h \circ f)(x)$             (f)  $(h \circ j \circ f)(x)$

12. (a)  $(f \circ j)(x)$                      (b)  $(g \circ h)(x)$                     (c)  $(h \circ h)(x)$

    (d)  $(f \circ f)(x)$                      (e)  $(j \circ g \circ f)(x)$             (f)  $(g \circ f \circ h)(x)$

13.

| g(x) | f(x) | $(f \circ g)(x)$ |
|---|---|---|
| (a)  $x - 7$ | $\sqrt{x}$ | $\sqrt{x-7}$ |
| (b)  $x + 2$ | $3x$ | $3(x+2) = 3x+6$ |
| (c)  $x^2$ | $\sqrt{x-5}$ | $\sqrt{x^2-5}$ |
| (d)  $\frac{x}{x-1}$ | $\frac{x}{x-1}$ | $\frac{\frac{x}{x-1}}{\frac{x}{x-1}-1} = \frac{x}{x-(x-1)} = x$ |
| (e)  $\frac{1}{x-1}$ | $1 + \frac{1}{x}$ | $x$ |
| (f)  $\frac{1}{x}$ | $\frac{1}{x}$ | $x$ |

14. (a)  $(f \circ g)(x) = |g(x)| = \frac{1}{|x-1|}$.

    (b)  $(f \circ g)(x) = \frac{g(x)-1}{g(x)} = \frac{x}{x+1} \Rightarrow 1 - \frac{1}{g(x)} = \frac{x}{x+1} \Rightarrow 1 - \frac{x}{x+1} = \frac{1}{g(x)} \Rightarrow \frac{1}{x+1} = \frac{1}{g(x)}$, so $g(x) = x + 1$.

    (c)  Since $(f \circ g)(x) = \sqrt{g(x)} = |x|$, $g(x) = x^2$.

    (d)  Since $(f \circ g)(x) = f\left(\sqrt{x}\right) = |x|$, $f(x) = x^2$. (Note that the domain of the composite is $[0, \infty)$.)

    The completed table is shown. Note that the absolute value sign in part (d) is optional.

| g(x) | f(x) | $(f \circ g)(x)$ |
|---|---|---|
| $\frac{1}{x-1}$ | $|x|$ | $\frac{1}{|x-1|}$ |
| $x + 1$ | $\frac{x-1}{x}$ | $\frac{x}{x+1}$ |
| $x^2$ | $\sqrt{x}$ | $|x|$ |
| $\sqrt{x}$ | $x^2$ | $|x|$ |

15. (a)  $f(g(-1)) = f(1) = 1$            (b)  $g(f(0)) = g(-2) = 2$            (c)  $f(f(-1)) = f(0) = -2$

    (d)  $g(g(2)) = g(0) = 0$             (e)  $g(f(-2)) = g(1) = -1$           (f)  $f(g(1)) = f(-1) = 0$

16. (a)  $f(g(0)) = f(-1) = 2 - (-1) = 3$, where $g(0) = 0 - 1 = -1$

    (b)  $g(f(3)) = g(-1) = -(-1) = 1$, where $f(3) = 2 - 3 = -1$

    (c)  $g(g(-1)) = g(1) = 1 - 1 = 0$, where $g(-1) = -(-1) = 1$

(d)  $f(f(2)) = f(0) = 2 - 0 = 2$, where $f(2) = 2 - 2 = 0$

(e)  $g(f(0)) = g(2) = 2 - 1 = 1$, where $f(0) = 2 - 0 = 2$

(f)  $f\left(g\left(\frac{1}{2}\right)\right) = f\left(-\frac{1}{2}\right) = 2 - \left(-\frac{1}{2}\right) = \frac{5}{2}$, where $g\left(\frac{1}{2}\right) = \frac{1}{2} - 1 = -\frac{1}{2}$

17. (a)  $(f \circ g)(x) = f(g(x)) = \sqrt{\frac{1}{x} + 1} = \sqrt{\frac{1+x}{x}}$

   $(g \circ f)(x) = g(f(x)) = \frac{1}{\sqrt{x+1}}$

   (b)  Domain $(f \circ g)$: $(-\infty, -1] \cup (0, \infty)$, domain $(g \circ f)$: $(-1, \infty)$

   (c)  Range $(f \circ g)$: $(1, \infty)$, range $(g \circ f)$: $(0, \infty)$

18. (a)  $(f \circ g)(x) = f(g(x)) = 1 - 2\sqrt{x} + x$

   $(g \circ f)(x) = g(f(x)) = 1 - |x|$

   (b)  Domain $(f \circ g)$: $[0, \infty)$, domain $(g \circ f)$: $(-\infty, \infty)$

   (c)  Range $(f \circ g)$: $[0, \infty)$, range $(g \circ f)$: $(-\infty, 1]$

19. $(f \circ g)(x) = x \Rightarrow f(g(x)) = x \Rightarrow \frac{g(x)}{g(x) - 2} = x \Rightarrow g(x) = (g(x) - 2)x = x \cdot g(x) - 2x$

   $\Rightarrow g(x) - x \cdot g(x) = -2x \Rightarrow g(x) = -\frac{2x}{1 - x} = \frac{2x}{x - 1}$

20. $(f \circ g)(x) = x + 2 \Rightarrow f(g(x)) = x + 2 \Rightarrow 2(g(x))^3 - 4 = x + 2 \Rightarrow (g(x))^3 = \frac{x+6}{2} \Rightarrow g(x) = \sqrt[3]{\frac{x+6}{2}}$

21. (a)  $y = -(x + 7)^2$          (b)  $y = -(x - 4)^2$

22. (a)  $y = x^2 + 3$          (b)  $y = x^2 - 5$

23. (a)  Position 4          (b)  Position 1          (c)  Position 2          (d)  Position 3

24. (a)  $y = -(x - 1)^2 + 4$    (b)  $y = -(x + 2)^2 + 3$    (c)  $y = -(x + 4)^2 - 1$    (d)  $y = -(x - 2)^2$

25.

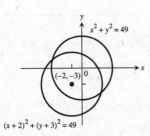

26.

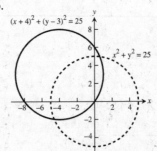

27.

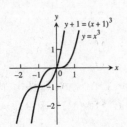

28.

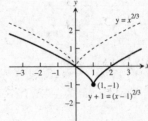

29.

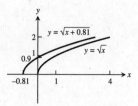

30.

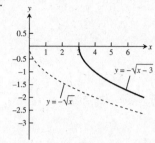

31.

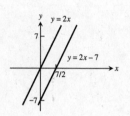

32.

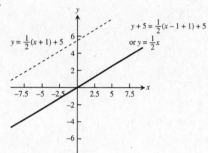

33.

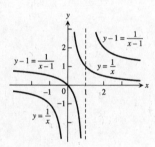

34.

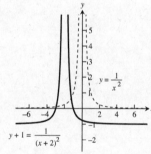

35.

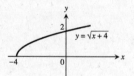

36.

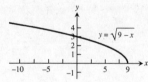

37.

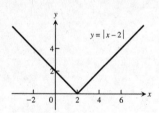

38.

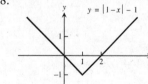

39.

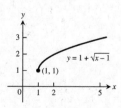

40.

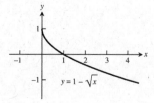

41.

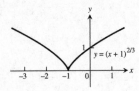

42.

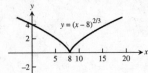

43.

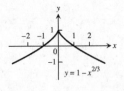

44.

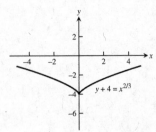

45.

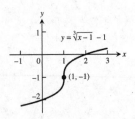

46.

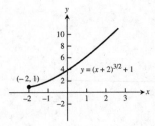

47.

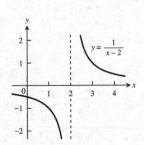

48.

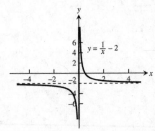

49.

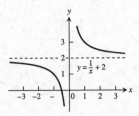

50.

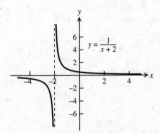

51.

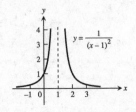

52.

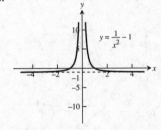

53.

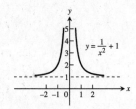

54.

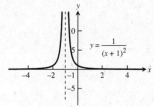

55. (a)  domain:  $[0, 2]$; range:  $[2, 3]$

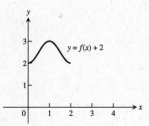

(b)  domain:  $[0, 2]$; range:  $[-1, 0]$

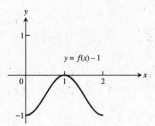

(c)  domain:  $[0, 2]$; range:  $[0, 2]$

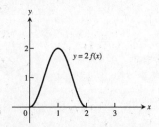

(d)  domain:  $[0, 2]$; range:  $[-1, 0]$

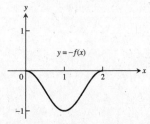

(e)  domain:  $[-2, 0]$; range:  $[0, 1]$

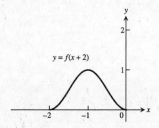

(f)  domain:  $[1, 3]$; range:  $[0, 1]$

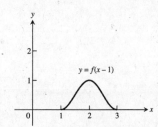

(g)  domain:  $[-2, 0]$; range:  $[0, 1]$

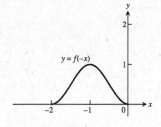

(h)  domain:  $[-1, 1]$; range:  $[0, 1]$

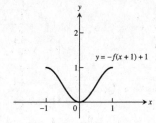

56. (a) domain: $[0, 4]$; range: $[-3, 0]$

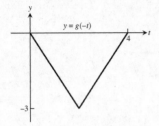

(b) domain: $[-4, 0]$; range: $[0, 3]$

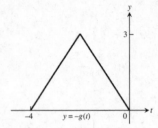

(c) domain: $[-4, 0]$; range: $[0, 3]$

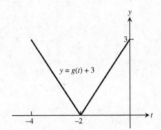

(d) domain: $[-4, 0]$; range: $[1, 4]$

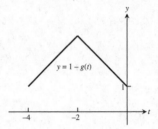

(e) domain: $[2, 4]$; range: $[-3, 0]$

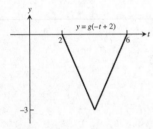

(f) domain: $[-2, 2]$; range: $[-3, 0]$

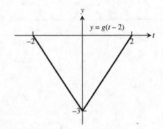

(g) domain: $[1, 5]$; range: $[-3, 0]$

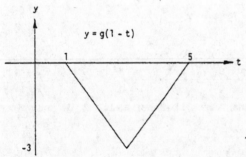

(h) domain: $[0, 4]$; range: $[0, 3]$

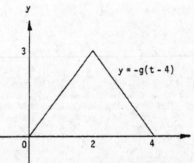

57. $y = 3x^2 - 3$

58. $y = (2x)^2 - 1 = 4x^2 - 1$

59. $y = \frac{1}{2}\left(1 + \frac{1}{x^2}\right) = \frac{1}{2} + \frac{1}{2x^2}$

60. $y = 1 + \frac{1}{(x/3)^2} = 1 + \frac{9}{x^2}$

61. $y = \sqrt{4x + 1}$

62. $y = 3\sqrt{x + 1}$

63. $y = \sqrt{4 - \left(\frac{x}{2}\right)^2} = \frac{1}{2}\sqrt{16 - x^2}$

64. $y = \frac{1}{3}\sqrt{4 - x^2}$

65. $y = 1 - (3x)^3 = 1 - 27x^3$

66. $y = 1 - \left(\frac{x}{2}\right)^3 = 1 - \frac{x^3}{8}$

67. Let $y = -\sqrt{2x+1} = f(x)$ and let $g(x) = x^{1/2}$, $h(x) = \left(x + \frac{1}{2}\right)^{1/2}$, $i(x) = \sqrt{2}\left(x + \frac{1}{2}\right)^{1/2}$, and $j(x) = -\left[\sqrt{2}\left(x + \frac{1}{2}\right)^{1/2}\right] = f(x)$. The graph of $h(x)$ is the graph of $g(x)$ shifted left $\frac{1}{2}$ unit; the graph of $i(x)$ is the graph of $h(x)$ stretched vertically by a factor of $\sqrt{2}$; and the graph of $j(x) = f(x)$ is the graph of $i(x)$ reflected across the x-axis.

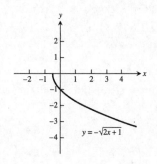

68. Let $y = \sqrt{1 - \frac{x}{2}} = f(x)$. Let $g(x) = (-x)^{1/2}$, $h(x) = (-x + 2)^{1/2}$, and $i(x) = \frac{1}{\sqrt{2}}(-x + 2)^{1/2}$ $= \sqrt{1 - \frac{x}{2}} = f(x)$. The graph of $g(x)$ is the graph of $y = \sqrt{x}$ reflected across the x-axis. The graph of $h(x)$ is the graph of $g(x)$ shifted right two units. And the graph of $i(x)$ is the graph of $h(x)$ compressed vertically by a factor of $\sqrt{2}$.

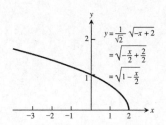

69. $y = f(x) = x^3$. Shift $f(x)$ one unit right followed by a shift two units up to get $g(x) = (x - 1)^3 + 2$.

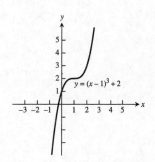

70. $y = (1 - x)^3 + 2 = -[(x - 1)^3 + (-2)] = f(x)$.
Let $g(x) = x^3$, $h(x) = (x - 1)^3$, $i(x) = (x - 1)^3 + (-2)$, and $j(x) = -[(x - 1)^3 + (-2)]$. The graph of $h(x)$ is the graph of $g(x)$ shifted right one unit; the graph of $i(x)$ is the graph of $h(x)$ shifted down two units; and the graph of $f(x)$ is the graph of $i(x)$ reflected across the x-axis.

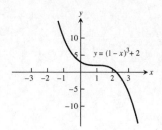

71. Compress the graph of $f(x) = \frac{1}{x}$ horizontally by a factor of 2 to get $g(x) = \frac{1}{2x}$. Then shift $g(x)$ vertically down 1 unit to get $h(x) = \frac{1}{2x} - 1$.

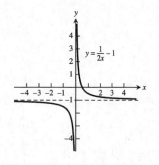

72. Let $f(x) = \frac{1}{x^2}$ and $g(x) = \frac{2}{x^2} + 1 = \frac{1}{\left(\frac{x^2}{2}\right)} + 1$

$= \frac{1}{\left(x/\sqrt{2}\right)^2} + 1 = \frac{1}{\left[\left(1/\sqrt{2}\right)x\right]^2} + 1$. Since

$\sqrt{2} \approx 1.4$, we see that the graph of $f(x)$ stretched horizontally by a factor of 1.4 and shifted up 1 unit is the graph of $g(x)$.

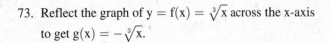

73. Reflect the graph of $y = f(x) = \sqrt[3]{x}$ across the x-axis to get $g(x) = -\sqrt[3]{x}$.

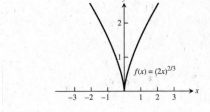

74. $y = f(x) = (-2x)^{2/3} = [(-1)(2)x]^{2/3}$

$= (-1)^{2/3}(2x)^{2/3} = (2x)^{2/3}$. So the graph of $f(x)$ is the graph of $g(x) = x^{2/3}$ compressed horizontally by a factor of 2.

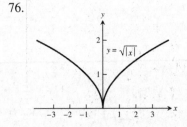

75.

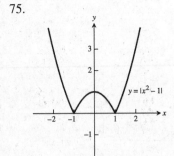

76.

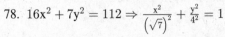

77. $9x^2 + 25y^2 = 225 \Rightarrow \frac{x^2}{5^2} + \frac{y^2}{3^2} = 1$

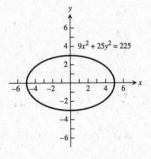

78. $16x^2 + 7y^2 = 112 \Rightarrow \frac{x^2}{\left(\sqrt{7}\right)^2} + \frac{y^2}{4^2} = 1$

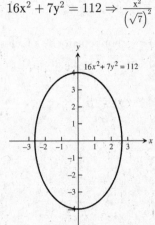

79. $3x^2 + (y-2)^2 = 3 \Rightarrow \frac{x^2}{1^2} + \frac{(y-2)^2}{\left(\sqrt{3}\right)^2} = 1$

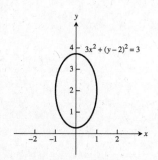

80. $(x+1)^2 + 2y^2 = 4 \Rightarrow \frac{\left[x-(-1)\right]^2}{2^2} + \frac{y^2}{\left(\sqrt{2}\right)^2} = 1$

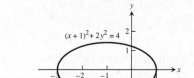

81. $3(x-1)^2 + 2(y+2)^2 = 6$

$\Rightarrow \frac{(x-1)^2}{\left(\sqrt{2}\right)^2} + \frac{\left[y-(-2)\right]^2}{\left(\sqrt{3}\right)^2} = 1$

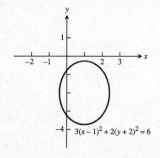

82. $6\left(x + \frac{3}{2}\right)^2 + 9\left(y - \frac{1}{2}\right)^2 = 54$

$\Rightarrow \frac{\left[x-\left(-\frac{3}{2}\right)\right]^2}{3^2} + \frac{\left(y-\frac{1}{2}\right)^2}{\left(\sqrt{6}\right)^2} = 1$

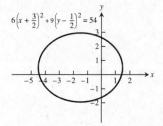

83. $\frac{x^2}{16} + \frac{y^2}{9} = 1$ has its center at $(0, 0)$. Shiftinig 4 units left and 3 units up gives the center at $(h, k) = (-4, 3)$. So the equation is $\frac{\left[x-(-4)\right]^2}{4^2} + \frac{(y-3)^2}{3^2} = 1$

$\Rightarrow \frac{(x+4)^2}{4^2} + \frac{(y-3)^2}{3^2} = 1$. Center, C, is $(-4, 3)$, and major axis, $\overline{AB}$, is the segment from $(-8, 3)$ to $(0, 3)$.

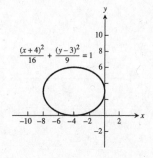

84. The ellipse $\frac{x^2}{4} + \frac{y^2}{25} = 1$ has center $(h, k) = (0, 0)$. Shifting the ellipse 3 units right and 2 units down produces an ellipse with center at $(h, k) = (3, -2)$ and an equation $\frac{(x-3)^2}{4} + \frac{\left[y-(-2)\right]^2}{25} = 1$. Center, C, is $(3, -2)$, and $\overline{AB}$, the segment from $(3, 3)$ to $(3, -7)$ is the major axis.

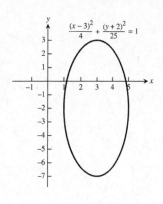

85. (a) $(fg)(-x) = f(-x)g(-x) = f(x)(-g(x)) = -(fg)(x)$, odd

(b) $\left(\frac{f}{g}\right)(-x) = \frac{f(-x)}{g(-x)} = \frac{f(x)}{-g(x)} = -\left(\frac{f}{g}\right)(x)$, odd

(c)  $\left(\frac{g}{f}\right)(-x) = \frac{g(-x)}{f(-x)} = \frac{-g(x)}{f(x)} = -\left(\frac{g}{f}\right)(x)$, odd

(d)  $f^2(-x) = f(-x)f(-x) = f(x)f(x) = f^2(x)$, even

(e)  $g^2(-x) = (g(-x))^2 = (-g(x))^2 = g^2(x)$, even

(f)  $(f \circ g)(-x) = f(g(-x)) = f(-g(x)) = f(g(x)) = (f \circ g)(x)$, even

(g)  $(g \circ f)(-x) = g(f(-x)) = g(f(x)) = (g \circ f)(x)$, even

(h)  $(f \circ f)(-x) = f(f(-x)) = f(f(x)) = (f \circ f)(x)$, even

(i)  $(g \circ g)(-x) = g(g(-x)) = g(-g(x)) = -g(g(x)) = -(g \circ g)(x)$, odd

86.  Yes, $f(x) = 0$ is both even and odd since $f(-x) = 0 = f(x)$ and $f(-x) = 0 = -f(x)$.

87. (a)

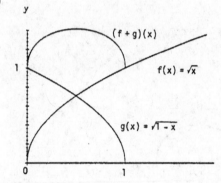

(b)

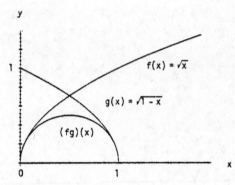

(c)

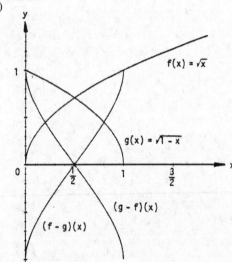

(d)

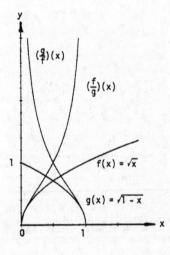

88.

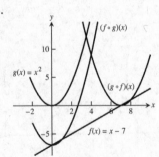

## 1.3 TRIGONOMETRIC FUNCTIONS

1. (a) $s = r\theta = (10)\left(\frac{4\pi}{5}\right) = 8\pi$ m

   (b) $s = r\theta = (10)(110°)\left(\frac{\pi}{180°}\right) = \frac{110\pi}{18} = \frac{55\pi}{9}$ m

2. $\theta = \frac{s}{r} = \frac{10\pi}{8} = \frac{5\pi}{4}$ radians and $\frac{5\pi}{4}\left(\frac{180°}{\pi}\right) = 225°$

3. $\theta = 80° \Rightarrow \theta = 80°\left(\frac{\pi}{180°}\right) = \frac{4\pi}{9} \Rightarrow s = (6)\left(\frac{4\pi}{9}\right) = 8.4$ in. (since the diameter = 12 in. $\Rightarrow$ radius = 6 in.)

4. $d = 1$ meter $\Rightarrow r = 50$ cm $\Rightarrow \theta = \frac{s}{r} = \frac{30}{50} = 0.6$ rad or $0.6\left(\frac{180°}{\pi}\right) \approx 34°$

5.

| $\theta$ | $-\pi$ | $-\frac{2\pi}{3}$ | $0$ | $\frac{\pi}{2}$ | $\frac{3\pi}{4}$ |
|---|---|---|---|---|---|
| $\sin\theta$ | $0$ | $-\frac{\sqrt{3}}{2}$ | $0$ | $1$ | $\frac{1}{\sqrt{2}}$ |
| $\cos\theta$ | $-1$ | $-\frac{1}{2}$ | $1$ | $0$ | $-\frac{1}{\sqrt{2}}$ |
| $\tan\theta$ | $0$ | $\sqrt{3}$ | $0$ | und. | $-1$ |
| $\cot\theta$ | und. | $\frac{1}{\sqrt{3}}$ | und. | $0$ | $-1$ |
| $\sec\theta$ | $-1$ | $-2$ | $1$ | und. | $-\sqrt{2}$ |
| $\csc\theta$ | und. | $-\frac{2}{\sqrt{3}}$ | und. | $1$ | $\sqrt{2}$ |

6.

| $\theta$ | $-\frac{3\pi}{2}$ | $-\frac{\pi}{3}$ | $-\frac{\pi}{6}$ | $\frac{\pi}{4}$ | $\frac{5\pi}{6}$ |
|---|---|---|---|---|---|
| $\sin\theta$ | $1$ | $-\frac{\sqrt{3}}{2}$ | $-\frac{1}{2}$ | $\frac{1}{\sqrt{2}}$ | $\frac{1}{2}$ |
| $\cos\theta$ | $0$ | $\frac{1}{2}$ | $\frac{\sqrt{3}}{2}$ | $\frac{1}{\sqrt{2}}$ | $-\frac{\sqrt{3}}{2}$ |
| $\tan\theta$ | und. | $-\sqrt{3}$ | $-\frac{1}{\sqrt{3}}$ | $1$ | $-\frac{1}{\sqrt{3}}$ |
| $\cot\theta$ | $0$ | $-\frac{1}{\sqrt{3}}$ | $-\sqrt{3}$ | $1$ | $-\sqrt{3}$ |
| $\sec\theta$ | und. | $2$ | $\frac{2}{\sqrt{3}}$ | $\sqrt{2}$ | $-\frac{2}{\sqrt{3}}$ |
| $\csc\theta$ | $1$ | $-\frac{2}{\sqrt{3}}$ | $-2$ | $\sqrt{2}$ | $2$ |

7. $\cos x = -\frac{4}{5}$, $\tan x = -\frac{3}{4}$

8. $\sin x = \frac{2}{\sqrt{5}}$, $\cos x = \frac{1}{\sqrt{5}}$

9. $\sin x = -\frac{\sqrt{8}}{3}$, $\tan x = -\sqrt{8}$

10. $\sin x = \frac{12}{13}$, $\tan x = -\frac{12}{5}$

11. $\sin x = -\frac{1}{\sqrt{5}}$, $\cos x = -\frac{2}{\sqrt{5}}$

12. $\cos x = -\frac{\sqrt{3}}{2}$, $\tan x = \frac{1}{\sqrt{3}}$

13.

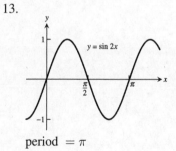

$y = \sin 2x$

period $= \pi$

14.

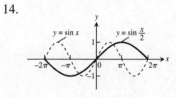

$y = \sin x$     $y = \sin\frac{x}{2}$

period $= 4\pi$

15.

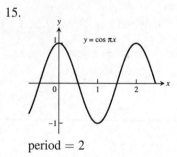

$y = \cos \pi x$

period $= 2$

16.

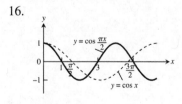

$y = \cos\frac{\pi x}{2}$     $y = \cos x$

period $= 4$

17.

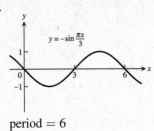

period = 6

18.

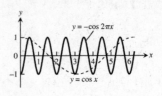

period = 1

19.

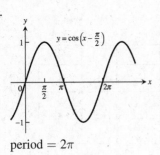

period = $2\pi$

20.

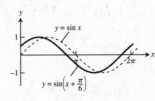

period = $2\pi$

21.

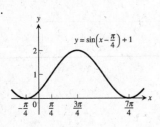

period = $2\pi$

22.

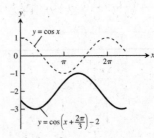

period = $2\pi$

23. period = $\frac{\pi}{2}$, symmetric about the origin

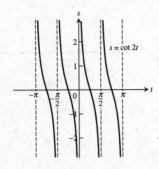

24. period = 1, symmetric about the origin

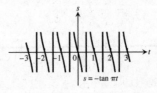

25. period = 4, symmetric about the s-axis

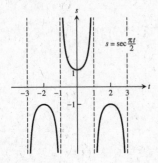

26. period = $4\pi$, symmetric about the origin

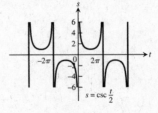

27. (a)  Cos x and sec x are positive for x in the interval
$\left(-\frac{\pi}{2}, \frac{\pi}{2}\right)$; and cos x and sec x are negative for x in the
intervals $\left(-\frac{3\pi}{2}, -\frac{\pi}{2}\right)$ and $\left(\frac{\pi}{2}, \frac{3\pi}{2}\right)$.  Sec x is undefined
when cos x is 0.  The range of sec x is
$(-\infty, -1] \cup [1, \infty)$; the range of cos x is $[-1, 1]$.

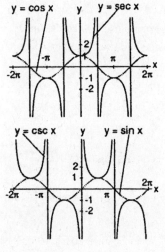

(b)  Sin x and csc x are positive for x in the intervals
$\left(-\frac{3\pi}{2}, -\pi\right)$ and $(0, \pi)$; and sin x and csc x are negative
for x in the intervals $(-\pi, 0)$ and $\left(\pi, \frac{3\pi}{2}\right)$.  Csc x is
undefined when sin x is 0.  The range of csc x is
$(-\infty, -1] \cup [1, \infty)$; the range of sin x is $[-1, 1]$.

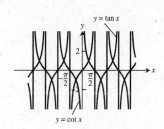

28. Since $\cot x = \frac{1}{\tan x}$, cot x is undefined when $\tan x = 0$
and is zero when tan x is undefined.  As tan x approaches
zero through positive values, cot x approaches infinity.
Also, cot x approaches negative infinity as tan x
approaches zero through negative values.

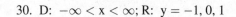

29. D: $-\infty < x < \infty$; R: $y = -1, 0, 1$

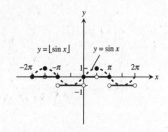

30. D: $-\infty < x < \infty$; R: $y = -1, 0, 1$

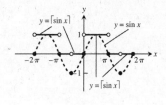

31. $\cos \left(x - \frac{\pi}{2}\right) = \cos x \cos \left(-\frac{\pi}{2}\right) - \sin x \sin \left(-\frac{\pi}{2}\right) = (\cos x)(0) - (\sin x)(-1) = \sin x$

32. $\cos \left(x + \frac{\pi}{2}\right) = \cos x \cos \left(\frac{\pi}{2}\right) - \sin x \sin \left(\frac{\pi}{2}\right) = (\cos x)(0) - (\sin x)(1) = -\sin x$

33. $\sin \left(x + \frac{\pi}{2}\right) = \sin x \cos \left(\frac{\pi}{2}\right) + \cos x \sin \left(\frac{\pi}{2}\right) = (\sin x)(0) + (\cos x)(1) = \cos x$

34. $\sin \left(x - \frac{\pi}{2}\right) = \sin x \cos \left(-\frac{\pi}{2}\right) + \cos x \sin \left(-\frac{\pi}{2}\right) = (\sin x)(0) + (\cos x)(-1) = -\cos x$

35. $\cos (A - B) = \cos (A + (-B)) = \cos A \cos (-B) - \sin A \sin (-B) = \cos A \cos B - \sin A (-\sin B)$
$= \cos A \cos B + \sin A \sin B$

36. $\sin (A - B) = \sin (A + (-B)) = \sin A \cos (-B) + \cos A \sin (-B) = \sin A \cos B + \cos A (-\sin B)$
$= \sin A \cos B - \cos A \sin B$

37. If $B = A$, $A - B = 0 \Rightarrow \cos (A - B) = \cos 0 = 1$.  Also $\cos (A - B) = \cos (A - A) = \cos A \cos A + \sin A \sin A$
$= \cos^2 A + \sin^2 A$.  Therefore, $\cos^2 A + \sin^2 A = 1$.

38. If $B = 2\pi$, then $\cos{(A + 2\pi)} = \cos{A}\cos{2\pi} - \sin{A}\sin{2\pi} = (\cos{A})(1) - (\sin{A})(0) = \cos{A}$ and $\sin{(A + 2\pi)} = \sin{A}\cos{2\pi} + \cos{A}\sin{2\pi} = (\sin{A})(1) + (\cos{A})(0) = \sin{A}$. The result agrees with the fact that the cosine and sine functions have period $2\pi$.

39. $\cos{(\pi + x)} = \cos{\pi}\cos{x} - \sin{\pi}\sin{x} = (-1)(\cos{x}) - (0)(\sin{x}) = -\cos{x}$

40. $\sin{(2\pi - x)} = \sin{2\pi}\cos{(-x)} + \cos{(2\pi)}\sin{(-x)} = (0)(\cos{(-x)}) + (1)(\sin{(-x)}) = -\sin{x}$

41. $\sin{\left(\frac{3\pi}{2} - x\right)} = \sin{\left(\frac{3\pi}{2}\right)}\cos{(-x)} + \cos{\left(\frac{3\pi}{2}\right)}\sin{(-x)} = (-1)(\cos{x}) + (0)(\sin{(-x)}) = -\cos{x}$

42. $\cos{\left(\frac{3\pi}{2} + x\right)} = \cos{\left(\frac{3\pi}{2}\right)}\cos{x} - \sin{\left(\frac{3\pi}{2}\right)}\sin{x} = (0)(\cos{x}) - (-1)(\sin{x}) = \sin{x}$

43. $\sin{\frac{7\pi}{12}} = \sin{\left(\frac{\pi}{4} + \frac{\pi}{3}\right)} = \sin{\frac{\pi}{4}}\cos{\frac{\pi}{3}} + \cos{\frac{\pi}{4}}\sin{\frac{\pi}{3}} = \left(\frac{\sqrt{2}}{2}\right)\left(\frac{1}{2}\right) + \left(\frac{\sqrt{2}}{2}\right)\left(\frac{\sqrt{3}}{2}\right) = \frac{\sqrt{6}+\sqrt{2}}{4}$

44. $\cos{\frac{11\pi}{12}} = \cos{\left(\frac{\pi}{4} + \frac{2\pi}{3}\right)} = \cos{\frac{\pi}{4}}\cos{\frac{2\pi}{3}} - \sin{\frac{\pi}{4}}\sin{\frac{2\pi}{3}} = \left(\frac{\sqrt{2}}{2}\right)\left(-\frac{1}{2}\right) - \left(\frac{\sqrt{2}}{2}\right)\left(\frac{\sqrt{3}}{2}\right) = -\frac{\sqrt{2}+\sqrt{6}}{4}$

45. $\cos{\frac{\pi}{12}} = \cos{\left(\frac{\pi}{3} - \frac{\pi}{4}\right)} = \cos{\frac{\pi}{3}}\cos{\left(-\frac{\pi}{4}\right)} - \sin{\frac{\pi}{3}}\sin{\left(-\frac{\pi}{4}\right)} = \left(\frac{1}{2}\right)\left(\frac{\sqrt{2}}{2}\right) - \left(\frac{\sqrt{3}}{2}\right)\left(-\frac{\sqrt{2}}{2}\right) = \frac{1+\sqrt{3}}{2\sqrt{2}}$

46. $\sin{\frac{5\pi}{12}} = \sin{\left(\frac{2\pi}{3} - \frac{\pi}{4}\right)} = \sin{\left(\frac{2\pi}{3}\right)}\cos{\left(-\frac{\pi}{4}\right)} + \cos{\left(\frac{2\pi}{3}\right)}\sin{\left(-\frac{\pi}{4}\right)} = \left(\frac{\sqrt{3}}{2}\right)\left(\frac{\sqrt{2}}{2}\right) + \left(-\frac{1}{2}\right)\left(-\frac{\sqrt{2}}{2}\right) = \frac{1+\sqrt{3}}{2\sqrt{2}}$

47. $\cos^2{\frac{\pi}{8}} = \frac{1 + \cos{\left(\frac{2\pi}{8}\right)}}{2} = \frac{1 + \frac{\sqrt{2}}{2}}{2} = \frac{2+\sqrt{2}}{4}$         48. $\cos^2{\frac{5\pi}{12}} = \frac{1 + \cos{\left(\frac{10\pi}{12}\right)}}{2} = \frac{1 + \left(-\frac{\sqrt{3}}{2}\right)}{2} = \frac{2-\sqrt{3}}{4}$

49. $\sin^2{\frac{\pi}{12}} = \frac{1 - \cos{\left(\frac{2\pi}{12}\right)}}{2} = \frac{1 - \frac{\sqrt{3}}{2}}{2} = \frac{2-\sqrt{3}}{4}$         50. $\sin^2{\frac{3\pi}{8}} = \frac{1 - \cos{\left(\frac{6\pi}{8}\right)}}{2} = \frac{1 - \left(-\frac{\sqrt{2}}{2}\right)}{2} = \frac{2+\sqrt{2}}{4}$

51. $\sin^2{\theta} = \frac{3}{4} \Rightarrow \sin{\theta} = \pm\frac{\sqrt{3}}{2} \Rightarrow \theta = \frac{\pi}{3}, \frac{2\pi}{3}, \frac{4\pi}{3}, \frac{5\pi}{3}$

52. $\sin^2{\theta} = \cos^2{\theta} \Rightarrow \frac{\sin^2{\theta}}{\cos^2{\theta}} = \frac{\cos^2{\theta}}{\cos^2{\theta}} \Rightarrow \tan^2{\theta} = 1 \Rightarrow \tan{\theta} = \pm1 \Rightarrow \theta = \frac{\pi}{4}, \frac{3\pi}{4}, \frac{5\pi}{4}, \frac{7\pi}{4}$

53. $\sin{2\theta} - \cos{\theta} = 0 \Rightarrow 2\sin{\theta}\cos{\theta} - \cos{\theta} = 0 \Rightarrow \cos{\theta}(2\sin{\theta} - 1) = 0 \Rightarrow \cos{\theta} = 0$ or $2\sin{\theta} - 1 = 0 \Rightarrow \cos{\theta} = 0$ or $\sin{\theta} = \frac{1}{2} \Rightarrow \theta = \frac{\pi}{2}, \frac{3\pi}{2},$ or $\theta = \frac{\pi}{6}, \frac{5\pi}{6} \Rightarrow \theta = \frac{\pi}{6}, \frac{\pi}{2}, \frac{5\pi}{6}, \frac{3\pi}{2}$

54. $\cos{2\theta} + \cos{\theta} = 0 \Rightarrow 2\cos^2{\theta} - 1 + \cos{\theta} = 0 \Rightarrow 2\cos^2{\theta} + \cos{\theta} - 1 = 0 \Rightarrow (\cos{\theta} + 1)(2\cos{\theta} - 1) = 0$
    $\Rightarrow \cos{\theta} + 1 = 0$ or $2\cos{\theta} - 1 = 0 \Rightarrow \cos{\theta} = -1$ or $\cos{\theta} = \frac{1}{2} \Rightarrow \theta = \pi$ or $\theta = \frac{\pi}{3}, \frac{5\pi}{3} \Rightarrow \theta = \frac{\pi}{3}, \pi, \frac{5\pi}{3}$

55. $\tan{(A + B)} = \frac{\sin{(A+B)}}{\cos{(A+B)}} = \frac{\sin{A}\cos{B}+\cos{A}\cos{B}}{\cos{A}\cos{B}-\sin{A}\sin{B}} = \frac{\frac{\sin{A}\cos{B}}{\cos{A}\cos{B}} + \frac{\cos{A}\sin{B}}{\cos{A}\cos{B}}}{\frac{\cos{A}\cos{B}}{\cos{A}\cos{B}} - \frac{\sin{A}\sin{B}}{\cos{A}\cos{B}}} = \frac{\tan{A}+\tan{B}}{1-\tan{A}\tan{B}}$

56. $\tan{(A - B)} = \frac{\sin{(A-B)}}{\cos{(A-B)}} = \frac{\sin{A}\cos{B}-\cos{A}\cos{B}}{\cos{A}\cos{B}+\sin{A}\sin{B}} = \frac{\frac{\sin{A}\cos{B}}{\cos{A}\cos{B}} - \frac{\cos{A}\sin{B}}{\cos{A}\cos{B}}}{\frac{\cos{A}\cos{B}}{\cos{A}\cos{B}} + \frac{\sin{A}\sin{B}}{\cos{A}\cos{B}}} = \frac{\tan{A}-\tan{B}}{1+\tan{A}\tan{B}}$

57. According to the figure in the text, we have the following: By the law of cosines, $c^2 = a^2 + b^2 - 2ab\cos{\theta}$
    $= 1^2 + 1^2 - 2\cos{(A - B)} = 2 - 2\cos{(A - B)}$. By distance formula, $c^2 = (\cos{A} - \cos{B})^2 + (\sin{A} - \sin{B})^2$
    $= \cos^2{A} - 2\cos{A}\cos{B} + \cos^2{B} + \sin^2{A} - 2\sin{A}\sin{B} + \sin^2{B} = 2 - 2(\cos{A}\cos{B} + \sin{A}\sin{B})$. Thus
    $c^2 = 2 - 2\cos{(A - B)} = 2 - 2(\cos{A}\cos{B} + \sin{A}\sin{B}) \Rightarrow \cos{(A - B)} = \cos{A}\cos{B} + \sin{A}\sin{B}$.

58. (a)  $\cos(A - B) = \cos A \cos B + \sin A \sin B$

   $\sin \theta = \cos\left(\frac{\pi}{2} - \theta\right)$ and $\cos \theta = \sin\left(\frac{\pi}{2} - \theta\right)$

   Let $\theta = A + B$

   $\sin(A + B) = \cos\left[\frac{\pi}{2} - (A + B)\right] = \cos\left[\left(\frac{\pi}{2} - A\right) - B\right] = \cos\left(\frac{\pi}{2} - A\right) \cos B + \sin\left(\frac{\pi}{2} - A\right) \sin B$

   $= \sin A \cos B + \cos A \sin B$

   (b)  $\cos(A - B) = \cos A \cos B + \sin A \sin B$

   $\cos(A - (-B)) = \cos A \cos(-B) + \sin A \sin(-B)$

   $\Rightarrow \cos(A + B) = \cos A \cos(-B) + \sin A \sin(-B) = \cos A \cos B + \sin A (-\sin B)$

   $= \cos A \cos B - \sin A \sin B$

   Because the cosine function is even and the sine functions is odd.

59.  $c^2 = a^2 + b^2 - 2ab \cos C = 2^2 + 3^2 - 2(2)(3) \cos(60°) = 4 + 9 - 12 \cos(60°) = 13 - 12\left(\frac{1}{2}\right) = 7.$
   Thus, $c = \sqrt{7} \approx 2.65$.

60.  $c^2 = a^2 + b^2 - 2ab \cos C = 2^2 + 3^2 - 2(2)(3) \cos(40°) = 13 - 12 \cos(40°).$ Thus, $c = \sqrt{13 - 12 \cos 40°} \approx 1.951$.

61.  From the figures in the text, we see that $\sin B = \frac{h}{c}$. If C is an acute angle, then $\sin C = \frac{h}{b}$. On the other hand,
   if C is obtuse (as in the figure on the right), then $\sin C = \sin(\pi - C) = \frac{h}{b}$. Thus, in either case,
   $h = b \sin C = c \sin B \Rightarrow ah = ab \sin C = ac \sin B.$

   By the law of cosines, $\cos C = \frac{a^2 + b^2 - c^2}{2ab}$ and $\cos B = \frac{a^2 + c^2 - b^2}{2ac}$. Moreover, since the sum of the
   interior angles of a triangle is $\pi$, we have $\sin A = \sin(\pi - (B + C)) = \sin(B + C) = \sin B \cos C + \cos B \sin C$
   $= \left(\frac{h}{c}\right)\left[\frac{a^2 + b^2 - c^2}{2ab}\right] + \left[\frac{a^2 + c^2 - b^2}{2ac}\right]\left(\frac{h}{b}\right) = \left(\frac{h}{2abc}\right)(2a^2 + b^2 - c^2 + c^2 - b^2) = \frac{ah}{bc} \Rightarrow ah = bc \sin A.$
   Combining our results we have $ah = ab \sin C$, $ah = ac \sin B$, and $ah = bc \sin A$. Dividing by abc gives
   $\underbrace{\frac{h}{bc} = \frac{\sin A}{a} = \frac{\sin C}{c} = \frac{\sin B}{b}}_{\text{law of sines}}.$

62.  By the law of sines, $\frac{\sin A}{2} = \frac{\sin B}{3} = \frac{\sqrt{3}/2}{c}$. By Exercise 61 we know that $c = \sqrt{7}$. Thus $\sin B = \frac{3\sqrt{3}}{2\sqrt{7}} \simeq 0.982$.

63.  From the figure at the right and the law of cosines,
   $b^2 = a^2 + 2^2 - 2(2a) \cos B$
   $= a^2 + 4 - 4a\left(\frac{1}{2}\right) = a^2 - 2a + 4.$
   Applying the law of sines to the figure, $\frac{\sin A}{a} = \frac{\sin B}{b}$
   $\Rightarrow \frac{\sqrt{2}/2}{a} = \frac{\sqrt{3}/2}{b} \Rightarrow b = \sqrt{\frac{3}{2}}\,a.$ Thus, combining results,
   $a^2 - 2a + 4 = b^2 = \frac{3}{2}a^2 \Rightarrow 0 = \frac{1}{2}a^2 + 2a - 4$
   $\Rightarrow 0 = a^2 + 4a - 8.$ From the quadratic formula and the fact that $a > 0$, we have
   $a = \frac{-4 + \sqrt{4^2 - 4(1)(-8)}}{2} = \frac{4\sqrt{3} - 4}{2} \simeq 1.464.$

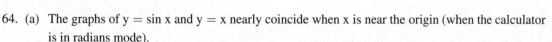

64.  (a)  The graphs of $y = \sin x$ and $y = x$ nearly coincide when x is near the origin (when the calculator
       is in radians mode).

   (b)  In degree mode, when x is near zero degrees the sine of x is much closer to zero than x itself. The
       curves look like intersecting straight lines near the origin when the calculator is in degree mode.

65. $A = 2, B = 2\pi, C = -\pi, D = -1$

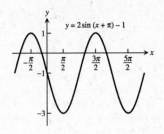

66. $A = \frac{1}{2}, B = 2, C = 1, D = \frac{1}{2}$

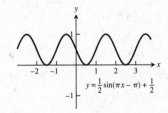

67. $A = -\frac{2}{\pi}, B = 4, C = 0, D = \frac{1}{\pi}$

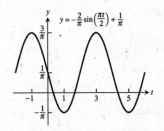

68. $A = \frac{L}{2\pi}, B = L, C = 0, D = 0$

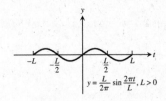

69-72.  Example CAS commands:

Maple

```
f := x -> A*sin((2*Pi/B)*(x-C))+D1;
A:=3; C:=0; D1:=0;
f_list := [seq( f(x), B=[1,3,2*Pi,5*Pi] )];
plot( f_list, x=-4*Pi..4*Pi, scaling=constrained,
      color=[red,blue,green,cyan], linestyle=[1,3,4,7],
      legend=["B=1","B=3","B=2*Pi","B=3*Pi"],
      title="#69 (Section 1.3)" );
```

Mathematica

```
Clear[a, b, c, d, f, x]
f[x_]:=a  Sin[2π/b (x − c)] + d
Plot[f[x]/.{a → 3, b → 1, c → 0, d → 0}, {x, −4π, 4π }]
```

69. (a)  The graph stretches horizontally.

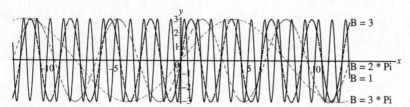

(b)  The period remains the same: period $= \mid B \mid$. The graph has a horizontal shift of $\frac{1}{2}$ period.

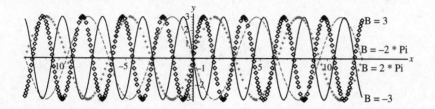

70. (a)  The graph is shifted right C units.

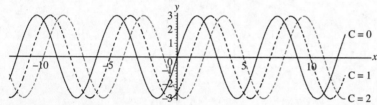

(b)  The graph is shifted left C units.

(c)  A shift of $\pm$ one period will produce no apparent shift. $\mid C \mid = 6$

71. (a)  The graph shifts upwards $\mid D \mid$ units for $D > 0$

(b)  The graph shifts down $\mid D \mid$ units for $D < 0$.

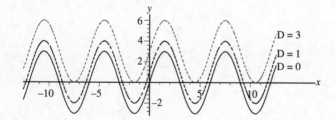

72. (a)  The graph stretches $\mid A \mid$ units.                    (b)  For $A < 0$, the graph is inverted.

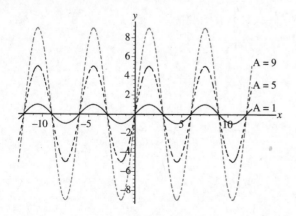

## 1.4 GRAPHING WITH CALCULATORS AND COMPUTERS

1-4.    The most appropriate viewing window displays the maxima, minima, intercepts, and end behavior of the graphs and has little unused space.

1.  d.

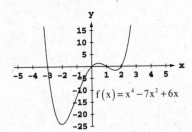

$f(x) = x^4 - 7x^2 + 6x$

2.  c.

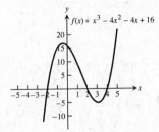

$f(x) = x^3 - 4x^2 - 4x + 16$

3.  d.

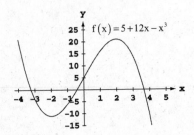

$f(x) = 5 + 12x - x^3$

4.  b.

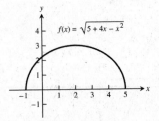

$f(x) = \sqrt{5 + 4x - x^2}$

5-30.    For any display there are many appropriate display widows. The graphs given as answers in Exercises 5−30 are not unique in appearance.

5.  $[-2, 5]$ by $[-15, 40]$

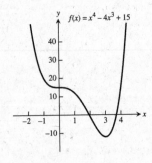

$f(x) = x^4 - 4x^3 + 15$

6.  $[-4, 4]$ by $[-4, 4]$

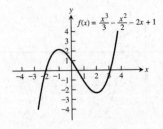

$f(x) = \frac{x^3}{3} - \frac{x^2}{2} - 2x + 1$

7.  $[-2, 6]$ by $[-250, 50]$

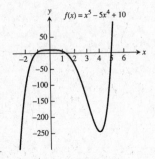

$f(x) = x^5 - 5x^4 + 10$

8.  $[-1, 5]$ by $[-5, 30]$

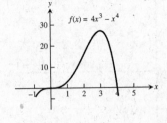

$f(x) = 4x^3 - x^4$

9.  $[-4, 4]$ by $[-5, 5]$

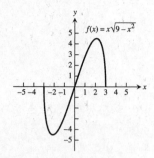

$f(x) = x\sqrt{9 - x^2}$

10.  $[-2, 2]$ by $[-2, 8]$

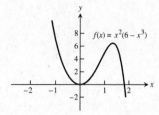

$f(x) = x^2(6 - x^3)$

11.  $[-2, 6]$ by $[-5, 4]$

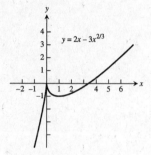

$y = 2x - 3x^{2/3}$

12.  $[-4, 4]$ by $[-8, 8]$

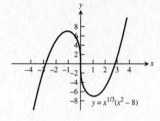

$y = x^{1/3}(x^2 - 8)$

13.  $[-1, 6]$ by $[-1, 4]$

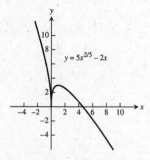

$y = 5x^{2/5} - 2x$

14.  $[-1, 6]$ by $[-1, 5]$

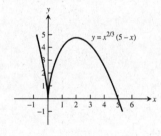

$y = x^{2/3}(5 - x)$

15.  $[-3, 3]$ by $[0, 10]$

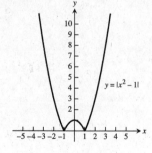

$y = |x^2 - 1|$

16.  $[-1, 2]$ by $[0, 1]$

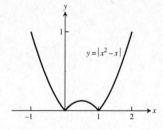

$y = |x^2 - x|$

17. $[-5, 1]$ by $[-5, 5]$

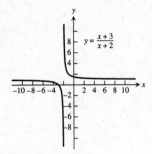

$$y = \frac{x+3}{x+2}$$

18. $[-5, 1]$ by $[-2, 4]$

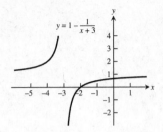

$$y = 1 - \frac{1}{x+3}$$

19. $[-4, 4]$ by $[0, 3]$

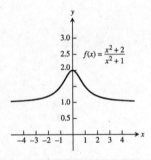

$$f(x) = \frac{x^2+2}{x^2+1}$$

20. $[-5, 5]$ by $[-2, 2]$

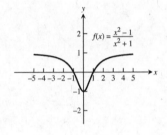

$$f(x) = \frac{x^2-1}{x^2+1}$$

21. $[-10, 10]$ by $[-6, 6]$

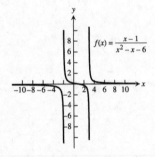

$$f(x) = \frac{x-1}{x^2-x-6}$$

22. $[-5, 5]$ by $[-2, 2]$

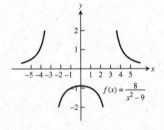

$$f(x) = \frac{8}{x^2-9}$$

23. $[-6, 10]$ by $[-6, 6]$

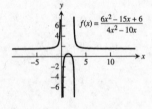

$$f(x) = \frac{6x^2-15x+6}{4x^2-10x}$$

24. $[-3, 5]$ by $[-2, 10]$

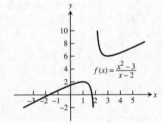

$$f(x) = \frac{x^2-3}{x-2}$$

25. $[-0.03, 0.03]$ by $[-1.25, 1.25]$

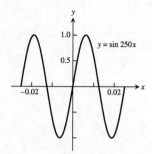

26. $[-0.1, 0.1]$ by $[-3, 3]$

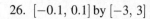
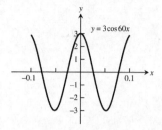

27. $[-300, 300]$ by $[-1.25, 1.25]$

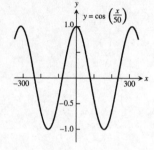

28. $[-50, 50]$ by $[-0.1, 0.1]$

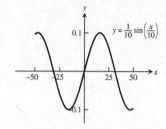

29. $[-0.25, 0.25]$ by $[-0.3, 0.3]$

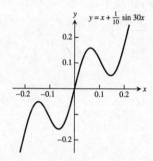

30. $[-0.15, 0.15]$ by $[-0.02, 0.05]$

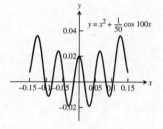

31. $x^2 + 2x = 4 + 4y - y^2 \Rightarrow y = 2 \pm \sqrt{-x^2 - 2x + 8}$.
The lower half is produced by graphing
$y = 2 - \sqrt{-x^2 - 2x + 8}$.

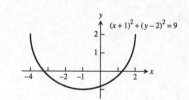

32. $y^2 - 16x^2 = 1 \Rightarrow y = \pm \sqrt{1 + 16x^2}$. The upper branch
is produced by graphing $y = \sqrt{1 + 16x^2}$.

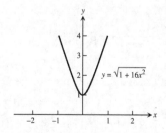

33.

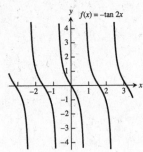

34.

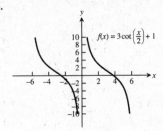

35.

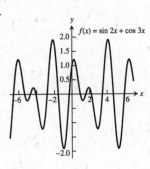

36.

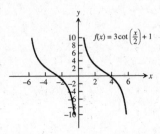

37.

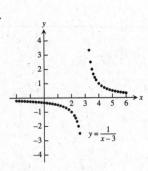

38.

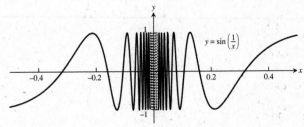

39.

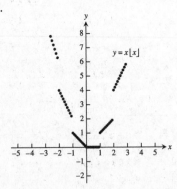

40.

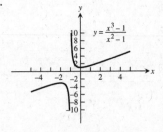

## CHAPTER 1 PRACTICE EXERCISES

1.  The area is $A = \pi r^2$ and the circumference is $C = 2\pi r$. Thus, $r = \frac{C}{2\pi} \Rightarrow A = \pi \left(\frac{C}{2\pi}\right)^2 = \frac{C^2}{4\pi}$.

2.  The surface area is $S = 4\pi r^2 \Rightarrow r = \left(\frac{S}{4\pi}\right)^{1/2}$. The volume is $V = \frac{4}{3}\pi r^3 \Rightarrow r = \sqrt[3]{\frac{3V}{4\pi}}$. Substitution into the formula for surface area gives $S = 4\pi r^2 = 4\pi \left(\frac{3V}{4\pi}\right)^{2/3}$.

3. The coordinates of a point on the parabola are $(x, x^2)$. The angle of inclination $\theta$ joining this point to the origin satisfies the equation $\tan \theta = \frac{x^2}{x} = x$. Thus the point has coordinates $(x, x^2) = (\tan \theta, \tan^2 \theta)$.

4. $\tan \theta = \frac{\text{rise}}{\text{run}} = \frac{h}{500} \Rightarrow h = 500 \tan \theta$ ft.

5.

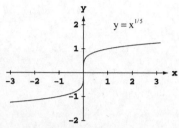

Symmetric about the origin.

6.

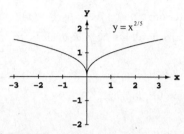

Symmetric about the y-axis.

7.

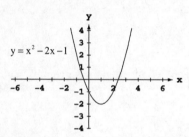

Neither

8.

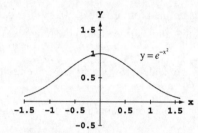

Symmetric about the y-axis.

9. $y(-x) = (-x)^2 + 1 = x^2 + 1 = y(x)$. Even.

10. $y(-x) = (-x)^5 - (-x)^3 - (-x) = -x^5 + x^3 + x = -y(x)$. Odd.

11. $y(-x) = 1 - \cos(-x) = 1 - \cos x = y(x)$. Even.

12. $y(-x) = \sec(-x)\tan(-x) = \frac{\sin(-x)}{\cos^2(-x)} = \frac{-\sin x}{\cos^2 x} = -\sec x \tan x = -y(x)$. Odd.

13. $y(-x) = \frac{(-x)^4 + 1}{(-x)^3 - 2(-x)} = \frac{x^4 + 1}{-x^3 + 2x} = -\frac{x^4 + 1}{x^3 - 2x} = -y(x)$. Odd.

14. $y(-x) = (-x) - \sin(-x) = (-x) + \sin x = -(x - \sin x) = -y(x)$. Odd.

15. $y(-x) = -x + \cos(-x) = -x + \cos x$. Neither even nor odd.

16. $y(-x) = (-x)\cos(-x) = -x \cos x = -y(x)$. Odd.

17. Since f and g are odd $\Rightarrow f(-x) = -f(x)$ and $g(-x) = -g(x)$.
   (a) $(f \cdot g)(-x) = f(-x)g(-x) = [-f(x)][-g(x)] = f(x)g(x) = (f \cdot g)(x) \Rightarrow f \cdot g$ is even
   (b) $f^3(-x) = f(-x)f(-x)f(-x) = [-f(x)][-f(x)][-f(x)] = -f(x) \cdot f(x) \cdot f(x) = -f^3(x) \Rightarrow f^3$ is odd.
   (c) $f(\sin(-x)) = f(-\sin(x)) = -f(\sin(x)) \Rightarrow f(\sin(x))$ is odd.
   (d) $g(\sec(-x)) = g(\sec(x)) \Rightarrow g(\sec(x))$ is even.
   (e) $|g(-x)| = |-g(x)| = |g(x)| \Rightarrow |g|$ is even.

18. Let $f(a - x) = f(a + x)$ and define $g(x) = f(x + a)$. Then $g(-x) = f((-x) + a) = f(a - x) = f(a + x) = f(x + a) = g(x)$
    $\Rightarrow g(x) = f(x + a)$ is even.

19. (a) The function is defined for all values of x, so the domain is $(-\infty, \infty)$.
    (b) Since $|x|$ attains all nonnegative values, the range is $[-2, \infty)$.

20. (a) Since the square root requires $1 - x \geq 0$, the domain is $(-\infty, 1]$.
    (b) Since $\sqrt{1 - x}$ attains all nonnegative values, the range is $[-2, \infty)$.

21. (a) Since the square root requires $16 - x^2 \geq 0$, the domain is $[-4, 4]$.
    (b) For values of x in the domain, $0 \leq 16 - x^2 \leq 16$, so $0 \leq \sqrt{16 - x^2} \leq 4$. The range is $[0, 4]$.

22. (a) The function is defined for all values of x, so the domain is $(-\infty, \infty)$.
    (b) Since $3^{2-x}$ attains all positive values, the range is $(1, \infty)$.

23. (a) The function is defined for all values of x, so the domain is $(-\infty, \infty)$.
    (b) Since $2e^{-x}$ attains all positive values, the range is $(-3, \infty)$.

24. (a) The function is equivalent to $y = \tan 2x$, so we require $2x \neq \frac{k\pi}{2}$ for odd integers k. The domain is given by $x \neq \frac{k\pi}{4}$ for
    odd integers k.
    (b) Since the tangent function attains all values, the range is $(-\infty, \infty)$.

25. (a) The function is defined for all values of x, so the domain is $(-\infty, \infty)$.
    (b) The sine function attains values from $-1$ to 1, so $-2 \leq 2\sin(3x + \pi) \leq 2$ and hence $-3 \leq 2\sin(3x + \pi) - 1 \leq 1$. The
    range is $[-3, 1]$.

26. (a) The function is defined for all values of x, so the domain is $(-\infty, \infty)$.
    (b) The function is equivalent to $y = \sqrt[5]{x^2}$, which attains all nonnegative values. The range is $[0, \infty)$.

27. (a) The logarithm requires $x - 3 > 0$, so the domain is $(3, \infty)$.
    (b) The logarithm attains all real values, so the range is $(-\infty, \infty)$.

28. (a) The function is defined for all values of x, so the domain is $(-\infty, \infty)$.
    (b) The cube root attains all real values, so the range is $(-\infty, \infty)$.

29. (a) Increasing because volume increases as radius increases
    (b) Neither, since the greatest integer function is composed of horizontal (constant) line segments
    (c) Decreasing because as the height increases, the atmospheric pressure decreases.
    (d) Increasing because the kinetic (motion) energy increases as the particles velocity increases.

30. (a) Increasing on $[2, \infty)$            (b) Increasing on $[-1, \infty)$
    (c) Increasing on $(-\infty, \infty)$          (d) Increasing on $[\frac{1}{2}, \infty)$

31. (a) The function is defined for $-4 \leq x \leq 4$, so the domain is $[-4, 4]$.
    (b) The function is equivalent to $y = \sqrt{|x|}$, $-4 \leq x \leq 4$, which attains values from 0 to 2 for x in the domain. The
    range is $[0, 2]$.

32. (a) The function is defined for $-2 \le x \le 2$, so the domain is $[-2, 2]$.

   (b) The range is $[-1, 1]$.

33. First piece: Line through $(0, 1)$ and $(1, 0)$. $m = \frac{0-1}{1-0} = \frac{-1}{1} = -1 \Rightarrow y = -x + 1 = 1 - x$

   Second piece: Line through $(1, 1)$ and $(2, 0)$. $m = \frac{0-1}{2-1} = \frac{-1}{1} = -1 \Rightarrow y = -(x-1) + 1 = -x + 2 = 2 - x$

   $f(x) = \begin{cases} 1 - x, & 0 \le x < 1 \\ 2 - x, & 1 \le x \le 2 \end{cases}$

34. First piece: Line through $(0, 0)$ and $(2, 5)$. $m = \frac{5-0}{2-0} = \frac{5}{2} \Rightarrow y = \frac{5}{2}x$

   Second piece: Line through $(2, 5)$ and $(4, 0)$. $m = \frac{0-5}{4-2} = \frac{-5}{2} = -\frac{5}{2} \Rightarrow y = -\frac{5}{2}(x - 2) + 5 = -\frac{5}{2}x + 10 = 10 - \frac{5x}{2}$

   $f(x) = \begin{cases} \frac{5}{2}x, & 0 \le x < 2 \\ 10 - \frac{5x}{2}, & 2 \le x \le 4 \end{cases}$   (Note: $x = 2$ can be included on either piece.)

35. (a) $(f \circ g)(-1) = f(g(-1)) = f\left(\frac{1}{\sqrt{-1+2}}\right) = f(1) = \frac{1}{1} = 1$

   (b) $(g \circ f)(2) = g(f(2)) = g\left(\frac{1}{2}\right) = \frac{1}{\sqrt{\frac{1}{2}+2}} = \frac{1}{\sqrt{2.5}}$ or $\sqrt{\frac{2}{5}}$

   (c) $(f \circ f)(x) = f(f(x)) = f\left(\frac{1}{x}\right) = \frac{1}{1/x} = x, \, x \ne 0$

   (d) $(g \circ g)(x) = g(g(x)) = g\left(\frac{1}{\sqrt{x+2}}\right) = \frac{1}{\sqrt{\frac{1}{\sqrt{x+2}}+2}} = \frac{\sqrt[4]{x+2}}{\sqrt{1+2\sqrt{x+2}}}$

36. (a) $(f \circ g)(-1) = f(g(-1)) = f\left(\sqrt[3]{-1+1}\right) = f(0) = 2 - 0 = 2$

   (b) $(g \circ f)(2) = f(g(2)) = g(2 - 2) = g(0) = \sqrt[3]{0+1} = 1$

   (c) $(f \circ f)(x) = f(f(x)) = f(2 - x) = 2 - (2 - x) = x$

   (d) $(g \circ g)(x) = g(g(x)) = g\left(\sqrt[3]{x+1}\right) = \sqrt[3]{\sqrt[3]{x+1}+1}$

37. (a) $(f \circ g)(x) = f(g(x)) = f\left(\sqrt{x+2}\right) = 2 - \left(\sqrt{x+2}\right)^2 = -x, \, x \ge -2.$

   $(g \circ f)(x) = f(g(x)) = g(2 - x^2) = \sqrt{(2 - x^2) + 2} = \sqrt{4 - x^2}$

   (b) Domain of $f \circ g$: $[-2, \infty)$.          (c) Range of $f \circ g$: $(-\infty, 2]$.

   Domain of $g \circ f$: $[-2, 2]$.             Range of $g \circ f$: $[0, 2]$.

38. (a) $(f \circ g)(x) = f(g(x)) = f\left(\sqrt{1-x}\right) = \sqrt{\sqrt{1-x}} = \sqrt[4]{1-x}.$

   $(g \circ f)(x) = f(g(x)) = g\left(\sqrt{x}\right) = \sqrt{1 - \sqrt{x}}$

   (b) Domain of $f \circ g$: $(-\infty, 1]$.          (c) Range of $f \circ g$: $[0, \infty)$.

   Domain of $g \circ f$: $[0, 1]$.             Range of $g \circ f$: $[0, 1]$.

39.

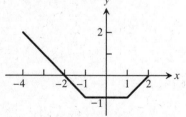

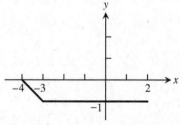

40.

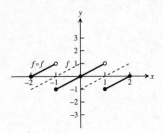

41.

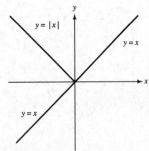

The graph of $f_2(x) = f_1(|x|)$ is the same as the graph of $f_1(x)$ to the right of the y-axis. The graph of $f_2(x)$ to the left of the y-axis is the reflection of $y = f_1(x)$, $x \geq 0$ across the y-axis.

42.

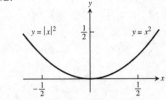

It does not change the graph.

43.

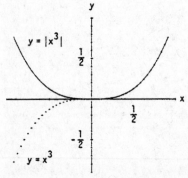

Whenever $g_1(x)$ is positive, the graph of $y = g_2(x) = |g_1(x)|$ is the same as the graph of $y = g_1(x)$. When $g_1(x)$ is negative, the graph of $y = g_2(x)$ is the reflection of the graph of $y = g_1(x)$ across the x-axis.

44.

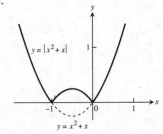

Whenever $g_1(x)$ is positive, the graph of $y = g_2(x) = |g_1(x)|$ is the same as the graph of $y = g_1(x)$. When $g_1(x)$ is negative, the graph of $y = g_2(x)$ is the reflection of the graph of $y = g_1(x)$ across the x-axis.

45.

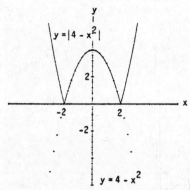

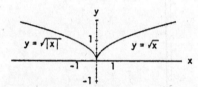

Whenever $g_1(x)$ is positive, the graph of $y = g_2(x) = |g_1(x)|$ is the same as the graph of $y = g_1(x)$. When $g_1(x)$ is negative, the graph of $y = g_2(x)$ is the reflection of the graph of $y = g_1(x)$ across the x-axis.

46.

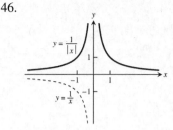

The graph of $f_2(x) = f_1(|x|)$ is the same as the graph of $f_1(x)$ to the right of the y-axis. The graph of $f_2(x)$ to the left of the y-axis is the reflection of $y = f_1(x)$, $x \geq 0$ across the y-axis.

47.

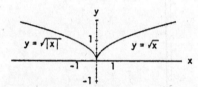

The graph of $f_2(x) = f_1(|x|)$ is the same as the graph of $f_1(x)$ to the right of the y-axis. The graph of $f_2(x)$ to the left of the y-axis is the reflection of $y = f_1(x)$, $x \geq 0$ across the y-axis.

48.

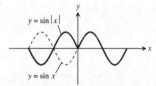

The graph of $f_2(x) = f_1(|x|)$ is the same as the graph of $f_1(x)$ to the right of the y-axis. The graph of $f_2(x)$ to the left of the y-axis is the reflection of $y = f_1(x)$, $x \geq 0$ across the y-axis.

49. (a) $y = g(x - 3) + \frac{1}{2}$

(b) $y = g\left(x + \frac{2}{3}\right) - 2$

(c) $y = g(-x)$

(d) $y = -g(x)$

(e) $y = 5 \cdot g(x)$

(f) $y = g(5x)$

50. (a) Shift the graph of f right 5 units

(b) Horizontally compress the graph of f by a factor of 4

(c) Horizontally compress the graph of f by a factor of 3 and a then reflect the graph about the y-axis

(d) Horizontally compress the graph of f by a factor of 2 and then shift the graph left $\frac{1}{2}$ unit.

(e) Horizontally stretch the graph of f by a factor of 3 and then shift the graph down 4 units.

(f) Vertically stretch the graph of f by a factor of 3, then reflect the graph about the x-axis, and finally shift the graph up $\frac{1}{4}$ unit.

51. Reflection of the grpah of $y = \sqrt{x}$ about the x-axis followed by a horizontal compression by a factor of $\frac{1}{2}$ then a shift left 2 units.

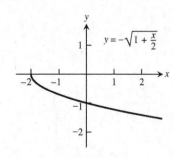

52. Reflect the graph of y = x about the x-axis, followed by a vertical compression of the graph by a factor of 3, then shift the graph up 1 unit.

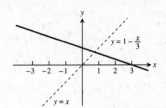

53. Vertical compression of the graph of $y = \frac{1}{x^2}$ by a factor of 2, then shift the graph up 1 unit.

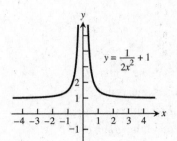

54. Reflect the graph of $y = x^{1/3}$ about the y-axis, then compress the graph horizontally by a factor of 5.

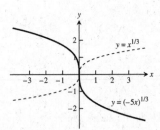

55.

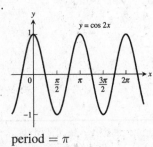

period = $\pi$

56.

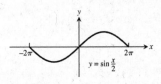

period = $4\pi$

57.

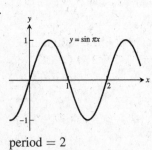

period = 2

58.

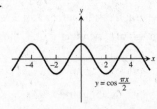

period = 4

59.

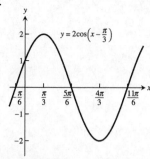

period $= 2\pi$

60.

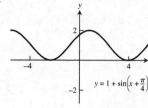

period $= 2\pi$

61. (a)  $\sin B = \sin \frac{\pi}{3} = \frac{b}{c} = \frac{b}{2} \Rightarrow b = 2 \sin \frac{\pi}{3} = 2\left(\frac{\sqrt{3}}{2}\right) = \sqrt{3}$. By the theorem of Pythagoras,

$a^2 + b^2 = c^2 \Rightarrow a = \sqrt{c^2 - b^2} = \sqrt{4 - 3} = 1.$

(b)  $\sin B = \sin \frac{\pi}{3} = \frac{b}{c} = \frac{2}{c} \Rightarrow c = \frac{2}{\sin \frac{\pi}{3}} = \frac{2}{\left(\frac{\sqrt{3}}{2}\right)} = \frac{4}{\sqrt{3}}$. Thus, $a = \sqrt{c^2 - b^2} = \sqrt{\left(\frac{4}{\sqrt{3}}\right)^2 - (2)^2} = \sqrt{\frac{4}{3}} = \frac{2}{\sqrt{3}}.$

62. (a)  $\sin A = \frac{a}{c} \Rightarrow a = c \sin A$  (b)  $\tan A = \frac{a}{b} \Rightarrow a = b \tan A$

63. (a)  $\tan B = \frac{b}{a} \Rightarrow a = \frac{b}{\tan B}$  (b)  $\sin A = \frac{a}{c} \Rightarrow c = \frac{a}{\sin A}$

64. (a)  $\sin A = \frac{a}{c}$  (c)  $\sin A = \frac{a}{c} = \frac{\sqrt{c^2 - b^2}}{c}$

65. Let h = height of vertical pole, and let b and c denote the distances of points B and C from the base of the pole, measured along the flatground, respectively. Then, $\tan 50° = \frac{h}{c}$, $\tan 35° = \frac{h}{b}$, and $b - c = 10$. Thus, $h = c \tan 50°$ and $h = b \tan 35° = (c + 10) \tan 35°$
$\Rightarrow c \tan 50° = (c + 10) \tan 35°$
$\Rightarrow c (\tan 50° - \tan 35°) = 10 \tan 35°$
$\Rightarrow c = \frac{10 \tan 35°}{\tan 50° - \tan 35°} \Rightarrow h = c \tan 50°$
$= \frac{10 \tan 35° \tan 50°}{\tan 50° - \tan 35°} \approx 16.98$ m.

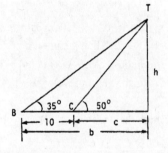

66. Let h = height of balloon above ground. From the figure at the right, $\tan 40° = \frac{h}{a}$, $\tan 70° = \frac{h}{b}$, and $a + b = 2$. Thus, $h = b \tan 70° \Rightarrow h = (2 - a) \tan 70°$ and $h = a \tan 40°$
$\Rightarrow (2 - a) \tan 70° = a \tan 40° \Rightarrow a(\tan 40° + \tan 70°)$
$= 2 \tan 70° \Rightarrow a = \frac{2 \tan 70°}{\tan 40° + \tan 70°} \Rightarrow h = a \tan 40°$
$= \frac{2 \tan 70° \tan 40°}{\tan 40° + \tan 70°} \approx 1.3$ km.

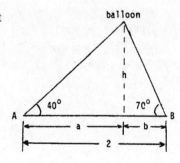

67. (a)

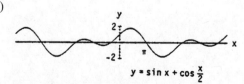

(b)  The period appears to be $4\pi$.

(c) $f(x + 4\pi) = \sin(x + 4\pi) + \cos\left(\frac{x+4\pi}{2}\right) = \sin(x + 2\pi) + \cos\left(\frac{x}{2} + 2\pi\right) = \sin x + \cos\frac{x}{2}$
since the period of sine and cosine is $2\pi$. Thus, $f(x)$ has period $4\pi$.

68. (a)

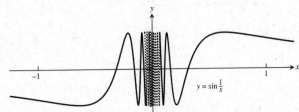

(b) $D = (-\infty, 0) \cup (0, \infty); R = [-1, 1]$

(c) f is not periodic. For suppose f has period p. Then $f\left(\frac{1}{2\pi} + kp\right) = f\left(\frac{1}{2\pi}\right) = \sin 2\pi = 0$ for all
integers k. Choose k so large that $\frac{1}{2\pi} + kp > \frac{1}{\pi} \Rightarrow 0 < \frac{1}{(1/2\pi)+kp} < \pi$. But then
$f\left(\frac{1}{2\pi} + kp\right) = \sin\left(\frac{1}{(1/2\pi)+kp}\right) > 0$ which is a contradiction. Thus f has no period, as claimed.

## CHAPTER 1 ADDITIONAL AND ADVANCED EXERCISES

1. There are (infinitely) many such function pairs. For example, $f(x) = 3x$ and $g(x) = 4x$ satisfy
   $f(g(x)) = f(4x) = 3(4x) = 12x = 4(3x) = g(3x) = g(f(x))$.

2. Yes, there are many such function pairs. For example, if $g(x) = (2x + 3)^3$ and $f(x) = x^{1/3}$, then
   $(f \circ g)(x) = f(g(x)) = f\left((2x + 3)^3\right) = \left((2x + 3)^3\right)^{1/3} = 2x + 3$.

3. If f is odd and defined at x, then $f(-x) = -f(x)$. Thus $g(-x) = f(-x) - 2 = -f(x) - 2$ whereas
   $-g(x) = -(f(x) - 2) = -f(x) + 2$. Then g cannot be odd because $g(-x) = -g(x) \Rightarrow -f(x) - 2 = -f(x) + 2$
   $\Rightarrow 4 = 0$, which is a contradiction. Also, $g(x)$ is not even unless $f(x) = 0$ for all x. On the other hand, if f is
   even, then $g(x) = f(x) - 2$ is also even: $g(-x) = f(-x) - 2 = f(x) - 2 = g(x)$.

4. If g is odd and g(0) is defined, then $g(0) = g(-0) = -g(0)$. Therefore, $2g(0) = 0 \Rightarrow g(0) = 0$.

5. For $(x, y)$ in the 1st quadrant, $|x| + |y| = 1 + x$
   $\Leftrightarrow x + y = 1 + x \Leftrightarrow y = 1$. For $(x, y)$ in the 2nd
   quadrant, $|x| + |y| = x + 1 \Leftrightarrow -x + y = x + 1$
   $\Leftrightarrow y = 2x + 1$. In the 3rd quadrant, $|x| + |y| = x + 1$
   $\Leftrightarrow -x - y = x + 1 \Leftrightarrow y = -2x - 1$. In the 4th
   quadrant, $|x| + |y| = x + 1 \Leftrightarrow x + (-y) = x + 1$
   $\Leftrightarrow y = -1$. The graph is given at the right.

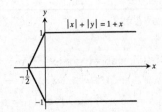

6.  We use reasoning similar to Exercise 5.

    (1) 1st quadrant: $y + |y| = x + |x|$

    $\Leftrightarrow 2y = 2x \Leftrightarrow y = x$.

    (2) 2nd quadrant: $y + |y| = x + |x|$

    $\Leftrightarrow 2y = x + (-x) = 0 \Leftrightarrow y = 0$.

    (3) 3rd quadrant: $y + |y| = x + |x|$

    $\Leftrightarrow y + (-y) = x + (-x) \Leftrightarrow 0 = 0$

    $\Rightarrow$ all points in the 3rd quadrant

    satisfy the equation.

    (4) 4th quadrant: $y + |y| = x + |x|$

    $\Leftrightarrow y + (-y) = 2x \Leftrightarrow 0 = x$. Combining

    these results we have the graph given at the

    right:

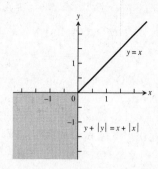

7.  (a) $\sin^2 x + \cos^2 x = 1 \Rightarrow \sin^2 x = 1 - \cos^2 x = (1 - \cos x)(1 + \cos x) \Rightarrow (1 - \cos x) = \frac{\sin^2 x}{1 + \cos x}$

    $\Rightarrow \frac{1 - \cos x}{\sin x} = \frac{\sin x}{1 + \cos x}$

    (b) Using the definition of the tangent function and the double angle formulas, we have

    $\tan^2\left(\frac{x}{2}\right) = \frac{\sin^2\left(\frac{x}{2}\right)}{\cos^2\left(\frac{x}{2}\right)} = \frac{\frac{1 - \cos\left(2\left(\frac{x}{2}\right)\right)}{2}}{\frac{1 + \cos\left(2\left(\frac{x}{2}\right)\right)}{2}} = \frac{1 - \cos x}{1 + \cos x}$.

8.  The angles labeled $\gamma$ in the accompanying figure are

    equal since both angles subtend arc CD. Similarly, the

    two angles labeled $\alpha$ are equal since they both subtend

    arc AB. Thus, triangles AED and BEC are similar which

    implies $\frac{a - c}{b} = \frac{2a \cos \theta - b}{a + c}$

    $\Rightarrow (a - c)(a + c) = b(2a \cos \theta - b)$

    $\Rightarrow a^2 - c^2 = 2ab \cos \theta - b^2$

    $\Rightarrow c^2 = a^2 + b^2 - 2ab \cos \theta$.

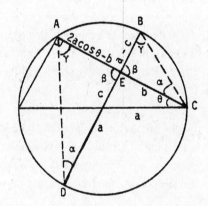

9.  As in the proof of the law of sines of Section 1.3, Exercise 61, $ah = bc \sin A = ab \sin C = ac \sin B$

    $\Rightarrow$ the area of ABC $= \frac{1}{2}$ (base)(height) $= \frac{1}{2} ah = \frac{1}{2} bc \sin A = \frac{1}{2} ab \sin C = \frac{1}{2} ac \sin B$.

10. As in Section 1.3, Exercise 61, (Area of ABC)$^2 = \frac{1}{4}$ (base)$^2$(height)$^2 = \frac{1}{4} a^2 h^2 = \frac{1}{4} a^2 b^2 \sin^2 C$

    $= \frac{1}{4} a^2 b^2 \left(1 - \cos^2 C\right)$. By the law of cosines, $c^2 = a^2 + b^2 - 2ab \cos C \Rightarrow \cos C = \frac{a^2 + b^2 - c^2}{2ab}$.

    Thus, (area of ABC)$^2 = \frac{1}{4} a^2 b^2 \left(1 - \cos^2 C\right) = \frac{1}{4} a^2 b^2 \left(1 - \left(\frac{a^2 + b^2 - c^2}{2ab}\right)^2\right) = \frac{a^2 b^2}{4} \left(1 - \frac{(a^2 + b^2 - c^2)^2}{4a^2 b^2}\right)$

    $= \frac{1}{16} \left(4a^2 b^2 - (a^2 + b^2 - c^2)^2\right) = \frac{1}{16} \left[(2ab + (a^2 + b^2 - c^2))(2ab - (a^2 + b^2 - c^2))\right]$

    $= \frac{1}{16} \left[((a + b)^2 - c^2)(c^2 - (a - b)^2)\right] = \frac{1}{16} \left[((a + b) + c)((a + b) - c)(c + (a - b))(c - (a - b))\right]$

    $= \left[\left(\frac{a + b + c}{2}\right)\left(\frac{-a + b + c}{2}\right)\left(\frac{a - b + c}{2}\right)\left(\frac{a + b - c}{2}\right)\right] = s(s - a)(s - b)(s - c)$, where $s = \frac{a + b + c}{2}$.

    Therefore, the area of ABC equals $\sqrt{s(s - a)(s - b)(s - c)}$.

11. If f is even and odd, then $f(-x) = -f(x)$ and $f(-x) = f(x) \Rightarrow f(x) = -f(x)$ for all x in the domain of f.

    Thus $2f(x) = 0 \Rightarrow f(x) = 0$.

12. (a) As suggested, let $E(x) = \frac{f(x)+f(-x)}{2} \Rightarrow E(-x) = \frac{f(-x)+f(-(-x))}{2} = \frac{f(x)+f(-x)}{2} = E(x) \Rightarrow$ E is an

even function. Define $O(x) = f(x) - E(x) = f(x) - \frac{f(x)+f(-x)}{2} = \frac{f(x)-f(-x)}{2}$. Then

$O(-x) = \frac{f(-x)-f(-(-x))}{2} = \frac{f(-x)-f(x)}{2} = -\left(\frac{f(x)-f(-x)}{2}\right) = -O(x) \Rightarrow$ O is an odd function

$\Rightarrow f(x) = E(x) + O(x)$ is the sum of an even and an odd function.

(b) Part (a) shows that $f(x) = E(x) + O(x)$ is the sum of an even and an odd function. If also
$f(x) = E_1(x) + O_1(x)$, where $E_1$ is even and $O_1$ is odd, then $f(x) - f(x) = 0 = (E_1(x) + O_1(x))$
$- (E(x) + O(x))$. Thus, $E(x) - E_1(x) = O_1(x) - O(x)$ for all x in the domain of f (which is the same as the
domain of $E - E_1$ and $O - O_1$). Now $(E - E_1)(-x) = E(-x) - E_1(-x) = E(x) - E_1(x)$ (since E and $E_1$ are
even) $= (E - E_1)(x) \Rightarrow E - E_1$ is even. Likewise, $(O_1 - O)(-x) = O_1(-x) - O(-x) = -O_1(x) - (-O(x))$
(since O and $O_1$ are odd) $= -(O_1(x) - O(x)) = -(O_1 - O)(x) \Rightarrow O_1 - O$ is odd. Therefore, $E - E_1$ and
$O_1 - O$ are both even and odd so they must be zero at each x in the domain of f by Exercise 11. That is,
$E_1 = E$ and $O_1 = O$, so the decomposition of f found in part (a) is unique.

13. $y = ax^2 + bx + c = a\left(x^2 + \frac{b}{a}x + \frac{b^2}{4a^2}\right) - \frac{b^2}{4a} + c = a\left(x + \frac{b}{2a}\right)^2 - \frac{b^2}{4a} + c$

(a) If $a > 0$ the graph is a parabola that opens upward. Increasing a causes a vertical stretching and a shift
of the vertex toward the y-axis and upward. If $a < 0$ the graph is a parabola that opens downward.
Decreasing a causes a vertical stretching and a shift of the vertex toward the y-axis and downward.

(b) If $a > 0$ the graph is a parabola that opens upward. If also $b > 0$, then increasing b causes a shift of the
graph downward to the left; if $b < 0$, then decreasing b causes a shift of the graph downward and to the
right.
    If $a < 0$ the graph is a parabola that opens downward. If $b > 0$, increasing b shifts the graph upward
to the right. If $b < 0$, decreasing b shifts the graph upward to the left.

(c) Changing c (for fixed a and b) by $\Delta c$ shifts the graph upward $\Delta c$ units if $\Delta c > 0$, and downward $-\Delta c$
units if $\Delta c < 0$.

14. (a) If $a > 0$, the graph rises to the right of the vertical line $x = -b$ and falls to the left. If $a < 0$, the graph
falls to the right of the line $x = -b$ and rises to the left. If $a = 0$, the graph reduces to the horizontal
line $y = c$. As $|a|$ increases, the slope at any given point $x = x_0$ increases in magnitude and the graph
becomes steeper. As $|a|$ decreases, the slope at $x_0$ decreases in magnitude and the graph rises or falls
more gradually.

(b) Increasing b shifts the graph to the left; decreasing b shifts it to the right.

(c) Increasing c shifts the graph upward; decreasing c shifts it downward.

15. Each of the triangles pictured has the same base
$b = v\Delta t = v(1 \text{ sec})$. Moreover, the height of each
triangle is the same value h. Thus $\frac{1}{2}$ (base)(height) $= \frac{1}{2}$ bh
$= A_1 = A_2 = A_3 = \dots$ . In conclusion, the object sweeps
out equal areas in each one second interval.

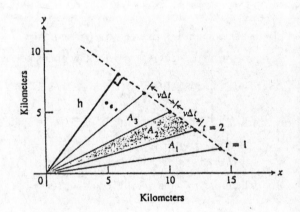

16. (a) Using the midpoint formula, the coordinates of P are $\left(\frac{a+0}{2}, \frac{b+0}{2}\right) = \left(\frac{a}{2}, \frac{b}{2}\right)$. Thus the slope
of $\overline{OP} = \frac{\Delta y}{\Delta x} = \frac{b/2}{a/2} = \frac{b}{a}$.

(b) The slope of $\overline{AB} = \frac{b-0}{0-a} = -\frac{b}{a}$. The line segments $\overline{AB}$ and $\overline{OP}$ are perpendicular when the product

of their slopes is $-1 = \left(\frac{b}{a}\right)\left(-\frac{b}{a}\right) = -\frac{b^2}{a^2}$. Thus, $b^2 = a^2 \Rightarrow a = b$ (since both are positive). Therefore, $\overline{AB}$

is perpendicular to $\overline{OP}$ when $a = b$.

17. From the figure we see that $0 \leq \theta \leq \frac{\pi}{2}$ and $AB = AD = 1$. From trigonometry we have the following: $\sin\theta = \frac{EB}{AB} = EB$,

$\cos\theta = \frac{AE}{AB} = AE$, $\tan\theta = \frac{CD}{AD} = CD$, and $\tan\theta = \frac{EB}{AE} = \frac{\sin\theta}{\cos\theta}$. We can see that:

area $\triangle AEB <$ area sector $\overparen{DB} <$ area $\triangle ADC \Rightarrow \frac{1}{2}(AE)(EB) < \frac{1}{2}(AD)^2\theta < \frac{1}{2}(AD)(CD)$

$\Rightarrow \frac{1}{2}\sin\theta\cos\theta < \frac{1}{2}(1)^2\theta < \frac{1}{2}(1)(\tan\theta) \Rightarrow \frac{1}{2}\sin\theta\cos\theta < \frac{1}{2}\theta < \frac{1}{2}\frac{\sin\theta}{\cos\theta}$

18. $(f\circ g)(x) = f(g(x)) = a(cx + d) + b = acx + ad + b$ and $(g\circ f)(x) = g(f(x)) = c(ax + b) + d = acx + cb + d$

Thus $(f\circ g)(x) = (g\circ f)(x) \Rightarrow acx + ad + b = acx + bc + d \Rightarrow ad + b = bc + d$. Note that $f(d) = ad + b$ and

$g(b) = cb + d$, thus $(f\circ g)(x) = (g\circ f)(x)$ if $f(d) = g(b)$.

**NOTES:**

# CHAPTER 2  LIMITS AND CONTINUITY

## 2.1 RATES OF CHANGE AND TANGENTS TO CURVES

1. (a) $\frac{\Delta f}{\Delta x} = \frac{f(3) - f(2)}{3 - 2} = \frac{28 - 9}{1} = 19$

   (b) $\frac{\Delta f}{\Delta x} = \frac{f(1) - f(-1)}{1 - (-1)} = \frac{2 - 0}{2} = 1$

2. (a) $\frac{\Delta g}{\Delta x} = \frac{g(1) - g(-1)}{1 - (-1)} = \frac{1 - 1}{2} = 0$

   (b) $\frac{\Delta g}{\Delta x} = \frac{g(0) - g(-2)}{0 - (-2)} = \frac{0 - 4}{2} = -2$

3. (a) $\frac{\Delta h}{\Delta t} = \frac{h\left(\frac{3\pi}{4}\right) - h\left(\frac{\pi}{4}\right)}{\frac{3\pi}{4} - \frac{\pi}{4}} = \frac{-1 - 1}{\frac{\pi}{2}} = -\frac{4}{\pi}$

   (b) $\frac{\Delta h}{\Delta t} = \frac{h\left(\frac{\pi}{2}\right) - h\left(\frac{\pi}{6}\right)}{\frac{\pi}{2} - \frac{\pi}{6}} = \frac{0 - \sqrt{3}}{\frac{\pi}{3}} = \frac{-3\sqrt{3}}{\pi}$

4. (a) $\frac{\Delta g}{\Delta t} = \frac{g(\pi) - g(0)}{\pi - 0} = \frac{(2 - 1) - (2 + 1)}{\pi - 0} = -\frac{2}{\pi}$

   (b) $\frac{\Delta g}{\Delta t} = \frac{g(\pi) - g(-\pi)}{\pi - (-\pi)} = \frac{(2 - 1) - (2 - 1)}{2\pi} = 0$

5. $\frac{\Delta R}{\Delta \theta} = \frac{R(2) - R(0)}{2 - 0} = \frac{\sqrt{8 + 1} - \sqrt{1}}{2} = \frac{3 - 1}{2} = 1$

6. $\frac{\Delta P}{\Delta \theta} = \frac{P(2) - P(1)}{2 - 1} = \frac{(8 - 16 + 10) - (1 - 4 + 5)}{1} = 2 - 2 = 0$

7. (a) $\frac{\Delta y}{\Delta x} = \frac{\left((2 + h)^2 - 3\right) - (2^2 - 3)}{h} = \frac{4 + 4h + h^2 - 3 - 1}{h} = \frac{4h + h^2}{h} = 4 + h$. As $h \to 0$, $4 + h \to 4 \Rightarrow$ at $P(2, 1)$ the slope is 4.

   (b) $y - 1 = 4(x - 2) \Rightarrow y - 1 = 4x - 8 \Rightarrow y = 4x - 7$

8. (a) $\frac{\Delta y}{\Delta x} = \frac{\left(5 - (1 + h)^2\right) - (5 - 1^2)}{h} = \frac{5 - 1 - 2h - h^2 - 4}{h} = \frac{-2h - h^2}{h} = -2 - h$. As $h \to 0$, $-2 - h \to -2 \Rightarrow$ at $P(1, 4)$ the slope is $-2$.

   (b) $y - 4 = (-2)(x - 1) \Rightarrow y - 4 = -2x + 2 \Rightarrow y = -2x + 6$

9. (a) $\frac{\Delta y}{\Delta x} = \frac{\left((2 + h)^2 - 2(2 + h) - 3\right) - (2^2 - 2(2) - 3)}{h} = \frac{4 + 4h + h^2 - 4 - 2h - 3 - (-3)}{h} = \frac{2h + h^2}{h} = 2 + h$. As $h \to 0$, $2 + h \to 2 \Rightarrow$ at $P(2, -3)$ the slope is 2.

   (b) $y - (-3) = 2(x - 2) \Rightarrow y + 3 = 2x - 4 \Rightarrow y = 2x - 7$.

10. (a) $\frac{\Delta y}{\Delta x} = \frac{\left((1 + h)^2 - 4(1 + h)\right) - (1^2 - 4(1))}{h} = \frac{1 + 2h + h^2 - 4 - 4h - (-3)}{h} = \frac{h^2 - 2h}{h} = h - 2$. As $h \to 0$, $h - 2 \to -2 \Rightarrow$ at $P(1, -3)$ the slope is $-2$.

    (b) $y - (-3) = (-2)(x - 1) \Rightarrow y + 3 = -2x + 2 \Rightarrow y = -2x - 1$.

11. (a) $\frac{\Delta y}{\Delta x} = \frac{(2 + h)^3 - 2^3}{h} = \frac{8 + 12h + 4h^2 + h^3 - 8}{h} = \frac{12h + 4h^2 + h^3}{h} = 12 + 4h + h^2$. As $h \to 0$, $12 + 4h + h^2 \to 12$, $\Rightarrow$ at $P(2, 8)$ the slope is 12.

    (b) $y - 8 = 12(x - 2) \Rightarrow y - 8 = 12x - 24 \Rightarrow y = 12x - 16$.

12. (a) $\frac{\Delta y}{\Delta x} = \frac{2 - (1 + h)^3 - (2 - 1^3)}{h} = \frac{2 - 1 - 3h - 3h^2 - h^3 - 1}{h} = \frac{-3h - 3h^2 - h^3}{h} = -3 - 3h - h^2$. As $h \to 0$, $-3 - 3h - h^2 \to -3$, $\Rightarrow$ at $P(1, 1)$ the slope is $-3$.

    (b) $y - 1 = (-3)(x - 1) \Rightarrow y - 1 = -3x + 3 \Rightarrow y = -3x + 4$.

13. (a) $\frac{\Delta y}{\Delta x} = \frac{(1 + h)^3 - 12(1 + h) - (1^3 - 12(1))}{h} = \frac{1 + 3h + 3h^2 + h^3 - 12 - 12h - (-11)}{h} = \frac{-9h + 3h^2 + h^3}{h} = -9 + 3h + h^2$. As $h \to 0$, $-9 + 3h + h^2 \to -9 \Rightarrow$ at $P(1, -11)$ the slope is $-9$.

    (b) $y - (-11) = (-9)(x - 1) \Rightarrow y + 11 = -9x + 9 \Rightarrow y = -9x - 2$.

14. (a) $\frac{\Delta y}{\Delta x} = \frac{(2+h)^3 - 3(2+h)^2 + 4 - (2^3 - 3(2)^2 + 4)}{h} = \frac{8 + 12h + 6h^2 + h^3 - 12 - 12h - 3h^2 + 4 - 0}{h} = \frac{3h^2 + h^3}{h} = 3h + h^2.$ As $h \to 0$,
$3h + h^2 \to 0 \Rightarrow$ at $P(2, 0)$ the slope is 0.

(b) $y - 0 = 0(x - 2) \Rightarrow y = 0.$

15. (a)

| Q | Slope of PQ = $\frac{\Delta p}{\Delta t}$ |
|---|---|
| $Q_1(10, 225)$ | $\frac{650 - 225}{20 - 10} = 42.5$ m/sec |
| $Q_2(14, 375)$ | $\frac{650 - 375}{20 - 14} = 45.83$ m/sec |
| $Q_3(16.5, 475)$ | $\frac{650 - 475}{20 - 16.5} = 50.00$ m/sec |
| $Q_4(18, 550)$ | $\frac{650 - 550}{20 - 18} = 50.00$ m/sec |

(b) At $t = 20$, the sportscar was traveling approximately 50 m/sec or 180 km/h.

16. (a)

| Q | Slope of PQ = $\frac{\Delta p}{\Delta t}$ |
|---|---|
| $Q_1(5, 20)$ | $\frac{80 - 20}{10 - 5} = 12$ m/sec |
| $Q_2(7, 39)$ | $\frac{80 - 39}{10 - 7} = 13.7$ m/sec |
| $Q_3(8.5, 58)$ | $\frac{80 - 58}{10 - 8.5} = 14.7$ m/sec |
| $Q_4(9.5, 72)$ | $\frac{80 - 72}{10 - 9.5} = 16$ m/sec |

(b) Approximately 16 m/sec

17. (a)

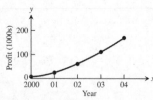

(b) $\frac{\Delta p}{\Delta t} = \frac{174 - 62}{2004 - 2002} = \frac{112}{2} = 56$ thousand dollars per year

(c) The average rate of change from 2001 to 2002 is $\frac{\Delta p}{\Delta t} = \frac{62 - 27}{2002 - 2001} = 35$ thousand dollars per year.

The average rate of change from 2002 to 2003 is $\frac{\Delta p}{\Delta t} = \frac{111 - 62}{2003 - 2002} = 49$ thousand dollars per year.

So, the rate at which profits were changing in 2002 is approximatley $\frac{1}{2}(35 + 49) = 42$ thousand dollars per year.

18. (a) $F(x) = (x + 2)/(x - 2)$

| x | 1.2 | 1.1 | 1.01 | 1.001 | 1.0001 | 1 |
|---|---|---|---|---|---|---|
| F(x) | −4.0 | −3.$\overline{4}$ | −3.$\overline{04}$ | −3.$\overline{004}$ | −3.$\overline{0004}$ | −3 |

$\frac{\Delta F}{\Delta x} = \frac{-4.0 - (-3)}{1.2 - 1} = -5.0;$     $\frac{\Delta F}{\Delta x} = \frac{-3.\overline{4} - (-3)}{1.1 - 1} = -4.\overline{4};$

$\frac{\Delta F}{\Delta x} = \frac{-3.\overline{04} - (-3)}{1.01 - 1} = -4.\overline{04};$     $\frac{\Delta F}{\Delta x} = \frac{-3.\overline{004} - (-3)}{1.001 - 1} = -4.\overline{004};$

$\frac{\Delta F}{\Delta x} = \frac{-3.\overline{0004} - (-3)}{1.0001 - 1} = -4.\overline{0004};$

(b) The rate of change of F(x) at $x = 1$ is −4.

19. (a) $\frac{\Delta g}{\Delta x} = \frac{g(2) - g(1)}{2 - 1} = \frac{\sqrt{2} - 1}{2 - 1} \approx 0.414213$     $\frac{\Delta g}{\Delta x} = \frac{g(1.5) - g(1)}{1.5 - 1} = \frac{\sqrt{1.5} - 1}{0.5} \approx 0.449489$

$\frac{\Delta g}{\Delta x} = \frac{g(1 + h) - g(1)}{(1 + h) - 1} = \frac{\sqrt{1 + h} - 1}{h}$

(b) $g(x) = \sqrt{x}$

| 1 + h | 1.1 | 1.01 | 1.001 | 1.0001 | 1.00001 | 1.000001 |
|---|---|---|---|---|---|---|
| $\sqrt{1 + h}$ | 1.04880 | 1.004987 | 1.0004998 | 1.0000499 | 1.000005 | 1.0000005 |
| $\left(\sqrt{1 + h} - 1\right)/h$ | 0.4880 | 0.4987 | 0.4998 | 0.499 | 0.5 | 0.5 |

(c) The rate of change of g(x) at $x = 1$ is 0.5.

(d) The calculator gives $\lim\limits_{h \to 0} \frac{\sqrt{1+h}-1}{h} = \frac{1}{2}$.

20. (a) i) $\frac{f(3) - f(2)}{3 - 2} = \frac{\frac{1}{3} - \frac{1}{2}}{1} = \frac{\frac{-1}{6}}{1} = -\frac{1}{6}$

   ii) $\frac{f(T) - f(2)}{T - 2} = \frac{\frac{1}{T} - \frac{1}{2}}{T - 2} = \frac{\frac{2}{2T} - \frac{T}{2T}}{T - 2} = \frac{2 - T}{2T(T - 2)} = \frac{2 - T}{-2T(2 - T)} = -\frac{1}{2T}, T \neq 2$

   (b)

| T | 2.1 | 2.01 | 2.001 | 2.0001 | 2.00001 | 2.000001 |
|---|---|---|---|---|---|---|
| f(T) | 0.476190 | 0.497512 | 0.499750 | 0.4999750 | 0.499997 | 0.499999 |
| (f(T) − f(2))/(T − 2) | −0.2381 | −0.2488 | −0.2500 | −0.2500 | −0.2500 | −0.2500 |

   (c) The table indicates the rate of change is −0.25 at t = 2.

   (d) $\lim\limits_{T \to 2} \left( \frac{1}{-2T} \right) = -\frac{1}{4}$

NOTE: Answers will vary in Exercises 21 and 22.

21. (a) $[0, 1]$: $\frac{\Delta s}{\Delta t} = \frac{15 - 0}{1 - 0} = 15$ mph; $[1, 2.5]$: $\frac{\Delta s}{\Delta t} = \frac{20 - 15}{2.5 - 1} = \frac{10}{3}$ mph; $[2.5, 3.5]$: $\frac{\Delta s}{\Delta t} = \frac{30 - 20}{3.5 - 2.5} = 10$ mph

   (b) At $P\left(\frac{1}{2}, 7.5\right)$: Since the portion of the graph from t = 0 to t = 1 is nearly linear, the instantaneous rate of change will be almost the same as the average rate of change, thus the instantaneous speed at t = $\frac{1}{2}$ is $\frac{15 - 7.5}{1 - 0.5} = 15$ mi/hr.

   At $P(2, 20)$: Since the portion of the graph from t = 2 to t = 2.5 is nearly linear, the instantaneous rate of change will be nearly the same as the average rate of change, thus $v = \frac{20 - 20}{2.5 - 2} = 0$ mi/hr. For values of t less than 2, we have

| Q | Slope of PQ $= \frac{\Delta s}{\Delta t}$ |
|---|---|
| $Q_1(1, 15)$ | $\frac{15 - 20}{1 - 2} = 5$ mi/hr |
| $Q_2(1.5, 19)$ | $\frac{19 - 20}{1.5 - 2} = 2$ mi/hr |
| $Q_3(1.9, 19.9)$ | $\frac{19.9 - 20}{1.9 - 2} = 1$ mi/hr |

   Thus, it appears that the instantaneous speed at t = 2 is 0 mi/hr.

   At $P(3, 22)$:

| Q | Slope of PQ $= \frac{\Delta s}{\Delta t}$ | Q | Slope of PQ $= \frac{\Delta s}{\Delta t}$ |
|---|---|---|---|
| $Q_1(4, 35)$ | $\frac{35 - 22}{4 - 3} = 13$ mi/hr | $Q_1(2, 20)$ | $\frac{20 - 22}{2 - 3} = 2$ mi/hr |
| $Q_2(3.5, 30)$ | $\frac{30 - 22}{3.5 - 3} = 16$ mi/hr | $Q_2(2.5, 20)$ | $\frac{20 - 22}{2.5 - 3} = 4$ mi/hr |
| $Q_3(3.1, 23)$ | $\frac{23 - 22}{3.1 - 3} = 10$ mi/hr | $Q_3(2.9, 21.6)$ | $\frac{21.6 - 22}{2.9 - 3} = 4$ mi/hr |

   Thus, it appears that the instantaneous speed at t = 3 is about 7 mi/hr.

   (c) It appears that the curve is increasing the fastest at t = 3.5. Thus for $P(3.5, 30)$

| Q | Slope of PQ $= \frac{\Delta s}{\Delta t}$ | Q | Slope of PQ $= \frac{\Delta s}{\Delta t}$ |
|---|---|---|---|
| $Q_1(4, 35)$ | $\frac{35 - 30}{4 - 3.5} = 10$ mi/hr | $Q_1(3, 22)$ | $\frac{22 - 30}{3 - 3.5} = 16$ mi/hr |
| $Q_2(3.75, 34)$ | $\frac{34 - 30}{3.75 - 3.5} = 16$ mi/hr | $Q_2(3.25, 25)$ | $\frac{25 - 30}{3.25 - 3.5} = 20$ mi/hr |
| $Q_3(3.6, 32)$ | $\frac{32 - 30}{3.6 - 3.5} = 20$ mi/hr | $Q_3(3.4, 28)$ | $\frac{28 - 30}{3.4 - 3.5} = 20$ mi/hr |

   Thus, it appears that the instantaneous speed at t = 3.5 is about 20 mi/hr.

22. (a) $[0, 3]$: $\frac{\Delta A}{\Delta t} = \frac{10 - 15}{3 - 0} \approx -1.67$ $\frac{gal}{day}$; $[0, 5]$: $\frac{\Delta A}{\Delta t} = \frac{3.9 - 15}{5 - 0} \approx -2.2$ $\frac{gal}{day}$; $[7, 10]$: $\frac{\Delta A}{\Delta t} = \frac{0 - 1.4}{10 - 7} \approx -0.5$ $\frac{gal}{day}$

   (b) At $P(1, 14)$:

| Q | Slope of PQ $= \frac{\Delta A}{\Delta t}$ | Q | Slope of PQ $= \frac{\Delta A}{\Delta t}$ |
|---|---|---|---|
| $Q_1(2, 12.2)$ | $\frac{12.2 - 14}{2 - 1} = -1.8$ gal/day | $Q_1(0, 15)$ | $\frac{15 - 14}{0 - 1} = -1$ gal/day |
| $Q_2(1.5, 13.2)$ | $\frac{13.2 - 14}{1.5 - 1} = -1.6$ gal/day | $Q_2(0.5, 14.6)$ | $\frac{14.6 - 14}{0.5 - 1} = -1.2$ gal/day |
| $Q_3(1.1, 13.85)$ | $\frac{13.85 - 14}{1.1 - 1} = -1.5$ gal/day | $Q_3(0.9, 14.86)$ | $\frac{14.86 - 14}{0.9 - 1} = -1.4$ gal/day |

   Thus, it appears that the instantaneous rate of consumption at t = 1 is about −1.45 gal/day.

   At $P(4, 6)$:

| Q | Slope of PQ $= \frac{\Delta A}{\Delta t}$ |
|---|---|
| $Q_1(5, 3.9)$ | $\frac{3.9-6}{5-4} = -2.1$ gal/day |
| $Q_2(4.5, 4.8)$ | $\frac{4.8-6}{4.5-4} = -2.4$ gal/day |
| $Q_3(4.1, 5.7)$ | $\frac{5.7-6}{4.1-4} = -3$ gal/day |

| Q | Slope of PQ $= \frac{\Delta A}{\Delta t}$ |
|---|---|
| $Q_1(3, 10)$ | $\frac{10-6}{3-4} = -4$ gal/day |
| $Q_2(3.5, 7.8)$ | $\frac{7.8-6}{3.5-4} = -3.6$ gal/day |
| $Q_3(3.9, 6.3)$ | $\frac{6.3-6}{3.9-4} = -3$ gal/day |

Thus, it appears that the instantaneous rate of consumption at $t = 1$ is $-3$ gal/day.

At P(8, 1):

| Q | Slope of PQ $= \frac{\Delta A}{\Delta t}$ |
|---|---|
| $Q_1(9, 0.5)$ | $\frac{0.5-1}{9-8} = -0.5$ gal/day |
| $Q_2(8.5, 0.7)$ | $\frac{0.7-1}{8.5-8} = -0.6$ gal/day |
| $Q_3(8.1, 0.95)$ | $\frac{0.95-1}{8.1-8} = -0.5$ gal/day |

| Q | Slope of PQ $= \frac{\Delta A}{\Delta t}$ |
|---|---|
| $Q_1(7, 1.4)$ | $\frac{1.4-1}{7-8} = -0.6$ gal/day |
| $Q_2(7.5, 1.3)$ | $\frac{1.3-1}{7.5-8} = -0.6$ gal/day |
| $Q_3(7.9, 1.04)$ | $\frac{1.04-1}{7.9-8} = -0.6$ gal/day |

Thus, it appears that the instantaneous rate of consumption at $t = 1$ is $-0.55$ gal/day.

(c) It appears that the curve (the consumption) is decreasing the fastest at $t = 3.5$. Thus for P(3.5, 7.8)

| Q | Slope of PQ $= \frac{\Delta A}{\Delta t}$ |
|---|---|
| $Q_1(4.5, 4.8)$ | $\frac{4.8-7.8}{4.5-3.5} = -3$ gal/day |
| $Q_2(4, 6)$ | $\frac{6-7.8}{4-3.5} = -3.6$ gal/day |
| $Q_3(3.6, 7.4)$ | $\frac{7.4-7.8}{3.6-3.5} = -4$ gal/day |

| Q | Slope of PQ $= \frac{\Delta s}{\Delta t}$ |
|---|---|
| $Q_1(2.5, 11.2)$ | $\frac{11.2-7.8}{2.5-3.5} = -3.4$ gal/day |
| $Q_2(3, 10)$ | $\frac{10-7.8}{3-3.5} = -4.4$ gal/day |
| $Q_3(3.4, 8.2)$ | $\frac{8.2-7.8}{3.4-3.5} = -4$ gal/day |

Thus, it appears that the rate of consumption at $t = 3.5$ is about $-4$ gal/day.

## 2.2 LIMIT OF A FUNCTION AND LIMIT LAWS

1. (a) Does not exist. As x approaches 1 from the right, g(x) approaches 0. As x approaches 1 from the left, g(x) approaches 1. There is no single number L that all the values g(x) get arbitrarily close to as x $\to$ 1.

   (b) 1            (c) 0            (d) 0.5

2. (a) 0

   (b) $-1$

   (c) Does not exist. As t approaches 0 from the left, f(t) approaches $-1$. As t approaches 0 from the right, f(t) approaches 1. There is no single number L that f(t) gets arbitrarily close to as t $\to$ 0.

   (d) $-1$

3. (a) True            (b) True            (c) False

   (d) False          (e) False          (f) True

   (g) True

4. (a) False          (b) False          (c) True

   (d) True           (e) True

5. $\lim_{x \to 0} \frac{x}{|x|}$ does not exist because $\frac{x}{|x|} = \frac{x}{x} = 1$ if $x > 0$ and $\frac{x}{|x|} = \frac{x}{-x} = -1$ if $x < 0$. As x approaches 0 from the left, $\frac{x}{|x|}$ approaches $-1$. As x approaches 0 from the right, $\frac{x}{|x|}$ approaches 1. There is no single number L that all the function values get arbitrarily close to as x $\to$ 0.

6. As x approaches 1 from the left, the values of $\frac{1}{x-1}$ become increasingly large and negative. As x approaches 1 from the right, the values become increasingly large and positive. There is no one number L that all the function values get arbitrarily close to as x $\to$ 1, so $\lim_{x \to 1} \frac{1}{x-1}$ does not exist.

7. Nothing can be said about f(x) because the existence of a limit as $x \to x_0$ does not depend on how the function is defined at $x_0$. In order for a limit to exist, f(x) must be arbitrarily close to a single real number L when x is close enough to $x_0$. That is, the existence of a limit depends on the values of f(x) for x <u>near</u> $x_0$, not on the definition of f(x) at $x_0$ itself.

8. Nothing can be said. In order for $\lim_{x \to 0} f(x)$ to exist, f(x) must close to a single value for x near 0 regardless of the value f(0) itself.

9. No, the definition does not require that f be defined at $x = 1$ in order for a limiting value to exist there. If f(1) is defined, it can be any real number, so we can conclude nothing about f(1) from $\lim_{x \to 1} f(x) = 5$.

10. No, because the existence of a limit depends on the values of f(x) when x is near 1, not on f(1) itself. If $\lim_{x \to 1} f(x)$ exists, its value may be some number other than f(1) = 5. We can conclude nothing about $\lim_{x \to 1} f(x)$, whether it exists or what its value is if it does exist, from knowing the value of f(1) alone.

11. $\lim_{x \to -7} (2x + 5) = 2(-7) + 5 = -14 + 5 = -9$

12. $\lim_{x \to 2} (-x^2 + 5x - 2) = -(2)^2 + 5(2) - 2 = -4 + 10 - 2 = 4$

13. $\lim_{t \to 6} 8(t - 5)(t - 7) = 8(6 - 5)(6 - 7) = -8$

14. $\lim_{x \to -2} (x^3 - 2x^2 + 4x + 8) = (-2)^3 - 2(-2)^2 + 4(-2) + 8 = -8 - 8 - 8 + 8 = -16$

15. $\lim_{x \to 2} \frac{x+3}{x+6} = \frac{2+3}{2+6} = \frac{5}{8}$

16. $\lim_{s \to \frac{2}{3}} 3s(2s - 1) = 3\left(\frac{2}{3}\right)\left[2\left(\frac{2}{3}\right) - 1\right] = 2\left(\frac{4}{3} - 1\right) = \frac{2}{3}$

17. $\lim_{x \to -1} 3(2x - 1)^2 = 3(2(-1) - 1)^2 = 3(-3)^2 = 27$

18. $\lim_{y \to 2} \frac{y+2}{y^2 + 5y + 6} = \frac{2+2}{(2)^2 + 5(2) + 6} = \frac{4}{4 + 10 + 6} = \frac{4}{20} = \frac{1}{5}$

19. $\lim_{y \to -3} (5 - y)^{4/3} = [5 - (-3)]^{4/3} = (8)^{4/3} = \left((8)^{1/3}\right)^4 = 2^4 = 16$

20. $\lim_{z \to 0} (2z - 8)^{1/3} = (2(0) - 8)^{1/3} = (-8)^{1/3} = -2$

21. $\lim_{h \to 0} \frac{3}{\sqrt{3h + 1} + 1} = \frac{3}{\sqrt{3(0) + 1} + 1} = \frac{3}{\sqrt{1} + 1} = \frac{3}{2}$

22. $\lim_{h \to 0} \frac{\sqrt{5h + 4} - 2}{h} = \lim_{h \to 0} \frac{\sqrt{5h + 4} - 2}{h} \cdot \frac{\sqrt{5h + 4} + 2}{\sqrt{5h + 4} + 2} = \lim_{h \to 0} \frac{(5h + 4) - 4}{h\left(\sqrt{5h + 4} + 2\right)} = \lim_{h \to 0} \frac{5h}{h\left(\sqrt{5h + 4} + 2\right)} = \lim_{h \to 0} \frac{5}{\sqrt{5h + 4} + 2}$
$= \frac{5}{\sqrt{4} + 2} = \frac{5}{4}$

23. $\lim_{x \to 5} \frac{x - 5}{x^2 - 25} = \lim_{x \to 5} \frac{x - 5}{(x + 5)(x - 5)} = \lim_{x \to 5} \frac{1}{x + 5} = \frac{1}{5 + 5} = \frac{1}{10}$

24. $\lim_{x \to -3} \frac{x + 3}{x^2 + 4x + 3} = \lim_{x \to -3} \frac{x + 3}{(x + 3)(x + 1)} = \lim_{x \to -3} \frac{1}{x + 1} = \frac{1}{-3 + 1} = -\frac{1}{2}$

25. $\lim\limits_{x \to -5} \frac{x^2+3x-10}{x+5} = \lim\limits_{x \to -5} \frac{(x+5)(x-2)}{x+5} = \lim\limits_{x \to -5} (x-2) = -5-2 = -7$

26. $\lim\limits_{x \to 2} \frac{x^2-7x+10}{x-2} = \lim\limits_{x \to 2} \frac{(x-5)(x-2)}{x-2} = \lim\limits_{x \to 2} (x-5) = 2-5 = -3$

27. $\lim\limits_{t \to 1} \frac{t^2+t-2}{t^2-1} = \lim\limits_{t \to 1} \frac{(t+2)(t-1)}{(t-1)(t+1)} = \lim\limits_{t \to 1} \frac{t+2}{t+1} = \frac{1+2}{1+1} = \frac{3}{2}$

28. $\lim\limits_{t \to -1} \frac{t^2+3t+2}{t^2-t-2} = \lim\limits_{t \to -1} \frac{(t+2)(t+1)}{(t-2)(t+1)} = \lim\limits_{t \to -1} \frac{t+2}{t-2} = \frac{-1+2}{-1-2} = -\frac{1}{3}$

29. $\lim\limits_{x \to -2} \frac{-2x-4}{x^3+2x^2} = \lim\limits_{x \to -2} \frac{-2(x+2)}{x^2(x+2)} = \lim\limits_{x \to -2} \frac{-2}{x^2} = \frac{-2}{4} = -\frac{1}{2}$

30. $\lim\limits_{y \to 0} \frac{5y^3+8y^2}{3y^4-16y^2} = \lim\limits_{y \to 0} \frac{y^2(5y+8)}{y^2(3y^2-16)} = \lim\limits_{y \to 0} \frac{5y+8}{3y^2-16} = \frac{8}{-16} = -\frac{1}{2}$

31. $\lim\limits_{x \to 1} \frac{\frac{1}{x}-1}{x-1} = \lim\limits_{x \to 1} \frac{\frac{1-x}{x}}{x-1} = \lim\limits_{x \to 1} \left( \frac{1-x}{x} \cdot \frac{1}{x-1} \right) = \lim\limits_{x \to 1} -\frac{1}{x} = -1$

32. $\lim\limits_{x \to 0} \frac{\frac{1}{x-1}+\frac{1}{x+1}}{x} = \lim\limits_{x \to 1} \frac{\frac{(x+1)+(x-1)}{(x-1)(x+1)}}{x} = \lim\limits_{x \to 1} \left( \frac{2x}{(x-1)(x+1)} \cdot \frac{1}{x} \right) = \lim\limits_{x \to 1} \frac{2}{(x-1)(x+1)} = \frac{2}{-1} = -2$

33. $\lim\limits_{u \to 1} \frac{u^4-1}{u^3-1} = \lim\limits_{u \to 1} \frac{(u^2+1)(u+1)(u-1)}{(u^2+u+1)(u-1)} = \lim\limits_{u \to 1} \frac{(u^2+1)(u+1)}{u^2+u+1} = \frac{(1+1)(1+1)}{1+1+1} = \frac{4}{3}$

34. $\lim\limits_{v \to 2} \frac{v^3-8}{v^4-16} = \lim\limits_{v \to 2} \frac{(v-2)(v^2+2v+4)}{(v-2)(v+2)(v^2+4)} = \lim\limits_{v \to 2} \frac{v^2+2v+4}{(v+2)(v^2+4)} = \frac{4+4+4}{(4)(8)} = \frac{12}{32} = \frac{3}{8}$

35. $\lim\limits_{x \to 9} \frac{\sqrt{x}-3}{x-9} = \lim\limits_{x \to 9} \frac{\sqrt{x}-3}{(\sqrt{x}-3)(\sqrt{x}+3)} = \lim\limits_{x \to 9} \frac{1}{\sqrt{x}+3} = \frac{1}{\sqrt{9}+3} = \frac{1}{6}$

36. $\lim\limits_{x \to 4} \frac{4x-x^2}{2-\sqrt{x}} = \lim\limits_{x \to 4} \frac{x(4-x)}{2-\sqrt{x}} = \lim\limits_{x \to 4} \frac{x(2+\sqrt{x})(2-\sqrt{x})}{2-\sqrt{x}} = \lim\limits_{x \to 4} x(2+\sqrt{x}) = 4(2+2) = 16$

37. $\lim\limits_{x \to 1} \frac{x-1}{\sqrt{x+3}-2} = \lim\limits_{x \to 1} \frac{(x-1)(\sqrt{x+3}+2)}{(\sqrt{x+3}-2)(\sqrt{x+3}+2)} = \lim\limits_{x \to 1} \frac{(x-1)(\sqrt{x+3}+2)}{(x+3)-4} = \lim\limits_{x \to 1} \left( \sqrt{x+3}+2 \right) = \sqrt{4}+2 = 4$

38. $\lim\limits_{x \to -1} \frac{\sqrt{x^2+8}-3}{x+1} = \lim\limits_{x \to -1} \frac{\left(\sqrt{x^2+8}-3\right)\left(\sqrt{x^2+8}+3\right)}{(x+1)\left(\sqrt{x^2+8}+3\right)} = \lim\limits_{x \to -1} \frac{(x^2+8)-9}{(x+1)\left(\sqrt{x^2+8}+3\right)}$

$= \lim\limits_{x \to -1} \frac{(x+1)(x-1)}{(x+1)\left(\sqrt{x^2+8}+3\right)} = \lim\limits_{x \to -1} \frac{x-1}{\sqrt{x^2+8}+3} = \frac{-2}{3+3} = -\frac{1}{3}$

39. $\lim\limits_{x \to 2} \frac{\sqrt{x^2+12}-4}{x-2} = \lim\limits_{x \to 2} \frac{\left(\sqrt{x^2+12}-4\right)\left(\sqrt{x^2+12}+4\right)}{(x-2)\left(\sqrt{x^2+12}+4\right)} = \lim\limits_{x \to 2} \frac{(x^2+12)-16}{(x-2)\left(\sqrt{x^2+12}+4\right)}$

$= \lim\limits_{x \to 2} \frac{(x-2)(x+2)}{(x-2)\left(\sqrt{x^2+12}+4\right)} = \lim\limits_{x \to 2} \frac{x+2}{\sqrt{x^2+12}+4} = \frac{4}{\sqrt{16}+4} = \frac{1}{2}$

40. $\lim\limits_{x \to -2} \frac{x+2}{\sqrt{x^2+5}-3} = \lim\limits_{x \to -2} \frac{(x+2)\left(\sqrt{x^2+5}+3\right)}{\left(\sqrt{x^2+5}-3\right)\left(\sqrt{x^2+5}+3\right)} = \lim\limits_{x \to -2} \frac{(x+2)\left(\sqrt{x^2+5}+3\right)}{(x^2+5)-9}$

$= \lim\limits_{x \to -2} \frac{(x+2)\left(\sqrt{x^2+5}+3\right)}{(x+2)(x-2)} = \lim\limits_{x \to -2} \frac{\sqrt{x^2+5}+3}{x-2} = \frac{\sqrt{9}+3}{-4} = -\frac{3}{2}$

41. $\displaystyle\lim_{x \to -3} \frac{2 - \sqrt{x^2 - 5}}{x + 3} = \lim_{x \to -3} \frac{\left(2 - \sqrt{x^2 - 5}\right)\left(2 + \sqrt{x^2 - 5}\right)}{(x + 3)\left(2 + \sqrt{x^2 - 5}\right)} = \lim_{x \to -3} \frac{4 - (x^2 - 5)}{(x + 3)\left(2 + \sqrt{x^2 - 5}\right)}$

$\displaystyle = \lim_{x \to -3} \frac{9 - x^2}{(x + 3)\left(2 + \sqrt{x^2 - 5}\right)} = \lim_{x \to -3} \frac{(3 - x)(3 + x)}{(x + 3)\left(2 + \sqrt{x^2 - 5}\right)} = \lim_{x \to -3} \frac{3 - x}{2 + \sqrt{x^2 - 5}} = \frac{6}{2 + \sqrt{4}} = \frac{3}{2}$

42. $\displaystyle\lim_{x \to 4} \frac{4 - x}{5 - \sqrt{x^2 + 9}} = \lim_{x \to 4} \frac{(4 - x)\left(5 + \sqrt{x^2 + 9}\right)}{\left(5 - \sqrt{x^2 + 9}\right)\left(5 + \sqrt{x^2 + 9}\right)} = \lim_{x \to 4} \frac{(4 - x)\left(5 + \sqrt{x^2 + 9}\right)}{25 - (x^2 + 9)}$

$\displaystyle = \lim_{x \to 4} \frac{(4 - x)\left(5 + \sqrt{x^2 + 9}\right)}{16 - x^2} = \lim_{x \to 4} \frac{(4 - x)\left(5 + \sqrt{x^2 + 9}\right)}{(4 - x)(4 + x)} = \lim_{x \to 4} \frac{5 + \sqrt{x^2 + 9}}{4 + x} = \frac{5 + \sqrt{25}}{8} = \frac{5}{4}$

43. $\displaystyle\lim_{x \to 0} (2\sin x - 1) = 2\sin 0 - 1 = 0 - 1 = -1$    44. $\displaystyle\lim_{x \to 0} \sin^2 x = \left(\lim_{x \to 0} \sin x\right)^2 = (\sin 0)^2 = 0^2 = 0$

45. $\displaystyle\lim_{x \to 0} \sec x = \lim_{x \to 0} \frac{1}{\cos x} = \frac{1}{\cos 0} = \frac{1}{1} = 1$    46. $\displaystyle\lim_{x \to 0} \tan x = \lim_{x \to 0} \frac{\sin x}{\cos x} = \frac{\sin 0}{\cos 0} = \frac{0}{1} = 0$

47. $\displaystyle\lim_{x \to 0} \frac{1 + x + \sin x}{3\cos x} = \frac{1 + 0 + \sin 0}{3\cos 0} = \frac{1 + 0 + 0}{3} = \frac{1}{3}$

48. $\displaystyle\lim_{x \to 0} (x^2 - 1)(2 - \cos x) = (0^2 - 1)(2 - \cos 0) = (-1)(2 - 1) = (-1)(1) = -1$

49. $\displaystyle\lim_{x \to -\pi} \sqrt{x + 4}\, \cos(x + \pi) = \lim_{x \to -\pi} \sqrt{x + 4} \cdot \lim_{x \to -\pi} \cos(x + \pi) = \sqrt{-\pi + 4} \cdot \cos 0 = \sqrt{4 - \pi} \cdot 1 = \sqrt{4 - \pi}$

50. $\displaystyle\lim_{x \to 0} \sqrt{7 + \sec^2 x} = \sqrt{\lim_{x \to 0}(7 + \sec^2 x)} = \sqrt{7 + \lim_{x \to 0} \sec^2 x} = \sqrt{7 + \sec^2 0} = \sqrt{7 + (1)^2} = 2\sqrt{2}$

51. (a) quotient rule                              (b) difference and power rules
    (c) sum and constant multiple rules

52. (a) quotient rule                              (b) power and product rules
    (c) difference and constant multiple rules

53. (a) $\displaystyle\lim_{x \to c} f(x)\, g(x) = \left[\lim_{x \to c} f(x)\right]\left[\lim_{x \to c} g(x)\right] = (5)(-2) = -10$

    (b) $\displaystyle\lim_{x \to c} 2f(x)\, g(x) = 2\left[\lim_{x \to c} f(x)\right]\left[\lim_{x \to c} g(x)\right] = 2(5)(-2) = -20$

    (c) $\displaystyle\lim_{x \to c} [f(x) + 3g(x)] = \lim_{x \to c} f(x) + 3\lim_{x \to c} g(x) = 5 + 3(-2) = -1$

    (d) $\displaystyle\lim_{x \to c} \frac{f(x)}{f(x) - g(x)} = \frac{\lim_{x \to c} f(x)}{\lim_{x \to c} f(x) - \lim_{x \to c} g(x)} = \frac{5}{5 - (-2)} = \frac{5}{7}$

54. (a) $\displaystyle\lim_{x \to 4} [g(x) + 3] = \lim_{x \to 4} g(x) + \lim_{x \to 4} 3 = -3 + 3 = 0$

    (b) $\displaystyle\lim_{x \to 4} xf(x) = \lim_{x \to 4} x \cdot \lim_{x \to 4} f(x) = (4)(0) = 0$

    (c) $\displaystyle\lim_{x \to 4} [g(x)]^2 = \left[\lim_{x \to 4} g(x)\right]^2 = [-3]^2 = 9$

    (d) $\displaystyle\lim_{x \to 4} \frac{g(x)}{f(x) - 1} = \frac{\lim_{x \to 4} g(x)}{\lim_{x \to 4} f(x) - \lim_{x \to 4} 1} = \frac{-3}{0 - 1} = 3$

55. (a) $\displaystyle\lim_{x \to b} [f(x) + g(x)] = \lim_{x \to b} f(x) + \lim_{x \to b} g(x) = 7 + (-3) = 4$

    (b) $\displaystyle\lim_{x \to b} f(x) \cdot g(x) = \left[\lim_{x \to b} f(x)\right]\left[\lim_{x \to b} g(x)\right] = (7)(-3) = -21$

(c) $\lim\limits_{x \to b} 4g(x) = \left[\lim\limits_{x \to b} 4\right]\left[\lim\limits_{x \to b} g(x)\right] = (4)(-3) = -12$

(d) $\lim\limits_{x \to b} f(x)/g(x) = \lim\limits_{x \to b} f(x)/\lim\limits_{x \to b} g(x) = \frac{7}{-3} = -\frac{7}{3}$

56. (a) $\lim\limits_{x \to -2} [p(x) + r(x) + s(x)] = \lim\limits_{x \to -2} p(x) + \lim\limits_{x \to -2} r(x) + \lim\limits_{x \to -2} s(x) = 4 + 0 + (-3) = 1$

(b) $\lim\limits_{x \to -2} p(x) \cdot r(x) \cdot s(x) = \left[\lim\limits_{x \to -2} p(x)\right]\left[\lim\limits_{x \to -2} r(x)\right]\left[\lim\limits_{x \to -2} s(x)\right] = (4)(0)(-3) = 0$

(c) $\lim\limits_{x \to -2} [-4p(x) + 5r(x)]/s(x) = \left[-4 \lim\limits_{x \to -2} p(x) + 5 \lim\limits_{x \to -2} r(x)\right] \bigg/ \lim\limits_{x \to -2} s(x) = [-4(4) + 5(0)]/-3 = \frac{16}{3}$

57. $\lim\limits_{h \to 0} \frac{(1+h)^2 - 1^2}{h} = \lim\limits_{h \to 0} \frac{1 + 2h + h^2 - 1}{h} = \lim\limits_{h \to 0} \frac{h(2+h)}{h} = \lim\limits_{h \to 0} (2 + h) = 2$

58. $\lim\limits_{h \to 0} \frac{(-2+h)^2 - (-2)^2}{h} = \lim\limits_{h \to 0} \frac{4 - 4h + h^2 - 4}{h} = \lim\limits_{h \to 0} \frac{h(h-4)}{h} = \lim\limits_{h \to 0} (h - 4) = -4$

59. $\lim\limits_{h \to 0} \frac{[3(2+h) - 4] - [3(2) - 4]}{h} = \lim\limits_{h \to 0} \frac{3h}{h} = 3$

60. $\lim\limits_{h \to 0} \frac{\left(\frac{1}{-2+h}\right) - \left(\frac{1}{-2}\right)}{h} = \lim\limits_{h \to 0} \frac{\frac{-2}{-2+h} - 1}{-2h} = \lim\limits_{h \to 0} \frac{-2 - (-2+h)}{-2h(-2+h)} = \lim\limits_{h \to 0} \frac{-h}{h(4 - 2h)} = -\frac{1}{4}$

61. $\lim\limits_{h \to 0} \frac{\sqrt{7+h} - \sqrt{7}}{h} = \lim\limits_{h \to 0} \frac{\left(\sqrt{7+h} - \sqrt{7}\right)\left(\sqrt{7+h} + \sqrt{7}\right)}{h\left(\sqrt{7+h} + \sqrt{7}\right)} = \lim\limits_{h \to 0} \frac{(7+h) - 7}{h\left(\sqrt{7+h} + \sqrt{7}\right)} = \lim\limits_{h \to 0} \frac{h}{h\left(\sqrt{7+h} + \sqrt{7}\right)} = \lim\limits_{h \to 0} \frac{1}{\sqrt{7+h} + \sqrt{7}}$

$= \frac{1}{2\sqrt{7}}$

62. $\lim\limits_{h \to 0} \frac{\sqrt{3(0+h) + 1} - \sqrt{3(0) + 1}}{h} = \lim\limits_{h \to 0} \frac{\left(\sqrt{3h+1} - 1\right)\left(\sqrt{3h+1} + 1\right)}{h\left(\sqrt{3h+1} + 1\right)} = \lim\limits_{h \to 0} \frac{(3h+1) - 1}{h\left(\sqrt{3h+1} + 1\right)} = \lim\limits_{h \to 0} \frac{3h}{h\left(\sqrt{3h+1} + 1\right)}$

$= \lim\limits_{h \to 0} \frac{3}{\sqrt{3h+1} + 1} = \frac{3}{2}$

63. $\lim\limits_{x \to 0} \sqrt{5 - 2x^2} = \sqrt{5 - 2(0)^2} = \sqrt{5}$ and $\lim\limits_{x \to 0} \sqrt{5 - x^2} = \sqrt{5 - (0)^2} = \sqrt{5}$; by the sandwich theorem,

$\lim\limits_{x \to 0} f(x) = \sqrt{5}$

64. $\lim\limits_{x \to 0} (2 - x^2) = 2 - 0 = 2$ and $\lim\limits_{x \to 0} 2 \cos x = 2(1) = 2$; by the sandwich theorem, $\lim\limits_{x \to 0} g(x) = 2$

65. (a) $\lim\limits_{x \to 0} \left(1 - \frac{x^2}{6}\right) = 1 - \frac{0}{6} = 1$ and $\lim\limits_{x \to 0} 1 = 1$; by the sandwich theorem, $\lim\limits_{x \to 0} \frac{x \sin x}{2 - 2 \cos x} = 1$

(b) For $x \neq 0$, $y = (x \sin x)/(2 - 2 \cos x)$
lies between the other two graphs in the
figure, and the graphs converge as $x \to 0$.

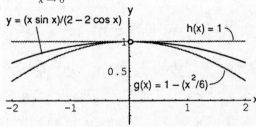

66. (a) $\lim\limits_{x \to 0} \left(\frac{1}{2} - \frac{x^2}{24}\right) = \lim\limits_{x \to 0} \frac{1}{2} - \lim\limits_{x \to 0} \frac{x^2}{24} = \frac{1}{2} - 0 = \frac{1}{2}$ and $\lim\limits_{x \to 0} \frac{1}{2} = \frac{1}{2}$; by the sandwich theorem,

$\lim\limits_{x \to 0} \frac{1 - \cos x}{x^2} = \frac{1}{2}$.

(b)  For all x ≠ 0, the graph of f(x) = (1 − cos x)/x²
lies between the line y = $\frac{1}{2}$ and the parabola
y = $\frac{1}{2}$ − x²/24, and the graphs converge as x → 0.

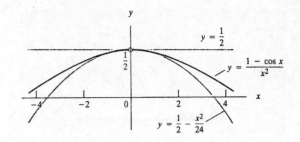

67. (a)  f(x) = (x² − 9)/(x + 3)

| x | −3.1 | −3.01 | −3.001 | −3.0001 | −3.00001 | −3.000001 |
|---|---|---|---|---|---|---|
| f(x) | −6.1 | −6.01 | −6.001 | −6.0001 | −6.00001 | −6.000001 |

| x | −2.9 | −2.99 | −2.999 | −2.9999 | −2.99999 | −2.999999 |
|---|---|---|---|---|---|---|
| f(x) | −5.9 | −5.99 | −5.999 | −5.9999 | −5.99999 | −5.999999 |

The estimate is $\lim_{x \to -3} f(x) = -6$.

(b)

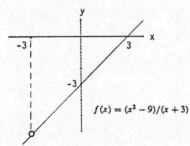

$f(x) = (x^2 - 9)/(x + 3)$

(c)  f(x) = $\frac{x^2 - 9}{x + 3}$ = $\frac{(x + 3)(x - 3)}{x + 3}$ = x − 3 if x ≠ −3, and $\lim_{x \to -3}$ (x − 3) = −3 − 3 = −6.

68. (a)  g(x) = (x² − 2)/$\left(x - \sqrt{2}\right)$

| x | 1.4 | 1.41 | 1.414 | 1.4142 | 1.41421 | 1.414213 |
|---|---|---|---|---|---|---|
| g(x) | 2.81421 | 2.82421 | 2.82821 | 2.828413 | 2.828423 | 2.828426 |

(b)

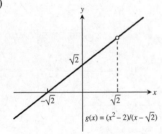

$g(x) = (x^2 - 2)/(x - \sqrt{2})$

(c)  g(x) = $\frac{x^2 - 2}{x - \sqrt{2}}$ = $\frac{\left(x + \sqrt{2}\right)\left(x - \sqrt{2}\right)}{\left(x - \sqrt{2}\right)}$ = x + $\sqrt{2}$ if x ≠ $\sqrt{2}$, and $\lim_{x \to \sqrt{2}}$ $\left(x + \sqrt{2}\right)$ = $\sqrt{2} + \sqrt{2} = 2\sqrt{2}$.

69. (a)  G(x) = (x + 6)/(x² + 4x − 12)

| x | −5.9 | −5.99 | −5.999 | −5.9999 | −5.99999 | −5.999999 |
|---|---|---|---|---|---|---|
| G(x) | −.126582 | −.1251564 | −.1250156 | −.1250015 | −.1250001 | −.1250000 |

| x | −6.1 | −6.01 | −6.001 | −6.0001 | −6.00001 | −6.000001 |
|---|---|---|---|---|---|---|
| G(x) | −.123456 | −.124843 | −.124984 | −.124998 | −.124999 | −.124999 |

(b)

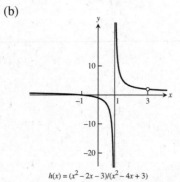

$$G(x) = (x + 6)/(x^2 + 4x - 12)$$

(c)  $G(x) = \frac{x+6}{(x^2+4x-12)} = \frac{x+6}{(x+6)(x-2)} = \frac{1}{x-2}$ if $x \neq -6$, and $\lim\limits_{x \to -6} \frac{1}{x-2} = \frac{1}{-6-2} = -\frac{1}{8} = -0.125.$

70. (a)  $h(x) = (x^2 - 2x - 3)/(x^2 - 4x + 3)$

| x | 2.9 | 2.99 | 2.999 | 2.9999 | 2.99999 | 2.999999 |
|---|---|---|---|---|---|---|
| h(x) | 2.052631 | 2.005025 | 2.000500 | 2.000050 | 2.000005 | 2.0000005 |

| x | 3.1 | 3.01 | 3.001 | 3.0001 | 3.00001 | 3.000001 |
|---|---|---|---|---|---|---|
| h(x) | 1.952380 | 1.995024 | 1.999500 | 1.999950 | 1.999995 | 1.999999 |

(b)

$$h(x) = (x^2 - 2x - 3)/(x^2 - 4x + 3)$$

(c)  $h(x) = \frac{x^2-2x-3}{x^2-4x+3} = \frac{(x-3)(x+1)}{(x-3)(x-1)} = \frac{x+1}{x-1}$ if $x \neq 3$, and $\lim\limits_{x \to 3} \frac{x+1}{x-1} = \frac{3+1}{3-1} = \frac{4}{2} = 2.$

71. (a)  $f(x) = (x^2 - 1)/(|x| - 1)$

| x | −1.1 | −1.01 | −1.001 | −1.0001 | −1.00001 | −1.000001 |
|---|---|---|---|---|---|---|
| f(x) | 2.1 | 2.01 | 2.001 | 2.0001 | 2.00001 | 2.000001 |

| x | −.9 | −.99 | −.999 | −.9999 | −.99999 | −.999999 |
|---|---|---|---|---|---|---|
| f(x) | 1.9 | 1.99 | 1.999 | 1.9999 | 1.99999 | 1.999999 |

(b)

$$f(x) = (x^2 - 1)/(|x| - 1)$$

(c)  $f(x) = \frac{x^2-1}{|x|-1} = \begin{cases} \frac{(x+1)(x-1)}{x-1} = x+1, & x \geq 0 \text{ and } x \neq 1 \\ \frac{(x+1)(x-1)}{-(x+1)} = 1-x, & x < 0 \text{ and } x \neq -1 \end{cases}$, and $\lim\limits_{x \to -1} (1-x) = 1 - (-1) = 2.$

72. (a) $F(x) = (x^2 + 3x + 2)/(2 - |x|)$

| x | −2.1 | −2.01 | −2.001 | −2.0001 | −2.00001 | −2.000001 |
|---|------|-------|--------|---------|----------|-----------|
| F(x) | −1.1 | −1.01 | −1.001 | −1.0001 | −1.00001 | −1.000001 |

| x | −1.9 | −1.99 | −1.999 | −1.9999 | −1.99999 | −1.999999 |
|---|------|-------|--------|---------|----------|-----------|
| F(x) | −.9 | −.99 | −.999 | −.9999 | −.99999 | −.999999 |

(b)

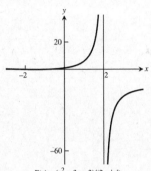

$F(x) = (x^2 + 3x + 2)/(2 - |x|)$

(c) $F(x) = \dfrac{x^2 + 3x + 2}{2 - |x|} = \begin{cases} \dfrac{(x+2)(x+1)}{2-x}, & x \geq 0 \\ \dfrac{(x+2)(x+1)}{2+x} = x + 1, & x < 0 \text{ and } x \neq -2 \end{cases}$, and $\lim\limits_{x \to -2} (x + 1) = -2 + 1 = -1$.

73. (a) $g(\theta) = (\sin \theta)/\theta$

| $\theta$ | .1 | .01 | .001 | .0001 | .00001 | .000001 |
|---|------|-------|--------|---------|----------|-----------|
| $g(\theta)$ | .998334 | .999983 | .999999 | .999999 | .999999 | .999999 |

| $\theta$ | −.1 | −.01 | −.001 | −.0001 | −.00001 | −.000001 |
|---|------|-------|--------|---------|----------|-----------|
| $g(\theta)$ | .998334 | .999983 | .999999 | .999999 | .999999 | .999999 |

$\lim\limits_{\theta \to 0} g(\theta) = 1$

(b)

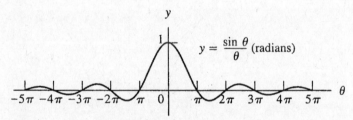

$y = \dfrac{\sin \theta}{\theta}$ (radians)

NOT TO SCALE

74. (a) $G(t) = (1 - \cos t)/t^2$

| t | .1 | .01 | .001 | .0001 | .00001 | .000001 |
|---|------|-------|--------|---------|----------|-----------|
| G(t) | .499583 | .499995 | .499999 | .5 | .5 | .5 |

| t | −.1 | −.01 | −.001 | −.0001 | −.00001 | −.000001 |
|---|------|-------|--------|---------|----------|-----------|
| G(t) | .499583 | .499995 | .499999 | .5 | .5 | .5 |

$\lim\limits_{t \to 0} G(t) = 0.5$

(b)

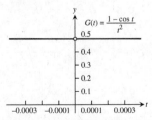

$G(t) = \dfrac{1 - \cos t}{t^2}$

Graph is NOT TO SCALE

75. $\lim\limits_{x \to c} f(x)$ exists at those points c where $\lim\limits_{x \to c} x^4 = \lim\limits_{x \to c} x^2$. Thus, $c^4 = c^2 \Rightarrow c^2(1 - c^2) = 0 \Rightarrow c = 0, 1,$ or $-1$.

Moreover, $\lim\limits_{x \to 0} f(x) = \lim\limits_{x \to 0} x^2 = 0$ and $\lim\limits_{x \to -1} f(x) = \lim\limits_{x \to 1} f(x) = 1$.

76. Nothing can be concluded about the values of f, g, and h at x = 2.  Yes, f(2) could be 0.  Since the conditions of the sandwich theorem are satisfied, $\lim\limits_{x \to 2} f(x) = -5 \neq 0$.

77. $1 = \lim\limits_{x \to 4} \frac{f(x)-5}{x-2} = \frac{\lim\limits_{x \to 4} f(x) - \lim\limits_{x \to 4} 5}{\lim\limits_{x \to 4} x - \lim\limits_{x \to 4} 2} = \frac{\lim\limits_{x \to 4} f(x) - 5}{4 - 2} \Rightarrow \lim\limits_{x \to 4} f(x) - 5 = 2(1) \Rightarrow \lim\limits_{x \to 4} f(x) = 2 + 5 = 7$.

78. (a) $1 = \lim\limits_{x \to -2} \frac{f(x)}{x^2} = \frac{\lim\limits_{x \to -2} f(x)}{\lim\limits_{x \to -2} x^2} = \frac{\lim\limits_{x \to -2} f(x)}{4} \Rightarrow \lim\limits_{x \to -2} f(x) = 4$.

(b) $1 = \lim\limits_{x \to -2} \frac{f(x)}{x^2} = \left[\lim\limits_{x \to -2} \frac{f(x)}{x}\right]\left[\lim\limits_{x \to -2} \frac{1}{x}\right] = \left[\lim\limits_{x \to -2} \frac{f(x)}{x}\right]\left(\frac{1}{-2}\right) \Rightarrow \lim\limits_{x \to -2} \frac{f(x)}{x} = -2$.

79. (a) $0 = 3 \cdot 0 = \left[\lim\limits_{x \to 2} \frac{f(x)-5}{x-2}\right]\left[\lim\limits_{x \to 2}(x-2)\right] = \lim\limits_{x \to 2}\left[\left(\frac{f(x)-5}{x-2}\right)(x-2)\right] = \lim\limits_{x \to 2}[f(x) - 5] = \lim\limits_{x \to 2} f(x) - 5$

$\Rightarrow \lim\limits_{x \to 2} f(x) = 5$.

(b) $0 = 4 \cdot 0 = \left[\lim\limits_{x \to 2} \frac{f(x)-5}{x-2}\right]\left[\lim\limits_{x \to 2}(x-2)\right] \Rightarrow \lim\limits_{x \to 2} f(x) = 5$ as in part (a).

80. (a) $0 = 1 \cdot 0 = \left[\lim\limits_{x \to 0} \frac{f(x)}{x^2}\right]\left[\lim\limits_{x \to 0} x\right]^2 = \left[\lim\limits_{x \to 0} \frac{f(x)}{x^2}\right]\left[\lim\limits_{x \to 0} x^2\right] = \lim\limits_{x \to 0}\left[\frac{f(x)}{x^2} \cdot x^2\right] = \lim\limits_{x \to 0} f(x)$.  That is, $\lim\limits_{x \to 0} f(x) = 0$.

(b) $0 = 1 \cdot 0 = \left[\lim\limits_{x \to 0} \frac{f(x)}{x^2}\right]\left[\lim\limits_{x \to 0} x\right] = \lim\limits_{x \to 0}\left[\frac{f(x)}{x^2} \cdot x\right] = \lim\limits_{x \to 0} \frac{f(x)}{x}$.  That is, $\lim\limits_{x \to 0} \frac{f(x)}{x} = 0$.

81. (a) $\lim\limits_{x \to 0} x \sin \frac{1}{x} = 0$

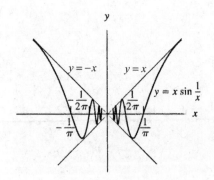

(b) $-1 \le \sin \frac{1}{x} \le 1$ for $x \neq 0$:

$x > 0 \Rightarrow -x \le x \sin \frac{1}{x} \le x \Rightarrow \lim\limits_{x \to 0} x \sin \frac{1}{x} = 0$ by the sandwich theorem;

$x < 0 \Rightarrow -x \ge x \sin \frac{1}{x} \ge x \Rightarrow \lim\limits_{x \to 0} x \sin \frac{1}{x} = 0$ by the sandwich theorem.

82. (a) $\lim\limits_{x \to 0} x^2 \cos\left(\frac{1}{x^3}\right) = 0$

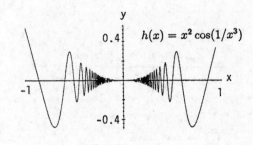

(b)  $-1 \le \cos\left(\frac{1}{x^3}\right) \le 1$ for $x \ne 0 \Rightarrow -x^2 \le x^2 \cos\left(\frac{1}{x^3}\right) \le x^2 \Rightarrow \lim\limits_{x \to 0} x^2 \cos\left(\frac{1}{x^3}\right) = 0$ by the sandwich

theorem since $\lim\limits_{x \to 0} x^2 = 0$.

83-88.  Example CAS commands:

Maple:

    f := x -> (x^4 − 16)/(x − 2);

    x0 := 2;

    plot( f(x), x = x0-1..x0+1, color = black,

        title = "Section 2.2, #83(a)" );

    limit( f(x), x = x0 );

In Exercise 85, note that the standard cube root, x^(1/3), is not defined for x<0 in many CASs.  This can be overcome in Maple by entering the function as f := x -> (surd(x+1, 3) − 1)/x.

Mathematica: (assigned function and values for x0 and h may vary)

    Clear[f, x]

    f[x_]:=(x³ − x² − 5x − 3)/(x + 1)²

    x0= −1; h = 0.1;

    Plot[f[x],{x, x0 − h, x0 + h}]

    Limit[f[x], x → x0]

## 2.3 THE PRECISE DEFINITION OF A LIMIT

1.

    Step 1:   $|x - 5| < \delta \Rightarrow -\delta < x - 5 < \delta \Rightarrow -\delta + 5 < x < \delta + 5$

    Step 2:   $\delta + 5 = 7 \Rightarrow \delta = 2$, or $-\delta + 5 = 1 \Rightarrow \delta = 4$.

              The value of $\delta$ which assures $|x - 5| < \delta \Rightarrow 1 < x < 7$ is the smaller value, $\delta = 2$.

2.

    Step 1:   $|x - 2| < \delta \Rightarrow -\delta < x - 2 < \delta \Rightarrow -\delta + 2 < x < \delta + 2$

    Step 2:   $-\delta + 2 = 1 \Rightarrow \delta = 1$, or $\delta + 2 = 7 \Rightarrow \delta = 5$.

              The value of $\delta$ which assures $|x - 2| < \delta \Rightarrow 1 < x < 7$ is the smaller value, $\delta = 1$.

3.

    Step 1:   $|x - (-3)| < \delta \Rightarrow -\delta < x + 3 < \delta \Rightarrow -\delta - 3 < x < \delta - 3$

    Step 2:   $-\delta - 3 = -\frac{7}{2} \Rightarrow \delta = \frac{1}{2}$, or $\delta - 3 = -\frac{1}{2} \Rightarrow \delta = \frac{5}{2}$.

              The value of $\delta$ which assures $|x - (-3)| < \delta \Rightarrow -\frac{7}{2} < x < -\frac{1}{2}$ is the smaller value, $\delta = \frac{1}{2}$.

4.

    Step 1:   $\left|x - \left(-\frac{3}{2}\right)\right| < \delta \Rightarrow -\delta < x + \frac{3}{2} < \delta \Rightarrow -\delta - \frac{3}{2} < x < \delta - \frac{3}{2}$

    Step 2:   $-\delta - \frac{3}{2} = -\frac{7}{2} \Rightarrow \delta = 2$, or $\delta - \frac{3}{2} = -\frac{1}{2} \Rightarrow \delta = 1$.

              The value of $\delta$ which assures $\left|x - \left(-\frac{3}{2}\right)\right| < \delta \Rightarrow -\frac{7}{2} < x < -\frac{1}{2}$ is the smaller value, $\delta = 1$.

5.

    Step 1:   $\left|x - \frac{1}{2}\right| < \delta \Rightarrow -\delta < x - \frac{1}{2} < \delta \Rightarrow -\delta + \frac{1}{2} < x < \delta + \frac{1}{2}$

Step 2:    $-\delta + \frac{1}{2} = \frac{4}{9} \Rightarrow \delta = \frac{1}{18}$, or $\delta + \frac{1}{2} = \frac{4}{7} \Rightarrow \delta = \frac{1}{14}$.

The value of $\delta$ which assures $\left|x - \frac{1}{2}\right| < \delta \Rightarrow \frac{4}{9} < x < \frac{4}{7}$ is the smaller value, $\delta = \frac{1}{18}$.

6.

```
    ←——( ———— | ———— )——→  x
      2.7591    3    3.2391
```

Step 1:    $|x - 3| < \delta \Rightarrow -\delta < x - 3 < \delta \Rightarrow -\delta + 3 < x < \delta + 3$

Step 2:    $-\delta + 3 = 2.7591 \Rightarrow \delta = 0.2409$, or $\delta + 3 = 3.2391 \Rightarrow \delta = 0.2391$.

The value of $\delta$ which assures $|x - 3| < \delta \Rightarrow 2.7591 < x < 3.2391$ is the smaller value, $\delta = 0.2391$.

7.  Step 1:    $|x - 5| < \delta \Rightarrow -\delta < x - 5 < \delta \Rightarrow -\delta + 5 < x < \delta + 5$

Step 2:    From the graph, $-\delta + 5 = 4.9 \Rightarrow \delta = 0.1$, or $\delta + 5 = 5.1 \Rightarrow \delta = 0.1$; thus $\delta = 0.1$ in either case.

8.  Step 1:    $|x - (-3)| < \delta \Rightarrow -\delta < x + 3 < \delta \Rightarrow -\delta - 3 < x < \delta - 3$

Step 2:    From the graph, $-\delta - 3 = -3.1 \Rightarrow \delta = 0.1$, or $\delta - 3 = -2.9 \Rightarrow \delta = 0.1$; thus $\delta = 0.1$.

9.  Step 1:    $|x - 1| < \delta \Rightarrow -\delta < x - 1 < \delta \Rightarrow -\delta + 1 < x < \delta + 1$

Step 2:    From the graph, $-\delta + 1 = \frac{9}{16} \Rightarrow \delta = \frac{7}{16}$, or $\delta + 1 = \frac{25}{16} \Rightarrow \delta = \frac{9}{16}$; thus $\delta = \frac{7}{16}$.

10.  Step 1:    $|x - 3| < \delta \Rightarrow -\delta < x - 3 < \delta \Rightarrow -\delta + 3 < x < \delta + 3$

Step 2:    From the graph, $-\delta + 3 = 2.61 \Rightarrow \delta = 0.39$, or $\delta + 3 = 3.41 \Rightarrow \delta = 0.41$; thus $\delta = 0.39$.

11.  Step 1:    $|x - 2| < \delta \Rightarrow -\delta < x - 2 < \delta \Rightarrow -\delta + 2 < x < \delta + 2$

Step 2:    From the graph, $-\delta + 2 = \sqrt{3} \Rightarrow \delta = 2 - \sqrt{3} \approx 0.2679$, or $\delta + 2 = \sqrt{5} \Rightarrow \delta = \sqrt{5} - 2 \approx 0.2361$;

thus $\delta = \sqrt{5} - 2$.

12.  Step 1:    $|x - (-1)| < \delta \Rightarrow -\delta < x + 1 < \delta \Rightarrow -\delta - 1 < x < \delta - 1$

Step 2:    From the graph, $-\delta - 1 = -\frac{\sqrt{5}}{2} \Rightarrow \delta = \frac{\sqrt{5} - 2}{2} \approx 0.1180$, or $\delta - 1 = -\frac{\sqrt{3}}{2} \Rightarrow \delta = \frac{2 - \sqrt{3}}{2} \approx 0.1340$;

thus $\delta = \frac{\sqrt{5} - 2}{2}$.

13.  Step 1:    $|x - (-1)| < \delta \Rightarrow -\delta < x + 1 < \delta \Rightarrow -\delta - 1 < x < \delta - 1$

Step 2:    From the graph, $-\delta - 1 = -\frac{16}{9} \Rightarrow \delta = \frac{7}{9} \approx 0.77$, or $\delta - 1 = -\frac{16}{25} \Rightarrow \frac{9}{25} = 0.36$; thus $\delta = \frac{9}{25} = 0.36$.

14.  Step 1:    $\left|x - \frac{1}{2}\right| < \delta \Rightarrow -\delta < x - \frac{1}{2} < \delta \Rightarrow -\delta + \frac{1}{2} < x < \delta + \frac{1}{2}$

Step 2:    From the graph, $-\delta + \frac{1}{2} = \frac{1}{2.01} \Rightarrow \delta = \frac{1}{2} - \frac{1}{2.01} \approx 0.00248$, or $\delta + \frac{1}{2} = \frac{1}{1.99} \Rightarrow \delta = \frac{1}{1.99} - \frac{1}{2} \approx 0.00251$;

thus $\delta = 0.00248$.

15.  Step 1:    $|(x + 1) - 5| < 0.01 \Rightarrow |x - 4| < 0.01 \Rightarrow -0.01 < x - 4 < 0.01 \Rightarrow 3.99 < x < 4.01$

Step 2:    $|x - 4| < \delta \Rightarrow -\delta < x - 4 < \delta \Rightarrow -\delta + 4 < x < \delta + 4 \Rightarrow \delta = 0.01$.

16.  Step 1:    $|(2x - 2) - (-6)| < 0.02 \Rightarrow |2x + 4| < 0.02 \Rightarrow -0.02 < 2x + 4 < 0.02 \Rightarrow -4.02 < 2x < -3.98$

$\Rightarrow -2.01 < x < -1.99$

Step 2:    $|x - (-2)| < \delta \Rightarrow -\delta < x + 2 < \delta \Rightarrow -\delta - 2 < x < \delta - 2 \Rightarrow \delta = 0.01$.

17.  Step 1:    $\left|\sqrt{x + 1} - 1\right| < 0.1 \Rightarrow -0.1 < \sqrt{x + 1} - 1 < 0.1 \Rightarrow 0.9 < \sqrt{x + 1} < 1.1 \Rightarrow 0.81 < x + 1 < 1.21$

$\Rightarrow -0.19 < x < 0.21$

Step 2:    $|x - 0| < \delta \Rightarrow -\delta < x < \delta$. Then, $-\delta = -0.19 \Rightarrow \delta = 0.19$ or $\delta = 0.21$; thus, $\delta = 0.19$.

18. Step 1: $\left|\sqrt{x} - \frac{1}{2}\right| < 0.1 \Rightarrow -0.1 < \sqrt{x} - \frac{1}{2} < 0.1 \Rightarrow 0.4 < \sqrt{x} < 0.6 \Rightarrow 0.16 < x < 0.36$

    Step 2: $\left|x - \frac{1}{4}\right| < \delta \Rightarrow -\delta < x - \frac{1}{4} < \delta \Rightarrow -\delta + \frac{1}{4} < x < \delta + \frac{1}{4}.$

    Then, $-\delta + \frac{1}{4} = 0.16 \Rightarrow \delta = 0.09$ or $\delta + \frac{1}{4} = 0.36 \Rightarrow \delta = 0.11$; thus $\delta = 0.09$.

19. Step 1: $\left|\sqrt{19 - x} - 3\right| < 1 \Rightarrow -1 < \sqrt{19 - x} - 3 < 1 \Rightarrow 2 < \sqrt{19 - x} < 4 \Rightarrow 4 < 19 - x < 16$

    $\Rightarrow -4 > x - 19 > -16 \Rightarrow 15 > x > 3$ or $3 < x < 15$

    Step 2: $|x - 10| < \delta \Rightarrow -\delta < x - 10 < \delta \Rightarrow -\delta + 10 < x < \delta + 10.$

    Then $-\delta + 10 = 3 \Rightarrow \delta = 7$, or $\delta + 10 = 15 \Rightarrow \delta = 5$; thus $\delta = 5$.

20. Step 1: $\left|\sqrt{x - 7} - 4\right| < 1 \Rightarrow -1 < \sqrt{x - 7} - 4 < 1 \Rightarrow 3 < \sqrt{x - 7} < 5 \Rightarrow 9 < x - 7 < 25 \Rightarrow 16 < x < 32$

    Step 2: $|x - 23| < \delta \Rightarrow -\delta < x - 23 < \delta \Rightarrow -\delta + 23 < x < \delta + 23.$

    Then $-\delta + 23 = 16 \Rightarrow \delta = 7$, or $\delta + 23 = 32 \Rightarrow \delta = 9$; thus $\delta = 7$.

21. Step 1: $\left|\frac{1}{x} - \frac{1}{4}\right| < 0.05 \Rightarrow -0.05 < \frac{1}{x} - \frac{1}{4} < 0.05 \Rightarrow 0.2 < \frac{1}{x} < 0.3 \Rightarrow \frac{10}{2} > x > \frac{10}{3}$ or $\frac{10}{3} < x < 5$.

    Step 2: $|x - 4| < \delta \Rightarrow -\delta < x - 4 < \delta \Rightarrow -\delta + 4 < x < \delta + 4.$

    Then $-\delta + 4 = \frac{10}{3}$ or $\delta = \frac{2}{3}$, or $\delta + 4 = 5$ or $\delta = 1$; thus $\delta = \frac{2}{3}$.

22. Step 1: $|x^2 - 3| < 0.1 \Rightarrow -0.1 < x^2 - 3 < 0.1 \Rightarrow 2.9 < x^2 < 3.1 \Rightarrow \sqrt{2.9} < x < \sqrt{3.1}$

    Step 2: $\left|x - \sqrt{3}\right| < \delta \Rightarrow -\delta < x - \sqrt{3} < \delta \Rightarrow -\delta + \sqrt{3} < x < \delta + \sqrt{3}.$

    Then $-\delta + \sqrt{3} = \sqrt{2.9} \Rightarrow \delta = \sqrt{3} - \sqrt{2.9} \approx 0.0291$, or $\delta + \sqrt{3} = \sqrt{3.1} \Rightarrow \delta = \sqrt{3.1} - \sqrt{3} \approx 0.0286$;

    thus $\delta = 0.0286$.

23. Step 1: $|x^2 - 4| < 0.5 \Rightarrow -0.5 < x^2 - 4 < 0.5 \Rightarrow 3.5 < x^2 < 4.5 \Rightarrow \sqrt{3.5} < |x| < \sqrt{4.5} \Rightarrow -\sqrt{4.5} < x < -\sqrt{3.5},$

    for x near $-2$.

    Step 2: $|x - (-2)| < \delta \Rightarrow -\delta < x + 2 < \delta \Rightarrow -\delta - 2 < x < \delta - 2.$

    Then $-\delta - 2 = -\sqrt{4.5} \Rightarrow \delta = \sqrt{4.5} - 2 \approx 0.1213$, or $\delta - 2 = -\sqrt{3.5} \Rightarrow \delta = 2 - \sqrt{3.5} \approx 0.1292$;

    thus $\delta = \sqrt{4.5} - 2 \approx 0.12$.

24. Step 1: $\left|\frac{1}{x} - (-1)\right| < 0.1 \Rightarrow -0.1 < \frac{1}{x} + 1 < 0.1 \Rightarrow -\frac{11}{10} < \frac{1}{x} < -\frac{9}{10} \Rightarrow -\frac{10}{11} > x > -\frac{10}{9}$ or $-\frac{10}{9} < x < -\frac{10}{11}$.

    Step 2: $|x - (-1)| < \delta \Rightarrow -\delta < x + 1 < \delta \Rightarrow -\delta - 1 < x < \delta - 1.$

    Then $-\delta - 1 = -\frac{10}{9} \Rightarrow \delta = \frac{1}{9}$, or $\delta - 1 = -\frac{10}{11} \Rightarrow \delta = \frac{1}{11}$; thus $\delta = \frac{1}{11}$.

25. Step 1: $|(x^2 - 5) - 11| < 1 \Rightarrow |x^2 - 16| < 1 \Rightarrow -1 < x^2 - 16 < 1 \Rightarrow 15 < x^2 < 17 \Rightarrow \sqrt{15} < x < \sqrt{17}.$

    Step 2: $|x - 4| < \delta \Rightarrow -\delta < x - 4 < \delta \Rightarrow -\delta + 4 < x < \delta + 4.$

    Then $-\delta + 4 = \sqrt{15} \Rightarrow \delta = 4 - \sqrt{15} \approx 0.1270$, or $\delta + 4 = \sqrt{17} \Rightarrow \delta = \sqrt{17} - 4 \approx 0.1231$;

    thus $\delta = \sqrt{17} - 4 \approx 0.12$.

26. Step 1: $\left|\frac{120}{x} - 5\right| < 1 \Rightarrow -1 < \frac{120}{x} - 5 < 1 \Rightarrow 4 < \frac{120}{x} < 6 \Rightarrow \frac{1}{4} > \frac{x}{120} > \frac{1}{6} \Rightarrow 30 > x > 20$ or $20 < x < 30$.

    Step 2: $|x - 24| < \delta \Rightarrow -\delta < x - 24 < \delta \Rightarrow -\delta + 24 < x < \delta + 24.$

    Then $-\delta + 24 = 20 \Rightarrow \delta = 4$, or $\delta + 24 = 30 \Rightarrow \delta = 6$; thus $\Rightarrow \delta = 4$.

27. Step 1: $|mx - 2m| < 0.03 \Rightarrow -0.03 < mx - 2m < 0.03 \Rightarrow -0.03 + 2m < mx < 0.03 + 2m \Rightarrow$

    $2 - \frac{0.03}{m} < x < 2 + \frac{0.03}{m}.$

    Step 2: $|x - 2| < \delta \Rightarrow -\delta < x - 2 < \delta \Rightarrow -\delta + 2 < x < \delta + 2.$

    Then $-\delta + 2 = 2 - \frac{0.03}{m} \Rightarrow \delta = \frac{0.03}{m}$, or $\delta + 2 = 2 + \frac{0.03}{m} \Rightarrow \delta = \frac{0.03}{m}$. In either case, $\delta = \frac{0.03}{m}$.

28. Step 1:   $|mx - 3m| < c \Rightarrow -c < mx - 3m < c \Rightarrow -c + 3m < mx < c + 3m \Rightarrow 3 - \frac{c}{m} < x < 3 + \frac{c}{m}$

    Step 2:   $|x - 3| < \delta \Rightarrow -\delta < x - 3 < \delta \Rightarrow -\delta + 3 < x < \delta + 3$.

    Then $-\delta + 3 = 3 - \frac{c}{m} \Rightarrow \delta = \frac{c}{m}$, or $\delta + 3 = 3 + \frac{c}{m} \Rightarrow \delta = \frac{c}{m}$. In either case, $\delta = \frac{c}{m}$.

29. Step 1:   $\left|(mx + b) - \left(\frac{m}{2} + b\right)\right| < c \Rightarrow -c < mx - \frac{m}{2} < c \Rightarrow -c + \frac{m}{2} < mx < c + \frac{m}{2} \Rightarrow \frac{1}{2} - \frac{c}{m} < x < \frac{1}{2} + \frac{c}{m}$.

    Step 2:   $\left|x - \frac{1}{2}\right| < \delta \Rightarrow -\delta < x - \frac{1}{2} < \delta \Rightarrow -\delta + \frac{1}{2} < x < \delta + \frac{1}{2}$.

    Then $-\delta + \frac{1}{2} = \frac{1}{2} - \frac{c}{m} \Rightarrow \delta = \frac{c}{m}$, or $\delta + \frac{1}{2} = \frac{1}{2} + \frac{c}{m} \Rightarrow \delta = \frac{c}{m}$. In either case, $\delta = \frac{c}{m}$.

30. Step 1:   $|(mx + b) - (m + b)| < 0.05 \Rightarrow -0.05 < mx - m < 0.05 \Rightarrow -0.05 + m < mx < 0.05 + m$

    $\Rightarrow 1 - \frac{0.05}{m} < x < 1 + \frac{0.05}{m}$.

    Step 2:   $|x - 1| < \delta \Rightarrow -\delta < x - 1 < \delta \Rightarrow -\delta + 1 < x < \delta + 1$.

    Then $-\delta + 1 = 1 - \frac{0.05}{m} \Rightarrow \delta = \frac{0.05}{m}$, or $\delta + 1 = 1 + \frac{0.05}{m} \Rightarrow \delta = \frac{0.05}{m}$. In either case, $\delta = \frac{0.05}{m}$.

31. $\lim\limits_{x \to 3} (3 - 2x) = 3 - 2(3) = -3$

    Step 1:   $|(3 - 2x) - (-3)| < 0.02 \Rightarrow -0.02 < 6 - 2x < 0.02 \Rightarrow -6.02 < -2x < -5.98 \Rightarrow 3.01 > x > 2.99$ or
    $2.99 < x < 3.01$.

    Step 2:   $0 < |x - 3| < \delta \Rightarrow -\delta < x - 3 < \delta \Rightarrow -\delta + 3 < x < \delta + 3$.

    Then $-\delta + 3 = 2.99 \Rightarrow \delta = 0.01$, or $\delta + 3 = 3.01 \Rightarrow \delta = 0.01$; thus $\delta = 0.01$.

32. $\lim\limits_{x \to -1} (-3x - 2) = (-3)(-1) - 2 = 1$

    Step 1:   $|(-3x - 2) - 1| < 0.03 \Rightarrow -0.03 < -3x - 3 < 0.03 \Rightarrow 0.01 > x + 1 > -0.01 \Rightarrow -1.01 < x < -0.99$.

    Step 2:   $|x - (-1)| < \delta \Rightarrow -\delta < x + 1 < \delta \Rightarrow -\delta - 1 < x < \delta - 1$.

    Then $-\delta - 1 = -1.01 \Rightarrow \delta = 0.01$, or $\delta - 1 = -0.99 \Rightarrow \delta = 0.01$; thus $\delta = 0.01$.

33. $\lim\limits_{x \to 2} \frac{x^2 - 4}{x - 2} = \lim\limits_{x \to 2} \frac{(x + 2)(x - 2)}{(x - 2)} = \lim\limits_{x \to 2} (x + 2) = 2 + 2 = 4, x \neq 2$

    Step 1:   $\left|\left(\frac{x^2 - 4}{x - 2}\right) - 4\right| < 0.05 \Rightarrow -0.05 < \frac{(x + 2)(x - 2)}{(x - 2)} - 4 < 0.05 \Rightarrow 3.95 < x + 2 < 4.05, x \neq 2$

    $\Rightarrow 1.95 < x < 2.05, x \neq 2$.

    Step 2:   $|x - 2| < \delta \Rightarrow -\delta < x - 2 < \delta \Rightarrow -\delta + 2 < x < \delta + 2$.

    Then $-\delta + 2 = 1.95 \Rightarrow \delta = 0.05$, or $\delta + 2 = 2.05 \Rightarrow \delta = 0.05$; thus $\delta = 0.05$.

34. $\lim\limits_{x \to -5} \frac{x^2 + 6x + 5}{x + 5} = \lim\limits_{x \to -5} \frac{(x + 5)(x + 1)}{(x + 5)} = \lim\limits_{x \to -5} (x + 1) = -4, x \neq -5$.

    Step 1:   $\left|\left(\frac{x^2 + 6x + 5}{x + 5}\right) - (-4)\right| < 0.05 \Rightarrow -0.05 < \frac{(x + 5)(x + 1)}{(x + 5)} + 4 < 0.05 \Rightarrow -4.05 < x + 1 < -3.95, x \neq -5$

    $\Rightarrow -5.05 < x < -4.95, x \neq -5$.

    Step 2:   $|x - (-5)| < \delta \Rightarrow -\delta < x + 5 < \delta \Rightarrow -\delta - 5 < x < \delta - 5$.

    Then $-\delta - 5 = -5.05 \Rightarrow \delta = 0.05$, or $\delta - 5 = -4.95 \Rightarrow \delta = 0.05$; thus $\delta = 0.05$.

35. $\lim\limits_{x \to -3} \sqrt{1 - 5x} = \sqrt{1 - 5(-3)} = \sqrt{16} = 4$

    Step 1:   $\left|\sqrt{1 - 5x} - 4\right| < 0.5 \Rightarrow -0.5 < \sqrt{1 - 5x} - 4 < 0.5 \Rightarrow 3.5 < \sqrt{1 - 5x} < 4.5 \Rightarrow 12.25 < 1 - 5x < 20.25$

    $\Rightarrow 11.25 < -5x < 19.25 \Rightarrow -3.85 < x < -2.25$.

    Step 2:   $|x - (-3)| < \delta \Rightarrow -\delta < x + 3 < \delta \Rightarrow -\delta - 3 < x < \delta - 3$.

    Then $-\delta - 3 = -3.85 \Rightarrow \delta = 0.85$, or $\delta - 3 = -2.25 \Rightarrow 0.75$; thus $\delta = 0.75$.

36. $\lim\limits_{x \to 2} \frac{4}{x} = \frac{4}{2} = 2$

    Step 1:   $\left|\frac{4}{x} - 2\right| < 0.4 \Rightarrow -0.4 < \frac{4}{x} - 2 < 0.4 \Rightarrow 1.6 < \frac{4}{x} < 2.4 \Rightarrow \frac{10}{16} > \frac{x}{4} > \frac{10}{24} \Rightarrow \frac{10}{4} > x > \frac{10}{6}$ or $\frac{5}{3} < x < \frac{5}{2}$.

Step 2:    $|x - 2| < \delta \Rightarrow -\delta < x - 2 < \delta \Rightarrow -\delta + 2 < x < \delta + 2.$

Then $-\delta + 2 = \frac{5}{3} \Rightarrow \delta = \frac{1}{3}$, or $\delta + 2 = \frac{5}{2} \Rightarrow \delta = \frac{1}{2}$; thus $\delta = \frac{1}{3}$.

37. Step 1:    $|(9 - x) - 5| < \epsilon \Rightarrow -\epsilon < 4 - x < \epsilon \Rightarrow -\epsilon - 4 < -x < \epsilon - 4 \Rightarrow \epsilon + 4 > x > 4 - \epsilon \Rightarrow 4 - \epsilon < x < 4 + \epsilon.$

Step 2:    $|x - 4| < \delta \Rightarrow -\delta < x - 4 < \delta \Rightarrow -\delta + 4 < x < \delta + 4.$

Then $-\delta + 4 = -\epsilon + 4 \Rightarrow \delta = \epsilon$, or $\delta + 4 = \epsilon + 4 \Rightarrow \delta = \epsilon$. Thus choose $\delta = \epsilon$.

38. Step 1:    $|(3x - 7) - 2| < \epsilon \Rightarrow -\epsilon < 3x - 9 < \epsilon \Rightarrow 9 - \epsilon < 3x < 9 + \epsilon \Rightarrow 3 - \frac{\epsilon}{3} < x < 3 + \frac{\epsilon}{3}.$

Step 2:    $|x - 3| < \delta \Rightarrow -\delta < x - 3 < \delta \Rightarrow -\delta + 3 < x < \delta + 3.$

Then $-\delta + 3 = 3 - \frac{\epsilon}{3} \Rightarrow \delta = \frac{\epsilon}{3}$, or $\delta + 3 = 3 + \frac{\epsilon}{3} \Rightarrow \delta = \frac{\epsilon}{3}$. Thus choose $\delta = \frac{\epsilon}{3}$.

39. Step 1:    $\left| \sqrt{x - 5} - 2 \right| < \epsilon \Rightarrow -\epsilon < \sqrt{x - 5} - 2 < \epsilon \Rightarrow 2 - \epsilon < \sqrt{x - 5} < 2 + \epsilon \Rightarrow (2 - \epsilon)^2 < x - 5 < (2 + \epsilon)^2$

$\Rightarrow (2 - \epsilon)^2 + 5 < x < (2 + \epsilon)^2 + 5.$

Step 2:    $|x - 9| < \delta \Rightarrow -\delta < x - 9 < \delta \Rightarrow -\delta + 9 < x < \delta + 9.$

Then $-\delta + 9 = \epsilon^2 - 4\epsilon + 9 \Rightarrow \delta = 4\epsilon - \epsilon^2$, or $\delta + 9 = \epsilon^2 + 4\epsilon + 9 \Rightarrow \delta = 4\epsilon + \epsilon^2$. Thus choose the smaller distance, $\delta = 4\epsilon - \epsilon^2.$

40. Step 1:    $\left| \sqrt{4 - x} - 2 \right| < \epsilon \Rightarrow -\epsilon < \sqrt{4 - x} - 2 < \epsilon \Rightarrow 2 - \epsilon < \sqrt{4 - x} < 2 + \epsilon \Rightarrow (2 - \epsilon)^2 < 4 - x < (2 + \epsilon)^2$

$\Rightarrow -(2 + \epsilon)^2 < x - 4 < -(2 - \epsilon)^2 \Rightarrow -(2 + \epsilon)^2 + 4 < x < -(2 - \epsilon)^2 + 4.$

Step 2:    $|x - 0| < \delta \Rightarrow -\delta < x < \delta.$

Then $-\delta = -(2 + \epsilon)^2 + 4 = -\epsilon^2 - 4\epsilon \Rightarrow \delta = 4\epsilon + \epsilon^2$, or $\delta = -(2 - \epsilon)^2 + 4 = 4\epsilon - \epsilon^2$. Thus choose the smaller distance, $\delta = 4\epsilon - \epsilon^2.$

41. Step 1:    For $x \neq 1$, $|x^2 - 1| < \epsilon \Rightarrow -\epsilon < x^2 - 1 < \epsilon \Rightarrow 1 - \epsilon < x^2 < 1 + \epsilon \Rightarrow \sqrt{1 - \epsilon} < |x| < \sqrt{1 + \epsilon}$

$\Rightarrow \sqrt{1 - \epsilon} < x < \sqrt{1 + \epsilon}$ near $x = 1$.

Step 2:    $|x - 1| < \delta \Rightarrow -\delta < x - 1 < \delta \Rightarrow -\delta + 1 < x < \delta + 1.$

Then $-\delta + 1 = \sqrt{1 - \epsilon} \Rightarrow \delta = 1 - \sqrt{1 - \epsilon}$, or $\delta + 1 = \sqrt{1 + \epsilon} \Rightarrow \delta = \sqrt{1 + \epsilon} - 1$. Choose

$\delta = \min \left\{ 1 - \sqrt{1 - \epsilon}, \sqrt{1 + \epsilon} - 1 \right\}$, that is, the smaller of the two distances.

42. Step 1:    For $x \neq -2$, $|x^2 - 4| < \epsilon \Rightarrow -\epsilon < x^2 - 4 < \epsilon \Rightarrow 4 - \epsilon < x^2 < 4 + \epsilon \Rightarrow \sqrt{4 - \epsilon} < |x| < \sqrt{4 + \epsilon}$

$\Rightarrow -\sqrt{4 + \epsilon} < x < -\sqrt{4 - \epsilon}$ near $x = -2$.

Step 2:    $|x - (-2)| < \delta \Rightarrow -\delta < x + 2 < \delta \Rightarrow -\delta - 2 < x < \delta - 2.$

Then $-\delta - 2 = -\sqrt{4 + \epsilon} \Rightarrow \delta = \sqrt{4 + \epsilon} - 2$, or $\delta - 2 = -\sqrt{4 - \epsilon} \Rightarrow \delta = 2 - \sqrt{4 - \epsilon}$. Choose

$\delta = \min \left\{ \sqrt{4 + \epsilon} - 2, 2 - \sqrt{4 - \epsilon} \right\}.$

43. Step 1:    $\left| \frac{1}{x} - 1 \right| < \epsilon \Rightarrow -\epsilon < \frac{1}{x} - 1 < \epsilon \Rightarrow 1 - \epsilon < \frac{1}{x} < 1 + \epsilon \Rightarrow \frac{1}{1 + \epsilon} < x < \frac{1}{1 - \epsilon}.$

Step 2:    $|x - 1| < \delta \Rightarrow -\delta < x - 1 < \delta \Rightarrow 1 - \delta < x < 1 + \delta.$

Then $1 - \delta = \frac{1}{1 + \epsilon} \Rightarrow \delta = 1 - \frac{1}{1 + \epsilon} = \frac{\epsilon}{1 + \epsilon}$, or $1 + \delta = \frac{1}{1 - \epsilon} \Rightarrow \delta = \frac{1}{1 - \epsilon} - 1 = \frac{\epsilon}{1 - \epsilon}.$

Choose $\delta = \frac{\epsilon}{1 + \epsilon}$, the smaller of the two distances.

44. Step 1:    $\left| \frac{1}{x^2} - \frac{1}{3} \right| < \epsilon \Rightarrow -\epsilon < \frac{1}{x^2} - \frac{1}{3} < \epsilon \Rightarrow \frac{1}{3} - \epsilon < \frac{1}{x^2} < \frac{1}{3} + \epsilon \Rightarrow \frac{1 - 3\epsilon}{3} < \frac{1}{x^2} < \frac{1 + 3\epsilon}{3} \Rightarrow \frac{3}{1 - 3\epsilon} > x^2 > \frac{3}{1 + 3\epsilon}$

$\Rightarrow \sqrt{\frac{3}{1 + 3\epsilon}} < |x| < \sqrt{\frac{3}{1 - 3\epsilon}}$, or $\sqrt{\frac{3}{1 + 3\epsilon}} < x < \sqrt{\frac{3}{1 - 3\epsilon}}$ for x near $\sqrt{3}$.

Step 2:   $\left|x - \sqrt{3}\right| < \delta \Rightarrow -\delta < x - \sqrt{3} < \delta \Rightarrow \sqrt{3} - \delta < x < \sqrt{3} + \delta.$

Then $\sqrt{3} - \delta = \sqrt{\frac{3}{1+3\epsilon}} \Rightarrow \delta = \sqrt{3} - \sqrt{\frac{3}{1+3\epsilon}}$, or $\sqrt{3} + \delta = \sqrt{\frac{3}{1-3\epsilon}} \Rightarrow \delta = \sqrt{\frac{3}{1-3\epsilon}} - \sqrt{3}.$

Choose $\delta = \min\left\{\sqrt{3} - \sqrt{\frac{3}{1+3\epsilon}}, \sqrt{\frac{3}{1-3\epsilon}} - \sqrt{3}\right\}.$

45.  Step 1:   $\left|\left(\frac{x^2-9}{x+3}\right) - (-6)\right| < \epsilon \Rightarrow -\epsilon < (x-3) + 6 < \epsilon, x \neq -3 \Rightarrow -\epsilon < x+3 < \epsilon \Rightarrow -\epsilon - 3 < x < \epsilon - 3.$

Step 2:   $|x - (-3)| < \delta \Rightarrow -\delta < x+3 < \delta \Rightarrow -\delta - 3 < x < \delta - 3.$

Then $-\delta - 3 = -\epsilon - 3 \Rightarrow \delta = \epsilon$, or $\delta - 3 = \epsilon - 3 \Rightarrow \delta = \epsilon$.  Choose $\delta = \epsilon$.

46.  Step 1:   $\left|\left(\frac{x^2-1}{x-1}\right) - 2\right| < \epsilon \Rightarrow -\epsilon < (x+1) - 2 < \epsilon, x \neq 1 \Rightarrow 1 - \epsilon < x < 1 + \epsilon.$

Step 2:   $|x - 1| < \delta \Rightarrow -\delta < x-1 < \delta \Rightarrow 1 - \delta < x < 1 + \delta.$

Then $1 - \delta = 1 - \epsilon \Rightarrow \delta = \epsilon$, or $1 + \delta = 1 + \epsilon \Rightarrow \delta = \epsilon$.  Choose $\delta = \epsilon$.

47.  Step 1:   $x < 1$: $|(4-2x) - 2| < \epsilon \Rightarrow 0 < 2 - 2x < \epsilon$ since $x < 1$. Thus, $1 - \frac{\epsilon}{2} < x < 0$;

$x \geq 1$: $|(6x-4) - 2| < \epsilon \Rightarrow 0 \leq 6x - 6 < \epsilon$ since $x \geq 1$. Thus, $1 \leq x < 1 + \frac{\epsilon}{6}$.

Step 2:   $|x - 1| < \delta \Rightarrow -\delta < x-1 < \delta \Rightarrow 1 - \delta < x < 1 + \delta.$

Then $1 - \delta = 1 - \frac{\epsilon}{2} \Rightarrow \delta = \frac{\epsilon}{2}$, or $1 + \delta = 1 + \frac{\epsilon}{6} \Rightarrow \delta = \frac{\epsilon}{6}$.  Choose $\delta = \frac{\epsilon}{6}$.

48.  Step 1:   $x < 0$: $|2x - 0| < \epsilon \Rightarrow -\epsilon < 2x < 0 \Rightarrow -\frac{\epsilon}{2} < x < 0$;

$x \geq 0$: $\left|\frac{x}{2} - 0\right| < \epsilon \Rightarrow 0 \leq x < 2\epsilon.$

Step 2:   $|x - 0| < \delta \Rightarrow -\delta < x < \delta.$

Then $-\delta = -\frac{\epsilon}{2} \Rightarrow \delta = \frac{\epsilon}{2}$, or $\delta = 2\epsilon \Rightarrow \delta = 2\epsilon$.  Choose $\delta = \frac{\epsilon}{2}$.

49.  By the figure, $-x \leq x \sin \frac{1}{x} \leq x$ for all $x > 0$ and $-x \geq x \sin \frac{1}{x} \geq x$ for $x < 0$. Since $\lim\limits_{x \to 0} (-x) = \lim\limits_{x \to 0} x = 0$, then by the sandwich theorem, in either case, $\lim\limits_{x \to 0} x \sin \frac{1}{x} = 0.$

50.  By the figure, $-x^2 \leq x^2 \sin \frac{1}{x} \leq x^2$ for all $x$ except possibly at $x = 0$. Since $\lim\limits_{x \to 0} (-x^2) = \lim\limits_{x \to 0} x^2 = 0$, then by the sandwich theorem, $\lim\limits_{x \to 0} x^2 \sin \frac{1}{x} = 0.$

51.  As $x$ approaches the value 0, the values of $g(x)$ approach $k$. Thus for every number $\epsilon > 0$, there exists a $\delta > 0$ such that $0 < |x - 0| < \delta \Rightarrow |g(x) - k| < \epsilon.$

52.  Write $x = h + c$. Then $0 < |x - c| < \delta \Leftrightarrow -\delta < x - c < \delta, x \neq c \Leftrightarrow -\delta < (h+c) - c < \delta, h + c \neq c$
$\Leftrightarrow -\delta < h < \delta, h \neq 0 \Leftrightarrow 0 < |h - 0| < \delta.$

Thus, $\lim\limits_{x \to c} f(x) = L \Leftrightarrow$ for any $\epsilon > 0$, there exists $\delta > 0$ such that $|f(x) - L| < \epsilon$ whenever $0 < |x - c| < \delta$
$\Leftrightarrow |f(h+c) - L| < \epsilon$ whenever $0 < |h - 0| < \delta \Leftrightarrow \lim\limits_{h \to 0} f(h+c) = L.$

53.  Let $f(x) = x^2$. The function values do get closer to $-1$ as $x$ approaches 0, but $\lim\limits_{x \to 0} f(x) = 0$, not $-1$. The function $f(x) = x^2$ never gets <u>arbitrarily</u> <u>close</u> to $-1$ for $x$ near 0.

54. Let $f(x) = \sin x$, $L = \frac{1}{2}$, and $x_0 = 0$. There exists a value of x (namely, $x = \frac{\pi}{6}$) for which $\left|\sin x - \frac{1}{2}\right| < \epsilon$ for any given $\epsilon > 0$. However, $\lim\limits_{x \to 0} \sin x = 0$, not $\frac{1}{2}$. The wrong statement does not require x to be arbitrarily close to $x_0$. As another\ example, let $g(x) = \sin \frac{1}{x}$, $L = \frac{1}{2}$, and $x_0 = 0$. We can choose infinitely many values of x near 0 such that $\sin \frac{1}{x} = \frac{1}{2}$ as you can see from the accompanying figure. However, $\lim\limits_{x \to 0} \sin \frac{1}{x}$ fails to exist. The wrong statement does not require <u>all</u> values of x arbitrarily close to $x_0 = 0$ to lie within $\epsilon > 0$ of $L = \frac{1}{2}$. Again you can see from the figure that there are also infinitely many values of x near 0 such that $\sin \frac{1}{x} = 0$. If we choose $\epsilon < \frac{1}{4}$ we cannot satisfy the inequality $\left|\sin \frac{1}{x} - \frac{1}{2}\right| < \epsilon$ for all values of x sufficiently near $x_0 = 0$.

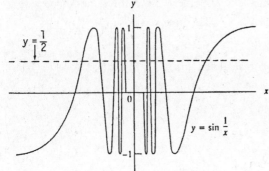

55. $|A - 9| \le 0.01 \Rightarrow -0.01 \le \pi \left(\frac{x}{2}\right)^2 - 9 \le 0.01 \Rightarrow 8.99 \le \frac{\pi x^2}{4} \le 9.01 \Rightarrow \frac{4}{\pi}(8.99) \le x^2 \le \frac{4}{\pi}(9.01)$

$\Rightarrow 2\sqrt{\frac{8.99}{\pi}} \le x \le 2\sqrt{\frac{9.01}{\pi}}$ or $3.384 \le x \le 3.387$. To be safe, the left endpoint was rounded up and the right endpoint was rounded down.

56. $V = RI \Rightarrow \frac{V}{R} = I \Rightarrow \left|\frac{V}{R} - 5\right| \le 0.1 \Rightarrow -0.1 \le \frac{120}{R} - 5 \le 0.1 \Rightarrow 4.9 \le \frac{120}{R} \le 5.1 \Rightarrow \frac{10}{49} \ge \frac{R}{120} \ge \frac{10}{51} \Rightarrow$

$\frac{(120)(10)}{51} \le R \le \frac{(120)(10)}{49} \Rightarrow 23.53 \le R \le 24.48$.

To be safe, the left endpoint was rounded up and the right endpoint was rounded down.

57. (a) $-\delta < x - 1 < 0 \Rightarrow 1 - \delta < x < 1 \Rightarrow f(x) = x$. Then $|f(x) - 2| = |x - 2| = 2 - x > 2 - 1 = 1$. That is, $|f(x) - 2| \ge 1 \ge \frac{1}{2}$ no matter how small $\delta$ is taken when $1 - \delta < x < 1 \Rightarrow \lim\limits_{x \to 1} f(x) \ne 2$.

(b) $0 < x - 1 < \delta \Rightarrow 1 < x < 1 + \delta \Rightarrow f(x) = x + 1$. Then $|f(x) - 1| = |(x + 1) - 1| = |x| = x > 1$. That is, $|f(x) - 1| \ge 1$ no matter how small $\delta$ is taken when $1 < x < 1 + \delta \Rightarrow \lim\limits_{x \to 1} f(x) \ne 1$.

(c) $-\delta < x - 1 < 0 \Rightarrow 1 - \delta < x < 1 \Rightarrow f(x) = x$. Then $|f(x) - 1.5| = |x - 1.5| = 1.5 - x > 1.5 - 1 = 0.5$. Also, $0 < x - 1 < \delta \Rightarrow 1 < x < 1 + \delta \Rightarrow f(x) = x + 1$. Then $|f(x) - 1.5| = |(x + 1) - 1.5| = |x - 0.5|$ $= x - 0.5 > 1 - 0.5 = 0.5$. Thus, no matter how small $\delta$ is taken, there exists a value of x such that $-\delta < x - 1 < \delta$ but $|f(x) - 1.5| \ge \frac{1}{2} \Rightarrow \lim\limits_{x \to 1} f(x) \ne 1.5$.

58. (a) For $2 < x < 2 + \delta \Rightarrow h(x) = 2 \Rightarrow |h(x) - 4| = 2$. Thus for $\epsilon < 2$, $|h(x) - 4| \ge \epsilon$ whenever $2 < x < 2 + \delta$ no matter how small we choose $\delta > 0 \Rightarrow \lim\limits_{x \to 2} h(x) \ne 4$.

(b) For $2 < x < 2 + \delta \Rightarrow h(x) = 2 \Rightarrow |h(x) - 3| = 1$. Thus for $\epsilon < 1$, $|h(x) - 3| \ge \epsilon$ whenever $2 < x < 2 + \delta$ no matter how small we choose $\delta > 0 \Rightarrow \lim\limits_{x \to 2} h(x) \ne 3$.

(c) For $2 - \delta < x < 2 \Rightarrow h(x) = x^2$ so $|h(x) - 2| = |x^2 - 2|$. No matter how small $\delta > 0$ is chosen, $x^2$ is close to 4 when x is near 2 and to the left on the real line $\Rightarrow |x^2 - 2|$ will be close to 2. Thus if $\epsilon < 1$, $|h(x) - 2| \ge \epsilon$ whenever $2 - \delta < x < 2$ no mater how small we choose $\delta > 0 \Rightarrow \lim\limits_{x \to 2} h(x) \ne 2$.

59. (a) For $3 - \delta < x < 3 \Rightarrow f(x) > 4.8 \Rightarrow |f(x) - 4| \geq 0.8$. Thus for $\epsilon < 0.8$, $|f(x) - 4| \geq \epsilon$ whenever $3 - \delta < x < 3$ no matter how small we choose $\delta > 0 \Rightarrow \lim_{x \to 3} f(x) \neq 4$.

   (b) For $3 < x < 3 + \delta \Rightarrow f(x) < 3 \Rightarrow |f(x) - 4.8| \geq 1.8$. Thus for $\epsilon < 1.8$, $|f(x) - 4.8| \geq \epsilon$ whenever $3 < x < 3 + \delta$ no matter how small we choose $\delta > 0 \Rightarrow \lim_{x \to 3} f(x) \neq 4.8$.

   (c) For $3 - \delta < x < 3 \Rightarrow f(x) > 4.8 \Rightarrow |f(x) - 3| \geq 1.8$. Again, for $\epsilon < 1.8$, $|f(x) - 3| \geq \epsilon$ whenever $3 - \delta < x < 3$ no matter how small we choose $\delta > 0 \Rightarrow \lim_{x \to 3} f(x) \neq 3$.

60. (a) No matter how small we choose $\delta > 0$, for x near $-1$ satisfying $-1 - \delta < x < -1 + \delta$, the values of g(x) are near $1 \Rightarrow |g(x) - 2|$ is near 1. Then, for $\epsilon = \frac{1}{2}$ we have $|g(x) - 2| \geq \frac{1}{2}$ for some x satisfying $-1 - \delta < x < -1 + \delta$, or $0 < |x + 1| < \delta \Rightarrow \lim_{x \to -1} g(x) \neq 2$.

   (b) Yes, $\lim_{x \to -1} g(x) = 1$ because from the graph we can find a $\delta > 0$ such that $|g(x) - 1| < \epsilon$ if $0 < |x - (-1)| < \delta$.

61-66. Example CAS commands (values of del may vary for a specified eps):
   Maple:

```
f := x -> (x^4-81)/(x-3);x0 := 3;
plot( f(x), x=x0-1..x0+1, color=black,              # (a)
      title="Section 2.3, #61(a)" );
L := limit( f(x), x=x0 );                           # (b)
epsilon := 0.2;                                     # (c)
plot( [f(x),L-epsilon,L+epsilon], x=x0-0.01..x0+0.01,
      color=black, linestyle=[1,3,3], title="Section 2.3, #61(c)" );
q := fsolve( abs( f(x)-L ) = epsilon, x=x0-1..x0+1 );   # (d)
delta := abs(x0-q);
plot( [f(x),L-epsilon,L+epsilon], x=x0-delta..x0+delta, color=black, title="Section 2.3, #61(d)" );
for eps in [0.1, 0.005, 0.001 ] do                      # (e)
 q := fsolve( abs( f(x)-L ) = eps, x=x0-1..x0+1 );
 delta := abs(x0-q);
 head := sprintf("Section 2.3, #61(e)\n epsilon = %5f, delta = %5f\n", eps, delta );
 print(plot( [f(x),L-eps,L+eps], x=x0-delta..x0+delta,
            color=black, linestyle=[1,3,3], title=head ));
end do:
```

   Mathematica (assigned function and values for x0, eps and del may vary):

```
Clear[f, x]
y1: = L - eps; y2: = L + eps; x0 = 1;
f[x_]: = (3x^2 - (7x + 1)Sqrt[x] + 5)/(x - 1)
Plot[f[x], {x, x0 - 0.2, x0 + 0.2}]
L: = Limit[f[x], x -> x0]
eps = 0.1; del = 0.2;
Plot[{f[x], y1, y2},{x, x0 - del, x0 + del}, PlotRange -> {L - 2eps, L + 2eps}]
```

## 2.4 ONE-SIDED LIMITS

1.  (a) True         (b) True         (c) False        (d) True
    (e) True         (f) True         (g) False        (h) False
    (i) False        (j) False        (k) True         (l) False

2.  (a) True         (b) False        (c) False        (d) True
    (e) True         (f) True         (g) True         (h) True
    (i) True         (j) False        (k) True

3.  (a) $\lim\limits_{x \to 2^+} f(x) = \frac{2}{2} + 1 = 2, \lim\limits_{x \to 2^-} f(x) = 3 - 2 = 1$

    (b) No, $\lim\limits_{x \to 2} f(x)$ does not exist because $\lim\limits_{x \to 2^+} f(x) \neq \lim\limits_{x \to 2^-} f(x)$

    (c) $\lim\limits_{x \to 4^-} f(x) = \frac{4}{2} + 1 = 3, \lim\limits_{x \to 4^+} f(x) = \frac{4}{2} + 1 = 3$

    (d) Yes, $\lim\limits_{x \to 4} f(x) = 3$ because $3 = \lim\limits_{x \to 4^-} f(x) = \lim\limits_{x \to 4^+} f(x)$

4.  (a) $\lim\limits_{x \to 2^+} f(x) = \frac{2}{2} = 1, \lim\limits_{x \to 2^-} f(x) = 3 - 2 = 1, f(2) = 2$

    (b) Yes, $\lim\limits_{x \to 2} f(x) = 1$ because $1 = \lim\limits_{x \to 2^+} f(x) = \lim\limits_{x \to 2^-} f(x)$

    (c) $\lim\limits_{x \to -1^-} f(x) = 3 - (-1) = 4, \lim\limits_{x \to -1^+} f(x) = 3 - (-1) = 4$

    (d) Yes, $\lim\limits_{x \to -1} f(x) = 4$ because $4 = \lim\limits_{x \to -1^-} f(x) = \lim\limits_{x \to -1^+} f(x)$

5.  (a) No, $\lim\limits_{x \to 0^+} f(x)$ does not exist since $\sin\left(\frac{1}{x}\right)$ does not approach any single value as x approaches 0

    (b) $\lim\limits_{x \to 0^-} f(x) = \lim\limits_{x \to 0^-} 0 = 0$

    (c) $\lim\limits_{x \to 0} f(x)$ does not exist because $\lim\limits_{x \to 0^+} f(x)$ does not exist

6.  (a) Yes, $\lim\limits_{x \to 0^+} g(x) = 0$ by the sandwich theorem since $-\sqrt{x} \leq g(x) \leq \sqrt{x}$ when x > 0

    (b) No, $\lim\limits_{x \to 0^-} g(x)$ does not exist since $\sqrt{x}$ is not defined for x < 0

    (c) No, $\lim\limits_{x \to 0} g(x)$ does not exist since $\lim\limits_{x \to 0^-} g(x)$ does not exist

7.  (a)
    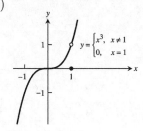

    $y = \begin{cases} x^3, & x \neq 1 \\ 0, & x = 1 \end{cases}$

    (b) $\lim\limits_{x \to 1^-} f(x) = 1 = \lim\limits_{x \to 1^+} f(x)$

    (c) Yes, $\lim\limits_{x \to 1} f(x) = 1$ since the right-hand and left-hand limits exist and equal 1

8.  (a)
    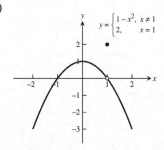

    $y = \begin{cases} 1 - x^2, & x \neq 1 \\ 2, & x = 1 \end{cases}$

    (b) $\lim\limits_{x \to 1^+} f(x) = 0 = \lim\limits_{x \to 1^-} f(x)$

    (c) Yes, $\lim\limits_{x \to 1} f(x) = 0$ since the right-hand and left-hand limits exist and equal 0

9. (a) domain: $0 \leq x \leq 2$
    range: $0 < y \leq 1$ and $y = 2$

   (b) $\lim_{x \to c} f(x)$ exists for c belonging to
       $(0, 1) \cup (1, 2)$

   (c) $x = 2$

   (d) $x = 0$

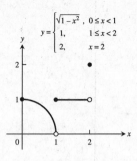

10. (a) domain: $-\infty < x < \infty$
    range: $-1 \leq y \leq 1$

   (b) $\lim_{x \to c} f(x)$ exists for c belonging to
       $(-\infty, -1) \cup (-1, 1) \cup (1, \infty)$

   (c) none

   (d) none

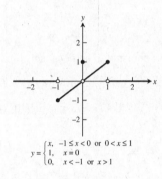

$$y = \begin{cases} x, & -1 \leq x < 0 \text{ or } 0 < x \leq 1 \\ 1, & x = 0 \\ 0, & x < -1 \text{ or } x > 1 \end{cases}$$

11. $\displaystyle\lim_{x \to -0.5^-} \sqrt{\frac{x+2}{x-1}} = \sqrt{\frac{-0.5+2}{-0.5+1}} = \sqrt{\frac{3/2}{1/2}} = \sqrt{3}$       12. $\displaystyle\lim_{x \to 1^+} \sqrt{\frac{x-1}{x+2}} = \sqrt{\frac{1-1}{1+2}} = \sqrt{0} = 0$

13. $\displaystyle\lim_{x \to -2^+} \left(\frac{x}{x+1}\right)\left(\frac{2x+5}{x^2+x}\right) = \left(\frac{-2}{-2+1}\right)\left(\frac{2(-2)+5}{(-2)^2+(-2)}\right) = (2)\left(\frac{1}{2}\right) = 1$

14. $\displaystyle\lim_{x \to 1^-} \left(\frac{1}{x+1}\right)\left(\frac{x+6}{x}\right)\left(\frac{3-x}{7}\right) = \left(\frac{1}{1+1}\right)\left(\frac{1+6}{1}\right)\left(\frac{3-1}{7}\right) = \left(\frac{1}{2}\right)\left(\frac{7}{1}\right)\left(\frac{2}{7}\right) = 1$

15. $\displaystyle\lim_{h \to 0^+} \frac{\sqrt{h^2+4h+5}-\sqrt{5}}{h} = \lim_{h \to 0^+} \left(\frac{\sqrt{h^2+4h+5}-\sqrt{5}}{h}\right)\left(\frac{\sqrt{h^2+4h+5}+\sqrt{5}}{\sqrt{h^2+4h+5}+\sqrt{5}}\right)$

$= \displaystyle\lim_{h \to 0^+} \frac{(h^2+4h+5)-5}{h\left(\sqrt{h^2+4h+5}+\sqrt{5}\right)} = \lim_{h \to 0^+} \frac{h(h+4)}{h\left(\sqrt{h^2+4h+5}+\sqrt{5}\right)} = \frac{0+4}{\sqrt{5}+\sqrt{5}} = \frac{2}{\sqrt{5}}$

16. $\displaystyle\lim_{h \to 0^-} \frac{\sqrt{6}-\sqrt{5h^2+11h+6}}{h} = \lim_{h \to 0^-} \left(\frac{\sqrt{6}-\sqrt{5h^2+11h+6}}{h}\right)\left(\frac{\sqrt{6}+\sqrt{5h^2+11h+6}}{\sqrt{6}+\sqrt{5h^2+11h+6}}\right)$

$= \displaystyle\lim_{h \to 0^-} \frac{6-(5h^2+11h+6)}{h\left(\sqrt{6}+\sqrt{5h^2+11h+6}\right)} = \lim_{h \to 0^-} \frac{-h(5h+11)}{h\left(\sqrt{6}+\sqrt{5h^2+11h+6}\right)} = \frac{-(0+11)}{\sqrt{6}+\sqrt{6}} = -\frac{11}{2\sqrt{6}}$

17. (a) $\displaystyle\lim_{x \to -2^+} (x+3)\frac{|x+2|}{x+2} = \lim_{x \to -2^+} (x+3)\frac{(x+2)}{(x+2)}$       $(|x+2| = (x+2)$ for $x > -2)$

$= \displaystyle\lim_{x \to -2^+} (x+3) = ((-2)+3) = 1$

   (b) $\displaystyle\lim_{x \to -2^-} (x+3)\frac{|x+2|}{x+2} = \lim_{x \to -2^-} (x+3)\left[\frac{-(x+2)}{(x+2)}\right]$       $(|x+2| = -(x+2)$ for $x < -2)$

$= \displaystyle\lim_{x \to -2^-} (x+3)(-1) = -(-2+3) = -1$

18. (a) $\displaystyle\lim_{x \to 1^+} \frac{\sqrt{2x}\,(x-1)}{|x-1|} = \lim_{x \to 1^+} \frac{\sqrt{2x}\,(x-1)}{(x-1)}$       $(|x-1| = x-1$ for $x > 1)$

$= \displaystyle\lim_{x \to 1^+} \sqrt{2x} = \sqrt{2}$

   (b) $\displaystyle\lim_{x \to 1^-} \frac{\sqrt{2x}\,(x-1)}{|x-1|} = \lim_{x \to 1^-} \frac{\sqrt{2x}\,(x-1)}{-(x-1)}$       $(|x-1| = -(x-1)$ for $x < 1)$

$= \displaystyle\lim_{x \to 1^-} -\sqrt{2x} = -\sqrt{2}$

19. (a) $\lim\limits_{\theta \to 3^+} \frac{|\theta|}{\theta} = \frac{3}{3} = 1$ 　　　　　　　　　　　(b) $\lim\limits_{\theta \to 3^-} \frac{|\theta|}{\theta} = \frac{2}{3}$

20. (a) $\lim\limits_{t \to 4^+} (t - \lfloor t \rfloor) = 4 - 4 = 0$ 　　　　　　　(b) $\lim\limits_{t \to 4^-} (t - \lfloor t \rfloor) = 4 - 3 = 1$

21. $\lim\limits_{\theta \to 0} \frac{\sin \sqrt{2}\theta}{\sqrt{2}\theta} = \lim\limits_{x \to 0} \frac{\sin x}{x} = 1$ 　　　(where $x = \sqrt{2}\theta$)

22. $\lim\limits_{t \to 0} \frac{\sin kt}{t} = \lim\limits_{t \to 0} \frac{k \sin kt}{kt} = \lim\limits_{\theta \to 0} \frac{k \sin \theta}{\theta} = k \lim\limits_{\theta \to 0} \frac{\sin \theta}{\theta} = k \cdot 1 = k$ 　　(where $\theta = kt$)

23. $\lim\limits_{y \to 0} \frac{\sin 3y}{4y} = \frac{1}{4} \lim\limits_{y \to 0} \frac{3 \sin 3y}{3y} = \frac{3}{4} \lim\limits_{y \to 0} \frac{\sin 3y}{3y} = \frac{3}{4} \lim\limits_{\theta \to 0} \frac{\sin \theta}{\theta} = \frac{3}{4}$ 　　(where $\theta = 3y$)

24. $\lim\limits_{h \to 0^-} \frac{h}{\sin 3h} = \lim\limits_{h \to 0^-} \left( \frac{1}{3} \cdot \frac{3h}{\sin 3h} \right) = \frac{1}{3} \lim\limits_{h \to 0^-} \frac{1}{\left( \frac{\sin 3h}{3h} \right)} = \frac{1}{3} \left( \frac{1}{\lim\limits_{\theta \to 0^-} \frac{\sin \theta}{\theta}} \right) = \frac{1}{3} \cdot 1 = \frac{1}{3}$ 　(where $\theta = 3h$)

25. $\lim\limits_{x \to 0} \frac{\tan 2x}{x} = \lim\limits_{x \to 0} \frac{\left( \frac{\sin 2x}{\cos 2x} \right)}{x} = \lim\limits_{x \to 0} \frac{\sin 2x}{x \cos 2x} = \left( \lim\limits_{x \to 0} \frac{1}{\cos 2x} \right) \left( \lim\limits_{x \to 0} \frac{2 \sin 2x}{2x} \right) = 1 \cdot 2 = 2$

26. $\lim\limits_{t \to 0} \frac{2t}{\tan t} = 2 \lim\limits_{t \to 0} \frac{t}{\left( \frac{\sin t}{\cos t} \right)} = 2 \lim\limits_{t \to 0} \frac{t \cos t}{\sin t} = 2 \left( \lim\limits_{t \to 0} \cos t \right) \left( \frac{1}{\lim\limits_{t \to 0} \frac{\sin t}{t}} \right) = 2 \cdot 1 \cdot 1 = 2$

27. $\lim\limits_{x \to 0} \frac{x \csc 2x}{\cos 5x} = \lim\limits_{x \to 0} \left( \frac{x}{\sin 2x} \cdot \frac{1}{\cos 5x} \right) = \left( \frac{1}{2} \lim\limits_{x \to 0} \frac{2x}{\sin 2x} \right) \left( \lim\limits_{x \to 0} \frac{1}{\cos 5x} \right) = \left( \frac{1}{2} \cdot 1 \right) (1) = \frac{1}{2}$

28. $\lim\limits_{x \to 0} 6x^2 (\cot x)(\csc 2x) = \lim\limits_{x \to 0} \frac{6x^2 \cos x}{\sin x \sin 2x} = \lim\limits_{x \to 0} \left( 3 \cos x \cdot \frac{x}{\sin x} \cdot \frac{2x}{\sin 2x} \right) = 3 \cdot 1 \cdot 1 = 3$

29. $\lim\limits_{x \to 0} \frac{x + x \cos x}{\sin x \cos x} = \lim\limits_{x \to 0} \left( \frac{x}{\sin x \cos x} + \frac{x \cos x}{\sin x \cos x} \right) = \lim\limits_{x \to 0} \left( \frac{x}{\sin x} \cdot \frac{1}{\cos x} \right) + \lim\limits_{x \to 0} \frac{x}{\sin x}$

$= \lim\limits_{x \to 0} \left( \frac{1}{\frac{\sin x}{x}} \right) \cdot \lim\limits_{x \to 0} \left( \frac{1}{\cos x} \right) + \lim\limits_{x \to 0} \left( \frac{1}{\frac{\sin x}{x}} \right) = (1)(1) + 1 = 2$

30. $\lim\limits_{x \to 0} \frac{x^2 - x + \sin x}{2x} = \lim\limits_{x \to 0} \left( \frac{x}{2} - \frac{1}{2} + \frac{1}{2} \left( \frac{\sin x}{x} \right) \right) = 0 - \frac{1}{2} + \frac{1}{2} (1) = 0$

31. $\lim\limits_{\theta \to 0} \frac{1 - \cos \theta}{\sin 2\theta} = \lim\limits_{\theta \to 0} \frac{(1 - \cos \theta)(1 + \cos \theta)}{(2 \sin \theta \cos \theta)(1 + \cos \theta)} = \lim\limits_{\theta \to 0} \frac{1 - \cos^2 \theta}{(2 \sin \theta \cos \theta)(1 + \cos \theta)} = \lim\limits_{\theta \to 0} \frac{\sin^2 \theta}{(2 \sin \theta \cos \theta)(1 + \cos \theta)}$

$= \lim\limits_{\theta \to 0} \frac{\sin \theta}{(2 \cos \theta)(1 + \cos \theta)} = \frac{0}{(2)(2)} = 0$

32. $\lim\limits_{x \to 0} \frac{x - x \cos x}{\sin^2 3x} = \lim\limits_{x \to 0} \frac{x(1 - \cos x)}{\sin^2 3x} = \lim\limits_{x \to 0} \frac{\frac{x(1 - \cos x)}{9x^2}}{\frac{\sin^2 3x}{9x^2}} = \lim\limits_{x \to 0} \frac{\frac{1 - \cos x}{9x}}{\left( \frac{\sin 3x}{3x} \right)^2} = \frac{\frac{1}{9} \lim\limits_{x \to 0} \left( \frac{1 - \cos x}{x} \right)}{\lim\limits_{x \to 0} \left( \frac{\sin 3x}{3x} \right)^2} = \frac{\frac{1}{9}(0)}{1^2} = 0$ 　*multiply N & D by (1 + cos x) to get* $\frac{0}{18} = 0$

33. $\lim\limits_{t \to 0} \frac{\sin(1 - \cos t)}{1 - \cos t} = \lim\limits_{\theta \to 0} \frac{\sin \theta}{\theta} = 1$ since $\theta = 1 - \cos t \to 0$ as $t \to 0$

34. $\lim\limits_{h \to 0} \frac{\sin(\sin h)}{\sin h} = \lim\limits_{\theta \to 0} \frac{\sin \theta}{\theta} = 1$ since $\theta = \sin h \to 0$ as $h \to 0$

35. $\lim\limits_{\theta \to 0} \frac{\sin \theta}{\sin 2\theta} = \lim\limits_{\theta \to 0} \left( \frac{\sin \theta}{\sin 2\theta} \cdot \frac{2\theta}{2\theta} \right) = \frac{1}{2} \lim\limits_{\theta \to 0} \left( \frac{\sin \theta}{\theta} \cdot \frac{2\theta}{\sin 2\theta} \right) = \frac{1}{2} \cdot 1 \cdot 1 = \frac{1}{2}$

36. $\lim\limits_{x \to 0} \frac{\sin 5x}{\sin 4x} = \lim\limits_{x \to 0} \left( \frac{\sin 5x}{\sin 4x} \cdot \frac{4x}{5x} \cdot \frac{5}{4} \right) = \frac{5}{4} \lim\limits_{x \to 0} \left( \frac{\sin 5x}{5x} \cdot \frac{4x}{\sin 4x} \right) = \frac{5}{4} \cdot 1 \cdot 1 = \frac{5}{4}$

37. $\lim\limits_{\theta \to 0} \theta \cos \theta = 0 \cdot 1 = 0$

38. $\lim\limits_{\theta \to 0} \sin \theta \cot 2\theta = \lim\limits_{\theta \to 0} \sin \theta \frac{\cos 2\theta}{\sin 2\theta} = \lim\limits_{\theta \to 0} \sin \theta \frac{\cos 2\theta}{2\sin \theta \cos \theta} = \lim\limits_{\theta \to 0} \frac{\cos 2\theta}{2\cos \theta} = \frac{1}{2}$

39. $\lim\limits_{x \to 0} \frac{\tan 3x}{\sin 8x} = \lim\limits_{x \to 0} \left( \frac{\sin 3x}{\cos 3x} \cdot \frac{1}{\sin 8x} \right) = \lim\limits_{x \to 0} \left( \frac{\sin 3x}{\cos 3x} \cdot \frac{1}{\sin 8x} \cdot \frac{8x}{3x} \cdot \frac{3}{8} \right)$

    $= \frac{3}{8} \lim\limits_{x \to 0} \left( \frac{1}{\cos 3x} \right) \left( \frac{\sin 3x}{3x} \right) \left( \frac{8x}{\sin 8x} \right) = \frac{3}{8} \cdot 1 \cdot 1 \cdot 1 = \frac{3}{8}$

40. $\lim\limits_{y \to 0} \frac{\sin 3y \cot 5y}{y \cot 4y} = \lim\limits_{y \to 0} \frac{\sin 3y \sin 4y \cos 5y}{y \cos 4y \sin 5y} = \lim\limits_{y \to 0} \left( \frac{\sin 3y}{y} \right) \left( \frac{\sin 4y}{\cos 4y} \right) \left( \frac{\cos 5y}{\sin 5y} \right) \left( \frac{3 \cdot 4 \cdot 5y}{3 \cdot 4 \cdot 5y} \right)$

    $= \lim\limits_{y \to 0} \left( \frac{\sin 3y}{3y} \right) \left( \frac{\sin 4y}{4y} \right) \left( \frac{5y}{\sin 5y} \right) \left( \frac{\cos 5y}{\cos 4y} \right) \left( \frac{3 \cdot 4}{5} \right) = 1 \cdot 1 \cdot 1 \cdot 1 \cdot \frac{12}{5} = \frac{12}{5}$

41. $\lim\limits_{\theta \to 0} \frac{\tan \theta}{\theta^2 \cot 3\theta} = \lim\limits_{\theta \to 0} \frac{\frac{\sin \theta}{\cos \theta}}{\theta^2 \frac{\cos 3\theta}{\sin 3\theta}} = \lim\limits_{\theta \to 0} \frac{\sin \theta \sin 3\theta}{\theta^2 \cos \theta \cos 3\theta} = \lim\limits_{\theta \to 0} \left( \frac{\sin \theta}{\theta} \right) \left( \frac{\sin 3\theta}{3\theta} \right) \left( \frac{3}{\cos \theta \cos 3\theta} \right) = (1)(1)\left( \frac{3}{1 \cdot 1} \right) = 3$

42. $\lim\limits_{\theta \to 0} \frac{\theta \cot 4\theta}{\sin^2 \theta \cot^2 2\theta} = \lim\limits_{\theta \to 0} \frac{\theta \frac{\cos 4\theta}{\sin 4\theta}}{\sin^2 \theta \frac{\cos^2 2\theta}{\sin^2 2\theta}} = \lim\limits_{\theta \to 0} \frac{\theta \cos 4\theta \sin^2 2\theta}{\sin^2 \theta \cos^2 2\theta \sin 4\theta} = \lim\limits_{\theta \to 0} \frac{\theta \cos 4\theta (2\sin \theta \cos \theta)^2}{\sin^2 \theta \cos^2 2\theta \sin 4\theta} = \lim\limits_{\theta \to 0} \frac{\theta \cos 4\theta (4\sin^2 \theta \cos^2 \theta)}{\sin^2 \theta \cos^2 2\theta \sin 4\theta}$

    $= \lim\limits_{\theta \to 0} \frac{4\theta \cos 4\theta \cos^2 \theta}{\cos^2 2\theta \sin 4\theta} = \lim\limits_{\theta \to 0} \left( \frac{4\theta}{\sin 4\theta} \right) \left( \frac{\cos 4\theta \cos^2 \theta}{\cos^2 2\theta} \right) = \lim\limits_{\theta \to 0} \left( \frac{1}{\frac{\sin 4\theta}{4\theta}} \right) \left( \frac{\cos 4\theta \cos^2 \theta}{\cos^2 2\theta} \right) = \left( \frac{1}{1} \right) \left( \frac{1 \cdot 1^2}{1^2} \right) = 1$

43. Yes. If $\lim\limits_{x \to a^+} f(x) = L = \lim\limits_{x \to a^-} f(x)$, then $\lim\limits_{x \to a} f(x) = L$. If $\lim\limits_{x \to a^+} f(x) \neq \lim\limits_{x \to a^-} f(x)$, then $\lim\limits_{x \to a} f(x)$ does not exist.

44. Since $\lim\limits_{x \to c} f(x) = L$ if and only if $\lim\limits_{x \to c^+} f(x) = L$ and $\lim\limits_{x \to c^-} f(x) = L$, then $\lim\limits_{x \to c} f(x)$ can be found by calculating

    $\lim\limits_{x \to c^+} f(x)$.

45. If f is an odd function of x, then $f(-x) = -f(x)$. Given $\lim\limits_{x \to 0^+} f(x) = 3$, then $\lim\limits_{x \to 0^-} f(x) = -3$.

46. If f is an even function of x, then $f(-x) = f(x)$. Given $\lim\limits_{x \to 2^-} f(x) = 7$ then $\lim\limits_{x \to -2^+} f(x) = 7$. However, nothing

    can be said about $\lim\limits_{x \to -2^-} f(x)$ because we don't know $\lim\limits_{x \to 2^+} f(x)$.

47. $I = (5, 5 + \delta) \Rightarrow 5 < x < 5 + \delta$. Also, $\sqrt{x - 5} < \epsilon \Rightarrow x - 5 < \epsilon^2 \Rightarrow x < 5 + \epsilon^2$. Choose $\delta = \epsilon^2$

    $\Rightarrow \lim\limits_{x \to 5^+} \sqrt{x - 5} = 0$.

48. $I = (4 - \delta, 4) \Rightarrow 4 - \delta < x < 4$. Also, $\sqrt{4 - x} < \epsilon \Rightarrow 4 - x < \epsilon^2 \Rightarrow x > 4 - \epsilon^2$. Choose $\delta = \epsilon^2$

    $\Rightarrow \lim\limits_{x \to 4^-} \sqrt{4 - x} = 0$.

49. As $x \to 0^-$ the number x is always negative. Thus, $\left| \frac{x}{|x|} - (-1) \right| < \epsilon \Rightarrow \left| \frac{x}{-x} + 1 \right| < \epsilon \Rightarrow 0 < \epsilon$ which is always

    true independent of the value of x. Hence we can choose any $\delta > 0$ with $-\delta < x < 0 \Rightarrow \lim\limits_{x \to 0^-} \frac{x}{|x|} = -1$.

50. Since $x \to 2^+$ we have $x > 2$ and $|x - 2| = x - 2$. Then, $\left| \frac{x-2}{|x-2|} - 1 \right| = \left| \frac{x-2}{x-2} - 1 \right| < \epsilon \Rightarrow 0 < \epsilon$

    which is always true so long as $x > 2$. Hence we can choose any $\delta > 0$, and thus $2 < x < 2 + \delta$

    $\Rightarrow \left| \frac{x-2}{|x-2|} - 1 \right| < \epsilon$. Thus, $\lim\limits_{x \to -2^+} \frac{x-2}{|x-2|} = 1$.

51. (a)   $\lim\limits_{x \to 400^+} \lfloor x \rfloor = 400$. Just observe that if $400 < x < 401$, then $\lfloor x \rfloor = 400$. Thus if we choose $\delta = 1$, we have for any

      number $\epsilon > 0$ that $400 < x < 400 + \delta \Rightarrow |\lfloor x \rfloor - 400| = |400 - 400| = 0 < \epsilon$.

  (b)   $\lim\limits_{x \to 400^-} \lfloor x \rfloor = 399$. Just observe that if $399 < x < 400$ then $\lfloor x \rfloor = 399$. Thus if we choose $\delta = 1$, we have for any

      number $\epsilon > 0$ that $400 - \delta < x < 400 \Rightarrow |\lfloor x \rfloor - 399| = |399 - 399| = 0 < \epsilon$.

  (c)   Since $\lim\limits_{x \to 400^+} \lfloor x \rfloor \neq \lim\limits_{x \to 400^-} \lfloor x \rfloor$ we conclude that $\lim\limits_{x \to 400} \lfloor x \rfloor$ does not exist.

52. (a)   $\lim\limits_{x \to 0^+} f(x) = \lim\limits_{x \to 0^+} \sqrt{x} = \sqrt{0} = 0; \left| \sqrt{x} - 0 \right| < \epsilon \Rightarrow -\epsilon < \sqrt{x} < \epsilon \Rightarrow 0 < x < \epsilon^2$ for x positive.  Choose $\delta = \epsilon^2$

      $\Rightarrow \lim\limits_{x \to 0^+} f(x) = 0$.

  (b)   $\lim\limits_{x \to 0^-} f(x) = \lim\limits_{x \to 0^-} x^2 \sin\left(\frac{1}{x}\right) = 0$ by the sandwich theorem since $-x^2 \leq x^2 \sin\left(\frac{1}{x}\right) \leq x^2$ for all $x \neq 0$.

      Since $|x^2 - 0| = |-x^2 - 0| = x^2 < \epsilon$ whenever $|x| < \sqrt{\epsilon}$, we choose $\delta = \sqrt{\epsilon}$ and obtain $\left| x^2 \sin\left(\frac{1}{x}\right) - 0 \right| < \epsilon$

      if $-\delta < x < 0$.

  (c)   The function f has limit 0 at $x_0 = 0$ since both the right-hand and left-hand limits exist and equal 0.

## 2.5 CONTINUITY

1.  No, discontinuous at $x = 2$, not defined at $x = 2$

2.  No, discontinuous at $x = 3$, $1 = \lim\limits_{x \to 3^-} g(x) \neq g(3) = 1.5$

3.  Continuous on $[-1, 3]$

4.  No, discontinuous at $x = 1$, $1.5 = \lim\limits_{x \to 1^-} k(x) \neq \lim\limits_{x \to 1^+} k(x) = 0$

5.  (a)  Yes                              (b)  Yes, $\lim\limits_{x \to -1^+} f(x) = 0$

  (c)  Yes                              (d)  Yes

6.  (a)  Yes, $f(1) = 1$                   (b)  Yes, $\lim\limits_{x \to 1} f(x) = 2$

  (c)  No                              (d)  No

7.  (a)  No                              (b)  No

8.  $[-1, 0) \cup (0, 1) \cup (1, 2) \cup (2, 3)$

9.  $f(2) = 0$, since $\lim\limits_{x \to 2^-} f(x) = -2(2) + 4 = 0 = \lim\limits_{x \to 2^+} f(x)$

10.  $f(1)$ should be changed to $2 = \lim\limits_{x \to 1} f(x)$

11.  Nonremovable discontinuity at $x = 1$ because $\lim\limits_{x \to 1} f(x)$ fails to exist ( $\lim\limits_{x \to 1^-} f(x) = 1$ and $\lim\limits_{x \to 1^+} f(x) = 0$).

    Removable discontinuity at $x = 0$ by assigning the number $\lim\limits_{x \to 0} f(x) = 0$ to be the value of $f(0)$ rather than $f(0) = 1$.

12.  Nonremovable discontinuity at $x = 1$ because $\lim\limits_{x \to 1} f(x)$ fails to exist ( $\lim\limits_{x \to 1^-} f(x) = 2$ and $\lim\limits_{x \to 1^+} f(x) = 1$).

    Removable discontinuity at $x = 2$ by assigning the number $\lim\limits_{x \to 2} f(x) = 1$ to be the value of $f(2)$ rather than $f(2) = 2$.

13. Discontinuous only when $x - 2 = 0 \Rightarrow x = 2$      14. Discontinuous only when $(x + 2)^2 = 0 \Rightarrow x = -2$

15. Discontinuous only when $x^2 - 4x + 3 = 0 \Rightarrow (x - 3)(x - 1) = 0 \Rightarrow x = 3$ or $x = 1$

16. Discontinuous only when $x^2 - 3x - 10 = 0 \Rightarrow (x - 5)(x + 2) = 0 \Rightarrow x = 5$ or $x = -2$

17. Continuous everywhere. ( $|x - 1| + \sin x$ defined for all x; limits exist and are equal to function values.)

18. Continuous everywhere. ( $|x| + 1 \neq 0$ for all x; limits exist and are equal to function values.)

19. Discontinuous only at $x = 0$

20. Discontinuous at odd integer multiples of $\frac{\pi}{2}$, i.e., $x = (2n - 1) \frac{\pi}{2}$, n an integer, but continuous at all other x.

21. Discontinuous when 2x is an integer multiple of $\pi$, i.e., $2x = n\pi$, n an integer $\Rightarrow x = \frac{n\pi}{2}$, n an integer, but continuous at all other x.

22. Discontinuous when $\frac{\pi x}{2}$ is an odd integer multiple of $\frac{\pi}{2}$, i.e., $\frac{\pi x}{2} = (2n - 1) \frac{\pi}{2}$, n an integer $\Rightarrow x = 2n - 1$, n an integer (i.e., x is an odd integer). Continuous everywhere else.

23. Discontinuous at odd integer multiples of $\frac{\pi}{2}$, i.e., $x = (2n - 1) \frac{\pi}{2}$, n an integer, but continuous at all other x.

24. Continuous everywhere since $x^4 + 1 \geq 1$ and $-1 \leq \sin x \leq 1 \Rightarrow 0 \leq \sin^2 x \leq 1 \Rightarrow 1 + \sin^2 x \geq 1$; limits exist and are equal to the function values.

25. Discontinuous when $2x + 3 < 0$ or $x < -\frac{3}{2} \Rightarrow$ continuous on the interval $\left[-\frac{3}{2}, \infty\right)$.

26. Discontinuous when $3x - 1 < 0$ or $x < \frac{1}{3} \Rightarrow$ continuous on the interval $\left[\frac{1}{3}, \infty\right)$.

27. Continuous everywhere: $(2x - 1)^{1/3}$ is defined for all x; limits exist and are equal to function values.

28. Continuous everywhere: $(2 - x)^{1/5}$ is defined for all x; limits exist and are equal to function values.

29. Continuous everywhere since $\lim_{x \to 3} \frac{x^2 - x - 6}{x - 3} = \lim_{x \to 3} \frac{(x - 3)(x + 2)}{x - 3} = \lim_{x \to 3} (x + 2) = 5 = g(3)$

30. Discontinuous at $x = -2$ since $\lim_{x \to -2} f(x)$ does not exist while $f(-2) = 4$.

31. $\lim_{x \to \pi} \sin (x - \sin x) = \sin (\pi - \sin \pi) = \sin (\pi - 0) = \sin \pi = 0$, and function continuous at $x = \pi$.

32. $\lim_{t \to 0} \sin \left(\frac{\pi}{2} \cos (\tan t)\right) = \sin \left(\frac{\pi}{2} \cos (\tan (0))\right) = \sin \left(\frac{\pi}{2} \cos (0)\right) = \sin \left(\frac{\pi}{2}\right) = 1$, and function continuous at $t = 0$.

33. $\lim_{y \to 1} \sec (y \sec^2 y - \tan^2 y - 1) = \lim_{y \to 1} \sec (y \sec^2 y - \sec^2 y) = \lim_{y \to 1} \sec ((y - 1) \sec^2 y) = \sec ((1 - 1) \sec^2 1)$
    $= \sec 0 = 1$, and function continuous at $y = 1$.

34. $\lim_{x \to 0} \tan \left[\frac{\pi}{4} \cos \left(\sin x^{1/3}\right)\right] = \tan \left[\frac{\pi}{4} \cos (\sin(0))\right] = \tan \left(\frac{\pi}{4} \cos (0)\right) = \tan \left(\frac{\pi}{4}\right) = 1$, and function continuous at $x = 0$.

35. $\lim_{t \to 0} \cos\left[\dfrac{\pi}{\sqrt{19 - 3 \sec 2t}}\right] = \cos\left[\dfrac{\pi}{\sqrt{19 - 3 \sec 0}}\right] = \cos\dfrac{\pi}{\sqrt{16}} = \cos\dfrac{\pi}{4} = \dfrac{\sqrt{2}}{2}$, and function continuous at $t = 0$.

36. $\lim_{x \to \frac{\pi}{6}} \sqrt{\csc^2 x + 5\sqrt{3}\tan x} = \sqrt{\csc^2\left(\frac{\pi}{6}\right) + 5\sqrt{3}\tan\left(\frac{\pi}{6}\right)} = \sqrt{4 + 5\sqrt{3}\left(\frac{1}{\sqrt{3}}\right)} = \sqrt{9} = 3$, and function continuous at $x = \frac{\pi}{6}$.

37. $g(x) = \dfrac{x^2 - 9}{x - 3} = \dfrac{(x+3)(x-3)}{(x-3)} = x + 3, x \neq 3 \Rightarrow g(3) = \lim_{x \to 3}(x + 3) = 6$

38. $h(t) = \dfrac{t^2 + 3t - 10}{t - 2} = \dfrac{(t+5)(t-2)}{t-2} = t + 5, t \neq 2 \Rightarrow h(2) = \lim_{t \to 2}(t + 5) = 7$

39. $f(s) = \dfrac{s^3 - 1}{s^2 - 1} = \dfrac{(s^2 + s + 1)(s - 1)}{(s+1)(s-1)} = \dfrac{s^2 + s + 1}{s + 1}, s \neq 1 \Rightarrow f(1) = \lim_{s \to 1}\left(\dfrac{s^2 + s + 1}{s + 1}\right) = \dfrac{3}{2}$

40. $g(x) = \dfrac{x^2 - 16}{x^2 - 3x - 4} = \dfrac{(x+4)(x-4)}{(x-4)(x+1)} = \dfrac{x+4}{x+1}, x \neq 4 \Rightarrow g(4) = \lim_{x \to 4}\left(\dfrac{x+4}{x+1}\right) = \dfrac{8}{5}$

41. As defined, $\lim_{x \to 3^-} f(x) = (3)^2 - 1 = 8$ and $\lim_{x \to 3^+}(2a)(3) = 6a$. For $f(x)$ to be continuous we must have
$6a = 8 \Rightarrow a = \dfrac{4}{3}$.

42. As defined, $\lim_{x \to -2^-} g(x) = -2$ and $\lim_{x \to -2^+} g(x) = b(-2)^2 = 4b$. For $g(x)$ to be continuous we must have
$4b = -2 \Rightarrow b = -\dfrac{1}{2}$.

43. As defined, $\lim_{x \to 2^-} f(x) = 12$ and $\lim_{x \to 2^+} f(x) = a^2(2) - 2a = 2a^2 - 2a$. For $f(x)$ to be continuous we must have
$12 = 2a^2 - 2a \Rightarrow a = 3$ or $a = -2$.

44. As defined, $\lim_{x \to 0^-} g(x) = \dfrac{0-b}{b+1} = \dfrac{-b}{b+1}$ and $\lim_{x \to 0^+} g(x) = (0)^2 + b = b$. For $g(x)$ to be continuous we must have
$\dfrac{-b}{b+1} = b \Rightarrow b = 0$ or $b = -2$.

45. As defined, $\lim_{x \to -1^-} f(x) = -2$ and $\lim_{x \to -1^+} f(x) = a(-1) + b = -a + b$, and $\lim_{x \to 1^-} f(x) = a(1) + b = a + b$ and
$\lim_{x \to 1^+} f(x) = 3$. For $f(x)$ to be continuous we must have $-2 = -a + b$ and $a + b = 3 \Rightarrow a = \dfrac{5}{2}$ and $b = \dfrac{1}{2}$.

46. As defined, $\lim_{x \to 0^-} g(x) = a(0) + 2b = 2b$ and $\lim_{x \to 0^+} g(x) = (0)^2 + 3a - b = 3a - b$, and
$\lim_{x \to 2^-} g(x) = (2)^2 + 3a - b = 4 + 3a - b$ and $\lim_{x \to 0^+} g(x) = 3(2) - 5 = 1$. For $g(x)$ to be continuous we must
have $2b = 3a - b$ and $4 + 3a - b = 1 \Rightarrow a = -\dfrac{3}{2}$ and $b = -\dfrac{3}{2}$.

47. The function can be extended: $f(0) \approx 2.3$.

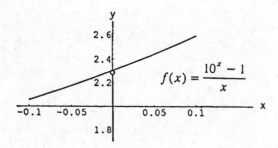

48. The function cannot be extended to be continuous at $x = 0$. If $f(0) \approx 2.3$, it will be continuous from the right. Or if $f(0) \approx -2.3$, it will be continuous from the left.

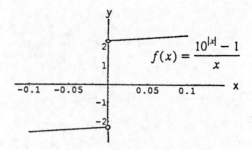

49. The function cannot be extended to be continuous at $x = 0$. If $f(0) = 1$, it will be continuous from the right. Or if $f(0) = -1$, it will be continuous from the left.

50. The function can be extended: $f(0) \approx 7.39$.

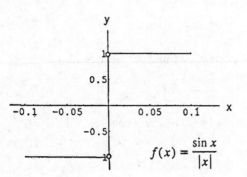

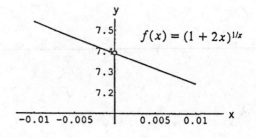

51. $f(x)$ is continuous on $[0, 1]$ and $f(0) < 0$, $f(1) > 0$ $\Rightarrow$ by the Intermediate Value Theorem $f(x)$ takes on every value between $f(0)$ and $f(1)$ $\Rightarrow$ the equation $f(x) = 0$ has at least one solution between $x = 0$ and $x = 1$.

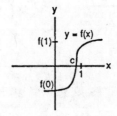

52. $\cos x = x \Rightarrow (\cos x) - x = 0$. If $x = -\frac{\pi}{2}$, $\cos\left(-\frac{\pi}{2}\right) - \left(-\frac{\pi}{2}\right) > 0$. If $x = \frac{\pi}{2}$, $\cos\left(\frac{\pi}{2}\right) - \frac{\pi}{2} < 0$. Thus $\cos x - x = 0$ for some x between $-\frac{\pi}{2}$ and $\frac{\pi}{2}$ according to the Intermediate Value Theorem, since the function $\cos x - x$ is continuous.

53. Let $f(x) = x^3 - 15x + 1$, which is continuous on $[-4, 4]$. Then $f(-4) = -3$, $f(-1) = 15$, $f(1) = -13$, and $f(4) = 5$. By the Intermediate Value Theorem, $f(x) = 0$ for some x in each of the intervals $-4 < x < -1$, $-1 < x < 1$, and $1 < x < 4$. That is, $x^3 - 15x + 1 = 0$ has three solutions in $[-4, 4]$. Since a polynomial of degree 3 can have at most 3 solutions, these are the only solutions.

54. Without loss of generality, assume that $a < b$. Then $F(x) = (x - a)^2 (x - b)^2 + x$ is continuous for all values of x, so it is continuous on the interval $[a, b]$. Moreover $F(a) = a$ and $F(b) = b$. By the Intermediate Value Theorem, since $a < \frac{a+b}{2} < b$, there is a number c between a and b such that $F(x) = \frac{a+b}{2}$.

55. Answers may vary. Note that f is continuous for every value of x.
    (a)  $f(0) = 10, f(1) = 1^3 - 8(1) + 10 = 3$. Since $3 < \pi < 10$, by the Intermediate Value Theorem, there exists a c
         so that $0 < c < 1$ and $f(c) = \pi$.
    (b)  $f(0) = 10, f(-4) = (-4)^3 - 8(-4) + 10 = -22$. Since $-22 < -\sqrt{3} < 10$, by the Intermediate Value
         Theorem, there exists a c so that $-4 < c < 0$ and $f(c) = -\sqrt{3}$.
    (c)  $f(0) = 10, f(1000) = (1000)^3 - 8(1000) + 10 = 999,992,010$. Since $10 < 5,000,000 < 999,992,010$, by the
         Intermediate Value Theorem, there exists a c so that $0 < c < 1000$ and $f(c) = 5,000,000$.

56. All five statements ask for the same information because of the intermediate value property of continuous functions.
    (a)  A root of $f(x) = x^3 - 3x - 1$ is a point c where $f(c) = 0$.
    (b)  The points where $y = x^3$ crosses $y = 3x + 1$ have the same y-coordinate, or $y = x^3 = 3x + 1$
         $\Rightarrow f(x) = x^3 - 3x - 1 = 0$.
    (c)  $x^3 - 3x = 1 \Rightarrow x^3 - 3x - 1 = 0$. The solutions to the equation are the roots of $f(x) = x^3 - 3x - 1$.
    (d)  The points where $y = x^3 - 3x$ crosses $y = 1$ have common y-coordinates, or $y = x^3 - 3x = 1$
         $\Rightarrow f(x) = x^3 - 3x - 1 = 0$.
    (e)  The solutions of $x^3 - 3x - 1 = 0$ are those points where $f(x) = x^3 - 3x - 1$ has value 0.

57. Answers may vary. For example, $f(x) = \frac{\sin(x-2)}{x-2}$ is discontinuous at $x = 2$ because it is not defined there.
    However, the discontinuity can be removed because f has a limit (namely 1) as $x \rightarrow 2$.

58. Answers may vary. For example, $g(x) = \frac{1}{x+1}$ has a discontinuity at $x = -1$ because $\lim\limits_{x \rightarrow -1} g(x)$ does not exist.
    $\left( \lim\limits_{x \rightarrow -1^-} g(x) = -\infty \text{ and } \lim\limits_{x \rightarrow -1^+} g(x) = +\infty. \right)$

59. (a)  Suppose $x_0$ is rational $\Rightarrow f(x_0) = 1$. Choose $\epsilon = \frac{1}{2}$. For any $\delta > 0$ there is an irrational number x (actually
         infinitely many) in the interval $(x_0 - \delta, x_0 + \delta) \Rightarrow f(x) = 0$. Then $0 < |x - x_0| < \delta$ but $|f(x) - f(x_0)|$
         $= 1 > \frac{1}{2} = \epsilon$, so $\lim\limits_{x \rightarrow x_0} f(x)$ fails to exist $\Rightarrow$ f is discontinuous at $x_0$ rational.
         On the other hand, $x_0$ irrational $\Rightarrow f(x_0) = 0$ and there is a rational number x in $(x_0 - \delta, x_0 + \delta) \Rightarrow f(x)$
         $= 1$. Again $\lim\limits_{x \rightarrow x_0} f(x)$ fails to exist $\Rightarrow$ f is discontinuous at $x_0$ irrational. That is, f is discontinuous at
         every point.
    (b)  f is neither right-continuous nor left-continuous at any point $x_0$ because in every interval $(x_0 - \delta, x_0)$ or
         $(x_0, x_0 + \delta)$ there exist both rational and irrational real numbers. Thus neither limits $\lim\limits_{x \rightarrow x_0^-} f(x)$ and
         $\lim\limits_{x \rightarrow x_0^+} f(x)$ exist by the same arguments used in part (a).

60. Yes. Both $f(x) = x$ and $g(x) = x - \frac{1}{2}$ are continuous on $[0, 1]$. However $\frac{f(x)}{g(x)}$ is undefined at $x = \frac{1}{2}$ since
    $g\left(\frac{1}{2}\right) = 0 \Rightarrow \frac{f(x)}{g(x)}$ is discontinuous at $x = \frac{1}{2}$.

61. No. For instance, if $f(x) = 0, g(x) = \lceil x \rceil$, then $h(x) = 0(\lceil x \rceil) = 0$ is continuous at $x = 0$ and $g(x)$ is not.

62. Let $f(x) = \frac{1}{x-1}$ and $g(x) = x + 1$. Both functions are continuous at $x = 0$. The composition $f \circ g = f(g(x))$
    $= \frac{1}{(x+1)-1} = \frac{1}{x}$ is discontinuous at $x = 0$, since it is not defined there. Theorem 10 requires that $f(x)$ be
    continuous at $g(0)$, which is not the case here since $g(0) = 1$ and f is undefined at 1.

63. Yes, because of the Intermediate Value Theorem. If $f(a)$ and $f(b)$ did have different signs then f would have to
    equal zero at some point between a and b since f is continuous on $[a, b]$.

64. Let f(x) be the new position of point x and let d(x) = f(x) − x. The displacement function d is negative if x is the left-hand point of the rubber band and positive if x is the right-hand point of the rubber band. By the Intermediate Value Theorem, d(x) = 0 for some point in between. That is, f(x) = x for some point x, which is then in its original position.

65. If f(0) = 0 or f(1) = 1, we are done (i.e., c = 0 or c = 1 in those cases). Then let f(0) = a > 0 and f(1) = b < 1 because 0 ≤ f(x) ≤ 1. Define g(x) = f(x) − x ⇒ g is continuous on [0, 1]. Moreover, g(0) = f(0) − 0 = a > 0 and g(1) = f(1) − 1 = b − 1 < 0 ⇒ by the Intermediate Value Theorem there is a number c in (0, 1) such that g(c) = 0 ⇒ f(c) − c = 0 or f(c) = c.

66. Let $\epsilon = \frac{|f(c)|}{2} > 0$. Since f is continuous at x = c there is a δ > 0 such that |x − c| < δ ⇒ |f(x) − f(c)| < ε ⇒ f(c) − ε < f(x) < f(c) + ε.

If f(c) > 0, then $\epsilon = \frac{1}{2}$ f(c) ⇒ $\frac{1}{2}$ f(c) < f(x) < $\frac{3}{2}$ f(c) ⇒ f(x) > 0 on the interval (c − δ, c + δ).

If f(c) < 0, then $\epsilon = -\frac{1}{2}$ f(c) ⇒ $\frac{3}{2}$ f(c) < f(x) < $\frac{1}{2}$ f(c) ⇒ f(x) < 0 on the interval (c − δ, c + δ).

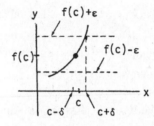 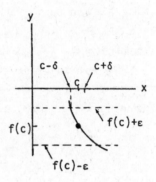

67. By Exercises 52 in Section 2.3, we have $\lim_{x \to c} f(x) = L \Leftrightarrow \lim_{h \to 0} f(c + h) = L$.

Thus, f(x) is continuous at x = c ⇔ $\lim_{x \to c} f(x) = f(c) \Leftrightarrow \lim_{h \to 0} f(c + h) = f(c)$.

68. By Exercise 67, it suffices to show that $\lim_{h \to 0} \sin(c + h) = \sin c$ and $\lim_{h \to 0} \cos(c + h) = \cos c$.

Now $\lim_{h \to 0} \sin(c + h) = \lim_{h \to 0} [(\sin c)(\cos h) + (\cos c)(\sin h)] = (\sin c)\left(\lim_{h \to 0} \cos h\right) + (\cos c)\left(\lim_{h \to 0} \sin h\right)$

By Example 11 Section 2.2, $\lim_{h \to 0} \cos h = 1$ and $\lim_{h \to 0} \sin h = 0$. So $\lim_{h \to 0} \sin(c + h) = \sin c$ and thus f(x) = sin x is continuous at x = c. Similarly,

$\lim_{h \to 0} \cos(c + h) = \lim_{h \to 0} [(\cos c)(\cos h) - (\sin c)(\sin h)] = (\cos c)\left(\lim_{h \to 0} \cos h\right) - (\sin c)\left(\lim_{h \to 0} \sin h\right) = \cos c$.

Thus, g(x) = cos x is continuous at x = c.

69. x ≈ 1.8794, −1.5321, −0.3473

70. x ≈ 1.4516, −0.8547, 0.4030

71. x ≈ 1.7549

72. x ≈ 1.5596

73. x ≈ 3.5156

74. x ≈ −3.9058, 3.8392, 0.0667

75. x ≈ 0.7391

76. x ≈ −1.8955, 0, 1.8955

## 2.6 LIMITS INVOLVING INFINITY; ASMYPTOTES OF GRAPHS

1. (a) $\lim\limits_{x \to 2} f(x) = 0$

   (b) $\lim\limits_{x \to -3^+} f(x) = -2$

   (c) $\lim\limits_{x \to -3^-} f(x) = 2$

   (d) $\lim\limits_{x \to 3} f(x) = $ does not exist

   (e) $\lim\limits_{x \to 0^+} f(x) = -1$

   (f) $\lim\limits_{x \to 0^-} f(x) = +\infty$

   (g) $\lim\limits_{x \to 0} f(x) = $ does not exist

   (h) $\lim\limits_{x \to \infty} f(x) = 1$

   (i) $\lim\limits_{x \to -\infty} f(x) = 0$

2. (a) $\lim\limits_{x \to 4} f(x) = 2$

   (b) $\lim\limits_{x \to 2^+} f(x) = -3$

   (c) $\lim\limits_{x \to 2^-} f(x) = 1$

   (d) $\lim\limits_{x \to 2} f(x) = $ does not exist

   (e) $\lim\limits_{x \to -3^+} f(x) = +\infty$

   (f) $\lim\limits_{x \to -3^-} f(x) = +\infty$

   (g) $\lim\limits_{x \to -3} f(x) = +\infty$

   (h) $\lim\limits_{x \to 0^+} f(x) = +\infty$

   (i) $\lim\limits_{x \to 0^-} f(x) = -\infty$

   (j) $\lim\limits_{x \to 0} f(x) = $ does not exist

   (k) $\lim\limits_{x \to \infty} f(x) = 0$

   (l) $\lim\limits_{x \to -\infty} f(x) = -1$

Note: In these exercises we use the result $\lim\limits_{x \to \pm\infty} \frac{1}{x^{m/n}} = 0$ whenever $\frac{m}{n} > 0$. This result follows immediately from Theorem 8 and the power rule in Theorem 1: $\lim\limits_{x \to \pm\infty} \left(\frac{1}{x^{m/n}}\right) = \lim\limits_{x \to \pm\infty} \left(\frac{1}{x}\right)^{m/n} = \left(\lim\limits_{x \to \pm\infty} \frac{1}{x}\right)^{m/n} = 0^{m/n} = 0.$

3. (a) $-3$

   (b) $-3$

4. (a) $\pi$

   (b) $\pi$

5. (a) $\frac{1}{2}$

   (b) $\frac{1}{2}$

6. (a) $\frac{1}{8}$

   (b) $\frac{1}{8}$

7. (a) $-\frac{5}{3}$

   (b) $-\frac{5}{3}$

8. (a) $\frac{3}{4}$

   (b) $\frac{3}{4}$

9. $-\frac{1}{x} \le \frac{\sin 2x}{x} \le \frac{1}{x} \Rightarrow \lim\limits_{x \to \infty} \frac{\sin 2x}{x} = 0$ by the Sandwich Theorem

10. $-\frac{1}{3\theta} \le \frac{\cos \theta}{3\theta} \le \frac{1}{3\theta} \Rightarrow \lim\limits_{\theta \to -\infty} \frac{\cos \theta}{3\theta} = 0$ by the Sandwich Theorem

11. $\lim\limits_{t \to \infty} \frac{2 - t + \sin t}{t + \cos t} = \lim\limits_{t \to \infty} \frac{\frac{2}{t} - 1 + \left(\frac{\sin t}{t}\right)}{1 + \left(\frac{\cos t}{t}\right)} = \frac{0 - 1 + 0}{1 + 0} = -1$

12. $\lim\limits_{r \to \infty} \frac{r + \sin r}{2r + 7 - 5\sin r} = \lim\limits_{r \to \infty} \frac{1 + \left(\frac{\sin r}{r}\right)}{2 + \frac{7}{r} - 5\left(\frac{\sin r}{r}\right)} = \lim\limits_{r \to \infty} \frac{1 + 0}{2 + 0 - 0} = \frac{1}{2}$

13. (a) $\lim\limits_{x \to \infty} \frac{2x + 3}{5x + 7} = \lim\limits_{x \to \infty} \frac{2 + \frac{3}{x}}{5 + \frac{7}{x}} = \frac{2}{5}$

   (b) $\frac{2}{5}$ (same process as part (a))

14. (a) $\lim\limits_{x \to \infty} \frac{2x^3+7}{x^3-x^2+x+7} = \lim\limits_{x \to \infty} \frac{2+\left(\frac{7}{x^3}\right)}{1-\frac{1}{x}+\frac{1}{x^2}+\frac{7}{x^3}} = 2$

(b) 2 (same process as part (a))

15. (a) $\lim\limits_{x \to \infty} \frac{x+1}{x^2+3} = \lim\limits_{x \to \infty} \frac{\frac{1}{x}+\frac{1}{x^2}}{1+\frac{3}{x^2}} = 0$     (b) 0 (same process as part (a))

16. (a) $\lim\limits_{x \to \infty} \frac{3x+7}{x^2-2} = \lim\limits_{x \to \infty} \frac{\frac{3}{x}+\frac{7}{x^2}}{1-\frac{2}{x^2}} = 0$     (b) 0 (same process as part (a))

17. (a) $\lim\limits_{x \to \infty} \frac{7x^3}{x^3-3x^2+6x} = \lim\limits_{x \to \infty} \frac{7}{1-\frac{3}{x}+\frac{6}{x^2}} = 7$     (b) 7 (same process as part (a))

18. (a) $\lim\limits_{x \to \infty} \frac{1}{x^3-4x+1} = \lim\limits_{x \to \infty} \frac{\frac{1}{x^3}}{1-\frac{4}{x^2}+\frac{1}{x^3}} = 0$     (b) 0 (same process as part (a))

19. (a) $\lim\limits_{x \to \infty} \frac{10x^5+x^4+31}{x^6} = \lim\limits_{x \to \infty} \frac{\frac{10}{x}+\frac{1}{x^2}+\frac{31}{x^6}}{1} = 0$     (b) 0 (same process as part (a))

20. (a) $\lim\limits_{x \to \infty} \frac{9x^4+x}{2x^4+5x^2-x+6} = \lim\limits_{x \to \infty} \frac{9+\frac{1}{x^3}}{2+\frac{5}{x^2}-\frac{1}{x^3}+\frac{6}{x^4}} = \frac{9}{2}$

(b) $\frac{9}{2}$ (same process as part (a))

21. (a) $\lim\limits_{x \to \infty} \frac{-2x^3-2x+3}{3x^3+3x^2-5x} = \lim\limits_{x \to \infty} \frac{-2-\frac{2}{x^2}+\frac{3}{x^3}}{3+\frac{3}{x}-\frac{5}{x^2}} = -\frac{2}{3}$

(b) $-\frac{2}{3}$ (same process as part (a))

22. (a) $\lim\limits_{x \to \infty} \frac{-x^4}{x^4-7x^3+7x^2+9} = \lim\limits_{x \to \infty} \frac{-1}{1-\frac{7}{x}+\frac{7}{x^2}+\frac{9}{x^4}} = -1$

(b) $-1$ (same process as part (a))

23. $\lim\limits_{x \to \infty} \sqrt{\frac{8x^2-3}{2x^2+x}} = \lim\limits_{x \to \infty} \sqrt{\frac{8-\frac{3}{x^2}}{2+\frac{1}{x}}} = \sqrt{\lim\limits_{x \to \infty} \frac{8-\frac{3}{x^2}}{2+\frac{1}{x}}} = \sqrt{\frac{8-0}{2+0}} = \sqrt{4} = 2$

24. $\lim\limits_{x \to -\infty} \left(\frac{x^2+x-1}{8x^2-3}\right)^{1/3} = \lim\limits_{x \to -\infty} \left(\frac{1+\frac{1}{x}-\frac{1}{x^2}}{8-\frac{3}{x^2}}\right)^{1/3} = \left(\lim\limits_{x \to -\infty} \frac{1+\frac{1}{x}-\frac{1}{x^2}}{8-\frac{3}{x^2}}\right)^{1/3} = \left(\frac{1+0-0}{8-0}\right)^{1/3} = \left(\frac{1}{8}\right)^{1/3} = \frac{1}{2}$

25. $\lim\limits_{x \to -\infty} \left(\frac{1-x^3}{x^2-7x}\right)^5 = \lim\limits_{x \to -\infty} \left(\frac{\frac{1}{x^2}-x}{1-\frac{7}{x}}\right)^5 = \left(\lim\limits_{x \to -\infty} \frac{\frac{1}{x^2}-x}{1-\frac{7}{x}}\right)^5 = \left(\frac{0+\infty}{1-0}\right)^5 = \infty$

26. $\lim\limits_{x \to \infty} \sqrt{\frac{x^2-5x}{x^3+x-2}} = \lim\limits_{x \to \infty} \sqrt{\frac{\frac{1}{x}-\frac{5}{x^2}}{1+\frac{1}{x^2}-\frac{2}{x^3}}} = \sqrt{\lim\limits_{x \to \infty} \frac{\frac{1}{x}-\frac{5}{x^2}}{1+\frac{1}{x^2}-\frac{2}{x^3}}} = \sqrt{\frac{0-0}{1+0-0}} = \sqrt{0} = 0$

27. $\lim\limits_{x \to \infty} \frac{2\sqrt{x}+x^{-1}}{3x-7} = \lim\limits_{x \to \infty} \frac{\left(\frac{2}{x^{1/2}}\right)+\left(\frac{1}{x^2}\right)}{3-\frac{7}{x}} = 0$     28. $\lim\limits_{x \to \infty} \frac{2+\sqrt{x}}{2-\sqrt{x}} = \lim\limits_{x \to \infty} \frac{\left(\frac{2}{x^{1/2}}\right)+1}{\left(\frac{2}{x^{1/2}}\right)-1} = -1$

29. $\lim\limits_{x \to -\infty} \frac{\sqrt[3]{x}-\sqrt[5]{x}}{\sqrt[3]{x}+\sqrt[5]{x}} = \lim\limits_{x \to -\infty} \frac{1-x^{(1/5)-(1/3)}}{1+x^{(1/5)-(1/3)}} = \lim\limits_{x \to -\infty} \frac{1-\left(\frac{1}{x^{2/15}}\right)}{1+\left(\frac{1}{x^{2/15}}\right)} = 1$

30. $\lim\limits_{x \to \infty} \frac{x^{-1}+x^{-4}}{x^{-2}-x^{-3}} = \lim\limits_{x \to \infty} \frac{x+\frac{1}{x^2}}{1-\frac{1}{x}} = \infty$

31. $\lim\limits_{x \to \infty} \dfrac{2x^{5/3} - x^{1/3} + 7}{x^{8/5} + 3x + \sqrt{x}} = \lim\limits_{x \to \infty} \dfrac{2x^{1/15} - \frac{1}{x^{19/15}} + \frac{7}{x^{8/5}}}{1 + \frac{3}{x^{3/5}} + \frac{1}{x^{11/10}}} = \infty$

32. $\lim\limits_{x \to -\infty} \dfrac{\sqrt[3]{x} - 5x + 3}{2x + x^{2/3} - 4} = \lim\limits_{x \to -\infty} \dfrac{\frac{1}{x^{2/3}} - 5 + \frac{3}{x}}{2 + \frac{1}{x^{1/3}} - \frac{4}{x}} = -\dfrac{5}{2}\sqrt[3]{x}$

33. $\lim\limits_{x \to \infty} \dfrac{\sqrt{x^2 + 1}}{x + 1} = \lim\limits_{x \to \infty} \dfrac{\sqrt{x^2 + 1}/\sqrt{x^2}}{(x + 1)/\sqrt{x^2}} = \lim\limits_{x \to \infty} \dfrac{\sqrt{(x^2 + 1)/x^2}}{(x + 1)/x} = \lim\limits_{x \to \infty} \dfrac{\sqrt{1 + 1/x^2}}{(1 + 1/x)} = \dfrac{\sqrt{1 + 0}}{(1 + 0)} = 1$

34. $\lim\limits_{x \to -\infty} \dfrac{\sqrt{x^2 + 1}}{x + 1} = \lim\limits_{x \to -\infty} \dfrac{\sqrt{x^2 + 1}/\sqrt{x^2}}{(x + 1)/\sqrt{x^2}} = \lim\limits_{x \to -\infty} \dfrac{\sqrt{(x^2 + 1)/x^2}}{(x + 1)/(-x)} = \lim\limits_{x \to -\infty} \dfrac{\sqrt{1 + 1/x^2}}{(-1 - 1/x)} = \dfrac{\sqrt{1 + 0}}{(-1 - 0)} = -1$

35. $\lim\limits_{x \to \infty} \dfrac{x - 3}{\sqrt{4x^2 + 25}} = \lim\limits_{x \to \infty} \dfrac{(x - 3)/\sqrt{x^2}}{\sqrt{4x^2 + 25}/\sqrt{x^2}} = \lim\limits_{x \to \infty} \dfrac{(x - 3)/x}{\sqrt{(4x^2 + 25)/x^2}} = \lim\limits_{x \to \infty} \dfrac{(1 - 3/x)}{\sqrt{4 + 25/x^2}} = \dfrac{(1 - 0)}{\sqrt{4 + 0}} = \dfrac{1}{2}$

36. $\lim\limits_{x \to -\infty} \dfrac{4 - 3x^3}{\sqrt{x^6 + 9}} = \lim\limits_{x \to -\infty} \dfrac{(4 - 3x^3)/\sqrt{x^6}}{\sqrt{x^6 + 9}/\sqrt{x^6}} = \lim\limits_{x \to -\infty} \dfrac{(4 - 3x^3)/(-x^3)}{\sqrt{(x^6 + 9)/x^6}} = \lim\limits_{x \to \infty} \dfrac{(-4/x^3 + 3)}{\sqrt{1 + 9/x^6}} = \dfrac{(0 + 3)}{\sqrt{1 + 0}} = 3$

37. $\lim\limits_{x \to 0^+} \dfrac{1}{3x} = \infty \qquad \left(\dfrac{\text{positive}}{\text{positive}}\right)$

38. $\lim\limits_{x \to 0^-} \dfrac{5}{2x} = -\infty \qquad \left(\dfrac{\text{positive}}{\text{negative}}\right)$

39. $\lim\limits_{x \to 2^-} \dfrac{3}{x - 2} = -\infty \qquad \left(\dfrac{\text{positive}}{\text{negative}}\right)$

40. $\lim\limits_{x \to 3^+} \dfrac{1}{x - 3} = \infty \qquad \left(\dfrac{\text{positive}}{\text{positive}}\right)$

41. $\lim\limits_{x \to -8^+} \dfrac{2x}{x + 8} = -\infty \qquad \left(\dfrac{\text{negative}}{\text{positive}}\right)$

42. $\lim\limits_{x \to -5^-} \dfrac{3x}{2x + 10} = \infty \qquad \left(\dfrac{\text{negative}}{\text{negative}}\right)$

43. $\lim\limits_{x \to 7} \dfrac{4}{(x - 7)^2} = \infty \qquad \left(\dfrac{\text{positive}}{\text{positive}}\right)$

44. $\lim\limits_{x \to 0} \dfrac{-1}{x^2(x + 1)} = -\infty \qquad \left(\dfrac{\text{negative}}{\text{positive} \cdot \text{positive}}\right)$

45. (a) $\lim\limits_{x \to 0^+} \dfrac{2}{3x^{1/3}} = \infty$

(b) $\lim\limits_{x \to 0^-} \dfrac{2}{3x^{1/3}} = -\infty$

46. (a) $\lim\limits_{x \to 0^+} \dfrac{2}{x^{1/5}} = \infty$

(b) $\lim\limits_{x \to 0^-} \dfrac{2}{x^{1/5}} = -\infty$

47. $\lim\limits_{x \to 0} \dfrac{4}{x^{2/5}} = \lim\limits_{x \to 0} \dfrac{4}{(x^{1/5})^2} = \infty$

48. $\lim\limits_{x \to 0} \dfrac{1}{x^{2/3}} = \lim\limits_{x \to 0} \dfrac{1}{(x^{1/3})^2} = \infty$

49. $\lim\limits_{x \to \left(\frac{\pi}{2}\right)^-} \tan x = \infty$

50. $\lim\limits_{x \to \left(\frac{-\pi}{2}\right)^+} \sec x = \infty$

51. $\lim\limits_{\theta \to 0^-} (1 + \csc \theta) = -\infty$

52. $\lim\limits_{\theta \to 0^+} (2 - \cot \theta) = -\infty$ and $\lim\limits_{\theta \to 0^-} (2 - \cot \theta) = \infty$, so the limit does not exist

53. (a) $\lim\limits_{x \to 2^+} \dfrac{1}{x^2 - 4} = \lim\limits_{x \to 2^+} \dfrac{1}{(x + 2)(x - 2)} = \infty \qquad \left(\dfrac{1}{\text{positive} \cdot \text{positive}}\right)$

(b) $\lim\limits_{x \to 2^-} \dfrac{1}{x^2 - 4} = \lim\limits_{x \to 2^-} \dfrac{1}{(x + 2)(x - 2)} = -\infty \qquad \left(\dfrac{1}{\text{positive} \cdot \text{negative}}\right)$

(c) $\lim\limits_{x \to -2^+} \dfrac{1}{x^2 - 4} = \lim\limits_{x \to -2^+} \dfrac{1}{(x + 2)(x - 2)} = -\infty \qquad \left(\dfrac{1}{\text{positive} \cdot \text{negative}}\right)$

(d) $\lim\limits_{x \to -2^-} \dfrac{1}{x^2 - 4} = \lim\limits_{x \to -2^-} \dfrac{1}{(x + 2)(x - 2)} = \infty \qquad \left(\dfrac{1}{\text{negative} \cdot \text{negative}}\right)$

54. (a) $\lim\limits_{x \to 1^+} \frac{x}{x^2-1} = \lim\limits_{x \to 1^+} \frac{x}{(x+1)(x-1)} = \infty$  $\left(\frac{\text{positive}}{\text{positive}\cdot\text{positive}}\right)$

   (b) $\lim\limits_{x \to 1^-} \frac{x}{x^2-1} = \lim\limits_{x \to 1^-} \frac{x}{(x+1)(x-1)} = -\infty$  $\left(\frac{\text{positive}}{\text{positive}\cdot\text{negative}}\right)$

   (c) $\lim\limits_{x \to -1^+} \frac{x}{x^2-1} = \lim\limits_{x \to -1^+} \frac{x}{(x+1)(x-1)} = \infty$  $\left(\frac{\text{negative}}{\text{positive}\cdot\text{negative}}\right)$

   (d) $\lim\limits_{x \to -1^-} \frac{x}{x^2-1} = \lim\limits_{x \to -1^-} \frac{x}{(x+1)(x-1)} = -\infty$  $\left(\frac{\text{negative}}{\text{negative}\cdot\text{negative}}\right)$

55. (a) $\lim\limits_{x \to 0^+} \frac{x^2}{2} - \frac{1}{x} = 0 + \lim\limits_{x \to 0^+} \frac{1}{-x} = -\infty$  $\left(\frac{1}{\text{negative}}\right)$

   (b) $\lim\limits_{x \to 0^-} \frac{x^2}{2} - \frac{1}{x} = 0 + \lim\limits_{x \to 0^-} \frac{1}{-x} = \infty$  $\left(\frac{1}{\text{positive}}\right)$

   (c) $\lim\limits_{x \to \sqrt[3]{2}} \frac{x^2}{2} - \frac{1}{x} = \frac{2^{2/3}}{2} - \frac{1}{2^{1/3}} = 2^{-1/3} - 2^{-1/3} = 0$

   (d) $\lim\limits_{x \to -1} \frac{x^2}{2} - \frac{1}{x} = \frac{1}{2} - \left(\frac{1}{-1}\right) = \frac{3}{2}$

56. (a) $\lim\limits_{x \to -2^+} \frac{x^2-1}{2x+4} = \infty$  $\left(\frac{\text{positive}}{\text{positive}}\right)$    (b) $\lim\limits_{x \to -2^-} \frac{x^2-1}{2x+4} = -\infty$  $\left(\frac{\text{positive}}{\text{negative}}\right)$

   (c) $\lim\limits_{x \to 1^+} \frac{x^2-1}{2x+4} = \lim\limits_{x \to 1^+} \frac{(x+1)(x-1)}{2x+4} = \frac{2\cdot 0}{2+4} = 0$

   (d) $\lim\limits_{x \to 0^-} \frac{x^2-1}{2x+4} = \frac{-1}{4}$

57. (a) $\lim\limits_{x \to 0^+} \frac{x^2-3x+2}{x^3-2x^2} = \lim\limits_{x \to 0^+} \frac{(x-2)(x-1)}{x^2(x-2)} = -\infty$  $\left(\frac{\text{negative}\cdot\text{negative}}{\text{positive}\cdot\text{negative}}\right)$

   (b) $\lim\limits_{x \to 2^+} \frac{x^2-3x+2}{x^3-2x^2} = \lim\limits_{x \to 2^+} \frac{(x-2)(x-1)}{x^2(x-2)} = \lim\limits_{x \to 2^+} \frac{x-1}{x^2} = \frac{1}{4}, x \neq 2$

   (c) $\lim\limits_{x \to 2^-} \frac{x^2-3x+2}{x^3-2x^2} = \lim\limits_{x \to 2^-} \frac{(x-2)(x-1)}{x^2(x-2)} = \lim\limits_{x \to 2^-} \frac{x-1}{x^2} = \frac{1}{4}, x \neq 2$

   (d) $\lim\limits_{x \to 2} \frac{x^2-3x+2}{x^3-2x^2} = \lim\limits_{x \to 2} \frac{(x-2)(x-1)}{x^2(x-2)} = \lim\limits_{x \to 2} \frac{x-1}{x^2} = \frac{1}{4}, x \neq 2$

   (e) $\lim\limits_{x \to 0} \frac{x^2-3x+2}{x^3-2x^2} = \lim\limits_{x \to 0} \frac{(x-2)(x-1)}{x^2(x-2)} = -\infty$  $\left(\frac{\text{negative}\cdot\text{negative}}{\text{positive}\cdot\text{negative}}\right)$

58. (a) $\lim\limits_{x \to 2^+} \frac{x^2-3x+2}{x^3-4x} = \lim\limits_{x \to 2^+} \frac{(x-2)(x-1)}{x(x-2)(x+2)} = \lim\limits_{x \to 2^+} \frac{(x-1)}{x(x+2)} = \frac{1}{2(4)} = \frac{1}{8}$

   (b) $\lim\limits_{x \to -2^+} \frac{x^2-3x+2}{x^3-4x} = \lim\limits_{x \to -2^+} \frac{(x-2)(x-1)}{x(x-2)(x+2)} = \lim\limits_{x \to -2^+} \frac{(x-1)}{x(x+2)} = \infty$  $\left(\frac{\text{negative}}{\text{negative}\cdot\text{positive}}\right)$

   (c) $\lim\limits_{x \to 0^-} \frac{x^2-3x+2}{x^3-4x} = \lim\limits_{x \to 0^-} \frac{(x-2)(x-1)}{x(x-2)(x+2)} = \lim\limits_{x \to 0^-} \frac{(x-1)}{x(x+2)} = \infty$  $\left(\frac{\text{negative}}{\text{negative}\cdot\text{positive}}\right)$

   (d) $\lim\limits_{x \to 1^+} \frac{x^2-3x+2}{x^3-4x} = \lim\limits_{x \to 1^+} \frac{(x-2)(x-1)}{x(x-2)(x+2)} = \lim\limits_{x \to 1^+} \frac{(x-1)}{x(x+2)} = \frac{0}{(1)(3)} = 0$

   (e) $\lim\limits_{x \to 0^+} \frac{x-1}{x(x+2)} = -\infty$  $\left(\frac{\text{negative}}{\text{positive}\cdot\text{positive}}\right)$

   and $\lim\limits_{x \to 0^-} \frac{x-1}{x(x+2)} = \infty$  $\left(\frac{\text{negative}}{\text{negative}\cdot\text{positive}}\right)$

   so the function has no limit as $x \to 0$.

59. (a) $\lim\limits_{t \to 0^+} \left[2 - \frac{3}{t^{1/3}}\right] = -\infty$    (b) $\lim\limits_{t \to 0^-} \left[2 - \frac{3}{t^{1/3}}\right] = \infty$

60. (a) $\lim\limits_{t \to 0^+} \left[\frac{1}{t^{3/5}} + 7\right] = \infty$    (b) $\lim\limits_{t \to 0^-} \left[\frac{1}{t^{3/5}} + 7\right] = -\infty$

61. (a) $\lim\limits_{x \to 0^+} \left[\frac{1}{x^{2/3}} + \frac{2}{(x-1)^{2/3}}\right] = \infty$    (b) $\lim\limits_{x \to 0^-} \left[\frac{1}{x^{2/3}} + \frac{2}{(x-1)^{2/3}}\right] = \infty$

   (c) $\lim\limits_{x \to 1^+} \left[\frac{1}{x^{2/3}} + \frac{2}{(x-1)^{2/3}}\right] = \infty$    (d) $\lim\limits_{x \to 1^-} \left[\frac{1}{x^{2/3}} + \frac{2}{(x-1)^{2/3}}\right] = \infty$

62. (a) $\lim\limits_{x \to 0^+} \left[ \frac{1}{x^{1/3}} - \frac{1}{(x-1)^{4/3}} \right] = \infty$    (b) $\lim\limits_{x \to 0^-} \left[ \frac{1}{x^{1/3}} - \frac{1}{(x-1)^{4/3}} \right] = -\infty$

(c) $\lim\limits_{x \to 1^+} \left[ \frac{1}{x^{1/3}} - \frac{1}{(x-1)^{4/3}} \right] = -\infty$    (d) $\lim\limits_{x \to 1^-} \left[ \frac{1}{x^{1/3}} - \frac{1}{(x-1)^{4/3}} \right] = -\infty$

63. $y = \frac{1}{x-1}$

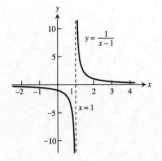

64. $y = \frac{1}{x+1}$

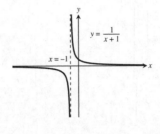

65. $y = \frac{1}{2x+4}$

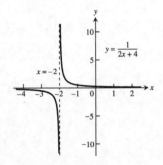

66. $y = \frac{-3}{x-3}$

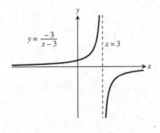

67. $y = \frac{x+3}{x+2} = 1 + \frac{1}{x+2}$

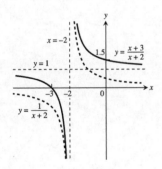

68. $y = \frac{2x}{x+1} = 2 - \frac{2}{x+1}$

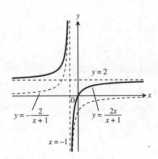

69. Here is one possibility.

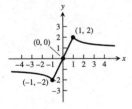

70. Here is one possibility.

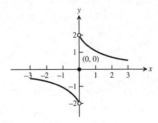

71. Here is one possibility.

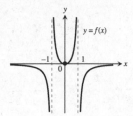

72. Here is one possibility.

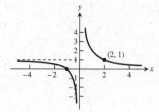

73. Here is one possibility.

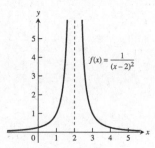

74. Here is one possibility.

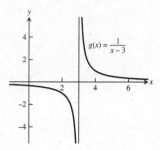

75. Here is one possibility.

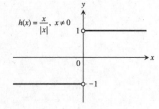

76. Here is one possibility.

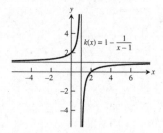

77. Yes. If $\lim\limits_{x \to \infty} \frac{f(x)}{g(x)} = 2$ then the ratio of the polynomials' leading coefficients is 2, so $\lim\limits_{x \to -\infty} \frac{f(x)}{g(x)} = 2$ as well.

78. Yes, it can have a horizontal or oblique asymptote.

79. At most 1 horizontal asymptote: If $\lim\limits_{x \to \infty} \frac{f(x)}{g(x)} = L$, then the ratio of the polynomials' leading coefficients is L, so $\lim\limits_{x \to -\infty} \frac{f(x)}{g(x)} = L$ as well.

80. $\lim\limits_{x \to \infty} \left( \sqrt{x+9} - \sqrt{x+4} \right) = \lim\limits_{x \to \infty} \left[ \sqrt{x+9} - \sqrt{x+4} \right] \cdot \left[ \frac{\sqrt{x+9} + \sqrt{x+4}}{\sqrt{x+9} + \sqrt{x+4}} \right] = \lim\limits_{x \to \infty} \frac{(x+9) - (x+4)}{\sqrt{x+9} + \sqrt{x+4}}$

$= \lim\limits_{x \to \infty} \frac{5}{\sqrt{x+9} + \sqrt{x+4}} = \lim\limits_{x \to \infty} \frac{\frac{5}{\sqrt{x}}}{\sqrt{1 + \frac{9}{x}} + \sqrt{1 + \frac{4}{x}}} = \frac{0}{1+1} = 0$

81. $\lim\limits_{x \to \infty} \left( \sqrt{x^2+25} - \sqrt{x^2-1} \right) = \lim\limits_{x \to \infty} \left[ \sqrt{x^2+25} - \sqrt{x^2-1} \right] \cdot \left[ \frac{\sqrt{x^2+25} + \sqrt{x^2-1}}{\sqrt{x^2+25} + \sqrt{x^2-1}} \right] = \lim\limits_{x \to \infty} \frac{(x^2+25) - (x^2-1)}{\sqrt{x^2+25} + \sqrt{x^2-1}}$

$= \lim\limits_{x \to \infty} \frac{26}{\sqrt{x^2+25} + \sqrt{x^2-1}} = \lim\limits_{x \to \infty} \frac{\frac{26}{x}}{\sqrt{1 + \frac{25}{x^2}} + \sqrt{1 - \frac{1}{x^2}}} = \frac{0}{1+1} = 0$

82. $\lim\limits_{x \to -\infty} \left( \sqrt{x^2+3} + x \right) = \lim\limits_{x \to -\infty} \left[ \sqrt{x^2+3} + x \right] \cdot \left[ \frac{\sqrt{x^2+3} - x}{\sqrt{x^2+3} - x} \right] = \lim\limits_{x \to -\infty} \frac{(x^2+3) - (x^2)}{\sqrt{x^2+3} - x}$

$= \lim\limits_{x \to -\infty} \frac{3}{\sqrt{x^2+3} - x} = \lim\limits_{x \to -\infty} \frac{\frac{3}{\sqrt{x^2}}}{\sqrt{1 + \frac{3}{x^2}} - \frac{x}{\sqrt{x^2}}} = \lim\limits_{x \to -\infty} \frac{-\frac{3}{x}}{\sqrt{1 + \frac{3}{x^2}} + 1} = \frac{0}{1+1} = 0$

83. $\displaystyle\lim_{x\to-\infty}\left(2x+\sqrt{4x^2+3x-2}\right)=\lim_{x\to-\infty}\left[2x+\sqrt{4x^2+3x-2}\right]\cdot\left[\frac{2x-\sqrt{4x^2+3x-2}}{2x-\sqrt{4x^2+3x-2}}\right]=\lim_{x\to-\infty}\frac{(4x^2)-(4x^2+3x-2)}{2x-\sqrt{4x^2+3x-2}}$

$=\displaystyle\lim_{x\to-\infty}\frac{-3x+2}{2x-\sqrt{4x^2+3x-2}}=\lim_{x\to-\infty}\frac{\frac{-3x+2}{\sqrt{x^2}}}{\frac{2x}{\sqrt{x^2}}-\sqrt{4+\frac{3}{x}-\frac{2}{x^2}}}=\lim_{x\to-\infty}\frac{\frac{-3x+2}{-x}}{\frac{2x}{-x}-\sqrt{4+\frac{3}{x}-\frac{2}{x^2}}}=\lim_{x\to-\infty}\frac{3-\frac{2}{x}}{-2-\sqrt{4+\frac{3}{x}-\frac{2}{x^2}}}$

$=\dfrac{3-0}{-2-2}=-\dfrac{3}{4}$

84. $\displaystyle\lim_{x\to\infty}\left(\sqrt{9x^2-x}-3x\right)==\lim_{x\to\infty}\left[\sqrt{9x^2-x}-3x\right]\cdot\left[\frac{\sqrt{9x^2-x}+3x}{\sqrt{9x^2-x}+3x}\right]=\lim_{x\to\infty}\frac{(9x^2-x)-(9x^2)}{\sqrt{9x^2-x}+3x}$

$=\displaystyle\lim_{x\to\infty}\frac{-x}{\sqrt{9x^2-x}+3x}=\lim_{x\to\infty}\frac{-\frac{x}{x}}{\sqrt{\frac{9x^2}{x^2}-\frac{x}{x^2}}+\frac{3x}{x}}=\lim_{x\to\infty}\frac{-1}{\sqrt{9-\frac{1}{x}}+3}=\frac{-1}{3+3}=-\frac{1}{6}$

85. $\displaystyle\lim_{x\to\infty}\left(\sqrt{x^2+3x}-\sqrt{x^2-2x}\right)=\lim_{x\to\infty}\left[\sqrt{x^2+3x}-\sqrt{x^2-2x}\right]\cdot\left[\frac{\sqrt{x^2+3x}+\sqrt{x^2-2x}}{\sqrt{x^2+3x}+\sqrt{x^2-2x}}\right]=\lim_{x\to\infty}\frac{(x^2+3x)-(x^2-2x)}{\sqrt{x^2+3x}+\sqrt{x^2-2x}}$

$=\displaystyle\lim_{x\to\infty}\frac{5x}{\sqrt{x^2+3x}+\sqrt{x^2-2x}}=\lim_{x\to\infty}\frac{5}{\sqrt{1+\frac{3}{x}}+\sqrt{1-\frac{2}{x}}}=\frac{5}{1+1}=\frac{5}{2}$

86. $\displaystyle\lim_{x\to\infty}\sqrt{x^2+x}-\sqrt{x^2-x}=\lim_{x\to\infty}\left[\sqrt{x^2+x}-\sqrt{x^2-x}\right]\cdot\left[\frac{\sqrt{x^2+x}+\sqrt{x^2-x}}{\sqrt{x^2+x}+\sqrt{x^2-x}}\right]=\lim_{x\to\infty}\frac{(x^2+x)-(x^2-x)}{\sqrt{x^2+x}+\sqrt{x^2-x}}$

$=\displaystyle\lim_{x\to\infty}\frac{2x}{\sqrt{x^2+x}+\sqrt{x^2-x}}=\lim_{x\to\infty}\frac{2}{\sqrt{1+\frac{1}{x}}+\sqrt{1-\frac{1}{x}}}=\frac{2}{1+1}=1$

87. For any $\epsilon>0$, take $N=1$. Then for all $x>N$ we have that $|f(x)-k|=|k-k|=0<\epsilon$.

88. For any $\epsilon>0$, take $N=1$. Then for all $y<-N$ we have that $|f(x)-k|=|k-k|=0<\epsilon$.

89. For every real number $-B<0$, we must find a $\delta>0$ such that for all x, $0<|x-0|<\delta\Rightarrow\frac{-1}{x^2}<-B$. Now,

$-\frac{1}{x^2}<-B<0\Leftrightarrow\frac{1}{x^2}>B>0\Leftrightarrow x^2<\frac{1}{B}\Leftrightarrow|x|<\frac{1}{\sqrt{B}}$. Choose $\delta=\frac{1}{\sqrt{B}}$, then $0<|x|<\delta\Rightarrow|x|<\frac{1}{\sqrt{B}}$

$\Rightarrow\frac{-1}{x^2}<-B$ so that $\displaystyle\lim_{x\to0}-\frac{1}{x^2}=-\infty$.

90. For every real number $B>0$, we must find a $\delta>0$ such that for all x, $0<|x-0|<\delta\Rightarrow\frac{1}{|x|}>B$. Now,

$\frac{1}{|x|}>B>0\Leftrightarrow|x|<\frac{1}{B}$. Choose $\delta=\frac{1}{B}$. Then $0<|x-0|<\delta\Rightarrow|x|<\frac{1}{B}\Rightarrow\frac{1}{|x|}>B$ so that $\displaystyle\lim_{x\to0}\frac{1}{|x|}=\infty$.

91. For every real number $-B<0$, we must find a $\delta>0$ such that for all x, $0<|x-3|<\delta\Rightarrow\frac{-2}{(x-3)^2}<-B$.

Now, $\frac{-2}{(x-3)^2}<-B<0\Leftrightarrow\frac{2}{(x-3)^2}>B>0\Leftrightarrow\frac{(x-3)^2}{2}<\frac{1}{B}\Leftrightarrow(x-3)^2<\frac{2}{B}\Leftrightarrow0<|x-3|<\sqrt{\frac{2}{B}}$. Choose

$\delta=\sqrt{\frac{2}{B}}$, then $0<|x-3|<\delta\Rightarrow\frac{-2}{(x-3)^2}<-B<0$ so that $\displaystyle\lim_{x\to3}\frac{-2}{(x-3)^2}=-\infty$.

92. For every real number $B>0$, we must find a $\delta>0$ such that for all x, $0<|x-(-5)|<\delta\Rightarrow\frac{1}{(x+5)^2}>B$.

Now, $\frac{1}{(x+5)^2}>B>0\Leftrightarrow(x+5)^2<\frac{1}{B}\Leftrightarrow|x+5|<\frac{1}{\sqrt{B}}$. Choose $\delta=\frac{1}{\sqrt{B}}$. Then $0<|x-(-5)|<\delta$

$\Rightarrow|x+5|<\frac{1}{\sqrt{B}}\Rightarrow\frac{1}{(x+5)^2}>B$ so that $\displaystyle\lim_{x\to-5}\frac{1}{(x+5)^2}=\infty$.

93. (a) We say that f(x) approaches infinity as x approaches $x_0$ from the left, and write $\displaystyle\lim_{x\to x_0^-}f(x)=\infty$, if

for every positive number B, there exists a corresponding number $\delta>0$ such that for all x,
$x_0-\delta<x<x_0\Rightarrow f(x)>B$.

(b) We say that f(x) approaches minus infinity as x approaches $x_0$ from the right, and write $\displaystyle\lim_{x\to x_0^+}f(x)=-\infty$,

if for every positive number B (or negative number $-B$) there exists a corresponding number $\delta>0$ such
that for all x, $x_0<x<x_0+\delta\Rightarrow f(x)<-B$.

(c) We say that f(x) approaches minus infinity as x approaches $x_0$ from the left, and write $\lim\limits_{x \to x_0^-} f(x) = -\infty$, if for every positive number B (or negative number $-$B) there exists a corresponding number $\delta > 0$ such that for all x, $x_0 - \delta < x < x_0 \Rightarrow f(x) < -B$.

94. For $B > 0$, $\frac{1}{x} > B > 0 \Leftrightarrow x < \frac{1}{B}$. Choose $\delta = \frac{1}{B}$. Then $0 < x < \delta \Rightarrow 0 < x < \frac{1}{B} \Rightarrow \frac{1}{x} > B$ so that $\lim\limits_{x \to 0^+} \frac{1}{x} = \infty$.

95. For $B > 0$, $\frac{1}{x} < -B < 0 \Leftrightarrow -\frac{1}{x} > B > 0 \Leftrightarrow -x < \frac{1}{B} \Leftrightarrow -\frac{1}{B} < x$. Choose $\delta = \frac{1}{B}$. Then $-\delta < x < 0$ $\Rightarrow -\frac{1}{B} < x \Rightarrow \frac{1}{x} < -B$ so that $\lim\limits_{x \to 0^-} \frac{1}{x} = -\infty$.

96. For $B > 0$, $\frac{1}{x-2} < -B \Leftrightarrow -\frac{1}{x-2} > B \Leftrightarrow -(x-2) < \frac{1}{B} \Leftrightarrow x - 2 > -\frac{1}{B} \Leftrightarrow x > 2 - \frac{1}{B}$. Choose $\delta = \frac{1}{B}$. Then $2 - \delta < x < 2 \Rightarrow -\delta < x - 2 < 0 \Rightarrow -\frac{1}{B} < x - 2 < 0 \Rightarrow \frac{1}{x-2} < -B < 0$ so that $\lim\limits_{x \to 2^-} \frac{1}{x-2} = -\infty$.

97. For $B > 0$, $\frac{1}{x-2} > B \Leftrightarrow 0 < x - 2 < \frac{1}{B}$. Choose $\delta = \frac{1}{B}$. Then $2 < x < 2 + \delta \Rightarrow 0 < x - 2 < \delta \Rightarrow 0 < x - 2 < \frac{1}{B}$ $\Rightarrow \frac{1}{x-2} > B > 0$ so that $\lim\limits_{x \to 2^+} \frac{1}{x-2} = \infty$.

98. For $B > 0$ and $0 < x < 1$, $\frac{1}{1-x^2} > B \Leftrightarrow 1 - x^2 < \frac{1}{B} \Leftrightarrow (1-x)(1+x) < \frac{1}{B}$. Now $\frac{1+x}{2} < 1$ since $x < 1$. Choose $\delta < \frac{1}{2B}$. Then $1 - \delta < x < 1 \Rightarrow -\delta < x - 1 < 0 \Rightarrow 1 - x < \delta < \frac{1}{2B} \Rightarrow (1-x)(1+x) < \frac{1}{B}\left(\frac{1+x}{2}\right) < \frac{1}{B}$ $\Rightarrow \frac{1}{1-x^2} > B$ for $0 < x < 1$ and x near $1 \Rightarrow \lim\limits_{x \to 1^-} \frac{1}{1-x^2} = \infty$.

99. $y = \frac{x^2}{x-1} = x + 1 + \frac{1}{x-1}$

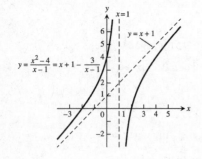

100. $y = \frac{x^2+1}{x-1} = x + 1 + \frac{2}{x-1}$

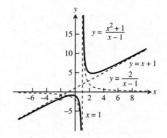

101. $y = \frac{x^2-4}{x-1} = x + 1 - \frac{3}{x-1}$

102. $y = \frac{x^2-1}{2x+4} = \frac{1}{2}x - 1 + \frac{3}{2x+4}$

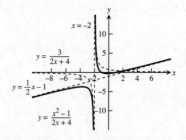

103. $y = \frac{x^2-1}{x} = x - \frac{1}{x}$

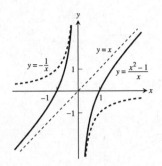

104. $y = \frac{x^3+1}{x^2} = x + \frac{1}{x^2}$

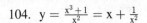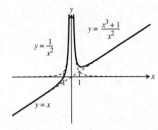

105. $y = \frac{x}{\sqrt{4-x^2}}$

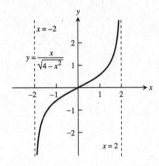

106. $y = \frac{-1}{\sqrt{4-x^2}}$

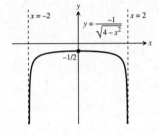

107. $y = x^{2/3} + \frac{1}{x^{1/3}}$

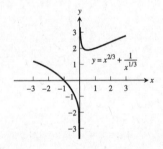

108. $y = \sin\left(\frac{\pi}{x^2+1}\right)$

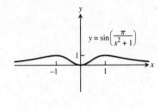

109. (a) $y \to \infty$ (see accompanying graph)
   (b) $y \to \infty$ (see accompanying graph)
   (c) cusps at $x = \pm 1$ (see accompanying graph)

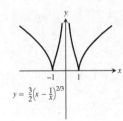

110. (a) $y \to 0$ and a cusp at $x = 0$ (see the accompanying graph)
   (b) $y \to \frac{3}{2}$ (see accompanying graph)
   (c) a vertical asymptote at $x = 1$ and contains the point $\left(-1, \frac{3}{2\sqrt[3]{4}}\right)$ (see accompanying graph)

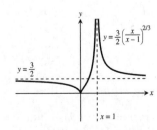

**CHAPTER 2 PRACTICE EXERCISES**

1.  At $x = -1$: $\lim\limits_{x \to -1^-} f(x) = \lim\limits_{x \to -1^+} f(x) = 1$

    $\Rightarrow \lim\limits_{x \to -1} f(x) = 1 = f(-1)$

    $\Rightarrow$ f is continuous at $x = -1$.

    At $x = 0$: $\lim\limits_{x \to 0^-} f(x) = \lim\limits_{x \to 0^+} f(x) = 0 \Rightarrow \lim\limits_{x \to 0} f(x) = 0.$

    But $f(0) = 1 \neq \lim\limits_{x \to 0} f(x)$

    $\Rightarrow$ f is discontinuous at $x = 0$.

    If we define $f(0) = 0$, then the discontinuity at $x = 0$ is removable.

    At $x = 1$: $\lim\limits_{x \to 1^-} f(x) = -1$ and $\lim\limits_{x \to 1^+} f(x) = 1$

    $\Rightarrow \lim\limits_{x \to 1} f(x)$ does not exist

    $\Rightarrow$ f is discontinuous at $x = 1$.

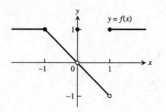

2.  At $x = -1$: $\lim\limits_{x \to -1^-} f(x) = 0$ and $\lim\limits_{x \to -1^+} f(x) = -1$

    $\Rightarrow \lim\limits_{x \to -1} f(x)$ does not exist

    $\Rightarrow$ f is discontinuous at $x = -1$.

    At $x = 0$: $\lim\limits_{x \to 0^-} f(x) = -\infty$ and $\lim\limits_{x \to 0^+} f(x) = \infty$

    $\Rightarrow \lim\limits_{x \to 0} f(x)$ does not exist

    $\Rightarrow$ f is discontinuous at $x = 0$.

    At $x = 1$: $\lim\limits_{x \to 1^-} f(x) = \lim\limits_{x \to 1^+} f(x) = 1 \Rightarrow \lim\limits_{x \to 1} f(x) = 1.$

    But $f(1) = 0 \neq \lim\limits_{x \to 1} f(x)$

    $\Rightarrow$ f is discontinuous at $x = 1$.

    If we define $f(1) = 1$, then the discontinuity at $x = 1$ is removable.

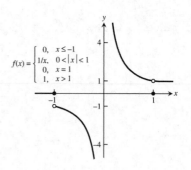

$$f(x) = \begin{cases} 0, & x \leq -1 \\ 1/x, & 0 < |x| < 1 \\ 0, & x = 1 \\ 1, & x > 1 \end{cases}$$

3.  (a) $\lim\limits_{t \to t_0} (3f(t)) = 3 \lim\limits_{t \to t_0} f(t) = 3(-7) = -21$

    (b) $\lim\limits_{t \to t_0} (f(t))^2 = \left( \lim\limits_{t \to t_0} f(t) \right)^2 = (-7)^2 = 49$

    (c) $\lim\limits_{t \to t_0} (f(t) \cdot g(t)) = \lim\limits_{t \to t_0} f(t) \cdot \lim\limits_{t \to t_0} g(t) = (-7)(0) = 0$

    (d) $\lim\limits_{t \to t_0} \dfrac{f(t)}{g(t)-7} = \dfrac{\lim\limits_{t \to t_0} f(t)}{\lim\limits_{t \to t_0} (g(t) - 7)} = \dfrac{\lim\limits_{t \to t_0} f(t)}{\lim\limits_{t \to t_0} g(t) - \lim\limits_{t \to t_0} 7} = \dfrac{-7}{0-7} = 1$

    (e) $\lim\limits_{t \to t_0} \cos(g(t)) = \cos\left( \lim\limits_{t \to t_0} g(t) \right) = \cos 0 = 1$

    (f) $\lim\limits_{t \to t_0} |f(t)| = \left| \lim\limits_{t \to t_0} f(t) \right| = |-7| = 7$

    (g) $\lim\limits_{t \to t_0} (f(t) + g(t)) = \lim\limits_{t \to t_0} f(t) + \lim\limits_{t \to t_0} g(t) = -7 + 0 = -7$

    (h) $\lim\limits_{t \to t_0} \left( \dfrac{1}{f(t)} \right) = \dfrac{1}{\lim\limits_{t \to t_0} f(t)} = \dfrac{1}{-7} = -\dfrac{1}{7}$

4.  (a) $\lim\limits_{x \to 0} -g(x) = -\lim\limits_{x \to 0} g(x) = -\sqrt{2}$

    (b) $\lim\limits_{x \to 0} (g(x) \cdot f(x)) = \lim\limits_{x \to 0} g(x) \cdot \lim\limits_{x \to 0} f(x) = \left( \sqrt{2} \right) \left( \tfrac{1}{2} \right) = \dfrac{\sqrt{2}}{2}$

    (c) $\lim\limits_{x \to 0} (f(x) + g(x)) = \lim\limits_{x \to 0} f(x) + \lim\limits_{x \to 0} g(x) = \tfrac{1}{2} + \sqrt{2}$

    (d) $\lim\limits_{x \to 0} \dfrac{1}{f(x)} = \dfrac{1}{\lim\limits_{x \to 0} f(x)} = \dfrac{1}{\tfrac{1}{2}} = 2$

(b)

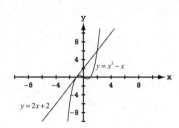

(c) $\left.\begin{array}{l} y = x^3 - x \\ y = 2x + 2 \end{array}\right\}$ $\Rightarrow$ $x^3 - x = 2x + 2$ $\Rightarrow$ $x^3 - 3x - 2 = (x - 2)(x + 1)^2 = 0$ $\Rightarrow$ $x = 2$ or $x = -1$. Since

$y = 2(2) + 2 = 6$; the other intersection point is $(2, 6)$

54. (a) $y = x^3 - 6x^2 + 5x$ $\Rightarrow$ $y' = 3x^2 - 12x + 5$. When $x = 0$, $y = 0$ and $y' = 5$ $\Rightarrow$ the tangent line to the curve at
    $(0, 0)$ is $y = 5x$.

(b)

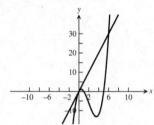

(c) $\left.\begin{array}{l} y = x^3 - 6x^2 + 5x \\ y = 5x \end{array}\right\}$ $\Rightarrow$ $x^3 - 6x^2 + 5x = 5x$ $\Rightarrow$ $x^3 - 6x^2 = 0$ $\Rightarrow$ $x^2(x - 6) = 0$ $\Rightarrow$ $x = 0$ or $x = 6$.

Since $y = 5(6) = 30$, the other intersection point is $(6, 30)$.

55. $\lim\limits_{x \to 1} \dfrac{x^{50} - 1}{x - 1} = 50 x^{49}\Big|_{x = 1} = 50 (1)^{49} = 50$

56. $\lim\limits_{x \to -1} \dfrac{x^{2/9} - 1}{x + 1} = \dfrac{2}{9} x^{-7/9}\Big|_{x = -1} = \dfrac{2}{9(-1)^{7/9}} = -\dfrac{2}{9}$

57. $g'(x) = \begin{cases} 2x - 3 & x > 0 \\ a & x < 0 \end{cases}$, since $g$ is differentiable at $x = 0$ $\Rightarrow$ $\lim\limits_{x \to 0^+} (2x - 3) = -3$ and $\lim\limits_{x \to 0^-} a = a \Rightarrow a = -3$

58. $f'(x) = \begin{cases} a & x > -1 \\ 2bx & x < -1 \end{cases}$, since $f$ is differentiable at $x = -1$ $\Rightarrow$ $\lim\limits_{x \to -1^+} a = a$ and $\lim\limits_{x \to -1^-} (2bx) = -2b \Rightarrow a = -2b$, and

since $f$ is continuous at $x = -1$ $\Rightarrow$ $\lim\limits_{x \to -1^+} (ax + b) = -a + b$ and $\lim\limits_{x \to -1^-} (bx^2 - 3) = b - 3 \Rightarrow -a + b = b - 3$

$\Rightarrow a = 3 \Rightarrow 3 = -2b \Rightarrow b = -\dfrac{3}{2}$.

59. $P(x) = a_n x^n + a_{n-1} x^{n-1} + \cdots + a_2 x^2 + a_1 x + a_0$ $\Rightarrow$ $P'(x) = n a_n x^{n-1} + (n - 1) a_{n-1} x^{n-2} + \cdots + 2 a_2 x + a_1$

60. $R = M^2 \left(\dfrac{C}{2} - \dfrac{M}{3}\right) = \dfrac{C}{2} M^2 - \dfrac{1}{3} M^3$, where C is a constant $\Rightarrow$ $\dfrac{dR}{dM} = CM - M^2$

61. Let c be a constant $\Rightarrow$ $\dfrac{dc}{dx} = 0$ $\Rightarrow$ $\dfrac{d}{dx} (u \cdot c) = u \cdot \dfrac{dc}{dx} + c \cdot \dfrac{du}{dx} = u \cdot 0 + c \dfrac{du}{dx} = c \dfrac{du}{dx}$. Thus when one of the
    functions is a constant, the Product Rule is just the Constant Multiple Rule $\Rightarrow$ the Constant Multiple Rule is
    a special case of the Product Rule.

62. (a) We use the Quotient rule to derive the Reciprocal Rule (with $u = 1$): $\dfrac{d}{dx} \left(\dfrac{1}{v}\right) = \dfrac{v \cdot 0 - 1 \cdot \frac{dv}{dx}}{v^2} = \dfrac{-1 \cdot \frac{dv}{dx}}{v^2} = -\dfrac{1}{v^2} \cdot \dfrac{dv}{dx}$.

(b) Now, using the Reciprocal Rule and the Product Rule, we'll derive the Quotient Rule: $\frac{d}{dx}\left(\frac{u}{v}\right) = \frac{d}{dx}\left(u \cdot \frac{1}{v}\right)$

$= u \cdot \frac{d}{dx}\left(\frac{1}{v}\right) + \frac{1}{v} \cdot \frac{du}{dx}$ (Product Rule) $= u \cdot \left(\frac{-1}{v^2}\right)\frac{dv}{dx} + \frac{1}{v}\frac{du}{dx}$ (Reciprocal Rule) $\Rightarrow \frac{d}{dx}\left(\frac{u}{v}\right) = \frac{-u\frac{dv}{dx} + v\frac{du}{dx}}{v^2}$

$= \frac{v\frac{du}{dx} - u\frac{dv}{dx}}{v^2}$, the Quotient Rule.

63. (a) $\frac{d}{dx}(uvw) = \frac{d}{dx}((uv) \cdot w) = (uv)\frac{dw}{dx} + w \cdot \frac{d}{dx}(uv) = uv\frac{dw}{dx} + w\left(u\frac{dv}{dx} + v\frac{du}{dx}\right) = uv\frac{dw}{dx} + wu\frac{dv}{dx} + wv\frac{du}{dx}$

$= uvw' + uv'w + u'vw$

(b) $\frac{d}{dx}(u_1u_2u_3u_4) = \frac{d}{dx}((u_1u_2u_3)u_4) = (u_1u_2u_3)\frac{du_4}{dx} + u_4\frac{d}{dx}(u_1u_2u_3) \Rightarrow \frac{d}{dx}(u_1u_2u_3u_4)$

$= u_1u_2u_3\frac{du_4}{dx} + u_4\left(u_1u_2\frac{du_3}{dx} + u_3u_1\frac{du_2}{dx} + u_3u_2\frac{du_1}{dx}\right)$    (using (a) above)

$\Rightarrow \frac{d}{dx}(u_1u_2u_3u_4) = u_1u_2u_3\frac{du_4}{dx} + u_1u_2u_4\frac{du_3}{dx} + u_1u_3u_4\frac{du_2}{dx} + u_2u_3u_4\frac{du_1}{dx}$

$= u_1u_2u_3u_4' + u_1u_2u_3'u_4 + u_1u_2'u_3u_4 + u_1'u_2u_3u_4$

(c) Generalizing (a) and (b) above, $\frac{d}{dx}(u_1\cdots u_n) = u_1u_2\cdots u_{n-1}u_n' + u_1u_2\cdots u_{n-2}u_{n-1}'u_n + \ldots + u_1'u_2\cdots u_n$

64. $\frac{d}{dx}(x^{-m}) = \frac{d}{dx}\left(\frac{1}{x^m}\right) = \frac{x^m \cdot 0 - 1(m \cdot x^{m-1})}{(x^m)^2} = \frac{-m \cdot x^{m-1}}{x^{2m}} = -m \cdot x^{m-1-2m} = -m \cdot x^{-m-1}$

65. $P = \frac{nRT}{V-nb} - \frac{an^2}{V^2}$. We are holding T constant, and a, b, n, R are also constant so their derivatives are zero

$\Rightarrow \frac{dP}{dV} = \frac{(V-nb)\cdot 0 - (nRT)(1)}{(V-nb)^2} - \frac{V^2(0) - (an^2)(2V)}{(V^2)^2} = \frac{-nRT}{(V-nb)^2} + \frac{2an^2}{V^3}$

66. $A(q) = \frac{km}{q} + cm + \frac{hq}{2} = (km)q^{-1} + cm + \left(\frac{h}{2}\right)q \Rightarrow \frac{dA}{dq} = -(km)q^{-2} + \left(\frac{h}{2}\right) = -\frac{km}{q^2} + \frac{h}{2} \Rightarrow \frac{d^2A}{dt^2} = 2(km)q^{-3} = \frac{2km}{q^3}$

## 3.4  THE DERIVATIVE AS A RATE OF CHANGE

1. $s = t^2 - 3t + 2, 0 \le t \le 2$

   (a) displacement $= \Delta s = s(2) - s(0) = 0m - 2m = -2$ m, $v_{av} = \frac{\Delta s}{\Delta t} = \frac{-2}{2} = -1$ m/sec

   (b) $v = \frac{ds}{dt} = 2t - 3 \Rightarrow |v(0)| = |-3| = 3$ m/sec and $|v(2)| = 1$ m/sec;

   $a = \frac{d^2s}{dt^2} = 2 \Rightarrow a(0) = 2$ m/sec$^2$ and $a(2) = 2$ m/sec$^2$

   (c) $v = 0 \Rightarrow 2t - 3 = 0 \Rightarrow t = \frac{3}{2}$. v is negative in the interval $0 < t < \frac{3}{2}$ and v is positive when $\frac{3}{2} < t < 2 \Rightarrow$ the body

   changes direction at $t = \frac{3}{2}$.

2. $s = 6t - t^2, 0 \le t \le 6$

   (a) displacement $= \Delta s = s(6) - s(0) = 0$ m, $v_{av} = \frac{\Delta s}{\Delta t} = \frac{0}{6} = 0$ m/sec

   (b) $v = \frac{ds}{dt} = 6 - 2t \Rightarrow |v(0)| = |6| = 6$ m/sec and $|v(6)| = |-6| = 6$ m/sec;

   $a = \frac{d^2s}{dt^2} = -2 \Rightarrow a(0) = -2$ m/sec$^2$ and $a(6) = -2$ m/sec$^2$

   (c) $v = 0 \Rightarrow 6 - 2t = 0 \Rightarrow t = 3$. v is positive in the interval $0 < t < 3$ and v is negative when $3 < t < 6 \Rightarrow$ the body

   changes direction at $t = 3$.

3. $s = -t^3 + 3t^2 - 3t, 0 \le t \le 3$

   (a) displacement $= \Delta s = s(3) - s(0) = -9$ m, $v_{av} = \frac{\Delta s}{\Delta t} = \frac{-9}{3} = -3$ m/sec

   (b) $v = \frac{ds}{dt} = -3t^2 + 6t - 3 \Rightarrow |v(0)| = |-3| = 3$ m/sec and $|v(3)| = |-12| = 12$ m/sec; $a = \frac{d^2s}{dt^2} = -6t + 6$

   $\Rightarrow a(0) = 6$ m/sec$^2$ and $a(3) = -12$ m/sec$^2$

   (c) $v = 0 \Rightarrow -3t^2 + 6t - 3 = 0 \Rightarrow t^2 - 2t + 1 = 0 \Rightarrow (t-1)^2 = 0 \Rightarrow t = 1$. For all other values of t in the

   interval the velocity v is negative (the graph of $v = -3t^2 + 6t - 3$ is a parabola with vertex at $t = 1$ which

   opens downward $\Rightarrow$ ~~the body never changes direction~~).

   *It does at $t = 1$ sec*

4.  $s = \frac{t^4}{4} - t^3 + t^2, 0 \leq t \leq 3$

    (a)  $\Delta s = s(3) - s(0) = \frac{9}{4}$ m, $v_{av} = \frac{\Delta s}{\Delta t} = \frac{\frac{9}{4}}{3} = \frac{3}{4}$ m/sec

    (b)  $v = t^3 - 3t^2 + 2t \Rightarrow |v(0)| = 0$ m/sec and $|v(3)| = 6$ m/sec; $a = 3t^2 - 6t + 2 \Rightarrow a(0) = 2$ m/sec$^2$ and
         $a(3) = 11$ m/sec$^2$

    (c)  $v = 0 \Rightarrow t^3 - 3t^2 + 2t = 0 \Rightarrow t(t-2)(t-1) = 0 \Rightarrow t = 0, 1, 2 \Rightarrow v = t(t-2)(t-1)$ is positive in the interval
         for $0 < t < 1$ and v is negative for $1 < t < 2$ and v is positive for $2 < t < 3 \Rightarrow$ the body changes direction at
         $t = 1$ and at $t = 2$.

5.  $s = \frac{25}{t^2} - \frac{5}{t}, 1 \leq t \leq 5$

    (a)  $\Delta s = s(5) - s(1) = -20$ m, $v_{av} = \frac{-20}{4} = -5$ m/sec

    (b)  $v = \frac{-50}{t^3} + \frac{5}{t^2} \Rightarrow |v(1)| = 45$ m/sec and $|v(5)| = \frac{1}{5}$ m/sec; $a = \frac{150}{t^4} - \frac{10}{t^3} \Rightarrow a(1) = 140$ m/sec$^2$ and
         $a(5) = \frac{4}{25}$ m/sec$^2$

    (c)  $v = 0 \Rightarrow \frac{-50 + 5t}{t^3} = 0 \Rightarrow -50 + 5t = 0 \Rightarrow t = 10 \Rightarrow$ the body does not change direction in the interval

6.  $s = \frac{25}{t+5}, -4 \leq t \leq 0$

    (a)  $\Delta s = s(0) - s(-4) = -20$ m, $v_{av} = -\frac{20}{4} = -5$ m/sec

    (b)  $v = \frac{-25}{(t+5)^2} \Rightarrow |v(-4)| = 25$ m/sec and $|v(0)| = 1$ m/sec; $a = \frac{50}{(t+5)^3} \Rightarrow a(-4) = 50$ m/sec$^2$ and
         $a(0) = \frac{2}{5}$ m/sec$^2$

    (c)  $v = 0 \Rightarrow \frac{-25}{(t+5)^2} = 0 \Rightarrow$ v is never $0 \Rightarrow$ the body never changes direction

7.  $s = t^3 - 6t^2 + 9t$ and let the positive direction be to the right on the s-axis.

    (a)  $v = 3t^2 - 12t + 9$ so that $v = 0 \Rightarrow t^2 - 4t + 3 = (t-3)(t-1) = 0 \Rightarrow t = 1$ or $3$; $a = 6t - 12 \Rightarrow a(1)$
         $= -6$ m/sec$^2$ and $a(3) = 6$ m/sec$^2$. Thus the body is motionless but being accelerated left when $t = 1$, and
         motionless but being accelerated right when $t = 3$.

    (b)  $a = 0 \Rightarrow 6t - 12 = 0 \Rightarrow t = 2$ with speed $|v(2)| = |12 - 24 + 9| = 3$ m/sec

    (c)  The body moves to the right or forward on $0 \leq t < 1$, and to the left or backward on $1 < t < 2$. The
         positions are $s(0) = 0, s(1) = 4$ and $s(2) = 2 \Rightarrow$ total distance $= |s(1) - s(0)| + |s(2) - s(1)| = |4| + |-2| = 6$ m.

8.  $v = t^2 - 4t + 3 \Rightarrow a = 2t - 4$

    (a)  $v = 0 \Rightarrow t^2 - 4t + 3 = 0 \Rightarrow t = 1$ or $3 \Rightarrow a(1) = -2$ m/sec$^2$ and $a(3) = 2$ m/sec$^2$

    (b)  $v > 0 \Rightarrow (t-3)(t-1) > 0 \Rightarrow 0 \leq t < 1$ or $t > 3$ and the body is moving forward; $v < 0 \Rightarrow (t-3)(t-1) < 0$
         $\Rightarrow 1 < t < 3$ and the body is moving backward

    (c)  velocity increasing $\Rightarrow a > 0 \Rightarrow 2t - 4 > 0 \Rightarrow t > 2$; velocity decreasing $\Rightarrow a < 0 \Rightarrow 2t - 4 < 0 \Rightarrow 0 \leq t < 2$

9.  $s_m = 1.86t^2 \Rightarrow v_m = 3.72t$ and solving $3.72t = 27.8 \Rightarrow t \approx 7.5$ sec on Mars; $s_j = 11.44t^2 \Rightarrow v_j = 22.88t$ and
    solving $22.88t = 27.8 \Rightarrow t \approx 1.2$ sec on Jupiter.

10. (a)  $v(t) = s'(t) = 24 - 1.6t$ m/sec, and $a(t) = v'(t) = s''(t) = -1.6$ m/sec$^2$

    (b)  Solve $v(t) = 0 \Rightarrow 24 - 1.6t = 0 \Rightarrow t = 15$ sec

    (c)  $s(15) = 24(15) - .8(15)^2 = 180$ m

    (d)  Solve $s(t) = 90 \Rightarrow 24t - .8t^2 = 90 \Rightarrow t = \frac{30 \pm 15\sqrt{2}}{2} \approx 4.39$ sec going up and 25.6 sec going down

    (e)  Twice the time it took to reach its highest point or 30 sec

11. $s = 15t - \frac{1}{2}g_s t^2 \Rightarrow v = 15 - g_s t$ so that $v = 0 \Rightarrow 15 - g_s t = 0 \Rightarrow g_s = \frac{15}{t}$. Therefore $g_s = \frac{15}{20} = \frac{3}{4} = 0.75$ m/sec$^2$

12. Solving $s_m = 832t - 2.6t^2 = 0 \Rightarrow t(832 - 2.6t) = 0 \Rightarrow t = 0$ or $320 \Rightarrow 320$ sec on the moon; solving
    $s_e = 832t - 16t^2 = 0 \Rightarrow t(832 - 16t) = 0 \Rightarrow t = 0$ or $52 \Rightarrow 52$ sec on the earth.  Also, $v_m = 832 - 5.2t = 0$
    $\Rightarrow t = 160$ and $s_m(160) = 66,560$ ft, the height it reaches above the moon's surface; $v_e = 832 - 32t = 0$
    $\Rightarrow t = 26$ and $s_e(26) = 10,816$ ft, the height it reaches above the earth's surface.

13. (a)  $s = 179 - 16t^2 \Rightarrow v = -32t \Rightarrow$ speed $= |v| = 32t$ ft/sec and $a = -32$ ft/sec$^2$

    (b)  $s = 0 \Rightarrow 179 - 16t^2 = 0 \Rightarrow t = \sqrt{\frac{179}{16}} \approx 3.3$ sec

    (c)  When $t = \sqrt{\frac{179}{16}}$, $v = -32\sqrt{\frac{179}{16}} = -8\sqrt{179} \approx -107.0$ ft/sec

14. (a)  $\lim\limits_{\theta \to \frac{\pi}{2}} v = \lim\limits_{\theta \to \frac{\pi}{2}} 9.8(\sin\theta)t = 9.8t$ so we expect $v = 9.8t$ m/sec in free fall

    (b)  $a = \frac{dv}{dt} = 9.8$ m/sec$^2$

15. (a)  at 2 and 7 seconds                              (b)  between 3 and 6 seconds:  $3 \le t \le 6$
    (c)                                                  (d)

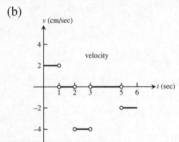            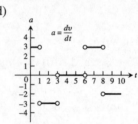

16. (a)  P is moving to the left when $2 < t < 3$ or $5 < t < 6$; P is moving to the right when $0 < t < 1$; P is standing
         still when $1 < t < 2$ or $3 < t < 5$
    (b)

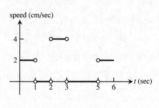

17. (a)  190 ft/sec                                      (b)  2 sec
    (c)  at 8 sec, 0 ft/sec                              (d)  10.8 sec, 90 ft/sec
    (e)  From $t = 8$ until $t = 10.8$ sec, a total of 2.8 sec
    (f)  Greatest acceleration happens 2 sec after launch
    (g)  From $t = 2$ to $t = 10.8$ sec; during this period, $a = \frac{v(10.8) - v(2)}{10.8 - 2} \approx -32$ ft/sec$^2$

18. (a)  Forward:  $0 \le t < 1$ and $5 < t < 7$; Backward:  $1 < t < 5$; Speeds up:  $1 < t < 2$ and $5 < t < 6$;
         Slows down:  $0 \le t < 1, 3 < t < 5$, and $6 < t < 7$
    (b)  Positive:  $3 < t < 6$; negative:  $0 \le t < 2$ and $6 < t < 7$; zero:  $2 < t < 3$ and $7 < t < 9$
    (c)  $t = 0$ and $2 \le t \le 3$
    (d)  $7 \le t \le 9$

19. $s = 490t^2 \Rightarrow v = 980t \Rightarrow a = 980$
    (a)  Solving $160 = 490t^2 \Rightarrow t = \frac{4}{7}$ sec.  The average velocity was $\frac{s(4/7) - s(0)}{4/7} = 280$ cm/sec.

(b)  At the 160 cm mark the balls are falling at v(4/7) = 560 cm/sec.  The acceleration at the 160 cm mark
    was 980 cm/sec$^2$.

(c)  The light was flashing at a rate of $\frac{17}{4/7}$ = 29.75 flashes per second.

20. (a)

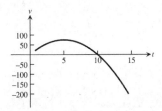    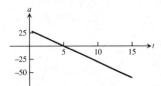

(b)

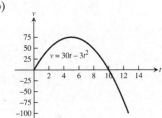    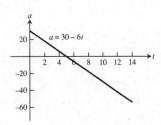

21.  C = position, A = velocity, and B = acceleration.  Neither A nor C can be the derivative of B because B's derivative
    is constant.  Graph C cannot be the derivative of A either, because A has some negative slopes while C has only
    positive values.  So, C (being the derivative of neither A nor B) must be the graph of position. Curve C has both
    positive and negative slopes, so its derivative, the velocity, must be A and not B.  That leaves B for acceleration.

22.  C = position, B = velocity, and A = acceleration.  Curve C cannot be the derivative of either A or B because
    C has only negative values while both A and B have some positive slopes.  So, C represents position.  Curve C
    has no positive slopes, so its derivative, the velocity, must be B.  That leaves A for acceleration.  Indeed, A is
    negative where B has negative slopes and positive where B has positive slopes.

23. (a)  c(100) = 11,000 $\Rightarrow$ c$_{av}$ = $\frac{11,000}{100}$ = \$110

(b)  c(x) = 2000 + 100x − .1x$^2$ $\Rightarrow$ c'(x) = 100 − .2x. Marginal cost = c'(x) $\Rightarrow$ the marginal cost of producing 100
    machines is c'(100) = \$80

(c)  The cost of producing the 101$^{st}$ machine is c(101) − c(100) = 100 − $\frac{201}{10}$ = \$79.90

24. (a)  r(x) = 20000 $\left(1 - \frac{1}{x}\right)$ $\Rightarrow$ r'(x) = $\frac{20000}{x^2}$ , which is marginal revenue. r'(100) = $\frac{20000}{100^2}$ = \$2.

(b)  r'(101) = \$1.96.

(c)  $\lim\limits_{x \to \infty}$ r'(x) = $\lim\limits_{x \to \infty}$ $\frac{20000}{x^2}$ = 0.  The increase in revenue as the number of items increases without bound
    will approach zero.

25.  b(t) = 10$^6$ + 10$^4$t − 10$^3$t$^2$ $\Rightarrow$ b'(t) = 10$^4$ − (2) (10$^3$t) = 10$^3$(10 − 2t)

(a)  b'(0) = 10$^4$ bacteria/hr                       (b)  b'(5) = 0 bacteria/hr

(c)  b'(10) = −10$^4$ bacteria/hr

26.  Q(t) = 200(30 − t)$^2$ = 200 $\left(900 - 60t + t^2\right)$ $\Rightarrow$ Q'(t) = 200(−60 + 2t) $\Rightarrow$ Q'(10) = −8,000 gallons/min is the rate
    the water is running at the end of 10 min.  Then $\frac{Q(10) - Q(0)}{10}$ = −10,000 gallons/min is the average rate the water flows
    during the first 10 min.  The negative signs indicate water is <u>leaving</u> the tank.

27. (a) $y = 6\left(1 - \frac{t}{12}\right)^2 = 6\left(1 - \frac{t}{6} + \frac{t^2}{144}\right) \Rightarrow \frac{dy}{dt} = \frac{t}{12} - 1$

   (b) The largest value of $\frac{dy}{dt}$ is 0 m/h when t = 12 and the fluid level is falling the slowest at that time. The smallest value of $\frac{dy}{dt}$ is −1 m/h, when t = 0, and the fluid level is falling the fastest at that time.

   (c) In this situation, $\frac{dy}{dt} \le 0 \Rightarrow$ the graph of y is always decreasing. As $\frac{dy}{dt}$ increases in value, the slope of the graph of y increases from −1 to 0 over the interval $0 \le t \le 12$.

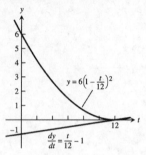

28. (a) $V = \frac{4}{3}\pi r^3 \Rightarrow \frac{dV}{dr} = 4\pi r^2 \Rightarrow \frac{dV}{dr}\Big|_{r=2} = 4\pi(2)^2 = 16\pi$ ft³/ft

   (b) When r = 2, $\frac{dV}{dr} = 16\pi$ so that when r changes by 1 unit, we expect V to change by approximately $16\pi$. Therefore when r changes by 0.2 units V changes by approximately $(16\pi)(0.2) = 3.2\pi \approx 10.05$ ft³. Note that $V(2.2) - V(2) \approx 11.09$ ft³.

29. 200 km/hr = $55\frac{5}{9}$ m/sec = $\frac{500}{9}$ m/sec, and D = $\frac{10}{9}t^2 \Rightarrow$ V = $\frac{20}{9}t$. Thus V = $\frac{500}{9} \Rightarrow \frac{20}{9}t = \frac{500}{9} \Rightarrow$ t = 25 sec. When t = 25, D = $\frac{10}{9}(25)^2 = \frac{6250}{9}$ m

30. $s = v_0 t - 16t^2 \Rightarrow v = v_0 - 32t$; v = 0 $\Rightarrow t = \frac{v_0}{32}$ ; $1900 = v_0 t - 16t^2$ so that t = $\frac{v_0}{32} \Rightarrow 1900 = \frac{v_0^2}{32} - \frac{v_0^2}{64}$

   $\Rightarrow v_0 = \sqrt{(64)(1900)} = 80\sqrt{19}$ ft/sec and, finally, $\frac{80\sqrt{19}\text{ ft}}{\text{sec}} \cdot \frac{60\text{ sec}}{1\text{ min}} \cdot \frac{60\text{ min}}{1\text{ hr}} \cdot \frac{1\text{ mi}}{5280\text{ ft}} \approx 238$ mph.

31.

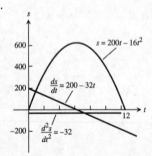

   (a) v = 0 when t = 6.25 sec
   (b) v > 0 when $0 \le t < 6.25 \Rightarrow$ body moves right (up); v < 0 when $6.25 < t \le 12.5 \Rightarrow$ body moves left (down)
   (c) body changes direction at t = 6.25 sec
   (d) body speeds up on (6.25, 12.5] and slows down on [0, 6.25)
   (e) The body is moving fastest at the endpoints t = 0 and t = 12.5 when it is traveling 200 ft/sec. It's moving slowest at t = 6.25 when the speed is 0.
   (f) When t = 6.25 the body is s = 625 m from the origin and farthest away.

32.

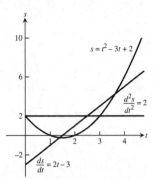

(a)  $v = 0$ when $t = \frac{3}{2}$ sec

(b)  $v < 0$ when $0 \le t < 1.5 \Rightarrow$ body moves left (down); $v > 0$ when $1.5 < t \le 5 \Rightarrow$ body moves right (up)

(c)  body changes direction at $t = \frac{3}{2}$ sec

(d)  body speeds up on $\left(\frac{3}{2}, 5\right]$ and slows down on $\left[0, \frac{3}{2}\right)$

(e)  body is moving fastest at $t = 5$ when the speed $= |v(5)| = 7$ units/sec; it is moving slowest at $t = \frac{3}{2}$ when the speed is 0

(f)  When $t = 5$ the body is $s = 12$ units from the origin and farthest away.

33.

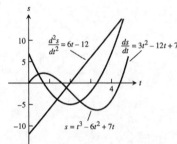

(a)  $v = 0$ when $t = \frac{6 \pm \sqrt{15}}{3}$ sec

(b)  $v < 0$ when $\frac{6 - \sqrt{15}}{3} < t < \frac{6 + \sqrt{15}}{3} \Rightarrow$ body moves left (down); $v > 0$ when $0 \le t < \frac{6 - \sqrt{15}}{3}$ or $\frac{6 + \sqrt{15}}{3} < t \le 4$
$\Rightarrow$ body moves right (up)

(c)  body changes direction at $t = \frac{6 \pm \sqrt{15}}{3}$ sec

(d)  body speeds up on $\left(\frac{6 - \sqrt{15}}{3}, 2\right) \cup \left(\frac{6 + \sqrt{15}}{3}, 4\right]$ and slows down on $\left[0, \frac{6 - \sqrt{15}}{3}\right) \cup \left(2, \frac{6 + \sqrt{15}}{3}\right)$.

(e)  The body is moving fastest at $t = 0$ and $t = 4$ when it is moving 7 units/sec and slowest at $t = \frac{6 \pm \sqrt{15}}{3}$ sec

(f)  When $t = \frac{6 + \sqrt{15}}{3}$ the body is at position $s \approx -6.303$ units and farthest from the origin.

34.

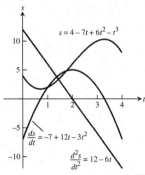

(a)  $v = 0$ when $t = \frac{6 \pm \sqrt{15}}{3}$

(b)  $v < 0$ when $0 \le t < \frac{6-\sqrt{15}}{3}$ or $\frac{6+\sqrt{15}}{3} < t \le 4 \Rightarrow$ body is moving left (down); $v > 0$ when

$\frac{6-\sqrt{15}}{3} < t < \frac{6+\sqrt{15}}{3} \Rightarrow$ body is moving right (up)

(c)  body changes direction at $t = \frac{6\pm\sqrt{15}}{3}$ sec

(d)  body speeds up on $\left(\frac{6-\sqrt{15}}{3}, 2\right) \cup \left(\frac{6+\sqrt{15}}{3}, 4\right]$ and slows down on $\left[0, \frac{6-\sqrt{15}}{3}\right) \cup \left(2, \frac{6+\sqrt{15}}{3}\right)$

(e)  The body is moving fastest at 7 units/sec when $t = 0$ and $t = 4$; it is moving slowest and stationary at $t = \frac{6\pm\sqrt{15}}{3}$

(f)  When $t = \frac{6+\sqrt{15}}{3}$ the position is $s \approx 10.303$ units and the body is farthest from the origin.

## 3.5 DERIVATIVES OF TRIGONOMETRIC FUNCTIONS

1.  $y = -10x + 3\cos x \Rightarrow \frac{dy}{dx} = -10 + 3\frac{d}{dx}(\cos x) = -10 - 3\sin x$

2.  $y = \frac{3}{x} + 5\sin x \Rightarrow \frac{dy}{dx} = \frac{-3}{x^2} + 5\frac{d}{dx}(\sin x) = \frac{-3}{x^2} + 5\cos x$

3.  $y = x^2\cos x \Rightarrow \frac{dy}{dx} = x^2(-\sin x) + 2x\cos x = -x^2\sin x + 2x\cos x$

4.  $y = \sqrt{x}\sec x + 3 \Rightarrow \frac{dy}{dx} = \sqrt{x}\sec x\tan x + \frac{\sec x}{2\sqrt{x}} + 0 = \sqrt{x}\sec x\tan x + \frac{\sec x}{2\sqrt{x}}$

5.  $y = \csc x - 4\sqrt{x} + 7 \Rightarrow \frac{dy}{dx} = -\csc x\cot x - \frac{4}{2\sqrt{x}} + 0 = -\csc x\cot x - \frac{2}{\sqrt{x}}$

6.  $y = x^2\cot x - \frac{1}{x^2} \Rightarrow \frac{dy}{dx} = x^2\frac{d}{dx}(\cot x) + \cot x \cdot \frac{d}{dx}(x^2) + \frac{2}{x^3} = -x^2\csc^2 x + (\cot x)(2x) + \frac{2}{x^3}$

    $= -x^2\csc^2 x + 2x\cot x + \frac{2}{x^3}$

7.  $f(x) = \sin x\tan x \Rightarrow f'(x) = \sin x\sec^2 x + \cos x\tan x = \sin x\sec^2 x + \cos x\frac{\sin x}{\cos x} = \sin x(\sec^2 x + 1)$

8.  $g(x) = \csc x\cot x \Rightarrow g'(x) = \csc x(-\csc^2 x) + (-\csc x\cot x)\cot x = -\csc^3 x - \csc x\cot^2 x = -\csc x(\csc^2 x + \cot^2 x)$

9.  $y = (\sec x + \tan x)(\sec x - \tan x) \Rightarrow \frac{dy}{dx} = (\sec x + \tan x)\frac{d}{dx}(\sec x - \tan x) + (\sec x - \tan x)\frac{d}{dx}(\sec x + \tan x)$

    $= (\sec x + \tan x)(\sec x\tan x - \sec^2 x) + (\sec x - \tan x)(\sec x\tan x + \sec^2 x)$

    $= (\sec^2 x\tan x + \sec x\tan^2 x - \sec^3 x - \sec^2 x\tan x) + (\sec^2 x\tan x - \sec x\tan^2 x + \sec^3 x - \tan x\sec^2 x) = 0$.

    $\left(\text{Note also that } y = \sec^2 x - \tan^2 x = (\tan^2 x + 1) - \tan^2 x = 1 \Rightarrow \frac{dy}{dx} = 0.\right)$

10. $y = (\sin x + \cos x)\sec x \Rightarrow \frac{dy}{dx} = (\sin x + \cos x)\frac{d}{dx}(\sec x) + \sec x\frac{d}{dx}(\sin x + \cos x)$

    $= (\sin x + \cos x)(\sec x\tan x) + (\sec x)(\cos x - \sin x) = \frac{(\sin x + \cos x)\sin x}{\cos^2 x} + \frac{\cos x - \sin x}{\cos x}$

    $= \frac{\sin^2 x + \cos x\sin x + \cos^2 x - \cos x\sin x}{\cos^2 x} = \frac{1}{\cos^2 x} = \sec^2 x$

    $\left(\text{Note also that } y = \sin x\sec x + \cos x\sec x = \tan x + 1 \Rightarrow \frac{dy}{dx} = \sec^2 x.\right)$

11. $y = \frac{\cot x}{1 + \cot x} \Rightarrow \frac{dy}{dx} = \frac{(1 + \cot x)\frac{d}{dx}(\cot x) - (\cot x)\frac{d}{dx}(1 + \cot x)}{(1 + \cot x)^2} = \frac{(1 + \cot x)(-\csc^2 x) - (\cot x)(-\csc^2 x)}{(1 + \cot x)^2}$

    $= \frac{-\csc^2 x - \csc^2 x\cot x + \csc^2 x\cot x}{(1 + \cot x)^2} = \frac{-\csc^2 x}{(1 + \cot x)^2}$

12. $y = \frac{\cos x}{1 + \sin x} \Rightarrow \frac{dy}{dx} = \frac{(1 + \sin x)\frac{d}{dx}(\cos x) - (\cos x)\frac{d}{dx}(1 + \sin x)}{(1 + \sin x)^2} = \frac{(1 + \sin x)(-\sin x) - (\cos x)(\cos x)}{(1 + \sin x)^2}$

    $= \frac{-\sin x - \sin^2 x - \cos^2 x}{(1 + \sin x)^2} = \frac{-\sin x - 1}{(1 + \sin x)^2} = \frac{-(1 + \sin x)}{(1 + \sin x)^2} = \frac{-1}{1 + \sin x}$

13. $y = \frac{4}{\cos x} + \frac{1}{\tan x} = 4 \sec x + \cot x \Rightarrow \frac{dy}{dx} = 4 \sec x \tan x - \csc^2 x$

14. $y = \frac{\cos x}{x} + \frac{x}{\cos x} \Rightarrow \frac{dy}{dx} = \frac{x(-\sin x) - (\cos x)(1)}{x^2} + \frac{(\cos x)(1) - x(-\sin x)}{\cos^2 x} = \frac{-x \sin x - \cos x}{x^2} + \frac{\cos x + x \sin x}{\cos^2 x}$

15. $y = x^2 \sin x + 2x \cos x - 2 \sin x \Rightarrow \frac{dy}{dx} = (x^2 \cos x + (\sin x)(2x)) + ((2x)(-\sin x) + (\cos x)(2)) - 2 \cos x$
$= x^2 \cos x + 2x \sin x - 2x \sin x + 2 \cos x - 2 \cos x = x^2 \cos x$

16. $y = x^2 \cos x - 2x \sin x - 2 \cos x \Rightarrow \frac{dy}{dx} = (x^2(-\sin x) + (\cos x)(2x)) - (2x \cos x + (\sin x)(2)) - 2(-\sin x)$
$= -x^2 \sin x + 2x \cos x - 2x \cos x - 2 \sin x + 2 \sin x = -x^2 \sin x$

17. $f(x) = x^3 \sin x \cos x \Rightarrow f'(x) = x^3 \sin x(-\sin x) + x^3 \cos x(\cos x) + 3x^2 \sin x \cos x = -x^3 \sin^2 x + x^3 \cos^2 x + 3x^2 \sin x \cos x$

18. $g(x) = (2 - x)\tan^2 x \Rightarrow g'(x) = (2 - x)(2 \tan x \sec^2 x) + (-1)\tan^2 x = 2(2 - x)\tan x \sec^2 x - \tan^2 x$
$= 2(2 - x)\tan x(\sec^2 x - \tan x)$

19. $s = \tan t - t \Rightarrow \frac{ds}{dt} = \sec^2 t - 1$ 

20. $s = t^2 - \sec t + 1 \Rightarrow \frac{ds}{dt} = 2t - \sec t \tan t$

21. $s = \frac{1 + \csc t}{1 - \csc t} \Rightarrow \frac{ds}{dt} = \frac{(1 - \csc t)(-\csc t \cot t) - (1 + \csc t)(\csc t \cot t)}{(1 - \csc t)^2}$
$= \frac{-\csc t \cot t + \csc^2 t \cot t - \csc t \cot t - \csc^2 t \cot t}{(1 - \csc t)^2} = \frac{-2 \csc t \cot t}{(1 - \csc t)^2}$

22. $s = \frac{\sin t}{1 - \cos t} \Rightarrow \frac{ds}{dt} = \frac{(1 - \cos t)(\cos t) - (\sin t)(\sin t)}{(1 - \cos t)^2} = \frac{\cos t - \cos^2 t - \sin^2 t}{(1 - \cos t)^2} = \frac{\cos t - 1}{(1 - \cos t)^2} = -\frac{1}{1 - \cos t} = \frac{1}{\cos t - 1}$

23. $r = 4 - \theta^2 \sin \theta \Rightarrow \frac{dr}{d\theta} = -\left(\theta^2 \frac{d}{d\theta}(\sin \theta) + (\sin \theta)(2\theta)\right) = -(\theta^2 \cos \theta + 2\theta \sin \theta) = -\theta(\theta \cos \theta + 2 \sin \theta)$

24. $r = \theta \sin \theta + \cos \theta \Rightarrow \frac{dr}{d\theta} = (\theta \cos \theta + (\sin \theta)(1)) - \sin \theta = \theta \cos \theta$

25. $r = \sec \theta \csc \theta \Rightarrow \frac{dr}{d\theta} = (\sec \theta)(-\csc \theta \cot \theta) + (\csc \theta)(\sec \theta \tan \theta)$
$= \left(\frac{-1}{\cos \theta}\right)\left(\frac{1}{\sin \theta}\right)\left(\frac{\cos \theta}{\sin \theta}\right) + \left(\frac{1}{\sin \theta}\right)\left(\frac{1}{\cos \theta}\right)\left(\frac{\sin \theta}{\cos \theta}\right) = \frac{-1}{\sin^2 \theta} + \frac{1}{\cos^2 \theta} = \sec^2 \theta - \csc^2 \theta$

26. $r = (1 + \sec \theta) \sin \theta \Rightarrow \frac{dr}{d\theta} = (1 + \sec \theta) \cos \theta + (\sin \theta)(\sec \theta \tan \theta) = (\cos \theta + 1) + \tan^2 \theta = \cos \theta + \sec^2 \theta$

27. $p = 5 + \frac{1}{\cot q} = 5 + \tan q \Rightarrow \frac{dp}{dq} = \sec^2 q$

28. $p = (1 + \csc q) \cos q \Rightarrow \frac{dp}{dq} = (1 + \csc q)(-\sin q) + (\cos q)(-\csc q \cot q) = (-\sin q - 1) - \cot^2 q = -\sin q - \csc^2 q$

29. $p = \frac{\sin q + \cos q}{\cos q} \Rightarrow \frac{dp}{dq} = \frac{(\cos q)(\cos q - \sin q) - (\sin q + \cos q)(-\sin q)}{\cos^2 q}$
$= \frac{\cos^2 q - \cos q \sin q + \sin^2 q + \cos q \sin q}{\cos^2 q} = \frac{1}{\cos^2 q} = \sec^2 q$

30. $p = \frac{\tan q}{1 + \tan q} \Rightarrow \frac{dp}{dq} = \frac{(1 + \tan q)(\sec^2 q) - (\tan q)(\sec^2 q)}{(1 + \tan q)^2} = \frac{\sec^2 q + \tan q \sec^2 q - \tan q \sec^2 q}{(1 + \tan q)^2} = \frac{\sec^2 q}{(1 + \tan q)^2}$

31. $p = \frac{q \sin q}{q^2 - 1} \Rightarrow \frac{dp}{dq} = \frac{(q^2 - 1)(q \cos q + \sin q(1)) - (q \sin q)(2q)}{(q^2 - 1)^2} = \frac{q^3 \cos q + q^2 \sin q - q \cos q - \sin q - 2q^2 \sin q}{(q^2 - 1)^2}$
$= \frac{q^3 \cos q - q^2 \sin q - q \cos q - \sin q}{(q^2 - 1)^2}$

32. $p = \frac{3q + \tan q}{q \sec q} \Rightarrow \frac{dp}{dq} = \frac{(q \sec q)(3 + \sec^2 q) - (3q + \tan q)(q \sec q \tan q + \sec q(1))}{(q \sec q)^2}$

$= \frac{3q \sec q + q \sec^3 q - (3q^2 \sec q \tan q + 3q \sec q + q \sec q \tan^2 q + \sec q \tan q)}{(q \sec q)^2} = \frac{q \sec^3 q - 3q^2 \sec q \tan q - q \sec q \tan^2 q - \sec q \tan q}{(q \sec q)^2}$

33. (a)  $y = \csc x \Rightarrow y' = -\csc x \cot x \Rightarrow y'' = -((\csc x)(-\csc^2 x) + (\cot x)(-\csc x \cot x)) = \csc^3 x + \csc x \cot^2 x$

   $= (\csc x)(\csc^2 x + \cot^2 x) = (\csc x)(\csc^2 x + \csc^2 x - 1) = 2 \csc^3 x - \csc x$

   (b)  $y = \sec x \Rightarrow y' = \sec x \tan x \Rightarrow y'' = (\sec x)(\sec^2 x) + (\tan x)(\sec x \tan x) = \sec^3 x + \sec x \tan^2 x$

   $= (\sec x)(\sec^2 x + \tan^2 x) = (\sec x)(\sec^2 x + \sec^2 x - 1) = 2 \sec^3 x - \sec x$

34. (a)  $y = -2 \sin x \Rightarrow y' = -2 \cos x \Rightarrow y'' = -2(-\sin x) = 2 \sin x \Rightarrow y''' = 2 \cos x \Rightarrow y^{(4)} = -2 \sin x$

   (b)  $y = 9 \cos x \Rightarrow y' = -9 \sin x \Rightarrow y'' = -9 \cos x \Rightarrow y''' = -9(-\sin x) = 9 \sin x \Rightarrow y^{(4)} = 9 \cos x$

35. $y = \sin x \Rightarrow y' = \cos x \Rightarrow$ slope of tangent at
    $x = -\pi$ is $y'(-\pi) = \cos(-\pi) = -1$; slope of
    tangent at $x = 0$ is $y'(0) = \cos(0) = 1$; and
    slope of tangent at $x = \frac{3\pi}{2}$ is $y'\left(\frac{3\pi}{2}\right) = \cos \frac{3\pi}{2}$
    $= 0$. The tangent at $(-\pi, 0)$ is $y - 0 = -1(x + \pi)$,
    or $y = -x - \pi$; the tangent at $(0, 0)$ is
    $y - 0 = 1(x - 0)$, or $y = x$; and the tangent at
    $\left(\frac{3\pi}{2}, -1\right)$ is $y = -1$.

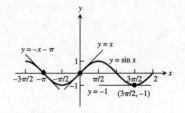

36. $y = \tan x \Rightarrow y' = \sec^2 x \Rightarrow$ slope of tangent at $x = -\frac{\pi}{3}$
    is $\sec^2\left(-\frac{\pi}{3}\right) = 4$; slope of tangent at $x = 0$ is $\sec^2(0) = 1$;
    and slope of tangent at $x = \frac{\pi}{3}$ is $\sec^2\left(\frac{\pi}{3}\right) = 4$. The tangent
    at $\left(-\frac{\pi}{3}, \tan\left(-\frac{\pi}{3}\right)\right) = \left(-\frac{\pi}{3}, -\sqrt{3}\right)$ is $y + \sqrt{3} = 4\left(x + \frac{\pi}{3}\right)$;
    the tangent at $(0, 0)$ is $y = x$; and the tangent at $\left(\frac{\pi}{3}, \tan\left(\frac{\pi}{3}\right)\right)$
    $= \left(\frac{\pi}{3}, \sqrt{3}\right)$ is $y - \sqrt{3} = 4\left(x - \frac{\pi}{3}\right)$.

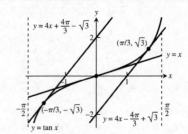

37. $y = \sec x \Rightarrow y' = \sec x \tan x \Rightarrow$ slope of tangent at
    $x = -\frac{\pi}{3}$ is $\sec\left(-\frac{\pi}{3}\right) \tan\left(-\frac{\pi}{3}\right) = -2\sqrt{3}$; slope of tangent
    at $x = \frac{\pi}{4}$ is $\sec\left(\frac{\pi}{4}\right) \tan\left(\frac{\pi}{4}\right) = \sqrt{2}$. The tangent at the point
    $\left(-\frac{\pi}{3}, \sec\left(-\frac{\pi}{3}\right)\right) = \left(-\frac{\pi}{3}, 2\right)$ is $y - 2 = -2\sqrt{3}\left(x + \frac{\pi}{3}\right)$;
    the tangent at the point $\left(\frac{\pi}{4}, \sec\left(\frac{\pi}{4}\right)\right) = \left(\frac{\pi}{4}, \sqrt{2}\right)$ is $y - \sqrt{2}$
    $= \sqrt{2}\left(x - \frac{\pi}{4}\right)$.

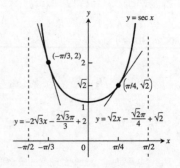

38. $y = 1 + \cos x \Rightarrow y' = -\sin x \Rightarrow$ slope of tangent at
    $x = -\frac{\pi}{3}$ is $-\sin\left(-\frac{\pi}{3}\right) = \frac{\sqrt{3}}{2}$; slope of tangent at $x = \frac{3\pi}{2}$
    is $-\sin\left(\frac{3\pi}{2}\right) = 1$. The tangent at the point
    $\left(-\frac{\pi}{3}, 1 + \cos\left(-\frac{\pi}{3}\right)\right) = \left(-\frac{\pi}{3}, \frac{3}{2}\right)$
    is $y - \frac{3}{2} = \frac{\sqrt{3}}{2}\left(x + \frac{\pi}{3}\right)$; the tangent at the point
    $\left(\frac{3\pi}{2}, 1 + \cos\left(\frac{3\pi}{2}\right)\right) = \left(\frac{3\pi}{2}, 1\right)$ is $y - 1 = x - \frac{3\pi}{2}$

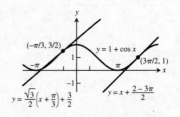

39. Yes, $y = x + \sin x \Rightarrow y' = 1 + \cos x$; horizontal tangent occurs where $1 + \cos x = 0 \Rightarrow \cos x = -1 \Rightarrow x = \pi$

40. No, $y = 2x + \sin x \Rightarrow y' = 2 + \cos x$; horizontal tangent occurs where $2 + \cos x = 0 \Rightarrow \cos x = -2$. But there are no x-values for which $\cos x = -2$.

41. No, $y = x - \cot x \Rightarrow y' = 1 + \csc^2 x$; horizontal tangent occurs where $1 + \csc^2 x = 0 \Rightarrow \csc^2 x = -1$. But there are no x-values for which $\csc^2 x = -1$.

42. Yes, $y = x + 2\cos x \Rightarrow y' = 1 - 2\sin x$; horizontal tangent occurs where $1 - 2\sin x = 0 \Rightarrow 1 = 2\sin x$
    $\Rightarrow \frac{1}{2} = \sin x \Rightarrow x = \frac{\pi}{6}$ or $x = \frac{5\pi}{6}$

43. We want all points on the curve where the tangent line has slope 2. Thus, $y = \tan x \Rightarrow y' = \sec^2 x$ so that $y' = 2 \Rightarrow \sec^2 x = 2 \Rightarrow \sec x = \pm\sqrt{2}$
    $\Rightarrow x = \pm\frac{\pi}{4}$. Then the tangent line at $\left(\frac{\pi}{4}, 1\right)$ has equation $y - 1 = 2\left(x - \frac{\pi}{4}\right)$; the tangent line at $\left(-\frac{\pi}{4}, -1\right)$ has equation $y + 1 = 2\left(x + \frac{\pi}{4}\right)$.

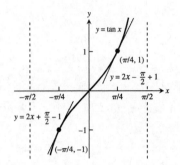

44. We want all points on the curve $y = \cot x$ where the tangent line has slope $-1$. Thus $y = \cot x$
    $\Rightarrow y' = -\csc^2 x$ so that $y' = -1 \Rightarrow -\csc^2 x = -1$
    $\Rightarrow \csc^2 x = 1 \Rightarrow \csc x = \pm 1 \Rightarrow x = \frac{\pi}{2}$. The tangent line at $\left(\frac{\pi}{2}, 0\right)$ is $y = -x + \frac{\pi}{2}$.

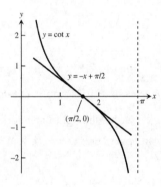

45. $y = 4 + \cot x - 2\csc x \Rightarrow y' = -\csc^2 x + 2\csc x \cot x = -\left(\frac{1}{\sin x}\right)\left(\frac{1 - 2\cos x}{\sin x}\right)$
    (a) When $x = \frac{\pi}{2}$, then $y' = -1$; the tangent line is $y = -x + \frac{\pi}{2} + 2$.
    (b) To find the location of the horizontal tangent set $y' = 0 \Rightarrow 1 - 2\cos x = 0 \Rightarrow x = \frac{\pi}{3}$ radians. When $x = \frac{\pi}{3}$, then $y = 4 - \sqrt{3}$ is the horizontal tangent.

46. $y = 1 + \sqrt{2}\csc x + \cot x \Rightarrow y' = -\sqrt{2}\csc x \cot x - \csc^2 x = -\left(\frac{1}{\sin x}\right)\left(\frac{\sqrt{2}\cos x + 1}{\sin x}\right)$
    (a) If $x = \frac{\pi}{4}$, then $y' = -4$; the tangent line is $y = -4x + \pi + 4$.
    (b) To find the location of the horizontal tangent set $y' = 0 \Rightarrow \sqrt{2}\cos x + 1 = 0 \Rightarrow x = \frac{3\pi}{4}$ radians. When $x = \frac{3\pi}{4}$, then $y = 2$ is the horizontal tangent.

47. $\lim\limits_{x \to 2} \sin\left(\frac{1}{x} - \frac{1}{2}\right) = \sin\left(\frac{1}{2} - \frac{1}{2}\right) = \sin 0 = 0$

48. $\lim\limits_{x \to -\frac{\pi}{6}} \sqrt{1 + \cos(\pi \csc x)} = \sqrt{1 + \cos\left(\pi \csc\left(-\frac{\pi}{6}\right)\right)} = \sqrt{1 + \cos(\pi \cdot (-2))} = \sqrt{2}$

49. $\lim\limits_{\theta \to \frac{\pi}{6}} \frac{\sin\theta - \frac{1}{2}}{\theta - \frac{\pi}{6}} = \frac{d}{d\theta}(\sin\theta)\Big|_{\theta = \frac{\pi}{6}} = \cos\theta\Big|_{\theta = \frac{\pi}{6}} = \cos\left(\frac{\pi}{6}\right) = \frac{\sqrt{3}}{2}$

50. $\lim\limits_{\theta \to \frac{\pi}{4}} \frac{\tan\theta - 1}{\theta - \frac{\pi}{4}} = \frac{d}{d\theta}(\tan\theta)\Big|_{\theta = \frac{\pi}{4}} = \sec^2\theta\Big|_{\theta = \frac{\pi}{4}} = \sec^2\left(\frac{\pi}{4}\right) = 2$

51. $\lim\limits_{x \to 0} \sec\left[\cos x + \pi\tan\left(\frac{\pi}{4\sec x}\right) - 1\right] = \sec\left[1 + \pi\tan\left(\frac{\pi}{4\sec 0}\right) - 1\right] = = \sec\left[\pi\tan\left(\frac{\pi}{4}\right)\right] = \sec\pi = -1$

52. $\lim\limits_{x \to 0} \sin\left(\frac{\pi + \tan x}{\tan x - 2\sec x}\right) = \sin\left(\frac{\pi + \tan 0}{\tan 0 - 2\sec 0}\right) = \sin\left(-\frac{\pi}{2}\right) = -1$

53. $\lim\limits_{t \to 0} \tan\left(1 - \frac{\sin t}{t}\right) = \tan\left(1 - \lim\limits_{t \to 0}\frac{\sin t}{t}\right) = \tan(1 - 1) = 0$

54. $\lim\limits_{\theta \to 0} \cos\left(\frac{\pi\theta}{\sin\theta}\right) = \cos\left(\pi\lim\limits_{\theta \to 0}\frac{\theta}{\sin\theta}\right) = \cos\left(\pi \cdot \frac{1}{\lim\limits_{\theta \to 0}\frac{\sin\theta}{\theta}}\right) = \cos\left(\pi \cdot \frac{1}{1}\right) = -1$

55. $s = 2 - 2\sin t \Rightarrow v = \frac{ds}{dt} = -2\cos t \Rightarrow a = \frac{dv}{dt} = 2\sin t \Rightarrow j = \frac{da}{dt} = 2\cos t$. Therefore, velocity $= v\left(\frac{\pi}{4}\right)$
$= -\sqrt{2}$ m/sec; speed $= \left|v\left(\frac{\pi}{4}\right)\right| = \sqrt{2}$ m/sec; acceleration $= a\left(\frac{\pi}{4}\right) = \sqrt{2}$ m/sec$^2$; jerk $= j\left(\frac{\pi}{4}\right) = \sqrt{2}$ m/sec$^3$.

56. $s = \sin t + \cos t \Rightarrow v = \frac{ds}{dt} = \cos t - \sin t \Rightarrow a = \frac{dv}{dt} = -\sin t - \cos t \Rightarrow j = \frac{da}{dt} = -\cos t + \sin t$. Therefore
velocity $= v\left(\frac{\pi}{4}\right) = 0$ m/sec; speed $= \left|v\left(\frac{\pi}{4}\right)\right| = 0$ m/sec; acceleration $= a\left(\frac{\pi}{4}\right) = -\sqrt{2}$ m/sec$^2$; jerk $= j\left(\frac{\pi}{4}\right) = 0$ m/sec$^3$.

57. $\lim\limits_{x \to 0} f(x) = \lim\limits_{x \to 0}\frac{\sin^2 3x}{x^2} = \lim\limits_{x \to 0} 9\left(\frac{\sin 3x}{3x}\right)\left(\frac{\sin 3x}{3x}\right) = 9$ so that f is continuous at $x = 0 \Rightarrow \lim\limits_{x \to 0} f(x) = f(0) \Rightarrow 9 = c$.

58. $\lim\limits_{x \to 0^-} g(x) = \lim\limits_{x \to 0^-} (x + b) = b$ and $\lim\limits_{x \to 0^+} g(x) = \lim\limits_{x \to 0^+} \cos x = 1$ so that g is continuous at $x = 0 \Rightarrow \lim\limits_{x \to 0^-} g(x)$
$= \lim\limits_{x \to 0^+} g(x) \Rightarrow b = 1$. Now g is not differentiable at $x = 0$: At $x = 0$, the left-hand derivative is
$\frac{d}{dx}(x + b)\Big|_{x=0} = 1$, but the right-hand derivative is $\frac{d}{dx}(\cos x)\Big|_{x=0} = -\sin 0 = 0$. The left- and right-hand
derivatives can never agree at $x = 0$, so g is not differentiable at $x = 0$ for any value of b (including $b = 1$).

59. $\frac{d^{999}}{dx^{999}}(\cos x) = \sin x$ because $\frac{d^4}{dx^4}(\cos x) = \cos x \Rightarrow$ the derivative of cos x any number of times that is a
multiple of 4 is cos x. Thus, dividing 999 by 4 gives $999 = 249 \cdot 4 + 3 \Rightarrow \frac{d^{999}}{dx^{999}}(\cos x)$
$= \frac{d^3}{dx^3}\left[\frac{d^{249 \cdot 4}}{dx^{249 \cdot 4}}(\cos x)\right] = \frac{d^3}{dx^3}(\cos x) = \sin x$.

60. (a) $y = \sec x = \frac{1}{\cos x} \Rightarrow \frac{dy}{dx} = \frac{(\cos x)(0) - (1)(-\sin x)}{(\cos x)^2} = \frac{\sin x}{\cos^2 x} = \left(\frac{1}{\cos x}\right)\left(\frac{\sin x}{\cos x}\right) = \sec x\tan x$
$\Rightarrow \frac{d}{dx}(\sec x) = \sec x\tan x$
   (b) $y = \csc x = \frac{1}{\sin x} \Rightarrow \frac{dy}{dx} = \frac{(\sin x)(0) - (1)(\cos x)}{(\sin x)^2} = \frac{-\cos x}{\sin^2 x} = \left(\frac{-1}{\sin x}\right)\left(\frac{\cos x}{\sin x}\right) = -\csc x\cot x$
$\Rightarrow \frac{d}{dx}(\csc x) = -\csc x\cot x$
   (c) $y = \cot x = \frac{\cos x}{\sin x} \Rightarrow \frac{dy}{dx} = \frac{(\sin x)(-\sin x) - (\cos x)(\cos x)}{(\sin x)^2} = \frac{-\sin^2 x - \cos^2 x}{\sin^2 x} = \frac{-1}{\sin^2 x} = -\csc^2 x$
$\Rightarrow \frac{d}{dx}(\cot x) = -\csc^2 x$

61. (a) $t = 0 \to x = 10\cos(0) = 10$ cm; $t = \frac{\pi}{3} \to x = 10\cos\left(\frac{\pi}{3}\right) = 5$ cm; $t = \frac{3\pi}{4} \to x = 10\cos\left(\frac{3\pi}{4}\right) = -5\sqrt{2}$ cm
   (b) $t = 0 \to v = -10\sin(0) = 0\,\frac{cm}{sec}$; $t = \frac{\pi}{3} \to v = -10\sin\left(\frac{\pi}{3}\right) = -5\sqrt{3}\,\frac{cm}{sec}$; $t = \frac{3\pi}{4} \to v = -10\sin\left(\frac{3\pi}{4}\right) = -5\sqrt{2}\,\frac{cm}{sec}$

62. (a) $t = 0 \to x = 3\cos(0) + 4\sin(0) = 3$ ft; $t = \frac{\pi}{2} \to x = 3\cos\left(\frac{\pi}{2}\right) + 4\sin\left(\frac{\pi}{2}\right) = 4$ ft;
       $t = \pi \to x = 3\cos(\pi) + 4\sin(\pi) = -3$ ft
   (b) $t = 0 \to v = -3\sin(0) + 4\cos(0) = 4\,\frac{ft}{sec}$; $t = \frac{\pi}{2} \to v = -3\sin\left(\frac{\pi}{2}\right) + 4\cos\left(\frac{\pi}{2}\right) = -3\,\frac{ft}{sec}$;
       $t = \pi \to v = -3\sin(\pi) + 4\cos(\pi) = -4\,\frac{ft}{sec}$

63.

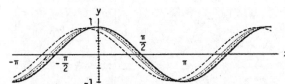 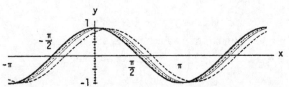

As h takes on the values of 1, 0.5, 0.3 and 0.1 the corresponding dashed curves of $y = \frac{\sin(x+h) - \sin x}{h}$ get

closer and closer to the black curve $y = \cos x$ because $\frac{d}{dx}(\sin x) = \lim_{h \to 0} \frac{\sin(x+h) - \sin x}{h} = \cos x$. The same

is true as h takes on the values of $-1, -0.5, -0.3$ and $-0.1$.

64.

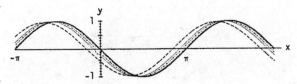 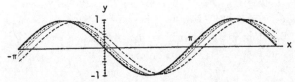

As h takes on the values of 1, 0.5, 0.3, and 0.1 the corresponding dashed curves of $y = \frac{\cos(x+h) - \cos x}{h}$ get

closer and closer to the black curve $y = -\sin x$ because $\frac{d}{dx}(\cos x) = \lim_{h \to 0} \frac{\cos(x+h) - \cos x}{h} = -\sin x$. The

same is true as h takes on the values of $-1, -0.5, -0.3$, and $-0.1$.

65. (a)

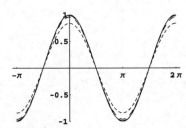

The dashed curves of $y = \frac{\sin(x+h) - \sin(x-h)}{2h}$ are closer to the black curve $y = \cos x$ than the corresponding dashed

curves in Exercise 63 illustrating that the centered difference quotient is a better approximation of the derivative of

this function.

(b)

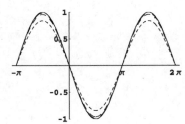

The dashed curves of $y = \frac{\cos(x+h) - \cos(x-h)}{2h}$ are closer to the black curve $y = -\sin x$ than the corresponding dashed

curves in Exercise 64 illustrating that the centered difference quotient is a better approximation of the derivative of

this function.

66. $\lim_{h \to 0} \frac{|0+h| - |0-h|}{2h} = \lim_{x \to 0} \frac{|h| - |h|}{2h} = \lim_{h \to 0} 0 = 0 \Rightarrow$ the limits of the centered difference quotient exists even

though the derivative of $f(x) = |x|$ does not exist at $x = 0$.

67. $y = \tan x \Rightarrow y' = \sec^2 x$, so the smallest value
$y' = \sec^2 x$ takes on is $y' = 1$ when $x = 0$;
$y'$ has no maximum value since $\sec^2 x$ has no
largest value on $\left(-\frac{\pi}{2}, \frac{\pi}{2}\right)$; $y'$ is never negative
since $\sec^2 x \geq 1$.

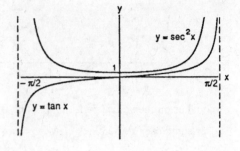

68. $y = \cot x \Rightarrow y' = -\csc^2 x$ so $y'$ has no smallest
value since $-\csc^2 x$ has no minimum value on
$(0, \pi)$; the largest value of $y'$ is $-1$, when $x = \frac{\pi}{2}$;
the slope is never positive since the largest
value $y' = -\csc^2 x$ takes on is $-1$.

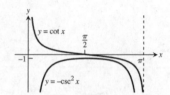

69. $y = \frac{\sin x}{x}$ appears to cross the y-axis at $y = 1$, since
$\lim\limits_{x \to 0} \frac{\sin x}{x} = 1$; $y = \frac{\sin 2x}{x}$ appears to cross the y-axis
at $y = 2$, since $\lim\limits_{x \to 0} \frac{\sin 2x}{x} = 2$; $y = \frac{\sin 4x}{x}$ appears to
cross the y-axis at $y = 4$, since $\lim\limits_{x \to 0} \frac{\sin 4x}{x} = 4$.
However, none of these graphs actually cross the y-axis
since $x = 0$ is not in the domain of the functions.  Also,
$\lim\limits_{x \to 0} \frac{\sin 5x}{x} = 5$, $\lim\limits_{x \to 0} \frac{\sin(-3x)}{x} = -3$, and $\lim\limits_{x \to 0} \frac{\sin kx}{x}$
$= k \Rightarrow$ the graphs of $y = \frac{\sin 5x}{x}$, $y = \frac{\sin(-3x)}{x}$, and
$y = \frac{\sin kx}{x}$ approach 5, $-3$, and k, respectively, as
$x \to 0$. However, the graphs do not actually cross the
y-axis.

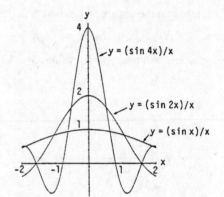

70. (a)

| h | $\frac{\sin h}{h}$ | $\left(\frac{\sin h}{h}\right)\left(\frac{180}{\pi}\right)$ |
|---|---|---|
| 1 | .017452406 | .99994923 |
| 0.01 | .017453292 | 1 |
| 0.001 | .017453292 | 1 |
| 0.0001 | .017453292 | 1 |

$\lim\limits_{h \to 0} \frac{\sin h^\circ}{h} = \lim\limits_{x \to 0} \frac{\sin\left(h \cdot \frac{\pi}{180}\right)}{h} = \lim\limits_{h \to 0} \frac{\frac{\pi}{180}\sin\left(h \cdot \frac{\pi}{180}\right)}{\frac{\pi}{180} \cdot h} = \lim\limits_{\theta \to 0} \frac{\frac{\pi}{180}\sin\theta}{\theta} = \frac{\pi}{180}$     $\left(\theta = h \cdot \frac{\pi}{180}\right)$

(converting to radians)

(b)

| h | $\frac{\cos h - 1}{h}$ |
|---|---|
| 1 | $-0.0001523$ |
| 0.01 | $-0.0000015$ |
| 0.001 | $-0.0000001$ |
| 0.0001 | 0 |

$\lim\limits_{h \to 0} \frac{\cos h - 1}{h} = 0$, whether h is measured in degrees or radians.

(c)  In degrees, $\frac{d}{dx}(\sin x) = \lim\limits_{h \to 0} \frac{\sin(x+h) - \sin x}{h} = \lim\limits_{h \to 0} \frac{(\sin x \cos h + \cos x \sin h) - \sin x}{h}$

$= \lim\limits_{h \to 0}\left(\sin x \cdot \frac{\cos h - 1}{h}\right) + \lim\limits_{h \to 0}\left(\cos x \cdot \frac{\sin h}{h}\right) = (\sin x) \cdot \lim\limits_{h \to 0}\left(\frac{\cos h - 1}{h}\right) + (\cos x) \cdot \lim\limits_{h \to 0}\left(\frac{\sin h}{h}\right)$

$= (\sin x)(0) + (\cos x)\left(\frac{\pi}{180}\right) = \frac{\pi}{180}\cos x$

(d) In degrees, $\frac{d}{dx}(\cos x) = \lim\limits_{h \to 0} \frac{\cos(x+h) - \cos x}{h} = \lim\limits_{h \to 0} \frac{(\cos x \cos h - \sin x \sin h) - \cos x}{h}$

$= \lim\limits_{h \to 0} \frac{(\cos x)(\cos h - 1) - \sin x \sin h}{h} = \lim\limits_{h \to 0} \left(\cos x \cdot \frac{\cos h - 1}{h}\right) - \lim\limits_{h \to 0} \left(\sin x \cdot \frac{\sin h}{h}\right)$

$= (\cos x) \lim\limits_{h \to 0} \left(\frac{\cos h - 1}{h}\right) - (\sin x) \lim\limits_{h \to 0} \left(\frac{\sin h}{h}\right) = (\cos x)(0) - (\sin x)\left(\frac{\pi}{180}\right) = -\frac{\pi}{180}\sin x$

(e) $\frac{d^2}{dx^2}(\sin x) = \frac{d}{dx}\left(\frac{\pi}{180}\cos x\right) = -\left(\frac{\pi}{180}\right)^2 \sin x;\ \frac{d^3}{dx^3}(\sin x) = \frac{d}{dx}\left(-\left(\frac{\pi}{180}\right)^2 \sin x\right) = -\left(\frac{\pi}{180}\right)^3 \cos x;$

$\frac{d^2}{dx^2}(\cos x) = \frac{d}{dx}\left(-\frac{\pi}{180}\sin x\right) = -\left(\frac{\pi}{180}\right)^2 \cos x;\ \frac{d^3}{dx^3}(\cos x) = \frac{d}{dx}\left(-\left(\frac{\pi}{180}\right)^2 \cos x\right) = \left(\frac{\pi}{180}\right)^3 \sin x$

## 3.6 THE CHAIN RULE

1. $f(u) = 6u - 9 \Rightarrow f'(u) = 6 \Rightarrow f'(g(x)) = 6;\ g(x) = \frac{1}{2}x^4 \Rightarrow g'(x) = 2x^3;$ therefore $\frac{dy}{dx} = f'(g(x))g'(x) = 6 \cdot 2x^3 = 12x^3$

2. $f(u) = 2u^3 \Rightarrow f'(u) = 6u^2 \Rightarrow f'(g(x)) = 6(8x - 1)^2;\ g(x) = 8x - 1 \Rightarrow g'(x) = 8;$ therefore $\frac{dy}{dx} = f'(g(x))g'(x)$
   $= 6(8x - 1)^2 \cdot 8 = 48(8x - 1)^2$

3. $f(u) = \sin u \Rightarrow f'(u) = \cos u \Rightarrow f'(g(x)) = \cos(3x + 1);\ g(x) = 3x + 1 \Rightarrow g'(x) = 3;$ therefore $\frac{dy}{dx} = f'(g(x))g'(x)$
   $= (\cos(3x + 1))(3) = 3\cos(3x + 1)$

4. $f(u) = \cos u \Rightarrow f'(u) = -\sin u \Rightarrow f'(g(x)) = -\sin\left(\frac{-x}{3}\right);\ g(x) = \frac{-x}{3} \Rightarrow g'(x) = -\frac{1}{3};$ therefore $\frac{dy}{dx} = f'(g(x))g'(x)$
   $= -\sin\left(\frac{-x}{3}\right) \cdot \left(\frac{-1}{3}\right) = \frac{1}{3}\sin\left(\frac{-x}{3}\right)$

5. $f(u) = \cos u \Rightarrow f'(u) = -\sin u \Rightarrow f'(g(x)) = -\sin(\sin x);\ g(x) = \sin x \Rightarrow g'(x) = \cos x;$ therefore
   $\frac{dy}{dx} = f'(g(x))g'(x) = -(\sin(\sin x))\cos x$

6. $f(u) = \sin u \Rightarrow f'(u) = \cos u \Rightarrow f'(g(x)) = \cos(x - \cos x);\ g(x) = x - \cos x \Rightarrow g'(x) = 1 + \sin x;$ therefore
   $\frac{dy}{dx} = f'(g(x))g'(x) = (\cos(x - \cos x))(1 + \sin x)$

7. $f(u) = \tan u \Rightarrow f'(u) = \sec^2 u \Rightarrow f'(g(x)) = \sec^2(10x - 5);\ g(x) = 10x - 5 \Rightarrow g'(x) = 10;$ therefore
   $\frac{dy}{dx} = f'(g(x))g'(x) = (\sec^2(10x - 5))(10) = 10\sec^2(10x - 5)$

8. $f(u) = -\sec u \Rightarrow f'(u) = -\sec u \tan u \Rightarrow f'(g(x)) = -\sec(x^2 + 7x)\tan(x^2 + 7x);\ g(x) = x^2 + 7x$
   $\Rightarrow g'(x) = 2x + 7;$ therefore $\frac{dy}{dx} = f'(g(x))g'(x) = -(2x + 7)\sec(x^2 + 7x)\tan(x^2 + 7x)$

9. With $u = (2x + 1),\ y = u^5$: $\frac{dy}{dx} = \frac{dy}{du}\frac{du}{dx} = 5u^4 \cdot 2 = 10(2x + 1)^4$

10. With $u = (4 - 3x),\ y = u^9$: $\frac{dy}{dx} = \frac{dy}{du}\frac{du}{dx} = 9u^8 \cdot (-3) = -27(4 - 3x)^8$

11. With $u = \left(1 - \frac{x}{7}\right),\ y = u^{-7}$: $\frac{dy}{dx} = \frac{dy}{du}\frac{du}{dx} = -7u^{-8} \cdot \left(-\frac{1}{7}\right) = \left(1 - \frac{x}{7}\right)^{-8}$

12. With $u = \left(\frac{x}{2} - 1\right),\ y = u^{-10}$: $\frac{dy}{dx} = \frac{dy}{du}\frac{du}{dx} = -10u^{-11} \cdot \left(\frac{1}{2}\right) = -5\left(\frac{x}{2} - 1\right)^{-11}$

13. With $u = \left(\frac{x^2}{8} + x - \frac{1}{x}\right),\ y = u^4$: $\frac{dy}{dx} = \frac{dy}{du}\frac{du}{dx} = 4u^3 \cdot \left(\frac{x}{4} + 1 + \frac{1}{x^2}\right) = 4\left(\frac{x^2}{8} + x - \frac{1}{x}\right)^3 \left(\frac{x}{4} + 1 + \frac{1}{x^2}\right)$

14. With $u = 3x^2 - 4x + 6,\ y = u^{1/2}$: $\frac{dy}{dx} = \frac{dy}{du}\frac{du}{dx} = \frac{1}{2}u^{-1/2} \cdot (6x - 4) = \frac{3x - 2}{\sqrt{3x^2 - 4x + 6}}$

15. With $u = \tan x$, $y = \sec u$: $\frac{dy}{dx} = \frac{dy}{du}\frac{du}{dx} = (\sec u \tan u)(\sec^2 x) = (\sec(\tan x)\tan(\tan x))\sec^2 x$

16. With $u = \pi - \frac{1}{x}$, $y = \cot u$: $\frac{dy}{dx} = \frac{dy}{du}\frac{du}{dx} = (-\csc^2 u)\left(\frac{1}{x^2}\right) = -\frac{1}{x^2}\csc^2\left(\pi - \frac{1}{x}\right)$

17. With $u = \sin x$, $y = u^3$: $\frac{dy}{dx} = \frac{dy}{du}\frac{du}{dx} = 3u^2\cos x = 3(\sin^2 x)(\cos x)$

18. With $u = \cos x$, $y = 5u^{-4}$: $\frac{dy}{dx} = \frac{dy}{du}\frac{du}{dx} = (-20u^{-5})(-\sin x) = 20(\cos^{-5}x)(\sin x)$

19. $p = \sqrt{3-t} = (3-t)^{1/2} \Rightarrow \frac{dp}{dt} = \frac{1}{2}(3-t)^{-1/2}\cdot\frac{d}{dt}(3-t) = -\frac{1}{2}(3-t)^{-1/2} = \frac{-1}{2\sqrt{3-t}}$

20. $q = \sqrt[3]{2r-r^2} = (2r-r^2)^{1/3} \Rightarrow \frac{dq}{dr} = \frac{1}{3}(2r-r^2)^{-2/3}\cdot\frac{d}{dr}(2r-r^2) = \frac{1}{3}(2r-r^2)^{-2/3}(2-2r) = \frac{2-2r}{3(2r-r^2)^{2/3}}$

21. $s = \frac{4}{3\pi}\sin 3t + \frac{4}{5\pi}\cos 5t \Rightarrow \frac{ds}{dt} = \frac{4}{3\pi}\cos 3t\cdot\frac{d}{dt}(3t) + \frac{4}{5\pi}(-\sin 5t)\cdot\frac{d}{dt}(5t) = \frac{4}{\pi}\cos 3t - \frac{4}{\pi}\sin 5t$
$= \frac{4}{\pi}(\cos 3t - \sin 5t)$

22. $s = \sin\left(\frac{3\pi t}{2}\right) + \cos\left(\frac{3\pi t}{2}\right) \Rightarrow \frac{ds}{dt} = \cos\left(\frac{3\pi t}{2}\right)\cdot\frac{d}{dt}\left(\frac{3\pi t}{2}\right) - \sin\left(\frac{3\pi t}{2}\right)\cdot\frac{d}{dt}\left(\frac{3\pi t}{2}\right) = \frac{3\pi}{2}\cos\left(\frac{3\pi t}{2}\right) - \frac{3\pi}{2}\sin\left(\frac{3\pi t}{2}\right)$
$= \frac{3\pi}{2}\left(\cos\frac{3\pi t}{2} - \sin\frac{3\pi t}{2}\right)$

23. $r = (\csc\theta + \cot\theta)^{-1} \Rightarrow \frac{dr}{d\theta} = -(\csc\theta + \cot\theta)^{-2}\frac{d}{d\theta}(\csc\theta + \cot\theta) = \frac{\csc\theta\cot\theta + \csc^2\theta}{(\csc\theta + \cot\theta)^2} = \frac{\csc\theta(\cot\theta + \csc\theta)}{(\csc\theta + \cot\theta)^2} = \frac{\csc\theta}{\csc\theta + \cot\theta}$

24. $r = 6(\sec\theta - \tan\theta)^{3/2} \Rightarrow \frac{dr}{d\theta} = 6\cdot\frac{3}{2}(\sec\theta - \tan\theta)^{1/2}\frac{d}{d\theta}(\sec\theta - \tan\theta) = 9\sqrt{\sec\theta - \tan\theta}(\sec\theta\tan\theta - \sec^2\theta)$

25. $y = x^2\sin^4 x + x\cos^{-2}x \Rightarrow \frac{dy}{dx} = x^2\frac{d}{dx}(\sin^4 x) + \sin^4 x\cdot\frac{d}{dx}(x^2) + x\frac{d}{dx}(\cos^{-2}x) + \cos^{-2}x\cdot\frac{d}{dx}(x)$
$= x^2\left(4\sin^3 x\frac{d}{dx}(\sin x)\right) + 2x\sin^4 x + x\left(-2\cos^{-3}x\cdot\frac{d}{dx}(\cos x)\right) + \cos^{-2}x$
$= x^2\left(4\sin^3 x\cos x\right) + 2x\sin^4 x + x((-2\cos^{-3}x)(-\sin x)) + \cos^{-2}x$
$= 4x^2\sin^3 x\cos x + 2x\sin^4 x + 2x\sin x\cos^{-3}x + \cos^{-2}x$

26. $y = \frac{1}{x}\sin^{-5}x - \frac{x}{3}\cos^3 x \Rightarrow y' = \frac{1}{x}\frac{d}{dx}(\sin^{-5}x) + \sin^{-5}x\cdot\frac{d}{dx}\left(\frac{1}{x}\right) - \frac{x}{3}\frac{d}{dx}(\cos^3 x) - \cos^3 x\cdot\frac{d}{dx}\left(\frac{x}{3}\right)$
$= \frac{1}{x}(-5\sin^{-6}x\cos x) + (\sin^{-5}x)\left(-\frac{1}{x^2}\right) - \frac{x}{3}((3\cos^2 x)(-\sin x)) - (\cos^3 x)\left(\frac{1}{3}\right)$
$= -\frac{5}{x}\sin^{-6}x\cos x - \frac{1}{x^2}\sin^{-5}x + x\cos^2 x\sin x - \frac{1}{3}\cos^3 x$

27. $y = \frac{1}{21}(3x-2)^7 + \left(4 - \frac{1}{2x^2}\right)^{-1} \Rightarrow \frac{dy}{dx} = \frac{7}{21}(3x-2)^6\cdot\frac{d}{dx}(3x-2) + (-1)\left(4 - \frac{1}{2x^2}\right)^{-2}\cdot\frac{d}{dx}\left(4 - \frac{1}{2x^2}\right)$
$= \frac{7}{21}(3x-2)^6\cdot 3 + (-1)\left(4 - \frac{1}{2x^2}\right)^{-2}\left(\frac{1}{x^3}\right) = (3x-2)^6 - \frac{1}{x^3\left(4 - \frac{1}{2x^2}\right)^2}$

28. $y = (5-2x)^{-3} + \frac{1}{8}\left(\frac{2}{x}+1\right)^4 \Rightarrow \frac{dy}{dx} = -3(5-2x)^{-4}(-2) + \frac{4}{8}\left(\frac{2}{x}+1\right)^3\left(-\frac{2}{x^2}\right) = 6(5-2x)^{-4} - \left(\frac{1}{x^2}\right)\left(\frac{2}{x}+1\right)^3$
$= \frac{6}{(5-2x)^4} - \frac{\left(\frac{2}{x}+1\right)^3}{x^2}$

29. $y = (4x+3)^4(x+1)^{-3} \Rightarrow \frac{dy}{dx} = (4x+3)^4(-3)(x+1)^{-4}\cdot\frac{d}{dx}(x+1) + (x+1)^{-3}(4)(4x+3)^3\cdot\frac{d}{dx}(4x+3)$
$= (4x+3)^4(-3)(x+1)^{-4}(1) + (x+1)^{-3}(4)(4x+3)^3(4) = -3(4x+3)^4(x+1)^{-4} + 16(4x+3)^3(x+1)^{-3}$
$= \frac{(4x+3)^3}{(x+1)^4}[-3(4x+3) + 16(x+1)] = \frac{(4x+3)^3(4x+7)}{(x+1)^4}$

30. $y = (2x - 5)^{-1} (x^2 - 5x)^6 \Rightarrow \frac{dy}{dx} = (2x - 5)^{-1}(6)(x^2 - 5x)^5(2x - 5) + (x^2 - 5x)^6(-1)(2x - 5)^{-2}(2)$

$= 6(x^2 - 5x)^5 - \frac{2(x^2 - 5x)^6}{(2x - 5)^2}$

31. $h(x) = x \tan(2\sqrt{x}) + 7 \Rightarrow h'(x) = x \frac{d}{dx}\left(\tan(2x^{1/2})\right) + \tan(2x^{1/2}) \cdot \frac{d}{dx}(x) + 0$

$= x \sec^2(2x^{1/2}) \cdot \frac{d}{dx}(2x^{1/2}) + \tan(2x^{1/2}) = x \sec^2(2\sqrt{x}) \cdot \frac{1}{\sqrt{x}} + \tan(2\sqrt{x}) = \sqrt{x} \sec^2(2\sqrt{x}) + \tan(2\sqrt{x})$

32. $k(x) = x^2 \sec\left(\frac{1}{x}\right) \Rightarrow k'(x) = x^2 \frac{d}{dx}\left(\sec\frac{1}{x}\right) + \sec\left(\frac{1}{x}\right) \cdot \frac{d}{dx}(x^2) = x^2 \sec\left(\frac{1}{x}\right)\tan\left(\frac{1}{x}\right) \cdot \frac{d}{dx}\left(\frac{1}{x}\right) + 2x \sec\left(\frac{1}{x}\right)$

$= x^2 \sec\left(\frac{1}{x}\right)\tan\left(\frac{1}{x}\right) \cdot \left(-\frac{1}{x^2}\right) + 2x \sec\left(\frac{1}{x}\right) = 2x \sec\left(\frac{1}{x}\right) - \sec\left(\frac{1}{x}\right)\tan\left(\frac{1}{x}\right)$

33. $f(x) = \sqrt{7 + x \sec x} \Rightarrow f'(x) = \frac{1}{2}(7 + x \sec x)^{-1/2}(x \cdot (\sec x \tan x) + (\sec x) \cdot 1) = \frac{x \sec x \tan x + \sec x}{2\sqrt{7 + x \sec x}}$

34. $g(x) = \frac{\tan 3x}{(x + 7)^4} \Rightarrow g'(x) = \frac{(x + 7)^4(\sec^2 3x \cdot 3) - (\tan 3x)4(x + 7)^3 \cdot 1}{[(x + 7)^4]^2} = \frac{(x + 7)^3(3(x + 7)\sec^2 3x - 4\tan 3x)}{(x + 7)^8}$

$= \frac{(3(x + 7)\sec^2 3x - 4\tan 3x)}{(x + 7)^5}$

35. $f(\theta) = \left(\frac{\sin \theta}{1 + \cos \theta}\right)^2 \Rightarrow f'(\theta) = 2\left(\frac{\sin \theta}{1 + \cos \theta}\right) \cdot \frac{d}{d\theta}\left(\frac{\sin \theta}{1 + \cos \theta}\right) = \frac{2\sin \theta}{1 + \cos \theta} \cdot \frac{(1 + \cos \theta)(\cos \theta) - (\sin \theta)(-\sin \theta)}{(1 + \cos \theta)^2}$

$= \frac{(2\sin \theta)(\cos \theta + \cos^2 \theta + \sin^2 \theta)}{(1 + \cos \theta)^3} = \frac{(2\sin \theta)(\cos \theta + 1)}{(1 + \cos \theta)^3} = \frac{2\sin \theta}{(1 + \cos \theta)^2}$

36. $g(t) = \left(\frac{1 + \sin 3t}{3 - 2t}\right)^{-1} = \frac{3 - 2t}{1 + \sin 3t} \Rightarrow g'(t) = \frac{(1 + \sin 3t)(-2) - (3 - 2t)(3\cos 3t)}{(1 + \sin 3t)^2} = \frac{-2 - 2\sin 3t - 9\cos 3t + 6t\cos 3t}{(1 + \sin 3t)^2}$

37. $r = \sin(\theta^2)\cos(2\theta) \Rightarrow \frac{dr}{d\theta} = \sin(\theta^2)(-\sin 2\theta)\frac{d}{d\theta}(2\theta) + \cos(2\theta)(\cos(\theta^2)) \cdot \frac{d}{d\theta}(\theta^2)$

$= \sin(\theta^2)(-\sin 2\theta)(2) + (\cos 2\theta)(\cos(\theta^2))(2\theta) = -2\sin(\theta^2)\sin(2\theta) + 2\theta\cos(2\theta)\cos(\theta^2)$

38. $r = \left(\sec \sqrt{\theta}\right)\tan\left(\frac{1}{\theta}\right) \Rightarrow \frac{dr}{d\theta} = \left(\sec \sqrt{\theta}\right)\left(\sec^2 \frac{1}{\theta}\right)\left(-\frac{1}{\theta^2}\right) + \tan\left(\frac{1}{\theta}\right)\left(\sec \sqrt{\theta}\tan \sqrt{\theta}\right)\left(\frac{1}{2\sqrt{\theta}}\right)$

$= -\frac{1}{\theta^2}\sec \sqrt{\theta}\sec^2\left(\frac{1}{\theta}\right) + \frac{1}{2\sqrt{\theta}}\tan\left(\frac{1}{\theta}\right)\sec \sqrt{\theta}\tan \sqrt{\theta} = \left(\sec \sqrt{\theta}\right)\left[\frac{\tan \sqrt{\theta}\tan\left(\frac{1}{\theta}\right)}{2\sqrt{\theta}} - \frac{\sec^2\left(\frac{1}{\theta}\right)}{\theta^2}\right]$

39. $q = \sin\left(\frac{t}{\sqrt{t + 1}}\right) \Rightarrow \frac{dq}{dt} = \cos\left(\frac{t}{\sqrt{t + 1}}\right) \cdot \frac{d}{dt}\left(\frac{t}{\sqrt{t + 1}}\right) = \cos\left(\frac{t}{\sqrt{t + 1}}\right) \cdot \frac{\sqrt{t + 1}(1) - t \cdot \frac{d}{dt}\left(\sqrt{t + 1}\right)}{\left(\sqrt{t + 1}\right)^2}$

$= \cos\left(\frac{t}{\sqrt{t + 1}}\right) \cdot \frac{\sqrt{t + 1} - \frac{t}{2\sqrt{t + 1}}}{t + 1} = \cos\left(\frac{t}{\sqrt{t + 1}}\right)\left(\frac{2(t + 1) - t}{2(t + 1)^{3/2}}\right) = \left(\frac{t + 2}{2(t + 1)^{3/2}}\right)\cos\left(\frac{t}{\sqrt{t + 1}}\right)$

40. $q = \cot\left(\frac{\sin t}{t}\right) \Rightarrow \frac{dq}{dt} = -\csc^2\left(\frac{\sin t}{t}\right) \cdot \frac{d}{dt}\left(\frac{\sin t}{t}\right) = \left(-\csc^2\left(\frac{\sin t}{t}\right)\right)\left(\frac{t\cos t - \sin t}{t^2}\right)$

41. $y = \sin^2(\pi t - 2) \Rightarrow \frac{dy}{dt} = 2\sin(\pi t - 2) \cdot \frac{d}{dt}\sin(\pi t - 2) = 2\sin(\pi t - 2) \cdot \cos(\pi t - 2) \cdot \frac{d}{dt}(\pi t - 2)$

$= 2\pi \sin(\pi t - 2)\cos(\pi t - 2)$

42. $y = \sec^2 \pi t \Rightarrow \frac{dy}{dt} = (2\sec \pi t) \cdot \frac{d}{dt}(\sec \pi t) = (2\sec \pi t)(\sec \pi t \tan \pi t) \cdot \frac{d}{dt}(\pi t) = 2\pi \sec^2 \pi t \tan \pi t$

43. $y = (1 + \cos 2t)^{-4} \Rightarrow \frac{dy}{dt} = -4(1 + \cos 2t)^{-5} \cdot \frac{d}{dt}(1 + \cos 2t) = -4(1 + \cos 2t)^{-5}(-\sin 2t) \cdot \frac{d}{dt}(2t) = \frac{8\sin 2t}{(1 + \cos 2t)^5}$

44. $y = \left(1 + \cot\left(\frac{t}{2}\right)\right)^{-2} \Rightarrow \frac{dy}{dt} = -2\left(1 + \cot\left(\frac{t}{2}\right)\right)^{-3} \cdot \frac{d}{dt}\left(1 + \cot\left(\frac{t}{2}\right)\right) = -2\left(1 + \cot\left(\frac{t}{2}\right)\right)^{-3} \cdot \left(-\csc^2\left(\frac{t}{2}\right)\right) \cdot \frac{d}{dt}\left(\frac{t}{2}\right)$

$= \frac{\csc^2\left(\frac{t}{2}\right)}{\left(1 + \cot\left(\frac{t}{2}\right)\right)^3}$

45. $y = (t\tan t)^{10} \Rightarrow \frac{dy}{dt} = 10(t\tan t)^9 (t \cdot \sec^2 t + 1 \cdot \tan t) = 10t^9 \tan^9 t(t\sec^2 t + \tan t) = 10t^{10}\tan^9 t\sec^2 t + 10t^9\tan^{10}t$

46. $y = \left(t^{-3/4}\sin t\right)^{4/3} = t^{-1}(\sin t)^{4/3} \Rightarrow \frac{dy}{dt} = t^{-1}\left(\frac{4}{3}\right)(\sin t)^{1/3}\cos t - t^{-2}(\sin t)^{4/3} = \frac{4(\sin t)^{1/3}\cos t}{3t} - \frac{(\sin t)^{4/3}}{t^2}$

$= \frac{(\sin t)^{1/3}(4t\cos t - 3\cos t)}{3t^2}$

47. $y = \left(\frac{t^2}{t^3-4t}\right)^3 \Rightarrow \frac{dy}{dt} = 3\left(\frac{t^2}{t^3-4t}\right)^2 \cdot \frac{(t^3-4t)(2t) - t^2(3t^2-4)}{(t^3-4t)^2} = \frac{3t^4}{(t^3-4t)^2} \cdot \frac{2t^4 - 8t^2 - 3t^4 + 4t^2}{(t^3-4t)^2} = \frac{3t^4(-t^4-4t^2)}{t^4(t^2-4)^4} = \frac{-3t^2(t^2+4)}{(t^2-4)^4}$

48. $y = \left(\frac{3t-4}{5t+2}\right)^{-5} \Rightarrow \frac{dy}{dt} = -5\left(\frac{3t-4}{5t+2}\right)^{-6} \cdot \frac{(5t+2)\cdot 3 - (3t-4)\cdot 5}{(5t+2)^2} = -5\left(\frac{5t+2}{3t-4}\right)^6 \cdot \frac{15t+6 - 15t+20}{(5t+2)^2} = -5\frac{(5t+2)^6}{(3t-4)^6} \cdot \frac{26}{(5t+2)^2}$

$= \frac{-130(5t+2)^4}{(3t-4)^6}$

49. $y = \sin(\cos(2t-5)) \Rightarrow \frac{dy}{dt} = \cos(\cos(2t-5)) \cdot \frac{d}{dt}\cos(2t-5) = \cos(\cos(2t-5)) \cdot (-\sin(2t-5)) \cdot \frac{d}{dt}(2t-5)$

$= -2\cos(\cos(2t-5))(\sin(2t-5))$

50. $y = \cos\left(5\sin\left(\frac{t}{3}\right)\right) \Rightarrow \frac{dy}{dt} = -\sin\left(5\sin\left(\frac{t}{3}\right)\right) \cdot \frac{d}{dt}\left(5\sin\left(\frac{t}{3}\right)\right) = -\sin\left(5\sin\left(\frac{t}{3}\right)\right)\left(5\cos\left(\frac{t}{3}\right)\right) \cdot \frac{d}{dt}\left(\frac{t}{3}\right)$

$= -\frac{5}{3}\sin\left(5\sin\left(\frac{t}{3}\right)\right)\left(\cos\left(\frac{t}{3}\right)\right)$

51. $y = \left[1+\tan^4\left(\frac{t}{12}\right)\right]^3 \Rightarrow \frac{dy}{dt} = 3\left[1+\tan^4\left(\frac{t}{12}\right)\right]^2 \cdot \frac{d}{dt}\left[1+\tan^4\left(\frac{t}{12}\right)\right] = 3\left[1+\tan^4\left(\frac{t}{12}\right)\right]^2\left[4\tan^3\left(\frac{t}{12}\right) \cdot \frac{d}{dt}\tan\left(\frac{t}{12}\right)\right]$

$= 12\left[1+\tan^4\left(\frac{t}{12}\right)\right]^2\left[\tan^3\left(\frac{t}{12}\right)\sec^2\left(\frac{t}{12}\right) \cdot \frac{1}{12}\right] = \left[1+\tan^4\left(\frac{t}{12}\right)\right]^2\left[\tan^3\left(\frac{t}{12}\right)\sec^2\left(\frac{t}{12}\right)\right]$

52. $y = \frac{1}{6}\left[1+\cos^2(7t)\right]^3 \Rightarrow \frac{dy}{dt} = \frac{3}{6}\left[1+\cos^2(7t)\right]^2 \cdot 2\cos(7t)(-\sin(7t))(7) = -7\left[1+\cos^2(7t)\right]^2(\cos(7t)\sin(7t))$

53. $y = \left(1+\cos(t^2)\right)^{1/2} \Rightarrow \frac{dy}{dt} = \frac{1}{2}\left(1+\cos(t^2)\right)^{-1/2} \cdot \frac{d}{dt}\left(1+\cos(t^2)\right) = \frac{1}{2}\left(1+\cos(t^2)\right)^{-1/2}\left(-\sin(t^2) \cdot \frac{d}{dt}(t^2)\right)$

$= -\frac{1}{2}\left(1+\cos(t^2)\right)^{-1/2}(\sin(t^2)) \cdot 2t = -\frac{t\sin(t^2)}{\sqrt{1+\cos(t^2)}}$

54. $y = 4\sin\left(\sqrt{1+\sqrt{t}}\right) \Rightarrow \frac{dy}{dt} = 4\cos\left(\sqrt{1+\sqrt{t}}\right) \cdot \frac{d}{dt}\left(\sqrt{1+\sqrt{t}}\right) = 4\cos\left(\sqrt{1+\sqrt{t}}\right) \cdot \frac{1}{2\sqrt{1+\sqrt{t}}} \cdot \frac{d}{dt}\left(1+\sqrt{t}\right)$

$= \frac{2\cos\left(\sqrt{1+\sqrt{t}}\right)}{\sqrt{1+\sqrt{t}}\cdot 2\sqrt{t}} = \frac{\cos\left(\sqrt{1+\sqrt{t}}\right)}{\sqrt{t+t\sqrt{t}}}$

55. $y = \tan^2(\sin^3 t) \Rightarrow \frac{dy}{dt} = 2\tan(\sin^3 t) \cdot \sec^2(\sin^3 t) \cdot (3\sin^2 t \cdot (\cos t)) = 6\tan(\sin^3 t)\sec^2(\sin^3 t)\sin^2 t\cos t$

56. $y = \cos^4(\sec^2 3t) \Rightarrow \frac{dy}{dt} = 4\cos^3(\sec^2(3t))(-\sin(\sec^2(3t)) \cdot 2(\sec(3t))(\sec(3t)\tan(3t)\cdot 3))$

$= -24\cos^3(\sec^2(3t))\sin(\sec^2(3t))\sec^2(3t)\tan(3t)$

57. $y = 3t(2t^2-5)^4 \Rightarrow \frac{dy}{dt} = 3t \cdot 4(2t^2-5)^3(4t) + 3 \cdot (2t^2-5)^4 = 3(2t^2-5)^3\left[16t^2 + 2t^2 - 5\right] = 3(2t^2-5)^3(18t^2-5)$

58. $y = \sqrt{3t+\sqrt{2+\sqrt{1-t}}} \Rightarrow \frac{dy}{dt} = \frac{1}{2}\left(3t+\sqrt{2+\sqrt{1-t}}\right)^{-1/2}\left(3 + \frac{1}{2}\left(2+\sqrt{1-t}\right)^{-1/2}\frac{1}{2}(1-t)^{-1/2}(-1)\right)$

$= \frac{1}{2\sqrt{3t+\sqrt{2+\sqrt{1-t}}}}\left(3 + \frac{1}{2\sqrt{2+\sqrt{1-t}}} \cdot \frac{-1}{2\sqrt{1-t}}\right) = \frac{1}{2\sqrt{3t+\sqrt{2+\sqrt{1-t}}}}\left(\frac{12\sqrt{1-t}\sqrt{2+\sqrt{1-t}}-1}{4\sqrt{1-t}\sqrt{2+\sqrt{1-t}}}\right) = \frac{12\sqrt{1-t}\sqrt{2+\sqrt{1-t}}-1}{8\sqrt{1-t}\sqrt{2+\sqrt{1-t}}\sqrt{3t+\sqrt{2+\sqrt{1-t}}}}$

59. $y = \left(1 + \frac{1}{x}\right)^3 \Rightarrow y' = 3\left(1 + \frac{1}{x}\right)^2\left(-\frac{1}{x^2}\right) = -\frac{3}{x^2}\left(1 + \frac{1}{x}\right)^2 \Rightarrow y'' = \left(-\frac{3}{x^2}\right) \cdot \frac{d}{dx}\left(1 + \frac{1}{x}\right)^2 - \left(1 + \frac{1}{x}\right)^2 \cdot \frac{d}{dx}\left(\frac{3}{x^2}\right)$

$= \left(-\frac{3}{x^2}\right)\left(2\left(1 + \frac{1}{x}\right)\left(-\frac{1}{x^2}\right)\right) + \left(\frac{6}{x^3}\right)\left(1 + \frac{1}{x}\right)^2 = \frac{6}{x^4}\left(1 + \frac{1}{x}\right) + \frac{6}{x^3}\left(1 + \frac{1}{x}\right)^2 = \frac{6}{x^3}\left(1 + \frac{1}{x}\right)\left(\frac{1}{x} + 1 + \frac{1}{x}\right)$

$= \frac{6}{x^3}\left(1 + \frac{1}{x}\right)\left(1 + \frac{2}{x}\right)$

60. $y = \left(1 - \sqrt{x}\right)^{-1} \Rightarrow y' = -\left(1 - \sqrt{x}\right)^{-2}\left(-\frac{1}{2}x^{-1/2}\right) = \frac{1}{2}\left(1 - \sqrt{x}\right)^{-2}x^{-1/2}$

$\Rightarrow y'' = \frac{1}{2}\left[\left(1 - \sqrt{x}\right)^{-2}\left(-\frac{1}{2}x^{-3/2}\right) + x^{-1/2}(-2)\left(1 - \sqrt{x}\right)^{-3}\left(-\frac{1}{2}x^{-1/2}\right)\right]$

$= \frac{1}{2}\left[\frac{-1}{2}x^{-3/2}\left(1 - \sqrt{x}\right)^{-2} + x^{-1}\left(1 - \sqrt{x}\right)^{-3}\right] = \frac{1}{2}x^{-1}\left(1 - \sqrt{x}\right)^{-3}\left[-\frac{1}{2}x^{-1/2}\left(1 - \sqrt{x}\right) + 1\right]$

$= \frac{1}{2x}\left(1 - \sqrt{x}\right)^{-3}\left(-\frac{1}{2\sqrt{x}} + \frac{1}{2} + 1\right) = \frac{1}{2x}\left(1 - \sqrt{x}\right)^{-3}\left(\frac{3}{2} - \frac{1}{2\sqrt{x}}\right)$

61. $y = \frac{1}{9}\cot(3x - 1) \Rightarrow y' = -\frac{1}{9}\csc^2(3x - 1)(3) = -\frac{1}{3}\csc^2(3x - 1) \Rightarrow y'' = \left(-\frac{2}{3}\right)(\csc(3x - 1) \cdot \frac{d}{dx}\csc(3x - 1))$

$= -\frac{2}{3}\csc(3x - 1)(-\csc(3x - 1)\cot(3x - 1) \cdot \frac{d}{dx}(3x - 1)) = 2\csc^2(3x - 1)\cot(3x - 1)$

62. $y = 9\tan\left(\frac{x}{3}\right) \Rightarrow y' = 9\left(\sec^2\left(\frac{x}{3}\right)\right)\left(\frac{1}{3}\right) = 3\sec^2\left(\frac{x}{3}\right) \Rightarrow y'' = 3 \cdot 2\sec\left(\frac{x}{3}\right)\left(\sec\left(\frac{x}{3}\right)\tan\left(\frac{x}{3}\right)\right)\left(\frac{1}{3}\right) = 2\sec^2\left(\frac{x}{3}\right)\tan\left(\frac{x}{3}\right)$

63. $y = x(2x + 1)^4 \Rightarrow y' = x \cdot 4(2x + 1)^3(2) + 1 \cdot (2x + 1)^4 = (2x + 1)^3(8x + (2x + 1)) = (2x + 1)^3(10x + 1)$

$\Rightarrow y'' = (2x + 1)^3(10) + 3(2x + 1)^2(2)(10x + 1) = 2(2x + 1)^2(5(2x + 1) + 3(10x + 1)) = 2(2x + 1)^2(40x + 8)$

$= 16(2x + 1)^2(5x + 1)$

64. $y = x^2(x^3 - 1)^5 \Rightarrow y' = x^2 \cdot 5(x^3 - 1)^4(3x^2) + 2x(x^3 - 1)^5 = x(x^3 - 1)^4\left[15x^3 + 2(x^3 - 1)\right] = (x^3 - 1)^4(17x^4 - 2x)$

$\Rightarrow y'' = (x^3 - 1)^4(68x^3 - 2) + 4(x^3 - 1)^3(3x^2)(17x^4 - 2x) = 2(x^3 - 1)^3\left[(x^3 - 1)(34x^3 - 1) + 6x^2(17x^4 - 2x)\right]$

$= 2(x^3 - 1)^3(136x^6 - 47x^3 + 1)$

65. $g(x) = \sqrt{x} \Rightarrow g'(x) = \frac{1}{2\sqrt{x}} \Rightarrow g(1) = 1$ and $g'(1) = \frac{1}{2}$; $f(u) = u^5 + 1 \Rightarrow f'(u) = 5u^4 \Rightarrow f'(g(1)) = f'(1) = 5$;

therefore, $(f \circ g)'(1) = f'(g(1)) \cdot g'(1) = 5 \cdot \frac{1}{2} = \frac{5}{2}$

66. $g(x) = (1 - x)^{-1} \Rightarrow g'(x) = -(1 - x)^{-2}(-1) = \frac{1}{(1-x)^2} \Rightarrow g(-1) = \frac{1}{2}$ and $g'(-1) = \frac{1}{4}$; $f(u) = 1 - \frac{1}{u}$

$\Rightarrow f'(u) = \frac{1}{u^2} \Rightarrow f'(g(-1)) = f'\left(\frac{1}{2}\right) = 4$; therefore, $(f \circ g)'(-1) = f'(g(-1))g'(-1) = 4 \cdot \frac{1}{4} = 1$

67. $g(x) = 5\sqrt{x} \Rightarrow g'(x) = \frac{5}{2\sqrt{x}} \Rightarrow g(1) = 5$ and $g'(1) = \frac{5}{2}$; $f(u) = \cot\left(\frac{\pi u}{10}\right) \Rightarrow f'(u) = -\csc^2\left(\frac{\pi u}{10}\right)\left(\frac{\pi}{10}\right) = \frac{-\pi}{10}\csc^2\left(\frac{\pi u}{10}\right)$

$\Rightarrow f'(g(1)) = f'(5) = -\frac{\pi}{10}\csc^2\left(\frac{\pi}{2}\right) = -\frac{\pi}{10}$; therefore, $(f \circ g)'(1) = f'(g(1))g'(1) = -\frac{\pi}{10} \cdot \frac{5}{2} = -\frac{\pi}{4}$

68. $g(x) = \pi x \Rightarrow g'(x) = \pi \Rightarrow g\left(\frac{1}{4}\right) = \frac{\pi}{4}$ and $g'\left(\frac{1}{4}\right) = \pi$; $f(u) = u + \sec^2 u \Rightarrow f'(u) = 1 + 2\sec u \cdot \sec u \tan u$

$= 1 + 2\sec^2 u \tan u \Rightarrow f'\left(g\left(\frac{1}{4}\right)\right) = f'\left(\frac{\pi}{4}\right) = 1 + 2\sec^2\frac{\pi}{4}\tan\frac{\pi}{4} = 5$; therefore, $(f \circ g)'\left(\frac{1}{4}\right) = f'\left(g\left(\frac{1}{4}\right)\right)g'\left(\frac{1}{4}\right) = 5\pi$

69. $g(x) = 10x^2 + x + 1 \Rightarrow g'(x) = 20x + 1 \Rightarrow g(0) = 1$ and $g'(0) = 1$; $f(u) = \frac{2u}{u^2 + 1} \Rightarrow f'(u) = \frac{(u^2 + 1)(2) - (2u)(2u)}{(u^2 + 1)^2}$

$= \frac{-2u^2 + 2}{(u^2 + 1)^2} \Rightarrow f'(g(0)) = f'(1) = 0$; therefore, $(f \circ g)'(0) = f'(g(0))g'(0) = 0 \cdot 1 = 0$

70. $g(x) = \frac{1}{x^2} - 1 \Rightarrow g'(x) = -\frac{2}{x^3} \Rightarrow g(-1) = 0$ and $g'(-1) = 2$; $f(u) = \left(\frac{u-1}{u+1}\right)^2 \Rightarrow f'(u) = 2\left(\frac{u-1}{u+1}\right)\frac{d}{du}\left(\frac{u-1}{u+1}\right)$

$= 2\left(\frac{u-1}{u+1}\right) \cdot \frac{(u+1)(1) - (u-1)(1)}{(u+1)^2} = \frac{2(u-1)(2)}{(u+1)^3} = \frac{4(u-1)}{(u+1)^3} \Rightarrow f'(g(-1)) = f'(0) = -4$; therefore,

$(f \circ g)'(-1) = f'(g(-1))g'(-1) = (-4)(2) = -8$

71. $y = f(g(x)), f'(3) = -1, g'(2) = 5, g(2) = 3 \Rightarrow y' = f'(g(x))g'(x) \Rightarrow y'\big|_{x=2} = f'(g(2))g'(2) = f'(3) \cdot 5$

    $= (-1) \cdot 5 = -5$

72. $r = \sin(f(t)), f(0) = \frac{\pi}{3}, f'(0) = 4 \Rightarrow \frac{dr}{dt} = \cos(f(t)) \cdot f'(t) \Rightarrow \frac{dr}{dt}\big|_{t=0} = \cos(f(0)) \cdot f'(0) = \cos\left(\frac{\pi}{3}\right) \cdot 4 = \left(\frac{1}{2}\right) \cdot 4 = 2$

73. (a) $y = 2f(x) \Rightarrow \frac{dy}{dx} = 2f'(x) \Rightarrow \frac{dy}{dx}\big|_{x=2} = 2f'(2) = 2\left(\frac{1}{3}\right) = \frac{2}{3}$

    (b) $y = f(x) + g(x) \Rightarrow \frac{dy}{dx} = f'(x) + g'(x) \Rightarrow \frac{dy}{dx}\big|_{x=3} = f'(3) + g'(3) = 2\pi + 5$

    (c) $y = f(x) \cdot g(x) \Rightarrow \frac{dy}{dx} = f(x)g'(x) + g(x)f'(x) \Rightarrow \frac{dy}{dx}\big|_{x=3} = f(3)g'(3) + g(3)f'(3) = 3 \cdot 5 + (-4)(2\pi) = 15 - 8\pi$

    (d) $y = \frac{f(x)}{g(x)} \Rightarrow \frac{dy}{dx} = \frac{g(x)f'(x) - f(x)g'(x)}{[g(x)]^2} \Rightarrow \frac{dy}{dx}\big|_{x=2} = \frac{g(2)f'(2) - f(2)g'(2)}{[g(2)]^2} = \frac{(2)\left(\frac{1}{3}\right) - (8)(-3)}{2^2} = \frac{37}{6}$

    (e) $y = f(g(x)) \Rightarrow \frac{dy}{dx} = f'(g(x))g'(x) \Rightarrow \frac{dy}{dx}\big|_{x=2} = f'(g(2))g'(2) = f'(2)(-3) = \frac{1}{3}(-3) = -1$

    (f) $y = (f(x))^{1/2} \Rightarrow \frac{dy}{dx} = \frac{1}{2}(f(x))^{-1/2} \cdot f'(x) = \frac{f'(x)}{2\sqrt{f(x)}} \Rightarrow \frac{dy}{dx}\big|_{x=2} = \frac{f'(2)}{2\sqrt{f(2)}} = \frac{\left(\frac{1}{3}\right)}{2\sqrt{8}} = \frac{1}{6\sqrt{8}} = \frac{1}{12\sqrt{2}} = \frac{\sqrt{2}}{24}$

    (g) $y = (g(x))^{-2} \Rightarrow \frac{dy}{dx} = -2(g(x))^{-3} \cdot g'(x) \Rightarrow \frac{dy}{dx}\big|_{x=3} = -2(g(3))^{-3}g'(3) = -2(-4)^{-3} \cdot 5 = \frac{5}{32}$

    (h) $y = \left((f(x))^2 + (g(x))^2\right)^{1/2} \Rightarrow \frac{dy}{dx} = \frac{1}{2}\left((f(x))^2 + (g(x))^2\right)^{-1/2}(2f(x) \cdot f'(x) + 2g(x) \cdot g'(x))$

    $\Rightarrow \frac{dy}{dx}\big|_{x=2} = \frac{1}{2}\left((f(2))^2 + (g(2))^2\right)^{-1/2}(2f(2)f'(2) + 2g(2)g'(2)) = \frac{1}{2}\left(8^2 + 2^2\right)^{-1/2}\left(2 \cdot 8 \cdot \frac{1}{3} + 2 \cdot 2 \cdot (-3)\right) = -\frac{5}{3\sqrt{17}}$

74. (a) $y = 5f(x) - g(x) \Rightarrow \frac{dy}{dx} = 5f'(x) - g'(x) \Rightarrow \frac{dy}{dx}\big|_{x=1} = 5f'(1) - g'(1) = 5\left(-\frac{1}{3}\right) - \left(\frac{-8}{3}\right) = 1$

    (b) $y = f(x)(g(x))^3 \Rightarrow \frac{dy}{dx} = f(x)\left(3(g(x))^2g'(x)\right) + (g(x))^3f'(x) \Rightarrow \frac{dy}{dx}\big|_{x=0} = 3f(0)(g(0))^2g'(0) + (g(0))^3f'(0)$

    $= 3(1)(1)^2\left(\frac{1}{3}\right) + (1)^3(5) = 6$

    (c) $y = \frac{f(x)}{g(x)+1} \Rightarrow \frac{dy}{dx} = \frac{(g(x)+1)f'(x) - f(x)g'(x)}{(g(x)+1)^2} \Rightarrow \frac{dy}{dx}\big|_{x=1} = \frac{(g(1)+1)f'(1) - f(1)g'(1)}{(g(1)+1)^2}$

    $= \frac{(-4+1)\left(-\frac{1}{3}\right) - (3)\left(-\frac{8}{3}\right)}{(-4+1)^2} = 1$

    (d) $y = f(g(x)) \Rightarrow \frac{dy}{dx} = f'(g(x))g'(x) \Rightarrow \frac{dy}{dx}\big|_{x=0} = f'(g(0))g'(0) = f'(1)\left(\frac{1}{3}\right) = \left(-\frac{1}{3}\right)\left(\frac{1}{3}\right) = -\frac{1}{9}$

    (e) $y = g(f(x)) \Rightarrow \frac{dy}{dx} = g'(f(x))f'(x) \Rightarrow \frac{dy}{dx}\big|_{x=0} = g'(f(0))f'(0) = g'(1)(5) = \left(-\frac{8}{3}\right)(5) = -\frac{40}{3}$

    (f) $y = \left(x^{11} + f(x)\right)^{-2} \Rightarrow \frac{dy}{dx} = -2\left(x^{11} + f(x)\right)^{-3}\left(11x^{10} + f'(x)\right) \Rightarrow \frac{dy}{dx}\big|_{x=1} = -2(1 + f(1))^{-3}(11 + f'(1))$

    $= -2(1+3)^{-3}\left(11 - \frac{1}{3}\right) = \left(-\frac{2}{4^3}\right)\left(\frac{32}{3}\right) = -\frac{1}{3}$

    (g) $y = f(x + g(x)) \Rightarrow \frac{dy}{dx} = f'(x + g(x))(1 + g'(x)) \Rightarrow \frac{dy}{dx}\big|_{x=0} = f'(0 + g(0))(1 + g'(0)) = f'(1)\left(1 + \frac{1}{3}\right)$

    $= \left(-\frac{1}{3}\right)\left(\frac{4}{3}\right) = -\frac{4}{9}$

75. $\frac{ds}{dt} = \frac{ds}{d\theta} \cdot \frac{d\theta}{dt}: s = \cos\theta \Rightarrow \frac{ds}{d\theta} = -\sin\theta \Rightarrow \frac{ds}{d\theta}\big|_{\theta=\frac{3\pi}{2}} = -\sin\left(\frac{3\pi}{2}\right) = 1$ so that $\frac{ds}{dt} = \frac{ds}{d\theta} \cdot \frac{d\theta}{dt} = 1 \cdot 5 = 5$

76. $\frac{dy}{dt} = \frac{dy}{dx} \cdot \frac{dx}{dt}: y = x^2 + 7x - 5 \Rightarrow \frac{dy}{dx} = 2x + 7 \Rightarrow \frac{dy}{dx}\big|_{x=1} = 9$ so that $\frac{dy}{dt} = \frac{dy}{dx} \cdot \frac{dx}{dt} = 9 \cdot \frac{1}{3} = 3$

77. With $y = x$, we should get $\frac{dy}{dx} = 1$ for both (a) and (b):

    (a) $y = \frac{u}{5} + 7 \Rightarrow \frac{dy}{du} = \frac{1}{5}; u = 5x - 35 \Rightarrow \frac{du}{dx} = 5$; therefore, $\frac{dy}{dx} = \frac{dy}{du} \cdot \frac{du}{dx} = \frac{1}{5} \cdot 5 = 1$, as expected

    (b) $y = 1 + \frac{1}{u} \Rightarrow \frac{dy}{du} = -\frac{1}{u^2}; u = (x-1)^{-1} \Rightarrow \frac{du}{dx} = -(x-1)^{-2}(1) = \frac{-1}{(x-1)^2}$; therefore $\frac{dy}{dx} = \frac{dy}{du} \cdot \frac{du}{dx}$

    $= \frac{-1}{u^2} \cdot \frac{-1}{(x-1)^2} = \frac{-1}{\left((x-1)^{-1}\right)^2} \cdot \frac{-1}{(x-1)^2} = (x-1)^2 \cdot \frac{1}{(x-1)^2} = 1$, again as expected

78. With $y = x^{3/2}$, we should get $\frac{dy}{dx} = \frac{3}{2} x^{1/2}$ for both (a) and (b):

(a) $y = u^3 \Rightarrow \frac{dy}{du} = 3u^2; u = \sqrt{x} \Rightarrow \frac{du}{dx} = \frac{1}{2\sqrt{x}}$; therefore, $\frac{dy}{dx} = \frac{dy}{du} \cdot \frac{du}{dx} = 3u^2 \cdot \frac{1}{2\sqrt{x}} = 3\left(\sqrt{x}\right)^2 \cdot \frac{1}{2\sqrt{x}} = \frac{3}{2}\sqrt{x}$,

as expected.

(b) $y = \sqrt{u} \Rightarrow \frac{dy}{du} = \frac{1}{2\sqrt{u}}; u = x^3 \Rightarrow \frac{du}{dx} = 3x^2$; therefore, $\frac{dy}{dx} = \frac{dy}{du} \cdot \frac{du}{dx} = \frac{1}{2\sqrt{u}} \cdot 3x^2 = \frac{1}{2\sqrt{x^3}} \cdot 3x^2 = \frac{3}{2} x^{1/2}$,

again as expected.

79. $y = \left(\frac{x-1}{x+1}\right)^2$ and $x = 0 \Rightarrow y = \left(\frac{0-1}{0+1}\right)^2 = (-1)^2 = 1.$ $y' = 2\left(\frac{x-1}{x+1}\right) \cdot \frac{(x+1)\cdot 1 - (x-1)\cdot 1}{(x+1)^2} = 2\frac{(x-1)}{(x+1)}\frac{2}{(x+1)^2} = \frac{4(x-1)}{(x+1)^3}$

$y'\Big|_{x=0} = \frac{4(0-1)}{(0+1)^3} = \frac{-4}{1^3} = -4 \Rightarrow y - 1 = -4(x-0) \Rightarrow y = -4x + 1$

80. $y = \sqrt{x^2 - x + 7}$ and $x = 2 \Rightarrow y = \sqrt{(2)^2 - (2) + 7} = \sqrt{9} = 3.$ $y' = \frac{1}{2}(x^2 - x + 7)^{-1/2}(2x - 1) = \frac{2x-1}{2\sqrt{x^2-x+7}}$

$y'\Big|_{x=2} = \frac{2(2)-1}{2\sqrt{(2)^2-(2)+7}} = \frac{3}{6} = \frac{1}{2} \Rightarrow y - 3 = \frac{1}{2}(x-2) \Rightarrow y = \frac{1}{2}x + 2$

81. $y = 2\tan\left(\frac{\pi x}{4}\right) \Rightarrow \frac{dy}{dx} = \left(2\sec^2\frac{\pi x}{4}\right)\left(\frac{\pi}{4}\right) = \frac{\pi}{2}\sec^2\frac{\pi x}{4}$

(a) $\frac{dy}{dx}\Big|_{x=1} = \frac{\pi}{2}\sec^2\left(\frac{\pi}{4}\right) = \pi \Rightarrow$ slope of tangent is 2; thus, $y(1) = 2\tan\left(\frac{\pi}{4}\right) = 2$ and $y'(1) = \pi \Rightarrow$ tangent line is

given by $y - 2 = \pi(x - 1) \Rightarrow y = \pi x + 2 - \pi$

(b) $y' = \frac{\pi}{2}\sec^2\left(\frac{\pi x}{4}\right)$ and the smallest value the secant function can have in $-2 < x < 2$ is $1 \Rightarrow$ the minimum

value of $y'$ is $\frac{\pi}{2}$ and that occurs when $\frac{\pi}{2} = \frac{\pi}{2}\sec^2\left(\frac{\pi x}{4}\right) \Rightarrow 1 = \sec^2\left(\frac{\pi x}{4}\right) \Rightarrow \pm 1 = \sec\left(\frac{\pi x}{4}\right) \Rightarrow x = 0.$

82. (a) $y = \sin 2x \Rightarrow y' = 2\cos 2x \Rightarrow y'(0) = 2\cos(0) = 2 \Rightarrow$ tangent to $y = \sin 2x$ at the origin is $y = 2x$;

$y = -\sin\left(\frac{x}{2}\right) \Rightarrow y' = -\frac{1}{2}\cos\left(\frac{x}{2}\right) \Rightarrow y'(0) = -\frac{1}{2}\cos 0 = -\frac{1}{2} \Rightarrow$ tangent to $y = -\sin\left(\frac{x}{2}\right)$ at the origin is

$y = -\frac{1}{2}x$. The tangents are perpendicular to each other at the origin since the product of their slopes is $-1$.

(b) $y = \sin(mx) \Rightarrow y' = m\cos(mx) \Rightarrow y'(0) = m\cos 0 = m; y = -\sin\left(\frac{x}{m}\right) \Rightarrow y' = -\frac{1}{m}\cos\left(\frac{x}{m}\right)$

$\Rightarrow y'(0) = -\frac{1}{m}\cos(0) = -\frac{1}{m}$. Since $m \cdot \left(-\frac{1}{m}\right) = -1$, the tangent lines are perpendicular at the origin.

(c) $y = \sin(mx) \Rightarrow y' = m\cos(mx)$. The largest value $\cos(mx)$ can attain is 1 at $x = 0 \Rightarrow$ the largest value

$y'$ can attain is $|m|$ because $|y'| = |m\cos(mx)| = |m||\cos mx| \leq |m| \cdot 1 = |m|$. Also, $y = -\sin\left(\frac{x}{m}\right)$

$\Rightarrow y' = -\frac{1}{m}\cos\left(\frac{x}{m}\right) \Rightarrow |y'| = \left|\frac{-1}{m}\cos\left(\frac{x}{m}\right)\right| \leq \left|\frac{1}{m}\right|\left|\cos\left(\frac{x}{m}\right)\right| \leq \frac{1}{|m|} \Rightarrow$ the largest value $y'$ can attain is $\left|\frac{1}{m}\right|$.

(d) $y = \sin(mx) \Rightarrow y' = m\cos(mx) \Rightarrow y'(0) = m \Rightarrow$ slope of curve at the origin is m. Also, $\sin(mx)$ completes

m periods on $[0, 2\pi]$. Therefore the slope of the curve $y = \sin(mx)$ at the origin is the same as the number

of periods it completes on $[0, 2\pi]$. In particular, for large m, we can think of "compressing" the graph of

$y = \sin x$ horizontally which gives more periods completed on $[0, 2\pi]$, but also increases the slope of the

graph at the origin.

83. $s = A\cos(2\pi bt) \Rightarrow v = \frac{ds}{dt} = -A\sin(2\pi bt)(2\pi b) = -2\pi bA\sin(2\pi bt)$. If we replace b with 2b to double the

frequency, the velocity formula gives $v = -4\pi bA\sin(4\pi bt) \Rightarrow$ doubling the frequency causes the velocity to

double. Also $v = -2\pi bA\sin(2\pi bt) \Rightarrow a = \frac{dv}{dt} = -4\pi^2 b^2 A\cos(2\pi bt)$. If we replace b with 2b in the

acceleration formula, we get $a = -16\pi^2 b^2 A\cos(4\pi bt) \Rightarrow$ doubling the frequency causes the acceleration to

quadruple. Finally, $a = -4\pi^2 b^2 A\cos(2\pi bt) \Rightarrow j = \frac{da}{dt} = 8\pi^3 b^3 A\sin(2\pi bt)$. If we replace b with 2b in the jerk

formula, we get $j = 64\pi^3 b^3 A\sin(4\pi bt) \Rightarrow$ doubling the frequency multiplies the jerk by a factor of 8.

84. (a) $y = 37\sin\left[\frac{2\pi}{365}(x - 101)\right] + 25 \Rightarrow y' = 37\cos\left[\frac{2\pi}{365}(x - 101)\right]\left(\frac{2\pi}{365}\right) = \frac{74\pi}{365}\cos\left[\frac{2\pi}{365}(x - 101)\right].$

The temperature is increasing the fastest when $y'$ is as large as possible. The largest value of

$\cos\left[\frac{2\pi}{365}(x - 101)\right]$ is 1 and occurs when $\frac{2\pi}{365}(x - 101) = 0 \Rightarrow x = 101 \Rightarrow$ on day 101 of the year

($\sim$ April 11), the temperature is increasing the fastest.

(b)  $y'(101) = \frac{74\pi}{365} \cos\left[\frac{2\pi}{365}(101 - 101)\right] = \frac{74\pi}{365} \cos(0) = \frac{74\pi}{365} \approx 0.64$ °F/day

85.  $s = (1 + 4t)^{1/2} \Rightarrow v = \frac{ds}{dt} = \frac{1}{2}(1 + 4t)^{-1/2}(4) = 2(1 + 4t)^{-1/2} \Rightarrow v(6) = 2(1 + 4 \cdot 6)^{-1/2} = \frac{2}{5}$ m/sec;

$v = 2(1 + 4t)^{-1/2} \Rightarrow a = \frac{dv}{dt} = -\frac{1}{2} \cdot 2(1 + 4t)^{-3/2}(4) = -4(1 + 4t)^{-3/2} \Rightarrow a(6) = -4(1 + 4 \cdot 6)^{-3/2} = -\frac{4}{125}$ m/sec$^2$

86.  We need to show $a = \frac{dv}{dt}$ is constant: $a = \frac{dv}{dt} = \frac{dv}{ds} \cdot \frac{ds}{dt}$ and $\frac{dv}{ds} = \frac{d}{ds}\left(k\sqrt{s}\right) = \frac{k}{2\sqrt{s}} \Rightarrow a = \frac{dv}{ds} \cdot \frac{ds}{dt} = \frac{dv}{ds} \cdot v$

$= \frac{k}{2\sqrt{s}} \cdot k\sqrt{s} = \frac{k^2}{2}$ which is a constant.

87.  $v$ proportional to $\frac{1}{\sqrt{s}} \Rightarrow v = \frac{k}{\sqrt{s}}$ for some constant $k \Rightarrow \frac{dv}{ds} = -\frac{k}{2s^{3/2}}$. Thus, $a = \frac{dv}{dt} = \frac{dv}{ds} \cdot \frac{ds}{dt} = \frac{dv}{ds} \cdot v$

$= -\frac{k}{2s^{3/2}} \cdot \frac{k}{\sqrt{s}} = -\frac{k^2}{2}\left(\frac{1}{s^2}\right) \Rightarrow$ acceleration is a constant times $\frac{1}{s^2}$ so $a$ is inversely proportional to $s^2$.

88.  Let $\frac{dx}{dt} = f(x)$. Then, $a = \frac{dv}{dt} = \frac{dv}{dx} \cdot \frac{dx}{dt} = \frac{dv}{dx} \cdot f(x) = \frac{d}{dx}\left(\frac{dx}{dt}\right) \cdot f(x) = \frac{d}{dx}(f(x)) \cdot f(x) = f'(x)f(x)$, as required.

89.  $T = 2\pi\sqrt{\frac{L}{g}} \Rightarrow \frac{dT}{dL} = 2\pi \cdot \frac{1}{2\sqrt{\frac{L}{g}}} \cdot \frac{1}{g} = \frac{\pi}{g\sqrt{\frac{L}{g}}} = \frac{\pi}{\sqrt{gL}}$. Therefore, $\frac{dT}{du} = \frac{dT}{dL} \cdot \frac{dL}{du} = \frac{\pi}{\sqrt{gL}} \cdot kL = \frac{\pi k\sqrt{L}}{\sqrt{g}} = \frac{1}{2} \cdot 2\pi k\sqrt{\frac{L}{g}}$

$= \frac{kT}{2}$, as required.

90.  No.  The chain rule says that when g is differentiable at 0 and f is differentiable at g(0), then f ∘ g is differentiable at 0.  But the chain rule says nothing about what happens when g is not differentiable at 0 so there is no contradiction.

91.  As $h \to 0$, the graph of $y = \frac{\sin 2(x+h) - \sin 2x}{h}$
approaches the graph of $y = 2\cos 2x$ because
$\lim\limits_{h \to 0} \frac{\sin 2(x+h) - \sin 2x}{h} = \frac{d}{dx}(\sin 2x) = 2\cos 2x.$

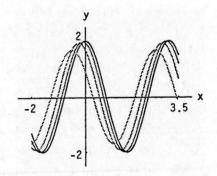

92.  As $h \to 0$, the graph of $y = \frac{\cos[(x+h)^2] - \cos(x^2)}{h}$
approaches the graph of $y = -2x\sin(x^2)$ because
$\lim\limits_{h \to 0} \frac{\cos[(x+h)^2] - \cos(x^2)}{h} = \frac{d}{dx}[\cos(x^2)] = -2x\sin(x^2).$

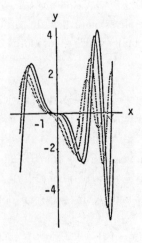

93. (a)

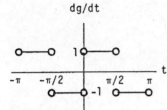

(b) $\frac{df}{dt} = 1.27324 \sin 2t + 0.42444 \sin 6t + 0.2546 \sin 10t + 0.18186 \sin 14t$

(c) The curve of $y = \frac{df}{dt}$ approximates $y = \frac{dg}{dt}$
the best when t is not $-\pi, -\frac{\pi}{2}, 0, \frac{\pi}{2},$ nor $\pi$.

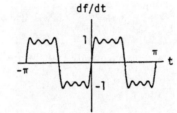

94. (a)

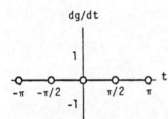

(b) $\frac{dh}{dt} = 2.5464 \cos(2t) + 2.5464 \cos(6t) + 2.5465 \cos(10t) + 2.54646 \cos(14t) + 2.54646 \cos(18t)$

(c)

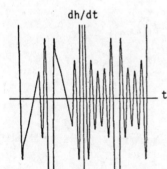

## 3.7  IMPLICIT DIFFERENTIATION

1. $x^2y + xy^2 = 6$:

   Step 1:   $\left(x^2 \frac{dy}{dx} + y \cdot 2x\right) + \left(x \cdot 2y \frac{dy}{dx} + y^2 \cdot 1\right) = 0$

   Step 2:   $x^2 \frac{dy}{dx} + 2xy \frac{dy}{dx} = -2xy - y^2$

   Step 3:   $\frac{dy}{dx}(x^2 + 2xy) = -2xy - y^2$

   Step 4:   $\frac{dy}{dx} = \frac{-2xy - y^2}{x^2 + 2xy}$

2. $x^3 + y^3 = 18xy \Rightarrow 3x^2 + 3y^2 \frac{dy}{dx} = 18y + 18x \frac{dy}{dx} \Rightarrow (3y^2 - 18x) \frac{dy}{dx} = 18y - 3x^2 \Rightarrow \frac{dy}{dx} = \frac{6y - x^2}{y^2 - 6x}$

3. $2xy + y^2 = x + y$:

   Step 1:   $\left(2x \frac{dy}{dx} + 2y\right) + 2y \frac{dy}{dx} = 1 + \frac{dy}{dx}$

   Step 2:   $2x \frac{dy}{dx} + 2y \frac{dy}{dx} - \frac{dy}{dx} = 1 - 2y$

Step 3: $\frac{dy}{dx}(2x + 2y - 1) = 1 - 2y$

Step 4: $\frac{dy}{dx} = \frac{1 - 2y}{2x + 2y - 1}$

4. $x^3 - xy + y^3 = 1 \Rightarrow 3x^2 - y - x\frac{dy}{dx} + 3y^2\frac{dy}{dx} = 0 \Rightarrow (3y^2 - x)\frac{dy}{dx} = y - 3x^2 \Rightarrow \frac{dy}{dx} = \frac{y - 3x^2}{3y^2 - x}$

5. $x^2(x - y)^2 = x^2 - y^2$:

Step 1: $x^2\left[2(x - y)\left(1 - \frac{dy}{dx}\right)\right] + (x - y)^2(2x) = 2x - 2y\frac{dy}{dx}$

Step 2: $-2x^2(x - y)\frac{dy}{dx} + 2y\frac{dy}{dx} = 2x - 2x^2(x - y) - 2x(x - y)^2$

Step 3: $\frac{dy}{dx}\left[-2x^2(x - y) + 2y\right] = 2x\left[1 - x(x - y) - (x - y)^2\right]$

Step 4: $\frac{dy}{dx} = \frac{2x\left[1 - x(x - y) - (x - y)^2\right]}{-2x^2(x - y) + 2y} = \frac{x\left[1 - x(x - y) - (x - y)^2\right]}{y - x^2(x - y)} = \frac{x\left(1 - x^2 + xy - x^2 + 2xy - y^2\right)}{x^2y - x^3 + y}$

$= \frac{x - 2x^3 + 3x^2y - xy^2}{x^2y - x^3 + y}$

6. $(3xy + 7)^2 = 6y \Rightarrow 2(3xy + 7)\cdot\left(3x\frac{dy}{dx} + 3y\right) = 6\frac{dy}{dx} \Rightarrow 2(3xy + 7)(3x)\frac{dy}{dx} - 6\frac{dy}{dx} = -6y(3xy + 7)$

$\Rightarrow \frac{dy}{dx}[6x(3xy + 7) - 6] = -6y(3xy + 7) \Rightarrow \frac{dy}{dx} = -\frac{y(3xy + 7)}{x(3xy + 7) - 1} = \frac{3xy^2 + 7y}{1 - 3x^2y - 7x}$

7. $y^2 = \frac{x - 1}{x + 1} \Rightarrow 2y\frac{dy}{dx} = \frac{(x + 1) - (x - 1)}{(x + 1)^2} = \frac{2}{(x + 1)^2} \Rightarrow \frac{dy}{dx} = \frac{1}{y(x + 1)^2}$

8. $x^3 = \frac{2x - y}{x + 3y} \Rightarrow x^4 + 3x^3y = 2x - y \Rightarrow 4x^3 + 9x^2y + 3x^3y' = 2 - y' \Rightarrow (3x^3 + 1)y' = 2 - 4x^3 - 9x^2y$

$\Rightarrow y' = \frac{2 - 4x^3 - 9x^2y}{3x^3 + 1}$

9. $x = \tan y \Rightarrow 1 = (\sec^2 y)\frac{dy}{dx} \Rightarrow \frac{dy}{dx} = \frac{1}{\sec^2 y} = \cos^2 y$

10. $xy = \cot(xy) \Rightarrow x\frac{dy}{dx} + y = -\csc^2(xy)\left(x\frac{dy}{dx} + y\right) \Rightarrow x\frac{dy}{dx} + x\csc^2(xy)\frac{dy}{dx} = -y\csc^2(xy) - y$

$\Rightarrow \frac{dy}{dx}\left[x + x\csc^2(xy)\right] = -y\left[\csc^2(xy) + 1\right] \Rightarrow \frac{dy}{dx} = \frac{-y\left[\csc^2(xy) + 1\right]}{x\left[1 + \csc^2(xy)\right]} = -\frac{y}{x}$

11. $x + \tan(xy) = 0 \Rightarrow 1 + [\sec^2(xy)]\left(y + x\frac{dy}{dx}\right) = 0 \Rightarrow x\sec^2(xy)\frac{dy}{dx} = -1 - y\sec^2(xy) \Rightarrow \frac{dy}{dx} = \frac{-1 - y\sec^2(xy)}{x\sec^2(xy)}$

$= \frac{-1}{x\sec^2(xy)} - \frac{y}{x} = \frac{-\cos^2(xy)}{x} - \frac{y}{x} = \frac{-\cos^2(xy) - y}{x}$

12. $x^4 + \sin y = x^3y^2 \Rightarrow 4x^3 + (\cos y)\frac{dy}{dx} = 3x^2y^2 + x^3 \cdot 2y\frac{dy}{dx} \Rightarrow (\cos y - 2x^3y)\frac{dy}{dx} = 3x^2y^2 - 4x^3 \Rightarrow \frac{dy}{dx} = \frac{3x^2y^2 - 4x^3}{\cos y - 2x^3y}$

13. $y\sin\left(\frac{1}{y}\right) = 1 - xy \Rightarrow y\left[\cos\left(\frac{1}{y}\right)\cdot(-1)\frac{1}{y^2}\cdot\frac{dy}{dx}\right] + \sin\left(\frac{1}{y}\right)\cdot\frac{dy}{dx} = -x\frac{dy}{dx} - y \Rightarrow$

$\frac{dy}{dx}\left[-\frac{1}{y}\cos\left(\frac{1}{y}\right) + \sin\left(\frac{1}{y}\right) + x\right] = -y \Rightarrow \frac{dy}{dx} = \frac{-y}{-\frac{1}{y}\cos\left(\frac{1}{y}\right) + \sin\left(\frac{1}{y}\right) + x} = \frac{-y^2}{y\sin\left(\frac{1}{y}\right) - \cos\left(\frac{1}{y}\right) + xy}$

14. $x\cos(2x + 3y) = y\sin x \Rightarrow -x\sin(2x + 3y)(2 + 3y') + \cos(2x + 3y) = y\cos x + y'\sin x$

$\Rightarrow -2x\sin(2x + 3y) - 3xy'\sin(2x + 3y) + \cos(2x + 3y) = y\cos x + y'\sin x$

$\Rightarrow \cos(2x + 3y) - 2x\sin(2x + 3y) - y\cos x = (\sin x + 3x\sin(2x + 3y))y' \Rightarrow y' = \frac{\cos(2x + 3y) - 2x\sin(2x + 3y) - y\cos x}{\sin x + 3x\sin(2x + 3y)}$

15. $\theta^{1/2} + r^{1/2} = 1 \Rightarrow \frac{1}{2}\theta^{-1/2} + \frac{1}{2}r^{-1/2}\cdot\frac{dr}{d\theta} = 0 \Rightarrow \frac{dr}{d\theta}\left[\frac{1}{2\sqrt{r}}\right] = \frac{-1}{2\sqrt{\theta}} \Rightarrow \frac{dr}{d\theta} = -\frac{2\sqrt{r}}{2\sqrt{\theta}} = -\frac{\sqrt{r}}{\sqrt{\theta}}$

16. $r - 2\sqrt{\theta} = \frac{3}{2}\theta^{2/3} + \frac{4}{3}\theta^{3/4} \Rightarrow \frac{dr}{d\theta} - \theta^{-1/2} = \theta^{-1/3} + \theta^{-1/4} \Rightarrow \frac{dr}{d\theta} = \theta^{-1/2} + \theta^{-1/3} + \theta^{-1/4}$

17. $\sin{(r\,\theta)} = \frac{1}{2} \Rightarrow [\cos{(r\,\theta)}]\left(r + \theta\,\frac{dr}{d\theta}\right) = 0 \Rightarrow \frac{d}{d\theta}[\theta\cos{(r\,\theta)}] = -r\cos{(r\,\theta)} \Rightarrow \frac{dr}{d\theta} = \frac{-r\cos{(r\,\theta)}}{\theta\cos{(r\,\theta)}} = -\frac{r}{\theta}\,,\ \cos{(r\,\theta)} \neq 0$

18. $\cos r + \cot\theta = r\,\theta \Rightarrow (-\sin r)\,\frac{dr}{d\theta} - \csc^2\theta = r + \theta\,\frac{dr}{d\theta} \Rightarrow \frac{dr}{d\theta}\left[-\sin r - \theta\right] = r + \csc^2\theta \Rightarrow \frac{dr}{d\theta} = -\frac{r + \csc^2\theta}{\sin r + \theta}$

19. $x^2 + y^2 = 1 \Rightarrow 2x + 2yy' = 0 \Rightarrow 2yy' = -2x \Rightarrow \frac{dy}{dx} = y' = -\frac{x}{y}$; now to find $\frac{d^2y}{dx^2}$, $\frac{d}{dx}(y') = \frac{d}{dx}\left(-\frac{x}{y}\right)$

   $\Rightarrow y'' = \frac{y(-1) + xy'}{y^2} = \frac{-y + x\left(-\frac{x}{y}\right)}{y^2}$ since $y' = -\frac{x}{y} \Rightarrow \frac{d^2y}{dx^2} = y'' = \frac{-y^2 - x^2}{y^3} = \frac{-y^2 - (1 - y^2)}{y^3} = \frac{-1}{y^3}$

20. $x^{2/3} + y^{2/3} = 1 \Rightarrow \frac{2}{3}x^{-1/3} + \frac{2}{3}y^{-1/3}\frac{dy}{dx} = 0 \Rightarrow \frac{dy}{dx}\left[\frac{2}{3}y^{-1/3}\right] = -\frac{2}{3}x^{-1/3} \Rightarrow y' = \frac{dy}{dx} = -\frac{x^{-1/3}}{y^{-1/3}} = -\left(\frac{y}{x}\right)^{1/3}$;

   Differentiating again, $y'' = \frac{x^{1/3}\cdot\left(-\frac{1}{3}y^{-2/3}\right)y' + y^{1/3}\left(\frac{1}{3}x^{-2/3}\right)}{x^{2/3}} = \frac{x^{1/3}\cdot\left(-\frac{1}{3}y^{-2/3}\right)\left(-\frac{y^{1/3}}{x^{1/3}}\right) + y^{1/3}\left(\frac{1}{3}x^{-2/3}\right)}{x^{2/3}}$

   $\Rightarrow \frac{d^2y}{dx^2} = \frac{1}{3}x^{-2/3}y^{-1/3} + \frac{1}{3}y^{1/3}x^{-4/3} = \frac{y^{1/3}}{3x^{4/3}} + \frac{1}{3y^{1/3}x^{2/3}}$

21. $y^2 = x^2 + 2x \Rightarrow 2yy' = 2x + 2 \Rightarrow y' = \frac{2x + 2}{2y} = \frac{x + 1}{y}$; then $y'' = \frac{y - (x+1)y'}{y^2} = \frac{y - (x+1)\left(\frac{x+1}{y}\right)}{y^2}$

   $\Rightarrow \frac{d^2y}{dx^2} = y'' = \frac{y^2 - (x+1)^2}{y^3}$

22. $y^2 - 2x = 1 - 2y \Rightarrow 2y\cdot y' - 2 = -2y' \Rightarrow y'(2y + 2) = 2 \Rightarrow y' = \frac{1}{y+1} = (y+1)^{-1}$; then $y'' = -(y+1)^{-2}\cdot y'$

   $= -(y+1)^{-2}(y+1)^{-1} \Rightarrow \frac{d^2y}{dx^2} = y'' = \frac{-1}{(y+1)^3}$

23. $2\sqrt{y} = x - y \Rightarrow y^{-1/2}y' = 1 - y' \Rightarrow y'\left(y^{-1/2} + 1\right) = 1 \Rightarrow \frac{dy}{dx} = y' = \frac{1}{y^{-1/2} + 1} = \frac{\sqrt{y}}{\sqrt{y} + 1}$; we can

   differentiate the equation $y'\left(y^{-1/2} + 1\right) = 1$ again to find $y''$: $y'\left(-\frac{1}{2}y^{-3/2}y'\right) + \left(y^{-1/2} + 1\right)y'' = 0$

   $\Rightarrow \left(y^{-1/2} + 1\right)y'' = \frac{1}{2}[y']^2 y^{-3/2} \Rightarrow \frac{d^2y}{dx^2} = y'' = \frac{\frac{1}{2}\left(\frac{1}{y^{-1/2} + 1}\right)^2 y^{-3/2}}{\left(y^{-1/2} + 1\right)} = \frac{1}{2y^{3/2}\left(y^{-1/2} + 1\right)^3} = \frac{1}{2\left(1 + \sqrt{y}\right)^3}$

24. $xy + y^2 = 1 \Rightarrow xy' + y + 2yy' = 0 \Rightarrow xy' + 2yy' = -y \Rightarrow y'(x + 2y) = -y \Rightarrow y' = \frac{-y}{(x + 2y)}$; $\frac{d^2y}{dx^2} = y''$

   $= \frac{-(x + 2y)y' + y(1 + 2y')}{(x + 2y)^2} = \frac{-(x + 2y)\left[\frac{-y}{(x + 2y)}\right] + y\left[1 + 2\left(\frac{-y}{(x + 2y)}\right)\right]}{(x + 2y)^2} = \frac{\frac{1}{(x + 2y)}[y(x + 2y) + y(x + 2y) - 2y^2]}{(x + 2y)^2}$

   $= \frac{2y(x + 2y) - 2y^2}{(x + 2y)^3} = \frac{2y^2 + 2xy}{(x + 2y)^3} = \frac{2y(x + y)}{(x + 2y)^3}$

25. $x^3 + y^3 = 16 \Rightarrow 3x^2 + 3y^2 y' = 0 \Rightarrow 3y^2 y' = -3x^2 \Rightarrow y' = -\frac{x^2}{y^2}$; we differentiate $y^2 y' = -x^2$ to find $y''$:

   $y^2 y'' + y'[2y\cdot y'] = -2x \Rightarrow y^2 y'' = -2x - 2y[y']^2 \Rightarrow y'' = \frac{-2x - 2y\left(-\frac{x^2}{y^2}\right)^2}{y^2} = \frac{-2x - \frac{2x^4}{y^3}}{y^2}$

   $= \frac{-2xy^3 - 2x^4}{y^5} \Rightarrow \frac{d^2y}{dx^2}\bigg|_{(2,2)} = \frac{-32 - 32}{32} = -2$

26. $xy + y^2 = 1 \Rightarrow xy' + y + 2yy' = 0 \Rightarrow y'(x + 2y) = -y \Rightarrow y' = \frac{-y}{(x + 2y)} \Rightarrow y'' = \frac{(x + 2y)(-y') - (-y)(1 + 2y')}{(x + 2y)^2}$;

   since $y'\big|_{(0,-1)} = -\frac{1}{2}$ we obtain $y''\big|_{(0,-1)} = \frac{(-2)\left(\frac{1}{2}\right) - (1)(0)}{4} = -\frac{1}{4}$

27. $y^2 + x^2 = y^4 - 2x$ at $(-2, 1)$ and $(-2, -1) \Rightarrow 2y\frac{dy}{dx} + 2x = 4y^3\frac{dy}{dx} - 2 \Rightarrow 2y\frac{dy}{dx} - 4y^3\frac{dy}{dx} = -2 - 2x$

   $\Rightarrow \frac{dy}{dx}(2y - 4y^3) = -2 - 2x \Rightarrow \frac{dy}{dx} = \frac{x + 1}{2y^3 - y} \Rightarrow \frac{dy}{dx}\bigg|_{(-2,1)} = -1$ and $\frac{dy}{dx}\bigg|_{(-2,-1)} = 1$

28. $(x^2 + y^2)^2 = (x - y)^2$ at $(1, 0)$ and $(1, -1)$ $\Rightarrow$ $2(x^2 + y^2)\left(2x + 2y\,\frac{dy}{dx}\right) = 2(x - y)\left(1 - \frac{dy}{dx}\right)$

$\Rightarrow$ $\frac{dy}{dx}[2y(x^2 + y^2) + (x - y)] = -2x(x^2 + y^2) + (x - y)$ $\Rightarrow$ $\frac{dy}{dx} = \frac{-2x(x^2 + y^2) + (x - y)}{2y(x^2 + y^2) + (x - y)}$ $\Rightarrow$ $\frac{dy}{dx}\Big|_{(1,0)} = -1$

and $\frac{dy}{dx}\Big|_{(1,-1)} = 1$

29. $x^2 + xy - y^2 = 1$ $\Rightarrow$ $2x + y + xy' - 2yy' = 0$ $\Rightarrow$ $(x - 2y)y' = -2x - y$ $\Rightarrow$ $y' = \frac{2x + y}{2y - x}$;

  (a) the slope of the tangent line $m = y'|_{(2,3)} = \frac{7}{4}$ $\Rightarrow$ the tangent line is $y - 3 = \frac{7}{4}(x - 2)$ $\Rightarrow$ $y = \frac{7}{4}x - \frac{1}{2}$

  (b) the normal line is $y - 3 = -\frac{4}{7}(x - 2)$ $\Rightarrow$ $y = -\frac{4}{7}x + \frac{29}{7}$

30. $x^2 + y^2 = 25$ $\Rightarrow$ $2x + 2yy' = 0$ $\Rightarrow$ $y' = -\frac{x}{y}$;

  (a) the slope of the tangent line $m = y'|_{(3,-4)} = -\frac{x}{y}\Big|_{(3,-4)} = \frac{3}{4}$ $\Rightarrow$ the tangent line is $y + 4 = \frac{3}{4}(x - 3) \Rightarrow y = \frac{3}{4}x - \frac{25}{4}$

  (b) the normal line is $y + 4 = -\frac{4}{3}(x - 3)$ $\Rightarrow$ $y = -\frac{4}{3}x$

31. $x^2 y^2 = 9$ $\Rightarrow$ $2xy^2 + 2x^2 yy' = 0$ $\Rightarrow$ $x^2 yy' = -xy^2$ $\Rightarrow$ $y' = -\frac{y}{x}$;

  (a) the slope of the tangent line $m = y'|_{(-1,3)} = -\frac{y}{x}\Big|_{(-1,3)} = 3 \Rightarrow$ the tangent line is $y - 3 = 3(x + 1)$ $\Rightarrow y = 3x + 6$

  (b) the normal line is $y - 3 = -\frac{1}{3}(x + 1)$ $\Rightarrow$ $y = -\frac{1}{3}x + \frac{8}{3}$

32. $y^2 - 2x - 4y - 1 = 0$ $\Rightarrow$ $2yy' - 2 - 4y' = 0$ $\Rightarrow$ $2(y - 2)y' = 2$ $\Rightarrow$ $y' = \frac{1}{y - 2}$;

  (a) the slope of the tangent line $m = y'|_{(-2,1)} = -1$ $\Rightarrow$ the tangent line is $y - 1 = -1(x + 2)$ $\Rightarrow$ $y = -x - 1$

  (b) the normal line is $y - 1 = 1(x + 2)$ $\Rightarrow$ $y = x + 3$

33. $6x^2 + 3xy + 2y^2 + 17y - 6 = 0$ $\Rightarrow$ $12x + 3y + 3xy' + 4yy' + 17y' = 0$ $\Rightarrow$ $y'(3x + 4y + 17) = -12x - 3y$

  $\Rightarrow$ $y' = \frac{-12x - 3y}{3x + 4y + 17}$;

  (a) the slope of the tangent line $m = y'|_{(-1,0)} = \frac{-12x - 3y}{3x + 4y + 17}\Big|_{(-1,0)} = \frac{6}{7}$ $\Rightarrow$ the tangent line is $y - 0 = \frac{6}{7}(x + 1)$

  $\Rightarrow$ $y = \frac{6}{7}x + \frac{6}{7}$

  (b) the normal line is $y - 0 = -\frac{7}{6}(x + 1)$ $\Rightarrow$ $y = -\frac{7}{6}x - \frac{7}{6}$

34. $x^2 - \sqrt{3}xy + 2y^2 = 5$ $\Rightarrow$ $2x - \sqrt{3}xy' - \sqrt{3}y + 4yy' = 0$ $\Rightarrow$ $y'\left(4y - \sqrt{3}x\right) = \sqrt{3}y - 2x$ $\Rightarrow$ $y' = \frac{\sqrt{3}y - 2x}{4y - \sqrt{3}x}$;

  (a) the slope of the tangent line $m = y'|_{\left(\sqrt{3},2\right)} = \frac{\sqrt{3}y - 2x}{4y - \sqrt{3}x}\Big|_{\left(\sqrt{3},2\right)} = 0$ $\Rightarrow$ the tangent line is $y = 2$

  (b) the normal line is $x = \sqrt{3}$

35. $2xy + \pi \sin y = 2\pi$ $\Rightarrow$ $2xy' + 2y + \pi(\cos y)y' = 0$ $\Rightarrow$ $y'(2x + \pi \cos y) = -2y$ $\Rightarrow$ $y' = \frac{-2y}{2x + \pi \cos y}$;

  (a) the slope of the tangent line $m = y'|_{\left(1,\frac{\pi}{2}\right)} = \frac{-2y}{2x + \pi \cos y}\Big|_{\left(1,\frac{\pi}{2}\right)} = -\frac{\pi}{2}$ $\Rightarrow$ the tangent line is

  $y - \frac{\pi}{2} = -\frac{\pi}{2}(x - 1)$ $\Rightarrow$ $y = -\frac{\pi}{2}x + \pi$

  (b) the normal line is $y - \frac{\pi}{2} = \frac{2}{\pi}(x - 1)$ $\Rightarrow$ $y = \frac{2}{\pi}x - \frac{2}{\pi} + \frac{\pi}{2}$

36. $x \sin 2y = y \cos 2x$ $\Rightarrow$ $x(\cos 2y)2y' + \sin 2y = -2y \sin 2x + y' \cos 2x$ $\Rightarrow$ $y'(2x \cos 2y - \cos 2x)$

  $= -\sin 2y - 2y \sin 2x$ $\Rightarrow$ $y' = \frac{\sin 2y + 2y \sin 2x}{\cos 2x - 2x \cos 2y}$;

  (a) the slope of the tangent line $m = y'|_{\left(\frac{\pi}{4},\frac{\pi}{2}\right)} = \frac{\sin 2y + 2y \sin 2x}{\cos 2x - 2x \cos 2y}\Big|_{\left(\frac{\pi}{4},\frac{\pi}{2}\right)} = \frac{\pi}{\frac{\pi}{2}} = 2$ $\Rightarrow$ the tangent line is

  $y - \frac{\pi}{2} = 2\left(x - \frac{\pi}{4}\right)$ $\Rightarrow$ $y = 2x$

  (b) the normal line is $y - \frac{\pi}{2} = -\frac{1}{2}\left(x - \frac{\pi}{4}\right)$ $\Rightarrow$ $y = -\frac{1}{2}x + \frac{5\pi}{8}$

37. $y = 2\sin(\pi x - y) \Rightarrow y' = 2[\cos(\pi x - y)] \cdot (\pi - y') \Rightarrow y'[1 + 2\cos(\pi x - y)] = 2\pi\cos(\pi x - y) \Rightarrow y' = \frac{2\pi\cos(\pi x - y)}{1 + 2\cos(\pi x - y)}$;

   (a) the slope of the tangent line $m = y'|_{(1,0)} = \frac{2\pi\cos(\pi x - y)}{1 + 2\cos(\pi x - y)}\Big|_{(1,0)} = 2\pi \Rightarrow$ the tangent line is

   $y - 0 = 2\pi(x - 1) \Rightarrow y = 2\pi x - 2\pi$

   (b) the normal line is $y - 0 = -\frac{1}{2\pi}(x - 1) \Rightarrow y = -\frac{x}{2\pi} + \frac{1}{2\pi}$

38. $x^2\cos^2 y - \sin y = 0 \Rightarrow x^2(2\cos y)(-\sin y)y' + 2x\cos^2 y - y'\cos y = 0 \Rightarrow y'[-2x^2\cos y\sin y - \cos y]$

   $= -2x\cos^2 y \Rightarrow y' = \frac{2x\cos^2 y}{2x^2\cos y\sin y + \cos y}$;

   (a) the slope of the tangent line $m = y'|_{(0,\pi)} = \frac{2x\cos^2 y}{2x^2\cos y\sin y + \cos y}\Big|_{(0,\pi)} = 0 \Rightarrow$ the tangent line is $y = \pi$

   (b) the normal line is $x = 0$

39. Solving $x^2 + xy + y^2 = 7$ and $y = 0 \Rightarrow x^2 = 7 \Rightarrow x = \pm\sqrt{7} \Rightarrow \left(-\sqrt{7}, 0\right)$ and $\left(\sqrt{7}, 0\right)$ are the points where the

   curve crosses the x-axis. Now $x^2 + xy + y^2 = 7 \Rightarrow 2x + y + xy' + 2yy' = 0 \Rightarrow (x + 2y)y' = -2x - y$

   $\Rightarrow y' = -\frac{2x + y}{x + 2y} \Rightarrow m = -\frac{2x + y}{x + 2y} \Rightarrow$ the slope at $\left(-\sqrt{7}, 0\right)$ is $m = -\frac{-2\sqrt{7}}{-\sqrt{7}} = -2$ and the slope at $\left(\sqrt{7}, 0\right)$ is

   $m = -\frac{2\sqrt{7}}{\sqrt{7}} = -2$. Since the slope is $-2$ in each case, the corresponding tangents must be parallel.

40. $xy + 2x - y = 0 \Rightarrow x\frac{dy}{dx} + y + 2 - \frac{dy}{dx} = 0 \Rightarrow \frac{dy}{dx} = \frac{y+2}{1-x}$; the slope of the line $2x + y = 0$ is $-2$. In order to be

   parallel, the normal lines must also have slope of $-2$. Since a normal is perpendicular to a tangent, the slope of

   the tangent is $\frac{1}{2}$. Therefore, $\frac{y+2}{1-x} = \frac{1}{2} \Rightarrow 2y + 4 = 1 - x \Rightarrow x = -3 - 2y$. Substituting in the original equation,

   $y(-3 - 2y) + 2(-3 - 2y) - y = 0 \Rightarrow y^2 + 4y + 3 = 0 \Rightarrow y = -3$ or $y = -1$. If $y = -3$, then $x = 3$ and

   $y + 3 = -2(x - 3) \Rightarrow y = -2x + 3$. If $y = -1$, then $x = -1$ and $y + 1 = -2(x + 1) \Rightarrow y = -2x - 3$.

41. $y^4 = y^2 - x^2 \Rightarrow 4y^3 y' = 2yy' - 2x \Rightarrow 2(2y^3 - y)y' = -2x \Rightarrow y' = \frac{x}{y - 2y^3}$; the slope of the tangent line at

   $\left(\frac{\sqrt{3}}{4}, \frac{\sqrt{3}}{2}\right)$ is $\frac{x}{y - 2y^3}\Big|_{\left(\frac{\sqrt{3}}{4}, \frac{\sqrt{3}}{2}\right)} = \frac{\frac{\sqrt{3}}{4}}{\frac{\sqrt{3}}{2} - \frac{6\sqrt{3}}{8}} = \frac{\frac{1}{4}}{\frac{1}{2} - \frac{3}{4}} = \frac{1}{2 - 3} = -1$; the slope of the tangent line at $\left(\frac{\sqrt{3}}{4}, \frac{1}{2}\right)$

   is $\frac{x}{y - 2y^3}\Big|_{\left(\frac{\sqrt{3}}{4}, \frac{1}{2}\right)} = \frac{\frac{\sqrt{3}}{4}}{\frac{1}{2} - \frac{2}{8}} = \frac{2\sqrt{3}}{4 - 2} = \sqrt{3}$

42. $y^2(2 - x) = x^3 \Rightarrow 2yy'(2 - x) + y^2(-1) = 3x^2 \Rightarrow y' = \frac{y^2 + 3x^2}{2y(2 - x)}$; the slope of the tangent line is $m = \frac{y^2 + 3x^2}{2y(2 - x)}\Big|_{(1,1)}$

   $= \frac{4}{2} = 2 \Rightarrow$ the tangent line is $y - 1 = 2(x - 1) \Rightarrow y = 2x - 1$; the normal line is $y - 1 = -\frac{1}{2}(x - 1) \Rightarrow y = -\frac{1}{2}x + \frac{3}{2}$

43. $y^4 - 4y^2 = x^4 - 9x^2 \Rightarrow 4y^3 y' - 8yy' = 4x^3 - 18x \Rightarrow y'(4y^3 - 8y) = 4x^3 - 18x \Rightarrow y' = \frac{4x^3 - 18x}{4y^3 - 8y} = \frac{2x^3 - 9x}{2y^3 - 4y}$

   $= \frac{x(2x^2 - 9)}{y(2y^2 - 4)} = m$; $(-3, 2)$: $m = \frac{(-3)(18 - 9)}{2(8 - 4)} = -\frac{27}{8}$; $(-3, -2)$: $m = \frac{27}{8}$; $(3, 2)$: $m = \frac{27}{8}$; $(3, -2)$: $m = -\frac{27}{8}$

44. $x^3 + y^3 - 9xy = 0 \Rightarrow 3x^2 + 3y^2 y' - 9xy' - 9y = 0 \Rightarrow y'(3y^2 - 9x) = 9y - 3x^2 \Rightarrow y' = \frac{9y - 3x^2}{3y^2 - 9x} = \frac{3y - x^2}{y^2 - 3x}$

   (a) $y'|_{(4,2)} = \frac{5}{4}$ and $y'|_{(2,4)} = \frac{4}{5}$;

   (b) $y' = 0 \Rightarrow \frac{3y - x^2}{y^2 - 3x} = 0 \Rightarrow 3y - x^2 = 0 \Rightarrow y = \frac{x^2}{3} \Rightarrow x^3 + \left(\frac{x^2}{3}\right)^3 - 9x\left(\frac{x^2}{3}\right) = 0 \Rightarrow x^6 - 54x^3 = 0$

   $\Rightarrow x^3(x^3 - 54) = 0 \Rightarrow x = 0$ or $x = \sqrt[3]{54} = 3\sqrt[3]{2} \Rightarrow$ there is a horizontal tangent at $x = 3\sqrt[3]{2}$. To find the

   corresponding y-value, we will use part (c).

   (c) $\frac{dx}{dy} = 0 \Rightarrow \frac{y^2 - 3x}{3y - x^2} = 0 \Rightarrow y^2 - 3x = 0 \Rightarrow y = \pm\sqrt{3x}$; $y = \sqrt{3x} \Rightarrow x^3 + \left(\sqrt{3x}\right)^3 - 9x\sqrt{3x} = 0$

   $\Rightarrow x^3 - 6\sqrt{3}x^{3/2} = 0 \Rightarrow x^{3/2}\left(x^{3/2} - 6\sqrt{3}\right) = 0 \Rightarrow x^{3/2} = 0$ or $x^{3/2} = 6\sqrt{3} \Rightarrow x = 0$ or $x = \sqrt[3]{108} = 3\sqrt[3]{4}$.

   Since the equation $x^3 + y^3 - 9xy = 0$ is symmetric in x and y, the graph is symmetric about the line $y = x$. That is, if (a, b) is a point on the folium, then so is (b, a). Moreover, if $y'|_{(a,b)} = m$, then $y'|_{(b,a)} = \frac{1}{m}$. Thus, if the folium has a horizontal tangent at (a, b), it has a vertical tangent at (b, a) so one might expect that with a horizontal tangent at $x = \sqrt[3]{54}$ and a vertical tangent at $x = 3\sqrt[3]{4}$, the points of tangency are $\left(\sqrt[3]{54}, 3\sqrt[3]{4}\right)$ and $\left(3\sqrt[3]{4}, \sqrt[3]{54}\right)$, respectively. One can check that these points do satisfy the equation $x^3 + y^3 - 9xy = 0$.

45. $x^2 + 2xy - 3y^2 = 0 \Rightarrow 2x + 2xy' + 2y - 6yy' = 0 \Rightarrow y'(2x - 6y) = -2x - 2y \Rightarrow y' = \frac{x+y}{3y-x} \Rightarrow$ the slope of the tangent line $m = y'|_{(1,1)} = \frac{x+y}{3y-x}\big|_{(1,1)} = 1 \Rightarrow$ the equation of the normal line at (1, 1) is $y - 1 = -1(x - 1) \Rightarrow y = -x + 2$. To find where the normal line intersects the curve we substitute into its equation: $x^2 + 2x(2 - x) - 3(2 - x)^2 = 0$
$\Rightarrow x^2 + 4x - 2x^2 - 3(4 - 4x + x^2) = 0 \Rightarrow -4x^2 + 16x - 12 = 0 \Rightarrow x^2 - 4x + 3 = 0 \Rightarrow (x - 3)(x - 1) = 0$
$\Rightarrow x = 3$ and $y = -x + 2 = -1$. Therefore, the normal to the curve at (1, 1) intersects the curve at the point (3, -1). Note that it also intersects the curve at (1, 1).

46. Let p and q be integers with $q > 0$ and suppose that $y = \sqrt[q]{x^p} = x^{p/q}$. Then $y^q = x^p$. Since p and q are integers and assuming y is a differentiable function of x, $\frac{d}{dx}(y^q) = \frac{d}{dx}(x^p) \Rightarrow qy^{q-1}\frac{dy}{dx} = px^{p-1} \Rightarrow \frac{dy}{dx} = \frac{px^{p-1}}{qy^{q-1}} = \frac{p}{q} \cdot \frac{x^{p-1}}{y^{q-1}}$
$= \frac{p}{q} \cdot \frac{x^{p-1}}{(x^{p/q})^{q-1}} = \frac{p}{q} \cdot \frac{x^{p-1}}{x^{p-p/q}} = \frac{p}{q} \cdot x^{p-1-(p-p/q)} = \frac{p}{q} \cdot x^{(p/q)-1}$

47. $y^2 = x \Rightarrow \frac{dy}{dx} = \frac{1}{2y}$. If a normal is drawn from (a, 0) to $(x_1, y_1)$ on the curve its slope satisfies $\frac{y_1 - 0}{x_1 - a} = -2y_1$
$\Rightarrow y_1 = -2y_1(x_1 - a)$ or $a = x_1 + \frac{1}{2}$. Since $x_1 \geq 0$ on the curve, we must have that $a \geq \frac{1}{2}$. By symmetry, the two points on the parabola are $(x_1, \sqrt{x_1})$ and $(x_1, -\sqrt{x_1})$. For the normal to be perpendicular, $\left(\frac{\sqrt{x_1}}{x_1 - a}\right)\left(\frac{\sqrt{x_1}}{a - x_1}\right) = -1$
$\Rightarrow \frac{x_1}{(a - x_1)^2} = 1 \Rightarrow x_1 = (a - x_1)^2 \Rightarrow x_1 = \left(x_1 + \frac{1}{2} - x_1\right)^2 \Rightarrow x_1 = \frac{1}{4}$ and $y_1 = \pm\frac{1}{2}$. Therefore, $\left(\frac{1}{4}, \pm\frac{1}{2}\right)$ and $a = \frac{3}{4}$.

48. $2x^2 + 3y^2 = 5 \Rightarrow 4x + 6yy' = 0 \Rightarrow y' = -\frac{2x}{3y} \Rightarrow y'|_{(1,1)} = -\frac{2x}{3y}\big|_{(1,1)} = -\frac{2}{3}$ and $y'|_{(1,-1)} = -\frac{2x}{3y}\big|_{(1,-1)} = \frac{2}{3}$; also, $y^2 = x^3 \Rightarrow 2yy' = 3x^2 \Rightarrow y' = \frac{3x^2}{2y} \Rightarrow y'|_{(1,1)} = \frac{3x^2}{2y}\big|_{(1,1)} = \frac{3}{2}$ and $y'|_{(1,-1)} = \frac{3x^2}{2y}\big|_{(1,-1)} = -\frac{3}{2}$. Therefore the tangents to the curves are perpendicular at (1, 1) and (1, -1) (i.e., the curves are orthogonal at these two points of intersection).

49. (a) $x^2 + y^2 = 4, x^2 = 3y^2 \Rightarrow (3y^2) + y^2 = 4 \Rightarrow y^2 = 1 \Rightarrow y = \pm 1$. If $y = 1 \Rightarrow x^2 + (1)^2 = 4 \Rightarrow x^2 = 3$
$\Rightarrow x = \pm\sqrt{3}$. If $y = -1 \Rightarrow x^2 + (-1)^2 = 4 \Rightarrow x^2 = 3 \Rightarrow x = \pm\sqrt{3}$.
$x^2 + y^2 = 4 \Rightarrow 2x + 2y\frac{dy}{dx} = 0 \Rightarrow m_1 = \frac{dy}{dx} = -\frac{x}{y}$ and $x^2 = 3y^2 \Rightarrow 2x = 6y\frac{dy}{dx} \Rightarrow m_2 = \frac{dy}{dx} = \frac{x}{3y}$
At $\left(\sqrt{3}, 1\right)$: $m_1 = \frac{dy}{dx} = -\frac{\sqrt{3}}{1} = -\sqrt{3}$ and $m_2 = \frac{dy}{dx} = \frac{\sqrt{3}}{3(1)} = \frac{\sqrt{3}}{3} \Rightarrow m_1 \cdot m_2 = \left(-\sqrt{3}\right)\left(\frac{\sqrt{3}}{3}\right) = -1$
At $\left(\sqrt{3}, -1\right)$: $m_1 = \frac{dy}{dx} = -\frac{\sqrt{3}}{(-1)} = \sqrt{3}$ and $m_2 = \frac{dy}{dx} = \frac{\sqrt{3}}{3(-1)} = -\frac{\sqrt{3}}{3} \Rightarrow m_1 \cdot m_2 = \left(\sqrt{3}\right)\left(-\frac{\sqrt{3}}{3}\right) = -1$
At $\left(-\sqrt{3}, 1\right)$: $m_1 = \frac{dy}{dx} = -\frac{\left(-\sqrt{3}\right)}{1} = \sqrt{3}$ and $m_2 = \frac{dy}{dx} = \frac{-\sqrt{3}}{3(1)} = -\frac{\sqrt{3}}{3} \Rightarrow m_1 \cdot m_2 = \left(\sqrt{3}\right)\left(-\frac{\sqrt{3}}{3}\right) = -1$
At $\left(-\sqrt{3}, -1\right)$: $m_1 = \frac{dy}{dx} = -\frac{\left(-\sqrt{3}\right)}{(-1)} = -\sqrt{3}$ and $m_2 = \frac{dy}{dx} = \frac{\left(-\sqrt{3}\right)}{3(-1)} = \frac{\sqrt{3}}{3} \Rightarrow m_1 \cdot m_2 = \left(-\sqrt{3}\right)\left(\frac{\sqrt{3}}{3}\right) = -1$

(b) $x = 1 - y^2, x = \frac{1}{3}y^2 \Rightarrow \left(\frac{1}{3}y^2\right) = 1 - y^2 \Rightarrow y^2 = \frac{3}{4} \Rightarrow y = \pm\frac{\sqrt{3}}{2}$. If $y = \frac{\sqrt{3}}{2} \Rightarrow x = 1 - \left(\frac{\sqrt{3}}{2}\right)^2 = \frac{1}{4}$. If
$y = -\frac{\sqrt{3}}{2} \Rightarrow x = 1 - \left(-\frac{\sqrt{3}}{2}\right)^2 = \frac{1}{4}$. $x = 1 - y^2 \Rightarrow 1 = -2y\frac{dy}{dx} \Rightarrow m_1 = \frac{dy}{dx} = -\frac{1}{2y}$ and $x = \frac{1}{3}y^2$
$\Rightarrow 1 = \frac{2}{3}y\frac{dy}{dx} \Rightarrow m_2 = \frac{dy}{dx} = \frac{3}{2y}$
At $\left(\frac{1}{4}, \frac{\sqrt{3}}{2}\right)$: $m_1 = \frac{dy}{dx} = -\frac{1}{2\left(\sqrt{3}/2\right)} = -\frac{1}{\sqrt{3}}$ and $m_2 = \frac{dy}{dx} = \frac{3}{2\left(\sqrt{3}/2\right)} = \frac{3}{\sqrt{3}} \Rightarrow m_1 \cdot m_2 = \left(-\frac{1}{\sqrt{3}}\right)\left(\frac{3}{\sqrt{3}}\right) = -1$
At $\left(\frac{1}{4}, -\frac{\sqrt{3}}{2}\right)$: $m_1 = \frac{dy}{dx} = -\frac{1}{2\left(-\sqrt{3}/2\right)} = \frac{1}{\sqrt{3}}$ and $m_2 = \frac{dy}{dx} = \frac{3}{2\left(-\sqrt{3}/2\right)} = -\frac{3}{\sqrt{3}} \Rightarrow m_1 \cdot m_2 = \left(\frac{1}{\sqrt{3}}\right)\left(-\frac{3}{\sqrt{3}}\right) = -1$

50. $y = -\frac{1}{3}x + b$, $y^2 = x^3 \Rightarrow \frac{dy}{dx} = -\frac{1}{3}$ and $2y\frac{dy}{dx} = 3x^2 \Rightarrow \frac{dy}{dx} = \frac{3x^2}{2y} \Rightarrow \left(-\frac{1}{3}\right)\left(\frac{3x^2}{2y}\right) = -1 \Rightarrow \frac{x^2}{2} = y \Rightarrow \left(\frac{x^2}{2}\right)^2 = x^3$

$\Rightarrow \frac{x^4}{4} = x^3 \Rightarrow x^4 - 4x^3 = 0 \Rightarrow x^3(x-4) = 0 \Rightarrow x = 0$ or $x = 4$. If $x = 0 \Rightarrow y = \frac{(0)^2}{2} = 0$ and $\left(-\frac{1}{3}\right)\left(\frac{3x^2}{2y}\right) = -1$ is

indeterminant at $(0,0)$. If $x = 4 \Rightarrow y = \frac{(4)^2}{2} = 8$. At $(4, 8)$, $y = -\frac{1}{3}x + b \Rightarrow 8 = -\frac{1}{3}(4) + b \Rightarrow b = \frac{28}{3}$.

51. $xy^3 + x^2y = 6 \Rightarrow x\left(3y^2 \frac{dy}{dx}\right) + y^3 + x^2 \frac{dy}{dx} + 2xy = 0 \Rightarrow \frac{dy}{dx}(3xy^2 + x^2) = -y^3 - 2xy \Rightarrow \frac{dy}{dx} = \frac{-y^3 - 2xy}{3xy^2 + x^2}$

$= -\frac{y^3 + 2xy}{3xy^2 + x^2}$ ; also, $xy^3 + x^2y = 6 \Rightarrow x(3y^2) + y^3 \frac{dx}{dy} + x^2 + y\left(2x\frac{dx}{dy}\right) = 0 \Rightarrow \frac{dx}{dy}(y^3 + 2xy) = -3xy^2 - x^2$

$\Rightarrow \frac{dx}{dy} = -\frac{3xy^2 + x^2}{y^3 + 2xy}$ ; thus $\frac{dx}{dy}$ appears to equal $\frac{1}{\frac{dy}{dx}}$ . The two different treatments view the graphs as functions

symmetric across the line $y = x$, so their slopes are reciprocals of one another at the corresponding points

$(a, b)$ and $(b, a)$.

52. $x^3 + y^2 = \sin^2 y \Rightarrow 3x^2 + 2y\frac{dy}{dx} = (2\sin y)(\cos y)\frac{dy}{dx} \Rightarrow \frac{dy}{dx}(2y - 2\sin y \cos y) = -3x^2 \Rightarrow \frac{dy}{dx} = \frac{-3x^2}{2y - 2\sin y \cos y}$

$= \frac{3x^2}{2\sin y \cos y - 2y}$ ; also, $x^3 + y^2 = \sin^2 y \Rightarrow 3x^2 \frac{dx}{dy} + 2y = 2\sin y \cos y \Rightarrow \frac{dx}{dy} = \frac{2\sin y \cos y - 2y}{3x^2}$ ; thus $\frac{dx}{dy}$

appears to equal $\frac{1}{\frac{dy}{dx}}$ . The two different treatments view the graphs as functions symmetric across the line

$y = x$ so their slopes are reciprocals of one another at the corresponding points $(a, b)$ and $(b, a)$.

53-60.  Example CAS commands:
   Maple:
```
q1 := x^3-x*y+y^3 = 7;
pt := [x=2,y=1];
p1 := implicitplot( q1, x=-3..3, y=-3..3 ):
p1;
eval( q1, pt );
q2 := implicitdiff( q1, y, x );
m := eval( q2, pt );
tan_line := y = 1 + m*(x-2);
p2 := implicitplot( tan_line, x=-5..5, y=-5..5, color=green ):
p3 := pointplot( eval([x,y],pt), color=blue ):
display( [p1,p2,p3], ="Section 3.7 #57(c)" );
```
   Mathematica: (functions and x0 may vary):
   Note use of double equal sign (logic statement) in definition of eqn and tanline.
```
<<Graphics`ImplicitPlot`
Clear[x, y]
{x0, y0}={1, π/4};
eqn=x + Tan[y/x]==2;
ImplicitPlot[eqn,{ x, x0 − 3, x0 + 3},{y, y0 − 3, y0 + 3}]
eqn/.{x → x0, y → y0}
eqn/.{ y → y[x]}
D[%, x]
Solve[%, y'[x]]
slope=y'[x]/.First[%]
m=slope/.{x → x0, y[x] → y0}
tanline=y==y0 + m (x − x0)
ImplicitPlot[{eqn, tanline}, {x, x0 − 3, x0 + 3},{y, y0 − 3, y0 + 3}]
```

## 3.8 RELATED RATES

1. $A = \pi r^2 \Rightarrow \frac{dA}{dt} = 2\pi r \frac{dr}{dt}$

2. $S = 4\pi r^2 \Rightarrow \frac{dS}{dt} = 8\pi r \frac{dr}{dt}$

3. $y = 5x, \frac{dx}{dt} = 2 \Rightarrow \frac{dy}{dt} = 5\frac{dx}{dt} \Rightarrow \frac{dy}{dt} = 5(2) = 10$

4. $2x + 3y = 12, \frac{dy}{dt} = -2 \Rightarrow 2\frac{dx}{dt} + 3\frac{dy}{dt} = 0 \Rightarrow 2\frac{dx}{dt} + 3(-2) = 0 \Rightarrow \frac{dx}{dt} = 3$

5. $y = x^2, \frac{dx}{dt} = 3 \Rightarrow \frac{dy}{dt} = 2x\frac{dx}{dt}$; when $x = -1 \Rightarrow \frac{dy}{dt} = 2(-1)(3) = -6$

6. $x = y^3 - y, \frac{dy}{dt} = 5 \Rightarrow \frac{dx}{dt} = 3y^2\frac{dy}{dt} - \frac{dy}{dt}$; when $y = 2 \Rightarrow \frac{dx}{dt} = 3(2)^2(5) - (5) = 55$

7. $x^2 + y^2 = 25, \frac{dx}{dt} = -2 \Rightarrow 2x\frac{dx}{dt} + 2y\frac{dy}{dt} = 0$; when $x = 3$ and $y = -4 \Rightarrow 2(3)(-2) + 2(-4)\frac{dy}{dt} = 0 \Rightarrow \frac{dy}{dt} = -\frac{3}{2}$

8. $x^2 y^3 = \frac{4}{27}, \frac{dy}{dt} = \frac{1}{2} \Rightarrow 3x^2 y^2\frac{dy}{dt} + 2xy^3\frac{dx}{dt} = 0$; when $x = 2 \Rightarrow (2)^2 y^3 = \frac{4}{27} \Rightarrow y = \frac{1}{3}$. Thus
   $3(2)^2 \left(\frac{1}{3}\right)^2 \left(\frac{1}{2}\right) + 2(2)\left(\frac{1}{3}\right)^3 \frac{dx}{dt} = 0 \Rightarrow \frac{dx}{dt} = -\frac{9}{2}$

9. $L = \sqrt{x^2 + y^2}, \frac{dx}{dt} = -1, \frac{dy}{dt} = 3 \Rightarrow \frac{dL}{dt} = \frac{1}{2\sqrt{x^2+y^2}}\left(2x\frac{dx}{dt} + 2y\frac{dy}{dt}\right) = \frac{x\frac{dx}{dt} + y\frac{dy}{dt}}{\sqrt{x^2+y^2}}$; when $x = 5$ and $y = 12$
   $\Rightarrow \frac{dL}{dt} = \frac{(5)(-1) + (12)(3)}{\sqrt{(5)^2+(12)^2}} = \frac{31}{13}$

10. $r + s^2 + v^3 = 12, \frac{dr}{dt} = 4, \frac{ds}{dt} = -3 \Rightarrow \frac{dr}{dt} + 2s\frac{ds}{dt} + 3v^2\frac{dv}{dt} = 0$; when $r = 3$ and $s = 1 \Rightarrow (3) + (1)^2 + v^3 = 12 \Rightarrow v = 2$
    $\Rightarrow 4 + 2(1)(-3) + 3(2)^2\frac{dv}{dt} = 0 \Rightarrow \frac{dv}{dt} = \frac{1}{6}$

11. (a) $S = 6x^2, \frac{dx}{dt} = -5\frac{m}{min} \Rightarrow \frac{dS}{dt} = 12x\frac{dx}{dt}$; when $x = 3 \Rightarrow \frac{dS}{dt} = 12(3)(-5) = -180 \frac{m^2}{min}$
    (b) $V = x^3, \frac{dx}{dt} = -5\frac{m}{min} \Rightarrow \frac{dV}{dt} = 3x^2\frac{dx}{dt}$; when $x = 3 \Rightarrow \frac{dV}{dt} = 3(3)^2(-5) = -135 \frac{m^3}{min}$

12. $S = 6x^2, \frac{dS}{dt} = 72\frac{in^2}{sec} \Rightarrow \frac{dS}{dt} = 12x\frac{dx}{dt} \Rightarrow 72 = 12(3)\frac{dx}{dt} \Rightarrow \frac{dx}{dt} = 2\frac{in}{sec}; V = x^3 \Rightarrow \frac{dV}{dt} = 3x^2\frac{dx}{dt}$; when $x = 3$
    $\Rightarrow \frac{dV}{dt} = 3(3)^2(2) = 54 \frac{in^3}{sec}$

13. (a) $V = \pi r^2 h \Rightarrow \frac{dV}{dt} = \pi r^2 \frac{dh}{dt}$         (b) $V = \pi r^2 h \Rightarrow \frac{dV}{dt} = 2\pi rh \frac{dr}{dt}$
    (c) $V = \pi r^2 h \Rightarrow \frac{dV}{dt} = \pi r^2 \frac{dh}{dt} + 2\pi rh \frac{dr}{dt}$

14. (a) $V = \frac{1}{3}\pi r^2 h \Rightarrow \frac{dV}{dt} = \frac{1}{3}\pi r^2 \frac{dh}{dt}$         (b) $V = \frac{1}{3}\pi r^2 h \Rightarrow \frac{dV}{dt} = \frac{2}{3}\pi rh \frac{dr}{dt}$
    (c) $\frac{dV}{dt} = \frac{1}{3}\pi r^2 \frac{dh}{dt} + \frac{2}{3}\pi rh \frac{dr}{dt}$

15. (a) $\frac{dV}{dt} = 1$ volt/sec         (b) $\frac{dI}{dt} = -\frac{1}{3}$ amp/sec
    (c) $\frac{dV}{dt} = R\left(\frac{dI}{dt}\right) + I\left(\frac{dR}{dt}\right) \Rightarrow \frac{dR}{dt} = \frac{1}{I}\left(\frac{dV}{dt} - R\frac{dI}{dt}\right) \Rightarrow \frac{dR}{dt} = \frac{1}{I}\left(\frac{dV}{dt} - \frac{V}{I}\frac{dI}{dt}\right)$
    (d) $\frac{dR}{dt} = \frac{1}{2}\left[1 - \frac{12}{2}\left(-\frac{1}{3}\right)\right] = \left(\frac{1}{2}\right)(3) = \frac{3}{2}$ ohms/sec, R is increasing

16. (a) $P = RI^2 \Rightarrow \frac{dP}{dt} = I^2\frac{dR}{dt} + 2RI\frac{dI}{dt}$
    (b) $P = RI^2 \Rightarrow 0 = \frac{dP}{dt} = I^2\frac{dR}{dt} + 2RI\frac{dI}{dt} \Rightarrow \frac{dR}{dt} = -\frac{2RI}{I^2}\frac{dI}{dt} = -\frac{2\left(\frac{P}{I}\right)}{I^2}\frac{dI}{dt} = -\frac{2P}{I^3}\frac{dI}{dt}$

17. (a) $s = \sqrt{x^2 + y^2} = (x^2 + y^2)^{1/2} \Rightarrow \frac{ds}{dt} = \frac{x}{\sqrt{x^2+y^2}} \frac{dx}{dt}$

(b) $s = \sqrt{x^2 + y^2} = (x^2 + y^2)^{1/2} \Rightarrow \frac{ds}{dt} = \frac{x}{\sqrt{x^2+y^2}} \frac{dx}{dt} + \frac{y}{\sqrt{x^2+y^2}} \frac{dy}{dt}$

(c) $s = \sqrt{x^2 + y^2} \Rightarrow s^2 = x^2 + y^2 \Rightarrow 2s \frac{ds}{dt} = 2x \frac{dx}{dt} + 2y \frac{dy}{dt} \Rightarrow 2s \cdot 0 = 2x \frac{dx}{dt} + 2y \frac{dy}{dt} \Rightarrow \frac{dx}{dt} = -\frac{y}{x} \frac{dy}{dt}$

18. (a) $s = \sqrt{x^2 + y^2 + z^2} \Rightarrow s^2 = x^2 + y^2 + z^2 \Rightarrow 2s \frac{ds}{dt} = 2x \frac{dx}{dt} + 2y \frac{dy}{dt} + 2z \frac{dz}{dt}$

$\Rightarrow \frac{ds}{dt} = \frac{x}{\sqrt{x^2+y^2+z^2}} \frac{dx}{dt} + \frac{y}{\sqrt{x^2+y^2+z^2}} \frac{dy}{dt} + \frac{z}{\sqrt{x^2+y^2+z^2}} \frac{dz}{dt}$

(b) From part (a) with $\frac{dx}{dt} = 0 \Rightarrow \frac{ds}{dt} = \frac{y}{\sqrt{x^2+y^2+z^2}} \frac{dy}{dt} + \frac{z}{\sqrt{x^2+y^2+z^2}} \frac{dz}{dt}$

(c) From part (a) with $\frac{ds}{dt} = 0 \Rightarrow 0 = 2x \frac{dx}{dt} + 2y \frac{dy}{dt} + 2z \frac{dz}{dt} \Rightarrow \frac{dx}{dt} + \frac{y}{x} \frac{dy}{dt} + \frac{z}{x} \frac{dz}{dt} = 0$

19. (a) $A = \frac{1}{2} ab \sin \theta \Rightarrow \frac{dA}{dt} = \frac{1}{2} ab \cos \theta \frac{d\theta}{dt}$       (b) $A = \frac{1}{2} ab \sin \theta \Rightarrow \frac{dA}{dt} = \frac{1}{2} ab \cos \theta \frac{d\theta}{dt} + \frac{1}{2} b \sin \theta \frac{da}{dt}$

(c) $A = \frac{1}{2} ab \sin \theta \Rightarrow \frac{dA}{dt} = \frac{1}{2} ab \cos \theta \frac{d\theta}{dt} + \frac{1}{2} b \sin \theta \frac{da}{dt} + \frac{1}{2} a \sin \theta \frac{db}{dt}$

20. Given $A = \pi r^2$, $\frac{dr}{dt} = 0.01$ cm/sec, and $r = 50$ cm. Since $\frac{dA}{dt} = 2\pi r \frac{dr}{dt}$, then $\frac{dA}{dt} \Big|_{r=50} = 2\pi(50)\left(\frac{1}{100}\right) = \pi$ cm$^2$/min.

21. Given $\frac{d\ell}{dt} = -2$ cm/sec, $\frac{dw}{dt} = 2$ cm/sec, $\ell = 12$ cm and $w = 5$ cm.

(a) $A = \ell w \Rightarrow \frac{dA}{dt} = \ell \frac{dw}{dt} + w \frac{d\ell}{dt} \Rightarrow \frac{dA}{dt} = 12(2) + 5(-2) = 14$ cm$^2$/sec, increasing

(b) $P = 2\ell + 2w \Rightarrow \frac{dP}{dt} = 2 \frac{d\ell}{dt} + 2 \frac{dw}{dt} = 2(-2) + 2(2) = 0$ cm/sec, constant

(c) $D = \sqrt{w^2 + \ell^2} = (w^2 + \ell^2)^{1/2} \Rightarrow \frac{dD}{dt} = \frac{1}{2} (w^2 + \ell^2)^{-1/2} \left(2w \frac{dw}{dt} + 2\ell \frac{d\ell}{dt}\right) \Rightarrow \frac{dD}{dt} = \frac{w \frac{dw}{dt} + \ell \frac{d\ell}{dt}}{\sqrt{w^2+\ell^2}}$

$= \frac{(5)(2) + (12)(-2)}{\sqrt{25+144}} = -\frac{14}{13}$ cm/sec, decreasing

22. (a) $V = xyz \Rightarrow \frac{dV}{dt} = yz \frac{dx}{dt} + xz \frac{dy}{dt} + xy \frac{dz}{dt} \Rightarrow \frac{dV}{dt}\Big|_{(4,3,2)} = (3)(2)(1) + (4)(2)(-2) + (4)(3)(1) = 2$ m$^3$/sec

(b) $S = 2xy + 2xz + 2yz \Rightarrow \frac{dS}{dt} = (2y + 2z) \frac{dx}{dt} + (2x + 2z) \frac{dy}{dt} + (2x + 2y) \frac{dz}{dt}$

$\Rightarrow \frac{dS}{dt}\Big|_{(4,3,2)} = (10)(1) + (12)(-2) + (14)(1) = 0$ m$^2$/sec

(c) $\ell = \sqrt{x^2 + y^2 + z^2} = (x^2 + y^2 + z^2)^{1/2} \Rightarrow \frac{d\ell}{dt} = \frac{x}{\sqrt{x^2+y^2+z^2}} \frac{dx}{dt} + \frac{y}{\sqrt{x^2+y^2+z^2}} \frac{dy}{dt} + \frac{z}{\sqrt{x^2+y^2+z^2}} \frac{dz}{dt}$

$\Rightarrow \frac{d\ell}{dt}\Big|_{(4,3,2)} = \left(\frac{4}{\sqrt{29}}\right)(1) + \left(\frac{3}{\sqrt{29}}\right)(-2) + \left(\frac{2}{\sqrt{29}}\right)(1) = 0$ m/sec

23. Given: $\frac{dx}{dt} = 5$ ft/sec, the ladder is 13 ft long, and $x = 12$, $y = 5$ at the instant of time

(a) Since $x^2 + y^2 = 169 \Rightarrow \frac{dy}{dt} = -\frac{x}{y} \frac{dx}{dt} = -\left(\frac{12}{5}\right)(5) = -12$ ft/sec, the ladder is sliding down the wall

(b) The area of the triangle formed by the ladder and walls is $A = \frac{1}{2} xy \Rightarrow \frac{dA}{dt} = \left(\frac{1}{2}\right)\left(x \frac{dy}{dt} + y \frac{dx}{dt}\right)$. The area

is changing at $\frac{1}{2} [12(-12) + 5(5)] = -\frac{119}{2} = -59.5$ ft$^2$/sec.

(c) $\cos \theta = \frac{x}{13} \Rightarrow -\sin \theta \frac{d\theta}{dt} = \frac{1}{13} \cdot \frac{dx}{dt} \Rightarrow \frac{d\theta}{dt} = -\frac{1}{13 \sin \theta} \cdot \frac{dx}{dt} = -\left(\frac{1}{5}\right)(5) = -1$ rad/sec

24. $s^2 = y^2 + x^2 \Rightarrow 2s \frac{ds}{dt} = 2x \frac{dx}{dt} + 2y \frac{dy}{dt} \Rightarrow \frac{ds}{dt} = \frac{1}{s}\left(x \frac{dx}{dt} + y \frac{dy}{dt}\right) \Rightarrow \frac{ds}{dt} = \frac{1}{\sqrt{169}} [5(-442) + 12(-481)] = -614$ knots

25. Let s represent the distance between the girl and the kite and x represents the horizontal distance between the girl and kite

$\Rightarrow s^2 = (300)^2 + x^2 \Rightarrow \frac{ds}{dt} = \frac{x}{s} \frac{dx}{dt} = \frac{400(25)}{500} = 20$ ft/sec.

26. When the diameter is 3.8 in., the radius is 1.9 in. and $\frac{dr}{dt} = \frac{1}{3000}$ in/min. Also $V = 6\pi r^2 \Rightarrow \frac{dV}{dt} = 12\pi r \frac{dr}{dt}$

$\Rightarrow \frac{dV}{dt} = 12\pi(1.9)\left(\frac{1}{3000}\right) = 0.0076\pi$. The volume is changing at about 0.0239 in$^3$/min.

27. $V = \frac{1}{3}\pi r^2 h$, $h = \frac{3}{8}(2r) = \frac{3r}{4} \Rightarrow r = \frac{4h}{3} \Rightarrow V = \frac{1}{3}\pi\left(\frac{4h}{3}\right)^2 h = \frac{16\pi h^3}{27} \Rightarrow \frac{dV}{dt} = \frac{16\pi h^2}{9}\frac{dh}{dt}$

   (a) $\left.\frac{dh}{dt}\right|_{h=4} = \left(\frac{9}{16\pi 4^2}\right)(10) = \frac{90}{256\pi} \approx 0.1119$ m/sec $= 11.19$ cm/sec

   (b) $r = \frac{4h}{3} \Rightarrow \frac{dr}{dt} = \frac{4}{3}\frac{dh}{dt} = \frac{4}{3}\left(\frac{90}{256\pi}\right) = \frac{15}{32\pi} \approx 0.1492$ m/sec $= 14.92$ cm/sec

28. (a) $V = \frac{1}{3}\pi r^2 h$ and $r = \frac{15h}{2} \Rightarrow V = \frac{1}{3}\pi\left(\frac{15h}{2}\right)^2 h = \frac{75\pi h^3}{4} \Rightarrow \frac{dV}{dt} = \frac{225\pi h^2}{4}\frac{dh}{dt} \Rightarrow \left.\frac{dh}{dt}\right|_{h=5} = \frac{4(-50)}{225\pi(5)^2} = \frac{-8}{225\pi}$

   $\approx -0.0113$ m/min $= -1.13$ cm/min

   (b) $r = \frac{15h}{2} \Rightarrow \frac{dr}{dt} = \frac{15}{2}\frac{dh}{dt} \Rightarrow \left.\frac{dr}{dt}\right|_{h=5} = \left(\frac{15}{2}\right)\left(\frac{-8}{225\pi}\right) = \frac{-4}{15\pi} \approx -0.0849$ m/sec $= -8.49$ cm/sec

29. (a) $V = \frac{\pi}{3}y^2(3R - y) \Rightarrow \frac{dV}{dt} = \frac{\pi}{3}\left[2y(3R - y) + y^2(-1)\right]\frac{dy}{dt} \Rightarrow \frac{dy}{dt} = \left[\frac{\pi}{3}(6Ry - 3y^2)\right]^{-1}\frac{dV}{dt} \Rightarrow$ at $R = 13$ and

   $y = 8$ we have $\frac{dy}{dt} = \frac{1}{144\pi}(-6) = \frac{-1}{24\pi}$ m/min

   (b) The hemisphere is on the circle $r^2 + (13 - y)^2 = 169 \Rightarrow r = \sqrt{26y - y^2}$ m

   (c) $r = (26y - y^2)^{1/2} \Rightarrow \frac{dr}{dt} = \frac{1}{2}(26y - y^2)^{-1/2}(26 - 2y)\frac{dy}{dt} \Rightarrow \frac{dr}{dt} = \frac{13 - y}{\sqrt{26y - y^2}}\frac{dy}{dt} \Rightarrow \left.\frac{dr}{dt}\right|_{y=8} = \frac{13 - 8}{\sqrt{26\cdot 8 - 64}}\left(\frac{-1}{24\pi}\right)$

   $= \frac{-5}{288\pi}$ m/min

30. If $V = \frac{4}{3}\pi r^3$, $S = 4\pi r^2$, and $\frac{dV}{dt} = kS = 4k\pi r^2$, then $\frac{dV}{dt} = 4\pi r^2\frac{dr}{dt} \Rightarrow 4k\pi r^2 = 4\pi r^2\frac{dr}{dt} \Rightarrow \frac{dr}{dt} = k$, a constant.
    Therefore, the radius is increasing at a constant rate.

31. If $V = \frac{4}{3}\pi r^3$, $r = 5$, and $\frac{dV}{dt} = 100\pi$ ft$^3$/min, then $\frac{dV}{dt} = 4\pi r^2\frac{dr}{dt} \Rightarrow \frac{dr}{dt} = 1$ ft/min. Then $S = 4\pi r^2 \Rightarrow \frac{dS}{dt}$
    $= 8\pi r\frac{dr}{dt} = 8\pi(5)(1) = 40\pi$ ft$^2$/min, the rate at which the surface area is increasing.

32. Let s represent the length of the rope and x the horizontal distance of the boat from the dock.

   (a) We have $s^2 = x^2 + 36 \Rightarrow \frac{dx}{dt} = \frac{s}{x}\frac{ds}{dt} = \frac{s}{\sqrt{s^2 - 36}}\frac{ds}{dt}$. Therefore, the boat is approaching the dock at

   $\left.\frac{dx}{dt}\right|_{s=10} = \frac{10}{\sqrt{10^2 - 36}}(-2) = -2.5$ ft/sec.

   (b) $\cos\theta = \frac{6}{r} \Rightarrow -\sin\theta\frac{d\theta}{dt} = -\frac{6}{r^2}\frac{dr}{dt} \Rightarrow \frac{d\theta}{dt} = \frac{6}{r^2\sin\theta}\frac{dr}{dt}$. Thus, $r = 10$, $x = 8$, and $\sin\theta = \frac{8}{10}$

   $\Rightarrow \frac{d\theta}{dt} = \frac{6}{10^2\left(\frac{8}{10}\right)}\cdot(-2) = -\frac{3}{20}$ rad/sec

33. Let s represent the distance between the bicycle and balloon, h the height of the balloon and x the horizontal
    distance between the balloon and the bicycle. The relationship between the variables is $s^2 = h^2 + x^2$
    $\Rightarrow \frac{ds}{dt} = \frac{1}{s}\left(h\frac{dh}{dt} + x\frac{dx}{dt}\right) \Rightarrow \frac{ds}{dt} = \frac{1}{85}[68(1) + 51(17)] = 11$ ft/sec.

34. (a) Let h be the height of the coffee in the pot. Since the radius of the pot is 3, the volume of the coffee is
    $V = 9\pi h \Rightarrow \frac{dV}{dt} = 9\pi\frac{dh}{dt} \Rightarrow$ the rate the coffee is rising is $\frac{dh}{dt} = \frac{1}{9\pi}\frac{dV}{dt} = \frac{10}{9\pi}$ in/min.

   (b) Let h be the height of the coffee in the pot. From the figure, the radius of the filter $r = \frac{h}{2} \Rightarrow V = \frac{1}{3}\pi r^2 h$
   $= \frac{\pi h^3}{12}$, the volume of the filter. The rate the coffee is falling is $\frac{dh}{dt} = \frac{4}{\pi h^2}\frac{dV}{dt} = \frac{4}{25\pi}(-10) = -\frac{8}{5\pi}$ in/min.

35. $y = QD^{-1} \Rightarrow \frac{dy}{dt} = D^{-1}\frac{dQ}{dt} - QD^{-2}\frac{dD}{dt} = \frac{1}{41}(0) - \frac{233}{(41)^2}(-2) = \frac{466}{1681}$ L/min $\Rightarrow$ increasing about 0.2772 L/min

36. Let $P(x, y)$ represent a point on the curve $y = x^2$ and $\theta$ the angle of inclination of a line containing P and the
    origin. Consequently, $\tan\theta = \frac{y}{x} \Rightarrow \tan\theta = \frac{x^2}{x} = x \Rightarrow \sec^2\theta\frac{d\theta}{dt} = \frac{dx}{dt} \Rightarrow \frac{d\theta}{dt} = \cos^2\theta\frac{dx}{dt}$. Since $\frac{dx}{dt} = 10$ m/sec
    and $\cos^2\theta\big|_{x=3} = \frac{x^2}{y^2 + x^2} = \frac{3^2}{9^2 + 3^2} = \frac{1}{10}$, we have $\left.\frac{d\theta}{dt}\right|_{x=3} = 1$ rad/sec.

37. The distance from the origin is $s = \sqrt{x^2 + y^2}$ and we wish to find $\frac{ds}{dt}\big|_{(5,12)} = \frac{1}{2}\left(x^2 + y^2\right)^{-1/2}\left(2x\frac{dx}{dt} + 2y\frac{dy}{dt}\right)\big|_{(5,12)}$

$= \frac{(5)(-1)+(12)(-5)}{\sqrt{25+144}} = -5$ m/sec

38. Let s = distance of car from foot of perpendicular in the textbook diagram $\Rightarrow \tan\theta = \frac{s}{132} \Rightarrow \sec^2\theta\frac{d\theta}{dt} = \frac{1}{132}\frac{ds}{dt}$

$\Rightarrow \frac{d\theta}{dt} = \frac{\cos^2\theta}{132}\frac{ds}{dt}$; $\frac{ds}{dt} = -264$ and $\theta = 0 \Rightarrow \frac{d\theta}{dt} = -2$ rad/sec. A half second later the car has traveled 132 ft

right of the perpendicular $\Rightarrow |\theta| = \frac{\pi}{4}$, $\cos^2\theta = \frac{1}{2}$, and $\frac{ds}{dt} = 264$ (since s increases) $\Rightarrow \frac{d\theta}{dt} = \frac{\left(\frac{1}{2}\right)}{132}(264) = 1$ rad/sec.

39. Let $s = 16t^2$ represent the distance the ball has fallen, h the distance between the ball and the ground, and I the distance between the shadow and the point directly beneath the ball. Accordingly, $s + h = 50$ and since the triangle LOQ and triangle PRQ are similar we have $I = \frac{30h}{50-h} \Rightarrow h = 50 - 16t^2$ and $I = \frac{30\left(50-16t^2\right)}{50-\left(50-16t^2\right)} = \frac{1500}{16t^2} - 30 \Rightarrow \frac{dI}{dt} = -\frac{1500}{8t^3}$

$\Rightarrow \frac{dI}{dt}\big|_{t=\frac{1}{2}} = -1500$ ft/sec.

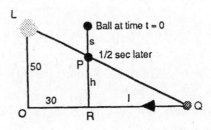

40. When x represents the length of the shadow, then $\tan\theta = \frac{80}{x} \Rightarrow \sec^2\theta\frac{d\theta}{dt} = -\frac{80}{x^2}\frac{dx}{dt} \Rightarrow \frac{dx}{dt} = \frac{-x^2\sec^2\theta}{80}\frac{d\theta}{dt}$. We are

given that $\frac{d\theta}{dt} = 0.27° = \frac{3\pi}{2000}$ rad/min. At x = 60, $\cos\theta = \frac{3}{5} \Rightarrow \left|\frac{dx}{dt}\right| = \left|\frac{-x^2\sec^2\theta}{80}\frac{d\theta}{dt}\right|_{\left(\frac{d\theta}{dt}=\frac{3\pi}{2000}\text{ and }\sec\theta=\frac{5}{3}\right)} = \frac{3\pi}{16}$ ft/min

$\approx 0.589$ ft/min $\approx 7.1$ in./min.

41. The volume of the ice is $V = \frac{4}{3}\pi r^3 - \frac{4}{3}\pi 4^3 \Rightarrow \frac{dV}{dt} = 4\pi r^2\frac{dr}{dt} \Rightarrow \frac{dr}{dt}\big|_{r=6} = \frac{-5}{72\pi}$ in./min when $\frac{dV}{dt} = -10$ in³/min, the

thickness of the ice is decreasing at $\frac{5}{72\pi}$ in./min. The surface area is $S = 4\pi r^2 \Rightarrow \frac{dS}{dt} = 8\pi r\frac{dr}{dt} \Rightarrow \frac{dS}{dt}\big|_{r=6} = 48\pi\left(\frac{-5}{72\pi}\right)$

$= -\frac{10}{3}$ in²/min, the outer surface of the ice is decreasing at $\frac{10}{3}$ in²/min.

42. Let s represent the horizontal distance between the car and plane while r is the line-of-sight distance between the car and

plane $\Rightarrow 9 + s^2 = r^2 \Rightarrow \frac{ds}{dt} = \frac{r}{\sqrt{r^2-9}}\frac{dr}{dt} \Rightarrow \frac{ds}{dt}\big|_{r=5} = \frac{5}{\sqrt{16}}(-160) = -200$ mph $\Rightarrow$ speed of plane + speed of car

$= 200$ mph $\Rightarrow$ the speed of the car is 80 mph.

43. Let x represent distance of the player from second base and s the distance to third base. Then $\frac{dx}{dt} = -16$ ft/sec

(a) $s^2 = x^2 + 8100 \Rightarrow 2s\frac{ds}{dt} = 2x\frac{dx}{dt} \Rightarrow \frac{ds}{dt} = \frac{x}{s}\frac{dx}{dt}$. When the player is 30 ft from first base, x = 60

$\Rightarrow s = 30\sqrt{13}$ and $\frac{ds}{dt} = \frac{60}{30\sqrt{13}}(-16) = \frac{-32}{\sqrt{13}} \approx -8.875$ ft/sec

(b) $\sin\theta_1 = \frac{90}{s} \Rightarrow \cos\theta_1\frac{d\theta_1}{dt} = -\frac{90}{s^2}\frac{ds}{dt} \Rightarrow \frac{d\theta_1}{dt} = -\frac{90}{s^2\cos\theta_1}\cdot\frac{ds}{dt} = -\frac{90}{s\cdot x}\cdot\frac{ds}{dt}$. Therefore, x = 60 and s = $30\sqrt{13}$

$\Rightarrow \frac{d\theta_1}{dt} = -\frac{90}{\left(30\sqrt{13}\right)(60)}\cdot\left(\frac{-32}{\sqrt{13}}\right) = \frac{8}{65}$ rad/sec; $\cos\theta_2 = \frac{90}{s} \Rightarrow -\sin\theta_2\frac{d\theta_2}{dt} = -\frac{90}{s^2}\frac{ds}{dt} \Rightarrow \frac{d\theta_2}{dt} = \frac{90}{s^2\sin\theta_2}\cdot\frac{ds}{dt}$

$= \frac{90}{s\cdot x}\cdot\frac{ds}{dt}$. Therefore, x = 60 and s = $30\sqrt{13} \Rightarrow \frac{d\theta_2}{dt} = \frac{90}{\left(30\sqrt{13}\right)(60)}\cdot\left(\frac{-32}{\sqrt{13}}\right) = -\frac{8}{65}$ rad/sec.

(c) $\frac{d\theta_1}{dt} = -\frac{90}{s^2\cos\theta_1}\cdot\frac{ds}{dt} = -\frac{90}{\left(s^2\cdot\frac{x}{s}\right)}\cdot\left(\frac{x}{s}\right)\cdot\left(\frac{dx}{dt}\right) = \left(-\frac{90}{s^2}\right)\left(\frac{dx}{dt}\right) = \left(-\frac{90}{x^2+8100}\right)\frac{dx}{dt} \Rightarrow \lim_{x\to 0}\frac{d\theta_1}{dt}$

$= \lim_{x\to 0}\left(-\frac{90}{x^2+8100}\right)(-15) = \frac{1}{6}$ rad/sec; $\frac{d\theta_2}{dt} = \frac{90}{s^2\sin\theta_2}\cdot\frac{ds}{dt} = \left(\frac{90}{s^2\cdot\frac{x}{s}}\right)\left(\frac{x}{s}\right)\left(\frac{dx}{dt}\right) = \left(\frac{90}{s^2}\right)\left(\frac{dx}{dt}\right)$

$= \left(\frac{90}{x^2+8100}\right)\frac{dx}{dt} \Rightarrow \lim_{x\to 0}\frac{d\theta_2}{dt} = -\frac{1}{6}$ rad/sec

44. Let a represent the distance between point O and ship A, b the distance between point O and ship B, and D the distance

between the ships. By the Law of Cosines, $D^2 = a^2 + b^2 - 2ab\cos 120° \Rightarrow \frac{dD}{dt} = \frac{1}{2D}\left[2a\frac{da}{dt} + 2b\frac{db}{dt} + a\frac{db}{dt} + b\frac{da}{dt}\right]$.

When a = 5, $\frac{da}{dt} = 14$, b = 3, and $\frac{db}{dt} = 21$, then $\frac{dD}{dt} = \frac{413}{2D}$ where D = 7. The ships are moving $\frac{dD}{dt} = 29.5$ knots apart.

## 3.9 LINEARIZATION AND DIFFERENTIALS

1. $f(x) = x^3 - 2x + 3 \Rightarrow f'(x) = 3x^2 - 2 \Rightarrow L(x) = f'(2)(x - 2) + f(2) = 10(x - 2) + 7 \Rightarrow L(x) = 10x - 13$ at $x = 2$

2. $f(x) = \sqrt{x^2 + 9} = (x^2 + 9)^{1/2} \Rightarrow f'(x) = \left(\frac{1}{2}\right)(x^2 + 9)^{-1/2}(2x) = \frac{x}{\sqrt{x^2 + 9}} \Rightarrow L(x) = f'(-4)(x + 4) + f(-4)$
   $= -\frac{4}{5}(x + 4) + 5 \Rightarrow L(x) = -\frac{4}{5}x + \frac{9}{5}$ at $x = -4$

3. $f(x) = x + \frac{1}{x} \Rightarrow f'(x) = 1 - x^{-2} \Rightarrow L(x) = f(1) + f'(1)(x - 1) = 2 + 0(x - 1) = 2$

4. $f(x) = x^{1/3} \Rightarrow f'(x) = \frac{1}{3x^{2/3}} \Rightarrow L(x) = f'(-8)(x - (-8)) + f(-8) = \frac{1}{12}(x + 8) - 2 \Rightarrow L(x) = \frac{1}{12}x - \frac{4}{3}$

5. $f(x) = \tan x \Rightarrow f'(x) = \sec^2 x \Rightarrow L(x) = f(\pi) + f'(\pi)(x - \pi) = 0 + 1(x - \pi) = x - \pi$

6. (a) $f(x) = \sin x \Rightarrow f'(x) = \cos x \Rightarrow L(x) = f(0) + f'(0)(x - 0) = x \Rightarrow L(x) = x$
   (b) $f(x) = \cos x \Rightarrow f'(x) = -\sin x \Rightarrow L(x) = f(0) + f'(0)(x - 0) = 1 \Rightarrow L(x) = 1$
   (c) $f(x) = \tan x \Rightarrow f'(x) = \sec^2 x \Rightarrow L(x) = f(0) + f'(0)(x - 0) = x \Rightarrow L(x) = x$

7. $f(x) = x^2 + 2x \Rightarrow f'(x) = 2x + 2 \Rightarrow L(x) = f'(0)(x - 0) + f(0) = 2(x - 0) + 0 \Rightarrow L(x) = 2x$ at $x = 0$

8. $f(x) = x^{-1} \Rightarrow f'(x) = -x^{-2} \Rightarrow L(x) = f'(1)(x - 1) + f(1) = (-1)(x - 1) + 1 \Rightarrow L(x) = -x + 2$ at $x = 1$

9. $f(x) = 2x^2 + 4x - 3 \Rightarrow f'(x) = 4x + 4 \Rightarrow L(x) = f'(-1)(x + 1) + f(-1) = 0(x + 1) + (-5) \Rightarrow L(x) = -5$ at $x = -1$

10. $f(x) = 1 + x \Rightarrow f'(x) = 1 \Rightarrow L(x) = f'(8)(x - 8) + f(8) = 1(x - 8) + 9 \Rightarrow L(x) = x + 1$ at $x = 8$

11. $f(x) = \sqrt[3]{x} = x^{1/3} \Rightarrow f'(x) = \left(\frac{1}{3}\right)x^{-2/3} \Rightarrow L(x) = f'(8)(x - 8) + f(8) = \frac{1}{12}(x - 8) + 2 \Rightarrow L(x) = \frac{1}{12}x + \frac{4}{3}$ at $x = 8$

12. $f(x) = \frac{x}{x + 1} \Rightarrow f'(x) = \frac{(1)(x + 1) - (1)(x)}{(x + 1)^2} = \frac{1}{(x + 1)^2} \Rightarrow L(x) = f'(1)(x - 1) + f(1) = \frac{1}{4}(x - 1) + \frac{1}{2}$
    $\Rightarrow L(x) = \frac{1}{4}x + \frac{1}{4}$ at $x = 1$

13. $f'(x) = k(1 + x)^{k-1}$. We have $f(0) = 1$ and $f'(0) = k$. $L(x) = f(0) + f'(0)(x - 0) = 1 + k(x - 0) = 1 + kx$

14. (a) $f(x) = (1 - x)^6 = \left[1 + (-x)\right]^6 \approx 1 + 6(-x) = 1 - 6x$
    (b) $f(x) = \frac{2}{1 - x} = 2\left[1 + (-x)\right]^{-1} \approx 2\left[1 + (-1)(-x)\right] = 2 + 2x$
    (c) $f(x) = (1 + x)^{-1/2} \approx 1 + \left(-\frac{1}{2}\right)x = 1 - \frac{x}{2}$
    (d) $f(x) = \sqrt{2 + x^2} = \sqrt{2}\left(1 + \frac{x^2}{2}\right)^{1/2} \approx \sqrt{2}\left(1 + \frac{1}{2}\frac{x^2}{2}\right) = \sqrt{2}\left(1 + \frac{x^2}{4}\right)$
    (e) $f(x) = (4 + 3x)^{1/3} = 4^{1/3}\left(1 + \frac{3x}{4}\right)^{1/3} \approx 4^{1/3}\left(1 + \frac{1}{3}\frac{3x}{4}\right) = 4^{1/3}\left(1 + \frac{x}{4}\right)$
    (f) $f(x) = \left(1 - \frac{1}{2 + x}\right)^{2/3} = \left[1 + \left(-\frac{1}{2 + x}\right)\right]^{2/3} \approx 1 + \frac{2}{3}\left(-\frac{1}{2 + x}\right) = 1 - \frac{2}{6 + 3x}$

15. (a) $(1.0002)^{50} = (1 + 0.0002)^{50} \approx 1 + 50(0.0002) = 1 + .01 = 1.01$
    (b) $\sqrt[3]{1.009} = (1 + 0.009)^{1/3} \approx 1 + \left(\frac{1}{3}\right)(0.009) = 1 + 0.003 = 1.003$

16. $f(x) = \sqrt{x + 1} + \sin x = (x + 1)^{1/2} + \sin x \Rightarrow f'(x) = \left(\frac{1}{2}\right)(x + 1)^{-1/2} + \cos x \Rightarrow L_f(x) = f'(0)(x - 0) + f(0)$
    $= \frac{3}{2}(x - 0) + 1 \Rightarrow L_f(x) = \frac{3}{2}x + 1$, the linearization of $f(x)$; $g(x) = \sqrt{x + 1} = (x + 1)^{1/2} \Rightarrow g'(x)$

$= \left(\frac{1}{2}\right)(x+1)^{-1/2} \Rightarrow L_g(x) = g'(0)(x-0) + g(0) = \frac{1}{2}(x-0) + 1 \Rightarrow L_g(x) = \frac{1}{2}x + 1$, the linearization of $g(x)$;

$h(x) = \sin x \Rightarrow h'(x) = \cos x \Rightarrow L_h(x) = h'(0)(x-0) + h(0) = (1)(x-0) + 0 \Rightarrow L_h(x) = x$, the linearization of $h(x)$. $L_f(x) = L_g(x) + L_h(x)$ implies that the linearization of a sum is equal to the sum of the linearizations.

17. $y = x^3 - 3\sqrt{x} = x^3 - 3x^{1/2} \Rightarrow dy = \left(3x^2 - \frac{3}{2}x^{-1/2}\right) dx \Rightarrow dy = \left(3x^2 - \frac{3}{2\sqrt{x}}\right) dx$

18. $y = x\sqrt{1-x^2} = x(1-x^2)^{1/2} \Rightarrow dy = \left[(1)(1-x^2)^{1/2} + (x)\left(\frac{1}{2}\right)(1-x^2)^{-1/2}(-2x)\right] dx$

$= (1-x^2)^{-1/2}\left[(1-x^2) - x^2\right] dx = \frac{(1-2x^2)}{\sqrt{1-x^2}} dx$

19. $y = \frac{2x}{1+x^2} \Rightarrow dy = \left(\frac{(2)(1+x^2) - (2x)(2x)}{(1+x^2)^2}\right) dx = \frac{2-2x^2}{(1+x^2)^2} dx$

20. $y = \frac{2\sqrt{x}}{3(1+\sqrt{x})} = \frac{2x^{1/2}}{3(1+x^{1/2})} \Rightarrow dy = \left(\frac{x^{-1/2}\left(3\left(1+x^{1/2}\right)\right) - 2x^{1/2}\left(\frac{3}{2}x^{-1/2}\right)}{9\left(1+x^{1/2}\right)^2}\right) dx = \frac{3x^{-1/2}+3-3}{9\left(1+x^{1/2}\right)^2} dx$

$\Rightarrow dy = \frac{1}{3\sqrt{x}\left(1+\sqrt{x}\right)^2} dx$

21. $2y^{3/2} + xy - x = 0 \Rightarrow 3y^{1/2} dy + y dx + x dy - dx = 0 \Rightarrow \left(3y^{1/2} + x\right) dy = (1-y) dx \Rightarrow dy = \frac{1-y}{3\sqrt{y}+x} dx$

22. $xy^2 - 4x^{3/2} - y = 0 \Rightarrow y^2 dx + 2xy dy - 6x^{1/2} dx - dy = 0 \Rightarrow (2xy-1) dy = \left(6x^{1/2} - y^2\right) dx$

$\Rightarrow dy = \frac{6\sqrt{x}-y^2}{2xy-1} dx$

23. $y = \sin\left(5\sqrt{x}\right) = \sin\left(5x^{1/2}\right) \Rightarrow dy = \left(\cos\left(5x^{1/2}\right)\right)\left(\frac{5}{2}x^{-1/2}\right) dx \Rightarrow dy = \frac{5\cos\left(5\sqrt{x}\right)}{2\sqrt{x}} dx$

24. $y = \cos\left(x^2\right) \Rightarrow dy = \left[-\sin\left(x^2\right)\right](2x) dx = -2x\sin\left(x^2\right) dx$

25. $y = 4\tan\left(\frac{x^3}{3}\right) \Rightarrow dy = 4\left(\sec^2\left(\frac{x^3}{3}\right)\right)(x^2) dx \Rightarrow dy = 4x^2\sec^2\left(\frac{x^3}{3}\right) dx$

26. $y = \sec\left(x^2 - 1\right) \Rightarrow dy = \left[\sec\left(x^2 - 1\right)\tan\left(x^2 - 1\right)\right](2x) dx = 2x\left[\sec\left(x^2 - 1\right)\tan\left(x^2 - 1\right)\right] dx$

27. $y = 3\csc\left(1 - 2\sqrt{x}\right) = 3\csc\left(1 - 2x^{1/2}\right) \Rightarrow dy = 3\left(-\csc\left(1 - 2x^{1/2}\right)\right)\cot\left(1 - 2x^{1/2}\right)\left(-x^{-1/2}\right) dx$

$\Rightarrow dy = \frac{3}{\sqrt{x}}\csc\left(1 - 2\sqrt{x}\right)\cot\left(1 - 2\sqrt{x}\right) dx$

28. $y = 2\cot\left(\frac{1}{\sqrt{x}}\right) = 2\cot\left(x^{-1/2}\right) \Rightarrow dy = -2\csc^2\left(x^{-1/2}\right)\left(-\frac{1}{2}\right)\left(x^{-3/2}\right) dx \Rightarrow dy = \frac{1}{\sqrt{x^3}}\csc^2\left(\frac{1}{\sqrt{x}}\right) dx$

29. $f(x) = x^2 + 2x, x_0 = 1, dx = 0.1 \Rightarrow f'(x) = 2x + 2$

(a) $\Delta f = f(x_0 + dx) - f(x_0) = f(1.1) - f(1) = 3.41 - 3 = 0.41$

(b) $df = f'(x_0) dx = [2(1) + 2](0.1) = 0.4$

(c) $|\Delta f - df| = |0.41 - 0.4| = 0.01$

30. $f(x) = 2x^2 + 4x - 3, x_0 = -1, dx = 0.1 \Rightarrow f'(x) = 4x + 4$

(a) $\Delta f = f(x_0 + dx) - f(x_0) = f(-.9) - f(-1) = .02$

(b) $df = f'(x_0) dx = [4(-1) + 4](.1) = 0$

(c) $|\Delta f - df| = |.02 - 0| = .02$

31. $f(x) = x^3 - x$, $x_0 = 1$, $dx = 0.1 \Rightarrow f'(x) = 3x^2 - 1$
    (a) $\Delta f = f(x_0 + dx) - f(x_0) = f(1.1) - f(1) = .231$
    (b) $df = f'(x_0)\, dx = [3(1)^2 - 1](.1) = .2$
    (c) $|\Delta f - df| = |.231 - .2| = .031$

32. $f(x) = x^4$, $x_0 = 1$, $dx = 0.1 \Rightarrow f'(x) = 4x^3$
    (a) $\Delta f = f(x_0 + dx) - f(x_0) = f(1.1) - f(1) = .4641$
    (b) $df = f'(x_0)\, dx = 4(1)^3(.1) = .4$
    (c) $|\Delta f - df| = |.4641 - .4| = .0641$

33. $f(x) = x^{-1}$, $x_0 = 0.5$, $dx = 0.1 \Rightarrow f'(x) = -x^{-2}$
    (a) $\Delta f = f(x_0 + dx) - f(x_0) = f(.6) - f(.5) = -\frac{1}{3}$
    (b) $df = f'(x_0)\, dx = (-4)\left(\frac{1}{10}\right) = -\frac{2}{5}$
    (c) $|\Delta f - df| = \left|-\frac{1}{3} + \frac{2}{5}\right| = \frac{1}{15}$

34. $f(x) = x^3 - 2x + 3$, $x_0 = 2$, $dx = 0.1 \Rightarrow f'(x) = 3x^2 - 2$
    (a) $\Delta f = f(x_0 + dx) - f(x_0) = f(2.1) - f(2) = 1.061$
    (b) $df = f'(x_0)\, dx = (10)(0.10) = 1$
    (c) $|\Delta f - df| = |1.061 - 1| = .061$

35. $V = \frac{4}{3}\pi r^3 \Rightarrow dV = 4\pi r_0^2\, dr$      36. $V = x^3 \Rightarrow dV = 3x_0^2\, dx$

37. $S = 6x^2 \Rightarrow dS = 12x_0\, dx$

38. $S = \pi r\sqrt{r^2 + h^2} = \pi r\left(r^2 + h^2\right)^{1/2}$, h constant $\Rightarrow \frac{dS}{dr} = \pi\left(r^2 + h^2\right)^{1/2} + \pi r \cdot r\left(r^2 + h^2\right)^{-1/2}$
    $\Rightarrow \frac{dS}{dr} = \frac{\pi\left(r^2 + h^2\right) + \pi r^2}{\sqrt{r^2 + h^2}} \Rightarrow dS = \frac{\pi\left(2r_0^2 + h^2\right)}{\sqrt{r_0^2 + h^2}}\, dr$, h constant

39. $V = \pi r^2 h$, height constant $\Rightarrow dV = 2\pi r_0 h\, dr$      40. $S = 2\pi r h \Rightarrow dS = 2\pi r\, dh$

41. Given $r = 2$ m, $dr = .02$ m
    (a) $A = \pi r^2 \Rightarrow dA = 2\pi r\, dr = 2\pi(2)(.02) = .08\pi$ m$^2$
    (b) $\left(\frac{.08\pi}{4\pi}\right)(100\%) = 2\%$

42. $C = 2\pi r$ and $dC = 2$ in. $\Rightarrow dC = 2\pi\, dr \Rightarrow dr = \frac{1}{\pi} \Rightarrow$ the diameter grew about $\frac{2}{\pi}$ in.; $A = \pi r^2 \Rightarrow dA = 2\pi r\, dr$
    $= 2\pi(5)\left(\frac{1}{\pi}\right) = 10$ in.$^2$

43. The volume of a cylinder is $V = \pi r^2 h$. When h is held fixed, we have $\frac{dV}{dr} = 2\pi r h$, and so $dV = 2\pi r h\, dr$. For $h = 30$ in., $r = 6$ in., and $dr = 0.5$ in., the volume of the material in the shell is approximately $dV = 2\pi r h\, dr = 2\pi(6)(30)(0.5)$
    $= 180\pi \approx 565.5$ in$^3$.

44. Let $\theta = $ angle of elevation and $h = $ height of building. Then $h = 30\tan\theta$, so $dh = 30\sec^2\theta\, d\theta$. We want $|dh| < 0.04h$, which gives: $|30\sec^2\theta\, d\theta| < 0.04|30\tan\theta| \Rightarrow \frac{1}{\cos^2\theta}|d\theta| < \frac{0.04\sin\theta}{\cos\theta} \Rightarrow |d\theta| < 0.04\sin\theta\cos\theta \Rightarrow |d\theta| < 0.04\sin\frac{5\pi}{12}\cos\frac{5\pi}{12}$
    $= 0.01$ radian. The angle should be measured with an error of less than 0.01 radian (or approximatley 0.57 degrees), which is a percentage error of approximately 0.76%.

45. The percentage error in the radius is $\frac{\left(\frac{dr}{dt}\right)}{r} \times 100 \le 2\%$.

(a) Since $C = 2\pi r \Rightarrow \frac{dC}{dt} = 2\pi \frac{dr}{dt}$. The percentage error in calculating the circle's circumference is $\frac{\left(\frac{dC}{dt}\right)}{C} \times 100$

$= \frac{\left(2\pi \frac{dr}{dt}\right)}{2\pi r} \times 100 = \frac{\left(\frac{dr}{dt}\right)}{r} \times 100 \le 2\%$.

(b) Since $A = \pi r^2 \Rightarrow \frac{dA}{dt} = 2\pi r \frac{dr}{dt}$. The percentage error in calculating the circle's area is given by $\frac{\left(\frac{dA}{dt}\right)}{A} \times 100$

$= \frac{\left(2\pi r \frac{dr}{dt}\right)}{\pi r^2} \times 100 = 2\frac{\left(\frac{dr}{dt}\right)}{r} \times 100 \le 2(2\%) = 4\%$.

46. The percentage error in the edge of the cube is $\frac{\left(\frac{dx}{dt}\right)}{x} \times 100 \le 0.5\%$.

(a) Since $S = 6x^2 \Rightarrow \frac{dS}{dt} = 12x \frac{dx}{dt}$. The percentage error in the cube's surface area is $\frac{\left(\frac{dS}{dt}\right)}{S} \times 100 = \frac{\left(12x \frac{dx}{dt}\right)}{6x^2} \times 100$

$= 2\frac{\left(\frac{dx}{dt}\right)}{x} \times 100 \le 2(0.5\%) = 1\%$

(b) Since $V = x^3 \Rightarrow \frac{dV}{dt} = 3x^2 \frac{dx}{dt}$. The percentage error in the cube's volume is $\frac{\left(\frac{dV}{dt}\right)}{V} \times 100 = \frac{\left(3x^2 \frac{dx}{dt}\right)}{x^3} \times 100$

$= 3\frac{\left(\frac{dx}{dt}\right)}{x} \times 100 \le 3(0.5\%) = 1.5\%$

47. $V = \pi h^3 \Rightarrow dV = 3\pi h^2\, dh$; recall that $\Delta V \approx dV$. Then $|\Delta V| \le (1\%)(V) = \frac{(1)(\pi h^3)}{100} \Rightarrow |dV| \le \frac{(1)(\pi h^3)}{100}$

$\Rightarrow |3\pi h^2\, dh| \le \frac{(1)(\pi h^3)}{100} \Rightarrow |dh| \le \frac{1}{300} h = \left(\frac{1}{3}\%\right) h$. Therefore the greatest tolerated error in the measurement of h is $\frac{1}{3}\%$.

48. (a) Let $D_i$ represent the interior diameter. Then $V = \pi r^2 h = \pi \left(\frac{D_i}{2}\right)^2 h = \frac{\pi D_i^2 h}{4}$ and $h = 10 \Rightarrow V = \frac{5\pi D_i^2}{2} \Rightarrow$

$dV = 5\pi D_i\, dD_i$. Recall that $\Delta V \approx dV$. We want $|\Delta V| \le (1\%)(V) \Rightarrow |dV| \le \left(\frac{1}{100}\right)\left(\frac{5\pi D_i^2}{2}\right) = \frac{\pi D_i^2}{40}$

$\Rightarrow 5\pi D_i\, dD_i \le \frac{\pi D_i^2}{40} \Rightarrow \frac{dD_i}{D_i} \le 200$. The inside diameter must be measured to within 0.5%.

(b) Let $D_e$ represent the exterior diameter, h the height and S the area of the painted surface. $S = \pi D_e h \Rightarrow dS = \pi h dD_e$

$\Rightarrow \frac{dS}{S} = \frac{dD_e}{D_e}$. Thus for small changes in exterior diameter, the approximate percentage change in the exterior diameter is equal to the approximate percentage change in the area painted, and to estimate the amount of paint required to within 5%, the tanks's exterior diameter must be measured to within 5%.

49. Given $D = 100$ cm, $dD = 1$ cm, $V = \frac{4}{3}\pi \left(\frac{D}{2}\right)^3 = \frac{\pi D^3}{6} \Rightarrow dV = \frac{\pi}{2} D^2\, dD = \frac{\pi}{2}(100)^2(1) = \frac{10^4 \pi}{2}$. Then $\frac{dV}{V}(100\%)$

$= \left[\frac{\frac{10^4 \pi}{2}}{\frac{10^6 \pi}{6}}\right](10^2\%) = \left[\frac{\frac{10^6 \pi}{2}}{\frac{10^6 \pi}{6}}\right]\% = 3\%$

50. $V = \frac{4}{3}\pi r^3 = \frac{4}{3}\pi \left(\frac{D}{2}\right)^3 = \frac{\pi D^3}{6} \Rightarrow dV = \frac{\pi D^2}{2}\, dD$; recall that $\Delta V \approx dV$. Then $|\Delta V| \le (3\%)V = \left(\frac{3}{100}\right)\left(\frac{\pi D^3}{6}\right)$

$= \frac{\pi D^3}{200} \Rightarrow |dV| \le \frac{\pi D^3}{200} \Rightarrow \left|\frac{\pi D^2}{2}\, dD\right| \le \frac{\pi D^3}{200} \Rightarrow |dD| \le \frac{D}{100} = (1\%)\, D \Rightarrow$ the allowable percentage error in measuring the diameter is 1%.

51. $W = a + \frac{b}{g} = a + bg^{-1} \Rightarrow dW = -bg^{-2}\, dg = -\frac{b\, dg}{g^2} \Rightarrow \frac{dW_{\text{moon}}}{dW_{\text{earth}}} = \frac{\left(-\frac{b\, dg}{(5.2)^2}\right)}{\left(-\frac{b\, dg}{(32)^2}\right)} = \left(\frac{32}{5.2}\right)^2 = 37.87$, so a change of

gravity on the moon has about 38 times the effect that a change of the same magnitude has on Earth.

52. (a) $T = 2\pi \left(\frac{L}{g}\right)^{1/2} \Rightarrow dT = 2\pi \sqrt{L}\left(-\frac{1}{2}g^{-3/2}\right)dg = -\pi\sqrt{L}\, g^{-3/2}\, dg$

(b) If g increases, then $dg > 0 \Rightarrow dT < 0$. The period T decreases and the clock ticks more frequently. Both the pendulum speed and clock speed increase.

(c) $0.001 = -\pi\sqrt{100}\left(980^{-3/2}\right)dg \Rightarrow dg \approx -0.977$ cm/sec$^2 \Rightarrow$ the new $g \approx 979$ cm/sec$^2$

53. $E(x) = f(x) - g(x) \Rightarrow E(x) = f(x) - m(x - a) - c$. Then $E(a) = 0 \Rightarrow f(a) - m(a - a) - c = 0 \Rightarrow c = f(a)$. Next we calculate m: $\lim_{x \to a} \frac{E(x)}{x - a} = 0 \Rightarrow \lim_{x \to a} \frac{f(x) - m(x - a) - c}{x - a} = 0 \Rightarrow \lim_{x \to a} \left[ \frac{f(x) - f(a)}{x - a} - m \right] = 0$ (since $c = f(a)$)

$\Rightarrow f'(a) - m = 0 \Rightarrow m = f'(a)$. Therefore, $g(x) = m(x - a) + c = f'(a)(x - a) + f(a)$ is the linear approximation, as claimed.

54. (a) i.    $Q(a) = f(a)$ implies that $b_0 = f(a)$.

ii.    Since $Q'(x) = b_1 + 2b_2(x - a)$, $Q'(a) = f'(a)$ implies that $b_1 = f'(a)$.

iii.    Since $Q''(x) = 2b_2$, $Q''(a) = f''(a)$ implies that $b_2 = \frac{f''(a)}{2}$.

In summary, $b_0 = f(a)$, $b_1 = f'(a)$, and $b_2 = \frac{f''(a)}{2}$.

(b) $f(x) = (1 - x)^{-1}$; $f'(x) = -1(1 - x)^{-2}(-1) = (1 - x)^{-2}$; $f''(x) = -2(1 - x)^{-3}(-1) = 2(1 - x)^{-3}$

Since $f(0) = 1$, $f'(0) = 1$, and $f''(0) = 2$, the coefficients are $b_0 = 1$, $b_1 = 1$, $b_2 = \frac{2}{2} = 1$. The quadratic approximation is $Q(x) = 1 + x + x^2$.

(c)

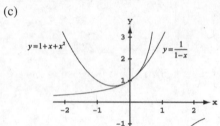

[-2.35, 2.35] by [-1.25, 3.25]

As one zooms in, the two graphs quickly become indistinguishable. They appear to be identical.

(d) $g(x) = x^{-1}$; $g'(x) = -1x^{-2}$; $g''(x) = 2x^{-3}$

Since $g(1) = 1$, $g'(1) = -1$, and $g''(1) = 2$, the coefficients are $b_0 = 1$, $b_1 = -1$, $b_2 = \frac{2}{2} = 1$. The quadratic approximation is $Q(x) = 1 - (x - 1) + (x - 1)^2$.

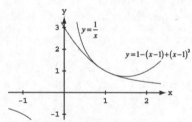

[-1.35, 3.35] by [-1.25, 3.25]

As one zooms in, the two graphs quickly become indistinguishable. They appear to be identical.

(e) $h(x) = (1 + x)^{1/2}$; $h'(x) = \frac{1}{2}(1 + x)^{-1/2}$; $h''(x) = -\frac{1}{4}(1 + x)^{-3/2}$

Since $h(0) = 1$, $h'(0) = \frac{1}{2}$, and $h''(0) = -\frac{1}{4}$, the coefficients are $b_0 = 1$, $b_1 = \frac{1}{2}$, $b_2 = \frac{-\frac{1}{4}}{2} = -\frac{1}{8}$. The quadratic approximation is $Q(x) = 1 + \frac{x}{2} - \frac{x^2}{8}$.

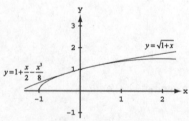

As one zooms in, the two graphs quickly become indistinguishable. They appear to be identical.

(f) The linearization of any differentiable function u(x) at $x = a$ is $L(x) = u(a) + u'(a)(x - a) = b_0 + b_1(x - a)$, where $b_0$ and $b_1$ are the coefficients of the constant and linear terms of the quadratic approximation. Thus, the linearization for f(x) at $x = 0$ is $1 + x$; the linearization for g(x) at $x = 1$ is $1 - (x - 1)$ or $2 - x$; and the linearization for h(x) at $x = 0$ is $1 + \frac{x}{2}$.

55-58.   Example CAS commands:

Maple:

    with(plots):

    a:= 1: f:=x -> x ∧ 3 + x ∧ 2 − 2*x;

    plot(f(x), x=−1..2);

    diff(f(x),x);

    fp := unapply ("",x);

    L:=x -> f(a) + fp(a)*(x − a);

    plot({f(x), L(x)}, x=−1..2);

    err:=x -> abs(f(x) − L(x));

    plot(err(x), x=−1..2, title = #absolute error function#);

    err(−1);

Mathematica: (function, x1, x2, and a may vary):

    Clear[f, x]

    {x1, x2} = {−1, 2}; a = 1;

    f[x_]:=x³ + x² − 2x

    Plot[f[x], {x, x1, x2}]

    lin[x_]=f[a] + f'[a](x − a)

    Plot[{f[x], lin[x]}, {x, x1, x2}]

    err[x_]=Abs[f[x] − lin[x]]

    Plot[err[x], {x, x1,x 2}]

    err//N

After reviewing the error function, plot the error function and epsilon for differing values of epsilon (eps) and delta (del)

    eps = 0.5; del = 0.4

    Plot[{err[x], eps},{x, a − del, a + del}]

# CHAPTER 3 PRACTICE EXERCISES

1.  $y = x^5 - 0.125x^2 + 0.25x \Rightarrow \frac{dy}{dx} = 5x^4 - 0.25x + 0.25$

2.  $y = 3 - 0.7x^3 + 0.3x^7 \Rightarrow \frac{dy}{dx} = -2.1x^2 + 2.1x^6$

3.  $y = x^3 - 3\left(x^2 + \pi^2\right) \Rightarrow \frac{dy}{dx} = 3x^2 - 3(2x + 0) = 3x^2 - 6x = 3x(x - 2)$

4.  $y = x^7 + \sqrt{7}x - \frac{1}{\pi+1} \Rightarrow \frac{dy}{dx} = 7x^6 + \sqrt{7}$

5.  $y = (x + 1)^2\left(x^2 + 2x\right) \Rightarrow \frac{dy}{dx} = (x + 1)^2(2x + 2) + \left(x^2 + 2x\right)(2(x + 1)) = 2(x + 1)\left[(x + 1)^2 + x(x + 2)\right]$
    $= 2(x + 1)\left(2x^2 + 4x + 1\right)$

6.  $y = (2x - 5)(4 - x)^{-1} \Rightarrow \frac{dy}{dx} = (2x - 5)(-1)(4 - x)^{-2}(-1) + (4 - x)^{-1}(2) = (4 - x)^{-2}\left[(2x - 5) + 2(4 - x)\right]$
    $= 3(4 - x)^{-2}$

7.  $y = \left(\theta^2 + \sec\theta + 1\right)^3 \Rightarrow \frac{dy}{d\theta} = 3\left(\theta^2 + \sec\theta + 1\right)^2(2\theta + \sec\theta\tan\theta)$

8.  $y = \left(-1 - \frac{\csc\theta}{2} - \frac{\theta^2}{4}\right)^2 \Rightarrow \frac{dy}{d\theta} = 2\left(-1 - \frac{\csc\theta}{2} - \frac{\theta^2}{4}\right)\left(\frac{\csc\theta\cot\theta}{2} - \frac{\theta}{2}\right) = \left(-1 - \frac{\csc\theta}{2} - \frac{\theta^2}{4}\right)(\csc\theta\cot\theta - \theta)$

9. $s = \frac{\sqrt{t}}{1+\sqrt{t}} \Rightarrow \frac{ds}{dt} = \frac{(1+\sqrt{t})\cdot\frac{1}{2\sqrt{t}} - \sqrt{t}\left(\frac{1}{2\sqrt{t}}\right)}{(1+\sqrt{t})^2} = \frac{(1+\sqrt{t}) - \sqrt{t}}{2\sqrt{t}(1+\sqrt{t})^2} = \frac{1}{2\sqrt{t}(1+\sqrt{t})^2}$

10. $s = \frac{1}{\sqrt{t}-1} \Rightarrow \frac{ds}{dt} = \frac{(\sqrt{t}-1)(0) - 1\left(\frac{1}{2\sqrt{t}}\right)}{(\sqrt{t}-1)^2} = \frac{-1}{2\sqrt{t}(\sqrt{t}-1)^2}$

11. $y = 2\tan^2 x - \sec^2 x \Rightarrow \frac{dy}{dx} = (4\tan x)(\sec^2 x) - (2\sec x)(\sec x \tan x) = 2\sec^2 x \tan x$

12. $y = \frac{1}{\sin^2 x} - \frac{2}{\sin x} = \csc^2 x - 2\csc x \Rightarrow \frac{dy}{dx} = (2\csc x)(-\csc x \cot x) - 2(-\csc x \cot x) = (2\csc x \cot x)(1 - \csc x)$

13. $s = \cos^4(1-2t) \Rightarrow \frac{ds}{dt} = 4\cos^3(1-2t)(-\sin(1-2t))(-2) = 8\cos^3(1-2t)\sin(1-2t)$

14. $s = \cot^3\left(\frac{2}{t}\right) \Rightarrow \frac{ds}{dt} = 3\cot^2\left(\frac{2}{t}\right)\left(-\csc^2\left(\frac{2}{t}\right)\right)\left(\frac{-2}{t^2}\right) = \frac{6}{t^2}\cot^2\left(\frac{2}{t}\right)\csc^2\left(\frac{2}{t}\right)$

15. $s = (\sec t + \tan t)^5 \Rightarrow \frac{ds}{dt} = 5(\sec t + \tan t)^4(\sec t \tan t + \sec^2 t) = 5(\sec t)(\sec t + \tan t)^5$

16. $s = \csc^5(1 - t + 3t^2) \Rightarrow \frac{ds}{dt} = 5\csc^4(1-t+3t^2)(-\csc(1-t+3t^2)\cot(1-t+3t^2))(-1+6t)$
$= -5(6t-1)\csc^5(1-t+3t^2)\cot(1-t+3t^2)$

17. $r = \sqrt{2\theta\sin\theta} = (2\theta\sin\theta)^{1/2} \Rightarrow \frac{dr}{d\theta} = \frac{1}{2}(2\theta\sin\theta)^{-1/2}(2\theta\cos\theta + 2\sin\theta) = \frac{\theta\cos\theta + \sin\theta}{\sqrt{2\theta\sin\theta}}$

18. $r = 2\theta\sqrt{\cos\theta} = 2\theta(\cos\theta)^{1/2} \Rightarrow \frac{dr}{d\theta} = 2\theta\left(\frac{1}{2}\right)(\cos\theta)^{-1/2}(-\sin\theta) + 2(\cos\theta)^{1/2} = \frac{-\theta\sin\theta}{\sqrt{\cos\theta}} + 2\sqrt{\cos\theta}$
$= \frac{2\cos\theta - \theta\sin\theta}{\sqrt{\cos\theta}}$

19. $r = \sin\sqrt{2\theta} = \sin(2\theta)^{1/2} \Rightarrow \frac{dr}{d\theta} = \cos(2\theta)^{1/2}\left(\frac{1}{2}(2\theta)^{-1/2}(2)\right) = \frac{\cos\sqrt{2\theta}}{\sqrt{2\theta}}$

20. $r = \sin\left(\theta + \sqrt{\theta+1}\right) \Rightarrow \frac{dr}{d\theta} = \cos\left(\theta + \sqrt{\theta+1}\right)\left(1 + \frac{1}{2\sqrt{\theta+1}}\right) = \frac{2\sqrt{\theta+1}+1}{2\sqrt{\theta+1}}\cos\left(\theta + \sqrt{\theta+1}\right)$

21. $y = \frac{1}{2}x^2\csc\frac{2}{x} \Rightarrow \frac{dy}{dx} = \frac{1}{2}x^2\left(-\csc\frac{2}{x}\cot\frac{2}{x}\right)\left(\frac{-2}{x^2}\right) + \left(\csc\frac{2}{x}\right)\left(\frac{1}{2}\cdot 2x\right) = \csc\frac{2}{x}\cot\frac{2}{x} + x\csc\frac{2}{x}$

22. $y = 2\sqrt{x}\sin\sqrt{x} \Rightarrow \frac{dy}{dx} = 2\sqrt{x}\left(\cos\sqrt{x}\right)\left(\frac{1}{2\sqrt{x}}\right) + \left(\sin\sqrt{x}\right)\left(\frac{2}{2\sqrt{x}}\right) = \cos\sqrt{x} + \frac{\sin\sqrt{x}}{\sqrt{x}}$

23. $y = x^{-1/2}\sec(2x)^2 \Rightarrow \frac{dy}{dx} = x^{-1/2}\sec(2x)^2\tan(2x)^2(2(2x)\cdot 2) + \sec(2x)^2\left(-\frac{1}{2}x^{-3/2}\right)$
$= 8x^{1/2}\sec(2x)^2\tan(2x)^2 - \frac{1}{2}x^{-3/2}\sec(2x)^2 = \frac{1}{2}x^{1/2}\sec(2x)^2\left[16\tan(2x)^2 - x^{-2}\right]$ or $\frac{1}{2x^{3/2}}\sec(2x)^2\left[16x^2\tan(2x)^2 - 1\right]$

24. $y = \sqrt{x}\csc(x+1)^3 = x^{1/2}\csc(x+1)^3$
$\Rightarrow \frac{dy}{dx} = x^{1/2}\left(-\csc(x+1)^3\cot(x+1)^3\right)(3(x+1)^2) + \csc(x+1)^3\left(\frac{1}{2}x^{-1/2}\right)$
$= -3\sqrt{x}(x+1)^2\csc(x+1)^3\cot(x+1)^3 + \frac{\csc(x+1)^3}{2\sqrt{x}} = \frac{1}{2}\sqrt{x}\csc(x+1)^3\left[\frac{1}{x} - 6(x+1)^2\cot(x+1)^3\right]$
or $\frac{1}{2\sqrt{x}}\csc(x+1)^3\left[1 - 6x(x+1)^2\cot(x+1)^3\right]$

25. $y = 5\cot x^2 \Rightarrow \frac{dy}{dx} = 5(-\csc^2 x^2)(2x) = -10x\csc^2(x^2)$

26. $y = x^2\cot 5x \Rightarrow \frac{dy}{dx} = x^2(-\csc^2 5x)(5) + (\cot 5x)(2x) = -5x^2\csc^2 5x + 2x\cot 5x$

27. $y = x^2 \sin^2(2x^2) \Rightarrow \frac{dy}{dx} = x^2 \left(2\sin(2x^2)\right)\left(\cos(2x^2)\right)(4x) + \sin^2(2x^2)(2x) = 8x^3 \sin(2x^2)\cos(2x^2) + 2x\sin^2(2x^2)$

28. $y = x^{-2}\sin^2(x^3) \Rightarrow \frac{dy}{dx} = x^{-2}\left(2\sin(x^3)\right)\left(\cos(x^3)\right)(3x^2) + \sin^2(x^3)(-2x^{-3}) = 6\sin(x^3)\cos(x^3) - 2x^{-3}\sin^2(x^3)$

29. $s = \left(\frac{4t}{t+1}\right)^{-2} \Rightarrow \frac{ds}{dt} = -2\left(\frac{4t}{t+1}\right)^{-3}\left(\frac{(t+1)(4)-(4t)(1)}{(t+1)^2}\right) = -2\left(\frac{4t}{t+1}\right)^{-3}\frac{4}{(t+1)^2} = -\frac{(t+1)}{8t^3}$

30. $s = \frac{-1}{15(15t-1)^3} = -\frac{1}{15}(15t-1)^{-3} \Rightarrow \frac{ds}{dt} = -\frac{1}{15}(-3)(15t-1)^{-4}(15) = \frac{3}{(15t-1)^4}$

31. $y = \left(\frac{\sqrt{x}}{x+1}\right)^2 \Rightarrow \frac{dy}{dx} = 2\left(\frac{\sqrt{x}}{x+1}\right)\cdot\frac{(x+1)\left(\frac{1}{2\sqrt{x}}\right)-(\sqrt{x})(1)}{(x+1)^2} = \frac{(x+1)-2x}{(x+1)^3} = \frac{1-x}{(x+1)^3}$

32. $y = \left(\frac{2\sqrt{x}}{2\sqrt{x}+1}\right)^2 \Rightarrow \frac{dy}{dx} = 2\left(\frac{2\sqrt{x}}{2\sqrt{x}+1}\right)\left(\frac{(2\sqrt{x}+1)\left(\frac{1}{\sqrt{x}}\right)-(2\sqrt{x})\left(\frac{1}{\sqrt{x}}\right)}{(2\sqrt{x}+1)^2}\right) = \frac{4\sqrt{x}\left(\frac{1}{\sqrt{x}}\right)}{(2\sqrt{x}+1)^3} = \frac{4}{(2\sqrt{x}+1)^3}$

33. $y = \sqrt{\frac{x^2+x}{x^2}} = \left(1+\frac{1}{x}\right)^{1/2} \Rightarrow \frac{dy}{dx} = \frac{1}{2}\left(1+\frac{1}{x}\right)^{-1/2}\left(-\frac{1}{x^2}\right) = -\frac{1}{2x^2\sqrt{1+\frac{1}{x}}}$

34. $y = 4x\sqrt{x+\sqrt{x}} = 4x\left(x+x^{1/2}\right)^{1/2} \Rightarrow \frac{dy}{dx} = 4x\left(\frac{1}{2}\right)\left(x+x^{1/2}\right)^{-1/2}\left(1+\frac{1}{2}x^{-1/2}\right) + \left(x+x^{1/2}\right)^{1/2}(4)$

$= \left(x+\sqrt{x}\right)^{-1/2}\left[2x\left(1+\frac{1}{2\sqrt{x}}\right) + 4\left(x+\sqrt{x}\right)\right] = \left(x+\sqrt{x}\right)^{-1/2}\left(2x+\sqrt{x}+4x+4\sqrt{x}\right) = \frac{6x+5\sqrt{x}}{\sqrt{x+\sqrt{x}}}$

35. $r = \left(\frac{\sin\theta}{\cos\theta-1}\right)^2 \Rightarrow \frac{dr}{d\theta} = 2\left(\frac{\sin\theta}{\cos\theta-1}\right)\left[\frac{(\cos\theta-1)(\cos\theta)-(\sin\theta)(-\sin\theta)}{(\cos\theta-1)^2}\right] = 2\left(\frac{\sin\theta}{\cos\theta-1}\right)\left(\frac{\cos^2\theta-\cos\theta+\sin^2\theta}{(\cos\theta-1)^2}\right)$

$= \frac{(2\sin\theta)(1-\cos\theta)}{(\cos\theta-1)^3} = \frac{-2\sin\theta}{(\cos\theta-1)^2}$

36. $r = \left(\frac{\sin\theta+1}{1-\cos\theta}\right)^2 \Rightarrow \frac{dr}{d\theta} = 2\left(\frac{\sin\theta+1}{1-\cos\theta}\right)\left[\frac{(1-\cos\theta)(\cos\theta)-(\sin\theta+1)(\sin\theta)}{(1-\cos\theta)^2}\right] = \frac{2(\sin\theta+1)}{(1-\cos\theta)^3}\left(\cos\theta-\cos^2\theta-\sin^2\theta-\sin\theta\right)$

$= \frac{2(\sin\theta+1)(\cos\theta-\sin\theta-1)}{(1-\cos\theta)^3}$

37. $y = (2x+1)\sqrt{2x+1} = (2x+1)^{3/2} \Rightarrow \frac{dy}{dx} = \frac{3}{2}(2x+1)^{1/2}(2) = 3\sqrt{2x+1}$

38. $y = 20(3x-4)^{1/4}(3x-4)^{-1/5} = 20(3x-4)^{1/20} \Rightarrow \frac{dy}{dx} = 20\left(\frac{1}{20}\right)(3x-4)^{-19/20}(3) = \frac{3}{(3x-4)^{19/20}}$

39. $y = 3\left(5x^2+\sin 2x\right)^{-3/2} \Rightarrow \frac{dy}{dx} = 3\left(-\frac{3}{2}\right)\left(5x^2+\sin 2x\right)^{-5/2}[10x+(\cos 2x)(2)] = \frac{-9(5x+\cos 2x)}{(5x^2+\sin 2x)^{5/2}}$

40. $y = (3+\cos^3 3x)^{-1/3} \Rightarrow \frac{dy}{dx} = -\frac{1}{3}(3+\cos^3 3x)^{-4/3}(3\cos^2 3x)(-\sin 3x)(3) = \frac{3\cos^2 3x \sin 3x}{(3+\cos^3 3x)^{4/3}}$

41. $xy + 2x + 3y = 1 \Rightarrow (xy'+y)+2+3y' = 0 \Rightarrow xy'+3y' = -2-y \Rightarrow y'(x+3) = -2-y \Rightarrow y' = -\frac{y+2}{x+3}$

42. $x^2 + xy + y^2 - 5x = 2 \Rightarrow 2x + \left(x\frac{dy}{dx}+y\right) + 2y\frac{dy}{dx} - 5 = 0 \Rightarrow x\frac{dy}{dx} + 2y\frac{dy}{dx} = 5-2x-y \Rightarrow \frac{dy}{dx}(x+2y) = 5-2x-y$

$\Rightarrow \frac{dy}{dx} = \frac{5-2x-y}{x+2y}$

43. $x^3 + 4xy - 3y^{4/3} = 2x \Rightarrow 3x^2 + \left(4x\frac{dy}{dx}+4y\right) - 4y^{1/3}\frac{dy}{dx} = 2 \Rightarrow 4x\frac{dy}{dx} - 4y^{1/3}\frac{dy}{dx} = 2-3x^2-4y$

$\Rightarrow \frac{dy}{dx}\left(4x-4y^{1/3}\right) = 2-3x^2-4y \Rightarrow \frac{dy}{dx} = \frac{2-3x^2-4y}{4x-4y^{1/3}}$

44. $5x^{4/5} + 10y^{6/5} = 15 \Rightarrow 4x^{-1/5} + 12y^{1/5} \frac{dy}{dx} = 0 \Rightarrow 12y^{1/5} \frac{dy}{dx} = -4x^{-1/5} \Rightarrow \frac{dy}{dx} = -\frac{1}{3} x^{-1/5} y^{-1/5} = -\frac{1}{3(xy)^{1/5}}$

45. $(xy)^{1/2} = 1 \Rightarrow \frac{1}{2}(xy)^{-1/2} \left( x \frac{dy}{dx} + y \right) = 0 \Rightarrow x^{1/2} y^{-1/2} \frac{dy}{dx} = -x^{-1/2} y^{1/2} \Rightarrow \frac{dy}{dx} = -x^{-1}y \Rightarrow \frac{dy}{dx} = -\frac{y}{x}$

46. $x^2 y^2 = 1 \Rightarrow x^2 \left( 2y \frac{dy}{dx} \right) + y^2 (2x) = 0 \Rightarrow 2x^2 y \frac{dy}{dx} = -2xy^2 \Rightarrow \frac{dy}{dx} = -\frac{y}{x}$

47. $y^2 = \frac{x}{x+1} \Rightarrow 2y \frac{dy}{dx} = \frac{(x+1)(1) - (x)(1)}{(x+1)^2} \Rightarrow \frac{dy}{dx} = \frac{1}{2y(x+1)^2}$

48. $y^2 = \left( \frac{1+x}{1-x} \right)^{1/2} \Rightarrow y^4 = \frac{1+x}{1-x} \Rightarrow 4y^3 \frac{dy}{dx} = \frac{(1-x)(1) - (1+x)(-1)}{(1-x)^2} \Rightarrow \frac{dy}{dx} = \frac{1}{2y^3(1-x)^2}$

49. $p^3 + 4pq - 3q^2 = 2 \Rightarrow 3p^2 \frac{dp}{dq} + 4 \left( p + q \frac{dp}{dq} \right) - 6q = 0 \Rightarrow 3p^2 \frac{dp}{dq} + 4q \frac{dp}{dq} = 6q - 4p \Rightarrow \frac{dp}{dq}(3p^2 + 4q) = 6q - 4p$

   $\Rightarrow \frac{dp}{dq} = \frac{6q - 4p}{3p^2 + 4q}$

50. $q = (5p^2 + 2p)^{-3/2} \Rightarrow 1 = -\frac{3}{2}(5p^2 + 2p)^{-5/2} \left( 10p \frac{dp}{dq} + 2 \frac{dp}{dq} \right) \Rightarrow -\frac{2}{3}(5p^2 + 2p)^{5/2} = \frac{dp}{dq}(10p + 2)$

   $\Rightarrow \frac{dp}{dq} = -\frac{(5p^2 + 2p)^{5/2}}{3(5p+1)}$

51. $r \cos 2s + \sin^2 s = \pi \Rightarrow r(-\sin 2s)(2) + (\cos 2s) \left( \frac{dr}{ds} \right) + 2 \sin s \cos s = 0 \Rightarrow \frac{dr}{ds}(\cos 2s) = 2r \sin 2s - 2 \sin s \cos s$

   $\Rightarrow \frac{dr}{ds} = \frac{2r \sin 2s - \sin 2s}{\cos 2s} = \frac{(2r-1)(\sin 2s)}{\cos 2s} = (2r-1)(\tan 2s)$

52. $2rs - r - s + s^2 = -3 \Rightarrow 2 \left( r + s \frac{dr}{ds} \right) - \frac{dr}{ds} - 1 + 2s = 0 \Rightarrow \frac{dr}{ds}(2s-1) = 1 - 2s - 2r \Rightarrow \frac{dr}{ds} = \frac{1 - 2s - 2r}{2s-1}$

53. (a) $x^3 + y^3 = 1 \Rightarrow 3x^2 + 3y^2 \frac{dy}{dx} = 0 \Rightarrow \frac{dy}{dx} = -\frac{x^2}{y^2} \Rightarrow \frac{d^2y}{dx^2} = \frac{y^2(-2x) - (-x^2)\left( 2y \frac{dy}{dx} \right)}{y^4}$

   $\Rightarrow \frac{d^2y}{dx^2} = \frac{-2xy^2 + (2yx^2)\left( -\frac{x^2}{y^2} \right)}{y^4} = \frac{-2xy^2 - \frac{2x^4}{y}}{y^4} = \frac{-2xy^3 - 2x^4}{y^5}$

   (b) $y^2 = 1 - \frac{2}{x} \Rightarrow 2y \frac{dy}{dx} = \frac{2}{x^2} \Rightarrow \frac{dy}{dx} = \frac{1}{yx^2} \Rightarrow \frac{dy}{dx} = (yx^2)^{-1} \Rightarrow \frac{d^2y}{dx^2} = -(yx^2)^{-2} \left[ y(2x) + x^2 \frac{dy}{dx} \right]$

   $\Rightarrow \frac{d^2y}{dx^2} = \frac{-2xy - x^2 \left( \frac{1}{yx^2} \right)}{y^2 x^4} = \frac{-2xy^2 - 1}{y^3 x^4}$

54. (a) $x^2 - y^2 = 1 \Rightarrow 2x - 2y \frac{dy}{dx} = 0 \Rightarrow -2y \frac{dy}{dx} = -2x \Rightarrow \frac{dy}{dx} = \frac{x}{y}$

   (b) $\frac{dy}{dx} = \frac{x}{y} \Rightarrow \frac{d^2y}{dx^2} = \frac{y(1) - x \frac{dy}{dx}}{y^2} = \frac{y - x \left( \frac{x}{y} \right)}{y^2} = \frac{y^2 - x^2}{y^3} = \frac{-1}{y^3}$ (since $y^2 - x^2 = -1$)

55. (a) Let $h(x) = 6f(x) - g(x) \Rightarrow h'(x) = 6f'(x) - g'(x) \Rightarrow h'(1) = 6f'(1) - g'(1) = 6 \left( \frac{1}{2} \right) - (-4) = 7$

   (b) Let $h(x) = f(x)g^2(x) \Rightarrow h'(x) = f(x)\left( 2g(x) \right)g'(x) + g^2(x)f'(x) \Rightarrow h'(0) = 2f(0)g(0)g'(0) + g^2(0)f'(0)$

      $= 2(1)(1) \left( \frac{1}{2} \right) + (1)^2(-3) = -2$

   (c) Let $h(x) = \frac{f(x)}{g(x)+1} \Rightarrow h'(x) = \frac{(g(x)+1)f'(x) - f(x)g'(x)}{(g(x)+1)^2} \Rightarrow h'(1) = \frac{(g(1)+1)f'(1) - f(1)g'(1)}{(g(1)+1)^2} = \frac{(5+1)\left( \frac{1}{2} \right) - 3(-4)}{(5+1)^2} = \frac{5}{12}$

   (d) Let $h(x) = f(g(x)) \Rightarrow h'(x) = f'(g(x))g'(x) \Rightarrow h'(0) = f'(g(0))g'(0) = f'(1) \left( \frac{1}{2} \right) = \left( \frac{1}{2} \right) \left( \frac{1}{2} \right) = \frac{1}{4}$

   (e) Let $h(x) = g(f(x)) \Rightarrow h'(x) = g'(f(x))f'(x) \Rightarrow h'(0) = g'(f(0))f'(0) = g'(1)f'(0) = (-4)(-3) = 12$

   (f) Let $h(x) = (x + f(x))^{3/2} \Rightarrow h'(x) = \frac{3}{2}(x + f(x))^{1/2}(1 + f'(x)) \Rightarrow h'(1) = \frac{3}{2}(1 + f(1))^{1/2}(1 + f'(1))$

      $= \frac{3}{2}(1 + 3)^{1/2} \left( 1 + \frac{1}{2} \right) = \frac{9}{2}$

   (g) Let $h(x) = f(x + g(x)) \Rightarrow h'(x) = f'(x + g(x))(1 + g'(x)) \Rightarrow h'(0) = f'(g(0))(1 + g'(0))$

      $= f'(1) \left( 1 + \frac{1}{2} \right) = \left( \frac{1}{2} \right) \left( \frac{3}{2} \right) = \frac{3}{4}$

56. (a) Let $h(x) = \sqrt{x}\,f(x) \Rightarrow h'(x) = \sqrt{x}\,f'(x) + f(x) \cdot \frac{1}{2\sqrt{x}} \Rightarrow h'(1) = \sqrt{1}\,f'(1) + f(1) \cdot \frac{1}{2\sqrt{1}} = \frac{1}{5} + (-3)\left(\frac{1}{2}\right) = -\frac{13}{10}$

(b) Let $h(x) = (f(x))^{1/2} \Rightarrow h'(x) = \frac{1}{2}\,(f(x))^{-1/2}\,(f'(x)) \Rightarrow h'(0) = \frac{1}{2}\,(f(0))^{-1/2}f'(0) = \frac{1}{2}\,(9)^{-1/2}(-2) = -\frac{1}{3}$

(c) Let $h(x) = f\left(\sqrt{x}\right) \Rightarrow h'(x) = f'\left(\sqrt{x}\right) \cdot \frac{1}{2\sqrt{x}} \Rightarrow h'(1) = f'\left(\sqrt{1}\right) \cdot \frac{1}{2\sqrt{1}} = \frac{1}{5} \cdot \frac{1}{2} = \frac{1}{10}$

(d) Let $h(x) = f(1 - 5\tan x) \Rightarrow h'(x) = f'(1 - 5\tan x)\,(-5\sec^2 x) \Rightarrow h'(0) = f'(1 - 5\tan 0)\,(-5\sec^2 0)$
$= f'(1)(-5) = \frac{1}{5}\,(-5) = -1$

(e) Let $h(x) = \frac{f(x)}{2 + \cos x} \Rightarrow h'(x) = \frac{(2 + \cos x)f'(x) - f(x)(-\sin x)}{(2 + \cos x)^2} \Rightarrow h'(0) = \frac{(2 + 1)f'(0) - f(0)(0)}{(2 + 1)^2} = \frac{3(-2)}{9} = -\frac{2}{3}$

(f) Let $h(x) = 10\sin\left(\frac{\pi x}{2}\right)f^2(x) \Rightarrow h'(x) = 10\sin\left(\frac{\pi x}{2}\right)(2f(x)f'(x)) + f^2(x)\left(10\cos\left(\frac{\pi x}{2}\right)\right)\left(\frac{\pi}{2}\right)$
$\Rightarrow h'(1) = 10\sin\left(\frac{\pi}{2}\right)(2f(1)f'(1)) + f^2(1)\left(10\cos\left(\frac{\pi}{2}\right)\right)\left(\frac{\pi}{2}\right) = 20(-3)\left(\frac{1}{5}\right) + 0 = -12$

57. $x = t^2 + \pi \Rightarrow \frac{dx}{dt} = 2t;\ y = 3\sin 2x \Rightarrow \frac{dy}{dx} = 3(\cos 2x)(2) = 6\cos 2x = 6\cos(2t^2 + 2\pi) = 6\cos(2t^2)$; thus,
$\frac{dy}{dt} = \frac{dy}{dx} \cdot \frac{dx}{dt} = 6\cos(2t^2) \cdot 2t \Rightarrow \left.\frac{dy}{dt}\right|_{t=0} = 6\cos(0) \cdot 0 = 0$

58. $t = (u^2 + 2u)^{1/3} \Rightarrow \frac{dt}{du} = \frac{1}{3}\,(u^2 + 2u)^{-2/3}(2u + 2) = \frac{2}{3}\,(u^2 + 2u)^{-2/3}(u + 1);\ s = t^2 + 5t \Rightarrow \frac{ds}{dt} = 2t + 5$
$= 2\,(u^2 + 2u)^{1/3} + 5;$ thus $\frac{ds}{du} = \frac{ds}{dt} \cdot \frac{dt}{du} = \left[2\,(u^2 + 2u)^{1/3} + 5\right]\left(\frac{2}{3}\right)(u^2 + 2u)^{-2/3}(u + 1)$
$\Rightarrow \left.\frac{ds}{du}\right|_{u=2} = \left[2\,(2^2 + 2(2))^{1/3} + 5\right]\left(\frac{2}{3}\right)(2^2 + 2(2))^{-2/3}(2 + 1) = 2\,(2 \cdot 8^{1/3} + 5)\,(8^{-2/3}) = 2(2 \cdot 2 + 5)\left(\frac{1}{4}\right) = \frac{9}{2}$

59. $r = 8\sin\left(s + \frac{\pi}{6}\right) \Rightarrow \frac{dr}{ds} = 8\cos\left(s + \frac{\pi}{6}\right);\ w = \sin\left(\sqrt{r} - 2\right) \Rightarrow \frac{dw}{dr} = \cos\left(\sqrt{r} - 2\right)\left(\frac{1}{2\sqrt{r}}\right)$
$= \frac{\cos\sqrt{8\sin\left(s + \frac{\pi}{6}\right)} - 2}{2\sqrt{8\sin\left(s + \frac{\pi}{6}\right)}};$ thus, $\frac{dw}{ds} = \frac{dw}{dr} \cdot \frac{dr}{ds} = \frac{\cos\left(\sqrt{8\sin\left(s + \frac{\pi}{6}\right)} - 2\right)}{2\sqrt{8\sin\left(s + \frac{\pi}{6}\right)}} \cdot \left[8\cos\left(s + \frac{\pi}{6}\right)\right]$
$\Rightarrow \left.\frac{dw}{ds}\right|_{s=0} = \frac{\cos\left(\sqrt{8\sin\left(\frac{\pi}{6}\right)} - 2\right) \cdot 8\cos\left(\frac{\pi}{6}\right)}{2\sqrt{8\sin\left(\frac{\pi}{6}\right)}} = \frac{(\cos 0)(8)\left(\frac{\sqrt{3}}{2}\right)}{2\sqrt{4}} = \sqrt{3}$

60. $\theta^2 t + \theta = 1 \Rightarrow \left(\theta^2 + t\left(2\theta\,\frac{d\theta}{dt}\right)\right) + \frac{d\theta}{dt} = 0 \Rightarrow \frac{d\theta}{dt}\,(2\theta t + 1) = -\theta^2 \Rightarrow \frac{d\theta}{dt} = \frac{-\theta^2}{2\theta t + 1};\ r = (\theta^2 + 7)^{1/3}$
$\Rightarrow \frac{dr}{d\theta} = \frac{1}{3}\,(\theta^2 + 7)^{-2/3}(2\theta) = \frac{2}{3}\,\theta\,(\theta^2 + 7)^{-2/3};$ now $t = 0$ and $\theta^2 t + \theta = 1 \Rightarrow \theta = 1$ so that $\left.\frac{d\theta}{dt}\right|_{t=0,\,\theta=1} = \frac{-1}{1} = -1$
and $\left.\frac{dr}{d\theta}\right|_{\theta=1} = \frac{2}{3}\,(1 + 7)^{-2/3} = \frac{1}{6} \Rightarrow \left.\frac{dr}{dt}\right|_{t=0} = \left.\frac{dr}{d\theta}\right|_{t=0} \cdot \left.\frac{d\theta}{dt}\right|_{t=0} = \left(\frac{1}{6}\right)(-1) = -\frac{1}{6}$

61. $y^3 + y = 2\cos x \Rightarrow 3y^2\,\frac{dy}{dx} + \frac{dy}{dx} = -2\sin x \Rightarrow \frac{dy}{dx}\,(3y^2 + 1) = -2\sin x \Rightarrow \frac{dy}{dx} = \frac{-2\sin x}{3y^2 + 1} \Rightarrow \left.\frac{dy}{dx}\right|_{(0,1)}$
$= \frac{-2\sin(0)}{3+1} = 0;\ \frac{d^2y}{dx^2} = \frac{(3y^2 + 1)(-2\cos x) - (-2\sin x)\left(6y\,\frac{dy}{dx}\right)}{(3y^2 + 1)^2}$
$\Rightarrow \left.\frac{d^2y}{dx^2}\right|_{(0,1)} = \frac{(3+1)(-2\cos 0) - (-2\sin 0)(6 \cdot 0)}{(3+1)^2} = -\frac{1}{2}$

62. $x^{1/3} + y^{1/3} = 4 \Rightarrow \frac{1}{3}\,x^{-2/3} + \frac{1}{3}\,y^{-2/3}\,\frac{dy}{dx} = 0 \Rightarrow \frac{dy}{dx} = -\frac{y^{2/3}}{x^{2/3}} \Rightarrow \left.\frac{dy}{dx}\right|_{(8,8)} = -1;\ \frac{dy}{dx} = \frac{-y^{2/3}}{x^{2/3}}$
$\Rightarrow \frac{d^2y}{dx^2} = \frac{(x^{2/3})\left(-\frac{2}{3}\,y^{-1/3}\,\frac{dy}{dx}\right) - (-y^{2/3})\left(\frac{2}{3}\,x^{-1/3}\right)}{(x^{2/3})^2} \Rightarrow \left.\frac{d^2y}{dx^2}\right|_{(8,8)} = \frac{(8^{2/3})\left[-\frac{2}{3} \cdot 8^{-1/3} \cdot (-1)\right] + (8^{2/3})\left(\frac{2}{3} \cdot 8^{-1/3}\right)}{8^{4/3}}$
$= \frac{\frac{1}{3} + \frac{1}{3}}{8^{2/3}} = \frac{\frac{2}{3}}{4} = \frac{1}{6}$

63. $f(t) = \frac{1}{2t + 1}$ and $f(t + h) = \frac{1}{2(t + h) + 1} \Rightarrow \frac{f(t + h) - f(t)}{h} = \frac{\frac{1}{2(t+h)+1} - \frac{1}{2t+1}}{h} = \frac{2t + 1 - (2t + 2h + 1)}{(2t + 2h + 1)(2t + 1)h}$
$= \frac{-2h}{(2t + 2h + 1)(2t + 1)h} = \frac{-2}{(2t + 2h + 1)(2t + 1)} \Rightarrow f'(t) = \lim_{h \to 0} \frac{f(t + h) - f(t)}{h} = \lim_{h \to 0} \frac{-2}{(2t + 2h + 1)(2t + 1)}$
$= \frac{-2}{(2t + 1)^2}$

64. $g(x) = 2x^2 + 1$ and $g(x + h) = 2(x + h)^2 + 1 = 2x^2 + 4xh + 2h^2 + 1 \Rightarrow \frac{g(x+h) - g(x)}{h} = \frac{(2x^2 + 4xh + 2h^2 + 1) - (2x^2 + 1)}{h}$

$= \frac{4xh + 2h^2}{h} = 4x + 2h \Rightarrow g'(x) = \lim_{h \to 0} \frac{g(x+h) - g(x)}{h} = \lim_{h \to 0} (4x + 2h) = 4x$

65. (a)

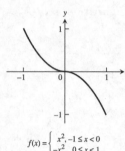

$$f(x) = \begin{cases} x^2, & -1 \le x < 0 \\ -x^2, & 0 \le x < 1 \end{cases}$$

(b)   $\lim_{x \to 0^-} f(x) = \lim_{x \to 0^-} x^2 = 0$ and $\lim_{x \to 0^+} f(x) = \lim_{x \to 0^+} -x^2 = 0 \Rightarrow \lim_{x \to 0} f(x) = 0$. Since $\lim_{x \to 0} f(x) = 0 = f(0)$ it

follows that f is continuous at x = 0.

(c)   $\lim_{x \to 0^-} f'(x) = \lim_{x \to 0^-} (2x) = 0$ and $\lim_{x \to 0^+} f'(x) = \lim_{x \to 0^+} (-2x) = 0 \Rightarrow \lim_{x \to 0} f'(x) = 0$. Since this limit exists, it

follows that f is differentiable at x = 0.

66. (a)

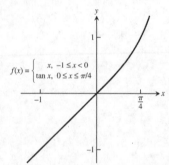

$$f(x) = \begin{cases} x, & -1 \le x < 0 \\ \tan x, & 0 \le x \le \pi/4 \end{cases}$$

(b)   $\lim_{x \to 0^-} f(x) = \lim_{x \to 0^-} x = 0$ and $\lim_{x \to 0^+} f(x) = \lim_{x \to 0^+} \tan x = 0 \Rightarrow \lim_{x \to 0} f(x) = 0$. Since $\lim_{x \to 0} f(x) = 0 = f(0)$, it

follows that f is continuous at x = 0.

(c)   $\lim_{x \to 0^-} f'(x) = \lim_{x \to 0^-} 1 = 1$ and $\lim_{x \to 0^+} f'(x) = \lim_{x \to 0^+} \sec^2 x = 1 \Rightarrow \lim_{x \to 0} f'(x) = 1$. Since this limit exists it

follows that f is differentiable at x = 0.

67. (a)

$$y = \begin{cases} x, & 0 \le x \le 1 \\ 2 - x, & 1 < x \le 2 \end{cases}$$

(b)   $\lim_{x \to 1^-} f(x) = \lim_{x \to 1^-} x = 1$ and $\lim_{x \to 1^+} f(x) = \lim_{x \to 1^+} (2 - x) = 1 \Rightarrow \lim_{x \to 1} f(x) = 1$. Since $\lim_{x \to 1} f(x) = 1 = f(1)$, it

follows that f is continuous at x = 1.

(c)   $\lim_{x \to 1^-} f'(x) = \lim_{x \to 1^-} 1 = 1$ and $\lim_{x \to 1^+} f'(x) = \lim_{x \to 1^+} -1 = -1 \Rightarrow \lim_{x \to 1^-} f'(x) \neq \lim_{x \to 1^+} f'(x)$, so $\lim_{x \to 1} f'(x)$ does

not exist $\Rightarrow$ f is not differentiable at x = 1.

68. (a)   $\lim_{x \to 0^-} f(x) = \lim_{x \to 0^-} \sin 2x = 0$ and $\lim_{x \to 0^+} f(x) = \lim_{x \to 0^+} mx = 0 \Rightarrow \lim_{x \to 0} f(x) = 0$, independent of m; since

$f(0) = 0 = \lim_{x \to 0} f(x)$ it follows that f is continuous at x = 0 for all values of m.

(b)   $\lim_{x \to 0^-} f'(x) = \lim_{x \to 0^-} (\sin 2x)' = \lim_{x \to 0^-} 2 \cos 2x = 2$ and $\lim_{x \to 0^+} f'(x) = \lim_{x \to 0^+} (mx)' = \lim_{x \to 0^+} m = m \Rightarrow$ f is

differentiable at x = 0 provided that $\lim_{x \to 0^-} f'(x) = \lim_{x \to 0^+} f'(x) \Rightarrow m = 2$.

69. $y = \frac{x}{2} + \frac{1}{2x-4} = \frac{1}{2}x + (2x-4)^{-1} \Rightarrow \frac{dy}{dx} = \frac{1}{2} - 2(2x-4)^{-2}$; the slope of the tangent is $-\frac{3}{2} \Rightarrow -\frac{3}{2} = \frac{1}{2} - 2(2x-4)^{-2}$

$\Rightarrow -2 = -2(2x-4)^{-2} \Rightarrow 1 = \frac{1}{(2x-4)^2} \Rightarrow (2x-4)^2 = 1 \Rightarrow 4x^2 - 16x + 16 = 1 \Rightarrow 4x^2 - 16x + 15 = 0$

$\Rightarrow (2x-5)(2x-3) = 0 \Rightarrow x = \frac{5}{2}$ or $x = \frac{3}{2} \Rightarrow \left(\frac{5}{2}, \frac{9}{4}\right)$ and $\left(\frac{3}{2}, -\frac{1}{4}\right)$ are points on the curve where the slope is $-\frac{3}{2}$.

70. $y = x - \frac{1}{2x} \Rightarrow \frac{dy}{dx} = 1 + \frac{2}{(2x)^2} = 1 + \frac{1}{2x^2}$; the slope of the tangent is $3 \Rightarrow 3 = 1 + \frac{1}{2x^2} \Rightarrow 2 = \frac{1}{2x^2} \Rightarrow x^2 = \frac{1}{4}$

$\Rightarrow x = \pm\frac{1}{2} \Rightarrow \left(\frac{1}{2}, -\frac{1}{2}\right)$ and $\left(-\frac{1}{2}, \frac{1}{2}\right)$ are points on the curve where the slope is 3.

71. $y = 2x^3 - 3x^2 - 12x + 20 \Rightarrow \frac{dy}{dx} = 6x^2 - 6x - 12$; the tangent is parallel to the x-axis when $\frac{dy}{dx} = 0$

$\Rightarrow 6x^2 - 6x - 12 = 0 \Rightarrow x^2 - x - 2 = 0 \Rightarrow (x-2)(x+1) = 0 \Rightarrow x = 2$ or $x = -1 \Rightarrow (2,0)$ and $(-1,27)$ are points on the curve where the tangent is parallel to the x-axis.

72. $y = x^3 \Rightarrow \frac{dy}{dx} = 3x^2 \Rightarrow \frac{dy}{dx}\Big|_{(-2,-8)} = 12$; an equation of the tangent line at $(-2,-8)$ is $y + 8 = 12(x+2)$

$\Rightarrow y = 12x + 16$; x-intercept: $0 = 12x + 16 \Rightarrow x = -\frac{4}{3} \Rightarrow \left(-\frac{4}{3}, 0\right)$; y-intercept: $y = 12(0) + 16 = 16 \Rightarrow (0,16)$

73. $y = 2x^3 - 3x^2 - 12x + 20 \Rightarrow \frac{dy}{dx} = 6x^2 - 6x - 12$

(a) The tangent is perpendicular to the line $y = 1 - \frac{x}{24}$ when $\frac{dy}{dx} = -\left(\frac{1}{-\left(\frac{1}{24}\right)}\right) = 24$; $6x^2 - 6x - 12 = 24$

$\Rightarrow x^2 - x - 2 = 4 \Rightarrow x^2 - x - 6 = 0 \Rightarrow (x-3)(x+2) = 0 \Rightarrow x = -2$ or $x = 3 \Rightarrow (-2,16)$ and $(3,11)$ are points where the tangent is perpendicular to $y = 1 - \frac{x}{24}$.

(b) The tangent is parallel to the line $y = \sqrt{2} - 12x$ when $\frac{dy}{dx} = -12 \Rightarrow 6x^2 - 6x - 12 = -12 \Rightarrow x^2 - x = 0$

$\Rightarrow x(x-1) = 0 \Rightarrow x = 0$ or $x = 1 \Rightarrow (0,20)$ and $(1,7)$ are points where the tangent is parallel to $y = \sqrt{2} - 12x$.

74. $y = \frac{\pi \sin x}{x} \Rightarrow \frac{dy}{dx} = \frac{x(\pi \cos x) - (\pi \sin x)(1)}{x^2} \Rightarrow m_1 = \frac{dy}{dx}\Big|_{x=\pi} = \frac{-\pi^2}{\pi^2} = -1$ and $m_2 = \frac{dy}{dx}\Big|_{x=-\pi} = \frac{\pi^2}{\pi^2} = 1$. Since $m_1 = -\frac{1}{m_2}$ the tangents intersect at right angles.

75. $y = \tan x$, $-\frac{\pi}{2} < x < \frac{\pi}{2} \Rightarrow \frac{dy}{dx} = \sec^2 x$; now the slope of $y = -\frac{x}{2}$ is $-\frac{1}{2} \Rightarrow$ the normal line is parallel to $y = -\frac{x}{2}$ when $\frac{dy}{dx} = 2$. Thus, $\sec^2 x = 2 \Rightarrow \frac{1}{\cos^2 x} = 2$

$\Rightarrow \cos^2 x = \frac{1}{2} \Rightarrow \cos x = \frac{\pm 1}{\sqrt{2}} \Rightarrow x = -\frac{\pi}{4}$ and $x = \frac{\pi}{4}$ for $-\frac{\pi}{2} < x < \frac{\pi}{2} \Rightarrow \left(-\frac{\pi}{4}, -1\right)$ and $\left(\frac{\pi}{4}, 1\right)$ are points where the normal is parallel to $y = -\frac{x}{2}$.

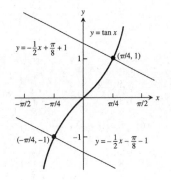

76. $y = 1 + \cos x \Rightarrow \frac{dy}{dx} = -\sin x \Rightarrow \frac{dy}{dx}\Big|_{\left(\frac{\pi}{2}, 1\right)} = -1$

$\Rightarrow$ the tangent at $\left(\frac{\pi}{2}, 1\right)$ is the line $y - 1 = -\left(x - \frac{\pi}{2}\right)$

$\Rightarrow y = -x + \frac{\pi}{2} + 1$; the normal at $\left(\frac{\pi}{2}, 1\right)$ is $y - 1 = (1)\left(x - \frac{\pi}{2}\right) \Rightarrow y = x - \frac{\pi}{2} + 1$

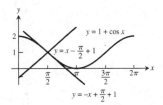

77. $y = x^2 + C \Rightarrow \frac{dy}{dx} = 2x$ and $y = x \Rightarrow \frac{dy}{dx} = 1$; the parabola is tangent to $y = x$ when $2x = 1 \Rightarrow x = \frac{1}{2} \Rightarrow y = \frac{1}{2}$; thus,

$\frac{1}{2} = \left(\frac{1}{2}\right)^2 + C \Rightarrow C = \frac{1}{4}$

78. $y = x^3 \Rightarrow \frac{dy}{dx} = 3x^2 \Rightarrow \frac{dy}{dx}\Big|_{x=a} = 3a^2 \Rightarrow$ the tangent line at $(a, a^3)$ is $y - a^3 = 3a^2(x - a)$. The tangent line

intersects $y = x^3$ when $x^3 - a^3 = 3a^2(x - a) \Rightarrow (x - a)(x^2 + xa + a^2) = 3a^2(x - a) \Rightarrow (x - a)(x^2 + xa - 2a^2) = 0$

$\Rightarrow (x - a)^2(x + 2a) = 0 \Rightarrow x = a$ or $x = -2a$. Now $\frac{dy}{dx}\Big|_{x=-2a} = 3(-2a)^2 = 12a^2 = 4(3a^2)$, so the slope at

$x = -2a$ is 4 times as large as the slope at $(a, a^3)$ where $x = a$.

79. The line through $(0, 3)$ and $(5, -2)$ has slope $m = \frac{3 - (-2)}{0 - 5} = -1 \Rightarrow$ the line through $(0, 3)$ and $(5, -2)$ is

$y = -x + 3; \ y = \frac{c}{x+1} \Rightarrow \frac{dy}{dx} = \frac{-c}{(x+1)^2}$, so the curve is tangent to $y = -x + 3 \Rightarrow \frac{dy}{dx} = -1 = \frac{-c}{(x+1)^2}$

$\Rightarrow (x + 1)^2 = c, \ x \neq -1$. Moreover, $y = \frac{c}{x+1}$ intersects $y = -x + 3 \Rightarrow \frac{c}{x+1} = -x + 3, \ x \neq -1$

$\Rightarrow c = (x + 1)(-x + 3), \ x \neq -1$. Thus $c = c \Rightarrow (x + 1)^2 = (x + 1)(-x + 3) \Rightarrow (x + 1)[x + 1 - (-x + 3)]$

$= 0, \ x \neq -1 \Rightarrow (x + 1)(2x - 2) = 0 \Rightarrow x = 1$ (since $x \neq -1$) $\Rightarrow c = 4$.

80. Let $\left(b, \pm\sqrt{a^2 - b^2}\right)$ be a point on the circle $x^2 + y^2 = a^2$. Then $x^2 + y^2 = a^2 \Rightarrow 2x + 2y\frac{dy}{dx} = 0 \Rightarrow \frac{dy}{dx} = -\frac{x}{y}$

$\Rightarrow \frac{dy}{dx}\Big|_{x=b} = \frac{-b}{\pm\sqrt{a^2 - b^2}} \Rightarrow$ normal line through $\left(b, \pm\sqrt{a^2 - b^2}\right)$ has slope $\frac{\pm\sqrt{a^2 - b^2}}{b} \Rightarrow$ normal line is

$y - \left(\pm\sqrt{a^2 - b^2}\right) = \frac{\pm\sqrt{a^2 - b^2}}{b}(x - b) \Rightarrow y \mp \sqrt{a^2 - b^2} = \frac{\pm\sqrt{a^2 - b^2}}{b}x \mp \sqrt{a^2 - b^2} \Rightarrow y = \pm\frac{\sqrt{a^2 - b^2}}{b}x$

which passes through the origin.

81. $x^2 + 2y^2 = 9 \Rightarrow 2x + 4y\frac{dy}{dx} = 0 \Rightarrow \frac{dy}{dx} = -\frac{x}{2y} \Rightarrow \frac{dy}{dx}\Big|_{(1,2)} = -\frac{1}{4} \Rightarrow$ the tangent line is $y = 2 - \frac{1}{4}(x - 1)$

$= -\frac{1}{4}x + \frac{9}{4}$ and the normal line is $y = 2 + 4(x - 1) = 4x - 2$.

82. $x^3 + y^2 = 2 \Rightarrow 3x^2 + 2y\frac{dy}{dx} = 0 \Rightarrow \frac{dy}{dx} = \frac{-3x^2}{2y} \Rightarrow \frac{dy}{dx}\Big|_{(1,1)} = -\frac{3}{2} \Rightarrow$ the tangent line is $y = 1 + \frac{-3}{2}(x - 1)$

$= -\frac{3}{2}x + \frac{5}{2}$ and the normal line is $y = 1 + \frac{2}{3}(x - 1) = \frac{2}{3}x + \frac{1}{3}$.

83. $xy + 2x - 5y = 2 \Rightarrow \left(x\frac{dy}{dx} + y\right) + 2 - 5\frac{dy}{dx} = 0 \Rightarrow \frac{dy}{dx}(x - 5) = -y - 2 \Rightarrow \frac{dy}{dx} = \frac{-y-2}{x-5} \Rightarrow \frac{dy}{dx}\Big|_{(3,2)} = 2$

$\Rightarrow$ the tangent line is $y = 2 + 2(x - 3) = 2x - 4$ and the normal line is $y = 2 + \frac{-1}{2}(x - 3) = -\frac{1}{2}x + \frac{7}{2}$.

84. $(y - x)^2 = 2x + 4 \Rightarrow 2(y - x)\left(\frac{dy}{dx} - 1\right) = 2 \Rightarrow (y - x)\frac{dy}{dx} = 1 + (y - x) \Rightarrow \frac{dy}{dx} = \frac{1+y-x}{y-x} \Rightarrow \frac{dy}{dx}\Big|_{(6,2)} = \frac{3}{4}$

$\Rightarrow$ the tangent line is $y = 2 + \frac{3}{4}(x - 6) = \frac{3}{4}x - \frac{5}{2}$ and the normal line is $y = 2 - \frac{4}{3}(x - 6) = -\frac{4}{3}x + 10$.

85. $x + \sqrt{xy} = 6 \Rightarrow 1 + \frac{1}{2\sqrt{xy}}\left(x\frac{dy}{dx} + y\right) = 0 \Rightarrow x\frac{dy}{dx} + y = -2\sqrt{xy} \Rightarrow \frac{dy}{dx} = \frac{-2\sqrt{xy}-y}{x} \Rightarrow \frac{dy}{dx}\Big|_{(4,1)} = \frac{-5}{4}$

$\Rightarrow$ the tangent line is $y = 1 - \frac{5}{4}(x - 4) = -\frac{5}{4}x + 6$ and the normal line is $y = 1 + \frac{4}{5}(x - 4) = \frac{4}{5}x - \frac{11}{5}$.

86. $x^{3/2} + 2y^{3/2} = 17 \Rightarrow \frac{3}{2}x^{1/2} + 3y^{1/2}\frac{dy}{dx} = 0 \Rightarrow \frac{dy}{dx} = \frac{-x^{1/2}}{2y^{1/2}} \Rightarrow \frac{dy}{dx}\Big|_{(1,4)} = -\frac{1}{4} \Rightarrow$ the tangent line is

$y = 4 - \frac{1}{4}(x - 1) = -\frac{1}{4}x + \frac{17}{4}$ and the normal line is $y = 4 + 4(x - 1) = 4x$.

87. $x^3y^3 + y^2 = x + y \Rightarrow \left[x^3\left(3y^2\frac{dy}{dx}\right) + y^3(3x^2)\right] + 2y\frac{dy}{dx} = 1 + \frac{dy}{dx} \Rightarrow 3x^3y^2\frac{dy}{dx} + 2y\frac{dy}{dx} - \frac{dy}{dx} = 1 - 3x^2y^3$

$\Rightarrow \frac{dy}{dx}(3x^3y^2 + 2y - 1) = 1 - 3x^2y^3 \Rightarrow \frac{dy}{dx} = \frac{1 - 3x^2y^3}{3x^3y^2 + 2y - 1} \Rightarrow \frac{dy}{dx}\Big|_{(1,1)} = -\frac{2}{4}$, but $\frac{dy}{dx}\Big|_{(1,-1)}$ is undefined.

Therefore, the curve has slope $-\frac{1}{2}$ at $(1, 1)$ but the slope is undefined at $(1, -1)$.

88. $y = \sin(x - \sin x) \Rightarrow \frac{dy}{dx} = [\cos(x - \sin x)](1 - \cos x); y = 0 \Rightarrow \sin(x - \sin x) = 0 \Rightarrow x - \sin x = k\pi,$

$k = -2, -1, 0, 1, 2$ (for our interval) $\Rightarrow \cos(x - \sin x) = \cos(k\pi) = \pm 1.$ Therefore, $\frac{dy}{dx} = 0$ and $y = 0$ when

$1 - \cos x = 0$ and $x = k\pi.$ For $-2\pi \le x \le 2\pi,$ these equations hold when $k = -2, 0,$ and 2 (since

$\cos(-\pi) = \cos \pi = -1$). Thus the curve has horizontal tangents at the x-axis for the x-values $-2\pi, 0,$ and $2\pi$

(which are even integer multiples of $\pi$) $\Rightarrow$ the curve has an infinite number of horizontal tangents.

89. B = graph of f, A = graph of f'. Curve B cannot be the derivative of A because A has only negative slopes
while some of B's values are positive.

90. A = graph of f, B = graph of f'. Curve A cannot be the derivative of B because B has only negative slopes
while A has positive values for $x > 0.$

91.

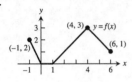

92.

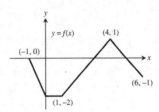

93. (a) 0, 0

(b) largest 1700, smallest about 1400

94. rabbits/day and foxes/day

95. $\lim\limits_{x \to 0} \frac{\sin x}{2x^2 - x} = \lim\limits_{x \to 0} \left[ \left( \frac{\sin x}{x} \right) \cdot \frac{1}{(2x - 1)} \right] = (1) \left( \frac{1}{-1} \right) = -1$

96. $\lim\limits_{x \to 0} \frac{3x - \tan 7x}{2x} = \lim\limits_{x \to 0} \left( \frac{3x}{2x} - \frac{\sin 7x}{2x \cos 7x} \right) = \frac{3}{2} - \lim\limits_{x \to 0} \left( \frac{1}{\cos 7x} \cdot \frac{\sin 7x}{7x} \cdot \frac{1}{\left( \frac{2}{7} \right)} \right) = \frac{3}{2} - \left( 1 \cdot 1 \cdot \frac{7}{2} \right) = -2$

97. $\lim\limits_{r \to 0} \frac{\sin r}{\tan 2r} = \lim\limits_{r \to 0} \left( \frac{\sin r}{r} \cdot \frac{2r}{\tan 2r} \cdot \frac{1}{2} \right) = \left( \frac{1}{2} \right) (1) \lim\limits_{r \to 0} \frac{\cos 2r}{\left( \frac{\sin 2r}{2r} \right)} = \left( \frac{1}{2} \right) (1) \left( \frac{1}{1} \right) = \frac{1}{2}$

98. $\lim\limits_{\theta \to 0} \frac{\sin(\sin \theta)}{\theta} = \lim\limits_{\theta \to 0} \left( \frac{\sin(\sin \theta)}{\sin \theta} \right) \left( \frac{\sin \theta}{\theta} \right) = \lim\limits_{\theta \to 0} \frac{\sin(\sin \theta)}{\sin \theta}.$ Let $x = \sin \theta.$ Then $x \to 0$ as $\theta \to 0$

$\Rightarrow \lim\limits_{\theta \to 0} \frac{\sin(\sin \theta)}{\sin \theta} = \lim\limits_{x \to 0} \frac{\sin x}{x} = 1$

99. $\lim\limits_{\theta \to \left( \frac{\pi}{2} \right)^-} \frac{4 \tan^2 \theta + \tan \theta + 1}{\tan^2 \theta + 5} = \lim\limits_{\theta \to \left( \frac{\pi}{2} \right)^-} \frac{\left( 4 + \frac{1}{\tan \theta} + \frac{1}{\tan^2 \theta} \right)}{\left( 1 + \frac{5}{\tan^2 \theta} \right)} = \frac{(4 + 0 + 0)}{(1 + 0)} = 4$

100. $\lim\limits_{\theta \to 0^+} \frac{1 - 2 \cot^2 \theta}{5 \cot^2 \theta - 7 \cot \theta - 8} = \lim\limits_{\theta \to 0^+} \frac{\left( \frac{1}{\cot^2 \theta} - 2 \right)}{\left( 5 - \frac{7}{\cot \theta} - \frac{8}{\cot^2 \theta} \right)} = \frac{(0 - 2)}{(5 - 0 - 0)} = -\frac{2}{5}$

101. $\lim\limits_{x \to 0} \frac{x \sin x}{2 - 2 \cos x} = \lim\limits_{x \to 0} \frac{x \sin x}{2(1 - \cos x)} = \lim\limits_{x \to 0} \frac{x \sin x}{2 \left( 2 \sin^2 \left( \frac{x}{2} \right) \right)} = \lim\limits_{x \to 0} \left[ \frac{\frac{x}{2} \cdot \frac{x}{2}}{\sin^2 \left( \frac{x}{2} \right)} \cdot \frac{\sin x}{x} \right] = \lim\limits_{x \to 0} \left[ \frac{\left( \frac{x}{2} \right)}{\sin \left( \frac{x}{2} \right)} \cdot \frac{\left( \frac{x}{2} \right)}{\sin \left( \frac{x}{2} \right)} \cdot \frac{\sin x}{x} \right]$

$= (1)(1)(1) = 1$

102. $\lim\limits_{\theta \to 0} \frac{1 - \cos \theta}{\theta^2} = \lim\limits_{\theta \to 0} \frac{2 \sin^2 \left( \frac{\theta}{2} \right)}{\theta^2} = \lim\limits_{\theta \to 0} \left[ \frac{\sin \left( \frac{\theta}{2} \right)}{\left( \frac{\theta}{2} \right)} \cdot \frac{\sin \left( \frac{\theta}{2} \right)}{\left( \frac{\theta}{2} \right)} \cdot \frac{1}{2} \right] = (1)(1) \left( \frac{1}{2} \right) = \frac{1}{2}$

103. $\lim\limits_{x \to 0} \frac{\tan x}{x} = \lim\limits_{x \to 0} \left( \frac{1}{\cos x} \cdot \frac{\sin x}{x} \right) = 1$; let $\theta = \tan x \Rightarrow \theta \to 0$ as $x \to 0 \Rightarrow \lim\limits_{x \to 0} g(x) = \lim\limits_{x \to 0} \frac{\tan (\tan x)}{\tan x}$

$= \lim\limits_{\theta \to 0} \frac{\tan \theta}{\theta} = 1$. Therefore, to make g continuous at the origin, define $g(0) = 1$.

104. $\lim\limits_{x \to 0} f(x) = \lim\limits_{x \to 0} \frac{\tan (\tan x)}{\sin (\sin x)} = \lim\limits_{x \to 0} \left[ \frac{\tan (\tan x)}{\tan x} \cdot \frac{\sin x}{\sin (\sin x)} \cdot \frac{1}{\cos x} \right] = 1 \cdot \lim\limits_{x \to 0} \frac{\sin x}{\sin (\sin x)}$ (using the result of #105);

let $\theta = \sin x \Rightarrow \theta \to 0$ as $x \to 0 \Rightarrow \lim\limits_{x \to 0} \frac{\sin x}{\sin (\sin x)} = \lim\limits_{\theta \to 0} \frac{\theta}{\sin \theta} = 1$. Therefore, to make f continuous at the origin,

define $f(0) = 1$.

105. (a) $S = 2\pi r^2 + 2\pi r h$ and h constant $\Rightarrow \frac{dS}{dt} = 4\pi r \frac{dr}{dt} + 2\pi h \frac{dr}{dt} = (4\pi r + 2\pi h) \frac{dr}{dt}$

(b) $S = 2\pi r^2 + 2\pi r h$ and r constant $\Rightarrow \frac{dS}{dt} = 2\pi r \frac{dh}{dt}$

(c) $S = 2\pi r^2 + 2\pi r h \Rightarrow \frac{dS}{dt} = 4\pi r \frac{dr}{dt} + 2\pi \left( r \frac{dh}{dt} + h \frac{dr}{dt} \right) = (4\pi r + 2\pi h) \frac{dr}{dt} + 2\pi r \frac{dh}{dt}$

(d) S constant $\Rightarrow \frac{dS}{dt} = 0 \Rightarrow 0 = (4\pi r + 2\pi h) \frac{dr}{dt} + 2\pi r \frac{dh}{dt} \Rightarrow (2r + h) \frac{dr}{dt} = -r \frac{dh}{dt} \Rightarrow \frac{dr}{dt} = \frac{-r}{2r+h} \frac{dh}{dt}$

106. $S = \pi r \sqrt{r^2 + h^2} \Rightarrow \frac{dS}{dt} = \pi r \cdot \frac{\left( r \frac{dr}{dt} + h \frac{dh}{dt} \right)}{\sqrt{r^2 + h^2}} + \pi \sqrt{r^2 + h^2} \frac{dr}{dt}$;

(a) h constant $\Rightarrow \frac{dh}{dt} = 0 \Rightarrow \frac{dS}{dt} = \frac{\pi r^2 \frac{dr}{dt}}{\sqrt{r^2 + h^2}} + \pi \sqrt{r^2 + h^2} \frac{dr}{dt} = \left[ \pi \sqrt{r^2 + h^2} + \frac{\pi r^2}{\sqrt{r^2 + h^2}} \right] \frac{dr}{dt}$

(b) r constant $\Rightarrow \frac{dr}{dt} = 0 \Rightarrow \frac{dS}{dt} = \frac{\pi r h}{\sqrt{r^2 + h^2}} \frac{dh}{dt}$

(c) In general, $\frac{dS}{dt} = \left[ \pi \sqrt{r^2 + h^2} + \frac{\pi r^2}{\sqrt{r^2 + h^2}} \right] \frac{dr}{dt} + \frac{\pi r h}{\sqrt{r^2 + h^2}} \frac{dh}{dt}$

107. $A = \pi r^2 \Rightarrow \frac{dA}{dt} = 2\pi r \frac{dr}{dt}$; so $r = 10$ and $\frac{dr}{dt} = -\frac{2}{\pi}$ m/sec $\Rightarrow \frac{dA}{dt} = (2\pi)(10) \left( -\frac{2}{\pi} \right) = -40$ m$^2$/sec

108. $V = s^3 \Rightarrow \frac{dV}{dt} = 3s^2 \cdot \frac{ds}{dt} \Rightarrow \frac{ds}{dt} = \frac{1}{3s^2} \frac{dV}{dt}$; so $s = 20$ and $\frac{dV}{dt} = 1200$ cm$^3$/min $\Rightarrow \frac{ds}{dt} = \frac{1}{3(20)^2} (1200) = 1$ cm/min

109. $\frac{dR_1}{dt} = -1$ ohm/sec, $\frac{dR_2}{dt} = 0.5$ ohm/sec; and $\frac{1}{R} = \frac{1}{R_1} + \frac{1}{R_2} \Rightarrow \frac{-1}{R^2} \frac{dR}{dt} = \frac{-1}{R_1^2} \frac{dR_1}{dt} - \frac{1}{R_2^2} \frac{dR_2}{dt}$. Also, $R_1 = 75$ ohms and

$R_2 = 50$ ohms $\Rightarrow \frac{1}{R} = \frac{1}{75} + \frac{1}{50} \Rightarrow R = 30$ ohms. Therefore, from the derivative equation,

$\frac{-1}{(30)^2} \frac{dR}{dt} = \frac{-1}{(75)^2} (-1) - \frac{1}{(50)^2} (0.5) = \left( \frac{1}{5625} - \frac{1}{5000} \right) \Rightarrow \frac{dR}{dt} = (-900) \left( \frac{5000 - 5625}{5625 \cdot 5000} \right) = \frac{9(625)}{50(5625)} = \frac{1}{50} = 0.02$ ohm/sec.

110. $\frac{dR}{dt} = 3$ ohms/sec and $\frac{dX}{dt} = -2$ ohms/sec; $Z = \sqrt{R^2 + X^2} \Rightarrow \frac{dZ}{dt} = \frac{R \frac{dR}{dt} + X \frac{dX}{dt}}{\sqrt{R^2 + X^2}}$ so that $R = 10$ ohms and

$X = 20$ ohms $\Rightarrow \frac{dZ}{dt} = \frac{(10)(3) + (20)(-2)}{\sqrt{10^2 + 20^2}} = \frac{-1}{\sqrt{5}} \approx -0.45$ ohm/sec.

111. Given $\frac{dx}{dt} = 10$ m/sec and $\frac{dy}{dt} = 5$ m/sec, let D be the distance from the origin $\Rightarrow D^2 = x^2 + y^2 \Rightarrow 2D \frac{dD}{dt}$

$= 2x \frac{dx}{dt} + 2y \frac{dy}{dt} \Rightarrow D \frac{dD}{dt} = x \frac{dx}{dt} + y \frac{dy}{dt}$. When $(x, y) = (3, -4)$, $D = \sqrt{3^2 + (-4)^2} = 5$ and

$5 \frac{dD}{dt} = (3)(10) + (-4)(5) \Rightarrow \frac{dD}{dt} = \frac{10}{5} = 2$. Therefore, the particle is moving <u>away from</u> the origin at 2 m/sec

(because the distance D is increasing).

112. Let D be the distance from the origin. We are given that $\frac{dD}{dt} = 11$ units/sec. Then $D^2 = x^2 + y^2 = x^2 + \left( x^{3/2} \right)^2$

$= x^2 + x^3 \Rightarrow 2D \frac{dD}{dt} = 2x \frac{dx}{dt} + 3x^2 \frac{dx}{dt} = x(2 + 3x) \frac{dx}{dt}$; $x = 3 \Rightarrow D = \sqrt{3^2 + 3^3} = 6$ and substitution in the

derivative equation gives $(2)(6)(11) = (3)(2 + 9) \frac{dx}{dt} \Rightarrow \frac{dx}{dt} = 4$ units/sec.

113. (a) From the diagram we have $\frac{10}{h} = \frac{4}{r} \Rightarrow r = \frac{2}{5} h$.

(b) $V = \frac{1}{3} \pi r^2 h = \frac{1}{3} \pi \left( \frac{2}{5} h \right)^2 h = \frac{4\pi h^3}{75} \Rightarrow \frac{dV}{dt} = \frac{4\pi h^2}{25} \frac{dh}{dt}$, so $\frac{dV}{dt} = -5$ and $h = 6 \Rightarrow \frac{dh}{dt} = -\frac{125}{144\pi}$ ft/min.

114. From the sketch in the text, $s = r\theta \Rightarrow \frac{ds}{dt} = r\frac{d\theta}{dt} + \theta\frac{dr}{dt}$. Also $r = 1.2$ is constant $\Rightarrow \frac{dr}{dt} = 0 \Rightarrow \frac{ds}{dt} = r\frac{d\theta}{dt} = (1.2)\frac{d\theta}{dt}$.
Therefore, $\frac{ds}{dt} = 6$ ft/sec and $r = 1.2$ ft $\Rightarrow \frac{d\theta}{dt} = 5$ rad/sec

115. (a)  From the sketch in the text, $\frac{d\theta}{dt} = -0.6$ rad/sec and $x = \tan\theta$. Also $x = \tan\theta \Rightarrow \frac{dx}{dt} = \sec^2\theta\,\frac{d\theta}{dt}$; at point A, $x = 0$
$\Rightarrow \theta = 0 \Rightarrow \frac{dx}{dt} = (\sec^2 0)(-0.6) = -0.6$. Therefore the speed of the light is $0.6 = \frac{3}{5}$ km/sec when it reaches
point A.

(b)  $\frac{(3/5)\text{ rad}}{\text{sec}} \cdot \frac{1\text{ rev}}{2\pi\text{ rad}} \cdot \frac{60\text{ sec}}{\text{min}} = \frac{18}{\pi}$ revs/min

116. From the figure, $\frac{a}{r} = \frac{b}{BC} \Rightarrow \frac{a}{r} = \frac{b}{\sqrt{b^2 - r^2}}$. We are given

that r is constant. Differentiation gives,

$\frac{1}{r} \cdot \frac{da}{dt} = \frac{\left(\sqrt{b^2 - r^2}\right)\left(\frac{db}{dt}\right) - (b)\left(\frac{b}{\sqrt{b^2 - r^2}}\right)\left(\frac{db}{dt}\right)}{b^2 - r^2}$. Then,

$b = 2r$ and $\frac{db}{dt} = -0.3r$

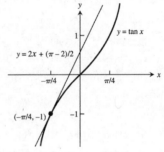

$\Rightarrow \frac{da}{dt} = r\left[\dfrac{\sqrt{(2r)^2 - r^2}\,(-0.3r) - (2r)\left(\frac{2r(-0.3r)}{\sqrt{(2r)^2 - r^2}}\right)}{(2r)^2 - r^2}\right]$

$= \dfrac{\sqrt{3r^2}\,(-0.3r) + \frac{4r^2(0.3r)}{\sqrt{3r^2}}}{3r} = \dfrac{(3r^2)(-0.3r) + (4r^2)(0.3r)}{3\sqrt{3}\,r^2} = \dfrac{0.3r}{3\sqrt{3}} = \dfrac{r}{10\sqrt{3}}$ m/sec. Since $\frac{da}{dt}$ is positive, the distance OA is increasing

when $OB = 2r$, and B is moving toward O at the rate of $0.3r$ m/sec.

117. (a)  If $f(x) = \tan x$ and $x = -\frac{\pi}{4}$, then $f'(x) = \sec^2 x$,
$f\left(-\frac{\pi}{4}\right) = -1$ and $f'\left(-\frac{\pi}{4}\right) = 2$. The linearization of
$f(x)$ is $L(x) = 2\left(x + \frac{\pi}{4}\right) + (-1) = 2x + \frac{\pi - 2}{2}$.

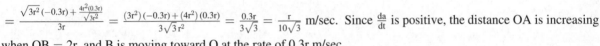

(b)  If $f(x) = \sec x$ and $x = -\frac{\pi}{4}$, then $f'(x) = \sec x \tan x$,
$f\left(-\frac{\pi}{4}\right) = \sqrt{2}$ and $f'\left(-\frac{\pi}{4}\right) = -\sqrt{2}$. The
linearization of $f(x)$ is $L(x) = -\sqrt{2}\left(x + \frac{\pi}{4}\right) + \sqrt{2}$
$= -\sqrt{2}x + \frac{\sqrt{2}(4 - \pi)}{4}$.

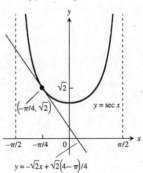

118. $f(x) = \frac{1}{1 + \tan x} \Rightarrow f'(x) = \frac{-\sec^2 x}{(1 + \tan x)^2}$. The linearization at $x = 0$ is $L(x) = f'(0)(x - 0) + f(0) = 1 - x$.

119. $f(x) = \sqrt{x + 1} + \sin x - 0.5 = (x + 1)^{1/2} + \sin x - 0.5 \Rightarrow f'(x) = \left(\frac{1}{2}\right)(x + 1)^{-1/2} + \cos x$
$\Rightarrow L(x) = f'(0)(x - 0) + f(0) = 1.5(x - 0) + 0.5 \Rightarrow L(x) = 1.5x + 0.5$, the linearization of $f(x)$.

120. $f(x) = \frac{2}{1 - x} + \sqrt{1 + x} - 3.1 = 2(1 - x)^{-1} + (1 + x)^{1/2} - 3.1 \Rightarrow f'(x) = -2(1 - x)^{-2}(-1) + \frac{1}{2}(1 + x)^{-1/2}$
$= \frac{2}{(1 - x)^2} + \frac{1}{2\sqrt{1 + x}} \Rightarrow L(x) = f'(0)(x - 0) + f(0) = 2.5x - 0.1$, the linearization of $f(x)$.

121. $S = \pi\, r\sqrt{r^2 + h^2}$, r constant $\Rightarrow dS = \pi\, r \cdot \frac{1}{2}(r^2 + h^2)^{-1/2} 2h\, dh = \frac{\pi\, r\, h}{\sqrt{r^2 + h^2}} dh$. Height changes from $h_0$ to $h_0 + dh$

$\Rightarrow dS = \frac{\pi\, r\, h_0\, (dh)}{\sqrt{r^2 + h_0^2}}$

122. (a)  $S = 6r^2 \Rightarrow dS = 12r\, dr$. We want $|dS| \le (2\%)\, S \Rightarrow |12r\, dr| \le \frac{12r^2}{100} \Rightarrow |dr| \le \frac{r}{100}$. The measurement of the edge r  must have an error less than 1%.

(b)  When $V = r^3$, then $dV = 3r^2\, dr$. The accuracy of the volume is $\left(\frac{dV}{V}\right)(100\%) = \left(\frac{3r^2\, dr}{r^3}\right)(100\%)$

$= \left(\frac{3}{r}\right)(dr)(100\%) = \left(\frac{3}{r}\right)\left(\frac{r}{100}\right)(100\%) = 3\%$

123.  $C = 2\pi r \Rightarrow r = \frac{C}{2\pi}$, $S = 4\pi r^2 = \frac{C^2}{\pi}$, and $V = \frac{4}{3}\pi r^3 = \frac{C^3}{6\pi^2}$. It also follows that $dr = \frac{1}{2\pi}\, dC$, $dS = \frac{2C}{\pi}\, dC$ and

$dV = \frac{C^2}{2\pi^2}\, dC$. Recall that $C = 10$ cm and $dC = 0.4$ cm.

(a)  $dr = \frac{0.4}{2\pi} = \frac{0.2}{\pi}$ cm $\Rightarrow \left(\frac{dr}{r}\right)(100\%) = \left(\frac{0.2}{\pi}\right)\left(\frac{2\pi}{10}\right)(100\%) = (.04)(100\%) = 4\%$

(b)  $dS = \frac{20}{\pi}(0.4) = \frac{8}{\pi}$ cm $\Rightarrow \left(\frac{dS}{S}\right)(100\%) = \left(\frac{8}{\pi}\right)\left(\frac{\pi}{100}\right)(100\%) = 8\%$

(c)  $dV = \frac{10^2}{2\pi^2}(0.4) = \frac{20}{\pi^2}$ cm $\Rightarrow \left(\frac{dV}{V}\right)(100\%) = \left(\frac{20}{\pi^2}\right)\left(\frac{6\pi^2}{1000}\right)(100\%) = 12\%$

124. Similar triangles yield $\frac{35}{h} = \frac{15}{6} \Rightarrow h = 14$ ft. The same triangles imply that $\frac{20+a}{h} = \frac{a}{6} \Rightarrow h = 120a^{-1} + 6$

$\Rightarrow dh = -120a^{-2}\, da = -\frac{120}{a^2}\, da = \left(-\frac{120}{a^2}\right)\left(\pm\frac{1}{12}\right) = \left(-\frac{120}{15^2}\right)\left(\pm\frac{1}{12}\right) = \pm\frac{2}{45} \approx \pm.0444$ ft $= \pm 0.53$ inches.

## CHAPTER 3  ADDITIONAL AND ADVANCED EXERCISES

1.  (a)  $\sin 2\theta = 2\sin\theta\cos\theta \Rightarrow \frac{d}{d\theta}(\sin 2\theta) = \frac{d}{d\theta}(2\sin\theta\cos\theta) \Rightarrow 2\cos 2\theta = 2[(\sin\theta)(-\sin\theta) + (\cos\theta)(\cos\theta)]$

$\Rightarrow \cos 2\theta = \cos^2\theta - \sin^2\theta$

(b)  $\cos 2\theta = \cos^2\theta - \sin^2\theta \Rightarrow \frac{d}{d\theta}(\cos 2\theta) = \frac{d}{d\theta}(\cos^2\theta - \sin^2\theta) \Rightarrow -2\sin 2\theta = (2\cos\theta)(-\sin\theta) - (2\sin\theta)(\cos\theta)$

$\Rightarrow \sin 2\theta = \cos\theta\sin\theta + \sin\theta\cos\theta \Rightarrow \sin 2\theta = 2\sin\theta\cos\theta$

2.  The derivative of $\sin(x + a) = \sin x \cos a + \cos x \sin a$ with respect to x is $\cos(x + a) = \cos x \cos a - \sin x \sin a$, which is also an identity. This principle does not apply to the equation $x^2 - 2x - 8 = 0$, since $x^2 - 2x - 8 = 0$ is not an identity: it holds for 2 values of x ($-2$ and 4), but not for all x.

3.  (a)  $f(x) = \cos x \Rightarrow f'(x) = -\sin x \Rightarrow f''(x) = -\cos x$, and $g(x) = a + bx + cx^2 \Rightarrow g'(x) = b + 2cx \Rightarrow g''(x) = 2c$; also, $f(0) = g(0) \Rightarrow \cos(0) = a \Rightarrow a = 1$; $f'(0) = g'(0) \Rightarrow -\sin(0) = b \Rightarrow b = 0$; $f''(0) = g''(0) \Rightarrow -\cos(0) = 2c$ $\Rightarrow c = -\frac{1}{2}$. Therefore, $g(x) = 1 - \frac{1}{2}x^2$.

(b)  $f(x) = \sin(x + a) \Rightarrow f'(x) = \cos(x + a)$, and $g(x) = b\sin x + c\cos x \Rightarrow g'(x) = b\cos x - c\sin x$; also, $f(0) = g(0)$ $\Rightarrow \sin(a) = b\sin(0) + c\cos(0) \Rightarrow c = \sin a$; $f'(0) = g'(0) \Rightarrow \cos(a) = b\cos(0) - c\sin(0) \Rightarrow b = \cos a$. Therefore, $g(x) = \sin x \cos a + \cos x \sin a$.

(c)  When $f(x) = \cos x$, $f'''(x) = \sin x$ and $f^{(4)}(x) = \cos x$; when $g(x) = 1 - \frac{1}{2}x^2$, $g'''(x) = 0$ and $g^{(4)}(x) = 0$. Thus $f'''(0) = 0 = g'''(0)$ so the third derivatives agree at $x = 0$. However, the fourth derivatives do not agree since $f^{(4)}(0) = 1$ but $g^{(4)}(0) = 0$. In case (b), when $f(x) = \sin(x + a)$ and $g(x) = \sin x \cos a + \cos x \sin a$, notice that $f(x) = g(x)$ for all x, not just $x = 0$. Since this is an identity, we have $f^{(n)}(x) = g^{(n)}(x)$ for any x and any positive integer n.

4.  (a)  $y = \sin x \Rightarrow y' = \cos x \Rightarrow y'' = -\sin x \Rightarrow y'' + y = -\sin x + \sin x = 0$; $y = \cos x \Rightarrow y' = -\sin x$ $\Rightarrow y'' = -\cos x \Rightarrow y'' + y = -\cos x + \cos x = 0$; $y = a\cos x + b\sin x \Rightarrow y' = -a\sin x + b\cos x$ $\Rightarrow y'' = -a\cos x - b\sin x \Rightarrow y'' + y = (-a\cos x - b\sin x) + (a\cos x + b\sin x) = 0$

(b) $y = \sin(2x) \Rightarrow y' = 2\cos(2x) \Rightarrow y'' = -4\sin(2x) \Rightarrow y'' + 4y = -4\sin(2x) + 4\sin(2x) = 0$. Similarly, $y = \cos(2x)$ and $y = a\cos(2x) + b\sin(2x)$ satisfy the differential equation $y'' + 4y = 0$. In general, $y = \cos(mx)$, $y = \sin(mx)$ and $y = a\cos(mx) + b\sin(mx)$ satisfy the differential equation $y'' + m^2y = 0$.

5. If the circle $(x - h)^2 + (y - k)^2 = a^2$ and $y = x^2 + 1$ are tangent at $(1, 2)$, then the slope of this tangent is $m = 2x\big|_{(1,2)} = 2$ and the tangent line is $y = 2x$. The line containing $(h, k)$ and $(1, 2)$ is perpendicular to $y = 2x \Rightarrow \frac{k-2}{h-1} = -\frac{1}{2} \Rightarrow h = 5 - 2k \Rightarrow$ the location of the center is $(5 - 2k, k)$. Also, $(x - h)^2 + (y - k)^2 = a^2$ $\Rightarrow x - h + (y - k)y' = 0 \Rightarrow 1 + (y')^2 + (y - k)y'' = 0 \Rightarrow y'' = \frac{1 + (y')^2}{k - y}$. At the point $(1, 2)$ we know $y' = 2$ from the tangent line and that $y'' = 2$ from the parabola. Since the second derivatives are equal at $(1, 2)$ we obtain $2 = \frac{1 + (2)^2}{k - 2} \Rightarrow k = \frac{9}{2}$. Then $h = 5 - 2k = -4 \Rightarrow$ the circle is $(x + 4)^2 + \left(y - \frac{9}{2}\right)^2 = a^2$. Since $(1, 2)$ lies on the circle we have that $a = \frac{5\sqrt{5}}{2}$.

6. The total revenue is the number of people times the price of the fare: $r(x) = xp = x\left(3 - \frac{x}{40}\right)^2$, where $0 \le x \le 60$. The marginal revenue is $\frac{dr}{dx} = \left(3 - \frac{x}{40}\right)^2 + 2x\left(3 - \frac{x}{40}\right)\left(-\frac{1}{40}\right) \Rightarrow \frac{dr}{dx} = \left(3 - \frac{x}{40}\right)\left[\left(3 - \frac{x}{40}\right) - \frac{2x}{40}\right]$ $= 3\left(3 - \frac{x}{40}\right)\left(1 - \frac{x}{40}\right)$. Then $\frac{dr}{dx} = 0 \Rightarrow x = 40$ (since $x = 120$ does not belong to the domain). When 40 people are on the bus the marginal revenue is zero and the fare is $p(40) = \left(3 - \frac{x}{40}\right)^2\Big|_{x=40} = \$4.00$.

7. (a) $y = uv \Rightarrow \frac{dy}{dt} = \frac{du}{dt}v + u\frac{dv}{dt} = (0.04u)v + u(0.05v) = 0.09uv = 0.09y \Rightarrow$ the rate of growth of the total production is 9% per year.

   (b) If $\frac{du}{dt} = -0.02u$ and $\frac{dv}{dt} = 0.03v$, then $\frac{dy}{dt} = (-0.02u)v + (0.03v)u = 0.01uv = 0.01y$, increasing at 1% per year.

8. When $x^2 + y^2 = 225$, then $y' = -\frac{x}{y}$. The tangent line to the balloon at $(12, -9)$ is $y + 9 = \frac{4}{3}(x - 12)$ $\Rightarrow y = \frac{4}{3}x - 25$. The top of the gondola is $15 + 8$ $= 23$ ft below the center of the balloon. The intersection of $y = -23$ and $y = \frac{4}{3}x - 25$ is at the far right edge of the gondola $\Rightarrow -23 = \frac{4}{3}x - 25$ $\Rightarrow x = \frac{3}{2}$. Thus the gondola is $2x = 3$ ft wide.

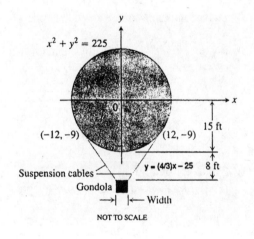

9. Answers will vary. Here is one possibility.

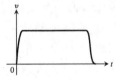

10. $s(t) = 10\cos\left(t + \frac{\pi}{4}\right) \Rightarrow v(t) = \frac{ds}{dt} = -10\sin\left(t + \frac{\pi}{4}\right) \Rightarrow a(t) = \frac{dv}{dt} = \frac{d^2s}{dt^2} = -10\cos\left(t + \frac{\pi}{4}\right)$

   (a) $s(0) = 10\cos\left(\frac{\pi}{4}\right) = \frac{10}{\sqrt{2}}$

   (b) Left: $-10$, Right: $10$

(c)  Solving $10\cos\left(t + \frac{\pi}{4}\right) = -10 \Rightarrow \cos\left(t + \frac{\pi}{4}\right) = -1 \Rightarrow t = \frac{3\pi}{4}$ when the particle is farthest to the left.

Solving $10\cos\left(t + \frac{\pi}{4}\right) = 10 \Rightarrow \cos\left(t + \frac{\pi}{4}\right) = 1 \Rightarrow t = -\frac{\pi}{4}$, but $t \geq 0 \Rightarrow t = 2\pi + \frac{-\pi}{4} = \frac{7\pi}{4}$ when the particle is farthest to the right. Thus, $v\left(\frac{3\pi}{4}\right) = 0$, $v\left(\frac{7\pi}{4}\right) = 0$, $a\left(\frac{3\pi}{4}\right) = 10$, and $a\left(\frac{7\pi}{4}\right) = -10$.

(d)  Solving $10\cos\left(t + \frac{\pi}{4}\right) = 0 \Rightarrow t = \frac{\pi}{4} \Rightarrow v\left(\frac{\pi}{4}\right) = -10$, $\left|v\left(\frac{\pi}{4}\right)\right| = 10$ and $a\left(\frac{\pi}{4}\right) = 0$.

11. (a)  $s(t) = 64t - 16t^2 \Rightarrow v(t) = \frac{ds}{dt} = 64 - 32t = 32(2 - t)$. The maximum height is reached when $v(t) = 0$

$\Rightarrow t = 2$ sec. The velocity when it leaves the hand is $v(0) = 64$ ft/sec.

(b)  $s(t) = 64t - 2.6t^2 \Rightarrow v(t) = \frac{ds}{dt} = 64 - 5.2t$. The maximum height is reached when $v(t) = 0 \Rightarrow t \approx 12.31$ sec.

The maximum height is about $s(12.31) = 393.85$ ft.

12. $s_1 = 3t^3 - 12t^2 + 18t + 5$ and $s_2 = -t^3 + 9t^2 - 12t \Rightarrow v_1 = 9t^2 - 24t + 18$ and $v_2 = -3t^2 + 18t - 12$; $v_1 = v_2$

$\Rightarrow 9t^2 - 24t + 18 = -3t^2 + 18t - 12 \Rightarrow 2t^2 - 7t + 5 = 0 \Rightarrow (t - 1)(2t - 5) = 0 \Rightarrow t = 1$ sec and $t = 2.5$ sec.

13. $m\left(v^2 - v_0^2\right) = k\left(x_0^2 - x^2\right) \Rightarrow m\left(2v\frac{dv}{dt}\right) = k\left(-2x\frac{dx}{dt}\right) \Rightarrow m\frac{dv}{dt} = k\left(-\frac{2x}{2v}\right)\frac{dx}{dt} \Rightarrow m\frac{dv}{dt} = -kx\left(\frac{1}{v}\right)\frac{dx}{dt}$. Then

substituting $\frac{dx}{dt} = v \Rightarrow m\frac{dv}{dt} = -kx$, as claimed.

14. (a)  $x = At^2 + Bt + C$ on $[t_1, t_2] \Rightarrow v = \frac{dx}{dt} = 2At + B \Rightarrow v\left(\frac{t_1 + t_2}{2}\right) = 2A\left(\frac{t_1 + t_2}{2}\right) + B = A(t_1 + t_2) + B$ is the

instantaneous velocity at the midpoint. The average velocity over the time interval is $v_{av} = \frac{\Delta x}{\Delta t}$

$= \frac{\left(At_2^2 + Bt_2 + C\right) - \left(At_1^2 + Bt_1 + C\right)}{t_2 - t_1} = \frac{(t_2 - t_1)\left[A(t_2 + t_1) + B\right]}{t_2 - t_1} = A(t_2 + t_1) + B.$

(b)  On the graph of the parabola $x = At^2 + Bt + C$, the slope of the curve at the midpoint of the interval $[t_1, t_2]$ is the same as the average slope of the curve over the interval.

15. (a)  To be continuous at $x = \pi$ requires that $\lim_{x \to \pi^-} \sin x = \lim_{x \to \pi^+} (mx + b) \Rightarrow 0 = m\pi + b \Rightarrow m = -\frac{b}{\pi}$;

(b)  If $y' = \begin{cases} \cos x, & x < \pi \\ m, & x \geq \pi \end{cases}$ is differentiable at $x = \pi$, then $\lim_{x \to \pi^-} \cos x = m \Rightarrow m = -1$ and $b = \pi$.

16. $f(x)$ is continuous at 0 because $\lim_{x \to 0} \frac{1 - \cos x}{x} = 0 = f(0)$. $f'(0) = \lim_{x \to 0} \frac{f(x) - f(0)}{x - 0} = \lim_{x \to 0} \frac{\frac{1 - \cos x}{x} - 0}{x}$

$= \lim_{x \to 0} \left(\frac{1 - \cos x}{x^2}\right)\left(\frac{1 + \cos x}{1 + \cos x}\right) = \lim_{x \to 0} \left(\frac{\sin x}{x}\right)^2 \left(\frac{1}{1 + \cos x}\right) = \frac{1}{2}$. Therefore $f'(0)$ exists with value $\frac{1}{2}$.

17. (a)  For all a, b and for all $x \neq 2$, f is differentiable at x. Next, f differentiable at $x = 2 \Rightarrow$ f continuous at $x = 2$

$\Rightarrow \lim_{x \to 2^-} f(x) = f(2) \Rightarrow 2a = 4a - 2b + 3 \Rightarrow 2a - 2b + 3 = 0$. Also, f differentiable at $x \neq 2$

$\Rightarrow f'(x) = \begin{cases} a, & x < 2 \\ 2ax - b, & x > 2 \end{cases}$. In order that $f'(2)$ exist we must have $a = 2a(2) - b \Rightarrow a = 4a - b \Rightarrow 3a = b$.

Then $2a - 2b + 3 = 0$ and $3a = b \Rightarrow a = \frac{3}{4}$ and $b = \frac{9}{4}$.

(b)  For $x < 2$, the graph of f is a straight line having a slope of $\frac{3}{4}$ and passing through the origin; for $x \geq 2$, the graph of f is a parabola. At $x = 2$, the value of the y-coordinate on the parabola is $\frac{3}{2}$ which matches the y-coordinate of the point on the straight line at $x = 2$. In addition, the slope of the parabola at the match up point is $\frac{3}{4}$ which is equal to the slope of the straight line. Therefore, since the graph is differentiable at the match up point, the graph is smooth there.

18. (a)  For any a, b and for any $x \neq -1$, g is differentiable at x. Next, g differentiable at $x = -1 \Rightarrow$ g continuous at

$x = -1 \Rightarrow \lim_{x \to -1^+} g(x) = g(-1) \Rightarrow -a - 1 + 2b = -a + b \Rightarrow b = 1$. Also, g differentiable at $x \neq -1$

$\Rightarrow g'(x) = \begin{cases} a, & x < -1 \\ 3ax^2 + 1, & x > -1 \end{cases}$. In order that $g'(-1)$ exist we must have $a = 3a(-1)^2 + 1 \Rightarrow a = 3a + 1$

$\Rightarrow a = -\frac{1}{2}$.

(b) For $x \le -1$, the graph of g is a straight line having a slope of $-\frac{1}{2}$ and a y-intercept of 1. For $x > -1$, the graph of g is a cubic. At $x = -1$, the value of the y-coordinate on the cubic is $\frac{3}{2}$ which matches the y-coordinate of the point on the straight line at $x = -1$. In addition, the slope of the cubic at the match up point is $-\frac{1}{2}$ which is equal to the slope of the straight line. Therefore, since the graph is differentiable at the match up point, the graph is smooth there.

19. f odd $\Rightarrow$ $f(-x) = -f(x)$ $\Rightarrow$ $\frac{d}{dx}(f(-x)) = \frac{d}{dx}(-f(x))$ $\Rightarrow$ $f'(-x)(-1) = -f'(x)$ $\Rightarrow$ $f'(-x) = f'(x)$ $\Rightarrow$ $f'$ is even.

20. f even $\Rightarrow$ $f(-x) = f(x)$ $\Rightarrow$ $\frac{d}{dx}(f(-x)) = \frac{d}{dx}(f(x))$ $\Rightarrow$ $f'(-x)(-1) = f'(x)$ $\Rightarrow$ $f'(-x) = -f'(x)$ $\Rightarrow$ $f'$ is odd.

21. Let $h(x) = (fg)(x) = f(x)\,g(x)$ $\Rightarrow$ $h'(x) = \lim\limits_{x \to x_0} \frac{h(x) - h(x_0)}{x - x_0} = \lim\limits_{x \to x_0} \frac{f(x)\,g(x) - f(x_0)\,g(x_0)}{x - x_0}$

$= \lim\limits_{x \to x_0} \frac{f(x)\,g(x) - f(x)\,g(x_0) + f(x)\,g(x_0) - f(x_0)\,g(x_0)}{x - x_0} = \lim\limits_{x \to x_0} \left[ f(x) \left[ \frac{g(x) - g(x_0)}{x - x_0} \right] \right] + \lim\limits_{x \to x_0} \left[ g(x_0) \left[ \frac{f(x) - f(x_0)}{x - x_0} \right] \right]$

$= f(x_0) \lim\limits_{x \to x_0} \left[ \frac{g(x) - g(x_0)}{x - x_0} \right] + g(x_0)\,f'(x_0) = 0 \cdot \lim\limits_{x \to x_0} \left[ \frac{g(x) - g(x_0)}{x - x_0} \right] + g(x_0)\,f'(x_0) = g(x_0)\,f'(x_0)$, if g is

continuous at $x_0$. Therefore (fg)(x) is differentiable at $x_0$ if $f(x_0) = 0$, and $(fg)'(x_0) = g(x_0)\,f'(x_0)$.

22. From Exercise 21 we have that fg is differentiable at 0 if f is differentiable at 0, $f(0) = 0$ and g is continuous at 0.
   (a) If $f(x) = \sin x$ and $g(x) = |x|$, then $|x| \sin x$ is differentiable because $f'(0) = \cos(0) = 1$, $f(0) = \sin(0) = 0$ and $g(x) = |x|$ is continuous at $x = 0$.
   (b) If $f(x) = \sin x$ and $g(x) = x^{2/3}$, then $x^{2/3} \sin x$ is differentiable because $f'(0) = \cos(0) = 1$, $f(0) = \sin(0) = 0$ and $g(x) = x^{2/3}$ is continuous at $x = 0$.
   (c) If $f(x) = 1 - \cos x$ and $g(x) = \sqrt[3]{x}$, then $\sqrt[3]{x}\,(1 - \cos x)$ is differentiable because $f'(0) = \sin(0) = 0$, $f(0) = 1 - \cos(0) = 0$ and $g(x) = x^{1/3}$ is continuous at $x = 0$.
   (d) If $f(x) = x$ and $g(x) = x \sin\left(\frac{1}{x}\right)$, then $x^2 \sin\left(\frac{1}{x}\right)$ is differentiable because $f'(0) = 1$, $f(0) = 0$ and
   $$\lim\limits_{x \to 0} x \sin\left(\tfrac{1}{x}\right) = \lim\limits_{x \to 0} \frac{\sin\left(\frac{1}{x}\right)}{\frac{1}{x}} = \lim\limits_{t \to \infty} \frac{\sin t}{t} = 0 \text{ (so g is continuous at } x = 0).$$

23. If $f(x) = x$ and $g(x) = x \sin\left(\frac{1}{x}\right)$, then $x^2 \sin\left(\frac{1}{x}\right)$ is differentiable at $x = 0$ because $f'(0) = 1$, $f(0) = 0$ and
   $$\lim\limits_{x \to 0} x \sin\left(\tfrac{1}{x}\right) = \lim\limits_{x \to 0} \frac{\sin\left(\frac{1}{x}\right)}{\frac{1}{x}} = \lim\limits_{t \to \infty} \frac{\sin t}{t} = 0 \text{ (so g is continuous at } x = 0). \text{ In fact, from Exercise 21,}$$
   $h'(0) = g(0)\,f'(0) = 0$. However, for $x \ne 0$, $h'(x) = \left[ x^2 \cos\left(\tfrac{1}{x}\right) \right]\left( -\tfrac{1}{x^2} \right) + 2x \sin\left(\tfrac{1}{x}\right)$. But
   $\lim\limits_{x \to 0} h'(x) = \lim\limits_{x \to 0} \left[ -\cos\left(\tfrac{1}{x}\right) + 2x \sin\left(\tfrac{1}{x}\right) \right]$ does not exist because $\cos\left(\tfrac{1}{x}\right)$ has no limit as $x \to 0$. Therefore, the derivative is not continuous at $x = 0$ because it has no limit there.

24. From the given conditions we have $f(x + h) = f(x)\,f(h)$, $f(h) - 1 = hg(h)$ and $\lim\limits_{h \to 0} g(h) = 1$. Therefore,
   $$f'(x) = \lim\limits_{h \to 0} \frac{f(x+h) - f(x)}{h} = \lim\limits_{h \to 0} \frac{f(x)\,f(h) - f(x)}{h} = \lim\limits_{h \to 0} f(x) \left[ \frac{f(h) - 1}{h} \right] = f(x) \left[ \lim\limits_{h \to 0} g(h) \right] = f(x) \cdot 1 = f(x)$$
   $\Rightarrow f'(x) = f(x)$ and $f'(x)$ exists at every value of x.

25. Step 1:  The formula holds for $n = 2$ (a single product) since $y = u_1 u_2 \Rightarrow \frac{dy}{dx} = \frac{du_1}{dx} u_2 + u_1 \frac{du_2}{dx}$.
   Step 2:  Assume the formula holds for $n = k$:
   $$y = u_1 u_2 \cdots u_k \Rightarrow \frac{dy}{dx} = \frac{du_1}{dx} u_2 u_3 \cdots u_k + u_1 \frac{du_2}{dx} u_3 \cdots u_k + \ldots + u_1 u_2 \cdots u_{k-1} \frac{du_k}{dx}.$$
   If $y = u_1 u_2 \cdots u_k u_{k+1} = (u_1 u_2 \cdots u_k)\,u_{k+1}$, then $\frac{dy}{dx} = \frac{d(u_1 u_2 \cdots u_k)}{dx} u_{k+1} + u_1 u_2 \cdots u_k \frac{du_{k+1}}{dx}$
   $$= \left( \frac{du_1}{dx} u_2 u_3 \cdots u_k + u_1 \frac{du_2}{dx} u_3 \cdots u_k + \cdots + u_1 u_2 \cdots u_{k-1} \frac{du_k}{dx} \right) u_{k+1} + u_1 u_2 \cdots u_k \frac{du_{k+1}}{dx}$$
   $$= \frac{du_1}{dx} u_2 u_3 \cdots u_{k+1} + u_1 \frac{du_2}{dx} u_3 \cdots u_{k+1} + \cdots + u_1 u_2 \cdots u_{k-1} \frac{du_k}{dx} u_{k+1} + u_1 u_2 \cdots u_k \frac{du_{k+1}}{dx}.$$
   Thus the original formula holds for $n = (k+1)$ whenever it holds for $n = k$.

26. Recall $\binom{m}{k} = \frac{m!}{k!\,(m-k)!}$. Then $\binom{m}{1} = \frac{m!}{1!\,(m-1)!} = m$ and $\binom{m}{k} + \binom{m}{k+1} = \frac{m!}{k!\,(m-k)!} + \frac{m!}{(k+1)!\,(m-k-1)!}$

$= \frac{m!\,(k+1) + m!\,(m-k)}{(k+1)!\,(m-k)!} = \frac{m!\,(m+1)}{(k+1)!\,(m-k)!} = \frac{(m+1)!}{(k+1)!\,((m+1)-(k+1))!} = \binom{m+1}{k+1}$. Now, we prove

Leibniz's rule by mathematical induction.

Step 1: If $n = 1$, then $\frac{d(uv)}{dx} = u\,\frac{dv}{dx} + v\,\frac{du}{dx}$. Assume that the statement is true for $n = k$, that is:

$\frac{d^k(uv)}{dx^k} = \frac{d^k u}{dx^k}\,v + k\,\frac{d^{k-1}u}{dx^{k-1}}\,\frac{dv}{dx} + \binom{k}{2}\,\frac{d^{k-2}u}{dx^{k-2}}\,\frac{d^2 v}{dx^2} + \ldots + \binom{k}{k-1}\,\frac{du}{dv}\,\frac{d^{k-1}v}{dx^{k-1}} + u\,\frac{d^k v}{dx^k}$.

Step 2: If $n = k+1$, then $\frac{d^{k+1}(uv)}{dx^{k+1}} = \frac{d}{dx}\left(\frac{d^k(uv)}{dx^k}\right) = \left[\frac{d^{k+1}u}{dx^{k+1}}\,v + \frac{d^k u}{dx^k}\,\frac{dv}{dx}\right] + \left[k\,\frac{d^k u}{dx^k}\,\frac{dv}{dx} + k\,\frac{d^{k-1}u}{dx^{k-1}}\,\frac{d^2 v}{dx^2}\right]$

$+ \left[\binom{k}{2}\,\frac{d^{k-1}u}{dx^{k-1}}\,\frac{d^2 v}{dx^2} + \binom{k}{2}\,\frac{d^{k-2}u}{dx^{k-2}}\,\frac{d^3 v}{dx^3}\right] + \ldots + \left[\binom{k}{k-1}\,\frac{d^2 u}{dx^2}\,\frac{d^{k-1}v}{dx^{k-1}} + \binom{k}{k-1}\,\frac{du}{dx}\,\frac{d^k u}{dx^k}\,v\right]$

$+ \left[\frac{du}{dx}\,\frac{d^k v}{dx^k} + u\,\frac{d^{k+1}u}{dx^{k+1}}\right] = \frac{d^{k+1}u}{dx^{k+1}}\,v + (k+1)\,\frac{d^k u}{dx^k}\,\frac{dv}{dx} + \left[\binom{k}{1} + \binom{k}{2}\right]\,\frac{d^{k-1}u}{dx^{k-1}}\,\frac{d^2 v}{dx^2} + \ldots$

$+ \left[\binom{k}{k-1} + \binom{k}{k}\right]\,\frac{du}{dx}\,\frac{d^k v}{dx^k} + u\,\frac{d^{k+1}v}{dx^{k+1}} = \frac{d^{k+1}u}{dx^{k+1}}\,v + (k+1)\,\frac{d^k u}{dx^k}\,\frac{dv}{dx} + \binom{k+1}{2}\,\frac{d^{k-1}u}{dx^{k-1}}\,\frac{d^2 v}{dx^2} + \ldots$

$+ \binom{k+1}{k}\,\frac{du}{dx}\,\frac{d^k v}{dx^k} + u\,\frac{d^{k+1}v}{dx^{k+1}}$.

Therefore the formula (c) holds for $n = (k+1)$ whenever it holds for $n = k$.

27. (a) $T^2 = \frac{4\pi^2 L}{g} \Rightarrow L = \frac{T^2 g}{4\pi^2} \Rightarrow L = \frac{(1\ \text{sec}^2)(32.2\ \text{ft/sec}^2)}{4\pi^2} \Rightarrow L \approx 0.8156\ \text{ft}$

(b) $T^2 = \frac{4\pi^2 L}{g} \Rightarrow T = \frac{2\pi}{\sqrt{g}}\,\sqrt{L}$; $dT = \frac{2\pi}{\sqrt{g}} \cdot \frac{1}{2\sqrt{L}}\,dL = \frac{\pi}{\sqrt{Lg}}\,dL$; $dT = \frac{\pi}{\sqrt{(0.8156\ \text{ft})(32.2\ \text{ft/sec}^2)}}\,(0.01\ \text{ft}) \approx 0.00613\ \text{sec}$.

(c) Since there are 86,400 sec in a day, we have $(0.00613\ \text{sec})(86,400\ \text{sec/day}) \approx 529.6\ \text{sec/day}$, or 8.83 min/day; the clock will lose about 8.83 min/day.

28. $v = s^3 \Rightarrow \frac{dv}{dt} = 3s^2\,\frac{ds}{dt} = -k(6s^2) \Rightarrow \frac{ds}{dt} = -2k$. If $s_0 =$ the initial length of the cube's side, then $s_1 = s_0 - 2k$

$\Rightarrow 2k = s_0 - s_1$. Let $t =$ the time it will take the ice cube to melt. Now, $t = \frac{s_0}{2k} = \frac{s_0}{s_0 - s_1} = \frac{(v_0)^{1/3}}{(v_0)^{1/3} - \left(\frac{3}{4}v_0\right)^{1/3}}$

$= \frac{1}{1 - \left(\frac{3}{4}\right)^{1/3}} \approx 11\ \text{hr}$.

# CHAPTER 4 APPLICATIONS OF DERIVATIVES

## 4.1 EXTREME VALUES OF FUNCTIONS

1. An absolute minimum at $x = c_2$, an absolute maximum at $x = b$. Theorem 1 guarantees the existence of such extreme values because h is continuous on $[a, b]$.

2. An absolute minimum at $x = b$, an absolute maximum at $x = c$. Theorem 1 guarantees the existence of such extreme values because f is continuous on $[a, b]$.

3. No absolute minimum. An absolute maximum at $x = c$. Since the function's domain is an open interval, the function does not satisfy the hypotheses of Theorem 1 and need not have absolute extreme values.

4. No absolute extrema. The function is neither continuous nor defined on a closed interval, so it need not fulfill the conclusions of Theorem 1.

5. An absolute minimum at $x = a$ and an absolute maximum at $x = c$. Note that $y = g(x)$ is not continuous but still has extrema. When the hypothesis of Theorem 1 is satisfied then extrema are guaranteed, but when the hypothesis is not satisfied, absolute extrema may or may not occur.

6. Absolute minimum at $x = c$ and an absolute maximum at $x = a$. Note that $y = g(x)$ is not continuous but still has absolute extrema. When the hypothesis of Theorem 1 is satisfied then extrema are guaranteed, but when the hypothesis is not satisfied, absolute extrema may or may not occur.

7. Local minimum at $(-1, 0)$, local maximum at $(1, 0)$

8. Minima at $(-2, 0)$ and $(2, 0)$, maximum at $(0, 2)$

9. Maximum at $(0, 5)$. Note that there is no minimum since the endpoint $(2, 0)$ is excluded from the graph.

10. Local maximum at $(-3, 0)$, local minimum at $(2, 0)$, maximum at $(1, 2)$, minimum at $(0, -1)$

11. Graph (c), since this the only graph that has positive slope at c.

12. Graph (b), since this is the only graph that represents a differentiable function at a and b and has negative slope at c.

13. Graph (d), since this is the only graph representing a funtion that is differentiable at b but not at a.

14. Graph (a), since this is the only graph that represents a function that is not differentiable at a or b.

15. f has an absolute min at $x = 0$ but does not have an absolute max. Since the interval on which f is defined, $-1 < x < 2$, is an open interval, we do not meet the conditions of Theorem 1.

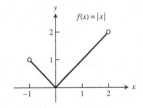

16. f has an absolute max at x = 0 but does not have an absolute min. Since the interval on which f is defined, $-1 < x < 1$, is an open interval, we do not meet the conditions of Theorem 1.

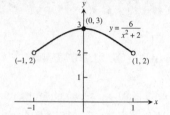

17. f has an absolute max at x = 2 but does not have an absolute min. Since the function is not continuous at x = 1, we do not meet the conditions of Theorem 1.

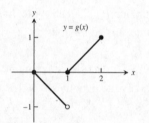

18. f has an absolute max at x = 4 but does not have an absolute min. Since the function is not continuous at x = 0, we do not meet the conditions of Theorem 1.

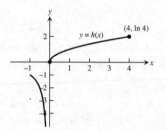

19. f has an absolute max at $x = \frac{\pi}{2}$ and an absolute min at $x = \frac{3\pi}{2}$. Since the interval on which f is defined, $0 < x < 2\pi$, is an open interval, we do not meet the conditions of Theorem 1.

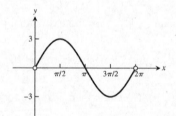

20. f has an absolute max at x = 0 and an absolute min at $x = \frac{\pi}{2}$ and x = -1. Since f is continuous on the closed interval on which it is defined, $-1 \le x \le 2\pi$, we do meet the conditions of Theorem 1.

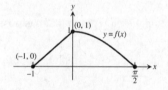

21. $f(x) = \frac{2}{3}x - 5 \Rightarrow f'(x) = \frac{2}{3} \Rightarrow$ no critical points; $f(-2) = -\frac{19}{3}$, $f(3) = -3 \Rightarrow$ the absolute maximum is $-3$ at $x = 3$ and the absolute minimum is $-\frac{19}{3}$ at $x = -2$

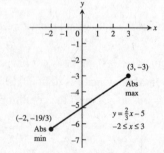

23. (a) $f(\theta) = 3\theta^2 - 4\theta^3 \Rightarrow f'(\theta) = 6\theta - 12\theta^2 = 6\theta(1 - 2\theta) \Rightarrow$ critical points at $\theta = 0, \frac{1}{2} \Rightarrow f' = --- \mid +++ \mid ---$,
$$\phantom{xxxxxxxxxxxxxxxxxxxxxxxxxxxxxxxxxxxxxxxxxxxxxxxxxxxxxxxxxxxxxx} 0 \qquad 1/2$$

increasing on $\left(0, \frac{1}{2}\right)$, decreasing on $(-\infty, 0)$ and $\left(\frac{1}{2}, \infty\right)$

(b) a local maximum is $f\left(\frac{1}{2}\right) = \frac{1}{4}$ at $\theta = \frac{1}{2}$, a local minimum is $f(0) = 0$ at $\theta = 0$, no absolute extrema

24. (a) $f(\theta) = 6\theta - \theta^3 \Rightarrow f'(\theta) = 6 - 3\theta^2 = 3\left(\sqrt{2} - \theta\right)\left(\sqrt{2} + \theta\right) \Rightarrow$ critical points at $\theta = \pm\sqrt{2} \Rightarrow$

$f' = --- \mid +++ \mid ---$, increasing on $\left(-\sqrt{2}, \sqrt{2}\right)$, decreasing on $\left(-\infty, -\sqrt{2}\right)$ and $\left(\sqrt{2}, \infty\right)$
$$\phantom{xxxxxx} -\sqrt{2} \quad \sqrt{2}$$

(b) a local maximum is $f\left(\sqrt{2}\right) = 4\sqrt{2}$ at $\theta = \sqrt{2}$, a local minimum is $f\left(-\sqrt{2}\right) = -4\sqrt{2}$ at $\theta = -\sqrt{2}$, no absolute extrema

25. (a) $f(r) = 3r^3 + 16r \Rightarrow f'(r) = 9r^2 + 16 \Rightarrow$ no critical points $\Rightarrow f' = +++++$, increasing on $(-\infty, \infty)$, never decreasing

(b) no local extrema, no absolute extrema

26. (a) $h(r) = (r + 7)^3 \Rightarrow h'(r) = 3(r + 7)^2 \Rightarrow$ a critical point at $r = -7 \Rightarrow h' = +++ \mid +++$, increasing on
$$\phantom{xxxxxxxxxxxxxxxxxxxxxxxxxxxxxxxxxxxxxxxxxxxxxxxxxxxxxxxxxxxxxxxxxxx} -7$$

$(-\infty, -7) \cup (-7, \infty)$, never decreasing

(b) no local extrema, no absolute extrema

27. (a) $f(x) = x^4 - 8x^2 + 16 \Rightarrow f'(x) = 4x^3 - 16x = 4x(x + 2)(x - 2) \Rightarrow$ critical points at $x = 0$ and $x = \pm 2$
$\Rightarrow f' = --- \mid +++ \mid --- \mid +++$, increasing on $(-2, 0)$ and $(2, \infty)$, decreasing on $(-\infty, -2)$ and $(0, 2)$
$$\phantom{xxxxxxxx} -2 \qquad 0 \qquad 2$$

(b) a local maximum is $f(0) = 16$ at $x = 0$, local minima are $f(\pm 2) = 0$ at $x = \pm 2$, no absolute maximum; absolute minimum is $0$ at $x = \pm 2$

28. (a) $g(x) = x^4 - 4x^3 + 4x^2 \Rightarrow g'(x) = 4x^3 - 12x^2 + 8x = 4x(x - 2)(x - 1) \Rightarrow$ critical points at $x = 0, 1, 2$
$\Rightarrow g' = --- \mid +++ \mid --- \mid +++$, increasing on $(0, 1)$ and $(2, \infty)$, decreasing on $(-\infty, 0)$ and $(1, 2)$
$$\phantom{xxxxxxx} 0 \qquad 1 \qquad 2$$

(b) a local maximum is $g(1) = 1$ at $x = 1$, local minima are $g(0) = 0$ at $x = 0$ and $g(2) = 0$ at $x = 2$, no absolute maximum; absolute minimum is $0$ at $x = 0, 2$

29. (a) $H(t) = \frac{3}{2}t^4 - t^6 \Rightarrow H'(t) = 6t^3 - 6t^5 = 6t^3(1 + t)(1 - t) \Rightarrow$ critical points at $t = 0, \pm 1$
$\Rightarrow H' = +++ \mid --- \mid +++ \mid ---$, increasing on $(-\infty, -1)$ and $(0, 1)$, decreasing on $(-1, 0)$ and $(1, \infty)$
$$\phantom{xxxxxxx} -1 \qquad 0 \qquad 1$$

(b) the local maxima are $H(-1) = \frac{1}{2}$ at $t = -1$ and $H(1) = \frac{1}{2}$ at $t = 1$, the local minimum is $H(0) = 0$ at $t = 0$, absolute maximum is $\frac{1}{2}$ at $t = \pm 1$; no absolute minimum

30. (a) $K(t) = 15t^3 - t^5 \Rightarrow K'(t) = 45t^2 - 5t^4 = 5t^2(3 + t)(3 - t) \Rightarrow$ critical points at $t = 0, \pm 3$
$\Rightarrow K' = --- \mid +++ \mid +++ \mid ---$, increasing on $(-3, 0) \cup (0, 3)$, decreasing on $(-\infty, -3)$ and $(3, \infty)$
$$\phantom{xxxxxxx} -3 \qquad 0 \qquad 3$$

(b) a local maximum is $K(3) = 162$ at $t = 3$, a local minimum is $K(-3) = -162$ at $t = -3$, no absolute extrema

31. (a) $f(x) = x - 6\sqrt{x - 1} \Rightarrow f'(x) = 1 - \frac{3}{\sqrt{x-1}} = \frac{\sqrt{x-1} - 3}{\sqrt{x-1}} \Rightarrow$ critical points at $x = 1$ and $x = 10$

$\Rightarrow f' = ( \phantom{x} --- \mid +++$, increasing on $(10, \infty)$, decreasing on $(1, 10)$
$$\phantom{xxxxxxx} 1 \qquad 10$$

(b) a local minimum is $f(10) = -8$, a local and absolute maximum is $f(1) = 1$, absolute minimum of $-8$ at $x = 10$

32. (a) $g(x) = 4\sqrt{x} - x^2 + 3 \Rightarrow g'(x) = \frac{2}{\sqrt{x}} - 2x = \frac{2 - 2x^{3/2}}{\sqrt{x}} \Rightarrow$ critical points at $x = 1$ and $x = 0$

$\Rightarrow g' = (\ +++\ |\ ---$, increasing on $(0, 1)$, decreasing on $(1, \infty)$
$\qquad\quad\ \ 0\quad\ \ 1$

(b) a local minimum is $f(0) = 3$, a local maximum is $f(1) = 6$, absolute maximum of 6 at $x = 1$

33. (a) $g(x) = x\sqrt{8 - x^2} = x(8 - x^2)^{1/2} \Rightarrow g'(x) = (8 - x^2)^{1/2} + x\left(\frac{1}{2}\right)(8 - x^2)^{-1/2}(-2x) = \frac{2(2 - x)(2 + x)}{\sqrt{\left(2\sqrt{2} - x\right)\left(2\sqrt{2} + x\right)}}$

$\Rightarrow$ critical points at $x = \pm 2, \pm 2\sqrt{2} \Rightarrow g' = (\quad ---\ |\ +++\ |\ ---\ )$ , increasing on $(-2, 2)$, decreasing on
$\qquad\qquad\qquad\qquad\qquad\qquad\qquad\quad\ -2\sqrt{2}\quad\ -2\quad\ \ 2\quad\ 2\sqrt{2}$

$\left(-2\sqrt{2}, -2\right)$ and $\left(2, 2\sqrt{2}\right)$

(b) local maxima are $g(2) = 4$ at $x = 2$ and $g\left(-2\sqrt{2}\right) = 0$ at $x = -2\sqrt{2}$, local minima are $g(-2) = -4$ at

$x = -2$ and $g\left(2\sqrt{2}\right) = 0$ at $x = 2\sqrt{2}$, absolute maximum is 4 at $x = 2$; absolute minimum is $-4$ at $x = -2$

34. (a) $g(x) = x^2\sqrt{5 - x} = x^2(5 - x)^{1/2} \Rightarrow g'(x) = 2x(5 - x)^{1/2} + x^2\left(\frac{1}{2}\right)(5 - x)^{-1/2}(-1) = \frac{5x(4 - x)}{2\sqrt{5 - x}} \Rightarrow$ critical points at

$x = 0, 4$ and $5 \Rightarrow g' = ---\ |\ +++\ |\ ---\ )$, increasing on $(0, 4)$, decreasing on $(-\infty, 0)$ and $(4, 5)$
$\qquad\qquad\qquad\qquad\qquad\quad\ 0\quad\quad\ 4\quad\ \ 5$

(b) a local maximum is $g(4) = 16$ at $x = 4$, a local minimum is 0 at $x = 0$ and $x = 5$, no absolute maximum; absolute minimum is 0 at $x = 0, 5$

35. (a) $f(x) = \frac{x^2 - 3}{x - 2} \Rightarrow f'(x) = \frac{2x(x - 2) - (x^2 - 3)(1)}{(x - 2)^2} = \frac{(x - 3)(x - 1)}{(x - 2)^2} \Rightarrow$ critical points at $x = 1, 3$

$\Rightarrow f' = +++\ |\ ---\ )(---\ |\ +++$, increasing on $(-\infty, 1)$ and $(3, \infty)$, decreasing on $(1, 2)$ and $(2, 3)$,
$\qquad\qquad\quad\ 1\qquad\ \ 2\qquad\ \ 3$

discontinuous at $x = 2$

(b) a local maximum is $f(1) = 2$ at $x = 1$, a local minimum is $f(3) = 6$ at $x = 3$, no absolute extrema

36. (a) $f(x) = \frac{x^3}{3x^2 + 1} \Rightarrow f'(x) = \frac{3x^2(3x^2 + 1) - x^3(6x)}{(3x^2 + 1)^2} = \frac{3x^2(x^2 + 1)}{(3x^2 + 1)^2} \Rightarrow$ a critical point at $x = 0$

$\Rightarrow f' = +++\ |\ +++$, increasing on $(-\infty, 0) \cup (0, \infty)$, and never decreasing
$\qquad\qquad\quad\ 0$

(b) no local extrema, no absolute extrema

37. (a) $f(x) = x^{1/3}(x + 8) = x^{4/3} + 8x^{1/3} \Rightarrow f'(x) = \frac{4}{3}x^{1/3} + \frac{8}{3}x^{-2/3} = \frac{4(x + 2)}{3x^{2/3}} \Rightarrow$ critical points at $x = 0, -2$

$\Rightarrow f' = ---\ |\ +++\ )(+++$, increasing on $(-2, 0) \cup (0, \infty)$, decreasing on $(-\infty, -2)$
$\qquad\qquad\qquad -2\qquad\ 0$

(b) no local maximum, a local minimum is $f(-2) = -6\sqrt[3]{2} \approx -7.56$ at $x = -2$, no absolute maximum; absolute

minimum is $-6\sqrt[3]{2}$ at $x = -2$

38. (a) $g(x) = x^{2/3}(x + 5) = x^{5/3} + 5x^{2/3} \Rightarrow g'(x) = \frac{5}{3}x^{2/3} + \frac{10}{3}x^{-1/3} = \frac{5(x + 2)}{3\sqrt[3]{x}} \Rightarrow$ critical points at $x = -2$ and

$x = 0 \Rightarrow g' = +++\ |\ ---\ )(+++$, increasing on $(-\infty, -2)$ and $(0, \infty)$, decreasing on $(-2, 0)$
$\qquad\qquad\qquad\qquad\ -2\quad\ \ 0$

(b) local maximum is $g(-2) = 3\sqrt[3]{4} \approx 4.762$ at $x = -2$, a local minimum is $g(0) = 0$ at $x = 0$, no absolute extrema

39. (a) $h(x) = x^{1/3}(x^2 - 4) = x^{7/3} - 4x^{1/3} \Rightarrow h'(x) = \frac{7}{3}x^{4/3} - \frac{4}{3}x^{-2/3} = \frac{\left(\sqrt{7}x + 2\right)\left(\sqrt{7}x - 2\right)}{3\sqrt[3]{x^2}} \Rightarrow$ critical points at

$x = 0, \frac{\pm 2}{\sqrt{7}} \Rightarrow h' = +++\ |\quad ---\ )(---\ |\quad +++$, increasing on $\left(-\infty, \frac{-2}{\sqrt{7}}\right)$ and $\left(\frac{2}{\sqrt{7}}, \infty\right)$, decreasing on
$\qquad\qquad\qquad\qquad\qquad\quad -2/\sqrt{7}\quad\ \ 0\quad\ \ 2/\sqrt{7}$

$\left(\frac{-2}{\sqrt{7}}, 0\right)$ and $\left(0, \frac{2}{\sqrt{7}}\right)$

(b) local maximum is $h\left(\frac{-2}{\sqrt{7}}\right) = \frac{24\sqrt[3]{2}}{7^{7/6}} \approx 3.12$ at $x = \frac{-2}{\sqrt{7}}$, the local minimum is $h\left(\frac{2}{\sqrt{7}}\right) = -\frac{24\sqrt[3]{2}}{7^{7/6}} \approx -3.12$, no absolute extrema

40. (a) $k(x) = x^{2/3}\left(x^2 - 4\right) = x^{8/3} - 4x^{2/3} \Rightarrow k'(x) = \frac{8}{3}x^{5/3} - \frac{8}{3}x^{-1/3} = \frac{8(x+1)(x-1)}{3\sqrt[3]{x}} \Rightarrow$ critical points at

$x = 0, \pm 1 \Rightarrow k' = ---\underset{-1}{|} +++)(---\underset{0}{|} +++$, increasing on $(-1, 0)$ and $(1, \infty)$, decreasing on $(-\infty, -1)$

and $(0, 1)$

(b) local maximum is $k(0) = 0$ at $x = 0$, local minima are $k(\pm 1) = -3$ at $x = \pm 1$, no absolute maximum; absolute minimum is $-3$ at $x = \pm 1$

41. (a) $f(x) = 2x - x^2 \Rightarrow f'(x) = 2 - 2x \Rightarrow$ a critical point at $x = 1 \Rightarrow f' = +++\underset{1}{|} ---\underset{2}{]}$ and $f(1) = 1$ and $f(2) = 0$

a local maximum is 1 at $x = 1$, a local minimum is 0 at $x = 2$.

(b) There is an absolute maximum of 1 at $x = 1$; no absolute minimum.

(c)

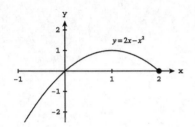

42. (a) $f(x) = (x + 1)^2 \Rightarrow f'(x) = 2(x + 1) \Rightarrow$ a critical point at $x = -1 \Rightarrow f' = ---\underset{-1}{|} +++\underset{0}{]}$ and $f(-1) = 0$, $f(0) = 1$

$\Rightarrow$ a local maximum is 1 at $x = 0$, a local minimum is 0 at $x = -1$

(b) no absolute maximum; absolute minimum is 0 at $x = -1$

(c)

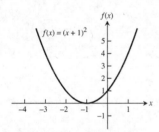

43. (a) $g(x) = x^2 - 4x + 4 \Rightarrow g'(x) = 2x - 4 = 2(x - 2) \Rightarrow$ a critical point at $x = 2 \Rightarrow g' = \underset{1}{[} ---\underset{2}{|} +++$ and

$g(1) = 1$, $g(2) = 0 \Rightarrow$ a local maximum is 1 at $x = 1$, a local minimum is $g(2) = 0$ at $x = 2$

(b) no absolute maximum; absolute minimum is 0 at $x = 2$

(c)

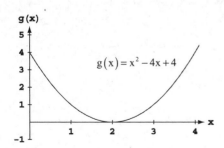

44. (a) $g(x) = -x^2 - 6x - 9 \Rightarrow g'(x) = -2x - 6 = -2(x + 3) \Rightarrow$ a critical point at $x = -3 \Rightarrow g' = \underset{-4}{[} +++\underset{-3}{|} ---$ and

$g(-4) = -1$, $g(-3) = 0 \Rightarrow$ a local maximum is 0 at $x = -3$, a local minimum is $-1$ at $x = -4$

(b) absolute maximum is 0 at x = −3; no absolute minimum

(c)

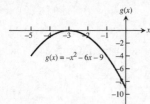

45. (a) $f(t) = 12t - t^3 \Rightarrow f'(t) = 12 - 3t^2 = 3(2 + t)(2 - t) \Rightarrow$ critical points at $t = \pm 2 \Rightarrow f' = [\ ---\ |\ +++\ |\ ---$

    $\phantom{xxxxxxxxxxxxxxxxxxxxxxxxxxxxxxxxxxxxxxxxxxxxxxxxxxxxxxxxxxxxxxxxxxxxx}-3 \qquad -2 \qquad 2$

    and $f(-3) = -9, f(-2) = -16, f(2) = 16 \Rightarrow$ local maxima are −9 at t = −3 and 16 at t = 2, a local minimum is −16 at t = −2

(b) absolute maximum is 16 at t = 2; no absolute minimum

(c)

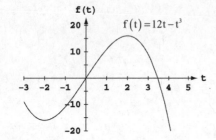

46. (a) $f(t) = t^3 - 3t^2 \Rightarrow f'(t) = 3t^2 - 6t = 3t(t - 2) \Rightarrow$ critical points at t = 0 and t = 2

    $\Rightarrow f' = +++\ |\ ---\ |\ +++\ ]$ and $f(0) = 0, f(2) = -4, f(3) = 0 \Rightarrow$ a local maximum is 0 at t = 0 and t = 3, a

    $\phantom{xxxxxxxxxxx}0 \qquad 2 \qquad 3$

    local minimum is −4 at t = 2

(b) absolute maximum is 0 at t = 0, 3; no absolute minimum

(c)

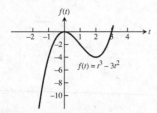

47. (a) $h(x) = \frac{x^3}{3} - 2x^2 + 4x \Rightarrow h'(x) = x^2 - 4x + 4 = (x - 2)^2 \Rightarrow$ a critical point at x = 2 $\Rightarrow h' = [\ +++\ |\ +++$ and

    $\phantom{xxxxxxxxxxxxxxxxxxxxxxxxxxxxxxxxxxxxxxxxxxxxxxxxxxxxxxxxxxxxxxxxxxxxxxxxxxxxxxxxxxxxxxxx}0 \qquad 2$

    $h(0) = 0 \Rightarrow$ no local maximum, a local minimum is 0 at x = 0

(b) no absolute maximum; absolute minimum is 0 at x = 0

(c)

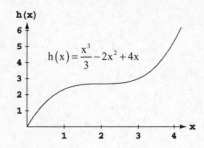

48. (a) $k(x) = x^3 + 3x^2 + 3x + 1 \Rightarrow k'(x) = 3x^2 + 6x + 3 = 3(x+1)^2 \Rightarrow$ a critical point at $x = -1$

$\Rightarrow k' = +++ \mid +++ ]$ and $k(-1) = 0$, $k(0) = 1 \Rightarrow$ a local maximum is 1 at $x = 0$, no local minimum
$\qquad\quad -1 \qquad 0$

(b) absolute maximum is 1 at $x = 0$; no absolute minimum

(c)

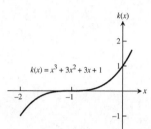

49. (a) $f(x) = \sqrt{25 - x^2} \Rightarrow f'(x) = \frac{-x}{\sqrt{25-x^2}} \Rightarrow$ critical points at $x = 0$, $x = -5$, and $x = 5$

$\Rightarrow f' = (\ +++ \mid --- )$, $f(-5) = 0$, $f(0) = 5$, $f(5) = 0 \Rightarrow$ local maximum is 5 at $x = 0$; local minimum of 0 at
$\qquad\quad -5 \quad 0 \quad 5$

$x = -5$ and $x = 5$

(b) absolute maximum is 5 at $x = 0$; absolute minimum of 0 at $x = -5$ and $x = 5$

(c)

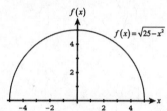

50. (a) $f(x) = \sqrt{x^2 - 2x - 3}$, $3 \le x < \infty \Rightarrow f'(x) = \frac{2x-2}{\sqrt{x^2-2x-3}} \Rightarrow$ only critical point in $3 \le x < \infty$ is at $x = 3$

$\Rightarrow f' = [\ +++$, $f(3) = 0 \Rightarrow$ local minimum of 0 at $x = 3$, no local maximum
$\qquad\quad 3$

(b) absolute minimum of 0 at $x = 3$, no absolute maximum

(c)

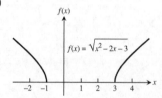

51. (a) $g(x) = \frac{x-2}{x^2-1}$, $0 \le x < 1 \Rightarrow g'(x) = \frac{-x^2+4x-1}{(x^2-1)^2} \Rightarrow$ only critical point in $0 \le x < 1$ is $x = 2 - \sqrt{3} \approx 0.268$

$\Rightarrow g' = [\ --- \mid +++ )$, $g\left(2 - \sqrt{3}\right) = \frac{\sqrt{3}}{4\sqrt{3}-6} \approx 1.866 \Rightarrow$ local minimum of $\frac{\sqrt{3}}{4\sqrt{3}-6}$ at $x = 2 - \sqrt{3}$, local
$\qquad\quad 0 \qquad 0.268 \quad 1$

maximum at $x = 0$.

(b) absolute minimum of $\frac{\sqrt{3}}{4\sqrt{3}-6}$ at $x = 2 - \sqrt{3}$, no absolute maximum

(c)

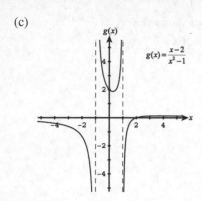

$g(x) = \frac{x-2}{x^2-1}$

52. (a) $g(x) = \frac{x^2}{4-x^2}, -2 < x \leq 1 \Rightarrow g'(x) = \frac{8x}{(4-x^2)^2} \Rightarrow$ only critical point in $-2 < x \leq 1$ is $x = 0$

$\Rightarrow g' = (\ \underset{-2}{\quad} \ \underset{0}{---\ |} \ \underset{1}{+++\ ]}, g(0) = 0 \Rightarrow$ local minimum of 0 at $x = 0$, local maximum of $\frac{1}{3}$ at $x = 1$.

(b) absolute minimum of 0 at $x = 0$, no absolute maximum

(c)

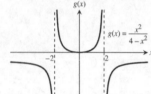

$g(x) = \frac{x^2}{4-x^2}$

53. (a) $f(x) = \sin 2x, 0 \leq x \leq \pi \Rightarrow f'(x) = 2\cos 2x, f'(x) = 0 \Rightarrow \cos 2x = 0 \Rightarrow$ critical points are $x = \frac{\pi}{4}$ and $x = \frac{3\pi}{4}$

$\Rightarrow f' = [\underset{0}{+++\ |} \ \underset{\frac{\pi}{4}}{---\ |} \ \underset{\frac{3\pi}{4}}{+++\ ]} \ \underset{\pi}{}, f(0) = 0, f(\frac{\pi}{4}) = 1, f(\frac{3\pi}{4}) = -1, f(\pi) = 0 \Rightarrow$ local maxima are 1 at $x = \frac{\pi}{4}$ and 0

at $x = \pi$, and local minima are $-1$ at $x = \frac{3\pi}{4}$ and 0 at $x = 0$.

(b) The graph of f rises when $f' > 0$, falls when $f' < 0$, and has local extreme values where $f' = 0$. The function f has a local minimum value at $x = 0$ and $x = \frac{3\pi}{4}$, where the values of $f'$ change from negative to positive. The function f has a local maximum value at $x = \pi$ and $x = \frac{\pi}{4}$, where the values of $f'$ change from positive to negative.

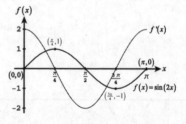

54. (a) $f(x) = \sin x - \cos x, 0 \leq x \leq 2\pi \Rightarrow f'(x) = \cos x + \sin x, f'(x) = 0 \Rightarrow \tan x = -1 \Rightarrow$ critical points are $x = \frac{3\pi}{4}$ and

$x = \frac{7\pi}{4} \Rightarrow f' = [\underset{0}{+++\ |} \ \underset{\frac{3\pi}{4}}{---\ |} \ \underset{\frac{7\pi}{4}}{+++\ ]} \ \underset{2\pi}{}, f(0) = -1, f(\frac{3\pi}{4}) = \sqrt{2}, f(\frac{7\pi}{4}) = -\sqrt{2}, f(2\pi) = -1 \Rightarrow$ local maxima are

$\sqrt{2}$ at $x = \frac{3\pi}{4}$ and $-1$ at $x = 2\pi$, and local minima are $-\sqrt{2}$ at $x = \frac{7\pi}{4}$ and $-1$ at $x = 0$.

(b) The graph of f rises when $f' > 0$, falls when $f' < 0$, and has local extreme values where $f' = 0$. The function f has a local minimum value at $x = 0$ and $x = \frac{7\pi}{4}$, where the values of $f'$ change from negative to positive. The function f has a local maximum value at $x = 2\pi$ and $x = \frac{3\pi}{4}$, where the values of $f'$ change from positive to negative.

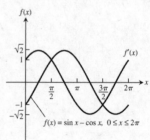

55. (a) $f(x) = \sqrt{3}\cos x + \sin x, 0 \le x \le 2\pi \Rightarrow f'(x) = -\sqrt{3}\sin x + \cos x, f'(x) = 0 \Rightarrow \tan x = \frac{1}{\sqrt{3}} \Rightarrow$ critical points are

$x = \frac{\pi}{6}$ and $x = \frac{7\pi}{6} \Rightarrow f' = [+++ \mid --- \mid +++]$ , $f(0) = \sqrt{3}, f(\frac{\pi}{6}) = 2, f(\frac{7\pi}{6}) = -2, f(2\pi) = \sqrt{3} \Rightarrow$ local
$\qquad\qquad\qquad\qquad\qquad 0 \quad\quad \frac{\pi}{6} \quad\quad \frac{7\pi}{6} \quad\quad 2\pi$

maxima are 2 at $x = \frac{\pi}{6}$ and $\sqrt{3}$ at $x = 2\pi$, and local minima are $-2$ at $x = \frac{7\pi}{6}$ and $\sqrt{3}$ at $x = 0$.

(b) The graph of f rises when $f' > 0$, falls when $f' < 0$,
and has local extreme values where $f' = 0$. The function
f has a local minimum value at $x = 0$ and $x = \frac{7\pi}{6}$, where
the values of $f'$ change from negative to positive. The
function f has a local maximum value at $x = 2\pi$ and
$x = \frac{\pi}{6}$, where the values of $f'$ change from positive to
negative.

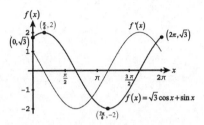

56. (a) $f(x) = -2x + \tan x, -\frac{\pi}{2} < x < \frac{\pi}{2} \Rightarrow f'(x) = -2 + \sec^2 x, f'(x) = 0 \Rightarrow \sec^2 x = 2 \Rightarrow$ critical points are

$x = -\frac{\pi}{4}$ and $x = \frac{\pi}{4} \Rightarrow f' = ( +++ \mid --- \mid +++ )$ , $f(-\frac{\pi}{4}) = \frac{\pi}{2} - 1, f(\frac{\pi}{4}) = 1 - \frac{\pi}{2} \Rightarrow$ local
$\qquad\qquad\qquad\qquad\qquad -\frac{\pi}{2} \quad -\frac{\pi}{4} \quad\quad \frac{\pi}{4} \quad\quad \frac{\pi}{2}$

maximum is $\frac{\pi}{2} - 1$ at $x = -\frac{\pi}{4}$, and local minimum is $1 - \frac{\pi}{2}$ at $x = \frac{\pi}{4}$.

(b) The graph of f rises when $f' > 0$, falls when $f' < 0$,
and has local extreme values where $f' = 0$. The function
f has a local minimum value at $x = \frac{\pi}{4}$, where the values
of $f'$ change from negative to positive. The function f
has a local maximum value at $x = -\frac{\pi}{4}$, where the values
of $f'$ change from positive to negative.

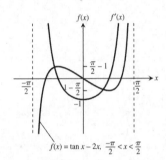

57. (a) $f(x) = \frac{x}{2} - 2\sin\left(\frac{x}{2}\right) \Rightarrow f'(x) = \frac{1}{2} - \cos\left(\frac{x}{2}\right), f'(x) = 0 \Rightarrow \cos\left(\frac{x}{2}\right) = \frac{1}{2} \Rightarrow$ a critical point at $x = \frac{2\pi}{3}$

$\Rightarrow f' = [ --- \mid +++]$ and $f(0) = 0, f\left(\frac{2\pi}{3}\right) = \frac{\pi}{3} - \sqrt{3}, f(2\pi) = \pi \Rightarrow$ local maxima are 0 at $x = 0$ and $\pi$
$\qquad\qquad 0 \quad 2\pi/3 \quad 2\pi$

at $x = 2\pi$, a local minimum is $\frac{\pi}{3} - \sqrt{3}$ at $x = \frac{2\pi}{3}$

(b) The graph of f rises when $f' > 0$, falls when $f' < 0$,
and has a local minimum value at the point where $f'$
changes from negative to positive.

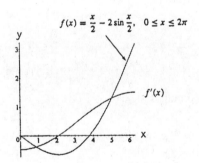

58. (a) $f(x) = -2\cos x - \cos^2 x \Rightarrow f'(x) = 2\sin x + 2\cos x \sin x = 2(\sin x)(1 + \cos x) \Rightarrow$ critical points at $x = -\pi, 0, \pi$

$\Rightarrow f' = [ --- \mid +++]$ and $f(-\pi) = 1, f(0) = -3, f(\pi) = 1 \Rightarrow$ a local maximum is 1 at $x = \pm\pi$, a local
$\qquad\quad -\pi \quad 0 \quad \pi$

minimum is $-3$ at $x = 0$

(b) The graph of f rises when $f' > 0$, falls when $f' < 0$, and has local extreme values where $f' = 0$. The function f has a local minimum value at $x = 0$, where the values of $f'$ change from negative to positive.

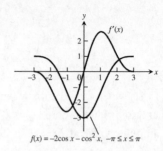

$f(x) = -2\cos x - \cos^2 x, \ -\pi \le x \le \pi$

59. (a) $f(x) = \csc^2 x - 2 \cot x \Rightarrow f'(x) = 2(\csc x)(-\csc x)(\cot x) - 2(-\csc^2 x) = -2(\csc^2 x)(\cot x - 1) \Rightarrow$ a critical point at $x = \frac{\pi}{4} \Rightarrow f' = (\ ---\ |\ +++)$ and $f\left(\frac{\pi}{4}\right) = 0 \Rightarrow$ no local maximum, a local minimum is 0 at $x = \frac{\pi}{4}$
$$\phantom{x}\quad 0\quad \pi/4\quad \pi$$

(b) The graph of f rises when $f' > 0$, falls when $f' < 0$, and has a local minimum value at the point where $f' = 0$ and the values of $f'$ change from negative to positive. The graph of f steepens as $f'(x) \rightarrow \pm\infty$.

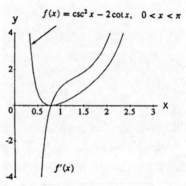

$f(x) = \csc^2 x - 2\cot x, \ \ 0 < x < \pi$

60. (a) $f(x) = \sec^2 x - 2 \tan x \Rightarrow f'(x) = 2(\sec x)(\sec x)(\tan x) - 2 \sec^2 x = (2 \sec^2 x)(\tan x - 1) \Rightarrow$ a critical point at $x = \frac{\pi}{4} \Rightarrow f' = (\quad ---\ |\ +++)$ and $f\left(\frac{\pi}{4}\right) = 0 \Rightarrow$ no local maximum, a local minimum is 0 at $x = \frac{\pi}{4}$
$$\phantom{x}\quad -\pi/2\quad \pi/4\quad \pi/2$$

(b) The graph of f rises when $f' > 0$, falls when $f' < 0$, and has a local minimum value where $f' = 0$ and the values of $f'$ change from negative to positive.

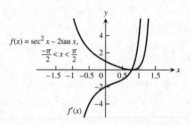

$f(x) = \sec^2 x - 2\tan x, \ -\frac{\pi}{2} < x < \frac{\pi}{2}$

61. $h(\theta) = 3 \cos\left(\frac{\theta}{2}\right) \Rightarrow h'(\theta) = -\frac{3}{2} \sin\left(\frac{\theta}{2}\right) \Rightarrow h' = [\ ---\ ]$ , $(0, 3)$ and $(2\pi, -3) \Rightarrow$ a local maximum is 3 at $\theta = 0$,
$$\phantom{x}\quad 0\quad\quad 2\pi$$
a local minimum is $-3$ at $\theta = 2\pi$

62. $h(\theta) = 5 \sin\left(\frac{\theta}{2}\right) \Rightarrow h'(\theta) = \frac{5}{2} \cos\left(\frac{\theta}{2}\right) \Rightarrow h' = [\ +++\ ]$ , $(0, 0)$ and $(\pi, 5) \Rightarrow$ a local maximum is 5 at $\theta = \pi$, a local
$$\phantom{x}\quad 0\quad\quad \pi$$
minimum is 0 at $\theta = 0$

63. (a)

(a)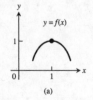

(b)

(c)

(d)

64. (a)

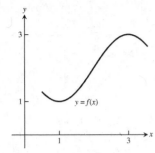

(b)

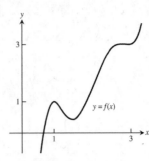

(c)

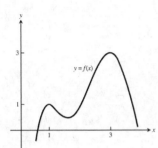

(d)

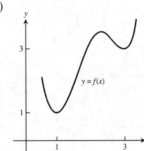

65. (a)

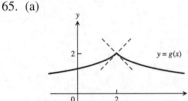

(b)

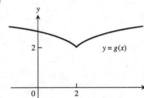

66. (a)

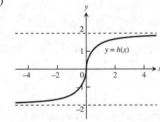

(b)

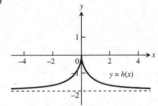

67. The function $f(x) = x \sin\left(\frac{1}{x}\right)$ has an infinite number of local maxima and minima. The function $\sin x$ has the following properties: a) it is continuous on $(-\infty, \infty)$; b) it is periodic; and c) its range is $[-1, 1]$. Also, for $a > 0$, the function $\frac{1}{x}$ has a range of $(-\infty, -a] \cup [a, \infty)$ on $\left[-\frac{1}{a}, \frac{1}{a}\right]$. In particular, if $a = 1$, then $\frac{1}{x} \leq -1$ or $\frac{1}{x} \geq 1$ when $x$ is in $[-1, 1]$. This means $\sin\left(\frac{1}{x}\right)$ takes on the values of 1 and $-1$ infinitely many times in times on the interval $[-1, 1]$, which occur when $\frac{1}{x} = \pm\frac{\pi}{2}, \pm\frac{3\pi}{2}, \pm\frac{5\pi}{2}, \ldots \Rightarrow x = \pm\frac{2}{\pi}, \pm\frac{2}{3\pi}, \pm\frac{2}{5\pi}, \ldots$. Thus $\sin\left(\frac{1}{x}\right)$ has infinitely many local maxima and minima in the interval $[-1, 1]$. On the interval $[0, 1]$, $-1 \leq \sin\left(\frac{1}{x}\right) \leq 1$ and since $x > 0$ we have $-x \leq x \sin\left(\frac{1}{x}\right) \leq x$. On the interval $[-1, 0]$, $-1 \leq \sin\left(\frac{1}{x}\right) \leq 1$ and since $x < 0$ we have $-x \geq x \sin\left(\frac{1}{x}\right) \geq x$. Thus $f(x)$ is bounded by the lines $y = x$ and $y = -x$. Since $\sin\left(\frac{1}{x}\right)$ oscillates between 1 and $-1$ infinitely many times on $[-1, 1]$ then $f$ will oscillate between $y = x$ and $y = -x$ infinitely many times. Thus $f$ has infinitely many local maxima and minima. We can see from the graph (and verify later in Chapter 7) that $\lim_{x \to \infty} x \sin\left(\frac{1}{x}\right) = 1$ and $\lim_{x \to -\infty} x \sin\left(\frac{1}{x}\right) = 1$. The graph of $f$ does not have any absolute maxima., but it does have two absolute minima.

68. $f(x) = a\,x^2 + b\,x + c = a\left(x^2 + \frac{b}{a}x\right) + c = a\left(x^2 + \frac{b}{a}x + \frac{b^2}{4a^2}\right) - \frac{b^2}{4a} + c = a\left(x + \frac{b}{2a}\right)^2 - \frac{b^2 - 4ac}{4a}$, a parabola whose

vertex is at $x = -\frac{b}{2a}$. Thus when $a > 0$, f is increasing on $\left(\frac{-b}{2a}, \infty\right)$ and decreasing on $\left(-\infty, \frac{-b}{2a}\right)$; when $a < 0$,

f is increasing on $\left(-\infty, \frac{-b}{2a}\right)$ and decreasing on $\left(\frac{-b}{2a}, \infty\right)$. Also note that $f'(x) = 2ax + b = 2a\left(x + \frac{b}{2a}\right) \Rightarrow$ for

$a > 0, f' = {-}{-}{-}\Big|_{-b/2a} {+}{+}{+}$ ; for $a < 0, f' = {+}{+}{+}\Big|_{-b/2a} {-}{-}{-}$ .

69. $f(x) = a\,x^2 + b\,x \Rightarrow f'(x) = 2a\,x + b, f(1) = 2 \Rightarrow a + b = 2, f'(1) = 0 \Rightarrow 2a + b = 0 \Rightarrow a = -2, b = 4$
    $\Rightarrow f(x) = -2x^2 + 4x$

70. $f(x) = a\,x^3 + b\,x^2 + c\,x + d \Rightarrow f'(x) = 3a\,x^2 + 2b\,x + c, f(0) = 0 \Rightarrow d = 0, f(1) = -1 \Rightarrow a + b + c + d = -1,$
    $f'(0) = 0 \Rightarrow c = 0, f'(1) = 0 \Rightarrow 3a + 2b + c = 0 \Rightarrow a = 2, b = -3, c = 0, d = 0 \Rightarrow f(x) = 2x^3 - 3x^2$

## 4.4 CONCAVITY AND CURVE SKETCHING

1. $y = \frac{x^3}{3} - \frac{x^2}{2} - 2x + \frac{1}{3} \Rightarrow y' = x^2 - x - 2 = (x - 2)(x + 1) \Rightarrow y'' = 2x - 1 = 2\left(x - \frac{1}{2}\right)$. The graph is rising on
   $(-\infty, -1)$ and $(2, \infty)$, falling on $(-1, 2)$, concave up on $\left(\frac{1}{2}, \infty\right)$ and concave down on $\left(-\infty, \frac{1}{2}\right)$. Consequently,
   a local maximum is $\frac{3}{2}$ at $x = -1$, a local minimum is $-3$ at $x = 2$, and $\left(\frac{1}{2}, -\frac{3}{4}\right)$ is a point of inflection.

2. $y = \frac{x^4}{4} - 2x^2 + 4 \Rightarrow y' = x^3 - 4x = x\left(x^2 - 4\right) = x(x + 2)(x - 2) \Rightarrow y'' = 3x^2 - 4 = \left(\sqrt{3}x + 2\right)\left(\sqrt{3}x - 2\right)$. The
   graph is rising on $(-2, 0)$ and $(2, \infty)$, falling on $(-\infty, -2)$ and $(0, 2)$, concave up on $\left(-\infty, -\frac{2}{\sqrt{3}}\right)$ and $\left(\frac{2}{\sqrt{3}}, \infty\right)$ and
   concave down on $\left(-\frac{2}{\sqrt{3}}, \frac{2}{\sqrt{3}}\right)$. Consequently, a local maximum is 4 at $x = 0$, local minima are 0 at $x = \pm 2$, and
   $\left(-\frac{2}{\sqrt{3}}, \frac{16}{9}\right)$ and $\left(\frac{2}{\sqrt{3}}, \frac{16}{9}\right)$ are points of inflection.

3. $y = \frac{3}{4}\left(x^2 - 1\right)^{2/3} \Rightarrow y' = \left(\frac{3}{4}\right)\left(\frac{2}{3}\right)\left(x^2 - 1\right)^{-1/3}(2x) = x\left(x^2 - 1\right)^{-1/3}, y' = {-}{-}{-})\underset{-1}{(}{+}{+}{+}\underset{0}{\Big|}{-}{-}{-})\underset{1}{(}{+}{+}{+}$
   $\Rightarrow$ the graph is rising on $(-1, 0)$ and $(1, \infty)$, falling on $(-\infty, -1)$ and $(0, 1) \Rightarrow$ a local maximum is $\frac{3}{4}$ at $x = 0$, local
   minima are 0 at $x = \pm 1$; $y'' = \left(x^2 - 1\right)^{-1/3} + (x)\left(-\frac{1}{3}\right)\left(x^2 - 1\right)^{-4/3}(2x) = \frac{x^2 - 3}{3\sqrt[3]{(x^2-1)^4}}$,
   $y'' = {+}{+}{+}\underset{-\sqrt{3}}{\Big|}{-}{-}{-})\underset{-1}{(}{-}{-}{-})\underset{1}{(}{-}{-}{-}\underset{\sqrt{3}}{\Big|}{+}{+}{+} \Rightarrow$ the graph is concave up on $\left(-\infty, -\sqrt{3}\right)$ and $\left(\sqrt{3}, \infty\right)$, concave
   down on $\left(-\sqrt{3}, \sqrt{3}\right) \Rightarrow$ points of inflection at $\left(\pm\sqrt{3}, \frac{3\sqrt[3]{4}}{4}\right)$

4. $y = \frac{9}{14}x^{1/3}\left(x^2 - 7\right) \Rightarrow y' = \frac{3}{14}x^{-2/3}\left(x^2 - 7\right) + \frac{9}{14}x^{1/3}(2x) = \frac{3}{2}x^{-2/3}\left(x^2 - 1\right), y' = {+}{+}{+}\underset{-1}{\Big|}{-}{-}{-})\underset{0}{(}{-}{-}{-}\underset{1}{\Big|}{+}{+}{+}$
   $\Rightarrow$ the graph is rising on $(-\infty, -1)$ and $(1, \infty)$, falling on $(-1, 1) \Rightarrow$ a local maximum is $\frac{27}{7}$ at $x = -1$, a local
   minimum is $-\frac{27}{7}$ at $x = 1$; $y'' = -x^{-5/3}\left(x^2 - 1\right) + 3x^{1/3} = 2x^{1/3} + x^{-5/3} = x^{-5/3}\left(2x^2 + 1\right)$,
   $y'' = {-}{-}{-})\underset{0}{(}{+}{+}{+} \Rightarrow$ the graph is concave up on $(0, \infty)$, concave down on $(-\infty, 0) \Rightarrow$ a point of inflection at $(0, 0)$.

5. $y = x + \sin 2x \Rightarrow y' = 1 + 2\cos 2x, y' = [{-}{-}{-}\underset{-2\pi/3}{\Big|}\underset{-\pi/3}{\,} {+}{+}{+}\underset{\pi/3}{\Big|}\underset{2\pi/3}{\,} {-}{-}{-}] \Rightarrow$ the graph is rising on $\left(-\frac{\pi}{3}, \frac{\pi}{3}\right)$, falling
   on $\left(-\frac{2\pi}{3}, -\frac{\pi}{3}\right)$ and $\left(\frac{\pi}{3}, \frac{2\pi}{3}\right) \Rightarrow$ local maxima are $-\frac{2\pi}{3} + \frac{\sqrt{3}}{2}$ at $x = -\frac{2\pi}{3}$ and $\frac{\pi}{3} + \frac{\sqrt{3}}{2}$ at $x = \frac{\pi}{3}$, local minima are
   $-\frac{\pi}{3} - \frac{\sqrt{3}}{2}$ at $x = -\frac{\pi}{3}$ and $\frac{2\pi}{3} - \frac{\sqrt{3}}{2}$ at $x = \frac{2\pi}{3}$; $y'' = -4\sin 2x, y'' = [\underset{-2\pi/3}{\,}{-}{-}{-}\underset{-\pi/2}{\Big|}{+}{+}{+}\underset{0}{\Big|}{-}{-}{-}\underset{\pi/2}{\Big|}{+}{+}{+}\underset{2\pi/3}{\,}] \Rightarrow$ the
   graph is concave up on $\left(-\frac{\pi}{2}, 0\right)$ and $\left(\frac{\pi}{2}, \frac{2\pi}{3}\right)$, concave down on $\left(-\frac{2\pi}{3}, -\frac{\pi}{2}\right)$ and $\left(0, \frac{\pi}{2}\right) \Rightarrow$ points of inflection at
   $\left(-\frac{\pi}{2}, -\frac{\pi}{2}\right), (0, 0)$, and $\left(\frac{\pi}{2}, \frac{\pi}{2}\right)$

6. $y = \tan x - 4x \Rightarrow y' = \sec^2 x - 4$, $y' = ( \ +++ \ | \ ---- \ | \ +++ \ ) \Rightarrow$ the graph is rising on $\left(-\frac{\pi}{2}, -\frac{\pi}{3}\right)$ and
$\qquad\qquad -\pi/2 \quad -\pi/3 \quad \pi/3 \quad \pi/2$

$\left(\frac{\pi}{3}, \frac{\pi}{2}\right)$, falling on $\left(-\frac{\pi}{3}, \frac{\pi}{3}\right) \Rightarrow$ a local maximum is $-\sqrt{3} + \frac{4\pi}{3}$ at $x = -\frac{\pi}{3}$, a local minimum is $\sqrt{3} - \frac{4\pi}{3}$ at $x = \frac{\pi}{3}$;

$y'' = 2(\sec x)(\sec x)(\tan x) = 2(\sec^2 x)(\tan x)$, $y'' = ( \ ---- \ | \ +++ \ ) \Rightarrow$ the graph is concave up on $\left(0, \frac{\pi}{2}\right)$,
$\qquad\qquad\qquad\qquad\qquad\qquad\qquad\qquad\qquad\qquad\quad -\pi/2 \quad 0 \quad \pi/2$

concave down on $\left(-\frac{\pi}{2}, 0\right) \Rightarrow$ a point of inflection at $(0, 0)$

7. If $x \geq 0$, $\sin |x| = \sin x$ and if $x < 0$, $\sin |x| = \sin(-x)$
$= -\sin x$. From the sketch the graph is rising on
$\left(-\frac{3\pi}{2}, -\frac{\pi}{2}\right)$, $\left(0, \frac{\pi}{2}\right)$ and $\left(\frac{3\pi}{2}, 2\pi\right)$, falling on $\left(-2\pi, -\frac{3\pi}{2}\right)$,
$\left(-\frac{\pi}{2}, 0\right)$ and $\left(\frac{\pi}{2}, \frac{3\pi}{2}\right)$; local minima are $-1$ at $x = \pm\frac{3\pi}{2}$
and $0$ at $x = 0$; local maxima are $1$ at $x = \pm\frac{\pi}{2}$ and $0$ at
$x = \pm 2\pi$; concave up on $(-2\pi, -\pi)$ and $(\pi, 2\pi)$, and
concave down on $(-\pi, 0)$ and $(0, \pi) \Rightarrow$ points of inflection
are $(-\pi, 0)$ and $(\pi, 0)$

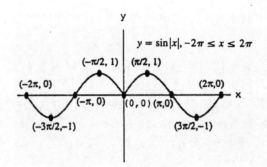

8. $y = 2\cos x - \sqrt{2}\,x \Rightarrow y' = -2\sin x - \sqrt{2}$, $y' = [ \ ---- \ | \ +++ \ | \ ---- \ | \ +++ \ ] \Rightarrow$ rising on
$\qquad\qquad\qquad\qquad\qquad\qquad\qquad\qquad\qquad -\pi \quad -3\pi/4 \quad -\pi/4 \quad 5\pi/4 \quad 3\pi/2$

$\left(-\frac{3\pi}{4}, -\frac{\pi}{4}\right)$ and $\left(\frac{5\pi}{4}, \frac{3\pi}{2}\right)$, falling on $\left(-\pi, -\frac{3\pi}{4}\right)$ and $\left(-\frac{\pi}{4}, \frac{5\pi}{4}\right) \Rightarrow$ local maxima are $-2 + \pi\sqrt{2}$ at $x = -\pi$, $\sqrt{2} + \frac{\pi\sqrt{2}}{4}$

at $x = -\frac{\pi}{4}$ and $-\frac{3\pi\sqrt{2}}{2}$ at $x = \frac{3\pi}{2}$, and local minima are $-\sqrt{2} + \frac{3\pi\sqrt{2}}{4}$ at $x = -\frac{3\pi}{4}$ and $-\sqrt{2} - \frac{5\pi\sqrt{2}}{4}$ at $x = \frac{5\pi}{4}$;

$y'' = -2\cos x$, $y'' = [ \ +++ \ | \ ---- \ | \ +++ \ ] \Rightarrow$ concave up on $\left(-\pi, -\frac{\pi}{2}\right)$ and $\left(\frac{\pi}{2}, \frac{3\pi}{2}\right)$, concave down on
$\qquad\qquad\qquad\qquad -\pi \quad -\pi/2 \quad \pi/2 \quad 3\pi/2$

$\left(-\frac{\pi}{2}, \frac{\pi}{2}\right) \Rightarrow$ points of inflection at $\left(-\frac{\pi}{2}, \frac{\sqrt{2}\pi}{2}\right)$ and $\left(\frac{\pi}{2}, -\frac{\sqrt{2}\pi}{2}\right)$

9. When $y = x^2 - 4x + 3$, then $y' = 2x - 4 = 2(x - 2)$ and
$y'' = 2$. The curve rises on $(2, \infty)$ and falls on $(-\infty, 2)$.
At $x = 2$ there is a minimum. Since $y'' > 0$, the curve is
concave up for all x.

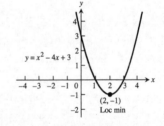

10. When $y = 6 - 2x - x^2$, then $y' = -2 - 2x = -2(1 + x)$ and
$y'' = -2$. The curve rises on $(-\infty, -1)$ and falls on
$(-1, \infty)$. At $x = -1$ there is a maximum. Since $y'' < 0$, the
curve is concave down for all x.

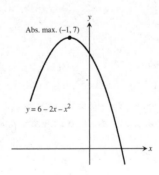

11. When $y = x^3 - 3x + 3$, then $y' = 3x^2 - 3 = 3(x - 1)(x + 1)$ and $y'' = 6x$. The curve rises on $(-\infty, -1) \cup (1, \infty)$ and falls on $(-1, 1)$. At $x = -1$ there is a local maximum and at $x = 1$ a local minimum. The curve is concave down on $(-\infty, 0)$ and concave up on $(0, \infty)$. There is a point of inflection at x = 0.

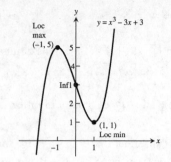

12. When $y = x(6 - 2x)^2$, then $y' = -4x(6 - 2x) + (6 - 2x)^2$ $= 12(3 - x)(1 - x)$ and $y'' = -12(3 - x) - 12(1 - x)$ $= 24(x - 2)$. The curve rises on $(-\infty, 1) \cup (3, \infty)$ and falls on $(1, 3)$. The curve is concave down on $(-\infty, 2)$ and concave up on $(2, \infty)$. At $x = 2$ there is a point of inflection.

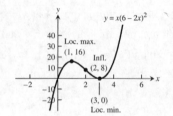

13. When $y = -2x^3 + 6x^2 - 3$, then $y' = -6x^2 + 12x$ $= -6x(x - 2)$ and $y'' = -12x + 12 = -12(x - 1)$. The curve rises on $(0, 2)$ and falls on $(-\infty, 0)$ and $(2, \infty)$. At $x = 0$ there is a local minimum and at $x = 2$ a local maximum. The curve is concave up on $(-\infty, 1)$ and concave down on $(1, \infty)$. At $x = 1$ there is a point of inflection.

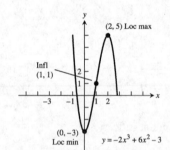

14. When $y = 1 - 9x - 6x^2 - x^3$, then $y' = -9 - 12x - 3x^2$ $= -3(x + 3)(x + 1)$ and $y'' = -12 - 6x = -6(x + 2)$. The curve rises on $(-3, -1)$ and falls on $(-\infty, -3)$ and $(-1, \infty)$. At $x = -1$ there is a local maximum and at $x = -3$ a local minimum. The curve is concave up on $(-\infty, -2)$ and concave down on $(-2, \infty)$. At $x = -2$ there is a point of inflection.

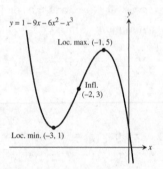

15. When $y = (x - 2)^3 + 1$, then $y' = 3(x - 2)^2$ and $y'' = 6(x - 2)$. The curve never falls and there are no local extrema. The curve is concave down on $(-\infty, 2)$ and concave up on $(2, \infty)$. At $x = 2$ there is a point of inflection.

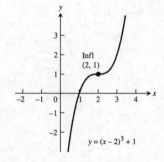

16. When $y = 1 - (x + 1)^3$, then $y' = -3(x + 1)^2$ and $y'' = -6(x + 1)$. The curve never rises and there are no local extrema. The curve is concave up on $(-\infty, -1)$ and concave down on $(-1, \infty)$. At $x = -1$ there is a point of inflection.

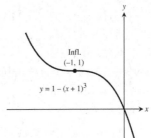

17. When $y = x^4 - 2x^2$, then $y' = 4x^3 - 4x = 4x(x + 1)(x - 1)$ and $y'' = 12x^2 - 4 = 12\left(x + \frac{1}{\sqrt{3}}\right)\left(x - \frac{1}{\sqrt{3}}\right)$. The curve rises on $(-1, 0)$ and $(1, \infty)$ and falls on $(-\infty, -1)$ and $(0, 1)$. At $x = \pm 1$ there are local minima and at $x = 0$ a local maximum. The curve is concave up on $\left(-\infty, -\frac{1}{\sqrt{3}}\right)$ and $\left(\frac{1}{\sqrt{3}}, \infty\right)$ and concave down on $\left(-\frac{1}{\sqrt{3}}, \frac{1}{\sqrt{3}}\right)$. At $x = \frac{\pm 1}{\sqrt{3}}$ there are points of inflection.

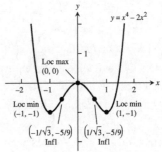

18. When $y = -x^4 + 6x^2 - 4$, then $y' = -4x^3 + 12x = -4x\left(x + \sqrt{3}\right)\left(x - \sqrt{3}\right)$ and $y'' = -12x^2 + 12 = -12(x + 1)(x - 1)$. The curve rises on $\left(-\infty, -\sqrt{3}\right)$ and $\left(0, \sqrt{3}\right)$, and falls on $\left(-\sqrt{3}, 0\right)$ and $\left(\sqrt{3}, \infty\right)$. At $x = \pm \sqrt{3}$ there are local maxima and at $x = 0$ a local minimum. The curve is concave up on $(-1, 1)$ and concave down on $(-\infty, -1)$ and $(1, \infty)$. At $x = \pm 1$ there are points of inflection.

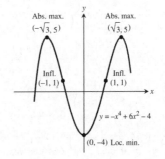

19. When $y = 4x^3 - x^4$, then $y' = 12x^2 - 4x^3 = 4x^2(3 - x)$ and $y'' = 24x - 12x^2 = 12x(2 - x)$. The curve rises on $(-\infty, 3)$ and falls on $(3, \infty)$. At $x = 3$ there is a local maximum, but there is no local minimum. The graph is concave up on $(0, 2)$ and concave down on $(-\infty, 0)$ and $(2, \infty)$. There are inflection points at $x = 0$ and $x = 2$.

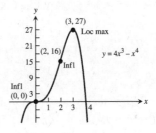

20. When $y = x^4 + 2x^3$, then $y' = 4x^3 + 6x^2 = 2x^2(2x + 3)$ and $y'' = 12x^2 + 12x = 12x(x + 1)$. The curve rises on $\left(-\frac{3}{2}, \infty\right)$ and falls on $\left(-\infty, -\frac{3}{2}\right)$. There is a local minimum at $x = -\frac{3}{2}$, but no local maximum. The curve is concave up on $(-\infty, -1)$ and $(0, \infty)$, and concave down on $(-1, 0)$. At $x = -1$ and $x = 0$ there are points of inflection.

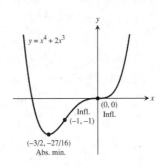

21. When $y = x^5 - 5x^4$, then $y' = 5x^4 - 20x^3 = 5x^3(x - 4)$ and $y'' = 20x^3 - 60x^2 = 20x^2(x - 3)$. The curve rises on $(-\infty, 0)$ and $(4, \infty)$, and falls on $(0, 4)$. There is a local maximum at $x = 0$, and a local minimum at $x = 4$. The curve is concave down on $(-\infty, 3)$ and concave up on $(3, \infty)$. At $x = 3$ there is a point of inflection.

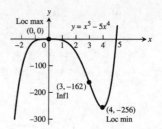

22. When $y = x\left(\frac{x}{2} - 5\right)^4$, then $y' = \left(\frac{x}{2} - 5\right)^4 + x(4)\left(\frac{x}{2} - 5\right)^3\left(\frac{1}{2}\right)$ $= \left(\frac{x}{2} - 5\right)^3\left(\frac{5x}{2} - 5\right)$, and $y'' = 3\left(\frac{x}{2} - 5\right)^2\left(\frac{1}{2}\right)\left(\frac{5x}{2} - 5\right)$ $+ \left(\frac{x}{2} - 5\right)^3\left(\frac{5}{2}\right) = 5\left(\frac{x}{2} - 5\right)^2(x - 4)$. The curve is rising on $(-\infty, 2)$ and $(10, \infty)$, and falling on $(2, 10)$. There is a local maximum at $x = 2$ and a local minimum at $x = 10$. The curve is concave down on $(-\infty, 4)$ and concave up on $(4, \infty)$. At $x = 4$ there is a point of inflection.

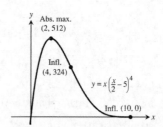

23. When $y = x + \sin x$, then $y' = 1 + \cos x$ and $y'' = -\sin x$. The curve rises on $(0, 2\pi)$. At $x = 0$ there is a local and absolute minimum and at $x = 2\pi$ there is a local and absolute maximum. The curve is concave down on $(0, \pi)$ and concave up on $(\pi, 2\pi)$. At $x = \pi$ there is a point of inflection.

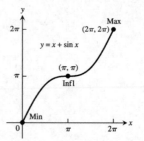

24. When $y = x - \sin x$, then $y' = 1 - \cos x$ and $y'' = \sin x$. The curve rises on $(0, 2\pi)$. At $x = 0$ there is a local and absolute minimum and at $x = 2\pi$ there is a local and absolute maximum. The curve is concave up on $(0, \pi)$ and concave down on $(\pi, 2\pi)$. At $x = \pi$ there is a point of inflection.

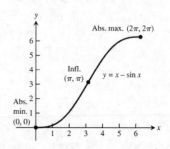

25. When $y = \sqrt{3}x - 2\cos x$, then $y' = \sqrt{3} + 2\sin x$ and $y'' = 2\cos x$. The curve is increasing on $\left(0, \frac{4\pi}{3}\right)$ and $\left(\frac{5\pi}{3}, 2\pi\right)$, and decreasing on $\left(\frac{4\pi}{3}, \frac{5\pi}{3}\right)$. At $x = 0$ there is a local and absolute minimum, at $x = \frac{4\pi}{3}$ there is a local maximum, at $x = \frac{5\pi}{3}$ there is a local minimum, and and at $x = 2\pi$ there is a local and absolute maximum. The curve is concave up on $\left(0, \frac{\pi}{2}\right)$ and $\left(\frac{3\pi}{2}, 2\pi\right)$, and is concave down on $\left(\frac{\pi}{2}, \frac{3\pi}{2}\right)$. At $x = \frac{\pi}{2}$ and $x = \frac{3\pi}{2}$ there are points of inflection.

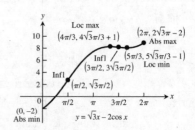

26. When $y = \frac{4}{3}x - \tan x$, then $y' = \frac{4}{3} - \sec^2 x$ and
$y'' = -2\sec^2 x \tan x$. The curve is increasing on $\left(-\frac{\pi}{6}, \frac{\pi}{6}\right)$,
and decreasing on $\left(-\frac{\pi}{2}, -\frac{\pi}{6}\right)$ and $\left(\frac{\pi}{6}, \frac{\pi}{2}\right)$. At $x = -\frac{\pi}{6}$
there is a local minimum, at $x = \frac{\pi}{6}$ there is a local
maximum, there are no absolute maxima or absolute minima.
The curve is concave up on $\left(-\frac{\pi}{2}, 0\right)$, and is concave
down on $\left(0, \frac{\pi}{2}\right)$. At $x = 0$ there is a point of inflection.

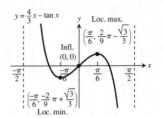

27. When $y = \sin x \cos x$, then $y' = -\sin^2 x + \cos^2 x = \cos 2x$
and $y'' = -2\sin 2x$. The curve is increasing on $\left(0, \frac{\pi}{4}\right)$ and
$\left(\frac{3\pi}{4}, \pi\right)$, and decreasing on $\left(\frac{\pi}{4}, \frac{3\pi}{4}\right)$. At $x = 0$ there is a
local minimum, at $x = \frac{\pi}{4}$ there is a local and absolute
maximum, at $x = \frac{3\pi}{4}$ there is a local and absolute minimum,
and at $x = \pi$ there is a local maximum. The curve is concave
down on $\left(0, \frac{\pi}{2}\right)$, and is concave up on $\left(\frac{\pi}{2}, \pi\right)$. At $x = \frac{\pi}{2}$
there is a point of inflection.

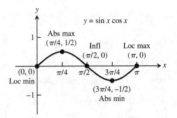

28. When $y = \cos x + \sqrt{3}\sin x$, then $y' = -\sin x + \sqrt{3}\cos x$
and $y'' = -\cos x - \sqrt{3}\sin x$. The curve is increasing on
$\left(0, \frac{\pi}{3}\right)$ and $\left(\frac{4\pi}{3}, 2\pi\right)$, and decreasing on $\left(\frac{\pi}{3}, \frac{4\pi}{3}\right)$. At
$x = 0$ there is a local minimum, at $x = \frac{\pi}{3}$ there is a local
and absolute maximum, at $x = \frac{4\pi}{3}$ there is a local and
absolute minimum, and at $x = 2\pi$ there is a local maximum.
The curve is concave down on $\left(0, \frac{5\pi}{6}\right)$ and $\left(\frac{11\pi}{6}, 2\pi\right)$,
and is concave up on $\left(\frac{5\pi}{6}, \frac{11\pi}{6}\right)$. At $x = \frac{5\pi}{6}$ and $x = \frac{11\pi}{6}$
there are points of inflection.

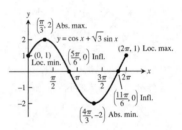

29. When $y = x^{1/5}$, then $y' = \frac{1}{5}x^{-4/5}$ and $y'' = -\frac{4}{25}x^{-9/5}$.
The curve rises on $(-\infty, \infty)$ and there are no extrema.
The curve is concave up on $(-\infty, 0)$ and concave down
on $(0, \infty)$. At $x = 0$ there is a point of inflection.

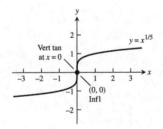

30. When $y = x^{2/5}$, then $y' = \frac{2}{5}x^{-3/5}$ and $y'' = -\frac{6}{25}x^{-8/5}$.
The curve is rising on $(0, \infty)$ and falling on $(-\infty, 0)$. At
$x = 0$ there is a local and absolute minimum. There is
no local or absolute maximum. The curve is concave
down on $(-\infty, 0)$ and $(0, \infty)$. There are no points of
inflection, but a cusp exists at $x = 0$.

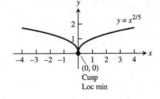

31. When $y = \frac{x}{\sqrt{x^2+1}}$, then $y' = \frac{1}{(x^2+1)^{3/2}}$ and
    $y'' = \frac{-3x}{(x^2+1)^{5/2}}$. The curve is increasing on $(-\infty, \infty)$.
    There are no local or absolute extrema. The curve is
    concave up on $(-\infty, 0)$ and concave down on $(0, \infty)$.
    At $x = 0$ there is a point of inflection.

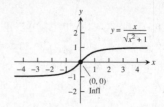

32. When $y = \frac{\sqrt{1-x^2}}{2x+1}$, then $y' = \frac{-(x+2)}{(2x+1)^2\sqrt{1-x^2}}$ and
    $y'' = \frac{-4x^3 - 12x^2 + 7}{(2x+1)^3(1-x^2)^{3/2}}$. The curve is decreasing on
    $\left(-1, -\frac{1}{2}\right)$ and $\left(-\frac{1}{2}, 1\right)$. There are no absolute extrrema,
    there is a local maximum at $x = -1$ and a local minimum
    at $x = 1$. The curve is concave up on $(-1, -0.92)$ and
    $\left(-\frac{1}{2}, 0.69\right)$, and concave down on $\left(-0.92, -\frac{1}{2}\right)$ and
    $(0.69, 1)$. At $x \approx -0.92$ and $x \approx 0.69$ there are points of
    inflection.

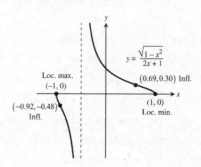

33. When $y = 2x - 3x^{2/3}$, then $y' = 2 - 2x^{-1/3}$ and
    $y'' = \frac{2}{3}x^{-4/3}$. The curve is rising on $(-\infty, 0)$ and
    $(1, \infty)$, and falling on $(0, 1)$. There is a local maximum
    at $x = 0$ and a local minimum at $x = 1$. The curve is
    concave up on $(-\infty, 0)$ and $(0, \infty)$. There are no
    points of inflection, but a cusp exists at $x = 0$.

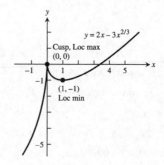

34. When $y = 5x^{2/5} - 2x$, then $y' = 2x^{-3/5} - 2 = 2\left(x^{-3/5} - 1\right)$
    and $y'' = -\frac{6}{5}x^{-8/5}$. The curve is rising on $(0, 1)$ and
    falling on $(-\infty, 0)$ and $(1, \infty)$. There is a local minimum
    at $x = 0$ and a local maximum at $x = 1$. The curve is
    concave down on $(-\infty, 0)$ and $(0, \infty)$. There are no
    points of inflection, but a cusp exists at $x = 0$.

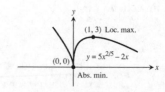

35. When $y = x^{2/3}\left(\frac{5}{2} - x\right) = \frac{5}{2}x^{2/3} - x^{5/3}$, then
    $y' = \frac{5}{3}x^{-1/3} - \frac{5}{3}x^{2/3} = \frac{5}{3}x^{-1/3}(1 - x)$ and
    $y'' = -\frac{5}{9}x^{-4/3} - \frac{10}{9}x^{-1/3} = -\frac{5}{9}x^{-4/3}(1 + 2x)$.
    The curve is rising on $(0, 1)$ and falling on $(-\infty, 0)$ and
    $(1, \infty)$. There is a local minimum at $x = 0$ and a local
    maximum at $x = 1$. The curve is concave up on $\left(-\infty, -\frac{1}{2}\right)$
    and concave down on $\left(-\frac{1}{2}, 0\right)$ and $(0, \infty)$. There is a point
    of inflection at $x = -\frac{1}{2}$ and a cusp at $x = 0$.

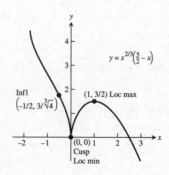

36. When $y = x^{2/3}(x - 5) = x^{5/3} - 5x^{2/3}$, then
$y' = \frac{5}{3}x^{2/3} - \frac{10}{3}x^{-1/3} = \frac{5}{3}x^{-1/3}(x - 2)$ and
$y'' = \frac{10}{9}x^{-1/3} + \frac{10}{9}x^{-4/3} = \frac{10}{9}x^{-4/3}(x + 1)$. The curve
is rising on $(-\infty, 0)$ and $(2, \infty)$, and falling on $(0, 2)$.
There is a local minimum at $x = 2$ and a local maximum
at $x = 0$. The curve is concave up on $(-1, 0)$ and $(0, \infty)$,
and concave down on $(-\infty, -1)$. There is a point of
inflection at $x = -1$ and a cusp at $x = 0$.

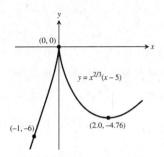

37. When $y = x\sqrt{8 - x^2} = x(8 - x^2)^{1/2}$, then
$y' = (8 - x^2)^{1/2} + (x)\left(\frac{1}{2}\right)(8 - x^2)^{-1/2}(-2x)$
$= (8 - x^2)^{-1/2}(8 - 2x^2) = \dfrac{2(2 - x)(2 + x)}{\sqrt{(2\sqrt{2} + x)(2\sqrt{2} - x)}}$ and
$y'' = \left(-\frac{1}{2}\right)(8 - x^2)^{-\frac{3}{2}}(-2x)(8 - 2x^2) + (8 - x^2)^{-\frac{1}{2}}(-4x)$
$= \dfrac{2x(x^2 - 12)}{\sqrt{(8 - x^2)^3}}$. The curve is rising on $(-2, 2)$, and falling
on $\left(-2\sqrt{2}, -2\right)$ and $\left(2, 2\sqrt{2}\right)$. There are local minima
$x = -2$ and $x = 2\sqrt{2}$, and local maxima at $x = -2\sqrt{2}$ and
$x = 2$. The curve is concave up on $\left(-2\sqrt{2}, 0\right)$ and
concave down on $\left(0, 2\sqrt{2}\right)$. There is a point of inflection
at $x = 0$.

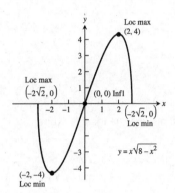

38. When $y = (2 - x^2)^{3/2}$, then $y' = \left(\frac{3}{2}\right)(2 - x^2)^{1/2}(-2x)$
$= -3x\sqrt{2 - x^2} = -3x\sqrt{\left(\sqrt{2} - x\right)\left(\sqrt{2} + x\right)}$ and
$y'' = (-3)(2 - x^2)^{1/2} + (-3x)\left(\frac{1}{2}\right)(2 - x^2)^{-1/2}(-2x)$
$= \dfrac{-6(1 - x)(1 + x)}{\sqrt{\left(\sqrt{2} - x\right)\left(\sqrt{2} + x\right)}}$. The curve is rising on
$\left(-\sqrt{2}, 0\right)$ and falling on $\left(0, \sqrt{2}\right)$. There is a local
maximum at $x = 0$, and local minima at $x = \pm\sqrt{2}$. The
curve is concave down on $(-1, 1)$ and concave up on
$\left(-\sqrt{2}, -1\right)$ and $\left(1, \sqrt{2}\right)$. There are points of inflection at
$x = \pm 1$.

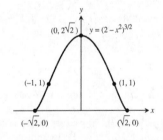

39. When $y = \sqrt{16 - x^2}$, then $y' = \dfrac{-x}{\sqrt{16 - x^2}}$ and
$y'' = \dfrac{-16}{(16 - x^2)^{3/2}}$. The curve is rising on $(-4, 0)$ and falling
on $(0, 4)$. There is a local and absolute maximum at $x = 0$
and local and absolute minima at $x = -4$ and $x = 4$. The
curve is concave down on $(-4, 4)$. There are no points
of inflection.

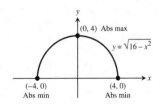

40. When $y = x^2 + \frac{2}{x}$, then $y' = 2x - \frac{2}{x^2} = \frac{2x^3 - 2}{x^2}$ and
$y'' = 2 + \frac{4}{x^3} = \frac{2x^3 + 4}{x^3}$. The curve is falling on $(-\infty, 0)$
and $(0, 1)$, and rising on $(1, \infty)$. There is a local minimum
at $x = 1$. There are no absolute maxima or absolute minima.
The curve is concave up on $\left(-\infty, -\sqrt[3]{2}\right)$ and $(0, \infty)$, and
concave down on $\left(-\sqrt[3]{2}, 0\right)$. There is a point of
inflection at $x = -\sqrt[3]{2}$.

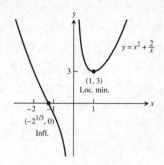

41. When $y = \frac{x^2 - 3}{x - 2}$, then $y' = \frac{2x(x-2) - (x^2 - 3)(1)}{(x-2)^2}$
$= \frac{(x-3)(x-1)}{(x-2)^2}$ and
$y'' = \frac{(2x-4)(x-2)^2 - (x^2 - 4x + 3)2(x-2)}{(x-2)^4} = \frac{2}{(x-2)^3}$.
The curve is rising on $(-\infty, 1)$ and $(3, \infty)$, and falling on
$(1, 2)$ and $(2, 3)$. There is a local maximum at $x = 1$ and a
local minimum at $x = 3$. The curve is concave down on
$(-\infty, 2)$ and concave up on $(2, \infty)$. There are no points
of inflection because $x = 2$ is not in the domain.

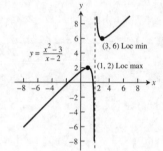

42. When $y = \sqrt[3]{x^3 + 1}$, then $y' = \frac{x^2}{(x^3 + 1)^{2/3}}$ and
$y'' = \frac{2x}{(x^3 + 1)^{5/3}}$. The curve is risng on $(-\infty, -1)$,
$(-1, 0)$, and $(0, \infty)$. There is are no local or absolute
extrema. The curve is concave up on $(-\infty, -1)$ and
$(0, \infty)$, and concave down on $(-1, 0)$. There are points of
inflection at $x = -1$ and $x = 0$.

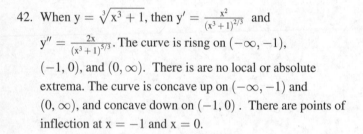

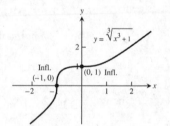

43. When $y = \frac{8x}{x^2 + 4}$, then $y' = \frac{-8(x^2 - 4)}{(x^2 + 4)^2}$ and
$y'' = \frac{16x(x^2 - 12)}{(x^2 + 4)^3}$. The curve is fallng on $(-\infty, -2)$
and $(2, \infty)$, and is rising on $(-2, 2)$. There is a local and
absolute minimum at $x = -2$, and a local and absolute
maximum at $x = 2$. The curve is concave down on
$\left(-\infty, -2\sqrt{3}\right)$ and $\left(0, 2\sqrt{3}\right)$, and concave up on
$\left(-2\sqrt{3}, 0\right)$ and $\left(2\sqrt{3}, \infty\right)$. There are points of inflection at $x = -2\sqrt{3}$, $x = 0$, and $x = 2\sqrt{3}$.
$y = 0$ is a horizontal asymptote.

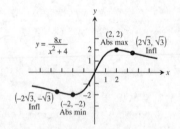

44. When $y = \frac{5}{x^4 + 5}$, then $y' = \frac{-20x^3}{(x^4 + 5)^2}$ and
$y'' = \frac{100x^2(x^4 - 3)}{(x^4 + 5)^3}$. The curve is risng on $(-\infty, 0)$,
and is falling on $(0, \infty)$. There is a local and
absolute maximum at $x = 0$, and there is no local or
aboslute minimum. The curve is concave up on
$\left(-\infty, -\sqrt[4]{3}\right)$ and $\left(\sqrt[4]{3}, \infty\right)$, and concave down on $\left(-\sqrt[4]{3}, 0\right)$ and $\left(0, \sqrt[4]{3}\right)$. There are points of inflection at $x = -\sqrt[4]{3}$
and $x = \sqrt[4]{3}$. There is a horizontal asymptote of $y = 0$.

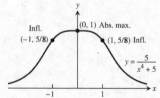

45. When $y = |x^2 - 1| = \begin{cases} x^2 - 1, & |x| \geq 1 \\ 1 - x^2, & |x| < 1 \end{cases}$, then

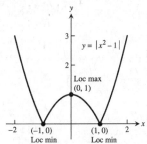

$y' = \begin{cases} 2x, & |x| > 1 \\ -2x, & |x| < 1 \end{cases}$ and $y'' = \begin{cases} 2, & |x| > 1 \\ -2, & |x| < 1 \end{cases}$. The

curve rises on $(-1, 0)$ and $(1, \infty)$ and falls on $(-\infty, -1)$
and $(0, 1)$. There is a local maximum at $x = 0$ and local
minima at $x = \pm 1$. The curve is concave up on $(-\infty, -1)$
and $(1, \infty)$, and concave down on $(-1, 1)$. There are no
points of inflection because y is not differentiable at $x = \pm 1$ (so there is no tangent line at those points).

46. When $y = |x^2 - 2x| = \begin{cases} x^2 - 2x, & x < 0 \\ 2x - x^2, & 0 \leq x \leq 2 \\ x^2 - 2x, & x > 2 \end{cases}$, then

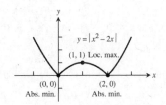

$y' = \begin{cases} 2x - 2, & x < 0 \\ 2 - 2x, & 0 < x < 2 \\ 2x - 2, & x > 2 \end{cases}$, and $y'' = \begin{cases} 2, & x < 0 \\ -2, & 0 < x < 2 \\ 2, & x > 2 \end{cases}$.

The curve is rising on $(0, 1)$ and $(2, \infty)$, and falling on
$(-\infty, 0)$ and $(1, 2)$. There is a local maximum at $x = 1$ and local minima at $x = 0$ and $x = 2$. The curve is concave up
on $(-\infty, 0)$ and $(2, \infty)$, and concave down on $(0, 2)$. There are no points of inflection because y is not
differentiable at $x = 0$ and $x = 2$ (so there is no tangent at those points).

47. When $y = \sqrt{|x|} = \begin{cases} \sqrt{x}, & x \geq 0 \\ \sqrt{-x}, & x < 0 \end{cases}$, then

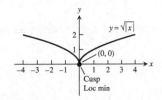

$y' = \begin{cases} \frac{1}{2\sqrt{x}}, & x > 0 \\ \frac{-1}{2\sqrt{-x}}, & x < 0 \end{cases}$ and $y'' = \begin{cases} \frac{-x^{-3/2}}{4}, & x > 0 \\ \frac{-(-x)^{-3/2}}{4}, & x < 0 \end{cases}$.

Since $\lim_{x \to 0^-} y' = -\infty$ and $\lim_{x \to 0^+} y' = \infty$ there is a

cusp at $x = 0$. There is a local minimum at $x = 0$, but no local maximum. The curve is concave down on $(-\infty, 0)$
and $(0, \infty)$. There are no points of inflection.

48. When $y = \sqrt{|x - 4|} = \begin{cases} \sqrt{x - 4}, & x \geq 4 \\ \sqrt{4 - x}, & x < 4 \end{cases}$, then

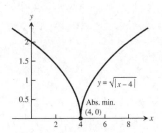

$y' = \begin{cases} \frac{1}{2\sqrt{x-4}}, & x > 4 \\ \frac{-1}{2\sqrt{4-x}}, & x < 4 \end{cases}$ and $y'' = \begin{cases} \frac{-(x-4)^{-3/2}}{4}, & x > 4 \\ \frac{-(4-x)^{-3/2}}{4}, & x < 4 \end{cases}$.

Since $\lim_{x \to 4^-} y' = -\infty$ and $\lim_{x \to 4^+} y' = \infty$ there is a cusp

at $x = 4$. There is a local minimum at $x = 4$, but no local
maximum. The curve is concave down on $(-\infty, 4)$ and $(4, \infty)$. There are no points of inflection.

49. $y' = 2 + x - x^2 = (1 + x)(2 - x)$, $y' = \underset{-1}{- - -} \mid +++ \underset{2}{\mid} - - -$

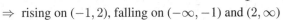

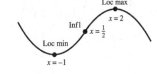

$\Rightarrow$ rising on $(-1, 2)$, falling on $(-\infty, -1)$ and $(2, \infty)$
$\Rightarrow$ there is a local maximum at $x = 2$ and a local minimum
at $x = -1$; $y'' = 1 - 2x$, $y'' = +++ \underset{1/2}{\mid} - - -$

$\Rightarrow$ concave up on $\left(-\infty, \frac{1}{2}\right)$, concave down on $\left(\frac{1}{2}, \infty\right)$ $\Rightarrow$ a point of inflection at $x = \frac{1}{2}$

50. $y' = x^2 - x - 6 = (x - 3)(x + 2)$, $y' = +++ \mid --- \mid +++$
$\qquad\qquad\qquad\qquad\qquad\qquad\qquad -2 \qquad 3$

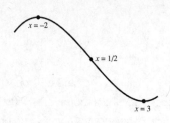

$\Rightarrow$ rising on $(-\infty, -2)$ and $(3, \infty)$, falling on $(-2, 3)$

$\Rightarrow$ there is a local maximum at $x = -2$ and a local

minimum at $x = 3$; $y'' = 2x - 1$, $y'' = --- \mid +++$
$\qquad\qquad\qquad\qquad\qquad\qquad\qquad\qquad 1/2$

$\Rightarrow$ concave up on $\left(\frac{1}{2}, \infty\right)$, concave down on $\left(-\infty, \frac{1}{2}\right)$

$\Rightarrow$ a point of inflection at $x = \frac{1}{2}$

51. $y' = x(x - 3)^2$, $y' = --- \mid +++ \mid +++$ $\Rightarrow$ rising on
$\qquad\qquad\qquad\qquad\qquad\quad 0 \qquad\quad 3$

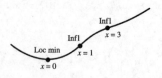

$(0, \infty)$, falling on $(-\infty, 0)$ $\Rightarrow$ no local maximum, but there

is a local minimum at $x = 0$; $y'' = (x - 3)^2 + x(2)(x - 3)$

$= 3(x - 3)(x - 1)$, $y'' = +++ \mid --- \mid +++$ $\Rightarrow$ concave
$\qquad\qquad\qquad\qquad\qquad\qquad\quad 1 \qquad 3$

up on $(-\infty, 1)$ and $(3, \infty)$, concave down on $(1, 3)$ $\Rightarrow$ points of inflection at $x = 1$ and $x = 3$

52. $y' = x^2(2 - x)$, $y' = +++ \mid +++ \mid ---$ $\Rightarrow$ rising on
$\qquad\qquad\qquad\qquad\qquad\quad 0 \qquad\quad 2$

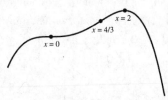

$(-\infty, 2)$, falling on $(2, \infty)$ $\Rightarrow$ there is a local maximum at

$x = 2$, but no local minimum; $y'' = 2x(2 - x) + x^2(-1)$

$= x(4 - 3x)$, $y'' = --- \mid +++ \mid ---$ $\Rightarrow$ concave up
$\qquad\qquad\qquad\qquad\quad 0 \qquad 4/3$

on $\left(0, \frac{4}{3}\right)$, concave down on $(-\infty, 0)$ and $\left(\frac{4}{3}, \infty\right)$ $\Rightarrow$ points of inflection at $x = 0$ and $x = \frac{4}{3}$

53. $y' = x(x^2 - 12) = x\left(x - 2\sqrt{3}\right)\left(x + 2\sqrt{3}\right)$,

$y' = --- \mid +++ \mid --- \mid +++ \Rightarrow$ rising on
$\qquad\quad -2\sqrt{3} \qquad 0 \qquad 2\sqrt{3}$

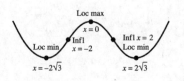

$\left(-2\sqrt{3}, 0\right)$ and $\left(2\sqrt{3}, \infty\right)$, falling on $\left(-\infty, -2\sqrt{3}\right)$

and $\left(0, 2\sqrt{3}\right)$ $\Rightarrow$ a local maximum at $x = 0$, local minima at $x = \pm 2\sqrt{3}$; $y'' = 1(x^2 - 12) + x(2x) = 3(x - 2)(x + 2)$,

$y'' = +++ \mid --- \mid +++$ $\Rightarrow$ concave up on $(-\infty, -2)$ and $(2, \infty)$, concave down on $(-2, 2)$ $\Rightarrow$ points of inflection
$\qquad\quad -2 \qquad 2$

at $x = \pm 2$

54. $y' = (x - 1)^2(2x + 3)$, $y' = --- \mid +++ \mid +++$
$\qquad\qquad\qquad\qquad\qquad\qquad -3/2 \qquad 1$

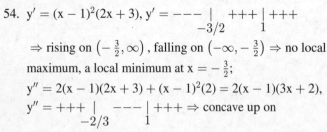

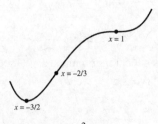

$\Rightarrow$ rising on $\left(-\frac{3}{2}, \infty\right)$, falling on $\left(-\infty, -\frac{3}{2}\right)$ $\Rightarrow$ no local

maximum, a local minimum at $x = -\frac{3}{2}$;

$y'' = 2(x - 1)(2x + 3) + (x - 1)^2(2) = 2(x - 1)(3x + 2)$,

$y'' = +++ \mid --- \mid +++$ $\Rightarrow$ concave up on
$\qquad\quad -2/3 \qquad 1$

$\left(-\infty, -\frac{2}{3}\right)$ and $(1, \infty)$, concave down on $\left(-\frac{2}{3}, 1\right)$ $\Rightarrow$ points of inflection at $x = -\frac{2}{3}$ and $x = 1$

55. $y' = (8x - 5x^2)(4 - x)^2 = x(8 - 5x)(4 - x)^2$,

$y' = --- | +++ | --- | --- \Rightarrow$ rising on $\left(0, \frac{8}{5}\right)$,
   0      8/5      4

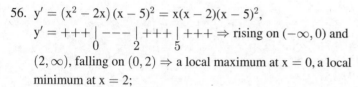

falling on $(-\infty, 0)$ and $\left(\frac{8}{5}, \infty\right) \Rightarrow$ a local maximum at

$x = \frac{8}{5}$, a local minimum at $x = 0$;

$y'' = (8 - 10x)(4 - x)^2 + (8x - 5x^2)(2)(4 - x)(-1) = 4(4 - x)(5x^2 - 16x + 8)$,

$y'' = +++ | --- | +++ | --- \Rightarrow$ concave up on $\left(-\infty, \frac{8 - 2\sqrt{6}}{5}\right)$ and $\left(\frac{8 + 2\sqrt{6}}{5}, 4\right)$, concave down on
        $\frac{8-2\sqrt{6}}{5}$    $\frac{8+2\sqrt{6}}{5}$    4

$\left(\frac{8 - 2\sqrt{6}}{5}, \frac{8 + 2\sqrt{6}}{5}\right)$ and $(4, \infty) \Rightarrow$ points of inflection at $x = \frac{8 \pm 2\sqrt{6}}{5}$ and $x = 4$

56. $y' = (x^2 - 2x)(x - 5)^2 = x(x - 2)(x - 5)^2$,

$y' = +++ | --- | +++ | +++ \Rightarrow$ rising on $(-\infty, 0)$ and
        0      2      5

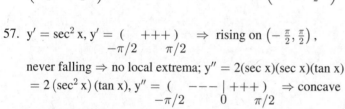

$(2, \infty)$, falling on $(0, 2) \Rightarrow$ a local maximum at $x = 0$, a local

minimum at $x = 2$;

$y'' = (2x - 2)(x - 5)^2 + 2(x^2 - 2x)(x - 5)$

$= 2(x - 5)(2x^2 - 8x + 5)$,

$y'' = --- | +++ | --- | +++ \Rightarrow$ concave up on
        $\frac{4-\sqrt{6}}{2}$    $\frac{4+\sqrt{6}}{2}$    5

$\left(\frac{4 - \sqrt{6}}{2}, \frac{4 + \sqrt{6}}{2}\right)$ and $(5, \infty)$, concave down on $\left(-\infty, \frac{4 - \sqrt{6}}{2}\right)$ and $\left(\frac{4 + \sqrt{6}}{2}, 5\right) \Rightarrow$ points of inflection at $x = \frac{4 \pm \sqrt{6}}{2}$ and $x = 5$

57. $y' = \sec^2 x$, $y' = ( \quad +++ ) \Rightarrow$ rising on $\left(-\frac{\pi}{2}, \frac{\pi}{2}\right)$,
              $-\pi/2 \quad \pi/2$

never falling $\Rightarrow$ no local extrema; $y'' = 2(\sec x)(\sec x)(\tan x)$

$= 2(\sec^2 x)(\tan x)$, $y'' = ( \quad --- | +++ ) \Rightarrow$ concave
                                  $-\pi/2 \quad 0 \quad \pi/2$

up on $\left(0, \frac{\pi}{2}\right)$, concave down on $\left(-\frac{\pi}{2}, 0\right)$, 0 is a point of

inflection.

58. $y' = \tan x$, $y' = ( \quad --- | +++ ) \Rightarrow$ rising on $\left(0, \frac{\pi}{2}\right)$,
              $-\pi/2 \quad 0 \quad \pi/2$

falling on $\left(-\frac{\pi}{2}, 0\right) \Rightarrow$ no local maximum, a local minimum

at $x = 0$; $y'' = \sec^2 x$, $y'' = ( \quad +++ ) \Rightarrow$ concave up
                                  $-\pi/2 \quad \pi/2$

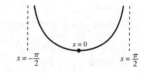

on $\left(-\frac{\pi}{2}, \frac{\pi}{2}\right) \Rightarrow$ no points of inflection

59. $y' = \cot \frac{\theta}{2}$, $y' = ( +++ | --- ) \Rightarrow$ rising on $(0, \pi)$,
                          0    $\pi$    $2\pi$

falling on $(\pi, 2\pi) \Rightarrow$ a local maximum at $\theta = \pi$, no local

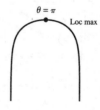

minimum; $y'' = -\frac{1}{2} \csc^2 \frac{\theta}{2}$, $y'' = ( --- ) \Rightarrow$ never
                                              0    $2\pi$

concave up, concave down on $(0, 2\pi) \Rightarrow$ no points of

inflection

60. $y' = \csc^2 \frac{\theta}{2}$, $y' = \underset{0 \qquad 2\pi}{(\; +++\; )} \;\Rightarrow\;$ rising on $(0, 2\pi)$, never

falling $\Rightarrow$ no local extrema;

$y'' = 2\left(\csc \frac{\theta}{2}\right)\left(-\csc \frac{\theta}{2}\right)\left(\cot \frac{\theta}{2}\right)\left(\frac{1}{2}\right)$

$= -\left(\csc^2 \frac{\theta}{2}\right)\left(\cot \frac{\theta}{2}\right)$, $y'' = \underset{0 \qquad \pi \qquad 2\pi}{(\; ---\; |\; +++\; )}$

$\Rightarrow$ concave up on $(\pi, 2\pi)$, concave down on $(0, \pi)$

$\Rightarrow$ a point of inflection at $\theta = \pi$

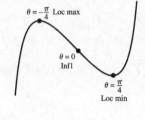

61. $y' = \tan^2 \theta - 1 = (\tan \theta - 1)(\tan \theta + 1)$,

$y' = \underset{-\pi/2 \quad\; -\pi/4 \quad\; \pi/4 \quad\; \pi/2}{(\quad +++ \;|\quad --- \;|\; +++ \;)} \;\Rightarrow\;$ rising on

$\left(-\frac{\pi}{2}, -\frac{\pi}{4}\right)$ and $\left(\frac{\pi}{4}, \frac{\pi}{2}\right)$, falling on $\left(-\frac{\pi}{4}, \frac{\pi}{4}\right)$

$\Rightarrow$ a local maximum at $\theta = -\frac{\pi}{4}$, a local minimum at $\theta = \frac{\pi}{4}$;

$y'' = 2 \tan \theta \sec^2 \theta$, $y'' = \underset{-\pi/2 \qquad 0 \qquad \pi/2}{(\quad --- \;|\; +++ \;)}$

$\Rightarrow$ concave up on $\left(0, \frac{\pi}{2}\right)$, concave down on $\left(-\frac{\pi}{2}, 0\right)$

$\Rightarrow$ a point of inflection at $\theta = 0$

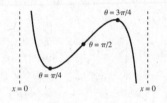

62. $y' = 1 - \cot^2 \theta = (1 - \cot \theta)(1 + \cot \theta)$,

$y' = \underset{0 \quad\; \pi/4 \quad\; 3\pi/4 \quad\; \pi}{(\; --- \;|\; +++ \;|\quad --- \;)} \;\Rightarrow\;$ rising on $\left(\frac{\pi}{4}, \frac{3\pi}{4}\right)$,

falling on $\left(0, \frac{\pi}{4}\right)$ and $\left(\frac{3\pi}{4}, \pi\right)$ $\Rightarrow$ a local maximum at

$\theta = \frac{3\pi}{4}$, a local minimum at $\theta = \frac{\pi}{4}$;

$y'' = -2(\cot \theta)\left(-\csc^2 \theta\right)$, $y'' = \underset{0 \qquad \pi/2 \qquad \pi}{(\; +++ \;|\quad --- \;)}$

$\Rightarrow$ concave up on $\left(0, \frac{\pi}{2}\right)$, concave down on $\left(\frac{\pi}{2}, \pi\right)$

$\Rightarrow$ a point of inflection at $\theta = \frac{\pi}{2}$

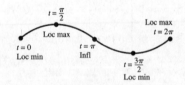

63. $y' = \cos t$, $y' = \underset{0 \qquad \pi/2 \qquad 3\pi/2 \qquad 2\pi}{[\; +++ \;|\quad --- \;|\quad +++ \;]} \;\Rightarrow\;$ rising on

$\left(0, \frac{\pi}{2}\right)$ and $\left(\frac{3\pi}{2}, 2\pi\right)$, falling on $\left(\frac{\pi}{2}, \frac{3\pi}{2}\right)$ $\Rightarrow$ local maxima at

$t = \frac{\pi}{2}$ and $t = 2\pi$, local minima at $t = 0$ and $t = \frac{3\pi}{2}$;

$y'' = -\sin t$, $y'' = \underset{0 \qquad \pi \qquad 2\pi}{[\; --- \;|\; +++ \;]}$

$\Rightarrow$ concave up on $(\pi, 2\pi)$, concave down

on $(0, \pi)$ $\Rightarrow$ a point of inflection at $t = \pi$

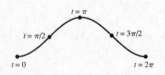

64. $y' = \sin t$, $y' = \underset{0 \qquad \pi \qquad 2\pi}{[\; +++ \;|\; --- \;]} \;\Rightarrow\;$ rising on $(0, \pi)$,

falling on $(\pi, 2\pi)$ $\Rightarrow$ a local maximum at $t = \pi$, local

minima at $t = 0$ and $t = 2\pi$; $y'' = \cos t$,

$y'' = \underset{0 \qquad \pi/2 \qquad 3\pi/2 \qquad 2\pi}{[\; +++ \;|\quad --- \;|\quad +++ \;]} \;\Rightarrow\;$ concave up on $\left(0, \frac{\pi}{2}\right)$

and $\left(\frac{3\pi}{2}, 2\pi\right)$, concave down on $\left(\frac{\pi}{2}, \frac{3\pi}{2}\right)$ $\Rightarrow$ points

of inflection at $t = \frac{\pi}{2}$ and $t = \frac{3\pi}{2}$

65. $y' = (x + 1)^{-2/3}$, $y' = +++ ) \; (+++ \; \Rightarrow$ rising on
$\quad\quad\quad\quad\quad\quad\quad\quad\;\; {}_{-1}$

$(-\infty, \infty)$, never falling $\Rightarrow$ no local extrema;

$y'' = -\frac{2}{3}(x + 1)^{-5/3}$, $y'' = +++ ) \; (---$
$\quad\quad\quad\quad\quad\quad\quad\quad\quad\quad\quad\;\; {}_{-1}$

$\Rightarrow$ concave up on $(-\infty, -1)$, concave down on $(-1, \infty)$

$\Rightarrow$ a point of inflection and vertical tangent at $x = -1$

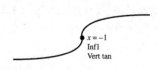

66. $y' = (x - 2)^{-1/3}$, $y' = --- )(+++ \; \Rightarrow$ rising on $(2, \infty)$,
$\quad\quad\quad\quad\quad\quad\quad\quad\;\; {}_{2}$

falling on $(-\infty, 2) \Rightarrow$ no local maximum, but a local

minimum at $x = 2$; $y'' = -\frac{1}{3}(x - 2)^{-4/3}$,

$y'' = --- )(--- \; \Rightarrow$ concave down on $(-\infty, 2)$ and
$\quad\quad\quad\;\; {}_{2}$

$(2, \infty) \Rightarrow$ no points of inflection, but there is a cusp at

$x = 2$

67. $y' = x^{-2/3}(x - 1)$, $y' = --- )(--- \mid +++ \; \Rightarrow$ rising on
$\quad\quad\quad\quad\quad\quad\quad\quad\;\; {}_{0} \quad\quad {}_{1}$

$(1, \infty)$, falling on $(-\infty, 1) \Rightarrow$ no local maximum, but a

local minimum at $x = 1$; $y'' = \frac{1}{3}x^{-2/3} + \frac{2}{3}x^{-5/3}$

$= \frac{1}{3}x^{-5/3}(x + 2)$, $y'' = +++ \mid --- )(+++$
$\quad\quad\quad\quad\quad\quad\quad\quad\;\; {}_{-2} \quad\quad {}_{0}$

$\Rightarrow$ concave up on $(-\infty, -2)$ and $(0, \infty)$, concave down on

$(-2, 0) \Rightarrow$ points of inflection at $x = -2$ and $x = 0$, and a

vertical tangent at $x = 0$

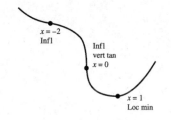

68. $y' = x^{-4/5}(x + 1)$, $y' = --- \mid \; +++ )(+++ \; \Rightarrow$ rising on
$\quad\quad\quad\quad\quad\quad\quad\quad\;\; {}_{-1} \quad\quad {}_{0}$

$(-1, 0)$ and $(0, \infty)$, falling on $(-\infty, -1) \Rightarrow$ no local

maximum, but a local minimum at $x = -1$;

$y'' = \frac{1}{5}x^{-4/5} - \frac{4}{5}x^{-9/5} = \frac{1}{5}x^{-9/5}(x - 4)$,

$y'' = +++ )(--- \mid +++ \; \Rightarrow$ concave up on $(-\infty, 0)$ and
$\quad\quad\quad\quad\;\; {}_{0} \quad\quad {}_{4}$

$(4, \infty)$, concave down on $(0, 4) \Rightarrow$ points of inflection at

$x = 0$ and $x = 4$, and a vertical tangent at $x = 0$

69. $y' = \begin{cases} -2x, & x \le 0 \\ 2x, & x > 0 \end{cases}$, $y' = +++ \mid +++ \; \Rightarrow$ rising on
$\quad\quad\quad\quad\quad\quad\quad\quad\quad\quad\quad\;\; {}_{0}$

$(-\infty, \infty) \Rightarrow$ no local extrema; $y'' = \begin{cases} -2, & x < 0 \\ 2, & x > 0 \end{cases}$,

$y'' = --- )(+++ \; \Rightarrow$ concave up on $(0, \infty)$, concave
$\quad\quad\quad\;\; {}_{0}$

down on $(-\infty, 0) \Rightarrow$ a point of inflection at $x = 0$

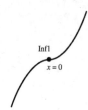

70. $y' = \begin{cases} -x^2, & x \le 0 \\ x^2, & x > 0 \end{cases}$, $y' = --- \mid +++ \; \Rightarrow$ rising on
$\quad\quad\quad\quad\quad\quad\quad\quad\quad\;\; {}_{0}$

$(0, \infty)$, falling on $(-\infty, 0) \Rightarrow$ no local maximum, but a

local minimum at $x = 0$; $y'' = \begin{cases} -2x, & x \le 0 \\ 2x, & x > 0 \end{cases}$,

$y'' = +++ \mid +++ \; \Rightarrow$ concave up on $(-\infty, \infty)$
$\quad\quad\quad\;\; {}_{0}$

$\Rightarrow$ no point of inflection

71. The graph of $y = f''(x) \Rightarrow$ the graph of $y = f(x)$ is concave up on $(0, \infty)$, concave down on $(-\infty, 0) \Rightarrow$ a point of inflection at $x = 0$; the graph of $y = f'(x)$
$\Rightarrow y' = +++ \mid --- \mid +++ \Rightarrow$ the graph $y = f(x)$ has both a local maximum and a local minimum

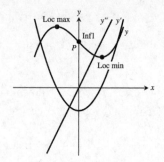

72. The graph of $y = f''(x) \Rightarrow y'' = +++ \mid --- \Rightarrow$ the graph of $y = f(x)$ has a point of inflection, the graph of $y = f'(x) \Rightarrow y' = --- \mid +++ \mid --- \Rightarrow$ the graph of $y = f(x)$ has both a local maximum and a local minimum

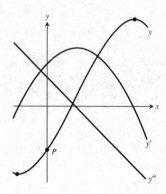

73. The graph of $y = f''(x) \Rightarrow y'' = --- \mid +++ \mid ---$
$\Rightarrow$ the graph of $y = f(x)$ has two points of inflection, the graph of $y = f'(x) \Rightarrow y' = --- \mid +++ \Rightarrow$ the graph of $y = f(x)$ has a local minimum

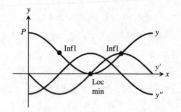

74. The graph of $y = f''(x) \Rightarrow y'' = +++ \mid --- \Rightarrow$ the graph of $y = f(x)$ has a point of inflection; the graph of $y = f'(x) \Rightarrow y' = --- \mid +++ \mid --- \Rightarrow$ the graph of $y = f(x)$ has both a local maximum and a local minimum

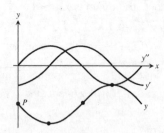

75. $y = \frac{2x^2 + x - 1}{x^2 - 1}$

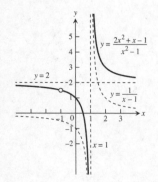

76. $y = \frac{x^2 - 49}{x^2 + 5x - 14} = 1 - \frac{5}{x - 2}$

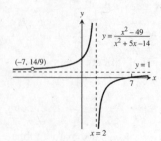

77. $y = \dfrac{x^4+1}{x^2} = x^2 + \dfrac{1}{x^2}$

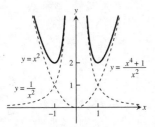

78. $y = \dfrac{x^2+4}{2x} = \dfrac{x}{2} + \dfrac{2}{x}$

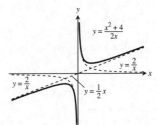

79. $y = \dfrac{1}{x^2-1}$

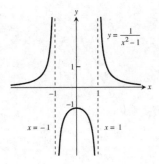

80. $y = \dfrac{x^2}{x^2-1} = 1 + \dfrac{1}{x^2-1}$

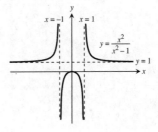

81. $y = -\dfrac{x^2-2}{x^2-1} = -1 + \dfrac{1}{x^2-1}$

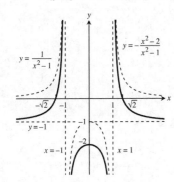

82. $y = \dfrac{x^2-4}{x^2-2} = 1 - \dfrac{2}{x^2-2}$

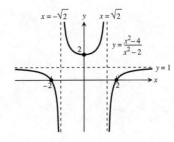

83. $y = \dfrac{x^2}{x+1} = x - 1 + \dfrac{1}{x+1}$

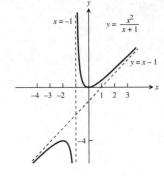

84. $y = -\dfrac{x^2-4}{x+1} = 1 - x + \dfrac{3}{x+1}$

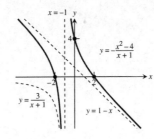

85. $y = \dfrac{x^2 - x + 1}{x - 1} = x + \dfrac{1}{x - 1}$

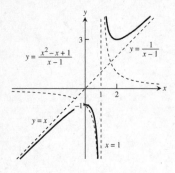

86. $y = -\dfrac{x^2 - x + 1}{x - 1} = -x - \dfrac{1}{x - 1}$

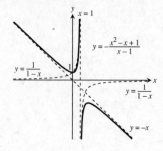

87. $y = \dfrac{x^3 - 3x^2 + 3x - 1}{x^2 + x + 2} = x - 4 + \dfrac{5x + 7}{x^2 + x + 2}$

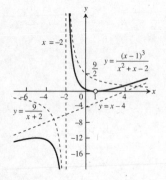

88. $y = \dfrac{x^3 + x - 2}{x - x^2} = -x - 1 + \dfrac{2x - 2}{x - x^2}$

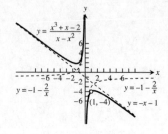

89. $y = \dfrac{x}{x^2 - 1}$

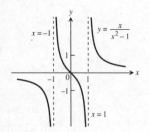

90. $y = \dfrac{x - 1}{x^2(x - 2)}$

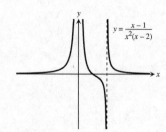

91. $y = \dfrac{8}{x^2 + 4}$

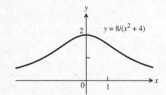

92. $y = \dfrac{4x}{x^2 + 4}$

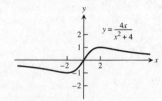

93.

| Point | $y'$ | $y''$ |
|-------|------|-------|
| P | $-$ | $+$ |
| Q | $+$ | $0$ |
| R | $+$ | $-$ |
| S | $0$ | $-$ |
| T | $-$ | $-$ |

94.

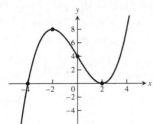

95.

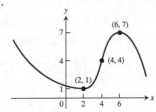

96.

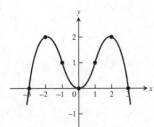

97. Graphs printed in color can shift during a press run, so your values may differ somewhat from those given here.

   (a) The body is moving away from the origin when |displacement| is increasing as t increases, $0 < t < 2$ and $6 < t < 9.5$; the body is moving toward the origin when |displacement| is decreasing as t increases, $2 < t < 6$ and $9.5 < t < 15$

   (b) The velocity will be zero when the slope of the tangent line for $y = s(t)$ is horizontal. The velocity is zero when t is approximately 2, 6, or 9.5 sec.

   (c) The acceleration will be zero at those values of t where the curve $y = s(t)$ has points of inflection. The acceleration is zero when t is approximately 4, 7.5, or 12.5 sec.

   (d) The acceleration is positive when the concavity is up, $4 < t < 7.5$ and $12.5 < t < 15$; the acceleration is negative when the concavity is down, $0 < t < 4$ and $7.5 < t < 12.5$

98. (a) The body is moving away from the origin when |displacement| is increasing as t increases, $1.5 < t < 4$, $10 < t < 12$ and $13.5 < t < 16$; the body is moving toward the origin when |displacement| is decreasing as t increases, $0 < t < 1.5$, $4 < t < 10$ and $12 < t < 13.5$

   (b) The velocity will be zero when the slope of the tangent line for $y = s(t)$ is horizontal. The velocity is zero when t is approximately 0, 4, 12 or 16 sec.

   (c) The acceleration will be zero at those values of t where the curve $y = s(t)$ has points of inflection. The acceleration is zero when t is approximately 1.5, 6, 8, 10.5, or 13.5 sec.

   (d) The acceleration is positive when the concavity is up, $0 < t < 1.5$, $6 < t < 8$ and $10 < t < 13.5$, the acceleration is negative when the concavity is down, $1.5 < t < 6$, $8 < t < 10$ and $13.5 < t < 16$.

99. The marginal cost is $\frac{dc}{dx}$ which changes from decreasing to increasing when its derivative $\frac{d^2c}{dx^2}$ is zero. This is a point of inflection of the cost curve and occurs when the production level x is approximately 60 thousand units.

100. The marginal revenue is $\frac{dy}{dx}$ and it is increasing when its derivative $\frac{d^2y}{dx^2}$ is positive $\Rightarrow$ the curve is concave up $\Rightarrow$ $0 < t < 2$ and $5 < t < 9$; marginal revenue is decreasing when $\frac{d^2y}{dx^2} < 0 \Rightarrow$ the curve is concave down $\Rightarrow$ $2 < t < 5$ and $9 < t < 12$.

101. When $y' = (x - 1)^2(x - 2)$, then $y'' = 2(x - 1)(x - 2) + (x - 1)^2$. The curve falls on $(-\infty, 2)$ and rises on $(2, \infty)$. At $x = 2$ there is a local minimum. There is no local maximum. The curve is concave upward on $(-\infty, 1)$ and $\left(\frac{5}{3}, \infty\right)$, and concave downward on $\left(1, \frac{5}{3}\right)$. At $x = 1$ or $x = \frac{5}{3}$ there are inflection points.

102. When $y' = (x - 1)^2(x - 2)(x - 4)$, then $y'' = 2(x - 1)(x - 2)(x - 4) + (x - 1)^2(x - 4) + (x - 1)^2(x - 2)$
$= (x - 1)[2(x^2 - 6x + 8) + (x^2 - 5x + 4) + (x^2 - 3x + 2)] = 2(x - 1)(2x^2 - 10x + 11)$. The curve rises on $(-\infty, 2)$ and $(4, \infty)$ and falls on $(2, 4)$. At $x = 2$ there is a local maximum and at $x = 4$ a local minimum. The curve is concave downward on $(-\infty, 1)$ and $\left(\frac{5 - \sqrt{3}}{2}, \frac{5 + \sqrt{3}}{2}\right)$ and concave upward on $\left(1, \frac{5 - \sqrt{3}}{2}\right)$ and $\left(\frac{5 + \sqrt{3}}{2}, \infty\right)$. At $x = 1, \frac{5 - \sqrt{3}}{2}$ and $\frac{5 + \sqrt{3}}{2}$ there are inflection points.

103. The graph must be concave down for $x > 0$ because $f''(x) = -\frac{1}{x^2} < 0$.

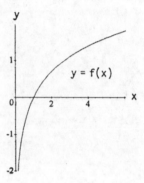

104. The second derivative, being continuous and never zero, cannot change sign. Therefore the graph will always be concave up or concave down so it will have no inflection points and no cusps or corners.

105. The curve will have a point of inflection at $x = 1$ if 1 is a solution of $y'' = 0$; $y = x^3 + bx^2 + cx + d$
$\Rightarrow y' = 3x^2 + 2bx + c \Rightarrow y'' = 6x + 2b$ and $6(1) + 2b = 0 \Rightarrow b = -3$.

106. (a) $f(x) = ax^2 + bx + c = a\left(x^2 + \frac{b}{a}x\right) + c = a\left(x^2 + \frac{b}{a}x + \frac{b^2}{4a^2}\right) - \frac{b^2}{4a} + c = a\left(x + \frac{b}{2a}\right)^2 - \frac{b^2 - 4ac}{4a}$ a parabola whose vertex is at $x = -\frac{b}{2a} \Rightarrow$ the coordinates of the vertex are $\left(-\frac{b}{2a}, -\frac{b^2 - 4ac}{4a}\right)$

(b) The second derivative, $f''(x) = 2a$, describes concavity $\Rightarrow$ when $a > 0$ the parabola is concave up and when $a < 0$ the parabola is concave down.

107. A quadratic curve never has an inflection point. If $y = ax^2 + bx + c$ where $a \neq 0$, then $y' = 2ax + b$ and $y'' = 2a$. Since $2a$ is a constant, it is not possible for $y''$ to change signs.

108. A cubic curve always has exactly one inflection point. If $y = ax^3 + bx^2 + cx + d$ where $a \neq 0$, then $y' = 3ax^2 + 2bx + c$ and $y'' = 6ax + 2b$. Since $\frac{-b}{3a}$ is a solution of $y'' = 0$, we have that $y''$ changes its sign at $x = -\frac{b}{3a}$ and $y'$ exists everywhere (so there is a tangent at $x = -\frac{b}{3a}$). Thus the curve has an inflection point at $x = -\frac{b}{3a}$. There are no other inflection points because $y''$ changes sign only at this zero.

109. $y'' = (x + 1)(x - 2)$, when $y'' = 0 \Rightarrow x = -1$ or $x = 2$; $y'' = +++ \underset{-1}{|} --- \underset{2}{|} +++ \Rightarrow$ points of inflection at $x = -1$ and $x = 2$

110. $y'' = x^2(x - 2)^3(x + 3)$, when $y'' = 0 \Rightarrow x = -3, x = 0,$ or $x = 2$; $y'' = +++ \underset{-3}{|} --- \underset{0}{|} --- \underset{2}{|} +++ \Rightarrow$ points of inflection at $x = -3$ and $x = 2$

111. $y = ax^3 + bx^2 + cx \Rightarrow y' = 3ax^2 + 2bx + c$ and $y'' = 6ax + 2b$; local maximum at $x = 3$
$\Rightarrow 3a(3)^2 + 2b(3) + c = 0 \Rightarrow 27a + 6b + c = 0$; local minimum at $x = -1 \Rightarrow 3a(-1)^2 + 2b(-1) + c = 0$
$\Rightarrow 3a - 2b + c = 0$; point of inflection at $(1, 11) \Rightarrow a(1)^3 + b(1)^2 + c(1) = 11 \Rightarrow a + b + c = 11$ and
$6a(1) + 2b = 0 \Rightarrow 6a + 2b = 0$. Solving $27a + 6b + c = 0$, $3a - 2b + c = 0$, $a + b + c = 11$, and $6a + 2b = 0$
$\Rightarrow a = -1, b = 3,$ and $c = 9 \Rightarrow y = -x^3 + 3x^2 + 9x$

112. $y = \frac{x^2 + a}{bx + c} \Rightarrow y' = \frac{bx^2 + 2cx - ab}{(bx+c)^2}$; local maximum at $x = 3 \Rightarrow \frac{b(3)^2 + 2c(3) - ab}{(b(3)+c)^2} = 0 \Rightarrow 9b + 6c - ab = 0$; local minimum at

$(-1, -2) \Rightarrow \frac{b(-1)^2 + 2c(-1) - ab}{(b(-1)+c)^2} = 0 \Rightarrow b - 2c - ab = 0$ and $\frac{(-1)^2 + a}{b(-1) + c} = -2 \Rightarrow -a + 2b - 2c = 1$. Solving

$9b + 6c - ab = 0$, $b - 2c - ab = 0$, and $-a + 2b - 2c = 1 \Rightarrow a = 3, b = 1$, and $c = -1 \Rightarrow y = \frac{x^2 + 3}{x - 1}$.

113. If $y = x^5 - 5x^4 - 240$, then $y' = 5x^3(x - 4)$ and $y'' = 20x^2(x - 3)$. The zeros of $y'$ are extrema, and there is a point of inflection at $x = 3$.

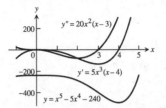

114. If $y = x^3 - 12x^2$, then $y' = 3x(x - 8)$ and $y'' = 6(x - 4)$. The zeros of $y'$ and $y''$ are extrema and points of inflection, respectively.

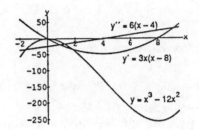

115. If $y = \frac{4}{5}x^5 + 16x^2 - 25$, then $y' = 4x(x^3 + 8)$ and $y'' = 16(x^3 + 2)$. The zeros of $y'$ and $y''$ are extrema and points of inflection, respectively.

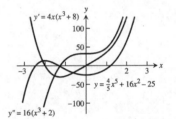

116. If $y = \frac{x^4}{4} - \frac{x^3}{3} - 4x^2 + 12x + 20$, then $y' = x^3 - x^2 - 8x + 12 = (x + 3)(x - 2)^2$.
So y has a local minimum at $x = -3$ as its only extreme value. Also $y'' = 3x^2 - 2x - 8 = (3x + 4)(x - 2)$ and there are inflection points at both zeros, $-\frac{4}{3}$ and 2, of $y''$.

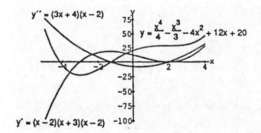

117. The graph of f falls where $f' < 0$, rises where $f' > 0$, and has horizontal tangents where $f' = 0$. It has local minima at points where $f'$ changes from negative to positive and local maxima where $f'$ changes from positive to negative. The graph of f is concave down where $f'' < 0$ and concave up where $f'' > 0$. It has an inflection point each time $f''$ changes sign, provided a tangent line exists there.

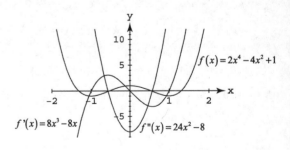

118. The graph f is concave down where $f'' < 0$, and concave
up where $f'' > 0$. It has an inflection point each time
$f''$ changes sign, provided a tangent line exists there.

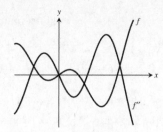

## 4.5 APPLIED OPTIMIZATION

1. Let $\ell$ and w represent the length and width of the rectangle, respectively. With an area of 16 in.$^2$, we have
that $(\ell)(w) = 16 \Rightarrow w = 16\ell^{-1} \Rightarrow$ the perimeter is $P = 2\ell + 2w = 2\ell + 32\ell^{-1}$ and $P'(\ell) = 2 - \frac{32}{\ell^2} = \frac{2(\ell^2 - 16)}{\ell^2}$.
Solving $P'(\ell) = 0 \Rightarrow \frac{2(\ell + 4)(\ell - 4)}{\ell^2} = 0 \Rightarrow \ell = -4, 4$. Since $\ell > 0$ for the length of a rectangle, $\ell$ must be 4 and
$w = 4 \Rightarrow$ the perimeter is 16 in., a minimum since $P''(\ell) = \frac{16}{\ell^3} > 0$.

2. Let x represent the length of the rectangle in meters ($0 < x < 4$) Then the width is $4 - x$ and the area is
$A(x) = x(4 - x) = 4x - x^2$. Since $A'(x) = 4 - 2x$, the critical point occurs at $x = 2$. Since, $A'(x) > 0$ for $0 < x < 2$ and
$A'(x) < 0$ for $2 < x < 4$, this critical point corresponds to the maximum area. The rectangle with the largest area measures
2 m by $4 - 2 = 2$ m, so it is a square.
Graphical Support:

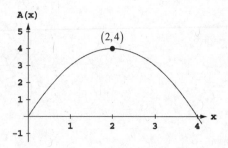

3. (a) The line containing point P also contains the points $(0, 1)$ and $(1, 0) \Rightarrow$ the line containing P is $y = 1 - x$
$\Rightarrow$ a general point on that line is $(x, 1 - x)$.
   (b) The area $A(x) = 2x(1 - x)$, where $0 \le x \le 1$.
   (c) When $A(x) = 2x - 2x^2$, then $A'(x) = 0 \Rightarrow 2 - 4x = 0 \Rightarrow x = \frac{1}{2}$. Since $A(0) = 0$ and $A(1) = 0$, we conclude
that $A\left(\frac{1}{2}\right) = \frac{1}{2}$ sq units is the largest area. The dimensions are 1 unit by $\frac{1}{2}$ unit.

4. The area of the rectangle is $A = 2xy = 2x\left(12 - x^2\right)$,
where $0 \le x \le \sqrt{12}$. Solving $A'(x) = 0 \Rightarrow 24 - 6x^2 = 0$
$\Rightarrow x = -2$ or 2. Now $-2$ is not in the domain, and since
$A(0) = 0$ and $A\left(\sqrt{12}\right) = 0$, we conclude that $A(2) = 32$
square units is the maximum area. The dimensions are 4 units
by 8 units.

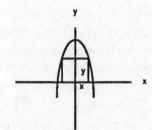

5. The volume of the box is $V(x) = x(15 - 2x)(8 - 2x)$
$= 120x - 46x^2 + 4x^3$, where $0 \le x \le 4$. Solving $V'(x) = 0$
$\Rightarrow 120 - 92x + 12x^2 = 4(6 - x)(5 - 3x) = 0 \Rightarrow x = \frac{5}{3}$
or 6, but 6 is not in the domain. Since $V(0) = V(4) = 0$,
$V\left(\frac{5}{3}\right) = \frac{2450}{27} \approx 91$ in$^3$ must be the maximum volume of
the box with dimensions $\frac{14}{3} \times \frac{35}{3} \times \frac{5}{3}$ inches.

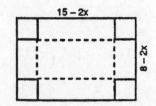

6. The area of the triangle is $A = \frac{1}{2}ba = \frac{b}{2}\sqrt{400 - b^2}$, where $0 \le b \le 20$. Then $\frac{dA}{db} = \frac{1}{2}\sqrt{400 - b^2} - \frac{b^2}{2\sqrt{400 - b^2}}$

$= \frac{200 - b^2}{\sqrt{400 - b^2}} = 0 \Rightarrow$ the interior critical point is $b = 10\sqrt{2}$.

When $b = 0$ or $20$, the area is zero $\Rightarrow A\left(10\sqrt{2}\right)$ is the

maximum area. When $a^2 + b^2 = 400$ and $b = 10\sqrt{2}$, the

value of a is also $10\sqrt{2} \Rightarrow$ the maximum area occurs when

$a = b$.

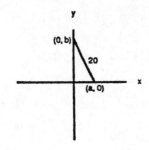

7. The area is $A(x) = x(800 - 2x)$, where $0 \le x \le 400$.
Solving $A'(x) = 800 - 4x = 0 \Rightarrow x = 200$. With
$A(0) = A(400) = 0$, the maximum area is
$A(200) = 80{,}000 \text{ m}^2$. The dimensions are 200 m by 400 m.

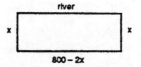

8. The area is $2xy = 216 \Rightarrow y = \frac{108}{x}$. The amount of fence
needed is $P = 4x + 3y = 4x + 324x^{-1}$, where $0 < x$;
$\frac{dP}{dx} = 4 - \frac{324}{x^2} = 0 \Rightarrow x^2 - 81 = 0 \Rightarrow$ the critical points are
0 and $\pm 9$, but 0 and $-9$ are not in the domain. Then
$P''(9) > 0 \Rightarrow$ at $x = 9$ there is a minimum $\Rightarrow$ the
dimensions of the outer rectangle are 18 m by 12 m
$\Rightarrow$ 72 meters of fence will be needed.

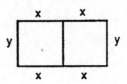

9. (a) We minimize the weight $= tS$ where S is the surface area, and t is the thickness of the steel walls of the tank. The surface area is $S = x^2 + 4xy$ where x is the length of a side of the square base of the tank, and y is its depth. The volume of the tank must be $500\text{ft}^3 \Rightarrow y = \frac{500}{x^2}$. Therefore, the weight of the tank is $w(x) = t\left(x^2 + \frac{2000}{x}\right)$. Treating the thickness as a constant gives $w'(x) = t\left(2x - \frac{2000}{x^2}\right)$. The critical value is at $x = 10$. Since $w''(10) = t\left(2 + \frac{4000}{10^3}\right) > 0$, there is a minimum at $x = 10$. Therefore, the optimum dimensions of the tank are 10 ft on the base edges and 5 ft deep.

(b) Minimizing the surface area of the tank minimizes its weight for a given wall thickness. The thickness of the steel walls would likely be determined by other considerations such as structural requirements.

10. (a) The volume of the tank being $1125 \text{ ft}^3$, we have that $yx^2 = 1125 \Rightarrow y = \frac{1125}{x^2}$. The cost of building the tank is $c(x) = 5x^2 + 30x\left(\frac{1125}{x^2}\right)$, where $0 < x$. Then $c'(x) = 10x - \frac{33750}{x^2} = 0 \Rightarrow$ the critical points are 0 and 15, but 0 is not in the domain. Thus, $c''(15) > 0 \Rightarrow$ at $x = 15$ we have a minimum. The values of $x = 15$ ft and $y = 5$ ft will minimize the cost.

(b) The cost function $c = 5(x^2 + 4xy) + 10xy$, can be separated into two items: (1) the cost of the materials and labor to fabricate the tank, and (2) the cost for the excavation. Since the area of the sides and bottom of the tanks is $(x^2 + 4xy)$, it can be deduced that the unit cost to fabricate the tanks is $\$5/\text{ft}^2$. Normally, excavation costs are per unit volume of excavated material. Consequently, the total excavation cost can be taken as $10xy = \left(\frac{10}{x}\right)(x^2y)$. This suggests that the unit cost of excavation is $\frac{\$10/\text{ft}^2}{x}$ where x is the length of a side of the square base of the tank in feet. For the least expensive tank, the unit cost for the excavation is $\frac{\$10/\text{ft}^2}{15 \text{ ft}} = \frac{\$0.67}{\text{ft}^3} = \frac{\$18}{\text{yd}^3}$. The total cost of the least expensive tank is $\$3375$, which is the sum of $\$2625$ for fabrication and $\$750$ for the excavation.

11. The area of the printing is $(y-4)(x-8) = 50$.
    Consequently, $y = \left(\frac{50}{x-8}\right) + 4$. The area of the paper is
    $A(x) = x\left(\frac{50}{x-8} + 4\right)$, where $8 < x$. Then
    $A'(x) = \left(\frac{50}{x-8} + 4\right) - x\left(\frac{50}{(x-8)^2}\right) = \frac{4(x-8)^2 - 400}{(x-8)^2} = 0$
    $\Rightarrow$ the critical points are $-2$ and $18$, but $-2$ is not in the
    domain. Thus $A''(18) > 0 \Rightarrow$ at $x = 18$ we have a minimum
    Therefore the dimensions 18 by 9 inches minimize the
    amount minimize the amount of paper.

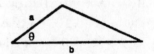

12. The volume of the cone is $V = \frac{1}{3}\pi r^2 h$, where $r = x = \sqrt{9-y^2}$ and $h = y + 3$ (from the figure in the text). Thus,
    $V(y) = \frac{\pi}{3}(9-y^2)(y+3) = \frac{\pi}{3}(27 + 9y - 3y^2 - y^3) \Rightarrow V'(y) = \frac{\pi}{3}(9 - 6y - 3y^2) = \pi(1-y)(3+y)$. The critical
    points are $-3$ and $1$, but $-3$ is not in the domain. Thus $V''(1) = \frac{\pi}{3}(-6 - 6(1)) < 0 \Rightarrow$ at $y = 1$ we have a maximum
    volume of $V(1) = \frac{\pi}{3}(8)(4) = \frac{32\pi}{3}$ cubic units.

13. The area of the triangle is $A(\theta) = \frac{ab \sin \theta}{2}$, where $0 < \theta < \pi$.
    Solving $A'(\theta) = 0 \Rightarrow \frac{ab \cos \theta}{2} = 0 \Rightarrow \theta = \frac{\pi}{2}$. Since $A''(\theta)$
    $= -\frac{ab \sin \theta}{2} \Rightarrow A''\left(\frac{\pi}{2}\right) < 0$, there is a maximum at $\theta = \frac{\pi}{2}$.

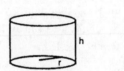

14. A volume $V = \pi r^2 h = 1000 \Rightarrow h = \frac{1000}{\pi r^2}$. The amount of
    material is the surface area given by the sides and bottom of
    the can $\Rightarrow S = 2\pi rh + \pi r^2 = \frac{2000}{r} + \pi r^2, 0 < r$. Then
    $\frac{dS}{dr} = -\frac{2000}{r^2} + 2\pi r = 0 \Rightarrow \frac{\pi r^3 - 1000}{r^2} = 0$. The critical points
    are 0 and $\frac{10}{\sqrt[3]{\pi}}$, but 0 is not in the domain. Since
    $\frac{d^2 S}{dr^2} = \frac{4000}{r^3} + 2\pi > 0$, we have a minimum surface area when
    $r = \frac{10}{\sqrt[3]{\pi}}$ cm and $h = \frac{1000}{\pi r^2} = \frac{10}{\sqrt[3]{\pi}}$ cm. Comparing this result to
    the result found in Example 2, if we include both ends of the
    can, then we have a minimum surface area when the can is
    shorter-specifically, when the height of the can is the same as
    its diameter.

15. With a volume of 1000 cm and $V = \pi r^2 h$, then $h = \frac{1000}{\pi r^2}$. The amount of aluminum used per can is
    $A = 8r^2 + 2\pi rh = 8r^2 + \frac{2000}{r}$. Then $A'(r) = 16r - \frac{2000}{r^2} = 0 \Rightarrow \frac{8r^3 - 1000}{r^2} = 0 \Rightarrow$ the critical points are 0 and 5,
    but $r = 0$ results in no can. Since $A''(r) = 16 + \frac{1000}{r^3} > 0$ we have a minimum at $r = 5 \Rightarrow h = \frac{40}{\pi}$ and $h:r = 8:\pi$.

16. (a)  The base measures $10 - 2x$ in. by $\frac{15-2x}{2}$ in., so the volume formula is $V(x) = \frac{x(10-2x)(15-2x)}{2} = 2x^3 - 25x^2 + 75x$.
    (b)  We require $x > 0$, $2x < 10$, and $2x < 15$. Combining these requirements, the domain is the interval $(0, 5)$.

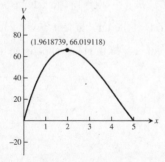

(c) The maximum volume is approximately 66.02 in.$^3$ when x $\approx$ 1.96 in.

(d) $V'(x) = 6x^2 - 50x + 75$. The critical point occurs when $V'(x) = 0$, at $x = \dfrac{50 \pm \sqrt{(-50)^2 - 4(6)(75)}}{2(6)} = \dfrac{50 \pm \sqrt{700}}{12}$

$= \dfrac{25 \pm 5\sqrt{7}}{6}$, that is, x $\approx$ 1.96 or x $\approx$ 6.37. We discard the larger value because it is not in the domain. Since $V''(x) = 12x - 50$, which is negative when x $\approx$ 1.96 , the critical point corresponds to the maximum volume. The maximum volume occurs when $x = \dfrac{25 - 5\sqrt{7}}{6} \approx 1.96$, which comfimrs the result in (c).

17. (a) The "sides" of the suitcase will measure $24 - 2x$ in. by $18 - 2x$ in. and will be 2x in. apart, so the volume formula is $V(x) = 2x(24 - 2x)(18 - 2x) = 8x^3 - 168x^2 + 862x$.

(b) We require x $>$ 0, 2x $<$ 18, and 2x $<$ 12. Combining these requirements, the domain is the interval (0, 9).

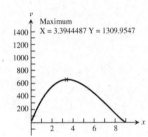

(c) The maximum volume is approximately 1309.95 in.$^3$ when x $\approx$ 3.39 in.

(d) $V'(x) = 24x^2 - 336x + 864 = 24(x^2 - 14x + 36)$. The critical point is at $x = \dfrac{14 \pm \sqrt{(-14)^2 - 4(1)(36)}}{2(1)} = \dfrac{14 \pm \sqrt{52}}{2}$

$= 7 \pm \sqrt{13}$, that is, x $\approx$ 3.39 or x $\approx$ 10.61. We discard the larger value because it is not in the domain. Since $V''(x) = 24(2x - 14)$ which is negative when x $\approx$ 3.39, the critical point corresponds to the maximum volume. The maximum value occurs at $x = 7 - \sqrt{13} \approx 3.39$, which confirms the results in (c).

(e) $8x^3 - 168x^2 + 862x = 1120 \Rightarrow 8(x^3 - 21x^2 + 108x - 140) = 0 \Rightarrow 8(x - 2)(x - 5)(x - 14) = 0$. Since 14 is not in the fomain, the possible values of x are x = 2 in. or x = 5 in.

(f) The dimensions of the resulting box are 2x in., $(24 - 2x)$ in., and $(18 - 2x)$. Each of these measurements must be positive, so that gives the domain of (0, 9).

18. If the upper right vertex of the rectangle is located at $(x, 4 \cos 0.5 x)$ for $0 < x < \pi$, then the rectangle has width 2x and height 4 cos 0.5x, so the area is $A(x) = 8x \cos 0.5x$. Solving $A'(x) = 0$ graphically for $0 < x < \pi$, we find that x $\approx$ 2.214. Evaluating 2x and 4 cos 0.5x for x $\approx$ 2.214, the dimensions of the rectangle are approximately 4.43 (width) by 1.79 (height), and the maximum area is approximately 7.923.

19. Let the radius of the cylinder be r cm, 0 $<$ r $<$ 10. Then the height is $2\sqrt{100 - r^2}$ and the volume is

$V(r) = 2\pi r^2 \sqrt{100 - r^2}$ cm$^3$. Then, $V'(r) = 2\pi r^2 \left(\dfrac{1}{\sqrt{100 - r^2}}\right)(-2r) + \left(2\pi \sqrt{100 - r^2}\right)(2r)$

$= \dfrac{-2\pi r^3 + 4\pi r(100 - r^2)}{\sqrt{100 - r^2}} = \dfrac{2\pi r(200 - 3r^2)}{\sqrt{100 - r^2}}$. The critical point for 0 $<$ r $<$ 10 occurs at $r = \sqrt{\dfrac{200}{3}} = 10\sqrt{\dfrac{2}{3}}$. Since $V'(r) > 0$ for

$0 < r < 10\sqrt{\dfrac{2}{3}}$ and $V'(r) < 0$ for $10\sqrt{\dfrac{2}{3}} < r < 10$, the critical point corresponds to the maximum volume. The

dimensions are $r = 10\sqrt{\dfrac{2}{3}} \approx 8.16$ cm and $h = \dfrac{20}{\sqrt{3}} \approx 11.55$ cm, and the volume is $\dfrac{4000\pi}{3\sqrt{3}} \approx 2418.40$ cm$^3$.

20. (a)  From the diagram we have $4x + \ell = 108$ and $V = x^2\ell$.
The volume of the box is $V(x) = x^2(108 - 4x)$, where
$0 \le x < 27$. Then
$V'(x) = 216x - 12x^2 = 12x(18 - x) = 0$
$\Rightarrow$ the critical points are 0 and 18, but $x = 0$ results in
no box. Since $V''(x) = 216 - 24x < 0$ at $x = 18$ we
have a maximum. The dimensions of the box are
$18 \times 18 \times 36$ in.

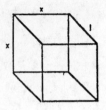

(b)  In terms of length, $V(\ell) = x^2\ell = \left(\frac{108 - \ell}{4}\right)^2 \ell$. The graph
indicates that the maximum volume occurs near $\ell = 36$,
which is consistent with the result of part (a).

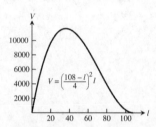

21. (a)  From the diagram we have $3h + 2w = 108$ and
$V = h^2w \Rightarrow V(h) = h^2\left(54 - \frac{3}{2}h\right) = 54h^2 - \frac{3}{2}h^3$.
Then $V'(h) = 108h - \frac{9}{2}h^2 = \frac{9}{2}h(24 - h) = 0$
$\Rightarrow h = 0$ or $h = 24$, but $h = 0$ results in no box. Since
$V''(h) = 108 - 9h < 0$ at $h = 24$, we have a maximum
volume at $h = 24$ and $w = 54 - \frac{3}{2}h = 18$.

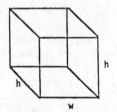

(b)

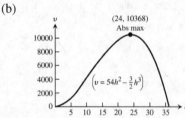

22.  From the diagram the perimeter is $P = 2r + 2h + \pi r$,
where r is the radius of the semicircle and h is the
height of the rectangle. The amount of light transmitted
proportional to
$A = 2rh + \frac{1}{4}\pi r^2 = r(P - 2r - \pi r) + \frac{1}{4}\pi r^2$
$= rP - 2r^2 - \frac{3}{4}\pi r^2$. Then $\frac{dA}{dr} = P - 4r - \frac{3}{2}\pi r = 0$
$\Rightarrow r = \frac{2P}{8 + 3\pi} \Rightarrow 2h = P - \frac{4P}{8 + 3\pi} - \frac{2\pi P}{8 + 3\pi} = \frac{(4 + \pi)P}{8 + 3\pi}$.
Therefore, $\frac{2r}{h} = \frac{8}{4 + \pi}$ gives the proportions that admit the
most light since $\frac{d^2A}{dr^2} = -4 - \frac{3}{2}\pi < 0$.

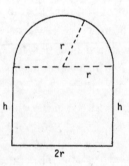

23.  The fixed volume is $V = \pi r^2 h + \frac{2}{3}\pi r^3 \Rightarrow h = \frac{V}{\pi r^2} - \frac{2r}{3}$, where h is the height of the cylinder and r is the radius
of the hemisphere. To minimize the cost we must minimize surface area of the cylinder added to twice the
surface area of the hemisphere. Thus, we minimize $C = 2\pi rh + 4\pi r^2 = 2\pi r\left(\frac{V}{\pi r^2} - \frac{2r}{3}\right) + 4\pi r^2 = \frac{2V}{r} + \frac{8}{3}\pi r^2$.
Then $\frac{dC}{dr} = -\frac{2V}{r^2} + \frac{16}{3}\pi r = 0 \Rightarrow V = \frac{8}{3}\pi r^3 \Rightarrow r = \left(\frac{3V}{8\pi}\right)^{1/3}$. From the volume equation, $h = \frac{V}{\pi r^2} - \frac{2r}{3}$
$= \frac{4V^{1/3}}{\pi^{1/3}\cdot 3^{2/3}} - \frac{2\cdot 3^{1/3}\cdot V^{1/3}}{3\cdot 2\cdot \pi^{1/3}} = \frac{3^{1/3}\cdot 2\cdot 4\cdot V^{1/3} - 2\cdot 3^{1/3}\cdot V^{1/3}}{3\cdot 2\cdot \pi^{1/3}} = \left(\frac{3V}{\pi}\right)^{1/3}$. Since $\frac{d^2C}{dr^2} = \frac{4V}{r^3} + \frac{16}{3}\pi > 0$, these
dimensions do minimize the cost.

24. The volume of the trough is maximized when the area of the cross section is maximized. From the diagram the area of the cross section is $A(\theta) = \cos\theta + \sin\theta\cos\theta$, $0 < \theta < \frac{\pi}{2}$. Then $A'(\theta) = -\sin\theta + \cos^2\theta - \sin^2\theta$

$= -(2\sin^2\theta + \sin\theta - 1) = -(2\sin\theta - 1)(\sin\theta + 1)$ so $A'(\theta) = 0 \Rightarrow \sin\theta = \frac{1}{2}$ or $\sin\theta = -1 \Rightarrow \theta = \frac{\pi}{6}$ because

$\sin\theta \neq -1$ when $0 < \theta < \frac{\pi}{2}$. Also, $A'(\theta) > 0$ for $0 < \theta < \frac{\pi}{6}$ and $A'(\theta) < 0$ for $\frac{\pi}{6} < \theta < \frac{\pi}{2}$. Therefore, at $\theta = \frac{\pi}{6}$ there is a maximum.

25. (a) From the diagram we have: $\overline{AP} = x$, $\overline{RA} = \sqrt{L - x^2}$,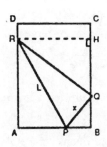

$\overline{PB} = 8.5 - x$, $\overline{CH} = \overline{DR} = 11 - \overline{RA} = 11 - \sqrt{L - x^2}$,

$\overline{QB} = \sqrt{x^2 - (8.5 - x)^2}$, $\overline{HQ} = 11 - \overline{CH} - \overline{QB}$

$= 11 - \left[11 - \sqrt{L - x^2} + \sqrt{x^2 - (8.5 - x)^2}\right]$

$= \sqrt{L - x^2} - \sqrt{x^2 - (8.5 - x)^2}$, $\overline{RQ}^2 = \overline{RH}^2 + \overline{HQ}^2$

$= (8.5)^2 + \left(\sqrt{L - x^2} - \sqrt{x^2 - (8.5 - x)^2}\right)^2$. It

follows that $\overline{RP}^2 = \overline{PQ}^2 + \overline{RQ}^2 \Rightarrow L^2 = x^2 + \left(\sqrt{L^2 - x^2} - \sqrt{x^2 - (x - 8.5)^2}\right)^2 + (8.5)^2$

$\Rightarrow L^2 = x^2 + L^2 - x^2 - 2\sqrt{L^2 - x^2}\sqrt{17x - (8.5)^2} + 17x - (8.5)^2 + (8.5)^2$

$\Rightarrow 17^2x^2 = 4(L^2 - x^2)(17x - (8.5)^2) \Rightarrow L^2 = x^2 + \frac{17^2x^2}{4[17x - (8.5)^2]} = \frac{17x^3}{17x - (8.5)^2} = \frac{17x^3}{17x - \left(\frac{17}{2}\right)^2}$

$= \frac{4x^3}{4x - 17} = \frac{2x^3}{2x - 8.5}$.

(b) If $f(x) = \frac{4x^3}{4x - 17}$ is minimized, then $L^2$ is minimized. Now $f'(x) = \frac{4x^2(8x - 51)}{(4x - 17)^2} \Rightarrow f'(x) < 0$ when $x < \frac{51}{8}$

and $f'(x) > 0$ when $x > \frac{51}{8}$. Thus $L^2$ is minimized when $x = \frac{51}{8}$.

(c) When $x = \frac{51}{8}$, then $L \approx 11.0$ in.

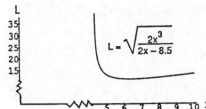

26. (a) From the figure in the text we have $P = 2x + 2y \Rightarrow y = \frac{P}{2} - x$. If $P = 36$, then $y = 18 - x$. When the cylinder is formed, $x = 2\pi r \Rightarrow r = \frac{x}{2\pi}$ and $h = y \Rightarrow h = 18 - x$. The volume of the cylinder is $V = \pi r^2 h$

$\Rightarrow V(x) = \frac{18x^2 - x^3}{4\pi}$. Solving $V'(x) = \frac{3x(12 - x)}{4\pi} = 0 \Rightarrow x = 0$ or $12$; but when $x = 0$, there is no cylinder. Then $V''(x) = \frac{3}{\pi}\left(3 - \frac{x}{2}\right) \Rightarrow V''(12) < 0 \Rightarrow$ there is a maximum at $x = 12$. The values of $x = 12$ cm and $y = 6$ cm give the largest volume.

(b) In this case $V(x) = \pi x^2(18 - x)$. Solving $V'(x) = 3\pi x(12 - x) = 0 \Rightarrow x = 0$ or $12$; but $x = 0$ would result in no cylinder. Then $V''(x) = 6\pi(6 - x) \Rightarrow V''(12) < 0 \Rightarrow$ there is a maximum at $x = 12$. The values of $x = 12$ cm and $y = 6$ cm give the largest volume.

27. Note that $h^2 + r^2 = 3$ and so $r = \sqrt{3 - h^2}$. Then the volume is given by $V = \frac{\pi}{3}r^2h = \frac{\pi}{3}(3 - h^2)h = \pi h - \frac{\pi}{3}h^3$ for $0 < h < \sqrt{3}$, and so $\frac{dV}{dh} = \pi - \pi r^2 = \pi(1 - r^2)$. The critical point (for $h > 0$) occurs at $h = 1$. Since $\frac{dV}{dh} > 0$ for $0 < h < 1$, and $\frac{dV}{dh} < 0$ for $1 < h < \sqrt{3}$, the critical point corresponds to the maximum volume. The cone of greatest volume has radius $\sqrt{2}$ m, height 1m, and volume $\frac{2\pi}{3}$ m$^3$.

28. Let $d = \sqrt{(x - 0)^2 + (y - 0)^2} = \sqrt{x^2 + y^2}$ and $\frac{x}{a} + \frac{y}{b} = 1 \Rightarrow y = -\frac{b}{a}x + b$. We can minimize $d$ by minimizing

$D = \left(\sqrt{x^2 + y^2}\right)^2 = x^2 + \left(-\frac{b}{a}x + b\right)^2 \Rightarrow D' = 2x + 2\left(-\frac{b}{a}x + b\right)\left(-\frac{b}{a}\right) = 2x + \frac{2b^2}{a^2}x - \frac{2b^2}{a}$. $D' = 0$

$\Rightarrow 2\left(x + \frac{b^2}{a^2}x - \frac{b^2}{a}\right) = 0 \Rightarrow x = \frac{ab^2}{a^2 + b^2}$ is the critical point $\Rightarrow y = -\frac{b}{a}\left(\frac{ab^2}{a^2 + b^2}\right) + b = \frac{a^2b}{a^2 + b^2}$.

$D'' = 2 + \frac{2b^2}{a^2} \Rightarrow D''\left(\frac{ab^2}{a^2+b^2}\right) = 2 + \frac{2b^2}{a^2} > 0 \Rightarrow$ the critical point is local minimum $\Rightarrow \left(\frac{ab^2}{a^2+b^2}, \frac{a^2b}{a^2+b^2}\right)$ is the point on the line $\frac{x}{a} + \frac{y}{b} = 1$ that is closest to the origin.

29. Let $S(x) = x + \frac{1}{x}, x > 0 \Rightarrow S'(x) = 1 - \frac{1}{x^2} = \frac{x^2-1}{x^2}$. $S'(x) = 0 \Rightarrow \frac{x^2-1}{x^2} = 0 \Rightarrow x^2 - 1 = 0 \Rightarrow x = \pm 1$. Since $x > 0$, we only consider $x = 1$. $S''(x) = \frac{2}{x^3} \Rightarrow S''(1) = \frac{2}{1^3} > 0 \Rightarrow$ local minimum when $x = 1$

30. Let $S(x) = \frac{1}{x} + 4x^2, x > 0 \Rightarrow S'(x) = -\frac{1}{x^2} + 8x = \frac{8x^3-1}{x^2}$. $S'(x) = 0 \Rightarrow \frac{8x^3-1}{x^2} = 0 \Rightarrow 8x^3 - 1 = 0 \Rightarrow x = \frac{1}{2}$. $S''(x) = \frac{2}{x^3} + 8 \Rightarrow S''\left(\frac{1}{2}\right) = \frac{2}{(1/2)^3} + 8 > 0 \Rightarrow$ local minimum when $x = \frac{1}{2}$.

31. The length of the wire $b =$ perimeter of the triangle $+$ circumference of the circle. Let $x =$ length of a side of the equilateral triangle $\Rightarrow P = 3x$, and let $r =$ radius of the circle $\Rightarrow C = 2\pi r$. Thus $b = 3x + 2\pi r \Rightarrow r = \frac{b-3x}{2\pi}$. The area of the circle is $\pi r^2$ and the area of an equilateral triangle whose sides are $x$ is $\frac{1}{2}(x)\left(\frac{\sqrt{3}}{2}x\right) = \frac{\sqrt{3}}{4}x^2$. Thus, the total area is given by $A = \frac{\sqrt{3}}{4}x^2 + \pi r^2 = \frac{\sqrt{3}}{4}x^2 + \pi\left(\frac{b-3x}{2\pi}\right)^2 = \frac{\sqrt{3}}{4}x^2 + \frac{(b-3x)^2}{4\pi} \Rightarrow A' = \frac{\sqrt{3}}{2}x - \frac{3}{2\pi}(b-3x) = \frac{\sqrt{3}}{2}x - \frac{3b}{2\pi} + \frac{9}{2\pi}x$
$A' = 0 \Rightarrow \frac{\sqrt{3}}{2}x - \frac{3b}{2\pi} + \frac{9}{2\pi}x = 0 \Rightarrow x = \frac{3b}{\sqrt{3}\pi+9}$. $A'' = \frac{\sqrt{3}}{2} + \frac{9}{2\pi} > 0 \Rightarrow$ local minimum at the critical point.
$P = 3\left(\frac{3b}{\sqrt{3}\pi+9}\right) = \frac{9b}{\sqrt{3}\pi+9}$ m is the length of the trianglular segment and $C = 2\pi\left(\frac{b-3x}{2\pi}\right) = b - 3x$
$= b - \frac{9b}{\sqrt{3}\pi+9} = \frac{\sqrt{3}\pi b}{\sqrt{3}\pi+9}$ m is the length of the circular segment.

32. The length of the wire $b =$ perimeter of the square $+$ circunference of the circle. Let $x =$ length of a side of the square $\Rightarrow P = 4x$, and let $r =$ radius of the circle $\Rightarrow C = 2\pi r$. Thus $b = 4x + 2\pi r \Rightarrow r = \frac{b-4x}{2\pi}$. The area of the circle is $\pi r^2$ and the area of a square whose sides are $x$ is $x^2$. Thus, the total area is given by $A = x^2 + \pi r^2$
$= x^2 + \pi\left(\frac{b-4x}{2\pi}\right)^2 = x^2 + \frac{(b-4x)^2}{4\pi} \Rightarrow A' = 2x - \frac{4}{2\pi}(b-4x) = 2x - \frac{2b}{\pi} + \frac{8}{\pi}x$, $A' = 0 \Rightarrow 2x - \frac{2b}{\pi} + \frac{8}{\pi}x = 0$
$\Rightarrow x = \frac{b}{4+\pi}$. $A'' = 2 + \frac{8}{\pi} > 0 \Rightarrow$ local minimum at the critical point. $P = 4\left(\frac{b}{4+\pi}\right) = \frac{4b}{4+\pi}$ m is the length of the square segment and $C = 2\pi\left(\frac{b-4x}{2\pi}\right) = b - 4x = b - \frac{4b}{4+\pi} = \frac{b\pi}{4+\pi}$ m is the length of the circular segment.

33. Let $(x, y) = \left(x, \frac{4}{3}x\right)$ be the coordinates of the corner that intersects the line. Then base $= 3 - x$ and height $= y = \frac{4}{3}x$, thus the area of therectangle is given by $A = (3-x)\left(\frac{4}{3}x\right) = 4x - \frac{4}{3}x^2, 0 \le x \le 3$. $A' = 4 - \frac{8}{3}x$, $A' = 0 \Rightarrow x = \frac{3}{2}$. $A'' = -\frac{4}{3}$
$\Rightarrow A''\left(\frac{3}{2}\right) < 0 \Rightarrow$ local maximum at the critical point. The base $= 3 - \frac{3}{2} = \frac{3}{2}$ and the height $= \frac{4}{3}\left(\frac{3}{2}\right) = 2$.

34. Let $(x, y) = \left(x, \sqrt{9 - x^2}\right)$ be the coordinates of the corner that intersects the semicircle. Then base $= 2x$ and height $= y$
$= \sqrt{9 - x^2}$, thus the area of the inscribed rectangle is given by $A = (2x)\sqrt{9 - x^2}, 0 \le x \le 3$. Then
$A' = 2\sqrt{9 - x^2} + (2x)\frac{-x}{\sqrt{9-x^2}} = \frac{2(9-x^2)-2x^2}{\sqrt{9-x^2}} = \frac{18-4x^2}{\sqrt{4-x^2}}$, $A' = 0 \Rightarrow 18 - 4x^2 = 0 \Rightarrow x = \pm\frac{3\sqrt{2}}{2}$, only $x = \frac{3\sqrt{2}}{2}$ lies in $0 \le x \le 3$. $A$ is continuous on the closed interval $0 \le x \le 3 \Rightarrow A$ has an absolute maxima and absolute minima. $A(0) = 0, A(3) = 0$, and $A\left(\frac{3\sqrt{2}}{2}\right) = \left(3\sqrt{2}\right)\left(\frac{3\sqrt{2}}{2}\right) = 9 \Rightarrow$ absolute maxima. Base of rectangle is $3\sqrt{2}$ and height is $\frac{3\sqrt{2}}{2}$.

35. (a) $f(x) = x^2 + \frac{a}{x} \Rightarrow f'(x) = x^{-2}\left(2x^3 - a\right)$, so that $f'(x) = 0$ when $x = 2$ implies $a = 16$
    (b) $f(x) = x^2 + \frac{a}{x} \Rightarrow f''(x) = 2x^{-3}\left(x^3 + a\right)$, so that $f''(x) = 0$ when $x = 1$ implies $a = -1$

36. If $f(x) = x^3 + ax^2 + bx$, then $f'(x) = 3x^2 + 2ax + b$ and $f''(x) = 6x + 2a$.

    (a) A local maximum at $x = -1$ and local minimum at $x = 3 \Rightarrow f'(-1) = 0$ and $f'(3) = 0 \Rightarrow 3 - 2a + b = 0$ and $27 + 6a + b = 0 \Rightarrow a = -3$ and $b = -9$.

    (b) A local minimum at $x = 4$ and a point of inflection at $x = 1 \Rightarrow f'(4) = 0$ and $f''(1) = 0 \Rightarrow 48 + 8a + b = 0$ and $6 + 2a = 0 \Rightarrow a = -3$ and $b = -24$.

37. (a) $s(t) = -16t^2 + 96t + 112 \Rightarrow v(t) = s'(t) = -32t + 96$. At $t = 0$, the velocity is $v(0) = 96$ ft/sec.

    (b) The maximum height ocurs when $v(t) = 0$, when $t = 3$. The maximum height is $s(3) = 256$ ft and it occurs at $t = 3$ sec.

    (c) Note that $s(t) = -16t^2 + 96t + 112 = -16(t + 1)(t - 7)$, so $s = 0$ at $t = -1$ or $t = 7$. Choosing the positive value of $t$, the velocity when $s = 0$ is $v(7) = -128$ ft/sec.

38.

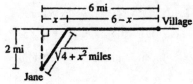

Let $x$ be the distance from the point on the shoreline nearest Jane's boat to the point where she lands her boat. Then she needs to row $\sqrt{4 + x^2}$ mi at 2 mph and walk $6 - x$ mi at 5 mph. The total amount of time to reach the village is

$f(x) = \frac{\sqrt{4 + x^2}}{2} + \frac{6 - x}{5}$ hours $(0 \le x \le 6)$. Then $f'(x) = \frac{1}{2} \frac{1}{2\sqrt{4 + x^2}} (2x) - \frac{1}{5} = \frac{x}{2\sqrt{4 + x^2}} - \frac{1}{5}$. Solving $f'(x) = 0$, we

have: $\frac{x}{2\sqrt{4 + x^2}} = \frac{1}{5} \Rightarrow 5x = 2\sqrt{4 + x^2} \Rightarrow 25x^2 = 4(4 + x^2) \Rightarrow 21x^2 = 16 \Rightarrow x = \pm \frac{4}{\sqrt{21}}$. We discard the negative

value of $x$ because it is not in the domain. Checking the endpoints and critical point, we have $f(0) = 2.2$,

$f\left(\frac{4}{\sqrt{21}}\right) \approx 2.12$, and $f(6) \approx 3.16$. Jane should land her boat $\frac{4}{\sqrt{21}} \approx 0.87$ miles down the shoreline from the point nearest her boat.

39. $\frac{8}{x} = \frac{h}{x + 27} \Rightarrow h = 8 + \frac{216}{x}$ and $L(x) = \sqrt{h^2 + (x + 27)^2}$

    $= \sqrt{\left(8 + \frac{216}{x}\right)^2 + (x + 27)^2}$ when $x \ge 0$. Note that $L(x)$ is

    minimized when $f(x) = \left(8 + \frac{216}{x}\right)^2 + (x + 27)^2$ is

    minimized. If $f'(x) = 0$, then

    $2\left(8 + \frac{216}{x}\right)\left(-\frac{216}{x^2}\right) + 2(x + 27) = 0$

    $\Rightarrow (x + 27)\left(1 - \frac{1728}{x^3}\right) = 0 \Rightarrow x = -27$ (not acceptable

    since distance is never negative or $x = 12$. Then $L(12) = \sqrt{2197} \approx 46.87$ ft.

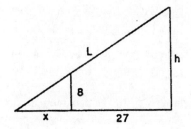

40. (a) $s_1 = s_2 \Rightarrow \sin t = \sin\left(t + \frac{\pi}{3}\right) \Rightarrow \sin t = \sin t \cos \frac{\pi}{3} + \sin \frac{\pi}{3} \cos t \Rightarrow \sin t = \frac{1}{2} \sin t + \frac{\sqrt{3}}{2} \cos t \Rightarrow \tan t = \sqrt{3}$

    $\Rightarrow t = \frac{\pi}{3}$ or $\frac{4\pi}{3}$

    (b) The distance between the particles is $s(t) = |s_1 - s_2| = \left|\sin t - \sin\left(t + \frac{\pi}{3}\right)\right| = \frac{1}{2}\left|\sin t - \sqrt{3} \cos t\right|$

    $\Rightarrow s'(t) = \frac{\left(\sin t - \sqrt{3} \cos t\right)\left(\cos t + \sqrt{3} \sin t\right)}{2\left|\sin t - \sqrt{3} \cos t\right|}$ since $\frac{d}{dx}|x| = \frac{x}{|x|} \Rightarrow$ critical times and endpoints are $0, \frac{\pi}{3}, \frac{5\pi}{6}, \frac{4\pi}{3}, \frac{11\pi}{6}, 2\pi$;

    then $s(0) = \frac{\sqrt{3}}{2}$, $s\left(\frac{\pi}{3}\right) = 0$, $s\left(\frac{5\pi}{6}\right) = 1$, $s\left(\frac{4\pi}{3}\right) = 0$, $s\left(\frac{11\pi}{6}\right) = 1$, $s(2\pi) = \frac{\sqrt{3}}{2} \Rightarrow$ the greatest distance between the particles is 1.

    (c) Since $s'(t) = \frac{\left(\sin t - \sqrt{3} \cos t\right)\left(\cos t + \sqrt{3} \sin t\right)}{2\left|\sin t - \sqrt{3} \cos t\right|}$ we can conclude that at $t = \frac{\pi}{3}$ and $\frac{4\pi}{3}$, $s'(t)$ has cusps and the distance

    between the particles is changing the fastest near these points.

41. $I = \frac{k}{d^2}$, let x = distance the point is from the stronger light source $\Rightarrow$ 6 − x = distance the point is from the other light source. The intensity of illumination at the point from the stronger light is $I_1 = \frac{k_1}{x^2}$, and intensity of illumination at the point from the weaker light is $I_2 = \frac{k_2}{(6-x)^2}$. Since the intensity of the first light is eight times the intensity of the second light $\Rightarrow k_1 = 8k_2$. $\Rightarrow I_1 = \frac{8k_2}{x^2}$. The total intensity is given by $I = I_1 + I_2 = \frac{8k_2}{x^2} + \frac{k_2}{(6-x)^2} \Rightarrow I' = -\frac{16k_2}{x^3} + \frac{2k_2}{(6-x)^3}$

$= \frac{-16(6-x)^3 k_2 + 2x^3 k_2}{x^3(6-x)^3}$ and $I' = 0 \Rightarrow \frac{-16(6-x)^3 k_2 + 2x^3 k_2}{x^3(6-x)^3} = 0 \Rightarrow -16(6-x)^3 k_2 + 2x^3 k_2 = 0 \Rightarrow x = 4$ m. $I'' = \frac{48k_2}{x^4} + \frac{6k_2}{(6-x)^4}$

$\Rightarrow I''(4) = \frac{48k_2}{4^4} + \frac{6k_2}{(6-4)^4} > 0 \Rightarrow$ local minimum. The point should be 4 m from the stronger light source.

42. $R = \frac{v_0^2}{g}\sin 2\alpha \Rightarrow \frac{dR}{d\alpha} = \frac{2v_0^2}{g}\cos 2\alpha$ and $\frac{dR}{d\alpha} = 0 \Rightarrow \frac{2v_0^2}{g}\cos 2\alpha = 0 \Rightarrow \alpha = \frac{\pi}{4}$. $\frac{d^2R}{d\alpha^2} = -\frac{4v_0^2}{g}\sin 2\alpha \Rightarrow \frac{d^2R}{d\alpha^2}\Big|_{\alpha=\frac{\pi}{4}} = -\frac{4v_0^2}{g}\sin 2\left(\frac{\pi}{4}\right)$

$= -\frac{4v_0^2}{g} < 0 \Rightarrow$ local maximum. Thus, the firing angle of $\alpha = \frac{\pi}{4} = 45°$ will maximize the range R.

43. (a) From the diagram we have $d^2 = 4r^2 - w^2$. The strength of the beam is $S = kwd^2 = kw(4r^2 - w^2)$. When r = 6, then $S = 144kw - kw^3$. Also, $S'(w) = 144k - 3kw^2 = 3k(48 - w^2)$ so $S'(w) = 0 \Rightarrow w = \pm 4\sqrt{3}$; $S''(4\sqrt{3}) < 0$ and $-4\sqrt{3}$ is not acceptable. Therefore $S(4\sqrt{3})$ is the maximum strength. The dimensions of the strongest beam are $4\sqrt{3}$ by $4\sqrt{6}$ inches.

(b) 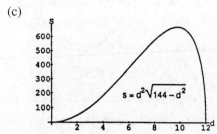     (c)

Both graphs indicate the same maximum value and are consistent with each other. Changing k does not change the dimensions that give the strongest beam (i.e., do not change the values of w and d that produce the strongest beam).

44. (a) From the situation we have $w^2 = 144 - d^2$. The stiffness of the beam is $S = kwd^3 = kd^3(144 - d^2)^{1/2}$, where $0 \le d \le 12$. Also, $S'(d) = \frac{4kd^2(108 - d^2)}{\sqrt{144 - d^2}} \Rightarrow$ critical points at 0, 12, and $6\sqrt{3}$. Both d = 0 and d = 12 cause S = 0. The maximum occurs at $d = 6\sqrt{3}$. The dimensions are 6 by $6\sqrt{3}$ inches.

(b) 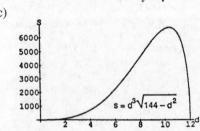     (c)

Both graphs indicate the same maximum value and are consistent with each other. The changing of k has no effect.

45. (a) $s = 10\cos(\pi t) \Rightarrow v = -10\pi\sin(\pi t) \Rightarrow$ speed $= |10\pi\sin(\pi t)| = 10\pi|\sin(\pi t)| \Rightarrow$ the maximum speed is $10\pi \approx 31.42$ cm/sec since the maximum value of $|\sin(\pi t)|$ is 1; the cart is moving the fastest at t = 0.5 sec, 1.5 sec, 2.5 sec and 3.5 sec when $|\sin(\pi t)|$ is 1. At these times the distance is $s = 10\cos\left(\frac{\pi}{2}\right) = 0$ cm and $a = -10\pi^2\cos(\pi t) \Rightarrow |a| = 10\pi^2|\cos(\pi t)| \Rightarrow |a| = 0$ cm/sec$^2$

(b) $|a| = 10\pi^2|\cos(\pi t)|$ is greatest at t = 0.0 sec, 1.0 sec, 2.0 sec, 3.0 sec and 4.0 sec, and at these times the magnitude of the cart's position is $|s| = 10$ cm from the rest position and the speed is 0 cm/sec.

46. (a)  $2 \sin t = \sin 2t \Rightarrow 2 \sin t - 2 \sin t \cos t = 0 \Rightarrow (2 \sin t)(1 - \cos t) = 0 \Rightarrow t = k\pi$ where k is a positive integer

(b)  The vertical distance between the masses is $s(t) = |s_1 - s_2| = \left((s_1 - s_2)^2\right)^{1/2} = \left((\sin 2t - 2 \sin t)^2\right)^{1/2}$

$\Rightarrow s'(t) = \left(\frac{1}{2}\right) \left((\sin 2t - 2 \sin t)^2\right)^{-1/2} (2)(\sin 2t - 2 \sin t)(2 \cos 2t - 2 \cos t) = \frac{2(\cos 2t - \cos t)(\sin 2t - 2 \sin t)}{|\sin 2t - 2 \sin t|}$

$= \frac{4(2 \cos t + 1)(\cos t - 1)(\sin t)(\cos t - 1)}{|\sin 2t - 2 \sin t|} \Rightarrow$ critical times at $0, \frac{2\pi}{3}, \pi, \frac{4\pi}{3}, 2\pi$; then $s(0) = 0$,

$s\left(\frac{2\pi}{3}\right) = \left|\sin\left(\frac{4\pi}{3}\right) - 2 \sin\left(\frac{2\pi}{3}\right)\right| = \frac{3\sqrt{3}}{2}$, $s(\pi) = 0$, $s\left(\frac{4\pi}{3}\right) = \left|\sin\left(\frac{8\pi}{3}\right) - 2 \sin\left(\frac{4\pi}{3}\right)\right| = \frac{3\sqrt{3}}{2}$, $s(2\pi) = 0$

$\Rightarrow$ the greatest distance is $\frac{3\sqrt{3}}{2}$ at $t = \frac{2\pi}{3}$ and $\frac{4\pi}{3}$

47. (a)  $s = \sqrt{(12 - 12t)^2 + (8t)^2} = \left((12 - 12t)^2 + 64t^2\right)^{1/2}$

(b)  $\frac{ds}{dt} = \frac{1}{2}\left((12 - 12t)^2 + 64t^2\right)^{-1/2}[2(12 - 12t)(-12) + 128t] = \frac{208t - 144}{\sqrt{(12 - 12t)^2 + 64t^2}} \Rightarrow \frac{ds}{dt}\big|_{t=0} = -12$ knots and

$\frac{ds}{dt}\big|_{t=1} = 8$ knots

(c)  The graph indicates that the ships did not see each other because $s(t) > 5$ for all values of t.

(d)  The graph supports the conclusions in parts (b) and (c).

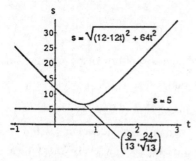

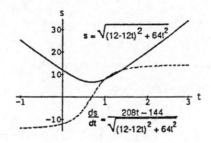

(e)  $\lim_{t \to \infty} \frac{ds}{dt} = \sqrt{\lim_{t \to \infty} \frac{(208t - 144)^2}{144(1 - t)^2 + 64t^2}} = \sqrt{\lim_{t \to \infty} \frac{\left(208 - \frac{144}{t}\right)^2}{144\left(\frac{1}{t} - 1\right)^2 + 64}} = \sqrt{\frac{208^2}{144 + 64}} = \sqrt{208} = 4\sqrt{13}$

which equals the square root of the sums of the squares of the individual speeds.

48.  The distance $\overline{OT} + \overline{TB}$ is minimized when $\overline{OB}$ is a straight line. Hence $\angle\alpha = \angle\beta \Rightarrow \theta_1 = \theta_2$.

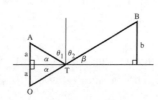

49.  If $v = kax - kx^2$, then $v' = ka - 2kx$ and $v'' = -2k$, so $v' = 0 \Rightarrow x = \frac{a}{2}$. At $x = \frac{a}{2}$ there is a maximum since $v''\left(\frac{a}{2}\right) = -2k < 0$. The maximum value of v is $\frac{ka^2}{4}$.

50. (a)  According to the graph, $y'(0) = 0$.

(b)  According to the graph, $y'(-L) = 0$.

(c)  $y(0) = 0$, so $d = 0$. Now $y'(x) = 3ax^2 + 2bx + c$, so $y'(0) = 0$ implies that $c = 0$. There fore, $y(x) = ax^3 + bx^2$ and $y'(x) = 3ax^2 + 2bx$. Then $y(-L) = -aL^3 + bL^2 = H$ and $y'(-L) = 3aL^2 - 2bL = 0$, so we have two linear equations in two unknowns a and b. The second equation gives $b = \frac{3aL}{2}$. Substituting into the first equation, we have $-aL^3 + \frac{3aL^3}{2} = H$, or $\frac{aL^3}{2} = H$, so $a = 2\frac{H}{L^3}$. Therefore, $b = 3\frac{H}{L^2}$ and the equation for y is $y(x) = 2\frac{H}{L^3}x^3 + 3\frac{H}{L^2}x^2$, or $y(x) = H\left[2\left(\frac{x}{L}\right)^3 + 3\left(\frac{x}{L}\right)^2\right]$.

51. The profit is $p = nx - nc = n(x - c) = [a(x - c)^{-1} + b(100 - x)](x - c) = a + b(100 - x)(x - c)$
    $= a + (bc + 100b)x - 100bc - bx^2$. Then $p'(x) = bc + 100b - 2bx$ and $p''(x) = -2b$. Solving $p'(x) = 0 \Rightarrow x = \frac{c}{2} + 50$.
    At $x = \frac{c}{2} + 50$ there is a maximum profit since $p''(x) = -2b < 0$ for all x.

52. Let x represent the number of people over 50. The profit is $p(x) = (50 + x)(200 - 2x) - 32(50 + x) - 6000$
    $= -2x^2 + 68x + 2400$. Then $p'(x) = -4x + 68$ and $p'' = -4$. Solving $p'(x) = 0 \Rightarrow x = 17$. At $x = 17$ there is a
    maximum since $p''(17) < 0$. It would take 67 people to maximize the profit.

53. (a) $A(q) = kmq^{-1} + cm + \frac{h}{2}q$, where $q > 0 \Rightarrow A'(q) = -kmq^{-2} + \frac{h}{2} = \frac{hq^2 - 2km}{2q^2}$ and $A''(q) = 2kmq^{-3}$. The
    critical points are $-\sqrt{\frac{2km}{h}}$, 0, and $\sqrt{\frac{2km}{h}}$, but only $\sqrt{\frac{2km}{h}}$ is in the domain. Then $A''\left(\sqrt{\frac{2km}{h}}\right) > 0 \Rightarrow$ at
    $q = \sqrt{\frac{2km}{h}}$ there is a minimum average weekly cost.

    (b) $A(q) = \frac{(k+bq)m}{q} + cm + \frac{h}{2}q = kmq^{-1} + bm + cm + \frac{h}{2}q$, where $q > 0 \Rightarrow A'(q) = 0$ at $q = \sqrt{\frac{2km}{h}}$ as in (a).
    Also $A''(q) = 2kmq^{-3} > 0$ so the most economical quantity to order is still $q = \sqrt{\frac{2km}{h}}$ which minimizes the
    average weekly cost.

54. We start with $c(x) =$ the cost of producing x items, $x > 0$, and $\frac{c(x)}{x} =$ the average cost of producing x items, assumed to
    be differentiable. If the average cost can be minimized, it will be at a production level at which $\frac{d}{dx}\left(\frac{c(x)}{x}\right) = 0$
    $\Rightarrow \frac{x\,c'(x) - c(x)}{x^2} = 0$ (by the quotient rule) $\Rightarrow x\,c'(x) - c(x) = 0$ (multiply both sides by $x^2$) $\Rightarrow c'(x) = \frac{c(x)}{x}$ where $c'(x)$ is
    the marginal cost. This concludes the proof. (Note: The theorem does not assure a production level that will give a
    minimum cost, but rather, it indicates where to look to see if there is one. Find the production levels where the average cost
    equals the marginal cost, then check to see if any of them give a mimimum.)

55. The profit $p(x) = r(x) - c(x) = 6x - (x^3 - 6x^2 + 15x) = -x^3 + 6x^2 - 9x$, where $x \geq 0$. Then $p'(x) = -3x^2 + 12x - 9$
    $= -3(x - 3)(x - 1)$ and $p''(x) = -6x + 12$. The critical points are 1 and 3. Thus $p''(1) = 6 > 0 \Rightarrow$ at $x = 1$ there is a
    local minimum, and $p''(3) = -6 < 0 \Rightarrow$ at $x = 3$ there is a local maximum. But $p(3) = 0 \Rightarrow$ the best you can do is
    break even.

56. The average cost of producing x items is $\bar{c}(x) = \frac{c(x)}{x} = x^2 - 20x + 20,000 \Rightarrow \bar{c}'(x) = 2x - 20 = 0 \Rightarrow x = 10$, the
    only critical value. The average cost is $\bar{c}(10) = \$19,900$ per item is a minimum cost because $\bar{c}''(10) = 2 > 0$.

57. Let x = the length of a side of the square base of the box and h = the height of the box. $V = x^2h = 48 \Rightarrow h = \frac{48}{x^2}$. The
    total cost is given by $C = 6 \cdot x^2 + 4(4 \cdot xh) = 6x^2 + 16x\left(\frac{48}{x^2}\right) = 6x^2 + \frac{768}{x}$, $x > 0 \Rightarrow C' = 12x - \frac{768}{x^2} = \frac{12x^3 - 768}{x^2}$
    $C' = 0 \Rightarrow \frac{12x^3 - 768}{x^2} = 0 \Rightarrow 12x^3 - 768 = 0 \Rightarrow x = 4$; $C'' = 12 + \frac{1536}{x^2} \Rightarrow C''(4) = 12 + \frac{1536}{4^2} > 0 \Rightarrow$ local minimum.
    $x = 4 \Rightarrow h = \frac{48}{4^2} = 3$ and $C(4) = 6(4)^2 + \frac{768}{4} = 288 \Rightarrow$ the box is 4 ft $\times$ 4 ft $\times$ 3 ft, with a minimum cost of \$288

58. Let x = the number of \$10 increases in the charge per room, then price per room = $50 + 10x$, and the number of rooms
    filled each night $= 800 - 40x \Rightarrow$ the total revenue is $R(x) = (50 + 10x)(800 - 40x) = -400x^2 + 6000x + 40000$,
    $0 \leq x \leq 20 \Rightarrow R'(x) = -800x + 6000$; $R'(x) = 0 \Rightarrow -800x + 6000 = 0 \Rightarrow x = \frac{15}{2}$; $R''(x) = -800$
    $\Rightarrow R''\left(\frac{15}{2}\right) = -800 < 0 \Rightarrow$ local maximum. The price per room is $50 + 10\left(\frac{15}{2}\right) = \$125$.

59. We have $\frac{dR}{dM} = CM - M^2$. Solving $\frac{d^2R}{dM^2} = C - 2M = 0 \Rightarrow M = \frac{C}{2}$. Also, $\frac{d^3R}{dM^3} = -2 < 0 \Rightarrow$ at $M = \frac{C}{2}$ there is a
    maximum.

60. (a) If $v = cr_0 r^2 - cr^3$, then $v' = 2cr_0 r - 3cr^2 = cr(2r_0 - 3r)$ and $v'' = 2cr_0 - 6cr = 2c(r_0 - 3r)$. The solution of $v' = 0$ is $r = 0$ or $\frac{2r_0}{3}$, but 0 is not in the domain. Also, $v' > 0$ for $r < \frac{2r_0}{3}$ and $v' < 0$ for $r > \frac{2r_0}{3}$ $\Rightarrow$ at $r = \frac{2r_0}{3}$ there is a maximum.

(b) The graph confirms the findings in (a).

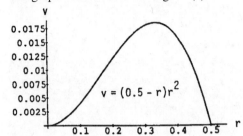

61. If $x > 0$, then $(x-1)^2 \geq 0 \Rightarrow x^2 + 1 \geq 2x \Rightarrow \frac{x^2+1}{x} \geq 2$. In particular if a, b, c and d are positive integers, then $\left(\frac{a^2+1}{a}\right)\left(\frac{b^2+1}{b}\right)\left(\frac{c^2+1}{c}\right)\left(\frac{d^2+1}{d}\right) \geq 16$.

62. (a) $f(x) = \frac{x}{\sqrt{a^2+x^2}} \Rightarrow f'(x) = \frac{(a^2+x^2)^{1/2} - x^2(a^2+x^2)^{-1/2}}{(a^2+x^2)} = \frac{a^2+x^2-x^2}{(a^2+x^2)^{3/2}} = \frac{a^2}{(a^2+x^2)^{3/2}} > 0$

$\Rightarrow$ $f(x)$ is an increasing function of x

(b) $g(x) = \frac{d-x}{\sqrt{b^2+(d-x)^2}} \Rightarrow g'(x) = \frac{-(b^2+(d-x)^2)^{1/2} + (d-x)^2(b^2+(d-x)^2)^{-1/2}}{b^2+(d-x)^2}$

$= \frac{-(b^2+(d-x)^2)+(d-x)^2}{(b^2+(d-x)^2)^{3/2}} = \frac{-b^2}{(b^2+(d-x)^2)^{3/2}} < 0 \Rightarrow$ $g(x)$ is a decreasing function of x

(c) Since $c_1, c_2 > 0$, the derivative $\frac{dt}{dx}$ is an increasing function of x (from part (a)) minus a decreasing function of x (from part (b)): $\frac{dt}{dx} = \frac{1}{c_1}f(x) - \frac{1}{c_2}g(x) \Rightarrow \frac{d^2t}{dx^2} = \frac{1}{c_1}f'(x) - \frac{1}{c_2}g'(x) > 0$ since $f'(x) > 0$ and $g'(x) < 0 \Rightarrow \frac{dt}{dx}$ is an increasing function of x.

63. At $x = c$, the tangents to the curves are parallel. Justification: The vertical distance between the curves is $D(x) = f(x) - g(x)$, so $D'(x) = f'(x) - g'(x)$. The maximum value of D will occur at a point c where $D' = 0$. At such a point, $f'(c) - g'(c) = 0$, or $f'(c) = g'(c)$.

64. (a) $f(x) = 3 + 4\cos x + \cos 2x$ is a periodic function with period $2\pi$

(b) No, $f(x) = 3 + 4\cos x + \cos 2x = 3 + 4\cos x + (2\cos^2 x - 1) = 2(1 + 2\cos x + \cos^2 x) = 2(1 + \cos x)^2 \geq 0$

$\Rightarrow$ $f(x)$ is never negative.

65. (a) If $y = \cot x - \sqrt{2}\csc x$ where $0 < x < \pi$, then $y' = (\csc x)\left(\sqrt{2}\cot x - \csc x\right)$. Solving $y' = 0 \Rightarrow \cos x = \frac{1}{\sqrt{2}}$ $\Rightarrow x = \frac{\pi}{4}$. For $0 < x < \frac{\pi}{4}$ we have $y' > 0$, and $y' < 0$ when $\frac{\pi}{4} < x < \pi$. Therefore, at $x = \frac{\pi}{4}$ there is a maximum value of $y = -1$.

(b)

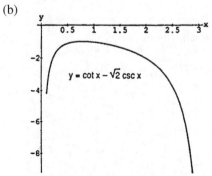

The graph confirms the findings in (a).

66. (a) If $y = \tan x + 3 \cot x$ where $0 < x < \frac{\pi}{2}$, then $y' = \sec^2 x - 3 \csc^2 x$. Solving $y' = 0 \Rightarrow \tan x = \pm \sqrt{3}$

$\Rightarrow x = \pm \frac{\pi}{3}$, but $-\frac{\pi}{3}$ is not in the domain. Also, $y'' = 2 \sec^2 x \tan x + 6 \csc^2 x \cot x > 0$ for all $0 < x < \frac{\pi}{2}$.

Therefore at $x = \frac{\pi}{3}$ there is a minimum value of $y = 2\sqrt{3}$.

(b)

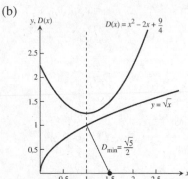

The graph confirms the findings in (a).

67. (a) The square of the distance is $D(x) = \left(x - \frac{3}{2}\right)^2 + \left(\sqrt{x} + 0\right)^2 = x^2 - 2x + \frac{9}{4}$, so $D'(x) = 2x - 2$ and the critical

point occurs at $x = 1$. Since $D'(x) < 0$ for $x < 1$ and $D'(x) > 0$ for $x > 1$, the critical point corresponds to the

minimum distance. The minimum distance is $\sqrt{D(1)} = \frac{\sqrt{5}}{2}$.

(b)

The minimum distance is from the point $\left(\frac{3}{2}, 0\right)$ to the point $(1, 1)$ on the graph of $y = \sqrt{x}$, and this occurs at the

value $x = 1$ where $D(x)$, the distance squared, has its minimum value.

68. (a) Calculus Method:

The square of the distance from the point $\left(1, \sqrt{3}\right)$ to $\left(x, \sqrt{16 - x^2}\right)$ is given by

$D(x) = (x - 1)^2 + \left(\sqrt{16 - x^2} - \sqrt{3}\right)^2 = x^2 - 2x + 1 + 16 - x^2 - 2\sqrt{48 - 3x^2} + 3 = -2x + 20 - 2\sqrt{48 - 3x^2}$.

Then $D'(x) = -2 - \frac{1}{2} \cdot \frac{2}{\sqrt{48 - 3x^2}}(-6x) = -2 + \frac{6x}{\sqrt{48 - 3x^2}}$. Solving $D'(x) = 0$ we have: $6x = 2\sqrt{48 - 3x^2}$

$\Rightarrow 36x^2 = 4(48 - 3x^2) \Rightarrow 9x^2 = 48 - 3x^2 \Rightarrow 12x^2 = 48 \Rightarrow x = \pm 2$. We discard $x = -2$ as an extraneous solution,

leaving $x = 2$. Since $D'(x) < 0$ for $-4 < x < 2$ and $D'(x) > 0$ for $2 < x < 4$, the critical point corresponds to the

minimum distance. The minimum distance is $\sqrt{D(2)} = 2$.

Geometry Method:

The semicircle is centered at the origin and has radius 4. The distance from the origin to $\left(1, \sqrt{3}\right)$ is

$\sqrt{1^2 + \left(\sqrt{3}\right)^2} = 2$. The shortest distance from the point to the semicircle is the distance along the radius

containing the point $\left(1, \sqrt{3}\right)$. That distance is $4 - 2 = 2$.

(b)

The minimum distance is from the point $\left(1, \sqrt{3}\right)$ to the point $\left(2, 2\sqrt{3}\right)$ on the graph of $y = \sqrt{16 - x^2}$, and this occurs at the value $x = 2$ where $D(x)$, the distance squared, has its minimum value.

## 4.6 NEWTON'S METHOD

1. $y = x^2 + x - 1 \Rightarrow y' = 2x + 1 \Rightarrow x_{n+1} = x_n - \frac{x_n^2 + x_n - 1}{2x_n + 1}$ ; $x_0 = 1 \Rightarrow x_1 = 1 - \frac{1+1-1}{2+1} = \frac{2}{3}$

$\Rightarrow x_2 = \frac{2}{3} - \frac{\frac{4}{9} + \frac{2}{3} - 1}{\frac{4}{3} + 1} \Rightarrow x_2 = \frac{2}{3} - \frac{4+6-9}{12+9} = \frac{2}{3} - \frac{1}{21} = \frac{13}{21} \approx .61905$; $x_0 = -1 \Rightarrow x_1 = 1 - \frac{1-1-1}{-2+1} = -2$

$\Rightarrow x_2 = -2 - \frac{4-2-1}{-4+1} = -\frac{5}{3} \approx -1.66667$

2. $y = x^3 + 3x + 1 \Rightarrow y' = 3x^2 + 3 \Rightarrow x_{n+1} = x_n - \frac{x_n^3 + 3x_n + 1}{3x_n^2 + 3}$ ; $x_0 = 0 \Rightarrow x_1 = 0 - \frac{1}{3} = -\frac{1}{3}$

$\Rightarrow x_2 = -\frac{1}{3} - \frac{-\frac{1}{27} - 1 + 1}{\frac{1}{3} + 3} = -\frac{1}{3} + \frac{1}{90} = -\frac{29}{90} \approx -0.32222$

3. $y = x^4 + x - 3 \Rightarrow y' = 4x^3 + 1 \Rightarrow x_{n+1} = x_n - \frac{x_n^4 + x_n - 3}{4x_n^3 + 1}$ ; $x_0 = 1 \Rightarrow x_1 = 1 - \frac{1+1-3}{4+1} = \frac{6}{5}$

$\Rightarrow x_2 = \frac{6}{5} - \frac{\frac{1296}{625} + \frac{6}{5} - 3}{\frac{864}{125} + 1} = \frac{6}{5} - \frac{1296 + 750 - 1875}{4320 + 625} = \frac{6}{5} - \frac{171}{4945} = \frac{5763}{4945} \approx 1.16542$; $x_0 = -1 \Rightarrow x_1 = -1 - \frac{1-1-3}{-4+1}$

$= -2 \Rightarrow x_2 = -2 - \frac{16-2-3}{-32+1} = -2 + \frac{11}{31} = -\frac{51}{31} \approx -1.64516$

4. $y = 2x - x^2 + 1 \Rightarrow y' = 2 - 2x \Rightarrow x_{n+1} = x_n - \frac{2x_n - x_n^2 + 1}{2 - 2x_n}$ ; $x_0 = 0 \Rightarrow x_1 = 0 - \frac{0-0+1}{2-0} = -\frac{1}{2}$

$\Rightarrow x_2 = -\frac{1}{2} - \frac{-1-\frac{1}{4}+1}{2+1} = -\frac{1}{2} + \frac{1}{12} = -\frac{5}{12} \approx -.41667$; $x_0 = 2 \Rightarrow x_1 = 2 - \frac{4-4+1}{2-4} = \frac{5}{2} \Rightarrow x_2 = \frac{5}{2} - \frac{5-\frac{25}{4}+1}{2-5}$

$= \frac{5}{2} - \frac{20-25+4}{-12} = \frac{5}{2} - \frac{1}{12} = \frac{29}{12} \approx 2.41667$

5. $y = x^4 - 2 \Rightarrow y' = 4x^3 \Rightarrow x_{n+1} = x_n - \frac{x_n^4 - 2}{4x_n^3}$; $x_0 = 1 \Rightarrow x_1 = 1 - \frac{1-2}{4} = \frac{5}{4} \Rightarrow x_2 = \frac{5}{4} - \frac{\frac{625}{256}-2}{\frac{125}{16}} = \frac{5}{4} - \frac{625-512}{2000}$

$= \frac{5}{4} - \frac{113}{2000} = \frac{2500-113}{2000} = \frac{2387}{2000} \approx 1.1935$

6. From Exercise 5, $x_{n+1} = x_n - \frac{x_n^4 - 2}{4x_n^3}$ ; $x_0 = -1 \Rightarrow x_1 = -1 - \frac{1-2}{-4} = -1 - \frac{1}{4} = -\frac{5}{4} \Rightarrow x_2 = -\frac{5}{4} - \frac{\frac{625}{256}-2}{-\frac{125}{16}}$

$= -\frac{5}{4} - \frac{625-512}{-2000} = -\frac{5}{4} + \frac{113}{2000} \approx -1.1935$

7. $f(x_0) = 0$ and $f'(x_0) \neq 0 \Rightarrow x_{n+1} = x_n - \frac{f(x_n)}{f'(x_n)}$ gives $x_1 = x_0 \Rightarrow x_2 = x_0 \Rightarrow x_n = x_0$ for all $n \geq 0$. That is, all of the approximations in Newton's method will be the root of $f(x) = 0$.

8. It does matter. If you start too far away from $x = \frac{\pi}{2}$, the calculated values may approach some other root. Starting with $x_0 = -0.5$, for instance, leads to $x = -\frac{\pi}{2}$ as the root, not $x = \frac{\pi}{2}$.

9.  If $x_0 = h > 0 \Rightarrow x_1 = x_0 - \frac{f(x_0)}{f'(x_0)} = h - \frac{f(h)}{f'(h)}$

$= h - \frac{\sqrt{h}}{\left(\frac{1}{2\sqrt{h}}\right)} = h - \left(\sqrt{h}\right)\left(2\sqrt{h}\right) = -h;$

if $x_0 = -h < 0 \Rightarrow x_1 = x_0 - \frac{f(x_0)}{f'(x_0)} = -h - \frac{f(-h)}{f'(-h)}$

$= -h - \frac{\sqrt{h}}{\left(\frac{-1}{2\sqrt{h}}\right)} = -h + \left(\sqrt{h}\right)\left(2\sqrt{h}\right) = h.$

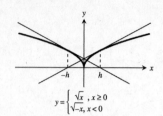

$y = \begin{cases} \sqrt{x} & ,x \ge 0 \\ \sqrt{-x}, & x < 0 \end{cases}$

10. $f(x) = x^{1/3} \Rightarrow f'(x) = \left(\frac{1}{3}\right)x^{-2/3} \Rightarrow x_{n+1} = x_n - \frac{x_n^{1/3}}{\left(\frac{1}{3}\right)x_n^{-2/3}}$

$= -2x_n; x_0 = 1 \Rightarrow x_1 = -2, x_2 = 4, x_3 = -8,$ and
$x_4 = 16$ and so forth. Since $|x_n| = 2|x_{n-1}|$ we may conclude
that $n \to \infty \Rightarrow |x_n| \to \infty$.

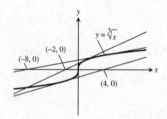

11. i) is equivalent to solving $x^3 - 3x - 1 = 0$.
    ii) is equivalent to solving $x^3 - 3x - 1 = 0$.
    iii) is equivalent to solving $x^3 - 3x - 1 = 0$.
    iv) is equivalent to solving $x^3 - 3x - 1 = 0$.
    All four equations are equivalent.

12. $f(x) = x - 1 - 0.5 \sin x \Rightarrow f'(x) = 1 - 0.5 \cos x \Rightarrow x_{n+1} = x_n - \frac{x_n - 1 - 0.5 \sin x_n}{1 - 0.5 \cos x_n}$ ; if $x_0 = 1.5$, then $x_1 = 1.49870$

13. $f(x) = \tan x - 2x \Rightarrow f'(x) = \sec^2 x - 2 \Rightarrow x_{n+1} = x_n - \frac{\tan(x_n) - 2x_n}{\sec^2(x_n)}$ ; $x_0 = 1 \Rightarrow x_1 = 1.2920445$

$\Rightarrow x_2 = 1.155327774 \Rightarrow x_{16} = x_{17} = 1.165561185$

14. $f(x) = x^4 - 2x^3 - x^2 - 2x + 2 \Rightarrow f'(x) = 4x^3 - 6x^2 - 2x - 2 \Rightarrow x_{n+1} = x_n - \frac{x_n^4 - 2x_n^3 - x_n^2 - 2x_n + 2}{4x_n^3 - 6x_n^2 - 2x_n - 2}$ ;

if $x_0 = 0.5$, then $x_4 = 0.630115396$; if $x_0 = 2.5$, then $x_4 = 2.57327196$

15. (a) The graph of $f(x) = \sin 3x - 0.99 + x^2$ in the window
        $-2 \le x \le 2, -2 \le y \le 3$ suggests three roots.
        However, when you zoom in on the x-axis near $x = 1.2$,
        you can see that the graph lies above the axis there.
        There are only two roots, one near $x = -1$, the other
        near $x = 0.4$.

    (b) $f(x) = \sin 3x - 0.99 + x^2 \Rightarrow f'(x) = 3 \cos 3x + 2x$

        $\Rightarrow x_{n+1} = x_n - \frac{\sin(3x_n) - 0.99 + x_n^2}{3 \cos(3x_n) + 2x_n}$ and the solutions
        are approximately $0.35003501505249$ and
        $-1.0261731615301$

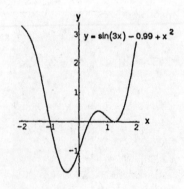

16. (a) Yes, three times as indicted by the graphs

(b) $f(x) = \cos 3x - x \Rightarrow f'(x)$
$= -3 \sin 3x - 1 \Rightarrow x_{n+1}$
$= x_n - \dfrac{\cos(3x_n) - x_n}{-3\sin(3x_n) - 1}$ ; at
approximately $-0.979367$,
$-0.887726$, and $0.39004$ we have
$\cos 3x = x$

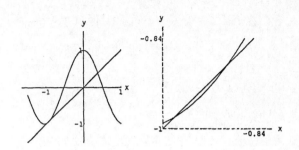

17. $f(x) = 2x^4 - 4x^2 + 1 \Rightarrow f'(x) = 8x^3 - 8x \Rightarrow x_{n+1} = x_n - \dfrac{2x_n^4 - 4x_n^2 + 1}{8x_n^3 - 8x_n}$ ; if $x_0 = -2$, then $x_6 = -1.30656296$; if
$x_0 = -0.5$, then $x_3 = -0.5411961$; the roots are approximately $\pm 0.5411961$ and $\pm 1.30656296$ because $f(x)$ is
an even function.

18. $f(x) = \tan x \Rightarrow f'(x) = \sec^2 x \Rightarrow x_{n+1} = x_n - \dfrac{\tan(x_n)}{\sec^2(x_n)}$ ; $x_0 = 3 \Rightarrow x_1 = 3.13971 \Rightarrow x_2 = 3.14159$ and we
approximate $\pi$ to be $3.14159$.

19. From the graph we let $x_0 = 0.5$ and $f(x) = \cos x - 2x$
$\Rightarrow x_{n+1} = x_n - \dfrac{\cos(x_n) - 2x_n}{-\sin(x_n) - 2} \Rightarrow x_1 = .45063$
$\Rightarrow x_2 = .45018 \Rightarrow$ at $x \approx 0.45$ we have $\cos x = 2x$.

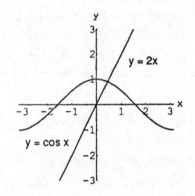

20. From the graph we let $x_0 = -0.7$ and $f(x) = \cos x + x$
$\Rightarrow x_{n+1} = x_n - \dfrac{x_n + \cos(x_n)}{1 - \sin(x_n)} \Rightarrow x_1 = -.73944$
$\Rightarrow x_2 = -.73908 \Rightarrow$ at $x \approx -0.74$ we have $\cos x = -x$.

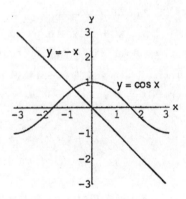

21. The x-coordinate of the point of intersection of $y = x^2(x+1)$ and $y = \frac{1}{x}$ is the solution of $x^2(x+1) = \frac{1}{x}$
$\Rightarrow x^3 + x^2 - \frac{1}{x} = 0 \Rightarrow$ The x-coordinate is the root of $f(x) = x^3 + x^2 - \frac{1}{x} \Rightarrow f'(x) = 3x^2 + 2x + \frac{1}{x^2}$. Let $x_0 = 1$
$\Rightarrow x_{n+1} = x_n - \dfrac{x_n^3 + x_n^2 - \frac{1}{x_n}}{3x_n^2 + 2x_n + \frac{1}{x_n^2}} \Rightarrow x_1 = 0.83333 \Rightarrow x_2 = 0.81924 \Rightarrow x_3 = 0.81917 \Rightarrow x_7 = 0.81917 \Rightarrow r \approx 0.8192$

22. The x-coordinate of the point of intersection of $y = \sqrt{x}$ and $y = 3 - x^2$ is the solution of $\sqrt{x} = 3 - x^2$
$\Rightarrow \sqrt{x} - 3 + x^2 = 0 \Rightarrow$ The x-coordinate is the root of $f(x) = \sqrt{x} - 3 + x^2 \Rightarrow f'(x) = \frac{1}{2\sqrt{x}} + 2x$. Let $x_0 = 1$
$\Rightarrow x_{n+1} = x_n - \dfrac{\sqrt{x_n} - 3 + x_n^2}{\frac{1}{2\sqrt{x_n}} + 2x_n} \Rightarrow x_1 = 1.4 \Rightarrow x_2 = 1.35556 \Rightarrow x_3 = 1.35498 \Rightarrow x_7 = 1.35498 \Rightarrow r \approx 1.3550$

23. If $f(x) = x^3 + 2x - 4$, then $f(1) = -1 < 0$ and $f(2) = 8 > 0$ $\Rightarrow$ by the Intermediate Value Theorem the equation $x^3 + 2x - 4 = 0$ has a solution between 1 and 2. Consequently, $f'(x) = 3x^2 + 2$ and $x_{n+1} = x_n - \frac{x_n^3 + 2x_n - 4}{3x_n^2 + 2}$.

Then $x_0 = 1$ $\Rightarrow$ $x_1 = 1.2$ $\Rightarrow$ $x_2 = 1.17975$ $\Rightarrow$ $x_3 = 1.179509$ $\Rightarrow$ $x_4 = 1.1795090$ $\Rightarrow$ the root is approximately 1.17951.

24. We wish to solve $8x^4 - 14x^3 - 9x^2 + 11x - 1 = 0$. Let $f(x) = 8x^4 - 14x^3 - 9x^2 + 11x - 1$, then $f'(x) = 32x^3 - 42x^2 - 18x + 11$ $\Rightarrow$ $x_{n+1} = x_n - \frac{8x_n^4 - 14x_n^3 - 9x_n^2 + 11x_n - 1}{32x_n^3 - 42x_n^2 - 18x_n + 11}$.

| $x_0$ | approximation of corresponding root |
|---|---|
| $-1.0$ | $-0.976823589$ |
| $0.1$ | $0.100363332$ |
| $0.6$ | $0.642746671$ |
| $2.0$ | $1.983713587$ |

25. $f(x) = 4x^4 - 4x^2$ $\Rightarrow$ $f'(x) = 16x^3 - 8x$ $\Rightarrow$ $x_{i+1} = x_i - \frac{f(x_i)}{f'(x_i)} = x_i - \frac{x_i^3 - x_i}{4x_i^2 - 2}$. Iterations are performed using the procedure in problem 13 in this section.

(a) For $x_0 = -2$ or $x_0 = -0.8$, $x_i \to -1$ as i gets large.

(b) For $x_0 = -0.5$ or $x_0 = 0.25$, $x_i \to 0$ as i gets large.

(c) For $x_0 = 0.8$ or $x_0 = 2$, $x_i \to 1$ as i gets large.

(d) (If your calculator has a CAS, put it in exact mode, otherwise approximate the radicals with a decimal value.)

For $x_0 = -\frac{\sqrt{21}}{7}$ or $x_0 = -\frac{\sqrt{21}}{7}$, Newton's method does not converge. The values of $x_i$ alternate between $x_0 = -\frac{\sqrt{21}}{7}$ or $x_0 = -\frac{\sqrt{21}}{7}$ as i increases.

26. (a) The distance can be represented by

$D(x) = \sqrt{(x-2)^2 + \left(x^2 + \frac{1}{2}\right)^2}$, where $x \geq 0$. The distance $D(x)$ is minimized when

$f(x) = (x-2)^2 + \left(x^2 + \frac{1}{2}\right)^2$ is minimized. If

$f(x) = (x-2)^2 + \left(x^2 + \frac{1}{2}\right)^2$, then

$f'(x) = 4\left(x^3 + x - 1\right)$ and $f''(x) = 4\left(3x^2 + 1\right) > 0$.

Now $f'(x) = 0$ $\Rightarrow$ $x^3 + x - 1 = 0$ $\Rightarrow$ $x\left(x^2 + 1\right) = 1$

$\Rightarrow$ $x = \frac{1}{x^2 + 1}$.

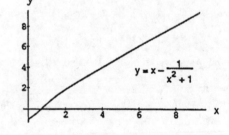

(b) Let $g(x) = \frac{1}{x^2+1} - x = \left(x^2 + 1\right)^{-1} - x$ $\Rightarrow$ $g'(x) = -\left(x^2 + 1\right)^{-2}(2x) - 1 = \frac{-2x}{\left(x^2 + 1\right)^2} - 1$

$\Rightarrow$ $x_{n+1} = x_n - \frac{\left(\frac{1}{x_n^2 + 1} - x_n\right)}{\left(\frac{-2x_n}{\left(x_n^2 + 1\right)^2} - 1\right)}$; $x_0 = 1$ $\Rightarrow$ $x_4 = 0.68233$ to five decimal places.

27. $f(x) = (x-1)^{40}$ $\Rightarrow$ $f'(x) = 40(x-1)^{39}$ $\Rightarrow$ $x_{n+1} = x_n - \frac{(x_n - 1)^{40}}{40(x_n - 1)^{39}} = \frac{39x_n + 1}{40}$. With $x_0 = 2$, our computer gave $x_{87} = x_{88} = x_{89} = \cdots = x_{200} = 1.11051$, coming within $0.11051$ of the root $x = 1$.

28. Since $s = r\theta$ $\Rightarrow$ $3 = r\theta$ $\Rightarrow$ $\theta = \frac{3}{r}$. Bisect the angle $\theta$ to obtain a right tringle with hypotenuse r and opposite side of length 1. Then $\sin\frac{\theta}{2} = \frac{1}{r}$ $\Rightarrow$ $\sin\frac{\left(\frac{3}{r}\right)}{2} = \frac{1}{r}$ $\Rightarrow$ $\sin\left(\frac{3}{2r}\right) = \frac{1}{r}$ $\Rightarrow$ $\sin\frac{3}{2r} - \frac{1}{r} = 0$. Thus the solution r is a root of

$f(r) = \sin\left(\frac{3}{2r}\right) - \frac{1}{r}$ $\Rightarrow$ $f'(r) = -\frac{3}{2r^2}\cos\left(\frac{3}{2r}\right) + \frac{1}{r^2}$; $r_0 = 1$ $\Rightarrow$ $r_{n+1} = r_n - \frac{\sin\left(\frac{3}{2r_n}\right) - \frac{1}{r_n}}{-\frac{3}{2r_n^2}\cos\left(\frac{3}{2r_n}\right) + \frac{1}{r_n^2}}$ $\Rightarrow$ $r_1 = 1.00280$

$\Rightarrow$ $r_2 = 1.00282$ $\Rightarrow$ $r_3 = 1.00282$ $\Rightarrow$ $r \approx 1.0028$ $\Rightarrow$ $\theta = \frac{3}{1.00282} \approx 2.9916$

**4.7 ANTIDERIVATIVES**

1. (a) $x^2$
   (b) $\frac{x^3}{3}$
   (c) $\frac{x^3}{3} - x^2 + x$

2. (a) $3x^2$
   (b) $\frac{x^8}{8}$
   (c) $\frac{x^8}{8} - 3x^2 + 8x$

3. (a) $x^{-3}$
   (b) $-\frac{x^{-3}}{3}$
   (c) $-\frac{x^{-3}}{3} + x^2 + 3x$

4. (a) $-x^{-2}$
   (b) $-\frac{x^{-2}}{4} + \frac{x^3}{3}$
   (c) $\frac{x^{-2}}{2} + \frac{x^2}{2} - x$

5. (a) $\frac{-1}{x}$
   (b) $\frac{-5}{x}$
   (c) $2x + \frac{5}{x}$

6. (a) $\frac{1}{x^2}$
   (b) $\frac{-1}{4x^2}$
   (c) $\frac{x^4}{4} + \frac{1}{2x^2}$

7. (a) $\sqrt{x^3}$
   (b) $\sqrt{x}$
   (c) $\frac{2}{3}\sqrt{x^3} + 2\sqrt{x}$

8. (a) $x^{4/3}$
   (b) $\frac{1}{2}x^{2/3}$
   (c) $\frac{3}{4}x^{4/3} + \frac{3}{2}x^{2/3}$

9. (a) $x^{2/3}$
   (b) $x^{1/3}$
   (c) $x^{-1/3}$

10. (a) $x^{1/2}$
    (b) $x^{-1/2}$
    (c) $x^{-3/2}$

11. (a) $\cos(\pi x)$
    (b) $-3\cos x$
    (c) $\frac{-\cos(\pi x)}{\pi} + \cos(3x)$

12. (a) $\sin(\pi x)$
    (b) $\sin\left(\frac{\pi x}{2}\right)$
    (c) $\left(\frac{2}{\pi}\right)\sin\left(\frac{\pi x}{2}\right) + \pi \sin x$

13. (a) $\tan x$
    (b) $2\tan\left(\frac{x}{3}\right)$
    (c) $-\frac{2}{3}\tan\left(\frac{3x}{2}\right)$

14. (a) $-\cot x$
    (b) $\cot\left(\frac{3x}{2}\right)$
    (c) $x + 4\cot(2x)$

15. (a) $-\csc x$
    (b) $\frac{1}{5}\csc(5x)$
    (c) $2\csc\left(\frac{\pi x}{2}\right)$

16. (a) $\sec x$
    (b) $\frac{4}{3}\sec(3x)$
    (c) $\frac{2}{\pi}\sec\left(\frac{\pi x}{2}\right)$

17. $\int (x+1)\,dx = \frac{x^2}{2} + x + C$

18. $\int (5 - 6x)\,dx = 5x - 3x^2 + C$

19. $\int \left(3t^2 + \frac{1}{2}\right) dt = t^3 + \frac{t}{4} + C$

20. $\int \left(\frac{t^2}{2} + 4t^3\right) dt = \frac{t^3}{6} + t^4 + C$

21. $\int (2x^3 - 5x + 7)\,dx = \frac{1}{2}x^4 - \frac{5}{2}x^2 + 7x + C$

22. $\int (1 - x^2 - 3x^5)\,dx = x - \frac{1}{3}x^3 - \frac{1}{2}x^6 + C$

23. $\int \left(\frac{1}{x^2} - x^2 - \frac{1}{3}\right) dx = \int \left(x^{-2} - x^2 - \frac{1}{3}\right) dx = \frac{x^{-1}}{-1} - \frac{x^3}{3} - \frac{1}{3}x + C = -\frac{1}{x} - \frac{x^3}{3} - \frac{x}{3} + C$

24. $\int \left(\frac{1}{5} - \frac{2}{x^3} + 2x\right) dx = \int \left(\frac{1}{5} - 2x^{-3} + 2x\right) dx = \frac{1}{5}x - \left(\frac{2x^{-2}}{-2}\right) + \frac{2x^2}{2} + C = \frac{x}{5} + \frac{1}{x^2} + x^2 + C$

25. $\int x^{-1/3}\, dx = \frac{x^{2/3}}{\frac{2}{3}} + C = \frac{3}{2}\, x^{2/3} + C$       26. $\int x^{-5/4}\, dx = \frac{x^{-1/4}}{-\frac{1}{4}} + C = \frac{-4}{\sqrt[4]{x}} + C$

27. $\int \left( \sqrt{x} + \sqrt[3]{x} \right) dx = \int \left( x^{1/2} + x^{1/3} \right) dx = \frac{x^{3/2}}{\frac{3}{2}} + \frac{x^{4/3}}{\frac{4}{3}} + C = \frac{2}{3}\, x^{3/2} + \frac{3}{4}\, x^{4/3} + C$

28. $\int \left( \frac{\sqrt{x}}{2} + \frac{2}{\sqrt{x}} \right) dx = \int \left( \frac{1}{2}\, x^{1/2} + 2x^{-1/2} \right) dx = \frac{1}{2} \left( \frac{x^{3/2}}{\frac{3}{2}} \right) + 2 \left( \frac{x^{1/2}}{\frac{1}{2}} \right) + C = \frac{1}{3}\, x^{3/2} + 4x^{1/2} + C$

29. $\int \left( 8y - \frac{2}{y^{1/4}} \right) dy = \int \left( 8y - 2y^{-1/4} \right) dy = \frac{8y^2}{2} - 2 \left( \frac{y^{3/4}}{\frac{3}{4}} \right) + C = 4y^2 - \frac{8}{3}\, y^{3/4} + C$

30. $\int \left( \frac{1}{7} - \frac{1}{y^{5/4}} \right) dy = \int \left( \frac{1}{7} - y^{-5/4} \right) dy = \frac{1}{7}\, y - \left( \frac{y^{-1/4}}{-\frac{1}{4}} \right) + C = \frac{y}{7} + \frac{4}{y^{1/4}} + C$

31. $\int 2x \left( 1 - x^{-3} \right) dx = \int \left( 2x - 2x^{-2} \right) dx = \frac{2x^2}{2} - 2 \left( \frac{x^{-1}}{-1} \right) + C = x^2 + \frac{2}{x} + C$

32. $\int x^{-3} (x + 1)\, dx = \int \left( x^{-2} + x^{-3} \right) dx = \frac{x^{-1}}{-1} + \left( \frac{x^{-2}}{-2} \right) + C = -\frac{1}{x} - \frac{1}{2x^2} + C$

33. $\int \frac{t\sqrt{t} + \sqrt{t}}{t^2}\, dt = \int \left( \frac{t^{3/2}}{t^2} + \frac{t^{1/2}}{t^2} \right) dt = \int \left( t^{-1/2} + t^{-3/2} \right) dt = \frac{t^{1/2}}{\frac{1}{2}} + \left( \frac{t^{-1/2}}{-\frac{1}{2}} \right) + C = 2\sqrt{t} - \frac{2}{\sqrt{t}} + C$

34. $\int \frac{4 + \sqrt{t}}{t^3}\, dt = \int \left( \frac{4}{t^3} + \frac{t^{1/2}}{t^3} \right) dt = \int \left( 4t^{-3} + t^{-5/2} \right) dt = 4 \left( \frac{t^{-2}}{-2} \right) + \left( \frac{t^{-3/2}}{-\frac{3}{2}} \right) + C = -\frac{2}{t^2} - \frac{2}{3t^{3/2}} + C$

35. $\int -2 \cos t\, dt = -2 \sin t + C$       36. $\int -5 \sin t\, dt = 5 \cos t + C$

37. $\int 7 \sin \frac{\theta}{3}\, d\theta = -21 \cos \frac{\theta}{3} + C$       38. $\int 3 \cos 5\theta\, d\theta = \frac{3}{5} \sin 5\theta + C$

39. $\int -3 \csc^2 x\, dx = 3 \cot x + C$       40. $\int -\frac{\sec^2 x}{3}\, dx = -\frac{\tan x}{3} + C$

41. $\int \frac{\csc \theta \cot \theta}{2}\, d\theta = -\frac{1}{2} \csc \theta + C$       42. $\int \frac{2}{5} \sec \theta \tan \theta\, d\theta = \frac{2}{5} \sec \theta + C$

43. $\int (4 \sec x \tan x - 2 \sec^2 x)\, dx = 4 \sec x - 2 \tan x + C$

44. $\int \frac{1}{2} (\csc^2 x - \csc x \cot x)\, dx = -\frac{1}{2} \cot x + \frac{1}{2} \csc x + C$

45. $\int (\sin 2x - \csc^2 x)\, dx = -\frac{1}{2} \cos 2x + \cot x + C$       46. $\int (2 \cos 2x - 3 \sin 3x)\, dx = \sin 2x + \cos 3x + C$

47. $\int \frac{1 + \cos 4t}{2}\, dt = \int \left( \frac{1}{2} + \frac{1}{2} \cos 4t \right) dt = \frac{1}{2}\, t + \frac{1}{2} \left( \frac{\sin 4t}{4} \right) + C = \frac{t}{2} + \frac{\sin 4t}{8} + C$

48. $\int \frac{1 - \cos 6t}{2}\, dt = \int \left( \frac{1}{2} - \frac{1}{2} \cos 6t \right) dt = \frac{1}{2}\, t - \frac{1}{2} \left( \frac{\sin 6t}{6} \right) + C = \frac{t}{2} - \frac{\sin 6t}{12} + C$

49. $\int (1 + \tan^2 \theta)\, d\theta = \int \sec^2 \theta\, d\theta = \tan \theta + C$

50. $\int (2 + \tan^2 \theta)\, d\theta = \int (1 + 1 + \tan^2 \theta)\, d\theta = \int (1 + \sec^2 \theta)\, d\theta = \theta + \tan \theta + C$

51. $\int \cot^2 x\, dx = \int (\csc^2 x - 1)\, dx = -\cot x - x + C$

52. $\int \left(1 - \cot^2 x\right) dx = \int \left(1 - (\csc^2 x - 1)\right) dx = \int \left(2 - \csc^2 x\right) dx = 2x + \cot x + C$

53. $\int \cos\theta \left(\tan\theta + \sec\theta\right) d\theta = \int \left(\sin\theta + 1\right) d\theta = -\cos\theta + \theta + C$

54. $\int \frac{\csc\theta}{\csc\theta - \sin\theta} d\theta = \int \left(\frac{\csc\theta}{\csc\theta - \sin\theta}\right)\left(\frac{\sin\theta}{\sin\theta}\right) d\theta = \int \frac{1}{1 - \sin^2\theta} d\theta = \int \frac{1}{\cos^2\theta} d\theta = \int \sec^2\theta \, d\theta = \tan\theta + C$

55. $\frac{d}{dx}\left(\frac{(7x-2)^4}{28} + C\right) = \frac{4(7x-2)^3(7)}{28} = (7x-2)^3$

56. $\frac{d}{dx}\left(-\frac{(3x+5)^{-1}}{3} + C\right) = -\left(-\frac{(3x+5)^{-2}(3)}{3}\right) = (3x+5)^{-2}$

57. $\frac{d}{dx}\left(\frac{1}{5}\tan(5x-1) + C\right) = \frac{1}{5}\left(\sec^2(5x-1)\right)(5) = \sec^2(5x-1)$

58. $\frac{d}{dx}\left(-3\cot\left(\frac{x-1}{3}\right) + C\right) = -3\left(-\csc^2\left(\frac{x-1}{3}\right)\right)\left(\frac{1}{3}\right) = \csc^2\left(\frac{x-1}{3}\right)$

59. $\frac{d}{dx}\left(\frac{-1}{x+1} + C\right) = (-1)(-1)(x+1)^{-2} = \frac{1}{(x+1)^2}$   60. $\frac{d}{dx}\left(\frac{x}{x+1} + C\right) = \frac{(x+1)(1) - x(1)}{(x+1)^2} = \frac{1}{(x+1)^2}$

61. (a) Wrong: $\frac{d}{dx}\left(\frac{x^2}{2}\sin x + C\right) = \frac{2x}{2}\sin x + \frac{x^2}{2}\cos x = x\sin x + \frac{x^2}{2}\cos x \neq x\sin x$

    (b) Wrong: $\frac{d}{dx}(-x\cos x + C) = -\cos x + x\sin x \neq x\sin x$

    (c) Right: $\frac{d}{dx}(-x\cos x + \sin x + C) = -\cos x + x\sin x + \cos x = x\sin x$

62. (a) Wrong: $\frac{d}{d\theta}\left(\frac{\sec^3\theta}{3} + C\right) = \frac{3\sec^2\theta}{3}(\sec\theta\tan\theta) = \sec^3\theta\tan\theta \neq \tan\theta\sec^2\theta$

    (b) Right: $\frac{d}{d\theta}\left(\frac{1}{2}\tan^2\theta + C\right) = \frac{1}{2}(2\tan\theta)\sec^2\theta = \tan\theta\sec^2\theta$

    (c) Right: $\frac{d}{d\theta}\left(\frac{1}{2}\sec^2\theta + C\right) = \frac{1}{2}(2\sec\theta)\sec\theta\tan\theta = \tan\theta\sec^2\theta$

63. (a) Wrong: $\frac{d}{dx}\left(\frac{(2x+1)^3}{3} + C\right) = \frac{3(2x+1)^2(2)}{3} = 2(2x+1)^2 \neq (2x+1)^2$

    (b) Wrong: $\frac{d}{dx}\left((2x+1)^3 + C\right) = 3(2x+1)^2(2) = 6(2x+1)^2 \neq 3(2x+1)^2$

    (c) Right: $\frac{d}{dx}\left((2x+1)^3 + C\right) = 6(2x+1)^2$

64. (a) Wrong: $\frac{d}{dx}(x^2 + x + C)^{1/2} = \frac{1}{2}(x^2 + x + C)^{-1/2}(2x+1) = \frac{2x+1}{2\sqrt{x^2+x+C}} \neq \sqrt{2x+1}$

    (b) Wrong: $\frac{d}{dx}\left((x^2 + x)^{1/2} + C\right) = \frac{1}{2}(x^2 + x)^{-1/2}(2x+1) = \frac{2x+1}{2\sqrt{x^2+x}} \neq \sqrt{2x+1}$

    (c) Right: $\frac{d}{dx}\left(\frac{1}{3}\left(\sqrt{2x+1}\right)^3 + C\right) = \frac{d}{dx}\left(\frac{1}{3}(2x+1)^{3/2} + C\right) = \frac{3}{6}(2x+1)^{1/2}(2) = \sqrt{2x+1}$

65. Right: $\frac{d}{dx}\left(\left(\frac{x+3}{x-2}\right)^3 + C\right) = 3\left(\frac{x+3}{x-2}\right)^2 \frac{(x-2)\cdot 1 - (x+3)\cdot 1}{(x-2)^2} = 3\frac{(x+3)^2}{(x-2)^2}\frac{-5}{(x-2)^2} = \frac{-15(x+3)^2}{(x-2)^4}$

66. Wrong: $\frac{d}{dx}\left(\frac{\sin(x^2)}{x} + C\right) = \frac{x\cdot\cos(x^2)(2x) - \sin(x^2)\cdot 1}{x^2} = \frac{2x^2\cos(x^2) - \sin(x^2)}{x^2} \neq \frac{x\cos(x^2) - \sin(x^2)}{x^2}$

67. Graph (b), because $\frac{dy}{dx} = 2x \Rightarrow y = x^2 + C$. Then $y(1) = 4 \Rightarrow C = 3$.

68. Graph (b), because $\frac{dy}{dx} = -x \Rightarrow y = -\frac{1}{2}x^2 + C$. Then $y(-1) = 1 \Rightarrow C = \frac{3}{2}$.

69. $\frac{dy}{dx} = 2x - 7 \Rightarrow y = x^2 - 7x + C$; at $x = 2$ and $y = 0$ we have $0 = 2^2 - 7(2) + C \Rightarrow C = 10 \Rightarrow y = x^2 - 7x + 10$

70. $\frac{dy}{dx} = 10 - x \Rightarrow y = 10x - \frac{x^2}{2} + C$; at $x = 0$ and $y = -1$ we have $-1 = 10(0) - \frac{0^2}{2} + C \Rightarrow C = -1 \Rightarrow y = 10x - \frac{x^2}{2} - 1$

71. $\frac{dy}{dx} = \frac{1}{x^2} + x = x^{-2} + x \Rightarrow y = -x^{-1} + \frac{x^2}{2} + C$; at $x = 2$ and $y = 1$ we have $1 = -2^{-1} + \frac{2^2}{2} + C \Rightarrow C = -\frac{1}{2}$
    $\Rightarrow y = -x^{-1} + \frac{x^2}{2} - \frac{1}{2}$ or $y = -\frac{1}{x} + \frac{x^2}{2} - \frac{1}{2}$

72. $\frac{dy}{dx} = 9x^2 - 4x + 5 \Rightarrow y = 3x^3 - 2x^2 + 5x + C$; at $x = -1$ and $y = 0$ we have $0 = 3(-1)^3 - 2(-1)^2 + 5(-1) + C$
    $\Rightarrow C = 10 \Rightarrow y = 3x^3 - 2x^2 + 5x + 10$

73. $\frac{dy}{dx} = 3x^{-2/3} \Rightarrow y = \frac{3x^{1/3}}{\frac{1}{3}} + C = 9$; at $x = 9x^{1/3} + C$; at $x = -1$ and $y = -5$ we have $-5 = 9(-1)^{1/3} + C \Rightarrow C = 4$
    $\Rightarrow y = 9x^{1/3} + 4$

74. $\frac{dy}{dx} = \frac{1}{2\sqrt{x}} = \frac{1}{2}x^{-1/2} \Rightarrow y = x^{1/2} + C$; at $x = 4$ and $y = 0$ we have $0 = 4^{1/2} + C \Rightarrow C = -2 \Rightarrow y = x^{1/2} - 2$

75. $\frac{ds}{dt} = 1 + \cos t \Rightarrow s = t + \sin t + C$; at $t = 0$ and $s = 4$ we have $4 = 0 + \sin 0 + C \Rightarrow C = 4 \Rightarrow s = t + \sin t + 4$

76. $\frac{ds}{dt} = \cos t + \sin t \Rightarrow s = \sin t - \cos t + C$; at $t = \pi$ and $s = 1$ we have $1 = \sin \pi - \cos \pi + C \Rightarrow C = 0$
    $\Rightarrow s = \sin t - \cos t$

77. $\frac{dr}{d\theta} = -\pi \sin \pi\theta \Rightarrow r = \cos(\pi\theta) + C$; at $r = 0$ and $\theta = 0$ we have $0 = \cos(\pi 0) + C \Rightarrow C = -1 \Rightarrow r = \cos(\pi\theta) - 1$

78. $\frac{dr}{d\theta} = \cos \pi\theta \Rightarrow r = \frac{1}{\pi} \sin(\pi\theta) + C$; at $r = 1$ and $\theta = 0$ we have $1 = \frac{1}{\pi} \sin(\pi 0) + C \Rightarrow C = 1 \Rightarrow r = \frac{1}{\pi} \sin(\pi\theta) + 1$

79. $\frac{dv}{dt} = \frac{1}{2} \sec t \tan t \Rightarrow v = \frac{1}{2} \sec t + C$; at $v = 1$ and $t = 0$ we have $1 = \frac{1}{2} \sec(0) + C \Rightarrow C = \frac{1}{2} \Rightarrow v = \frac{1}{2} \sec t + \frac{1}{2}$

80. $\frac{dv}{dt} = 8t + \csc^2 t \Rightarrow v = 4t^2 - \cot t + C$; at $v = -7$ and $t = \frac{\pi}{2}$ we have $-7 = 4\left(\frac{\pi}{2}\right)^2 - \cot\left(\frac{\pi}{2}\right) + C \Rightarrow C = -7 - \pi^2$
    $\Rightarrow v = 4t^2 - \cot t - 7 - \pi^2$

81. $\frac{d^2y}{dx^2} = 2 - 6x \Rightarrow \frac{dy}{dx} = 2x - 3x^2 + C_1$; at $\frac{dy}{dx} = 4$ and $x = 0$ we have $4 = 2(0) - 3(0)^2 + C_1 \Rightarrow C_1 = 4$
    $\Rightarrow \frac{dy}{dx} = 2x - 3x^2 + 4 \Rightarrow y = x^2 - x^3 + 4x + C_2$; at $y = 1$ and $x = 0$ we have $1 = 0^2 - 0^3 + 4(0) + C_2 \Rightarrow C_2 = 1$
    $\Rightarrow y = x^2 - x^3 + 4x + 1$

82. $\frac{d^2y}{dx^2} = 0 \Rightarrow \frac{dy}{dx} = C_1$; at $\frac{dy}{dx} = 2$ and $x = 0$ we have $C_1 = 2 \Rightarrow \frac{dy}{dx} = 2 \Rightarrow y = 2x + C_2$; at $y = 0$ and $x = 0$ we have $0 = 2(0) + C_2 \Rightarrow C_2 = 0 \Rightarrow y = 2x$

83. $\frac{d^2r}{dt^2} = \frac{2}{t^3} = 2t^{-3} \Rightarrow \frac{dr}{dt} = -t^{-2} + C_1$; at $\frac{dr}{dt} = 1$ and $t = 1$ we have $1 = -(1)^{-2} + C_1 \Rightarrow C_1 = 2 \Rightarrow \frac{dr}{dt} = -t^{-2} + 2$
    $\Rightarrow r = t^{-1} + 2t + C_2$; at $r = 1$ and $t = 1$ we have $1 = 1^{-1} + 2(1) + C_2 \Rightarrow C_2 = -2 \Rightarrow r = t^{-1} + 2t - 2$ or
    $r = \frac{1}{t} + 2t - 2$

84. $\frac{d^2s}{dt^2} = \frac{3t}{8} \Rightarrow \frac{ds}{dt} = \frac{3t^2}{16} + C_1$; at $\frac{ds}{dt} = 3$ and $t = 4$ we have $3 = \frac{3(4)^2}{16} + C_1 \Rightarrow C_1 = 0 \Rightarrow \frac{ds}{dt} = \frac{3t^2}{16} \Rightarrow s = \frac{t^3}{16} + C_2$; at
    $s = 4$ and $t = 4$ we have $4 = \frac{4^3}{16} + C_2 \Rightarrow C_2 = 0 \Rightarrow s = \frac{t^3}{16}$

85. $\frac{d^3y}{dx^3} = 6 \Rightarrow \frac{d^2y}{dx^2} = 6x + C_1$; at $\frac{d^2y}{dx^2} = -8$ and $x = 0$ we have $-8 = 6(0) + C_1 \Rightarrow C_1 = -8 \Rightarrow \frac{d^2y}{dx^2} = 6x - 8$

$\Rightarrow \frac{dy}{dx} = 3x^2 - 8x + C_2$; at $\frac{dy}{dx} = 0$ and $x = 0$ we have $0 = 3(0)^2 - 8(0) + C_2 \Rightarrow C_2 = 0 \Rightarrow \frac{dy}{dx} = 3x^2 - 8x$

$\Rightarrow y = x^3 - 4x^2 + C_3$; at $y = 5$ and $x = 0$ we have $5 = 0^3 - 4(0)^2 + C_3 \Rightarrow C_3 = 5 \Rightarrow y = x^3 - 4x^2 + 5$

86. $\frac{d^3\theta}{dt^3} = 0 \Rightarrow \frac{d^2\theta}{dt^2} = C_1$; at $\frac{d^2\theta}{dt^2} = -2$ and $t = 0$ we have $\frac{d^2\theta}{dt^2} = -2 \Rightarrow \frac{d\theta}{dt} = -2t + C_2$; at $\frac{d\theta}{dt} = -\frac{1}{2}$ and $t = 0$ we

have $-\frac{1}{2} = -2(0) + C_2 \Rightarrow C_2 = -\frac{1}{2} \Rightarrow \frac{d\theta}{dt} = -2t - \frac{1}{2} \Rightarrow \theta = -t^2 - \frac{1}{2}t + C_3$; at $\theta = \sqrt{2}$ and $t = 0$ we have

$\sqrt{2} = -0^2 - \frac{1}{2}(0) + C_3 \Rightarrow C_3 = \sqrt{2} \Rightarrow \theta = -t^2 - \frac{1}{2}t + \sqrt{2}$

87. $y^{(4)} = -\sin t + \cos t \Rightarrow y''' = \cos t + \sin t + C_1$; at $y''' = 7$ and $t = 0$ we have $7 = \cos(0) + \sin(0) + C_1 \Rightarrow C_1 = 6$

$\Rightarrow y''' = \cos t + \sin t + 6 \Rightarrow y'' = \sin t - \cos t + 6t + C_2$; at $y'' = -1$ and $t = 0$ we have

$-1 = \sin(0) - \cos(0) + 6(0) + C_2 \Rightarrow C_2 = 0 \Rightarrow y'' = \sin t - \cos t + 6t \Rightarrow y' = -\cos t - \sin t + 3t^2 + C_3$; at

$y' = -1$ and $t = 0$ we have $-1 = -\cos(0) - \sin(0) + 3(0)^2 + C_3 \Rightarrow C_3 = 0 \Rightarrow y' = -\cos t - \sin t + 3t^2$

$\Rightarrow y = -\sin t + \cos t + t^3 + C_4$; at $y = 0$ and $t = 0$ we have $0 = -\sin(0) + \cos(0) + 0^3 + C_4 \Rightarrow C_4 = -1$

$\Rightarrow y = -\sin t + \cos t + t^3 - 1$

88. $y^{(4)} = -\cos x + 8\sin(2x) \Rightarrow y''' = -\sin x - 4\cos(2x) + C_1$; at $y''' = 0$ and $x = 0$ we have

$0 = -\sin(0) - 4\cos(2(0)) + C_1 \Rightarrow C_1 = 4 \Rightarrow y''' = -\sin x - 4\cos(2x) + 4 \Rightarrow y'' = \cos x - 2\sin(2x) + 4x + C_2$;

at $y'' = 1$ and $x = 0$ we have $1 = \cos(0) - 2\sin(2(0)) + 4(0) + C_2 \Rightarrow C_2 = 0 \Rightarrow y'' = \cos x - 2\sin(2x) + 4x$

$\Rightarrow y' = \sin x + \cos(2x) + 2x^2 + C_3$; at $y' = 1$ and $x = 0$ we have $1 = \sin(0) + \cos(2(0)) + 2(0)^2 + C_3 \Rightarrow C_3 = 0$

$\Rightarrow y' = \sin x + \cos(2x) + 2x^2 \Rightarrow y = -\cos x + \frac{1}{2}\sin(2x) + \frac{2}{3}x^3 + C_4$; at $y = 3$ and $x = 0$ we have

$3 = -\cos(0) + \frac{1}{2}\sin(2(0)) + \frac{2}{3}(0)^3 + C_4 \Rightarrow C_4 = 4 \Rightarrow y = -\cos x + \frac{1}{2}\sin(2x) + \frac{2}{3}x^3 + 4$

89. $m = y' = 3\sqrt{x} = 3x^{1/2} \Rightarrow y = 2x^{3/2} + C$; at $(9, 4)$ we have $4 = 2(9)^{3/2} + C \Rightarrow C = -50 \Rightarrow y = 2x^{3/2} - 50$

90. Yes. If $F(x)$ and $G(x)$ both solve the initial value problem on an interval I then they both have the same first derivative. Therefore, by Corollary 2 of the Mean Value Theorem there is a constant C such that $F(x) = G(x) + C$ for all x. In particular, $F(x_0) = G(x_0) + C$, so $C = F(x_0) - G(x_0) = 0$. Hence $F(x) = G(x)$ for all x.

91. $\frac{dy}{dx} = 1 - \frac{4}{3}x^{1/3} \Rightarrow y = \int \left(1 - \frac{4}{3}x^{1/3}\right) dx = x - x^{4/3} + C$; at $(1, 0.5)$ on the curve we have $0.5 = 1 - 1^{4/3} + C$

$\Rightarrow C = 0.5 \Rightarrow y = x - x^{4/3} + \frac{1}{2}$

92. $\frac{dy}{dx} = x - 1 \Rightarrow y = \int (x - 1) dx = \frac{x^2}{2} - x + C$; at $(-1, 1)$ on the curve we have $1 = \frac{(-1)^2}{2} - (-1) + C \Rightarrow C = -\frac{1}{2}$

$\Rightarrow y = \frac{x^2}{2} - x - \frac{1}{2}$

93. $\frac{dy}{dx} = \sin x - \cos x \Rightarrow y = \int (\sin x - \cos x) dx = -\cos x - \sin x + C$; at $(-\pi, -1)$ on the curve we have

$-1 = -\cos(-\pi) - \sin(-\pi) + C \Rightarrow C = -2 \Rightarrow y = -\cos x - \sin x - 2$

94. $\frac{dy}{dx} = \frac{1}{2\sqrt{x}} + \pi \sin \pi x = \frac{1}{2}x^{-1/2} + \pi \sin \pi x \Rightarrow y = \int \left(\frac{1}{2}x^{-1/2} + \sin \pi x\right) dx = x^{1/2} - \cos \pi x + C$; at $(1, 2)$ on the

curve we have $2 = 1^{1/2} - \cos \pi(1) + C \Rightarrow C = 0 \Rightarrow y = \sqrt{x} - \cos \pi x$

95. (a) $\frac{ds}{dt} = 9.8t - 3 \Rightarrow s = 4.9t^2 - 3t + C$; (i) at $s = 5$ and $t = 0$ we have $C = 5 \Rightarrow s = 4.9t^2 - 3t + 5$;

displacement $= s(3) - s(1) = ((4.9)(9) - 9 + 5) - (4.9 - 3 + 5) = 33.2$ units; (ii) at $s = -2$ and $t = 0$ we have

$C = -2 \Rightarrow s = 4.9t^2 - 3t - 2$; displacement $= s(3) - s(1) = ((4.9)(9) - 9 - 2) - (4.9 - 3 - 2) = 33.2$ units;

(iii) at $s = s_0$ and $t = 0$ we have $C = s_0 \Rightarrow s = 4.9t^2 - 3t + s_0$; displacement $= s(3) - s(1)$

$= ((4.9)(9) - 9 + s_0) - (4.9 - 3 + s_0) = 33.2$ units

(b)  True.  Given an antiderivative f(t) of the velocity function, we know that the body's position function is
s = f(t) + C for some constant C.  Therefore, the displacement from t = a to t = b is (f(b) + C) − (f(a) + C)
= f(b) − f(a).  Thus we can find the displacement from any antiderivative f as the numerical difference
f(b) − f(a) without knowing the exact values of C and s.

96.  $a(t) = v'(t) = 20 \Rightarrow v(t) = 20t + C$; at $(0, 0)$ we have $C = 0 \Rightarrow v(t) = 20t$.  When $t = 60$, then $v(60) = 20(60) = 1200 \, \frac{m}{sec}$.

97.  Step 1:  $\frac{d^2s}{dt^2} = -k \Rightarrow \frac{ds}{dt} = -kt + C_1$; at $\frac{ds}{dt} = 88$ and $t = 0$ we have $C_1 = 88 \Rightarrow \frac{ds}{dt} = -kt + 88 \Rightarrow$
$s = -k\left(\frac{t^2}{2}\right) + 88t + C_2$; at $s = 0$ and $t = 0$ we have $C_2 = 0 \Rightarrow s = -\frac{kt^2}{2} + 88t$

Step 2:  $\frac{ds}{dt} = 0 \Rightarrow 0 = -kt + 88 \Rightarrow t = \frac{88}{k}$

Step 3:  $242 = \frac{-k\left(\frac{88}{k}\right)^2}{2} + 88\left(\frac{88}{k}\right) \Rightarrow 242 = -\frac{(88)^2}{2k} + \frac{(88)^2}{k} \Rightarrow 242 = \frac{(88)^2}{2k} \Rightarrow k = 16$

98.  $\frac{d^2s}{dt^2} = -k \Rightarrow \frac{ds}{dt} = \int -k \, dt = -kt + C$; at $\frac{ds}{dt} = 44$ when $t = 0$ we have $44 = -k(0) + C \Rightarrow C = 44$
$\Rightarrow \frac{ds}{dt} = -kt + 44 \Rightarrow s = -\frac{kt^2}{2} + 44t + C_1$; at $s = 0$ when $t = 0$ we have $0 = -\frac{k(0)^2}{2} + 44(0) + C_1 \Rightarrow C_1 = 0$
$\Rightarrow s = -\frac{kt^2}{2} + 44t$.  Then $\frac{ds}{dt} = 0 \Rightarrow -kt + 44 = 0 \Rightarrow t = \frac{44}{k}$ and $s\left(\frac{44}{k}\right) = -\frac{k\left(\frac{44}{k}\right)^2}{2} + 44\left(\frac{44}{k}\right) = 45$
$\Rightarrow -\frac{968}{k} + \frac{1936}{k} = 45 \Rightarrow \frac{968}{k} = 45 \Rightarrow k = \frac{968}{45} \approx 21.5 \, \frac{ft}{sec^2}$.

99.  (a)  $v = \int a \, dt = \int \left(15t^{1/2} - 3t^{-1/2}\right) dt = 10t^{3/2} - 6t^{1/2} + C$; $\frac{ds}{dt}(1) = 4 \Rightarrow 4 = 10(1)^{3/2} - 6(1)^{1/2} + C \Rightarrow C = 0$
$\Rightarrow v = 10t^{3/2} - 6t^{1/2}$

(b)  $s = \int v \, dt = \int \left(10t^{3/2} - 6t^{1/2}\right) dt = 4t^{5/2} - 4t^{3/2} + C$; $s(1) = 0 \Rightarrow 0 = 4(1)^{5/2} - 4(1)^{3/2} + C \Rightarrow C = 0$
$\Rightarrow s = 4t^{5/2} - 4t^{3/2}$

100.  $\frac{d^2s}{dt^2} = -5.2 \Rightarrow \frac{ds}{dt} = -5.2t + C_1$; at $\frac{ds}{dt} = 0$ and $t = 0$ we have $C_1 = 0 \Rightarrow \frac{ds}{dt} = -5.2t \Rightarrow s = -2.6t^2 + C_2$; at $s = 4$
and $t = 0$ we have $C_2 = 4 \Rightarrow s = -2.6t^2 + 4$.  Then $s = 0 \Rightarrow 0 = -2.6t^2 + 4 \Rightarrow t = \sqrt{\frac{4}{2.6}} \approx 1.24$ sec, since $t > 0$

101.  $\frac{d^2s}{dt^2} = a \Rightarrow \frac{ds}{dt} = \int a \, dt = at + C$; $\frac{ds}{dt} = v_0$ when $t = 0 \Rightarrow C = v_0 \Rightarrow \frac{ds}{dt} = at + v_0 \Rightarrow s = \frac{at^2}{2} + v_0 t + C_1$; $s = s_0$
when $t = 0 \Rightarrow s_0 = \frac{a(0)^2}{2} + v_0(0) + C_1 \Rightarrow C_1 = s_0 \Rightarrow s = \frac{at^2}{2} + v_0 t + s_0$

102.  The appropriate initial value problem is:  Differential Equation:  $\frac{d^2s}{dt^2} = -g$ with Initial Conditions:  $\frac{ds}{dt} = v_0$ and
$s = s_0$ when $t = 0$.  Thus, $\frac{ds}{dt} = \int -g \, dt = -gt + C_1$; $\frac{ds}{dt}(0) = v_0 \Rightarrow v_0 = (-g)(0) + C_1 \Rightarrow C_1 = v_0$
$\Rightarrow \frac{ds}{dt} = -gt + v_0$.  Thus $s = \int (-gt + v_0) \, dt = -\frac{1}{2}gt^2 + v_0 t + C_2$; $s(0) = s_0 = -\frac{1}{2}(g)(0)^2 + v_0(0) + C_2 \Rightarrow C_2 = s_0$
Thus $s = -\frac{1}{2}gt^2 + v_0 t + s_0$.

103 − 106 Example CAS commands:
Maple:
    with(student):
    f := x -> cos(x)^2 + sin(x);
    ic := [x=Pi,y=1];
    F := unapply( int( f(x), x ) + C, x );
    eq := eval( y=F(x), ic );
    solnC := solve( eq, {C} );
    Y := unapply( eval( F(x), solnC ), x );
    DEplot( diff(y(x),x) = f(x), y(x), x=0..2*Pi, [[y(Pi)=1]],
        color=black, linecolor=black, stepsize=0.05, title="Section 4.7 #103" );

Mathematica: (functions and values may vary)

The following commands use the definite integral and the Fundamental Theorem of calculus to construct the solution of the initial value problems for exercises 103 - 105.

    Clear[x, y, yprime]
    yprime[x_] = Cos[x]² + Sin[x];
    initxvalue = π; inityvalue = 1;
    y[x_] = Integrate[yprime[t], {t, initxvalue, x}] + inityvalue

If the solution satisfies the differential equation and initial condition, the following yield True

    yprime[x]==D[y[x], x] //Simplify
    y[initxvalue]==inityvalue

Since exercise 106 is a second order differential equation, two integrations will be required.

    Clear[x, y, yprime]
    y2prime[x_] = 3 Exp[x/2] + 1;
    initxval = 0; inityval = 4; inityprimeval = −1;
    yprime[x_] = Integrate[y2prime[t],{t, initxval, x}] + inityprimeval
    y[x_] = Integrate[yprime[t], {t, initxval, x}] + inityval

Verify that y[x] solves the differential equation and initial condition and plot the solution (red) and its derivative (blue).

    y2prime[x]==D[y[x], {x, 2}]//Simplify
    y[initxval]==inityval
    yprime[initxval]==inityprimeval
    Plot[{y[x], yprime[x]}, {x, initxval − 3, initxval + 3}, PlotStyle → {RGBColor[1,0,0], RGBColor[0,0,1]}]

## CHAPTER 4 PRACTICE EXERCISES

1.  No, since $f(x) = x^3 + 2x + \tan x \Rightarrow f'(x) = 3x^2 + 2 + \sec^2 x > 0 \Rightarrow$ f(x) is always increasing on its domain

2.  No, since $g(x) = \csc x + 2 \cot x \Rightarrow g'(x) = -\csc x \cot x - 2 \csc^2 x = -\frac{\cos x}{\sin^2 x} - \frac{2}{\sin^2 x} = -\frac{1}{\sin^2 x}(\cos x + 2) < 0$
    $\Rightarrow$ g(x) is always decreasing on its domain

3.  No absolute minimum because $\lim_{x \to \infty} (7 + x)(11 - 3x)^{1/3} = -\infty$. Next $f'(x) =$
    $(11 - 3x)^{1/3} - (7 + x)(11 - 3x)^{-2/3} = \frac{(11 - 3x) - (7 + x)}{(11 - 3x)^{2/3}} = \frac{4(1 - x)}{(11 - 3x)^{2/3}} \Rightarrow x = 1$ and $x = \frac{11}{3}$ are critical points.
    Since $f' > 0$ if $x < 1$ and $f' < 0$ if $x > 1$, $f(1) = 16$ is the absolute maximum.

4.  $f(x) = \frac{ax + b}{x^2 - 1} \Rightarrow f'(x) = \frac{a(x^2 - 1) - 2x(ax + b)}{(x^2 - 1)^2} = \frac{-(ax^2 + 2bx + a)}{(x^2 - 1)^2}$; $f'(3) = 0 \Rightarrow -\frac{1}{64}(9a + 6b + a) = 0 \Rightarrow 5a + 3b = 0$.
    We require also that $f(3) = 1$. Thus $1 = \frac{3a + b}{8} \Rightarrow 3a + b = 8$. Solving both equations yields $a = 6$ and $b = -10$. Now,
    $f'(x) = \frac{-2(3x - 1)(x - 3)}{(x^2 - 1)^2}$ so that $f' = - - - \underset{-1}{|} - - - \underset{1/3}{|} + + + \underset{1}{|} + + + \underset{3}{|} - - -$. Thus $f'$ changes sign at $x = 3$ from
    positive to negative so there is a local maximum at $x = 3$ which has a value $f(3) = 1$.

5.  Yes, because at each point of $[0, 1)$ except $x = 0$, the function's value is a local minimum value as well as a local maximum value. At $x = 0$ the function's value, 0, is not a local minimum value because each open interval around $x = 0$ on the x-axis contains points to the left of 0 where f equals −1.

6.  (a)  The first derivative of the function $f(x) = x^3$ is zero at $x = 0$ even though f has no local extreme value at $x = 0$.
    (b)  Theorem 2 says only that if f is differentiable and f has a local extreme at $x = c$ then $f'(c) = 0$. It does not assert the (false) reverse implication $f'(c) = 0 \Rightarrow$ f has a local extreme at $x = c$.

7.  No, because the interval $0 < x < 1$ fails to be closed. The Extreme Value Theorem says that if the function is continuous throughout a finite closed interval $a \le x \le b$ then the existence of absolute extrema is guaranteed on that interval.

8.  The absolute maximum is $|-1| = 1$ and the absolute minimum is $|0| = 0$. This is not inconsistent with the Extreme Value Theorem for continuous functions, which says a continuous function on a closed interval attains its extreme values on that interval. The theorem says nothing about the behavior of a continuous function on an interval which is half open and half closed, such as $[-1, 1)$, so there is nothing to contradict.

9.  (a) There appear to be local minima at $x = -1.75$ and 1.8. Points of inflection are indicated at approximately $x = 0$ and $x = \pm 1$.

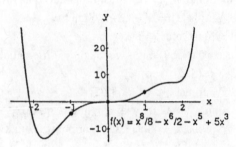

(b) $f'(x) = x^7 - 3x^5 - 5x^4 + 15x^2 = x^2(x^2 - 3)(x^3 - 5)$. The pattern $y' = ---\ |\ +++\ |\ +++\ |\ ---\ |\ +++$
$\qquad\qquad\qquad\qquad\qquad\qquad\qquad\qquad\qquad -\sqrt{3}\quad 0\quad \sqrt[3]{5}\quad \sqrt{3}$

indicates a local maximum at $x = \sqrt[3]{5}$ and local minima at $x = \pm\sqrt{3}$.

(c)

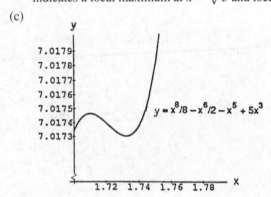

10. (a) The graph does not indicate any local extremum. Points of inflection are indicated at approximately $x = -\frac{3}{4}$ and $x = 1$.

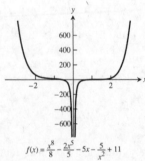

(b) $f'(x) = x^7 - 2x^4 - 5 + \frac{10}{x^3} = x^{-3}(x^3 - 2)(x^7 - 5)$. The pattern $f' = ---\ )(+++\ |\ ---\ |\ +++$ indicates
$\qquad\qquad\qquad\qquad\qquad\qquad\qquad\qquad\qquad\qquad\qquad 0\quad \sqrt[7]{5}\quad \sqrt[3]{2}$

a local maximum at $x = \sqrt[7]{5}$ and a local minimum at $x = \sqrt[3]{2}$.

(c)

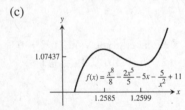

11. (a) $g(t) = \sin^2 t - 3t \Rightarrow g'(t) = 2 \sin t \cos t - 3 = \sin(2t) - 3 \Rightarrow g' < 0 \Rightarrow g(t)$ is always falling and hence must decrease on every interval in its domain.

(b) One, since $\sin^2 t - 3t - 5 = 0$ and $\sin^2 t - 3t = 5$ have the same solutions: $f(t) = \sin^2 t - 3t - 5$ has the same derivative as $g(t)$ in part (a) and is always decreasing with $f(-3) > 0$ and $f(0) < 0$. The Intermediate Value Theorem guarantees the continuous function f has a root in $[-3, 0]$.

12. (a) $y = \tan \theta \Rightarrow \frac{dy}{d\theta} = \sec^2 \theta > 0 \Rightarrow y = \tan \theta$ is always rising on its domain $\Rightarrow y = \tan \theta$ increases on every interval in its domain

(b) The interval $\left[\frac{\pi}{4}, \pi\right]$ is not in the tangent's domain because $\tan \theta$ is undefined at $\theta = \frac{\pi}{2}$. Thus the tangent need not increase on this interval.

13. (a) $f(x) = x^4 + 2x^2 - 2 \Rightarrow f'(x) = 4x^3 + 4x$. Since $f(0) = -2 < 0$, $f(1) = 1 > 0$ and $f'(x) \geq 0$ for $0 \leq x \leq 1$, we may conclude from the Intermediate Value Theorem that $f(x)$ has exactly one solution when $0 \leq x \leq 1$.

(b) $x^2 = \frac{-2 \pm \sqrt{4+8}}{2} > 0 \Rightarrow x^2 = \sqrt{3} - 1$ and $x \geq 0 \Rightarrow x \approx \sqrt{.7320508076} \approx .8555996772$

14. (a) $y = \frac{x}{x+1} \Rightarrow y' = \frac{1}{(x+1)^2} > 0$, for all x in the domain of $\frac{x}{x+1} \Rightarrow y = \frac{x}{x+1}$ is increasing in every interval in its domain.

(b) $y = x^3 + 2x \Rightarrow y' = 3x^2 + 2 > 0$ for all $x \Rightarrow$ the graph of $y = x^3 + 2x$ is always increasing and can never have a local maximum or minimum

15. Let $V(t)$ represent the volume of the water in the reservoir at time t, in minutes, let $V(0) = a_0$ be the initial amount and $V(1440) = a_0 + (1400)(43,560)(7.48)$ gallons be the amount of water contained in the reservoir after the rain, where 24 hr $= 1440$ min. Assume that $V(t)$ is continuous on $[0, 1440]$ and differentiable on $(0, 1440)$. The Mean Value Theorem says that for some $t_0$ in $(0, 1440)$ we have $V'(t_0) = \frac{V(1440) - V(0)}{1440 - 0} = \frac{a_0 + (1400)(43,560)(7.48) - a_0}{1440} = \frac{456,160,320 \text{ gal}}{1440 \text{ min}}$
$= 316,778$ gal/min. Therefore at $t_0$ the reservoir's volume was increasing at a rate in excess of 225,000 gal/min.

16. Yes, all differentiable functions $g(x)$ having 3 as a derivative differ by only a constant. Consequently, the difference $3x - g(x)$ is a constant K because $g'(x) = 3 = \frac{d}{dx}(3x)$. Thus $g(x) = 3x + K$, the same form as $F(x)$.

17. No, $\frac{x}{x+1} = 1 + \frac{-1}{x+1} \Rightarrow \frac{x}{x+1}$ differs from $\frac{-1}{x+1}$ by the constant 1. Both functions have the same derivative
$\frac{d}{dx}\left(\frac{x}{x+1}\right) = \frac{(x+1) - x(1)}{(x+1)^2} = \frac{1}{(x+1)^2} = \frac{d}{dx}\left(\frac{-1}{x+1}\right)$.

18. $f'(x) = g'(x) = \frac{2x}{(x^2+1)^2} \Rightarrow f(x) - g(x) = C$ for some constant $C \Rightarrow$ the graphs differ by a vertical shift.

19. The global minimum value of $\frac{1}{2}$ occurs at $x = 2$.

20. (a) The function is increasing on the intervals $[-3, -2]$ and $[1, 2]$.

(b) The function is decreasing on the intervals $[-2, 0)$ and $(0, 1]$.

(c) The local maximum values occur only at $x = -2$, and at $x = 2$; local minimum values occur at $x = -3$ and at $x = 1$ provided f is continuous at $x = 0$.

21. (a) $t = 0, 6, 12$    (b) $t = 3, 9$    (c) $6 < t < 12$    (d) $0 < t < 6$, $12 < t < 14$

22. (a) $t = 4$    (b) at no time    (c) $0 < t < 4$    (d) $4 < t < 8$

23.

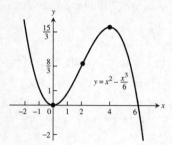

24.

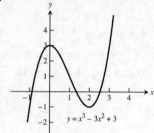

25.

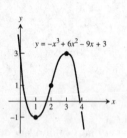

26.

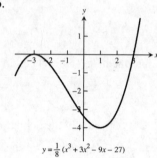

27.

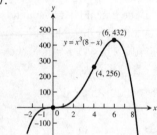

28.

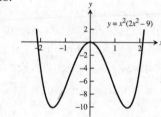

29.

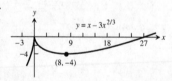

30.

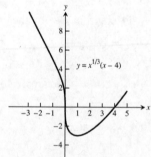

31.

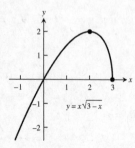

32.

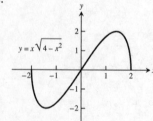

33. (a) $y' = 16 - x^2 \Rightarrow y' = ---\;|\;+++\;|\;---\;\Rightarrow$ the curve is rising on $(-4, 4)$, falling on $(-\infty, -4)$ and $(4, \infty)$
$\phantom{xxxxxxxxxxxxxxxxxxxxxx}{\scriptstyle -4}\;\;\;\;\;{\scriptstyle 4}$

$\Rightarrow$ a local maximum at $x = 4$ and a local minimum at $x = -4$; $y'' = -2x \Rightarrow y'' = +++\;|\;---\;\Rightarrow$ the curve
$\phantom{xxxxxxxxxxxxxxxxxxxxxxxxxxxxxxxxxxxxxxxxxxxxxxxxxxxxxxxxxxx}{\scriptstyle 0}$

is concave up on $(-\infty, 0)$, concave down on $(0, \infty) \Rightarrow$ a point of inflection at $x = 0$

(b)

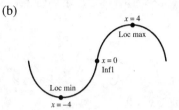

34. (a) $y' = x^2 - x - 6 = (x - 3)(x + 2) \Rightarrow y' = +++\;|\;---\;|\;+++ \Rightarrow$ the curve is rising on $(-\infty, -2)$ and $(3, \infty)$,
$\phantom{xxxxxxxxxxxxxxxxxxxxxxxxxxxxxxxxxxxx}{\scriptstyle -2}\;\;\;\;\;{\scriptstyle 3}$

falling on $(-2, 3) \Rightarrow$ local maximum at $x = -2$ and a local minimum at $x = 3$; $y'' = 2x - 1$

$\Rightarrow y'' = ---\;|\;+++ \Rightarrow$ concave up on $\left(\frac{1}{2}, \infty\right)$, concave down on $\left(-\infty, \frac{1}{2}\right) \Rightarrow$ a point of inflection at $x = \frac{1}{2}$
$\phantom{xxxxxx}{\scriptstyle 1/2}$

(b)

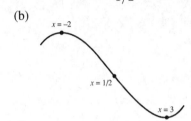

35. (a) $y' = 6x(x + 1)(x - 2) = 6x^3 - 6x^2 - 12x \Rightarrow y' = ---\;|\;+++\;|\;---\;|\;+++ \Rightarrow$ the graph is rising on $(-1, 0)$
$\phantom{xxxxxxxxxxxxxxxxxxxxxxxxxxxxxxxxxxxxxxxxxxxxxxxxxxx}{\scriptstyle -1}\;\;\;\;{\scriptstyle 0}\;\;\;\;{\scriptstyle 2}$

and $(2, \infty)$, falling on $(-\infty, -1)$ and $(0, 2) \Rightarrow$ a local maximum at $x = 0$, local minima at $x = -1$ and

$x = 2$; $y'' = 18x^2 - 12x - 12 = 6(3x^2 - 2x - 2) = 6\left(x - \frac{1 - \sqrt{7}}{3}\right)\left(x - \frac{1 + \sqrt{7}}{3}\right) \Rightarrow$

$y'' = +++\;|\;---\;|\;+++ \Rightarrow$ the curve is concave up on $\left(-\infty, \frac{1 - \sqrt{7}}{3}\right)$ and $\left(\frac{1 + \sqrt{7}}{3}, \infty\right)$, concave down
$\phantom{xxxxxxx}{\scriptstyle \frac{1-\sqrt{7}}{3}}\;\;\;{\scriptstyle \frac{1+\sqrt{7}}{3}}$

on $\left(\frac{1 - \sqrt{7}}{3}, \frac{1 + \sqrt{7}}{3}\right) \Rightarrow$ points of inflection at $x = \frac{1 \pm \sqrt{7}}{3}$

(b)

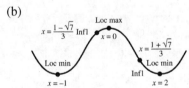

36. (a) $y' = x^2(6 - 4x) = 6x^2 - 4x^3 \Rightarrow y' = +++\;|\;+++\;|\;--- \Rightarrow$ the curve is rising on $\left(-\infty, \frac{3}{2}\right)$, falling on $\left(\frac{3}{2}, \infty\right)$
$\phantom{xxxxxxxxxxxxxxxxxxxxxxxxxxxxxxxxxxxxxxxx}{\scriptstyle 0}\;\;\;\;{\scriptstyle 3/2}$

$\Rightarrow$ a local maximum at $x = \frac{3}{2}$; $y'' = 12x - 12x^2 = 12x(1 - x) \Rightarrow y'' = ---\;|\;+++\;|\;--- \Rightarrow$ concave up on
$\phantom{xxxxxxxxxxxxxxxxxxxxxxxxxxxxxxxxxxxxxxxxxxxxxxxxxxxxxxxxxxxxx}{\scriptstyle 0}\;\;\;\;{\scriptstyle 1}$

$(0, 1)$, concave down on $(-\infty, 0)$ and $(1, \infty) \Rightarrow$ points of inflection at $x = 0$ and $x = 1$

(b)

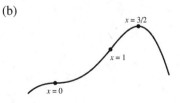

37. (a) $y' = x^4 - 2x^2 = x^2(x^2 - 2)$ ⇒ $y' = +++ |_{-\sqrt{2}} --- |_0 --- |_{\sqrt{2}} +++$ ⇒ the curve is rising on $\left(-\infty, -\sqrt{2}\right)$ and

$\left(\sqrt{2}, \infty\right)$, falling on $\left(-\sqrt{2}, \sqrt{2}\right)$ ⇒ a local maximum at $x = -\sqrt{2}$ and a local minimum at $x = \sqrt{2}$;

$y'' = 4x^3 - 4x = 4x(x-1)(x+1)$ ⇒ $y'' = --- |_{-1} +++ |_0 --- |_1 +++$ ⇒ concave up on $(-1, 0)$ and $(1, \infty)$,

concave down on $(-\infty, -1)$ and $(0, 1)$ ⇒ points of inflection at $x = 0$ and $x = \pm 1$

(b)

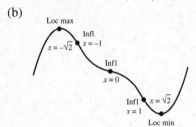

38. (a) $y' = 4x^2 - x^4 = x^2(4 - x^2)$ ⇒ $y' = --- |_{-2} +++ |_0 +++ |_2 ---$ ⇒ the curve is rising on $(-2, 0)$ and $(0, 2)$,

falling on $(-\infty, -2)$ and $(2, \infty)$ ⇒ a local maximum at $x = 2$, a local minimum at $x = -2$; $y'' = 8x - 4x^3$

$= 4x(2 - x^2)$ ⇒ $y'' = +++ |_{-\sqrt{2}} --- |_0 +++ |_{\sqrt{2}} ---$ ⇒ concave up on $\left(-\infty, -\sqrt{2}\right)$ and $\left(0, \sqrt{2}\right)$, concave

down on $\left(-\sqrt{2}, 0\right)$ and $\left(\sqrt{2}, \infty\right)$ ⇒ points of inflection at $x = 0$ and $x = \pm\sqrt{2}$

(b)

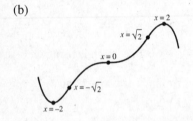

39. The values of the first derivative indicate that the curve is rising on $(0, \infty)$ and falling on $(-\infty, 0)$. The slope of the curve approaches $-\infty$ as $x \to 0^-$, and approaches $\infty$ as $x \to 0^+$ and $x \to 1$. The curve should therefore have a cusp and local minimum at $x = 0$, and a vertical tangent at $x = 1$.

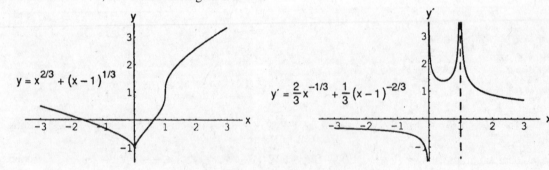

40. The values of the first derivative indicate that the curve is rising on $\left(0,\frac{1}{2}\right)$ and $(1,\infty)$, and falling on $(-\infty,0)$ and $\left(\frac{1}{2},1\right)$. The derivative changes from positive to negative at $x=\frac{1}{2}$, indicating a local maximum there. The slope of the curve approaches $-\infty$ as $x\to 0^-$ and $x\to 1^-$, and approaches $\infty$ as $x\to 0^+$ and as $x\to 1^+$, indicating cusps and local minima at both $x=0$ and $x=1$.

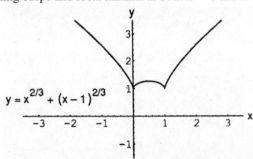 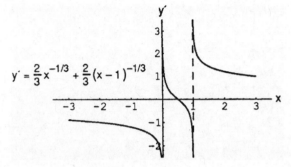

41. The values of the first derivative indicate that the curve is always rising. The slope of the curve approaches $\infty$ as $x\to 0$ and as $x\to 1$, indicating vertical tangents at both $x=0$ and $x=1$.

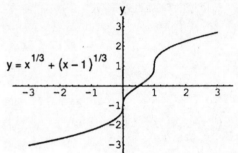 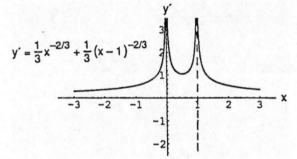

42. The graph of the first derivative indicates that the curve is rising on $\left(0,\frac{17-\sqrt{33}}{16}\right)$ and $\left(\frac{17+\sqrt{33}}{16},\infty\right)$, falling on $(-\infty,0)$ and $\left(\frac{17-\sqrt{33}}{16},\frac{17+\sqrt{33}}{16}\right)$ $\Rightarrow$ a local maximum at $x=\frac{17-\sqrt{33}}{16}$, a local minimum at $x=\frac{17+\sqrt{33}}{16}$. The derivative approaches $-\infty$ as $x\to 0^-$ and $x\to 1$, and approaches $\infty$ as $x\to 0^+$, indicating a cusp and local minimum at $x=0$ and a vertical tangent at $x=1$.

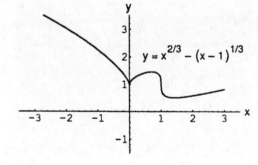 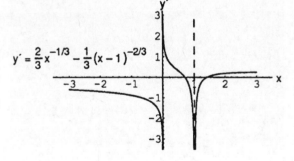

43. $y = \frac{x+1}{x-3} = 1 + \frac{4}{x-3}$

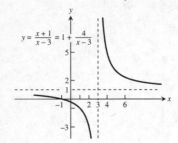

44. $y = \frac{2x}{x+5} = 2 - \frac{10}{x+5}$

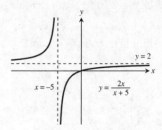

45. $y = \frac{x^2+1}{x} = x + \frac{1}{x}$

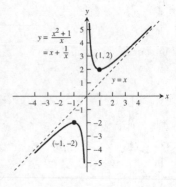

46. $y = \frac{x^2-x+1}{x} = x - 1 + \frac{1}{x}$

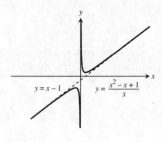

47. $y = \frac{x^3+2}{2x} = \frac{x^2}{2} + \frac{1}{x}$

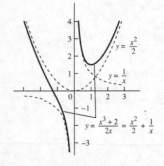

48. $y = \frac{x^4-1}{x^2} = x^2 - \frac{1}{x^2}$

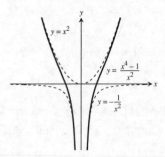

49. $y = \frac{x^2-4}{x^2-3} = 1 - \frac{1}{x^2-3}$

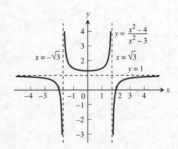

50. $y = \frac{x^2}{x^2-4} = 1 + \frac{4}{x^2-4}$

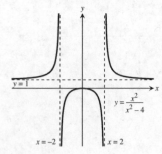

51. (a)  Maximize $f(x) = \sqrt{x} - \sqrt{36-x} = x^{1/2} - (36-x)^{1/2}$ where $0 \le x \le 36$

$\Rightarrow$  $f'(x) = \frac{1}{2}x^{-1/2} - \frac{1}{2}(36-x)^{-1/2}(-1) = \frac{\sqrt{36-x} + \sqrt{x}}{2\sqrt{x}\sqrt{36-x}}$  $\Rightarrow$  derivative fails to exist at 0 and 36;  $f(0) = -6$,

and $f(36) = 6$  $\Rightarrow$  the numbers are 0 and 36

(b)  Maximize $g(x) = \sqrt{x} + \sqrt{36-x} = x^{1/2} + (36-x)^{1/2}$ where $0 \le x \le 36$

$\Rightarrow g'(x) = \frac{1}{2}x^{-1/2} + \frac{1}{2}(36-x)^{-1/2}(-1) = \frac{\sqrt{36-x}-\sqrt{x}}{2\sqrt{x}\sqrt{36-x}} \Rightarrow$ critical points at 0, 18 and 36; $g(0) = 6$,

$g(18) = 2\sqrt{18} = 6\sqrt{2}$ and $g(36) = 6 \Rightarrow$ the numbers are 18 and 18

52.  (a)  Maximize $f(x) = \sqrt{x}(20-x) = 20x^{1/2} - x^{3/2}$ where $0 \le x \le 20 \Rightarrow f'(x) = 10x^{-1/2} - \frac{3}{2}x^{1/2}$

$= \frac{20-3x}{2\sqrt{x}} = 0 \Rightarrow x = 0$ and $x = \frac{20}{3}$ are critical points; $f(0) = f(20) = 0$ and $f\left(\frac{20}{3}\right) = \sqrt{\frac{20}{3}}\left(20 - \frac{20}{3}\right)$

$= \frac{40\sqrt{20}}{3\sqrt{3}} \Rightarrow$ the numbers are $\frac{20}{3}$ and $\frac{40}{3}$.

(b)  Maximize $g(x) = x + \sqrt{20-x} = x + (20-x)^{1/2}$ where $0 \le x \le 20 \Rightarrow g'(x) = \frac{2\sqrt{20-x}-1}{2\sqrt{20-x}} = 0$

$\Rightarrow \sqrt{20-x} = \frac{1}{2} \Rightarrow x = \frac{79}{4}$. The critical points are $x = \frac{79}{4}$ and $x = 20$. Since $g\left(\frac{79}{4}\right) = \frac{81}{4}$ and $g(20) = 20$,

the numbers must be $\frac{79}{4}$ and $\frac{1}{4}$.

53.  $A(x) = \frac{1}{2}(2x)(27 - x^2)$ for $0 \le x \le \sqrt{27}$

$\Rightarrow A'(x) = 3(3+x)(3-x)$ and $A''(x) = -6x$.
The critical points are $-3$ and 3, but $-3$ is not in the
domain. Since $A''(3) = -18 < 0$ and $A\left(\sqrt{27}\right) = 0$,
the maximum occurs at $x = 3 \Rightarrow$ the largest area is
$A(3) = 54$ sq units.

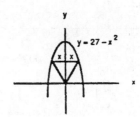

54.  The volume is $V = x^2h = 32 \Rightarrow h = \frac{32}{x^2}$. The
surface area is $S(x) = x^2 + 4x\left(\frac{32}{x^2}\right) = x^2 + \frac{128}{x}$,
where $x > 0 \Rightarrow S'(x) = \frac{2(x-4)(x^2+4x+16)}{x^2}$
$\Rightarrow$ the critical points are 0 and 4, but 0 is not in the
domain. Now $S''(4) = 2 + \frac{256}{4^3} > 0 \Rightarrow$ at $x = 4$ there
is a minimum. The dimensions 4 ft by 4 ft by 2 ft
minimize the surface area.

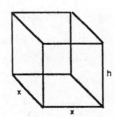

55.  From the diagram we have $\left(\frac{h}{2}\right)^2 + r^2 = \left(\sqrt{3}\right)^2$

$\Rightarrow r^2 = \frac{12-h^2}{4}$. The volume of the cylinder is

$V = \pi r^2h = \pi\left(\frac{12-h^2}{4}\right)h = \frac{\pi}{4}(12h - h^3)$, where

$0 \le h \le 2\sqrt{3}$. Then $V'(h) = \frac{3\pi}{4}(2+h)(2-h)$
$\Rightarrow$ the critical points are $-2$ and 2, but $-2$ is not in
the domain. At $h = 2$ there is a maximum since
$V''(2) = -3\pi < 0$. The dimensions of the largest
cylinder are radius $= \sqrt{2}$ and height $= 2$.

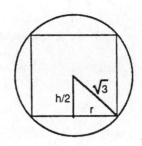

56.  From the diagram we have $x = $ radius and
$y = $ height $= 12 - 2x$ and $V(x) = \frac{1}{3}\pi x^2(12-2x)$, where
$0 \le x \le 6 \Rightarrow V'(x) = 2\pi x(4-x)$ and $V''(4) = -8\pi$. The
critical points are 0 and 4; $V(0) = V(6) = 0 \Rightarrow x = 4$
gives the maximum. Thus the values of $r = 4$ and
$h = 4$ yield the largest volume for the smaller cone.

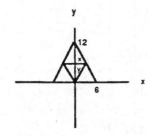

52. Let $\Delta x = \frac{b-0}{n} = \frac{b}{n}$ and let $x_0 = 0$, $x_1 = \Delta x$,

$x_2 = 2\Delta x, \ldots, x_{n-1} = (n-1)\Delta x$, $x_n = n\Delta x = b$.

Let the $c_k$'s be the right end-points of the subintervals

$\Rightarrow c_1 = x_1$, $c_2 = x_2$, and so on. The rectangles

defined have areas:

$\quad f(c_1)\,\Delta x = f(\Delta x)\,\Delta x = \pi(\Delta x)^2\,\Delta x = \pi(\Delta x)^3$

$\quad f(c_2)\,\Delta x = f(2\Delta x)\,\Delta x = \pi(2\Delta x)^2\,\Delta x = \pi(2)^2(\Delta x)^3$

$\quad f(c_3)\,\Delta x = f(3\Delta x)\,\Delta x = \pi(3\Delta x)^2\,\Delta x = \pi(3)^2(\Delta x)^3$

$\qquad \vdots$

$\quad f(c_n)\,\Delta x = f(n\Delta x)\,\Delta x = \pi(n\Delta x)^2\,\Delta x = \pi(n)^2(\Delta x)^3$

Then $S_n = \sum\limits_{k=1}^{n} f(c_k)\,\Delta x = \sum\limits_{k=1}^{n} \pi k^2(\Delta x)^3$

$= \pi(\Delta x)^3 \sum\limits_{k=1}^{n} k^2 = \pi\left(\frac{b^3}{n^3}\right)\left(\frac{n(n+1)(2n+1)}{6}\right)$

$= \frac{\pi b^3}{6}\left(2 + \frac{3}{n} + \frac{1}{n^2}\right) \Rightarrow \int_0^b \pi x^2\,dx = \lim\limits_{n\to\infty} \frac{\pi b^3}{6}\left(2 + \frac{3}{n} + \frac{1}{n^2}\right) = \frac{\pi b^3}{3}$.

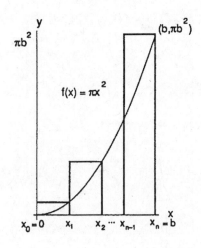

53. Let $\Delta x = \frac{b-0}{n} = \frac{b}{n}$ and let $x_0 = 0$, $x_1 = \Delta x$,

$x_2 = 2\Delta x, \ldots, x_{n-1} = (n-1)\Delta x$, $x_n = n\Delta x = b$.

Let the $c_k$'s be the right end-points of the subintervals

$\Rightarrow c_1 = x_1$, $c_2 = x_2$, and so on. The rectangles

defined have areas:

$\quad f(c_1)\,\Delta x = f(\Delta x)\,\Delta x = 2(\Delta x)(\Delta x) = 2(\Delta x)^2$

$\quad f(c_2)\,\Delta x = f(2\Delta x)\,\Delta x = 2(2\Delta x)(\Delta x) = 2(2)(\Delta x)^2$

$\quad f(c_3)\,\Delta x = f(3\Delta x)\,\Delta x = 2(3\Delta x)(\Delta x) = 2(3)(\Delta x)^2$

$\qquad \vdots$

$\quad f(c_n)\,\Delta x = f(n\Delta x)\,\Delta x = 2(n\Delta x)(\Delta x) = 2(n)(\Delta x)^2$

Then $S_n = \sum\limits_{k=1}^{n} f(c_k)\,\Delta x = \sum\limits_{k=1}^{n} 2k(\Delta x)^2$

$= 2(\Delta x)^2 \sum\limits_{k=1}^{n} k = 2\left(\frac{b^2}{n^2}\right)\left(\frac{n(n+1)}{2}\right)$

$= b^2\left(1 + \frac{1}{n}\right) \Rightarrow \int_0^b 2x\,dx = \lim\limits_{n\to\infty} b^2\left(1 + \frac{1}{n}\right) = b^2$.

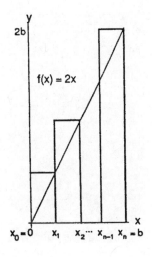

54. Let $\Delta x = \frac{b-0}{n} = \frac{b}{n}$ and let $x_0 = 0$, $x_1 = \Delta x$,

$x_2 = 2\Delta x, \ldots, x_{n-1} = (n-1)\Delta x$, $x_n = n\Delta x = b$.

Let the $c_k$'s be the right end-points of the subintervals

$\Rightarrow c_1 = x_1$, $c_2 = x_2$, and so on. The rectangles

defined have areas:

$\quad f(c_1)\,\Delta x = f(\Delta x)\,\Delta x = \left(\frac{\Delta x}{2} + 1\right)(\Delta x) = \frac{1}{2}(\Delta x)^2 + \Delta x$

$\quad f(c_2)\,\Delta x = f(2\Delta x)\,\Delta x = \left(\frac{2\Delta x}{2} + 1\right)(\Delta x) = \frac{1}{2}(2)(\Delta x)^2 + \Delta x$

$\quad f(c_3)\,\Delta x = f(3\Delta x)\,\Delta x = \left(\frac{3\Delta x}{2} + 1\right)(\Delta x) = \frac{1}{2}(3)(\Delta x)^2 + \Delta x$

$\qquad \vdots$

$\quad f(c_n)\,\Delta x = f(n\Delta x)\,\Delta x = \left(\frac{n\Delta x}{2} + 1\right)(\Delta x) = \frac{1}{2}(n)(\Delta x)^2 + \Delta x$

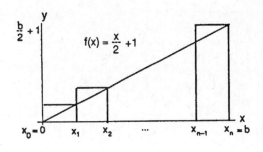

Then $S_n = \sum\limits_{k=1}^{n} f(c_k)\,\Delta x = \sum\limits_{k=1}^{n} \left(\frac{1}{2}k(\Delta x)^2 + \Delta x\right) = \frac{1}{2}(\Delta x)^2 \sum\limits_{k=1}^{n} k + \Delta x \sum\limits_{k=1}^{n} 1 = \frac{1}{2}\left(\frac{b^2}{n^2}\right)\left(\frac{n(n+1)}{2}\right) + \left(\frac{b}{n}\right)(n)$

$= \frac{1}{4}b^2\left(1 + \frac{1}{n}\right) + b \Rightarrow \int_0^b \left(\frac{x}{2} + 1\right)dx = \lim\limits_{n\to\infty} \left(\frac{1}{4}b^2\left(1 + \frac{1}{n}\right) + b\right) = \frac{1}{4}b^2 + b$.

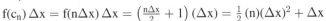

55.  $av(f) = \left(\frac{1}{\sqrt{3}-0}\right) \int_0^{\sqrt{3}} (x^2 - 1)\, dx$

$= \frac{1}{\sqrt{3}} \int_0^{\sqrt{3}} x^2\, dx - \frac{1}{\sqrt{3}} \int_0^{\sqrt{3}} 1\, dx$

$= \frac{1}{\sqrt{3}} \left(\frac{(\sqrt{3})^3}{3}\right) - \frac{1}{\sqrt{3}} \left(\sqrt{3} - 0\right) = 1 - 1 = 0.$

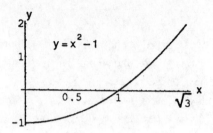

56.  $av(f) = \left(\frac{1}{3-0}\right) \int_0^3 \left(-\frac{x^2}{2}\right) dx = \frac{1}{3}\left(-\frac{1}{2}\right) \int_0^3 x^2\, dx$

$= -\frac{1}{6}\left(\frac{3^3}{3}\right) = -\frac{3}{2}\,;\, -\frac{x^2}{2} = -\frac{3}{2}.$

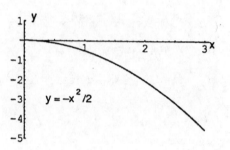

57.  $av(f) = \left(\frac{1}{1-0}\right) \int_0^1 (-3x^2 - 1)\, dx =$

$= -3 \int_0^1 x^2\, dx - \int_0^1 1\, dx = -3\left(\frac{1^3}{3}\right) - (1 - 0)$

$= -2.$

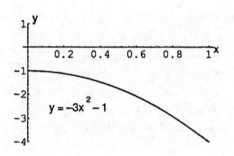

58.  $av(f) = \left(\frac{1}{1-0}\right) \int_0^1 (3x^2 - 3)\, dx =$

$= 3 \int_0^1 x^2\, dx - \int_0^1 3\, dx = 3\left(\frac{1^3}{3}\right) - 3(1 - 0)$

$= -2.$

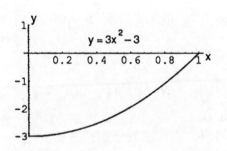

59.  $av(f) = \left(\frac{1}{3-0}\right) \int_0^3 (t - 1)^2\, dt$

$= \frac{1}{3} \int_0^3 t^2\, dt - \frac{2}{3} \int_0^3 t\, dt + \frac{1}{3} \int_0^3 1\, dt$

$= \frac{1}{3}\left(\frac{3^3}{3}\right) - \frac{2}{3}\left(\frac{3^2}{2} - \frac{0^2}{2}\right) + \frac{1}{3}(3 - 0) = 1.$

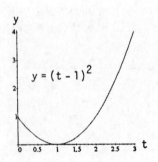

60. $\text{av}(f) = \left(\frac{1}{1-(-2)}\right) \int_{-2}^{1} (t^2 - t)\, dt$

$= \frac{1}{3} \int_{-2}^{1} t^2\, dt - \frac{1}{3} \int_{-2}^{1} t\, dt$

$= \frac{1}{3} \int_{0}^{1} t^2\, dt - \frac{1}{3} \int_{0}^{-2} t^2\, dt - \frac{1}{3} \left(\frac{1^2}{2} - \frac{(-2)^2}{2}\right)$

$= \frac{1}{3} \left(\frac{1^3}{3}\right) - \frac{1}{3} \left(\frac{(-2)^3}{3}\right) + \frac{1}{2} = \frac{3}{2}.$

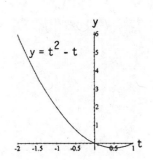

61. (a)  $\text{av}(g) = \left(\frac{1}{1-(-1)}\right) \int_{-1}^{1} (|x| - 1)\, dx$

$= \frac{1}{2} \int_{-1}^{0} (-x - 1)\, dx + \frac{1}{2} \int_{0}^{1} (x - 1)\, dx$

$= -\frac{1}{2} \int_{-1}^{0} x\, dx - \frac{1}{2} \int_{-1}^{0} 1\, dx + \frac{1}{2} \int_{0}^{1} x\, dx - \frac{1}{2} \int_{0}^{1} 1\, dx$

$= -\frac{1}{2} \left(\frac{0^2}{2} - \frac{(-1)^2}{2}\right) - \frac{1}{2} (0 - (-1)) + \frac{1}{2} \left(\frac{1^2}{2} - \frac{0^2}{2}\right) - \frac{1}{2} (1 - 0)$

$= -\frac{1}{2}.$

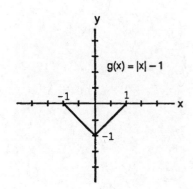

(b)  $\text{av}(g) = \left(\frac{1}{3-1}\right) \int_{1}^{3} (|x| - 1)\, dx = \frac{1}{2} \int_{1}^{3} (x - 1)\, dx$

$= \frac{1}{2} \int_{1}^{3} x\, dx - \frac{1}{2} \int_{1}^{3} 1\, dx = \frac{1}{2} \left(\frac{3^2}{2} - \frac{1^2}{2}\right) - \frac{1}{2} (3 - 1)$

$= 1.$

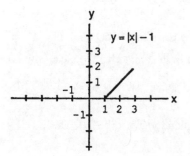

(c)  $\text{av}(g) = \left(\frac{1}{3-(-1)}\right) \int_{-1}^{3} (|x| - 1)\, dx$

$= \frac{1}{4} \int_{-1}^{1} (|x| - 1)\, dx + \frac{1}{4} \int_{1}^{3} (|x| - 1)\, dx$

$= \frac{1}{4} (-1 + 2) = \frac{1}{4}$ (see parts (a) and (b) above).

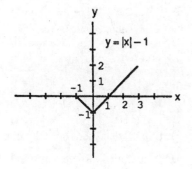

62. (a)  $\text{av}(h) = \left(\frac{1}{0-(-1)}\right) \int_{-1}^{0} -|x|\, dx = \int_{-1}^{0} -(-x)\, dx$

$= \int_{-1}^{0} x\, dx = \frac{0^2}{2} - \frac{(-1)^2}{2} = -\frac{1}{2}.$

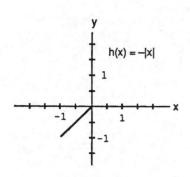

(b) $\text{av(h)} = \left(\frac{1}{1-0}\right)\int_0^1 -|x|\,dx = -\int_0^1 x\,dx$

$\quad = -\left(\frac{1^2}{2} - \frac{0^2}{2}\right) = -\frac{1}{2}.$

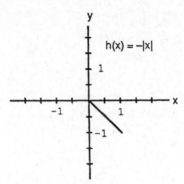

(c) $\text{av(h)} = \left(\frac{1}{1-(-1)}\right)\int_{-1}^1 -|x|\,dx$

$\quad = \frac{1}{2}\left(\int_{-1}^0 -|x|\,dx + \int_0^1 -|x|\,dx\right)$

$\quad = \frac{1}{2}\left(-\frac{1}{2} + \left(-\frac{1}{2}\right)\right) = -\frac{1}{2}$ (see parts (a) and (b)
above).

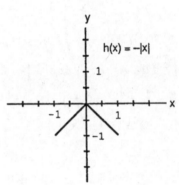

63. Consider the partition P that subdivides the interval [a, b] into n subintervals of width $\triangle x = \frac{b-a}{n}$ and let $c_k$ be the right endpoint of each subinterval. So the partition is $P = \{a, a+\frac{b-a}{n}, a+\frac{2(b-a)}{n}, \dots, a+\frac{n(b-a)}{n}\}$ and $c_k = a+\frac{k(b-a)}{n}$.
We get the Riemann sum $\sum_{k=1}^n f(c_k)\triangle x = \sum_{k=1}^n c \cdot \frac{b-a}{n} = \frac{c(b-a)}{n}\sum_{k=1}^n 1 = \frac{c(b-a)}{n} \cdot n = c(b-a)$. As $n \to \infty$ and $\|P\| \to 0$
this expression remains $c(b-a)$. Thus, $\int_a^b c\,dx = c(b-a)$.

64. Consider the partition P that subdivides the interval [0, 2] into n subintervals of width $\triangle x = \frac{2-0}{n} = \frac{2}{n}$ and let $c_k$ be the right endpoint of each subinterval. So the partition is $P = \{0, \frac{2}{n}, 2\cdot\frac{2}{n}, \dots, n\cdot\frac{2}{n} = 2\}$ and $c_k = k\cdot\frac{2}{n} = \frac{2k}{n}$. We get the
Riemann sum $\sum_{k=1}^n f(c_k)\triangle x = \sum_{k=1}^n \left[2\left(\frac{2k}{n}\right)+1\right]\cdot\frac{2}{n} = \frac{2}{n}\sum_{k=1}^n\left(\frac{4k}{n}+1\right) = \frac{8}{n^2}\sum_{k=1}^n k + \frac{2}{n}\sum_{k=1}^n 1 = \frac{8}{n^2}\cdot\frac{n(n+1)}{2} + \frac{2}{n}\cdot n = \frac{4(n+1)}{n} + 2.$
As $n \to \infty$ and $\|P\| \to 0$ the expression $\frac{4(n+1)}{n} + 2$ has the value $4 + 2 = 6$. Thus, $\int_0^2 (2x+1)\,dx = 6.$

65. Consider the partition P that subdivides the interval [a, b] into n subintervals of width $\triangle x = \frac{b-a}{n}$ and let $c_k$ be the right endpoint of each subinterval. So the partition is $P = \{a, a+\frac{b-a}{n}, a+\frac{2(b-a)}{n}, \dots, a+\frac{n(b-a)}{n}\}$ and $c_k = a+\frac{k(b-a)}{n}$.
We get the Riemann sum $\sum_{k=1}^n f(c_k)\triangle x = \sum_{k=1}^n c_k^2\left(\frac{b-a}{n}\right) = \frac{b-a}{n}\sum_{k=1}^n\left(a+\frac{k(b-a)}{n}\right)^2 = \frac{b-a}{n}\sum_{k=1}^n\left(a^2 + \frac{2ak(b-a)}{n} + \frac{k^2(b-a)^2}{n^2}\right)$

$= \frac{b-a}{n}\left(\sum_{k=1}^n a^2 + \frac{2a(b-a)}{n}\sum_{k=1}^n k + \frac{(b-a)^2}{n^2}\sum_{k=1}^n k^2\right) = \frac{b-a}{n}\cdot na^2 + \frac{2a(b-a)^2}{n^2}\cdot\frac{n(n+1)}{2} + \frac{(b-a)^3}{n^3}\cdot\frac{n(n+1)(2n+1)}{6}$

$= (b-a)a^2 + a(b-a)^2\cdot\frac{n+1}{n} + \frac{(b-a)^3}{6}\cdot\frac{(n+1)(2n+1)}{n^2} = (b-a)a^2 + a(b-a)^2\cdot\frac{1+\frac{1}{n}}{1} + \frac{(b-a)^3}{6}\cdot\frac{2+\frac{3}{n}+\frac{1}{n^2}}{1}$

As $n \to \infty$ and $\|P\| \to 0$ this expression has value $(b-a)a^2 + a(b-a)^2\cdot 1 + \frac{(b-a)^3}{6}\cdot 2$

$= ba^2 - a^3 + ab^2 - 2a^2b + a^3 + \frac{1}{3}(b^3 - 3b^2a + 3ba^2 - a^3) = \frac{b^3}{3} - \frac{a^3}{3}$. Thus, $\int_a^b x^2\,dx = \frac{b^3}{3} - \frac{a^3}{3}.$

66. Consider the partition P that subdivides the interval [−1, 0] into n subintervals of width $\triangle x = \frac{0-(-1)}{n} = \frac{1}{n}$ and let $c_k$ be the right endpoint of each subinterval. So the partition is $P = \{-1, -1+\frac{1}{n}, -1+2\cdot\frac{1}{n}, \dots, -1+n\cdot\frac{1}{n} = 0\}$ and

$c_k = -1 + k \cdot \frac{1}{n} = -1 + \frac{k}{n}$. We get the Riemann sum $\sum_{k=1}^{n} f(c_k) \triangle x = \sum_{k=1}^{n} \left( (-1 + \frac{k}{n}) - (-1 + \frac{k}{n})^2 \right) \cdot \frac{1}{n}$

$= \frac{1}{n} \sum_{k=1}^{n} \left( -1 + \frac{k}{n} - 1 + \frac{2k}{n} - (\frac{k}{n})^2 \right) = -\frac{2}{n} \sum_{k=1}^{n} 1 + \frac{3}{n^2} \sum_{k=1}^{n} k - \frac{1}{n^3} \sum_{k=1}^{n} k^2 = -\frac{2}{n} \cdot n + \frac{3}{n^2} \cdot \frac{n(n+1)}{2} - \frac{1}{n^3} \cdot \frac{n(n+1)(2n+1)}{6}$

$= -2 + \frac{3(n+1)}{2n} - \frac{(n+1)(2n+1)}{6n^2}$. As $n \to \infty$ and $\|P\| \to 0$ this expression has value $-2 + \frac{3}{2} - \frac{1}{3} = -\frac{5}{6}$. Thus,

$\int_{-1}^{0} (x - x^2) dx = -\frac{5}{6}$.

67. Consider the partition P that subdivides the interval $[-1, 2]$ into n subintervals of width $\triangle x = \frac{2-(-1)}{n} = \frac{3}{n}$ and let $c_k$ be the right endpoint of each subinterval. So the partition is $P = \{-1, -1 + \frac{3}{n}, -1 + 2 \cdot \frac{3}{n}, \ldots, -1 + n \cdot \frac{3}{n} = 2\}$ and

$c_k = -1 + k \cdot \frac{3}{n} = -1 + \frac{3k}{n}$. We get the Riemann sum $\sum_{k=1}^{n} f(c_k) \triangle x = \sum_{k=1}^{n} \left( 3(-1 + \frac{3k}{n})^2 - 2(-1 + \frac{3k}{n}) + 1 \right) \cdot \frac{3}{n}$

$= \frac{3}{n} \sum_{k=1}^{n} \left( 3 - \frac{18k}{n} + \frac{27k^2}{n^2} + 2 - \frac{6k}{n} + 1 \right) = \frac{18}{n} \sum_{k=1}^{n} 1 - \frac{72}{n^2} \sum_{k=1}^{n} k + \frac{81}{n^3} \sum_{k=1}^{n} k^2 = \frac{18}{n} \cdot n - \frac{72}{n^2} \cdot \frac{n(n+1)}{2} + \frac{81}{n^3} \cdot \frac{n(n+1)(2n+1)}{6}$

$= 18 - \frac{36(n+1)}{n} + \frac{27(n+1)(2n+1)}{2n^2}$. As $n \to \infty$ and $\|P\| \to 0$ this expression has value $18 - 36 + 27 = 9$. Thus,

$\int_{-1}^{2} (3x^2 - 2x + 1) dx = 9$.

68. Consider the partition P that subdivides the interval $[-1, 1]$ into n subintervals of width $\triangle x = \frac{1-(-1)}{n} = \frac{2}{n}$ and let $c_k$ be the right endpoint of each subinterval. So the partition is $P = \{-1, -1 + \frac{2}{n}, -1 + 2 \cdot \frac{2}{n}, \ldots, -1 + n \cdot \frac{2}{n} = 1\}$ and

$c_k = -1 + k \cdot \frac{2}{n} = -1 + \frac{2k}{n}$. We get the Riemann sum $\sum_{k=1}^{n} f(c_k) \triangle x = \sum_{k=1}^{n} c_k^3 (\frac{2}{n}) = \frac{2}{n} \sum_{k=1}^{n} (-1 + \frac{2k}{n})^3$

$= \frac{2}{n} \sum_{k=1}^{n} \left( -1 + \frac{6k}{n} - \frac{12k^2}{n^2} + \frac{8k^3}{n^3} \right) = \frac{2}{n} \left( -\sum_{k=1}^{n} 1 + \frac{6}{n} \sum_{k=1}^{n} k - \frac{12}{n^2} \sum_{k=1}^{n} k^2 + \frac{8}{n^3} \sum_{k=1}^{n} k^3 \right)$

$= -\frac{2}{n} \cdot n + \frac{12}{n^2} \cdot \frac{n(n+1)}{2} - \frac{24}{n^3} \cdot \frac{n(n+1)(2n+1)}{6} + \frac{16}{n^4} \cdot \left( \frac{n(n+1)}{2} \right)^2 = -2 + 6 \cdot \frac{n+1}{n} - 4 \cdot \frac{(n+1)(2n+1)}{n^2} + 4 \cdot \frac{(n+1)^2}{n^2}$

$= -2 + 6 \cdot \frac{1+\frac{1}{n}}{1} - 4 \cdot \frac{2+\frac{3}{n}+\frac{1}{n^2}}{1} + 4 \cdot \frac{1+\frac{2}{n}+\frac{1}{n^2}}{1}$. As $n \to \infty$ and $\|P\| \to 0$ this expression has value $-2 + 6 - 8 + 4 = 0$.

Thus, $\int_{-1}^{1} x^3 dx = 0$.

69. Consider the partition P that subdivides the interval $[a, b]$ into n subintervals of width $\triangle x = \frac{b-a}{n}$ and let $c_k$ be the right endpoint of each subinterval. So the partition is $P = \{a, a + \frac{b-a}{n}, a + \frac{2(b-a)}{n}, \ldots, a + \frac{n(b-a)}{n} = b\}$ and

$c_k = a + \frac{k(b-a)}{n}$. We get the Riemann sum $\sum_{k=1}^{n} f(c_k) \triangle x = \sum_{k=1}^{n} c_k^3 (\frac{b-a}{n}) = \frac{b-a}{n} \sum_{k=1}^{n} \left( a + \frac{k(b-a)}{n} \right)^3$

$= \frac{b-a}{n} \sum_{k=1}^{n} \left( a^3 + \frac{3a^2 k(b-a)}{n} + \frac{3ak^2(b-a)^2}{n^2} + \frac{k^3(b-a)^3}{n^3} \right) = \frac{b-a}{n} \left( \sum_{k=1}^{n} a^3 + \frac{3a^2(b-a)}{n} \sum_{k=1}^{n} k + \frac{3a(b-a)^2}{n^2} \sum_{k=1}^{n} k^2 + \frac{(b-a)^3}{n^3} \sum_{k=1}^{n} k^3 \right)$

$= \frac{b-a}{n} \cdot na^3 + \frac{3a^2(b-a)^2}{n^2} \cdot \frac{n(n+1)}{2} + \frac{3a(b-a)^3}{n^3} \cdot \frac{n(n+1)(2n+1)}{6} + \frac{(b-a)^4}{n^4} \cdot \left( \frac{n(n+1)}{2} \right)^2$

$= (b-a)a^3 + \frac{3a^2(b-a)^2}{2} \cdot \frac{n+1}{n} + \frac{a(b-a)^3}{2} \cdot \frac{(n+1)(2n+1)}{n^2} + \frac{(b-a)^4}{4} \cdot \frac{(n+1)^2}{n^2}$

$= (b-a)a^3 + \frac{3a^2(b-a)^2}{2} \cdot \frac{1+\frac{1}{n}}{1} + \frac{a(b-a)^3}{2} \cdot \frac{2+\frac{3}{n}+\frac{1}{n^2}}{1} + \frac{(b-a)^4}{4} \cdot \frac{1+\frac{2}{n}+\frac{1}{n^2}}{1}$. As $n \to \infty$ and $\|P\| \to 0$ this expression has value

$(b-a)a^3 + \frac{3a^2(b-a)^2}{2} + a(b-a)^3 + \frac{(b-a)^4}{4} = \frac{b^4}{4} - \frac{a^4}{4}$. Thus, $\int_{a}^{b} x^3 dx = \frac{b^4}{4} - \frac{a^4}{4}$.

70. Consider the partition P that subdivides the interval $[0, 1]$ into n subintervals of width $\triangle x = \frac{1-0}{n} = \frac{1}{n}$ and let $c_k$ be the right endpoint of each subinterval. So the partition is $P = \{0, 0 + \frac{1}{n}, 0 + 2 \cdot \frac{1}{n}, \ldots, 0 + n \cdot \frac{1}{n} = 1\}$ and $c_k = 0 + k \cdot \frac{1}{n} = \frac{k}{n}$.

We get the Riemann sum $\sum_{k=1}^{n} f(c_k) \triangle x = \sum_{k=1}^{n} (3c_k - c_k^3)(\frac{1}{n}) = \frac{1}{n} \sum_{k=1}^{n} \left( 3 \cdot \frac{k}{n} - (\frac{k}{n})^3 \right) = \frac{1}{n} \left( \frac{3}{n} \sum_{k=1}^{n} k - \frac{1}{n^3} \sum_{k=1}^{n} k^3 \right)$

$= \frac{3}{n^2} \cdot \frac{n(n+1)}{2} - \frac{1}{n^4} \cdot \left(\frac{n(n+1)}{2}\right)^2 = \frac{3}{2} \cdot \frac{n+1}{n} - \frac{1}{4} \cdot \frac{(n+1)^2}{n^2} = \frac{3}{2} \cdot \frac{1+\frac{1}{n}}{1} - \frac{1}{4} \cdot \frac{1+\frac{2}{n}+\frac{1}{n^2}}{1}$. As $n \to \infty$ and $\|P\| \to 0$ this expression

has value $\frac{3}{2} - \frac{1}{4} = \frac{5}{4}$. Thus, $\int_0^1 (3x - x^3)dx = \frac{5}{4}$.

71. To find where $x - x^2 \geq 0$, let $x - x^2 = 0 \Rightarrow x(1-x) = 0 \Rightarrow x = 0$ or $x = 1$. If $0 < x < 1$, then $0 < x - x^2 \Rightarrow a = 0$ and $b = 1$ maximize the integral.

72. To find where $x^4 - 2x^2 \leq 0$, let $x^4 - 2x^2 = 0 \Rightarrow x^2(x^2 - 2) = 0 \Rightarrow x = 0$ or $x = \pm\sqrt{2}$. By the sign graph,
$\underset{-\sqrt{2} \quad 0 \quad \sqrt{2}}{+++++ \; 0 \;--\; 0 \;--\; 0 \;+++++++}$, we can see that $x^4 - 2x^2 \leq 0$ on $\left[-\sqrt{2}, \sqrt{2}\right] \Rightarrow a = -\sqrt{2}$ and $b = \sqrt{2}$
minimize the integral.

73. $f(x) = \frac{1}{1+x^2}$ is decreasing on $[0, 1] \Rightarrow$ maximum value of f occurs at $0 \Rightarrow \max f = f(0) = 1$; minimum value of f occurs
at $1 \Rightarrow \min f = f(1) = \frac{1}{1+1^2} = \frac{1}{2}$. Therefore, $(1-0)\min f \leq \int_0^1 \frac{1}{1+x^2}\,dx \leq (1-0)\max f \Rightarrow \frac{1}{2} \leq \int_0^1 \frac{1}{1+x^2}\,dx \leq 1$.
That is, an upper bound $= 1$ and a lower bound $= \frac{1}{2}$.

74. See Exercise 73 above. On $[0, 0.5]$, $\max f = \frac{1}{1+0^2} = 1$, $\min f = \frac{1}{1+(0.5)^2} = 0.8$. Therefore
$(0.5 - 0)\min f \leq \int_0^{0.5} f(x)\,dx \leq (0.5 - 0)\max f \Rightarrow \frac{2}{5} \leq \int_0^{0.5} \frac{1}{1+x^2}\,dx \leq \frac{1}{2}$. On $[0.5, 1]$, $\max f = \frac{1}{1+(0.5)^2} = 0.8$ and
$\min f = \frac{1}{1+1^2} = 0.5$. Therefore $(1 - 0.5)\min f \leq \int_{0.5}^1 \frac{1}{1+x^2}\,dx \leq (1 - 0.5)\max f \Rightarrow \frac{1}{4} \leq \int_{0.5}^1 \frac{1}{1+x^2}\,dx \leq \frac{2}{5}$.
Then $\frac{1}{4} + \frac{2}{5} \leq \int_0^{0.5} \frac{1}{1+x^2}\,dx + \int_{0.5}^1 \frac{1}{1+x^2}\,dx \leq \frac{1}{2} + \frac{2}{5} \Rightarrow \frac{13}{20} \leq \int_0^1 \frac{1}{1+x^2}\,dx \leq \frac{9}{10}$.

75. $-1 \leq \sin(x^2) \leq 1$ for all $x \Rightarrow (1-0)(-1) \leq \int_0^1 \sin(x^2)\,dx \leq (1-0)(1)$ or $\int_0^1 \sin x^2\,dx \leq 1 \Rightarrow \int_0^1 \sin x^2\,dx$ cannot
equal 2.

76. $f(x) = \sqrt{x+8}$ is increasing on $[0, 1] \Rightarrow \max f = f(1) = \sqrt{1+8} = 3$ and $\min f = f(0) = \sqrt{0+8} = 2\sqrt{2}$.
Therefore, $(1-0)\min f \leq \int_0^1 \sqrt{x+8}\,dx \leq (1-0)\max f \Rightarrow 2\sqrt{2} \leq \int_0^1 \sqrt{x+8}\,dx \leq 3$.

77. If $f(x) \geq 0$ on $[a, b]$, then $\min f \geq 0$ and $\max f \geq 0$ on $[a, b]$. Now, $(b-a)\min f \leq \int_a^b f(x)\,dx \leq (b-a)\max f$.
Then $b \geq a \Rightarrow b - a \geq 0 \Rightarrow (b-a)\min f \geq 0 \Rightarrow \int_a^b f(x)\,dx \geq 0$.

78. If $f(x) \leq 0$ on $[a, b]$, then $\min f \leq 0$ and $\max f \leq 0$. Now, $(b-a)\min f \leq \int_a^b f(x)\,dx \leq (b-a)\max f$. Then
$b \geq a \Rightarrow b - a \geq 0 \Rightarrow (b-a)\max f \leq 0 \Rightarrow \int_a^b f(x)\,dx \leq 0$.

79. $\sin x \leq x$ for $x \geq 0 \Rightarrow \sin x - x \leq 0$ for $x \geq 0 \Rightarrow \int_0^1 (\sin x - x)\,dx \leq 0$ (see Exercise 78) $\Rightarrow \int_0^1 \sin x\,dx - \int_0^1 x\,dx \leq 0$
$\Rightarrow \int_0^1 \sin x\,dx \leq \int_0^1 x\,dx \Rightarrow \int_0^1 \sin x\,dx \leq \left(\frac{1^2}{2} - \frac{0^2}{2}\right) \Rightarrow \int_0^1 \sin x\,dx \leq \frac{1}{2}$. Thus an upper bound is $\frac{1}{2}$.

80. $\sec x \geq 1 + \frac{x^2}{2}$ on $\left(-\frac{\pi}{2}, \frac{\pi}{2}\right) \Rightarrow \sec x - \left(1 + \frac{x^2}{2}\right) \geq 0$ on $\left(-\frac{\pi}{2}, \frac{\pi}{2}\right) \Rightarrow \int_0^1 \left[\sec x - \left(1 + \frac{x^2}{2}\right)\right] dx \geq 0$ (see Exercise 77)

since $[0, 1]$ is contained in $\left(-\frac{\pi}{2}, \frac{\pi}{2}\right) \Rightarrow \int_0^1 \sec x \, dx - \int_0^1 \left(1 + \frac{x^2}{2}\right) dx \geq 0 \Rightarrow \int_0^1 \sec x \, dx \geq \int_0^1 \left(1 + \frac{x^2}{2}\right)$

$\Rightarrow \int_0^1 \sec x \, dx \geq \int_0^1 1 \, dx + \frac{1}{2}\int_0^1 x^2 \, dx \Rightarrow \int_0^1 \sec x \, dx \geq (1 - 0) + \frac{1}{2}\left(\frac{1^3}{3}\right) \Rightarrow \int_0^1 \sec x \, dx \geq \frac{7}{6}$. Thus a lower bound

is $\frac{7}{6}$.

81. Yes, for the following reasons: $\text{av}(f) = \frac{1}{b-a} \int_a^b f(x) \, dx$ is a constant K. Thus $\int_a^b \text{av}(f) \, dx = \int_a^b K \, dx = K(b - a)$

$\Rightarrow \int_a^b \text{av}(f) \, dx = (b - a)K = (b - a) \cdot \frac{1}{b-a}\int_a^b f(x) \, dx = \int_a^b f(x) \, dx$.

82. All three rules hold. The reasons: On any interval $[a, b]$ on which f and g are integrable, we have:

(a) $\text{av}(f + g) = \frac{1}{b-a} \int_a^b [f(x) + g(x)] \, dx = \frac{1}{b-a}\left[\int_a^b f(x) \, dx + \int_a^b g(x) \, dx\right] = \frac{1}{b-a}\int_a^b f(x) \, dx + \frac{1}{b-a}\int_a^b g(x) \, dx$

   $= \text{av}(f) + \text{av}(g)$

(b) $\text{av}(kf) = \frac{1}{b-a} \int_a^b kf(x) \, dx = \frac{1}{b-a}\left[k \int_a^b f(x) \, dx\right] = k \left[\frac{1}{b-a}\int_a^b f(x) \, dx\right] = k \, \text{av}(f)$

(c) $\text{av}(f) = \frac{1}{b-a}\int_a^b f(x) \, dx \leq \frac{1}{b-a}\int_a^b g(x) \, dx$ since $f(x) \leq g(x)$ on $[a, b]$, and $\frac{1}{b-a}\int_a^b g(x) \, dx = \text{av}(g)$.
   Therefore, $\text{av}(f) \leq \text{av}(g)$.

83. (a) $U = \max_1 \Delta x + \max_2 \Delta x + \ldots + \max_n \Delta x$ where $\max_1 = f(x_1), \max_2 = f(x_2), \ldots, \max_n = f(x_n)$ since f is
   increasing on $[a, b]$; $L = \min_1 \Delta x + \min_2 \Delta x + \ldots + \min_n \Delta x$ where $\min_1 = f(x_0), \min_2 = f(x_1), \ldots,$
   $\min_n = f(x_{n-1})$ since f is increasing on $[a, b]$. Therefore
   $U - L = (\max_1 - \min_1) \Delta x + (\max_2 - \min_2) \Delta x + \ldots + (\max_n - \min_n) \Delta x$
   $= (f(x_1) - f(x_0)) \Delta x + (f(x_2) - f(x_1))\Delta x + \ldots + (f(x_n) - f(x_{n-1})) \Delta x = (f(x_n) - f(x_0)) \Delta x = (f(b) - f(a)) \Delta x$.

   (b) $U = \max_1 \Delta x_1 + \max_2 \Delta x_2 + \ldots + \max_n \Delta x_n$ where $\max_1 = f(x_1), \max_2 = f(x_2), \ldots, \max_n = f(x_n)$ since f
   is increasing on$[a, b]$; $L = \min_1 \Delta x_1 + \min_2 \Delta x_2 + \ldots + \min_n \Delta x_n$ where
   $\min_1 = f(x_0), \min_2 = f(x_1), \ldots, \min_n = f(x_{n-1})$ since f is increasing on $[a, b]$. Therefore
   $U - L = (\max_1 - \min_1) \Delta x_1 + (\max_2 - \min_2) \Delta x_2 + \ldots + (\max_n - \min_n) \Delta x_n$
   $= (f(x_1) - f(x_0)) \Delta x_1 + (f(x_2) - f(x_1))\Delta x_2 + \ldots + (f(x_n) - f(x_{n-1})) \Delta x_n$
   $\leq (f(x_1) - f(x_0)) \Delta x_{\max} + (f(x_2) - f(x_1)) \Delta x_{\max} + \ldots + (f(x_n) - f(x_{n-1})) \Delta x_{\max}$. Then
   $U - L \leq (f(x_n) - f(x_0)) \Delta x_{\max} = (f(b) - f(a)) \Delta x_{\max} = |f(b) - f(a)| \Delta x_{\max}$ since $f(b) \geq f(a)$. Thus
   $\lim_{\|P\| \to 0} (U - L) = \lim_{\|P\| \to 0} (f(b) - f(a)) \Delta x_{\max} = 0$, since $\Delta x_{\max} = \|P\|$.

84. (a) $U = \max_1 \Delta x + \max_2 \Delta x + \ldots + \max_n \Delta x$ where
   $\max_1 = f(x_0), \max_2 = f(x_1), \ldots, \max_n = f(x_{n-1})$
   since f is decreasing on $[a, b]$;
   $L = \min_1 \Delta x + \min_2 \Delta x + \ldots + \min_n \Delta x$ where
   $\min_1 = f(x_1), \min_2 = f(x_2), \ldots, \min_n = f(x_n)$
   since f is decreasing on $[a, b]$. Therefore
   $U - L = (\max_1 - \min_1) \Delta x + (\max_2 - \min_2) \Delta x$
   $+ \ldots + (\max_n - \min_n) \Delta x$
   $= (f(x_0) - f(x_1)) \Delta x + (f(x_1) - f(x_2))\Delta x$
   $+ \ldots + (f(x_{n-1}) - f(x_n)) \Delta x = (f(x_0) - f(x_n)) \Delta x$
   $= (f(a) - f(b)) \Delta x$.

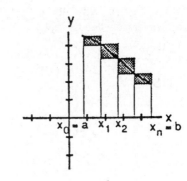

(b)  $U = \max_1 \Delta x_1 + \max_2 \Delta x_2 + \ldots + \max_n \Delta x_n$ where $\max_1 = f(x_0)$, $\max_2 = f(x_1)$, $\ldots$ , $\max_n = f(x_{n-1})$ since
f is decreasing on $[a, b]$; $L = \min_1 \Delta x_1 + \min_2 \Delta x_2 + \ldots + \min_n \Delta x_n$ where
$\min_1 = f(x_1)$, $\min_2 = f(x_2)$, $\ldots$ , $\min_n = f(x_n)$ since f is decreasing on $[a, b]$. Therefore
$U - L = (\max_1 - \min_1)\Delta x_1 + (\max_2 - \min_2)\Delta x_2 + \ldots + (\max_n - \min_n)\Delta x_n$
$\quad = (f(x_0) - f(x_1))\Delta x_1 + (f(x_1) - f(x_2))\Delta x_2 + \ldots + (f(x_{n-1}) - f(x_n))\Delta x_n$
$\quad \leq (f(x_0) - f(x_n))\Delta x_{max} = (f(a) - f(b))\Delta x_{max} = |f(b) - f(a)|\,\Delta x_{max}$ since $f(b) \leq f(a)$. Thus
$\lim\limits_{\|P\| \to 0} (U - L) = \lim\limits_{\|P\| \to 0} |f(b) - f(a)|\,\Delta x_{max} = 0$, since $\Delta x_{max} = \|P\|$ .

85. (a)  Partition $\left[0, \frac{\pi}{2}\right]$ into n subintervals, each of length $\Delta x = \frac{\pi}{2n}$ with points $x_0 = 0$, $x_1 = \Delta x$,
$x_2 = 2\Delta x, \ldots , x_n = n\Delta x = \frac{\pi}{2}$. Since sin x is increasing on $\left[0, \frac{\pi}{2}\right]$ , the upper sum U is the sum of the areas
of the circumscribed rectangles of areas $f(x_1)\,\Delta x = (\sin \Delta x)\Delta x$, $f(x_2)\,\Delta x = (\sin 2\Delta x)\,\Delta x, \ldots , f(x_n)\,\Delta x$
$= (\sin n\Delta x)\,\Delta x$. Then $U = (\sin \Delta x + \sin 2\Delta x + \ldots + \sin n\Delta x)\,\Delta x = \left[\dfrac{\cos \frac{\Delta x}{2} - \cos\left(\left(n + \frac{1}{2}\right)\Delta x\right)}{2\sin \frac{\Delta x}{2}}\right]\Delta x$
$= \left[\dfrac{\cos \frac{\pi}{4n} - \cos\left(\left(n + \frac{1}{2}\right)\frac{\pi}{2n}\right)}{2\sin \frac{\pi}{4n}}\right]\left(\dfrac{\pi}{2n}\right) = \dfrac{\pi\left(\cos \frac{\pi}{4n} - \cos\left(\frac{\pi}{2} + \frac{\pi}{4n}\right)\right)}{4n\sin \frac{\pi}{4n}} = \dfrac{\cos \frac{\pi}{4n} - \cos\left(\frac{\pi}{2} + \frac{\pi}{4n}\right)}{\left(\frac{\sin \frac{\pi}{4n}}{\frac{\pi}{4n}}\right)}$

(b)  The area is $\displaystyle\int_0^{\pi/2} \sin x \, dx = \lim_{n \to \infty} \dfrac{\cos \frac{\pi}{4n} - \cos\left(\frac{\pi}{2} + \frac{\pi}{4n}\right)}{\left(\frac{\sin \frac{\pi}{4n}}{\frac{\pi}{4n}}\right)} = \dfrac{1 - \cos \frac{\pi}{2}}{1} = 1$.

86. (a)  The area of the shaded region is $\sum\limits_{i=1}^{n} \Delta x_i \cdot m_i$ which is equal to L.

(b)  The area of the shaded region is $\sum\limits_{i=1}^{n} \Delta x_i \cdot M_i$ which is equal to U.

(c)  The area of the shaded region is the difference in the areas of the shaded regions shown in the second part of the figure
and the first part of the figure. Thus this area is $U - L$.

87.  By Exercise 86, $U - L = \sum\limits_{i=1}^{n} \Delta x_i \cdot M_i - \sum\limits_{i=1}^{n} \Delta x_i \cdot m_i$ where $M_i = \max\{f(x)$ on the ith subinterval$\}$ and

$m_i = \min\{f(x)$ on the ith subinterval$\}$. Thus $U - L = \sum\limits_{i=1}^{n}(M_i - m_i)\Delta x_i < \sum\limits_{i=1}^{n}\epsilon \cdot \Delta x_i$ provided $\Delta x_i < \delta$ for each

$i = 1, \ldots , n$. Since $\sum\limits_{i=1}^{n}\epsilon \cdot \Delta x_i = \epsilon \sum\limits_{i=1}^{n}\Delta x_i = \epsilon(b - a)$ the result, $U - L < \epsilon(b - a)$ follows.

88.  The car drove the first 150 miles in 5 hours and the
second 150 miles in 3 hours, which means it drove 300
miles in 8 hours, for an average of $\frac{300}{8}$ mi/hr
$= 37.5$ mi/hr.  In terms of average values of functions,
the function whose average value we seek is
$v(t) = \begin{cases} 30, & 0 \leq t \leq 5 \\ 50, & 5 < 1 \leq 8 \end{cases}$, and the average value is
$\frac{(30)(5) + (50)(3)}{8} = 37.5$.

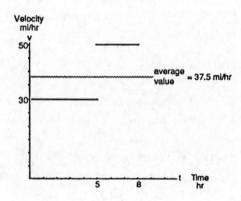

89-94.    Example CAS commands:

Maple:

```
with( plots );
with( Student[Calculus1] );
f := x -> 1-x;
a := 0;
b := 1;
N :=[ 4, 10, 20, 50 ];
P := [seq( RiemannSum( f(x), x=a..b, partition=n, method=random, output=plot ), n=N )]:
display( P, insequence=true );
```

95-98.    Example CAS commands:

Maple:

```
with( Student[Calculus1] );
f := x -> sin(x);
a := 0;
b := Pi;
plot( f(x), x=a..b, title="#95(a) (Section 5.3)" );
N := [ 100, 200, 1000 ];                          # (b)
for n in N do
  Xlist := [ a+1.*(b-a)/n*i $ i=0..n ];
  Ylist := map( f, Xlist );
end do:
for n in N do                              # (c)
  Avg[n] := evalf(add(y,y=Ylist)/nops(Ylist));
end do;
avg := FunctionAverage( f(x), x=a..b, output=value );
evalf( avg );
FunctionAverage(f(x),x=a..b,output=plot);      # (d)
fsolve( f(x)=avg, x=0.5 );
fsolve( f(x)=avg, x=2.5 );
fsolve( f(x)=Avg[1000], x=0.5 );
fsolve( f(x)=Avg[1000], x=2.5 );
```

89-98.    Example CAS commands:

Mathematica: (assigned function and values for a, b, and n may vary)

Sums of rectangles evaluated at left-hand endpoints can be represented and evaluated by this set of commands

```
Clear[x, f, a, b, n]
{a, b}={0, π}; n =10; dx = (b − a)/n;
f = Sin[x]²;
xvals =Table[N[x], {x, a, b − dx, dx}];
yvals = f /.x → xvals;
boxes = MapThread[Line[{{#1,0},{#1, #3},{#2, #3},{#2, 0}]&,{xvals, xvals + dx, yvals}];
Plot[f, {x, a, b}, Epilog → boxes];
Sum[yvals[[i]] dx, {i, 1, Length[yvals]}]//N
```

Sums of rectangles evaluated at right-hand endpoints can be represented and evaluated by this set of commands.

```
Clear[x, f, a, b, n]
{a, b}={0, π}; n =10; dx = (b − a)/n;
f = Sin[x]²;
```

xvals =Table[N[x], {x, a + dx, b, dx}];

yvals = f /.x $\rightarrow$ xvals;

boxes = MapThread[Line[{{#1,0},{#1, #3},{#2, #3},{#2, 0}]&,{xvals $-$ dx,xvals, yvals}];

Plot[f, {x, a, b}, Epilog $\rightarrow$ boxes];

Sum[yvals[[i]] dx, {i, 1,Length[yvals]}]//N

Sums of rectangles evaluated at midpoints can be represented and evaluated by this set of commands.

Clear[x, f, a, b, n]

{a, b}={0, $\pi$}; n =10; dx = (b $-$ a)/n;

f = Sin[x]$^2$;

xvals =Table[N[x], {x, a + dx/2, b $-$ dx/2, dx}];

yvals = f /.x $\rightarrow$ xvals;

boxes = MapThread[Line[{{#1,0},{#1, #3},{#2, #3},{#2, 0}]&,{xvals $-$ dx/2, xvals + dx/2, yvals}];

Plot[f, {x, a, b},Epilog $\rightarrow$ boxes];

Sum[yvals[[i]] dx, {i, 1, Length[yvals]}]//N

## 5.4  THE FUNDAMENTAL THEOREM OF CALCULUS

1.  $\displaystyle\int_{-2}^{0}(2x + 5)\, dx = [x^2 + 5x]_{-2}^{0} = (0^2 + 5(0)) - ((-2)^2 + 5(-2)) = 6$

2.  $\displaystyle\int_{-3}^{4}\left(5 - \frac{x}{2}\right) dx = \left[5x - \frac{x^2}{4}\right]_{-3}^{4} = \left(5(4) - \frac{4^2}{4}\right) - \left(5(-3) - \frac{(-3)^2}{4}\right) = \frac{133}{4}$

3.  $\displaystyle\int_{0}^{2}x(x - 3)\, dx = \int_{0}^{2}(x^2 - 3x)\, dx = \left[\frac{x^3}{3} - \frac{3x^2}{2}\right]_{0}^{2} = \left(\frac{(2)^3}{3} - \frac{3(2)^2}{2}\right) - \left(\frac{(0)^3}{3} - \frac{3(0)^2}{2}\right) = -\frac{10}{3}$

4.  $\displaystyle\int_{-1}^{1}(x^2 - 2x + 3)\, dx = \left[\frac{x^3}{3} - x^2 + 3x\right]_{-1}^{1} = \left(\frac{(1)^3}{3} - (1)^2 + 3(1)\right) - \left(\frac{(-1)^3}{3} - (-1)^2 + 3(-1)\right) = \frac{20}{3}$

5.  $\displaystyle\int_{0}^{4}\left(3x - \frac{x^3}{4}\right) dx = \left[\frac{3x^2}{2} - \frac{x^4}{16}\right]_{0}^{4} = \left(\frac{3(4)^2}{2} - \frac{4^4}{16}\right) - \left(\frac{3(0)^2}{2} - \frac{(0)^4}{16}\right) = 8$

6.  $\displaystyle\int_{-2}^{2}(x^3 - 2x + 3)\, dx = \left[\frac{x^4}{4} - x^2 + 3x\right]_{-2}^{2} = \left(\frac{2^4}{4} - 2^2 + 3(2)\right) - \left(\frac{(-2)^4}{4} - (-2)^2 + 3(-2)\right) = 12$

7.  $\displaystyle\int_{0}^{1}\left(x^2 + \sqrt{x}\right) dx = \left[\frac{x^3}{3} + \frac{2}{3}x^{3/2}\right]_{0}^{1} = \left(\frac{1}{3} + \frac{2}{3}\right) - 0 = 1$

8.  $\displaystyle\int_{1}^{32}x^{-6/5}\, dx = \left[-5x^{-1/5}\right]_{1}^{32} = \left(-\frac{5}{2}\right) - (-5) = \frac{5}{2}$

9.  $\displaystyle\int_{0}^{\pi/3}2\sec^2 x\, dx = [2\tan x]_{0}^{\pi/3} = \left(2\tan\left(\frac{\pi}{3}\right)\right) - (2\tan 0) = 2\sqrt{3} - 0 = 2\sqrt{3}$

10.  $\displaystyle\int_{0}^{\pi}(1 + \cos x)\, dx = [x + \sin x]_{0}^{\pi} = (\pi + \sin \pi) - (0 + \sin 0) = \pi$

11.  $\displaystyle\int_{\pi/4}^{3\pi/4}\csc\theta\cot\theta\, d\theta = [-\csc\theta]_{\pi/4}^{3\pi/4} = \left(-\csc\left(\frac{3\pi}{4}\right)\right) - \left(-\csc\left(\frac{\pi}{4}\right)\right) = -\sqrt{2} - \left(-\sqrt{2}\right) = 0$

12.  $\displaystyle\int_{0}^{\pi/3}4\sec u\tan u\, du = [4\sec u]_{0}^{\pi/3} = 4\sec\left(\frac{\pi}{3}\right) - 4\sec 0 = 4(2) - 4(1) = 4$

13. $\int_{\pi/2}^{0} \frac{1+\cos 2t}{2}\, dt = \int_{\pi/2}^{0} \left(\frac{1}{2} + \frac{1}{2}\cos 2t\right) dt = \left[\frac{1}{2}t + \frac{1}{4}\sin 2t\right]_{\pi/2}^{0} = \left(\frac{1}{2}(0) + \frac{1}{4}\sin 2(0)\right) - \left(\frac{1}{2}\left(\frac{\pi}{2}\right) + \frac{1}{4}\sin 2\left(\frac{\pi}{2}\right)\right) = -\frac{\pi}{4}$

14. $\int_{-\pi/3}^{\pi/3} \frac{1-\cos 2t}{2}\, dt = \int_{-\pi/3}^{\pi/3} \left(\frac{1}{2} - \frac{1}{2}\cos 2t\right) dt = \left[\frac{1}{2}t - \frac{1}{4}\sin 2t\right]_{-\pi/3}^{\pi/3}$

$= \left(\frac{1}{2}\left(\frac{\pi}{3}\right) - \frac{1}{4}\sin 2\left(\frac{\pi}{3}\right)\right) - \left(\frac{1}{2}\left(-\frac{\pi}{3}\right) - \frac{1}{4}\sin 2\left(-\frac{\pi}{3}\right)\right) = \frac{\pi}{6} - \frac{1}{4}\sin\frac{2\pi}{3} + \frac{\pi}{6} + \frac{1}{4}\sin\left(\frac{-2\pi}{3}\right) = \frac{\pi}{3} - \frac{\sqrt{3}}{4}$

15. $\int_{0}^{\pi/4} \tan^2 x\, dx = \int_{0}^{\pi/4} (\sec^2 x - 1) dx = [\tan x - x]_{0}^{\pi/4} = \left(\tan\left(\frac{\pi}{4}\right) - \frac{\pi}{4}\right) - (\tan(0) - 0) = 1 - \frac{\pi}{4}$

16. $\int_{0}^{\pi/6} (\sec x + \tan x)^2\, dx = \int_{0}^{\pi/6} (\sec^2 x + 2\sec x \tan x + \tan^2 x) dx = \int_{0}^{\pi/6} (2\sec^2 x + 2\sec x \tan x - 1) dx$

$= [2\tan x + 2\sec x - x]_{0}^{\pi/6} = \left(2\tan\left(\frac{\pi}{6}\right) + 2\sec\left(\frac{\pi}{6}\right) - \left(\frac{\pi}{6}\right)\right) - (2\tan 0 + 2\sec 0 - 0) = 2\sqrt{3} - \frac{\pi}{6} - 2$

17. $\int_{0}^{\pi/8} \sin 2x\, dx = \left[-\frac{1}{2}\cos 2x\right]_{0}^{\pi/8} = \left(-\frac{1}{2}\cos 2\left(\frac{\pi}{8}\right)\right) - \left(-\frac{1}{2}\cos 2(0)\right) = \frac{2-\sqrt{2}}{4}$

18. $\int_{-\pi/3}^{-\pi/4} \left(4\sec^2 t + \frac{\pi}{t^2}\right) dt = \int_{-\pi/3}^{-\pi/4} (4\sec^2 t + \pi t^{-2}) dt = \left[4\tan t - \frac{\pi}{t}\right]_{-\pi/3}^{-\pi/4}$

$= \left(4\tan\left(-\frac{\pi}{4}\right) - \frac{\pi}{\left(-\frac{\pi}{4}\right)}\right) - \left(4\tan\left(\frac{\pi}{3}\right) - \frac{\pi}{\left(-\frac{\pi}{3}\right)}\right) = (4(-1) + 4) - \left(4\left(-\sqrt{3}\right) + 3\right) = 4\sqrt{3} - 3$

19. $\int_{1}^{-1} (r+1)^2\, dr = \int_{1}^{-1} (r^2 + 2r + 1)\, dr = \left[\frac{r^3}{3} + r^2 + r\right]_{1}^{-1} = \left(\frac{(-1)^3}{3} + (-1)^2 + (-1)\right) - \left(\frac{1^3}{3} + 1^2 + 1\right) = -\frac{8}{3}$

20. $\int_{-\sqrt{3}}^{\sqrt{3}} (t+1)(t^2+4)\, dt = \int_{-\sqrt{3}}^{\sqrt{3}} (t^3 + t^2 + 4t + 4)\, dt = \left[\frac{t^4}{4} + \frac{t^3}{3} + 2t^2 + 4t\right]_{-\sqrt{3}}^{\sqrt{3}}$

$= \left(\frac{\left(\sqrt{3}\right)^4}{4} + \frac{\left(\sqrt{3}\right)^3}{3} + 2\left(\sqrt{3}\right)^2 + 4\sqrt{3}\right) - \left(\frac{\left(-\sqrt{3}\right)^4}{4} + \frac{\left(-\sqrt{3}\right)^3}{3} + 2\left(-\sqrt{3}\right)^2 + 4\left(-\sqrt{3}\right)\right) = 10\sqrt{3}$

21. $\int_{\sqrt{2}}^{1} \left(\frac{u^7}{2} - \frac{1}{u^5}\right) du = \int_{\sqrt{2}}^{1} \left(\frac{u^7}{2} - u^{-5}\right) du = \left[\frac{u^8}{16} + \frac{1}{4u^4}\right]_{\sqrt{2}}^{1} = \left(\frac{1^8}{16} + \frac{1}{4(1)^4}\right) - \left(\frac{\left(\sqrt{2}\right)^8}{16} + \frac{1}{4\left(\sqrt{2}\right)^4}\right) = -\frac{3}{4}$

22. $\int_{-3}^{-1} \frac{y^5 - 2y}{y^3}\, dy = \int_{-3}^{-1} (y^2 - 2y^{-2})\, dy = \left[\frac{y^3}{3} + 2y^{-1}\right]_{-3}^{-1} = \left(\frac{(-1)^3}{3} + \frac{2}{(-1)}\right) - \left(\frac{(-3)^3}{3} + \frac{2}{(-3)}\right) = \frac{22}{3}$

23. $\int_{1}^{\sqrt{2}} \frac{s^2 + \sqrt{s}}{s^2}\, ds = \int_{1}^{\sqrt{2}} (1 + s^{-3/2})\, ds = \left[s - \frac{2}{\sqrt{s}}\right]_{1}^{\sqrt{2}} = \left(\sqrt{2} - \frac{2}{\sqrt{\sqrt{2}}}\right) - \left(1 - \frac{2}{\sqrt{1}}\right) = \sqrt{2} - 2^{3/4} + 1$

$= \sqrt{2} - \sqrt[4]{8} + 1$

24. $\int_{1}^{8} \frac{(x^{1/3} + 1)(2 - x^{2/3})}{x^{1/3}}\, dx = \int_{1}^{8} \frac{2x^{1/3} - x + 2 - x^{2/3}}{x^{1/3}}\, dx = \int_{1}^{8} \left(2 - x^{2/3} + 2x^{-1/3} - x^{1/3}\right) dx =$

$\left[2x - \frac{3}{5}x^{5/3} + 3x^{2/3} - \frac{3}{4}x^{4/3}\right]_{1}^{8} = \left(2(8) - \frac{3}{5}(8)^{5/3} + 3(8)^{2/3} - \frac{3}{4}(8)^{4/3}\right) - \left(2(1) - \frac{3}{5}(1)^{5/3} + 3(1)^{2/3} - \frac{3}{4}(1)^{4/3}\right)$

$= -\frac{137}{20}$

25. $\int_{\pi/2}^{\pi} \frac{\sin 2x}{2\sin x}\, dx = \int_{\pi/2}^{\pi} \frac{2\sin x \cos x}{2\sin x}\, dx = \int_{\pi/2}^{\pi} \cos x\, dx = [\sin x]_{\pi/2}^{\pi} = (\sin(\pi)) - \left(\sin\left(\frac{\pi}{2}\right)\right) = -1$

26. $\displaystyle\int_0^{\pi/3} (\cos x + \sec x)^2\, dx = \int_0^{\pi/3} (\cos^2 x + 2 + \sec^2 x)dx = \int_0^{\pi/3} \left(\frac{\cos 2x + 1}{2} + 2 + \sec^2 x\right)dx$

$= \displaystyle\int_0^{\pi/3} \left(\tfrac{1}{2}\cos 2x + \tfrac{5}{2} + \sec^2 x\right)dx = \left[\tfrac{1}{4}\sin 2x + \tfrac{5}{2}x + \tan x\right]_0^{\pi/3}$

$= \left(\tfrac{1}{4}\sin 2\left(\tfrac{\pi}{3}\right) + \tfrac{5}{2}\left(\tfrac{\pi}{3}\right) + \tan\left(\tfrac{\pi}{3}\right)\right) - \left(\tfrac{1}{4}\sin 2(0) + \tfrac{5}{2}(0) + \tan(0)\right) = \tfrac{5\pi}{6} + \tfrac{9\sqrt{3}}{8}$

27. $\displaystyle\int_{-4}^4 |x|\, dx = \int_{-4}^0 |x|\, dx + \int_0^4 |x|\, dx = -\int_{-4}^0 x\, dx + \int_0^4 x\, dx = \left[-\tfrac{x^2}{2}\right]_{-4}^0 + \left[\tfrac{x^2}{2}\right]_0^4 = \left(-\tfrac{0^2}{2} + \tfrac{(-4)^2}{2}\right) + \left(\tfrac{4^2}{2} - \tfrac{0^2}{2}\right) = 16$

28. $\displaystyle\int_0^{\pi} \tfrac{1}{2}(\cos x + |\cos x|)\, dx = \int_0^{\pi/2} \tfrac{1}{2}(\cos x + \cos x)\, dx + \int_{\pi/2}^{\pi} \tfrac{1}{2}(\cos x - \cos x)\, dx = \int_0^{\pi/2} \cos x\, dx = [\sin x]_0^{\pi/2}$

$= \sin\tfrac{\pi}{2} - \sin 0 = 1$

29. (a) $\displaystyle\int_0^{\sqrt{x}} \cos t\, dt = [\sin t]_0^{\sqrt{x}} = \sin\sqrt{x} - \sin 0 = \sin\sqrt{x} \Rightarrow \frac{d}{dx}\left(\int_0^{\sqrt{x}} \cos t\, dt\right) = \frac{d}{dx}\left(\sin\sqrt{x}\right) = \cos\sqrt{x}\left(\tfrac{1}{2}x^{-1/2}\right)$

$= \dfrac{\cos\sqrt{x}}{2\sqrt{x}}$

(b) $\dfrac{d}{dx}\left(\displaystyle\int_0^{\sqrt{x}} \cos t\, dt\right) = (\cos\sqrt{x})\left(\tfrac{d}{dx}\left(\sqrt{x}\right)\right) = (\cos\sqrt{x})\left(\tfrac{1}{2}x^{-1/2}\right) = \dfrac{\cos\sqrt{x}}{2\sqrt{x}}$

30. (a) $\displaystyle\int_1^{\sin x} 3t^2\, dt = [t^3]_1^{\sin x} = \sin^3 x - 1 \Rightarrow \frac{d}{dx}\left(\int_1^{\sin x} 3t^2\, dt\right) = \frac{d}{dx}(\sin^3 x - 1) = 3\sin^2 x \cos x$

(b) $\dfrac{d}{dx}\left(\displaystyle\int_1^{\sin x} 3t^2\, dt\right) = (3\sin^2 x)\left(\tfrac{d}{dx}(\sin x)\right) = 3\sin^2 x \cos x$

31. (a) $\displaystyle\int_0^{t^4} \sqrt{u}\, du = \int_0^{t^4} u^{1/2}\, du = \left[\tfrac{2}{3}u^{3/2}\right]_0^{t^4} = \tfrac{2}{3}(t^4)^{3/2} - 0 = \tfrac{2}{3}t^6 \Rightarrow \frac{d}{dt}\left(\int_0^{t^4} \sqrt{u}\, du\right) = \frac{d}{dt}\left(\tfrac{2}{3}t^6\right) = 4t^5$

(b) $\dfrac{d}{dt}\left(\displaystyle\int_0^{t^4} \sqrt{u}\, du\right) = \sqrt{t^4}\left(\tfrac{d}{dt}(t^4)\right) = t^2(4t^3) = 4t^5$

32. (a) $\displaystyle\int_0^{\tan\theta} \sec^2 y\, dy = [\tan y]_0^{\tan\theta} = \tan(\tan\theta) - 0 = \tan(\tan\theta) \Rightarrow \frac{d}{d\theta}\left(\int_0^{\tan\theta} \sec^2 y\, dy\right) = \frac{d}{d\theta}(\tan(\tan\theta))$

$= (\sec^2(\tan\theta))\sec^2\theta$

(b) $\dfrac{d}{d\theta}\left(\displaystyle\int_0^{\tan\theta} \sec^2 y\, dy\right) = (\sec^2(\tan\theta))\left(\tfrac{d}{d\theta}(\tan\theta)\right) = (\sec^2(\tan\theta))\sec^2\theta$

33. $y = \displaystyle\int_0^x \sqrt{1+t^2}\, dt \Rightarrow \frac{dy}{dx} = \sqrt{1+x^2}$

34. $y = \displaystyle\int_1^x \tfrac{1}{t}\, dt \Rightarrow \frac{dy}{dx} = \tfrac{1}{x},\ x > 0$

35. $y = \displaystyle\int_{\sqrt{x}}^0 \sin t^2\, dt = -\int_0^{\sqrt{x}} \sin t^2\, dt \Rightarrow \frac{dy}{dx} = -\left(\sin\left(\sqrt{x}\right)^2\right)\left(\tfrac{d}{dx}\left(\sqrt{x}\right)\right) = -(\sin x)\left(\tfrac{1}{2}x^{-1/2}\right) = -\dfrac{\sin x}{2\sqrt{x}}$

36. $y = x\displaystyle\int_2^{x^2} \sin t^3\, dt \Rightarrow \frac{dy}{dx} = x\cdot\frac{d}{dx}\left(\int_2^{x^2} \sin t^3\, dt\right) + 1\cdot\int_2^{x^2} \sin t^3\, dt = x\cdot\sin(x^2)^3\tfrac{d}{dx}(x^2) + \int_2^{x^2} \sin t^3\, dt$

$= 2x^2\sin x^6 + \displaystyle\int_2^{x^2} \sin t^3\, dt$

37. $y = \displaystyle\int_{-1}^x \tfrac{t^2}{t^2+4}\, dt - \int_3^x \tfrac{t^2}{t^2+4}\, dt \Rightarrow \frac{dy}{dx} = \tfrac{x^2}{x^2+4} - \tfrac{x^2}{x^2+4} = 0$

38. $y = \left(\int_0^x (t^3 + 1)^{10}dt\right)^3 \Rightarrow \frac{dy}{dx} = 3\left(\int_0^x (t^3 + 1)^{10}dt\right)\frac{d}{dx}\left(\int_0^x (t^3 + 1)^{10}dt\right) = 3(x^3 + 1)^{10}\left(\int_0^x (t^3 + 1)^{10}dt\right)$

39. $y = \int_0^{\sin x} \frac{dt}{\sqrt{1 - t^2}}, |x| < \frac{\pi}{2} \Rightarrow \frac{dy}{dx} = \frac{1}{\sqrt{1 - \sin^2 x}}\left(\frac{d}{dx}(\sin x)\right) = \frac{1}{\sqrt{\cos^2 x}}(\cos x) = \frac{\cos x}{|\cos x|} = \frac{\cos x}{\cos x} = 1$ since $|x| < \frac{\pi}{2}$

40. $y = \int_0^{\tan x} \frac{dt}{1 + t^2} \Rightarrow \frac{dy}{dx} = \left(\frac{1}{1 + \tan^2 x}\right)\left(\frac{d}{dx}(\tan x)\right) = \left(\frac{1}{\sec^2 x}\right)(\sec^2 x) = 1$

41. $-x^2 - 2x = 0 \Rightarrow -x(x + 2) = 0 \Rightarrow x = 0$ or $x = -2$; Area

$= -\int_{-3}^{-2}(-x^2 - 2x)dx + \int_{-2}^{0}(-x^2 - 2x)dx - \int_{0}^{2}(-x^2 - 2x)dx$

$= -\left[-\frac{x^3}{3} - x^2\right]_{-3}^{-2} + \left[-\frac{x^3}{3} - x^2\right]_{-2}^{0} - \left[-\frac{x^3}{3} - x^2\right]_{0}^{2}$

$= -\left(\left(-\frac{(-2)^3}{3} - (-2)^2\right) - \left(-\frac{(-3)^3}{3} - (-3)^2\right)\right)$

$+ \left(\left(-\frac{0^3}{3} - 0^2\right) - \left(-\frac{(-2)^3}{3} - (-2)^2\right)\right)$

$- \left(\left(-\frac{2^3}{3} - 2^2\right) - \left(-\frac{0^3}{3} - 0^2\right)\right) = \frac{28}{3}$

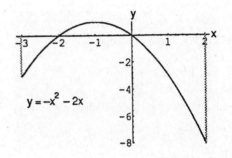

$y = -x^2 - 2x$

42. $3x^2 - 3 = 0 \Rightarrow x^2 = 1 \Rightarrow x = \pm 1$; because of symmetry about

the y-axis, Area $= 2\left(-\int_0^1 (3x^2 - 3)dx + \int_1^2 (3x^2 - 3)dx\right)$

$2\left(-[x^3 - 3x]_0^1 + [x^3 - 3x]_1^2\right) = 2[-((1^3 - 3(1)) - (0^3 - 3(0)))$

$+ ((2^3 - 3(2)) - (1^3 - 3(1)))] = 2(6) = 12$

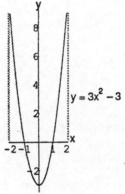

$y = 3x^2 - 3$

43. $x^3 - 3x^2 + 2x = 0 \Rightarrow x(x^2 - 3x + 2) = 0$

$\Rightarrow x(x - 2)(x - 1) = 0 \Rightarrow x = 0, 1,$ or $2;$

Area $= \int_0^1 (x^3 - 3x^2 + 2x)dx - \int_1^2 (x^3 - 3x^2 + 2x)dx$

$= \left[\frac{x^4}{4} - x^3 + x^2\right]_0^1 - \left[\frac{x^4}{4} - x^3 + x^2\right]_1^2$

$= \left(\frac{1^4}{4} - 1^3 + 1^2\right) - \left(\frac{0^4}{4} - 0^3 + 0^2\right)$

$- \left[\left(\frac{2^4}{4} - 2^3 + 2^2\right) - \left(\frac{1^4}{4} - 1^3 + 1^2\right)\right] = \frac{1}{2}$

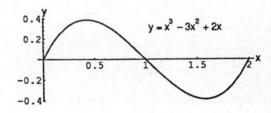

$y = x^3 - 3x^2 + 2x$

44. $x^{1/3} - x = 0 \Rightarrow x^{1/3}\left(1 - x^{2/3}\right) = 0 \Rightarrow x^{1/3} = 0$ or

$1 - x^{2/3} = 0 \Rightarrow x = 0$ or $1 = x^{2/3} \Rightarrow x = 0$ or

$1 = x^2 \Rightarrow x = 0$ or $\pm 1$;

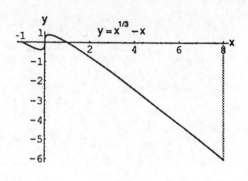

Area $= -\int_{-1}^{0}\left(x^{1/3} - x\right)dx + \int_{0}^{1}\left(x^{1/3} - x\right)dx - \int_{1}^{8}\left(x^{1/3} - x\right)dx$

$= -\left[\frac{3}{4}x^{4/3} - \frac{x^2}{2}\right]_{-1}^{0} + \left[\frac{3}{4}x^{4/3} - \frac{x^2}{2}\right]_{0}^{1} - \left[\frac{3}{4}x^{4/3} - \frac{x^2}{2}\right]_{1}^{8}$

$= -\left[\left(\frac{3}{4}(0)^{4/3} - \frac{0^2}{2}\right) - \left(\frac{3}{4}(-1)^{4/3} - \frac{(-1)^2}{2}\right)\right]$

$+ \left[\left(\frac{3}{4}(1)^{4/3} - \frac{1^2}{2}\right) - \left(\frac{3}{4}(0)^{4/3} - \frac{0^2}{2}\right)\right]$

$- \left[\left(\frac{3}{4}(8)^{4/3} - \frac{8^2}{2}\right) - \left(\frac{3}{4}(1)^{4/3} - \frac{1^2}{2}\right)\right]$

$= \frac{1}{4} + \frac{1}{4} - \left(-20 - \frac{3}{4} + \frac{1}{2}\right) = \frac{83}{4}$

45. The area of the rectangle bounded by the lines $y = 2$, $y = 0$, $x = \pi$, and $x = 0$ is $2\pi$. The area under the curve

$y = 1 + \cos x$ on $[0, \pi]$ is $\int_{0}^{\pi}(1 + \cos x)\,dx = [x + \sin x]_{0}^{\pi} = (\pi + \sin \pi) - (0 + \sin 0) = \pi$. Therefore the area of

the shaded region is $2\pi - \pi = \pi$.

46. The area of the rectangle bounded by the lines $x = \frac{\pi}{6}$, $x = \frac{5\pi}{6}$, $y = \sin \frac{\pi}{6} = \frac{1}{2} = \sin \frac{5\pi}{6}$, and $y = 0$ is

$\frac{1}{2}\left(\frac{5\pi}{6} - \frac{\pi}{6}\right) = \frac{\pi}{3}$. The area under the curve $y = \sin x$ on $\left[\frac{\pi}{6}, \frac{5\pi}{6}\right]$ is $\int_{\pi/6}^{5\pi/6} \sin x\,dx = [-\cos x]_{\pi/6}^{5\pi/6}$

$= \left(-\cos \frac{5\pi}{6}\right) - \left(-\cos \frac{\pi}{6}\right) = -\left(-\frac{\sqrt{3}}{2}\right) + \frac{\sqrt{3}}{2} = \sqrt{3}$. Therefore the area of the shaded region is $\sqrt{3} - \frac{\pi}{3}$.

47. On $\left[-\frac{\pi}{4}, 0\right]$: The area of the rectangle bounded by the lines $y = \sqrt{2}$, $y = 0$, $\theta = 0$, and $\theta = -\frac{\pi}{4}$ is $\sqrt{2}\left(\frac{\pi}{4}\right)$

$= \frac{\pi\sqrt{2}}{4}$. The area between the curve $y = \sec \theta \tan \theta$ and $y = 0$ is $-\int_{-\pi/4}^{0} \sec \theta \tan \theta\,d\theta = [-\sec \theta]_{-\pi/4}^{0}$

$= (-\sec 0) - \left(-\sec\left(-\frac{\pi}{4}\right)\right) = \sqrt{2} - 1$. Therefore the area of the shaded region on $\left[-\frac{\pi}{4}, 0\right]$ is $\frac{\pi\sqrt{2}}{4} + \left(\sqrt{2} - 1\right)$.

On $\left[0, \frac{\pi}{4}\right]$: The area of the rectangle bounded by $\theta = \frac{\pi}{4}$, $\theta = 0$, $y = \sqrt{2}$, and $y = 0$ is $\sqrt{2}\left(\frac{\pi}{4}\right) = \frac{\pi\sqrt{2}}{4}$. The area

under the curve $y = \sec \theta \tan \theta$ is $\int_{0}^{\pi/4} \sec \theta \tan \theta\,d\theta = [\sec \theta]_{0}^{\pi/4} = \sec \frac{\pi}{4} - \sec 0 = \sqrt{2} - 1$. Therefore the area

of the shaded region on $\left[0, \frac{\pi}{4}\right]$ is $\frac{\pi\sqrt{2}}{4} - \left(\sqrt{2} - 1\right)$. Thus, the area of the total shaded region is

$\left(\frac{\pi\sqrt{2}}{4} + \sqrt{2} - 1\right) + \left(\frac{\pi\sqrt{2}}{4} - \sqrt{2} + 1\right) = \frac{\pi\sqrt{2}}{2}$.

48. The area of the rectangle bounded by the lines $y = 2$, $y = 0$, $t = -\frac{\pi}{4}$, and $t = 1$ is $2\left(1 - \left(-\frac{\pi}{4}\right)\right) = 2 + \frac{\pi}{2}$. The

area under the curve $y = \sec^2 t$ on $\left[-\frac{\pi}{4}, 0\right]$ is $\int_{-\pi/4}^{0} \sec^2 t\,dt = [\tan t]_{-\pi/4}^{0} = \tan 0 - \tan\left(-\frac{\pi}{4}\right) = 1$. The area

under the curve $y = 1 - t^2$ on $[0, 1]$ is $\int_{0}^{1}(1 - t^2)\,dt = \left[t - \frac{t^3}{3}\right]_{0}^{1} = \left(1 - \frac{1^3}{3}\right) - \left(0 - \frac{0^3}{3}\right) = \frac{2}{3}$. Thus, the total

area under the curves on $\left[-\frac{\pi}{4}, 1\right]$ is $1 + \frac{2}{3} = \frac{5}{3}$. Therefore the area of the shaded region is $\left(2 + \frac{\pi}{2}\right) - \frac{5}{3} = \frac{1}{3} + \frac{\pi}{2}$.

49. $y = \int_{\pi}^{x} \frac{1}{t}\,dt - 3 \Rightarrow \frac{dy}{dx} = \frac{1}{x}$ and $y(\pi) = \int_{\pi}^{\pi} \frac{1}{t}\,dt - 3 = 0 - 3 = -3 \Rightarrow$ (d) is a solution to this problem.

50. $y = \int_{-1}^{x} \sec t\,dt + 4 \Rightarrow \frac{dy}{dx} = \sec x$ and $y(-1) = \int_{-1}^{-1} \sec t\,dt + 4 = 0 + 4 = 4 \Rightarrow$ (c) is a solution to this problem.

51. $y = \int_{0}^{x} \sec t\,dt + 4 \Rightarrow \frac{dy}{dx} = \sec x$ and $y(0) = \int_{0}^{0} \sec t\,dt + 4 = 0 + 4 = 4 \Rightarrow$ (b) is a solution to this problem.

52. $y = \int_1^x \frac{1}{t} dt - 3 \Rightarrow \frac{dy}{dx} = \frac{1}{x}$ and $y(1) = \int_1^1 \frac{1}{t} dt - 3 = 0 - 3 = -3 \Rightarrow$ (a) is a solution to this problem.

53. $y = \int_2^x \sec t \, dt + 3$                54. $y = \int_1^x \sqrt{1 + t^2} \, dt - 2$

55. Area $= \int_{-b/2}^{b/2} \left( h - \left( \frac{4h}{b^2} \right) x^2 \right) dx = \left[ hx - \frac{4hx^3}{3b^2} \right]_{-b/2}^{b/2}$

$= \left( h\left( \frac{b}{2} \right) - \frac{4h \left( \frac{b}{2} \right)^3}{3b^2} \right) - \left( h\left( -\frac{b}{2} \right) - \frac{4h \left( -\frac{b}{2} \right)^3}{3b^2} \right)$

$= \left( \frac{bh}{2} - \frac{bh}{6} \right) - \left( -\frac{bh}{2} + \frac{bh}{6} \right) = bh - \frac{bh}{3} = \frac{2}{3} bh$

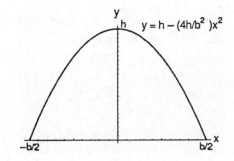

56. $k > 0 \Rightarrow$ one arch of $y = \sin kx$ will occur over the interval $\left[ 0, \frac{\pi}{k} \right] \Rightarrow$ the area $= \int_0^{\pi/k} \sin kx \, dx = \left[ -\frac{1}{k} \cos kx \right]_0^{\pi/k}$

$= -\frac{1}{k} \cos \left( k \left( \frac{\pi}{k} \right) \right) - \left( -\frac{1}{k} \cos (0) \right) = \frac{2}{k}$

57. $\frac{dc}{dx} = \frac{1}{2\sqrt{x}} = \frac{1}{2} x^{-1/2} \Rightarrow c = \int_0^x \frac{1}{2} t^{-1/2} dt = \left[ t^{1/2} \right]_0^x = \sqrt{x}$; $c(100) - c(1) = \sqrt{100} - \sqrt{1} = \$9.00$

58. $r = \int_0^3 \left( 2 - \frac{2}{(x+1)^2} \right) dx = 2 \int_0^3 \left( 1 - \frac{1}{(x+1)^2} \right) dx = 2 \left[ x - \left( \frac{-1}{x+1} \right) \right]_0^3 = 2 \left[ \left( 3 + \frac{1}{(3+1)} \right) - \left( 0 + \frac{1}{(0+1)} \right) \right]$

$= 2 \left[ 3 \frac{1}{4} - 1 \right] = 2 \left( 2 \frac{1}{4} \right) = 4.5$ or $\$4500$

59. (a) $t = 0 \Rightarrow T = 85 - 3\sqrt{25 - 0} = 70^\circ$ F; $t = 16 \Rightarrow T = 85 - 3\sqrt{25 - 16} = 76^\circ$ F;

$t = 25 \Rightarrow T = 85 - 3\sqrt{25 - 25} = 85^\circ$ F

(b) average temperatuve $= \frac{1}{25-0} \int_0^{25} \left( 85 - 3\sqrt{25 - t} \right) dt = \frac{1}{25} \left[ 85t + 2(25 - t)^{3/2} \right]_0^{25}$

$= \frac{1}{25} \left( 85(25) + 2(25 - 25)^{3/2} \right) - \frac{1}{25} \left( 85(0) + 2(25 - 0)^{3/2} \right) = 75^\circ$ F

60. (a) $t = 0 \Rightarrow H = \sqrt{0 + 1} + 5(0)^{1/3} = 1$ ft; $t = 4 \Rightarrow H = \sqrt{4 + 1} + 5(4)^{1/3} = \sqrt{5} + 5\sqrt[3]{4} \approx 10.17$ ft;

$t = 8 \Rightarrow H = \sqrt{8 + 1} + 5(8)^{1/3} = 13$ ft

(b) average height $= \frac{1}{8-0} \int_0^8 \left( \sqrt{t + 1} + 5t^{1/3} \right) dt = \frac{1}{8} \left[ \frac{2}{3}(t + 1)^{3/2} + \frac{15}{4} t^{4/3} \right]_0^8$

$= \frac{1}{8} \left( \frac{2}{3}(8 + 1)^{3/2} + \frac{15}{4} (8)^{4/3} \right) - \frac{1}{8} \left( \frac{2}{3}(0 + 1)^{3/2} + \frac{15}{4} (0)^{4/3} \right) = \frac{29}{3} \approx 9.67$ ft

61. $\int_1^x f(t) \, dt = x^2 - 2x + 1 \Rightarrow f(x) = \frac{d}{dx} \int_1^x f(t) \, dt = \frac{d}{dx} (x^2 - 2x + 1) = 2x - 2$

62. $\int_0^x f(t) \, dt = x \cos \pi x \Rightarrow f(x) = \frac{d}{dx} \int_0^x f(t) \, dt = \cos \pi x - \pi x \sin \pi x \Rightarrow f(4) = \cos \pi(4) - \pi(4) \sin \pi(4) = 1$

63. $f(x) = 2 - \int_2^{x+1} \frac{9}{1+t} \, dt \Rightarrow f'(x) = -\frac{9}{1+(x+1)} = \frac{-9}{x+2} \Rightarrow f'(1) = -3$; $f(1) = 2 - \int_2^{1+1} \frac{9}{1+t} \, dt = 2 - 0 = 2$;

$L(x) = -3(x - 1) + f(1) = -3(x - 1) + 2 = -3x + 5$

64. $g(x) = 3 + \int_1^{x^2} \sec(t-1)\, dt \Rightarrow g'(x) = (\sec(x^2-1))(2x) = 2x \sec(x^2-1) \Rightarrow g'(-1) = 2(-1)\sec((-1)^2-1)$

$= -2;\ g(-1) = 3 + \int_1^{(-1)^2} \sec(t-1)\, dt = 3 + \int_1^1 \sec(t-1)\, dt = 3 + 0 = 3;\ L(x) = -2(x-(-1)) + g(-1)$

$= -2(x+1) + 3 = -2x + 1$

65. (a)  True: since f is continuous, g is differentiable by Part 1 of the Fundamental Theorem of Calculus.

(b)  True:  g is continuous because it is differentiable.

(c)  True, since $g'(1) = f(1) = 0$.

(d)  False, since $g''(1) = f'(1) > 0$.

(e)  True, since $g'(1) = 0$ and $g''(1) = f'(1) > 0$.

(f)  False:  $g''(x) = f'(x) > 0$, so g'' never changes sign.

(g)  True, since $g'(1) = f(1) = 0$ and $g'(x) = f(x)$ is an increasing function of x (because $f'(x) > 0$).

66. Let $a = x_0 < x_1 < x_2 \cdots < x_n = b$ be any partition of [a, b] and let F be any antiderivative of f.

(a) $\sum_{i=1}^{n} \left[ F(x_i) - F(x_{i-1}) \right]$

$= \left[ F(x_1) - F(x_0) \right] + \left[ F(x_2) - F(x_1) \right] + \left[ F(x_3) - F(x_2) \right] + \cdots + \left[ F(x_{n-1}) - F(x_{n-2}) \right] + \left[ F(x_n) - F(x_{n-1}) \right]$

$= -F(x_0) + F(x_1) - F(x_1) + F(x_2) - F(x_2) + \cdots + F(x_{n-1}) - F(x_{n-1}) + F(x_n) = F(x_n) - F(x_0) = F(b) - F(a)$

(b)  Since F is any antiderivative of f on [a, b] $\Rightarrow$ F is differentiable on [a, b] $\Rightarrow$ F is continuous on [a, b]. Consider any subinterval $[x_{i-1}, x_i]$ in [a, b], then by the Mean Value Theorem there is at least one number $c_i$ in $(x_{i-1}, x_i)$ such that

$\left[ F(x_i) - F(x_{i-1}) \right] = F'(c_i)(x_i - x_{i-1}) = f(c_i)(x_i - x_{i-1}) = f(c_i)\Delta x_i$. Thus $F(b) - F(a) = \sum_{i=1}^{n} \left[ F(x_i) - F(x_{i-1}) \right]$

$= \sum_{i=1}^{n} f(c_i)\Delta x_i$.

(c)  Taking the limit of $F(b) - F(a) = \sum_{i=1}^{n} f(c_i)\Delta x_i$ we obtain $\lim_{\|P\|\to 0} (F(b) - F(a)) = \lim_{\|P\|\to 0} \left( \sum_{i=1}^{n} f(c_i)\Delta x_i \right)$

$\Rightarrow F(b) - F(a) = \int_a^b f(x)\, dx$

67-70.    Example CAS commands:

Maple:

```
with( plots );
f := x -> x^3-4*x^2+3*x;
a := 0;
b := 4;
F := unapply( int(f(t),t=a..x), x );                 # (a)
p1 := plot( [f(x),F(x)], x=a..b, legend=["y = f(x)","y = F(x)"], title="#67(a) (Section 5.4)" ):
p1;
dF := D(F);                                          # (b)
q1 := solve( dF(x)=0, x );
pts1 := [ seq( [x,f(x)], x=remove(has,evalf([q1]),I) ) ];
p2 := plot( pts1, style=point, color=blue, symbolsize=18, symbol=diamond, legend="(x,f(x)) where F '(x)=0" ):
display( [p1,p2], title="81(b) (Section 5.4)" );
incr := solve( dF(x)>0, x );                         # (c)
decr := solve( dF(x)<0, x );
df := D(f);                                          # (d)
p3 := plot( [df(x),F(x)], x=a..b, legend=["y = f '(x)","y = F(x)"], title="#67(d) (Section 5.4)" ):
p3;
q2 := solve( df(x)=0, x );
```

```
pts2 := [ seq( [x,F(x)], x=remove(has,evalf([q2]),I) ) ];
p4 := plot( pts2, style=point, color=blue, symbolsize=18, symbol=diamond, legend="(x,f(x)) where f '(x)=0" ):
display( [p3,p4], title="81(d) (Section 5.4)" );
```

71-74.   Example CAS commands:
   Maple:

```
a := 1;
u := x -> x^2;
f := x -> sqrt(1-x^2);
F := unapply( int( f(t), t=a..u(x) ), x );
dF := D(F);                    # (b)
cp := solve( dF(x)=0, x );
solve( dF(x)>0, x );
solve( dF(x)<0, x );
d2F := D(dF);                  # (c)
solve( d2F(x)=0, x );
plot( F(x), x=-1..1, title="#71(d) (Section 5.4)" );
```

75.     Example CAS commands:
   Maple:

```
f := `f`;
q1 := Diff( Int( f(t), t=a..u(x) ), x );
d1' := value( q1 );
```

76.     Example CAS commands:
   Maple:

```
f := `f`;
q2 := Diff( Int( f(t), t=a..u(x) ), x,x );
value( q2 );
```

67-76.   Example CAS commands:
   Mathematica: (assigned function and values for a, and b may vary)
   For transcendental functions the FindRoot is needed instead of the Solve command.
   The Map command executes FindRoot over a set of initial guesses
   Initial guesses will vary as the functions vary.

```
Clear[x, f, F]
{a, b}= {0, 2π}; f[x_] = Sin[2x] Cos[x/3]
F[x_] = Integrate[f[t], {t, a, x}]
Plot[{f[x], F[x]},{x, a, b}]
x/.Map[FindRoot[F'[x]==0, {x, #}] &,{2, 3, 5, 6}]
x/.Map[FindRoot[f'[x]==0, {x, #}] &,{1, 2, 4, 5, 6}]
```

   Slightly alter above commands for 75 - 80.

```
Clear[x, f, F, u]
a=0;  f[x_] = x² − 2x − 3
u[x_] = 1 − x²
F[x_] = Integrate[f[t], {t, a, u(x)}]
x/.Map[FindRoot[F'[x]==0,{x, #}] &,{1, 2, 3, 4}]
x/.Map[FindRoot[F''[x]==0,{x,#}] &,{1, 2, 3, 4}]
```

After determining an appropriate value for b, the following can be entered
    b = 4;
    Plot[{F[x], {x, a, b}]

## 5.5 INDEFINTE INTEGRALS AND THE SUBSTITUTION RULE

1. Let $u = 2x + 4 \Rightarrow du = 2\,dx \Rightarrow \frac{1}{2}\,du = dx$

$$\int 2(2x+4)^5 dx = \int 2u^5 \tfrac{1}{2}\,du = \int u^5\,du = \tfrac{1}{6}u^6 + C = \tfrac{1}{6}(2x+4)^6 + C$$

2. Let $u = 7x - 1 \Rightarrow du = 7\,dx \Rightarrow \frac{1}{7}\,du = dx$

$$\int 7\sqrt{7x-1}\,dx = \int 7(7x-1)^{1/2}\,dx = \int 7u^{1/2}\tfrac{1}{7}\,du = \int u^{1/2}\,du = \tfrac{2}{3}u^{3/2} + C = \tfrac{2}{3}(7x-1)^{3/2} + C$$

3. Let $u = x^2 + 5 \Rightarrow du = 2x\,dx \Rightarrow \frac{1}{2}\,du = x\,dx$

$$\int 2x(x^2+5)^{-4}dx = \int 2u^{-4}\tfrac{1}{2}du = \int u^{-4}\,du = -\tfrac{1}{3}u^{-3} + C = -\tfrac{1}{3}(x^2+5)^{-3} + C$$

4. Let $u = x^4 + 1 \Rightarrow du = 4x^3\,dx \Rightarrow \frac{1}{4}\,du = x^3\,dx$

$$\int \tfrac{4x^3}{(x^4+1)^2}dx = \int 4x^3(x^4+1)^{-2}dx = \int 4u^{-2}\tfrac{1}{4}du = \int u^{-2}\,du = -u^{-1} + C = \tfrac{-1}{x^4+1} + C$$

5. Let $u = 3x^2 + 4x \Rightarrow du = (6x+4)dx = 2(3x+2)\,dx \Rightarrow \frac{1}{2}\,du = (3x+2)\,dx$

$$\int (3x+2)(3x^2+4x)^4 dx = \int u^4 \tfrac{1}{2}du = \tfrac{1}{2}\int u^4\,du = \tfrac{1}{10}u^5 + C = \tfrac{1}{10}(3x^2+4x)^5 + C$$

6. Let $u = 1 + \sqrt{x} \Rightarrow du = \frac{1}{2\sqrt{x}}\,dx \Rightarrow 2\,du = \frac{1}{\sqrt{x}}\,dx$

$$\int \tfrac{(1+\sqrt{x})^{1/3}}{\sqrt{x}}dx = \int (1+\sqrt{x})^{1/3}\tfrac{1}{\sqrt{x}}dx = \int u^{1/3}\,2\,du = 2\int u^{1/3}\,du = 2\cdot\tfrac{3}{4}u^{4/3} + C = \tfrac{3}{2}(1+\sqrt{x})^{4/3} + C$$

7. Let $u = 3x \Rightarrow du = 3\,dx \Rightarrow \frac{1}{3}\,du = dx$

$$\int \sin 3x\,dx = \int \tfrac{1}{3}\sin u\,du = -\tfrac{1}{3}\cos u + C = -\tfrac{1}{3}\cos 3x + C$$

8. Let $u = 2x^2 \Rightarrow du = 4x\,dx \Rightarrow \frac{1}{4}\,du = x\,dx$

$$\int x\sin(2x^2)\,dx = \int \tfrac{1}{4}\sin u\,du = -\tfrac{1}{4}\cos u + C = -\tfrac{1}{4}\cos 2x^2 + C$$

9. Let $u = 2t \Rightarrow du = 2\,dt \Rightarrow \frac{1}{2}\,du = dt$

$$\int \sec 2t\,\tan 2t\,dt = \int \tfrac{1}{2}\sec u\,\tan u\,du = \tfrac{1}{2}\sec u + C = \tfrac{1}{2}\sec 2t + C$$

10. Let $u = 1 - \cos\frac{t}{2} \Rightarrow du = \frac{1}{2}\sin\frac{t}{2}\,dt \Rightarrow 2\,du = \sin\frac{t}{2}\,dt$

$$\int \left(1 - \cos\tfrac{t}{2}\right)^2 \left(\sin\tfrac{t}{2}\right)dt = \int 2u^2\,du = \tfrac{2}{3}u^3 + C = \tfrac{2}{3}\left(1 - \cos\tfrac{t}{2}\right)^3 + C$$

11. Let $u = 1 - r^3 \Rightarrow du = -3r^2\,dr \Rightarrow -3\,du = 9r^2\,dr$

$$\int \tfrac{9r^2\,dr}{\sqrt{1-r^3}} = \int -3u^{-1/2}\,du = -3(2)u^{1/2} + C = -6(1-r^3)^{1/2} + C$$

12. Let $u = y^4 + 4y^2 + 1 \Rightarrow du = (4y^3 + 8y)\,dy \Rightarrow 3\,du = 12(y^3+2y)\,dy$

$$\int 12(y^4+4y^2+1)^2(y^3+2y)\,dy = \int 3u^2\,du = u^3 + C = (y^4+4y^2+1)^3 + C$$

13. Let $u = x^{3/2} - 1 \Rightarrow du = \frac{3}{2} x^{1/2} dx \Rightarrow \frac{2}{3} du = \sqrt{x} \, dx$

$\int \sqrt{x} \sin^2 \left(x^{3/2} - 1\right) dx = \int \frac{2}{3} \sin^2 u \, du = \frac{2}{3} \left(\frac{u}{2} - \frac{1}{4} \sin 2u\right) + C = \frac{1}{3} \left(x^{3/2} - 1\right) - \frac{1}{6} \sin \left(2x^{3/2} - 2\right) + C$

14. Let $u = -\frac{1}{x} \Rightarrow du = \frac{1}{x^2} dx$

$\int \frac{1}{x^2} \cos^2 \left(\frac{1}{x}\right) dx = \int \cos^2 (-u) \, du = \int \cos^2 (u) \, du = \left(\frac{u}{2} + \frac{1}{4} \sin 2u\right) + C = -\frac{1}{2x} + \frac{1}{4} \sin \left(-\frac{2}{x}\right) + C$

$= -\frac{1}{2x} - \frac{1}{4} \sin \left(\frac{2}{x}\right) + C$

15. (a) Let $u = \cot 2\theta \Rightarrow du = -2 \csc^2 2\theta \, d\theta \Rightarrow -\frac{1}{2} du = \csc^2 2\theta \, d\theta$

$\int \csc^2 2\theta \cot 2\theta \, d\theta = -\int \frac{1}{2} u \, du = -\frac{1}{2} \left(\frac{u^2}{2}\right) + C = -\frac{u^2}{4} + C = -\frac{1}{4} \cot^2 2\theta + C$

(b) Let $u = \csc 2\theta \Rightarrow du = -2 \csc 2\theta \cot 2\theta \, d\theta \Rightarrow -\frac{1}{2} du = \csc 2\theta \cot 2\theta \, d\theta$

$\int \csc^2 2\theta \cot 2\theta \, d\theta = \int -\frac{1}{2} u \, du = -\frac{1}{2} \left(\frac{u^2}{2}\right) + C = -\frac{u^2}{4} + C = -\frac{1}{4} \csc^2 2\theta + C$

16. (a) Let $u = 5x + 8 \Rightarrow du = 5 \, dx \Rightarrow \frac{1}{5} du = dx$

$\int \frac{dx}{\sqrt{5x+8}} = \int \frac{1}{5} \left(\frac{1}{\sqrt{u}}\right) du = \frac{1}{5} \int u^{-1/2} du = \frac{1}{5} \left(2u^{1/2}\right) + C = \frac{2}{5} u^{1/2} + C = \frac{2}{5} \sqrt{5x+8} + C$

(b) Let $u = \sqrt{5x + 8} \Rightarrow du = \frac{1}{2} (5x+8)^{-1/2} (5) \, dx \Rightarrow \frac{2}{5} du = \frac{dx}{\sqrt{5x+8}}$

$\int \frac{dx}{\sqrt{5x+8}} = \int \frac{2}{5} du = \frac{2}{5} u + C = \frac{2}{5} \sqrt{5x+8} + C$

17. Let $u = 3 - 2s \Rightarrow du = -2 \, ds \Rightarrow -\frac{1}{2} du = ds$

$\int \sqrt{3 - 2s} \, ds = \int \sqrt{u} \left(-\frac{1}{2} du\right) = -\frac{1}{2} \int u^{1/2} du = \left(-\frac{1}{2}\right) \left(\frac{2}{3} u^{3/2}\right) + C = -\frac{1}{3} (3 - 2s)^{3/2} + C$

18. Let $u = 5s + 4 \Rightarrow du = 5 \, ds \Rightarrow \frac{1}{5} du = ds$

$\int \frac{1}{\sqrt{5s+4}} \, ds = \int \frac{1}{\sqrt{u}} \left(\frac{1}{5} du\right) = \frac{1}{5} \int u^{-1/2} du = \left(\frac{1}{5}\right) \left(2u^{1/2}\right) + C = \frac{2}{5} \sqrt{5s+4} + C$

19. Let $u = 1 - \theta^2 \Rightarrow du = -2\theta \, d\theta \Rightarrow -\frac{1}{2} du = \theta \, d\theta$

$\int \theta \sqrt[4]{1 - \theta^2} \, d\theta = \int \sqrt[4]{u} \left(-\frac{1}{2} du\right) = -\frac{1}{2} \int u^{1/4} du = \left(-\frac{1}{2}\right) \left(\frac{4}{5} u^{5/4}\right) + C = -\frac{2}{5} \left(1 - \theta^2\right)^{5/4} + C$

20. Let $u = 7 - 3y^2 \Rightarrow du = -6y \, dy \Rightarrow -\frac{1}{2} du = 3y \, dy$

$\int 3y \sqrt{7 - 3y^2} \, dy = \int \sqrt{u} \left(-\frac{1}{2} du\right) = -\frac{1}{2} \int u^{1/2} du = \left(-\frac{1}{2}\right) \left(\frac{2}{3} u^{3/2}\right) + C = -\frac{1}{3} \left(7 - 3y^2\right)^{3/2} + C$

21. Let $u = 1 + \sqrt{x} \Rightarrow du = \frac{1}{2\sqrt{x}} dx \Rightarrow 2 \, du = \frac{1}{\sqrt{x}} dx$

$\int \frac{1}{\sqrt{x} \left(1 + \sqrt{x}\right)^2} dx = \int \frac{2 \, du}{u^2} = -\frac{2}{u} + C = \frac{-2}{1 + \sqrt{x}} + C$

22. Let $u = 3z + 4 \Rightarrow du = 3 \, dz \Rightarrow \frac{1}{3} du = dz$

$\int \cos (3z + 4) \, dz = \int (\cos u) \left(\frac{1}{3} du\right) = \frac{1}{3} \int \cos u \, du = \frac{1}{3} \sin u + C = \frac{1}{3} \sin (3z + 4) + C$

23. Let $u = 3x + 2 \Rightarrow du = 3 \, dx \Rightarrow \frac{1}{3} du = dx$

$\int \sec^2 (3x + 2) \, dx = \int (\sec^2 u) \left(\frac{1}{3} du\right) = \frac{1}{3} \int \sec^2 u \, du = \frac{1}{3} \tan u + C = \frac{1}{3} \tan (3x + 2) + C$

24. Let $u = \tan x \Rightarrow du = \sec^2 x \, dx$

$\int \tan^2 x \sec^2 x \, dx = \int u^2 \, du = \frac{1}{3} u^3 + C = \frac{1}{3} \tan^3 x + C$

25. Let $u = \sin\left(\frac{x}{3}\right) \Rightarrow du = \frac{1}{3}\cos\left(\frac{x}{3}\right) dx \Rightarrow 3\,du = \cos\left(\frac{x}{3}\right) dx$

$\int \sin^5\left(\frac{x}{3}\right) \cos\left(\frac{x}{3}\right) dx = \int u^5 \, (3\,du) = 3\left(\frac{1}{6}u^6\right) + C = \frac{1}{2}\sin^6\left(\frac{x}{3}\right) + C$

26. Let $u = \tan\left(\frac{x}{2}\right) \Rightarrow du = \frac{1}{2}\sec^2\left(\frac{x}{2}\right) dx \Rightarrow 2\,du = \sec^2\left(\frac{x}{2}\right) dx$

$\int \tan^7\left(\frac{x}{2}\right) \sec^2\left(\frac{x}{2}\right) dx = \int u^7 \, (2\,du) = 2\left(\frac{1}{8}u^8\right) + C = \frac{1}{4}\tan^8\left(\frac{x}{2}\right) + C$

27. Let $u = \frac{r^3}{18} - 1 \Rightarrow du = \frac{r^2}{6}\,dr \Rightarrow 6\,du = r^2\,dr$

$\int r^2 \left(\frac{r^3}{18} - 1\right)^5 dr = \int u^5 \, (6\,du) = 6\int u^5\,du = 6\left(\frac{u^6}{6}\right) + C = \left(\frac{r^3}{18} - 1\right)^6 + C$

28. Let $u = 7 - \frac{r^5}{10} \Rightarrow du = -\frac{1}{2}r^4\,dr \Rightarrow -2\,du = r^4\,dr$

$\int r^4 \left(7 - \frac{r^5}{10}\right)^3 dr = \int u^3 \, (-2\,du) = -2\int u^3\,du = -2\left(\frac{u^4}{4}\right) + C = -\frac{1}{2}\left(7 - \frac{r^5}{10}\right)^4 + C$

29. Let $u = x^{3/2} + 1 \Rightarrow du = \frac{3}{2}x^{1/2}\,dx \Rightarrow \frac{2}{3}\,du = x^{1/2}\,dx$

$\int x^{1/2}\sin\left(x^{3/2} + 1\right) dx = \int (\sin u)\left(\frac{2}{3}\,du\right) = \frac{2}{3}\int \sin u\,du = \frac{2}{3}(-\cos u) + C = -\frac{2}{3}\cos\left(x^{3/2} + 1\right) + C$

30. Let $u = \csc\left(\frac{v-\pi}{2}\right) \Rightarrow du = -\frac{1}{2}\csc\left(\frac{v-\pi}{2}\right)\cot\left(\frac{v-\pi}{2}\right) dv \Rightarrow -2\,du = \csc\left(\frac{v-\pi}{2}\right)\cot\left(\frac{v-\pi}{2}\right) dv$

$\int \csc\left(\frac{v-\pi}{2}\right)\cot\left(\frac{v-\pi}{2}\right) dv = \int -2\,du = -2u + C = -2\csc\left(\frac{v-\pi}{2}\right) + C$

31. Let $u = \cos(2t+1) \Rightarrow du = -2\sin(2t+1)\,dt \Rightarrow -\frac{1}{2}\,du = \sin(2t+1)\,dt$

$\int \frac{\sin(2t+1)}{\cos^2(2t+1)}\,dt = \int -\frac{1}{2}\frac{du}{u^2} = \frac{1}{2u} + C = \frac{1}{2\cos(2t+1)} + C$

32. Let $u = \sec z \Rightarrow du = \sec z\tan z\,dz$

$\int \frac{\sec z\tan z}{\sqrt{\sec z}}\,dz = \int \frac{1}{\sqrt{u}}\,du = \int u^{-1/2}\,du = 2u^{1/2} + C = 2\sqrt{\sec z} + C$

33. Let $u = \frac{1}{t} - 1 = t^{-1} - 1 \Rightarrow du = -t^{-2}\,dt \Rightarrow -du = \frac{1}{t^2}\,dt$

$\int \frac{1}{t^2}\cos\left(\frac{1}{t} - 1\right) dt = \int (\cos u)(-du) = -\int \cos u\,du = -\sin u + C = -\sin\left(\frac{1}{t} - 1\right) + C$

34. Let $u = \sqrt{t} + 3 = t^{1/2} + 3 \Rightarrow du = \frac{1}{2}t^{-1/2}\,dt \Rightarrow 2\,du = \frac{1}{\sqrt{t}}\,dt$

$\int \frac{1}{\sqrt{t}}\cos\left(\sqrt{t} + 3\right) dt = \int (\cos u)(2\,du) = 2\int \cos u\,du = 2\sin u + C = 2\sin\left(\sqrt{t} + 3\right) + C$

35. Let $u = \sin\frac{1}{\theta} \Rightarrow du = \left(\cos\frac{1}{\theta}\right)\left(-\frac{1}{\theta^2}\right) d\theta \Rightarrow -du = \frac{1}{\theta^2}\cos\frac{1}{\theta}\,d\theta$

$\int \frac{1}{\theta^2}\sin\frac{1}{\theta}\cos\frac{1}{\theta}\,d\theta = \int -u\,du = -\frac{1}{2}u^2 + C = -\frac{1}{2}\sin^2\frac{1}{\theta} + C$

36. Let $u = \csc\sqrt{\theta} \Rightarrow du = \left(-\csc\sqrt{\theta}\cot\sqrt{\theta}\right)\left(\frac{1}{2\sqrt{\theta}}\right) d\theta \Rightarrow -2\,du = \frac{1}{\sqrt{\theta}}\cot\sqrt{\theta}\csc\sqrt{\theta}\,d\theta$

$\int \frac{\cos\sqrt{\theta}}{\sqrt{\theta}\sin^2\sqrt{\theta}}\,d\theta = \int \frac{1}{\sqrt{\theta}}\cot\sqrt{\theta}\csc\sqrt{\theta}\,d\theta = \int -2\,du = -2u + C = -2\csc\sqrt{\theta} + C = -\frac{2}{\sin\sqrt{\theta}} + C$

37. Let $u = 1 + t^4 \Rightarrow du = 4t^3\,dt \Rightarrow \frac{1}{4}\,du = t^3\,dt$

$\int t^3\left(1 + t^4\right)^3 dt = \int u^3\left(\frac{1}{4}\,du\right) = \frac{1}{4}\left(\frac{1}{4}u^4\right) + C = \frac{1}{16}\left(1 + t^4\right)^4 + C$

38. Let $u = 1 - \frac{1}{x} \Rightarrow du = \frac{1}{x^2} dx$

$\int \sqrt{\frac{x-1}{x^5}} dx = \int \frac{1}{x^2} \sqrt{\frac{x-1}{x}} dx = \int \frac{1}{x^2} \sqrt{1 - \frac{1}{x}} dx = \int \sqrt{u} \, du = \int u^{1/2} du = \frac{2}{3} u^{3/2} + C = \frac{2}{3} \left(1 - \frac{1}{x}\right)^{3/2} + C$

39. Let $u = 2 - \frac{1}{x} \Rightarrow du = \frac{1}{x^2} dx$

$\int \frac{1}{x^2} \sqrt{2 - \frac{1}{x}} dx = \int \sqrt{u} \, du = \int u^{1/2} du = \frac{2}{3} u^{3/2} + C = \frac{2}{3} \left(2 - \frac{1}{x}\right)^{3/2} + C$

40. Let $u = 1 - \frac{1}{x^2} \Rightarrow du = \frac{2}{x^3} dx \Rightarrow \frac{1}{2} du = \frac{1}{x^3} dx$

$\int \frac{1}{x^3} \sqrt{\frac{x^2-1}{x^2}} dx = \int \frac{1}{x^3} \sqrt{1 - \frac{1}{x^2}} dx = \int \sqrt{u} \, \frac{1}{2} du = \frac{1}{2} \int u^{1/2} du = \frac{1}{3} u^{3/2} + C = \frac{1}{3} \left(1 - \frac{1}{x^2}\right)^{3/2} + C$

41. Let $u = 1 - \frac{3}{x^3} \Rightarrow du = \frac{9}{x^4} dx \Rightarrow \frac{1}{9} du = \frac{1}{x^4} dx$

$\int \sqrt{\frac{x^3-3}{x^{11}}} dx = \int \frac{1}{x^4} \sqrt{\frac{x^3-3}{x^3}} dx = \int \frac{1}{x^4} \sqrt{1 - \frac{3}{x^3}} dx = \int \sqrt{u} \, \frac{1}{9} du = \frac{1}{9} \int u^{1/2} du = \frac{2}{27} u^{3/2} + C = \frac{2}{27} \left(1 - \frac{3}{x^3}\right)^{3/2} + C$

42. Let $u = x^3 - 1 \Rightarrow du = 3x^2 dx \Rightarrow \frac{1}{3} du = x^2 dx$

$\int \sqrt{\frac{x^4}{x^3-1}} dx = \int \frac{x^2}{\sqrt{x^3-1}} dx = \int \frac{1}{\sqrt{u}} \frac{1}{3} du = \frac{1}{3} \int u^{-1/2} du = \frac{2}{3} u^{1/2} + C = \frac{2}{3} (x^3 - 1)^{3/2} + C$

43. Let $u = x - 1$. Then $du = dx$ and $x = u + 1$. Thus $\int x(x-1)^{10} dx = \int (u+1)u^{10} du = \int (u^{11} + u^{10}) du$

$= \frac{1}{12} u^{12} + \frac{1}{11} u^{11} + C = \frac{1}{12} (x-1)^{12} + \frac{1}{11} (x-1)^{11} + C$

44. Let $u = 4 - x$. Then $du = -1 \, dx$ and $(-1) \, du = dx$ and $x = 4 - u$. Thus $\int x \sqrt{4-x} dx = \int (4-u) \sqrt{u} \, (-1) du$

$= \int (4-u)(-u^{1/2}) du = \int \left(u^{3/2} - 4u^{1/2}\right) du = \frac{2}{5} u^{5/2} - \frac{8}{3} u^{3/2} + C = \frac{2}{5} (4-x)^{5/2} - \frac{8}{3} (4-x)^{3/2} + C$

45. Let $u = 1 - x$. Then $du = -1 \, dx$ and $(-1) \, du = dx$ and $x = 1 - u$. Thus $\int (x+1)^2 (1-x)^5 dx$

$= \int (2-u)^2 u^5 (-1) du = \int (-u^7 + 4u^6 - 4u^5) du = -\frac{1}{8} u^8 + \frac{4}{7} u^7 - \frac{2}{3} u^6 + C$

$= -\frac{1}{8} (1-x)^8 + \frac{4}{7} (1-x)^7 - \frac{2}{3} (1-x)^6 + C$

46. Let $u = x - 5$. Then $du = dx$ and $x = u + 5$. Thus $\int (x+5)(x-5)^{1/3} dx = \int (u+10)u^{1/3} du = \int (u^{4/3} + 10u^{1/3}) du$

$= \frac{3}{7} u^{7/3} + \frac{15}{2} u^{4/3} + C = \frac{3}{7} (x-5)^{7/3} + \frac{15}{2} (x-5)^{4/3} + C$

47. Let $u = x^2 + 1$. Then $du = 2x \, dx$ and $\frac{1}{2} du = x \, dx$ and $x^2 = u - 1$. Thus $\int x^3 \sqrt{x^2+1} dx = \int (u-1) \frac{1}{2} \sqrt{u} \, du$

$= \frac{1}{2} \int \left(u^{3/2} - u^{1/2}\right) du = \frac{1}{2} \left[\frac{2}{5} u^{5/2} - \frac{2}{3} u^{3/2}\right] + C = \frac{1}{5} u^{5/2} - \frac{1}{3} u^{3/2} + C = \frac{1}{5} (x^2+1)^{5/2} - \frac{1}{3} (x^2+1)^{3/2} + C$

48. Let $u = x^3 + 1 \Rightarrow du = 3x^2 dx$ and $x^3 = u - 1$. So $\int 3x^5 \sqrt{x^3+1} dx = \int (u-1) \sqrt{u} \, du = \int \left(u^{3/2} - u^{1/2}\right) du$

$= \frac{2}{5} u^{5/2} - \frac{2}{3} u^{3/2} + C = \frac{2}{5} (x^3+1)^{5/2} - \frac{2}{3} (x^3+1)^{3/2} + C$

49. Let $u = x^2 - 4 \Rightarrow du = 2x \, dx$ and $\frac{1}{2} du = x \, dx$. Thus $\int \frac{x}{(x^2-4)^3} dx = \int (x^2-4)^{-3} x \, dx = \int u^{-3} \frac{1}{2} du = \frac{1}{2} \int u^{-3} du$

$= -\frac{1}{4} u^{-2} + C = -\frac{1}{4} (x^2-4)^{-2} + C$

50. Let $u = x - 4 \Rightarrow du = dx$ and $x = u + 4$. Thus $\int \frac{x}{(x-4)^3} dx = \int (x-4)^{-3} x \, dx = \int u^{-3} (u+4) du = \int \left(u^{-2} + 4u^{-3}\right) du$

$= -u^{-1} - 2u^{-2} + C = -(x-4)^{-1} - 2(x-4)^{-2} + C$

51. (a) Let $u = \tan x \Rightarrow du = \sec^2 x\, dx$; $v = u^3 \Rightarrow dv = 3u^2\, du \Rightarrow 6\, dv = 18u^2\, du$; $w = 2 + v \Rightarrow dw = dv$

$\int \frac{18 \tan^2 x \sec^2 x}{(2 + \tan^3 x)^2}\, dx = \int \frac{18u^2}{(2 + u^3)^2}\, du = \int \frac{6\, dv}{(2 + v)^2} = \int \frac{6\, dw}{w^2} = 6 \int w^{-2}\, dw = -6w^{-1} + C = -\frac{6}{2 + v} + C$

$\quad = -\frac{6}{2 + u^3} + C = -\frac{6}{2 + \tan^3 x} + C$

(b) Let $u = \tan^3 x \Rightarrow du = 3 \tan^2 x \sec^2 x\, dx \Rightarrow 6\, du = 18 \tan^2 x \sec^2 x\, dx$; $v = 2 + u \Rightarrow dv = du$

$\int \frac{18 \tan^2 x \sec^2 x}{(2 + \tan^3 x)^2}\, dx = \int \frac{6\, du}{(2 + u)^2} = \int \frac{6\, dv}{v^2} = -\frac{6}{v} + C = -\frac{6}{2 + u} + C = -\frac{6}{2 + \tan^3 x} + C$

(c) Let $u = 2 + \tan^3 x \Rightarrow du = 3 \tan^2 x \sec^2 x\, dx \Rightarrow 6\, du = 18 \tan^2 x \sec^2 x\, dx$

$\int \frac{18 \tan^2 x \sec^2 x}{(2 + \tan^3 x)^2}\, dx = \int \frac{6\, du}{u^2} = -\frac{6}{u} + C = -\frac{6}{2 + \tan^3 x} + C$

52. (a) Let $u = x - 1 \Rightarrow du = dx$; $v = \sin u \Rightarrow dv = \cos u\, du$; $w = 1 + v^2 \Rightarrow dw = 2v\, dv \Rightarrow \frac{1}{2}\, dw = v\, dv$

$\int \sqrt{1 + \sin^2(x - 1)} \sin(x - 1) \cos(x - 1)\, dx = \int \sqrt{1 + \sin^2 u} \sin u \cos u\, du = \int v \sqrt{1 + v^2}\, dv$

$\quad = \int \frac{1}{2} \sqrt{w}\, dw = \frac{1}{3} w^{3/2} + C = \frac{1}{3}(1 + v^2)^{3/2} + C = \frac{1}{3}(1 + \sin^2 u)^{3/2} + C = \frac{1}{3}(1 + \sin^2(x - 1))^{3/2} + C$

(b) Let $u = \sin(x - 1) \Rightarrow du = \cos(x - 1)\, dx$; $v = 1 + u^2 \Rightarrow dv = 2u\, du \Rightarrow \frac{1}{2}\, dv = u\, du$

$\int \sqrt{1 + \sin^2(x - 1)} \sin(x - 1) \cos(x - 1)\, dx = \int u \sqrt{1 + u^2}\, du = \int \frac{1}{2} \sqrt{v}\, dv = \int \frac{1}{2} v^{1/2}\, dv$

$\quad = \left(\frac{1}{2}\left(\frac{2}{3}\right) v^{3/2}\right) + C = \frac{1}{3} v^{3/2} + C = \frac{1}{3}(1 + u^2)^{3/2} + C = \frac{1}{3}(1 + \sin^2(x - 1))^{3/2} + C$

(c) Let $u = 1 + \sin^2(x - 1) \Rightarrow du = 2 \sin(x - 1) \cos(x - 1)\, dx \Rightarrow \frac{1}{2}\, du = \sin(x - 1) \cos(x - 1)\, dx$

$\int \sqrt{1 + \sin^2(x - 1)} \sin(x - 1) \cos(x - 1)\, dx = \int \frac{1}{2} \sqrt{u}\, du = \int \frac{1}{2} u^{1/2}\, du = \frac{1}{2}\left(\frac{2}{3} u^{3/2}\right) + C$

$\quad = \frac{1}{3}(1 + \sin^2(x - 1))^{3/2} + C$

53. Let $u = 3(2r - 1)^2 + 6 \Rightarrow du = 6(2r - 1)(2)\, dr \Rightarrow \frac{1}{12}\, du = (2r - 1)\, dr$; $v = \sqrt{u} \Rightarrow dv = \frac{1}{2\sqrt{u}}\, du \Rightarrow \frac{1}{6}\, dv = \frac{1}{12\sqrt{u}}\, du$

$\int \frac{(2r - 1) \cos \sqrt{3(2r - 1)^2 + 6}}{\sqrt{3(2r - 1)^2 + 6}}\, dr = \int \left(\frac{\cos \sqrt{u}}{\sqrt{u}}\right)\left(\frac{1}{12}\, du\right) = \int (\cos v)\left(\frac{1}{6}\, dv\right) = \frac{1}{6} \sin v + C = \frac{1}{6} \sin \sqrt{u} + C$

$\quad = \frac{1}{6} \sin \sqrt{3(2r - 1)^2 + 6} + C$

54. Let $u = \cos \sqrt{\theta} \Rightarrow du = \left(-\sin \sqrt{\theta}\right)\left(\frac{1}{2\sqrt{\theta}}\right) d\theta \Rightarrow -2\, du = \frac{\sin \sqrt{\theta}}{\sqrt{\theta}}\, d\theta$

$\int \frac{\sin \sqrt{\theta}}{\sqrt{\theta \cos^3 \sqrt{\theta}}}\, d\theta = \int \frac{\sin \sqrt{\theta}}{\sqrt{\theta} \sqrt{\cos^3 \sqrt{\theta}}}\, d\theta = \int \frac{-2\, du}{u^{3/2}} = -2 \int u^{-3/2}\, du = -2\left(-2u^{-1/2}\right) + C = \frac{4}{\sqrt{u}} + C$

$\quad = \frac{4}{\sqrt{\cos \sqrt{\theta}}} + C$

55. Let $u = 3t^2 - 1 \Rightarrow du = 6t\, dt \Rightarrow 2\, du = 12t\, dt$

$s = \int 12t (3t^2 - 1)^3\, dt = \int u^3 (2\, du) = 2\left(\frac{1}{4} u^4\right) + C = \frac{1}{2} u^4 + C = \frac{1}{2}(3t^2 - 1)^4 + C$;

$s = 3$ when $t = 1 \Rightarrow 3 = \frac{1}{2}(3 - 1)^4 + C \Rightarrow 3 = 8 + C \Rightarrow C = -5 \Rightarrow s = \frac{1}{2}(3t^2 - 1)^4 - 5$

56. Let $u = x^2 + 8 \Rightarrow du = 2x\, dx \Rightarrow 2\, du = 4x\, dx$

$y = \int 4x (x^2 + 8)^{-1/3}\, dx = \int u^{-1/3} (2\, du) = 2\left(\frac{3}{2} u^{2/3}\right) + C = 3u^{2/3} + C = 3(x^2 + 8)^{2/3} + C$;

$y = 0$ when $x = 0 \Rightarrow 0 = 3(8)^{2/3} + C \Rightarrow C = -12 \Rightarrow y = 3(x^2 + 8)^{2/3} - 12$

57. Let $u = t + \frac{\pi}{12} \Rightarrow du = dt$

$s = \int 8 \sin^2\left(t + \frac{\pi}{12}\right) dt = \int 8 \sin^2 u\, du = 8\left(\frac{u}{2} - \frac{1}{4} \sin 2u\right) + C = 4\left(t + \frac{\pi}{12}\right) - 2 \sin\left(2t + \frac{\pi}{6}\right) + C$;

$s = 8$ when $t = 0 \Rightarrow 8 = 4\left(\frac{\pi}{12}\right) - 2 \sin\left(\frac{\pi}{6}\right) + C \Rightarrow C = 8 - \frac{\pi}{3} + 1 = 9 - \frac{\pi}{3}$

$\Rightarrow s = 4\left(t + \frac{\pi}{12}\right) - 2 \sin\left(2t + \frac{\pi}{6}\right) + 9 - \frac{\pi}{3} = 4t - 2 \sin\left(2t + \frac{\pi}{6}\right) + 9$

58. Let $u = \frac{\pi}{4} - \theta \Rightarrow -du = d\theta$

$r = \int 3 \cos^2 \left(\frac{\pi}{4} - \theta\right) d\theta = -\int 3 \cos^2 u \, du = -3 \left(\frac{u}{2} + \frac{1}{4} \sin 2u\right) + C = -\frac{3}{2} \left(\frac{\pi}{4} - \theta\right) - \frac{3}{4} \sin \left(\frac{\pi}{2} - 2\theta\right) + C;$

$r = \frac{\pi}{8}$ when $\theta = 0 \Rightarrow \frac{\pi}{8} = -\frac{3\pi}{8} - \frac{3}{4} \sin \frac{\pi}{2} + C \Rightarrow C = \frac{\pi}{2} + \frac{3}{4} \Rightarrow r = -\frac{3}{2} \left(\frac{\pi}{4} - \theta\right) - \frac{3}{4} \sin \left(\frac{\pi}{2} - 2\theta\right) + \frac{\pi}{2} + \frac{3}{4}$

$\Rightarrow r = \frac{3}{2}\theta - \frac{3}{4} \sin \left(\frac{\pi}{2} - 2\theta\right) + \frac{\pi}{8} + \frac{3}{4} \Rightarrow r = \frac{3}{2}\theta - \frac{3}{4} \cos 2\theta + \frac{\pi}{8} + \frac{3}{4}$

59. Let $u = 2t - \frac{\pi}{2} \Rightarrow du = 2 \, dt \Rightarrow -2 \, du = -4 \, dt$

$\frac{ds}{dt} = \int -4 \sin \left(2t - \frac{\pi}{2}\right) dt = \int (\sin u)(-2 \, du) = 2 \cos u + C_1 = 2 \cos \left(2t - \frac{\pi}{2}\right) + C_1;$

at $t = 0$ and $\frac{ds}{dt} = 100$ we have $100 = 2 \cos \left(-\frac{\pi}{2}\right) + C_1 \Rightarrow C_1 = 100 \Rightarrow \frac{ds}{dt} = 2 \cos \left(2t - \frac{\pi}{2}\right) + 100$

$\Rightarrow s = \int \left(2 \cos \left(2t - \frac{\pi}{2}\right) + 100\right) dt = \int (\cos u + 50) \, du = \sin u + 50u + C_2 = \sin \left(2t - \frac{\pi}{2}\right) + 50 \left(2t - \frac{\pi}{2}\right) + C_2;$

at $t = 0$ and $s = 0$ we have $0 = \sin \left(-\frac{\pi}{2}\right) + 50 \left(-\frac{\pi}{2}\right) + C_2 \Rightarrow C_2 = 1 + 25\pi$

$\Rightarrow s = \sin \left(2t - \frac{\pi}{2}\right) + 100t - 25\pi + (1 + 25\pi) \Rightarrow s = \sin \left(2t - \frac{\pi}{2}\right) + 100t + 1$

60. Let $u = \tan 2x \Rightarrow du = 2 \sec^2 2x \, dx \Rightarrow 2 \, du = 4 \sec^2 2x \, dx; v = 2x \Rightarrow dv = 2 \, dx \Rightarrow \frac{1}{2} dv = dx$

$\frac{dy}{dx} = \int 4 \sec^2 2x \tan 2x \, dx = \int u(2 \, du) = u^2 + C_1 = \tan^2 2x + C_1;$

at $x = 0$ and $\frac{dy}{dx} = 4$ we have $4 = 0 + C_1 \Rightarrow C_1 = 4 \Rightarrow \frac{dy}{dx} = \tan^2 2x + 4 = (\sec^2 2x - 1) + 4 = \sec^2 2x + 3$

$\Rightarrow y = \int (\sec^2 2x + 3) \, dx = \int (\sec^2 v + 3) \left(\frac{1}{2} dv\right) = \frac{1}{2} \tan v + \frac{3}{2} v + C_2 = \frac{1}{2} \tan 2x + 3x + C_2;$

at $x = 0$ and $y = -1$ we have $-1 = \frac{1}{2}(0) + 0 + C_2 \Rightarrow C_2 = -1 \Rightarrow y = \frac{1}{2} \tan 2x + 3x - 1$

61. Let $u = 2t \Rightarrow du = 2 \, dt \Rightarrow 3 \, du = 6 \, dt$

$s = \int 6 \sin 2t \, dt = \int (\sin u)(3 \, du) = -3 \cos u + C = -3 \cos 2t + C;$

at $t = 0$ and $s = 0$ we have $0 = -3 \cos 0 + C \Rightarrow C = 3 \Rightarrow s = 3 - 3 \cos 2t \Rightarrow s \left(\frac{\pi}{2}\right) = 3 - 3 \cos (\pi) = 6$ m

62. Let $u = \pi t \Rightarrow du = \pi \, dt \Rightarrow \pi \, du = \pi^2 \, dt$

$v = \int \pi^2 \cos \pi t \, dt = \int (\cos u)(\pi \, du) = \pi \sin u + C_1 = \pi \sin (\pi t) + C_1;$

at $t = 0$ and $v = 8$ we have $8 = \pi(0) + C_1 \Rightarrow C_1 = 8 \Rightarrow v = \frac{ds}{dt} = \pi \sin (\pi t) + 8 \Rightarrow s = \int (\pi \sin (\pi t) + 8) \, dt$

$= \int \sin u \, du + 8t + C_2 = -\cos (\pi t) + 8t + C_2;$ at $t = 0$ and $s = 0$ we have $0 = -1 + C_2 \Rightarrow C_2 = 1$

$\Rightarrow s = 8t - \cos (\pi t) + 1 \Rightarrow s(1) = 8 - \cos \pi + 1 = 10$ m

63. All three integrations are correct. In each case, the derivative of the function on the right is the integrand on the left, and each formula has an arbitrary constant for generating the remaining antiderivatives. Moreover,

$\sin^2 x + C_1 = 1 - \cos^2 x + C_1 \Rightarrow C_2 = 1 + C_1;$ also $-\cos^2 x + C_2 = -\frac{\cos 2x}{2} - \frac{1}{2} + C_2 \Rightarrow C_3 = C_2 - \frac{1}{2} = C_1 + \frac{1}{2}.$

64. (a) $\left(\frac{1}{\frac{1}{60} - 0}\right) \int_0^{1/60} V_{max} \sin 120\pi t \, dt = 60 \left[-V_{max} \left(\frac{1}{120\pi}\right) \cos (120\pi t)\right]_0^{1/60} = -\frac{V_{max}}{2\pi} [\cos 2\pi - \cos 0]$

$= -\frac{V_{max}}{2\pi} [1 - 1] = 0$

(b) $V_{max} = \sqrt{2} V_{rms} = \sqrt{2} (240) \approx 339$ volts

(c) $\int_0^{1/60} (V_{max})^2 \sin^2 120\pi t \, dt = (V_{max})^2 \int_0^{1/60} \left(\frac{1 - \cos 240\pi t}{2}\right) dt = \frac{(V_{max})^2}{2} \int_0^{1/60} (1 - \cos 240\pi t) \, dt$

$= \frac{(V_{max})^2}{2} \left[t - \left(\frac{1}{240\pi}\right) \sin 240\pi t\right]_0^{1/60} = \frac{(V_{max})^2}{2} \left[\left(\frac{1}{60} - \left(\frac{1}{240\pi}\right) \sin (4\pi)\right) - \left(0 - \left(\frac{1}{240\pi}\right) \sin (0)\right)\right] = \frac{(V_{max})^2}{120}$

## 5.6 SUBSTITUTION AND AREA BETWEEN CURVES

1. (a) Let $u = y + 1 \Rightarrow du = dy; y = 0 \Rightarrow u = 1, y = 3 \Rightarrow u = 4$

$$\int_0^3 \sqrt{y+1}\, dy = \int_1^4 u^{1/2}\, du = \left[\tfrac{2}{3} u^{3/2}\right]_1^4 = \left(\tfrac{2}{3}\right)(4)^{3/2} - \left(\tfrac{2}{3}\right)(1)^{3/2} = \left(\tfrac{2}{3}\right)(8) - \left(\tfrac{2}{3}\right)(1) = \tfrac{14}{3}$$

(b) Use the same substitution for u as in part (a); $y = -1 \Rightarrow u = 0, y = 0 \Rightarrow u = 1$

$$\int_{-1}^0 \sqrt{y+1}\, dy = \int_0^1 u^{1/2}\, du = \left[\tfrac{2}{3} u^{3/2}\right]_0^1 = \left(\tfrac{2}{3}\right)(1)^{3/2} - 0 = \tfrac{2}{3}$$

2. (a) Let $u = 1 - r^2 \Rightarrow du = -2r\, dr \Rightarrow -\tfrac{1}{2} du = r\, dr; r = 0 \Rightarrow u = 1, r = 1 \Rightarrow u = 0$

$$\int_0^1 r\sqrt{1-r^2}\, dr = \int_1^0 -\tfrac{1}{2}\sqrt{u}\, du = \left[-\tfrac{1}{3} u^{3/2}\right]_1^0 = 0 - \left(-\tfrac{1}{3}\right)(1)^{3/2} = \tfrac{1}{3}$$

(b) Use the same substitution for u as in part (a); $r = -1 \Rightarrow u = 0, r = 1 \Rightarrow u = 0$

$$\int_{-1}^1 r\sqrt{1-r^2}\, dr = \int_0^0 -\tfrac{1}{2}\sqrt{u}\, du = 0$$

3. (a) Let $u = \tan x \Rightarrow du = \sec^2 x\, dx; x = 0 \Rightarrow u = 0, x = \tfrac{\pi}{4} \Rightarrow u = 1$

$$\int_0^{\pi/4} \tan x \sec^2 x\, dx = \int_0^1 u\, du = \left[\tfrac{u^2}{2}\right]_0^1 = \tfrac{1^2}{2} - 0 = \tfrac{1}{2}$$

(b) Use the same substitution as in part (a); $x = -\tfrac{\pi}{4} \Rightarrow u = -1, x = 0 \Rightarrow u = 0$

$$\int_{-\pi/4}^0 \tan x \sec^2 x\, dx = \int_{-1}^0 u\, du = \left[\tfrac{u^2}{2}\right]_{-1}^0 = 0 - \tfrac{1}{2} = -\tfrac{1}{2}$$

4. (a) Let $u = \cos x \Rightarrow du = -\sin x\, dx \Rightarrow -du = \sin x\, dx; x = 0 \Rightarrow u = 1, x = \pi \Rightarrow u = -1$

$$\int_0^\pi 3\cos^2 x \sin x\, dx = \int_1^{-1} -3u^2\, du = \left[-u^3\right]_1^{-1} = -(-1)^3 - (-(1)^3) = 2$$

(b) Use the same substitution as in part (a); $x = 2\pi \Rightarrow u = 1, x = 3\pi \Rightarrow u = -1$

$$\int_{2\pi}^{3\pi} 3\cos^2 x \sin x\, dx = \int_1^{-1} -3u^2\, du = 2$$

5. (a) $u = 1 + t^4 \Rightarrow du = 4t^3\, dt \Rightarrow \tfrac{1}{4} du = t^3\, dt; t = 0 \Rightarrow u = 1, t = 1 \Rightarrow u = 2$

$$\int_0^1 t^3(1+t^4)^3\, dt = \int_1^2 \tfrac{1}{4} u^3\, du = \left[\tfrac{u^4}{16}\right]_1^2 = \tfrac{2^4}{16} - \tfrac{1^4}{16} = \tfrac{15}{16}$$

(b) Use the same substitution as in part (a); $t = -1 \Rightarrow u = 2, t = 1 \Rightarrow u = 2$

$$\int_{-1}^1 t^3(1+t^4)^3\, dt = \int_2^2 \tfrac{1}{4} u^3\, du = 0$$

6. (a) Let $u = t^2 + 1 \Rightarrow du = 2t\, dt \Rightarrow \tfrac{1}{2} du = t\, dt; t = 0 \Rightarrow u = 1, t = \sqrt{7} \Rightarrow u = 8$

$$\int_0^{\sqrt{7}} t(t^2+1)^{1/3}\, dt = \int_1^8 \tfrac{1}{2} u^{1/3}\, du = \left[\left(\tfrac{1}{2}\right)\left(\tfrac{3}{4}\right) u^{4/3}\right]_1^8 = \left(\tfrac{3}{8}\right)(8)^{4/3} - \left(\tfrac{3}{8}\right)(1)^{4/3} = \tfrac{45}{8}$$

(b) Use the same substitution as in part (a); $t = -\sqrt{7} \Rightarrow u = 8, t = 0 \Rightarrow u = 1$

$$\int_{-\sqrt{7}}^0 t(t^2+1)^{1/3}\, dt = \int_8^1 \tfrac{1}{2} u^{1/3}\, du = -\int_1^8 \tfrac{1}{2} u^{1/3}\, du = -\tfrac{45}{8}$$

7. (a) Let $u = 4 + r^2 \Rightarrow du = 2r\, dr \Rightarrow \tfrac{1}{2} du = r\, dr; r = -1 \Rightarrow u = 5, r = 1 \Rightarrow u = 5$

$$\int_{-1}^1 \tfrac{5r}{(4+r^2)^2}\, dr = 5\int_5^5 \tfrac{1}{2} u^{-2}\, du = 0$$

(b) Use the same substitution as in part (a); $r = 0 \Rightarrow u = 4, r = 1 \Rightarrow u = 5$

$$\int_0^1 \tfrac{5r}{(4+r^2)^2}\, dr = 5\int_4^5 \tfrac{1}{2} u^{-2}\, du = 5\left[-\tfrac{1}{2} u^{-1}\right]_4^5 = 5\left(-\tfrac{1}{2}(5)^{-1}\right) - 5\left(-\tfrac{1}{2}(4)^{-1}\right) = \tfrac{1}{8}$$

8. (a) Let $u = 1 + v^{3/2} \Rightarrow du = \frac{3}{2} v^{1/2} dv \Rightarrow \frac{20}{3} du = 10\sqrt{v} \, dv; v = 0 \Rightarrow u = 1, v = 1 \Rightarrow u = 2$

$\int_0^1 \frac{10\sqrt{v}}{(1+v^{3/2})^2} \, dv = \int_1^2 \frac{1}{u^2} \left(\frac{20}{3} du\right) = \frac{20}{3} \int_1^2 u^{-2} \, du = -\frac{20}{3} \left[\frac{1}{u}\right]_1^2 = -\frac{20}{3} \left[\frac{1}{2} - \frac{1}{1}\right] = \frac{10}{3}$

(b) Use the same substitution as in part (a); $v = 1 \Rightarrow u = 2, v = 4 \Rightarrow u = 1 + 4^{3/2} = 9$

$\int_1^4 \frac{10\sqrt{v}}{(1+v^{3/2})^2} \, dv = \int_2^9 \frac{1}{u^2} \left(\frac{20}{3} du\right) = -\frac{20}{3} \left[\frac{1}{u}\right]_2^9 = -\frac{20}{3} \left(\frac{1}{9} - \frac{1}{2}\right) = -\frac{20}{3} \left(-\frac{7}{18}\right) = \frac{70}{27}$

9. (a) Let $u = x^2 + 1 \Rightarrow du = 2x \, dx \Rightarrow 2 \, du = 4x \, dx; x = 0 \Rightarrow u = 1, x = \sqrt{3} \Rightarrow u = 4$

$\int_0^{\sqrt{3}} \frac{4x}{\sqrt{x^2+1}} \, dx = \int_1^4 \frac{2}{\sqrt{u}} \, du = \int_1^4 2u^{-1/2} \, du = \left[4u^{1/2}\right]_1^4 = 4(4)^{1/2} - 4(1)^{1/2} = 4$

(b) Use the same substitution as in part (a); $x = -\sqrt{3} \Rightarrow u = 4, x = \sqrt{3} \Rightarrow u = 4$

$\int_{-\sqrt{3}}^{\sqrt{3}} \frac{4x}{\sqrt{x^2+1}} \, dx = \int_4^4 \frac{2}{\sqrt{u}} \, du = 0$

10. (a) Let $u = x^4 + 9 \Rightarrow du = 4x^3 \, dx \Rightarrow \frac{1}{4} du = x^3 \, dx; x = 0 \Rightarrow u = 9, x = 1 \Rightarrow u = 10$

$\int_0^1 \frac{x^3}{\sqrt{x^4+9}} \, dx = \int_9^{10} \frac{1}{4} u^{-1/2} \, du = \left[\frac{1}{4} (2)u^{1/2}\right]_9^{10} = \frac{1}{2} (10)^{1/2} - \frac{1}{2} (9)^{1/2} = \frac{\sqrt{10}-3}{2}$

(b) Use the same substitution as in part (a); $x = -1 \Rightarrow u = 10, x = 0 \Rightarrow u = 9$

$\int_{-1}^0 \frac{x^3}{\sqrt{x^4+9}} \, dx = \int_{10}^9 \frac{1}{4} u^{-1/2} \, du = -\int_9^{10} \frac{1}{4} u^{-1/2} \, du = \frac{3-\sqrt{10}}{2}$

11. (a) Let $u = 1 - \cos 3t \Rightarrow du = 3 \sin 3t \, dt \Rightarrow \frac{1}{3} du = \sin 3t \, dt; t = 0 \Rightarrow u = 0, t = \frac{\pi}{6} \Rightarrow u = 1 - \cos \frac{\pi}{2} = 1$

$\int_0^{\pi/6} (1 - \cos 3t) \sin 3t \, dt = \int_0^1 \frac{1}{3} u \, du = \left[\frac{1}{3} \left(\frac{u^2}{2}\right)\right]_0^1 = \frac{1}{6} (1)^2 - \frac{1}{6} (0)^2 = \frac{1}{6}$

(b) Use the same substitution as in part (a); $t = \frac{\pi}{6} \Rightarrow u = 1, t = \frac{\pi}{3} \Rightarrow u = 1 - \cos \pi = 2$

$\int_{\pi/6}^{\pi/3} (1 - \cos 3t) \sin 3t \, dt = \int_1^2 \frac{1}{3} u \, du = \left[\frac{1}{3} \left(\frac{u^2}{2}\right)\right]_1^2 = \frac{1}{6} (2)^2 - \frac{1}{6} (1)^2 = \frac{1}{2}$

12. (a) Let $u = 2 + \tan \frac{t}{2} \Rightarrow du = \frac{1}{2} \sec^2 \frac{t}{2} \, dt \Rightarrow 2 \, du = \sec^2 \frac{t}{2} \, dt; t = \frac{-\pi}{2} \Rightarrow u = 2 + \tan \left(\frac{-\pi}{4}\right) = 1, t = 0 \Rightarrow u = 2$

$\int_{-\pi/2}^0 \left(2 + \tan \frac{t}{2}\right) \sec^2 \frac{t}{2} \, dt = \int_1^2 u (2 \, du) = \left[u^2\right]_1^2 = 2^2 - 1^2 = 3$

(b) Use the same substitution as in part (a); $t = \frac{-\pi}{2} \Rightarrow u = 1, t = \frac{\pi}{2} \Rightarrow u = 3$

$\int_{-\pi/2}^{\pi/2} \left(2 + \tan \frac{t}{2}\right) \sec^2 \frac{t}{2} \, dt = 2 \int_1^3 u \, du = \left[u^2\right]_1^3 = 3^2 - 1^2 = 8$

13. (a) Let $u = 4 + 3 \sin z \Rightarrow du = 3 \cos z \, dz \Rightarrow \frac{1}{3} du = \cos z \, dz; z = 0 \Rightarrow u = 4, z = 2\pi \Rightarrow u = 4$

$\int_0^{2\pi} \frac{\cos z}{\sqrt{4+3 \sin z}} \, dz = \int_4^4 \frac{1}{\sqrt{u}} \left(\frac{1}{3} du\right) = 0$

(b) Use the same substitution as in part (a); $z = -\pi \Rightarrow u = 4 + 3 \sin (-\pi) = 4, z = \pi \Rightarrow u = 4$

$\int_{-\pi}^{\pi} \frac{\cos z}{\sqrt{4+3 \sin z}} \, dz = \int_4^4 \frac{1}{\sqrt{u}} \left(\frac{1}{3} du\right) = 0$

14. (a) Let $u = 3 + 2 \cos w \Rightarrow du = -2 \sin w \, dw \Rightarrow -\frac{1}{2} du = \sin w \, dw; w = -\frac{\pi}{2} \Rightarrow u = 3, w = 0 \Rightarrow u = 5$

$\int_{-\pi/2}^0 \frac{\sin w}{(3+2 \cos w)^2} \, dw = \int_3^5 u^{-2} \left(-\frac{1}{2} du\right) = \frac{1}{2} [u^{-1}]_3^5 = \frac{1}{2} \left(\frac{1}{5} - \frac{1}{3}\right) = -\frac{1}{15}$

(b) Use the same substitution as in part (a); $w = 0 \Rightarrow u = 5, w = \frac{\pi}{2} \Rightarrow u = 3$

$\int_0^{\pi/2} \frac{\sin w}{(3+2 \cos w)^2} \, dw = \int_5^3 u^{-2} \left(-\frac{1}{2} du\right) = \frac{1}{2} \int_3^5 u^{-2} \, du = \frac{1}{15}$

15. Let $u = t^5 + 2t \Rightarrow du = (5t^4 + 2)\, dt; t = 0 \Rightarrow u = 0, t = 1 \Rightarrow u = 3$

$$\int_0^1 \sqrt{t^5 + 2t}\, (5t^4 + 2)\, dt = \int_0^3 u^{1/2}\, du = \left[\tfrac{2}{3} u^{3/2}\right]_0^3 = \tfrac{2}{3}(3)^{3/2} - \tfrac{2}{3}(0)^{3/2} = 2\sqrt{3}$$

16. Let $u = 1 + \sqrt{y} \Rightarrow du = \frac{dy}{2\sqrt{y}}; y = 1 \Rightarrow u = 2, y = 4 \Rightarrow u = 3$

$$\int_1^4 \frac{dy}{2\sqrt{y}\,(1 + \sqrt{y})^2} = \int_2^3 \frac{1}{u^2}\, du = \int_2^3 u^{-2}\, du = [-u^{-1}]_2^3 = \left(-\tfrac{1}{3}\right) - \left(-\tfrac{1}{2}\right) = \tfrac{1}{6}$$

17. Let $u = \cos 2\theta \Rightarrow du = -2 \sin 2\theta\, d\theta \Rightarrow -\tfrac{1}{2}\, du = \sin 2\theta\, d\theta; \theta = 0 \Rightarrow u = 1, \theta = \tfrac{\pi}{6} \Rightarrow u = \cos 2\left(\tfrac{\pi}{6}\right) = \tfrac{1}{2}$

$$\int_0^{\pi/6} \cos^{-3} 2\theta \sin 2\theta\, d\theta = \int_1^{1/2} u^{-3} \left(-\tfrac{1}{2}\, du\right) = -\tfrac{1}{2} \int_1^{1/2} u^{-3}\, du = \left[-\tfrac{1}{2}\left(\tfrac{u^{-2}}{-2}\right)\right]_1^{1/2} = \tfrac{1}{4\left(\tfrac{1}{2}\right)^2} - \tfrac{1}{4(1)^2} = \tfrac{3}{4}$$

18. Let $u = \tan\left(\tfrac{\theta}{6}\right) \Rightarrow du = \tfrac{1}{6} \sec^2\left(\tfrac{\theta}{6}\right)\, d\theta \Rightarrow 6\, du = \sec^2\left(\tfrac{\theta}{6}\right)\, d\theta; \theta = \pi \Rightarrow u = \tan\left(\tfrac{\pi}{6}\right) = \tfrac{1}{\sqrt{3}}, \theta = \tfrac{3\pi}{2} \Rightarrow u = \tan\tfrac{\pi}{4} = 1$

$$\int_\pi^{3\pi/2} \cot^5\left(\tfrac{\theta}{6}\right) \sec^2\left(\tfrac{\theta}{6}\right)\, d\theta = \int_{1/\sqrt{3}}^1 u^{-5}\,(6\, du) = \left[6\left(\tfrac{u^{-4}}{-4}\right)\right]_{1/\sqrt{3}}^1 = \left[-\tfrac{3}{2u^4}\right]_{1/\sqrt{3}}^1 = -\tfrac{3}{2(1)^4} - \left(-\tfrac{3}{2\left(\tfrac{1}{\sqrt{3}}\right)^4}\right) = 12$$

19. Let $u = 5 - 4 \cos t \Rightarrow du = 4 \sin t\, dt \Rightarrow \tfrac{1}{4}\, du = \sin t\, dt; t = 0 \Rightarrow u = 5 - 4 \cos 0 = 1, t = \pi \Rightarrow u = 5 - 4 \cos \pi = 9$

$$\int_0^\pi 5\,(5 - 4 \cos t)^{1/4} \sin t\, dt = \int_1^9 5u^{1/4} \left(\tfrac{1}{4}\, du\right) = \tfrac{5}{4} \int_1^9 u^{1/4}\, du = \left[\tfrac{5}{4}\left(\tfrac{4}{5} u^{5/4}\right)\right]_1^9 = 9^{5/4} - 1 = 3^{5/2} - 1$$

20. Let $u = 1 - \sin 2t \Rightarrow du = -2 \cos 2t\, dt \Rightarrow -\tfrac{1}{2}\, du = \cos 2t\, dt; t = 0 \Rightarrow u = 1, t = \tfrac{\pi}{4} \Rightarrow u = 0$

$$\int_0^{\pi/4} (1 - \sin 2t)^{3/2} \cos 2t\, dt = \int_1^0 -\tfrac{1}{2} u^{3/2}\, du = \left[-\tfrac{1}{2}\left(\tfrac{2}{5} u^{5/2}\right)\right]_1^0 = \left(-\tfrac{1}{5}(0)^{5/2}\right) - \left(-\tfrac{1}{5}(1)^{5/2}\right) = \tfrac{1}{5}$$

21. Let $u = 4y - y^2 + 4y^3 + 1 \Rightarrow du = (4 - 2y + 12y^2)\, dy; y = 0 \Rightarrow u = 1, y = 1 \Rightarrow u = 4(1) - (1)^2 + 4(1)^3 + 1 = 8$

$$\int_0^1 (4y - y^2 + 4y^3 + 1)^{-2/3}\,(12y^2 - 2y + 4)\, dy = \int_1^8 u^{-2/3}\, du = \left[3u^{1/3}\right]_1^8 = 3(8)^{1/3} - 3(1)^{1/3} = 3$$

22. Let $u = y^3 + 6y^2 - 12y + 9 \Rightarrow du = (3y^2 + 12y - 12)\, dy \Rightarrow \tfrac{1}{3}\, du = (y^2 + 4y - 4)\, dy; y = 0 \Rightarrow u = 9, y = 1 \Rightarrow u = 4$

$$\int_0^1 (y^3 + 6y^2 - 12y + 9)^{-1/2}\,(y^2 + 4y - 4)\, dy = \int_9^4 \tfrac{1}{3} u^{-1/2}\, du = \left[\tfrac{1}{3}\left(2u^{1/2}\right)\right]_9^4 = \tfrac{2}{3}(4)^{1/2} - \tfrac{2}{3}(9)^{1/2} = \tfrac{2}{3}(2 - 3) = -\tfrac{2}{3}$$

23. Let $u = \theta^{3/2} \Rightarrow du = \tfrac{3}{2} \theta^{1/2}\, d\theta \Rightarrow \tfrac{2}{3}\, du = \sqrt{\theta}\, d\theta; \theta = 0 \Rightarrow u = 0, \theta = \sqrt[3]{\pi^2} \Rightarrow u = \pi$

$$\int_0^{\sqrt[3]{\pi^2}} \sqrt{\theta} \cos^2\left(\theta^{3/2}\right)\, d\theta = \int_0^\pi \cos^2 u \left(\tfrac{2}{3}\, du\right) = \left[\tfrac{2}{3}\left(\tfrac{u}{2} + \tfrac{1}{4} \sin 2u\right)\right]_0^\pi = \tfrac{2}{3}\left(\tfrac{\pi}{2} + \tfrac{1}{4} \sin 2\pi\right) - \tfrac{2}{3}(0) = \tfrac{\pi}{3}$$

24. Let $u = 1 + \tfrac{1}{t} \Rightarrow du = -t^{-2}\, dt; t = -1 \Rightarrow u = 0, t = -\tfrac{1}{2} \Rightarrow u = -1$

$$\int_{-1}^{-1/2} t^{-2} \sin^2\left(1 + \tfrac{1}{t}\right)\, dt = \int_0^{-1} -\sin^2 u\, du = \left[-\left(\tfrac{u}{2} - \tfrac{1}{4} \sin 2u\right)\right]_0^{-1} = -\left[\left(-\tfrac{1}{2} - \tfrac{1}{4} \sin(-2)\right) - \left(\tfrac{0}{2} - \tfrac{1}{4} \sin 0\right)\right]$$

$$= \tfrac{1}{2} - \tfrac{1}{4} \sin 2$$

25. Let $u = 4 - x^2 \Rightarrow du = -2x\, dx \Rightarrow -\tfrac{1}{2}\, du = x\, dx; x = -2 \Rightarrow u = 0, x = 0 \Rightarrow u = 4, x = 2 \Rightarrow u = 0$

$$A = -\int_{-2}^0 x\sqrt{4 - x^2}\, dx + \int_0^2 x\sqrt{4 - x^2}\, dx = -\int_0^4 -\tfrac{1}{2} u^{1/2}\, du + \int_4^0 -\tfrac{1}{2} u^{1/2}\, du = 2 \int_0^4 \tfrac{1}{2} u^{1/2}\, du = \int_0^4 u^{1/2}\, du$$

$$= \left[\tfrac{2}{3} u^{3/2}\right]_0^4 = \tfrac{2}{3}(4)^{3/2} - \tfrac{2}{3}(0)^{3/2} = \tfrac{16}{3}$$

26. Let $u = 1 - \cos x \Rightarrow du = \sin x\, dx; x = 0 \Rightarrow u = 0, x = \pi \Rightarrow u = 2$

$$\int_0^\pi (1 - \cos x) \sin x\, dx = \int_0^2 u\, du = \left[\tfrac{u^2}{2}\right]_0^2 = \tfrac{2^2}{2} - \tfrac{0^2}{2} = 2$$

27. Let $u = 1 + \cos x \Rightarrow du = -\sin x \, dx \Rightarrow -du = \sin x \, dx$; $x = -\pi \Rightarrow u = 1 + \cos(-\pi) = 0$, $x = 0 \Rightarrow u = 1 + \cos 0 = 2$

$A = -\int_{-\pi}^{0} 3(\sin x)\sqrt{1 + \cos x}\, dx = -\int_{0}^{2} 3u^{1/2}(-du) = 3\int_{0}^{2} u^{1/2}\, du = \left[2u^{3/2}\right]_{0}^{2} = 2(2)^{3/2} - 2(0)^{3/2} = 2^{5/2}$

28. Let $u = \pi + \pi \sin x \Rightarrow du = \pi \cos x \, dx \Rightarrow \frac{1}{\pi} du = \cos x \, dx$; $x = -\frac{\pi}{2} \Rightarrow u = \pi + \pi \sin\left(-\frac{\pi}{2}\right) = 0$, $x = 0 \Rightarrow u = \pi$

Because of symmetry about $x = -\frac{\pi}{2}$, $A = 2\int_{-\pi/2}^{0} \frac{\pi}{2}(\cos x)(\sin(\pi + \pi \sin x))\, dx = 2\int_{0}^{\pi} \frac{\pi}{2}(\sin u)\left(\frac{1}{\pi}\, du\right)$

$= \int_{0}^{\pi} \sin u \, du = [-\cos u]_{0}^{\pi} = (-\cos \pi) - (-\cos 0) = 2$

29. For the sketch given, $a = 0$, $b = \pi$; $f(x) - g(x) = 1 - \cos^2 x = \sin^2 x = \frac{1 - \cos 2x}{2}$;

$A = \int_{0}^{\pi} \frac{(1 - \cos 2x)}{2}\, dx = \frac{1}{2}\int_{0}^{\pi}(1 - \cos 2x)\, dx = \frac{1}{2}\left[x - \frac{\sin 2x}{2}\right]_{0}^{\pi} = \frac{1}{2}[(\pi - 0) - (0 - 0)] = \frac{\pi}{2}$

30. For the sketch given, $a = -\frac{\pi}{3}$, $b = \frac{\pi}{3}$; $f(t) - g(t) = \frac{1}{2}\sec^2 t - (-4\sin^2 t) = \frac{1}{2}\sec^2 t + 4\sin^2 t$;

$A = \int_{-\pi/3}^{\pi/3}\left(\frac{1}{2}\sec^2 t + 4\sin^2 t\right) dt = \frac{1}{2}\int_{-\pi/3}^{\pi/3}\sec^2 t \, dt + 4\int_{-\pi/3}^{\pi/3}\sin^2 t \, dt = \frac{1}{2}\int_{-\pi/3}^{\pi/3}\sec^2 t \, dt + 4\int_{-\pi/3}^{\pi/3}\frac{(1 - \cos 2t)}{2}\, dt$

$= \frac{1}{2}\int_{-\pi/3}^{\pi/3}\sec^2 t \, dt + 2\int_{-\pi/3}^{\pi/3}(1 - \cos 2t)\, dt = \frac{1}{2}[\tan t]_{-\pi/3}^{\pi/3} + 2[t - \frac{\sin 2t}{2}]_{-\pi/3}^{\pi/3} = \sqrt{3} + 4\cdot\frac{\pi}{3} - \sqrt{3} = \frac{4\pi}{3}$

31. For the sketch given, $a = -2$, $b = 2$; $f(x) - g(x) = 2x^2 - (x^4 - 2x^2) = 4x^2 - x^4$;

$A = \int_{-2}^{2}(4x^2 - x^4)\, dx = \left[\frac{4x^3}{3} - \frac{x^5}{5}\right]_{-2}^{2} = \left(\frac{32}{3} - \frac{32}{5}\right) - \left[-\frac{32}{3} - \left(-\frac{32}{5}\right)\right] = \frac{64}{3} - \frac{64}{5} = \frac{320 - 192}{15} = \frac{128}{15}$

32. For the sketch given, $c = 0$, $d = 1$; $f(y) - g(y) = y^2 - y^3$;

$A = \int_{0}^{1}(y^2 - y^3)\, dy = \int_{0}^{1} y^2\, dy - \int_{0}^{1} y^3\, dy = \left[\frac{y^3}{3}\right]_{0}^{1} - \left[\frac{y^4}{4}\right]_{0}^{1} = \frac{(1 - 0)}{3} - \frac{(1 - 0)}{4} = \frac{1}{3} - \frac{1}{4} = \frac{1}{12}$

33. For the sketch given, $c = 0$, $d = 1$; $f(y) - g(y) = (12y^2 - 12y^3) - (2y^2 - 2y) = 10y^2 - 12y^3 + 2y$;

$A = \int_{0}^{1}(10y^2 - 12y^3 + 2y)\, dy = \int_{0}^{1} 10y^2\, dy - \int_{0}^{1} 12y^3\, dy + \int_{0}^{1} 2y \, dy = \left[\frac{10}{3}y^3\right]_{0}^{1} - \left[\frac{12}{4}y^4\right]_{0}^{1} + \left[\frac{2}{2}y^2\right]_{0}^{1}$

$= \left(\frac{10}{3} - 0\right) - (3 - 0) + (1 - 0) = \frac{4}{3}$

34. For the sketch given, $a = -1$, $b = 1$; $f(x) - g(x) = x^2 - (-2x^4) = x^2 + 2x^4$;

$A = \int_{-1}^{1}(x^2 + 2x^4)\, dx = \left[\frac{x^3}{3} + \frac{2x^5}{5}\right]_{-1}^{1} = \left(\frac{1}{3} + \frac{2}{5}\right) - \left[-\frac{1}{3} + \left(-\frac{2}{5}\right)\right] = \frac{2}{3} + \frac{4}{5} = \frac{10 + 12}{15} = \frac{22}{15}$

35. We want the area between the line $y = 1$, $0 \le x \le 2$, and the curve $y = \frac{x^2}{4}$, *minus* the area of a triangle

(formed by $y = x$ and $y = 1$) with base 1 and height 1. Thus, $A = \int_{0}^{2}\left(1 - \frac{x^2}{4}\right) dx - \frac{1}{2}(1)(1) = \left[x - \frac{x^3}{12}\right]_{0}^{2} - \frac{1}{2}$

$= \left(2 - \frac{8}{12}\right) - \frac{1}{2} = 2 - \frac{2}{3} - \frac{1}{2} = \frac{5}{6}$

36. We want the area between the x-axis and the curve $y = x^2$, $0 \le x \le 1$ *plus* the area of a triangle (formed by $x = 1$,

$x + y = 2$, and the x-axis) with base 1 and height 1. Thus, $A = \int_{0}^{1} x^2\, dx + \frac{1}{2}(1)(1) = \left[\frac{x^3}{3}\right]_{0}^{1} + \frac{1}{2} = \frac{1}{3} + \frac{1}{2} = \frac{5}{6}$

37. AREA $= A1 + A2$

A1: For the sketch given, $a = -3$ and we find b by solving the equations $y = x^2 - 4$ and $y = -x^2 - 2x$

simultaneously for x: $x^2 - 4 = -x^2 - 2x \Rightarrow 2x^2 + 2x - 4 = 0 \Rightarrow 2(x + 2)(x - 1) \Rightarrow x = -2$ or $x = 1$ so

$b = -2$: $f(x) - g(x) = (x^2 - 4) - (-x^2 - 2x) = 2x^2 + 2x - 4 \Rightarrow A1 = \int_{-3}^{-2}(2x^2 + 2x - 4)\, dx$

$$= \left[ \tfrac{2x^3}{3} + \tfrac{2x^2}{2} - 4x \right]_{-3}^{-2} = \left( -\tfrac{16}{3} + 4 + 8 \right) - (-18 + 9 + 12) = 9 - \tfrac{16}{3} = \tfrac{11}{3};$$

A2:  For the sketch given, $a = -2$ and $b = 1$: $f(x) - g(x) = (-x^2 - 2x) - (x^2 - 4) = -2x^2 - 2x + 4$

$$\Rightarrow A2 = -\int_{-2}^{1} (2x^2 + 2x - 4)\, dx = -\left[ \tfrac{2x^3}{3} + x^2 - 4x \right]_{-2}^{1} = -\left( \tfrac{2}{3} + 1 - 4 \right) + \left( -\tfrac{16}{3} + 4 + 8 \right)$$

$$= -\tfrac{2}{3} - 1 + 4 - \tfrac{16}{3} + 4 + 8 = 9;$$

Therefore, AREA $= A1 + A2 = \tfrac{11}{3} + 9 = \tfrac{38}{3}$

38.  AREA $= A1 + A2$

A1:  For the sketch given, $a = -2$ and $b = 0$: $f(x) - g(x) = (2x^3 - x^2 - 5x) - (-x^2 + 3x) = 2x^3 - 8x$

$$\Rightarrow A1 = \int_{-2}^{0} (2x^3 - 8x)\, dx = \left[ \tfrac{2x^4}{4} - \tfrac{8x^2}{2} \right]_{-2}^{0} = 0 - (8 - 16) = 8;$$

A2:  For the sketch given, $a = 0$ and $b = 2$: $f(x) - g(x) = (-x^2 + 3x) - (2x^3 - x^2 - 5x) = 8x - 2x^3$

$$\Rightarrow A2 = \int_{0}^{2} (8x - 2x^3)\, dx = \left[ \tfrac{8x^2}{2} - \tfrac{2x^4}{4} \right]_{0}^{2} = (16 - 8) = 8;$$

Therefore, AREA $= A1 + A2 = 16$

39.  AREA $= A1 + A2 + A3$

A1:  For the sketch given, $a = -2$ and $b = -1$: $f(x) - g(x) = (-x + 2) - (4 - x^2) = x^2 - x - 2$

$$\Rightarrow A1 = \int_{-2}^{-1} (x^2 - x - 2)\, dx = \left[ \tfrac{x^3}{3} - \tfrac{x^2}{2} - 2x \right]_{-2}^{-1} = \left( -\tfrac{1}{3} - \tfrac{1}{2} + 2 \right) - \left( -\tfrac{8}{3} - \tfrac{4}{2} + 4 \right) = \tfrac{7}{3} - \tfrac{1}{2} = \tfrac{14-3}{6} = \tfrac{11}{6};$$

A2:  For the sketch given, $a = -1$ and $b = 2$: $f(x) - g(x) = (4 - x^2) - (-x + 2) = -(x^2 - x - 2)$

$$\Rightarrow A2 = -\int_{-1}^{2} (x^2 - x - 2)\, dx = -\left[ \tfrac{x^3}{3} - \tfrac{x^2}{2} - 2x \right]_{-1}^{2} = -\left( \tfrac{8}{3} - \tfrac{4}{2} - 4 \right) + \left( -\tfrac{1}{3} - \tfrac{1}{2} + 2 \right) = -3 + 8 - \tfrac{1}{2} = \tfrac{9}{2};$$

A3:  For the sketch given, $a = 2$ and $b = 3$: $f(x) - g(x) = (-x + 2) - (4 - x^2) = x^2 - x - 2$

$$\Rightarrow A3 = \int_{2}^{3} (x^2 - x - 2)\, dx = \left[ \tfrac{x^3}{3} - \tfrac{x^2}{2} - 2x \right]_{2}^{3} = \left( \tfrac{27}{3} - \tfrac{9}{2} - 6 \right) - \left( \tfrac{8}{3} - \tfrac{4}{2} - 4 \right) = 9 - \tfrac{9}{2} - \tfrac{8}{3};$$

Therefore, AREA $= A1 + A2 + A3 = \tfrac{11}{6} + \tfrac{9}{2} + \left( 9 - \tfrac{9}{2} - \tfrac{8}{3} \right) = 9 - \tfrac{5}{6} = \tfrac{49}{6}$

40.  AREA $= A1 + A2 + A3$

A1:  For the sketch given, $a = -2$ and $b = 0$: $f(x) - g(x) = \left( \tfrac{x^3}{3} - x \right) - \tfrac{x}{3} = \tfrac{x^3}{3} - \tfrac{4}{3}x = \tfrac{1}{3}(x^3 - 4x)$

$$\Rightarrow A1 = \tfrac{1}{3}\int_{-2}^{0} (x^3 - 4x)\, dx = \tfrac{1}{3}\left[ \tfrac{x^4}{4} - 2x^2 \right]_{-2}^{0} = 0 - \tfrac{1}{3}(4 - 8) = \tfrac{4}{3};$$

A2:  For the sketch given, $a = 0$ and we find b by solving the equations $y = \tfrac{x^3}{3} - x$ and $y = \tfrac{x}{3}$ simultaneously

for x:  $\tfrac{x^3}{3} - x = \tfrac{x}{3} \Rightarrow \tfrac{x^3}{3} - \tfrac{4}{3}x = 0 \Rightarrow \tfrac{x}{3}(x - 2)(x + 2) = 0 \Rightarrow x = -2, x = 0, $ or $x = 2$ so $b = 2$:

$$f(x) - g(x) = \tfrac{x}{3} - \left( \tfrac{x^3}{3} - x \right) = -\tfrac{1}{3}(x^3 - 4x) \Rightarrow A2 = -\tfrac{1}{3}\int_{0}^{2} (x^3 - 4x)\, dx = \tfrac{1}{3}\int_{0}^{2} (4x - x^3) = \tfrac{1}{3}\left[ 2x^2 - \tfrac{x^4}{4} \right]_{0}^{2}$$

$$= \tfrac{1}{3}(8 - 4) = \tfrac{4}{3};$$

A3:  For the sketch given, $a = 2$ and $b = 3$: $f(x) - g(x) = \left( \tfrac{x^3}{3} - x \right) - \tfrac{x}{3} = \tfrac{1}{3}(x^3 - 4x)$

$$\Rightarrow A3 = \tfrac{1}{3}\int_{2}^{3} (x^3 - 4x)\, dx = \tfrac{1}{3}\left[ \tfrac{x^4}{4} - 2x^2 \right]_{2}^{3} = \tfrac{1}{3}\left[ \left( \tfrac{81}{4} - 2 \cdot 9 \right) - \left( \tfrac{16}{4} - 8 \right) \right] = \tfrac{1}{3}\left( \tfrac{81}{4} - 14 \right) = \tfrac{25}{12};$$

Therefore, AREA $= A1 + A2 + A3 = \tfrac{4}{3} + \tfrac{4}{3} + \tfrac{25}{12} = \tfrac{32+25}{12} = \tfrac{19}{4}$

41.  $a = -2, b = 2$;

$f(x) - g(x) = 2 - (x^2 - 2) = 4 - x^2$

$$\Rightarrow A = \int_{-2}^{2} (4 - x^2)\, dx = \left[ 4x - \tfrac{x^3}{3} \right]_{-2}^{2} = \left( 8 - \tfrac{8}{3} \right) - \left( -8 + \tfrac{8}{3} \right)$$

$$= 2 \cdot \left( \tfrac{24}{3} - \tfrac{8}{3} \right) = \tfrac{32}{3}$$

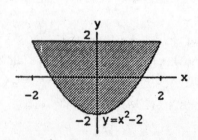

42. $a = -1, b = 3$;

$f(x) - g(x) = (2x - x^2) - (-3) = 2x - x^2 + 3$

$\Rightarrow A = \int_{-1}^{3} (2x - x^2 + 3)\,dx = \left[x^2 - \frac{x^3}{3} + 3x\right]_{-1}^{3}$

$= \left(9 - \frac{27}{3} + 9\right) - \left(1 + \frac{1}{3} - 3\right) = 11 - \frac{1}{3} = \frac{32}{3}$

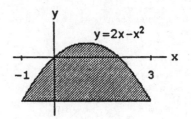

43. $a = 0, b = 2$;

$f(x) - g(x) = 8x - x^4 \Rightarrow A = \int_{0}^{2} (8x - x^4)\,dx$

$= \left[\frac{8x^2}{2} - \frac{x^5}{5}\right]_{0}^{2} = 16 - \frac{32}{5} = \frac{80 - 32}{5} = \frac{48}{5}$

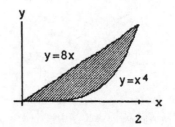

44. Limits of integration: $x^2 - 2x = x \Rightarrow x^2 = 3x$

$\Rightarrow x(x - 3) = 0 \Rightarrow a = 0$ and $b = 3$;

$f(x) - g(x) = x - (x^2 - 2x) = 3x - x^2$

$\Rightarrow A = \int_{0}^{3} (3x - x^2)\,dx = \left[\frac{3x^2}{2} - \frac{x^3}{3}\right]_{0}^{3}$

$= \frac{27}{2} - 9 = \frac{27 - 18}{2} = \frac{9}{2}$

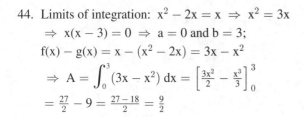
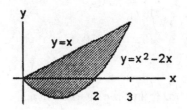

45. Limits of integration: $x^2 = -x^2 + 4x \Rightarrow 2x^2 - 4x = 0$

$\Rightarrow 2x(x - 2) = 0 \Rightarrow a = 0$ and $b = 2$;

$f(x) - g(x) = (-x^2 + 4x) - x^2 = -2x^2 + 4x$

$\Rightarrow A = \int_{0}^{2} (-2x^2 + 4x)\,dx = \left[\frac{-2x^3}{3} + \frac{4x^2}{2}\right]_{0}^{2}$

$= -\frac{16}{3} + \frac{16}{2} = \frac{-32 + 48}{6} = \frac{8}{3}$

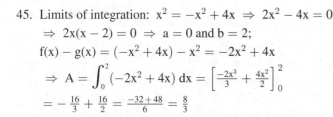
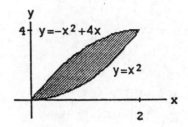

46. Limits of integration: $7 - 2x^2 = x^2 + 4 \Rightarrow 3x^2 - 3 = 0$

$\Rightarrow 3(x - 1)(x + 1) = 0 \Rightarrow a = -1$ and $b = 1$;

$f(x) - g(x) = (7 - 2x^2) - (x^2 + 4) = 3 - 3x^2$

$\Rightarrow A = \int_{-1}^{1} (3 - 3x^2)\,dx = 3\left[x - \frac{x^3}{3}\right]_{-1}^{1}$

$= 3\left[\left(1 - \frac{1}{3}\right) - \left(-1 + \frac{1}{3}\right)\right] = 6\left(\frac{2}{3}\right) = 4$

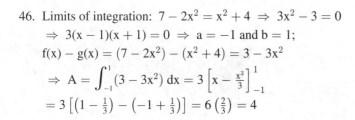
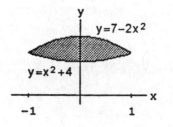

47. Limits of integration: $x^4 - 4x^2 + 4 = x^2$

$\Rightarrow x^4 - 5x^2 + 4 = 0 \Rightarrow (x^2 - 4)(x^2 - 1) = 0$

$\Rightarrow (x + 2)(x - 2)(x + 1)(x - 1) = 0 \Rightarrow x = -2, -1, 1, 2$;

$f(x) - g(x) = (x^4 - 4x^2 + 4) - x^2 = x^4 - 5x^2 + 4$ and

$g(x) - f(x) = x^2 - (x^4 - 4x^2 + 4) = -x^4 + 5x^2 - 4$

$\Rightarrow A = \int_{-2}^{-1} (-x^4 + 5x^2 - 4)\,dx + \int_{-1}^{1} (x^4 - 5x^2 + 4)\,dx$

$+ \int_{1}^{2} (-x^4 + 5x^2 - 4)\,dx$

$= \left[-\frac{x^5}{5} + \frac{5x^3}{3} - 4x\right]_{-2}^{-1} + \left[\frac{x^5}{5} - \frac{5x^3}{3} + 4x\right]_{-1}^{1} + \left[\frac{-x^5}{5} + \frac{5x^3}{3} - 4x\right]_{1}^{2}$

$= \left(\frac{1}{5} - \frac{5}{3} + 4\right) - \left(\frac{32}{5} - \frac{40}{3} + 8\right) + \left(\frac{1}{5} - \frac{5}{3} + 4\right) - \left(-\frac{1}{5} + \frac{5}{3} - 4\right) + \left(-\frac{32}{5} + \frac{40}{3} - 8\right) - \left(-\frac{1}{5} + \frac{5}{3} - 4\right)$

$= -\frac{60}{5} + \frac{60}{3} = \frac{300 - 180}{15} = 8$

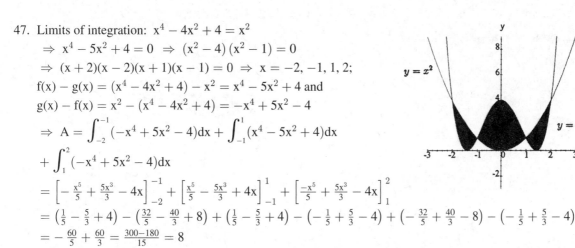
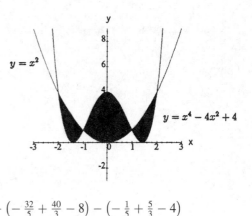

48. Limits of integration: $x\sqrt{a^2 - x^2} = 0 \Rightarrow x = 0$ or

$\sqrt{a^2 - x^2} = 0 \Rightarrow x = 0$ or $a^2 - x^2 = 0 \Rightarrow x = -a, 0, a$;

$A = \int_{-a}^{0} -x\sqrt{a^2 - x^2}\, dx + \int_{0}^{a} x\sqrt{a^2 - x^2}\, dx$

$= \frac{1}{2} \left[ \frac{2}{3} (a^2 - x^2)^{3/2} \right]_{-a}^{0} - \frac{1}{2} \left[ \frac{2}{3} (a^2 - x^2)^{3/2} \right]_{0}^{a}$

$= \frac{1}{3} (a^2)^{3/2} - \left[ -\frac{1}{3} (a^2)^{3/2} \right] = \frac{2a^3}{3}$

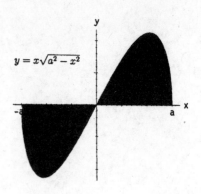

49. Limits of integration: $y = \sqrt{|x|} = \begin{cases} \sqrt{-x}, & x \le 0 \\ \sqrt{x}, & x \ge 0 \end{cases}$ and

$5y = x + 6$ or $y = \frac{x}{5} + \frac{6}{5}$; for $x \le 0$: $\sqrt{-x} = \frac{x}{5} + \frac{6}{5}$

$\Rightarrow 5\sqrt{-x} = x + 6 \Rightarrow 25(-x) = x^2 + 12x + 36$

$\Rightarrow x^2 + 37x + 36 = 0 \Rightarrow (x + 1)(x + 36) = 0$

$\Rightarrow x = -1, -36$ (but $x = -36$ is not a solution);

for $x \ge 0$: $5\sqrt{x} = x + 6 \Rightarrow 25x = x^2 + 12x + 36$

$\Rightarrow x^2 - 13x + 36 = 0 \Rightarrow (x - 4)(x - 9) = 0$

$\Rightarrow x = 4, 9$; there are three intersection points and

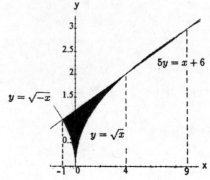

$A = \int_{-1}^{0} \left( \frac{x+6}{5} - \sqrt{-x} \right) dx + \int_{0}^{4} \left( \frac{x+6}{5} - \sqrt{x} \right) dx + \int_{4}^{9} \left( \sqrt{x} - \frac{x+6}{5} \right) dx$

$= \left[ \frac{(x+6)^2}{10} + \frac{2}{3} (-x)^{3/2} \right]_{-1}^{0} + \left[ \frac{(x+6)^2}{10} - \frac{2}{3} x^{3/2} \right]_{0}^{4} + \left[ \frac{2}{3} x^{3/2} - \frac{(x+6)^2}{10} \right]_{4}^{9}$

$= \left( \frac{36}{10} - \frac{25}{10} - \frac{2}{3} \right) + \left( \frac{100}{10} - \frac{2}{3} \cdot 4^{3/2} - \frac{36}{10} + 0 \right) + \left( \frac{2}{3} \cdot 9^{3/2} - \frac{225}{10} - \frac{2}{3} \cdot 4^{3/2} + \frac{100}{10} \right) = -\frac{50}{10} + \frac{20}{3} = \frac{5}{3}$

50. Limits of integration:

$y = |x^2 - 4| = \begin{cases} x^2 - 4, & x \le -2 \text{ or } x \ge 2 \\ 4 - x^2, & -2 \le x \le 2 \end{cases}$

for $x \le -2$ and $x \ge 2$: $x^2 - 4 = \frac{x^2}{2} + 4$

$\Rightarrow 2x^2 - 8 = x^2 + 8 \Rightarrow x^2 = 16 \Rightarrow x = \pm 4$;

for $-2 \le x \le 2$: $4 - x^2 = \frac{x^2}{2} + 4 \Rightarrow 8 - 2x^2 = x^2 + 8$

$\Rightarrow x^2 = 0 \Rightarrow x = 0$; by symmetry of the graph,

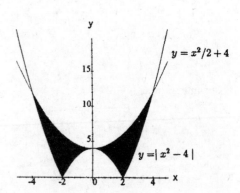

$A = 2\int_{0}^{2} \left[ \left( \frac{x^2}{2} + 4 \right) - (4 - x^2) \right] dx + 2\int_{2}^{4} \left[ \left( \frac{x^2}{2} + 4 \right) - (x^2 - 4) \right] dx = 2\left[ \frac{x^3}{2} \right]_{0}^{2} + 2\left[ 8x - \frac{x^3}{6} \right]_{2}^{4}$

$= 2 \left( \frac{8}{2} - 0 \right) + 2 \left( 32 - \frac{64}{6} - 16 + \frac{8}{6} \right) = 40 - \frac{56}{3} = \frac{64}{3}$

51. Limits of integration: $c = 0$ and $d = 3$;

$f(y) - g(y) = 2y^2 - 0 = 2y^2$

$\Rightarrow A = \int_{0}^{3} 2y^2\, dy = \left[ \frac{2y^3}{3} \right]_{0}^{3} = 2 \cdot 9 = 18$

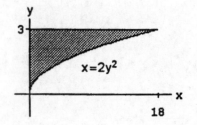

52. Limits of integration: $y^2 = y + 2 \Rightarrow (y+1)(y-2) = 0$
$\Rightarrow c = -1$ and $d = 2$; $f(y) - g(y) = (y+2) - y^2$
$\Rightarrow A = \int_{-1}^{2} (y + 2 - y^2)\, dy = \left[ \frac{y^2}{2} + 2y - \frac{y^3}{3} \right]_{-1}^{2}$
$= \left( \frac{4}{2} + 4 - \frac{8}{3} \right) - \left( \frac{1}{2} - 2 + \frac{1}{3} \right) = 6 - \frac{8}{3} - \frac{1}{2} + 2 - \frac{1}{3} = \frac{9}{2}$

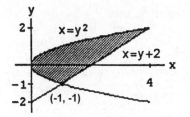

53. Limits of integration: $4x = y^2 - 4$ and $4x = 16 + y$
$\Rightarrow y^2 - 4 = 16 + y \Rightarrow y^2 - y - 20 = 0 \Rightarrow$
$(y - 5)(y + 4) = 0 \Rightarrow c = -4$ and $d = 5$;
$f(y) - g(y) = \left( \frac{16+y}{4} \right) - \left( \frac{y^2-4}{4} \right) = \frac{-y^2+y+20}{4}$
$\Rightarrow A = \frac{1}{4} \int_{-4}^{5} (-y^2 + y + 20)\, dy$
$= \frac{1}{4} \left[ -\frac{y^3}{3} + \frac{y^2}{2} + 20y \right]_{-4}^{5}$
$= \frac{1}{4} \left( -\frac{125}{3} + \frac{25}{2} + 100 \right) - \frac{1}{4} \left( \frac{64}{3} + \frac{16}{2} - 80 \right)$
$= \frac{1}{4} \left( -\frac{189}{3} + \frac{9}{2} + 180 \right) = \frac{243}{8}$

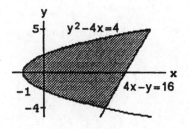

54. Limits of integration: $x = y^2$ and $x = 3 - 2y^2$
$\Rightarrow y^2 = 3 - 2y^2 \Rightarrow 3y^2 = 3 \Rightarrow 3(y-1)(y+1) = 0$
$\Rightarrow c = -1$ and $d = 1$; $f(y) - g(y) = (3 - 2y^2) - y^2$
$= 3 - 3y^2 = 3(1 - y^2) \Rightarrow A = 3 \int_{-1}^{1} (1 - y^2)\, dy$
$= 3 \left[ y - \frac{y^3}{3} \right]_{-1}^{1} = 3 \left( 1 - \frac{1}{3} \right) - 3 \left( -1 + \frac{1}{3} \right)$
$= 3 \cdot 2 \left( 1 - \frac{1}{3} \right) = 4$

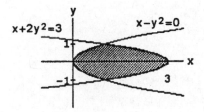

55. Limits of integration: $x = y^2 - y$ and $x = 2y^2 - 2y - 6$
$\Rightarrow y^2 - y = 2y^2 - 2y - 6 \Rightarrow y^2 - y - 6 = 0$
$\Rightarrow (y - 3)(y + 2) = 0 \Rightarrow c = -2$ and $d = 3$;
$f(y) - g(y) = (y^2 - y) - (2y^2 - 2y - 6) = -y^2 + y + 6$
$\Rightarrow A = \int_{-2}^{3} (-y^2 + y + 6)\, dy = \left[ -\frac{y^3}{3} + \frac{1}{2}y^2 + 6y \right]_{-2}^{3}$
$= \left( -9 + \frac{9}{2} + 18 \right) - \left( \frac{8}{3} + 2 - 12 \right) = \frac{125}{6}$

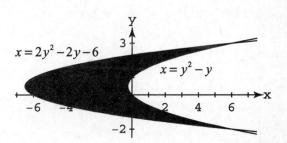

56. Limits of integration: $x = y^{2/3}$ and $x = 2 - y^4$
$\Rightarrow y^{2/3} = 2 - y^4 \Rightarrow c = -1$ and $d = 1$;
$f(y) - g(y) = (2 - y^4) - y^{2/3}$
$\Rightarrow A = \int_{-1}^{1} \left( 2 - y^4 - y^{2/3} \right) dy$
$= \left[ 2y - \frac{y^5}{5} - \frac{3}{5} y^{5/3} \right]_{-1}^{1}$
$= \left( 2 - \frac{1}{5} - \frac{3}{5} \right) - \left( -2 + \frac{1}{5} + \frac{3}{5} \right)$
$= 2 \left( 2 - \frac{1}{5} - \frac{3}{5} \right) = \frac{12}{5}$

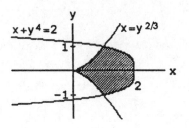

57. Limits of integration: $x = y^2 - 1$ and $x = |y| \sqrt{1 - y^2}$

$\Rightarrow y^2 - 1 = |y| \sqrt{1 - y^2} \Rightarrow y^4 - 2y^2 + 1 = y^2 (1 - y^2)$

$\Rightarrow y^4 - 2y^2 + 1 = y^2 - y^4 \Rightarrow 2y^4 - 3y^2 + 1 = 0$

$\Rightarrow (2y^2 - 1)(y^2 - 1) = 0 \Rightarrow 2y^2 - 1 = 0$ or $y^2 - 1 = 0$

$\Rightarrow y^2 = \frac{1}{2}$ or $y^2 = 1 \Rightarrow y = \pm \frac{\sqrt{2}}{2}$ or $y = \pm 1$.

Substitution shows that $\frac{\pm\sqrt{2}}{2}$ are not solutions $\Rightarrow y = \pm 1$;

for $-1 \le y \le 0$, $f(x) - g(x) = -y\sqrt{1 - y^2} - (y^2 - 1)$

$= 1 - y^2 - y(1 - y^2)^{1/2}$, and by symmetry of the graph,

$A = 2 \int_{-1}^{0} \left[ 1 - y^2 - y(1 - y^2)^{1/2} \right] dy$

$= 2 \int_{-1}^{0} (1 - y^2) \, dy - 2 \int_{-1}^{0} y(1 - y^2)^{1/2} \, dy = 2 \left[ y - \frac{y^3}{3} \right]_{-1}^{0} + 2 \left( \frac{1}{2} \right) \left[ \frac{2(1 - y^2)^{3/2}}{3} \right]_{-1}^{0}$

$= 2 \left[ (0 - 0) - \left( -1 + \frac{1}{3} \right) \right] + \left( \frac{2}{3} - 0 \right) = 2$

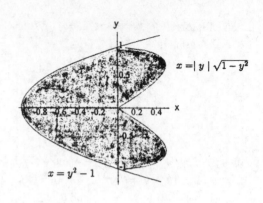

58. AREA = A1 + A2

Limits of integration: $x = 2y$ and $x = y^3 - y^2 \Rightarrow$

$y^3 - y^2 = 2y \Rightarrow y(y^2 - y - 2) = y(y + 1)(y - 2) = 0$

$\Rightarrow y = -1, 0, 2$:

for $-1 \le y \le 0$, $f(y) - g(y) = y^3 - y^2 - 2y$

$\Rightarrow A1 = \int_{-1}^{0} (y^3 - y^2 - 2y) \, dy = \left[ \frac{y^4}{4} - \frac{y^3}{3} - y^2 \right]_{-1}^{0}$

$= 0 - \left( \frac{1}{4} + \frac{1}{3} - 1 \right) = \frac{5}{12}$;

for $0 \le y \le 2$, $f(y) - g(y) = 2y - y^3 + y^2$

$\Rightarrow A2 = \int_{0}^{2} (2y - y^3 + y^2) \, dy = \left[ y^2 - \frac{y^4}{4} + \frac{y^3}{3} \right]_{0}^{2}$

$\Rightarrow \left( 4 - \frac{16}{4} + \frac{8}{3} \right) - 0 = \frac{8}{3}$;

Therefore, A1 + A2 $= \frac{5}{12} + \frac{8}{3} = \frac{37}{12}$

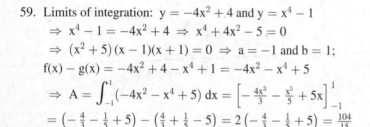

59. Limits of integration: $y = -4x^2 + 4$ and $y = x^4 - 1$

$\Rightarrow x^4 - 1 = -4x^2 + 4 \Rightarrow x^4 + 4x^2 - 5 = 0$

$\Rightarrow (x^2 + 5)(x - 1)(x + 1) = 0 \Rightarrow a = -1$ and $b = 1$;

$f(x) - g(x) = -4x^2 + 4 - x^4 + 1 = -4x^2 - x^4 + 5$

$\Rightarrow A = \int_{-1}^{1} (-4x^2 - x^4 + 5) \, dx = \left[ -\frac{4x^3}{3} - \frac{x^5}{5} + 5x \right]_{-1}^{1}$

$= \left( -\frac{4}{3} - \frac{1}{5} + 5 \right) - \left( \frac{4}{3} + \frac{1}{5} - 5 \right) = 2 \left( -\frac{4}{3} - \frac{1}{5} + 5 \right) = \frac{104}{15}$

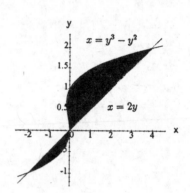

60. Limits of integration: $y = x^3$ and $y = 3x^2 - 4$

$\Rightarrow x^3 - 3x^2 + 4 = 0 \Rightarrow (x^2 - x - 2)(x - 2) = 0$

$\Rightarrow (x + 1)(x - 2)^2 = 0 \Rightarrow a = -1$ and $b = 2$;

$f(x) - g(x) = x^3 - (3x^2 - 4) = x^3 - 3x^2 + 4$

$\Rightarrow A = \int_{-1}^{2} (x^3 - 3x^2 + 4) \, dx = \left[ \frac{x^4}{4} - \frac{3x^3}{3} + 4x \right]_{-1}^{2}$

$= \left( \frac{16}{4} - \frac{24}{3} + 8 \right) - \left( \frac{1}{4} + 1 - 4 \right) = \frac{27}{4}$

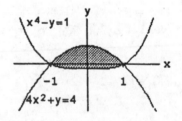

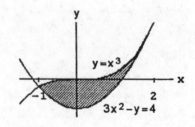

61. Limits of integration: $x = 4 - 4y^2$ and $x = 1 - y^4$

$\Rightarrow 4 - 4y^2 = 1 - y^4 \Rightarrow y^4 - 4y^2 + 3 = 0$

$\Rightarrow \left(y - \sqrt{3}\right)\left(y + \sqrt{3}\right)(y - 1)(y + 1) = 0 \Rightarrow c = -1$

and $d = 1$ since $x \geq 0$; $f(y) - g(y) = (4 - 4y^2) - (1 - y^4)$

$= 3 - 4y^2 + y^4 \Rightarrow A = \int_{-1}^{1}(3 - 4y^2 + y^4)\,dy$

$= \left[3y - \frac{4y^3}{3} + \frac{y^5}{5}\right]_{-1}^{1} = 2\left(3 - \frac{4}{3} + \frac{1}{5}\right) = \frac{56}{15}$

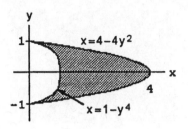

62. Limits of integration: $x = 3 - y^2$ and $x = -\frac{y^2}{4}$

$\Rightarrow 3 - y^2 = -\frac{y^2}{4} \Rightarrow \frac{3y^2}{4} - 3 = 0 \Rightarrow \frac{3}{4}(y - 2)(y + 2) = 0$

$\Rightarrow c = -2$ and $d = 2$; $f(y) - g(y) = (3 - y^2) - \left(\frac{-y^2}{4}\right)$

$= 3\left(1 - \frac{y^2}{4}\right) \Rightarrow A = 3\int_{-2}^{2}\left(1 - \frac{y^2}{4}\right)dy = 3\left[y - \frac{y^3}{12}\right]_{-2}^{2}$

$= 3\left[\left(2 - \frac{8}{12}\right) - \left(-2 + \frac{8}{12}\right)\right] = 3\left(4 - \frac{16}{12}\right) = 12 - 4 = 8$

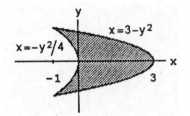

63. $a = 0, b = \pi$; $f(x) - g(x) = 2\sin x - \sin 2x$

$\Rightarrow A = \int_{0}^{\pi}(2\sin x - \sin 2x)\,dx = \left[-2\cos x + \frac{\cos 2x}{2}\right]_{0}^{\pi}$

$= \left[-2(-1) + \frac{1}{2}\right] - \left(-2 \cdot 1 + \frac{1}{2}\right) = 4$

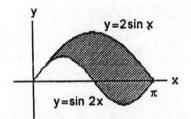

64. $a = -\frac{\pi}{3}, b = \frac{\pi}{3}$; $f(x) - g(x) = 8\cos x - \sec^2 x$

$\Rightarrow A = \int_{-\pi/3}^{\pi/3}(8\cos x - \sec^2 x)\,dx = [8\sin x - \tan x]_{-\pi/3}^{\pi/3}$

$= \left(8 \cdot \frac{\sqrt{3}}{2} - \sqrt{3}\right) - \left(-8 \cdot \frac{\sqrt{3}}{2} + \sqrt{3}\right) = 6\sqrt{3}$

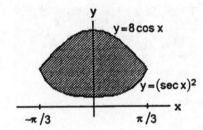

65. $a = -1, b = 1$; $f(x) - g(x) = (1 - x^2) - \cos\left(\frac{\pi x}{2}\right)$

$\Rightarrow A = \int_{-1}^{1}\left[1 - x^2 - \cos\left(\frac{\pi x}{2}\right)\right]dx = \left[x - \frac{x^3}{3} - \frac{2}{\pi}\sin\left(\frac{\pi x}{2}\right)\right]_{-1}^{1}$

$= \left(1 - \frac{1}{3} - \frac{2}{\pi}\right) - \left(-1 + \frac{1}{3} + \frac{2}{\pi}\right) = 2\left(\frac{2}{3} - \frac{2}{\pi}\right) = \frac{4}{3} - \frac{4}{\pi}$

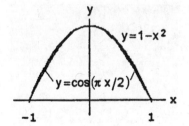

66. $A = A1 + A2$

$a_1 = -1, b_1 = 0$ and $a_2 = 0, b_2 = 1$;

$f_1(x) - g_1(x) = x - \sin\left(\frac{\pi x}{2}\right)$ and $f_2(x) - g_2(x) = \sin\left(\frac{\pi x}{2}\right) - x$

$\Rightarrow$ by symmetry about the origin,

$A_1 + A_2 = 2A_1 \Rightarrow A = 2\int_{0}^{1}\left[\sin\left(\frac{\pi x}{2}\right) - x\right]dx$

$= 2\left[-\frac{2}{\pi}\cos\left(\frac{\pi x}{2}\right) - \frac{x^2}{2}\right]_{0}^{1} = 2\left[\left(-\frac{2}{\pi} \cdot 0 - \frac{1}{2}\right) - \left(-\frac{2}{\pi} \cdot 1 - 0\right)\right]$

$= 2\left(\frac{2}{\pi} - \frac{1}{2}\right) = 2\left(\frac{4 - \pi}{2\pi}\right) = \frac{4 - \pi}{\pi}$

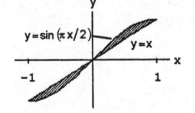

67. $a = -\frac{\pi}{4}$, $b = \frac{\pi}{4}$; $f(x) - g(x) = \sec^2 x - \tan^2 x$

$\Rightarrow A = \int_{-\pi/4}^{\pi/4} (\sec^2 x - \tan^2 x)\, dx$

$= \int_{-\pi/4}^{\pi/4} [\sec^2 x - (\sec^2 x - 1)]\, dx$

$= \int_{-\pi/4}^{\pi/4} 1 \cdot dx = [x]_{-\pi/4}^{\pi/4} = \frac{\pi}{4} - \left(-\frac{\pi}{4}\right) = \frac{\pi}{2}$

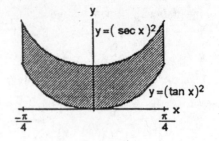

68. $c = -\frac{\pi}{4}$, $d = \frac{\pi}{4}$; $f(y) - g(y) = \tan^2 y - (-\tan^2 y) = 2\tan^2 y$

$= 2(\sec^2 y - 1) \Rightarrow A = \int_{-\pi/4}^{\pi/4} 2(\sec^2 y - 1)\, dy$

$= 2[\tan y - y]_{-\pi/4}^{\pi/4} = 2\left[\left(1 - \frac{\pi}{4}\right) - \left(-1 + \frac{\pi}{4}\right)\right]$

$= 4\left(1 - \frac{\pi}{4}\right) = 4 - \pi$

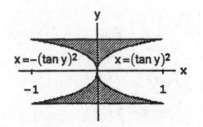

69. $c = 0$, $d = \frac{\pi}{2}$; $f(y) - g(y) = 3\sin y \sqrt{\cos y} - 0 = 3\sin y \sqrt{\cos y}$

$\Rightarrow A = 3\int_0^{\pi/2} \sin y \sqrt{\cos y}\, dy = -3\left[\frac{2}{3}(\cos y)^{3/2}\right]_0^{\pi/2}$

$= -2(0 - 1) = 2$

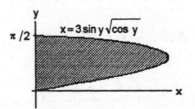

70. $a = -1$, $b = 1$; $f(x) - g(x) = \sec^2\left(\frac{\pi x}{3}\right) - x^{1/3}$

$\Rightarrow A = \int_{-1}^1 \left[\sec^2\left(\frac{\pi x}{3}\right) - x^{1/3}\right] dx = \left[\frac{3}{\pi}\tan\left(\frac{\pi x}{3}\right) - \frac{3}{4}x^{4/3}\right]_{-1}^1$

$= \left(\frac{3}{\pi}\sqrt{3} - \frac{3}{4}\right) - \left[\frac{3}{\pi}\left(-\sqrt{3}\right) - \frac{3}{4}\right] = \frac{6\sqrt{3}}{\pi}$

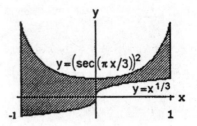

71. $A = A_1 + A_2$

Limits of integration: $x = y^3$ and $x = y \Rightarrow y = y^3$

$\Rightarrow y^3 - y = 0 \Rightarrow y(y - 1)(y + 1) = 0 \Rightarrow c_1 = -1, d_1 = 0$

and $c_2 = 0, d_2 = 1$; $f_1(y) - g_1(y) = y^3 - y$ and

$f_2(y) - g_2(y) = y - y^3 \Rightarrow$ by symmetry about the origin,

$A_1 + A_2 = 2A_2 \Rightarrow A = 2\int_0^1 (y - y^3)\, dy = 2\left[\frac{y^2}{2} - \frac{y^4}{4}\right]_0^1$

$= 2\left(\frac{1}{2} - \frac{1}{4}\right) = \frac{1}{2}$

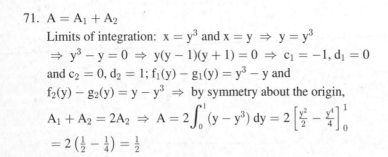

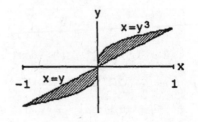

72. $A = A_1 + A_2$

Limits of integration: $y = x^3$ and $y = x^5 \Rightarrow x^3 = x^5$

$\Rightarrow x^5 - x^3 = 0 \Rightarrow x^3(x - 1)(x + 1) = 0 \Rightarrow a_1 = -1, b_1 = 0$

and $a_2 = 0, b_2 = 1$; $f_1(x) - g_1(x) = x^3 - x^5$ and

$f_2(x) - g_2(x) = x^5 - x^3 \Rightarrow$ by symmetry about the origin,

$A_1 + A_2 = 2A_2 \Rightarrow A = 2\int_0^1 (x^3 - x^5)\, dx = 2\left[\frac{x^4}{4} - \frac{x^6}{6}\right]_0^1$

$= 2\left(\frac{1}{4} - \frac{1}{6}\right) = \frac{1}{6}$

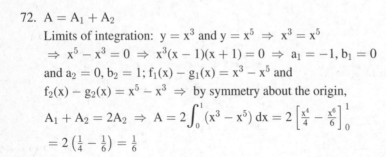

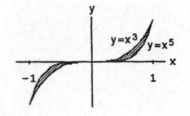

73. $A = A_1 + A_2$

Limits of integration: $y = x$ and $y = \frac{1}{x^2} \Rightarrow x = \frac{1}{x^2}, x \neq 0$

$\Rightarrow x^3 = 1 \Rightarrow x = 1$, $f_1(x) - g_1(x) = x - 0 = x$

$\Rightarrow A_1 = \int_0^1 x \, dx = \left[\frac{x^2}{2}\right]_0^1 = \frac{1}{2}$; $f_2(x) - g_2(x) = \frac{1}{x^2} - 0$

$= x^{-2} \Rightarrow A_2 = \int_1^2 x^{-2} \, dx = \left[\frac{-1}{x}\right]_1^2 = -\frac{1}{2} + 1 = \frac{1}{2}$;

$A = A_1 + A_2 = \frac{1}{2} + \frac{1}{2} = 1$

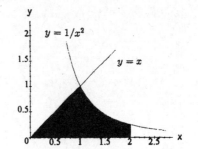

74. Limits of integration: $\sin x = \cos x \Rightarrow x = \frac{\pi}{4} \Rightarrow a = 0$

and $b = \frac{\pi}{4}$; $f(x) - g(x) = \cos x - \sin x$

$\Rightarrow A = \int_0^{\pi/4} (\cos x - \sin x) \, dx = [\sin x + \cos x]_0^{\pi/4}$

$= \left(\frac{\sqrt{2}}{2} + \frac{\sqrt{2}}{2}\right) - (0 + 1) = \sqrt{2} - 1$

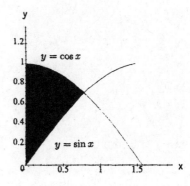

75. (a) The coordinates of the points of intersection of the
line and parabola are $c = x^2 \Rightarrow x = \pm\sqrt{c}$ and $y = c$

(b) $f(y) - g(y) = \sqrt{y} - (-\sqrt{y}) = 2\sqrt{y} \Rightarrow$ the area of the

lower section is, $A_L = \int_0^c [f(y) - g(y)] \, dy$

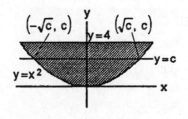

$= 2 \int_0^c \sqrt{y} \, dy = 2 \left[\frac{2}{3} y^{3/2}\right]_0^c = \frac{4}{3} c^{3/2}$. The area of the

entire shaded region can be found by setting $c = 4$: $A = \left(\frac{4}{3}\right) 4^{3/2} = \frac{4 \cdot 8}{3} = \frac{32}{3}$. Since we want c to divide the region

into subsections of equal area we have $A = 2A_L \Rightarrow \frac{32}{3} = 2\left(\frac{4}{3} c^{3/2}\right) \Rightarrow c = 4^{2/3}$

(c) $f(x) - g(x) = c - x^2 \Rightarrow A_L = \int_{-\sqrt{c}}^{\sqrt{c}} [f(x) - g(x)] \, dx = \int_{-\sqrt{c}}^{\sqrt{c}} (c - x^2) \, dx = \left[cx - \frac{x^3}{3}\right]_{-\sqrt{c}}^{\sqrt{c}} = 2\left[c^{3/2} - \frac{c^{3/2}}{3}\right]$

$= \frac{4}{3} c^{3/2}$. Again, the area of the whole shaded region can be found by setting $c = 4 \Rightarrow A = \frac{32}{3}$. From the

condition $A = 2A_L$, we get $\frac{4}{3} c^{3/2} = \frac{32}{3} \Rightarrow c = 4^{2/3}$ as in part (b).

76. (a) Limits of integration: $y = 3 - x^2$ and $y = -1$

$\Rightarrow 3 - x^2 = -1 \Rightarrow x^2 = 4 \Rightarrow a = -2$ and $b = 2$;

$f(x) - g(x) = (3 - x^2) - (-1) = 4 - x^2$

$\Rightarrow A = \int_{-2}^2 (4 - x^2) \, dx = \left[4x - \frac{x^3}{3}\right]_{-2}^2$

$= \left(8 - \frac{8}{3}\right) - \left(-8 + \frac{8}{3}\right) = 16 - \frac{16}{3} = \frac{32}{3}$

(b) Limits of integration: let $x = 0$ in $y = 3 - x^2$

$\Rightarrow y = 3$; $f(y) - g(y) = \sqrt{3 - y} - (-\sqrt{3 - y})$

$= 2(3 - y)^{1/2}$

$\Rightarrow A = 2\int_{-1}^3 (3 - y)^{1/2} \, dy = -2 \int_{-1}^3 (3 - y)^{1/2}(-1) \, dy = (-2)\left[\frac{2(3-y)^{3/2}}{3}\right]_{-1}^3 = \left(-\frac{4}{3}\right)\left[0 - (3 + 1)^{3/2}\right]$

$= \left(\frac{4}{3}\right)(8) = \frac{32}{3}$

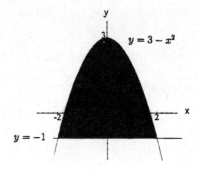

77. Limits of integration: $y = 1 + \sqrt{x}$ and $y = \frac{2}{\sqrt{x}}$

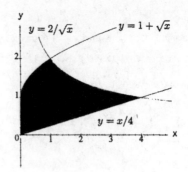

$\Rightarrow 1 + \sqrt{x} = \frac{2}{\sqrt{x}}, x \neq 0 \Rightarrow \sqrt{x} + x = 2 \Rightarrow x = (2 - x)^2$

$\Rightarrow x = 4 - 4x + x^2 \Rightarrow x^2 - 5x + 4 = 0$

$\Rightarrow (x - 4)(x - 1) = 0 \Rightarrow x = 1, 4$ (but $x = 4$ does not

satisfy the equation); $y = \frac{2}{\sqrt{x}}$ and $y = \frac{x}{4} \Rightarrow \frac{2}{\sqrt{x}} = \frac{x}{4}$

$\Rightarrow 8 = x\sqrt{x} \Rightarrow 64 = x^3 \Rightarrow x = 4.$

Therefore, AREA $= A_1 + A_2$: $f_1(x) - g_1(x) = \left(1 + x^{1/2}\right) - \frac{x}{4}$

$\Rightarrow A_1 = \int_0^1 \left(1 + x^{1/2} - \frac{x}{4}\right) dx = \left[x + \frac{2}{3} x^{3/2} - \frac{x^2}{8}\right]_0^1$

$= \left(1 + \frac{2}{3} - \frac{1}{8}\right) - 0 = \frac{37}{24}$; $f_2(x) - g_2(x) = 2x^{-1/2} - \frac{x}{4} \Rightarrow A_2 = \int_1^4 \left(2x^{-1/2} - \frac{x}{4}\right) dx = \left[4x^{1/2} - \frac{x^2}{8}\right]_1^4$

$= \left(4 \cdot 2 - \frac{16}{8}\right) - \left(4 - \frac{1}{8}\right) = 4 - \frac{15}{8} = \frac{17}{8}$; Therefore, AREA $= A_1 + A_2 = \frac{37}{24} + \frac{17}{8} = \frac{37+51}{24} = \frac{88}{24} = \frac{11}{3}$

78. Limits of integration: $(y - 1)^2 = 3 - y \Rightarrow y^2 - 2y + 1$

$= 3 - y \Rightarrow y^2 - y - 2 = 0 \Rightarrow (y - 2)(y + 1) = 0$

$\Rightarrow y = 2$ since $y > 0$; also, $2\sqrt{y} = 3 - y$

$\Rightarrow 4y = 9 - 6y + y^2 \Rightarrow y^2 - 10y + 9 = 0$

$\Rightarrow (y - 9)(y - 1) = 0 \Rightarrow y = 1$ since $y = 9$ does not

satisfy the equation;

AREA $= A_1 + A_2$

$f_1(y) - g_1(y) = 2\sqrt{y} - 0 = 2y^{1/2}$

$\Rightarrow A_1 = 2 \int_0^1 y^{1/2} dy = 2 \left[\frac{2y^{3/2}}{3}\right]_0^1 = \frac{4}{3}$; $f_2(y) - g_2(y) = (3 - y) - (y - 1)^2$

$\Rightarrow A_2 = \int_1^2 [3 - y - (y - 1)^2] dy = \left[3y - \frac{1}{2} y^2 - \frac{1}{3} (y - 1)^3\right]_1^2 = \left(6 - 2 - \frac{1}{3}\right) - \left(3 - \frac{1}{2} + 0\right) = 1 - \frac{1}{3} + \frac{1}{2} = \frac{7}{6}$;

Therefore, $A_1 + A_2 = \frac{4}{3} + \frac{7}{6} = \frac{15}{6} = \frac{5}{2}$

79. Area between parabola and $y = a^2$: $A = 2 \int_0^a (a^2 - x^2) dx = 2 \left[a^2 x - \frac{1}{3} x^3\right]_0^a = 2 \left(a^3 - \frac{a^3}{3}\right) - 0 = \frac{4a^3}{3}$;

Area of triangle AOC: $\frac{1}{2} (2a) (a^2) = a^3$; limit of ratio $= \lim\limits_{a \to 0^+} \frac{a^3}{\left(\frac{4a^3}{3}\right)} = \frac{3}{4}$ which is independent of a.

80. $A = \int_a^b 2f(x) dx - \int_a^b f(x) dx = 2 \int_a^b f(x) dx - \int_a^b f(x) dx = \int_a^b f(x) dx = 4$

81. The lower boundary of the region is the line through the points $(z, 1 - z^2)$ and $\left(z + 1, 1 - (z + 1)^2\right)$. The equation of this

line is $y - (1 - z^2) = \frac{(1-(z+1)^2) - (1-z^2)}{z+1-z} (x - 1) = -(2z + 1)(x - 1) \Rightarrow y = -(2z + 1)x + (z^2 + z + 1)$.

The area of theregion is given by $\int_z^{z+1} ((1 - x^2) - (-(2z + 1)x + (z^2 + z + 1)))dy$

$= \int_z^{z+1} (-x^2 + (2z + 1)x - z^2 - z)dy = \left[-\frac{1}{3}x^3 + \frac{1}{2}(2z + 1)x^2 - (z^2 + z)x\right]_z^{z+1}$

$= \left(-\frac{1}{3}(z + 1)^3 + \frac{1}{2}(2z + 1)(z + 1)^2 - (z^2 + z)(z + 1)\right) - \left(-\frac{1}{3}z^3 + \frac{1}{2}(2z + 1)z^2 - (z^2 + z)z\right) = \frac{1}{6}$. No matter where we

choose z, the area of the region bounded by $y = 1 - x^2$ and the line through the points $(z, 1 - z^2)$ and

$\left(z + 1, 1 - (z + 1)^2\right)$ is always $\frac{1}{6}$.

82. It is sometimes true. It is true if $f(x) \geq g(x)$ for all x between a and b. Otherwise it is false. If the graph of f
    lies below the graph of g for a portion of the interval of integration, the integral over that portion will be
    negative and the integral over [a, b] will be less than the area between the curves (see Exercise 71).

83. Let $u = 2x \Rightarrow du = 2\,dx \Rightarrow \frac{1}{2}\,du = dx;\, x = 1 \Rightarrow u = 2,\, x = 3 \Rightarrow u = 6$

$$\int_1^3 \frac{\sin 2x}{x}\,dx = \int_2^6 \frac{\sin u}{\left(\frac{u}{2}\right)}\left(\frac{1}{2}\,du\right) = \int_2^6 \frac{\sin u}{u}\,du = [F(u)]_2^6 = F(6) - F(2)$$

84. Let $u = 1 - x \Rightarrow du = -dx \Rightarrow -du = dx;\, x = 0 \Rightarrow u = 1,\, x = 1 \Rightarrow u = 0$

$$\int_0^1 f(1-x)\,dx = \int_1^0 f(u)\,(-du) = -\int_1^0 f(u)\,du = \int_0^1 f(u)\,du = \int_0^1 f(x)\,dx$$

85. (a) Let $u = -x \Rightarrow du = -dx;\, x = -1 \Rightarrow u = 1,\, x = 0 \Rightarrow u = 0$

   f odd $\Rightarrow f(-x) = -f(x)$. Then $\int_{-1}^0 f(x)\,dx = \int_1^0 f(-u)\,(-du) = \int_1^0 -f(u)\,(-du) = \int_1^0 f(u)\,du = -\int_0^1 f(u)\,du$
   $= -3$

   (b) Let $u = -x \Rightarrow du = -dx;\, x = -1 \Rightarrow u = 1,\, x = 0 \Rightarrow u = 0$

   f even $\Rightarrow f(-x) = f(x)$. Then $\int_{-1}^0 f(x)\,dx = \int_1^0 f(-u)\,(-du) = -\int_1^0 f(u)\,du = \int_0^1 f(u)\,du = 3$

86. (a) Consider $\int_{-a}^0 f(x)\,dx$ when f is odd. Let $u = -x \Rightarrow du = -dx \Rightarrow -du = dx$ and $x = -a \Rightarrow u = a$ and $x = 0$

   $\Rightarrow u = 0$. Thus $\int_{-a}^0 f(x)\,dx = \int_a^0 -f(-u)\,du = \int_a^0 f(u)\,du = -\int_0^a f(u)\,du = -\int_0^a f(x)\,dx$.

   Thus $\int_{-a}^a f(x)\,dx = \int_{-a}^0 f(x)\,dx + \int_0^a f(x)\,dx = -\int_0^a f(x)\,dx + \int_0^a f(x)\,dx = 0$.

   (b) $\int_{-\pi/2}^{\pi/2} \sin x\,dx = [-\cos x]_{-\pi/2}^{\pi/2} = -\cos\left(\frac{\pi}{2}\right) + \cos\left(-\frac{\pi}{2}\right) = 0 + 0 = 0.$

87. Let $u = a - x \Rightarrow du = -dx;\, x = 0 \Rightarrow u = a,\, x = a \Rightarrow u = 0$

$$I = \int_0^a \frac{f(x)\,dx}{f(x) + f(a-x)} = \int_a^0 \frac{f(a-u)}{f(a-u) + f(u)}\,(-du) = \int_0^a \frac{f(a-u)\,du}{f(u) + f(a-u)} = \int_0^a \frac{f(a-x)\,dx}{f(x) + f(a-x)}$$

$$\Rightarrow I + I = \int_0^a \frac{f(x)\,dx}{f(x) + f(a-x)} + \int_0^a \frac{f(a-x)\,dx}{f(x) + f(a-x)} = \int_0^a \frac{f(x) + f(a-x)}{f(x) + f(a-x)}\,dx = \int_0^a dx = [x]_0^a = a - 0 = a.$$

Therefore, $2I = a \Rightarrow I = \frac{a}{2}$.

88. Let $u = \frac{xy}{t} \Rightarrow du = -\frac{xy}{t^2}\,dt \Rightarrow -\frac{t}{xy}\,du = \frac{1}{t}\,dt \Rightarrow -\frac{1}{u}\,du = \frac{1}{t}\,dt;\, t = x \Rightarrow u = y,\, t = xy \Rightarrow u = 1.$ Therefore,

$$\int_x^{xy} \frac{1}{t}\,dt = \int_y^1 -\frac{1}{u}\,du = -\int_y^1 \frac{1}{u}\,du = \int_1^y \frac{1}{u}\,du = \int_1^y \frac{1}{t}\,dt$$

89. Let $u = x + c \Rightarrow du = dx;\, x = a - c \Rightarrow u = a,\, x = b - c \Rightarrow u = b$

$$\int_{a-c}^{b-c} f(x+c)\,dx = \int_a^b f(u)\,du = \int_a^b f(x)\,dx$$

90. (a)                                    (b)                                    (c)

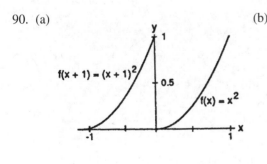

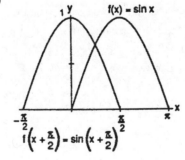

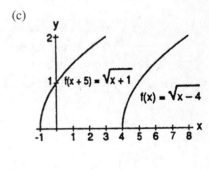

91-94.    Example CAS commands:

Maple:

```
f := x -> x^3/3-x^2/2-2*x+1/3;
g := x -> x-1;
plot( [f(x),g(x)], x=-5..5, legend=["y = f(x)","y = g(x)"], title="#91(a) (Section 5.6)" );
q1 := [ -5, -2, 1, 4 ];              # (b)
q2 := [seq( fsolve( f(x)=g(x), x=q1[i]..q1[i+1] ), i=1..nops(q1)-1 )];
for i from 1 to nops(q2)-1 do       # (c)
  area[i] := int( abs(f(x)-g(x)),x=q2[i]..q2[i+1] );
end do;
add( area[i], i=1..nops(q2)-1 );     # (d)
```

Mathematica: (assigned functions may vary)

```
Clear[x, f, g]
f[x_] = x^2 Cos[x]
g[x_] = x^3 - x
Plot[{f[x], g[x]}, {x, -2, 2}]
```

After examining the plots, the initial guesses for FindRoot can be determined.

```
pts = x/.Map[FindRoot[f[x]==g[x],{x, #}]&, {-1, 0, 1}]
i1=NIntegrate[f[x] - g[x], {x, pts[[1]], pts[[2]]}]
i2=NIntegrate[f[x] - g[x], {x, pts[[2]], pts[[3]]}]
i1 + i2
```

## CHAPTER 5 PRACTICE EXERCISES

1.  (a)  Each time subinterval is of length $\Delta t = 0.4$ sec.  The distance traveled over each subinterval, using the midpoint rule, is $\Delta h = \frac{1}{2}(v_i + v_{i+1})\Delta t$, where $v_i$ is the velocity at the left endpoint and $v_{i+1}$ the velocity at the right endpoint of the subinterval.  We then add $\Delta h$ to the height attained so far at the left endpoint $v_i$ to arrive at the height associated with velocity $v_{i+1}$ at the right endpoint.  Using this methodology we build the following table based on the figure in the text:

| t (sec) | 0 | 0.4 | 0.8 | 1.2 | 1.6 | 2.0 | 2.4 | 2.8 | 3.2 | 3.6 | 4.0 | 4.4 | 4.8 | 5.2 | 5.6 | 6.0 |
|---|---|---|---|---|---|---|---|---|---|---|---|---|---|---|---|---|
| v (fps) | 0 | 10 | 25 | 55 | 100 | 190 | 180 | 165 | 150 | 140 | 130 | 115 | 105 | 90 | 76 | 65 |
| h (ft) | 0 | 2 | 9 | 25 | 56 | 114 | 188 | 257 | 320 | 378 | 432 | 481 | 525 | 564 | 592 | 620.2 |

| t (sec) | 6.4 | 6.8 | 7.2 | 7.6 | 8.0 |
|---|---|---|---|---|---|
| v (fps) | 50 | 37 | 25 | 12 | 0 |
| h (ft) | 643.2 | 660.6 | 672 | 679.4 | 681.8 |

NOTE:  Your table values may vary slightly from ours depending on the v-values you read from the graph.  Remember that some shifting of the graph occurs in the printing process.

The total height attained is about 680 ft.

(b)  The graph is based on the table in part (a).

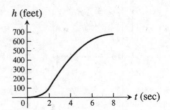

2. (a) Each time subinterval is of length $\Delta t = 1$ sec. The distance traveled over each subinterval, using the midpoint rule, is $\Delta s = \frac{1}{2}(v_i + v_{i+1})\Delta t$, where $v_i$ is the velocity at the left, and $v_{i+1}$ the velocity at the right, endpoint of the subinterval. We then add $\Delta s$ to the distance attained so far at the left endpoint $v_i$ to arrive at the distance associated with velocity $v_{i+1}$ at the right endpoint. Using this methodology we build the table given below based on the figure in the text, obtaining approximately 26 m for the total distance traveled:

| t (sec) | 0 | 1 | 2 | 3 | 4 | 5 | 6 | 7 | 8 | 9 | 10 |
|---|---|---|---|---|---|---|---|---|---|---|---|
| v (m/sec) | 0 | 0.5 | 1.2 | 2 | 3.4 | 4.5 | 4.8 | 4.5 | 3.5 | 2 | 0 |
| s (m) | 0 | 0.25 | 1.1 | 2.7 | 5.4 | 9.35 | 14 | 18.65 | 22.65 | 25.4 | 26.4 |

(b) The graph shows the distance traveled by the moving body as a function of time for $0 \le t \le 10$.

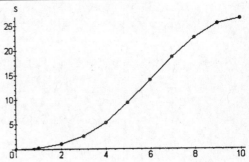

3. (a) $\displaystyle\sum_{k=1}^{10} \frac{a_k}{4} = \frac{1}{4}\sum_{k=1}^{10} a_k = \frac{1}{4}(-2) = -\frac{1}{2}$    (b) $\displaystyle\sum_{k=1}^{10}(b_k - 3a_k) = \sum_{k=1}^{10} b_k - 3\sum_{k=1}^{10} a_k = 25 - 3(-2) = 31$

(c) $\displaystyle\sum_{k=1}^{10}(a_k + b_k - 1) = \sum_{k=1}^{10} a_k + \sum_{k=1}^{10} b_k - \sum_{k=1}^{10} 1 = -2 + 25 - (1)(10) = 13$

(d) $\displaystyle\sum_{k=1}^{10}\left(\frac{5}{2} - b_k\right) = \sum_{k=1}^{10} \frac{5}{2} - \sum_{k=1}^{10} b_k = \frac{5}{2}(10) - 25 = 0$

4. (a) $\displaystyle\sum_{k=1}^{20} 3a_k = 3\sum_{k=1}^{20} a_k = 3(0) = 0$    (b) $\displaystyle\sum_{k=1}^{20}(a_k + b_k) = \sum_{k=1}^{20} a_k + \sum_{k=1}^{20} b_k = 0 + 7 = 7$

(c) $\displaystyle\sum_{k=1}^{20}\left(\frac{1}{2} - \frac{2b_k}{7}\right) = \sum_{k=1}^{20} \frac{1}{2} - \frac{2}{7}\sum_{k=1}^{20} b_k = \frac{1}{2}(20) - \frac{2}{7}(7) = 8$

(d) $\displaystyle\sum_{k=1}^{20}(a_k - 2) = \sum_{k=1}^{20} a_k - \sum_{k=1}^{20} 2 = 0 - 2(20) = -40$

5. Let $u = 2x - 1 \Rightarrow du = 2\,dx \Rightarrow \frac{1}{2}du = dx; x = 1 \Rightarrow u = 1, x = 5 \Rightarrow u = 9$

$\displaystyle\int_1^5 (2x-1)^{-1/2}\,dx = \int_1^9 u^{-1/2}\left(\frac{1}{2}du\right) = \left[u^{1/2}\right]_1^9 = 3 - 1 = 2$

6. Let $u = x^2 - 1 \Rightarrow du = 2x\,dx \Rightarrow \frac{1}{2}du = x\,dx; x = 1 \Rightarrow u = 0, x = 3 \Rightarrow u = 8$

$\displaystyle\int_1^3 x(x^2 - 1)^{1/3}\,dx = \int_0^8 u^{1/3}\left(\frac{1}{2}du\right) = \left[\frac{3}{8} u^{4/3}\right]_0^8 = \frac{3}{8}(16 - 0) = 6$

7. Let $u = \frac{x}{2} \Rightarrow 2\,du = dx; x = -\pi \Rightarrow u = -\frac{\pi}{2}, x = 0 \Rightarrow u = 0$

$\displaystyle\int_{-\pi}^0 \cos\left(\frac{x}{2}\right)dx = \int_{-\pi/2}^0 (\cos u)(2\,du) = [2\sin u]_{-\pi/2}^0 = 2\sin 0 - 2\sin\left(-\frac{\pi}{2}\right) = 2(0 - (-1)) = 2$

8. Let $u = \sin x \Rightarrow du = \cos x\,dx; x = 0 \Rightarrow u = 0, x = \frac{\pi}{2} \Rightarrow u = 1$

$\displaystyle\int_0^{\pi/2} (\sin x)(\cos x)\,dx = \int_0^1 u\,du = \left[\frac{u^2}{2}\right]_0^1 = \frac{1}{2}$

9. (a) $\int_{-2}^{2} f(x)\,dx = \frac{1}{3}\int_{-2}^{2} 3\,f(x)\,dx = \frac{1}{3}(12) = 4$    (b) $\int_{2}^{5} f(x)\,dx = \int_{-2}^{5} f(x)\,dx - \int_{-2}^{2} f(x)\,dx = 6 - 4 = 2$

(c) $\int_{5}^{-2} g(x)\,dx = -\int_{-2}^{5} g(x)\,dx = -2$    (d) $\int_{-2}^{5}(-\pi\,g(x))\,dx = -\pi\int_{-2}^{5} g(x)\,dx = -\pi(2) = -2\pi$

(e) $\int_{-2}^{5}\left(\frac{f(x)+g(x)}{5}\right)dx = \frac{1}{5}\int_{-2}^{5} f(x)\,dx + \frac{1}{5}\int_{-2}^{5} g(x)\,dx = \frac{1}{5}(6) + \frac{1}{5}(2) = \frac{8}{5}$

10. (a) $\int_{0}^{2} g(x)\,dx = \frac{1}{7}\int_{0}^{2} 7\,g(x)\,dx = \frac{1}{7}(7) = 1$    (b) $\int_{1}^{2} g(x)\,dx = \int_{0}^{2} g(x)\,dx - \int_{0}^{1} g(x)\,dx = 1 - 2 = -1$

(c) $\int_{2}^{0} f(x)\,dx = -\int_{0}^{2} f(x)\,dx = -\pi$    (d) $\int_{0}^{2}\sqrt{2}\,f(x)\,dx = \sqrt{2}\int_{0}^{2} f(x)\,dx = \sqrt{2}(\pi) = \pi\sqrt{2}$

(e) $\int_{0}^{2}[g(x) - 3\,f(x)]\,dx = \int_{0}^{2} g(x)\,dx - 3\int_{0}^{2} f(x)\,dx = 1 - 3\pi$

11. $x^2 - 4x + 3 = 0 \Rightarrow (x-3)(x-1) = 0 \Rightarrow x = 3$ or $x = 1$;

Area $= \int_{0}^{1}(x^2 - 4x + 3)\,dx - \int_{1}^{3}(x^2 - 4x + 3)\,dx$

$= \left[\frac{x^3}{3} - 2x^2 + 3x\right]_{0}^{1} - \left[\frac{x^3}{3} - 2x^2 + 3x\right]_{1}^{3}$

$= \left[\left(\frac{1^3}{3} - 2(1)^2 + 3(1)\right) - 0\right]$

$\quad - \left[\left(\frac{3^3}{3} - 2(3)^2 + 3(3)\right) - \left(\frac{1^3}{3} - 2(1)^2 + 3(1)\right)\right]$

$= \left(\frac{1}{3} + 1\right) - \left[0 - \left(\frac{1}{3} + 1\right)\right] = \frac{8}{3}$

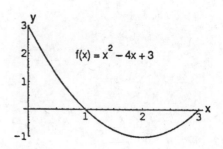

$f(x) = x^2 - 4x + 3$

12. $1 - \frac{x^2}{4} = 0 \Rightarrow 4 - x^2 - 0 \Rightarrow x = \pm 2$;

Area $= \int_{-2}^{2}\left(1 - \frac{x^2}{4}\right)dx - \int_{2}^{3}\left(1 - \frac{x^2}{4}\right)dx$

$= \left[x - \frac{x^3}{12}\right]_{-2}^{2} - \left[x - \frac{x^3}{12}\right]_{2}^{3}$

$= \left[\left(2 - \frac{2^3}{12}\right) - \left(-2 - \frac{(-2)^3}{12}\right)\right] - \left[\left(3 - \frac{3^3}{12}\right) - \left(2 - \frac{2^3}{12}\right)\right]$

$= \left[\frac{4}{3} - \left(-\frac{4}{3}\right)\right] - \left(\frac{3}{4} - \frac{4}{3}\right) = \frac{13}{4}$

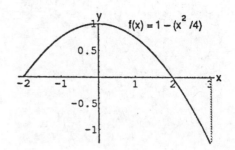

$f(x) = 1 - (x^2/4)$

13. $5 - 5x^{2/3} = 0 \Rightarrow 1 - x^{2/3} = 0 \Rightarrow x = \pm 1$;

Area $= \int_{-1}^{1}\left(5 - 5x^{2/3}\right)dx - \int_{1}^{8}\left(5 - 5x^{2/3}\right)dx$

$= \left[5x - 3x^{5/3}\right]_{-1}^{1} - \left[5x - 3x^{5/3}\right]_{1}^{8}$

$= \left[(5(1) - 3(1)^{5/3}) - (5(-1) - 3(-1)^{5/3})\right]$

$\quad - \left[(5(8) - 3(8)^{5/3}) - (5(1) - 3(1)^{5/3})\right]$

$= [2 - (-2)] - [(40 - 96) - 2] = 62$

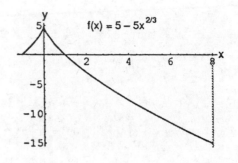

$f(x) = 5 - 5x^{2/3}$

14. $1 - \sqrt{x} = 0 \Rightarrow x = 1$;

Area $= \int_{0}^{1}\left(1 - \sqrt{x}\right)dx - \int_{1}^{4}\left(1 - \sqrt{x}\right)dx$

$= \left[x - \frac{2}{3}x^{3/2}\right]_{0}^{1} - \left[x - \frac{2}{3}x^{3/2}\right]_{1}^{4}$

$= \left[\left(1 - \frac{2}{3}(1)^{3/2}\right) - 0\right] - \left[\left(4 - \frac{2}{3}(4)^{3/2}\right) - \left(1 - \frac{2}{3}(1)^{3/2}\right)\right]$

$= \frac{1}{3} - \left[\left(4 - \frac{16}{3}\right) - \frac{1}{3}\right] = 2$

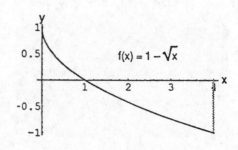

$f(x) = 1 - \sqrt{x}$

15. $f(x) = x, g(x) = \frac{1}{x^2}, a = 1, b = 2 \Rightarrow A = \int_a^b [f(x) - g(x)]\, dx$

$= \int_1^2 \left(x - \frac{1}{x^2}\right) dx = \left[\frac{x^2}{2} + \frac{1}{x}\right]_1^2 = \left(\frac{4}{2} + \frac{1}{2}\right) - \left(\frac{1}{2} + 1\right) = 1$

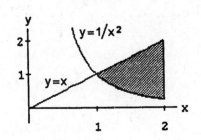

16. $f(x) = x, g(x) = \frac{1}{\sqrt{x}}, a = 1, b = 2 \Rightarrow A = \int_a^b [f(x) - g(x)]\, dx$

$= \int_1^2 \left(x - \frac{1}{\sqrt{x}}\right) dx = \left[\frac{x^2}{2} - 2\sqrt{x}\right]_1^2$

$= \left(\frac{4}{2} - 2\sqrt{2}\right) - \left(\frac{1}{2} - 2\right) = \frac{7 - 4\sqrt{2}}{2}$

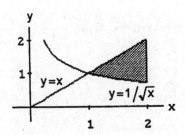

17. $f(x) = \left(1 - \sqrt{x}\right)^2, g(x) = 0, a = 0, b = 1 \Rightarrow A = \int_a^b [f(x) - g(x)]\, dx = \int_0^1 \left(1 - \sqrt{x}\right)^2 dx = \int_0^1 \left(1 - 2\sqrt{x} + x\right) dx$

$= \int_0^1 \left(1 - 2x^{1/2} + x\right) dx = \left[x - \frac{4}{3}x^{3/2} + \frac{x^2}{2}\right]_0^1 = 1 - \frac{4}{3} + \frac{1}{2} = \frac{1}{6}(6 - 8 + 3) = \frac{1}{6}$

18. $f(x) = (1 - x^3)^2, g(x) = 0, a = 0, b = 1 \Rightarrow A = \int_a^b [f(x) - g(x)]\, dx = \int_0^1 (1 - x^3)^2 dx = \int_0^1 (1 - 2x^3 + x^6) dx$

$= \left[x - \frac{x^4}{2} + \frac{x^7}{7}\right]_0^1 = 1 - \frac{1}{2} + \frac{1}{7} = \frac{9}{14}$

19. $f(y) = 2y^2, g(y) = 0, c = 0, d = 3$

$\Rightarrow A = \int_c^d [f(y) - g(y)]\, dy = \int_0^3 (2y^2 - 0)\, dy$

$= 2 \int_0^3 y^2\, dy = \frac{2}{3}[y^3]_0^3 = 18$

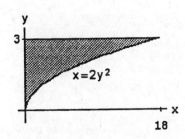

20. $f(y) = 4 - y^2, g(y) = 0, c = -2, d = 2$

$\Rightarrow A = \int_c^d [f(y) - g(y)]\, dy = \int_{-2}^2 (4 - y^2)\, dy$

$= \left[4y - \frac{y^3}{3}\right]_{-2}^2 = 2\left(8 - \frac{8}{3}\right) = \frac{32}{3}$

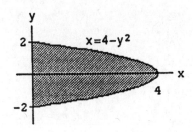

21. Let us find the intersection points: $\frac{y^2}{4} = \frac{y+2}{4}$

$\Rightarrow y^2 - y - 2 = 0 \Rightarrow (y-2)(y+1) = 0 \Rightarrow y = -1$

or $y = 2 \Rightarrow c = -1, d = 2; f(y) = \frac{y+2}{4}, g(y) = \frac{y^2}{4}$

$\Rightarrow A = \int_c^d [f(y) - g(y)] \, dy = \int_{-1}^2 \left(\frac{y+2}{4} - \frac{y^2}{4}\right) dy$

$= \frac{1}{4}\int_{-1}^2 (y + 2 - y^2) \, dy = \frac{1}{4}\left[\frac{y^2}{2} + 2y - \frac{y^3}{3}\right]_{-1}^2$

$= \frac{1}{4}\left[\left(\frac{4}{2} + 4 - \frac{8}{3}\right) - \left(\frac{1}{2} - 2 + \frac{1}{3}\right)\right] = \frac{9}{8}$

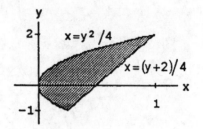

22. Let us find the intersection points: $\frac{y^2-4}{4} = \frac{y+16}{4}$

$\Rightarrow y^2 - y - 20 = 0 \Rightarrow (y-5)(y+4) = 0 \Rightarrow y = -4$

or $y = 5 \Rightarrow c = -4, d = 5; f(y) = \frac{y+16}{4}, g(y) = \frac{y^2-4}{4}$

$\Rightarrow A = \int_c^d [f(y) - g(y)] \, dy = \int_{-4}^5 \left(\frac{y+16}{4} - \frac{y^2-4}{4}\right) dy$

$= \frac{1}{4}\int_{-4}^5 (y + 20 - y^2) \, dy = \frac{1}{4}\left[\frac{y^2}{2} + 20y - \frac{y^3}{3}\right]_{-4}^5$

$= \frac{1}{4}\left[\left(\frac{25}{2} + 100 - \frac{125}{3}\right) - \left(\frac{16}{2} - 80 + \frac{64}{3}\right)\right]$

$= \frac{1}{4}\left(\frac{9}{2} + 180 - 63\right) = \frac{1}{4}\left(\frac{9}{2} + 117\right) = \frac{1}{8}(9 + 234) = \frac{243}{8}$

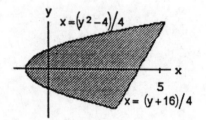

23. $f(x) = x, g(x) = \sin x, a = 0, b = \frac{\pi}{4}$

$\Rightarrow A = \int_a^b [f(x) - g(x)] \, dx = \int_0^{\pi/4} (x - \sin x) \, dx$

$= \left[\frac{x^2}{2} + \cos x\right]_0^{\pi/4} = \left(\frac{\pi^2}{32} + \frac{\sqrt{2}}{2}\right) - 1$

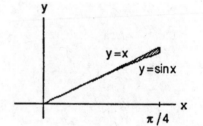

24. $f(x) = 1, g(x) = |\sin x|, a = -\frac{\pi}{2}, b = \frac{\pi}{2}$

$\Rightarrow A = \int_a^b [f(x) - g(x)] \, dx = \int_{-\pi/2}^{\pi/2} (1 - |\sin x|) \, dx$

$= \int_{-\pi/2}^0 (1 + \sin x) \, dx + \int_0^{\pi/2} (1 - \sin x) \, dx$

$= 2\int_0^{\pi/2} (1 - \sin x) \, dx = 2[x + \cos x]_0^{\pi/2}$

$= 2\left(\frac{\pi}{2} - 1\right) = \pi - 2$

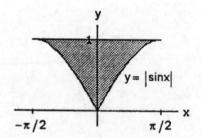

25. $a = 0, b = \pi, f(x) - g(x) = 2\sin x - \sin 2x$

$\Rightarrow A = \int_0^\pi (2\sin x - \sin 2x) \, dx = \left[-2\cos x + \frac{\cos 2x}{2}\right]_0^\pi$

$= \left[-2 \cdot (-1) + \frac{1}{2}\right] - \left(-2 \cdot 1 + \frac{1}{2}\right) = 4$

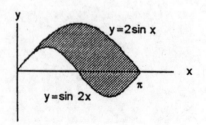

26. $a = -\frac{\pi}{3}, b = \frac{\pi}{3}, f(x) - g(x) = 8\cos x - \sec^2 x$

$\Rightarrow A = \int_{-\pi/3}^{\pi/3} (8\cos x - \sec^2 x)\, dx = [8\sin x - \tan x]_{-\pi/3}^{\pi/3}$

$= \left(8 \cdot \frac{\sqrt{3}}{2} - \sqrt{3}\right) - \left(-8 \cdot \frac{\sqrt{3}}{2} + \sqrt{3}\right) = 6\sqrt{3}$

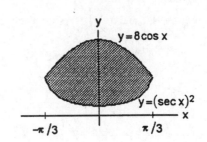

27. $f(y) = \sqrt{y}, g(y) = 2 - y, c = 1, d = 2$

$\Rightarrow A = \int_c^d [f(y) - g(y)]\, dy = \int_1^2 \left[\sqrt{y} - (2-y)\right] dy$

$= \int_1^2 \left(\sqrt{y} - 2 + y\right) dy = \left[\frac{2}{3}y^{3/2} - 2y + \frac{y^2}{2}\right]_1^2$

$= \left(\frac{4}{3}\sqrt{2} - 4 + 2\right) - \left(\frac{2}{3} - 2 + \frac{1}{2}\right) = \frac{4}{3}\sqrt{2} - \frac{7}{6} = \frac{8\sqrt{2}-7}{6}$

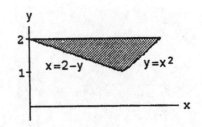

28. $f(y) = 6 - y, g(y) = y^2, c = 1, d = 2$

$\Rightarrow A = \int_c^d [f(y) - g(y)]\, dy = \int_1^2 (6 - y - y^2)\, dy$

$= \left[6y - \frac{y^2}{2} - \frac{y^3}{3}\right]_1^2 = \left(12 - 2 - \frac{8}{3}\right) - \left(6 - \frac{1}{2} - \frac{1}{3}\right)$

$= 4 - \frac{7}{3} + \frac{1}{2} = \frac{24 - 14 + 3}{6} = \frac{13}{6}$

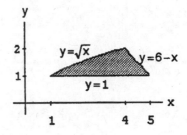

29. $f(x) = x^3 - 3x^2 = x^2(x - 3) \Rightarrow f'(x) = 3x^2 - 6x = 3x(x - 2) \Rightarrow f' = +++ \mid_0 ---- \mid_2 +++$

$\Rightarrow f(0) = 0$ is a maximum and $f(2) = -4$ is a minimum. $A = -\int_0^3 (x^3 - 3x^2)\, dx = -\left[\frac{x^4}{4} - x^3\right]_0^3 = -\left(\frac{81}{4} - 27\right) = \frac{27}{4}$

30. $A = \int_0^a \left(a^{1/2} - x^{1/2}\right)^2 dx = \int_0^a \left(a - 2\sqrt{a}\, x^{1/2} + x\right) dx = \left[ax - \frac{4}{3}\sqrt{a}\, x^{3/2} + \frac{x^2}{2}\right]_0^a = a^2 - \frac{4}{3}\sqrt{a} \cdot a\sqrt{a} + \frac{a^2}{2}$

$= a^2\left(1 - \frac{4}{3} + \frac{1}{2}\right) = \frac{a^2}{6}(6 - 8 + 3) = \frac{a^2}{6}$

31. The area above the x-axis is $A_1 = \int_0^1 \left(y^{2/3} - y\right) dy$

$= \left[\frac{3y^{5/3}}{5} - \frac{y^2}{2}\right]_0^1 = \frac{1}{10}$ ; the area below the x-axis is

$A_2 = \int_{-1}^0 \left(y^{2/3} - y\right) dy = \left[\frac{3y^{5/3}}{5} - \frac{y^2}{2}\right]_{-1}^0 = \frac{11}{10}$

$\Rightarrow$ the total area is $A_1 + A_2 = \frac{6}{5}$

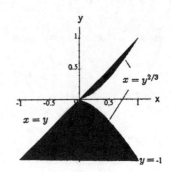

32. $A = \int_0^{\pi/4} (\cos x - \sin x)\, dx + \int_{\pi/4}^{5\pi/4} (\sin x - \cos x)\, dx$

$\quad + \int_{5\pi/4}^{3\pi/2} (\cos x - \sin x)\, dx = [\sin x + \cos x]_0^{\pi/4}$

$\quad + [-\cos x - \sin x]_{\pi/4}^{5\pi/4} + [\sin x + \cos x]_{5\pi/4}^{3\pi/2}$

$\quad = \left[\left(\frac{\sqrt{2}}{2} + \frac{\sqrt{2}}{2}\right) - (0+1)\right] + \left[\left(\frac{\sqrt{2}}{2} + \frac{\sqrt{2}}{2}\right) - \left(-\frac{\sqrt{2}}{2} - \frac{\sqrt{2}}{2}\right)\right]$

$\quad + \left[(-1+0) - \left(-\frac{\sqrt{2}}{2} - \frac{\sqrt{2}}{2}\right)\right] = \frac{8\sqrt{2}}{2} - 2 = 4\sqrt{2} - 2$

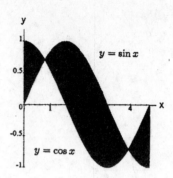

33. $y = x^2 + \int_1^x \frac{1}{t}\, dt \Rightarrow \frac{dy}{dx} = 2x + \frac{1}{x} \Rightarrow \frac{d^2y}{dx^2} = 2 - \frac{1}{x^2};\ y(1) = 1 + \int_1^1 \frac{1}{t}\, dt = 1$ and $y'(1) = 2 + 1 = 3$

34. $y = \int_0^x \left(1 + 2\sqrt{\sec t}\right) dt \Rightarrow \frac{dy}{dx} = 1 + 2\sqrt{\sec x} \Rightarrow \frac{d^2y}{dx^2} = 2\left(\frac{1}{2}\right)(\sec x)^{-1/2}(\sec x \tan x) = \sqrt{\sec x}\,(\tan x);$

$\quad x = 0 \Rightarrow y = \int_0^0 \left(1 + 2\sqrt{\sec t}\right) dt = 0$ and $x = 0 \Rightarrow \frac{dy}{dx} = 1 + 2\sqrt{\sec 0} = 3$

35. $y = \int_5^x \frac{\sin t}{t}\, dt - 3 \Rightarrow \frac{dy}{dx} = \frac{\sin x}{x};\ x = 5 \Rightarrow y = \int_5^5 \frac{\sin t}{t}\, dt - 3 = -3$

36. $y = \int_{-1}^x \sqrt{2 - \sin^2 t}\, dt + 2$ so that $\frac{dy}{dx} = \sqrt{2 - \sin^2 x};\ x = -1 \Rightarrow y = \int_{-1}^{-1} \sqrt{2 - \sin^2 t}\, dt + 2 = 2$

37. Let $u = \cos x \Rightarrow du = -\sin x\, dx \Rightarrow -du = \sin x\, dx$

$\quad \int 2(\cos x)^{-1/2} \sin x\, dx = \int 2u^{-1/2}(-du) = -2 \int u^{-1/2}\, du = -2\left(\frac{u^{1/2}}{\frac{1}{2}}\right) + C = -4u^{1/2} + C = -4(\cos x)^{1/2} + C$

38. Let $u = \tan x \Rightarrow du = \sec^2 x\, dx$

$\quad \int (\tan x)^{-3/2} \sec^2 x\, dx = \int u^{-3/2}\, du = \frac{u^{-1/2}}{\left(-\frac{1}{2}\right)} + C = -2u^{-1/2} + C = \frac{-2}{(\tan x)^{1/2}} + C$

39. Let $u = 2\theta + 1 \Rightarrow du = 2\, d\theta \Rightarrow \frac{1}{2}\, du = d\theta$

$\quad \int [2\theta + 1 + 2\cos(2\theta + 1)]\, d\theta = \int (u + 2\cos u)\left(\frac{1}{2}\, du\right) = \frac{u^2}{4} + \sin u + C_1 = \frac{(2\theta+1)^2}{4} + \sin(2\theta + 1) + C_1$

$\quad = \theta^2 + \theta + \sin(2\theta + 1) + C$, where $C = C_1 + \frac{1}{4}$ is still an arbitrary constant

40. Let $u = 2\theta - \pi \Rightarrow du = 2\, d\theta \Rightarrow \frac{1}{2}\, du = d\theta$

$\quad \int \left(\frac{1}{\sqrt{2\theta - \pi}} + 2\sec^2(2\theta - \pi)\right) d\theta = \int \left(\frac{1}{\sqrt{u}} + 2\sec^2 u\right)\left(\frac{1}{2}\, du\right) = \frac{1}{2} \int \left(u^{-1/2} + 2\sec^2 u\right) du$

$\quad = \frac{1}{2}\left(\frac{u^{1/2}}{\frac{1}{2}}\right) + \frac{1}{2}(2\tan u) + C = u^{1/2} + \tan u + C = (2\theta - \pi)^{1/2} + \tan(2\theta - \pi) + C$

41. $\int \left(t - \frac{2}{t}\right)\left(t + \frac{2}{t}\right) dt = \int \left(t^2 - \frac{4}{t^2}\right) dt = \int (t^2 - 4t^{-2})\, dt = \frac{t^3}{3} - 4\left(\frac{t^{-1}}{-1}\right) + C = \frac{t^3}{3} + \frac{4}{t} + C$

42. $\int \frac{(t+1)^2 - 1}{t^4}\, dt = \int \frac{t^2 + 2t}{t^4}\, dt = \int \left(\frac{1}{t^2} + \frac{2}{t^3}\right) dt = \int (t^{-2} + 2t^{-3})\, dt = \frac{t^{-1}}{(-1)} + 2\left(\frac{t^{-2}}{-2}\right) + C = -\frac{1}{t} - \frac{1}{t^2} + C$

43. Let $u = 2t^{3/2} \Rightarrow du = 3\sqrt{t}\, dt \Rightarrow \frac{1}{3}\, du = \sqrt{t}\, dt$

$\quad \int \sqrt{t}\, \sin\left(2t^{3/2}\right) dt = \frac{1}{3} \int \sin u\, du = -\frac{1}{3}\cos u + C = -\frac{1}{3}\cos\left(2t^{3/2}\right) + C$

44. Let $u = 1 + \sec\theta \Rightarrow du = \sec\theta\,\tan\theta\,d\theta \Rightarrow \int \sec\theta\,\tan\theta\,\sqrt{1+\sec\theta}\,d\theta = \int u^{1/2}du = \frac{2}{3}u^{3/2} + C = \frac{2}{3}(1+\sec\theta)^{3/2} + C$

45. $\int_{-1}^{1}(3x^2 - 4x + 7)\,dx = [x^3 - 2x^2 + 7x]_{-1}^{1} = [1^3 - 2(1)^2 + 7(1)] - [(-1)^3 - 2(-1)^2 + 7(-1)] = 6 - (-10) = 16$

46. $\int_{0}^{1}(8s^3 - 12s^2 + 5)\,ds = [2s^4 - 4s^3 + 5s]_{0}^{1} = [2(1)^4 - 4(1)^3 + 5(1)] - 0 = 3$

47. $\int_{1}^{2}\frac{4}{v^2}\,dv = \int_{1}^{2}4v^{-2}\,dv = [-4v^{-1}]_{1}^{2} = \left(\frac{-4}{2}\right) - \left(\frac{-4}{1}\right) = 2$

48. $\int_{1}^{27}x^{-4/3}\,dx = [-3x^{-1/3}]_{1}^{27} = -3(27)^{-1/3} - \left(-3(1)^{-1/3}\right) = -3\left(\frac{1}{3}\right) + 3(1) = 2$

49. $\int_{1}^{4}\frac{dt}{t\sqrt{t}} = \int_{1}^{4}\frac{dt}{t^{3/2}} = \int_{1}^{4}t^{-3/2}\,dt = [-2t^{-1/2}]_{1}^{4} = \frac{-2}{\sqrt{4}} - \frac{(-2)}{\sqrt{1}} = 1$

50. Let $x = 1 + \sqrt{u} \Rightarrow dx = \frac{1}{2}u^{-1/2}\,du \Rightarrow 2\,dx = \frac{du}{\sqrt{u}}; u = 1 \Rightarrow x = 2, u = 4 \Rightarrow x = 3$

$\int_{1}^{4}\frac{(1+\sqrt{u})^{1/2}}{\sqrt{u}}\,du = \int_{2}^{3}x^{1/2}(2\,dx) = \left[2\left(\frac{2}{3}\right)x^{3/2}\right]_{2}^{3} = \frac{4}{3}\left(3^{3/2}\right) - \frac{4}{3}\left(2^{3/2}\right) = 4\sqrt{3} - \frac{8}{3}\sqrt{2} = \frac{4}{3}\left(3\sqrt{3} - 2\sqrt{2}\right)$

51. Let $u = 2x + 1 \Rightarrow du = 2\,dx \Rightarrow 18\,du = 36\,dx; x = 0 \Rightarrow u = 1, x = 1 \Rightarrow u = 3$

$\int_{0}^{1}\frac{36\,dx}{(2x+1)^3} = \int_{1}^{3}18u^{-3}\,du = \left[\frac{18u^{-2}}{-2}\right]_{1}^{3} = \left[\frac{-9}{u^2}\right]_{1}^{3} = \left(\frac{-9}{3^2}\right) - \left(\frac{-9}{1^2}\right) = 8$

52. Let $u = 7 - 5r \Rightarrow du = -5\,dr \Rightarrow -\frac{1}{5}du = dr; r = 0 \Rightarrow u = 7, r = 1 \Rightarrow u = 2$

$\int_{0}^{1}\frac{dr}{\sqrt[3]{(7-5r)^2}} = \int_{0}^{1}(7-5r)^{-2/3}\,dr = \int_{7}^{2}u^{-2/3}\left(-\frac{1}{5}du\right) = -\frac{1}{5}\left[3u^{1/3}\right]_{7}^{2} = \frac{3}{5}\left(\sqrt[3]{7} - \sqrt[3]{2}\right)$

53. Let $u = 1 - x^{2/3} \Rightarrow du = -\frac{2}{3}x^{-1/3}\,dx \Rightarrow -\frac{3}{2}du = x^{-1/3}\,dx; x = \frac{1}{8} \Rightarrow u = 1 - \left(\frac{1}{8}\right)^{2/3} = \frac{3}{4}, x = 1 \Rightarrow u = 1 - 1^{2/3} = 0$

$\int_{1/8}^{1}x^{-1/3}\left(1 - x^{2/3}\right)^{3/2}\,dx = \int_{3/4}^{0}u^{3/2}\left(-\frac{3}{2}du\right) = \left[\left(-\frac{3}{2}\right)\left(\frac{u^{5/2}}{\frac{5}{2}}\right)\right]_{3/4}^{0} = \left[-\frac{3}{5}u^{5/2}\right]_{3/4}^{0} = -\frac{3}{5}(0)^{5/2} - \left(-\frac{3}{5}\right)\left(\frac{3}{4}\right)^{5/2}$

$= \frac{27\sqrt{3}}{160}$

54. Let $u = 1 + 9x^4 \Rightarrow du = 36x^3\,dx \Rightarrow \frac{1}{36}du = x^3\,dx; x = 0 \Rightarrow u = 1, x = \frac{1}{2} \Rightarrow u = 1 + 9\left(\frac{1}{2}\right)^4 = \frac{25}{16}$

$\int_{0}^{1/2}x^3\left(1 + 9x^4\right)^{-3/2}\,dx = \int_{1}^{25/16}u^{-3/2}\left(\frac{1}{36}du\right) = \left[\frac{1}{36}\left(\frac{u^{-1/2}}{-\frac{1}{2}}\right)\right]_{1}^{25/16} = \left[-\frac{1}{18}u^{-1/2}\right]_{1}^{25/16}$

$= -\frac{1}{18}\left(\frac{25}{16}\right)^{-1/2} - \left(-\frac{1}{18}(1)^{-1/2}\right) = \frac{1}{90}$

55. Let $u = 5r \Rightarrow du = 5\,dr \Rightarrow \frac{1}{5}du = dr; r = 0 \Rightarrow u = 0, r = \pi \Rightarrow u = 5\pi$

$\int_{0}^{\pi}\sin^2 5r\,dr = \int_{0}^{5\pi}(\sin^2 u)\left(\frac{1}{5}du\right) = \frac{1}{5}\left[\frac{u}{2} - \frac{\sin 2u}{4}\right]_{0}^{5\pi} = \left(\frac{\pi}{2} - \frac{\sin 10\pi}{20}\right) - \left(0 - \frac{\sin 0}{20}\right) = \frac{\pi}{2}$

56. Let $u = 4t - \frac{\pi}{4} \Rightarrow du = 4\,dt \Rightarrow \frac{1}{4}du = dt; t = 0 \Rightarrow u = -\frac{\pi}{4}, t = \frac{\pi}{4} \Rightarrow u = \frac{3\pi}{4}$

$\int_{0}^{\pi/4}\cos^2\left(4t - \frac{\pi}{4}\right)\,dt = \int_{-\pi/4}^{3\pi/4}(\cos^2 u)\left(\frac{1}{4}du\right) = \frac{1}{4}\left[\frac{u}{2} + \frac{\sin 2u}{4}\right]_{-\pi/4}^{3\pi/4} = \frac{1}{4}\left(\frac{3\pi}{8} + \frac{\sin\left(\frac{3\pi}{2}\right)}{4}\right) - \frac{1}{4}\left(-\frac{\pi}{8} + \frac{\sin\left(-\frac{\pi}{2}\right)}{4}\right)$

$= \frac{\pi}{8} - \frac{1}{16} + \frac{1}{16} = \frac{\pi}{8}$

57. $\displaystyle\int_0^{\pi/3} \sec^2\theta\, d\theta = [\tan\theta]_0^{\pi/3} = \tan\frac{\pi}{3} - \tan 0 = \sqrt{3}$

58. $\displaystyle\int_{\pi/4}^{3\pi/4} \csc^2 x\, dx = [-\cot x]_{\pi/4}^{3\pi/4} = \left(-\cot\frac{3\pi}{4}\right) - \left(-\cot\frac{\pi}{4}\right) = 2$

59. Let $u = \frac{x}{6} \Rightarrow du = \frac{1}{6}\, dx \Rightarrow 6\, du = dx$; $x = \pi \Rightarrow u = \frac{\pi}{6}$, $x = 3\pi \Rightarrow u = \frac{\pi}{2}$

$\displaystyle\int_\pi^{3\pi} \cot^2\frac{x}{6}\, dx = \int_{\pi/6}^{\pi/2} 6\cot^2 u\, du = 6\int_{\pi/6}^{\pi/2}(\csc^2 u - 1)\, du = [6(-\cot u - u)]_{\pi/6}^{\pi/2} = 6\left(-\cot\frac{\pi}{2} - \frac{\pi}{2}\right) - 6\left(-\cot\frac{\pi}{6} - \frac{\pi}{6}\right)$

$= 6\sqrt{3} - 2\pi$

60. Let $u = \frac{\theta}{3} \Rightarrow du = \frac{1}{3}\, d\theta \Rightarrow 3\, du = d\theta$; $\theta = 0 \Rightarrow u = 0$, $\theta = \pi \Rightarrow u = \frac{\pi}{3}$

$\displaystyle\int_0^\pi \tan^2\frac{\theta}{3}\, d\theta = \int_0^\pi\left(\sec^2\frac{\theta}{3} - 1\right)d\theta = \int_0^{\pi/3} 3(\sec^2 u - 1)\, du = [3\tan u - 3u]_0^{\pi/3} = \left[3\tan\frac{\pi}{3} - 3\left(\frac{\pi}{3}\right)\right] - (3\tan 0 - 0)$

$= 3\sqrt{3} - \pi$

61. $\displaystyle\int_{-\pi/3}^0 \sec x \tan x\, dx = [\sec x]_{-\pi/3}^0 = \sec 0 - \sec\left(-\frac{\pi}{3}\right) = 1 - 2 = -1$

62. $\displaystyle\int_{\pi/4}^{3\pi/4} \csc z \cot z\, dz = [-\csc z]_{\pi/4}^{3\pi/4} = \left(-\csc\frac{3\pi}{4}\right) - \left(-\csc\frac{\pi}{4}\right) = -\sqrt{2} + \sqrt{2} = 0$

63. Let $u = \sin x \Rightarrow du = \cos x\, dx$; $x = 0 \Rightarrow u = 0$, $x = \frac{\pi}{2} \Rightarrow u = 1$

$\displaystyle\int_0^{\pi/2} 5(\sin x)^{3/2}\cos x\, dx = \int_0^1 5u^{3/2}\, du = \left[5\left(\frac{2}{5}\right)u^{5/2}\right]_0^1 = \left[2u^{5/2}\right]_0^1 = 2(1)^{5/2} - 2(0)^{5/2} = 2$

64. Let $u = 1 - x^2 \Rightarrow du = -2x\, dx \Rightarrow -du = 2x\, dx$; $x = -1 \Rightarrow u = 0$, $x = 1 \Rightarrow u = 0$

$\displaystyle\int_{-1}^1 2x\sin(1 - x^2)\, dx = \int_0^0 -\sin u\, du = 0$

65. Let $u = \sin 3x \Rightarrow du = 3\cos 3x\, dx \Rightarrow \frac{1}{3}\, du = \cos 3x\, dx$; $x = -\frac{\pi}{2} \Rightarrow u = \sin\left(-\frac{3\pi}{2}\right) = 1$, $x = \frac{\pi}{2} \Rightarrow u = \sin\left(\frac{3\pi}{2}\right) = -1$

$\displaystyle\int_{-\pi/2}^{\pi/2} 15\sin^4 3x \cos 3x\, dx = \int_1^{-1} 15u^4\left(\frac{1}{3}\, du\right) = \int_1^{-1} 5u^4\, du = [u^5]_1^{-1} = (-1)^5 - (1)^5 = -2$

66. Let $u = \cos\left(\frac{x}{2}\right) \Rightarrow du = -\frac{1}{2}\sin\left(\frac{x}{2}\right)dx \Rightarrow -2\, du = \sin\left(\frac{x}{2}\right)dx$; $x = 0 \Rightarrow u = \cos\left(\frac{0}{2}\right) = 1$, $x = \frac{2\pi}{3} \Rightarrow u = \cos\left(\frac{2\pi}{3}{2}\right) = \frac{1}{2}$

$\displaystyle\int_0^{2\pi/3} \cos^{-4}\left(\frac{x}{2}\right)\sin\left(\frac{x}{2}\right)dx = \int_1^{1/2} u^{-4}(-2\, du) = \left[-2\left(\frac{u^{-3}}{-3}\right)\right]_1^{1/2} = \frac{2}{3}\left(\frac{1}{2}\right)^{-3} - \frac{2}{3}(1)^{-3} = \frac{2}{3}(8 - 1) = \frac{14}{3}$

67. Let $u = 1 + 3\sin^2 x \Rightarrow du = 6\sin x\cos x\, dx \Rightarrow \frac{1}{2}\, du = 3\sin x\cos x\, dx$; $x = 0 \Rightarrow u = 1$, $x = \frac{\pi}{2} \Rightarrow u = 1 + 3\sin^2\frac{\pi}{2} = 4$

$\displaystyle\int_0^{\pi/2} \frac{3\sin x\cos x}{\sqrt{1 + 3\sin^2 x}}\, dx = \int_1^4 \frac{1}{\sqrt{u}}\left(\frac{1}{2}\, du\right) = \int_1^4 \frac{1}{2}u^{-1/2}\, du = \left[\frac{1}{2}\left(\frac{u^{1/2}}{\frac{1}{2}}\right)\right]_1^4 = \left[u^{1/2}\right]_1^4 = 4^{1/2} - 1^{1/2} = 1$

68. Let $u = 1 + 7\tan x \Rightarrow du = 7\sec^2 x\, dx \Rightarrow \frac{1}{7}\, du = \sec^2 x\, dx$; $x = 0 \Rightarrow u = 1 + 7\tan 0 = 1$, $x = \frac{\pi}{4}$

$\Rightarrow u = 1 + 7\tan\frac{\pi}{4} = 8$

$\displaystyle\int_0^{\pi/4} \frac{\sec^2 x}{(1 + 7\tan x)^{2/3}}\, dx = \int_1^8 \frac{1}{u^{2/3}}\left(\frac{1}{7}\, du\right) = \int_1^8 \frac{1}{7}u^{-2/3}\, du = \left[\frac{1}{7}\left(\frac{u^{1/3}}{\frac{1}{3}}\right)\right]_1^8 = \left[\frac{3}{7}u^{1/3}\right]_1^8 = \frac{3}{7}(8)^{1/3} - \frac{3}{7}(1)^{1/3} = \frac{3}{7}$

69. Let $u = \sec\theta \Rightarrow du = \sec\theta\tan\theta\,d\theta;\ \theta = 0 \Rightarrow u = \sec 0 = 1,\ \theta = \frac{\pi}{3} \Rightarrow u = \sec\frac{\pi}{3} = 2$

$$\int_0^{\pi/3} \frac{\tan\theta}{\sqrt{2\sec\theta}}\,d\theta = \int_0^{\pi/3} \frac{\sec\theta\tan\theta}{\sec\theta\sqrt{2\sec\theta}}\,d\theta = \int_0^{\pi/3} \frac{\sec\theta\tan\theta}{\sqrt{2}\,(\sec\theta)^{3/2}}\,d\theta = \int_1^2 \frac{1}{\sqrt{2}\,u^{3/2}}\,du = \frac{1}{\sqrt{2}}\int_1^2 u^{-3/2}\,du$$

$$= \frac{1}{\sqrt{2}}\left[\frac{u^{-1/2}}{\left(-\frac{1}{2}\right)}\right]_1^2 = \left[-\frac{2}{\sqrt{2u}}\right]_1^2 = -\frac{2}{\sqrt{2(2)}} - \left(-\frac{2}{\sqrt{2(1)}}\right) = \sqrt{2} - 1$$

70. Let $u = \sin\sqrt{t} \Rightarrow du = \left(\cos\sqrt{t}\right)\left(\frac{1}{2}t^{-1/2}\right)dt = \frac{\cos\sqrt{t}}{2\sqrt{t}}\,dt \Rightarrow 2\,du = \frac{\cos\sqrt{t}}{\sqrt{t}}\,dt;\ t = \frac{\pi^2}{36} \Rightarrow u = \sin\frac{\pi}{6} = \frac{1}{2}$,

$t = \frac{\pi^2}{4} \Rightarrow u = \sin\frac{\pi}{2} = 1$

$$\int_{\pi^2/36}^{\pi^2/4} \frac{\cos\sqrt{t}}{\sqrt{t}\,\sin\sqrt{t}}\,dt = \int_{1/2}^1 \frac{1}{\sqrt{u}}\,(2\,du) = 2\int_{1/2}^1 u^{-1/2}\,du = \left[4\sqrt{u}\right]_{1/2}^1 = 4\sqrt{1} - 4\sqrt{\frac{1}{2}} = 2\left(2 - \sqrt{2}\right)$$

71. (a) $\operatorname{av}(f) = \frac{1}{1-(-1)}\int_{-1}^1 (mx+b)\,dx = \frac{1}{2}\left[\frac{mx^2}{2} + bx\right]_{-1}^1 = \frac{1}{2}\left[\left(\frac{m(1)^2}{2} + b(1)\right) - \left(\frac{m(-1)^2}{2} + b(-1)\right)\right] = \frac{1}{2}(2b) = b$

   (b) $\operatorname{av}(f) = \frac{1}{k-(-k)}\int_{-k}^k (mx+b)\,dx = \frac{1}{2k}\left[\frac{mx^2}{2} + bx\right]_{-k}^k = \frac{1}{2k}\left[\left(\frac{m(k)^2}{2} + b(k)\right) - \left(\frac{m(-k)^2}{2} + b(-k)\right)\right] = \frac{1}{2k}(2bk) = b$

72. (a) $y_{av} = \frac{1}{3-0}\int_0^3 \sqrt{3x}\,dx = \frac{1}{3}\int_0^3 \sqrt{3}\,x^{1/2}\,dx = \frac{\sqrt{3}}{3}\left[\frac{2}{3}x^{3/2}\right]_0^3 = \frac{\sqrt{3}}{3}\left[\frac{2}{3}(3)^{3/2} - \frac{2}{3}(0)^{3/2}\right] = \frac{\sqrt{3}}{3}\left(2\sqrt{3}\right) = 2$

   (b) $y_{av} = \frac{1}{a-0}\int_0^a \sqrt{ax}\,dx = \frac{1}{a}\int_0^a \sqrt{a}\,x^{1/2}\,dx = \frac{\sqrt{a}}{a}\left[\frac{2}{3}x^{3/2}\right]_0^a = \frac{\sqrt{a}}{a}\left(\frac{2}{3}(a)^{3/2} - \frac{2}{3}(0)^{3/2}\right) = \frac{\sqrt{a}}{a}\left(\frac{2}{3}a\sqrt{a}\right) = \frac{2}{3}a$

73. $f'_{av} = \frac{1}{b-a}\int_a^b f'(x)\,dx = \frac{1}{b-a}[f(x)]_a^b = \frac{1}{b-a}[f(b) - f(a)] = \frac{f(b)-f(a)}{b-a}$ so the average value of $f'$ over $[a,b]$ is the slope of the secant line joining the points $(a, f(a))$ and $(b, f(b))$, which is the average rate of change of $f$ over $[a,b]$.

74. Yes, because the average value of $f$ on $[a,b]$ is $\frac{1}{b-a}\int_a^b f(x)\,dx$. If the length of the interval is 2, then $b-a = 2$ and the average value of the function is $\frac{1}{2}\int_a^b f(x)\,dx$.

75. We want to evaluate

$$\frac{1}{365-0}\int_0^{365} f(x)\,dx = \frac{1}{365}\int_0^{365}\left(37\sin\left[\frac{2\pi}{365}(x-101)\right] + 25\right)dx = \frac{37}{365}\int_0^{365}\sin\left[\frac{2\pi}{365}(x-101)\right]dx + \frac{25}{365}\int_0^{365}dx$$

Notice that the period of $y = \sin\left[\frac{2\pi}{365}(x-101)\right]$ is $\frac{2\pi}{\frac{2\pi}{365}} = 365$ and that we are integrating this function over an iterval of

length 365. Thus the value of $\frac{37}{365}\int_0^{365}\sin\left[\frac{2\pi}{365}(x-101)\right]dx + \frac{25}{365}\int_0^{365}dx$ is $\frac{37}{365}\cdot 0 + \frac{25}{365}\cdot 365 = 25$.

76. $\frac{1}{675-20}\int_{20}^{675}(8.27 + 10^{-5}(26T - 1.87T^2))dT = \frac{1}{655}\left[8.27T + \frac{26T^2}{2\cdot10^5} - \frac{1.87T^3}{3\cdot10^5}\right]_{20}^{675}$

$= \frac{1}{655}\left(\left[8.27(675) + \frac{26(675)^2}{2\cdot10^5} - \frac{1.87(675)^3}{3\cdot10^5}\right] - \left[8.27(20) + \frac{26(20)^2}{2\cdot10^5} - \frac{1.87(20)^3}{3\cdot10^5}\right]\right) \approx \frac{1}{655}(3724.44 - 165.40)$

$= 5.43 =$ the average value of $C_v$ on $[20, 675]$. To find the temperature $T$ at which $C_v = 5.43$, solve

$5.43 = 8.27 + 10^{-5}(26T - 1.87T^2)$ for T. We obtain $1.87T^2 - 26T - 284000 = 0$

$\Rightarrow T = \frac{26 \pm \sqrt{(26)^2 - 4(1.87)(-284000)}}{2(1.87)} = \frac{26 \pm \sqrt{2124996}}{3.74}$. So $T = -382.82$ or $T = 396.72$. Only $T = 396.72$ lies in the

interval $[20, 675]$, so $T = 396.72°C$.

77. $\frac{dy}{dx} = \sqrt{2 + \cos^3 x}$

78. $\frac{dy}{dx} = \sqrt{2 + \cos^3(7x^2)} \cdot \frac{d}{dx}(7x^2) = 14x\sqrt{2 + \cos^3(7x^2)}$

79. $\frac{dy}{dx} = \frac{d}{dx}\left(-\int_1^x \frac{6}{3+t^4}\,dt\right) = -\frac{6}{3+x^4}$

80. $\frac{dy}{dx} = \frac{d}{dx}\left(\int_{\sec x}^2 \frac{1}{t^2+1}\,dt\right) = -\frac{d}{dx}\left(\int_2^{\sec x} \frac{1}{t^2+1}\,dt\right) = -\frac{1}{\sec^2 x + 1}\frac{d}{dx}(\sec x) = -\frac{\sec x \tan x}{1+\sec^2 x}$

81. Yes. The function f, being differentiable on [a, b], is then continuous on [a, b]. The Fundamental Theorem of Calculus says that every continuous function on [a, b] is the derivative of a function on [a, b].

82. The second part of the Fundamental Theorem of Calculus states that if F(x) is an antiderivative of f(x) on [a, b], then $\int_a^b f(x)\,dx = F(b) - F(a)$. In particular, if F(x) is an antiderivaitve of $\sqrt{1+x^4}$ on [0, 1], then $\int_0^1 \sqrt{1+x^4}\,dx$
$= F(1) - F(0)$.

83. $y = \int_x^1 \sqrt{1+t^2}\,dt = -\int_1^x \sqrt{1+t^2}\,dt \Rightarrow \frac{dy}{dx} = \frac{d}{dx}\left[-\int_1^x \sqrt{1+t^2}\,dt\right] = -\frac{d}{dx}\left[\int_1^x \sqrt{1+t^2}\,dt\right] = -\sqrt{1+x^2}$

84. $y = \int_{\cos x}^0 \frac{1}{1-t^2}\,dt = -\int_0^{\cos x} \frac{1}{1-t^2}\,dt \Rightarrow \frac{dy}{dx} = \frac{d}{dx}\left[-\int_0^{\cos x} \frac{1}{1-t^2}\,dt\right] = -\frac{d}{dx}\left[\int_0^{\cos x} \frac{1}{1-t^2}\,dt\right]$
$= -\left(\frac{1}{1-\cos^2 x}\right)\left(\frac{d}{dx}(\cos x)\right) = -\left(\frac{1}{\sin^2 x}\right)(-\sin x) = \frac{1}{\sin x} = \csc x$

85. We estimate the area A using midpoints of the vertical intervals, and we will estimate the width of the parking lot on each interval by averaging the widths at top and bottom. This gives the estimate
$A \approx 15 \cdot \left(\frac{0+36}{2} + \frac{36+54}{2} + \frac{54+51}{2} + \frac{51+49.5}{2} + \frac{49.5+54}{2} + \frac{54+64.4}{2} + \frac{64.4+67.5}{2} + \frac{67.5+42}{2}\right)$
$A \approx 5961\ ft^2$. The cost is Area $\cdot$ ($2.10/ft^2$) $\approx (5961\ ft^2)($2.10/ft^2$) = $12,518.10 \Rightarrow$ the job cannot be done for $11,000.

86. (a) Before the chute opens for A, $a = -32\ ft/sec^2$. Since the helicopter is hovering, $v_0 = 0\ ft/sec$
$\Rightarrow v = \int -32\,dt = -32t + v_0 = -32t$. Then $s_0 = 6400\ ft \Rightarrow s = \int -32t\,dt = -16t^2 + s_0 = -16t^2 + 6400$.
At $t = 4$ sec, $s = -16(4)^2 + 6400 = 6144\ ft$ when A's chute opens;

   (b) For B, $s_0 = 7000\ ft$, $v_0 = 0$, $a = -32\ ft/sec^2 \Rightarrow v = \int -32\,dt = -32t + v_0 = -32t \Rightarrow s = \int -32t\,dt$
$= -16t^2 + s_0 = -16t^2 + 7000$. At $t = 13$ sec, $s = -16(13)^2 + 7000 = 4296\ ft$ when B's chute opens;

   (c) After the chutes open, $v = -16\ ft/sec \Rightarrow s = \int -16\,dt = -16t + s_0$. For A, $s_0 = 6144\ ft$ and for B,
$s_0 = 4296\ ft$. Therefore, for A, $s = -16t + 6144$ and for B, $s = -16t + 4296$. When they hit the ground,
$s = 0 \Rightarrow$ for A, $0 = -16t + 6144 \Rightarrow t = \frac{6144}{16} = 384$ seconds, and for B, $0 = -16t + 4296 \Rightarrow t = \frac{4296}{16}$
$= 268.5$ seconds to hit the ground after the chutes open. Since B's chute opens 58 seconds after A's opens
$\Rightarrow$ B hits the ground first.

## CHAPTER 5  ADDITIONAL AND ADVANCED EXERCISES

1. (a) Yes, because $\int_0^1 f(x)\,dx = \frac{1}{7}\int_0^1 7f(x)\,dx = \frac{1}{7}(7) = 1$

   (b) No. For example, $\int_0^1 8x\,dx = [4x^2]_0^1 = 4$, but $\int_0^1 \sqrt{8x}\,dx = \left[2\sqrt{2}\left(\frac{x^{3/2}}{\frac{3}{2}}\right)\right]_0^1 = \frac{4\sqrt{2}}{3}(1^{3/2} - 0^{3/2}) = \frac{4\sqrt{2}}{3} \neq \sqrt{4}$

2. (a) True: $\int_5^2 f(x)\,dx = -\int_2^5 f(x)\,dx = -3$

   (b) True: $\int_{-2}^5 [f(x) + g(x)]\,dx = \int_{-2}^5 f(x)\,dx + \int_{-2}^5 g(x)\,dx = \int_{-2}^2 f(x)\,dx + \int_2^5 f(x)\,dx + \int_{-2}^5 g(x)\,dx = 4 + 3 + 2 = 9$

(c)  False: $\int_{-2}^{5} f(x)\,dx = 4 + 3 = 7 > 2 = \int_{-2}^{5} g(x)\,dx \Rightarrow \int_{-2}^{5}[f(x) - g(x)]\,dx > 0 \Rightarrow \int_{-2}^{5}[g(x) - f(x)]\,dx < 0.$

On the other hand, $f(x) \le g(x) \Rightarrow [g(x) - f(x)] \ge 0 \Rightarrow \int_{-2}^{5}[g(x) - f(x)]\,dx \ge 0$ which is a contradiction.

3.  $y = \frac{1}{a}\int_0^x f(t) \sin a(x - t)\,dt = \frac{1}{a}\int_0^x f(t) \sin ax \cos at\,dt - \frac{1}{a}\int_0^x f(t) \cos ax \sin at\,dt$

$= \frac{\sin ax}{a}\int_0^x f(t) \cos at\,dt - \frac{\cos ax}{a}\int_0^x f(t) \sin at\,dt \Rightarrow \frac{dy}{dx} = \cos ax \left(\int_0^x f(t) \cos at\,dt\right)$

$+ \frac{\sin ax}{a}\left(\frac{d}{dx}\int_0^x f(t) \cos at\,dt\right) + \sin ax \int_0^x f(t) \sin at\,dt - \frac{\cos ax}{a}\left(\frac{d}{dx}\int_0^x f(t) \sin at\,dt\right)$

$= \cos ax \int_0^x f(t) \cos at\,dt + \frac{\sin ax}{a}(f(x) \cos ax) + \sin ax \int_0^x f(t) \sin at\,dt - \frac{\cos ax}{a}(f(x) \sin ax)$

$\Rightarrow \frac{dy}{dx} = \cos ax \int_0^x f(t) \cos at\,dt + \sin ax \int_0^x f(t) \sin at\,dt.$  Next,

$\frac{d^2y}{dx^2} = -a \sin ax \int_0^x f(t) \cos at\,dt + (\cos ax)\left(\frac{d}{dx}\int_0^x f(t) \cos at\,dt\right) + a \cos ax \int_0^x f(t) \sin at\,dt$

$+ (\sin ax)\left(\frac{d}{dx}\int_0^x f(t) \sin at\,dt\right) = -a \sin ax \int_0^x f(t) \cos at\,dt + (\cos ax)f(x) \cos ax$

$+ a \cos ax \int_0^x f(t) \sin at\,dt + (\sin ax)f(x) \sin ax = -a \sin ax \int_0^x f(t) \cos at\,dt + a \cos ax \int_0^x f(t) \sin at\,dt + f(x).$

Therefore, $y'' + a^2y = a \cos ax \int_0^x f(t) \sin at\,dt - a \sin ax \int_0^x f(t) \cos at\,dt + f(x)$

$+ a^2\left(\frac{\sin ax}{a}\int_0^x f(t) \cos at\,dt - \frac{\cos ax}{a}\int_0^x f(t) \sin at\,dt\right) = f(x).$  Note also that $y'(0) = y(0) = 0.$

4.  $x = \int_0^y \frac{1}{\sqrt{1 + 4t^2}}\,dt \Rightarrow \frac{d}{dx}(x) = \frac{d}{dx}\int_0^y \frac{1}{\sqrt{1 + 4t^2}}\,dt = \frac{d}{dy}\left[\int_0^y \frac{1}{\sqrt{1 + 4t^2}}\,dt\right]\left(\frac{dy}{dx}\right)$ from the chain rule

$\Rightarrow 1 = \frac{1}{\sqrt{1 + 4y^2}}\left(\frac{dy}{dx}\right) \Rightarrow \frac{dy}{dx} = \sqrt{1 + 4y^2}.$ Then $\frac{d^2y}{dx^2} = \frac{d}{dx}\left(\sqrt{1 + 4y^2}\right) = \frac{d}{dy}\left(\sqrt{1 + 4y^2}\right)\left(\frac{dy}{dx}\right)$

$= \frac{1}{2}(1 + 4y^2)^{-1/2}(8y)\left(\frac{dy}{dx}\right) = \frac{4y\left(\frac{dy}{dx}\right)}{\sqrt{1 + 4y^2}} = \frac{4y\left(\sqrt{1 + 4y^2}\right)}{\sqrt{1 + 4y^2}} = 4y.$ Thus $\frac{d^2y}{dx^2} = 4y$, and the constant of

proportionality is 4.

5.  (a)  $\int_0^{x^2} f(t)\,dt = x \cos \pi x \Rightarrow \frac{d}{dx}\int_0^{x^2} f(t)\,dt = \cos \pi x - \pi x \sin \pi x \Rightarrow f(x^2)(2x) = \cos \pi x - \pi x \sin \pi x$

$\Rightarrow f(x^2) = \frac{\cos \pi x - \pi x \sin \pi x}{2x}.$ Thus, $x = 2 \Rightarrow f(4) = \frac{\cos 2\pi - 2\pi \sin 2\pi}{4} = \frac{1}{4}$

(b)  $\int_0^{f(x)} t^2\,dt = \left[\frac{t^3}{3}\right]_0^{f(x)} = \frac{1}{3}(f(x))^3 \Rightarrow \frac{1}{3}(f(x))^3 = x \cos \pi x \Rightarrow (f(x))^3 = 3x \cos \pi x \Rightarrow f(x) = \sqrt[3]{3x \cos \pi x}$

$\Rightarrow f(4) = \sqrt[3]{3(4) \cos 4\pi} = \sqrt[3]{12}$

6.  $\int_0^a f(x)\,dx = \frac{a^2}{2} + \frac{a}{2}\sin a + \frac{\pi}{2}\cos a.$ Let $F(a) = \int_0^a f(t)\,dt \Rightarrow f(a) = F'(a).$ Now $F(a) = \frac{a^2}{2} + \frac{a}{2}\sin a + \frac{\pi}{2}\cos a$

$\Rightarrow f(a) = F'(a) = a + \frac{1}{2}\sin a + \frac{a}{2}\cos a - \frac{\pi}{2}\sin a \Rightarrow f\left(\frac{\pi}{2}\right) = \frac{\pi}{2} + \frac{1}{2}\sin \frac{\pi}{2} + \frac{\left(\frac{\pi}{2}\right)}{2}\cos \frac{\pi}{2} - \frac{\pi}{2}\sin \frac{\pi}{2} = \frac{\pi}{2} + \frac{1}{2} - \frac{\pi}{2} = \frac{1}{2}$

7.  $\int_1^b f(x)\,dx = \sqrt{b^2 + 1} - \sqrt{2} \Rightarrow f(b) = \frac{d}{db}\int_1^b f(x)\,dx = \frac{1}{2}(b^2 + 1)^{-1/2}(2b) = \frac{b}{\sqrt{b^2 + 1}} \Rightarrow f(x) = \frac{x}{\sqrt{x^2 + 1}}$

8.  The derivative of the left side of the equation is: $\frac{d}{dx}\left[\int_0^x \left[\int_0^u f(t)\,dt\right]du\right] = \int_0^x f(t)\,dt$; the derivative of the right

side of the equation is: $\frac{d}{dx}\left[\int_0^x f(u)(x - u)\,du\right] = \frac{d}{dx}\int_0^x f(u)\,x\,du - \frac{d}{dx}\int_0^x u\,f(u)\,du$

$= \frac{d}{dx}\left[x\int_0^x f(u)\,du\right] - \frac{d}{dx}\int_0^x u\,f(u)\,du = \int_0^x f(u)\,du + x\left[\frac{d}{dx}\int_0^x f(u)\,du\right] - xf(x) = \int_0^x f(u)\,du + xf(x) - xf(x)$

$= \int_0^x f(u)\,du.$ Since each side has the same derivative, they differ by a constant, and since both sides equal 0

when $x = 0$, the constant must be 0. Therefore, $\int_0^x \left[\int_0^u f(t)\,dt\right] du = \int_0^x f(u)(x - u)\,du.$

9. $\frac{dy}{dx} = 3x^2 + 2 \Rightarrow y = \int (3x^2 + 2)\,dx = x^3 + 2x + C.$ Then $(1, -1)$ on the curve $\Rightarrow 1^3 + 2(1) + C = -1 \Rightarrow C = -4$
   $\Rightarrow y = x^3 + 2x - 4$

10. The acceleration due to gravity downward is $-32$ ft/sec$^2$ $\Rightarrow$ $v = \int -32\,dt = -32t + v_0$, where $v_0$ is the initial
    velocity $\Rightarrow$ $v = -32t + 32 \Rightarrow s = \int (-32t + 32)\,dt = -16t^2 + 32t + C.$ If the release point, at $t = 0$, is $s = 0$, then
    $C = 0 \Rightarrow s = -16t^2 + 32t.$ Then $s = 17 \Rightarrow 17 = -16t^2 + 32t \Rightarrow 16t^2 - 32t + 17 = 0.$ The discriminant of this
    quadratic equation is $-64$ which says there is no real time when $s = 17$ ft. You had better duck.

11. $\int_{-8}^3 f(x)\,dx = \int_{-8}^0 x^{2/3}\,dx + \int_0^3 -4\,dx$

    $= \left[\frac{3}{5}x^{5/3}\right]_{-8}^0 + [-4x]_0^3$

    $= \left(0 - \frac{3}{5}(-8)^{5/3}\right) + (-4(3) - 0) = \frac{96}{5} - 12$

    $= \frac{36}{5}$

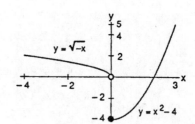

12. $\int_{-4}^3 f(x)\,dx = \int_{-4}^0 \sqrt{-x}\,dx + \int_0^3 (x^2 - 4)\,dx$

    $= \left[-\frac{2}{3}(-x)^{3/2}\right]_{-4}^0 + \left[\frac{x^3}{3} - 4x\right]_0^3$

    $= \left[0 - \left(-\frac{2}{3}(4)^{3/2}\right)\right] + \left[\left(\frac{3^3}{3} - 4(3)\right) - 0\right]$

    $= \frac{16}{3} - 3 = \frac{7}{3}$

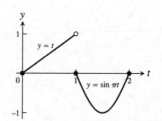

13. $\int_0^2 g(t)\,dt = \int_0^1 t\,dt + \int_1^2 \sin \pi t\,dt$

    $= \left[\frac{t^2}{2}\right]_0^1 + \left[-\frac{1}{\pi}\cos \pi t\right]_1^2$

    $= \left(\frac{1}{2} - 0\right) + \left[-\frac{1}{\pi}\cos 2\pi - \left(-\frac{1}{\pi}\cos \pi\right)\right]$

    $= \frac{1}{2} - \frac{2}{\pi}$

14. $\int_0^2 h(z)\,dz = \int_0^1 \sqrt{1 - z}\,dz + \int_1^2 (7z - 6)^{-1/3}\,dz$

    $= \left[-\frac{2}{3}(1 - z)^{3/2}\right]_0^1 + \left[\frac{3}{14}(7z - 6)^{2/3}\right]_1^2$

    $= \left[-\frac{2}{3}(1 - 1)^{3/2} - \left(-\frac{2}{3}(1 - 0)^{3/2}\right)\right]$

    $\quad + \left[\frac{3}{14}(7(2) - 6)^{2/3} - \frac{3}{14}(7(1) - 6)^{2/3}\right]$

    $= \frac{2}{3} + \left(\frac{6}{7} - \frac{3}{14}\right) = \frac{55}{42}$

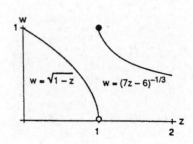

15. $\int_{-2}^{2} f(x)\,dx = \int_{-2}^{-1} dx + \int_{-1}^{1}(1-x^2)\,dx + \int_{1}^{2} 2\,dx$

$= [x]_{-2}^{-1} + \left[x - \frac{x^3}{3}\right]_{-1}^{1} + [2x]_{1}^{2}$

$= (-1 - (-2)) + \left[\left(1 - \frac{1^3}{3}\right) - \left(-1 - \frac{(-1)^3}{3}\right)\right] + \left[2(2) - 2(1)\right]$

$= 1 + \frac{2}{3} - \left(-\frac{2}{3}\right) + 4 - 2 = \frac{13}{3}$

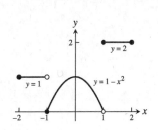

16. $\int_{-1}^{2} h(r)\,dr = \int_{-1}^{0} r\,dr + \int_{0}^{1}(1-r^2)\,dr + \int_{1}^{2} dr$

$= \left[\frac{r^2}{2}\right]_{-1}^{0} + \left[r - \frac{r^3}{3}\right]_{0}^{1} + [r]_{1}^{2}$

$= \left(0 - \frac{(-1)^2}{2}\right) + \left(\left(1 - \frac{1^3}{3}\right) - 0\right) + (2 - 1)$

$= -\frac{1}{2} + \frac{2}{3} + 1 = \frac{7}{6}$

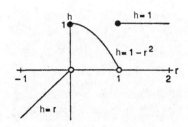

17. Ave. value $= \frac{1}{b-a}\int_{a}^{b} f(x)\,dx = \frac{1}{2-0}\int_{0}^{2} f(x)\,dx = \frac{1}{2}\left[\int_{0}^{1} x\,dx + \int_{1}^{2}(x-1)\,dx\right] = \frac{1}{2}\left[\frac{x^2}{2}\right]_{0}^{1} + \frac{1}{2}\left[\frac{x^2}{2} - x\right]_{1}^{2}$

$= \frac{1}{2}\left[\left(\frac{1^2}{2} - 0\right) + \left(\frac{2^2}{2} - 2\right) - \left(\frac{1^2}{2} - 1\right)\right] = \frac{1}{2}$

18. Ave. value $= \frac{1}{b-a}\int_{a}^{b} f(x)\,dx = \frac{1}{3-0}\int_{0}^{3} f(x)\,dx = \frac{1}{3}\left[\int_{0}^{1} dx + \int_{1}^{2} 0\,dx + \int_{2}^{3} dx\right] = \frac{1}{3}\left[1 - 0 + 0 + 3 - 2\right] = \frac{2}{3}$

19. Let $f(x) = x^5$ on $[0, 1]$. Partition $[0, 1]$ into n subintervals with $\Delta x = \frac{1-0}{n} = \frac{1}{n}$. Then $\frac{1}{n}, \frac{2}{n}, \ldots, \frac{n}{n}$ are the

right-hand endpoints of the subintervals. Since f is increasing on $[0, 1]$, $U = \sum_{j=1}^{\infty}\left(\frac{j}{n}\right)^5\left(\frac{1}{n}\right)$ is the upper sum for

$f(x) = x^5$ on $[0, 1] \Rightarrow \lim_{n\to\infty}\sum_{j=1}^{\infty}\left(\frac{j}{n}\right)^5\left(\frac{1}{n}\right) = \lim_{n\to\infty}\frac{1}{n}\left[\left(\frac{1}{n}\right)^5 + \left(\frac{2}{n}\right)^5 + \ldots + \left(\frac{n}{n}\right)^5\right] = \lim_{n\to\infty}\left[\frac{1^5 + 2^5 + \ldots + n^5}{n^6}\right]$

$= \int_{0}^{1} x^5\,dx = \left[\frac{x^6}{6}\right]_{0}^{1} = \frac{1}{6}$

20. Let $f(x) = x^3$ on $[0, 1]$. Partition $[0, 1]$ into n subintervals with $\Delta x = \frac{1-0}{n} = \frac{1}{n}$. Then $\frac{1}{n}, \frac{2}{n}, \ldots, \frac{n}{n}$ are the

right-hand endpoints of the subintervals. Since f is increasing on $[0, 1]$, $U = \sum_{j=1}^{\infty}\left(\frac{j}{n}\right)^3\left(\frac{1}{n}\right)$ is the upper sum for

$f(x) = x^3$ on $[0, 1] \Rightarrow \lim_{n\to\infty}\sum_{j=1}^{\infty}\left(\frac{j}{n}\right)^3\left(\frac{1}{n}\right) = \lim_{n\to\infty}\frac{1}{n}\left[\left(\frac{1}{n}\right)^3 + \left(\frac{2}{n}\right)^3 + \ldots + \left(\frac{n}{n}\right)^3\right] = \lim_{n\to\infty}\left[\frac{1^3 + 2^3 + \ldots + n^3}{n^4}\right]$

$= \int_{0}^{1} x^3\,dx = \left[\frac{x^4}{4}\right]_{0}^{1} = \frac{1}{4}$

21. Let $y = f(x)$ on $[0, 1]$. Partition $[0, 1]$ into n subintervals with $\Delta x = \frac{1-0}{n} = \frac{1}{n}$. Then $\frac{1}{n}, \frac{2}{n}, \ldots, \frac{n}{n}$ are the

right-hand endpoints of the subintervals. Since f is continuous on $[0, 1]$, $\sum_{j=1}^{\infty} f\left(\frac{j}{n}\right)\left(\frac{1}{n}\right)$ is a Riemann sum of

$y = f(x)$ on $[0, 1] \Rightarrow \lim_{n\to\infty}\sum_{j=1}^{\infty} f\left(\frac{j}{n}\right)\left(\frac{1}{n}\right) = \lim_{n\to\infty}\frac{1}{n}\left[f\left(\frac{1}{n}\right) + f\left(\frac{2}{n}\right) + \ldots + f\left(\frac{n}{n}\right)\right] = \int_{0}^{1} f(x)\,dx$

22. (a) $\lim_{n\to\infty}\frac{1}{n^2}[2 + 4 + 6 + \ldots + 2n] = \lim_{n\to\infty}\frac{1}{n}\left[\frac{2}{n} + \frac{4}{n} + \frac{6}{n} + \ldots + \frac{2n}{n}\right] = \int_{0}^{1} 2x\,dx = [x^2]_{0}^{1} = 1$, where $f(x) = 2x$

on $[0, 1]$ (see Exercise 21)

23. $y = 3 - 2x, 0 \le x \le 2 \Rightarrow \frac{dy}{dx} = -2 \Rightarrow L = \int_0^2 \sqrt{1 + (-2)^2}\, dx = \int_0^2 \sqrt{5}\, dx = \left[\sqrt{5}\, x\right]_0^2 = 2\sqrt{5}$.

$d = \sqrt{(2-0)^2 + (3-(-1))^2} = 2\sqrt{5}$

24. Consider the circle $x^2 + y^2 = r^2$, we will find the length of the portion in the first quadrant, and multiply our result by 4.

$y = \sqrt{r^2 - x^2}, 0 \le x \le r \Rightarrow \frac{dy}{dx} = \frac{-x}{\sqrt{r^2-x^2}} \Rightarrow L = 4\int_0^r \sqrt{1 + \left[\frac{-x}{\sqrt{r^2-x^2}}\right]^2}\, dx = 4\int_0^r \sqrt{1 + \frac{x^2}{r^2-x^2}}\, dx = 4\int_0^r \sqrt{\frac{r^2}{r^2-x^2}}\, dx$

$= 4\int_0^r \frac{r}{\sqrt{r^2-x^2}}\, dx = 4r\int_0^r \frac{dx}{\sqrt{r^2-x^2}}$

25. $9x^2 = y(y-3)^2 \Rightarrow \frac{d}{dy}\left[9x^2\right] = \frac{d}{dy}\left[y(y-3)^2\right] \Rightarrow 18x\frac{dx}{dy} = 2y(y-3) + (y-3)^2 = 3(y-3)(y-1) \Rightarrow \frac{dx}{dy} = \frac{(y-3)(y-1)}{6x}$

$\Rightarrow dx = \frac{(y-3)(y-1)}{6x}dy; ds^2 = dx^2 + dy^2 = \left[\frac{(y-3)(y-1)}{6x}dy\right]^2 + dy^2 = \frac{(y-3)^2(y-1)^2}{36x^2}dy^2 + dy^2 = \frac{(y-3)^2(y-1)^2}{4y(y-3)^2}dy^2 + dy^2$

$= \left[\frac{(y-1)^2}{4y} + 1\right]dy^2 = \frac{y^2-2y+1+4y}{4y}dy^2 = \frac{(y+1)^2}{4y}dy^2$

26. $4x^2 - y^2 = 64 \Rightarrow \frac{d}{dx}\left[4x^2 - y^2\right] = \frac{d}{dx}\left[64\right] \Rightarrow 8x - 2y\frac{dy}{dx} = 0 \Rightarrow \frac{dy}{dx} = \frac{4x}{y} \Rightarrow dy = \frac{4x}{y}dx; ds^2 = dx^2 + dy^2$

$= dx^2 + \left[\frac{4x}{y}dx\right]^2 = dx^2 + \frac{16x^2}{y^2}dx^2 = \left(1 + \frac{16x^2}{y^2}\right)dx^2 = \frac{y^2+16x^2}{y^2}dx^2 = \frac{4x^2-64+16x^2}{y^2}dx^2 = \frac{20x^2-64}{y^2}dx^2 = \frac{4}{y^2}(5x^2 - 16)dx^2$

27. $\sqrt{2}\,x = \int_0^x \sqrt{1 + \left(\frac{dy}{dt}\right)^2}\, dt, x \ge 0 \Rightarrow \sqrt{2} = \sqrt{1 + \left(\frac{dy}{dx}\right)^2} \Rightarrow \frac{dy}{dx} = \pm 1 \Rightarrow y = f(x) = \pm x + C$ where C is any real number.

28. (a) From the accompanying figure and definition of the differential (change along the tangent line) we see that $dy = f'(x_{k-1})\triangle x_k \Rightarrow$ length of kth tangent fin is $\sqrt{(\triangle x_k)^2 + (dy)^2} = \sqrt{(\triangle x_k)^2 + [f'(x_{k-1})\triangle x_k]^2}$.

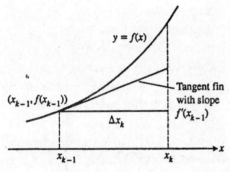

(b) Length of curve $= \lim\limits_{n \to \infty} \sum\limits_{k=1}^{n} (\text{length of kth tangent fin}) = \lim\limits_{n \to \infty} \sum\limits_{k=1}^{n} \sqrt{(\triangle x_k)^2 + [f'(x_{k-1})\triangle x_k]^2}$

$= \lim\limits_{n \to \infty} \sum\limits_{k=1}^{n} \sqrt{1 + [f'(x_{k-1})]^2}\, \triangle x_k = \int_a^b \sqrt{1 + [f'(x)]^2}\, dx$

29. $x^2 + y^2 = 1 \Rightarrow y = \sqrt{1 - x^2}; P = \{0, \frac{1}{4}, \frac{1}{2}, \frac{3}{4}, 1\} \Rightarrow L \approx \sum\limits_{k=1}^{4} \sqrt{(x_i - x_{i-1})^2 + (y_i - y_{i-1})^2} = \sqrt{\left(\frac{1}{4} - 0\right)^2 + \left(\frac{\sqrt{15}}{4} - 1\right)^2}$

$+ \sqrt{\left(\frac{1}{2} - \frac{1}{4}\right)^2 + \left(\frac{\sqrt{3}}{2} - \frac{\sqrt{15}}{4}\right)^2} + \sqrt{\left(\frac{3}{4} - \frac{1}{2}\right)^2 + \left(\frac{\sqrt{7}}{4} - \frac{\sqrt{3}}{2}\right)^2} + \sqrt{\left(1 - \frac{3}{4}\right)^2 + \left(0 - \frac{\sqrt{7}}{4}\right)^2} \approx 1.55225$

30. Let $(x_1, y_1)$ and $(x_2, y_2)$, with $x_2 > x_1$, lie on $y = mx + b$, where $m = \frac{y_2-y_1}{x_2-x_1}$, then $\frac{dy}{dx} = m \Rightarrow L = \int_{x_1}^{x_2} \sqrt{1 + m^2}\, dx$

$= \sqrt{1 + m^2}\,[x]_{x_1}^{x_2} = \sqrt{1 + m^2}(x_2 - x_1) = \sqrt{1 + \left(\frac{y_2-y_1}{x_2-x_1}\right)^2}(x_2 - x_1) = \sqrt{\frac{(x_2-x_1)^2 + (y_2-y_1)^2}{(x_2-x_1)^2}}(x_2 - x_1)$

$\frac{\sqrt{(x_2-x_1)^2 + (y_2-y_1)^2}}{(x_2-x_1)}(x_2 - x_1) = \sqrt{(x_2 - x_1)^2 + (y_2 - y_1)^2}$.

31. $y = 2x^{3/2} \Rightarrow \frac{dy}{dx} = 3x^{1/2}$; $L(x) = \int_0^x \sqrt{1 + \left[3t^{1/2}\right]^2}\, dt = \int_0^x \sqrt{1 + 9t}\, dt$; $[u = 1 + 9t \Rightarrow du = 9dt, t = 0 \Rightarrow u = 1,$

$t = x \Rightarrow u = 1 + 9x] \rightarrow \frac{1}{9} \int_1^{1+9x} \sqrt{u}\, du = \frac{2}{27}\left[u^{3/2}\right]_1^{1+9x} = \frac{2}{27}(1 + 9x)^{3/2} - \frac{2}{27}$; $L(1) = \frac{2}{27}(10)^{3/2} - \frac{2}{27} = \frac{2\left(10\sqrt{10} - 1\right)}{27}$

32. $y = \frac{x^3}{3} + x^2 + x + \frac{1}{4x+4} \Rightarrow \frac{dy}{dx} = x^2 + 2x + 1 - \frac{1}{4(x+1)^2} = (x+1)^2 - \frac{1}{4(x+1)^2}$;

$L(x) = \int_0^x \sqrt{1 + \left[(t+1)^2 - \frac{1}{4(t+1)^2}\right]^2}\, dt = \int_0^x \sqrt{1 + \left[\frac{4(t+1)^4 - 1}{4(t+1)^2}\right]^2}\, dt = \int_0^x \sqrt{1 + \frac{[4(t+1)^4 - 1]^2}{16(t+1)^4}}\, dt$

$= \int_0^x \sqrt{\frac{16(t+1)^4 + 16(t+1)^8 - 8(t+1)^4 + 1}{16(t+1)^4}}\, dt = \int_0^x \sqrt{\frac{16(t+1)^8 + 8(t+1)^4 + 1}{16(t+1)^4}}\, dt = \int_0^x \sqrt{\frac{[4(t+1)^4 + 1]^2}{16(t+1)^4}}\, dt$

$= \int_0^x \frac{4(t+1)^4 + 1}{4(t+1)^2}\, dt = \int_0^x \left[(t+1)^2 + \frac{1}{4(t+1)^2}\right] dt$; $[u = t + 1 \Rightarrow du = dt, t = 0 \Rightarrow u = 1, t = x \Rightarrow u = x + 1]$

$\rightarrow \int_1^{x+1} \left[u^2 + \frac{1}{4}u^{-2}\right] du = \left[\frac{1}{3}u^3 - \frac{1}{4}u^{-1}\right]_1^{x+1} = \left(\frac{1}{3}(x+1)^3 - \frac{1}{4(x+1)}\right) - \left(\frac{1}{3} - \frac{1}{4}\right) = \frac{1}{3}(x+1)^3 - \frac{1}{4(x+1)} - \frac{1}{12}$;

$L(1) = \frac{8}{3} - \frac{1}{8} - \frac{1}{12} = \frac{59}{24}$

33-38.    Example CAS commands:

Maple:

```
with( plots );
with( Student[Calculus1] );
with( student );
f := x -> sqrt(1-x^2);a := -1;
b := 1;
N := [2, 4, 8 ];
for n in N do
  xx := [seq( a+i*(b-a)/n, i=0..n )];
  pts := [seq([x,f(x)],x=xx)];
  L := simplify(add( distance(pts[i+1],pts[i]), i=1..n ));          # (b)
  T := sprintf("#33(a) (Section 6.3)\nn=%3d  L=%8.5f\n", n, L );
  P[n] := plot( [f(x),pts], x=a..b, title=T ):                      # (a)
end do:
display( [seq(P[n],n=N)], insequence=true, scaling=constrained );
L := ArcLength( f(x), x=a..b, output=integral ):
L = evalf( L );                                                      # (c)
```

33-38.    Example CAS commands:

Mathematica: (assigned function and values for a, b, and n may vary)

```
Clear[x, f]
{a, b} = {-1, 1}; f[x_] = Sqrt[1 - x^2]
p1 = Plot[f[x], {x, a, b}]
n = 8;
pts = Table[{xn, f[xn]}, {xn, a, b, (b - a)/n}]// N
Show[{p1,Graphics[{Line[pts]}]}]
Sum[ Sqrt[ (pts[[i + 1, 1]] - pts[[i, 1]])^2 + (pts[[i + 1, 2]] - pts[[i, 2]])^2], {i, 1, n}]
NIntegrate[ Sqrt[ 1 + f'[x]^2],{x, a, b}]
```

## 6.4 AREAS OF SURFACES OF REVOLUTION

1.  (a) $\frac{dy}{dx} = \sec^2 x \Rightarrow \left(\frac{dy}{dx}\right)^2 = \sec^4 x$

    $\Rightarrow S = 2\pi \int_0^{\pi/4} (\tan x) \sqrt{1 + \sec^4 x}\ dx$

    (c) $S \approx 3.84$

    (b)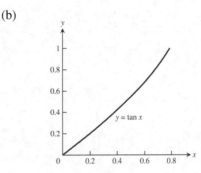

2.  (a) $\frac{dy}{dx} = 2x \Rightarrow \left(\frac{dy}{dx}\right)^2 = 4x^2$

    $\Rightarrow S = 2\pi \int_0^2 x^2 \sqrt{1 + 4x^2}\ dx$

    (c) $S \approx 53.23$

    (b)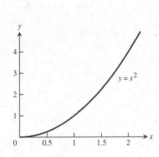

3.  (a) $xy = 1 \Rightarrow x = \frac{1}{y} \Rightarrow \frac{dx}{dy} = -\frac{1}{y^2} \Rightarrow \left(\frac{dx}{dy}\right)^2 = \frac{1}{y^4}$

    $\Rightarrow S = 2\pi \int_1^2 \frac{1}{y} \sqrt{1 + y^{-4}}\ dy$

    (c) $S \approx 5.02$

    (b)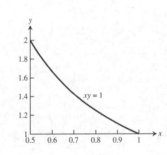

4.  (a) $\frac{dx}{dy} = \cos y \Rightarrow \left(\frac{dx}{dy}\right)^2 = \cos^2 y$

    $\Rightarrow S = 2\pi \int_0^{\pi} (\sin y) \sqrt{1 + \cos^2 y}\ dy$

    (c) $S \approx 14.42$

    (b)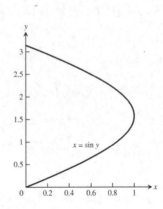

5.  (a) $x^{1/2} + y^{1/2} = 3 \Rightarrow y = \left(3 - x^{1/2}\right)^2$

    $\Rightarrow \frac{dy}{dx} = 2\left(3 - x^{1/2}\right)\left(-\frac{1}{2} x^{-1/2}\right)$

    $\Rightarrow \left(\frac{dy}{dx}\right)^2 = \left(1 - 3x^{-1/2}\right)^2$

    $\Rightarrow S = 2\pi \int_1^4 \left(3 - x^{1/2}\right)^2 \sqrt{1 + \left(1 - 3x^{-1/2}\right)^2}\ dx$

    (c) $S \approx 63.37$

    (b)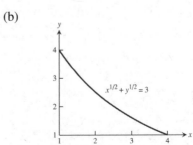

6.  (a) $\frac{dx}{dy} = 1 + y^{-1/2} \Rightarrow \left(\frac{dx}{dy}\right)^2 = \left(1 + y^{-1/2}\right)^2$

    $\Rightarrow S = 2\pi \int_1^2 \left(y + 2\sqrt{y}\right)\sqrt{1 + \left(1 + y^{-1/2}\right)^2}\, dx$

    (c) $S \approx 51.33$

(b)

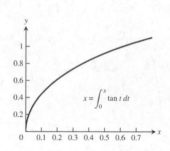

7.  (a) $\frac{dx}{dy} = \tan y \Rightarrow \left(\frac{dx}{dy}\right)^2 = \tan^2 y$

    $\Rightarrow S = 2\pi \int_0^{\pi/3}\left(\int_0^y \tan t\, dt\right)\sqrt{1 + \tan^2 y}\, dy$

    $= 2\pi \int_0^{\pi/3}\left(\int_0^y \tan t\, dt\right)\sec y\, dy$

    (c) $S \approx 2.08$

(b)

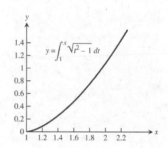

8.  (a) $\frac{dy}{dx} = \sqrt{x^2 - 1} \Rightarrow \left(\frac{dy}{dx}\right)^2 = x^2 - 1$

    $\Rightarrow S = 2\pi \int_1^{\sqrt{5}}\left(\int_1^x \sqrt{t^2 - 1}\, dt\right)\sqrt{1 + (x^2 - 1)}\, dx$

    $= 2\pi \int_1^{\sqrt{5}}\left(\int_1^x \sqrt{t^2 - 1}\, dt\right) x\, dx$

    (c) $S \approx 8.55$

(b)

9.  $y = \frac{x}{2} \Rightarrow \frac{dy}{dx} = \frac{1}{2};\ S = \int_a^b 2\pi y\sqrt{1 + \left(\frac{dy}{dx}\right)^2}\, dx \Rightarrow S = \int_0^4 2\pi \left(\frac{x}{2}\right)\sqrt{1 + \frac{1}{4}}\, dx = \frac{\pi\sqrt{5}}{2}\int_0^4 x\, dx$

    $= \frac{\pi\sqrt{5}}{2}\left[\frac{x^2}{2}\right]_0^4 = 4\pi\sqrt{5};$ Geometry formula: base circumference $= 2\pi(2)$, slant height $= \sqrt{4^2 + 2^2} = 2\sqrt{5}$

    $\Rightarrow$ Lateral surface area $= \frac{1}{2}(4\pi)\left(2\sqrt{5}\right) = 4\pi\sqrt{5}$ in agreement with the integral value

10. $y = \frac{x}{2} \Rightarrow x = 2y \Rightarrow \frac{dx}{dy} = 2;\ S = \int_c^d 2\pi x\sqrt{1 + \left(\frac{dx}{dy}\right)^2}\, dy = \int_0^2 2\pi \cdot 2y\sqrt{1 + 2^2}\, dy = 4\pi\sqrt{5}\int_0^2 y\, dy = 2\pi\sqrt{5}\left[y^2\right]_0^2$

    $= 2\pi\sqrt{5} \cdot 4 = 8\pi\sqrt{5};$ Geometry formula: base circumference $= 2\pi(4)$, slant height $= \sqrt{4^2 + 2^2} = 2\sqrt{5}$

    $\Rightarrow$ Lateral surface area $= \frac{1}{2}(8\pi)\left(2\sqrt{5}\right) = 8\pi\sqrt{5}$ in agreement with the integral value

11. $\frac{dy}{dx} = \frac{1}{2};\ S = \int_a^b 2\pi y\sqrt{1 + \left(\frac{dy}{dx}\right)^2}\, dx = \int_1^3 2\pi \frac{(x+1)}{2}\sqrt{1 + \left(\frac{1}{2}\right)^2}\, dx = \frac{\pi\sqrt{5}}{2}\int_1^3 (x + 1)\, dx = \frac{\pi\sqrt{5}}{2}\left[\frac{x^2}{2} + x\right]_1^3$

    $= \frac{\pi\sqrt{5}}{2}\left[\left(\frac{9}{2} + 3\right) - \left(\frac{1}{2} + 1\right)\right] = \frac{\pi\sqrt{5}}{2}(4 + 2) = 3\pi\sqrt{5};$ Geometry formula: $r_1 = \frac{1}{2} + \frac{1}{2} = 1,\ r_2 = \frac{3}{2} + \frac{1}{2} = 2,$

    slant height $= \sqrt{(2 - 1)^2 + (3 - 1)^2} = \sqrt{5} \Rightarrow$ Frustum surface area $= \pi(r_1 + r_2) \times$ slant height $= \pi(1 + 2)\sqrt{5}$

    $= 3\pi\sqrt{5}$ in agreement with the integral value

12. $y = \frac{x}{2} + \frac{1}{2} \Rightarrow x = 2y - 1 \Rightarrow \frac{dx}{dy} = 2;\ S = \int_c^d 2\pi x\sqrt{1 + \left(\frac{dx}{dy}\right)^2}\, dy = \int_1^2 2\pi(2y - 1)\sqrt{1 + 4}\, dy = 2\pi\sqrt{5}\int_1^2 (2y - 1)\, dy$

    $= 2\pi\sqrt{5}\left[y^2 - y\right]_1^2 = 2\pi\sqrt{5}\left[(4 - 2) - (1 - 1)\right] = 4\pi\sqrt{5};$ Geometry formula: $r_1 = 1,\ r_2 = 3,$

slant height $= \sqrt{(2-1)^2 + (3-1)^2} = \sqrt{5} \Rightarrow$ Frustum surface area $= \pi(1+3)\sqrt{5} = 4\pi\sqrt{5}$ in agreement with the integral value

13. $\frac{dy}{dx} = \frac{x^2}{3} \Rightarrow \left(\frac{dy}{dx}\right)^2 = \frac{x^4}{9} \Rightarrow S = \int_0^2 \frac{2\pi x^3}{9} \sqrt{1 + \frac{x^4}{9}}\, dx;$

$\left[ u = 1 + \frac{x^4}{9} \Rightarrow du = \frac{4}{9} x^3\, dx \Rightarrow \frac{1}{4} du = \frac{x^3}{9}\, dx; \right.$

$x = 0 \Rightarrow u = 1, x = 2 \Rightarrow u = \frac{25}{9} \Big]$

$\rightarrow S = 2\pi \int_1^{25/9} u^{1/2} \cdot \frac{1}{4}\, du = \frac{\pi}{2} \left[ \frac{2}{3} u^{3/2} \right]_1^{25/9}$

$= \frac{\pi}{3} \left( \frac{125}{27} - 1 \right) = \frac{\pi}{3} \left( \frac{125-27}{27} \right) = \frac{98\pi}{81}$

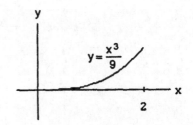

14. $\frac{dy}{dx} = \frac{1}{2} x^{-1/2} \Rightarrow \left(\frac{dy}{dx}\right)^2 = \frac{1}{4x}$

$\Rightarrow S = \int_{3/4}^{15/4} 2\pi \sqrt{x} \sqrt{1 + \frac{1}{4x}}\, dx$

$= 2\pi \int_{3/4}^{15/4} \sqrt{x + \frac{1}{4}}\, dx = 2\pi \left[ \frac{2}{3} \left( x + \frac{1}{4} \right)^{3/2} \right]_{3/4}^{15/4}$

$= \frac{4\pi}{3} \left[ \left( \frac{15}{4} + \frac{1}{4} \right)^{3/2} - \left( \frac{3}{4} + \frac{1}{4} \right)^{3/2} \right] = \frac{4\pi}{3} \left[ \left( \frac{4}{2} \right)^3 - 1 \right]$

$= \frac{4\pi}{3} (8 - 1) = \frac{28\pi}{3}$

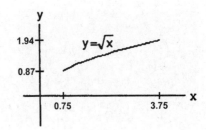

15. $\frac{dy}{dx} = \frac{1}{2} \frac{(2-2x)}{\sqrt{2x-x^2}} = \frac{1-x}{\sqrt{2x-x^2}} \Rightarrow \left(\frac{dy}{dx}\right)^2 = \frac{(1-x)^2}{2x-x^2}$

$\Rightarrow S = \int_{0.5}^{1.5} 2\pi \sqrt{2x-x^2} \sqrt{1 + \frac{(1-x)^2}{2x-x^2}}\, dx$

$= 2\pi \int_{0.5}^{1.5} \sqrt{2x-x^2} \frac{\sqrt{2x-x^2+1-2x+x^2}}{\sqrt{2x-x^2}}\, dx$

$= 2\pi \int_{0.5}^{1.5} dx = 2\pi [x]_{0.5}^{1.5} = 2\pi$

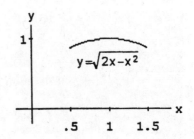

16. $\frac{dy}{dx} = \frac{1}{2\sqrt{x+1}} \Rightarrow \left(\frac{dy}{dx}\right)^2 = \frac{1}{4(x+1)}$

$\Rightarrow S = \int_1^5 2\pi \sqrt{x+1} \sqrt{1 + \frac{1}{4(x+1)}}\, dx$

$= 2\pi \int_1^5 \sqrt{(x+1) + \frac{1}{4}}\, dx = 2\pi \int_1^5 \sqrt{x + \frac{5}{4}}\, dx$

$= 2\pi \left[ \frac{2}{3} \left( x + \frac{5}{4} \right)^{3/2} \right]_1^5 = \frac{4\pi}{3} \left[ \left( 5 + \frac{5}{4} \right)^{3/2} - \left( 1 + \frac{5}{4} \right)^{3/2} \right]$

$= \frac{4\pi}{3} \left[ \left( \frac{25}{4} \right)^{3/2} - \left( \frac{9}{4} \right)^{3/2} \right] = \frac{4\pi}{3} \left( \frac{5^3}{2^3} - \frac{3^3}{2^3} \right)$

$= \frac{\pi}{6} (125 - 27) = \frac{98\pi}{6} = \frac{49\pi}{3}$

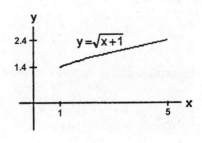

17. $\frac{dx}{dy} = y^2 \Rightarrow \left(\frac{dx}{dy}\right)^2 = y^4 \Rightarrow S = \int_0^1 \frac{2\pi y^3}{3} \sqrt{1 + y^4}\, dy;$

$\left[ u = 1 + y^4 \Rightarrow du = 4y^3\, dy \Rightarrow \frac{1}{4} du = y^3\, dy; y = 0 \right.$

$\Rightarrow u = 1, y = 1 \Rightarrow u = 2 \Big] \rightarrow S = \int_1^2 2\pi \left( \frac{1}{3} \right) u^{1/2} \left( \frac{1}{4}\, du \right)$

$= \frac{\pi}{6} \int_1^2 u^{1/2}\, du = \frac{\pi}{6} \left[ \frac{2}{3} u^{3/2} \right]_1^2 = \frac{\pi}{9} \left( \sqrt{8} - 1 \right)$

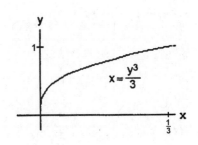

18. $x = \left(\frac{1}{3} y^{3/2} - y^{1/2}\right) \le 0$, when $1 \le y \le 3$. To get positive
area, we take $x = -\left(\frac{1}{3} y^{3/2} - y^{1/2}\right)$

$\Rightarrow \frac{dx}{dy} = -\frac{1}{2}\left(y^{1/2} - y^{-1/2}\right) \Rightarrow \left(\frac{dx}{dy}\right)^2 = \frac{1}{4}\left(y - 2 + y^{-1}\right)$

$\Rightarrow S = -\int_1^3 2\pi \left(\frac{1}{3} y^{3/2} - y^{1/2}\right) \sqrt{1 + \frac{1}{4}\left(y - 2 + y^{-1}\right)}\, dy$

$= -2\pi \int_1^3 \left(\frac{1}{3} y^{3/2} - y^{1/2}\right) \sqrt{\frac{1}{4}\left(y + 2 + y^{-1}\right)}\, dy$

$= -2\pi \int_1^3 \left(\frac{1}{3} y^{3/2} - y^{1/2}\right) \frac{\sqrt{\left(y^{1/2} + y^{-1/2}\right)^2}}{2}\, dy = -\pi \int_1^3 y^{1/2} \left(\frac{1}{3} y - 1\right) \left(y^{1/2} + \frac{1}{y^{1/2}}\right) dy = -\pi \int_1^3 \left(\frac{1}{3} y - 1\right)(y + 1)\, dy$

$= -\pi \int_1^3 \left(\frac{1}{3} y^2 - \frac{2}{3} y - 1\right) dy = -\pi \left[\frac{y^3}{9} - \frac{y^2}{3} - y\right]_1^3 = -\pi \left[\left(\frac{27}{9} - \frac{9}{3} - 3\right) - \left(\frac{1}{9} - \frac{1}{3} - 1\right)\right] = -\pi \left(-3 - \frac{1}{9} + \frac{1}{3} + 1\right)$

$= -\frac{\pi}{9}(-18 - 1 + 3) = \frac{16\pi}{9}$

19. $\frac{dx}{dy} = \frac{-1}{\sqrt{4-y}} \Rightarrow \left(\frac{dx}{dy}\right)^2 = \frac{1}{4-y} \Rightarrow S = \int_0^{15/4} 2\pi \cdot 2\sqrt{4-y}\, \sqrt{1 + \frac{1}{4-y}}\, dy = 4\pi \int_0^{15/4} \sqrt{(4-y)+1}\, dy$

$= 4\pi \int_0^{15/4} \sqrt{5-y}\, dy = -4\pi \left[\frac{2}{3}(5-y)^{3/2}\right]_0^{15/4} = -\frac{8\pi}{3}\left[\left(5 - \frac{15}{4}\right)^{3/2} - 5^{3/2}\right] = -\frac{8\pi}{3}\left[\left(\frac{5}{4}\right)^{3/2} - 5^{3/2}\right]$

$= \frac{8\pi}{3}\left(5\sqrt{5} - \frac{5\sqrt{5}}{8}\right) = \frac{8\pi}{3}\left(\frac{40\sqrt{5} - 5\sqrt{5}}{8}\right) = \frac{35\pi\sqrt{5}}{3}$

20. $\frac{dx}{dy} = \frac{1}{\sqrt{2y-1}} \Rightarrow \left(\frac{dx}{dy}\right)^2 = \frac{1}{2y-1} \Rightarrow S = \int_{5/8}^1 2\pi \sqrt{2y-1}\, \sqrt{1 + \frac{1}{2y-1}}\, dy = 2\pi \int_{5/8}^1 \sqrt{(2y-1)+1}\, dy = 2\pi \int_{5/8}^1 \sqrt{2}\, y^{1/2}\, dy$

$= 2\pi\sqrt{2}\left[\frac{2}{3} y^{3/2}\right]_{5/8}^1 = \frac{4\pi\sqrt{2}}{3}\left[1^{3/2} - \left(\frac{5}{8}\right)^{3/2}\right] = \frac{4\pi\sqrt{2}}{3}\left(1 - \frac{5\sqrt{5}}{8\sqrt{8}}\right) = \frac{4\pi\sqrt{2}}{3}\left(\frac{8\cdot 2\sqrt{2} - 5\sqrt{5}}{8\cdot 2\sqrt{2}}\right) = \frac{\pi}{12}\left(16\sqrt{2} - 5\sqrt{5}\right)$

21. $S = 2\pi \int_{1/2}^1 \sqrt{2y-1}\, \sqrt{1 + \left(\frac{1}{\sqrt{2y-1}}\right)^2}\, dy = 2\pi \int_{1/2}^1 \sqrt{2y-1}\, \sqrt{1 + \frac{1}{2y-1}}\, dy = 2\pi \int_{1/2}^1 \sqrt{2y-1}\, \sqrt{\frac{2y}{2y-1}}\, dy$

$= 2\pi \int_{1/2}^1 \sqrt{2y}\, dy = 2\sqrt{2}\pi \int_{1/2}^1 \sqrt{y}\, dy = 2\sqrt{2}\pi \left[\frac{2}{3} y^{3/2}\right]_{1/2}^1 = 2\sqrt{2}\pi \left[\left(\frac{2}{3}\sqrt{1^3}\right) - \left(\frac{2}{3}\sqrt{\left(\frac{1}{2}\right)^3}\right)\right] = 2\sqrt{2}\pi \left(\frac{2}{3} - \frac{1}{3\sqrt{2}}\right)$

$= 2\sqrt{2}\pi \left(\frac{2\sqrt{2}-1}{3\sqrt{2}}\right) = \frac{2\pi}{3}\left(2\sqrt{2} - 1\right)$

22. $y = \frac{1}{3}\left(x^2 + 2\right)^{3/2} \Rightarrow dy = x\sqrt{x^2 + 2}\, dx \Rightarrow ds = \sqrt{1 + (2x^2 + x^4)}\, dx \Rightarrow S = 2\pi \int_0^{\sqrt{2}} x\sqrt{1 + 2x^2 + x^4}\, dx$

$= 2\pi \int_0^{\sqrt{2}} x\sqrt{(x^2 + 1)^2}\, dx = 2\pi \int_0^{\sqrt{2}} x\left(x^2 + 1\right) dx = 2\pi \int_0^{\sqrt{2}} \left(x^3 + x\right) dx = 2\pi \left[\frac{x^4}{4} + \frac{x^2}{2}\right]_0^{\sqrt{2}} = 2\pi \left(\frac{4}{4} + \frac{2}{2}\right) = 4\pi$

23. $ds = \sqrt{dx^2 + dy^2} = \sqrt{\left(y^3 - \frac{1}{4y^3}\right)^2 + 1}\, dy = \sqrt{\left(y^6 - \frac{1}{2} + \frac{1}{16y^6}\right) + 1}\, dy = \sqrt{\left(y^6 + \frac{1}{2} + \frac{1}{16y^6}\right)}\, dy$

$= \sqrt{\left(y^3 + \frac{1}{4y^3}\right)^2}\, dy = \left(y^3 + \frac{1}{4y^3}\right) dy; S = \int_1^2 2\pi y\, ds = 2\pi \int_1^2 y\left(y^3 + \frac{1}{4y^3}\right) dy = 2\pi \int_1^2 \left(y^4 + \frac{1}{4} y^{-2}\right) dy$

$= 2\pi \left[\frac{y^5}{5} - \frac{1}{4} y^{-1}\right]_1^2 = 2\pi \left[\left(\frac{32}{5} - \frac{1}{8}\right) - \left(\frac{1}{5} - \frac{1}{4}\right)\right] = 2\pi \left(\frac{31}{5} + \frac{1}{8}\right) = \frac{2\pi}{40}(8 \cdot 31 + 5) = \frac{253\pi}{20}$

24. $y = \cos x \Rightarrow \frac{dy}{dx} = -\sin x \Rightarrow \left(\frac{dy}{dx}\right)^2 = \sin^2 x \Rightarrow S = 2\pi \int_{-\pi/2}^{\pi/2} (\cos x)\sqrt{1 + \sin^2 x}\, dx$

25. $y = \sqrt{a^2 - x^2} \Rightarrow \frac{dy}{dx} = \frac{1}{2}\left(a^2 - x^2\right)^{-1/2}(-2x) = \frac{-x}{\sqrt{a^2 - x^2}} \Rightarrow \left(\frac{dy}{dx}\right)^2 = \frac{x^2}{(a^2 - x^2)}$

$\Rightarrow S = 2\pi \int_{-a}^a \sqrt{a^2 - x^2}\, \sqrt{1 + \frac{x^2}{(a^2 - x^2)}}\, dx = 2\pi \int_{-a}^a \sqrt{(a^2 - x^2) + x^2}\, dx = 2\pi \int_{-a}^a a\, dx = 2\pi a[x]_{-a}^a$

$= 2\pi a[a - (-a)] = (2\pi a)(2a) = 4\pi a^2$

26. $y = \frac{r}{h}x \Rightarrow \frac{dy}{dx} = \frac{r}{h} \Rightarrow \left(\frac{dy}{dx}\right)^2 = \frac{r^2}{h^2} \Rightarrow S = 2\pi \int_0^h \frac{r}{h}x \sqrt{1 + \frac{r^2}{h^2}}\, dx = 2\pi \int_0^h \frac{r}{h}x \sqrt{\frac{h^2+r^2}{h^2}}\, dx$

$= \frac{2\pi r}{h}\sqrt{\frac{h^2+r^2}{h^2}} \int_0^h x\, dx = \frac{2\pi r}{h^2}\sqrt{h^2+r^2}\left[\frac{x^2}{2}\right]_0^h = \frac{2\pi r}{h^2}\sqrt{h^2+r^2}\left(\frac{h^2}{2}\right) = \pi r\sqrt{h^2+r^2}$

27. The area of the surface of one wok is $S = \int_c^d 2\pi x \sqrt{1 + \left(\frac{dx}{dy}\right)^2}\, dy$. Now, $x^2 + y^2 = 16^2 \Rightarrow x = \sqrt{16^2 - y^2}$

$\Rightarrow \frac{dx}{dy} = \frac{-y}{\sqrt{16^2-y^2}} \Rightarrow \left(\frac{dx}{dy}\right)^2 = \frac{y^2}{16^2-y^2}; S = \int_{-16}^{-7} 2\pi\sqrt{16^2-y^2}\sqrt{1+\frac{y^2}{16^2-y^2}}\, dy = 2\pi\int_{-16}^{-7}\sqrt{(16^2-y^2)+y^2}\, dy$

$= 2\pi\int_{-16}^{-7} 16\, dy = 32\pi \cdot 9 = 288\pi \approx 904.78 \text{ cm}^2$. The enamel needed to cover one surface of one wok is

$V = S \cdot 0.5 \text{ mm} = S \cdot 0.05 \text{ cm} = (904.78)(0.05) \text{ cm}^3 = 45.24 \text{ cm}^3$. For 5000 woks, we need

$5000 \cdot V = 5000 \cdot 45.24 \text{ cm}^3 = (5)(45.24)L = 226.2L \Rightarrow 226.2$ liters of each color are needed.

28. $y = \sqrt{r^2 - x^2} \Rightarrow \frac{dy}{dx} = -\frac{1}{2}\frac{2x}{\sqrt{r^2-x^2}} = \frac{-x}{\sqrt{r^2-x^2}} \Rightarrow \left(\frac{dx}{dy}\right)^2 = \frac{x^2}{r^2-x^2}; S = 2\pi\int_a^{a+h}\sqrt{r^2-x^2}\sqrt{1+\frac{x^2}{r^2-x^2}}\, dx$

$= 2\pi\int_a^{a+h}\sqrt{(r^2-x^2)+x^2}\, dx = 2\pi r\int_a^{a+h}dx = 2\pi rh$, which is independent of a.

29. $y = \sqrt{R^2 - x^2} \Rightarrow \frac{dy}{dx} = -\frac{1}{2}\frac{2x}{\sqrt{R^2-x^2}} = \frac{-x}{\sqrt{R^2-x^2}} \Rightarrow \left(\frac{dx}{dy}\right)^2 = \frac{x^2}{R^2-x^2}; S = 2\pi\int_a^{a+h}\sqrt{R^2-x^2}\sqrt{1+\frac{x^2}{R^2-x^2}}\, dx$

$= 2\pi\int_a^{a+h}\sqrt{(R^2-x^2)+x^2}\, dx = 2\pi R\int_a^{a+h}dx = 2\pi Rh$

30. (a) $x^2 + y^2 = 45^2 \Rightarrow x = \sqrt{45^2 - y^2} \Rightarrow \frac{dx}{dy} = \frac{-y}{\sqrt{45^2-y^2}} \Rightarrow \left(\frac{dx}{dy}\right)^2 = \frac{y^2}{45^2-y^2};$

$S = \int_{-22.5}^{45} 2\pi\sqrt{45^2-y^2}\sqrt{1+\frac{y^2}{45^2-y^2}}\, dy = 2\pi\int_{-22.5}^{45}\sqrt{(45^2-y^2)+y^2}\, dy = 2\pi \cdot 45\int_{-22.5}^{45} dy$

$= (2\pi)(45)(67.5) = 6075\pi$ square feet

(b) 19,085 square feet

31. (a) An equation of the tangent line segment is
(see figure) $y = f(m_k) + f'(m_k)(x - m_k)$.
When $x = x_{k-1}$ we have
$r_1 = f(m_k) + f'(m_k)(x_{k-1} - m_k)$
$= f(m_k) + f'(m_k)\left(-\frac{\Delta x_k}{2}\right) = f(m_k) - f'(m_k)\frac{\Delta x_k}{2};$
when $x = x_k$ we have
$r_2 = f(m_k) + f'(m_k)(x_k - m_k)$
$= f(m_k) + f'(m_k)\frac{\Delta x_k}{2};$

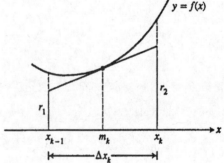

(b) $L_k^2 = (\Delta x_k)^2 + (r_2 - r_1)^2$

$= (\Delta x_k)^2 + \left[f'(m_k)\frac{\Delta x_k}{2} - \left(-f'(m_k)\frac{\Delta x_k}{2}\right)\right]^2$

$= (\Delta x_k)^2 + [f'(m_k)\Delta x_k]^2 \Rightarrow L_k = \sqrt{(\Delta x_k)^2 + [f'(m_k)\Delta x_k]^2}$, as claimed

(c) From geometry it is a fact that the lateral surface area of the frustum obtained by revolving the tangent

line segment about the x-axis is given by $\Delta S_k = \pi(r_1 + r_2)L_k = \pi[2f(m_k)]\sqrt{(\Delta x_k)^2 + [f'(m_k)\Delta x_k]^2}$

using parts (a) and (b) above. Thus, $\Delta S_k = 2\pi f(m_k)\sqrt{1 + [f'(m_k)]^2}\,\Delta x_k$.

(d) $S = \lim_{n \to \infty}\sum_{k=1}^n \Delta S_k = \lim_{n \to \infty}\sum_{k=1}^n 2\pi f(m_k)\sqrt{1 + [f'(m_k)]^2}\,\Delta x_k = \int_a^b 2\pi f(x)\sqrt{1 + [f'(x)]^2}\, dx$

32. $y = \left(1 - x^{2/3}\right)^{3/2} \Rightarrow \frac{dy}{dx} = \frac{3}{2}\left(1 - x^{2/3}\right)^{1/2}\left(-\frac{2}{3}x^{-1/3}\right) = -\frac{\left(1-x^{2/3}\right)^{1/2}}{x^{1/3}} \Rightarrow \left(\frac{dy}{dx}\right)^2 = \frac{1-x^{2/3}}{x^{2/3}} = \frac{1}{x^{2/3}} - 1$

$\Rightarrow S = 2\int_0^1 2\pi\left(1 - x^{2/3}\right)^{3/2}\sqrt{1 + \left(\frac{1}{x^{2/3}} - 1\right)}\, dx = 4\pi\int_0^1\left(1 - x^{2/3}\right)^{3/2}\sqrt{x^{-2/3}}\, dx$

$$= 4\pi \int_0^1 \left(1 - x^{2/3}\right)^{3/2} x^{-1/3} \, dx; \left[u = 1 - x^{2/3} \Rightarrow du = -\tfrac{2}{3} x^{-1/3} \, dx \Rightarrow -\tfrac{3}{2} \, du = x^{-1/3} \, dx; \right.$$

$$\left. x = 0 \Rightarrow u = 1, x = 1 \Rightarrow u = 0\right] \rightarrow S = 4\pi \int_1^0 u^{3/2} \left(-\tfrac{3}{2} \, du\right) = -6\pi \left[\tfrac{2}{5} u^{5/2}\right]_1^0 = -6\pi \left(0 - \tfrac{2}{5}\right) = \tfrac{12\pi}{5}$$

## 6.5 WORK AND FLUID FORCES

1. The force required to stretch the spring from its natural length of 2 m to a length of 5 m is $F(x) = kx$. The work done by F is $W = \int_0^3 F(x) \, dx = k \int_0^3 x \, dx = \tfrac{k}{2} [x^2]_0^3 = \tfrac{9k}{2}$. This work is equal to 1800 J $\Rightarrow \tfrac{9}{2} k = 1800 \Rightarrow k = 400$ N/m

2. (a) We find the force constant from Hooke's Law: $F = kx \Rightarrow k = \tfrac{F}{x} \Rightarrow k = \tfrac{800}{4} = 200$ lb/in.

   (b) The work done to stretch the spring 2 inches beyond its natural length is $W = \int_0^2 kx \, dx = 200 \int_0^2 x \, dx = 200 \left[\tfrac{x^2}{2}\right]_0^2$
   $= 200(2 - 0) = 400$ in $\cdot$ lb $= 33.3$ ft $\cdot$ lb

   (c) We substitute $F = 1600$ into the equation $F = 200x$ to find $1600 = 200x \Rightarrow x = 8$ in.

3. We find the force constant from Hooke's law: $F = kx$. A force of 2 N stretches the spring to 0.02 m $\Rightarrow 2 = k \cdot (0.02)$
   $\Rightarrow k = 100 \tfrac{N}{m}$. The force of 4 N will stretch the rubber band y m, where $F = ky \Rightarrow y = \tfrac{F}{k} \Rightarrow y = \tfrac{4N}{100 \tfrac{N}{m}} \Rightarrow y = 0.04$ m
   $= 4$ cm. The work done to stretch the rubber band 0.04 m is $W = \int_0^{0.04} kx \, dx = 100 \int_0^{0.04} x \, dx = 100 \left[\tfrac{x^2}{2}\right]_0^{0.04}$
   $= \tfrac{(100)(0.04)^2}{2} = 0.08$ J

4. We find the force constant from Hooke's law: $F = kx \Rightarrow k = \tfrac{F}{x} \Rightarrow k = \tfrac{90}{1} \Rightarrow k = 90 \tfrac{N}{m}$. The work done to stretch the spring 5 m beyond its natural length is $W = \int_0^5 kx \, dx = 90 \int_0^5 x \, dx = 90 \left[\tfrac{x^2}{2}\right]_0^5 = (90) \left(\tfrac{25}{2}\right) = 1125$ J

5. (a) We find the spring's constant from Hooke's law: $F = kx \Rightarrow k = \tfrac{F}{x} = \tfrac{21,714}{8-5} = \tfrac{21,714}{3} \Rightarrow k = 7238 \tfrac{lb}{in}$

   (b) The work done to compress the assembly the first half inch is $W = \int_0^{0.5} kx \, dx = 7238 \int_0^{0.5} x \, dx = 7238 \left[\tfrac{x^2}{2}\right]_0^{0.5}$
   $= (7238) \tfrac{(0.5)^2}{2} = \tfrac{(7238)(0.25)}{2} \approx 905$ in $\cdot$ lb. The work done to compress the assembly the second half inch is:
   $W = \int_{0.5}^{1.0} kx \, dx = 7238 \int_{0.5}^{1.0} x \, dx = 7238 \left[\tfrac{x^2}{2}\right]_{0.5}^{1.0} = \tfrac{7238}{2} [1 - (0.5)^2] = \tfrac{(7238)(0.75)}{2} \approx 2714$ in $\cdot$ lb

6. First, we find the force constant from Hooke's law: $F = kx \Rightarrow k = \tfrac{F}{x} = \tfrac{150}{\left(\tfrac{1}{16}\right)} = 16 \cdot 150 = 2,400 \tfrac{lb}{in}$. If someone compresses the scale $x = \tfrac{1}{8}$ in, he/she must weigh $F = kx = 2,400 \left(\tfrac{1}{8}\right) = 300$ lb. The work done to compress the scale this far is $W = \int_0^{1/8} kx \, dx = 2400 \left[\tfrac{x^2}{2}\right]_0^{1/8} = \tfrac{2400}{2 \cdot 64} = 18.75$ lb $\cdot$ in. $= \tfrac{25}{16}$ ft $\cdot$ lb

7. The force required to haul up the rope is equal to the rope's weight, which varies steadily and is proportional to x, the length of the rope still hanging: $F(x) = 0.624x$. The work done is: $W = \int_0^{50} F(x) \, dx = \int_0^{50} 0.624x \, dx = 0.624 \left[\tfrac{x^2}{2}\right]_0^{50}$
   $= 780$ J

8. The weight of sand decreases steadily by 72 lb over the 18 ft, at 4 lb/ft. So the weight of sand when the bag is x ft off the ground is $F(x) = 144 - 4x$. The work done is: $W = \int_a^b F(x) \, dx = \int_0^{18} (144 - 4x) \, dx = [144x - 2x^2]_0^{18} = 1944$ ft $\cdot$ lb

9. The force required to lift the cable is equal to the weight of the cable paid out: $F(x) = (4.5)(180 - x)$ where x is the position of the car off the first floor. The work done is: $W = \int_0^{180} F(x) \, dx = 4.5 \int_0^{180} (180 - x) \, dx$

$$= 4.5 \left[180x - \tfrac{x^2}{2}\right]_0^{180} = 4.5 \left(180^2 - \tfrac{180^2}{2}\right) = \tfrac{4.5 \cdot 180^2}{2} = 72{,}900 \text{ ft} \cdot \text{lb}$$

10. Since the force is acting <u>toward</u> the origin, it acts opposite to the positive x-direction. Thus $F(x) = -\tfrac{k}{x^2}$. The work done
    is $W = \int_a^b -\tfrac{k}{x^2} \, dx = k \int_a^b -\tfrac{1}{x^2} \, dx = k \left[\tfrac{1}{x}\right]_a^b = k \left(\tfrac{1}{b} - \tfrac{1}{a}\right) = \tfrac{k(a-b)}{ab}$

11. Let r = the constant rate of leakage. Since the bucket is leaking at a constant rate and the bucket is rising at a constant rate,
    the amount of water in the bucket is proportional to $(20 - x)$, the distance the bucket is being raised. The leakage rate of
    the water is 0.8 lb/ft raised and the weight of the water in the bucket is $F = 0.8(20 - x)$. So:
    $$W = \int_0^{20} 0.8(20 - x) \, dx = 0.8 \left[20x - \tfrac{x^2}{2}\right]_0^{20} = 160 \text{ ft} \cdot \text{lb}.$$

12. Let r = the constant rate of leakage. Since the bucket is leaking at a constant rate and the bucket is rising at a constant rate,
    the amount of water in the bucket is proportional to $(20 - x)$, the distance the bucket is being raised. The leakage rate of
    the water is 2 lb/ft raised and the weight of the water in the bucket is $F = 2(20 - x)$. So:
    $$W = \int_0^{20} 2(20 - x) \, dx = 2 \left[20x - \tfrac{x^2}{2}\right]_0^{20} = 400 \text{ ft} \cdot \text{lb}.$$
    Note that since the force in Exercise 12 is 2.5 times the force in Exercise 11 at each elevation, the total work is also 2.5
    times as great.

13. We will use the coordinate system given.
    (a) The typical slab between the planes at y and $y + \Delta y$ has
        a volume of $\Delta V = (10)(12) \, \Delta y = 120 \, \Delta y \text{ ft}^3$. The force
        F required to lift the slab is equal to its weight:
        $F = 62.4 \, \Delta V = 62.4 \cdot 120 \, \Delta y$ lb. The distance through
        which F must act is about y ft, so the work done lifting
        the slab is about $\Delta W = \text{force} \times \text{distance}$
        $= 62.4 \cdot 120 \cdot y \cdot \Delta y \text{ ft} \cdot \text{lb}$. The work it takes to lift all
        the water is approximately $W \approx \sum_0^{20} \Delta W$

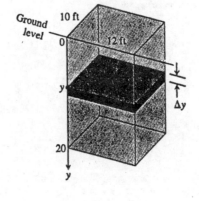

        $= \sum_0^{20} 62.4 \cdot 120y \cdot \Delta y \text{ ft} \cdot \text{lb}$. This is a Riemann sum for
        the function $62.4 \cdot 120y$ over the interval $0 \le y \le 20$. The work of pumping the tank empty is the limit of these sums:
        $$W = \int_0^{20} 62.4 \cdot 120y \, dy = (62.4)(120) \left[\tfrac{y^2}{2}\right]_0^{20} = (62.4)(120) \left(\tfrac{400}{2}\right) = (62.4)(120)(200) = 1{,}497{,}600 \text{ ft} \cdot \text{lb}$$
    (b) The time t it takes to empty the full tank with $\left(\tfrac{5}{11}\right)$–hp motor is $t = \tfrac{W}{250 \frac{\text{ft-lb}}{\text{sec}}} = \tfrac{1{,}497{,}600 \text{ ft-lb}}{250 \frac{\text{ft-lb}}{\text{sec}}} = 5990.4 \text{ sec} = 1.664 \text{ hr}$
        $\Rightarrow t \approx 1 \text{ hr and } 40 \text{ min}$
    (c) Following all the steps of part (a), we find that the work it takes to lower the water level 10 ft is
        $$W = \int_0^{10} 62.4 \cdot 120y \, dy = (62.4)(120) \left[\tfrac{y^2}{2}\right]_0^{10} = (62.4)(120) \left(\tfrac{100}{2}\right) = 374{,}400 \text{ ft} \cdot \text{lb and the time is } t = \tfrac{W}{250 \frac{\text{ft-lb}}{\text{sec}}}$$
        $= 1497.6 \text{ sec} = 0.416 \text{ hr} \approx 25 \text{ min}$
    (d) In a location where water weighs 62.26 $\tfrac{\text{lb}}{\text{ft}^3}$:
        a) $W = (62.26)(24{,}000) = 1{,}494{,}240 \text{ ft} \cdot \text{lb}.$
        b) $t = \tfrac{1{,}494{,}240}{250} = 5976.96 \text{ sec} \approx 1.660 \text{ hr} \Rightarrow t \approx 1 \text{ hr and } 40 \text{ min}$
        In a location where water weighs 62.59 $\tfrac{\text{lb}}{\text{ft}^3}$:
        a) $W = (62.59)(24{,}000) = 1{,}502{,}160 \text{ ft} \cdot \text{lb}$
        b) $t = \tfrac{1{,}502{,}160}{250} = 6008.64 \text{ sec} \approx 1.669 \text{ hr} \Rightarrow t \approx 1 \text{ hr and } 40.1 \text{ min}$

14. We will use the coordinate system given.

    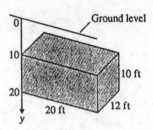
    Ground level

    (a) The typical slab between the planes at y and $y + \Delta y$ has a volume of $\Delta V = (20)(12)\,\Delta y = 240\,\Delta y$ ft$^3$. The force F required to lift the slab is equal to its weight: $F = 62.4\,\Delta V = 62.4 \cdot 240\,\Delta y$ lb. The distance through which F must act is about y ft, so the work done lifting the slab is about $\Delta W = \text{force} \times \text{distance}$

    $= 62.4 \cdot 240 \cdot y \cdot \Delta y$ ft $\cdot$ lb. The work it takes to lift all the water is approximately $W \approx \sum_{10}^{20} \Delta W$

    $= \sum_{10}^{20} 62.4 \cdot 240y \cdot \Delta y$ ft $\cdot$ lb. This is a Riemann sum for the function $62.4 \cdot 240y$ over the interval

    $10 \le y \le 20$. The work it takes to empty the cistern is the limit of these sums: $W = \int_{10}^{20} 62.4 \cdot 240y\,dy$

    $= (62.4)(240)\left[\frac{y^2}{2}\right]_{10}^{20} = (62.4)(240)(200 - 50) = (62.4)(240)(150) = 2{,}246{,}400$ ft $\cdot$ lb

    (b) $t = \frac{W}{275\,\frac{\text{ft-lb}}{\text{sec}}} = \frac{2{,}246{,}400 \text{ ft-lb}}{275} \approx 8168.73$ sec $\approx 2.27$ hours $\approx 2$ hr and 16.1 min

    (c) Following all the steps of part (a), we find that the work it takes to empty the tank halfway is

    $W = \int_{10}^{15} 62.4 \cdot 240y\,dy = (62.4)(240)\left[\frac{y^2}{2}\right]_{10}^{15} = (62.4)(240)\left(\frac{225}{2} - \frac{100}{2}\right) = (62.4)(240)\left(\frac{125}{2}\right) = 936{,}000$ ft.

    Then the time is $t = \frac{W}{275\,\frac{\text{ft-lb}}{\text{sec}}} = \frac{936{,}000}{275} \approx 3403.64$ sec $\approx 56.7$ min

    (d) In a location where water weighs $62.26\,\frac{\text{lb}}{\text{ft}^3}$:

    a) $W = (62.26)(240)(150) = 2{,}241{,}360$ ft $\cdot$ lb.

    b) $t = \frac{2{,}241{,}360}{275} = 8150.40$ sec $= 2.264$ hours $\approx 2$ hr and 15.8 min

    c) $W = (62.26)(240)\left(\frac{125}{2}\right) = 933{,}900$ ft $\cdot$ lb; $t = \frac{933{,}900}{275} = 3396$ sec $\approx 0.94$ hours $\approx 56.6$ min

    In a location where water weighs $62.59\,\frac{\text{lb}}{\text{ft}^3}$

    a) $W = (62.59)(240)(150) = 2{,}253{,}240$ ft $\cdot$ lb.

    b) $t = \frac{2{,}253{,}240}{275} = 8193.60$ sec $= 2.276$ hours $\approx 2$ hr and 16.56 min

    c) $W = (62.59)(240)\left(\frac{125}{2}\right) = 938{,}850$ ft $\cdot$ lb; $t = \frac{938{,}850}{275} \approx 3414$ sec $\approx 0.95$ hours $\approx 56.9$ min

15. The slab is a disk of area $\pi x^2 = \pi\left(\frac{y}{2}\right)^2$, thickness $\Delta y$, and height below the top of the tank $(10 - y)$. So the work to pump the oil in this slab, $\Delta W$, is $57(10 - y)\pi\left(\frac{y}{2}\right)^2$. The work to pump all the oil to the top of the tank is

    $W = \int_0^{10} \frac{57\pi}{4}(10y^2 - y^3)dy = \frac{57\pi}{4}\left[\frac{10y^3}{3} - \frac{y^4}{4}\right]_0^{10} = 11{,}875\pi$ ft $\cdot$ lb $\approx 37{,}306$ ft $\cdot$ lb.

    of thickness dy       dy

16. Each slab of oil is to be pumped to a height of 14 ft. So the work to pump a slab is $(14 - y)(\pi)\left(\frac{y}{2}\right)^2$ and since the tank is half full and the volume of the original cone is $V = \frac{1}{3}\pi r^2 h = \frac{1}{3}\pi(5^2)(10) = \frac{250\pi}{3}$ ft$^3$, half the volume $= \frac{250\pi}{6}$ ft$^3$, and

    with half the volume the cone is filled to a height y, $\frac{250\pi}{6} = \frac{1}{3}\pi\frac{y^2}{4}y \Rightarrow y = \sqrt[3]{500}$ ft. So $W = \int_0^{\sqrt[3]{500}} \frac{57\pi}{4}(14y^2 - y^3)\,dy$

    $= \frac{57\pi}{4}\left[\frac{14y^3}{3} - \frac{y^4}{4}\right]_0^{\sqrt[3]{500}} \approx 60{,}042$ ft $\cdot$ lb.

17. The typical slab between the planes at y and and $y + \Delta y$ has a volume of $\Delta V = \pi(\text{radius})^2(\text{thickness}) = \pi\left(\frac{20}{2}\right)^2\Delta y$

    $= \pi \cdot 100\,\Delta y$ ft$^3$. The force F required to lift the slab is equal to its weight: $F = 51.2\,\Delta V = 51.2 \cdot 100\pi\,\Delta y$ lb

    $\Rightarrow F = 5120\pi\,\Delta y$ lb. The distance through which F must act is about $(30 - y)$ ft. The work it takes to lift all the

    kerosene is approximately $W \approx \sum_0^{30} \Delta W = \sum_0^{30} 5120\pi(30 - y)\,\Delta y$ ft $\cdot$ lb which is a Riemann sum. The work to pump the

    tank dry is the limit of these sums: $W = \int_0^{30} 5120\pi(30 - y)\,dy = 5120\pi\left[30y - \frac{y^2}{2}\right]_0^{30} = 5120\pi\left(\frac{900}{2}\right) = (5120)(450\pi)$

    $\approx 7{,}238{,}229.48$ ft $\cdot$ lb

18. (a) Follow all the steps of Example 5 but make the substitution of $64.5 \frac{lb}{ft^3}$ for $57 \frac{lb}{ft^3}$. Then,

$$W = \int_0^8 \frac{64.5\pi}{4}(10-y)y^2\, dy = \frac{64.5\pi}{4}\left[\frac{10y^3}{3} - \frac{y^4}{4}\right]_0^8 = \frac{64.5\pi}{4}\left(\frac{10\cdot 8^3}{3} - \frac{8^4}{4}\right) = \left(\frac{64.5\pi}{4}\right)(8^3)\left(\frac{10}{3} - 2\right)$$

$$= \frac{64.5\pi\cdot 8^3}{3} = 21.5\pi\cdot 8^3 \approx 34{,}582.65 \text{ ft}\cdot\text{lb}$$

(b) Exactly as done in Example 5 but change the distance through which F acts to distance $\approx (13-y)$ ft. Then

$$W = \int_0^8 \frac{57\pi}{4}(13-y)y^2\, dy = \frac{57\pi}{4}\left[\frac{13y^3}{3} - \frac{y^4}{4}\right]_0^8 = \frac{57\pi}{4}\left(\frac{13\cdot 8^3}{3} - \frac{8^4}{4}\right) = \left(\frac{57\pi}{4}\right)(8^3)\left(\frac{13}{3} - 2\right) = \frac{57\pi\cdot 8^3\cdot 7}{3\cdot 4}$$

$$= (19\pi)(8^2)(7)(2) \approx 53{,}482.5 \text{ ft}\cdot\text{lb}$$

19. The typical slab between the planes at y and $y+\Delta y$ has a volume of about $\Delta V = \pi(\text{radius})^2(\text{thickness}) = \pi\left(\sqrt{y}\right)^2 \Delta y$ ft$^3$. The force F(y) required to lift this slab is equal to its weight: $F(y) = 73\cdot\Delta V = 73\pi\left(\sqrt{y}\right)^2\Delta y = 73\pi\, y\,\Delta y$ lb. The distance through which F(y) must act to lift the slab to the top of the reservoir is about $(4-y)$ ft, so the work done is approximately $\Delta W \approx 73\pi\, y\,(4-y)\Delta y$ ft$\cdot$lb. The work done lifting all the slabs from $y=0$ ft to $y=4$ ft is approximately $W \approx \sum_{k=0}^{n} 73\pi\, y_k\,(4-y_k)\Delta y$ ft$\cdot$lb. Taking the limit of these Riemann sums as $n\to\infty$, we get

$$W = \int_0^4 73\pi\, y\,(4-y)dy = 73\pi\int_0^4 (4y - y^2)dy = 73\pi\left[2y^2 - \tfrac{1}{3}y^3\right]_0^4 = 73\pi\left(32 - \tfrac{64}{3}\right) = \tfrac{2336\pi}{3} \text{ ft}\cdot\text{lb}.$$

20. The typical slab between the planes at y and $y+\Delta y$ has a volume of about $\Delta V = (\text{length})(\text{width})(\text{thickness})$
$= (2\sqrt{25-y^2})(10)\,\Delta y$ ft$^3$. The force F(y) required to lift this slab is equal to its weight: $F(y) = 53\cdot\Delta V$
$= 53(2\sqrt{25-y^2})(10)\,\Delta y = 1060\sqrt{25-y^2}\Delta y$ lb. The distance through which F(y) must act to lift the slab to the level of 15 m above the top of the reservoir is about $(20-y)$ ft, so the work done is approximately $\Delta W \approx 1060\sqrt{25-y^2}(20-y)\Delta y$ ft$\cdot$lb. The work done lifting all the slabs from $y=-5$ ft to $y=5$ ft is approximately $W \approx \sum_{k=0}^{n} 1060\sqrt{25-y_k^2}\,(20-y_k)\Delta y$ ft$\cdot$lb. Taking the limit of these Riemann sums as $n\to\infty$, we get

$$W = \int_{-5}^5 1060\sqrt{25-y^2}(20-y)dy = 1060\int_{-5}^5 (20-y)\sqrt{25-y^2}dy = 1060\left[\int_{-5}^5 20\sqrt{25-y^2}dy - \int_{-5}^5 y\sqrt{25-y^2}dy\right]$$

To evaluate the first integral, we use we can interpret $\int_{-5}^5 \sqrt{25-y^2}dy$ as the area of the semicircle whose radius is 5, thus
$\int_{-5}^5 20\sqrt{25-y^2}dy = 20\int_{-5}^5 \sqrt{25-y^2}dy = 20\left[\tfrac{1}{2}\pi(5)^2\right] = 250\pi$. To evaluate the second integral let $u = 25 - y^2$
$\Rightarrow du = -2y\, dy; y = -5 \Rightarrow u = 0, y = 5 \Rightarrow u = 0$, thus $\int_{-5}^5 y\sqrt{25-y^2}dy = -\tfrac{1}{2}\int_0^0 \sqrt{u}\, du = 0$. Thus,
$1060\left[\int_{-5}^5 20\sqrt{25-y^2}dy - \int_{-5}^5 y\sqrt{25-y^2}dy\right] = 1060(250\pi - 0) = 265000\pi \approx 832522$ ft$\cdot$lb.

21. The typical slab between the planes at y and $y+\Delta y$ has a volume of about $\Delta V = \pi(\text{radius})^2(\text{thickness})$
$= \pi\left(\sqrt{25-y^2}\right)^2 \Delta y$ m$^3$. The force F(y) required to lift this slab is equal to its weight: $F(y) = 9800\cdot\Delta V$
$= 9800\pi\left(\sqrt{25-y^2}\right)^2\Delta y = 9800\pi(25-y^2)\,\Delta y$ N. The distance through which F(y) must act to lift the slab to the level of 4 m above the top of the reservoir is about $(4-y)$ m, so the work done is approximately $\Delta W \approx 9800\pi(25-y^2)(4-y)\Delta y$ N$\cdot$m. The work done lifting all the slabs from $y=-5$ m to $y=0$ m is approximately $W \approx \sum_{-5}^{0} 9800\pi(25-y^2)(4-y)\Delta y$ N$\cdot$m. Taking the limit of these Riemann sums, we get

$$W = \int_{-5}^0 9800\pi(25-y^2)(4-y)\, dy = 9800\pi\int_{-5}^0 (100 - 25y - 4y^2 + y^3)\, dy = 9800\pi\left[100y - \tfrac{25}{2}y^2 - \tfrac{4}{3}y^3 + \tfrac{y^4}{4}\right]_{-5}^0$$

$$= -9800\pi\left(-500 - \tfrac{25\cdot 25}{2} + \tfrac{4}{3}\cdot 125 + \tfrac{625}{4}\right) \approx 15{,}073{,}099.75 \text{ J}$$

22. The typical slab between the planes at y and $y+\Delta y$ has a volume of about $\Delta V = \pi(\text{radius})^2(\text{thickness})$
$= \pi\left(\sqrt{100-y^2}\right)^2\Delta y = \pi(100-y^2)\,\Delta y$ ft$^3$. The force is $F(y) = \frac{56\,lb}{ft^3}\cdot\Delta V = 56\pi(100-y^2)\,\Delta y$ lb. The distance through which F(y) must act to lift the slab to the level of 2 ft above the top of the tank is about

$(12 - y)$ ft, so the work done is $\Delta W \approx 56\pi (100 - y^2)(12 - y)\,\Delta y$ lb · ft. The work done lifting all the slabs

from $y = 0$ ft to $y = 10$ ft is approximately $W \approx \sum_0^{10} 56\pi (100 - y^2)(12 - y)\,\Delta y$ lb · ft. Taking the limit of these

Riemann sums, we get $W = \int_0^{10} 56\pi (100 - y^2)(12 - y)\,dy = 56\pi \int_0^{10} (100 - y^2)(12 - y)\,dy$

$= 56\pi \int_0^{10} (1200 - 100y - 12y^2 + y^3)\,dy = 56\pi \left[ 1200y - \frac{100y^2}{2} - \frac{12y^3}{3} + \frac{y^4}{4} \right]_0^{10}$

$= 56\pi \left( 12{,}000 - \frac{10{,}000}{2} - 4 \cdot 1000 + \frac{10{,}000}{4} \right) = (56\pi)\left( 12 - 5 - 4 + \frac{5}{2} \right)(1000) \approx 967{,}611$ ft · lb.

It would cost $(0.5)(967{,}611) = 483{,}805¢ = \$4838.05$. Yes, you can afford to hire the firm.

23.  $F = m\frac{dv}{dt} = mv\frac{dv}{dx}$ by the chain rule $\Rightarrow W = \int_{x_1}^{x_2} mv\frac{dv}{dx}\,dx = m\int_{x_1}^{x_2}\left(v\frac{dv}{dx}\right)dx = m\left[\frac{1}{2}v^2(x)\right]_{x_1}^{x_2}$

$= \frac{1}{2}m\left[v^2(x_2) - v^2(x_1)\right] = \frac{1}{2}mv_2^2 - \frac{1}{2}mv_1^2$, as claimed.

24.  weight $= 2$ oz $= \frac{2}{16}$ lb; mass $= \frac{\text{weight}}{32} = \frac{\frac{1}{8}}{32} = \frac{1}{256}$ slugs; $W = \left(\frac{1}{2}\right)\left(\frac{1}{256}\text{ slugs}\right)(160\text{ ft/sec})^2 \approx 50$ ft · lb

25.  90 mph $= \frac{90\text{ mi}}{1\text{ hr}} \cdot \frac{1\text{ hr}}{60\text{ min}} \cdot \frac{1\text{ min}}{60\text{ sec}} \cdot \frac{5280\text{ ft}}{1\text{ mi}} = 132$ ft/sec; $m = \frac{0.3125\text{ lb}}{32\text{ ft/sec}^2} = \frac{0.3125}{32}$ slugs;

$W = \left(\frac{1}{2}\right)\left(\frac{0.3125\text{ lb}}{32\text{ ft/sec}^2}\right)(132\text{ ft/sec})^2 \approx 85.1$ ft · lb

26.  weight $= 1.6$ oz $= 0.1$ lb $\Rightarrow m = \frac{0.1\text{ lb}}{32\text{ ft/sec}^2} = \frac{1}{320}$ slugs; $W = \left(\frac{1}{2}\right)\left(\frac{1}{320}\text{ slugs}\right)(280\text{ ft/sec})^2 = 122.5$ ft · lb

27.  $v_1 = 0$ mph $= 0\frac{\text{ft}}{\text{sec}}$, $v_2 = 153$ mph $= 224.4\frac{\text{ft}}{\text{sec}}$; $2$ oz $= 0.125$ lb $\Rightarrow m = \frac{0.125\text{ lb}}{32\text{ ft/sec}^2} = \frac{1}{256}$ slugs;

$W = \int_{x_1}^{x_2} F(x)\,dx = \frac{1}{2}mv_2^2 - \frac{1}{2}mv_1^2 = \frac{1}{2}\left(\frac{1}{256}\right)(224.4)^2 - \frac{1}{2}\left(\frac{1}{256}\right)(0)^2 = 98.35$ ft-lb.

28.  weight $= 6.5$ oz $= \frac{6.5}{16}$ lb $\Rightarrow m = \frac{6.5}{(16)(32)}$ slugs; $W = \left(\frac{1}{2}\right)\left(\frac{6.5}{(16)(32)}\text{ slugs}\right)(132\text{ ft/sec})^2 \approx 110.6$ ft · lb

29.  We imagine the milkshake divided into thin slabs by planes perpendicular to the y-axis at the points of a partition of the
interval $[0, 7]$. The typical slab between the planes at $y$ and $y + \Delta y$ has a volume of about$\Delta V = \pi(\text{radius})^2(\text{thickness})$

$= \pi\left(\frac{y + 17.5}{14}\right)^2\Delta y$ in$^3$. The force $F(y)$ required to lift this slab is equal to its weight: $F(y) = \frac{4}{9}\,\Delta V = \frac{4\pi}{9}\left(\frac{y + 17.5}{14}\right)^2\Delta y$ oz.
The distance through which $F(y)$ must act to lift this slab to the level of 1 inch above the top is about $(8 - y)$ in. The work
done lifting the slab is about $\Delta W = \left(\frac{4\pi}{9}\right)\frac{(y + 17.5)^2}{14^2}(8 - y)\Delta y$ in · oz. The work done lifting all the slabs from $y = 0$ to

$y = 7$ is approximately $W = \sum_0^7 \frac{4\pi}{9 \cdot 14^2}(y + 17.5)^2(8 - y)\,\Delta y$ in · oz which is a Riemann sum. The work is the limit of these

sums as the norm of the partition goes to zero: $W = \int_0^7 \frac{4\pi}{9 \cdot 14^2}(y + 17.5)^2(8 - y)\,dy$

$= \frac{4\pi}{9 \cdot 14^2}\int_0^7 (2450 - 26.25y - 27y^2 - y^3)\,dy = \frac{4\pi}{9 \cdot 14^2}\left[ -\frac{y^4}{4} - 9y^3 - \frac{26.25}{2}y^2 + 2450y \right]_0^7$

$= \frac{4\pi}{9 \cdot 14^2}\left[ -\frac{7^4}{4} - 9 \cdot 7^3 - \frac{26.25}{2} \cdot 7^2 + 2450 \cdot 7 \right] \approx 91.32$ in · oz

30.  Work $= \int_{6{,}370{,}000}^{35{,}780{,}000} \frac{1000\,MG}{r^2}\,dr = 1000\,MG \int_{6{,}370{,}000}^{35{,}780{,}000} \frac{dr}{r^2} = 1000\,MG \left[ -\frac{1}{r} \right]_{6{,}370{,}000}^{35{,}780{,}000}$

$= (1000)(5.975 \cdot 10^{24})(6.672 \cdot 10^{-11})\left( \frac{1}{6{,}370{,}000} - \frac{1}{35{,}780{,}000} \right) \approx 5.144 \times 10^{10}$ J

31.  To find the width of the plate at a typical depth $y$, we first find an equation for the line of the plate's
right-hand edge: $y = x - 5$. If we let $x$ denote the width of the right-hand half of the triangle at depth $y$, then
$x = 5 + y$ and the total width is $L(y) = 2x = 2(5 + y)$. The depth of the strip is $(-y)$. The force exerted by the
water against one side of the plate is therefore $F = \int_{-5}^{-2} w(-y) \cdot L(y)\,dy = \int_{-5}^{-2} 62.4 \cdot (-y) \cdot 2(5 + y)\,dy$

$= 124.8 \int_{-5}^{-2} (-5y - y^2)\, dy = 124.8 \left[ -\frac{5}{2} y^2 - \frac{1}{3} y^3 \right]_{-5}^{-2} = 124.8 \left[ \left( -\frac{5}{2} \cdot 4 + \frac{1}{3} \cdot 8 \right) - \left( -\frac{5}{2} \cdot 25 + \frac{1}{3} \cdot 125 \right) \right]$

$= (124.8) \left( \frac{105}{2} - \frac{117}{3} \right) = (124.8) \left( \frac{315 - 234}{6} \right) = 1684.8 \text{ lb}$

32. An equation for the line of the plate's right-hand edge is $y = x - 3 \Rightarrow x = y + 3$. Thus the total width is $L(y) = 2x = 2(y + 3)$. The depth of the strip is $(2 - y)$. The force exerted by the water is

$F = \int_{-3}^{0} w(2 - y)L(y)\, dy = \int_{-3}^{0} 62.4 \cdot (2 - y) \cdot 2(3 + y)\, dy = 124.8 \int_{-3}^{0} (6 - y - y^2)\, dy = 124.8 \left[ 6y - \frac{y^2}{2} - \frac{y^3}{3} \right]_{-3}^{0}$

$= (-124.8)\left( -18 - \frac{9}{2} + 9 \right) = (-124.8)\left( -\frac{27}{2} \right) = 1684.8 \text{ lb}$

33. (a) The width of the strip is $L(y) = 4$, the depth of the strip is $(10 - y) \Rightarrow F = \int_{a}^{b} w \cdot \left( \frac{\text{strip}}{\text{depth}} \right) F(y)dy$

$= \int_{0}^{3} 62.4(10 - y)(4)dy = 249.6 \int_{0}^{3} (10 - y)dy = 249.6 \left[ 10y - \frac{y^2}{2} \right]_{0}^{3} = 249.6(30 - \frac{9}{2}) = 6364.8 \text{ lb}$

(b) The width of the strip is $L(y) = 3$, the depth of the strip is $(10 - y) \Rightarrow F = \int_{a}^{b} w \cdot \left( \frac{\text{strip}}{\text{depth}} \right) F(y)dy$

$= \int_{0}^{4} 62.4(10 - y)(3)dy = 187.2 \int_{0}^{4} (10 - y)dy = 187.2 \left[ 10y - \frac{y^2}{2} \right]_{0}^{4} = 187.2(40 - 8) = 5990.4 \text{ lb}$

34. The width of the strip is $L(y) = 2\sqrt{25 - y^2}$, the depth of the strip is $(6 - y) \Rightarrow F = \int_{a}^{b} w \cdot \left( \frac{\text{strip}}{\text{depth}} \right) F(y)dy$

$= \int_{0}^{5} 62.4(6 - y)(2\sqrt{25 - y^2})dy = 124.8 \int_{0}^{5} (6 - y)\sqrt{25 - y^2}dy = 124.8 \left[ \int_{0}^{5} 6\sqrt{25 - y^2}dy - \int_{0}^{5} y\sqrt{25 - y^2}dy \right]$

To evaluate the first integral, we use we can interpret $\int_{0}^{5} \sqrt{25 - y^2}dy$ as the area of a quarter circle whose radius is 5, thus

$\int_{0}^{5} 6\sqrt{25 - y^2}dy = 6 \int_{0}^{5} \sqrt{25 - y^2}dy = 6\left[ \frac{1}{4}\pi(5)^2 \right] = \frac{75\pi}{2}$. To evaluate the second integral let $u = 25 - y^2$

$\Rightarrow du = -2y\, dy; y = 0 \Rightarrow u = 25, y = 5 \Rightarrow u = 0$, thus $\int_{0}^{5} y\sqrt{25 - y^2}dy = -\frac{1}{2}\int_{25}^{0} \sqrt{u}\, du = \frac{1}{2}\int_{0}^{25} u^{1/2}\, du$

$= \frac{1}{3}\left[ u^{3/2} \right]_{0}^{25} = \frac{125}{3}$. Thus, $124.8 \left[ \int_{0}^{5} 6\sqrt{25 - y^2}dy - \int_{0}^{5} y\sqrt{25 - y^2}dy \right] = 124.8\left( \frac{75\pi}{2} - \frac{125}{3} \right) \approx 9502.7 \text{ lb}.$

35. Using the coordinate system of Exercise 32, we find the equation for the line of the plate's right-hand edge to be $y = 2x - 4 \Rightarrow x = \frac{y+4}{2}$ and $L(y) = 2x = y + 4$. The depth of the strip is $(1 - y)$.

(a) $F = \int_{-4}^{0} w(1 - y)L(y)\, dy = \int_{-4}^{0} 62.4 \cdot (1 - y)(y + 4)\, dy = 62.4 \int_{-4}^{0} (4 - 3y - y^2)\, dy = 62.4 \left[ 4y - \frac{3y^2}{2} - \frac{y^3}{3} \right]_{-4}^{0}$

$= (-62.4)\left[ (-4)(4) - \frac{(3)(16)}{2} + \frac{64}{3} \right] = (-62.4)\left( -16 - 24 + \frac{64}{3} \right) = \frac{(-62.4)(-120 + 64)}{3} = 1164.8 \text{ lb}$

(b) $F = (-64.0)\left[ (-4)(4) - \frac{(3)(16)}{2} + \frac{64}{3} \right] = \frac{(-64.0)(-120 + 64)}{3} \approx 1194.7 \text{ lb}$

36. Using the coordinate system given, we find an equation for the line of the plate's right-hand edge to be $y = -2x + 4$
$\Rightarrow x = \frac{4-y}{2}$ and $L(y) = 2x = 4 - y$. The depth of the strip is $(1 - y) \Rightarrow F = \int_{0}^{1} w(1 - y)(4 - y)\, dy$

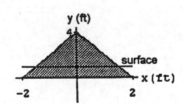

$= 62.4 \int_{0}^{1} (y^2 - 5y + 4)\, dy = 62.4 \left[ \frac{y^3}{3} - \frac{5y^2}{2} + 4y \right]_{0}^{1}$

$= (62.4)\left( \frac{1}{3} - \frac{5}{2} + 4 \right) = (62.4)\left( \frac{2 - 15 + 24}{6} \right) = \frac{(62.4)(11)}{6} = 114.4 \text{ lb}$

37. Using the coordinate system given in the accompanying
   figure, we see that the total width is $L(y) = 63$ and the depth
   of the strip is $(33.5 - y) \Rightarrow F = \int_0^{33} w(33.5 - y)L(y)\, dy$

   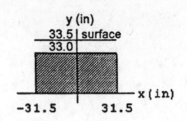

   $= \int_0^{33} \frac{64}{12^3} \cdot (33.5 - y) \cdot 63\, dy = \left(\frac{64}{12^3}\right)(63)\int_0^{33} (33.5 - y)\, dy$

   $= \left(\frac{64}{12^3}\right)(63)\left[33.5y - \frac{y^2}{2}\right]_0^{33} = \left(\frac{64 \cdot 63}{12^3}\right)\left[(33.5)(33) - \frac{33^2}{2}\right]$

   $= \frac{(64)(63)(33)(67 - 33)}{(2)(12^3)} = 1309$ lb

38. Using the coordinate system given in the accompanying
   figure, we see that the right-hand edge is $x = \sqrt{1 - y^2}$
   so the total width is $L(y) = 2x = 2\sqrt{1 - y^2}$ and the depth
   of the strip is $(-y)$. The force exerted by the water is

   therefore $F = \int_{-1}^0 w \cdot (-y) \cdot 2\sqrt{1 - y^2}\, dy$

   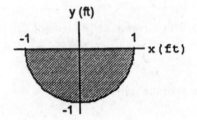

   $= 62.4\int_{-1}^0 \sqrt{1 - y^2}\, d(1 - y^2) = 62.4\left[\frac{2}{3}(1 - y^2)^{3/2}\right]_{-1}^0 = (62.4)\left(\frac{2}{3}\right)(1 - 0) = 41.6$ lb

39. (a)  $F = \left(62.4\, \frac{lb}{ft^3}\right)(8\, ft)(25\, ft^2) = 12480$ lb

   (b)  The width of the strip is $L(y) = 5$, the depth of the strip is $(8 - y) \Rightarrow F = \int_a^b w \cdot \left(\frac{strip}{depth}\right)F(y)\, dy$

   $= \int_0^5 62.4(8 - y)(5)\, dy = 312\int_0^5 (8 - y)\, dy = 312\left[8y - \frac{y^2}{2}\right]_0^5 = 312\left(40 - \frac{25}{2}\right) = 8580$ lb

   (c)  The width of the strip is $L(y) = 5$, the depth of the strip is $(8 - y)$, the height of the strip is $\sqrt{2}\, dy$

   $\Rightarrow F = \int_a^b w \cdot \left(\frac{strip}{depth}\right)F(y)\, dy = \int_0^{5/\sqrt{2}} 62.4(8 - y)(5)\sqrt{2}\, dy = 312\sqrt{2}\int_0^{5/\sqrt{2}} (8 - y)\, dy = 312\sqrt{2}\left[8y - \frac{y^2}{2}\right]_0^{5/\sqrt{2}}$

   $= 312\sqrt{2}\left(\frac{40}{\sqrt{2}} - \frac{25}{4}\right) = 9722.3$

40. The width of the strip is $L(y) = \frac{3}{4}\left(2\sqrt{3} - y\right)$, the depth of the strip is $(6 - y)$, the height of the strip is $\frac{2}{\sqrt{3}}\, dy$

   $\Rightarrow F = \int_a^b w \cdot \left(\frac{strip}{depth}\right)F(y)\, dy = \int_0^{2\sqrt{3}} 62.4(6 - y) \cdot \frac{3}{4}\left(2\sqrt{3} - y\right)\frac{2}{\sqrt{3}}\, dy = \frac{93.6}{\sqrt{3}}\int_0^{2\sqrt{3}}\left(12\sqrt{3} - 6y - 2y\sqrt{3} + y^2\right)dy$

   $= \frac{93.6}{\sqrt{3}}\left[12y\sqrt{3} - 3y^2 - y^2\sqrt{3} + \frac{y^3}{3}\right]_0^{2\sqrt{3}} = \frac{93.6}{\sqrt{3}}\left(72 - 36 - 12\sqrt{3} + 8\sqrt{3}\right) \approx 1571.04$ lb

41. The coordinate system is given in the text. The right-hand edge is $x = \sqrt{y}$ and the total width is $L(y) = 2x = 2\sqrt{y}$.

   (a)  The depth of the strip is $(2 - y)$ so the force exerted by the liquid on the gate is $F = \int_0^1 w(2 - y)L(y)\, dy$

   $= \int_0^1 50(2 - y) \cdot 2\sqrt{y}\, dy = 100\int_0^1 (2 - y)\sqrt{y}\, dy = 100\int_0^1 \left(2y^{1/2} - y^{3/2}\right)dy = 100\left[\frac{4}{3}y^{3/2} - \frac{2}{5}y^{5/2}\right]_0^1$

   $= 100\left(\frac{4}{3} - \frac{2}{5}\right) = \left(\frac{100}{15}\right)(20 - 6) = 93.33$ lb

   (b)  We need to solve $160 = \int_0^1 w(H - y) \cdot 2\sqrt{y}\, dy$ for h. $160 = 100\left(\frac{2H}{3} - \frac{2}{5}\right) \Rightarrow H = 3$ ft.

42. Suppose that h is the maximum height. Using the coordinate system given in the text, we find an equation for
   the line of the end plate's right-hand edge is $y = \frac{5}{2}x \Rightarrow x = \frac{2}{5}y$. The total width is $L(y) = 2x = \frac{4}{5}y$ and the

   depth of the typical horizontal strip at level y is $(h - y)$. Then the force is $F = \int_0^h w(h - y)L(y)\, dy = F_{max}$,

   where $F_{max} = 6667$ lb. Hence, $F_{max} = w\int_0^h (h - y) \cdot \frac{4}{5}y\, dy = (62.4)\left(\frac{4}{5}\right)\int_0^h (hy - y^2)\, dy$

   $= (62.4)\left(\frac{4}{5}\right)\left[\frac{hy^2}{2} - \frac{y^3}{3}\right]_0^h = (62.4)\left(\frac{4}{5}\right)\left(\frac{h^3}{2} - \frac{h^3}{3}\right) = (62.4)\left(\frac{4}{5}\right)\left(\frac{1}{6}\right)h^3 = (10.4)\left(\frac{4}{5}\right)h^3 \Rightarrow h = \sqrt[3]{\left(\frac{5}{4}\right)\left(\frac{F_{max}}{10.4}\right)}$

$= \sqrt[3]{\left(\frac{5}{4}\right)\left(\frac{6667}{10.4}\right)} \approx 9.288$ ft. The volume of water which the tank can hold is $V = \frac{1}{2}$ (Base)(Height) · 30, where

Height = h and $\frac{1}{2}$ (Base) = $\frac{2}{5}$ h $\Rightarrow$ $V = \left(\frac{2}{5} h^2\right)(30) = 12h^2 \approx 12(9.288)^2 \approx 1035$ ft³.

43. The pressure at level y is $p(y) = w \cdot y \Rightarrow$ the average

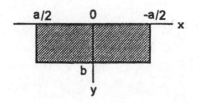

pressure is $\bar{p} = \frac{1}{b}\int_0^b p(y)\,dy = \frac{1}{b}\int_0^b w \cdot y\,dy = \frac{1}{b}w\left[\frac{y^2}{2}\right]_0^b$

$= \left(\frac{w}{b}\right)\left(\frac{b^2}{2}\right) = \frac{wb}{2}$. This is the pressure at level $\frac{b}{2}$, which

is the pressure at the middle of the plate.

44. The force exerted by the fluid is $F = \int_0^b w(\text{depth})(\text{length})\,dy = \int_0^b w \cdot y \cdot a\,dy = (w \cdot a)\int_0^b y\,dy = (w \cdot a)\left[\frac{y^2}{2}\right]_0^b$

$= w\left(\frac{ab^2}{2}\right) = \left(\frac{wb}{2}\right)(ab) = \bar{p} \cdot \text{Area}$, where $\bar{p}$ is the average value of the pressure.

45. When the water reaches the top of the tank the force on the movable side is $\int_{-2}^0 (62.4)\left(2\sqrt{4-y^2}\right)(-y)\,dy$

$= (62.4)\int_{-2}^0 (4-y^2)^{1/2}(-2y)\,dy = (62.4)\left[\frac{2}{3}(4-y^2)^{3/2}\right]_{-2}^0 = (62.4)\left(\frac{2}{3}\right)\left(4^{3/2}\right) = 332.8$ ft · lb. The force

compressing the spring is $F = 100x$, so when the tank is full we have $332.8 = 100x \Rightarrow x \approx 3.33$ ft. Therefore the

movable end does not reach the required 5 ft to allow drainage $\Rightarrow$ the tank will overflow.

46. (a) Using the given coordinate system we see that the total

width is $L(y) = 3$ and the depth of the strip is $(3-y)$.

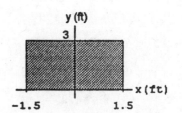

Thus, $F = \int_0^3 w(3-y)L(y)\,dy = \int_0^3 (62.4)(3-y) \cdot 3\,dy$

$= (62.4)(3)\int_0^3 (3-y)\,dy = (62.4)(3)\left[3y - \frac{y^2}{2}\right]_0^3$

$= (62.4)(3)\left(9 - \frac{9}{2}\right) = (62.4)(3)\left(\frac{9}{2}\right) = 842.4$ lb

(b) Find a new water level Y such that $F_Y = (0.75)(842.4 \text{ lb}) = 631.8$ lb. The new depth of the strip is $(Y-y)$ and Y is

the new upper limit of integration. Thus, $F_Y = \int_0^Y w(Y-y)L(y)\,dy = 62.4\int_0^Y (Y-y) \cdot 3\,dy$

$= (62.4)(3)\int_0^Y (Y-y)\,dy = (62.4)(3)\left[Yy - \frac{y^2}{2}\right]_0^Y = (62.4)(3)\left(Y^2 - \frac{Y^2}{2}\right) = (62.4)(3)\left(\frac{Y^2}{2}\right)$. Therefore,

$Y = \sqrt{\frac{2F_Y}{(62.4)(3)}} = \sqrt{\frac{1263.6}{187.2}} = \sqrt{6.75} \approx 2.598$ ft. So, $\Delta Y = 3 - Y \approx 3 - 2.598 \approx 0.402$ ft $\approx 4.8$ in

## 6.6 MOMENTS AND CENTERS OF MASS

1. Since the plate is symmetric about the y-axis and its density is

constant, the distribution of mass is symmetric about the y-axis

and the center of mass lies on the y-axis. This means that

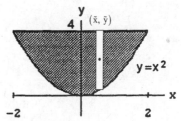

$\bar{x} = 0$. It remains to find $\bar{y} = \frac{M_x}{M}$. We model the distribution of

mass with *vertical* strips. The typical strip has center of mass:

$(\tilde{x}, \tilde{y}) = \left(x, \frac{x^2+4}{2}\right)$, length: $4 - x^2$, width: dx, area:

$dA = (4 - x^2)\,dx$, mass: $dm = \delta\,dA = \delta(4 - x^2)\,dx$. The moment of the strip about the x-axis is

$\tilde{y}\,dm = \left(\frac{x^2+4}{2}\right)\delta(4-x^2)\,dx = \frac{\delta}{2}(16-x^4)\,dx$. The moment of the plate about the x-axis is $M_x = \int \tilde{y}\,dm$

$= \int_{-2}^2 \frac{\delta}{2}(16-x^4)\,dx = \frac{\delta}{2}\left[16x - \frac{x^5}{5}\right]_{-2}^2 = \frac{\delta}{2}\left[\left(16 \cdot 2 - \frac{2^5}{5}\right) - \left(-16 \cdot 2 + \frac{2^5}{5}\right)\right] = \frac{\delta \cdot 2}{2}\left(32 - \frac{32}{5}\right) = \frac{128\delta}{5}$. The mass of the plate is $M = \int \delta \left(4 - x^2\right) dx = \delta \left[4x - \frac{x^3}{3}\right]_{-2}^{2} = 2\delta \left(8 - \frac{8}{3}\right) = \frac{32\delta}{3}$. Therefore $\overline{y} = \frac{M_x}{M} = \frac{\left(\frac{128\delta}{5}\right)}{\left(\frac{32\delta}{3}\right)} = \frac{12}{5}$. The plate's center of

mass is the point $(\overline{x}, \overline{y}) = \left(0, \frac{12}{5}\right)$.

2. Applying the symmetry argument analogous to the one in
   Exercise 1, we find $\overline{x} = 0$. To find $\overline{y} = \frac{M_x}{M}$, we use the
   *vertical* strips technique. The typical strip has center of

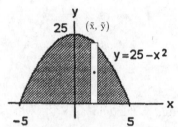

   mass: $(\widetilde{x}, \widetilde{y}) = \left(x, \frac{25 - x^2}{2}\right)$, length: $25 - x^2$, width: dx,

   area: $dA = (25 - x^2)dx$, mass: $dm = \delta\, dA = \delta \left(25 - x^2\right) dx$.
   The moment of the strip about the x-axis is

$\widetilde{y}\, dm = \left(\frac{25 - x^2}{2}\right) \delta \left(25 - x^2\right) dx = \frac{\delta}{2} \left(25 - x^2\right)^2 dx$. The moment of the plate about the x-axis is $M_x = \int \widetilde{y}\, dm$

$= \int_{-5}^{5} \frac{\delta}{2} \left(25 - x^2\right)^2 dx = \frac{\delta}{2} \int_{-5}^{5} \left(625 - 50x^2 + x^4\right) dx = \frac{\delta}{2} \left[625x - \frac{50}{3} x^3 + \frac{x^5}{5}\right]_{-5}^{5} = 2 \cdot \frac{\delta}{2} \left(625 \cdot 5 - \frac{50}{3} \cdot 5^3 + \frac{5^5}{5}\right)$

$= \delta \cdot 625 \left(5 - \frac{10}{3} + 1\right) = \delta \cdot 625 \cdot \left(\frac{8}{3}\right)$. The mass of the plate is $M = \int dm = \int_{-5}^{5} \delta \left(25 - x^2\right) dx = \delta \left[25x - \frac{x^3}{3}\right]_{-5}^{5}$

$= 2\delta \left(5^3 - \frac{5^3}{3}\right) = \frac{4}{3} \delta \cdot 5^3$. Therefore $\overline{y} = \frac{M_x}{M} = \frac{\delta \cdot 5^4 \cdot \left(\frac{8}{3}\right)}{\delta \cdot 5^3 \cdot \left(\frac{4}{3}\right)} = 10$. The plate's center of mass is the point $(\overline{x}, \overline{y}) = (0, 10)$.

3. Intersection points: $x - x^2 = -x \Rightarrow 2x - x^2 = 0$
   $\Rightarrow x(2 - x) = 0 \Rightarrow x = 0$ or $x = 2$. The typical *vertical*
   strip has center of mass: $(\widetilde{x}, \widetilde{y}) = \left(x, \frac{(x - x^2) + (-x)}{2}\right)$

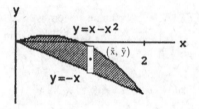

   $= \left(x, -\frac{x^2}{2}\right)$, length: $(x - x^2) - (-x) = 2x - x^2$, width: dx,
   area: $dA = (2x - x^2) dx$, mass: $dm = \delta\, dA = \delta \left(2x - x^2\right) dx$.
   The moment of the strip about the x-axis is

$\widetilde{y}\, dm = \left(-\frac{x^2}{2}\right) \delta \left(2x - x^2\right) dx$; about the y-axis it is $\widetilde{x}\, dm = x \cdot \delta \left(2x - x^2\right) dx$. Thus, $M_x = \int \widetilde{y}\, dm$

$= -\int_{0}^{2} \left(\frac{\delta}{2} x^2\right) \left(2x - x^2\right) dx = -\frac{\delta}{2} \int_{0}^{2} \left(2x^3 - x^4\right) dx = -\frac{\delta}{2} \left[\frac{x^4}{2} - \frac{x^5}{5}\right]_{0}^{2} = -\frac{\delta}{2} \left(2^3 - \frac{2^5}{5}\right) = -\frac{\delta}{2} \cdot 2^3 \left(1 - \frac{4}{5}\right)$

$= -\frac{4\delta}{5}$; $M_y = \int \widetilde{x}\, dm = \int_{0}^{2} x \cdot \delta \left(2x - x^2\right) dx = \delta \int_{0}^{2} \left(2x^2 - x^3\right) = \delta \left[\frac{2}{3} x^3 - \frac{x^4}{4}\right]_{0}^{2} = \delta \left(2 \cdot \frac{2^3}{3} - \frac{2^4}{4}\right) = \frac{\delta \cdot 2^4}{12} = \frac{4\delta}{3}$;

$M = \int dm = \int_{0}^{2} \delta \left(2x - x^2\right) dx = \delta \int_{0}^{2} \left(2x - x^2\right) dx = \delta \left[x^2 - \frac{x^3}{3}\right]_{0}^{2} = \delta \left(4 - \frac{8}{3}\right) = \frac{4\delta}{3}$. Therefore, $\overline{x} = \frac{M_y}{M}$

$= \left(\frac{4\delta}{3}\right) \left(\frac{3}{4\delta}\right) = 1$ and $\overline{y} = \frac{M_x}{M} = \left(-\frac{4\delta}{5}\right) \left(\frac{3}{4\delta}\right) = -\frac{3}{5} \Rightarrow (\overline{x}, \overline{y}) = \left(1, -\frac{3}{5}\right)$ is the center of mass.

4. Intersection points: $x^2 - 3 = -2x^2 \Rightarrow 3x^2 - 3 = 0$
   $\Rightarrow 3(x - 1)(x + 1) = 0 \Rightarrow x = -1$ or $x = 1$. Applying the
   symmetry argument analogous to the one in Exercise 1, we
   find $\overline{x} = 0$. The typical *vertical* strip has center of mass:

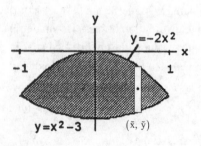

   $(\widetilde{x}, \widetilde{y}) = \left(x, \frac{-2x^2 + (x^2 - 3)}{2}\right) = \left(x, \frac{-x^2 - 3}{2}\right)$,
   length: $-2x^2 - (x^2 - 3) = 3\left(1 - x^2\right)$, width: dx,
   area: $dA = 3\left(1 - x^2\right) dx$, mass: $dm = \delta\, dA = 3\delta \left(1 - x^2\right) dx$.
   The moment of the strip about the x-axis is

$\widetilde{y}\, dm = \frac{3}{2} \delta \left(-x^2 - 3\right) \left(1 - x^2\right) dx = \frac{3}{2} \delta \left(x^4 + 3x^2 - x^2 - 3\right) dx = \frac{3}{2} \delta \left(x^4 + 2x^2 - 3\right) dx$; $M_x = \int \widetilde{y}\, dm$

$= \frac{3}{2} \delta \int_{-1}^{1} \left(x^4 + 2x^2 - 3\right) dx = \frac{3}{2} \delta \left[\frac{x^5}{5} + \frac{2x^3}{3} - 3x\right]_{-1}^{1} = \frac{3}{2} \cdot \delta \cdot 2 \left(\frac{1}{5} + \frac{2}{3} - 3\right) = 3\delta \left(\frac{3 + 10 - 45}{15}\right) = -\frac{32\delta}{5}$;

$M = \int dm = 3\delta \int_{-1}^{1} (1 - x^2)\, dx = 3\delta \left[ x - \frac{x^3}{3} \right]_{-1}^{1} = 3\delta \cdot 2 \left( 1 - \frac{1}{3} \right) = 4\delta$. Therefore, $\bar{y} = \frac{M_x}{M} = -\frac{\delta \cdot 32}{5 \cdot \delta \cdot 4} = -\frac{8}{5}$

$\Rightarrow (\bar{x}, \bar{y}) = \left( 0, -\frac{8}{5} \right)$ is the center of mass.

5. The typical *horizontal* strip has center of mass:

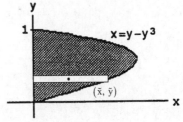

$(\tilde{x}, \tilde{y}) = \left( \frac{y - y^3}{2}, y \right)$, length: $y - y^3$, width: dy,

area: $dA = (y - y^3)\, dy$, mass: $dm = \delta\, dA = \delta (y - y^3)\, dy$.
The moment of the strip about the y-axis is

$\tilde{x}\, dm = \delta \left( \frac{y - y^3}{2} \right) (y - y^3)\, dy = \frac{\delta}{2} (y - y^3)^2\, dy$

$= \frac{\delta}{2} (y^2 - 2y^4 + y^6)\, dy$; the moment about the x-axis is

$\tilde{y}\, dm = \delta y (y - y^3)\, dy = \delta (y^2 - y^4)\, dy$. Thus, $M_x = \int \tilde{y}\, dm = \delta \int_0^1 (y^2 - y^4)\, dy = \delta \left[ \frac{y^3}{3} - \frac{y^5}{5} \right]_0^1 = \delta \left( \frac{1}{3} - \frac{1}{5} \right) = \frac{2\delta}{15}$;

$M_y = \int \tilde{x}\, dm = \frac{\delta}{2} \int_0^1 (y^2 - 2y^4 + y^6)\, dy = \frac{\delta}{2} \left[ \frac{y^3}{3} - \frac{2y^5}{5} + \frac{y^7}{7} \right]_0^1 = \frac{\delta}{2} \left( \frac{1}{3} - \frac{2}{5} + \frac{1}{7} \right) = \frac{\delta}{2} \left( \frac{35 - 42 + 15}{3 \cdot 5 \cdot 7} \right) = \frac{4\delta}{105}$ ; $M = \int dm$

$= \delta \int_0^1 (y - y^3)\, dy = \delta \left[ \frac{y^2}{2} - \frac{y^4}{4} \right]_0^1 = \delta \left( \frac{1}{2} - \frac{1}{4} \right) = \frac{\delta}{4}$. Therefore, $\bar{x} = \frac{M_y}{M} = \left( \frac{4\delta}{105} \right) \left( \frac{4}{\delta} \right) = \frac{16}{105}$ and $\bar{y} = \frac{M_x}{M} = \left( \frac{2\delta}{15} \right) \left( \frac{4}{\delta} \right)$

$= \frac{8}{15} \Rightarrow (\bar{x}, \bar{y}) = \left( \frac{16}{105}, \frac{8}{15} \right)$ is the center of mass.

6. Intersection points: $y = y^2 - y \Rightarrow y^2 - 2y = 0$

$\Rightarrow y(y - 2) = 0 \Rightarrow y = 0$ or $y = 2$. The typical

*horizontal* strip has center of mass:

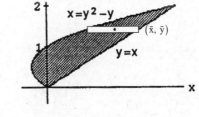

$(\tilde{x}, \tilde{y}) = \left( \frac{(y^2 - y) + y}{2}, y \right) = \left( \frac{y^2}{2}, y \right)$,

length: $y - (y^2 - y) = 2y - y^2$, width: dy,

area: $dA = (2y - y^2)\, dy$, mass: $dm = \delta\, dA = \delta (2y - y^2)\, dy$.
The moment about the y-axis is $\tilde{x}\, dm = \frac{\delta}{2} \cdot y^2 (2y - y^2)\, dy$

$= \frac{\delta}{2} (2y^3 - y^4)\, dy$; the moment about the x-axis is $\tilde{y}\, dm = \delta y (2y - y^2)\, dy = \delta (2y^2 - y^3)\, dy$. Thus,

$M_x = \int \tilde{y}\, dm = \int_0^2 \delta (2y^2 - y^3)\, dy = \delta \left[ \frac{2y^3}{3} - \frac{y^4}{4} \right]_0^2 = \delta \left( \frac{16}{3} - \frac{16}{4} \right) = \frac{16\delta}{12} (4 - 3) = \frac{4\delta}{3}$ ; $M_y = \int \tilde{x}\, dm$

$= \int_0^2 \frac{\delta}{2} (2y^3 - y^4)\, dy = \frac{\delta}{2} \left[ \frac{y^4}{2} - \frac{y^5}{5} \right]_0^2 = \frac{\delta}{2} \left( 8 - \frac{32}{5} \right) = \frac{\delta}{2} \left( \frac{40 - 32}{5} \right) = \frac{4\delta}{5}$ ; $M = \int dm = \int_0^2 \delta (2y - y^2)\, dy$

$= \delta \left[ y^2 - \frac{y^3}{3} \right]_0^2 = \delta \left( 4 - \frac{8}{3} \right) = \frac{4\delta}{3}$. Therefore, $\bar{x} = \frac{M_y}{M} = \left( \frac{4\delta}{5} \right) \left( \frac{3}{4\delta} \right) = \frac{3}{5}$ and $\bar{y} = \frac{M_x}{M} = \left( \frac{4\delta}{3} \right) \left( \frac{3}{4\delta} \right) = 1$

$\Rightarrow (\bar{x}, \bar{y}) = \left( \frac{3}{5}, 1 \right)$ is the center of mass.

7. Applying the symmetry argument analogous to the one used
in Exercise 1, we find $\bar{x} = 0$. The typical *vertical* strip has
center of mass: $(\tilde{x}, \tilde{y}) = \left( x, \frac{\cos x}{2} \right)$, length: $\cos x$, width: dx,

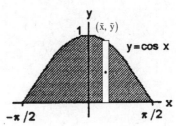

area: $dA = \cos x\, dx$, mass: $dm = \delta\, dA = \delta \cos x\, dx$. The
moment of the strip about the x-axis is $\tilde{y}\, dm = \delta \cdot \frac{\cos x}{2} \cdot \cos x\, dx$

$= \frac{\delta}{2} \cos^2 x\, dx = \frac{\delta}{2} \left( \frac{1 + \cos 2x}{2} \right) dx = \frac{\delta}{4} (1 + \cos 2x)\, dx$; thus,

$M_x = \int \tilde{y}\, dm = \int_{-\pi/2}^{\pi/2} \frac{\delta}{4} (1 + \cos 2x)\, dx = \frac{\delta}{4} \left[ x + \frac{\sin 2x}{2} \right]_{-\pi/2}^{\pi/2} = \frac{\delta}{4} \left[ \left( \frac{\pi}{2} + 0 \right) - \left( -\frac{\pi}{2} \right) \right] = \frac{\delta\pi}{4}$ ; $M = \int dm = \delta \int_{-\pi/2}^{\pi/2} \cos x\, dx$

$= \delta [\sin x]_{-\pi/2}^{\pi/2} = 2\delta$. Therefore, $\bar{y} = \frac{M_x}{M} = \frac{\delta\pi}{4 \cdot 2\delta} = \frac{\pi}{8} \Rightarrow (\bar{x}, \bar{y}) = \left( 0, \frac{\pi}{8} \right)$ is the center of mass.

8. Applying the symmetry argument analogous to the one used in Exercise 1, we find $\bar{x} = 0$. The typical vertical strip has center of mass: $(\tilde{x}, \tilde{y}) = \left(x, \frac{\sec^2 x}{2}\right)$, length: $\sec^2 x$, width: dx, area: $dA = \sec^2 x \, dx$, mass: $dm = \delta \, dA = \delta \sec^2 x \, dx$. The moment about the x-axis is $\tilde{y} \, dm = \left(\frac{\sec^2 x}{2}\right)(\delta \sec^2 x) \, dx$

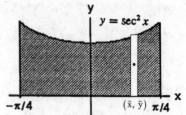

$= \frac{\delta}{2} \sec^4 x \, dx$. $M_x = \int_{-\pi/4}^{\pi/4} \tilde{y} \, dm = \frac{\delta}{2} \int_{-\pi/4}^{\pi/4} \sec^4 x \, dx$

$= \frac{\delta}{2} \int_{-\pi/4}^{\pi/4} (\tan^2 x + 1)(\sec^2 x) \, dx = \frac{\delta}{2} \int_{-\pi/4}^{\pi/4} (\tan x)^2 (\sec^2 x) \, dx + \frac{\delta}{2} \int_{-\pi/4}^{\pi/4} \sec^2 x \, dx = \frac{\delta}{2} \left[\frac{(\tan x)^3}{3}\right]_{-\pi/4}^{\pi/4} + \frac{\delta}{2} [\tan x]_{-\pi/4}^{\pi/4}$

$= \frac{\delta}{2}\left[\frac{1}{3} - \left(-\frac{1}{3}\right)\right] + \frac{\delta}{2}[1 - (-1)] = \frac{\delta}{3} + \delta = \frac{4\delta}{3}$; $M = \int dm = \delta \int_{-\pi/4}^{\pi/4} \sec^2 x \, dx = \delta[\tan x]_{-\pi/4}^{\pi/4} = \delta[1 - (-1)] = 2\delta$. Therefore, $\bar{y} = \frac{M_x}{M} = \left(\frac{4\delta}{3}\right)\left(\frac{1}{2\delta}\right) = \frac{2}{3} \Rightarrow (\bar{x}, \bar{y}) = \left(0, \frac{2}{3}\right)$ is the center of mass.

9. Since the plate is symmetric about the line $x = 1$ and its density is constant, the distribution of mass is symmetric about this line and the center of mass lies on it. This means that $\bar{x} = 1$. The typical *vertical* strip has center of mass: $(\tilde{x}, \tilde{y}) = \left(x, \frac{(2x - x^2) + (2x^2 - 4x)}{2}\right) = \left(x, \frac{x^2 - 2x}{2}\right)$, length: $(2x - x^2) - (2x^2 - 4x) = -3x^2 + 6x = 3(2x - x^2)$, width: dx, area: $dA = 3(2x - x^2) \, dx$, mass: $dm = \delta \, dA = 3\delta(2x - x^2) \, dx$. The moment about the x-axis is $\tilde{y} \, dm = \frac{3}{2}\delta(x^2 - 2x)(2x - x^2) \, dx = -\frac{3}{2}\delta(x^2 - 2x)^2 \, dx$

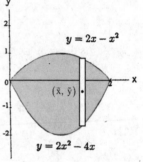

$= -\frac{3}{2}\delta(x^4 - 4x^3 + 4x^2) \, dx$. Thus, $M_x = \int \tilde{y} \, dm = -\int_0^2 \frac{3}{2}\delta(x^4 - 4x^3 + 4x^2) \, dx = -\frac{3}{2}\delta \left[\frac{x^5}{5} - x^4 + \frac{4}{3}x^3\right]_0^2$

$= -\frac{3}{2}\delta\left(\frac{2^5}{5} - 2^4 + \frac{4}{3} \cdot 2^3\right) = -\frac{3}{2}\delta \cdot 2^4 \left(\frac{2}{5} - 1 + \frac{2}{3}\right) = -\frac{3}{2}\delta \cdot 2^4 \left(\frac{6 - 15 + 10}{15}\right) = -\frac{8\delta}{5}$; $M = \int dm$

$= \int_0^2 3\delta(2x - x^2) \, dx = 3\delta\left[x^2 - \frac{x^3}{3}\right]_0^2 = 3\delta\left(4 - \frac{8}{3}\right) = 4\delta$. Therefore, $\bar{y} = \frac{M_x}{M} = \left(-\frac{8\delta}{5}\right)\left(\frac{1}{4\delta}\right) = -\frac{2}{5}$

$\Rightarrow (\bar{x}, \bar{y}) = \left(1, -\frac{2}{5}\right)$ is the center of mass.

10. (a) Since the plate is symmetric about the line $x = y$ and its density is constant, the distribution of mass is symmetric about this line. This means that $\bar{x} = \bar{y}$. The typical *vertical* strip has center of mass: $(\tilde{x}, \tilde{y}) = \left(x, \frac{\sqrt{9 - x^2}}{2}\right)$, length: $\sqrt{9 - x^2}$, width: dx, area: $dA = \sqrt{9 - x^2} \, dx$, mass: $dm = \delta \, dA = \delta\sqrt{9 - x^2} \, dx$. The moment about the x-axis is

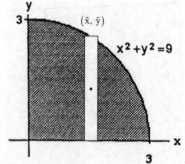

$\tilde{y} \, dm = \delta\left(\frac{\sqrt{9 - x^2}}{2}\right)\sqrt{9 - x^2} \, dx = \frac{\delta}{2}(9 - x^2) \, dx$. Thus, $M_x = \int \tilde{y} \, dm = \int_0^3 \frac{\delta}{2}(9 - x^2) \, dx = \frac{\delta}{2}\left[9x - \frac{x^3}{3}\right]_0^3$

$= \frac{\delta}{2}(27 - 9) = 9\delta$; $M = \int dm = \int \delta \, dA = \delta \int dA = \delta(\text{Area of a quarter of a circle of radius 3}) = \delta\left(\frac{9\pi}{4}\right) = \frac{9\pi\delta}{4}$. Therefore, $\bar{y} = \frac{M_x}{M} = (9\delta)\left(\frac{4}{9\pi\delta}\right) = \frac{4}{\pi} \Rightarrow (\bar{x}, \bar{y}) = \left(\frac{4}{\pi}, \frac{4}{\pi}\right)$ is the center of mass.

(b) Applying the symmetry argument analogous to the one used in Exercise 1, we find that $\bar{x} = 0$. The typical vertical strip has the same parameters as in part (a).

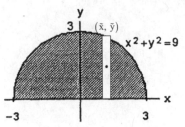

Thus, $M_x = \int \tilde{y} \, dm = \int_{-3}^{3} \frac{\delta}{2} \left(9 - x^2\right) dx$

$= 2 \int_{0}^{3} \frac{\delta}{2} \left(9 - x^2\right) dx = 2(9\delta) = 18\delta;$

$M = \int dm = \int \delta \, dA = \delta \int dA$

$= \delta(\text{Area of a semi-circle of radius 3}) = \delta \left(\frac{9\pi}{2}\right) = \frac{9\pi\delta}{2}.$ Therefore, $\bar{y} = \frac{M_x}{M} = (18\delta) \left(\frac{2}{9\pi\delta}\right) = \frac{4}{\pi}$, the same $\bar{y}$ as in part (a) $\Rightarrow (\bar{x}, \bar{y}) = \left(0, \frac{4}{\pi}\right)$ is the center of mass.

11. Since the plate is symmetric about the line $x = y$ and its density is constant, the distribution of mass is symmetric about this line. This means that $\bar{x} = \bar{y}$. The typical *vertical* strip has

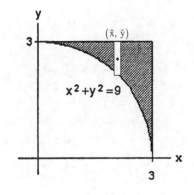

center of mass: $(\tilde{x}, \tilde{y}) = \left(x, \frac{3 + \sqrt{9 - x^2}}{2}\right),$

length: $3 - \sqrt{9 - x^2}$, width: $dx$,

area: $dA = \left(3 - \sqrt{9 - x^2}\right) dx,$

mass: $dm = \delta \, dA = \delta \left(3 - \sqrt{9 - x^2}\right) dx.$

The moment about the x-axis is

$\tilde{y} \, dm = \delta \frac{\left(3 + \sqrt{9 - x^2}\right)\left(3 - \sqrt{9 - x^2}\right)}{2} dx = \frac{\delta}{2} [9 - (9 - x^2)] \, dx = \frac{\delta x^2}{2} \, dx.$ Thus, $M_x = \int_{0}^{3} \frac{\delta x^2}{2} \, dx = \frac{\delta}{6} [x^3]_0^3 = \frac{9\delta}{2}.$ The area equals the area of a square with side length 3 minus one quarter the area of a disk with radius 3 $\Rightarrow A = 3^2 - \frac{\pi 9}{4}$

$= \frac{9}{4}(4 - \pi) \Rightarrow M = \delta A = \frac{9\delta}{4}(4 - \pi).$ Therefore, $\bar{y} = \frac{M_x}{M} = \left(\frac{9\delta}{2}\right)\left[\frac{4}{9\delta(4 - \pi)}\right] = \frac{2}{4 - \pi} \Rightarrow (\bar{x}, \bar{y}) = \left(\frac{2}{4 - \pi}, \frac{2}{4 - \pi}\right)$ is the center of mass.

12. Applying the symmetry argument analogous to the one used in Exercise 1, we find that $\bar{y} = 0$. The typical *vertical* strip

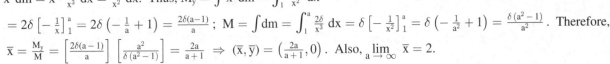

has center of mass: $(\tilde{x}, \tilde{y}) = \left(x, \frac{\frac{1}{x^3} - \frac{1}{x^3}}{2}\right) = (x, 0),$

length: $\frac{1}{x^3} - \left(-\frac{1}{x^3}\right) = \frac{2}{x^3}$, width: $dx$, area: $dA = \frac{2}{x^3} \, dx,$

mass: $dm = \delta \, dA = \frac{2\delta}{x^3} \, dx.$ The moment about the y-axis is

$\tilde{x} \, dm = x \cdot \frac{2\delta}{x^3} \, dx = \frac{2\delta}{x^2} \, dx.$ Thus, $M_y = \int \tilde{x} \, dm = \int_{1}^{a} \frac{2\delta}{x^2} \, dx$

$= 2\delta \left[-\frac{1}{x}\right]_1^a = 2\delta \left(-\frac{1}{a} + 1\right) = \frac{2\delta(a-1)}{a}; \quad M = \int dm = \int_{1}^{a} \frac{2\delta}{x^3} \, dx = \delta \left[-\frac{1}{x^2}\right]_1^a = \delta \left(-\frac{1}{a^2} + 1\right) = \frac{\delta(a^2 - 1)}{a^2}.$ Therefore,

$\bar{x} = \frac{M_y}{M} = \left[\frac{2\delta(a-1)}{a}\right]\left[\frac{a^2}{\delta(a^2-1)}\right] = \frac{2a}{a+1} \Rightarrow (\bar{x}, \bar{y}) = \left(\frac{2a}{a+1}, 0\right).$ Also, $\lim_{a \to \infty} \bar{x} = 2.$

13. $M_x = \int \tilde{y} \, dm = \int_{1}^{2} \frac{\left(\frac{2}{x^2}\right)}{2} \cdot \delta \cdot \left(\frac{2}{x^2}\right) dx$

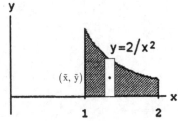

$= \int_{1}^{2} \left(\frac{1}{x^2}\right) (x^2) \left(\frac{2}{x^2}\right) dx = \int_{1}^{2} \frac{2}{x^2} \, dx = 2 \int_{1}^{2} x^{-2} \, dx$

$= 2 \left[-x^{-1}\right]_1^2 = 2 \left[\left(-\frac{1}{2}\right) - (-1)\right] = 2 \left(\frac{1}{2}\right) = 1;$

$M_y = \int \tilde{x} \, dm = \int_{1}^{2} x \cdot \delta \cdot \left(\frac{2}{x^2}\right) dx$

$= \int_{1}^{2} x (x^2) \left(\frac{2}{x^2}\right) dx = 2 \int_{1}^{2} x \, dx = 2 \left[\frac{x^2}{2}\right]_1^2$

$= 2 \left(2 - \frac{1}{2}\right) = 4 - 1 = 3; \quad M = \int dm = \int_{1}^{2} \delta \left(\frac{2}{x^2}\right) dx = \int_{1}^{2} x^2 \left(\frac{2}{x^2}\right) dx = 2 \int_{1}^{2} dx = 2[x]_1^2 = 2(2 - 1) = 2.$ So $\bar{x} = \frac{M_y}{M} = \frac{3}{2}$ and $\bar{y} = \frac{M_x}{M} = \frac{1}{2} \Rightarrow (\bar{x}, \bar{y}) = \left(\frac{3}{2}, \frac{1}{2}\right)$ is the center of mass.

14. We use the *vertical* strip approach:

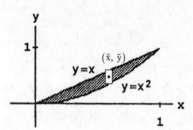

$$M_x = \int \tilde{y} \, dm = \int_0^1 \frac{(x+x^2)}{2} \left(x - x^2\right) \cdot \delta \, dx$$

$$= \frac{1}{2} \int_0^1 (x^2 - x^4) \cdot 12x \, dx$$

$$= 6 \int_0^1 (x^3 - x^5) \, dx = 6 \left[ \frac{x^4}{4} - \frac{x^6}{6} \right]_0^1$$

$$= 6 \left( \frac{1}{4} - \frac{1}{6} \right) = \frac{6}{4} - 1 = \frac{1}{2};$$

$$M_y = \int \tilde{x} \, dm = \int_0^1 x \left(x - x^2\right) \cdot \delta \, dx = \int_0^1 (x^2 - x^3) \cdot 12x \, dx = 12 \int_0^1 (x^3 - x^4) \, dx = 12 \left[ \frac{x^4}{4} - \frac{x^5}{5} \right]_0^1 = 12 \left( \frac{1}{4} - \frac{1}{5} \right)$$

$$= \frac{12}{20} = \frac{3}{5}; M = \int dm = \int_0^1 (x - x^2) \cdot \delta \, dx = 12 \int_0^1 (x^2 - x^3) \, dx = 12 \left[ \frac{x^3}{3} - \frac{x^4}{4} \right]_0^1 = 12 \left( \frac{1}{3} - \frac{1}{4} \right) = \frac{12}{12} = 1. \text{ So}$$

$$\bar{x} = \frac{M_y}{M} = \frac{3}{5} \text{ and } \bar{y} = \frac{M_x}{M} = \frac{1}{2} \Rightarrow \left( \frac{3}{5}, \frac{1}{2} \right) \text{ is the center of mass.}$$

15. (a) We use the shell method: $V = \int_a^b 2\pi \left( \substack{\text{shell} \\ \text{radius}} \right) \left( \substack{\text{shell} \\ \text{height}} \right) dx = \int_1^4 2\pi x \left[ \frac{4}{\sqrt{x}} - \left( -\frac{4}{\sqrt{x}} \right) \right] dx = 16\pi \int_1^4 \frac{x}{\sqrt{x}} \, dx$

$$= 16\pi \int_1^4 x^{1/2} \, dx = 16\pi \left[ \frac{2}{3} x^{3/2} \right]_1^4 = 16\pi \left( \frac{2}{3} \cdot 8 - \frac{2}{3} \right) = \frac{32\pi}{3} (8 - 1) = \frac{224\pi}{3}$$

   (b) Since the plate is symmetric about the x-axis and its density $\delta(x) = \frac{1}{x}$ is a function of x alone, the distribution of its mass is symmetric about the x-axis. This means that $\bar{y} = 0$. We use the vertical strip approach to find $\bar{x}$:

$$M_y = \int \tilde{x} \, dm = \int_1^4 x \cdot \left[ \frac{4}{\sqrt{x}} - \left( -\frac{4}{\sqrt{x}} \right) \right] \cdot \delta \, dx = \int_1^4 x \cdot \frac{8}{\sqrt{x}} \cdot \frac{1}{x} \, dx = 8 \int_1^4 x^{-1/2} \, dx = 8 \left[ 2x^{1/2} \right]_1^4 = 8(2 \cdot 2 - 2) = 16;$$

$$M = \int dm = \int_1^4 \left[ \frac{4}{\sqrt{x}} - \left( \frac{-4}{\sqrt{x}} \right) \right] \cdot \delta \, dx = 8 \int_1^4 \left( \frac{1}{\sqrt{x}} \right) \left( \frac{1}{x} \right) dx = 8 \int_1^4 x^{-3/2} \, dx = 8 \left[ -2x^{-1/2} \right]_1^4 = 8[-1 - (-2)] = 8.$$

   So $\bar{x} = \frac{M_y}{M} = \frac{16}{8} = 2 \Rightarrow (\bar{x}, \bar{y}) = (2, 0)$ is the center of mass.

   (c)

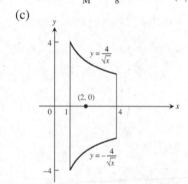

16. (a) We use the disk method: $V = \int_a^b \pi R^2(x) \, dx = \int_1^4 \pi \left( \frac{4}{x^2} \right) dx = 4\pi \int_1^4 x^{-2} \, dx = 4\pi \left[ -\frac{1}{x} \right]_1^4 = 4\pi \left[ \frac{-1}{4} - (-1) \right]$

$$= \pi[-1 + 4] = 3\pi$$

   (b) We model the distribution of mass with vertical strips: $M_x = \int \tilde{y} \, dm = \int_1^4 \frac{\left( \frac{2}{x} \right)}{2} \cdot \left( \frac{2}{x} \right) \cdot \delta \, dx = \int_1^4 \frac{2}{x^2} \cdot \sqrt{x} \, dx$

$$= 2 \int_1^4 x^{-3/2} \, dx = 2 \left[ \frac{-2}{\sqrt{x}} \right]_1^4 = 2[-1 - (-2)] = 2; M_y = \int \tilde{x} \, dm = \int_1^4 x \cdot \frac{2}{x} \cdot \delta \, dx = 2 \int_1^4 x^{1/2} \, dx = 2 \left[ \frac{2x^{3/2}}{3} \right]_1^4 =$$

$$2 \left[ \frac{16}{3} - \frac{2}{3} \right] = \frac{28}{3}; M = \int dm = \int_1^4 \frac{2}{x} \cdot \delta \, dx = 2 \int_1^4 \frac{\sqrt{x}}{x} \, dx = 2 \int_1^4 x^{-1/2} \, dx = 2 \left[ 2x^{1/2} \right]_1^4 = 2(4 - 2) = 4. \text{ So}$$

$$\bar{x} = \frac{M_y}{M} = \frac{\left( \frac{28}{3} \right)}{4} = \frac{7}{3} \text{ and } \bar{y} = \frac{M_x}{M} = \frac{2}{4} = \frac{1}{2} \Rightarrow (\bar{x}, \bar{y}) = \left( \frac{7}{3}, \frac{1}{2} \right) \text{ is the center of mass.}$$

(c)

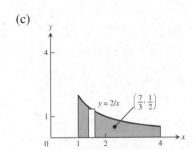

17. The mass of a horizontal strip is $dm = \delta \, dA = \delta L \, dy$, where L is the width of the triangle at a distance of y above its base on the x-axis as shown in the figure in the text. Also, by similar triangles we have $\frac{L}{b} = \frac{h-y}{h}$

$\Rightarrow L = \frac{b}{h}(h-y)$. Thus, $M_x = \int \tilde{y} \, dm = \int_0^h \delta y \left(\frac{b}{h}\right)(h-y) \, dy = \frac{\delta b}{h} \int_0^h (hy - y^2) \, dy = \frac{\delta b}{h} \left[\frac{hy^2}{2} - \frac{y^3}{3}\right]_0^h$

$= \frac{\delta b}{h} \left(\frac{h^3}{2} - \frac{h^3}{3}\right) = \delta b h^2 \left(\frac{1}{2} - \frac{1}{3}\right) = \frac{\delta b h^2}{6}$; $M = \int dm = \int_0^h \delta \left(\frac{b}{h}\right)(h-y) \, dy = \frac{\delta b}{h} \int_0^h (h-y) \, dy = \frac{\delta b}{h} \left[hy - \frac{y^2}{2}\right]_0^h$

$= \frac{\delta b}{h} \left(h^2 - \frac{h^2}{2}\right) = \frac{\delta b h}{2}$. So $\bar{y} = \frac{M_x}{M} = \left(\frac{\delta b h^2}{6}\right)\left(\frac{2}{\delta b h}\right) = \frac{h}{3}$ $\Rightarrow$ the center of mass lies above the base of the

triangle one-third of the way toward the opposite vertex. Similarly the other two sides of the triangle can be placed on the x-axis and the same results will occur. Therefore the centroid does lie at the intersection of the medians, as claimed.

18. From the symmetry about the y-axis it follows that $\bar{x} = 0$. It also follows that the line through the points $(0,0)$ and $(0,3)$ is a median $\Rightarrow \bar{y} = \frac{1}{3}(3-0) = 1 \Rightarrow (\bar{x},\bar{y}) = (0,1)$.

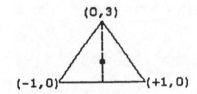

19. From the symmetry about the line $x = y$ it follows that $\bar{x} = \bar{y}$. It also follows that the line through the points $(0,0)$ and $\left(\frac{1}{2},\frac{1}{2}\right)$ is a median $\Rightarrow \bar{y} = \bar{x} = \frac{2}{3} \cdot \left(\frac{1}{2} - 0\right) = \frac{1}{3}$ $\Rightarrow (\bar{x},\bar{y}) = \left(\frac{1}{3},\frac{1}{3}\right)$.

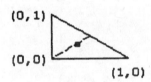

20. From the symmetry about the line $x = y$ it follows that $\bar{x} = \bar{y}$. It also follows that the line through the point $(0,0)$ and $\left(\frac{a}{2},\frac{a}{2}\right)$ is a median $\Rightarrow \bar{y} = \bar{x} = \frac{2}{3}\left(\frac{a}{2} - 0\right) = \frac{1}{3}a$ $\Rightarrow (\bar{x},\bar{y}) = \left(\frac{a}{3},\frac{a}{3}\right)$.

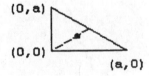

21. The point of intersection of the median from the vertex $(0,b)$ to the opposite side has coordinates $\left(0,\frac{a}{2}\right)$

$\Rightarrow \bar{y} = (b-0) \cdot \frac{1}{3} = \frac{b}{3}$ and $\bar{x} = \left(\frac{a}{2} - 0\right) \cdot \frac{2}{3} = \frac{a}{3}$

$\Rightarrow (\bar{x},\bar{y}) = \left(\frac{a}{3},\frac{b}{3}\right)$.

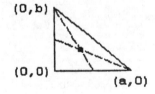

22. From the symmetry about the line $x = \frac{a}{2}$ it follows that $\bar{x} = \frac{a}{2}$. It also follows that the line through the points $\left(\frac{a}{2},0\right)$ and $\left(\frac{a}{2},b\right)$ is a median $\Rightarrow \bar{y} = \frac{1}{3}(b-0) = \frac{b}{3}$

$\Rightarrow (\bar{x},\bar{y}) = \left(\frac{a}{2},\frac{b}{3}\right)$.

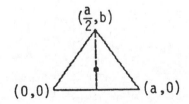

23. $y = x^{1/2} \Rightarrow dy = \frac{1}{2} x^{-1/2} dx$

$\Rightarrow ds = \sqrt{(dx)^2 + (dy)^2} = \sqrt{1 + \frac{1}{4x}} \, dx$;

$M_x = \delta \int_0^2 \sqrt{x} \sqrt{1 + \frac{1}{4x}} \, dx$

$= \delta \int_0^2 \sqrt{x + \frac{1}{4}} \, dx = \frac{2\delta}{3} \left[ \left( x + \frac{1}{4} \right)^{3/2} \right]_0^2$

$= \frac{2\delta}{3} \left[ \left( 2 + \frac{1}{4} \right)^{3/2} - \left( \frac{1}{4} \right)^{3/2} \right]$

$= \frac{2\delta}{3} \left[ \left( \frac{9}{4} \right)^{3/2} - \left( \frac{1}{4} \right)^{3/2} \right] = \frac{2\delta}{3} \left( \frac{27}{8} - \frac{1}{8} \right) = \frac{13\delta}{6}$

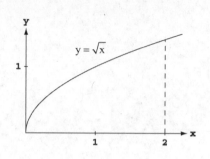

24. $y = x^3 \Rightarrow dy = 3x^2 \, dx$

$\Rightarrow dx = \sqrt{(dx)^2 + \left( 3x^2 \, dx \right)^2} = \sqrt{1 + 9x^4} \, dx$;

$M_x = \delta \int_0^1 x^3 \sqrt{1 + 9x^4} \, dx$;

$[u = 1 + 9x^4 \Rightarrow du = 36x^3 \, dx \Rightarrow \frac{1}{36} du = x^3 \, dx$;

$x = 0 \Rightarrow u = 1, x = 1 \Rightarrow u = 10]$

$\rightarrow M_x = \delta \int_1^{10} \frac{1}{36} u^{1/2} \, du = \frac{\delta}{36} \left[ \frac{2}{3} u^{3/2} \right]_1^{10} = \frac{\delta}{54} \left( 10^{3/2} - 1 \right)$

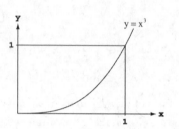

25. From Example 4 we have $M_x = \int_0^\pi a(a \sin \theta)(k \sin \theta) \, d\theta = a^2 k \int_0^\pi \sin^2 \theta \, d\theta = \frac{a^2 k}{2} \int_0^\pi (1 - \cos 2\theta) \, d\theta = \frac{a^2 k}{2} \left[ \theta - \frac{\sin 2\theta}{2} \right]_0^\pi$

$= \frac{a^2 k \pi}{2}$; $M_y = \int_0^\pi a(a \cos \theta)(k \sin \theta) \, d\theta = a^2 k \int_0^\pi \sin \theta \cos \theta \, d\theta = \frac{a^2 k}{2} \left[ \sin^2 \theta \right]_0^\pi = 0$; $M = \int_0^\pi ak \sin \theta \, d\theta = ak[- \cos \theta]_0^\pi$

$= 2ak$. Therefore, $\bar{x} = \frac{M_y}{M} = 0$ and $\bar{y} = \frac{M_x}{M} = \left( \frac{a^2 k \pi}{2} \right) \left( \frac{1}{2ak} \right) = \frac{a\pi}{4} \Rightarrow \left( 0, \frac{a\pi}{4} \right)$ is the center of mass.

26. $M_x = \int \tilde{y} \, dm = \int_0^\pi (a \sin \theta) \cdot \delta \cdot a \, d\theta$

$= \int_0^\pi (a^2 \sin \theta)(1 + k |\cos \theta|) \, d\theta$

$= a^2 \int_0^{\pi/2} (\sin \theta)(1 + k \cos \theta) \, d\theta$

$\quad + a^2 \int_{\pi/2}^\pi (\sin \theta)(1 - k \cos \theta) \, d\theta$

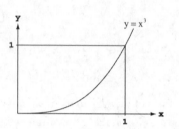

$= a^2 \int_0^{\pi/2} \sin \theta \, d\theta + a^2 k \int_0^{\pi/2} \sin \theta \cos \theta \, d\theta + a^2 \int_{\pi/2}^\pi \sin \theta \, d\theta - a^2 k \int_{\pi/2}^\pi \sin \theta \cos \theta \, d\theta$

$= a^2 [- \cos \theta]_0^{\pi/2} + a^2 k \left[ \frac{\sin^2 \theta}{2} \right]_0^{\pi/2} + a^2 [- \cos \theta]_{\pi/2}^\pi - a^2 k \left[ \frac{\sin^2 \theta}{2} \right]_{\pi/2}^\pi$

$= a^2 [0 - (-1)] + a^2 k \left( \frac{1}{2} - 0 \right) + a^2 [-(-1) - 0] - a^2 k \left( 0 - \frac{1}{2} \right) = a^2 + \frac{a^2 k}{2} + a^2 + \frac{a^2 k}{2} = 2a^2 + a^2 k = a^2 (2 + k)$;

$M_y = \int \tilde{x} \, dm = \int_0^\pi (a \cos \theta) \cdot \delta \cdot a \, d\theta = \int_0^\pi (a^2 \cos \theta)(1 + k |\cos \theta|) \, d\theta$

$= a^2 \int_0^{\pi/2} (\cos \theta)(1 + k \cos \theta) \, d\theta + a^2 \int_{\pi/2}^\pi (\cos \theta)(1 - k \cos \theta) \, d\theta$

$= a^2 \int_0^{\pi/2} \cos \theta \, d\theta + a^2 k \int_0^{\pi/2} \left( \frac{1 + \cos 2\theta}{2} \right) d\theta + a^2 \int_{\pi/2}^\pi \cos \theta \, d\theta - a^2 k \int_{\pi/2}^\pi \left( \frac{1 + \cos 2\theta}{2} \right) d\theta$

$= a^2 [\sin \theta]_0^{\pi/2} + \frac{a^2 k}{2} \left[ \theta + \frac{\sin 2\theta}{2} \right]_0^{\pi/2} + a^2 [\sin \theta]_{\pi/2}^\pi - \frac{a^2 k}{2} \left[ \theta + \frac{\sin 2\theta}{2} \right]_{\pi/2}^\pi$

$= a^2 (1 - 0) + \frac{a^2 k}{2} \left[ \left( \frac{\pi}{2} - 0 \right) - (0 + 0) \right] + a^2 (0 - 1) - \frac{a^2 k}{2} \left[ (\pi + 0) - \left( \frac{\pi}{2} + 0 \right) \right] = a^2 + \frac{a^2 k \pi}{4} - a^2 - \frac{a^2 k \pi}{4} = 0$;

$M = \int_0^\pi \delta \cdot a \, d\theta = a \int_0^\pi (1 + k |\cos \theta|) \, d\theta = a \int_0^{\pi/2} (1 + k \cos \theta) \, d\theta + a \int_{\pi/2}^\pi (1 - k \cos \theta) \, d\theta$

$= a[\theta + k \sin \theta]_0^{\pi/2} + a[\theta - k \sin \theta]_{\pi/2}^\pi = a \left[ \left( \frac{\pi}{2} + k \right) - 0 \right] + a \left[ (\pi + 0) - \left( \frac{\pi}{2} - k \right) \right]$

$= \frac{a\pi}{2} + ak + a \left( \frac{\pi}{2} + k \right) = a\pi + 2ak = a(\pi + 2k)$. So $\bar{x} = \frac{M_y}{M} = 0$ and $\bar{y} = \frac{M_x}{M} = \frac{a^2 (2 + k)}{a(\pi + 2k)} = \frac{a(2 + k)}{\pi + 2k}$

$\Rightarrow \left( 0, \frac{2a + ka}{\pi + 2k} \right)$ is the center of mass.

27. $f(x) = x + 6$, $g(x) = x^2$, $f(x) = g(x) \Rightarrow x + 6 = x^2$

$\Rightarrow x^2 - x - 6 = 0 \Rightarrow x = 3$, $x = -2$; $\delta = 1$

$M = \int_{-2}^{3} [(x + 6) - x^2]dx = \left[\frac{1}{2}x^2 + 6x - \frac{1}{3}x^3\right]_{-2}^{3}$

$= \left(\frac{9}{2} + 18 - 9\right) - \left(2 - 12 + \frac{8}{3}\right) = \frac{125}{6}$

$\bar{x} = \frac{1}{125/6}\int_{-2}^{3} x[(x + 6) - x^2]dx = \frac{6}{125}\int_{-2}^{3}[x^2 + 6x - x^3]dx$

$= \frac{6}{125}\left[\frac{1}{3}x^3 + 3x^2 - \frac{1}{4}x^4\right]_{-2}^{3}$

$= \frac{6}{125}\left(9 + 27 - \frac{81}{4}\right) - \frac{6}{125}\left(-\frac{8}{3} + 12 - 4\right) = \frac{1}{2}$; $\bar{y} = \frac{1}{125/6}\int_{-2}^{3}\frac{1}{2}\left[(x + 6)^2 - (x^2)^2\right]dx = \frac{3}{125}\int_{-2}^{3}[x^2 + 12x + 36 - x^4]dx$

$= \frac{3}{125}\left[\frac{1}{3}x^3 + 6x^2 + 36x - \frac{1}{5}x^5\right]_{-2}^{3} = \frac{3}{125}\left(9 + 54 + 108 - \frac{243}{5}\right) - \frac{3}{125}\left(-\frac{8}{3} + 24 - 72 + \frac{32}{5}\right) = 4$

$\Rightarrow \left(\frac{1}{2}, 4\right)$ is the center of mass.

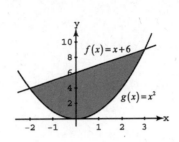

28. $f(x) = 2$, $g(x) = x^2(x + 1)$, $f(x) = g(x) \Rightarrow 2 = x^2(x + 1)$

$\Rightarrow x^3 + x^2 - 2 = 0 \Rightarrow x = 1$; $\delta = 1$

$M = \int_{0}^{1}[2 - x^2(x + 1)]\,dx = \int_{0}^{1}[2 - x^3 - x^2]\,dx$

$= \left[2x - \frac{1}{4}x^4 - \frac{1}{3}x^3\right]_{0}^{1} = \left(2 - \frac{1}{4} - \frac{1}{3}\right) - 0 = \frac{17}{12}$

$\bar{x} = \frac{1}{17/12}\int_{0}^{1}x[2 - x^2(x + 1)]dx = \frac{12}{17}\int_{0}^{1}[2x - x^4 - x^3]dx$

$= \frac{12}{17}\left[x^2 - \frac{1}{5}x^5 - \frac{1}{4}x^4\right]_{0}^{1}$

$= \frac{12}{17}\left(1 - \frac{1}{5} - \frac{1}{4}\right) - 0 = \frac{33}{85}$; $\bar{y} = \frac{1}{17/12}\int_{0}^{1}\frac{1}{2}\left[2^2 - (x^2(x + 1))^2\right]dx = \frac{6}{17}\int_{0}^{1}[4 - x^6 - 2x^5 - x^4]dx$

$= \frac{6}{17}\left[4x - \frac{1}{7}x^7 - \frac{1}{3}x^6 - \frac{1}{5}x^5\right]_{0}^{1} = \frac{6}{17}\left(4 - \frac{1}{7} - \frac{1}{3} - \frac{1}{5}\right) - 0 = \frac{698}{595} \Rightarrow \left(\frac{33}{85}, \frac{698}{595}\right)$ is the center of mass.

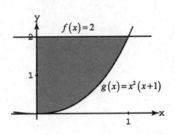

29. $f(x) = x^2$, $g(x) = x^2(x - 1)$, $f(x) = g(x) \Rightarrow x^2 = x^2(x - 1)$

$\Rightarrow x^3 - 2x^2 = 0 \Rightarrow x = 0$, $x = 2$; $\delta = 1$

$M = \int_{0}^{2}[x^2 - x^2(x - 1)]dx = \int_{0}^{2}[2x^2 - x^3]dx$

$= \left[\frac{2}{3}x^3 - \frac{1}{4}x^4\right]_{0}^{2} = \left(\frac{16}{3} - 4\right) - 0 = \frac{4}{3}$

$\bar{x} = \frac{1}{4/3}\int_{0}^{2}x[x^2 - x^2(x - 1)]dx = \frac{3}{4}\int_{0}^{2}[2x^3 - x^4]dx$

$= \frac{3}{4}\left[\frac{1}{2}x^4 - \frac{1}{5}x^5\right]_{0}^{2} = \frac{3}{4}\left(8 - \frac{32}{5}\right) - 0 = \frac{6}{5}$;

$\bar{y} = \frac{1}{4/3}\int_{0}^{2}\frac{1}{2}\left[(x^2)^2 - (x^2(x - 1))^2\right]dx = \frac{3}{8}\int_{0}^{2}[2x^5 - x^6]dx = \frac{3}{8}\left[\frac{1}{3}x^6 - \frac{1}{7}x^7\right]_{0}^{2} = \frac{3}{8}\left(\frac{64}{3} - \frac{128}{7}\right) - 0 = \frac{8}{7}$

$\Rightarrow \left(\frac{6}{5}, \frac{8}{7}\right)$ is the center of mass.

30. $f(x) = 2 + \sin x$, $g(x) = 0$, $x = 0$, $x = 2\pi$; $\delta = 1$;

$M = \int_{0}^{2\pi}[2 + \sin x]dx = [2x - \cos x]_{0}^{2\pi}$

$= (4\pi - 1) - (0 - 1) = 4\pi$

$\bar{x} = \frac{1}{4\pi}\int_{0}^{2\pi}x[2 + \sin x - 0]dx = \frac{1}{4\pi}\int_{0}^{2\pi}[2x + x\sin x]dx$

$= \frac{1}{4\pi}\int_{0}^{2\pi}2x\,dx + \frac{1}{4\pi}\int_{0}^{2\pi}x\sin x\,dx$

$= \frac{1}{4\pi}[x^2]_{0}^{2\pi} + \frac{1}{4\pi}[\sin x - x\cos x]_{0}^{2\pi}$

$= \frac{1}{4\pi}(4\pi^2) - 0 + \frac{1}{4\pi}(0 - 2\pi) - 0 = \frac{2\pi - 1}{2}$; $\bar{y} = \frac{1}{4\pi}\int_{0}^{2\pi}\frac{1}{2}\left[(2 + \sin x)^2 - (0)^2\right]dx = \frac{1}{8\pi}\int_{0}^{2\pi}[4 + 4\sin x + \sin^2 x]dx$

$= \frac{1}{8\pi}\int_{0}^{2\pi}[4 + 4\sin x]dx + \frac{1}{8\pi}\int_{0}^{2\pi}[\sin^2 x]dx = \frac{1}{8\pi}\int_{0}^{2\pi}[4 + 4\sin x]dx + \frac{1}{8\pi}\int_{0}^{2\pi}\left[\frac{1 - \cos 2x}{2}\right]dx$

$= \frac{1}{8\pi}[4x - 4\cos x + ]_{0}^{2\pi} + \frac{1}{16\pi}\int_{0}^{2\pi}dx - \frac{1}{16\pi}\int_{0}^{2\pi}\cos 2x\,dx$ [$u = 2x \Rightarrow du = 2dx$, $x = 0 \Rightarrow u = 0$, $x = 2\pi \Rightarrow u = 4\pi$]

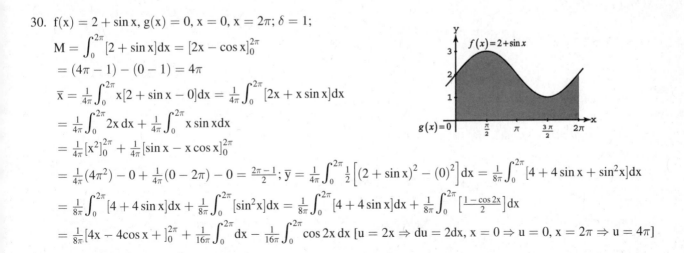

$\rightarrow \frac{1}{8\pi}[4x - 4\cos x]_0^{2\pi} + \frac{1}{16\pi}[x]_0^{2\pi} - \frac{1}{32\pi}\int_0^{4\pi}\cos u\, du = \frac{1}{8\pi}[4x - 4\cos x]_0^{2\pi} + \frac{1}{16\pi}[x]_0^{2\pi} - \frac{1}{32\pi}[\sin u]_0^{4\pi}$

$= \frac{1}{8\pi}(8\pi - 4) - \frac{1}{8\pi}(0 - 4) + \frac{1}{16\pi}(2\pi) - 0 - 0 = \frac{9}{8} \Rightarrow \left(\frac{2\pi - 1}{2}, \frac{9}{8}\right)$ is the center of mass.

31. Consider the curve as an infinite number of line segments joined together. From the derivation of arc length we have that

the length of a particular segment is ds $= \sqrt{(dx)^2 + (dy)^2}$ . This implies that $M_x = \int \delta y\, ds$, $M_y = \int \delta x\, ds$ and

$M = \int \delta\, ds$. If $\delta$ is constant, then $\overline{x} = \frac{M_y}{M} = \frac{\int x\, ds}{\int ds} = \frac{\int x\, ds}{\text{length}}$ and $\overline{y} = \frac{M_x}{M} = \frac{\int y\, ds}{\int ds} = \frac{\int y\, ds}{\text{length}}$ .

32. Applying the symmetry argument analogous to the one used in Exercise 1, we find that $\overline{x} = 0$. The typical vertical strip

has center of mass: $(\widetilde{x}, \widetilde{y}) = \left(x, \frac{a + \frac{x^2}{4p}}{2}\right)$, length: $a - \frac{x^2}{4p}$, width: dx, area: $dA = \left(a - \frac{x^2}{4p}\right)$ dx, mass: $dm = \delta\, dA$

$= \delta\left(a - \frac{x^2}{4p}\right)$ dx. Thus, $M_x = \int \widetilde{y}\, dm = \int_{-2\sqrt{pa}}^{2\sqrt{pa}}\frac{1}{2}\left(a + \frac{x^2}{4p}\right)\left(a - \frac{x^2}{4p}\right)\delta\, dx = \frac{\delta}{2}\int_{-2\sqrt{pa}}^{2\sqrt{pa}}\left(a^2 - \frac{x^4}{16p^2}\right)$ dx

$= \frac{\delta}{2}\left[a^2 x - \frac{x^5}{80p^2}\right]_{-2\sqrt{pa}}^{2\sqrt{pa}} = 2 \cdot \frac{\delta}{2}\left[a^2 x - \frac{x^5}{80p^2}\right]_0^{2\sqrt{pa}} = \delta\left(2a^2\sqrt{pa} - \frac{2^5 p^2 a^2\sqrt{pa}}{80p^2}\right) = 2a^2\delta\sqrt{pa}\left(1 - \frac{16}{80}\right) = 2a^2\delta\sqrt{pa}\left(\frac{80-16}{80}\right)$

$= 2a^2\delta\sqrt{pa}\left(\frac{64}{80}\right) = \frac{8a^2\delta\sqrt{pa}}{5}$; $M = \int dm = \delta\int_{-2\sqrt{pa}}^{2\sqrt{pa}}\left(a - \frac{x^2}{4p}\right)$ dx $= \delta\left[ax - \frac{x^3}{12p}\right]_{-2\sqrt{pa}}^{2\sqrt{pa}} = 2 \cdot \delta\left[ax - \frac{x^3}{12p}\right]_0^{2\sqrt{pa}}$

$= 2\delta\left(2a\sqrt{pa} - \frac{2^3 pa\sqrt{pa}}{12p}\right) = 4a\delta\sqrt{pa}\left(1 - \frac{4}{12}\right) = 4a\delta\sqrt{pa}\left(\frac{12-4}{12}\right) = \frac{8a\delta\sqrt{pa}}{3}$. So $\overline{y} = \frac{M_x}{M} = \left(\frac{8a^2\delta\sqrt{pa}}{5}\right)\left(\frac{3}{8a\delta\sqrt{pa}}\right)$

$= \frac{3}{5}$ a, as claimed.

33. The centroid of the square is located at $(2, 2)$. The volume is V $= (2\pi)(\overline{y})(A) = (2\pi)(2)(8) = 32\pi$ and the surface area is

S $= (2\pi)(\overline{y})(L) = (2\pi)(2)\left(4\sqrt{8}\right) = 32\sqrt{2}\pi$ (where $\sqrt{8}$ is the length of a side).

34. The midpoint of the hypotenuse of the triangle is $\left(\frac{3}{2}, 3\right)$

$\Rightarrow$ y $= 2x$ is an equation of the median $\Rightarrow$ the line
y $= 2x$ contains the centroid. The point $\left(\frac{3}{2}, 3\right)$ is

$\frac{3\sqrt{5}}{2}$ units from the origin $\Rightarrow$ the x-coordinate of the

centroid solves the equation $\sqrt{\left(x - \frac{3}{2}\right)^2 + (2x - 3)^2}$

$= \frac{\sqrt{5}}{2} \Rightarrow \left(x^2 - 3x + \frac{9}{4}\right) + (4x^2 - 12x + 9) = \frac{5}{4}$

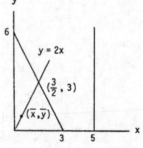

$\Rightarrow 5x^2 - 15x + 9 = -1$

$\Rightarrow x^2 - 3x + 2 = (x - 2)(x - 1) = 0 \Rightarrow \overline{x} = 1$ since the centroid must lie inside the triangle $\Rightarrow \overline{y} = 2$. By the

Theorem of Pappus, the volume is V $=$ (distance traveled by the centroid)(area of the region) $= 2\pi(5 - \overline{x})\left[\frac{1}{2}(3)(6)\right]$

$= (2\pi)(4)(9) = 72\pi$

35. The centroid is located at $(2, 0) \Rightarrow$ V $= (2\pi)(\overline{x})(A) = (2\pi)(2)(\pi) = 4\pi^2$

36. We create the cone by revolving the triangle with vertices
$(0, 0)$, $(h, r)$ and $(h, 0)$ about the x-axis (see the accompanying
figure). Thus, the cone has height h and base radius r. By
Theorem of Pappus, the lateral surface area swept out by the
hypotenuse L is given by S $= 2\pi\overline{y}L = 2\pi\left(\frac{r}{2}\right)\sqrt{h^2 + r^2}$

$= \pi r\sqrt{r^2 + h^2}$. To calculate the volume we need the position
of the centroid of the triangle. From the diagram we see that

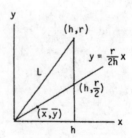

the centroid lies on the line y $= \frac{r}{2h}$ x. The x-coordinate of the centroid solves the equation $\sqrt{(x - h)^2 + \left(\frac{r}{2h} x - \frac{r}{2}\right)^2}$

$= \frac{1}{3}\sqrt{h^2 + \frac{r^2}{4}} \Rightarrow \left(\frac{4h^2 + r^2}{4h^2}\right)x^2 - \left(\frac{4h^2 + r^2}{2h}\right)x + \frac{r^2}{4} + \frac{2(r^2 + 4h^2)}{9} = 0 \Rightarrow x = \frac{2h}{3}$ or $\frac{4h}{3} \Rightarrow \bar{x} = \frac{2h}{3}$, since the centroid must lie inside the triangle $\Rightarrow \bar{y} = \frac{r}{2h}\bar{x} = \frac{r}{3}$. By the Theorem of Pappus, $V = \left[2\pi\left(\frac{r}{3}\right)\right]\left(\frac{1}{2}hr\right) = \frac{1}{3}\pi r^2 h$.

37. $S = 2\pi\bar{y}L \Rightarrow 4\pi a^2 = (2\pi\bar{y})(\pi a) \Rightarrow \bar{y} = \frac{2a}{\pi}$, and by symmetry $\bar{x} = 0$

38. $S = 2\pi\rho L \Rightarrow \left[2\pi\left(a - \frac{2a}{\pi}\right)\right](\pi a) = 2\pi a^2(\pi - 2)$

39. $V = 2\pi\bar{y}A \Rightarrow \frac{4}{3}\pi ab^2 = (2\pi\bar{y})\left(\frac{\pi ab}{2}\right) \Rightarrow \bar{y} = \frac{4b}{3\pi}$ and by symmetry $\bar{x} = 0$

40. $V = 2\pi\rho A \Rightarrow V = \left[2\pi\left(a + \frac{4a}{3\pi}\right)\right]\left(\frac{\pi a^2}{2}\right) = \frac{\pi a^3(3\pi + 4)}{3}$

41. $V = 2\pi\rho A = (2\pi)$(area of the region) · (distance from the centroid to the line $y = x - a$). We must find the distance from $\left(0, \frac{4a}{3\pi}\right)$ to $y = x - a$. The line containing the centroid and perpendicular to $y = x - a$ has slope $-1$ and contains the point $\left(0, \frac{4a}{3\pi}\right)$. This line is $y = -x + \frac{4a}{3\pi}$. The intersection of $y = x - a$ and $y = -x + \frac{4a}{3\pi}$ is the point $\left(\frac{4a + 3a\pi}{6\pi}, \frac{4a - 3a\pi}{6\pi}\right)$. Thus, the distance from the centroid to the line $y = x - a$ is $\sqrt{\left(\frac{4a + 3a\pi}{6\pi}\right)^2 + \left(\frac{4a}{3\pi} - \frac{4a}{6\pi} + \frac{3a\pi}{6\pi}\right)^2} = \frac{\sqrt{2}(4a + 3a\pi)}{6\pi}$
$\Rightarrow V = (2\pi)\left(\frac{\sqrt{2}(4a + 3a\pi)}{6\pi}\right)\left(\frac{\pi a^2}{2}\right) = \frac{\sqrt{2}\pi a^3(4 + 3\pi)}{6}$

42. The line perpendicular to $y = x - a$ and passing through the centroid $\left(0, \frac{2a}{\pi}\right)$ has equation $y = -x + \frac{2a}{\pi}$. The intersection of the two perpendicular lines occurs when $x - a = -x + \frac{2a}{\pi} \Rightarrow x = \frac{2a + a\pi}{2\pi} \Rightarrow y = \frac{2a - a\pi}{2\pi}$. Thus the distance from the centroid to the line $y = x - a$ is $\sqrt{\left(\frac{2a + \pi a}{2} - 0\right)^2 + \left(\frac{2a - \pi a}{2} - \frac{2a}{2}\right)^2} = \frac{a(2 + \pi)}{\sqrt{2}\pi}$. Therefore, by the Theorem of Pappus the surface area is $S = 2\pi\left[\frac{a(2 + \pi)}{\sqrt{2}\pi}\right](\pi a) = \sqrt{2}\pi a^2(2 + \pi)$.

43. If we revolve the region about the y-axis: $r = a$, $h = b \Rightarrow A = \frac{1}{2}ab$, $V = \frac{1}{3}\pi a^2 b$, and $\rho = \bar{x}$. By the Theorem of Pappus: $\frac{1}{3}\pi a^2 b = 2\pi\bar{x}\left(\frac{1}{2}ab\right) \Rightarrow \bar{x} = \frac{a}{3}$; If we revolve the region about the x-axis: $r = b$, $h = a \Rightarrow A = \frac{1}{2}ab$, $V = \frac{1}{3}\pi b^2 a$, and $\rho = \bar{y}$. By the Theorem of Pappus: $\frac{1}{3}\pi b^2 a = 2\pi\bar{y}\left(\frac{1}{2}ab\right) \Rightarrow \bar{y} = \frac{b}{3} \Rightarrow \left(\frac{a}{3}, \frac{b}{3}\right)$ is the center of mass.

44. Let $O(0, 0)$, $P(a, c)$, and $Q(a, b)$ be the vertices of the given triangle. If we revolve the region about the x-axis: Let R be the point $R(a, 0)$. The volume is given by the volume of the outer cone, radius $= RP = c$, minus the volume of the inner cone, radius $= RQ = b$, thus $V = \frac{1}{3}\pi c^2 a - \frac{1}{3}\pi b^2 a = \frac{1}{3}\pi a(c^2 - b^2)$, the area is given by the area of triangle OPR minus area of triangle OQR, $A = \frac{1}{2}ac - \frac{1}{2}ab = \frac{1}{2}a(c - b)$, and $\rho = \bar{y}$. By the Theorem of Pappus: $\frac{1}{3}\pi a(c^2 - b^2)$
$= 2\pi\bar{y}\left[\frac{1}{2}a(c - b)\right] \Rightarrow \bar{y} = \frac{c + b}{3}$; If we revolve the region about the y-axis: Let S and T be the points $S(0, c)$ and $T(0, b)$, respectively. Then the volume is the volume of the cylinder with radius $OR = a$ and height $RP = c$, minus the sum of the volumes of the cone with radius $= SP = a$ and height $= OS = c$ and the portion of the cylinder with height $= OT = b$ and radius $= TQ = a$ with a cone of height $= OT = b$ and radius $= TQ = a$ removed. Thus $V = \pi a^2 c - \left[\frac{1}{3}\pi a^2 c + \left(\pi a^2 b - \frac{1}{3}\pi a^2 b\right)\right] = \frac{2}{3}\pi a^2 c - \frac{2}{3}\pi a^2 b = \frac{2}{3}\pi a^2(a - b)$. The area of the triangle is the same as before, $A = \frac{1}{2}ac - \frac{1}{2}ab = \frac{1}{2}a(c - b)$, and $\rho = \bar{x}$. By the Theorem of Pappus: $\frac{2}{3}\pi a^2(a - b) = 2\pi\bar{x}\left[\frac{1}{2}a(c - b)\right]$
$\Rightarrow \bar{x} = \frac{2a(a - b)}{3(c - b)} \Rightarrow \left(\frac{2a(a - b)}{3(c - b)}, \frac{c + b}{2}\right)$ is the center of mass.

**CHAPTER 6 PRACTICE EXERCISES**

1.  $A(x) = \frac{\pi}{4} (\text{diameter})^2 = \frac{\pi}{4} \left(\sqrt{x} - x^2\right)^2$

    $= \frac{\pi}{4} \left(x - 2\sqrt{x} \cdot x^2 + x^4\right); a = 0, b = 1$

    $\Rightarrow V = \int_a^b A(x)\, dx = \frac{\pi}{4} \int_0^1 \left(x - 2x^{5/2} + x^4\right) dx$

    $= \frac{\pi}{4} \left[\frac{x^2}{2} - \frac{4}{7} x^{7/2} + \frac{x^5}{5}\right]_0^1 = \frac{\pi}{4} \left(\frac{1}{2} - \frac{4}{7} + \frac{1}{5}\right)$

    $= \frac{\pi}{4 \cdot 70} (35 - 40 + 14) = \frac{9\pi}{280}$

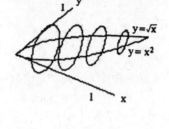

2.  $A(x) = \frac{1}{2} (\text{side})^2 \left(\sin \frac{\pi}{3}\right) = \frac{\sqrt{3}}{4} \left(2\sqrt{x} - x\right)^2$

    $= \frac{\sqrt{3}}{4} \left(4x - 4x\sqrt{x} + x^2\right); a = 0, b = 4$

    $\Rightarrow V = \int_a^b A(x)\, dx = \frac{\sqrt{3}}{4} \int_0^4 \left(4x - 4x^{3/2} + x^2\right) dx$

    $= \frac{\sqrt{3}}{4} \left[2x^2 - \frac{8}{5} x^{5/2} + \frac{x^3}{3}\right]_0^4 = \frac{\sqrt{3}}{4} \left(32 - \frac{8 \cdot 32}{5} + \frac{64}{3}\right)$

    $= \frac{32\sqrt{3}}{4} \left(1 - \frac{8}{5} + \frac{2}{3}\right) = \frac{8\sqrt{3}}{15} (15 - 24 + 10) = \frac{8\sqrt{3}}{15}$

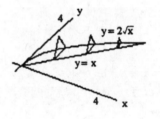

3.  $A(x) = \frac{\pi}{4} (\text{diameter})^2 = \frac{\pi}{4} (2 \sin x - 2 \cos x)^2$

    $= \frac{\pi}{4} \cdot 4 \left(\sin^2 x - 2 \sin x \cos x + \cos^2 x\right)$

    $= \pi(1 - \sin 2x); a = \frac{\pi}{4}, b = \frac{5\pi}{4}$

    $\Rightarrow V = \int_a^b A(x)\, dx = \pi \int_{\pi/4}^{5\pi/4} (1 - \sin 2x)\, dx$

    $= \pi \left[x + \frac{\cos 2x}{2}\right]_{\pi/4}^{5\pi/4}$

    $= \pi \left[\left(\frac{5\pi}{4} + \frac{\cos \frac{5\pi}{2}}{2}\right) - \left(\frac{\pi}{4} - \frac{\cos \frac{\pi}{2}}{2}\right)\right] = \pi^2$

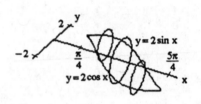

4.  $A(x) = (\text{edge})^2 = \left(\left(\sqrt{6} - \sqrt{x}\right)^2 - 0\right)^2 = \left(\sqrt{6} - \sqrt{x}\right)^4 = 36 - 24\sqrt{6}\sqrt{x} + 36x - 4\sqrt{6}x^{3/2} + x^2;$

    $a = 0, b = 6 \Rightarrow V = \int_a^b A(x)\, dx = \int_0^6 \left(36 - 24\sqrt{6}\sqrt{x} + 36x - 4\sqrt{6}x^{3/2} + x^2\right) dx$

    $= \left[36x - 24\sqrt{6} \cdot \frac{2}{3} x^{3/2} + 18x^2 - 4\sqrt{6} \cdot \frac{2}{5} x^{5/2} + \frac{x^3}{3}\right]_0^6 = 216 - 16 \cdot \sqrt{6}\sqrt{6} \cdot 6 + 18 \cdot 6^2 - \frac{8}{5} \sqrt{6}\sqrt{6} \cdot 6^2 + \frac{6^3}{3}$

    $= 216 - 576 + 648 - \frac{1728}{5} + 72 = 360 - \frac{1728}{5} = \frac{1800 - 1728}{5} = \frac{72}{5}$

5.  $A(x) = \frac{\pi}{4} (\text{diameter})^2 = \frac{\pi}{4} \left(2\sqrt{x} - \frac{x^2}{4}\right)^2 = \frac{\pi}{4} \left(4x - x^{5/2} + \frac{x^4}{16}\right); a = 0, b = 4 \Rightarrow V = \int_a^b A(x)\, dx$

    $= \frac{\pi}{4} \int_0^4 \left(4x - x^{5/2} + \frac{x^4}{16}\right) dx = \frac{\pi}{4} \left[2x^2 - \frac{2}{7} x^{7/2} + \frac{x^5}{5 \cdot 16}\right]_0^4 = \frac{\pi}{4} \left(32 - 32 \cdot \frac{8}{7} + \frac{2}{5} \cdot 32\right)$

    $= \frac{32\pi}{4} \left(1 - \frac{8}{7} + \frac{2}{5}\right) = \frac{8\pi}{35} (35 - 40 + 14) = \frac{72\pi}{35}$

6.  $A(x) = \frac{1}{2} (\text{edge})^2 \sin \left(\frac{\pi}{3}\right) = \frac{\sqrt{3}}{4} \left[2\sqrt{x} - \left(-2\sqrt{x}\right)\right]^2$

    $= \frac{\sqrt{3}}{4} \left(4\sqrt{x}\right)^2 = 4\sqrt{3}x; a = 0, b = 1$

    $\Rightarrow V = \int_a^b A(x)\, dx = \int_0^1 4\sqrt{3}x\, dx = \left[2\sqrt{3}x^2\right]_0^1$

    $= 2\sqrt{3}$

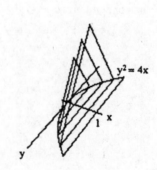

7.  (a)  *disk method*:

$$V = \int_a^b \pi R^2(x)\, dx = \int_{-1}^1 \pi\, (3x^4)^2\, dx = \pi \int_{-1}^1 9x^8\, dx$$

$$= \pi\, [x^9]_{-1}^1 = 2\pi$$

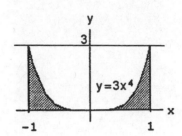

(b)  *shell method*:

$$V = \int_a^b 2\pi \left(\begin{smallmatrix}\text{shell}\\\text{radius}\end{smallmatrix}\right) \left(\begin{smallmatrix}\text{shell}\\\text{height}\end{smallmatrix}\right) dx = \int_0^1 2\pi x\, (3x^4)\, dx = 2\pi \cdot 3 \int_0^1 x^5\, dx = 2\pi \cdot 3 \left[\tfrac{x^6}{6}\right]_0^1 = \pi$$

Note:  The lower limit of integration is 0 rather than $-1$.

(c)  *shell method*:

$$V = \int_a^b 2\pi \left(\begin{smallmatrix}\text{shell}\\\text{radius}\end{smallmatrix}\right) \left(\begin{smallmatrix}\text{shell}\\\text{height}\end{smallmatrix}\right) dx = 2\pi \int_{-1}^1 (1-x)\, (3x^4)\, dx = 2\pi \left[\tfrac{3x^5}{5} - \tfrac{x^6}{2}\right]_{-1}^1 = 2\pi \left[\left(\tfrac{3}{5} - \tfrac{1}{2}\right) - \left(-\tfrac{3}{5} - \tfrac{1}{2}\right)\right] = \tfrac{12\pi}{5}$$

(d)  *washer method*:

$$R(x) = 3,\, r(x) = 3 - 3x^4 = 3\,(1 - x^4) \;\Rightarrow\; V = \int_a^b \pi\, [R^2(x) - r^2(x)]\, dx = \int_{-1}^1 \pi \left[9 - 9\,(1-x^4)^2\right] dx$$

$$= 9\pi \int_{-1}^1 [1 - (1 - 2x^4 + x^8)]\, dx = 9\pi \int_{-1}^1 (2x^4 - x^8)\, dx = 9\pi \left[\tfrac{2x^5}{5} - \tfrac{x^9}{9}\right]_{-1}^1 = 18\pi \left[\tfrac{2}{5} - \tfrac{1}{9}\right] = \tfrac{2\pi \cdot 13}{5} = \tfrac{26\pi}{5}$$

8.  (a)  *washer method*:

$$R(x) = \tfrac{4}{x^3},\, r(x) = \tfrac{1}{2} \;\Rightarrow\; V = \int_a^b \pi [R^2(x) - r^2(x)]\, dx = \int_1^2 \pi \left[\left(\tfrac{4}{x^3}\right)^2 - \left(\tfrac{1}{2}\right)^2\right] dx = \pi \left[-\tfrac{16}{5}\, x^{-5} - \tfrac{x}{4}\right]_1^2$$

$$= \pi \left[\left(\tfrac{-16}{5 \cdot 32} - \tfrac{1}{2}\right) - \left(-\tfrac{16}{5} - \tfrac{1}{4}\right)\right] = \pi \left(-\tfrac{1}{10} - \tfrac{1}{2} + \tfrac{16}{5} + \tfrac{1}{4}\right) = \tfrac{\pi}{20}\,(-2 - 10 + 64 + 5) = \tfrac{57\pi}{20}$$

(b)  *shell method*:

$$V = 2\pi \int_1^2 x \left(\tfrac{4}{x^3} - \tfrac{1}{2}\right) dx = 2\pi \left[-4x^{-1} - \tfrac{x^2}{4}\right]_1^2 = 2\pi \left[\left(-\tfrac{4}{2} - 1\right) - \left(-4 - \tfrac{1}{4}\right)\right] = 2\pi \left(\tfrac{5}{4}\right) = \tfrac{5\pi}{2}$$

(c)  *shell method*:

$$V = 2\pi \int_a^b \left(\begin{smallmatrix}\text{shell}\\\text{radius}\end{smallmatrix}\right) \left(\begin{smallmatrix}\text{shell}\\\text{height}\end{smallmatrix}\right) dx = 2\pi \int_1^2 (2-x) \left(\tfrac{4}{x^3} - \tfrac{1}{2}\right) dx = 2\pi \int_1^2 \left(\tfrac{8}{x^3} - \tfrac{4}{x^2} - 1 + \tfrac{x}{2}\right) dx$$

$$= 2\pi \left[-\tfrac{4}{x^2} + \tfrac{4}{x} - x + \tfrac{x^2}{4}\right]_1^2 = 2\pi \left[(-1 + 2 - 2 + 1) - \left(-4 + 4 - 1 + \tfrac{1}{4}\right)\right] = \tfrac{3\pi}{2}$$

(d)  *washer method*:

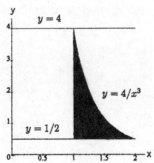

$$V = \int_a^b \pi [R^2(x) - r^2(x)]\, dx$$

$$= \pi \int_1^2 \left[\left(\tfrac{7}{2}\right)^2 - \left(4 - \tfrac{4}{x^3}\right)^2\right] dx$$

$$= \tfrac{49\pi}{4} - 16\pi \int_1^2 (1 - 2x^{-3} + x^{-6})\, dx$$

$$= \tfrac{49\pi}{4} - 16\pi \left[x + x^{-2} - \tfrac{x^{-5}}{5}\right]_1^2$$

$$= \tfrac{49\pi}{4} - 16\pi \left[\left(2 + \tfrac{1}{4} - \tfrac{1}{5 \cdot 32}\right) - \left(1 + 1 - \tfrac{1}{5}\right)\right]$$

$$= \tfrac{49\pi}{4} - 16\pi \left(\tfrac{1}{4} - \tfrac{1}{160} + \tfrac{1}{5}\right)$$

$$= \tfrac{49\pi}{4} - \tfrac{16\pi}{160}\,(40 - 1 + 32) = \tfrac{49\pi}{4} - \tfrac{71\pi}{10} = \tfrac{103\pi}{20}$$

9.  (a)  *disk method*:

$$V = \pi \int_1^5 \left(\sqrt{x - 1}\right)^2 dx = \pi \int_1^5 (x - 1)\, dx = \pi \left[\tfrac{x^2}{2} - x\right]_1^5$$

$$= \pi \left[\left(\tfrac{25}{2} - 5\right) - \left(\tfrac{1}{2} - 1\right)\right] = \pi \left(\tfrac{24}{2} - 4\right) = 8\pi$$

(b)  *washer method*:

$$R(y) = 5,\, r(y) = y^2 + 1 \;\Rightarrow\; V = \int_c^d \pi\, [R^2(y) - r^2(y)]\, dy = \pi \int_{-2}^2 \left[25 - (y^2 + 1)^2\right] dy$$

$$= \pi \int_{-2}^2 (25 - y^4 - 2y^2 - 1)\, dy = \pi \int_{-2}^2 (24 - y^4 - 2y^2)\, dy = \pi \left[24y - \tfrac{y^5}{5} - \tfrac{2}{3}\, y^3\right]_{-2}^2 = 2\pi \left(24 \cdot 2 - \tfrac{32}{5} - \tfrac{2}{3} \cdot 8\right)$$

$= 32\pi \left(3 - \frac{2}{5} - \frac{1}{3}\right) = \frac{32\pi}{15}(45 - 6 - 5) = \frac{1088\pi}{15}$

(c) *disk method*:

$R(y) = 5 - (y^2 + 1) = 4 - y^2$

$\Rightarrow V = \int_c^d \pi R^2(y)\, dy = \int_{-2}^2 \pi \left(4 - y^2\right)^2 dy$

$= \pi \int_{-2}^2 (16 - 8y^2 + y^4)\, dy$

$= \pi \left[16y - \frac{8y^3}{3} + \frac{y^5}{5}\right]_{-2}^2 = 2\pi \left(32 - \frac{64}{3} + \frac{32}{5}\right)$

$= 64\pi \left(1 - \frac{2}{3} + \frac{1}{5}\right) = \frac{64\pi}{15}(15 - 10 + 3) = \frac{512\pi}{15}$

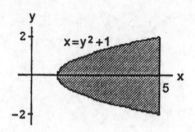

10. (a) *shell method*:

$V = \int_c^d 2\pi \binom{\text{shell}}{\text{radius}} \binom{\text{shell}}{\text{height}}\, dy = \int_0^4 2\pi y \left(y - \frac{y^2}{4}\right) dy$

$= 2\pi \int_0^4 \left(y^2 - \frac{y^3}{4}\right) dy = 2\pi \left[\frac{y^3}{3} - \frac{y^4}{16}\right]_0^4 = 2\pi \left(\frac{64}{3} - \frac{64}{4}\right)$

$= \frac{2\pi}{12} \cdot 64 = \frac{32\pi}{3}$

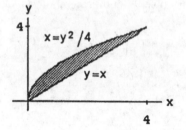

(b) *shell method*:

$V = \int_a^b 2\pi \binom{\text{shell}}{\text{radius}} \binom{\text{shell}}{\text{height}}\, dx = \int_0^4 2\pi x \left(2\sqrt{x} - x\right) dx = 2\pi \int_0^4 \left(2x^{3/2} - x^2\right) dx = 2\pi \left[\frac{4}{5} x^{5/2} - \frac{x^3}{3}\right]_0^4$

$= 2\pi \left(\frac{4}{5} \cdot 32 - \frac{64}{3}\right) = \frac{128\pi}{15}$

(c) *shell method*:

$V = \int_a^b 2\pi \binom{\text{shell}}{\text{radius}} \binom{\text{shell}}{\text{height}}\, dx = \int_0^4 2\pi(4 - x) \left(2\sqrt{x} - x\right) dx = 2\pi \int_0^4 \left(8x^{1/2} - 4x - 2x^{3/2} + x^2\right) dx$

$= 2\pi \left[\frac{16}{3} x^{3/2} - 2x^2 - \frac{4}{5} x^{5/2} + \frac{x^3}{3}\right]_0^4 = 2\pi \left(\frac{16}{3} \cdot 8 - 32 - \frac{4}{5} \cdot 32 + \frac{64}{3}\right) = 64\pi \left(\frac{4}{3} - 1 - \frac{4}{5} + \frac{2}{3}\right)$

$= 64\pi \left(1 - \frac{4}{5}\right) = \frac{64\pi}{5}$

(d) *shell method*:

$V = \int_c^d 2\pi \binom{\text{shell}}{\text{radius}} \binom{\text{shell}}{\text{height}}\, dy = \int_0^4 2\pi(4 - y) \left(y - \frac{y^2}{4}\right) dy = 2\pi \int_0^4 \left(4y - y^2 - y^2 + \frac{y^3}{4}\right) dy$

$= 2\pi \int_0^4 \left(4y - 2y^2 + \frac{y^3}{4}\right) dy = 2\pi \left[2y^2 - \frac{2}{3} y^3 + \frac{y^4}{16}\right]_0^4 = 2\pi \left(32 - \frac{2}{3} \cdot 64 + 16\right) = 32\pi \left(2 - \frac{8}{3} + 1\right) = \frac{32\pi}{3}$

11. *disk method*:

$R(x) = \tan x,\ a = 0,\ b = \frac{\pi}{3} \Rightarrow V = \pi \int_0^{\pi/3} \tan^2 x\, dx = \pi \int_0^{\pi/3} \left(\sec^2 x - 1\right) dx = \pi[\tan x - x]_0^{\pi/3} = \frac{\pi\left(3\sqrt{3} - \pi\right)}{3}$

12. *disk method*:

$V = \pi \int_0^\pi (2 - \sin x)^2 dx = \pi \int_0^\pi \left(4 - 4\sin x + \sin^2 x\right) dx = \pi \int_0^\pi \left(4 - 4\sin x + \frac{1 - \cos 2x}{2}\right) dx$

$= \pi \left[4x + 4\cos x + \frac{x}{2} - \frac{\sin 2x}{4}\right]_0^\pi = \pi \left[\left(4\pi - 4 + \frac{\pi}{2} - 0\right) - (0 + 4 + 0 - 0)\right] = \pi \left(\frac{9\pi}{2} - 8\right) = \frac{\pi}{2}(9\pi - 16)$

13. (a) *disk method*:

$V = \pi \int_0^2 \left(x^2 - 2x\right)^2 dx = \pi \int_0^2 \left(x^4 - 4x^3 + 4x^2\right) dx = \pi \left[\frac{x^5}{5} - x^4 + \frac{4}{3} x^3\right]_0^2 = \pi \left(\frac{32}{5} - 16 + \frac{32}{3}\right)$

$= \frac{16\pi}{15}(6 - 15 + 10) = \frac{16\pi}{15}$

(b) *washer method*:

$V = \int_0^2 \pi \left[1^2 - \left(x^2 - 2x + 1\right)^2\right] dx = \int_0^2 \pi\, dx - \int_0^2 \pi (x - 1)^4 dx = 2\pi - \left[\pi \frac{(x-1)^5}{5}\right]_0^2 = 2\pi - \pi \cdot \frac{2}{5} = \frac{8\pi}{5}$

(c) *shell method*:

$V = \int_a^b 2\pi \binom{\text{shell}}{\text{radius}} \binom{\text{shell}}{\text{height}}\, dx = 2\pi \int_0^2 (2 - x)\left[-(x^2 - 2x)\right] dx = 2\pi \int_0^2 (2 - x)\left(2x - x^2\right) dx$

$$= 2\pi \int_0^2 (4x - 2x^2 - 2x^2 + x^3)\, dx = 2\pi \int_0^2 (x^3 - 4x^2 + 4x)\, dx = 2\pi \left[\frac{x^4}{4} - \frac{4}{3}x^3 + 2x^2\right]_0^2 = 2\pi \left(4 - \frac{32}{3} + 8\right)$$

$$= \frac{2\pi}{3}(36 - 32) = \frac{8\pi}{3}$$

(d) *washer method:*

$$V = \pi \int_0^2 [2 - (x^2 - 2x)]^2\, dx - \pi \int_0^2 2^2\, dx = \pi \int_0^2 \left[4 - 4(x^2 - 2x) + (x^2 - 2x)^2\right] dx - 8\pi$$

$$= \pi \int_0^2 (4 - 4x^2 + 8x + x^4 - 4x^3 + 4x^2)\, dx - 8\pi = \pi \int_0^2 (x^4 - 4x^3 + 8x + 4)\, dx - 8\pi$$

$$= \pi \left[\frac{x^5}{5} - x^4 + 4x^2 + 4x\right]_0^2 - 8\pi = \pi \left(\frac{32}{5} - 16 + 16 + 8\right) - 8\pi = \frac{\pi}{5}(32 + 40) - 8\pi = \frac{72\pi}{5} - \frac{40\pi}{5} = \frac{32\pi}{5}$$

14. *disk method:*

$$V = 2\pi \int_0^{\pi/4} 4\tan^2 x\, dx = 8\pi \int_0^{\pi/4} (\sec^2 x - 1)\, dx = 8\pi[\tan x - x]_0^{\pi/4} = 2\pi(4 - \pi)$$

15. The material removed from the sphere consists of a cylinder and two "caps." From the diagram, the height of the cylinder is 2h, where $h^2 + \left(\sqrt{3}\right)^2 = 2^2$, i.e. $h = 1$. Thus

$V_{cyl} = (2h)\pi\left(\sqrt{3}\right)^2 = 6\pi$ ft$^3$. To get the volume of a cap,

use the disk method and $x^2 + y^2 = 2^2$: $V_{cap} = \int_1^2 \pi x^2 dy$

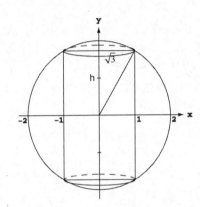

$$= \int_1^2 \pi(4 - y^2)dy = \pi\left[4y - \frac{y^3}{3}\right]_1^2$$

$$= \pi\left[\left(8 - \frac{8}{3}\right) - \left(4 - \frac{1}{3}\right)\right] = \frac{5\pi}{3} \text{ ft}^3. \text{ Therefore,}$$

$$V_{removed} = V_{cyl} + 2V_{cap} = 6\pi + \frac{10\pi}{3} = \frac{28\pi}{3} \text{ ft}^3.$$

16. We rotate the region enclosed by the curve $y = \sqrt{12\left(1 - \frac{4x^2}{121}\right)}$ and the x-axis around the x-axis. To find the

volume we use the *disk* method: $V = \int_a^b \pi R^2(x)\, dx = \int_{-11/2}^{11/2} \pi \left(\sqrt{12\left(1 - \frac{4x^2}{121}\right)}\right)^2 dx = \pi \int_{-11/2}^{11/2} 12\left(1 - \frac{4x^2}{121}\right) dx$

$$= 12\pi \int_{-11/2}^{11/2} \left(1 - \frac{4x^2}{121}\right) dx = 12\pi \left[x - \frac{4x^3}{363}\right]_{-11/2}^{11/2} = 24\pi \left[\frac{11}{2} - \left(\frac{4}{363}\right)\left(\frac{11}{2}\right)^3\right] = 132\pi \left[1 - \left(\frac{4}{363}\right)\left(\frac{11^2}{4}\right)\right]$$

$$= 132\pi \left(1 - \frac{1}{3}\right) = \frac{264\pi}{3} = 88\pi \approx 276 \text{ in}^3$$

17. $y = x^{1/2} - \frac{x^{3/2}}{3} \Rightarrow \frac{dy}{dx} = \frac{1}{2}x^{-1/2} - \frac{1}{2}x^{1/2} \Rightarrow \left(\frac{dy}{dx}\right)^2 = \frac{1}{4}\left(\frac{1}{x} - 2 + x\right) \Rightarrow L = \int_1^4 \sqrt{1 + \frac{1}{4}\left(\frac{1}{x} - 2 + x\right)}\, dx$

$$\Rightarrow L = \int_1^4 \sqrt{\frac{1}{4}\left(\frac{1}{x} + 2 + x\right)}\, dx = \int_1^4 \sqrt{\frac{1}{4}\left(x^{-1/2} + x^{1/2}\right)^2}\, dx = \int_1^4 \frac{1}{2}\left(x^{-1/2} + x^{1/2}\right) dx = \frac{1}{2}\left[2x^{1/2} + \frac{2}{3}x^{3/2}\right]_1^4$$

$$= \frac{1}{2}\left[\left(4 + \frac{2}{3}\cdot 8\right) - \left(2 + \frac{2}{3}\right)\right] = \frac{1}{2}\left(2 + \frac{14}{3}\right) = \frac{10}{3}$$

18. $x = y^{2/3} \Rightarrow \frac{dx}{dy} = \frac{2}{3}y^{-1/3} \Rightarrow \left(\frac{dx}{dy}\right)^2 = \frac{4y^{-2/3}}{9} \Rightarrow L = \int_1^8 \sqrt{1 + \left(\frac{dx}{dy}\right)^2}\, dy = \int_1^8 \sqrt{1 + \frac{4}{9y^{2/3}}}\, dy$

$$= \int_1^8 \frac{\sqrt{9y^{2/3} + 4}}{3y^{1/3}}\, dy = \frac{1}{3}\int_1^8 \sqrt{9y^{2/3} + 4}\,(y^{-1/3})\, dy; \ [u = 9y^{2/3} + 4 \Rightarrow du = 6y^{-1/3}\, dy; y = 1 \Rightarrow u = 13,$$

$$y = 8 \Rightarrow u = 40] \to L = \frac{1}{18}\int_{13}^{40} u^{1/2}\, du = \frac{1}{18}\left[\frac{2}{3}u^{3/2}\right]_{13}^{40} = \frac{1}{27}\left[40^{3/2} - 13^{3/2}\right] \approx 7.634$$

19. $y = \frac{5}{12}x^{6/5} - \frac{5}{8}x^{4/5} \Rightarrow \frac{dy}{dx} = \frac{1}{2}x^{1/5} - \frac{1}{2}x^{-1/5} \Rightarrow \left(\frac{dy}{dx}\right)^2 = \frac{1}{4}\left(x^{2/5} - 2 + x^{-2/5}\right)$

$$\Rightarrow L = \int_1^{32} \sqrt{1 + \frac{1}{4}\left(x^{2/5} - 2 + x^{-2/5}\right)}\, dx \Rightarrow L = \int_1^{32} \sqrt{\frac{1}{4}\left(x^{2/5} + 2 + x^{-2/5}\right)}\, dx = \int_1^{32} \sqrt{\frac{1}{4}\left(x^{1/5} + x^{-1/5}\right)^2}\, dx$$

$= \int_1^{32} \frac{1}{2} \left( x^{1/5} + x^{-1/5} \right) dx = \frac{1}{2} \left[ \frac{5}{6} x^{6/5} + \frac{5}{4} x^{4/5} \right]_1^{32} = \frac{1}{2} \left[ \left( \frac{5}{6} \cdot 2^6 + \frac{5}{4} \cdot 2^4 \right) - \left( \frac{5}{6} + \frac{5}{4} \right) \right] = \frac{1}{2} \left( \frac{315}{6} + \frac{75}{4} \right)$

$= \frac{1}{48} (1260 + 450) = \frac{1710}{48} = \frac{285}{8}$

20. $x = \frac{1}{12} y^3 + \frac{1}{y} \Rightarrow \frac{dx}{dy} = \frac{1}{4} y^2 - \frac{1}{y^2} \Rightarrow \left( \frac{dx}{dy} \right)^2 = \frac{1}{16} y^4 - \frac{1}{2} + \frac{1}{y^4} \Rightarrow L = \int_1^2 \sqrt{1 + \left( \frac{1}{16} y^4 - \frac{1}{2} + \frac{1}{y^4} \right)} \, dy$

$= \int_1^2 \sqrt{\frac{1}{16} y^4 + \frac{1}{2} + \frac{1}{y^4}} \, dy = \int_1^2 \sqrt{\left( \frac{1}{4} y^2 + \frac{1}{y^2} \right)^2} \, dy = \int_1^2 \left( \frac{1}{4} y^2 + \frac{1}{y^2} \right) dy = \left[ \frac{1}{12} y^3 - \frac{1}{y} \right]_1^2$

$= \left( \frac{8}{12} - \frac{1}{2} \right) - \left( \frac{1}{12} - 1 \right) = \frac{7}{12} + \frac{1}{2} = \frac{13}{12}$

21. $S = \int_a^b 2\pi y \sqrt{1 + \left( \frac{dy}{dx} \right)^2} \, dx; \; \frac{dy}{dx} = \frac{1}{\sqrt{2x+1}} \Rightarrow \left( \frac{dy}{dx} \right)^2 = \frac{1}{2x+1} \Rightarrow S = \int_0^3 2\pi \sqrt{2x+1} \sqrt{1 + \frac{1}{2x+1}} \, dx$

$= 2\pi \int_0^3 \sqrt{2x+1} \sqrt{\frac{2x+2}{2x+1}} \, dx = 2\sqrt{2} \pi \int_0^3 \sqrt{x+1} \, dx = 2\sqrt{2} \pi \left[ \frac{2}{3} (x+1)^{3/2} \right]_0^3 = 2\sqrt{2} \pi \cdot \frac{2}{3} (8 - 1) = \frac{28\pi\sqrt{2}}{3}$

22. $S = \int_a^b 2\pi y \sqrt{1 + \left( \frac{dy}{dx} \right)^2} \, dx; \; \frac{dy}{dx} = x^2 \Rightarrow \left( \frac{dy}{dx} \right)^2 = x^4 \Rightarrow S = \int_0^1 2\pi \cdot \frac{x^3}{3} \sqrt{1 + x^4} \, dx = \frac{\pi}{6} \int_0^1 \sqrt{1 + x^4} \, (4x^3) \, dx$

$= \frac{\pi}{6} \int_0^1 \sqrt{1 + x^4} \, d(1 + x^4) = \frac{\pi}{6} \left[ \frac{2}{3} (1 + x^4)^{3/2} \right]_0^1 = \frac{\pi}{9} \left[ 2\sqrt{2} - 1 \right]$

23. $S = \int_c^d 2\pi x \sqrt{1 + \left( \frac{dx}{dy} \right)^2} \, dy; \; \frac{dx}{dy} = \frac{\left( \frac{1}{2} \right)(4 - 2y)}{\sqrt{4y - y^2}} = \frac{2 - y}{\sqrt{4y - y^2}} \Rightarrow 1 + \left( \frac{dx}{dy} \right)^2 = \frac{4y - y^2 + 4 - 4y + y^2}{4y - y^2} = \frac{4}{4y - y^2}$

$\Rightarrow S = \int_1^2 2\pi \sqrt{4y - y^2} \sqrt{\frac{4}{4y - y^2}} \, dy = 4\pi \int_1^2 dx = 4\pi$

24. $S = \int_c^d 2\pi x \sqrt{1 + \left( \frac{dx}{dy} \right)^2} \, dy; \; \frac{dx}{dy} = \frac{1}{2\sqrt{y}} \Rightarrow 1 + \left( \frac{dx}{dy} \right)^2 = 1 + \frac{1}{4y} = \frac{4y + 1}{4y} \Rightarrow S = \int_2^6 2\pi \sqrt{y} \cdot \frac{\sqrt{4y+1}}{\sqrt{4y}} \, dy$

$= \pi \int_2^6 \sqrt{4y + 1} \, dy = \frac{\pi}{4} \left[ \frac{2}{3} (4y + 1)^{3/2} \right]_2^6 = \frac{\pi}{6} (125 - 27) = \frac{\pi}{6} (98) = \frac{49\pi}{3}$

25. The equipment alone: the force required to lift the equipment is equal to its weight $\Rightarrow F_1(x) = 100$ N.

The work done is $W_1 = \int_a^b F_1(x) \, dx = \int_0^{40} 100 \, dx = [100x]_0^{40} = 4000$ J; the rope alone: the force required to lift the rope is equal to the weight of the rope paid out at elevation x $\Rightarrow F_2(x) = 0.8(40 - x)$. The work done is $W_2 = \int_a^b F_2(x) \, dx = \int_0^{40} 0.8(40 - x) \, dx = 0.8 \left[ 40x - \frac{x^2}{2} \right]_0^{40} = 0.8 \left( 40^2 - \frac{40^2}{2} \right) = \frac{(0.8)(1600)}{2} = 640$ J; the total work is $W = W_1 + W_2 = 4000 + 640 = 4640$ J

26. The force required to lift the water is equal to the water's weight, which varies steadily from $8 \cdot 800$ lb to $8 \cdot 400$ lb over the 4750 ft elevation. When the truck is x ft off the base of Mt. Washington, the water weight is $F(x) = 8 \cdot 800 \cdot \left( \frac{2 \cdot 4750 - x}{2 \cdot 4750} \right) = (6400) \left( 1 - \frac{x}{9500} \right)$ lb. The work done is $W = \int_a^b F(x) \, dx$

$= \int_0^{4750} 6400 \left( 1 - \frac{x}{9500} \right) dx = 6400 \left[ x - \frac{x^2}{2 \cdot 9500} \right]_0^{4750} = 6400 \left( 4750 - \frac{4750^2}{4 \cdot 4750} \right) = \left( \frac{3}{4} \right) (6400)(4750)$

$= 22,800,000$ ft $\cdot$ lb

27. Force constant: $F = kx \Rightarrow 20 = k \cdot 1 \Rightarrow k = 20$ lb/ft; the work to stretch the spring 1 ft is

$W = \int_0^1 kx \, dx = k \int_0^1 x \, dx = \left[ 20 \frac{x^2}{2} \right]_0^1 = 10$ ft $\cdot$ lb; the work to stretch the spring an additional foot is

$W = \int_1^2 kx \, dx = k \int_1^2 x \, dx = 20 \left[ \frac{x^2}{2} \right]_1^2 = 20 \left( \frac{4}{2} - \frac{1}{2} \right) = 20 \left( \frac{3}{2} \right) = 30$ ft $\cdot$ lb

28. Force constant: $F = kx \Rightarrow 200 = k(0.8) \Rightarrow k = 250$ N/m; the 300 N force stretches the spring $x = \frac{F}{k}$

$= \frac{300}{250} = 1.2$ m; the work required to stretch the spring that far is then $W = \int_0^{1.2} F(x)\,dx = \int_0^{1.2} 250x\,dx$

$= [125x^2]_0^{1.2} = 125(1.2)^2 = 180$ J

29. We imagine the water divided into thin slabs by planes perpendicular to the y-axis at the points of a partition of the interval [0, 8]. The typical slab between the planes at y and $y + \Delta y$ has a volume of about $\Delta V = \pi(\text{radius})^2(\text{thickness})$
$= \pi\left(\frac{5}{4}y\right)^2\Delta y = \frac{25\pi}{16}y^2\,\Delta y$ ft$^3$. The force $F(y)$ required to lift this slab is equal to its weight: $F(y) = 62.4\,\Delta V$
$= \frac{(62.4)(25)}{16}\pi y^2\,\Delta y$ lb. The distance through which $F(y)$ must act to lift this slab to the level 6 ft above the top is

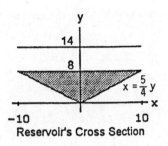

**Reservoir's Cross Section**

about $(6 + 8 - y)$ ft, so the work done lifting the slab is about $\Delta W = \frac{(62.4)(25)}{16}\pi y^2(14 - y)\,\Delta y$ ft · lb. The work done lifting all the slabs from $y = 0$ to $y = 8$ to the level 6 ft above the top is approximately

$W \approx \sum_0^8 \frac{(62.4)(25)}{16}\pi y^2 (14 - y)\,\Delta y$ ft · lb so the work to pump the water is the limit of these Riemann sums as the norm of

the partition goes to zero: $W = \int_0^8 \frac{(62.4)(25)}{(16)}\pi y^2(14 - y)\,dy = \frac{(62.4)(25)\pi}{16}\int_0^8 (14y^2 - y^3)\,dy = (62.4)\left(\frac{25\pi}{16}\right)\left[\frac{14}{3}y^3 - \frac{y^4}{4}\right]_0^8$

$= (62.4)\left(\frac{25\pi}{16}\right)\left(\frac{14}{3} \cdot 8^3 - \frac{8^4}{4}\right) \approx 418{,}208.81$ ft · lb

30. The same as in Exercise 29, but change the distance through which $F(y)$ must act to $(8 - y)$ rather than $(6 + 8 - y)$. Also change the upper limit of integration from 8 to 5. The integral is: $W = \int_0^5 \frac{(62.4)(25)\pi}{16}y^2(8 - y)\,dy$

$= (62.4)\left(\frac{25\pi}{16}\right)\int_0^5 (8y^2 - y^3)\,dy = (62.4)\left(\frac{25\pi}{16}\right)\left[\frac{8}{3}y^3 - \frac{y^4}{4}\right]_0^5 = (62.4)\left(\frac{25\pi}{16}\right)\left(\frac{8}{3} \cdot 5^3 - \frac{5^4}{4}\right) \approx 54{,}241.56$ ft · lb

31. The tank's cross section looks like the figure in Exercise 29 with right edge given by $x = \frac{5}{10}y = \frac{y}{2}$. A typical horizontal slab has volume $\Delta V = \pi(\text{radius})^2(\text{thickness}) = \pi\left(\frac{y}{2}\right)^2\Delta y = \frac{\pi}{4}y^2\,\Delta y$. The force required to lift this slab is its weight: $F(y) = 60 \cdot \frac{\pi}{4}y^2\,\Delta y$. The distance through which $F(y)$ must act is $(2 + 10 - y)$ ft, so the work to pump the liquid is

$W = 60\int_0^{10}\pi(12 - y)\left(\frac{y^2}{4}\right)dy = 15\pi\left[\frac{12y^3}{3} - \frac{y^4}{4}\right]_0^{10} = 22{,}500\pi$ ft · lb; the time needed to empty the tank is

$\frac{22{,}500\pi \text{ ft·lb}}{275 \text{ ft·lb/sec}} \approx 257$ sec

32. A typical horizontal slab has volume about $\Delta V = (20)(2x)\Delta y = (20)\left(2\sqrt{16 - y^2}\right)\Delta y$ and the force required to lift this slab is its weight $F(y) = (57)(20)\left(2\sqrt{16 - y^2}\right)\Delta y$. The distance through which $F(y)$ must act is $(6 + 4 - y)$ ft, so the work to pump the olive oil from the half-full tank is $W = 57\int_{-4}^0 (10 - y)(20)\left(2\sqrt{16 - y^2}\right)dy$

$= 2880\int_{-4}^0 10\sqrt{16 - y^2}\,dy + 1140\int_{-4}^0 (16 - y^2)^{1/2}(-2y)\,dy$

$= 22{,}800 \cdot (\text{area of a quarter circle having radius 4}) + \frac{2}{3}(1140)\left[(16 - y^2)^{3/2}\right]_{-4}^0 = (22{,}800)(4\pi) + 48{,}640$

$= 335{,}153.25$ ft · lb

33. Intersection points: $3 - x^2 = 2x^2 \Rightarrow 3x^2 - 3 = 0$

$\Rightarrow 3(x - 1)(x + 1) = 0 \Rightarrow x = -1$ or $x = 1$. Symmetry

suggests that $\bar{x} = 0$. The typical *vertical* strip has

center of mass: $(\tilde{x}, \tilde{y}) = \left(x, \frac{2x^2 + (3 - x^2)}{2}\right) = \left(x, \frac{x^2 + 3}{2}\right)$,

length: $(3 - x^2) - 2x^2 = 3(1 - x^2)$, width: dx,

area: $dA = 3(1 - x^2)\, dx$, and mass: $dm = \delta \cdot dA$

$= 3\delta(1 - x^2)\, dx \Rightarrow$ the moment about the x-axis is

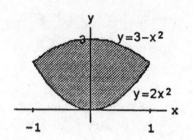

$\tilde{y}\, dm = \frac{3}{2}\delta(x^2 + 3)(1 - x^2)\, dx = \frac{3}{2}\delta(-x^4 - 2x^2 + 3)\, dx \Rightarrow M_x = \int \tilde{y}\, dm = \frac{3}{2}\delta\int_{-1}^{1}(-x^4 - 2x^2 + 3)\, dx$

$= \frac{3}{2}\delta\left[-\frac{x^5}{5} - \frac{2x^3}{3} + 3x\right]_{-1}^{1} = 3\delta\left(-\frac{1}{5} - \frac{2}{3} + 3\right) = \frac{3\delta}{15}(-3 - 10 + 45) = \frac{32\delta}{5}$; $M = \int dm = 3\delta\int_{-1}^{1}(1 - x^2)\, dx$

$= 3\delta\left[x - \frac{x^3}{3}\right]_{-1}^{1} = 6\delta\left(1 - \frac{1}{3}\right) = 4\delta \Rightarrow \bar{y} = \frac{M_x}{M} = \frac{32\delta}{5 \cdot 4\delta} = \frac{8}{5}$. Therefore, the centroid is $(\bar{x}, \bar{y}) = \left(0, \frac{8}{5}\right)$.

34. Symmetry suggests that $\bar{x} = 0$. The typical *vertical*

strip has center of mass: $(\tilde{x}, \tilde{y}) = \left(x, \frac{x^2}{2}\right)$, length: $x^2$,

width: dx, area: $dA = x^2\, dx$, mass: $dm = \delta \cdot dA = \delta x^2\, dx$

$\Rightarrow$ the moment about the x-axis is $\tilde{y}\, dm = \frac{\delta}{2}x^2 \cdot x^2\, dx$

$= \frac{\delta}{2}x^4\, dx \Rightarrow M_x = \int \tilde{y}\, dm = \frac{\delta}{2}\int_{-2}^{2}x^4\, dx = \frac{\delta}{10}[x^5]_{-2}^{2}$

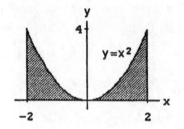

35. The typical *vertical* strip has: center of mass: $(\tilde{x}, \tilde{y})$

$= \left(x, \frac{4 + \frac{x^2}{4}}{2}\right)$, length: $4 - \frac{x^2}{4}$, width: dx,

area: $dA = \left(4 - \frac{x^2}{4}\right)dx$, mass: $dm = \delta \cdot dA$

$= \delta\left(4 - \frac{x^2}{4}\right)dx \Rightarrow$ the moment about the x-axis is

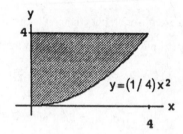

$\tilde{y}\, dm = \delta \cdot \frac{\left(4 + \frac{x^2}{4}\right)}{2}\left(4 - \frac{x^2}{4}\right)dx = \frac{\delta}{2}\left(16 - \frac{x^4}{16}\right)dx$; the

moment about the y-axis is $\tilde{x}\, dm = \delta\left(4 - \frac{x^2}{4}\right) \cdot x\, dx = \delta\left(4x - \frac{x^3}{4}\right)dx$. Thus, $M_x = \int \tilde{y}\, dm = \frac{\delta}{2}\int_{0}^{4}\left(16 - \frac{x^4}{16}\right)dx$

$= \frac{\delta}{2}\left[16x - \frac{x^5}{5 \cdot 16}\right]_{0}^{4} = \frac{\delta}{2}\left[64 - \frac{64}{5}\right] = \frac{128\delta}{5}$; $M_y = \int \tilde{x}\, dm = \delta\int_{0}^{4}\left(4x - \frac{x^3}{4}\right)dx = \delta\left[2x^2 - \frac{x^4}{16}\right]_{0}^{4}$

$= \delta(32 - 16) = 16\delta$; $M = \int dm = \delta\int_{0}^{4}\left(4 - \frac{x^2}{4}\right)dx = \delta\left[4x - \frac{x^3}{12}\right]_{0}^{4} = \delta\left(16 - \frac{64}{12}\right) = \frac{32\delta}{3}$

$\Rightarrow \bar{x} = \frac{M_y}{M} = \frac{16 \cdot \delta \cdot 3}{32 \cdot \delta} = \frac{3}{2}$ and $\bar{y} = \frac{M_x}{M} = \frac{128 \cdot \delta \cdot 3}{5 \cdot 32 \cdot \delta} = \frac{12}{5}$. Therefore, the centroid is $(\bar{x}, \bar{y}) = \left(\frac{3}{2}, \frac{12}{5}\right)$.

36. A typical *horizontal* strip has:

center of mass: $(\tilde{x}, \tilde{y}) = \left(\frac{y^2 + 2y}{2}, y\right)$, length: $2y - y^2$,

width: dy, area: $dA = (2y - y^2)\, dy$, mass: $dm = \delta \cdot dA$

$= \delta(2y - y^2)\, dy$; the moment about the x-axis is

$\tilde{y}\, dm = \delta \cdot y \cdot (2y - y^2)\, dy = \delta(2y^2 - y^3)$; the moment

about the y-axis is $\tilde{x}\, dm = \delta \cdot \frac{(y^2 + 2y)}{2} \cdot (2y - y^2)\, dy$

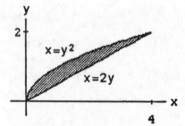

$= \frac{\delta}{2}(4y^2 - y^4)\, dy \Rightarrow M_x = \int \tilde{y}\, dm = \delta\int_{0}^{2}(2y^2 - y^3)\, dy$

$= \delta\left[\frac{2}{3}y^3 - \frac{y^4}{4}\right]_{0}^{2} = \delta\left(\frac{2}{3} \cdot 8 - \frac{16}{4}\right) = \delta\left(\frac{16}{3} - \frac{16}{4}\right) = \frac{\delta \cdot 16}{12} = \frac{4\delta}{3}$; $M_y = \int \tilde{x}\, dm = \frac{\delta}{2}\int_{0}^{2}(4y^2 - y^4)\, dy = \frac{\delta}{2}\left[\frac{4}{3}y^3 - \frac{y^5}{5}\right]_{0}^{2}$

$= \frac{\delta}{2}\left(\frac{4 \cdot 8}{3} - \frac{32}{5}\right) = \frac{32\delta}{15}$; $M = \int dm = \delta\int_{0}^{2}(2y - y^2)\, dy = \delta\left[y^2 - \frac{y^3}{3}\right]_{0}^{2} = \delta\left(4 - \frac{8}{3}\right) = \frac{4\delta}{3} \Rightarrow \bar{x} = \frac{M_y}{M} = \frac{32 \cdot \delta \cdot 3}{15 \cdot \delta \cdot 4} = \frac{8}{5}$ and

$\bar{y} = \frac{M_x}{M} = \frac{4 \cdot \delta \cdot 3}{3 \cdot 4 \cdot \delta} = 1$. Therefore, the centroid is $(\bar{x}, \bar{y}) = \left(\frac{8}{5}, 1\right)$.

37. A typical horizontal strip has:  center of mass: $(\widetilde{x}, \widetilde{y})$

$= \left(\frac{y^2+2y}{2}, y\right)$, length: $2y - y^2$, width: dy,

area: $dA = (2y - y^2)\, dy$,  mass: $dm = \delta \cdot dA$

$= (1 + y)(2y - y^2)\, dy \Rightarrow$ the moment about the

x-axis is $\widetilde{y}\, dm = y(1 + y)(2y - y^2)\, dy$

$= (2y^2 + 2y^3 - y^3 - y^4)\, dy$

$= (2y^2 + y^3 - y^4)\, dy$; the moment about the y-axis is

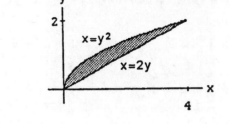

$\widetilde{x}\, dm = \left(\frac{y^2+2y}{2}\right)(1 + y)(2y - y^2)\, dy = \frac{1}{2}(4y^2 - y^4)(1 + y)\, dy = \frac{1}{2}(4y^2 + 4y^3 - y^4 - y^5)\, dy$

$\Rightarrow M_x = \int \widetilde{y}\, dm = \int_0^2 (2y^2 + y^3 - y^4)\, dy = \left[\frac{2}{3}y^3 + \frac{y^4}{4} - \frac{y^5}{5}\right]_0^2 = \left(\frac{16}{3} + \frac{16}{4} - \frac{32}{5}\right) = 16\left(\frac{1}{3} + \frac{1}{4} - \frac{2}{5}\right)$

$= \frac{16}{60}(20 + 15 - 24) = \frac{4}{15}(11) = \frac{44}{15}$;  $M_y = \int \widetilde{x}\, dm = \int_0^2 \frac{1}{2}(4y^2 + 4y^3 - y^4 - y^5)\, dy = \frac{1}{2}\left[\frac{4}{3}y^3 + y^4 - \frac{y^5}{5} - \frac{y^6}{6}\right]_0^2$

$= \frac{1}{2}\left(\frac{4\cdot2^3}{3} + 2^4 - \frac{2^5}{5} - \frac{2^6}{6}\right) = 4\left(\frac{4}{3} + 2 - \frac{4}{5} - \frac{8}{6}\right) = 4\left(2 - \frac{4}{5}\right) = \frac{24}{5}$;  $M = \int dm = \int_0^2 (1 + y)(2y - y^2)\, dy$

$= \int_0^2 (2y + y^2 - y^3)\, dy = \left[y^2 + \frac{y^3}{3} - \frac{y^4}{4}\right]_0^2 = \left(4 + \frac{8}{3} - \frac{16}{4}\right) = \frac{8}{3} \Rightarrow \overline{x} = \frac{M_y}{M} = \left(\frac{24}{5}\right)\left(\frac{3}{8}\right) = \frac{9}{5}$ and $\overline{y} = \frac{M_x}{M}$

$= \left(\frac{44}{15}\right)\left(\frac{3}{8}\right) = \frac{44}{40} = \frac{11}{10}$. Therefore, the center of mass is $(\overline{x}, \overline{y}) = \left(\frac{9}{5}, \frac{11}{10}\right)$.

38. A typical vertical strip has:  center of mass: $(\widetilde{x}, \widetilde{y}) = \left(x, \frac{3}{2x^{3/2}}\right)$, length: $\frac{3}{x^{3/2}}$, width: dx, area: $dA = \frac{3}{x^{3/2}}\, dx$,

mass: $dm = \delta \cdot dA = \delta \cdot \frac{3}{x^{3/2}}\, dx \Rightarrow$ the moment about the x-axis is $\widetilde{y}\, dm = \frac{3}{2x^{3/2}} \cdot \delta \frac{3}{x^{3/2}}\, dx = \frac{9\delta}{2x^3}\, dx$; the moment about

the y-axis is $\widetilde{x}\, dm = x \cdot \delta \frac{3}{x^{3/2}}\, dx = \frac{3\delta}{x^{1/2}}\, dx$.

(a)  $M_x = \delta \int_1^9 \frac{1}{2}\left(\frac{9}{x^3}\right)\, dx = \frac{9\delta}{2}\left[-\frac{x^{-2}}{2}\right]_1^9 = \frac{20\delta}{9}$;  $M_y = \delta \int_1^9 x\left(\frac{3}{x^{3/2}}\right)\, dx = 3\delta\left[2x^{1/2}\right]_1^9 = 12\delta$;

$M = \delta \int_1^9 \frac{3}{x^{3/2}}\, dx = -6\delta\left[x^{-1/2}\right]_1^9 = 4\delta \Rightarrow \overline{x} = \frac{M_y}{M} = \frac{12\delta}{4\delta} = 3$ and $\overline{y} = \frac{M_x}{M} = \frac{\left(\frac{20\delta}{9}\right)}{4\delta} = \frac{5}{9}$

(b)  $M_x = \int_1^9 \frac{x}{2}\left(\frac{9}{x^3}\right)\, dx = \frac{9}{2}\left[-\frac{1}{x}\right]_1^9 = 4$;  $M_y = \int_1^9 x^2\left(\frac{3}{x^{3/2}}\right)\, dx = \left[2x^{3/2}\right]_1^9 = 52$;  $M = \int_1^9 x\left(\frac{3}{x^{3/2}}\right)\, dx$

$= 6\left[x^{1/2}\right]_1^9 = 12 \Rightarrow \overline{x} = \frac{M_y}{M} = \frac{13}{3}$ and $\overline{y} = \frac{M_x}{M} = \frac{1}{3}$

39. $F = \int_a^b W \cdot \left(\begin{smallmatrix}\text{strip}\\\text{depth}\end{smallmatrix}\right) \cdot L(y)\, dy \Rightarrow F = 2\int_0^2 (62.4)(2 - y)(2y)\, dy = 249.6\int_0^2 (2y - y^2)\, dy = 249.6\left[y^2 - \frac{y^3}{3}\right]_0^2$

$= (249.6)\left(4 - \frac{8}{3}\right) = (249.6)\left(\frac{4}{3}\right) = 332.8$ lb

40. $F = \int_a^b W \cdot \left(\begin{smallmatrix}\text{strip}\\\text{depth}\end{smallmatrix}\right) \cdot L(y)\, dy \Rightarrow F = \int_0^{5/6} 75\left(\frac{5}{6} - y\right)(2y + 4)\, dy = 75\int_0^{5/6}\left(\frac{5}{3}y + \frac{10}{3} - 2y^2 - 4y\right)\, dy$

$= 75\int_0^{5/6}\left(\frac{10}{3} - \frac{7}{3}y - 2y^2\right)\, dy = 75\left[\frac{10}{3}y - \frac{7}{6}y^2 - \frac{2}{3}y^3\right]_0^{5/6} = (75)\left[\left(\frac{50}{18}\right) - \left(\frac{7}{6}\right)\left(\frac{25}{36}\right) - \left(\frac{2}{3}\right)\left(\frac{125}{216}\right)\right]$

$= (75)\left(\frac{25}{9} - \frac{175}{216} - \frac{250}{3\cdot216}\right) = \left(\frac{75}{9\cdot216}\right)(25 \cdot 216 - 175 \cdot 9 - 250 \cdot 3) = \frac{(75)(3075)}{9\cdot216} \approx 118.63$ lb.

41. $F = \int_a^b W \cdot \left(\begin{smallmatrix}\text{strip}\\\text{depth}\end{smallmatrix}\right) \cdot L(y)\, dy \Rightarrow F = 62.4\int_0^4 (9 - y)\left(2 \cdot \frac{\sqrt{y}}{2}\right)\, dy = 62.4\int_0^4 (9y^{1/2} - 3y^{3/2})\, dy$

$= 62.4\left[6y^{3/2} - \frac{2}{5}y^{5/2}\right]_0^4 = (62.4)\left(6 \cdot 8 - \frac{2}{5} \cdot 32\right) = \left(\frac{62.4}{5}\right)(48 \cdot 5 - 64) = \frac{(62.4)(176)}{5} = 2196.48$ lb

42. Place the origin at the bottom of the tank. Then $F = \int_0^h W \cdot \left(\begin{smallmatrix}\text{strip}\\\text{depth}\end{smallmatrix}\right) \cdot L(y)\, dy$, h = the height of the mercury column,

strip depth $= h - y$, $L(y) = 1 \Rightarrow F = \int_0^h 849(h - y)\, 1\, dy = (849)\int_0^h (h - y)\, dy = 849\left[hy - \frac{y^2}{2}\right]_0^h = 849\left(h^2 - \frac{h^2}{2}\right)$

$= \frac{849}{2}h^2$. Now solve $\frac{849}{2}h^2 = 40000$ to get $h \approx 9.707$ ft. The volume of the mercury is $s^2 h = 1^2 \cdot 9.707 = 9.707$ ft$^3$.

**CHAPTER 6 ADDITIONAL AND ADVANCED EXERCISES**

1. $V = \pi \int_a^b [f(x)]^2 \, dx = b^2 - ab \Rightarrow \pi \int_a^x [f(t)]^2 \, dt = x^2 - ax$ for all $x > a \Rightarrow \pi [f(x)]^2 = 2x - a \Rightarrow f(x) = \sqrt{\frac{2x-a}{\pi}}$

2. $V = \pi \int_0^a [f(x)]^2 \, dx = a^2 + a \Rightarrow \pi \int_0^x [f(t)]^2 \, dt = x^2 + x$ for all $x > a \Rightarrow \pi[f(x)]^2 = 2x + 1 \Rightarrow f(x) = \sqrt{\frac{2x+1}{\pi}}$

3. $s(x) = Cx \Rightarrow \int_0^x \sqrt{1 + [f'(t)]^2} \, dt = Cx \Rightarrow \sqrt{1 + [f'(x)]^2} = C \Rightarrow f'(x) = \sqrt{C^2 - 1}$ for $C \geq 1$

   $\Rightarrow f(x) = \int_0^x \sqrt{C^2 - 1} \, dt + k$. Then $f(0) = a \Rightarrow a = 0 + k \Rightarrow f(x) = \int_0^x \sqrt{C^2 - 1} \, dt + a \Rightarrow f(x) = x\sqrt{C^2 - 1} + a$,
   where $C \geq 1$.

4. (a) The graph of $f(x) = \sin x$ traces out a path from $(0,0)$ to $(\alpha, \sin \alpha)$ whose length is $L = \int_0^\alpha \sqrt{1 + \cos^2 \theta} \, d\theta$.
   The line segment from $(0,0)$ to $(\alpha, \sin \alpha)$ has length $\sqrt{(\alpha - 0)^2 + (\sin \alpha - 0)^2} = \sqrt{\alpha^2 + \sin^2 \alpha}$. Since the
   shortest distance between two points is the length of the straight line segment joining them, we have
   immediately that $\int_0^\alpha \sqrt{1 + \cos^2 \theta} \, d\theta > \sqrt{\alpha^2 + \sin^2 \alpha}$ if $0 < \alpha \leq \frac{\pi}{2}$.

   (b) In general, if $y = f(x)$ is continuously differentiable and $f(0) = 0$, then $\int_0^\alpha \sqrt{1 + [f'(t)]^2} \, dt > \sqrt{\alpha^2 + f^2(\alpha)}$
   for $\alpha > 0$.

5. We can find the centroid and then use Pappus' Theorem to calculate the volume. $f(x) = x$, $g(x) = x^2$, $f(x) = g(x)$
   $\Rightarrow x = x^2 \Rightarrow x^2 - x = 0 \Rightarrow x = 0, x = 1; \delta = 1; M = \int_0^1 [x - x^2] dx = \left[\frac{1}{2}x^2 - \frac{1}{3}x^3\right]_0^1 = \left(\frac{1}{2} - \frac{1}{3}\right) - 0 = \frac{1}{6}$

   $\bar{x} = \frac{1}{1/6} \int_0^1 x[x - x^2] dx = 6\int_0^1 [x^2 - x^3] dx = 6\left[\frac{1}{3}x^3 - \frac{1}{4}x^4\right]_0^1 = 6\left(\frac{1}{3} - \frac{1}{4}\right) - 0 = \frac{1}{2}$

   $\bar{y} = \frac{1}{1/6} \int_0^1 \frac{1}{2}\left[x^2 - (x^2)^2\right] dx = 3\int_0^1 [x^2 - x^4] dx = 3\left[\frac{1}{3}x^3 - \frac{1}{5}x^5\right]_0^1 = 3\left(\frac{1}{3} - \frac{1}{5}\right) - 0 = \frac{2}{5} \Rightarrow$ The centroid is $\left(\frac{1}{2}, \frac{2}{5}\right)$.

   $\rho$ is the distance from $\left(\frac{1}{2}, \frac{2}{5}\right)$ to the axis of rotation, $y = x$. To calculate this distance we must find the point on $y = x$ that
   also lies on the line perpendicular to $y = x$ that passes through $\left(\frac{1}{2}, \frac{2}{5}\right)$. The equation of this line is $y - \frac{2}{5} = -1\left(x - \frac{1}{2}\right)$
   $\Rightarrow x + y = \frac{9}{10}$. The point of intersection of the lines $x + y = \frac{9}{10}$ and $y = x$ is $\left(\frac{9}{20}, \frac{9}{20}\right)$. Thus,
   $\rho = \sqrt{\left(\frac{9}{20} - \frac{1}{2}\right)^2 + \left(\frac{9}{20} - \frac{2}{5}\right)^2} = \frac{1}{10\sqrt{2}}$. Thus $V = 2\pi\left(\frac{1}{10\sqrt{2}}\right)\left(\frac{1}{6}\right) = \frac{\pi}{30\sqrt{2}}$.

6. Since the slice is made at an angle of $45°$, the volume of the wedge is half the volume of the cylinder of radius $\frac{1}{2}$ and
   height 1. Thus, $V = \frac{1}{2}\left[\pi \left(\frac{1}{2}\right)^2 (1)\right] = \frac{\pi}{8}$.

7. $y = 2\sqrt{x} \Rightarrow ds = \sqrt{\frac{1}{x} + 1} \, dx \Rightarrow A = \int_0^3 2\sqrt{x} \sqrt{\frac{1}{x} + 1} \, dx = \frac{4}{3}\left[(1 + x)^{3/2}\right]_0^3 = \frac{28}{3}$

8. This surface is a triangle having a base of $2\pi a$ and a height of $2\pi ak$. Therefore the surface area is
   $\frac{1}{2}(2\pi a)(2\pi ak) = 2\pi^2 a^2 k$.

9. $F = ma = t^2 \Rightarrow \frac{d^2 x}{dt^2} = a = \frac{t^2}{m} \Rightarrow v = \frac{dx}{dt} = \frac{t^3}{3m} + C; v = 0$ when $t = 0 \Rightarrow C = 0 \Rightarrow \frac{dx}{dt} = \frac{t^3}{3m} \Rightarrow x = \frac{t^4}{12m} + C_1;$
   $x = 0$ when $t = 0 \Rightarrow C_1 = 0 \Rightarrow x = \frac{t^4}{12m}$. Then $x = h \Rightarrow t = (12mh)^{1/4}$. The work done is

   $W = \int F \, dx = \int_0^{(12mh)^{1/4}} F(t) \cdot \frac{dx}{dt} \, dt = \int_0^{(12mh)^{1/4}} t^2 \cdot \frac{t^3}{3m} \, dt = \frac{1}{3m}\left[\frac{t^6}{6}\right]_0^{(12mh)^{1/4}} = \left(\frac{1}{18m}\right)(12mh)^{6/4}$

   $= \frac{(12mh)^{3/2}}{18m} = \frac{12mh \cdot \sqrt{12mh}}{18m} = \frac{2h}{3} \cdot 2\sqrt{3mh} = \frac{4h}{3}\sqrt{3mh}$

10. Converting to pounds and feet, 2 lb/in = $\frac{2 \text{ lb}}{1 \text{ in}} \cdot \frac{12 \text{ in}}{1 \text{ ft}}$ = 24 lb/ft. Thus, F = 24x $\Rightarrow$ W = $\int_0^{1/2} 24x \, dx$

$= [12x^2]_0^{1/2} = 3 \text{ ft} \cdot \text{lb}$. Since W = $\frac{1}{2}mv_0^2 - \frac{1}{2}mv_1^2$, where W = 3 ft $\cdot$ lb, m = $\left(\frac{1}{10} \text{ lb}\right)\left(\frac{1}{32 \text{ ft/sec}^2}\right)$

$= \frac{1}{320}$ slugs, and $v_1 = 0$ ft/sec, we have 3 = $\left(\frac{1}{2}\right)\left(\frac{1}{320}v_0^2\right)$ $\Rightarrow$ $v_0^2 = 3 \cdot 640$. For the projectile height,

s = $-16t^2 + v_0 t$ (since s = 0 at t = 0) $\Rightarrow$ $\frac{ds}{dt} = v = -32t + v_0$. At the top of the ball's path, v = 0 $\Rightarrow$ t = $\frac{v_0}{32}$

and the height is s = $-16\left(\frac{v_0}{32}\right)^2 + v_0\left(\frac{v_0}{32}\right) = \frac{v_0^2}{64} = \frac{3 \cdot 640}{64} = 30$ ft.

11. From the symmetry of $y = 1 - x^n$, n even, about the y-axis for $-1 \le x \le 1$, we have $\bar{x} = 0$. To find $\bar{y} = \frac{M_x}{M}$, we

use the vertical strips technique. The typical strip has center of mass: $(\tilde{x}, \tilde{y}) = \left(x, \frac{1-x^n}{2}\right)$, length: $1 - x^n$,

width: dx, area: dA = $(1 - x^n)$ dx, mass: dm = $1 \cdot dA = (1 - x^n)$ dx. The moment of the strip about the

x-axis is $\tilde{y}$ dm = $\frac{(1-x^n)^2}{2}$ dx $\Rightarrow$ $M_x = \int_{-1}^1 \frac{(1-x^n)^2}{2} \, dx = 2\int_0^1 \frac{1}{2}\left(1 - 2x^n + x^{2n}\right) dx = \left[x - \frac{2x^{n+1}}{n+1} + \frac{x^{2n+1}}{2n+1}\right]_0^1$

$= 1 - \frac{2}{n+1} + \frac{1}{2n+1} = \frac{(n+1)(2n+1) - 2(2n+1) + (n+1)}{(n+1)(2n+1)} = \frac{2n^2 + 3n + 1 - 4n - 2 + n + 1}{(n+1)(2n+1)} = \frac{2n^2}{(n+1)(2n+1)}$.

Also, M = $\int_{-1}^1 dA = \int_{-1}^1 (1 - x^n) \, dx = 2\int_0^1 (1 - x^n) \, dx = 2\left[x - \frac{x^{n+1}}{n+1}\right]_0^1 = 2\left(1 - \frac{1}{n+1}\right) = \frac{2n}{n+1}$. Therefore,

$\bar{y} = \frac{M_x}{M} = \frac{2n^2}{(n+1)(2n+1)} \cdot \frac{(n+1)}{2n} = \frac{n}{2n+1}$ $\Rightarrow$ $\left(0, \frac{n}{2n+1}\right)$ is the location of the centroid. As n $\to \infty$, $\bar{y} \to \frac{1}{2}$ so

the limiting position of the centroid is $\left(0, \frac{1}{2}\right)$.

12. Align the telephone pole along the x-axis as shown in the
accompanying figure. The slope of the top length of pole is

$\frac{\left(\frac{14.5}{8\pi} - \frac{9}{8\pi}\right)}{40} = \frac{1}{8\pi} \cdot \frac{1}{40} \cdot (14.5 - 9) = \frac{5.5}{8\pi \cdot 40} = \frac{11}{8\pi \cdot 80}$. Thus,

y = $\frac{9}{8\pi} + \frac{11}{8\pi \cdot 80}x = \frac{1}{8\pi}\left(9 + \frac{11}{80}x\right)$ is an equation of the
line representing the top of the pole. Then,

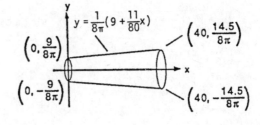

$M_y = \int_a^b x \cdot \pi y^2 \, dx = \pi \int_0^{40} x \left[\frac{1}{8\pi}\left(9 + \frac{11}{80}x\right)\right]^2 dx$

$= \frac{1}{64\pi}\int_0^{40} x \left(9 + \frac{11}{80}x\right)^2 dx$; M = $\int_a^b \pi y^2 \, dx$

$= \pi \int_0^{40}\left[\frac{1}{8\pi}\left(9 + \frac{11}{80}x\right)\right]^2 dx = \frac{1}{64\pi}\int_0^{40}\left(9 + \frac{11}{80}x\right)^2 dx$. Thus, $\bar{x} = \frac{M_y}{M} \approx \frac{129,700}{5623.3} \approx 23.06$ (using a calculator to compute

the integrals). By symmetry about the x-axis, $\bar{y} = 0$ so the center of mass is about 23 ft from the top of the pole.

13. (a) Consider a single vertical strip with center of mass $(\tilde{x}, \tilde{y})$. If the plate lies to the right of the line, then
the moment of this strip about the line x = b is $(\tilde{x} - b)$ dm = $(\tilde{x} - b)\delta$ dA $\Rightarrow$ the plate's first moment
about x = b is the integral $\int (x - b)\delta \, dA = \int \delta x \, dA - \int \delta b \, dA = M_y - b\delta A$.

(b) If the plate lies to the left of the line, the moment of a vertical strip about the line x = b is
$(b - \tilde{x})$ dm = $(b - \tilde{x})\delta$ dA $\Rightarrow$ the plate's first moment about x = b is $\int (b - x)\delta \, dA = \int b\delta \, dA - \int \delta x \, dA$
$= b\delta A - M_y$.

14. (a) By symmetry of the plate about the x-axis, $\bar{y} = 0$. A typical vertical strip has center of mass:
$(\tilde{x}, \tilde{y}) = (x, 0)$, length: $4\sqrt{ax}$, width: dx, area: $4\sqrt{ax}$ dx, mass: dm = $\delta$ dA = $kx \cdot 4\sqrt{ax}$ dx, for some

proportionality constant k. The moment of the strip about the y-axis is $M_y = \int \tilde{x} \, dm = \int_0^a 4kx^2\sqrt{ax} \, dx$

$= 4k\sqrt{a}\int_0^a x^{5/2} \, dx = 4k\sqrt{a}\left[\frac{2}{7}x^{7/2}\right]_0^a = 4ka^{1/2} \cdot \frac{2}{7}a^{7/2} = \frac{8ka^4}{7}$. Also, M = $\int dm = \int_0^a 4kx\sqrt{ax} \, dx$

$= 4k\sqrt{a}\int_0^a x^{3/2} \, dx = 4k\sqrt{a}\left[\frac{2}{5}x^{5/2}\right]_0^a = 4ka^{1/2} \cdot \frac{2}{5}a^{5/2} = \frac{8ka^3}{5}$. Thus, $\bar{x} = \frac{M_y}{M} = \frac{8ka^4}{7} \cdot \frac{5}{8ka^3} = \frac{5}{7}a$

$\Rightarrow (\bar{x}, \bar{y}) = \left(\frac{5a}{7}, 0\right)$ is the center of mass.

(b) A typical horizontal strip has center of mass: $(\tilde{x}, \tilde{y}) = \left(\frac{\frac{y^2}{4a} + a}{2}, y\right) = \left(\frac{y^2 + 4a^2}{8a}, y\right)$, length: $a - \frac{y^2}{4a}$,

width: dy, area: $\left(a - \frac{y^2}{4a}\right)$ dy, mass: dm = $\delta$ dA = $|y|\left(a - \frac{y^2}{4a}\right)$ dy. Thus, $M_x = \int \tilde{y} \, dm$

$= \int_{-2a}^{2a} y \, |y| \left(a - \frac{y^2}{4a}\right) dy = \int_{-2a}^0 -y^2\left(a - \frac{y^2}{4a}\right) dy + \int_0^{2a} y^2\left(a - \frac{y^2}{4a}\right) dy$

$$= \int_{-2a}^{0} \left(-ay^2 + \tfrac{y^4}{4a}\right) dy + \int_{0}^{2a} \left(ay^2 - \tfrac{y^4}{4a}\right) dy = \left[-\tfrac{a}{3}y^3 + \tfrac{y^5}{20a}\right]_{-2a}^{0} + \left[\tfrac{a}{3}y^3 - \tfrac{y^5}{20a}\right]_{0}^{2a}$$

$$= -\tfrac{8a^4}{3} + \tfrac{32a^5}{20a} + \tfrac{8a^4}{3} - \tfrac{32a^5}{20a} = 0; \quad M_y = \int \tilde{x} \, dm = \int_{-2a}^{2a} \left(\tfrac{y^2+4a^2}{8a}\right) |y| \left(a - \tfrac{y^2}{4a}\right) dy$$

$$= \tfrac{1}{8a} \int_{-2a}^{2a} |y| (y^2 + 4a^2) \left(\tfrac{4a^2-y^2}{4a}\right) dy = \tfrac{1}{32a^2} \int_{-2a}^{2a} |y| (16a^4 - y^4) \, dy$$

$$= \tfrac{1}{32a^2} \int_{-2a}^{0} (-16a^4 y + y^5) \, dy + \tfrac{1}{32a^2} \int_{0}^{2a} (16a^4 y - y^5) \, dy = \tfrac{1}{32a^2} \left[-8a^4 y^2 + \tfrac{y^6}{6}\right]_{-2a}^{0} + \tfrac{1}{32a^2} \left[8a^4 y^2 - \tfrac{y^6}{6}\right]_{0}^{2a}$$

$$= \tfrac{1}{32a^2} \left[8a^4 \cdot 4a^2 - \tfrac{64a^6}{6}\right] + \tfrac{1}{32a^2} \left[8a^4 \cdot 4a^2 - \tfrac{64a^6}{6}\right] = \tfrac{1}{16a^2} \left(32a^6 - \tfrac{32a^6}{3}\right) = \tfrac{1}{16a^2} \cdot \tfrac{2}{3} (32a^6) = \tfrac{4}{3} a^4;$$

$$M = \int dm = \int_{-2a}^{2a} |y| \left(\tfrac{4a^2-y^2}{4a}\right) dy = \tfrac{1}{4a} \int_{-2a}^{2a} |y| (4a^2 - y^2) \, dy$$

$$= \tfrac{1}{4a} \int_{-2a}^{0} (-4a^2 y + y^3) \, dy + \tfrac{1}{4a} \int_{0}^{2a} (4a^2 y - y^3) \, dy = \tfrac{1}{4a} \left[-2a^2 y^2 + \tfrac{y^4}{4}\right]_{-2a}^{0} + \tfrac{1}{4a} \left[2a^2 y^2 - \tfrac{y^4}{4}\right]_{0}^{2a}$$

$$= 2 \cdot \tfrac{1}{4a} \left(2a^2 \cdot 4a^2 - \tfrac{16a^4}{4}\right) = \tfrac{1}{2a} (8a^4 - 4a^4) = 2a^3. \text{ Therefore, } \bar{x} = \tfrac{M_y}{M} = \left(\tfrac{4}{3}a^4\right)\left(\tfrac{1}{2a^3}\right) = \tfrac{2a}{3} \text{ and}$$

$$\bar{y} = \tfrac{M_x}{M} = 0 \text{ is the center of mass.}$$

15. (a) On $[0, a]$ a typical *vertical* strip has center of mass: $(\tilde{x}, \tilde{y}) = \left(x, \tfrac{\sqrt{b^2-x^2}+\sqrt{a^2-x^2}}{2}\right)$,

length: $\sqrt{b^2-x^2} - \sqrt{a^2-x^2}$, width: $dx$, area: $dA = \left(\sqrt{b^2-x^2} - \sqrt{a^2-x^2}\right) dx$, mass: $dm = \delta \, dA$

$= \delta \left(\sqrt{b^2-x^2} - \sqrt{a^2-x^2}\right) dx$. On $[a, b]$ a typical *vertical* strip has center of mass:

$(\tilde{x}, \tilde{y}) = \left(x, \tfrac{\sqrt{b^2-x^2}}{2}\right)$, length: $\sqrt{b^2-x^2}$, width: $dx$, area: $dA = \sqrt{b^2-x^2} \, dx$,

mass: $dm = \delta \, dA = \delta \sqrt{b^2-x^2} \, dx$. Thus, $M_x = \int \tilde{y} \, dm$

$$= \int_{0}^{a} \tfrac{1}{2} \left(\sqrt{b^2-x^2} + \sqrt{a^2-x^2}\right) \delta \left(\sqrt{b^2-x^2} - \sqrt{a^2-x^2}\right) dx + \int_{a}^{b} \tfrac{1}{2} \sqrt{b^2-x^2} \, \delta \sqrt{b^2-x^2} \, dx$$

$$= \tfrac{\delta}{2} \int_{0}^{a} [(b^2-x^2) - (a^2-x^2)] \, dx + \tfrac{\delta}{2} \int_{a}^{b} (b^2-x^2) \, dx = \tfrac{\delta}{2} \int_{0}^{a} (b^2-a^2) \, dx + \tfrac{\delta}{2} \int_{a}^{b} (b^2-x^2) \, dx$$

$$= \tfrac{\delta}{2} \left[(b^2-a^2) x\right]_{0}^{a} + \tfrac{\delta}{2} \left[b^2 x - \tfrac{x^3}{3}\right]_{a}^{b} = \tfrac{\delta}{2} [(b^2-a^2) a] + \tfrac{\delta}{2} \left[\left(b^3 - \tfrac{b^3}{3}\right) - \left(b^2 a - \tfrac{a^3}{3}\right)\right]$$

$$= \tfrac{\delta}{2} (ab^2 - a^3) + \tfrac{\delta}{2} \left(\tfrac{2}{3} b^3 - ab^2 + \tfrac{a^3}{3}\right) = \tfrac{\delta b^3}{3} - \tfrac{\delta a^3}{3} = \delta \left(\tfrac{b^3 - a^3}{3}\right); \quad M_y = \int \tilde{x} \, dm$$

$$= \int_{0}^{a} x \delta \left(\sqrt{b^2-x^2} - \sqrt{a^2-x^2}\right) dx + \int_{a}^{b} x \delta \sqrt{b^2-x^2} \, dx$$

$$= \delta \int_{0}^{a} x (b^2-x^2)^{1/2} \, dx - \delta \int_{0}^{a} x (a^2-x^2)^{1/2} \, dx + \delta \int_{a}^{b} x (b^2-x^2)^{1/2} \, dx$$

$$= \tfrac{-\delta}{2} \left[\tfrac{2(b^2-x^2)^{3/2}}{3}\right]_{0}^{a} + \tfrac{\delta}{2} \left[\tfrac{2(a^2-x^2)^{3/2}}{3}\right]_{0}^{a} - \tfrac{\delta}{2} \left[\tfrac{2(b^2-x^2)^{3/2}}{3}\right]_{a}^{b}$$

$$= -\tfrac{\delta}{3} \left[(b^2-a^2)^{3/2} - (b^2)^{3/2}\right] + \tfrac{\delta}{3} \left[0 - (a^2)^{3/2}\right] - \tfrac{\delta}{3} \left[0 - (b^2-a^2)^{3/2}\right] = \tfrac{\delta b^3}{3} - \tfrac{\delta a^3}{3} = \tfrac{\delta(b^3-a^3)}{3} = M_x;$$

We calculate the mass geometrically: $M = \delta A = \delta \left(\tfrac{\pi b^2}{4}\right) - \delta \left(\tfrac{\pi a^2}{4}\right) = \tfrac{\delta \pi}{4} (b^2 - a^2)$. Thus, $\bar{x} = \tfrac{M_y}{M}$

$$= \tfrac{\delta(b^3-a^3)}{3} \cdot \tfrac{4}{\delta \pi (b^2-a^2)} = \tfrac{4}{3\pi} \left(\tfrac{b^3-a^3}{b^2-a^2}\right) = \tfrac{4}{3\pi} \tfrac{(b-a)(a^2+ab+b^2)}{(b-a)(b+a)} = \tfrac{4(a^2+ab+b^2)}{3\pi(a+b)}; \text{ likewise}$$

$$\bar{y} = \tfrac{M_x}{M} = \tfrac{4(a^2+ab+b^2)}{3\pi(a+b)}.$$

(b) $\lim_{b \to a} \tfrac{4}{3\pi} \left(\tfrac{a^2+ab+b^2}{a+b}\right) = \left(\tfrac{4}{3\pi}\right) \left(\tfrac{a^2+a^2+a^2}{a+a}\right) = \left(\tfrac{4}{3\pi}\right) \left(\tfrac{3a^2}{2a}\right) = \tfrac{2a}{\pi} \Rightarrow (\bar{x}, \bar{y}) = \left(\tfrac{2a}{\pi}, \tfrac{2a}{\pi}\right)$ is the limiting

position of the centroid as $b \to a$. This is the centroid of a circle of radius $a$ (and we note the two circles coincide when $b = a$).

16. Since the area of the triangle is 36, the diagram may be labeled as shown at the right. The centroid of the triangle is $\left(\frac{a}{3}, \frac{24}{a}\right)$. The shaded portion is $144 - 36 = 108$. Write $(\underline{x}, \underline{y})$ for the centroid of the remaining region. The centroid of the whole square is obviously $(6, 6)$. Think of the square as a sheet of uniform density, so that the centroid of the square is the average of the centroids of the two regions, weighted by area:

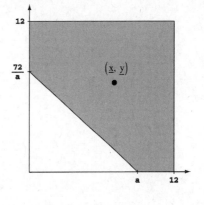

$6 = \frac{36\left(\frac{a}{3}\right) + 108(\underline{x})}{144}$ and $6 = \frac{36\left(\frac{24}{a}\right) + 108(\underline{y})}{144}$

which we solve to get $\underline{x} = 8 - \frac{a}{9}$ and $\underline{y} = \frac{8(a-1)}{a}$. Set $\underline{x} = 7$ in. (Given). It follows that $a = 9$, whence $\underline{y} = \frac{64}{9}$

$= 7\frac{1}{9}$ in. The distances of the centroid $(\underline{x}, \underline{y})$ from the other sides are easily computed. (Note that if we set $\underline{y} = 7$ in. above, we will find $\underline{x} = 7\frac{1}{9}$.)

17. The submerged triangular plate is depicted in the figure at the right. The hypotenuse of the triangle has slope $-1$ $\Rightarrow y - (-2) = -(x - 0) \Rightarrow x = -(y + 2)$ is an equation of the hypotenuse. Using a typical horizontal strip, the fluid pressure is $F = \int (62.4) \cdot \left(\begin{smallmatrix}\text{strip}\\\text{depth}\end{smallmatrix}\right) \cdot \left(\begin{smallmatrix}\text{strip}\\\text{length}\end{smallmatrix}\right) dy$

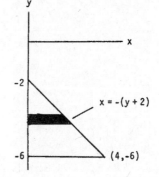

$= \int_{-6}^{-2} (62.4)(-y)[-(y + 2)]\, dy = 62.4 \int_{-6}^{-2} (y^2 + 2y)\, dy$

$= 62.4 \left[\frac{y^3}{3} + y^2\right]_{-6}^{-2} = (62.4)\left[\left(-\frac{8}{3} + 4\right) - \left(-\frac{216}{3} + 36\right)\right]$

$= (62.4)\left(\frac{208}{3} - 32\right) = \frac{(62.4)(112)}{3} \approx 2329.6$ lb

18. Consider a rectangular plate of length $\ell$ and width w. The length is parallel with the surface of the fluid of weight density $\omega$. The force on one side of the plate is

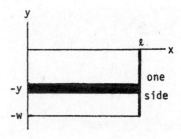

$F = \omega \int_{-w}^{0} (-y)(\ell)\, dy = -\omega\ell \left[\frac{y^2}{2}\right]_{-w}^{0} = \frac{\omega\ell w^2}{2}$. The

average force on one side of the plate is $F_{av} = \frac{\omega}{w} \int_{-w}^{0} (-y)\, dy$

$= \frac{\omega}{w}\left[-\frac{y^2}{2}\right]_{-w}^{0} = \frac{\omega w}{2}$. Therefore the force $\frac{\omega\ell w^2}{2}$

$= \left(\frac{\omega w}{2}\right)(\ell w) = $ (the average pressure up and down) $\cdot$ (the area of the plate).

**NOTES:**

# CHAPTER 7  TRANSCENDENTAL FUNCTIONS

## 7.1  INVERSE FUNCTIONS AND THEIR DERIVATIVES

1.  Yes one-to-one, the graph passes the horizontal line test.

2.  Not one-to-one, the graph fails the horizontal line test.

3.  Not one-to-one since (for example) the horizontal line $y = 2$ intersects the graph twice.

4.  Not one-to-one, the graph fails the horizontal line test.

5.  Yes one-to-one, the graph passes the horizontal line test

6.  Yes one-to-one, the graph passes the horizontal line test

7.  Not one-to-one since the horizontal line $y = 3$ intersects the graph an infinite number of times.

8.  Yes one-to-one, the graph passes the horizontal line test

9.  Yes one-to-one, the graph passes the horizontal line test

10. Not one-to-one since (for example) the horizontal line $y = 1$ intersects the graph twice.

11. Domain: $0 < x \leq 1$, Range: $0 \leq y$

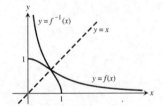

12. Domain: $x < 1$, Range: $y > 0$

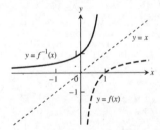

13. Domain: $-1 \leq x \leq 1$, Range: $-\frac{\pi}{2} \leq y \leq \frac{\pi}{2}$

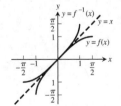

14. Domain: $-\infty < x < \infty$, Range: $-\frac{\pi}{2} < y \leq \frac{\pi}{2}$

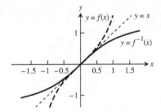

15. Domain: $0 \le x \le 6$, Range: $0 \le y \le 3$

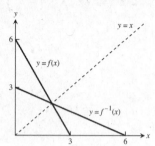

16. Domain: $-2 \le x \le 1$, Range: $-1 \le y < 3$

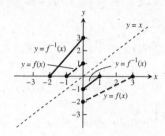

17. The graph is symmetric about $y = x$.

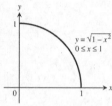

(b)  $y = \sqrt{1 - x^2} \Rightarrow y^2 = 1 - x^2 \Rightarrow x^2 = 1 - y^2 \Rightarrow x = \sqrt{1 - y^2} \Rightarrow y = \sqrt{1 - x^2} = f^{-1}(x)$

18. The graph is symmetric about $y = x$.

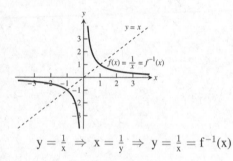

$y = \frac{1}{x} \Rightarrow x = \frac{1}{y} \Rightarrow y = \frac{1}{x} = f^{-1}(x)$

19. Step 1:  $y = x^2 + 1 \Rightarrow x^2 = y - 1 \Rightarrow x = \sqrt{y - 1}$
    Step 2:  $y = \sqrt{x - 1} = f^{-1}(x)$

20. Step 1:  $y = x^2 \Rightarrow x = -\sqrt{y}$, since $x \le 0$.
    Step 2:  $y = -\sqrt{x} = f^{-1}(x)$

21. Step 1:  $y = x^3 - 1 \Rightarrow x^3 = y + 1 \Rightarrow x = (y + 1)^{1/3}$
    Step 2:  $y = \sqrt[3]{x + 1} = f^{-1}(x)$

22. Step 1:  $y = x^2 - 2x + 1 \Rightarrow y = (x - 1)^2 \Rightarrow \sqrt{y} = x - 1$, since $x \ge 1 \Rightarrow x = 1 + \sqrt{y}$
    Step 2:  $y = 1 + \sqrt{x} = f^{-1}(x)$

23. Step 1:  $y = (x + 1)^2 \Rightarrow \sqrt{y} = x + 1$, since $x \ge -1 \Rightarrow x = \sqrt{y} - 1$
    Step 2:  $y = \sqrt{x} - 1 = f^{-1}(x)$

24. Step 1:  $y = x^{2/3} \Rightarrow x = y^{3/2}$
    Step 2:  $y = x^{3/2} = f^{-1}(x)$

25. Step 1:  $y = x^5 \Rightarrow x = y^{1/5}$

    Step 2:  $y = \sqrt[5]{x} = f^{-1}(x)$;

    Domain and Range of $f^{-1}$: all reals;

    $f(f^{-1}(x)) = \left(x^{1/5}\right)^5 = x$ and $f^{-1}(f(x)) = \left(x^5\right)^{1/5} = x$

26. Step 1:  $y = x^4 \Rightarrow x = y^{1/4}$

    Step 2:  $y = \sqrt[4]{x} = f^{-1}(x)$;

    Domain of $f^{-1}$: $x \geq 0$, Range of $f^{-1}$: $y \geq 0$;

    $f(f^{-1}(x)) = \left(x^{1/4}\right)^4 = x$ and $f^{-1}(f(x)) = \left(x^4\right)^{1/4} = x$

27. Step 1:  $y = x^3 + 1 \Rightarrow x^3 = y - 1 \Rightarrow x = (y - 1)^{1/3}$

    Step 2:  $y = \sqrt[3]{x - 1} = f^{-1}(x)$;

    Domain and Range of $f^{-1}$: all reals;

    $f(f^{-1}(x)) = \left((x - 1)^{1/3}\right)^3 + 1 = (x - 1) + 1 = x$ and $f^{-1}(f(x)) = \left((x^3 + 1) - 1\right)^{1/3} = \left(x^3\right)^{1/3} = x$

28. Step 1:  $y = \frac{1}{2}x - \frac{7}{2} \Rightarrow \frac{1}{2}x = y + \frac{7}{2} \Rightarrow x = 2y + 7$

    Step 2:  $y = 2x + 7 = f^{-1}(x)$;

    Domain and Range of $f^{-1}$: all reals;

    $f(f^{-1}(x)) = \frac{1}{2}(2x + 7) - \frac{7}{2} = \left(x + \frac{7}{2}\right) - \frac{7}{2} = x$ and $f^{-1}(f(x)) = 2\left(\frac{1}{2}x - \frac{7}{2}\right) + 7 = (x - 7) + 7 = x$

29. Step 1:  $y = \frac{1}{x^2} \Rightarrow x^2 = \frac{1}{y} \Rightarrow x = \frac{1}{\sqrt{y}}$

    Step 2:  $y = \frac{1}{\sqrt{x}} = f^{-1}(x)$

    Domain of $f^{-1}$: $x > 0$, Range of $f^{-1}$: $y > 0$;

    $f(f^{-1}(x)) = \frac{1}{\left(\frac{1}{\sqrt{x}}\right)^2} = \frac{1}{\left(\frac{1}{x}\right)} = x$ and $f^{-1}(f(x)) = \frac{1}{\sqrt{\frac{1}{x^2}}} = \frac{1}{\left(\frac{1}{x}\right)} = x$ since $x > 0$

30. Step 1:  $y = \frac{1}{x^3} \Rightarrow x^3 = \frac{1}{y} \Rightarrow x = \frac{1}{y^{1/3}}$

    Step 2:  $y = \frac{1}{x^{1/3}} = \sqrt[3]{\frac{1}{x}} = f^{-1}(x)$;

    Domain of $f^{-1}$: $x \neq 0$, Range of $f^{-1}$: $y \neq 0$;

    $f(f^{-1}(x)) = \frac{1}{(x^{-1/3})^3} = \frac{1}{x^{-1}} = x$ and $f^{-1}(f(x)) = \left(\frac{1}{x^3}\right)^{-1/3} = \left(\frac{1}{x}\right)^{-1} = x$

31. Step 1:  $y = \frac{x+3}{x-2} \Rightarrow y(x - 2) = x + 3 \Rightarrow xy - 2y = x + 3 \Rightarrow xy - x = 2y + 3 \Rightarrow x = \frac{2y+3}{y-1}$

    Step 2:  $y = \frac{2x+3}{x-1} = f^{-1}(x)$;

    Domain of $f^{-1}$: $x \neq 1$, Range of $f^{-1}$: $y \neq 2$;

    $f(f^{-1}(x)) = \frac{\left(\frac{2x+3}{x-1}\right)+3}{\left(\frac{2x+3}{x-1}\right)-2} = \frac{(2x+3)+3(x-1)}{(2x+3)-2(x-1)} = \frac{5x}{5} = x$ and $f^{-1}(f(x)) = \frac{2\left(\frac{x+3}{x-2}\right)+3}{\left(\frac{x+3}{x-2}\right)-1} = \frac{2(x+3)+3(x-2)}{(x+3)-(x-2)} = \frac{5x}{5} = x$

32. Step 1:  $y = \frac{\sqrt{x}}{\sqrt{x}-3} \Rightarrow y(\sqrt{x} - 3) = \sqrt{x} \Rightarrow y\sqrt{x} - 3y = \sqrt{x} \Rightarrow y\sqrt{x} - \sqrt{x} = 3y \Rightarrow x = \left(\frac{3y}{y-1}\right)^2$

    Step 2:  $y = \left(\frac{3x}{x-1}\right)^2 = f^{-1}(x)$;

    Domain of $f^{-1}$: $(-\infty, 0] \cup (1, \infty)$, Range of $f^{-1}$: $[0, 9) \cup (9, \infty)$;

    $f(f^{-1}(x)) = \frac{\sqrt{\left(\frac{3x}{x-1}\right)^2}}{\sqrt{\left(\frac{3x}{x-1}\right)^2}-3}$; If $x > 1$ or $x \leq 0 \Rightarrow \frac{3x}{x-1} \geq 0 \Rightarrow \frac{\sqrt{\left(\frac{3x}{x-1}\right)^2}}{\sqrt{\left(\frac{3x}{x-1}\right)^2}-3} = \frac{\frac{3x}{x-1}}{\frac{3x}{x-1}-3} = \frac{3x}{3x-3(x-1)} = \frac{3x}{3} = x$ and

    $f^{-1}(f(x)) = \left(\frac{3\left(\frac{\sqrt{x}}{\sqrt{x}-3}\right)}{\left(\frac{\sqrt{x}}{\sqrt{x}-3}\right)-1}\right)^2 = \frac{9x}{(\sqrt{x}-(\sqrt{x}-3))^2} = \frac{9x}{9} = x$

33. Step 1:  $y = x^2 - 2x, x \le 1 \Rightarrow y + 1 = (x - 1)^2, x \le 1 \Rightarrow -\sqrt{y + 1} = x - 1, x \le 1 \Rightarrow x = 1 - \sqrt{y + 1}$

Step 2:  $y = 1 - \sqrt{x + 1} = f^{-1}(x)$;

Domain of $f^{-1}$: $[-1, \infty)$, Range of $f^{-1}$: $(-\infty, 1]$;

$f(f^{-1}(x)) = \left(1 - \sqrt{x + 1}\right)^2 - 2\left(1 - \sqrt{x + 1}\right) = 1 - 2\sqrt{x + 1} + x + 1 - 2 + 2\sqrt{x + 1} = x$ and

$f^{-1}(f(x)) = 1 - \sqrt{(x^2 - 2x) + 1}, x \le 1 = 1 - \sqrt{(x - 1)^2}, x \le 1 = 1 - |x - 1| = 1 - (1 - x) = x$

34. Step 1:  $y = (2x^3 + 1)^{1/5} \Rightarrow y^5 = 2x^3 + 1 \Rightarrow y^5 - 1 = 2x^3 \Rightarrow \frac{y^5 - 1}{2} = x^3 \Rightarrow x = \sqrt[3]{\frac{y^5 - 1}{2}}$

Step 2:  $y = \sqrt[3]{\frac{x^5 - 1}{2}} = f^{-1}(x)$;

Domain of $f^{-1}$: $(-\infty, \infty)$, Range of $f^{-1}$: $(-\infty, \infty)$;

$f(f^{-1}(x)) = \left(2\left(\sqrt[3]{\frac{x^5 - 1}{2}}\right)^3 + 1\right)^{1/5} = \left(2\left(\frac{x^5 - 1}{2}\right) + 1\right)^{1/5} = ((x^5 - 1) + 1)^{1/5} = (x^5)^{1/5} = x$ and

$f^{-1}(f(x)) = \sqrt[3]{\frac{\left[(2x^3 + 1)^{1/5}\right]^5 - 1}{2}} = \sqrt[3]{\frac{(2x^3 + 1) - 1}{2}} = \sqrt[3]{\frac{2x^3}{2}} = x$

35. (a) $y = 2x + 3 \Rightarrow 2x = y - 3$

    $\Rightarrow x = \frac{y}{2} - \frac{3}{2} \Rightarrow f^{-1}(x) = \frac{x}{2} - \frac{3}{2}$

(c) $\frac{df}{dx}\Big|_{x=-1} = 2, \frac{df^{-1}}{dx}\Big|_{x=1} = \frac{1}{2}$

(b)

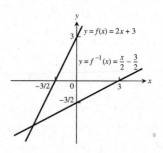

36. (a) $y = \frac{1}{5}x + 7 \Rightarrow \frac{1}{5}x = y - 7$

    $\Rightarrow x = 5y - 35 \Rightarrow f^{-1}(x) = 5x - 35$

(c) $\frac{df}{dx}\Big|_{x=-1} = \frac{1}{5}, \frac{df^{-1}}{dx}\Big|_{x=34/5} = 5$

(b)

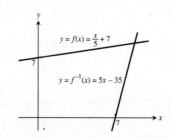

37. (a) $y = 5 - 4x \Rightarrow 4x = 5 - y$

    $\Rightarrow x = \frac{5}{4} - \frac{y}{4} \Rightarrow f^{-1}(x) = \frac{5}{4} - \frac{x}{4}$

(c) $\frac{df}{dx}\Big|_{x=1/2} = -4, \frac{df^{-1}}{dx}\Big|_{x=3} = -\frac{1}{4}$

(b)

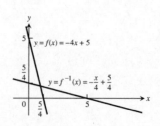

38. (a) $y = 2x^2 \Rightarrow x^2 = \frac{1}{2}y$

    $\Rightarrow x = \frac{1}{\sqrt{2}}\sqrt{y} \Rightarrow f^{-1}(x) = \sqrt{\frac{x}{2}}$

(c) $\frac{df}{dx}\Big|_{x=5} = 4x\Big|_{x=5} = 20$,

    $\frac{df^{-1}}{dx}\Big|_{x=50} = \frac{1}{2\sqrt{2}}x^{-1/2}\Big|_{x=50} = \frac{1}{20}$

(b)

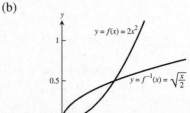

39. (a)  $f(g(x)) = \left(\sqrt[3]{x}\right)^3 = x$, $g(f(x)) = \sqrt[3]{x^3} = x$

(b)
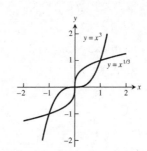

(c)  $f'(x) = 3x^2 \Rightarrow f'(1) = 3, f'(-1) = 3;$

$g'(x) = \frac{1}{3}x^{-2/3} \Rightarrow g'(1) = \frac{1}{3}, g'(-1) = \frac{1}{3}$

(d)  The line $y = 0$ is tangent to $f(x) = x^3$ at $(0,0)$;

the line $x = 0$ is tangent to $g(x) = \sqrt[3]{x}$ at $(0,0)$

40. (a)  $h(k(x)) = \frac{1}{4}\left((4x)^{1/3}\right)^3 = x,$

$k(h(x)) = \left(4 \cdot \frac{x^3}{4}\right)^{1/3} = x$

(b)
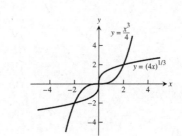

(c)  $h'(x) = \frac{3x^2}{4} \Rightarrow h'(2) = 3, h'(-2) = 3;$

$k'(x) = \frac{4}{3}(4x)^{-2/3} \Rightarrow k'(2) = \frac{1}{3}, k'(-2) = \frac{1}{3}$

(d)  The line $y = 0$ is tangent to $h(x) = \frac{x^3}{4}$ at $(0,0)$;

the line $x = 0$ is tangent to $k(x) = (4x)^{1/3}$ at

$(0,0)$

41.  $\frac{df}{dx} = 3x^2 - 6x \Rightarrow \left.\frac{df^{-1}}{dx}\right|_{x=f(3)} = \left.\frac{1}{\frac{df}{dx}}\right|_{x=3} = \frac{1}{9}$

42.  $\frac{df}{dx} = 2x - 4 \Rightarrow \left.\frac{df^{-1}}{dx}\right|_{x=f(5)} = \left.\frac{1}{\frac{df}{dx}}\right|_{x=5} = \frac{1}{6}$

43.  $\left.\frac{df^{-1}}{dx}\right|_{x=4} = \left.\frac{df^{-1}}{dx}\right|_{x=f(2)} = \left.\frac{1}{\frac{df}{dx}}\right|_{x=2} = \frac{1}{\left(\frac{1}{3}\right)} = 3$

44.  $\left.\frac{dg^{-1}}{dx}\right|_{x=0} = \left.\frac{dg^{-1}}{dx}\right|_{x=f(0)} = \left.\frac{1}{\frac{dg}{dx}}\right|_{x=0} = \frac{1}{2}$

45. (a)  $y = mx \Rightarrow x = \frac{1}{m}y \Rightarrow f^{-1}(x) = \frac{1}{m}x$

(b)  The graph of $y = f^{-1}(x)$ is a line through the origin with slope $\frac{1}{m}$.

46.  $y = mx + b \Rightarrow x = \frac{y}{m} - \frac{b}{m} \Rightarrow f^{-1}(x) = \frac{1}{m}x - \frac{b}{m}$; the graph of $f^{-1}(x)$ is a line with slope $\frac{1}{m}$ and y-intercept $-\frac{b}{m}$.

47. (a)  $y = x + 1 \Rightarrow x = y - 1 \Rightarrow f^{-1}(x) = x - 1$

(b)  $y = x + b \Rightarrow x = y - b \Rightarrow f^{-1}(x) = x - b$

(c)  Their graphs will be parallel to one another and lie on opposite sides of the line $y = x$ equidistant from that line.

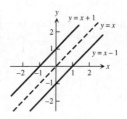

48. (a)  $y = -x + 1 \Rightarrow x = -y + 1 \Rightarrow f^{-1}(x) = 1 - x;$

the lines intersect at a right angle

(b)  $y = -x + b \Rightarrow x = -y + b \Rightarrow f^{-1}(x) = b - x;$

the lines intersect at a right angle

(c)  Such a function is its own inverse.

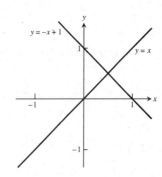

49. Let $x_1 \neq x_2$ be two numbers in the domain of an increasing function f. Then, either $x_1 < x_2$ or $x_1 > x_2$ which implies $f(x_1) < f(x_2)$ or $f(x_1) > f(x_2)$, since $f(x)$ is increasing. In either case, $f(x_1) \neq f(x_2)$ and f is one-to-one. Similar arguments hold if f is decreasing.

50. $f(x)$ is increasing since $x_2 > x_1 \Rightarrow \frac{1}{3} x_2 + \frac{5}{6} > \frac{1}{3} x_1 + \frac{5}{6}$; $\frac{df}{dx} = \frac{1}{3} \Rightarrow \frac{df^{-1}}{dx} = \frac{1}{\left(\frac{1}{3}\right)} = 3$

51. $f(x)$ is increasing since $x_2 > x_1 \Rightarrow 27x_2^3 > 27x_1^3$; $y = 27x^3 \Rightarrow x = \frac{1}{3} y^{1/3} \Rightarrow f^{-1}(x) = \frac{1}{3} x^{1/3}$; $\frac{df}{dx} = 81x^2 \Rightarrow \frac{df^{-1}}{dx} = \frac{1}{81x^2}\Big|_{\frac{1}{3} x^{1/3}} = \frac{1}{9x^{2/3}} = \frac{1}{9} x^{-2/3}$

52. $f(x)$ is decreasing since $x_2 > x_1 \Rightarrow 1 - 8x_2^3 < 1 - 8x_1^3$; $y = 1 - 8x^3 \Rightarrow x = \frac{1}{2} (1 - y)^{1/3} \Rightarrow f^{-1}(x) = \frac{1}{2} (1 - x)^{1/3}$; $\frac{df}{dx} = -24x^2 \Rightarrow \frac{df^{-1}}{dx} = \frac{1}{-24x^2}\Big|_{\frac{1}{2}(1-x)^{1/3}} = \frac{-1}{6(1-x)^{2/3}} = -\frac{1}{6} (1 - x)^{-2/3}$

53. $f(x)$ is decreasing since $x_2 > x_1 \Rightarrow (1 - x_2)^3 < (1 - x_1)^3$; $y = (1 - x)^3 \Rightarrow x = 1 - y^{1/3} \Rightarrow f^{-1}(x) = 1 - x^{1/3}$; $\frac{df}{dx} = -3(1 - x)^2 \Rightarrow \frac{df^{-1}}{dx} = \frac{1}{-3(1 - x)^2}\Big|_{1-x^{1/3}} = \frac{-1}{3x^{2/3}} = -\frac{1}{3} x^{-2/3}$

54. $f(x)$ is increasing since $x_2 > x_1 \Rightarrow x_2^{5/3} > x_1^{5/3}$; $y = x^{5/3} \Rightarrow x = y^{3/5} \Rightarrow f^{-1}(x) = x^{3/5}$; $\frac{df}{dx} = \frac{5}{3} x^{2/3} \Rightarrow \frac{df^{-1}}{dx} = \frac{1}{\frac{5}{3} x^{2/3}}\Big|_{x^{3/5}} = \frac{3}{5x^{2/5}} = \frac{3}{5} x^{-2/5}$

55. The function $g(x)$ is also one-to-one. The reasoning: $f(x)$ is one-to-one means that if $x_1 \neq x_2$ then $f(x_1) \neq f(x_2)$, so $-f(x_1) \neq -f(x_2)$ and therefore $g(x_1) \neq g(x_2)$. Therefore $g(x)$ is one-to-one as well.

56. The function $h(x)$ is also one-to-one. The reasoning: $f(x)$ is one-to-one means that if $x_1 \neq x_2$ then $f(x_1) \neq f(x_2)$, so $\frac{1}{f(x_1)} \neq \frac{1}{f(x_2)}$, and therefore $h(x_1) \neq h(x_2)$.

57. The composite is one-to-one also. The reasoning: If $x_1 \neq x_2$ then $g(x_1) \neq g(x_2)$ because g is one-to-one. Since $g(x_1) \neq g(x_2)$, we also have $f(g(x_1)) \neq f(g(x_2))$ because f is one-to-one. Thus, $f \circ g$ is one-to-one because $x_1 \neq x_2 \Rightarrow f(g(x_1)) \neq f(g(x_2))$.

58. Yes, g must be one-to-one. If g were not one-to-one, there would exist numbers $x_1 \neq x_2$ in the domain of g with $g(x_1) = g(x_2)$. For these numbers we would also have $f(g(x_1)) = f(g(x_2))$, contradicting the assumption that $f \circ g$ is one-to-one.

59. $(g \circ f)(x) = x \Rightarrow g(f(x)) = x \Rightarrow g'(f(x))f'(x) = 1$

60. $W(a) = \int_{f(a)}^{f(a)} \pi \left[ \left( f^{-1}(y) \right)^2 - a^2 \right] dy = 0 = \int_a^a 2\pi x[f(a) - f(x)] \, dx = S(a)$; $W'(t) = \pi \left[ \left( f^{-1}(f(t)) \right)^2 - a^2 \right] f'(t)$

    $= \pi (t^2 - a^2) f'(t)$; also $S(t) = 2\pi f(t) \int_a^t x \, dx - 2\pi \int_a^t xf(x) \, dx = \left[ \pi f(t)t^2 - \pi f(t)a^2 \right] - 2\pi \int_a^t xf(x) \, dx \Rightarrow S'(t)$

    $= \pi t^2 f'(t) + 2\pi t f(t) - \pi a^2 f'(t) - 2\pi t f(t) = \pi (t^2 - a^2) f'(t) \Rightarrow W'(t) = S'(t)$. Therefore, $W(t) = S(t)$ for all $t \in [a, b]$.

61-68.   Example CAS commands:
    Maple:

```
with( plots );#63
f := x -> sqrt(3*x-2);
domain := 2/3 .. 4;
x0 := 3;
Df := D(f);                        # (a)
```

```
plot( [f(x),Df(x)], x=domain, color=[red,blue], linestyle=[1,3], legend=["y=f(x)","y=f '(x)"],
    title="#61(a) (Section 7.1)" );
q1 := solve( y=f(x), x );          # (b)
g := unapply( q1, y );
m1 := Df(x0);                      # (c)
t1 := f(x0)+m1*(x-x0);
y=t1;
m2 := 1/Df(x0);                    # (d)
t2 := g(f(x0)) + m2*(x-f(x0));
y=t2;
domaing := map(f,domain);      # (e)
p1 := plot( [f(x),x], x=domain, color=[pink,green], linestyle=[1,9], thickness=[3,0] ):
p2 := plot( g(x), x=domaing, color=cyan, linestyle=3, thickness=4 ):
p3 := plot( t1, x=x0-1..x0+1, color=red, linestyle=4, thickness=0 ):
p4 := plot( t2, x=f(x0)-1..f(x0)+1, color=blue, linestyle=7, thickness=1 ):
p5 := plot( [ [x0,f(x0)], [f(x0),x0] ], color=green ):
display( [p1,p2,p3,p4,p5], scaling=constrained, title="#63(e) (Section 7.1)" );
```

Mathematica: (assigned function and values for a, b, and x0 may vary)

If a function requires the odd root of a negative number, begin by loading the RealOnly package that allows Mathematica to do this. See section 2.5 for details.

```
<<Miscellaneous `RealOnly`
Clear[x, y]
{a,b} = {−2, 1}; x0 = 1/2 ;
f[x_] = (3x + 2) / (2x − 11)
Plot[{f[x], f'[x]}, {x, a, b}]
solx = Solve[y == f[x], x]
g[y_] = x /. solx[[1]]
y0 = f[x0]
ftan[x_] = y0 + f'[x0] (x-x0)
gtan[y_] = x0 + 1/ f'[x0] (y − y0)
Plot[{f[x], ftan[x], g[x], gtan[x], Identity[x]},{x, a, b},
Epilog → Line[{{x0, y0},{y0, x0}}], PlotRange → {{a,b},{a,b}}, AspectRatio → Automatic]
```

69-70.  Example CAS commands:

Maple:

```
with( plots );
eq := cos(y) = x^(1/5);
domain := 0 .. 1;
x0 := 1/2;
f := unapply( solve( eq, y ), x );  # (a)
Df := D(f);
plot( [f(x),Df(x)], x=domain, color=[red,blue], linestyle=[1,3], legend=["y=f(x)","y=f '(x)"],
    title="#70(a) (Section 7.1)" );
q1 := solve( eq, x );              # (b)
g := unapply( q1, y );
m1 := Df(x0);                      # (c)
t1 := f(x0)+m1*(x-x0);
y=t1;
m2 := 1/Df(x0);                    # (d)
```

64. $\int_1^{e^{\pi/4}} \frac{4\,dt}{t(1+\ln^2 t)} = 4\int_0^{\pi/4} \frac{du}{1+u^2}$ , where $u = \ln t$ and $du = \frac{1}{t}\,dt$; $t = 1 \Rightarrow u = 0$, $t = e^{\pi/4} \Rightarrow u = \frac{\pi}{4}$

$\qquad = [4\tan^{-1} u]_0^{\pi/4} = 4\left(\tan^{-1}\frac{\pi}{4} - \tan^{-1} 0\right) = 4\tan^{-1}\frac{\pi}{4}$

65. $\int \frac{y\,dy}{\sqrt{1-y^4}} = \frac{1}{2}\int \frac{du}{\sqrt{1-u^2}}$ , where $u = y^2$ and $du = 2y\,dy$

$\qquad = \frac{1}{2}\sin^{-1} u + C = \frac{1}{2}\sin^{-1} y^2 + C$

66. $\int \frac{\sec^2 y\,dy}{\sqrt{1-\tan^2 y}} = \int \frac{du}{\sqrt{1-u^2}}$ , where $u = \tan y$ and $du = \sec^2 y\,dy$

$\qquad = \sin^{-1} u + C = \sin^{-1}(\tan y) + C$

67. $\int \frac{dx}{\sqrt{-x^2+4x-3}} = \int \frac{dx}{\sqrt{1-(x^2-4x+4)}} = \int \frac{dx}{\sqrt{1-(x-2)^2}} = \sin^{-1}(x-2) + C$

68. $\int \frac{dx}{\sqrt{2x-x^2}} = \int \frac{dx}{\sqrt{1-(x^2-2x+1)}} = \int \frac{dx}{\sqrt{1-(x-1)^2}} = \sin^{-1}(x-1) + C$

69. $\int_{-1}^0 \frac{6\,dt}{\sqrt{3-2t-t^2}} = 6\int_{-1}^0 \frac{dt}{\sqrt{4-(t^2+2t+1)}} = 6\int_{-1}^0 \frac{dt}{\sqrt{2^2-(t+1)^2}} = 6\left[\sin^{-1}\left(\frac{t+1}{2}\right)\right]_{-1}^0$

$\qquad = 6\left[\sin^{-1}\left(\frac{1}{2}\right) - \sin^{-1} 0\right] = 6\left(\frac{\pi}{6} - 0\right) = \pi$

70. $\int_{1/2}^1 \frac{6\,dt}{\sqrt{3+4t-4t^2}} = 3\int_{1/2}^1 \frac{2\,dt}{\sqrt{4-(4t^2-4t+1)}} = 3\int_{1/2}^1 \frac{2\,dt}{\sqrt{2^2-(2t-1)^2}} = 3\left[\sin^{-1}\left(\frac{2t-1}{2}\right)\right]_{1/2}^1$

$\qquad = 3\left[\sin^{-1}\left(\frac{1}{2}\right) - \sin^{-1} 0\right] = 3\left(\frac{\pi}{6} - 0\right) = \frac{\pi}{2}$

71. $\int \frac{dy}{y^2-2y+5} = \int \frac{dy}{4+y^2-2y+1} = \int \frac{dy}{2^2+(y-1)^2} = \frac{1}{2}\tan^{-1}\left(\frac{y-1}{2}\right) + C$

72. $\int \frac{dy}{y^2+6y+10} = \int \frac{dy}{1+(y^2+6y+9)} = \int \frac{dy}{1+(y+3)^2} = \tan^{-1}(y+3) + C$

73. $\int_1^2 \frac{8\,dx}{x^2-2x+2} = 8\int_1^2 \frac{dx}{1+(x^2-2x+1)} = 8\int_1^2 \frac{dx}{1+(x-1)^2} = 8\left[\tan^{-1}(x-1)\right]_1^2 = 8\left(\tan^{-1} 1 - \tan^{-1} 0\right) = 8\left(\frac{\pi}{4} - 0\right) = 2\pi$

74. $\int_2^4 \frac{2\,dx}{x^2-6x+10} = 2\int_2^4 \frac{dx}{1+(x^2-6x+9)} = 2\int_2^4 \frac{dx}{1+(x-3)^2} = 2\left[\tan^{-1}(x-3)\right]_2^4 = 2\left[\tan^{-1} 1 - \tan^{-1}(-1)\right] = 2\left[\frac{\pi}{4} - \left(-\frac{\pi}{4}\right)\right] = \pi$

75. $\int \frac{x+4}{x^2+4}\,dx = \int \frac{x}{x^2+4}\,dx + \int \frac{4}{x^2+4}\,dx$; $\int \frac{x}{x^2+4}\,dx = \frac{1}{2}\int \frac{1}{u}\,du$ where $u = x^2+4 \Rightarrow du = 2x\,dx \Rightarrow \frac{1}{2}du = x\,dx$

$\qquad \Rightarrow \int \frac{x+4}{x^2+4}\,dx = \frac{1}{2}\ln(x^2+4) + 2\tan^{-1}\left(\frac{x}{2}\right) + C$

76. $\int \frac{t-2}{t^2-6t+10}\,dt = \int \frac{t-2}{(t-3)^2+1}\,dt \left[\text{Let } w = t-3 \Rightarrow w+3 = t \Rightarrow dw = dt\right] \rightarrow \int \frac{w+1}{w^2+1}\,dw = \int \frac{w}{w^2+1}\,dw + \int \frac{1}{w^2+1}\,dw$;

$\qquad \int \frac{w}{w^2+1}\,dw = \frac{1}{2}\int \frac{1}{u}\,du$ where $u = w^2+1 \Rightarrow du = 2w\,dw \Rightarrow \frac{1}{2}du = w\,dw \Rightarrow \int \frac{w}{w^2+1}\,dw + \int \frac{1}{w^2+1}\,dw$

$\qquad = \frac{1}{2}\ln(w^2+1) + \tan^{-1}(w) + C = \frac{1}{2}\ln\left((t-3)^2+1\right) + \tan^{-1}(t-3) + C = \frac{1}{2}\ln(t^2-6t+10) + \tan^{-1}(t-3) + C$

77. $\int \frac{x^2+2x-1}{x^2+9}\,dx = \int \left(1 + \frac{2x-10}{x^2+9}\right)dx = \int dx + \int \frac{2x}{x^2+9}\,dx - 10\int \frac{1}{x^2+9}\,dx$; $\int \frac{2x}{x^2+9}\,dx = \int \frac{1}{u}\,du$ where $u = x^2+9$

$\qquad \Rightarrow du = 2x\,dx \Rightarrow \int dx + \int \frac{2x}{x^2+9}\,dx - 10\int \frac{1}{x^2+9}\,dx = x + \ln(x^2+9) - \frac{10}{3}\tan^{-1}\left(\frac{x}{3}\right) + C$

78. $\int \frac{t^3-2t^2+3t-4}{t^2+1}\,dt = \int \left(t - 2 + \frac{2t-2}{t^2+1}\right)dt = \int (t-2)\,dt + \int \frac{2t}{t^2+1}\,dt - 2\int \frac{1}{t^2+1}\,dt$; $\int \frac{2t}{t^2+1}\,dt = \int \frac{1}{u}\,du$ where $u = t^2+1$

$\qquad \Rightarrow du = 2t\,dt \Rightarrow \int (t-2)\,dt + \int \frac{2t}{t^2+1}\,dt - 2\int \frac{1}{t^2+1}\,dt = \frac{1}{2}t^2 - 2t + \ln(t^2+1) - 2\tan^{-1}(t) + C$

79. $\int \frac{dx}{(x+1)\sqrt{x^2+2x}} = \int \frac{dx}{(x+1)\sqrt{x^2+2x+1-1}} = \int \frac{dx}{(x+1)\sqrt{(x+1)^2-1}} = \int \frac{du}{u\sqrt{u^2-1}}$, where $u = x + 1$ and $du = dx$

$= \sec^{-1}|u| + C = \sec^{-1}|x+1| + C$

80. $\int \frac{dx}{(x-2)\sqrt{x^2-4x+3}} = \int \frac{dx}{(x-2)\sqrt{x^2-4x+4-1}} = \int \frac{dx}{(x-2)\sqrt{(x-2)^2-1}} = \int \frac{1}{u\sqrt{u^2-1}} du$, where $u = x - 2$ and $du = dx$

$= \sec^{-1}|u| + C = \sec^{-1}|x-2| + C$

81. $\int \frac{e^{\sin^{-1}x}}{\sqrt{1-x^2}} dx = \int e^u du$, where $u = \sin^{-1}x$ and $du = \frac{dx}{\sqrt{1-x^2}}$

$= e^u + C = e^{\sin^{-1}x} + C$

82. $\int \frac{e^{\cos^{-1}x}}{\sqrt{1-x^2}} dx = -\int e^u du$, where $u = \cos^{-1}x$ and $du = \frac{-dx}{\sqrt{1-x^2}}$

$= -e^u + C = -e^{\cos^{-1}x} + C$

83. $\int \frac{\left(\sin^{-1}x\right)^2}{\sqrt{1-x^2}} dx = \int u^2 du$, where $u = \sin^{-1}x$ and $du = \frac{dx}{\sqrt{1-x^2}}$

$= \frac{u^3}{3} + C = \frac{\left(\sin^{-1}x\right)^3}{3} + C$

84. $\int \frac{\sqrt{\tan^{-1}x}}{1+x^2} dx = \int u^{1/2} du$, where $u = \tan^{-1}x$ and $du = \frac{dx}{1+x^2}$

$= \frac{2}{3}u^{3/2} + C = \frac{2}{3}\left(\tan^{-1}x\right)^{3/2} + C = \frac{2}{3}\sqrt{\left(\tan^{-1}x\right)^3} + C$

85. $\int \frac{1}{(\tan^{-1}y)(1+y^2)} dy = \int \frac{\left(\frac{1}{1+y^2}\right)}{\tan^{-1}y} dy = \int \frac{1}{u} du$, where $u = \tan^{-1}y$ and $du = \frac{dy}{1+y^2}$

$= \ln|u| + C = \ln|\tan^{-1}y| + C$

86. $\int \frac{1}{(\sin^{-1}y)\sqrt{1+y^2}} dy = \int \frac{\left(\frac{1}{\sqrt{1-y^2}}\right)}{\sin^{-1}y} dy = \int \frac{1}{u} du$, where $u = \sin^{-1}y$ and $du = \frac{dy}{\sqrt{1-y^2}}$

$= \ln|u| + C = \ln|\sin^{-1}y| + C$

87. $\int_{\sqrt{2}}^2 \frac{\sec^2\left(\sec^{-1}x\right)}{x\sqrt{x^2-1}} dx = \int_{\pi/4}^{\pi/3} \sec^2 u \, du$, where $u = \sec^{-1}x$ and $du = \frac{dx}{x\sqrt{x^2-1}}$; $x = \sqrt{2} \Rightarrow u = \frac{\pi}{4}$, $x = 2 \Rightarrow u = \frac{\pi}{3}$

$= [\tan u]_{\pi/4}^{\pi/3} = \tan\frac{\pi}{3} - \tan\frac{\pi}{4} = \sqrt{3} - 1$

88. $\int_{2/\sqrt{3}}^2 \frac{\cos\left(\sec^{-1}x\right)}{x\sqrt{x^2-1}} dx = \int_{\pi/6}^{\pi/3} \cos u \, du$, where $u = \sec^{-1}x$ and $du = \frac{dx}{x\sqrt{x^2-1}}$; $x = \frac{2}{\sqrt{3}} \Rightarrow u = \frac{\pi}{6}$, $x = 2 \Rightarrow u = \frac{\pi}{3}$

$= [\sin u]_{\pi/6}^{\pi/3} = \sin\frac{\pi}{3} - \sin\frac{\pi}{6} = \frac{\sqrt{3}-1}{2}$

89. $\int \frac{1}{\sqrt{x}(x+1)\left[\left(\tan^{-1}\sqrt{x}\right)^2+9\right]} dx = 2\int \frac{1}{u^2+9} du$ where $u = \tan^{-1}\sqrt{x} \Rightarrow du = \frac{1}{1+\left(\sqrt{x}\right)^2}\frac{1}{2\sqrt{x}} dx \Rightarrow 2du = \frac{1}{(1+x)\sqrt{x}} dx$

$= \frac{2}{3}\tan^{-1}\left(\frac{\tan^{-1}\sqrt{x}}{3}\right) + C$

90. $\int \frac{e^x\sin^{-1}e^x}{\sqrt{1-e^{2x}}} dx = \int u \, du$ where $u = \sin^{-1}e^x \Rightarrow du = \frac{1}{\sqrt{1-e^{2x}}}e^x dx$

$= \frac{1}{2}\left(\sin^{-1}e^x\right)^2 + C$

91. $\lim_{x \to 0} \frac{\sin^{-1}5x}{x} = \lim_{x \to 0} \frac{\left(\frac{5}{\sqrt{1-25x^2}}\right)}{1} = 5$

92. $\displaystyle\lim_{x \to 1^+} \frac{\sqrt{x^2-1}}{\sec^{-1}x} = \lim_{x \to 1^+} \frac{(x^2-1)^{1/2}}{\sec^{-1}x} = \lim_{x \to 1^+} \frac{\left(\frac{1}{2}\right)(x^2-1)^{-1/2}(2x)}{\left(\frac{1}{|x|\sqrt{x^2-1}}\right)} = \lim_{x \to 1^+} x\,|x| = 1$

93. $\displaystyle\lim_{x \to \infty} x \tan^{-1}\left(\frac{2}{x}\right) = \lim_{x \to \infty} \frac{\tan^{-1}(2x^{-1})}{x^{-1}} = \lim_{x \to \infty} \frac{\left(\frac{-2x^{-2}}{1+4x^{-2}}\right)}{-x^{-2}} = \lim_{x \to \infty} \frac{2}{1+4x^{-2}} = 2$

94. $\displaystyle\lim_{x \to 0} \frac{2\tan^{-1}3x^2}{7x^2} = \lim_{x \to 0} \frac{\left(\frac{12x}{1+9x^4}\right)}{14x} = \lim_{x \to 0} \frac{6}{7(1+9x^4)} = \frac{6}{7}$

95. $\displaystyle\lim_{x \to 0} \frac{\tan^{-1}x^2}{x\sin^{-1}x} = \lim_{x \to 0} \left(\frac{\frac{2x}{1+x^4}}{x\frac{1}{\sqrt{1-x^2}}+\sin^{-1}x}\right) = \lim_{x \to 0} \left(\frac{\frac{-2(3x^4-1)}{(1+x^4)^2}}{\frac{-x^2+2}{(1-x^2)^{3/2}}}\right) = \frac{\frac{-2(0-1)}{1^2}}{\frac{-0+2}{(1-0)^{3/2}}} = \frac{2}{2} = 1$

96. $\displaystyle\lim_{x \to \infty} \frac{e^x \tan^{-1}e^x}{e^{2x}+x} = \lim_{x \to \infty} \frac{e^x \tan^{-1}e^x + \frac{e^{2x}}{e^{2x}+1}}{2e^{2x}+1} = \lim_{x \to \infty} \frac{e^x \tan^{-1}e^x + \frac{e^{2x}}{e^{2x}+1} + \frac{2e^{2x}}{(e^{2x}+1)^2}}{4e^{2x}} = \lim_{x \to \infty} \frac{e^x \tan^{-1}e^x + \frac{e^{2x}(e^{2x}+3)}{(e^{2x}+1)^2}}{4e^{2x}}$

$\displaystyle = \lim_{x \to \infty} \left[\frac{\tan^{-1}e^x}{4e^x} + \frac{(e^{2x}+3)}{4(e^{2x}+1)^2}\right] = \lim_{x \to \infty} \left[\frac{\tan^{-1}e^x}{4e^x} + \frac{(1+3e^{-2x})}{4(e^x+e^{-x})^2}\right] = 0 + 0 = 0$

97. $\displaystyle\lim_{x \to 0^+} \frac{\left[\tan^{-1}(\sqrt{x})\right]^2}{x\sqrt{x+1}} = \lim_{x \to 0^+} \frac{\tan^{-1}(\sqrt{x})\frac{1}{\sqrt{x}(1+x)}}{\frac{x}{2\sqrt{x+1}}+\sqrt{x+1}} = \lim_{x \to 0^+} \frac{\frac{\tan^{-1}(\sqrt{x})}{\sqrt{x}(1+x)}}{\frac{3x+2}{2\sqrt{x+1}}} = \lim_{x \to 0^+} \left(\frac{2\tan^{-1}(\sqrt{x})}{(3x+2)\sqrt{x}\sqrt{x+1}}\right) = \lim_{x \to 0^+} \left(\frac{\frac{1}{\sqrt{x}(1+x)}}{\frac{12x^2+13x+2}{2\sqrt{x}\sqrt{x+1}}}\right)$

$\displaystyle = \lim_{x \to 0^+} \left(\frac{2}{(12x^2+13x+2)\sqrt{x+1}}\right) = \frac{2}{2} = 1$

98. $\displaystyle\lim_{x \to 0^+} \frac{\sin^{-1}(x^2)}{(\sin^{-1}x)^2} = \lim_{x \to 0^+} \left(\frac{\frac{2x}{\sqrt{1-x^4}}}{2(\sin^{-1}x)\frac{1}{\sqrt{1-x^2}}}\right) = \lim_{x \to 0^+} \left(\frac{x}{\sin^{-1}x\,\sqrt{1+x^2}}\right) = \lim_{x \to 0^+} \left(\frac{1}{\sin^{-1}x\cdot\frac{x}{\sqrt{1+x^2}}+\frac{1}{\sqrt{1-x^2}}\sqrt{1+x^2}}\right) =$

$\displaystyle = \lim_{x \to 0^+} \left(\frac{\sqrt{1+x^2}\sqrt{1-x^2}}{1+x^2+x\sqrt{1-x^2}\sin^{-1}x}\right) = \frac{1}{1} = 1$

99. If $y = \ln x - \frac{1}{2}\ln(1+x^2) - \frac{\tan^{-1}x}{x} + C$, then $dy = \left[\frac{1}{x} - \frac{x}{1+x^2} - \frac{\left(\frac{x}{1+x^2}\right)-\tan^{-1}x}{x^2}\right] dx$

$= \left(\frac{1}{x} - \frac{x}{1+x^2} - \frac{1}{x(1+x^2)} + \frac{\tan^{-1}x}{x^2}\right) dx = \frac{x(1+x^2)-x^3-x+(\tan^{-1}x)(1+x^2)}{x^2(1+x^2)} dx = \frac{\tan^{-1}x}{x^2} dx,$

which verifies the formula

100. If $y = \frac{x^4}{4}\cos^{-1}5x + \frac{5}{4}\int \frac{x^4}{\sqrt{1-25x^2}} dx$, then $dy = \left[x^3\cos^{-1}5x + \left(\frac{x^4}{4}\right)\left(\frac{-5}{\sqrt{1-25x^2}}\right) + \frac{5}{4}\left(\frac{x^4}{\sqrt{1-25x^2}}\right)\right] dx$

$= (x^3\cos^{-1}5x)\,dx$, which verifies the formula

101. If $y = x\left(\sin^{-1}x\right)^2 - 2x + 2\sqrt{1-x^2}\sin^{-1}x + C$, then

$dy = \left[\left(\sin^{-1}x\right)^2 + \frac{2x(\sin^{-1}x)}{\sqrt{1-x^2}} - 2 + \frac{-2x}{\sqrt{1-x^2}}\sin^{-1}x + 2\sqrt{1-x^2}\left(\frac{1}{\sqrt{1-x^2}}\right)\right] dx = (\sin^{-1}x)^2\,dx$, which verifies

the formula

102. If $y = x\ln(a^2+x^2) - 2x + 2a\tan^{-1}\left(\frac{x}{a}\right) + C$, then $dy = \left[\ln(a^2+x^2) + \frac{2x^2}{a^2+x^2} - 2 + \frac{2}{1+\left(\frac{x^2}{a^2}\right)}\right] dx$

$= \left[\ln(a^2+x^2) + 2\left(\frac{a^2+x^2}{a^2+x^2}\right) - 2\right] dx = \ln(a^2+x^2)\,dx$, which verifies the formula

103. $\frac{dy}{dx} = \frac{1}{\sqrt{1-x^2}} \Rightarrow dy = \frac{dx}{\sqrt{1-x^2}} \Rightarrow y = \sin^{-1}x + C;\ x = 0$ and $y = 0 \Rightarrow 0 = \sin^{-1}0 + C \Rightarrow C = 0 \Rightarrow y = \sin^{-1}x$

104. $\frac{dy}{dx} = \frac{1}{x^2+1} - 1 \Rightarrow dy = \left(\frac{1}{1+x^2} - 1\right) dx \Rightarrow y = \tan^{-1}(x) - x + C;\ x = 0$ and $y = 1 \Rightarrow 1 = \tan^{-1} 0 - 0 + C$
$\Rightarrow C = 1 \Rightarrow y = \tan^{-1}(x) - x + 1$

105. $\frac{dy}{dx} = \frac{1}{x\sqrt{x^2-1}} \Rightarrow dy = \frac{dx}{x\sqrt{x^2-1}} \Rightarrow y = \sec^{-1}|x| + C;\ x = 2$ and $y = \pi \Rightarrow \pi = \sec^{-1} 2 + C \Rightarrow C = \pi - \sec^{-1} 2$
$= \pi - \frac{\pi}{3} = \frac{2\pi}{3} \Rightarrow y = \sec^{-1}(x) + \frac{2\pi}{3},\ x > 1$

106. $\frac{dy}{dx} = \frac{1}{1+x^2} - \frac{2}{\sqrt{1-x^2}} \Rightarrow dy = \left(\frac{1}{1+x^2} - \frac{2}{\sqrt{1-x^2}}\right) dx \Rightarrow y = \tan^{-1} x - 2\sin^{-1} x + C;\ x = 0$ and $y = 2$
$\Rightarrow 2 = \tan^{-1} 0 - 2\sin^{-1} 0 + C \Rightarrow C = 2 \Rightarrow y = \tan^{-1} x - 2\sin^{-1} x + 2$

107. (a) The angle $\alpha$ is the large angle between the wall and the right end of the blackboard minus the small angle between
the left end of the blackboard and the wall $\Rightarrow \alpha = \cot^{-1}\left(\frac{x}{15}\right) - \cot^{-1}\left(\frac{x}{3}\right)$.

(b) $\frac{d\alpha}{dt} = -\frac{\frac{1}{15}}{1+\left(\frac{x}{15}\right)^2} + \frac{\frac{1}{3}}{1+\left(\frac{x}{3}\right)^2} = -\frac{15}{225+x^2} + \frac{3}{9+x^2} = \frac{540-12x^2}{(225+x^2)(9+x^2)};\ \frac{d\alpha}{dt} = 0 \Rightarrow 540 - 12x^2 = 0 \Rightarrow x = \pm 3\sqrt{5}$

Since $x > 0$, consider only $x = 3\sqrt{5} \Rightarrow \alpha\left(3\sqrt{5}\right) = \cot^{-1}\left(\frac{3\sqrt{5}}{15}\right) - \cot^{-1}\left(\frac{3\sqrt{5}}{3}\right) \approx 0.729728 \approx 41.8103°$. Using

the first derivative test, $\frac{d\alpha}{dt}\Big|_{x=1} = \frac{132}{565} > 0$ and $\frac{d\alpha}{dt}\Big|_{x=10} = -\frac{132}{7085} < 0 \Rightarrow$ local maximum of $41.8103°$ when

$x = 3\sqrt{5} \approx 6.7082$ ft.

108. $V = \pi \int_0^{\pi/3} [2^2 - (\sec y)^2]\, dy = \pi [4y - \tan y]_0^{\pi/3} = \pi\left(\frac{4\pi}{3} - \sqrt{3}\right)$

109. $V = \left(\frac{1}{3}\right)\pi r^2 h = \left(\frac{1}{3}\right)\pi(3\sin\theta)^2(3\cos\theta) = 9\pi(\cos\theta - \cos^3\theta)$, where $0 \le \theta \le \frac{\pi}{2}$
$\Rightarrow \frac{dV}{d\theta} = -9\pi(\sin\theta)(1 - 3\cos^2\theta) = 0 \Rightarrow \sin\theta = 0$ or $\cos\theta = \pm\frac{1}{\sqrt{3}} \Rightarrow$ the critical points are: $0, \cos^{-1}\left(\frac{1}{\sqrt{3}}\right)$, and
$\cos^{-1}\left(-\frac{1}{\sqrt{3}}\right)$; but $\cos^{-1}\left(-\frac{1}{\sqrt{3}}\right)$ is not in the domain. When $\theta = 0$, we have a minimum and when $\theta = \cos^{-1}\left(\frac{1}{\sqrt{3}}\right)$
$\approx 54.7°$, we have a maximum volume.

110. $65° + (90° - \beta) + (90° - \alpha) = 180° \Rightarrow \alpha = 65° - \beta = 65° - \tan^{-1}\left(\frac{21}{50}\right) \approx 65° - 22.78° \approx 42.22°$

111. Take each square as a unit square. From the diagram we have the following: the smallest angle $\alpha$ has a
tangent of $1 \Rightarrow \alpha = \tan^{-1} 1$; the middle angle $\beta$ has a tangent of $2 \Rightarrow \beta = \tan^{-1} 2$; and the largest angle $\gamma$
has a tangent of $3 \Rightarrow \gamma = \tan^{-1} 3$. The sum of these three angles is $\pi \Rightarrow \alpha + \beta + \gamma = \pi$
$\Rightarrow \tan^{-1} 1 + \tan^{-1} 2 + \tan^{-1} 3 = \pi$.

112. (a) From the symmetry of the diagram, we see that $\pi - \sec^{-1} x$ is the vertical distance from the graph of $y = \sec^{-1} x$ to
the line $y = \pi$ and this distance is the same as the height of $y = \sec^{-1} x$ above the x-axis at $-x$;
i.e., $\pi - \sec^{-1} x = \sec^{-1}(-x)$.

(b) $\cos^{-1}(-x) = \pi - \cos^{-1} x$, where $-1 \le x \le 1 \Rightarrow \cos^{-1}\left(-\frac{1}{x}\right) = \pi - \cos^{-1}\left(\frac{1}{x}\right)$, where $x \ge 1$ or $x \le -1$
$\Rightarrow \sec^{-1}(-x) = \pi - \sec^{-1} x$

113. $\sin^{-1}(1) + \cos^{-1}(1) = \frac{\pi}{2} + 0 = \frac{\pi}{2}$; $\sin^{-1}(0) + \cos^{-1}(0) = 0 + \frac{\pi}{2} = \frac{\pi}{2}$; and $\sin^{-1}(-1) + \cos^{-1}(-1) = -\frac{\pi}{2} + \pi = \frac{\pi}{2}$.
If $x \in (-1, 0)$ and $x = -a$, then $\sin^{-1}(x) + \cos^{-1}(x) = \sin^{-1}(-a) + \cos^{-1}(-a) = -\sin^{-1} a + (\pi - \cos^{-1} a)$
$= \pi - (\sin^{-1} a + \cos^{-1} a) = \pi - \frac{\pi}{2} = \frac{\pi}{2}$ from Equations (3) and (4) in the text.

114.  $x \Rightarrow \tan \alpha = x$ and $\tan \beta = \frac{1}{x} \Rightarrow \frac{\pi}{2} = \alpha + \beta = \tan^{-1} x + \tan^{-1} \frac{1}{x}$.

115. $\csc^{-1} u = \frac{\pi}{2} - \sec^{-1} u \Rightarrow \frac{d}{dx} \left( \csc^{-1} u \right) = \frac{d}{dx} \left( \frac{\pi}{2} - \sec^{-1} u \right) = 0 - \frac{\frac{du}{dx}}{|u| \sqrt{u^2 - 1}} = -\frac{\frac{du}{dx}}{|u| \sqrt{u^2 - 1}}, |u| > 1$

116. $y = \tan^{-1} x \Rightarrow \tan y = x \Rightarrow \frac{d}{dx} (\tan y) = \frac{d}{dx} (x)$

$\Rightarrow (\sec^2 y) \frac{dy}{dx} = 1 \Rightarrow \frac{dy}{dx} = \frac{1}{\sec^2 y} = \frac{1}{\left( \sqrt{1 + x^2} \right)^2}$

$= \frac{1}{1 + x^2}$, as indicated by the triangle

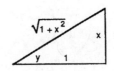

117. $f(x) = \sec x \Rightarrow f'(x) = \sec x \tan x \Rightarrow \frac{df^{-1}}{dx} \bigg|_{x=b} = \frac{1}{\frac{df}{dx} \big|_{x = f^{-1}(b)}} = \frac{1}{\sec(\sec^{-1} b) \tan(\sec^{-1} b)} = \frac{1}{b \left( \pm \sqrt{b^2 - 1} \right)}$.

Since the slope of $\sec^{-1} x$ is always positive, we the right sign by writing $\frac{d}{dx} \sec^{-1} x = \frac{1}{|x| \sqrt{x^2 - 1}}$.

118. $\cot^{-1} u = \frac{\pi}{2} - \tan^{-1} u \Rightarrow \frac{d}{dx} \left( \cot^{-1} u \right) = \frac{d}{dx} \left( \frac{\pi}{2} - \tan^{-1} u \right) = 0 - \frac{\frac{du}{dx}}{1 + u^2} = -\frac{\frac{du}{dx}}{1 + u^2}$

119. The functions f and g have the same derivative (for $x \geq 0$), namely $\frac{1}{\sqrt{x}(x+1)}$. The functions therefore differ

by a constant. To identify the constant we can set x equal to 0 in the equation $f(x) = g(x) + C$, obtaining

$\sin^{-1}(-1) = 2 \tan^{-1}(0) + C \Rightarrow -\frac{\pi}{2} = 0 + C \Rightarrow C = -\frac{\pi}{2}$. For $x \geq 0$, we have $\sin^{-1} \left( \frac{x-1}{x+1} \right) = 2 \tan^{-1} \sqrt{x} - \frac{\pi}{2}$.

120. The functions f and g have the same derivative for $x > 0$, namely $\frac{-1}{1+x^2}$. The functions therefore differ by a

constant for $x > 0$. To identify the constant we can set x equal to 1 in the equation $f(x) = g(x) + C$, obtaining

$\sin^{-1} \left( \frac{1}{\sqrt{2}} \right) = \tan^{-1} 1 + C \Rightarrow \frac{\pi}{4} = \frac{\pi}{4} + C \Rightarrow C = 0$. For $x > 0$, we have $\sin^{-1} \frac{1}{\sqrt{x^2 + 1}} = \tan^{-1} \frac{1}{x}$.

121. $V = \pi \int_{-\sqrt{3}/3}^{\sqrt{3}} \left( \frac{1}{\sqrt{1 + x^2}} \right)^2 dx = \pi \int_{-\sqrt{3}/3}^{\sqrt{3}} \frac{1}{1 + x^2} dx = \pi [\tan^{-1} x]_{-\sqrt{3}/3}^{\sqrt{3}} = \pi \left[ \tan^{-1} \sqrt{3} - \tan^{-1} \left( -\frac{\sqrt{3}}{3} \right) \right]$

$= \pi \left[ \frac{\pi}{3} - \left( -\frac{\pi}{6} \right) \right] = \frac{\pi^2}{2}$

122. Consider $y = \sqrt{r^2 - x^2} \Rightarrow \frac{dy}{dx} = \frac{-x}{\sqrt{r^2 - x^2}}$; Since $\frac{dy}{dx}$ is undefined at $x = r$ and $x = -r$, we will find the length from $x = 0$

to $x = \frac{r}{\sqrt{2}}$ (in other words, the length of $\frac{1}{8}$ of a circle) $\Rightarrow L = \int_0^{r/\sqrt{2}} \sqrt{1 + \left( \frac{-x}{\sqrt{r^2 - x^2}} \right)^2} dx = \int_0^{r/\sqrt{2}} \sqrt{1 + \frac{x^2}{r^2 - x^2}} dx$

$= \int_0^{r/\sqrt{2}} \sqrt{\frac{r^2}{r^2 - x^2}} dx = \int_0^{r/\sqrt{2}} \frac{r}{\sqrt{r^2 - x^2}} dx = \left[ r \sin^{-1} \left( \frac{x}{r} \right) \right]_0^{r/\sqrt{2}} = r \sin^{-1} \left( \frac{r/\sqrt{2}}{r} \right) - r \sin^{-1}(0)$

$= r \sin^{-1} \left( \frac{1}{\sqrt{2}} \right) - 0 = r \left( \frac{\pi}{4} \right) = \frac{\pi r}{4}$. The total circumference of the circle is $C = 8L = 8 \left( \frac{\pi r}{4} \right) = 2\pi r$.

123. (a)  $A(x) = \frac{\pi}{4} (\text{diameter})^2 = \frac{\pi}{4} \left[ \frac{1}{\sqrt{1 + x^2}} - \left( -\frac{1}{\sqrt{1 + x^2}} \right) \right]^2 = \frac{\pi}{1 + x^2} \Rightarrow V = \int_a^b A(x) \, dx = \int_{-1}^1 \frac{\pi \, dx}{1 + x^2}$

$= \pi [\tan^{-1} x]_{-1}^1 = (\pi)(2) \left( \frac{\pi}{4} \right) = \frac{\pi^2}{2}$

(b)  $A(x) = (\text{edge})^2 = \left[ \frac{1}{\sqrt{1 + x^2}} - \left( -\frac{1}{\sqrt{1 + x^2}} \right) \right]^2 = \frac{4}{1 + x^2} \Rightarrow V = \int_a^b A(x) \, dx = \int_{-1}^1 \frac{4 \, dx}{1 + x^2}$

$= 4 [\tan^{-1} x]_{-1}^1 = 4 [\tan^{-1}(1) - \tan^{-1}(-1)] = 4 \left[ \frac{\pi}{4} - \left( -\frac{\pi}{4} \right) \right] = 2\pi$

124. (a)  $A(x) = \frac{\pi}{4} (\text{diameter})^2 = \frac{\pi}{4} \left( \frac{2}{\sqrt[4]{1-x^2}} - 0 \right)^2 = \frac{\pi}{4} \left( \frac{4}{\sqrt{1-x^2}} \right) = \frac{\pi}{\sqrt{1-x^2}} \Rightarrow V = \int_a^b A(x)\, dx$

$= \int_{-\sqrt{2}/2}^{\sqrt{2}/2} \frac{\pi}{\sqrt{1-x^2}}\, dx = \pi \left[ \sin^{-1} x \right]_{-\sqrt{2}/2}^{\sqrt{2}/2} = \pi \left[ \sin^{-1} \left( \frac{\sqrt{2}}{2} \right) - \sin^{-1} \left( -\frac{\sqrt{2}}{2} \right) \right] = \pi \left[ \frac{\pi}{4} - \left( -\frac{\pi}{4} \right) \right] = \frac{\pi^2}{2}$

(b)  $A(x) = \frac{(\text{diagonal})^2}{2} = \frac{1}{2} \left( \frac{2}{\sqrt[4]{1-x^2}} - 0 \right)^2 = \frac{2}{\sqrt{1-x^2}} \Rightarrow V = \int_a^b A(x)\, dx = \int_{-\sqrt{2}/2}^{\sqrt{2}/2} \frac{2}{\sqrt{1-x^2}}\, dx$

$= 2 \left[ \sin^{-1} x \right]_{-\sqrt{2}/2}^{\sqrt{2}/2} = 2 \left( \frac{\pi}{4} \cdot 2 \right) = \pi$

125. (a)  $\sec^{-1} 1.5 = \cos^{-1} \frac{1}{1.5} \approx 0.84107$    (b)  $\csc^{-1}(-1.5) = \sin^{-1} \left( -\frac{1}{1.5} \right) \approx -0.72973$

(c)  $\cot^{-1} 2 = \frac{\pi}{2} - \tan^{-1} 2 \approx 0.46365$

126. (a)  $\sec^{-1}(-3) = \cos^{-1} \left( -\frac{1}{3} \right) \approx 1.91063$    (b)  $\csc^{-1} 1.7 = \sin^{-1} \left( \frac{1}{1.7} \right) \approx 0.62887$

(c)  $\cot^{-1}(-2) = \frac{\pi}{2} - \tan^{-1}(-2) \approx 2.67795$

127. (a)  Domain:  all real numbers except those having the form $\frac{\pi}{2} + k\pi$ where k is an integer.

Range:  $-\frac{\pi}{2} < y < \frac{\pi}{2}$

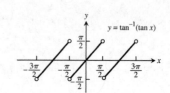

(b)  Domain: $-\infty < x < \infty$; Range: $-\infty < y < \infty$
The graph of $y = \tan^{-1}(\tan x)$ is periodic, the graph of $y = \tan(\tan^{-1} x) = x$ for $-\infty \le x < \infty$.

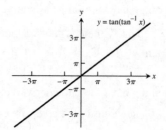

128. (a)  Domain: $-\infty < x < \infty$; Range: $-\frac{\pi}{2} \le y \le \frac{\pi}{2}$

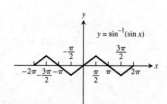

(b)  Domain: $-1 \le x \le 1$; Range: $-1 \le y \le 1$
The graph of $y = \sin^{-1}(\sin x)$ is periodic; the graph of $y = \sin(\sin^{-1} x) = x$ for $-1 \le x \le 1$.

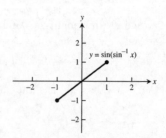

129. (a)  Domain: $-\infty < x < \infty$; Range: $0 \le y \le \pi$

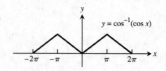

(b)  Domain: $-1 \le x \le 1$; Range: $-1 \le y \le 1$
The graph of $y = \cos^{-1}(\cos x)$ is periodic; the
graph of $y = \cos(\cos^{-1} x) = x$ for $-1 \le x \le 1$.

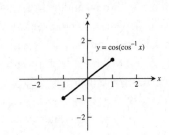

130.  Since the domain of $\sec^{-1} x$ is $(-\infty, -1] \cup [1, \infty)$, we
have $\sec(\sec^{-1} x) = x$ for $|x| \ge 1$.  The graph of
$y = \sec(\sec^{-1} x)$ is the line $y = x$ with the open
line segment from $(-1, -1)$ to $(1, 1)$ removed.

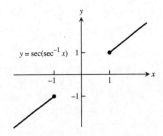

131.  The graphs are identical for $y = 2\sin(2\tan^{-1} x)$
$= 4\left[\sin(\tan^{-1} x)\right]\left[\cos(\tan^{-1} x)\right] = 4\left(\frac{x}{\sqrt{x^2+1}}\right)\left(\frac{1}{\sqrt{x^2+1}}\right)$

$= \frac{4x}{x^2+1}$ from the triangle

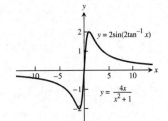

132.  The graphs are identical for $y = \cos(2\sec^{-1} x)$
$= \cos^2(\sec^{-1} x) - \sin^2(\sec^{-1} x) = \frac{1}{x^2} - \frac{x^2-1}{x^2}$

$= \frac{2-x^2}{x^2}$ from the triangle

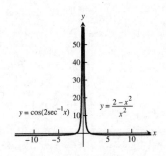

133.  The values of f increase over the interval $[-1, 1]$ because
$f' > 0$, and the graph of f steepens as the values of $f'$
increase towards the ends of the interval.  The graph of f
is concave down to the left of the origin where $f'' < 0$,
and concave up to the right of the origin where $f'' > 0$.
There is an inflection point at $x = 0$ where $f'' = 0$ and
$f'$ has a local minimum value.

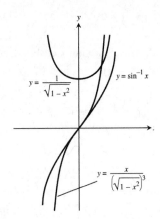

134. The values of f increase throughout the interval $(-\infty, \infty)$ because $f' > 0$, and they increase most rapidly near the origin where the values of $f'$ are relatively large. The graph of f is concave up to the left of the origin where $f'' > 0$, and concave down to the right of the origin where $f'' < 0$. There is an inflection point at $x = 0$ where $f'' = 0$ and $f'$ has a local maximum value.

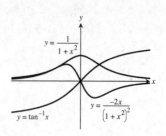

## 7.7 HYPERBOLIC FUNCTIONS

1.  $\sinh x = -\frac{3}{4} \Rightarrow \cosh x = \sqrt{1 + \sinh^2 x} = \sqrt{1 + \left(-\frac{3}{4}\right)^2} = \sqrt{1 + \frac{9}{16}} = \sqrt{\frac{25}{16}} = \frac{5}{4}$, $\tanh x = \frac{\sinh x}{\cosh x} = \frac{\left(-\frac{3}{4}\right)}{\left(\frac{5}{4}\right)} = -\frac{3}{5}$,

    $\coth x = \frac{1}{\tanh x} = -\frac{5}{3}$, $\text{sech } x = \frac{1}{\cosh x} = \frac{4}{5}$, and $\text{csch } x = \frac{1}{\sin x} = -\frac{4}{3}$

2.  $\sinh x = \frac{4}{3} \Rightarrow \cosh x = \sqrt{1 + \sinh^2 x} = \sqrt{1 + \frac{16}{9}} = \sqrt{\frac{25}{9}} = \frac{5}{3}$, $\tanh x = \frac{\sinh x}{\cosh x} = \frac{\left(\frac{4}{3}\right)}{\left(\frac{5}{3}\right)} = \frac{4}{5}$, $\coth x = \frac{1}{\tanh x} = \frac{5}{4}$,

    $\text{sech } x = \frac{1}{\cosh x} = \frac{3}{5}$, and $\text{csch } x = \frac{1}{\sinh x} = \frac{3}{4}$

3.  $\cosh x = \frac{17}{15}$, $x > 0 \Rightarrow \sinh x = \sqrt{\cosh^2 x - 1} = \sqrt{\left(\frac{17}{15}\right)^2 - 1} = \sqrt{\frac{289}{225} - 1} = \sqrt{\frac{64}{225}} = \frac{8}{15}$, $\tanh x = \frac{\sinh x}{\cosh x} = \frac{\left(\frac{8}{15}\right)}{\left(\frac{17}{15}\right)}$

    $= \frac{8}{17}$, $\coth x = \frac{1}{\tanh x} = \frac{17}{8}$, $\text{sech } x = \frac{1}{\cosh x} = \frac{15}{17}$, and $\text{csch } x = \frac{1}{\sinh x} = \frac{15}{8}$

4.  $\cosh x = \frac{13}{5}$, $x > 0 \Rightarrow \sinh x = \sqrt{\cosh^2 x - 1} = \sqrt{\frac{169}{25} - 1} = \sqrt{\frac{144}{25}} = \frac{12}{5}$, $\tanh x = \frac{\sinh x}{\cosh x} = \frac{\left(\frac{12}{5}\right)}{\left(\frac{13}{5}\right)} = \frac{12}{13}$,

    $\coth x = \frac{1}{\tanh x} = \frac{13}{12}$, $\text{sech } x = \frac{1}{\cosh x} = \frac{5}{13}$, and $\text{csch } x = \frac{1}{\sinh x} = \frac{5}{12}$

5.  $2 \cosh (\ln x) = 2 \left(\frac{e^{\ln x} + e^{-\ln x}}{2}\right) = e^{\ln x} + \frac{1}{e^{\ln x}} = x + \frac{1}{x}$

6.  $\sinh (2 \ln x) = \frac{e^{2 \ln x} - e^{-2 \ln x}}{2} = \frac{e^{\ln x^2} - e^{\ln x^{-2}}}{2} = \frac{\left(x^2 - \frac{1}{x^2}\right)}{2} = \frac{x^4 - 1}{2x^2}$

7.  $\cosh 5x + \sinh 5x = \frac{e^{5x} + e^{-5x}}{2} + \frac{e^{5x} - e^{-5x}}{2} = e^{5x}$        8.  $\cosh 3x - \sinh 3x = \frac{e^{3x} + e^{-3x}}{2} - \frac{e^{3x} - e^{-3x}}{2} = e^{-3x}$

9.  $(\sinh x + \cosh x)^4 = \left(\frac{e^x - e^{-x}}{2} + \frac{e^x + e^{-x}}{2}\right)^4 = (e^x)^4 = e^{4x}$

10. $\ln (\cosh x + \sinh x) + \ln (\cosh x - \sinh x) = \ln (\cosh^2 x - \sinh^2 x) = \ln 1 = 0$

11. (a)  $\sinh 2x = \sinh (x + x) = \sinh x \cosh x + \cosh x \sinh x = 2 \sinh x \cosh x$

    (b)  $\cosh 2x = \cosh (x + x) = \cosh x \cosh x + \sinh x \sin x = \cosh^2 x + \sinh^2 x$

12. $\cosh^2 x - \sinh^2 x = \left(\frac{e^x + e^{-x}}{2}\right)^2 - \left(\frac{e^x - e^{-x}}{2}\right)^2 = \frac{1}{4}[(e^x + e^{-x}) + (e^x - e^{-x})] [(e^x + e^{-x}) - (e^x - e^{-x})] = \frac{1}{4} (2e^x) (2e^{-x})$

    $= \frac{1}{4} (4e^0) = \frac{1}{4} (4) = 1$

13. $y = 6 \sinh \frac{x}{3} \Rightarrow \frac{dy}{dx} = 6 \left(\cosh \frac{x}{3}\right) \left(\frac{1}{3}\right) = 2 \cosh \frac{x}{3}$

14. $y = \frac{1}{2} \sinh (2x + 1) \Rightarrow \frac{dy}{dx} = \frac{1}{2} [\cosh (2x + 1)](2) = \cosh (2x + 1)$

15. $y = 2\sqrt{t} \tanh \sqrt{t} = 2t^{1/2} \tanh t^{1/2} \Rightarrow \frac{dy}{dt} = \left[\text{sech}^2 \left(t^{1/2}\right)\right] \left(\frac{1}{2} t^{-1/2}\right) \left(2t^{1/2}\right) + \left(\tanh t^{1/2}\right) \left(t^{-1/2}\right) = \text{sech}^2 \sqrt{t} + \frac{\tanh \sqrt{t}}{\sqrt{t}}$

16. $y = t^2 \tanh \frac{1}{t} = t^2 \tanh t^{-1} \Rightarrow \frac{dy}{dt} = [\text{sech}^2 (t^{-1})] (-t^{-2}) (t^2) + (2t) (\tanh t^{-1}) = -\text{sech}^2 \frac{1}{t} + 2t \tanh \frac{1}{t}$

17. $y = \ln (\sinh z) \Rightarrow \frac{dy}{dz} = \frac{\cosh z}{\sinh z} = \coth z$ 　　　　　18. $y = \ln (\cosh z) \Rightarrow \frac{dy}{dz} = \frac{\sinh z}{\cosh z} = \tanh z$

19. $y = (\text{sech } \theta)(1 - \ln \text{sech } \theta) \Rightarrow \frac{dy}{d\theta} = \left(- \frac{-\text{sech } \theta \tanh \theta}{\text{sech } \theta}\right) (\text{sech } \theta) + (- \text{sech } \theta \tanh \theta)(1 - \ln \text{sech } \theta)$
$= \text{sech } \theta \tanh \theta - (\text{sech } \theta \tanh \theta)(1 - \ln \text{sech } \theta) = (\text{sech } \theta \tanh \theta)[1 - (1 - \ln \text{sech } \theta)] = (\text{sech } \theta \tanh \theta)(\ln \text{sech } \theta)$

20. $y = (\text{csch } \theta)(1 - \ln \text{csch } \theta) \Rightarrow \frac{dy}{d\theta} = (\text{csch } \theta) \left(- \frac{-\text{csch } \theta \coth \theta}{\text{csch } \theta}\right) + (1 - \ln \text{csch } \theta)(- \text{csch } \theta \coth \theta)$
$= \text{csch } \theta \coth \theta - (1 - \ln \text{csch } \theta)(\text{csch } \theta \coth \theta) = (\text{csch } \theta \coth \theta)(1 - 1 + \ln \text{csch } \theta) = (\text{csch } \theta \coth \theta)(\ln \text{csch } \theta)$

21. $y = \ln \cosh v - \frac{1}{2} \tanh^2 v \Rightarrow \frac{dy}{dv} = \frac{\sinh v}{\cosh v} - \left(\frac{1}{2}\right) (2 \tanh v) (\text{sech}^2 v) = \tanh v - (\tanh v) (\text{sech}^2 v)$
$= (\tanh v) (1 - \text{sech}^2 v) = (\tanh v) (\tanh^2 v) = \tanh^3 v$

22. $y = \ln \sinh v - \frac{1}{2} \coth^2 v \Rightarrow \frac{dy}{dv} = \frac{\cosh v}{\sinh v} - \left(\frac{1}{2}\right) (2 \coth v) (- \text{csch}^2 v) = \coth v + (\coth v) (\text{csch}^2 v)$
$= (\coth v) (1 + \text{csch}^2 v) = (\coth v) (\coth^2 v) = \coth^3 v$

23. $y = (x^2 + 1) \text{sech} (\ln x) = (x^2 + 1) \left(\frac{2}{e^{\ln x} + e^{-\ln x}}\right) = (x^2 + 1) \left(\frac{2}{x + x^{-1}}\right) = (x^2 + 1) \left(\frac{2x}{x^2 + 1}\right) = 2x \Rightarrow \frac{dy}{dx} = 2$

24. $y = (4x^2 - 1) \text{csch} (\ln 2x) = (4x^2 - 1) \left(\frac{2}{e^{\ln 2x} - e^{-\ln 2x}}\right) = (4x^2 - 1) \left(\frac{2}{2x - (2x)^{-1}}\right) = (4x^2 - 1) \left(\frac{4x}{4x^2 - 1}\right) = 4x \Rightarrow \frac{dy}{dx} = 4$

25. $y = \sinh^{-1} \sqrt{x} = \sinh^{-1} \left(x^{1/2}\right) \Rightarrow \frac{dy}{dx} = \frac{\left(\frac{1}{2}\right) x^{-1/2}}{\sqrt{1 + (x^{1/2})^2}} = \frac{1}{2\sqrt{x} \sqrt{1 + x}} = \frac{1}{2\sqrt{x(1 + x)}}$

26. $y = \cosh^{-1} 2\sqrt{x + 1} = \cosh^{-1} \left(2(x + 1)^{1/2}\right) \Rightarrow \frac{dy}{dx} = \frac{(2) \left(\frac{1}{2}\right) (x + 1)^{-1/2}}{\sqrt{[2(x+1)^{1/2}]^2 - 1}} = \frac{1}{\sqrt{x + 1} \sqrt{4x + 3}} = \frac{1}{\sqrt{4x^2 + 7x + 3}}$

27. $y = (1 - \theta) \tanh^{-1} \theta \Rightarrow \frac{dy}{d\theta} = (1 - \theta) \left(\frac{1}{1 - \theta^2}\right) + (-1) \tanh^{-1} \theta = \frac{1}{1 + \theta} - \tanh^{-1} \theta$

28. $y = (\theta^2 + 2\theta) \tanh^{-1} (\theta + 1) \Rightarrow \frac{dy}{d\theta} = (\theta^2 + 2\theta) \left[\frac{1}{1 - (\theta+1)^2}\right] + (2\theta + 2) \tanh^{-1} (\theta + 1) = \frac{\theta^2 + 2\theta}{-\theta^2 - 2\theta} + (2\theta + 2) \tanh^{-1} (\theta + 1)$
$= (2\theta + 2) \tanh^{-1} (\theta + 1) - 1$

29. $y = (1 - t) \coth^{-1} \sqrt{t} = (1 - t) \coth^{-1} \left(t^{1/2}\right) \Rightarrow \frac{dy}{dt} = (1 - t) \left[\frac{\left(\frac{1}{2}\right) t^{-1/2}}{1 - (t^{1/2})^2}\right] + (-1) \coth^{-1} \left(t^{1/2}\right) = \frac{1}{2\sqrt{t}} - \coth^{-1} \sqrt{t}$

30. $y = (1 - t^2) \coth^{-1} t \Rightarrow \frac{dy}{dt} = (1 - t^2) \left(\frac{1}{1 - t^2}\right) + (-2t) \coth^{-1} t = 1 - 2t \coth^{-1} t$

31. $y = \cos^{-1} x - x \text{sech}^{-1} x \Rightarrow \frac{dy}{dx} = \frac{-1}{\sqrt{1 - x^2}} - \left[x \left(\frac{-1}{x\sqrt{1 - x^2}}\right) + (1) \text{sech}^{-1} x\right] = \frac{-1}{\sqrt{1 - x^2}} + \frac{1}{\sqrt{1 - x^2}} - \text{sech}^{-1} x = -\text{sech}^{-1} x$

32. $y = \ln x + \sqrt{1 - x^2} \text{ sech}^{-1} x = \ln x + (1 - x^2)^{1/2} \text{ sech}^{-1} x$
$\Rightarrow \frac{dy}{dx} = \frac{1}{x} + (1 - x^2)^{1/2} \left(\frac{-1}{x\sqrt{1 - x^2}}\right) + \left(\frac{1}{2}\right) (1 - x^2)^{-1/2} (-2x) \text{ sech}^{-1} x = \frac{1}{x} - \frac{1}{x} - \frac{x}{\sqrt{1 - x^2}} \text{ sech}^{-1} x = \frac{-x}{\sqrt{1 - x^2}} \text{ sech}^{-1} x$

33. $y = \text{csch}^{-1} \left(\frac{1}{2}\right)^{\theta} \Rightarrow \frac{dy}{d\theta} = - \frac{\left[\ln \left(\frac{1}{2}\right)\right] \left(\frac{1}{2}\right)^{\theta}}{\left(\frac{1}{2}\right)^{\theta} \sqrt{1 + \left[\left(\frac{1}{2}\right)^{\theta}\right]^2}} = - \frac{\ln (1) - \ln (2)}{\sqrt{1 + \left(\frac{1}{2}\right)^{2\theta}}} = \frac{\ln 2}{\sqrt{1 + \left(\frac{1}{2}\right)^{2\theta}}}$

34. $y = \operatorname{csch}^{-1} 2^\theta \Rightarrow \frac{dy}{d\theta} = -\frac{(\ln 2)\, 2^\theta}{2^\theta \sqrt{1 + (2^\theta)^2}} = \frac{-\ln 2}{\sqrt{1 + 2^{2\theta}}}$

35. $y = \sinh^{-1}(\tan x) \Rightarrow \frac{dy}{dx} = \frac{\sec^2 x}{\sqrt{1 + (\tan x)^2}} = \frac{\sec^2 x}{\sqrt{\sec^2 x}} = \frac{\sec^2 x}{|\sec x|} = \frac{|\sec x|\,|\sec x|}{|\sec x|} = |\sec x|$

36. $y = \cosh^{-1}(\sec x) \Rightarrow \frac{dy}{dx} = \frac{(\sec x)(\tan x)}{\sqrt{\sec^2 x - 1}} = \frac{(\sec x)(\tan x)}{\sqrt{\tan^2 x}} = \frac{(\sec x)(\tan x)}{|\tan x|} = \sec x,\ 0 < x < \frac{\pi}{2}$

37. (a) If $y = \tan^{-1}(\sinh x) + C$, then $\frac{dy}{dx} = \frac{\cosh x}{1 + \sinh^2 x} = \frac{\cosh x}{\cosh^2 x} = \operatorname{sech} x$, which verifies the formula

    (b) If $y = \sin^{-1}(\tanh x) + C$, then $\frac{dy}{dx} = \frac{\operatorname{sech}^2 x}{\sqrt{1 - \tanh^2 x}} = \frac{\operatorname{sech}^2 x}{\operatorname{sech} x} = \operatorname{sech} x$, which verifies the formula

38. If $y = \frac{x^2}{2} \operatorname{sech}^{-1} x - \frac{1}{2}\sqrt{1 - x^2} + C$, then $\frac{dy}{dx} = x \operatorname{sech}^{-1} x + \frac{x^2}{2}\left(\frac{-1}{x\sqrt{1 - x^2}}\right) + \frac{2x}{4\sqrt{1 - x^2}} = x \operatorname{sech}^{-1} x$, which verifies the formula

39. If $y = \frac{x^2 - 1}{2} \coth^{-1} x + \frac{x}{2} + C$, then $\frac{dy}{dx} = x \coth^{-1} x + \left(\frac{x^2 - 1}{2}\right)\left(\frac{1}{1 - x^2}\right) + \frac{1}{2} = x \coth^{-1} x$, which verifies the formula

40. If $y = x \tanh^{-1} x + \frac{1}{2} \ln(1 - x^2) + C$, then $\frac{dy}{dx} = \tanh^{-1} x + x\left(\frac{1}{1 - x^2}\right) + \frac{1}{2}\left(\frac{-2x}{1 - x^2}\right) = \tanh^{-1} x$, which verifies the formula

41. $\int \sinh 2x\, dx = \frac{1}{2}\int \sinh u\, du$, where $u = 2x$ and $du = 2\, dx$
    $= \frac{\cosh u}{2} + C = \frac{\cosh 2x}{2} + C$

42. $\int \sinh \frac{x}{5}\, dx = 5 \int \sinh u\, du$, where $u = \frac{x}{5}$ and $du = \frac{1}{5}\, dx$
    $= 5 \cosh u + C = 5 \cosh \frac{x}{5} + C$

43. $\int 6 \cosh\left(\frac{x}{2} - \ln 3\right) dx = 12 \int \cosh u\, du$, where $u = \frac{x}{2} - \ln 3$ and $du = \frac{1}{2}\, dx$
    $= 12 \sinh u + C = 12 \sinh\left(\frac{x}{2} - \ln 3\right) + C$

44. $\int 4 \cosh(3x - \ln 2)\, dx = \frac{4}{3}\int \cosh u\, du$, where $u = 3x - \ln 2$ and $du = 3\, dx$
    $= \frac{4}{3} \sinh u + C = \frac{4}{3} \sinh(3x - \ln 2) + C$

45. $\int \tanh \frac{x}{7}\, dx = 7 \int \frac{\sinh u}{\cosh u}\, du$, where $u = \frac{x}{7}$ and $du = \frac{1}{7}\, dx$
    $= 7 \ln|\cosh u| + C_1 = 7 \ln\left|\cosh \frac{x}{7}\right| + C_1 = 7 \ln\left|\frac{e^{x/7} + e^{-x/7}}{2}\right| + C_1 = 7 \ln\left|e^{x/7} + e^{-x/7}\right| - 7 \ln 2 + C_1$
    $= 7 \ln\left|e^{x/7} + e^{-x/7}\right| + C$

46. $\int \coth \frac{\theta}{\sqrt{3}}\, d\theta = \sqrt{3}\int \frac{\cosh u}{\sinh u}\, du$, where $u = \frac{\theta}{\sqrt{3}}$ and $du = \frac{d\theta}{\sqrt{3}}$
    $= \sqrt{3} \ln|\sinh u| + C_1 = \sqrt{3} \ln\left|\sinh \frac{\theta}{\sqrt{3}}\right| + C_1 = \sqrt{3} \ln\left|\frac{e^{\theta/\sqrt{3}} - e^{-\theta/\sqrt{3}}}{2}\right| + C_1$
    $= \sqrt{3} \ln\left|e^{\theta/\sqrt{3}} - e^{-\theta/\sqrt{3}}\right| - \sqrt{3} \ln 2 + C_1 = \sqrt{3} \ln\left|e^{\theta/\sqrt{3}} - e^{-\theta/\sqrt{3}}\right| + C$

47. $\int \operatorname{sech}^2\left(x - \frac{1}{2}\right) dx = \int \operatorname{sech}^2 u\, du$, where $u = \left(x - \frac{1}{2}\right)$ and $du = dx$
    $= \tanh u + C = \tanh\left(x - \frac{1}{2}\right) + C$

48. $\int \text{csch}^2 (5 - x) \, dx = - \int \text{csch}^2 u \, du$, where $u = (5 - x)$ and $du = - dx$

$= -(- \coth u) + C = \coth u + C = \coth (5 - x) + C$

49. $\int \frac{\text{sech} \sqrt{t} \tanh \sqrt{t}}{\sqrt{t}} \, dt = 2 \int \text{sech} \, u \tanh u \, du$, where $u = \sqrt{t} = t^{1/2}$ and $du = \frac{dt}{2\sqrt{t}}$

$= 2(- \text{sech} \, u) + C = -2 \, \text{sech} \sqrt{t} + C$

50. $\int \frac{\text{csch} (\ln t) \coth (\ln t)}{t} \, dt = \int \text{csch} \, u \coth u \, du$, where $u = \ln t$ and $du = \frac{dt}{t}$

$= - \text{csch} \, u + C = - \text{csch} (\ln t) + C$

51. $\int_{\ln 2}^{\ln 4} \coth x \, dx = \int_{\ln 2}^{\ln 4} \frac{\cosh x}{\sinh x} \, dx = \int_{3/4}^{15/8} \frac{1}{u} \, du = [\ln |u|]_{3/4}^{15/8} = \ln \left| \frac{15}{8} \right| - \ln \left| \frac{3}{4} \right| = \ln \left| \frac{15}{8} \cdot \frac{4}{3} \right| = \ln \frac{5}{2}$,

where $u = \sinh x$, $du = \cosh x \, dx$, the lower limit is $\sinh (\ln 2) = \frac{e^{\ln 2} - e^{-\ln 2}}{2} = \frac{2 - \left( \frac{1}{2} \right)}{2} = \frac{3}{4}$ and the upper

limit is $\sinh (\ln 4) = \frac{e^{\ln 4} - e^{-\ln 4}}{2} = \frac{4 - \left( \frac{1}{4} \right)}{2} = \frac{15}{8}$

52. $\int_{0}^{\ln 2} \tanh 2x \, dx = \int_{0}^{\ln 2} \frac{\sinh 2x}{\cosh 2x} \, dx = \frac{1}{2} \int_{1}^{17/8} \frac{1}{u} \, du = \frac{1}{2} [\ln |u|]_{1}^{17/8} = \frac{1}{2} \left[ \ln \left( \frac{17}{8} \right) - \ln 1 \right] = \frac{1}{2} \ln \frac{17}{8}$, where

$u = \cosh 2x$, $du = 2 \sinh (2x) \, dx$, the lower limit is $\cosh 0 = 1$ and the upper limit is $\cosh (2 \ln 2) = \cosh (\ln 4)$

$= \frac{e^{\ln 4} + e^{-\ln 4}}{2} = \frac{4 + \left( \frac{1}{4} \right)}{2} = \frac{17}{8}$

53. $\int_{-\ln 4}^{-\ln 2} 2e^{\theta} \cosh \theta \, d\theta = \int_{-\ln 4}^{-\ln 2} 2e^{\theta} \left( \frac{e^{\theta} + e^{-\theta}}{2} \right) d\theta = \int_{-\ln 4}^{-\ln 2} (e^{2\theta} + 1) \, d\theta = \left[ \frac{e^{2\theta}}{2} + \theta \right]_{-\ln 4}^{-\ln 2}$

$= \left( \frac{e^{-2\ln 2}}{2} - \ln 2 \right) - \left( \frac{e^{-2\ln 4}}{2} - \ln 4 \right) = \left( \frac{1}{8} - \ln 2 \right) - \left( \frac{1}{32} - \ln 4 \right) = \frac{3}{32} - \ln 2 + 2 \ln 2 = \frac{3}{32} + \ln 2$

54. $\int_{0}^{\ln 2} 4e^{-\theta} \sinh \theta \, d\theta = \int_{0}^{\ln 2} 4e^{-\theta} \left( \frac{e^{\theta} - e^{-\theta}}{2} \right) d\theta = 2 \int_{0}^{\ln 2} (1 - e^{-2\theta}) \, d\theta = 2 \left[ \theta + \frac{e^{-2\theta}}{2} \right]_{0}^{\ln 2}$

$= 2 \left[ \left( \ln 2 + \frac{e^{-2\ln 2}}{2} \right) - \left( 0 + \frac{e^{0}}{2} \right) \right] = 2 \left( \ln 2 + \frac{1}{8} - \frac{1}{2} \right) = 2 \ln 2 + \frac{1}{4} - 1 = \ln 4 - \frac{3}{4}$

55. $\int_{-\pi/4}^{\pi/4} \cosh (\tan \theta) \sec^2 \theta \, d\theta = \int_{-1}^{1} \cosh u \, du = [\sinh u]_{-1}^{1} = \sinh (1) - \sinh (-1) = \left( \frac{e^1 - e^{-1}}{2} \right) - \left( \frac{e^{-1} - e^1}{2} \right)$

$= \frac{e - e^{-1} - e^{-1} + e}{2} = e - e^{-1}$, where $u = \tan \theta$, $du = \sec^2 \theta \, d\theta$, the lower limit is $\tan \left( - \frac{\pi}{4} \right) = -1$ and the upper

limit is $\tan \left( \frac{\pi}{4} \right) = 1$

56. $\int_{0}^{\pi/2} 2 \sinh (\sin \theta) \cos \theta \, d\theta = 2 \int_{0}^{1} \sinh u \, du = 2 [\cosh u]_{0}^{1} = 2(\cosh 1 - \cosh 0) = 2 \left( \frac{e + e^{-1}}{2} - 1 \right)$

$= e + e^{-1} - 2$, where $u = \sin \theta$, $du = \cos \theta \, d\theta$, the lower limit is $\sin 0 = 0$ and the upper limit is $\sin \left( \frac{\pi}{2} \right) = 1$

57. $\int_{1}^{2} \frac{\cosh (\ln t)}{t} \, dt = \int_{0}^{\ln 2} \cosh u \, du = [\sinh u]_{0}^{\ln 2} = \sinh (\ln 2) - \sinh (0) = \frac{e^{\ln 2} - e^{-\ln 2}}{2} - 0 = \frac{2 - \frac{1}{2}}{2} = \frac{3}{4}$, where

$u = \ln t$, $du = \frac{1}{t} \, dt$, the lower limit is $\ln 1 = 0$ and the upper limit is $\ln 2$

58. $\int_{1}^{4} \frac{8 \cosh \sqrt{x}}{\sqrt{x}} \, dx = 16 \int_{1}^{2} \cosh u \, du = 16 [\sinh u]_{1}^{2} = 16(\sinh 2 - \sinh 1) = 16 \left[ \left( \frac{e^2 - e^{-2}}{2} \right) - \left( \frac{e - e^{-1}}{2} \right) \right]$

$= 8 (e^2 - e^{-2} - e + e^{-1})$, where $u = \sqrt{x} = x^{1/2}$, $du = \frac{1}{2} x^{-1/2} dx = \frac{dx}{2\sqrt{x}}$, the lower limit is $\sqrt{1} = 1$ and the upper

limit is $\sqrt{4} = 2$

59. $\int_{-\ln 2}^{0} \cosh^2\left(\frac{x}{2}\right) dx = \int_{-\ln 2}^{0} \frac{\cosh x + 1}{2} dx = \frac{1}{2}\int_{-\ln 2}^{0}(\cosh x + 1) dx = \frac{1}{2}\left[\sinh x + x\right]_{-\ln 2}^{0}$

$= \frac{1}{2}\left[(\sinh 0 + 0) - (\sinh(-\ln 2) - \ln 2)\right] = \frac{1}{2}\left[(0 + 0) - \left(\frac{e^{-\ln 2} - e^{\ln 2}}{2} - \ln 2\right)\right] = \frac{1}{2}\left[-\frac{\left(\frac{1}{2}\right) - 2}{2} + \ln 2\right]$

$= \frac{1}{2}\left(1 - \frac{1}{4} + \ln 2\right) = \frac{3}{8} + \frac{1}{2}\ln 2 = \frac{3}{8} + \ln\sqrt{2}$

60. $\int_{0}^{\ln 10} 4\sinh^2\left(\frac{x}{2}\right) dx = \int_{0}^{\ln 10} 4\left(\frac{\cosh x - 1}{2}\right) dx = 2\int_{0}^{\ln 10}(\cosh x - 1) dx = 2\left[\sinh x - x\right]_{0}^{\ln 10}$

$= 2[(\sinh(\ln 10) - \ln 10) - (\sinh 0 - 0)] = e^{\ln 10} - e^{-\ln 10} - 2\ln 10 = 10 - \frac{1}{10} - 2\ln 10 = 9.9 - 2\ln 10$

61. $\sinh^{-1}\left(\frac{-5}{12}\right) = \ln\left(-\frac{5}{12} + \sqrt{\frac{25}{144} + 1}\right) = \ln\left(\frac{2}{3}\right)$        62. $\cosh^{-1}\left(\frac{5}{3}\right) = \ln\left(\frac{5}{3} + \sqrt{\frac{25}{9} - 1}\right) = \ln 3$

63. $\tanh^{-1}\left(-\frac{1}{2}\right) = \frac{1}{2}\ln\left(\frac{1 - (1/2)}{1 + (1/2)}\right) = -\frac{\ln 3}{2}$        64. $\coth^{-1}\left(\frac{5}{4}\right) = \frac{1}{2}\ln\left(\frac{(9/4)}{(1/4)}\right) = \frac{1}{2}\ln 9 = \ln 3$

65. $\text{sech}^{-1}\left(\frac{3}{5}\right) = \ln\left(\frac{1 + \sqrt{1 - (9/25)}}{(3/5)}\right) = \ln 3$        66. $\text{csch}^{-1}\left(-\frac{1}{\sqrt{3}}\right) = \ln\left(-\sqrt{3} + \frac{\sqrt{4/3}}{(1/\sqrt{3})}\right) = \ln\left(-\sqrt{3} + 2\right)$

67. (a) $\int_{0}^{2\sqrt{3}} \frac{dx}{\sqrt{4 + x^2}} = \left[\sinh^{-1}\frac{x}{2}\right]_{0}^{2\sqrt{3}} = \sinh^{-1}\sqrt{3} - \sinh^{-1} 0 = \sinh^{-1}\sqrt{3}$

(b) $\sinh^{-1}\sqrt{3} = \ln\left(\sqrt{3} + \sqrt{3 + 1}\right) = \ln\left(\sqrt{3} + 2\right)$

68. (a) $\int_{0}^{1/3} \frac{6\, dx}{\sqrt{1 + 9x^2}} = 2\int_{0}^{1} \frac{dx}{\sqrt{a^2 + u^2}}$, where $u = 3x$, $du = 3\, dx$, $a = 1$

$= \left[2\sinh^{-1} u\right]_{0}^{1} = 2\left(\sinh^{-1} 1 - \sinh^{-1} 0\right) = 2\sinh^{-1} 1$

(b) $2\sinh^{-1} 1 = 2\ln\left(1 + \sqrt{1^2 + 1}\right) = 2\ln\left(1 + \sqrt{2}\right)$

69. (a) $\int_{5/4}^{2} \frac{1}{1 - x^2} dx = \left[\coth^{-1} x\right]_{5/4}^{2} = \coth^{-1} 2 - \coth^{-1}\frac{5}{4}$

(b) $\coth^{-1} 2 - \coth^{-1}\frac{5}{4} = \frac{1}{2}\left[\ln 3 - \ln\left(\frac{9/4}{1/4}\right)\right] = \frac{1}{2}\ln\frac{1}{3}$

70. (a) $\int_{0}^{1/2} \frac{1}{1 - x^2} dx = \left[\tanh^{-1} x\right]_{0}^{1/2} = \tanh^{-1}\frac{1}{2} - \tanh^{-1} 0 = \tanh^{-1}\frac{1}{2}$

(b) $\tanh^{-1}\frac{1}{2} = \frac{1}{2}\ln\left(\frac{1 + (1/2)}{1 - (1/2)}\right) = \frac{1}{2}\ln 3$

71. (a) $\int_{1/5}^{3/13} \frac{dx}{x\sqrt{1 - 16x^2}} = \int_{4/5}^{12/13} \frac{du}{u\sqrt{a^2 - u^2}}$, where $u = 4x$, $du = 4\, dx$, $a = 1$

$= \left[-\text{sech}^{-1} u\right]_{4/5}^{12/13} = -\text{sech}^{-1}\frac{12}{13} + \text{sech}^{-1}\frac{4}{5}$

(b) $-\text{sech}^{-1}\frac{12}{13} + \text{sech}^{-1}\frac{4}{5} = -\ln\left(\frac{1 + \sqrt{1 - (12/13)^2}}{(12/13)}\right) + \ln\left(\frac{1 + \sqrt{1 - (4/5)^2}}{(4/5)}\right)$

$= -\ln\left(\frac{13 + \sqrt{169 - 144}}{12}\right) + \ln\left(\frac{5 + \sqrt{25 - 16}}{4}\right) = \ln\left(\frac{5 + 3}{4}\right) - \ln\left(\frac{13 + 5}{12}\right) = \ln 2 - \ln\frac{3}{2} = \ln\left(2 \cdot \frac{2}{3}\right) = \ln\frac{4}{3}$

72. (a) $\int_{1}^{2} \frac{dx}{x\sqrt{4 + x^2}} = \left[-\frac{1}{2}\text{csch}^{-1}\left|\frac{x}{2}\right|\right]_{1}^{2} = -\frac{1}{2}\left(\text{csch}^{-1} 1 - \text{csch}^{-1}\frac{1}{2}\right) = \frac{1}{2}\left(\text{csch}^{-1}\frac{1}{2} - \text{csch}^{-1} 1\right)$

(b) $\frac{1}{2}\left(\text{csch}^{-1}\frac{1}{2} - \text{csch}^{-1} 1\right) = \frac{1}{2}\left[\ln\left(2 + \frac{\sqrt{5/4}}{(1/2)}\right) - \ln\left(1 + \sqrt{2}\right)\right] = \frac{1}{2}\ln\left(\frac{2 + \sqrt{5}}{1 + \sqrt{2}}\right)$

73. (a) $\int_{0}^{\pi} \frac{\cos x}{\sqrt{1 + \sin^2 x}} dx = \int_{0}^{0} \frac{1}{\sqrt{1 + u^2}} du = \left[\sinh^{-1} u\right]_{0}^{0} = \sinh^{-1} 0 - \sinh^{-1} 0 = 0$, where $u = \sin x$, $du = \cos x\, dx$

(b) $\sinh^{-1} 0 - \sinh^{-1} 0 = \ln\left(0 + \sqrt{0+1}\right) - \ln\left(0 + \sqrt{0+1}\right) = 0$

74. (a) $\int_1^e \frac{dx}{x\sqrt{1+(\ln x)^2}} = \int_0^1 \frac{du}{\sqrt{a^2+u^2}}$, where $u = \ln x$, $du = \frac{1}{x} dx$, $a = 1$

$= [\sinh^{-1} u]_0^1 = \sinh^{-1} 1 - \sinh^{-1} 0 = \sinh^{-1} 1$

(b) $\sinh^{-1} 1 - \sinh^{-1} 0 = \ln\left(1 + \sqrt{1^2+1}\right) - \ln\left(0 + \sqrt{0^2+1}\right) = \ln\left(1 + \sqrt{2}\right)$

75. Let $E(x) = \frac{f(x)+f(-x)}{2}$ and $O(x) = \frac{f(x)-f(-x)}{2}$. Then $E(x) + O(x) = \frac{f(x)+f(-x)}{2} + \frac{f(x)-f(-x)}{2} = \frac{2f(x)}{2} = f(x)$. Also,

$E(-x) = \frac{f(-x)+f(-(-x))}{2} = \frac{f(x)+f(-x)}{2} = E(x) \Rightarrow E(x)$ is even, and $O(-x) = \frac{f(-x)-f(-(-x))}{2} = -\frac{f(x)-f(-x)}{2} = -O(x)$

$\Rightarrow O(x)$ is odd. Consequently, $f(x)$ can be written as a sum of an even and an odd function.

$f(x) = \frac{f(x)+f(-x)}{2}$ because $\frac{f(x)-f(-x)}{2} = 0$ if f is even and $f(x) = \frac{f(x)-f(-x)}{2}$ because $\frac{f(x)+f(-x)}{2} = 0$ if f is odd.

Thus, if f is even $f(x) = \frac{2f(x)}{2} + 0$ and if f is odd, $f(x) = 0 + \frac{2f(x)}{2}$

76. $y = \sinh^{-1} x \Rightarrow x = \sinh y \Rightarrow x = \frac{e^y - e^{-y}}{2} \Rightarrow 2x = e^y - \frac{1}{e^y} \Rightarrow 2xe^y = e^{2y} - 1 \Rightarrow e^{2y} - 2xe^y - 1 = 0$

$\Rightarrow e^y = \frac{2x \pm \sqrt{4x^2+4}}{2} \Rightarrow e^y = x + \sqrt{x^2+1} \Rightarrow \sinh^{-1} x = y = \ln\left(x + \sqrt{x^2+1}\right)$. Since $e^y > 0$, we cannot

choose $e^y = x - \sqrt{x^2+1}$ because $x - \sqrt{x^2+1} < 0$.

77. (a) $v = \sqrt{\frac{mg}{k}} \tanh\left(\sqrt{\frac{gk}{m}} t\right) \Rightarrow \frac{dv}{dt} = \sqrt{\frac{mg}{k}}\left[\text{sech}^2\left(\sqrt{\frac{gk}{m}} t\right)\right]\left(\sqrt{\frac{gk}{m}}\right) = g\,\text{sech}^2\left(\sqrt{\frac{gk}{m}} t\right)$.

Thus $m\frac{dv}{dt} = mg\,\text{sech}^2\left(\sqrt{\frac{gk}{m}} t\right) = mg\left(1 - \tanh^2\left(\sqrt{\frac{gk}{m}} t\right)\right) = mg - kv^2$. Also, since $\tanh x = 0$ when $x = 0$, $v = 0$

when $t = 0$.

(b) $\lim_{t \to \infty} v = \lim_{t \to \infty} \sqrt{\frac{mg}{k}} \tanh\left(\sqrt{\frac{kg}{m}} t\right) = \sqrt{\frac{mg}{k}} \lim_{t \to \infty} \tanh\left(\sqrt{\frac{kg}{m}} t\right) = \sqrt{\frac{mg}{k}} (1) = \sqrt{\frac{mg}{k}}$

(c) $\sqrt{\frac{160}{0.005}} = \sqrt{\frac{160,000}{5}} = \frac{400}{\sqrt{5}} = 80\sqrt{5} \approx 178.89$ ft/sec

78. (a) $s(t) = a\cos kt + b\sin kt \Rightarrow \frac{ds}{dt} = -ak\sin kt + bk\cos kt \Rightarrow \frac{d^2s}{dt^2} = -ak^2\cos kt - bk^2\sin kt$

$= -k^2(a\cos kt + b\sin kt) = -k^2 s(t) \Rightarrow$ acceleration is proportional to s. The negative constant $-k^2$

implies that the acceleration is directed toward the origin.

(b) $s(t) = a\cosh kt + b\sinh kt \Rightarrow \frac{ds}{dt} = ak\sinh kt + bk\cosh kt \Rightarrow \frac{d^2s}{dt^2} = ak^2\cosh kt + bk^2\sinh kt$

$= k^2(a\cosh kt + b\sinh kt) = k^2 s(t) \Rightarrow$ acceleration is proportional to s. The positive constant $k^2$ implies

that the acceleration is directed away from the origin.

79. $V = \pi\int_0^2 (\cosh^2 x - \sinh^2 x)\,dx = \pi\int_0^2 1\,dx = 2\pi$

80. $V = 2\pi\int_0^{\ln\sqrt{3}} \text{sech}^2 x\,dx = 2\pi[\tanh x]_0^{\ln\sqrt{3}} = 2\pi\left[\frac{\sqrt{3}-(1/\sqrt{3})}{\sqrt{3}+(1/\sqrt{3})}\right] = \pi$

81. $y = \frac{1}{2}\cosh 2x \Rightarrow y' = \sinh 2x \Rightarrow L = \int_0^{\ln\sqrt{5}} \sqrt{1+(\sinh 2x)^2}\,dx = \int_0^{\ln\sqrt{5}} \cosh 2x\,dx = \left[\frac{1}{2}\sinh 2x\right]_0^{\ln\sqrt{5}}$

$= \left[\frac{1}{2}\left(\frac{e^{2x}-e^{-2x}}{2}\right)\right]_0^{\ln\sqrt{5}} = \frac{1}{4}\left(5 - \frac{1}{5}\right) = \frac{6}{5}$

82. (a) $\lim\limits_{x \to \infty} \tanh x = \lim\limits_{x \to \infty} \frac{e^x - e^{-x}}{e^x + e^{-x}} = \lim\limits_{x \to \infty} \frac{e^x - \frac{1}{e^x}}{e^x + \frac{1}{e^x}} = \lim\limits_{x \to \infty} \frac{\left(e^x - \frac{1}{e^x}\right)}{\left(e^x + \frac{1}{e^x}\right)} \cdot \frac{\frac{1}{e^x}}{\frac{1}{e^x}} = \lim\limits_{x \to \infty} \frac{1 - \frac{1}{e^{2x}}}{1 + \frac{1}{e^{2x}}} = \frac{1-0}{1+0} = 1$

(b) $\lim\limits_{x \to -\infty} \tanh x = \lim\limits_{x \to -\infty} \frac{e^x - e^{-x}}{e^x + e^{-x}} = \lim\limits_{x \to -\infty} \frac{e^x - \frac{1}{e^x}}{e^x + \frac{1}{e^x}} = \lim\limits_{x \to -\infty} \frac{\left(e^x - \frac{1}{e^x}\right)}{\left(e^x + \frac{1}{e^x}\right)} \cdot \frac{e^x}{e^x} = \lim\limits_{x \to -\infty} \frac{e^{2x} - 1}{e^{2x} + 1} = \frac{0-1}{0+1} = -1$

(c) $\lim\limits_{x \to \infty} \sinh x = \lim\limits_{x \to \infty} \frac{e^x - e^{-x}}{2} = \lim\limits_{x \to \infty} \frac{e^x - \frac{1}{e^x}}{2} = \lim\limits_{x \to \infty} \left(\frac{e^x}{2} - \frac{1}{2e^x}\right) = \infty - 0 = \infty$

(d) $\lim\limits_{x \to -\infty} \sinh x = \lim\limits_{x \to -\infty} \frac{e^x - e^{-x}}{2} = \lim\limits_{x \to -\infty} \left(\frac{e^x}{2} - \frac{e^{-x}}{2}\right) = 0 - \infty = -\infty$

(e) $\lim\limits_{x \to \infty} \operatorname{sech} x = \lim\limits_{x \to \infty} \frac{2}{e^x + e^{-x}} = \lim\limits_{x \to \infty} \frac{2}{e^x + \frac{1}{e^x}} \cdot \frac{\frac{1}{e^x}}{\frac{1}{e^x}} = \lim\limits_{x \to \infty} \frac{\frac{2}{e^x}}{1 + \frac{1}{e^{2x}}} = \frac{0}{1+0} = 0$

(f) $\lim\limits_{x \to \infty} \coth x = \lim\limits_{x \to \infty} \frac{e^x + e^{-x}}{e^x - e^{-x}} = \lim\limits_{x \to \infty} \frac{e^x + \frac{1}{e^x}}{e^x - \frac{1}{e^x}} = \lim\limits_{x \to \infty} \frac{\left(e^x + \frac{1}{e^x}\right)}{\left(e^x - \frac{1}{e^x}\right)} \cdot \frac{\frac{1}{e^x}}{\frac{1}{e^x}} = \lim\limits_{x \to \infty} \frac{1 + \frac{1}{e^{2x}}}{1 - \frac{1}{e^{2x}}} = \frac{1+0}{1-0} = 1$

(g) $\lim\limits_{x \to 0^+} \coth x = \lim\limits_{x \to 0^+} \frac{e^x + e^{-x}}{e^x - e^{-x}} = \lim\limits_{x \to 0^+} \frac{e^x + \frac{1}{e^x}}{e^x - \frac{1}{e^x}} \cdot \frac{e^x}{e^x} = \lim\limits_{x \to 0^+} \frac{e^{2x} + 1}{e^{2x} - 1} = +\infty$

(h) $\lim\limits_{x \to 0^-} \coth x = \lim\limits_{x \to 0^-} \frac{e^x + e^{-x}}{e^x - e^{-x}} = \lim\limits_{x \to 0^-} \frac{e^x + \frac{1}{e^x}}{e^x - \frac{1}{e^x}} \cdot \frac{e^x}{e^x} = \lim\limits_{x \to 0^-} \frac{e^{2x} + 1}{e^{2x} - 1} = -\infty$

(i) $\lim\limits_{x \to -\infty} \operatorname{csch} x = \lim\limits_{x \to -\infty} \frac{2}{e^x - e^{-x}} = \lim\limits_{x \to -\infty} \frac{2}{e^x - \frac{1}{e^x}} \cdot \frac{e^x}{e^x} = \lim\limits_{x \to -\infty} \frac{2e^x}{e^{2x} - 1} = \frac{0}{0-1} = 0$

83. (a) $y = \frac{H}{w} \cosh\left(\frac{w}{H} x\right) \Rightarrow \tan \phi = \frac{dy}{dx} = \left(\frac{H}{w}\right)\left[\frac{w}{H} \sinh\left(\frac{w}{H} x\right)\right] = \sinh\left(\frac{w}{H} x\right)$

(b) The tension at P is given by $T \cos \phi = H \Rightarrow T = H \sec \phi = H\sqrt{1 + \tan^2 \phi} = H\sqrt{1 + \left(\sinh \frac{w}{H} x\right)^2}$
$= H \cosh\left(\frac{w}{H} x\right) = w\left(\frac{H}{w}\right) \cosh\left(\frac{w}{H} x\right) = wy$

84. $s = \frac{1}{a} \sinh ax \Rightarrow \sinh ax = as \Rightarrow ax = \sinh^{-1} as \Rightarrow x = \frac{1}{a} \sinh^{-1} as; \ y = \frac{1}{a} \cosh ax = \frac{1}{a}\sqrt{\cosh^2 ax}$
$= \frac{1}{a}\sqrt{\sinh^2 ax + 1} = \frac{1}{a}\sqrt{a^2 s^2 + 1} = \sqrt{s^2 + \frac{1}{a^2}}$

85. To find the length of the curve: $y = \frac{1}{a} \cosh ax \Rightarrow y' = \sinh ax \Rightarrow L = \int_0^b \sqrt{1 + (\sinh ax)^2}\, dx$
$\Rightarrow L = \int_0^b \cosh ax\, dx = \left[\frac{1}{a} \sinh ax\right]_0^b = \frac{1}{a} \sinh ab$. The area under the curve is $A = \int_0^b \frac{1}{a} \cosh ax\, dx$
$= \left[\frac{1}{a^2} \sinh ax\right]_0^b = \frac{1}{a^2} \sinh ab = \left(\frac{1}{a}\right)\left(\frac{1}{a} \sinh ab\right)$ which is the area of the rectangle of height $\frac{1}{a}$ and length L
as claimed, and which is illustrated below.

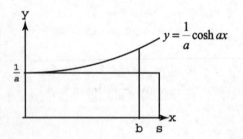

86. (a) Let the point located at $(\cosh u, 0)$ be called T. Then $A(u) =$ area of the triangle $\triangle OTP$ minus the area
under the curve $y = \sqrt{x^2 - 1}$ from A to T $\Rightarrow A(u) = \frac{1}{2} \cosh u \sinh u - \int_1^{\cosh u} \sqrt{x^2 - 1}\, dx$.

(b) $A(u) = \frac{1}{2} \cosh u \sinh u - \int_1^{\cosh u} \sqrt{x^2 - 1}\, dx \Rightarrow A'(u) = \frac{1}{2}(\cosh^2 u + \sinh^2 u) - \left(\sqrt{\cosh^2 u - 1}\right)(\sinh u)$
$= \frac{1}{2} \cosh^2 u + \frac{1}{2} \sinh^2 u - \sinh^2 u = \frac{1}{2}(\cosh^2 u - \sinh^2 u) = \left(\frac{1}{2}\right)(1) = \frac{1}{2}$

(c) $A'(u) = \frac{1}{2} \Rightarrow A(u) = \frac{u}{2} + C$, and from part (a) we have $A(0) = 0 \Rightarrow C = 0 \Rightarrow A(u) = \frac{u}{2} \Rightarrow u = 2A$

## 7.8  RELATIVE RATES OF GROWTH

1. (a) slower, $\displaystyle\lim_{x \to \infty} \frac{x+3}{e^x} = \lim_{x \to \infty} \frac{1}{e^x} = 0$

   (b) slower, $\displaystyle\lim_{x \to \infty} \frac{x^3 + \sin^2 x}{e^x} = \lim_{x \to \infty} \frac{3x^2 + 2\sin x \cos x}{e^x} = \lim_{x \to \infty} \frac{6x + 2\cos 2x}{e^x} = \lim_{x \to \infty} \frac{6 - 4\sin 2x}{e^x} = 0$ by the

   Sandwich Theorem because $\frac{2}{e^x} \le \frac{6 - 4\sin 2x}{e^x} \le \frac{10}{e^x}$ for all reals and $\displaystyle\lim_{x \to \infty} \frac{2}{e^x} = 0 = \lim_{x \to \infty} \frac{10}{e^x}$

   (c) slower, $\displaystyle\lim_{x \to \infty} \frac{\sqrt{x}}{e^x} = \lim_{x \to \infty} \frac{x^{1/2}}{e^x} = \lim_{x \to \infty} \frac{\left(\frac{1}{2}\right) x^{-1/2}}{e^x} = \lim_{x \to \infty} \frac{1}{2\sqrt{x}\, e^x} = 0$

   (d) faster, $\displaystyle\lim_{x \to \infty} \frac{4^x}{e^x} = \lim_{x \to \infty} \left(\frac{4}{e}\right)^x = \infty$ since $\frac{4}{e} > 1$

   (e) slower, $\displaystyle\lim_{x \to \infty} \frac{\left(\frac{3}{2}\right)^x}{e^x} = \lim_{x \to \infty} \left(\frac{3}{2e}\right)^x = 0$ since $\frac{3}{2e} < 1$

   (f) slower, $\displaystyle\lim_{x \to \infty} \frac{e^{x/2}}{e^x} = \lim_{x \to \infty} \frac{1}{e^{x/2}} = 0$

   (g) same, $\displaystyle\lim_{x \to \infty} \frac{\left(\frac{e^x}{2}\right)}{e^x} = \lim_{x \to \infty} \frac{1}{2} = \frac{1}{2}$

   (h) slower, $\displaystyle\lim_{x \to \infty} \frac{\log_{10} x}{e^x} = \lim_{x \to \infty} \frac{\ln x}{(\ln 10)\, e^x} = \lim_{x \to \infty} \frac{\frac{1}{x}}{(\ln 10)\, e^x} = \lim_{x \to \infty} \frac{1}{(\ln 10) x e^x} = 0$

2. (a) slower, $\displaystyle\lim_{x \to \infty} \frac{10x^4 + 30x + 1}{e^x} = \lim_{x \to \infty} \frac{40x^3 + 30}{e^x} = \lim_{x \to \infty} \frac{120x^2}{e^x} = \lim_{x \to \infty} \frac{240x}{e^x} = \lim_{x \to \infty} \frac{240}{e^x} = 0$

   (b) slower, $\displaystyle\lim_{x \to \infty} \frac{x \ln x - x}{e^x} = \lim_{x \to \infty} \frac{x(\ln x - 1)}{e^x} = \lim_{x \to \infty} \frac{\ln x - 1 + x\left(\frac{1}{x}\right)}{e^x} = \lim_{x \to \infty} \frac{\ln x - 1 + 1}{e^x} = \lim_{x \to \infty} \frac{\ln x}{e^x}$

   $= \displaystyle\lim_{x \to \infty} \frac{\left(\frac{1}{x}\right)}{e^x} = \lim_{x \to \infty} \frac{1}{x e^x} = 0$

   (c) slower, $\displaystyle\lim_{x \to \infty} \frac{\sqrt{1 + x^4}}{e^x} = \sqrt{\lim_{x \to \infty} \frac{1 + x^4}{e^{2x}}} = \sqrt{\lim_{x \to \infty} \frac{4x^3}{2e^{2x}}} = \sqrt{\lim_{x \to \infty} \frac{12x^2}{4e^{2x}}} = \sqrt{\lim_{x \to \infty} \frac{24x}{8e^{2x}}} = \sqrt{\lim_{x \to \infty} \frac{24}{16e^{2x}}}$

   $= \sqrt{0} = 0$

   (d) slower, $\displaystyle\lim_{x \to \infty} \frac{\left(\frac{5}{2}\right)^x}{e^x} = \lim_{x \to \infty} \left(\frac{5}{2e}\right)^x = 0$ since $\frac{5}{2e} < 1$

   (e) slower, $\displaystyle\lim_{x \to \infty} \frac{e^{-x}}{e^x} = \lim_{x \to \infty} \frac{1}{e^{2x}} = 0$

   (f) faster, $\displaystyle\lim_{x \to \infty} \frac{x e^x}{e^x} = \lim_{x \to \infty} x = \infty$

   (g) slower, since for all reals we have $-1 \le \cos x \le 1 \Rightarrow e^{-1} \le e^{\cos x} \le e^1 \Rightarrow \frac{e^{-1}}{e^x} \le \frac{e^{\cos x}}{e^x} \le \frac{e^1}{e^x}$ and also

   $\displaystyle\lim_{x \to \infty} \frac{e^{-1}}{e^x} = 0 = \lim_{x \to \infty} \frac{e^1}{e^x}$, so by the Sandwich Theorem we conclude that $\displaystyle\lim_{x \to \infty} \frac{e^{\cos x}}{e^x} = 0$

   (h) same, $\displaystyle\lim_{x \to \infty} \frac{e^{x-1}}{e^x} = \lim_{x \to \infty} \frac{1}{e^{(x-x+1)}} = \lim_{x \to \infty} \frac{1}{e} = \frac{1}{e}$

3. (a) same, $\displaystyle\lim_{x \to \infty} \frac{x^2 + 4x}{x^2} = \lim_{x \to \infty} \frac{2x+4}{2x} = \lim_{x \to \infty} \frac{2}{2} = 1$

   (b) faster, $\displaystyle\lim_{x \to \infty} \frac{x^5 - x^2}{x^2} = \lim_{x \to \infty} (x^3 - 1) = \infty$

   (c) same, $\displaystyle\lim_{x \to \infty} \frac{\sqrt{x^4 + x^3}}{x^2} = \sqrt{\lim_{x \to \infty} \frac{x^4 + x^3}{x^4}} = \sqrt{\lim_{x \to \infty} \left(1 + \frac{1}{x}\right)} = \sqrt{1} = 1$

   (d) same, $\displaystyle\lim_{x \to \infty} \frac{(x+3)^2}{x^2} = \lim_{x \to \infty} \frac{2(x+3)}{2x} = \lim_{x \to \infty} \frac{2}{2} = 1$

   (e) slower, $\displaystyle\lim_{x \to \infty} \frac{x \ln x}{x^2} = \lim_{x \to \infty} \frac{\ln x}{x} = \lim_{x \to \infty} \frac{\left(\frac{1}{x}\right)}{1} = 0$

   (f) faster, $\displaystyle\lim_{x \to \infty} \frac{2^x}{x^2} = \lim_{x \to \infty} \frac{(\ln 2)\, 2^x}{2x} = \lim_{x \to \infty} \frac{(\ln 2)^2\, 2^x}{2} = \infty$

   (g) slower, $\displaystyle\lim_{x \to \infty} \frac{x^3 e^{-x}}{x^2} = \lim_{x \to \infty} \frac{x}{e^x} = \lim_{x \to \infty} \frac{1}{e^x} = 0$

   (h) same, $\displaystyle\lim_{x \to \infty} \frac{8x^2}{x^2} = \lim_{x \to \infty} 8 = 8$

4. (a) same, $\displaystyle\lim_{x \to \infty} \frac{x^2 + \sqrt{x}}{x^2} = \lim_{x \to \infty} \left(1 + \frac{1}{x^{3/2}}\right) = 1$

   (b) same, $\displaystyle\lim_{x \to \infty} \frac{10x^2}{x^2} = \lim_{x \to \infty} 10 = 10$

   (c) slower, $\displaystyle\lim_{x \to \infty} \frac{x^2 e^{-x}}{x^2} = \lim_{x \to \infty} \frac{1}{e^x} = 0$

(d)  slower, $\displaystyle\lim_{x \to \infty} \frac{\log_{10} x^2}{x^2} = \lim_{x \to \infty} \frac{\left(\frac{\ln x^2}{\ln 10}\right)}{x^2} = \frac{1}{\ln 10} \lim_{x \to \infty} \frac{2 \ln x}{x^2} = \frac{2}{\ln 10} \lim_{x \to \infty} \frac{\left(\frac{1}{x}\right)}{2x} = \frac{1}{\ln 10} \lim_{x \to \infty} \frac{1}{x^2} = 0$

(e)  faster, $\displaystyle\lim_{x \to \infty} \frac{x^3 - x^2}{x^2} = \lim_{x \to \infty} (x - 1) = \infty$

(f)  slower, $\displaystyle\lim_{x \to \infty} \frac{\left(\frac{1}{10}\right)^x}{x^2} = \lim_{x \to \infty} \frac{1}{10^x x^2} = 0$

(g)  faster, $\displaystyle\lim_{x \to \infty} \frac{(1.1)^x}{x^2} = \lim_{x \to \infty} \frac{(\ln 1.1)(1.1)^x}{2x} = \lim_{x \to \infty} \frac{(\ln 1.1)^2 (1.1)^x}{2} = \infty$

(h)  same, $\displaystyle\lim_{x \to \infty} \frac{x^2 + 100x}{x^2} = \lim_{x \to \infty} \left(1 + \frac{100}{x}\right) = 1$

5.  (a)  same, $\displaystyle\lim_{x \to \infty} \frac{\log_3 x}{\ln x} = \lim_{x \to \infty} \frac{\left(\frac{\ln x}{\ln 3}\right)}{\ln x} = \lim_{x \to \infty} \frac{1}{\ln 3} = \frac{1}{\ln 3}$

(b)  same, $\displaystyle\lim_{x \to \infty} \frac{\ln 2x}{\ln x} = \lim_{x \to \infty} \frac{\left(\frac{2}{2x}\right)}{\left(\frac{1}{x}\right)} = 1$

(c)  same, $\displaystyle\lim_{x \to \infty} \frac{\ln \sqrt{x}}{\ln x} = \lim_{x \to \infty} \frac{\left(\frac{1}{2}\right) \ln x}{\ln x} = \lim_{x \to \infty} \frac{1}{2} = \frac{1}{2}$

(d)  faster, $\displaystyle\lim_{x \to \infty} \frac{\sqrt{x}}{\ln x} = \lim_{x \to \infty} \frac{x^{1/2}}{\ln x} = \lim_{x \to \infty} \frac{\left(\frac{1}{2}\right) x^{-1/2}}{\left(\frac{1}{x}\right)} = \lim_{x \to \infty} \frac{x}{2\sqrt{x}} = \lim_{x \to \infty} \frac{\sqrt{x}}{2} = \infty$

(e)  faster, $\displaystyle\lim_{x \to \infty} \frac{x}{\ln x} = \lim_{x \to \infty} \frac{1}{\left(\frac{1}{x}\right)} = \lim_{x \to \infty} x = \infty$

(f)  same, $\displaystyle\lim_{x \to \infty} \frac{5 \ln x}{\ln x} = \lim_{x \to \infty} 5 = 5$

(g)  slower, $\displaystyle\lim_{x \to \infty} \frac{\left(\frac{1}{x}\right)}{\ln x} = \lim_{x \to \infty} \frac{1}{x \ln x} = 0$

(h)  faster, $\displaystyle\lim_{x \to \infty} \frac{e^x}{\ln x} = \lim_{x \to \infty} \frac{e^x}{\left(\frac{1}{x}\right)} = \lim_{x \to \infty} x e^x = \infty$

6.  (a)  same, $\displaystyle\lim_{x \to \infty} \frac{\log_2 x^2}{\ln x} = \lim_{x \to \infty} \frac{\left(\frac{\ln x^2}{\ln 2}\right)}{\ln x} = \frac{1}{\ln 2} \lim_{x \to \infty} \frac{\ln x^2}{\ln x} = \frac{1}{\ln 2} \lim_{x \to \infty} \frac{2 \ln x}{\ln x} = \frac{1}{\ln 2} \lim_{x \to \infty} 2 = \frac{2}{\ln 2}$

(b)  same, $\displaystyle\lim_{x \to \infty} \frac{\log_{10} 10x}{\ln x} = \lim_{x \to \infty} \frac{\left(\frac{\ln 10x}{\ln 10}\right)}{\ln x} = \frac{1}{\ln 10} \lim_{x \to \infty} \frac{\ln 10x}{\ln x} = \frac{1}{\ln 10} \lim_{x \to \infty} \frac{\left(\frac{10}{10x}\right)}{\left(\frac{1}{x}\right)} = \frac{1}{\ln 10} \lim_{x \to \infty} 1 = \frac{1}{\ln 10}$

(c)  slower, $\displaystyle\lim_{x \to \infty} \frac{\left(\frac{1}{\sqrt{x}}\right)}{\ln x} = \lim_{x \to \infty} \frac{1}{(\sqrt{x})(\ln x)} = 0$

(d)  slower, $\displaystyle\lim_{x \to \infty} \frac{\left(\frac{1}{x^2}\right)}{\ln x} = \lim_{x \to \infty} \frac{1}{x^2 \ln x} = 0$

(e)  faster, $\displaystyle\lim_{x \to \infty} \frac{x - 2 \ln x}{\ln x} = \lim_{x \to \infty} \left(\frac{x}{\ln x} - 2\right) = \left(\lim_{x \to \infty} \frac{x}{\ln x}\right) - 2 = \left(\lim_{x \to \infty} \frac{1}{\left(\frac{1}{x}\right)}\right) - 2 = \left(\lim_{x \to \infty} x\right) - 2 = \infty$

(f)  slower, $\displaystyle\lim_{x \to \infty} \frac{e^{-x}}{\ln x} = \lim_{x \to \infty} \frac{1}{e^x \ln x} = 0$

(g)  slower, $\displaystyle\lim_{x \to \infty} \frac{\ln (\ln x)}{\ln x} = \lim_{x \to \infty} \frac{\left(\frac{1/x}{\ln x}\right)}{\left(\frac{1}{x}\right)} = \lim_{x \to \infty} \frac{1}{\ln x} = 0$

(h)  same, $\displaystyle\lim_{x \to \infty} \frac{\ln (2x+5)}{\ln x} = \lim_{x \to \infty} \frac{\left(\frac{2}{2x+5}\right)}{\left(\frac{1}{x}\right)} = \lim_{x \to \infty} \frac{2x}{2x+5} = \lim_{x \to \infty} \frac{2}{2} = \lim_{x \to \infty} 1 = 1$

7.  $\displaystyle\lim_{x \to \infty} \frac{e^x}{e^{x/2}} = \lim_{x \to \infty} e^{x/2} = \infty \Rightarrow e^x$ grows faster than $e^{x/2}$; since for $x > e^e$ we have $\ln x > e$ and $\displaystyle\lim_{x \to \infty} \frac{(\ln x)^x}{e^x}$
$= \displaystyle\lim_{x \to \infty} \left(\frac{\ln x}{e}\right)^x = \infty \Rightarrow (\ln x)^x$ grows faster than $e^x$; since $x > \ln x$ for all $x > 0$ and $\displaystyle\lim_{x \to \infty} \frac{x^x}{(\ln x)^x} = \lim_{x \to \infty} \left(\frac{x}{\ln x}\right)^x$
$= \infty \Rightarrow x^x$ grows faster than $(\ln x)^x$. Therefore, slowest to fastest are: $e^{x/2}, e^x, (\ln x)^x, x^x$ so the order is d, a, c, b

8.  $\displaystyle\lim_{x \to \infty} \frac{(\ln 2)^x}{x^2} = \lim_{x \to \infty} \frac{(\ln (\ln 2))(\ln 2)^x}{2x} = \lim_{x \to \infty} \frac{(\ln (\ln 2))^2 (\ln 2)^x}{2} = \frac{(\ln (\ln 2))^2}{2} \lim_{x \to \infty} (\ln 2)^x = 0$
$\Rightarrow (\ln 2)^x$ grows slower than $x^2$; $\displaystyle\lim_{x \to \infty} \frac{x^2}{2^x} = \lim_{x \to \infty} \frac{2x}{(\ln 2)2^x} = \lim_{x \to \infty} \frac{2}{(\ln 2)^2 2^x} = 0 \Rightarrow x^2$ grows slower than $2^x$;
$\displaystyle\lim_{x \to \infty} \frac{2^x}{e^x} = \lim_{x \to \infty} \left(\frac{2}{e}\right)^x = 0 \Rightarrow 2^x$ grows slower than $e^x$. Therefore, the slowest to the fastest is: $(\ln 2)^x, x^2, 2^x$
and $e^x$ so the order is c, b, a, d

9. (a) false; $\lim\limits_{x \to \infty} \frac{x}{x} = 1$

(b) false; $\lim\limits_{x \to \infty} \frac{x}{x+5} = \frac{1}{1} = 1$

(c) true; $x < x + 5 \Rightarrow \frac{x}{x+5} < 1$ if $x > 1$ (or sufficiently large)

(d) true; $x < 2x \Rightarrow \frac{x}{2x} < 1$ if $x > 1$ (or sufficiently large)

(e) true; $\lim\limits_{x \to \infty} \frac{e^x}{e^{2x}} = \lim\limits_{x \to 0} \frac{1}{e^x} = 0$

(f) true; $\frac{x + \ln x}{x} = 1 + \frac{\ln x}{x} < 1 + \frac{\sqrt{x}}{x} = 1 + \frac{1}{\sqrt{x}} < 2$ if $x > 1$ (or sufficiently large)

(g) false; $\lim\limits_{x \to \infty} \frac{\ln x}{\ln 2x} = \lim\limits_{x \to \infty} \frac{\left(\frac{1}{x}\right)}{\left(\frac{2}{2x}\right)} = \lim\limits_{x \to \infty} 1 = 1$

(h) true; $\frac{\sqrt{x^2 + 5}}{x} < \frac{\sqrt{(x+5)^2}}{x} < \frac{x+5}{x} = 1 + \frac{5}{x} < 6$ if $x > 1$ (or sufficiently large)

10. (a) true; $\frac{\left(\frac{1}{x+3}\right)}{\left(\frac{1}{x}\right)} = \frac{x}{x+3} < 1$ if $x > 1$ (or sufficiently large)

(b) true; $\frac{\left(\frac{1}{x} + \frac{1}{x^2}\right)}{\left(\frac{1}{x}\right)} = 1 + \frac{1}{x} < 2$ if $x > 1$ (or sufficiently large)

(c) false; $\lim\limits_{x \to \infty} \frac{\left(\frac{1}{x} - \frac{1}{x^2}\right)}{\left(\frac{1}{x}\right)} = \lim\limits_{x \to \infty} \left(1 - \frac{1}{x}\right) = 1$

(d) true; $2 + \cos x \le 3 \Rightarrow \frac{2 + \cos x}{2} \le \frac{3}{2}$ if $x$ is sufficiently large

(e) true; $\frac{e^x + x}{e^x} = 1 + \frac{x}{e^x}$ and $\frac{x}{e^x} \to 0$ as $x \to \infty \Rightarrow 1 + \frac{x}{e^x} < 2$ if $x$ is sufficiently large

(f) true; $\lim\limits_{x \to \infty} \frac{x \ln x}{x^2} = \lim\limits_{x \to \infty} \frac{\ln x}{x} = \lim\limits_{x \to \infty} \frac{\left(\frac{1}{x}\right)}{1} = 0$

(g) true; $\frac{\ln(\ln x)}{\ln x} < \frac{\ln x}{\ln x} = 1$ if $x$ is sufficiently large

(h) false; $\lim\limits_{x \to \infty} \frac{\ln x}{\ln(x^2 + 1)} = \lim\limits_{x \to \infty} \frac{\left(\frac{1}{x}\right)}{\left(\frac{2x}{x^2 + 1}\right)} = \lim\limits_{x \to \infty} \frac{x^2 + 1}{2x^2} = \lim\limits_{x \to \infty} \left(\frac{1}{2} + \frac{1}{2x^2}\right) = \frac{1}{2}$

11. If $f(x)$ and $g(x)$ grow at the same rate, then $\lim\limits_{x \to \infty} \frac{f(x)}{g(x)} = L \neq 0 \Rightarrow \lim\limits_{x \to \infty} \frac{g(x)}{f(x)} = \frac{1}{L} \neq 0$. Then $\left| \frac{f(x)}{g(x)} - L \right| < 1$ if $x$ is sufficiently large $\Rightarrow L - 1 < \frac{f(x)}{g(x)} < L + 1 \Rightarrow \frac{f(x)}{g(x)} \le |L| + 1$ if $x$ is sufficiently large $\Rightarrow f = O(g)$. Similarly, $\frac{g(x)}{f(x)} \le \left| \frac{1}{L} \right| + 1 \Rightarrow g = O(f)$.

12. When the degree of $f$ is less than the degree of $g$ since in that case $\lim\limits_{x \to \infty} \frac{f(x)}{g(x)} = 0$.

13. When the degree of $f$ is less than or equal to the degree of $g$ since $\lim\limits_{x \to \infty} \frac{f(x)}{g(x)} = 0$ when the degree of $f$ is smaller than the degree of $g$, and $\lim\limits_{x \to \infty} \frac{f(x)}{g(x)} = \frac{a}{b}$ (the ratio of the leading coefficients) when the degrees are the same.

14. Polynomials of a greater degree grow at a greater rate than polynomials of a lesser degree. Polynomials of the same degree grow at the same rate.

15. $\lim\limits_{x \to \infty} \frac{\ln(x+1)}{\ln x} = \lim\limits_{x \to \infty} \frac{\left(\frac{1}{x+1}\right)}{\left(\frac{1}{x}\right)} = \lim\limits_{x \to \infty} \frac{x}{x+1} = \lim\limits_{x \to \infty} \frac{1}{1} = 1$ and $\lim\limits_{x \to \infty} \frac{\ln(x+999)}{\ln x} = \lim\limits_{x \to \infty} \frac{\left(\frac{1}{x+999}\right)}{\left(\frac{1}{x}\right)}$ $= \lim\limits_{x \to \infty} \frac{x}{x+999} = 1$

16. $\lim\limits_{x \to \infty} \frac{\ln(x+a)}{\ln x} = \lim\limits_{x \to \infty} \frac{\left(\frac{1}{x+a}\right)}{\left(\frac{1}{x}\right)} = \lim\limits_{x \to \infty} \frac{x}{x+a} = \lim\limits_{x \to \infty} \frac{1}{1} = 1$. Therefore, the relative rates are the same.

17. $\lim\limits_{x \to \infty} \frac{\sqrt{10x+1}}{\sqrt{x}} = \sqrt{\lim\limits_{x \to \infty} \frac{10x+1}{x}} = \sqrt{10}$ and $\lim\limits_{x \to \infty} \frac{\sqrt{x+1}}{\sqrt{x}} = \sqrt{\lim\limits_{x \to \infty} \frac{x+1}{x}} = \sqrt{1} = 1$. Since the growth rate is transitive, we conclude that $\sqrt{10x+1}$ and $\sqrt{x+1}$ have the same growth rate $\left(\text{that of } \sqrt{x}\right)$.

18. $\lim\limits_{x \to \infty} \frac{\sqrt{x^4+x}}{x^2} = \sqrt{\lim\limits_{x \to \infty} \frac{x^4+x}{x^4}} = 1$ and $\lim\limits_{x \to \infty} \frac{\sqrt{x^4-x^3}}{x^2} = \sqrt{\lim\limits_{x \to \infty} \frac{x^4-x^3}{x^4}} = 1$. Since the growth rate is transitive, we conclude that $\sqrt{x^4+x}$ and $\sqrt{x^4-x^3}$ have the same growth rate $\left(\text{that of } x^2\right)$.

19. $\lim\limits_{x \to \infty} \frac{x^n}{e^x} = \lim\limits_{x \to \infty} \frac{nx^{n-1}}{e^x} = \ldots = \lim\limits_{x \to \infty} \frac{n!}{e^x} = 0 \Rightarrow x^n = o\left(e^x\right)$ for any non-negative integer n

20. If $p(x) = a_n x^n + a_{n-1} x^{n-1} + \ldots + a_1 x + a_0$, then $\lim\limits_{x \to \infty} \frac{p(x)}{e^x} = a_n \lim\limits_{x \to \infty} \frac{x^n}{e^x} + a_{n-1} \lim\limits_{x \to \infty} \frac{x^{n-1}}{e^x} + \ldots$
$+ a_1 \lim\limits_{x \to \infty} \frac{x}{e^x} + a_0 \lim\limits_{x \to \infty} \frac{1}{e^x}$ where each limit is zero (from Exercise 19). Therefore, $\lim\limits_{x \to \infty} \frac{p(x)}{e^x} = 0$
$\Rightarrow e^x$ grows faster than any polynomial.

21. (a) $\lim\limits_{x \to \infty} \frac{x^{1/n}}{\ln x} = \lim\limits_{x \to \infty} \frac{x^{(1-n)/n}}{n\left(\frac{1}{x}\right)} = \left(\frac{1}{n}\right) \lim\limits_{x \to \infty} x^{1/n} = \infty \Rightarrow \ln x = o\left(x^{1/n}\right)$ for any positive integer n

(b) $\ln\left(e^{17,000,000}\right) = 17,000,000 < \left(e^{17 \times 10^6}\right)^{1/10^6} = e^{17} \approx 24,154,952.75$

(c) $x \approx 3.430631121 \times 10^{15}$

(d) In the interval $[3.41 \times 10^{15}, 3.45 \times 10^{15}]$ we have $\ln x = 10 \ln(\ln x)$. The graphs cross at about $3.4306311 \times 10^{15}$.

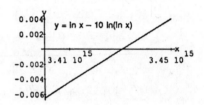

22. $\lim\limits_{x \to \infty} \frac{\ln x}{a_n x^n + a_{n-1} x^{n-1} + \ldots + a_1 x + a_0} = \frac{\lim\limits_{x \to \infty}\left(\frac{\ln x}{x^n}\right)}{\lim\limits_{x \to \infty}\left(a_n + \frac{a_{n-1}}{x} + \ldots + \frac{a_1}{x^{n-1}} + \frac{a_0}{x^n}\right)} = \frac{\lim\limits_{x \to \infty}\left[\frac{1/x}{nx^{n-1}}\right]}{a_n} = \lim\limits_{x \to \infty} \frac{1}{(a_n)(nx^n)} = 0$
$\Rightarrow \ln x$ grows slower than any non-constant polynomial ($n \geq 1$)

23. (a) $\lim\limits_{n \to \infty} \frac{n \log_2 n}{n(\log_2 n)^2} = \lim\limits_{n \to \infty} \frac{1}{\log_2 n} = 0 \Rightarrow n \log_2 n$ grows (b)
slower than $n(\log_2 n)^2$; $\lim\limits_{n \to \infty} \frac{n \log_2 n}{n^{3/2}} = \lim\limits_{n \to \infty} \frac{\left(\frac{\ln n}{\ln 2}\right)}{n^{1/2}}$
$= \frac{1}{\ln 2} \lim\limits_{n \to \infty} \frac{\left(\frac{1}{n}\right)}{\left(\frac{1}{2}\right)n^{-1/2}} = \frac{2}{\ln 2} \lim\limits_{n \to \infty} \frac{1}{n^{1/2}} = 0$
$\Rightarrow n \log_2 n$ grows slower than $n^{3/2}$. Therefore, $n \log_2 n$ grows at the slowest rate $\Rightarrow$ the algorithm that takes $O(n \log_2 n)$ steps is the most efficient in the long run.

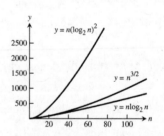

24. (a) $\lim\limits_{n \to \infty} \frac{(\log_2 n)^2}{n} = \lim\limits_{n \to \infty} \frac{\left(\frac{\ln n}{\ln 2}\right)^2}{n} = \lim\limits_{n \to \infty} \frac{(\ln n)^2}{n(\ln 2)^2}$ (b)
$= \lim\limits_{n \to \infty} \frac{2(\ln n)\left(\frac{1}{n}\right)}{(\ln 2)^2} = \frac{2}{(\ln 2)^2} \lim\limits_{n \to \infty} \frac{\ln n}{n}$
$= \frac{2}{(\ln 2)^2} \lim\limits_{n \to \infty} \frac{\left(\frac{1}{n}\right)}{1} = 0 \Rightarrow (\log_2 n)^2$ grows slower
than n; $\lim\limits_{n \to \infty} \frac{(\log_2 n)^2}{\sqrt{n} \log_2 n} = \lim\limits_{n \to \infty} \frac{\log_2 n}{\sqrt{n}}$
$= \lim\limits_{n \to \infty} \frac{\left(\frac{\ln n}{\ln 2}\right)}{n^{1/2}} = \frac{1}{\ln 2} \lim\limits_{n \to \infty} \frac{\ln n}{n^{1/2}}$

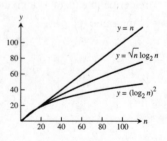

$= \frac{1}{\ln 2} \lim\limits_{x \to \infty} \frac{\left(\frac{1}{n}\right)}{\left(\frac{1}{2}\right)n^{-1/2}} = \frac{2}{\ln 2} \lim\limits_{n \to \infty} \frac{1}{n^{1/2}} = 0 \Rightarrow (\log_2 n)^2$ grows slower than $\sqrt{n} \log_2 n$. Therefore $(\log_2 n)^2$ grows at the slowest rate $\Rightarrow$ the algorithm that takes $O\left((\log_2 n)^2\right)$ steps is the most efficient in the long run.

25. It could take one million steps for a sequential search, but at most 20 steps for a binary search because
$2^{19} = 524,288 < 1,000,000 < 1,048,576 = 2^{20}$.

26. It could take 450,000 steps for a sequential search, but at most 19 steps for a binary search because
$2^{18} = 262,144 < 450,000 < 524,288 = 2^{19}$.

## CHAPTER 7 PRACTICE EXERCISES

1. $y = 10e^{-x/5} \Rightarrow \frac{dy}{dx} = (10)\left(-\frac{1}{5}\right)e^{-x/5} = -2e^{-x/5}$
   
   2. $y = \sqrt{2}\,e^{\sqrt{2}x} \Rightarrow \frac{dy}{dx} = \left(\sqrt{2}\right)\left(\sqrt{2}\right)e^{\sqrt{2}x} = 2e^{\sqrt{2}x}$

3. $y = \frac{1}{4}xe^{4x} - \frac{1}{16}e^{4x} \Rightarrow \frac{dy}{dx} = \frac{1}{4}\left[x\left(4e^{4x}\right) + e^{4x}(1)\right] - \frac{1}{16}\left(4e^{4x}\right) = xe^{4x} + \frac{1}{4}e^{4x} - \frac{1}{4}e^{4x} = xe^{4x}$

4. $y = x^2 e^{-2/x} = x^2 e^{-2x^{-1}} \Rightarrow \frac{dy}{dx} = x^2\left[\left(2x^{-2}\right)e^{-2x^{-1}}\right] + e^{-2x^{-1}}(2x) = (2 + 2x)e^{-2x^{-1}} = 2e^{-2/x}(1 + x)$

5. $y = \ln\left(\sin^2 \theta\right) \Rightarrow \frac{dy}{d\theta} = \frac{2(\sin \theta)(\cos \theta)}{\sin^2 \theta} = \frac{2\cos \theta}{\sin \theta} = 2\cot \theta$

6. $y = \ln\left(\sec^2 \theta\right) \Rightarrow \frac{dy}{d\theta} = \frac{2(\sec \theta)(\sec \theta \tan \theta)}{\sec^2 \theta} = 2\tan \theta$

7. $y = \log_2\left(\frac{x^2}{2}\right) = \frac{\ln\left(\frac{x^2}{2}\right)}{\ln 2} \Rightarrow \frac{dy}{dx} = \frac{1}{\ln 2}\left(\frac{x}{\left(\frac{x^2}{2}\right)}\right) = \frac{2}{(\ln 2)x}$

8. $y = \log_5\left(3x - 7\right) = \frac{\ln(3x-7)}{\ln 5} \Rightarrow \frac{dy}{dx} = \left(\frac{1}{\ln 5}\right)\left(\frac{3}{3x-7}\right) = \frac{3}{(\ln 5)(3x-7)}$

9. $y = 8^{-t} \Rightarrow \frac{dy}{dt} = 8^{-t}(\ln 8)(-1) = -8^{-t}(\ln 8)$
   
   10. $y = 9^{2t} \Rightarrow \frac{dy}{dt} = 9^{2t}(\ln 9)(2) = 9^{2t}(2\ln 9)$

11. $y = 5x^{3.6} \Rightarrow \frac{dy}{dx} = 5(3.6)x^{2.6} = 18x^{2.6}$

12. $y = \sqrt{2}\,x^{-\sqrt{2}} \Rightarrow \frac{dy}{dx} = \left(\sqrt{2}\right)\left(-\sqrt{2}\right)x^{\left(-\sqrt{2}-1\right)} = -2x^{\left(-\sqrt{2}-1\right)}$

13. $y = (x + 2)^{x+2} \Rightarrow \ln y = \ln(x + 2)^{x+2} = (x + 2)\ln(x + 2) \Rightarrow \frac{y'}{y} = (x + 2)\left(\frac{1}{x+2}\right) + (1)\ln(x + 2)$
    $\Rightarrow \frac{dy}{dx} = (x + 2)^{x+2}\left[\ln(x + 2) + 1\right]$

14. $y = 2(\ln x)^{x/2} \Rightarrow \ln y = \ln\left[2(\ln x)^{x/2}\right] = \ln(2) + \left(\frac{x}{2}\right)\ln(\ln x) \Rightarrow \frac{y'}{y} = 0 + \left(\frac{x}{2}\right)\left[\frac{\left(\frac{1}{x}\right)}{\ln x}\right] + (\ln(\ln x))\left(\frac{1}{2}\right)$
    $\Rightarrow y' = \left[\frac{1}{2\ln x} + \left(\frac{1}{2}\right)\ln(\ln x)\right]2(\ln x)^{x/2} = (\ln x)^{x/2}\left[\ln(\ln x) + \frac{1}{\ln x}\right]$

15. $y = \sin^{-1}\sqrt{1 - u^2} = \sin^{-1}\left(1 - u^2\right)^{1/2} \Rightarrow \frac{dy}{du} = \frac{\frac{1}{2}\left(1 - u^2\right)^{-1/2}(-2u)}{\sqrt{1 - \left[\left(1-u^2\right)^{1/2}\right]^2}} = \frac{-u}{\sqrt{1 - u^2}\sqrt{1 - \left(1 - u^2\right)}} = \frac{-u}{|u|\sqrt{1 - u^2}}$
    $= \frac{-u}{u\sqrt{1 - u^2}} = \frac{-1}{\sqrt{1 - u^2}}, \; 0 < u < 1$

16. $y = \sin^{-1}\left(\frac{1}{\sqrt{v}}\right) = \sin^{-1}v^{-1/2} \Rightarrow \frac{dy}{dv} = \frac{-\frac{1}{2}v^{-3/2}}{\sqrt{1 - \left(v^{-1/2}\right)^2}} = \frac{-1}{2v^{3/2}\sqrt{1 - v^{-1}}} = \frac{-1}{2v^{3/2}\sqrt{\frac{v-1}{v}}} = \frac{-\sqrt{v}}{2v^{3/2}\sqrt{v - 1}} = \frac{-1}{2v\sqrt{v - 1}}$

17. $y = \ln\left(\cos^{-1}x\right) \Rightarrow y' = \frac{\left(\frac{-1}{\sqrt{1-x^2}}\right)}{\cos^{-1}x} = \frac{-1}{\sqrt{1 - x^2}\cos^{-1}x}$

18. $y = z \cos^{-1} z - \sqrt{1 - z^2} = z \cos^{-1} z - (1 - z^2)^{1/2} \Rightarrow \frac{dy}{dz} = \cos^{-1} z - \frac{z}{\sqrt{1-z^2}} - \left(\frac{1}{2}\right)(1 - z^2)^{-1/2}(-2z)$

$= \cos^{-1} z - \frac{z}{\sqrt{1-z^2}} + \frac{z}{\sqrt{1-z^2}} = \cos^{-1} z$

19. $y = t \tan^{-1} t - \left(\frac{1}{2}\right) \ln t \Rightarrow \frac{dy}{dt} = \tan^{-1} t + t\left(\frac{1}{1+t^2}\right) - \left(\frac{1}{2}\right)\left(\frac{1}{t}\right) = \tan^{-1} t + \frac{t}{1+t^2} - \frac{1}{2t}$

20. $y = (1 + t^2) \cot^{-1} 2t \Rightarrow \frac{dy}{dt} = 2t \cot^{-1} 2t + (1 + t^2)\left(\frac{-2}{1+4t^2}\right)$

21. $y = z \sec^{-1} z - \sqrt{z^2 - 1} = z \sec^{-1} z - (z^2 - 1)^{1/2} \Rightarrow \frac{dy}{dz} = z\left(\frac{1}{|z|\sqrt{z^2-1}}\right) + (\sec^{-1} z)(1) - \frac{1}{2}(z^2 - 1)^{-1/2}(2z)$

$= \frac{z}{|z|\sqrt{z^2-1}} - \frac{z}{\sqrt{z^2-1}} + \sec^{-1} z = \frac{1-z}{\sqrt{z^2-1}} + \sec^{-1} z, z > 1$

22. $y = 2\sqrt{x - 1} \sec^{-1} \sqrt{x} = 2(x - 1)^{1/2} \sec^{-1} \left(x^{1/2}\right)$

$\Rightarrow \frac{dy}{dx} = 2\left[\left(\frac{1}{2}\right)(x - 1)^{-1/2} \sec^{-1}\left(x^{1/2}\right) + (x - 1)^{1/2}\left(\frac{\left(\frac{1}{2}\right)x^{-1/2}}{\sqrt{x}\sqrt{x-1}}\right)\right] = 2\left(\frac{\sec^{-1}\sqrt{x}}{2\sqrt{x-1}} + \frac{1}{2x}\right) = \frac{\sec^{-1}\sqrt{x}}{\sqrt{x-1}} + \frac{1}{x}$

23. $y = \csc^{-1}(\sec\theta) \Rightarrow \frac{dy}{d\theta} = \frac{-\sec\theta\tan\theta}{|\sec\theta|\sqrt{\sec^2\theta - 1}} = -\frac{\tan\theta}{|\tan\theta|} = -1, 0 < \theta < \frac{\pi}{2}$

24. $y = (1 + x^2) e^{\tan^{-1} x} \Rightarrow y' = 2xe^{\tan^{-1} x} + (1 + x^2)\left(\frac{e^{\tan^{-1} x}}{1 + x^2}\right) = 2xe^{\tan^{-1} x} + e^{\tan^{-1} x}$

25. $y = \frac{2(x^2 + 1)}{\sqrt{\cos 2x}} \Rightarrow \ln y = \ln\left(\frac{2(x^2 + 1)}{\sqrt{\cos 2x}}\right) = \ln(2) + \ln(x^2 + 1) - \frac{1}{2}\ln(\cos 2x) \Rightarrow \frac{y'}{y} = 0 + \frac{2x}{x^2+1} - \left(\frac{1}{2}\right)\frac{(-2\sin 2x)}{\cos 2x}$

$\Rightarrow y' = \left(\frac{2x}{x^2+1} + \tan 2x\right) y = \frac{2(x^2 + 1)}{\sqrt{\cos 2x}}\left(\frac{2x}{x^2+1} + \tan 2x\right)$

26. $y = \sqrt[10]{\frac{3x + 4}{2x - 4}} \Rightarrow \ln y = \ln \sqrt[10]{\frac{3x + 4}{2x - 4}} = \frac{1}{10}\left[\ln(3x + 4) - \ln(2x - 4)\right] \Rightarrow \frac{y'}{y} = \frac{1}{10}\left(\frac{3}{3x+4} - \frac{2}{2x-4}\right)$

$\Rightarrow y' = \frac{1}{10}\left(\frac{3}{3x+4} - \frac{1}{x-2}\right) y = \sqrt[10]{\frac{3x + 4}{2x - 4}}\left(\frac{1}{10}\right)\left(\frac{3}{3x+4} - \frac{1}{x-2}\right)$

27. $y = \left[\frac{(t + 1)(t - 1)}{(t - 2)(t + 3)}\right]^5 \Rightarrow \ln y = 5\left[\ln(t + 1) + \ln(t - 1) - \ln(t - 2) - \ln(t + 3)\right] \Rightarrow \left(\frac{1}{y}\right)\left(\frac{dy}{dt}\right)$

$= 5\left(\frac{1}{t+1} + \frac{1}{t-1} - \frac{1}{t-2} - \frac{1}{t+3}\right) \Rightarrow \frac{dy}{dt} = 5\left[\frac{(t + 1)(t - 1)}{(t - 2)(t + 3)}\right]^5\left(\frac{1}{t+1} + \frac{1}{t-1} - \frac{1}{t-2} - \frac{1}{t+3}\right)$

28. $y = \frac{2u2^u}{\sqrt{u^2 + 1}} \Rightarrow \ln y = \ln 2 + \ln u + u \ln 2 - \frac{1}{2}\ln(u^2 + 1) \Rightarrow \left(\frac{1}{y}\right)\left(\frac{dy}{du}\right) = \frac{1}{u} + \ln 2 - \frac{1}{2}\left(\frac{2u}{u^2+1}\right)$

$\Rightarrow \frac{dy}{du} = \frac{2u2^u}{\sqrt{u^2 + 1}}\left(\frac{1}{u} + \ln 2 - \frac{u}{u^2+1}\right)$

29. $y = (\sin\theta)^{\sqrt{\theta}} \Rightarrow \ln y = \sqrt{\theta} \ln(\sin\theta) \Rightarrow \left(\frac{1}{y}\right)\left(\frac{dy}{d\theta}\right) = \sqrt{\theta}\left(\frac{\cos\theta}{\sin\theta}\right) + \frac{1}{2}\theta^{-1/2}\ln(\sin\theta)$

$\Rightarrow \frac{dy}{d\theta} = (\sin\theta)^{\sqrt{\theta}}\left(\sqrt{\theta}\cot\theta + \frac{\ln(\sin\theta)}{2\sqrt{\theta}}\right)$

30. $y = (\ln x)^{1/\ln x} \Rightarrow \ln y = \left(\frac{1}{\ln x}\right)\ln(\ln x) \Rightarrow \frac{y'}{y} = \left(\frac{1}{\ln x}\right)\left(\frac{1}{\ln x}\right)\left(\frac{1}{x}\right) + \ln(\ln x)\left[\frac{-1}{(\ln x)^2}\right]\left(\frac{1}{x}\right)$

$\Rightarrow y' = (\ln x)^{1/\ln x}\left[\frac{1 - \ln(\ln x)}{x(\ln x)^2}\right]$

31. $\int e^x \sin(e^x) \, dx = \int \sin u \, du$, where $u = e^x$ and $du = e^x \, dx$

$= -\cos u + C = -\cos(e^x) + C$

32. $\int e^t \cos(3e^t - 2) \, dt = \frac{1}{3} \int \cos u \, du$, where $u = 3e^t - 2$ and $du = 3e^t \, dt$

$= \frac{1}{3} \sin u + C = \frac{1}{3} \sin(3e^t - 2) + C$

33. $\int e^x \sec^2(e^x - 7) \, dx = \int \sec^2 u \, du$, where $u = e^x - 7$ and $du = e^x \, dx$

$= \tan u + C = \tan(e^x - 7) + C$

34. $\int e^y \csc(e^y + 1) \cot(e^y + 1) \, dy = \int \csc u \cot u \, du$, where $u = e^y + 1$ and $du = e^y \, dy$

$= -\csc u + C = -\csc(e^y + 1) + C$

35. $\int (\sec^2 x) e^{\tan x} \, dx = \int e^u \, du$, where $u = \tan x$ and $du = \sec^2 x \, dx$

$= e^u + C = e^{\tan x} + C$

36. $\int (\csc^2 x) e^{\cot x} \, dx = -\int e^u \, du$, where $u = \cot x$ and $du = -\csc^2 x \, dx$

$= -e^u + C = -e^{\cot x} + C$

37. $\int_{-1}^{1} \frac{1}{3x-4} \, dx = \frac{1}{3} \int_{-7}^{-1} \frac{1}{u} \, du$, where $u = 3x - 4$, $du = 3 \, dx$; $x = -1 \Rightarrow u = -7$, $x = 1 \Rightarrow u = -1$

$= \frac{1}{3} \left[ \ln|u| \right]_{-7}^{-1} = \frac{1}{3} \left[ \ln|-1| - \ln|-7| \right] = \frac{1}{3} [0 - \ln 7] = -\frac{\ln 7}{3}$

38. $\int_{1}^{e} \frac{\sqrt{\ln x}}{x} \, dx = \int_{0}^{1} u^{1/2} \, du$, where $u = \ln x$, $du = \frac{1}{x} \, dx$; $x = 1 \Rightarrow u = 0$, $x = e \Rightarrow u = 1$

$= \left[ \frac{2}{3} u^{3/2} \right]_{0}^{1} = \left[ \frac{2}{3} 1^{3/2} - \frac{2}{3} 0^{3/2} \right] = \frac{2}{3}$

39. $\int_{0}^{\pi} \tan\left(\frac{x}{3}\right) dx = \int_{0}^{\pi} \frac{\sin\left(\frac{x}{3}\right)}{\cos\left(\frac{x}{3}\right)} \, dx = -3 \int_{1}^{1/2} \frac{1}{u} \, du$, where $u = \cos\left(\frac{x}{3}\right)$, $du = -\frac{1}{3} \sin\left(\frac{x}{3}\right) dx$; $x = 0 \Rightarrow u = 1$, $x = \pi$

$\Rightarrow u = \frac{1}{2}$

$= -3 \left[ \ln|u| \right]_{1}^{1/2} = -3 \left[ \ln\left|\frac{1}{2}\right| - \ln|1| \right] = -3 \ln\frac{1}{2} = \ln 2^3 = \ln 8$

40. $\int_{1/6}^{1/4} 2 \cot \pi x \, dx = 2 \int_{1/6}^{1/4} \frac{\cos \pi x}{\sin \pi x} \, dx = \frac{2}{\pi} \int_{1/2}^{1/\sqrt{2}} \frac{1}{u} \, du$, where $u = \sin \pi x$, $du = \pi \cos \pi x \, dx$; $x = \frac{1}{6} \Rightarrow u = \frac{1}{2}$, $x = \frac{1}{4}$

$\Rightarrow u = \frac{1}{\sqrt{2}}$

$= \frac{2}{\pi} \left[ \ln|u| \right]_{1/2}^{1/\sqrt{2}} = \frac{2}{\pi} \left[ \ln\left|\frac{1}{\sqrt{2}}\right| - \ln\left|\frac{1}{2}\right| \right] = \frac{2}{\pi} \left[ \ln 1 - \frac{1}{2} \ln 2 - \ln 1 + \ln 2 \right] = \frac{2}{\pi} \left[ \frac{1}{2} \ln 2 \right] = \frac{\ln 2}{\pi}$

41. $\int_{0}^{4} \frac{2t}{t^2 - 25} \, dt = \int_{-25}^{-9} \frac{1}{u} \, du$, where $u = t^2 - 25$, $du = 2t \, dt$; $t = 0 \Rightarrow u = -25$, $t = 4 \Rightarrow u = -9$

$= \left[ \ln|u| \right]_{-25}^{-9} = \ln|-9| - \ln|-25| = \ln 9 - \ln 25 = \ln\frac{9}{25}$

42. $\int_{-\pi/2}^{\pi/6} \frac{\cos t}{1 - \sin t} \, dt = -\int_{2}^{1/2} \frac{1}{u} \, du$, where $u = 1 - \sin t$, $du = -\cos t \, dt$; $t = -\frac{\pi}{2} \Rightarrow u = 2$, $t = \frac{\pi}{6} \Rightarrow u = \frac{1}{2}$

$= -\left[ \ln|u| \right]_{2}^{1/2} = -\left[ \ln\left|\frac{1}{2}\right| - \ln|2| \right] = -\ln 1 + \ln 2 + \ln 2 = 2 \ln 2 = \ln 4$

43. $\int \frac{\tan(\ln v)}{v} \, dv = \int \tan u \, du = \int \frac{\sin u}{\cos u} \, du$, where $u = \ln v$ and $du = \frac{1}{v} \, dv$

$= -\ln|\cos u| + C = -\ln|\cos(\ln v)| + C$

44. $\int \frac{1}{v \ln v} \, dv = \int \frac{1}{u} \, du$, where $u = \ln v$ and $du = \frac{1}{v} \, dv$

$= \ln|u| + C = \ln|\ln v| + C$

45. $\int \frac{(\ln x)^{-3}}{x}\, dx = \int u^{-3}\, du$, where $u = \ln x$ and $du = \frac{1}{x}\, dx$

$\quad = \frac{u^{-2}}{-2} + C = -\frac{1}{2}(\ln x)^{-2} + C$

46. $\int \frac{\ln(x-5)}{x-5}\, dx = \int u\, du$, where $u = \ln(x-5)$ and $du = \frac{1}{x-5}\, dx$

$\quad = \frac{u^2}{2} + C = \frac{[\ln(x-5)]^2}{2} + C$

47. $\int \frac{1}{r}\csc^2(1 + \ln r)\, dr = \int \csc^2 u\, du$, where $u = 1 + \ln r$ and $du = \frac{1}{r}\, dr$

$\quad = -\cot u + C = -\cot(1 + \ln r) + C$

48. $\int \frac{\cos(1 - \ln v)}{v}\, dv = -\int \cos u\, du$, where $u = 1 - \ln v$ and $du = -\frac{1}{v}\, dv$

$\quad = -\sin u + C = -\sin(1 - \ln v) + C$

49. $\int x3^{x^2}\, dx = \frac{1}{2}\int 3^u\, du$, where $u = x^2$ and $du = 2x\, dx$

$\quad = \frac{1}{2\ln 3}(3^u) + C = \frac{1}{2\ln 3}\left(3^{x^2}\right) + C$

50. $\int 2^{\tan x}\sec^2 x\, dx = \int 2^u\, du$, where $u = \tan x$ and $du = \sec^2 x\, dx$

$\quad = \frac{1}{\ln 2}(2^u) + C = \frac{2^{\tan x}}{\ln 2} + C$

51. $\int_1^7 \frac{3}{x}\, dx = 3\int_1^7 \frac{1}{x}\, dx = 3\left[\ln|x|\right]_1^7 = 3(\ln 7 - \ln 1) = 3\ln 7$

52. $\int_1^{32} \frac{1}{5x}\, dx = \frac{1}{5}\int_1^{32} \frac{1}{x}\, dx = \frac{1}{5}\left[\ln|x|\right]_1^{32} = \frac{1}{5}(\ln 32 - \ln 1) = \frac{1}{5}\ln 32 = \ln\left(\sqrt[5]{32}\right) = \ln 2$

53. $\int_1^4 \left(\frac{x}{8} + \frac{1}{2x}\right) dx = \frac{1}{2}\int_1^4 \left(\frac{1}{4}x + \frac{1}{x}\right) dx = \frac{1}{2}\left[\frac{1}{8}x^2 + \ln|x|\right]_1^4 = \frac{1}{2}\left[\left(\frac{16}{8} + \ln 4\right) - \left(\frac{1}{8} + \ln 1\right)\right] = \frac{15}{16} + \frac{1}{2}\ln 4$

$\quad = \frac{15}{16} + \ln\sqrt{4} = \frac{15}{16} + \ln 2$

54. $\int_1^8 \left(\frac{2}{3x} - \frac{8}{x^2}\right) dx = \frac{2}{3}\int_1^8 \left(\frac{1}{x} - 12x^{-2}\right) dx = \frac{2}{3}\left[\ln|x| + 12x^{-1}\right]_1^8 = \frac{2}{3}\left[\left(\ln 8 + \frac{12}{8}\right) - (\ln 1 + 12)\right]$

$\quad = \frac{2}{3}\left(\ln 8 + \frac{3}{2} - 12\right) = \frac{2}{3}\left(\ln 8 - \frac{21}{2}\right) = \frac{2}{3}(\ln 8) - 7 = \ln\left(8^{2/3}\right) - 7 = \ln 4 - 7$

55. $\int_{-2}^{-1} e^{-(x+1)}\, dx = -\int_1^0 e^u\, du$, where $u = -(x+1)$, $du = -dx$; $x = -2 \Rightarrow u = 1$, $x = -1 \Rightarrow u = 0$

$\quad = -\left[e^u\right]_1^0 = -(e^0 - e^1) = e - 1$

56. $\int_{-\ln 2}^0 e^{2w}\, dw = \frac{1}{2}\int_{\ln(1/4)}^0 e^u\, du$, where $u = 2w$, $du = 2\, dw$; $w = -\ln 2 \Rightarrow u = \ln\frac{1}{4}$, $w = 0 \Rightarrow u = 0$

$\quad = \frac{1}{2}\left[e^u\right]_{\ln(1/4)}^0 = \frac{1}{2}\left[e^0 - e^{\ln(1/4)}\right] = \frac{1}{2}\left(1 - \frac{1}{4}\right) = \frac{3}{8}$

57. $\int_1^{\ln 5} e^r(3e^r + 1)^{-3/2}\, dr = \frac{1}{3}\int_4^{16} u^{-3/2}\, du$, where $u = 3e^r + 1$, $du = 3e^r dr$; $r = 0 \Rightarrow u = 4$, $r = \ln 5 \Rightarrow u = 16$

$\quad = -\frac{2}{3}\left[u^{-1/2}\right]_4^{16} = -\frac{2}{3}\left(16^{-1/2} - 4^{-1/2}\right) = \left(-\frac{2}{3}\right)\left(\frac{1}{4} - \frac{1}{2}\right) = \left(-\frac{2}{3}\right)\left(-\frac{1}{4}\right) = \frac{1}{6}$

58. $\int_0^{\ln 9} e^\theta(e^\theta - 1)^{1/2}\, d\theta = \int_0^8 u^{1/2}\, du$, where $u = e^\theta - 1$, $du = e^\theta d\theta$; $\theta = 0 \Rightarrow u = 0$, $\theta = \ln 9 \Rightarrow u = 8$

$\quad = \frac{2}{3}\left[u^{3/2}\right]_0^8 = \frac{2}{3}\left(8^{3/2} - 0^{3/2}\right) = \frac{2}{3}\left(2^{9/2} - 0\right) = \frac{2^{11/2}}{3} = \frac{32\sqrt{2}}{3}$

**59.** $\int_1^e \frac{1}{x}(1+7\ln x)^{-1/3}\,dx = \frac{1}{7}\int_1^8 u^{-1/3}\,du$, where $u = 1 + 7\ln x$, $du = \frac{7}{x}\,dx$, $x = 1 \Rightarrow u = 1$, $x = e \Rightarrow u = 8$

$= \frac{3}{14}\left[u^{2/3}\right]_1^8 = \frac{3}{14}\left(8^{2/3} - 1^{2/3}\right) = \left(\frac{3}{14}\right)(4-1) = \frac{9}{14}$

**60.** $\int_e^{e^2} \frac{1}{x\sqrt{\ln x}}\,dx = \int_e^{e^2}(\ln x)^{-1/2}\frac{1}{x}\,dx = \int_1^2 u^{-1/2}\,du$, where $u = \ln x$, $du = \frac{1}{x}\,dx$; $x = e \Rightarrow u = 1$, $x = e^2 \Rightarrow u = 2$

$= 2\left[u^{1/2}\right]_1^2 = 2\left(\sqrt{2} - 1\right) = 2\sqrt{2} - 2$

**61.** $\int_1^3 \frac{[\ln(v+1)]^2}{v+1}\,dv = \int_1^3 [\ln(v+1)]^2\,\frac{1}{v+1}\,dv = \int_{\ln 2}^{\ln 4} u^2\,du$, where $u = \ln(v+1)$, $du = \frac{1}{v+1}\,dv$;

$v = 1 \Rightarrow u = \ln 2$, $v = 3 \Rightarrow u = \ln 4$;

$= \frac{1}{3}\left[u^3\right]_{\ln 2}^{\ln 4} = \frac{1}{3}\left[(\ln 4)^3 - (\ln 2)^3\right] = \frac{1}{3}\left[(2\ln 2)^3 - (\ln 2)^3\right] = \frac{(\ln 2)^3}{3}(8-1) = \frac{7}{3}(\ln 2)^3$

**62.** $\int_2^4 (1+\ln t)(t\ln t)\,dt = \int_2^4 (t\ln t)(1+\ln t)\,dt = \int_{2\ln 2}^{4\ln 4} u\,du$, where $u = t\ln t$, $du = \left((t)\left(\frac{1}{t}\right) + (\ln t)(1)\right)dt$

$= (1 + \ln t)\,dt$; $t = 2 \Rightarrow u = 2\ln 2$, $t = 4$

$\Rightarrow u = 4\ln 4$

$= \frac{1}{2}\left[u^2\right]_{2\ln 2}^{4\ln 4} = \frac{1}{2}\left[(4\ln 4)^2 - (2\ln 2)^2\right] = \frac{1}{2}\left[(8\ln 2)^2 - (2\ln 2)^2\right] = \frac{(2\ln 2)^2}{2}(16-1) = 30(\ln 2)^2$

**63.** $\int_1^8 \frac{\log_4 \theta}{\theta}\,d\theta = \frac{1}{\ln 4}\int_1^8 (\ln\theta)\left(\frac{1}{\theta}\right)d\theta = \frac{1}{\ln 4}\int_0^{\ln 8} u\,du$, where $u = \ln\theta$, $du = \frac{1}{\theta}\,d\theta$, $\theta = 1 \Rightarrow u = 0$, $\theta = 8 \Rightarrow u = \ln 8$

$= \frac{1}{2\ln 4}\left[u^2\right]_0^{\ln 8} = \frac{1}{\ln 16}\left[(\ln 8)^2 - 0^2\right] = \frac{(3\ln 2)^2}{4\ln 2} = \frac{9\ln 2}{4}$

**64.** $\int_1^e \frac{8(\ln 3)(\log_3 \theta)}{\theta}\,d\theta = \int_1^e \frac{8(\ln 3)(\ln\theta)}{\theta(\ln 3)}\,d\theta = 8\int_1^e (\ln\theta)\left(\frac{1}{\theta}\right)d\theta = 8\int_0^1 u\,du$, where $u = \ln\theta$, $du = \frac{1}{\theta}\,d\theta$;

$\theta = 1 \Rightarrow u = 0$, $\theta = e \Rightarrow u = 1$

$= 4\left[u^2\right]_0^1 = 4\left(1^2 - 0^2\right) = 4$

**65.** $\int_{-3/4}^{3/4} \frac{6}{\sqrt{9-4x^2}}\,dx = 3\int_{-3/4}^{3/4} \frac{2}{\sqrt{3^2-(2x)^2}}\,dx = 3\int_{-3/2}^{3/2} \frac{1}{\sqrt{3^2-u^2}}\,du$, where $u = 2x$, $du = 2\,dx$;

$x = -\frac{3}{4} \Rightarrow u = -\frac{3}{2}$, $x = \frac{3}{4} \Rightarrow u = \frac{3}{2}$

$= 3\left[\sin^{-1}\left(\frac{u}{3}\right)\right]_{-3/2}^{3/2} = 3\left[\sin^{-1}\left(\frac{1}{2}\right) - \sin^{-1}\left(-\frac{1}{2}\right)\right] = 3\left[\frac{\pi}{6} - \left(-\frac{\pi}{6}\right)\right] = 3\left(\frac{\pi}{3}\right) = \pi$

**66.** $\int_{-1/5}^{1/5} \frac{6}{\sqrt{4-25x^2}}\,dx = \frac{6}{5}\int_{-1/5}^{1/5} \frac{5}{\sqrt{2^2-(5x)^2}}\,dx = \frac{6}{5}\int_{-1}^{1} \frac{1}{\sqrt{2^2-u^2}}\,du$, where $u = 5x$, $du = 5\,dx$;

$x = -\frac{1}{5} \Rightarrow u = -1$, $x = \frac{1}{5} \Rightarrow u = 1$

$= \frac{6}{5}\left[\sin^{-1}\left(\frac{u}{2}\right)\right]_{-1}^{1} = \frac{6}{5}\left[\sin^{-1}\left(\frac{1}{2}\right) - \sin^{-1}\left(-\frac{1}{2}\right)\right] = \frac{6}{5}\left[\frac{\pi}{6} - \left(-\frac{\pi}{6}\right)\right] = \frac{6}{5}\left(\frac{\pi}{3}\right) = \frac{2\pi}{5}$

**67.** $\int_{-2}^{2} \frac{3}{4+3t^2}\,dt = \sqrt{3}\int_{-2}^{2} \frac{\sqrt{3}}{2^2+\left(\sqrt{3}t\right)^2}\,dt = \sqrt{3}\int_{-2\sqrt{3}}^{2\sqrt{3}} \frac{1}{2^2+u^2}\,du$, where $u = \sqrt{3}t$, $du = \sqrt{3}\,dt$;

$t = -2 \Rightarrow u = -2\sqrt{3}$, $t = 2 \Rightarrow u = 2\sqrt{3}$

$= \sqrt{3}\left[\frac{1}{2}\tan^{-1}\left(\frac{u}{2}\right)\right]_{-2\sqrt{3}}^{2\sqrt{3}} = \frac{\sqrt{3}}{2}\left[\tan^{-1}\left(\sqrt{3}\right) - \tan^{-1}\left(-\sqrt{3}\right)\right] = \frac{\sqrt{3}}{2}\left[\frac{\pi}{3} - \left(-\frac{\pi}{3}\right)\right] = \frac{\pi}{\sqrt{3}}$

**68.** $\int_{\sqrt{3}}^{3} \frac{1}{3+t^2}\,dt = \int_{\sqrt{3}}^{3} \frac{1}{\left(\sqrt{3}\right)^2+t^2}\,dt = \left[\frac{1}{\sqrt{3}}\tan^{-1}\left(\frac{t}{\sqrt{3}}\right)\right]_{\sqrt{3}}^{3} = \frac{1}{\sqrt{3}}\left(\tan^{-1}\sqrt{3} - \tan^{-1}1\right) = \frac{1}{\sqrt{3}}\left(\frac{\pi}{3} - \frac{\pi}{4}\right) = \frac{\sqrt{3}\pi}{36}$

**69.** $\int \frac{1}{y\sqrt{4y^2-1}}\,dy = \int \frac{2}{(2y)\sqrt{(2y)^2-1}}\,dy = \int \frac{1}{u\sqrt{u^2-1}}\,du$, where $u = 2y$ and $du = 2\,dy$

$= \sec^{-1}|u| + C = \sec^{-1}|2y| + C$

70. $\int \frac{24}{y\sqrt{y^2-16}}\,dy = 24\int \frac{1}{y\sqrt{y^2-4^2}}\,dy = 24\left(\frac{1}{4}\sec^{-1}\left|\frac{y}{4}\right|\right) + C = 6\sec^{-1}\left|\frac{y}{4}\right| + C$

71. $\int_{\sqrt{2}/3}^{2/3} \frac{1}{|y|\sqrt{9y^2-1}}\,dy = \int_{\sqrt{2}/3}^{2/3} \frac{3}{|3y|\sqrt{(3y)^2-1}}\,dy = \int_{\sqrt{2}}^{2} \frac{1}{|u|\sqrt{u^2-1}}\,du$, where $u = 3y$, $du = 3\,dy$;

$$y = \frac{\sqrt{2}}{3} \Rightarrow u = \sqrt{2}, y = \frac{2}{3} \Rightarrow u = 2$$

$$= \left[\sec^{-1} u\right]_{\sqrt{2}}^{2} = \left[\sec^{-1} 2 - \sec^{-1}\sqrt{2}\right] = \frac{\pi}{3} - \frac{\pi}{4} = \frac{\pi}{12}$$

72. $\int_{-2/\sqrt{5}}^{-\sqrt{6}/\sqrt{5}} \frac{1}{|y|\sqrt{5y^2-3}}\,dy = \int_{-2/\sqrt{5}}^{-\sqrt{6}/\sqrt{5}} \frac{\sqrt{5}}{-\sqrt{5}y\sqrt{\left(\sqrt{5}y\right)^2-\left(\sqrt{3}\right)^2}}\,dy = \int_{-2}^{-\sqrt{6}} \frac{1}{-u\sqrt{u^2-\left(\sqrt{3}\right)^2}}\,du$,

where $u = \sqrt{5}y$, $du = \sqrt{5}\,dy$; $y = -\frac{2}{\sqrt{5}} \Rightarrow u = -2, y = -\frac{\sqrt{6}}{\sqrt{5}} \Rightarrow u = -\sqrt{6}$

$$= \left[-\frac{1}{\sqrt{3}}\sec^{-1}\left|\frac{u}{\sqrt{3}}\right|\right]_{-2}^{-\sqrt{6}} = \frac{-1}{\sqrt{3}}\left[\sec^{-1}\sqrt{2} - \sec^{-1}\frac{2}{\sqrt{3}}\right] = \frac{-1}{\sqrt{3}}\left(\frac{\pi}{4} - \frac{\pi}{6}\right) = \frac{-1}{\sqrt{3}}\left[\frac{3\pi}{12} - \frac{2\pi}{12}\right] = \frac{-\pi}{12\sqrt{3}} = \frac{-\sqrt{3}\pi}{36}$$

73. $\int \frac{1}{\sqrt{-2x-x^2}}\,dx = \int \frac{1}{\sqrt{1-(x^2+2x+1)}}\,dx = \int \frac{1}{\sqrt{1-(x+1)^2}}\,dx = \int \frac{1}{\sqrt{1-u^2}}\,du$, where $u = x+1$ and

$$du = dx$$

$$= \sin^{-1} u + C = \sin^{-1}(x+1) + C$$

74. $\int \frac{1}{\sqrt{-x^2+4x-1}}\,dx = \int \frac{1}{\sqrt{3-(x^2-4x+4)}}\,dx = \int \frac{1}{\sqrt{\left(\sqrt{3}\right)^2-(x-2)^2}}\,dx = \int \frac{1}{\sqrt{\left(\sqrt{3}\right)^2-u^2}}\,du$

$$\text{where } u = x-2 \text{ and } du = dx$$

$$= \sin^{-1}\left(\frac{u}{\sqrt{3}}\right) + C = \sin^{-1}\left(\frac{x-2}{\sqrt{3}}\right) + C$$

75. $\int_{-2}^{-1} \frac{2}{v^2+4v+5}\,dv = 2\int_{-2}^{-1} \frac{1}{1+(v^2+4v+4)}\,dv = 2\int_{-2}^{-1} \frac{1}{1+(v+2)^2}\,dv = 2\int_{0}^{1} \frac{1}{1+u^2}\,du$,

$$\text{where } u = v+2, du = dv; v = -2 \Rightarrow u = 0, v = -1 \Rightarrow u = 1$$

$$= 2\left[\tan^{-1} u\right]_{0}^{1} = 2\left(\tan^{-1} 1 - \tan^{-1} 0\right) = 2\left(\frac{\pi}{4} - 0\right) = \frac{\pi}{2}$$

76. $\int_{-1}^{1} \frac{3}{4v^2+4v+4}\,dv = \frac{3}{4}\int_{-1}^{1} \frac{1}{\frac{3}{4}+\left(v^2+v+\frac{1}{4}\right)}\,dv = \frac{3}{4}\int_{-1}^{1} \frac{1}{\left(\frac{\sqrt{3}}{2}\right)^2+\left(v+\frac{1}{2}\right)^2}\,dv = \frac{3}{4}\int_{-1/2}^{3/2} \frac{1}{\left(\frac{\sqrt{3}}{2}\right)^2+u^2}\,du$

$$\text{where } u = v+\frac{1}{2}, du = dv; v = -1 \Rightarrow u = -\frac{1}{2}, v = 1 \Rightarrow u = \frac{3}{2}$$

$$= \frac{3}{4}\left[\frac{2}{\sqrt{3}}\tan^{-1}\left(\frac{2u}{\sqrt{3}}\right)\right]_{-1/2}^{3/2} = \frac{\sqrt{3}}{2}\left[\tan^{-1}\sqrt{3} - \tan^{-1}\left(-\frac{1}{\sqrt{3}}\right)\right] = \frac{\sqrt{3}}{2}\left[\frac{\pi}{3} - \left(-\frac{\pi}{6}\right)\right] = \frac{\sqrt{3}}{2}\left(\frac{2\pi}{6} + \frac{\pi}{6}\right) = \frac{\sqrt{3}}{2}\cdot\frac{\pi}{2}$$

$$= \frac{\sqrt{3}\pi}{4}$$

77. $\int \frac{1}{(t+1)\sqrt{t^2+2t-8}}\,dt = \int \frac{1}{(t+1)\sqrt{(t^2+2t+1)-9}}\,dt = \int \frac{1}{(t+1)\sqrt{(t+1)^2-3^2}}\,dt = \int \frac{1}{u\sqrt{u^2-3^2}}\,du$

$$\text{where } u = t+1 \text{ and } du = dt$$

$$= \frac{1}{3}\sec^{-1}\left|\frac{u}{3}\right| + C = \frac{1}{3}\sec^{-1}\left|\frac{t+1}{3}\right| + C$$

78. $\int \frac{1}{(3t+1)\sqrt{9t^2+6t}}\,dt = \int \frac{1}{(3t+1)\sqrt{(9t^2+6t+1)-1}}\,dt = \int \frac{1}{(3t+1)\sqrt{(3t+1)^2-1^2}}\,dt = \frac{1}{3}\int \frac{1}{u\sqrt{u^2-1}}\,du$

$$\text{where } u = 3t+1 \text{ and } du = 3\,dt$$

$$= \frac{1}{3}\sec^{-1}|u| + C = \frac{1}{3}\sec^{-1}|3t+1| + C$$

79. $3^y = 2^{y+1} \Rightarrow \ln 3^y = \ln 2^{y+1} \Rightarrow y(\ln 3) = (y+1)\ln 2 \Rightarrow (\ln 3 - \ln 2)y = \ln 2 \Rightarrow \left(\ln\frac{3}{2}\right)y = \ln 2 \Rightarrow y = \frac{\ln 2}{\ln\left(\frac{3}{2}\right)}$

80. $4^{-y} = 3^{y+2} \Rightarrow \ln 4^{-y} = \ln 3^{y+2} \Rightarrow -y \ln 4 = (y+2) \ln 3 \Rightarrow -2 \ln 3 = (\ln 3 + \ln 4)y \Rightarrow (\ln 12)y = -2 \ln 3$

$\Rightarrow y = -\frac{\ln 9}{\ln 12}$

81. $9e^{2y} = x^2 \Rightarrow e^{2y} = \frac{x^2}{9} \Rightarrow \ln e^{2y} = \ln\left(\frac{x^2}{9}\right) \Rightarrow 2y(\ln e) = \ln\left(\frac{x^2}{9}\right) \Rightarrow y = \frac{1}{2}\ln\left(\frac{x^2}{9}\right) = \ln\sqrt{\frac{x^2}{9}} = \ln\left|\frac{x}{3}\right| = \ln|x| - \ln 3$

82. $3^y = 3 \ln x \Rightarrow \ln 3^y = \ln(3 \ln x) \Rightarrow y \ln 3 = \ln(3 \ln x) \Rightarrow y = \frac{\ln(3 \ln x)}{\ln 3} = \frac{\ln 3 + \ln(\ln x)}{\ln 3}$

83. $\ln(y-1) = x + \ln y \Rightarrow e^{\ln(y-1)} = e^{(x+\ln y)} = e^x e^{\ln y} \Rightarrow y - 1 = ye^x \Rightarrow y - ye^x = 1 \Rightarrow y(1 - e^x) = 1 \Rightarrow y = \frac{1}{1-e^x}$

84. $\ln(10 \ln y) = \ln 5x \Rightarrow e^{\ln(10 \ln y)} = e^{\ln 5x} \Rightarrow 10 \ln y = 5x \Rightarrow \ln y = \frac{x}{2} \Rightarrow e^{\ln y} = e^{x/2} \Rightarrow y = e^{x/2}$

85. $\lim\limits_{x \to 1} \frac{x^2 + 3x - 4}{x - 1} = \lim\limits_{x \to 1} \frac{2x + 3}{1} = 5$

86. $\lim\limits_{x \to 1} \frac{x^a - 1}{x^b - 1} = \lim\limits_{x \to 1} \frac{ax^{a-1}}{bx^{b-1}} = \frac{a}{b}$

87. $\lim\limits_{x \to \pi} \frac{\tan x}{x} = \frac{\tan \pi}{\pi} = 0$

88. $\lim\limits_{x \to 0} \frac{\tan x}{x + \sin x} = \lim\limits_{x \to 0} \frac{\sec^2 x}{1 + \cos x} = \frac{1}{1+1} = \frac{1}{2}$

89. $\lim\limits_{x \to 0} \frac{\sin^2 x}{\tan(x^2)} = \lim\limits_{x \to 0} \frac{2\sin x \cdot \cos x}{2x \sec^2(x^2)} = \lim\limits_{x \to 0} \frac{\sin(2x)}{2x \sec^2(x^2)} = \lim\limits_{x \to 0} \frac{2\cos(2x)}{2x\left(2\sec^2(x^2)\tan(x^2)\cdot 2x\right) + 2\sec^2(x^2)} = \frac{2}{0 + 2 \cdot 1} = 1$

90. $\lim\limits_{x \to 0} \frac{\sin(mx)}{\sin(nx)} = \lim\limits_{x \to 0} \frac{m\cos(mx)}{n\cos(nx)} = \frac{m}{n}$

91. $\lim\limits_{x \to \pi/2^-} \sec(7x)\cos(3x) = \lim\limits_{x \to \pi/2^-} \frac{\cos(3x)}{\cos(7x)} = \lim\limits_{x \to \pi/2^-} \frac{-3\sin(3x)}{-7\sin(7x)} = \frac{3}{7}$

92. $\lim\limits_{x \to 0^+} \sqrt{x} \sec x = \lim\limits_{x \to 0^+} \frac{\sqrt{x}}{\cos x} = \frac{0}{1} = 0$

93. $\lim\limits_{x \to 0} (\csc x - \cot x) = \lim\limits_{x \to 0} \frac{1 - \cos x}{\sin x} = \lim\limits_{x \to 0} \frac{\sin x}{\cos x} = \frac{0}{1} = 0$

94. $\lim\limits_{x \to 0} \left(\frac{1}{x^4} - \frac{1}{x^2}\right) = \lim\limits_{x \to 0} \left(\frac{1 - x^2}{x^4}\right) = \lim\limits_{x \to 0} (1 - x^2) \cdot \frac{1}{x^4} = \lim\limits_{x \to 0} (1 - x^2) = \lim\limits_{x \to 0} \frac{1}{x^4} = 1 \cdot \infty = \infty$

95. $\lim\limits_{x \to \infty} \left(\sqrt{x^2 + x + 1} - \sqrt{x^2 - x}\right) = \lim\limits_{x \to \infty} \left(\sqrt{x^2 + x + 1} - \sqrt{x^2 - x}\right) \cdot \frac{\sqrt{x^2 + x + 1} + \sqrt{x^2 - x}}{\sqrt{x^2 + x + 1} + \sqrt{x^2 - x}}$

$= \lim\limits_{x \to \infty} \frac{2x + 1}{\sqrt{x^2 + x + 1} + \sqrt{x^2 - x}}$

Notice that $x = \sqrt{x^2}$ for $x > 0$ so this is equivalent to

$= \lim\limits_{x \to \infty} \frac{\frac{2x+1}{x}}{\sqrt{\frac{x^2+x+1}{x^2}} + \sqrt{\frac{x^2-x}{x^2}}} = \lim\limits_{x \to \infty} \frac{2 + \frac{1}{x}}{\sqrt{1 + \frac{1}{x} + \frac{1}{x^2}} + \sqrt{1 - \frac{1}{x}}} = \frac{2}{\sqrt{1} + \sqrt{1}} = 1$

96. $\lim\limits_{x \to \infty} \left(\frac{x^3}{x^2 - 1} - \frac{x^3}{x^2 + 1}\right) = \lim\limits_{x \to \infty} \frac{x^3(x^2 + 1) - x^3(x^2 - 1)}{(x^2 - 1)(x^2 + 1)} = \lim\limits_{x \to \infty} \frac{2x^3}{x^4 - 1} = \lim\limits_{x \to \infty} \frac{6x^2}{4x^3} = \lim\limits_{x \to \infty} \frac{12x}{12x^2}$

$= \lim\limits_{x \to \infty} \frac{12}{24x} = \lim\limits_{x \to \infty} \frac{1}{2x} = 0$

97. The limit leads to the indeterminate form $\frac{0}{0}$: $\lim\limits_{x \to 0} \frac{10^x - 1}{x} = \lim\limits_{x \to 0} \frac{(\ln 10)10^x}{1} = \ln 10$

98. The limit leads to the indeterminate form $\frac{0}{0}$: $\lim\limits_{\theta \to 0} \frac{3^\theta - 1}{\theta} = \lim\limits_{\theta \to 0} \frac{(\ln 3)3^\theta}{1} = \ln 3$

99. The limit leads to the indeterminate form $\frac{0}{0}$: $\lim\limits_{x \to 0} \frac{2^{\sin x} - 1}{e^x - 1} = \lim\limits_{x \to 0} \frac{2^{\sin x}(\ln 2)(\cos x)}{e^x} = \ln 2$

100. The limit leads to the indeterminate form $\frac{0}{0}$: $\lim\limits_{x \to 0} \frac{2^{-\sin x} - 1}{e^x - 1} = \lim\limits_{x \to 0} \frac{2^{-\sin x}(\ln 2)(-\cos x)}{e^x} = -\ln 2$

101. The limit leads to the indeterminate form $\frac{0}{0}$: $\lim\limits_{x \to 0} \frac{5 - 5\cos x}{e^x - x - 1} = \lim\limits_{x \to 0} \frac{5\sin x}{e^x - 1} = \lim\limits_{x \to 0} \frac{5\cos x}{e^x} = 5$

102. The limit leads to the indeterminate form $\frac{0}{0}$: $\lim\limits_{x \to 0} \frac{x \sin x^2}{\tan^3 x} = \lim\limits_{x \to 0} \frac{2x^2 \cos x^2 + \sin x^2}{3\tan^2 x \sec^2 x} = \lim\limits_{x \to 0} \frac{2x^2 \cos x^2 + \sin x^2}{3\tan^4 x + 3\tan^2 x}$

$= \lim\limits_{x \to 0} \frac{6x \cos x^2 - 4x^3 \sin x^2}{12\tan^3 x \sec^2 x + 6\tan x \sec^2 x} = \lim\limits_{x \to 0} \frac{6x \cos x^2 - 4x^3 \sin x^2}{12\tan^3 x + 18\tan^3 x + 6\tan x} = \lim\limits_{x \to 0} \frac{(6 - 8x^4)\cos x^2 - 24x^2 \sin x^2}{60\tan^4 x \sec^2 x + 54\tan^2 x \sec^2 x + 6\sec^2 x} = \frac{6}{6} = 1$

103. The limit leads to the indeterminate form $\frac{0}{0}$: $\lim\limits_{t \to 0^+} \frac{t - \ln(1 + 2t)}{t^2} = \lim\limits_{t \to 0^+} \frac{\left(1 - \frac{2}{1+2t}\right)}{2t} = -\infty$

104. The limit leads to the indeterminate form $\frac{0}{0}$: $\lim\limits_{x \to 4} \frac{\sin^2(\pi x)}{e^{x-4} + 3 - x} = \lim\limits_{x \to 4} \frac{2\pi(\sin \pi x)(\cos \pi x)}{e^{x-4} - 1}$

$= \lim\limits_{x \to 4} \frac{\pi \sin(2\pi x)}{e^{x-4} - 1} = \lim\limits_{x \to 4} \frac{2\pi^2 \cos(2\pi x)}{e^{x-4}} = 2\pi^2$

105. The limit leads to the indeterminate form $\frac{0}{0}$: $\lim\limits_{t \to 0^+} \left(\frac{e^t}{t} - \frac{1}{t}\right) = \lim\limits_{t \to 0^+} \left(\frac{e^t - 1}{t}\right) = \lim\limits_{t \to 0^+} \frac{e^t}{1} = 1$

106. The limit leads to the indeterminate form $\frac{\infty}{\infty}$: $\lim\limits_{y \to 0^+} e^{-1/y} \ln y = \lim\limits_{y \to 0^+} \frac{\ln y}{e^{y^{-1}}} = \lim\limits_{y \to 0^+} \frac{y^{-1}}{-e^{y^{-1}}(y^{-2})}$

$= \lim\limits_{y \to 0^+} \left(-\frac{y}{e^{y^{-1}}}\right) = 0$

107. Let $f(x) = \left(\frac{e^x + 1}{e^x - 1}\right)^{\ln x} \Rightarrow \ln f(x) = \ln x \ln \left(\frac{e^x + 1}{e^x - 1}\right) \Rightarrow \lim\limits_{x \to \infty} \ln f(x) = \lim\limits_{x \to \infty} \ln x \ln \left(\frac{e^x + 1}{e^x - 1}\right)$; this is limit is currently of

the form $0 \cdot \infty$. Before we put in one of the indeterminate forms, we rewrite $\frac{e^x + 1}{e^x - 1} = \frac{e^{x/2} + e^{-x/2}}{e^{x/2} - e^{-x/2}} = \coth\left(\frac{x}{2}\right)$; the limit is

$\lim\limits_{x \to \infty} \ln x \ln \coth\left(\frac{x}{2}\right) = \lim\limits_{x \to \infty} \frac{\ln \coth\left(\frac{x}{2}\right)}{\frac{1}{\ln x}}$; the limit leads to the indeterminate form $\frac{0}{0}$: $\lim\limits_{x \to \infty} \frac{\ln \coth\left(\frac{x}{2}\right)}{\frac{1}{\ln x}}$

$= \lim\limits_{x \to \infty} \left(\frac{\frac{\text{csch}^2\left(\frac{x}{2}\right)}{\coth\left(\frac{x}{2}\right)}\left(-\frac{1}{2}\right)}{-\frac{1}{(\ln x)^2}\left(\frac{1}{x}\right)}\right) = \lim\limits_{x \to \infty} \left(\frac{x(\ln x)^2}{2\sinh\left(\frac{x}{2}\right)\cosh\left(\frac{x}{2}\right)}\right) = \lim\limits_{x \to \infty} \left(\frac{x(\ln x)^2}{\sinh x}\right) = \lim\limits_{x \to \infty} \left(\frac{2x(\ln x)\left(\frac{1}{x}\right) + (\ln x)^2}{\cosh x}\right)$

$= \lim\limits_{x \to \infty} \left(\frac{2\ln x + (\ln x)^2}{\cosh x}\right) = \lim\limits_{x \to \infty} \left(\frac{2\left(\frac{1}{x}\right) + 2(\ln x)\left(\frac{1}{x}\right)}{\sinh x}\right) = \lim\limits_{x \to \infty} \left(\frac{2 + 2\ln x}{x\sinh x}\right) = \lim\limits_{x \to \infty} \left(\frac{\frac{2}{x}}{x\cosh x + \sinh x}\right)$

$= \lim\limits_{x \to \infty} \left(\frac{2}{x^2\cosh x + x\sinh x}\right) = 0 \Rightarrow \lim\limits_{x \to \infty} \left(\frac{e^x + 1}{e^x - 1}\right)^{\ln x} = \lim\limits_{x \to \infty} e^{\ln f(x)} = e^0 = 1$

108. Let $f(x) = \left(1 + \frac{3}{x}\right)^x \Rightarrow \ln f(x) = x \ln \left(1 + \frac{3}{x}\right) \Rightarrow \lim\limits_{x \to 0^+} \ln f(x) = \lim\limits_{x \to 0^+} \frac{\ln(1 + 3x^{-1})}{x^{-1}}$; the limit leads to the

indeterminate form $\frac{\infty}{\infty}$: $\lim\limits_{x \to 0^+} \frac{\left(\frac{-3x^{-2}}{1 + 3x^{-1}}\right)}{-x^{-2}} = \lim\limits_{x \to 0^+} \frac{3x}{x + 3} = 0 \Rightarrow \lim\limits_{x \to 0^+} \left(1 + \frac{3}{x}\right)^x = \lim\limits_{x \to 0^+} e^{\ln f(x)} = e^0 = 1$

109. (a) $\lim\limits_{x \to \infty} \frac{\log_2 x}{\log_3 x} = \lim\limits_{x \to \infty} \frac{\left(\frac{\ln x}{\ln 2}\right)}{\left(\frac{\ln x}{\ln 3}\right)} = \lim\limits_{x \to \infty} \frac{\ln 3}{\ln 2} = \frac{\ln 3}{\ln 2} \Rightarrow$ same rate

(b) $\lim\limits_{x \to \infty} \frac{x}{x + \left(\frac{1}{x}\right)} = \lim\limits_{x \to \infty} \frac{x^2}{x^2 + 1} = \lim\limits_{x \to \infty} \frac{2x}{2x} = \lim\limits_{x \to \infty} 1 = 1 \Rightarrow$ same rate

(c) $\lim\limits_{x \to \infty} \frac{\left(\frac{x}{100}\right)}{xe^{-x}} = \lim\limits_{x \to \infty} \frac{xe^x}{100x} = \lim\limits_{x \to \infty} \frac{e^x}{100} = \infty \Rightarrow$ faster

(d) $\lim\limits_{x \to \infty} \frac{x}{\tan^{-1} x} = \infty \Rightarrow$ faster

(e) $\lim\limits_{x \to \infty} \frac{\csc^{-1} x}{\left(\frac{1}{x}\right)} = \lim\limits_{x \to \infty} \frac{\sin^{-1}(x^{-1})}{x^{-1}} = \lim\limits_{x \to \infty} \frac{\frac{(-x^{-2})}{\sqrt{1 - (x^{-1})^2}}}{-x^{-2}} = \lim\limits_{x \to \infty} \frac{1}{\sqrt{1 - \left(\frac{1}{x^2}\right)}} = 1 \Rightarrow$ same rate

Chapter 7 Practice Exercises

(f) $\lim\limits_{x \to \infty} \frac{\sinh x}{e^x} = \lim\limits_{x \to \infty} \frac{(e^x - e^{-x})}{2e^x} = \lim\limits_{x \to \infty} \frac{1 - e^{-2x}}{2} = \frac{1}{2} \Rightarrow$ same rate

110. (a) $\lim\limits_{x \to \infty} \frac{3^{-x}}{2^{-x}} = \lim\limits_{x \to \infty} \left(\frac{2}{3}\right)^x = 0 \Rightarrow$ slower

(b) $\lim\limits_{x \to \infty} \frac{\ln 2x}{\ln x^2} = \lim\limits_{x \to \infty} \frac{\ln 2 + \ln x}{2(\ln x)} = \lim\limits_{x \to \infty} \left(\frac{\ln 2}{2\ln x} + \frac{1}{2}\right) = \frac{1}{2} \Rightarrow$ same rate

(c) $\lim\limits_{x \to \infty} \frac{10x^3 + 2x^2}{e^x} = \lim\limits_{x \to \infty} \frac{30x^2 + 4x}{e^x} = \lim\limits_{x \to \infty} \frac{60x + 4}{e^x} = \lim\limits_{x \to \infty} \frac{60}{e^x} = 0 \Rightarrow$ slower

(d) $\lim\limits_{x \to \infty} \frac{\tan^{-1}\left(\frac{1}{x}\right)}{\left(\frac{1}{x}\right)} = \lim\limits_{x \to \infty} \frac{\tan^{-1}(x^{-1})}{x^{-1}} = \lim\limits_{x \to \infty} \frac{\left(\frac{-x^{-2}}{1 + x^{-2}}\right)}{-x^{-2}} = \lim\limits_{x \to \infty} \frac{1}{1 + \frac{1}{x^2}} = 1 \Rightarrow$ same rate

(e) $\lim\limits_{x \to \infty} \frac{\sin^{-1}\left(\frac{1}{x}\right)}{\left(\frac{1}{x^2}\right)} = \lim\limits_{x \to \infty} \frac{\sin^{-1}(x^{-1})}{x^{-2}} = \lim\limits_{x \to \infty} \frac{\left(\frac{-x^{-2}}{\sqrt{1 - (x^{-1})^2}}\right)}{-2x^{-3}} = \lim\limits_{x \to \infty} \frac{x}{2\sqrt{1 - \frac{1}{x^2}}} = \infty \Rightarrow$ faster

(f) $\lim\limits_{x \to \infty} \frac{\operatorname{sech} x}{e^{-x}} = \lim\limits_{x \to \infty} \frac{\left(\frac{2}{e^x + e^{-x}}\right)}{e^{-x}} = \lim\limits_{x \to \infty} \frac{2}{e^{-x}(e^x + e^{-x})} = \lim\limits_{x \to \infty} \left(\frac{2}{1 + e^{-2x}}\right) = 2 \Rightarrow$ same rate

111. (a) $\frac{\left(\frac{1}{x^2} + \frac{1}{x^4}\right)}{\left(\frac{1}{x^2}\right)} = 1 + \frac{1}{x^2} \le 2$ for x sufficiently large $\Rightarrow$ true

(b) $\frac{\left(\frac{1}{x^2} + \frac{1}{x^4}\right)}{\left(\frac{1}{x^4}\right)} = x^2 + 1 > M$ for any positive integer M whenever $x > \sqrt{M} \Rightarrow$ false

(c) $\lim\limits_{x \to \infty} \frac{x}{x + \ln x} = \lim\limits_{x \to \infty} \frac{1}{1 + \frac{1}{x}} = 1 \Rightarrow$ the same growth rate $\Rightarrow$ false

(d) $\lim\limits_{x \to \infty} \frac{\ln(\ln x)}{\ln x} = \lim\limits_{x \to \infty} \frac{\left[\frac{\left(\frac{1}{x}\right)}{\ln x}\right]}{\left(\frac{1}{x}\right)} = \lim\limits_{x \to \infty} \frac{1}{\ln x} = 0 \Rightarrow$ grows slower $\Rightarrow$ true

(e) $\frac{\tan^{-1} x}{1} \le \frac{\pi}{2}$ for all $x \Rightarrow$ true

(f) $\frac{\cosh x}{e^x} = \frac{1}{2}(1 + e^{-2x}) \le \frac{1}{2}(1 + 1) = 1$ if $x > 0 \Rightarrow$ true

112. (a) $\frac{\left(\frac{1}{x^4}\right)}{\left(\frac{1}{x^2} + \frac{1}{x^4}\right)} = \frac{1}{x^2 + 1} \le 1$ if $x > 0 \Rightarrow$ true

(b) $\lim\limits_{x \to \infty} \frac{\left(\frac{1}{x^4}\right)}{\left(\frac{1}{x^2} + \frac{1}{x^4}\right)} = \lim\limits_{x \to \infty} \left(\frac{1}{x^2 + 1}\right) = 0 \Rightarrow$ true

(c) $\lim\limits_{x \to \infty} \frac{\ln x}{x + 1} = \lim\limits_{x \to \infty} \frac{\left(\frac{1}{x}\right)}{1} = 0 \Rightarrow$ true

(d) $\frac{\ln 2x}{\ln x} = \frac{\ln 2}{\ln x} + 1 \le 1 + 1 = 2$ if $x \ge 2 \Rightarrow$ true

(e) $\frac{\sec^{-1} x}{1} = \frac{\cos^{-1}\left(\frac{1}{x}\right)}{1} \le \frac{\left(\frac{\pi}{2}\right)}{1} = \frac{\pi}{2}$ if $x > 1 \Rightarrow$ true

(f) $\frac{\sinh x}{e^x} = \frac{1}{2}(1 - e^{-2x}) \le \frac{1}{2}$ if $x > 0 \Rightarrow$ true

113. $\frac{df}{dx} = e^x + 1 \Rightarrow \left(\frac{df^{-1}}{dx}\right)_{x = f(\ln 2)} = \frac{1}{\left(\frac{df}{dx}\right)_{x = \ln 2}} \Rightarrow \left(\frac{df^{-1}}{dx}\right)_{x = f(\ln 2)} = \frac{1}{(e^x + 1)_{x = \ln 2}} = \frac{1}{2 + 1} = \frac{1}{3}$

114. $y = f(x) \Rightarrow y = 1 + \frac{1}{x} \Rightarrow \frac{1}{x} = y - 1 \Rightarrow x = \frac{1}{y - 1} \Rightarrow f^{-1}(x) = \frac{1}{x - 1}; f^{-1}(f(x)) = \frac{1}{\left(1 + \frac{1}{x}\right) - 1} = \frac{1}{\left(\frac{1}{x}\right)} = x$ and

$f(f^{-1}(x)) = 1 + \frac{1}{\left(\frac{1}{x - 1}\right)} = 1 + (x - 1) = x; \left.\frac{df^{-1}}{dx}\right|_{f(x)} = \left.\frac{-1}{(x - 1)^2}\right|_{f(x)} = \frac{-1}{\left[\left(1 + \frac{1}{x}\right) - 1\right]^2} = -x^2;$

$f'(x) = -\frac{1}{x^2} \Rightarrow \left.\frac{df^{-1}}{dx}\right|_{f(x)} = \frac{1}{f'(x)}$

115. $y = x \ln 2x - x \Rightarrow y' = x\left(\frac{2}{2x}\right) + \ln(2x) - 1 = \ln 2x;$
solving $y' = 0 \Rightarrow x = \frac{1}{2}; y' > 0$ for $x > \frac{1}{2}$ and $y' < 0$ for
$x < \frac{1}{2} \Rightarrow$ relative minimum of $-\frac{1}{2}$ at $x = \frac{1}{2}; f\left(\frac{1}{2e}\right) = -\frac{1}{e}$
and $f\left(\frac{e}{2}\right) = 0 \Rightarrow$ absolute minimum is $-\frac{1}{2}$ at $x = \frac{1}{2}$ and
the absolute maximum is 0 at $x = \frac{e}{2}$

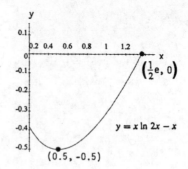

116. $y = 10x(2 - \ln x) \Rightarrow y' = 10(2 - \ln x) - 10x\left(\frac{1}{x}\right)$
$= 20 - 10 \ln x - 10 = 10(1 - \ln x);$ solving $y' = 0$
$\Rightarrow x = e; y' < 0$ for $x > e$ and $y' > 0$ for $x < e$
$\Rightarrow$ relative maximum at $x = e$ of $10e; y \geq 0$ on $(0, e^2]$ and
$y(e^2) = 10e^2(2 - 2\ln e) = 0 \Rightarrow$ absolute minimum is 0
at $x = e^2$ and the absolute maximum is $10e$ at $x = e$

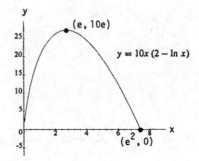

117. $A = \int_1^e \frac{2\ln x}{x}\, dx = \int_0^1 2u\, du = [u^2]_0^1 = 1,$ where $u = \ln x$ and $du = \frac{1}{x}\, dx; x = 1 \Rightarrow u = 0, x = e \Rightarrow u = 1$

118. (a) $A_1 = \int_{10}^{20} \frac{1}{x}\, dx = [\ln|x|]_{10}^{20} = \ln 20 - \ln 10 = \ln\frac{20}{10} = \ln 2,$ and $A_2 = \int_1^2 \frac{1}{x}\, dx = [\ln|x|]_1^2 = \ln 2 - \ln 1 = \ln 2$

(b) $A_1 = \int_{ka}^{kb} \frac{1}{x}\, dx = [\ln|x|]_{ka}^{kb} = \ln kb - \ln ka = \ln\frac{kb}{ka} = \ln\frac{b}{a} = \ln b - \ln a,$ and $A_2 = \int_a^b \frac{1}{x}\, dx = [\ln|x|]_a^b = \ln b - \ln a$

119. $y = \ln x \Rightarrow \frac{dy}{dx} = \frac{1}{x}; \frac{dy}{dt} = \frac{dy}{dx}\frac{dx}{dt} \Rightarrow \frac{dy}{dt} = \left(\frac{1}{x}\right)\sqrt{x} = \frac{1}{\sqrt{x}} \Rightarrow \left.\frac{dy}{dt}\right|_{e^2} = \frac{1}{e}$ m/sec

120. $y = 9e^{-x/3} \Rightarrow \frac{dy}{dx} = -3e^{-x/3}; \frac{dx}{dt} = \frac{(dy/dt)}{(dy/dx)} \Rightarrow \frac{dx}{dt} = \frac{\left(-\frac{1}{4}\right)\sqrt{9-y}}{-3e^{-x/3}}; x = 9 \Rightarrow y = 9e^{-3}$

$\Rightarrow \left.\frac{dx}{dt}\right|_{x=9} = \frac{\left(-\frac{1}{4}\right)\sqrt{9-\frac{9}{e^3}}}{\left(-\frac{3}{e^3}\right)} = \frac{1}{4}\sqrt{e^3}\sqrt{e^3 - 1} \approx 5$ ft/sec

121. $A = xy = xe^{-x^2} \Rightarrow \frac{dA}{dx} = e^{-x^2} + (x)(-2x)e^{-x^2} = e^{-x^2}(1 - 2x^2).$ Solving $\frac{dA}{dx} = 0 \Rightarrow 1 - 2x^2 = 0$
$\Rightarrow x = \frac{1}{\sqrt{2}}; \frac{dA}{dx} < 0$ for $x > \frac{1}{\sqrt{2}}$ and $\frac{dA}{dx} > 0$ for $0 < x < \frac{1}{\sqrt{2}} \Rightarrow$ absolute maximum of $\frac{1}{\sqrt{2}}e^{-1/2} = \frac{1}{\sqrt{2e}}$ at
$x = \frac{1}{\sqrt{2}}$ units long by $y = e^{-1/2} = \frac{1}{\sqrt{e}}$ units high.

122. $A = xy = x\left(\frac{\ln x}{x^2}\right) = \frac{\ln x}{x} \Rightarrow \frac{dA}{dx} = \frac{1}{x^2} - \frac{\ln x}{x^2} = \frac{1-\ln x}{x^2}.$ Solving $\frac{dA}{dx} = 0 \Rightarrow 1 - \ln x = 0 \Rightarrow x = e;$
$\frac{dA}{dx} < 0$ for $x > e$ and $\frac{dA}{dx} > 0$ for $x < e \Rightarrow$ absolute maximum of $\frac{\ln e}{e} = \frac{1}{e}$ at $x = e$ units long and $y = \frac{1}{e^2}$ units high.

123. (a) $y = \frac{\ln x}{\sqrt{x}} \Rightarrow y' = \frac{1}{x\sqrt{x}} - \frac{\ln x}{2x^{3/2}} = \frac{2-\ln x}{2x\sqrt{x}}$
$\Rightarrow y'' = -\frac{3}{4}x^{-5/2}(2 - \ln x) - \frac{1}{2}x^{-5/2} = x^{-5/2}\left(\frac{3}{4}\ln x - 2\right);$
solving $y' = 0 \Rightarrow \ln x = 2 \Rightarrow x = e^2; y' < 0$ for $x > e^2$ and
and $y' > 0$ for $x < e^2 \Rightarrow$ a maximum of $\frac{2}{e}; y'' = 0$
$\Rightarrow \ln x = \frac{8}{3} \Rightarrow x = e^{8/3};$ the curve is concave down on
$(0, e^{8/3})$ and concave up on $(e^{8/3}, \infty);$ so there is an
inflection point at $\left(e^{8/3}, \frac{8}{3e^{4/3}}\right).$

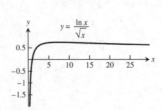

(b) $y = e^{-x^2} \Rightarrow y' = -2xe^{-x^2} \Rightarrow y'' = -2e^{-x^2} + 4x^2e^{-x^2}$
$= (4x^2 - 2)e^{-x^2}$; solving $y' = 0 \Rightarrow x = 0$; $y' < 0$ for
$x > 0$ and $y' > 0$ for $x < 0 \Rightarrow$ a maximum at $x = 0$ of
$e^0 = 1$; there are points of inflection at $x = \pm\frac{1}{\sqrt{2}}$; the
curve is concave down for $-\frac{1}{\sqrt{2}} < x < \frac{1}{\sqrt{2}}$ and concave
up otherwise.

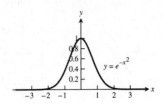

(c) $y = (1 + x)e^{-x} \Rightarrow y' = e^{-x} - (1 + x)e^{-x} = -xe^{-x}$
$\Rightarrow y'' = -e^{-x} + xe^{-x} = (x - 1)e^{-x}$; solving $y' = 0$
$\Rightarrow -xe^{-x} = 0 \Rightarrow x = 0$; $y' < 0$ for $x > 0$ and $y' > 0$
for $x < 0 \Rightarrow$ a maximum at $x = 0$ of $(1 + 0)e^0 = 1$;
there is a point of inflection at $x = 1$ and the curve is
concave up for $x > 1$ and concave down for $x < 1$.

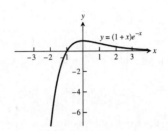

124. $y = x \ln x \Rightarrow y' = \ln x + x\left(\frac{1}{x}\right) = \ln x + 1$; solving $y' = 0$
$\Rightarrow \ln x + 1 = 0 \Rightarrow \ln x = -1 \Rightarrow x = e^{-1}$; $y' > 0$ for
$x > e^{-1}$ and $y' < 0$ for $x < e^{-1} \Rightarrow$ a minimum of $e^{-1} \ln e^{-1}$
$= -\frac{1}{e}$ at $x = e^{-1}$. This minimum is an absolute minimum
since $y'' = \frac{1}{x}$ is positive for all $x > 0$.

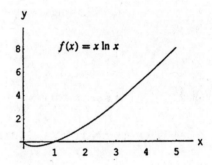

125. $\frac{dy}{dx} = \sqrt{y}\cos^2\sqrt{y} \Rightarrow \frac{dy}{\sqrt{y}\cos^2\sqrt{y}} = dx \Rightarrow 2\tan\sqrt{y} = x + C \Rightarrow y = \left(\tan^{-1}\left(\frac{x+C}{2}\right)\right)^2$

126. $y' = \frac{3y(x+1)^2}{y-1} \Rightarrow \frac{(y-1)}{y}dy = 3(x+1)^2 dx \Rightarrow y - \ln y = (x+1)^3 + C$

127. $yy' = \sec(y^2)\sec^2 x \Rightarrow \frac{y\,dy}{\sec(y^2)} = \sec^2 x\,dx \Rightarrow \frac{\sin(y^2)}{2} = \tan x + C \Rightarrow \sin(y^2) = 2\tan x + C_1$

128. $y\cos^2(x)\,dy + \sin x\,dx = 0 \Rightarrow y\,dy = -\frac{\sin x}{\cos^2(x)}dx \Rightarrow \frac{y^2}{2} = -\frac{1}{\cos(x)} + C \Rightarrow y = \pm\sqrt{\frac{-2}{\cos(x)} + C_1}$

129. $\frac{dy}{dx} = e^{-x-y-2} \Rightarrow e^y dy = e^{-(x+2)}dx \Rightarrow e^y = -e^{-(x+2)} + C$. We have $y(0) = -2$, so $e^{-2} = -e^{-2} + C \Rightarrow C = 2e^{-2}$ and
$e^y = -e^{-(x+2)} + 2e^{-2} \Rightarrow y = \ln\left(-e^{-(x+2)} + 2e^{-2}\right)$

130. $\frac{dy}{dx} = \frac{y\ln y}{1+x^2} \Rightarrow \frac{dy}{y\ln y} = \frac{dx}{1+x^2} \Rightarrow \ln(\ln y) = \tan^{-1}(x) + C \Rightarrow y = e^{e^{\tan^{-1}(x)+C}}$. We have $y(0) = e^2 \Rightarrow e^2 = e^{e^{\tan^{-1}(0)+C}}$
$\Rightarrow e^{\tan^{-1}(0)+C} = 2 \Rightarrow \tan^{-1}(0) + C = \ln 2 \Rightarrow 0 + C = \ln 2 \Rightarrow C = \ln 2 \Rightarrow y = e^{e^{\tan^{-1}(x)+\ln 2}}$

131. $x\,dy - \left(y + \sqrt{y}\right)dx = 0 \Rightarrow \frac{dy}{(y+\sqrt{y})} = \frac{dx}{x} \Rightarrow 2\ln\left(\sqrt{y} + 1\right) = \ln x + C$. We have $y(1) = 1 \Rightarrow 2\ln\left(\sqrt{1} + 1\right) = \ln 1 + C$
$\Rightarrow 2\ln 2 = C = \ln 2^2 = \ln 4$. So $2\ln\left(\sqrt{y} + 1\right) = \ln x + \ln 4 = \ln(4x) \Rightarrow \ln\left(\sqrt{y} + 1\right) = \frac{1}{2}\ln(4x) = \ln(4x)^{1/2}$
$\Rightarrow e^{\ln(\sqrt{y}+1)} = e^{\ln(4x)^{1/2}} \Rightarrow \sqrt{y} + 1 = 2\sqrt{x} \Rightarrow y = \left(2\sqrt{x} - 1\right)^2$

132. $y^{-2}\frac{dx}{dy} = \frac{e^x}{e^{2x}+1} \Rightarrow \frac{e^{2x}+1}{e^x}dx = \frac{dy}{y^{-2}} \Rightarrow \frac{y^3}{3} = e^x - e^{-x} + C$. We have $y(0) = 1 \Rightarrow \frac{(1)^3}{3} = e^0 - e^0 + C \Rightarrow C = \frac{1}{3}$.
So $\frac{y^3}{3} = e^x - e^{-x} + \frac{1}{3} \Rightarrow y^3 = 3(e^x - e^{-x}) + 1 \Rightarrow y = [3(e^x - e^{-x}) + 1]^{1/3}$

133. Since the half life is 5700 years and $A(t) = A_0 e^{kt}$ we have $\frac{A_0}{2} = A_0 e^{5700k} \Rightarrow \frac{1}{2} = e^{5700k} \Rightarrow \ln(0.5) = 5700k$

$\Rightarrow k = \frac{\ln(0.5)}{5700}$. With 10% of the original carbon-14 remaining we have $0.1 A_0 = A_0 e^{\frac{\ln(0.5)}{5700} t} \Rightarrow 0.1 = e^{\frac{\ln(0.5)}{5700} t}$

$\Rightarrow \ln(0.1) = \frac{\ln(0.5)}{5700} t \Rightarrow t = \frac{(5700)\ln(0.1)}{\ln(0.5)} \approx 18{,}935$ years (rounded to the nearest year).

134. $T - T_s = (T_o - T_s) e^{-kt} \Rightarrow 180 - 40 = (220 - 40) e^{-k/4}$, time in hours, $\Rightarrow k = -4\ln\left(\frac{7}{9}\right) = 4\ln\left(\frac{9}{7}\right) \Rightarrow 70 - 40$

$= (220 - 40) e^{-4\ln(9/7) t} \Rightarrow t = \frac{\ln 6}{4\ln\left(\frac{9}{7}\right)} \approx 1.78$ hr $\approx 107$ min, the total time $\Rightarrow$ the time it took to cool from $180°$ F to

$70°$ F was $107 - 15 = 92$ min

135. $\theta = \pi - \cot^{-1}\left(\frac{x}{60}\right) - \cot^{-1}\left(\frac{5}{3} - \frac{x}{30}\right), 0 < x < 50 \Rightarrow \frac{d\theta}{dx} = \frac{\left(\frac{1}{60}\right)}{1 + \left(\frac{x}{60}\right)^2} + \frac{\left(-\frac{1}{30}\right)}{1 + \left(\frac{50-x}{30}\right)^2}$

$= 30\left[\frac{2}{60^2 + x^2} - \frac{1}{30^2 + (50-x)^2}\right]$; solving $\frac{d\theta}{dx} = 0 \Rightarrow x^2 - 200x + 3200 = 0 \Rightarrow x = 100 \pm 20\sqrt{17}$, but

$100 + 20\sqrt{17}$ is not in the domain; $\frac{d\theta}{dx} > 0$ for $x < 20\left(5 - \sqrt{17}\right)$ and $\frac{d\theta}{dx} < 0$ for $20\left(5 - \sqrt{17}\right) < x < 50$

$\Rightarrow x = 20\left(5 - \sqrt{17}\right) \approx 17.54$ m maximizes $\theta$

136. $v = x^2 \ln\left(\frac{1}{x}\right) = x^2 (\ln 1 - \ln x) = -x^2 \ln x \Rightarrow \frac{dv}{dx} = -2x \ln x - x^2 \left(\frac{1}{x}\right) = -x(2\ln x + 1)$; solving $\frac{dv}{dx} = 0$

$\Rightarrow 2\ln x + 1 = 0 \Rightarrow \ln x = -\frac{1}{2} \Rightarrow x = e^{-1/2}; \frac{dv}{dx} < 0$ for $x > e^{-1/2}$ and $\frac{dv}{dx} > 0$ for $x < e^{-1/2} \Rightarrow$ a relative

maximum at $x = e^{-1/2}; \frac{r}{h} = x$ and $r = 1 \Rightarrow h = e^{1/2} = \sqrt{e} \approx 1.65$ cm

## CHAPTER 7 ADDITIONAL AND ADVANCED EXERCISES

1. $\lim\limits_{b \to 1^-} \int_0^b \frac{1}{\sqrt{1-x^2}} dx = \lim\limits_{b \to 1^-} [\sin^{-1} x]_0^b = \lim\limits_{b \to 1^-} (\sin^{-1} b - \sin^{-1} 0) = \lim\limits_{b \to 1^-} (\sin^{-1} b - 0) = \lim\limits_{b \to 1^-} \sin^{-1} b = \frac{\pi}{2}$

2. $\lim\limits_{x \to \infty} \frac{1}{x} \int_0^x \tan^{-1} t \, dt = \lim\limits_{x \to \infty} \frac{\int_0^x \tan^{-1} t \, dt}{x}$    $\left(\frac{\infty}{\infty} \text{ form}\right)$

   $= \lim\limits_{x \to \infty} \frac{\tan^{-1} x}{1} = \frac{\pi}{2}$

3. $y = \left(\cos\sqrt{x}\right)^{1/x} \Rightarrow \ln y = \frac{1}{x}\ln\left(\cos\sqrt{x}\right)$ and $\lim\limits_{x \to 0^+} \frac{\ln\left(\cos\sqrt{x}\right)}{x} = \lim\limits_{x \to 0^+} \frac{-\sin\sqrt{x}}{2\sqrt{x}\cos\sqrt{x}} = \frac{-1}{2}\lim\limits_{x \to 0^+} \frac{\tan\sqrt{x}}{\sqrt{x}}$

   $= -\frac{1}{2}\lim\limits_{x \to 0^+} \frac{\frac{1}{2}x^{-1/2}\sec^2\sqrt{x}}{\frac{1}{2}x^{-1/2}} = -\frac{1}{2} \Rightarrow \lim\limits_{x \to 0^+} \left(\cos\sqrt{x}\right)^{1/x} = e^{-1/2} = \frac{1}{\sqrt{e}}$

4. $y = (x + e^x)^{2/x} \Rightarrow \ln y = \frac{2\ln(x + e^x)}{x} \Rightarrow \lim\limits_{x \to \infty} \ln y = \lim\limits_{x \to \infty} \frac{2(1 + e^x)}{x + e^x} = \lim\limits_{x \to \infty} \frac{2e^x}{1 + e^x} = \lim\limits_{x \to \infty} \frac{2e^x}{e^x} = 2$

   $\Rightarrow \lim\limits_{x \to \infty} (x + e^x)^{2/x} = \lim\limits_{x \to \infty} e^y = e^2$

5. $\lim\limits_{x \to \infty} \left(\frac{1}{n+1} + \frac{1}{n+2} + \ldots + \frac{1}{2n}\right) = \lim\limits_{x \to \infty} \left(\left(\frac{1}{n}\right)\left[\frac{1}{1 + \left(\frac{1}{n}\right)}\right] + \left(\frac{1}{n}\right)\left[\frac{1}{1 + 2\left(\frac{1}{n}\right)}\right] + \ldots + \left(\frac{1}{n}\right)\left[\frac{1}{1 + n\left(\frac{1}{n}\right)}\right]\right)$

   which can be interpreted as a Riemann sum with partitioning $\Delta x = \frac{1}{n} \Rightarrow \lim\limits_{x \to \infty} \left(\frac{1}{n+1} + \frac{1}{n+2} + \ldots + \frac{1}{2n}\right)$

   $= \int_0^1 \frac{1}{1+x} dx = [\ln(1+x)]_0^1 = \ln 2$

6. $\lim\limits_{x \to \infty} \frac{1}{n}\left[e^{1/n} + e^{2/n} + \ldots + e\right] = \lim\limits_{x \to \infty} \left[\left(\frac{1}{n}\right)e^{(1/n)} + \left(\frac{1}{n}\right)e^{2(1/n)} + \ldots + \left(\frac{1}{n}\right)e^{n(1/n)}\right]$ which can be interpreted as a

   Riemann sum with partitioning $\Delta x = \frac{1}{n} \Rightarrow \lim\limits_{x \to \infty} \frac{1}{n}\left[e^{1/n} + e^{2/n} + \ldots + e\right] = \int_0^1 e^x dx = [e^x]_0^1 = e - 1$

7.  $A(t) = \int_0^t e^{-x}\,dx = \left[-e^{-x}\right]_0^t = 1 - e^{-t}$, $V(t) = \pi\int_0^t e^{-2x}\,dx = \left[-\frac{\pi}{2}e^{-2x}\right]_0^t = \frac{\pi}{2}\left(1 - e^{-2t}\right)$

(a)  $\lim\limits_{t \to \infty} A(t) = \lim\limits_{t \to \infty}\left(1 - e^{-t}\right) = 1$

(b)  $\lim\limits_{t \to \infty} \frac{V(t)}{A(t)} = \lim\limits_{t \to \infty} \frac{\frac{\pi}{2}\left(1 - e^{-2t}\right)}{1 - e^{-t}} = \frac{\pi}{2}$

(c)  $\lim\limits_{t \to 0^+} \frac{V(t)}{A(t)} = \lim\limits_{t \to 0^+} \frac{\frac{\pi}{2}\left(1 - e^{-2t}\right)}{1 - e^{-t}} = \lim\limits_{t \to 0^+} \frac{\frac{\pi}{2}\left(1 - e^{-t}\right)\left(1 + e^{-t}\right)}{\left(1 - e^{-t}\right)} = \lim\limits_{t \to 0^+} \frac{\pi}{2}\left(1 + e^{-t}\right) = \pi$

8.  (a)  $\lim\limits_{a \to 0^+}\log_a 2 = \lim\limits_{a \to 0^+} \frac{\ln 2}{\ln a} = 0$;

$\lim\limits_{a \to 1^-}\log_a 2 = \lim\limits_{a \to 1^-} \frac{\ln 2}{\ln a} = -\infty$;

$\lim\limits_{a \to 1^+}\log_a 2 = \lim\limits_{a \to 1^+} \frac{\ln 2}{\ln 1} = \infty$;

$\lim\limits_{a \to \infty}\log_a 2 = \lim\limits_{a \to \infty} \frac{\ln 2}{\ln a} = 0$

(b)

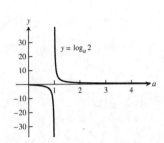

9.  $A_1 = \int_1^e \frac{2\log_2 x}{x}\,dx = \frac{2}{\ln 2}\int_1^e \frac{\ln x}{x}\,dx = \left[\frac{(\ln x)^2}{\ln 2}\right]_1^e = \frac{1}{\ln 2}$; $A_2 = \int_1^e \frac{2\log_4 x}{4}\,dx = \frac{2}{\ln 4}\int_1^e \frac{\ln x}{x}\,dx$

$= \left[\frac{(\ln x)^2}{2\ln 2}\right]_1^e = \frac{1}{2\ln 2} \Rightarrow A_1 : A_2 = 2 : 1$

10.  $y = \tan^{-1} x + \tan^{-1}\left(\frac{1}{x}\right) \Rightarrow y' = \frac{1}{1+x^2} + \frac{\left(-\frac{1}{x^2}\right)}{\left(1 + \frac{1}{x^2}\right)}$

$= \frac{1}{1+x^2} - \frac{1}{1+x^2} = 0 \Rightarrow \tan^{-1} x + \tan^{-1}\left(\frac{1}{x}\right)$ is a constant and the constant is $\frac{\pi}{2}$ for $x > 0$; it is $-\frac{\pi}{2}$ for $x < 0$ since $\tan^{-1} x + \tan^{-1}\left(\frac{1}{x}\right)$ is odd.  Next the

$\lim\limits_{x \to 0^+}\left[\tan^{-1} x + \tan^{-1}\left(\frac{1}{x}\right)\right] = 0 + \frac{\pi}{2} = \frac{\pi}{2}$

and  $\lim\limits_{x \to 0^-}\left(\tan^{-1} x + \tan^{-1}\left(\frac{1}{x}\right)\right) = 0 + \left(-\frac{\pi}{2}\right) = -\frac{\pi}{2}$

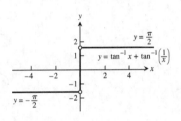

11.  $\ln x^{(x^x)} = x^x \ln x$ and $\ln\left(x^x\right)^x = x \ln x^x = x^2 \ln x$; then, $x^x \ln x = x^2 \ln x \Rightarrow \left(x^x - x^2\right)\ln x = 0 \Rightarrow x^x = x^2$ or $\ln x = 0$.

$\ln x = 0 \Rightarrow x = 1$; $x^x = x^2 \Rightarrow x \ln x = 2 \ln x \Rightarrow x = 2$.  Therefore, $x^{(x^x)} = \left(x^x\right)^x$ when $x = 2$ or $x = 1$.

12.  In the interval $\pi < x < 2\pi$ the function $\sin x < 0$

$\Rightarrow (\sin x)^{\sin x}$ is not defined for all values in that interval or its translation by $2\pi$.

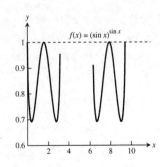

13.  $f(x) = e^{g(x)} \Rightarrow f'(x) = e^{g(x)}\,g'(x)$, where $g'(x) = \frac{x}{1+x^4} \Rightarrow f'(2) = e^0\left(\frac{2}{1+16}\right) = \frac{2}{17}$

14.  (a)  $\frac{df}{dx} = \frac{2\ln e^x}{e^x} \cdot e^x = 2x$

(b)  $f(0) = \int_1^1 \frac{2\ln t}{t}\,dt = 0$

(c)  $\frac{df}{dx} = 2x \Rightarrow f(x) = x^2 + C$; $f(0) = 0 \Rightarrow C = 0 \Rightarrow f(x) = x^2 \Rightarrow$ the graph of $f(x)$ is a parabola

15.  (a)  $g(x) + h(x) = 0 \Rightarrow g(x) = -h(x)$; also $g(x) + h(x) = 0 \Rightarrow g(-x) + h(-x) = 0 \Rightarrow g(x) - h(x) = 0$

$\Rightarrow g(x) = h(x)$; therefore $-h(x) = h(x) \Rightarrow h(x) = 0 \Rightarrow g(x) = 0$

(b) $\frac{f(x)+f(-x)}{2} = \frac{[f_E(x)+f_o(x)]+[f_E(-x)+f_o(-x)]}{2} = \frac{f_E(x)+f_o(x)+f_E(x)-f_o(x)}{2} = f_E(x);$

$\frac{f(x)-f(-x)}{2} = \frac{[f_E(x)+f_o(x)]-[f_E(-x)+f_o(-x)]}{2} = \frac{f_E(x)+f_o(x)-f_E(x)+f_o(x)}{2} = f_o(x)$

(c) Part b $\Rightarrow$ such a decomposition is unique.

16. (a) $g(0+0) = \frac{g(0)+g(0)}{1-g(0)g(0)} \Rightarrow [1-g^2(0)]g(0) = 2g(0) \Rightarrow g(0)-g^3(0) = 2g(0) \Rightarrow g^3(0)+g(0) = 0$

$\Rightarrow g(0)[g^2(0)+1] = 0 \Rightarrow g(0) = 0$

(b) $g'(x) = \lim_{h \to 0} \frac{g(x+h)-g(x)}{h} = \lim_{h \to 0} \frac{\left[\frac{g(x)+g(h)}{1-g(x)g(h)}\right]-g(x)}{h} = \lim_{h \to 0} \frac{g(x)+g(h)-g(x)+g^2(x)g(h)}{h[1-g(x)g(h)]}$

$= \lim_{h \to 0} \left[\frac{g(h)}{h}\right]\left[\frac{1+g^2(x)}{1-g(x)g(h)}\right] = 1 \cdot [1+g^2(x)] = 1+g^2(x) = 1+[g(x)]^2$

(c) $\frac{dy}{dx} = 1+y^2 \Rightarrow \frac{dy}{1+y^2} = dx \Rightarrow \tan^{-1}y = x+C \Rightarrow \tan^{-1}(g(x)) = x+C; g(0) = 0 \Rightarrow \tan^{-1}0 = 0+C$

$\Rightarrow C = 0 \Rightarrow \tan^{-1}(g(x)) = x \Rightarrow g(x) = \tan x$

17. $M = \int_0^1 \frac{2}{1+x^2}\, dx = 2\left[\tan^{-1}x\right]_0^1 = \frac{\pi}{2}$ and $M_y = \int_0^1 \frac{2x}{1+x^2}\, dx = \left[\ln(1+x^2)\right]_0^1 = \ln 2 \Rightarrow \bar{x} = \frac{M_y}{M}$

$= \frac{\ln 2}{\left(\frac{\pi}{2}\right)} = \frac{\ln 4}{\pi}; \bar{y} = 0$ by symmetry

18. (a) $V = \pi \int_{1/4}^4 \left(\frac{1}{2\sqrt{x}}\right)^2 dx = \frac{\pi}{4}\int_{1/4}^4 \frac{1}{x}\, dx = \frac{\pi}{4}\left[\ln|x|\right]_{1/4}^4 = \frac{\pi}{4}\left(\ln 4 - \ln\frac{1}{4}\right) = \frac{\pi}{4}\ln 16 = \frac{\pi}{4}\ln(2^4) = \pi\ln 2$

(b) $M_y = \int_{1/4}^4 x\left(\frac{1}{2\sqrt{x}}\right) dx = \frac{1}{2}\int_{1/4}^4 x^{1/2}\, dx = \left[\frac{1}{3}x^{3/2}\right]_{1/4}^4 = \left(\frac{8}{3}-\frac{1}{24}\right) = \frac{64-1}{24} = \frac{63}{24};$

$M_x = \int_{1/4}^4 \frac{1}{2}\left(\frac{1}{2\sqrt{x}}\right)\left(\frac{1}{2\sqrt{x}}\right) dx = \frac{1}{8}\int_{1/4}^4 \frac{1}{x}\, dx = \left[\frac{1}{8}\ln|x|\right]_{1/4}^4 = \frac{1}{8}\ln 16 = \frac{1}{2}\ln 2;$

$M = \int_{1/4}^4 \frac{1}{2\sqrt{x}}\, dx = \int_{1/4}^4 \frac{1}{2}x^{-1/2}\, dx = \left[x^{1/2}\right]_{1/4}^4 = 2-\frac{1}{2} = \frac{3}{2}$; therefore, $\bar{x} = \frac{M_y}{M} = \left(\frac{63}{24}\right)\left(\frac{2}{3}\right) = \frac{21}{12} = \frac{7}{4}$ and

$\bar{y} = \frac{M_x}{M} = \left(\frac{1}{2}\ln 2\right)\left(\frac{2}{3}\right) = \frac{\ln 2}{3}$

19. (a) $L = k\left(\frac{a-b\cot\theta}{R^4} + \frac{b\csc\theta}{r^4}\right) \Rightarrow \frac{dL}{d\theta} = k\left(\frac{b\csc^2\theta}{R^4} - \frac{b\csc\theta\cot\theta}{r^4}\right)$; solving $\frac{dL}{d\theta} = 0$

$\Rightarrow r^4 b\csc^2\theta - bR^4\csc\theta\cot\theta = 0 \Rightarrow (b\csc\theta)(r^4\csc\theta - R^4\cot\theta) = 0$; but $b\csc\theta \neq 0$ since

$\theta \neq \frac{\pi}{2} \Rightarrow r^4\csc\theta - R^4\cot\theta = 0 \Rightarrow \cos\theta = \frac{r^4}{R^4} \Rightarrow \theta = \cos^{-1}\left(\frac{r^4}{R^4}\right)$, the critical value of $\theta$

(b) $\theta = \cos^{-1}\left(\frac{5}{6}\right)^4 \approx \cos^{-1}(0.48225) \approx 61°$

20. In order to maximize the amount of sunlight, we need to maximize the angle $\theta$ formed by extending the two red line segments to their vertex. The angle between the two lines is given by $\theta = \pi - (\theta_1 + (\pi - \theta_2))$. From trig we have

$\tan\theta_1 = \frac{350}{450-x} \Rightarrow \theta_1 = \tan^{-1}\left(\frac{350}{450-x}\right)$ and $\tan(\pi-\theta_2) = \frac{200}{x} \Rightarrow (\pi-\theta_2) = \tan^{-1}\left(\frac{200}{x}\right)$

$\Rightarrow \theta = \pi - (\theta_1 + (\pi - \theta_2)) = \pi - \tan^{-1}\left(\frac{350}{450-x}\right) - \tan^{-1}\left(\frac{200}{x}\right)$

$\Rightarrow \frac{d\theta}{dx} = -\frac{1}{1+\left(\frac{350}{450-x}\right)^2} \cdot \frac{350}{(450-x)^2} - \frac{1}{1+\left(\frac{200}{x}\right)^2} \cdot \left(-\frac{200}{x^2}\right) = \frac{-350}{(450-x)^2+122500} + \frac{200}{x^2+40000}$

$\frac{d\theta}{dx} = 0 \Rightarrow \frac{-350}{(450-x)^2+122500} + \frac{200}{x^2+40000} = 0 \Rightarrow 200\left((450-x)^2+122500\right) = 350(x^2+40000)$

$\Rightarrow 3x^2 + 3600x - 1020000 = 0 \Rightarrow x = -600 \pm 100\sqrt{70}$. Since $x > 0$, consider only $x = -600+100\sqrt{70}$.

Using the first derivative test, $\frac{d\theta}{dx}\Big|_{x=100} = \frac{9}{3500} > 0$ and $\frac{d\theta}{dx}\Big|_{x=400} = \frac{-9}{5000} < 0 \Rightarrow$ local max when

$x = -600+100\sqrt{70} \approx 236.67$ ft.

# CHAPTER 8 TECHNIQUES OF INTEGRATION

## 8.1 INTEGRATION BY PARTS

1. $u = x, du = dx; dv = \sin \frac{x}{2} dx, v = -2 \cos \frac{x}{2}$ ;

   $\int x \sin \frac{x}{2} dx = -2x \cos \frac{x}{2} - \int \left(-2 \cos \frac{x}{2}\right) dx = -2x \cos \left(\frac{x}{2}\right) + 4 \sin \left(\frac{x}{2}\right) + C$

2. $u = \theta, du = d\theta; dv = \cos \pi\theta \, d\theta, v = \frac{1}{\pi} \sin \pi\theta;$

   $\int \theta \cos \pi\theta \, d\theta = \frac{\theta}{\pi} \sin \pi\theta - \int \frac{1}{\pi} \sin \pi\theta \, d\theta = \frac{\theta}{\pi} \sin \pi\theta + \frac{1}{\pi^2} \cos \pi\theta + C$

3. 

   $$
   \begin{array}{ll}
    & \cos t \\
   t^2 \xrightarrow{(+)} & \sin t \\
   2t \xrightarrow{(-)} & -\cos t \\
   2 \xrightarrow{(+)} & -\sin t \\
   0 &
   \end{array}
   $$

   $\int t^2 \cos t \, dt = t^2 \sin t + 2t \cos t - 2 \sin t + C$

4. 

   $$
   \begin{array}{ll}
    & \sin x \\
   x^2 \xrightarrow{(+)} & -\cos x \\
   2x \xrightarrow{(-)} & -\sin x \\
   2 \xrightarrow{(+)} & \cos x \\
   0 &
   \end{array}
   $$

   $\int x^2 \sin x \, dx = -x^2 \cos x + 2x \sin x + 2 \cos x + C$

5. $u = \ln x, du = \frac{dx}{x}; dv = x \, dx, v = \frac{x^2}{2}$ ;

   $\int_1^2 x \ln x \, dx = \left[\frac{x^2}{2} \ln x\right]_1^2 - \int_1^2 \frac{x^2}{2} \frac{dx}{x} = 2 \ln 2 - \left[\frac{x^2}{4}\right]_1^2 = 2 \ln 2 - \frac{3}{4} = \ln 4 - \frac{3}{4}$

6. $u = \ln x, du = \frac{dx}{x}; dv = x^3 \, dx, v = \frac{x^4}{4}$ ;

   $\int_1^e x^3 \ln x \, dx = \left[\frac{x^4}{4} \ln x\right]_1^e - \int_1^e \frac{x^4}{4} \frac{dx}{x} = \frac{e^4}{4} - \left[\frac{x^4}{16}\right]_1^e = \frac{3e^4 + 1}{16}$

7. $u = x, du = dx ; dv = e^x dx, v = e^x;$

   $\int x e^x dx = x e^x - \int e^x dx = x e^x - e^x + C$

8. $u = x, du = dx ; dv = e^{3x} dx, v = \frac{1}{3} e^{3x};$

   $\int x e^{3x} dx = \frac{x}{3} e^{3x} - \frac{1}{3} \int e^{3x} dx = \frac{x}{3} e^{3x} - \frac{1}{9} e^{3x} + C$

9.

$$e^{-x}$$

$$x^2 \xrightarrow{\ (+)\ } -e^{-x}$$

$$2x \xrightarrow{\ (-)\ } e^{-x}$$

$$2 \xrightarrow{\ (+)\ } -e^{-x}$$

$$0$$

$$\int x^2 e^{-x}\, dx = -x^2 e^{-x} - 2x\, e^{-x} - 2\, e^{-x} + C$$

10.

$$e^{2x}$$

$$x^2 - 2x + 1 \xrightarrow{\ (+)\ } \tfrac{1}{2}e^{2x}$$

$$2x - 2 \xrightarrow{\ (-)\ } \tfrac{1}{4}e^{2x}$$

$$2 \xrightarrow{\ (+)\ } \tfrac{1}{8}e^{2x}$$

$$0$$

$$\int (x^2 - 2x + 1)e^{2x}\, dx = \tfrac{1}{2}(x^2 - 2x + 1)e^{2x} - \tfrac{1}{4}(2x - 2)e^{2x} + \tfrac{1}{4}e^{2x} + C$$
$$= \left(\tfrac{1}{2}x^2 - \tfrac{3}{2}x + \tfrac{5}{4}\right)e^{2x} + C$$

11. $u = \tan^{-1} y,\ du = \frac{dy}{1+y^2}\, ;\ dv = dy,\ v = y;$

$$\int \tan^{-1} y\, dy = y \tan^{-1} y - \int \frac{y\, dy}{(1+y^2)} = y \tan^{-1} y - \tfrac{1}{2}\ln(1 + y^2) + C = y \tan^{-1} y - \ln\sqrt{1 + y^2} + C$$

12. $u = \sin^{-1} y,\ du = \frac{dy}{\sqrt{1-y^2}}\, ;\ dv = dy,\ v = y;$

$$\int \sin^{-1} y\, dy = y \sin^{-1} y - \int \frac{y\, dy}{\sqrt{1-y^2}} = y \sin^{-1} y + \sqrt{1 - y^2} + C$$

13. $u = x,\ du = dx;\ dv = \sec^2 x\, dx,\ v = \tan x;$

$$\int x \sec^2 x\, dx = x \tan x - \int \tan x\, dx = x \tan x + \ln|\cos x| + C$$

14. $\int 4x \sec^2 2x\, dx;\ [y = 2x] \ \rightarrow\ \int y \sec^2 y\, dy = y \tan y - \int \tan y\, dy = y \tan y - \ln|\sec y| + C$
$$= 2x \tan 2x - \ln|\sec 2x| + C$$

15.

$$e^{x}$$

$$x^3 \xrightarrow{\ (+)\ } e^{x}$$

$$3x^2 \xrightarrow{\ (-)\ } e^{x}$$

$$6x \xrightarrow{\ (+)\ } e^{x}$$

$$6 \xrightarrow{\ (-)\ } e^{x}$$

$$0$$

$$\int x^3 e^x\, dx = x^3 e^x - 3x^2 e^x + 6x e^x - 6e^x + C = (x^3 - 3x^2 + 6x - 6)\, e^x + C$$

**16.**

$$e^{-p}$$

$$p^4 \xrightarrow{(+)} -e^{-p}$$

$$4p^3 \xrightarrow{(-)} e^{-p}$$

$$12p^2 \xrightarrow{(+)} -e^{-p}$$

$$24p \xrightarrow{(-)} e^{-p}$$

$$24 \xrightarrow{(+)} -e^{-p}$$

$$0$$

$$\int p^4 e^{-p}\, dp = -p^4 e^{-p} - 4p^3 e^{-p} - 12p^2 e^{-p} - 24p e^{-p} - 24 e^{-p} + C$$
$$= \left(-p^4 - 4p^3 - 12p^2 - 24p - 24\right) e^{-p} + C$$

**17.**

$$e^{x}$$

$$x^2 - 5x \xrightarrow{(+)} e^{x}$$

$$2x - 5 \xrightarrow{(-)} e^{x}$$

$$2 \xrightarrow{(+)} e^{x}$$

$$0$$

$$\int (x^2 - 5x)\, e^{x}\, dx = (x^2 - 5x)\, e^{x} - (2x - 5)e^{x} + 2e^{x} + C = x^2 e^{x} - 7x e^{x} + 7 e^{x} + C$$
$$= (x^2 - 7x + 7)\, e^{x} + C$$

**18.**

$$e^{r}$$

$$r^2 + r + 1 \xrightarrow{(+)} e^{r}$$

$$2r + 1 \xrightarrow{(-)} e^{r}$$

$$2 \xrightarrow{(+)} e^{r}$$

$$0$$

$$\int (r^2 + r + 1)\, e^{r}\, dr = (r^2 + r + 1)\, e^{r} - (2r + 1)\, e^{r} + 2e^{r} + C$$
$$= \left[(r^2 + r + 1) - (2r + 1) + 2\right] e^{r} + C = (r^2 - r + 2)\, e^{r} + C$$

**19.**

$$e^{x}$$

$$x^5 \xrightarrow{(+)} e^{x}$$

$$5x^4 \xrightarrow{(-)} e^{x}$$

$$20x^3 \xrightarrow{(+)} e^{x}$$

$$60x^2 \xrightarrow{(-)} e^{x}$$

$$120x \xrightarrow{(+)} e^{x}$$

$$120 \xrightarrow{(-)} e^{x}$$

$$0$$

$$\int x^5 e^{x}\, dx = x^5 e^{x} - 5x^4 e^{x} + 20x^3 e^{x} - 60x^2 e^{x} + 120x e^{x} - 120 e^{x} + C$$
$$= (x^5 - 5x^4 + 20x^3 - 60x^2 + 120x - 120)\, e^{x} + C$$

32. $u = 25 + 4x^2 \Rightarrow du = 8x\,dx \Rightarrow \frac{1}{8}du = x\,dx$

$\int \frac{x}{25 + 4x^2}\,dx = \frac{1}{8}\int \frac{1}{u}du = \frac{1}{8}\ln|u| + C = \frac{1}{8}\ln(25 + 4x^2) + C$

33. $v = \sin\theta,\ -\frac{\pi}{2} < \theta < \frac{\pi}{2},\ dv = \cos\theta\,d\theta,\ (1 - v^2)^{5/2} = \cos^5\theta;$

$\int \frac{v^2\,dv}{(1 - v^2)^{5/2}} = \int \frac{\sin^2\theta\cos\theta\,d\theta}{\cos^5\theta} = \int \tan^2\theta\sec^2\theta\,d\theta = \frac{\tan^3\theta}{3} + C = \frac{1}{3}\left(\frac{v}{\sqrt{1 - v^2}}\right)^3 + C$

34. $r = \sin\theta,\ -\frac{\pi}{2} < \theta < \frac{\pi}{2};$

$\int \frac{(1 - r^2)^{5/2}\,dr}{r^8} = \int \frac{\cos^5\theta\cdot\cos\theta\,d\theta}{\sin^8\theta} = \int \cot^6\theta\csc^2\theta\,d\theta = -\frac{\cot^7\theta}{7} + C = -\frac{1}{7}\left[\frac{\sqrt{1 - r^2}}{r}\right]^7 + C$

35. Let $e^t = 3\tan\theta,\ t = \ln(3\tan\theta),\ \tan^{-1}\left(\frac{1}{3}\right) \le \theta \le \tan^{-1}\left(\frac{4}{3}\right),\ dt = \frac{\sec^2\theta}{\tan\theta}\,d\theta,\ \sqrt{e^{2t} + 9} = \sqrt{9\tan^2\theta + 9} = 3\sec\theta;$

$\int_0^{\ln 4} \frac{e^t\,dt}{\sqrt{e^{2t} + 9}} = \int_{\tan^{-1}(1/3)}^{\tan^{-1}(4/3)} \frac{3\tan\theta\cdot\sec^2\theta\,d\theta}{\tan\theta\cdot 3\sec\theta} = \int_{\tan^{-1}(1/3)}^{\tan^{-1}(4/3)} \sec\theta\,d\theta = \left[\ln|\sec\theta + \tan\theta|\right]_{\tan^{-1}(1/3)}^{\tan^{-1}(4/3)}$

$= \ln\left(\frac{5}{3} + \frac{4}{3}\right) - \ln\left(\frac{\sqrt{10}}{3} + \frac{1}{3}\right) = \ln 9 - \ln\left(1 + \sqrt{10}\right)$

36. Let $e^t = \tan\theta,\ t = \ln(\tan\theta),\ \tan^{-1}\left(\frac{3}{4}\right) \le \theta \le \tan^{-1}\left(\frac{4}{3}\right),\ dt = \frac{\sec^2\theta}{\tan\theta}\,d\theta,\ 1 + e^{2t} = 1 + \tan^2\theta = \sec^2\theta;$

$\int_{\ln(3/4)}^{\ln(4/3)} \frac{e^t\,dt}{(1 + e^{2t})^{3/2}} = \int_{\tan^{-1}(3/4)}^{\tan^{-1}(4/3)} \frac{(\tan\theta)\left(\frac{\sec^2\theta}{\tan\theta}\right)d\theta}{\sec^3\theta} = \int_{\tan^{-1}(3/4)}^{\tan^{-1}(4/3)} \cos\theta\,d\theta = \left[\sin\theta\right]_{\tan^{-1}(3/4)}^{\tan^{-1}(4/3)} = \frac{4}{5} - \frac{3}{5} = \frac{1}{5}$

37. $\int_{1/12}^{1/4} \frac{2\,dt}{\sqrt{t} + 4t\sqrt{t}};\ \left[u = 2\sqrt{t},\ du = \frac{1}{\sqrt{t}}\,dt\right] \to \int_{1/\sqrt{3}}^{1} \frac{2\,du}{1 + u^2};\ u = \tan\theta,\ \frac{\pi}{6} \le \theta \le \frac{\pi}{4},\ du = \sec^2\theta\,d\theta,\ 1 + u^2 = \sec^2\theta;$

$\int_{1/\sqrt{3}}^{1} \frac{2\,du}{1 + u^2} = \int_{\pi/6}^{\pi/4} \frac{2\sec^2\theta\,d\theta}{\sec^2\theta} = [2\theta]_{\pi/6}^{\pi/4} = 2\left(\frac{\pi}{4} - \frac{\pi}{6}\right) = \frac{\pi}{6}$

38. $y = e^{\tan\theta},\ 0 \le \theta \le \frac{\pi}{4},\ dy = e^{\tan\theta}\sec^2\theta\,d\theta,\ \sqrt{1 + (\ln y)^2} = \sqrt{1 + \tan^2\theta} = \sec\theta;$

$\int_1^e \frac{dy}{y\sqrt{1 + (\ln y)^2}} = \int_0^{\pi/4} \frac{e^{\tan\theta}\sec^2\theta}{e^{\tan\theta}\sec\theta}\,d\theta = \int_0^{\pi/4} \sec\theta\,d\theta = \left[\ln|\sec\theta + \tan\theta|\right]_0^{\pi/4} = \ln\left(1 + \sqrt{2}\right)$

39. $x = \sec\theta,\ 0 < \theta < \frac{\pi}{2},\ dx = \sec\theta\tan\theta\,d\theta,\ \sqrt{x^2 - 1} = \sqrt{\sec^2\theta - 1} = \tan\theta;$

$\int \frac{dx}{x\sqrt{x^2 - 1}} = \int \frac{\sec\theta\tan\theta\,d\theta}{\sec\theta\tan\theta} = \theta + C = \sec^{-1}x + C$

40. $x = \tan\theta,\ dx = \sec^2\theta\,d\theta,\ 1 + x^2 = \sec^2\theta;$

$\int \frac{dx}{x^2 + 1} = \int \frac{\sec^2\theta\,d\theta}{\sec^2\theta} = \theta + C = \tan^{-1}x + C$

41. $x = \sec\theta,\ dx = \sec\theta\tan\theta\,d\theta,\ \sqrt{x^2 - 1} = \sqrt{\sec^2\theta - 1} = \tan\theta;$

$\int \frac{x\,dx}{\sqrt{x^2 - 1}} = \int \frac{\sec\theta\cdot\sec\theta\tan\theta\,d\theta}{\tan\theta} = \int \sec^2\theta\,d\theta = \tan\theta + C = \sqrt{x^2 - 1} + C$

42. $x = \sin\theta,\ dx = \cos\theta\,d\theta,\ -\frac{\pi}{2} < \theta < \frac{\pi}{2};$

$\int \frac{dx}{\sqrt{1 - x^2}} = \int \frac{\cos\theta\,d\theta}{\cos\theta} = \theta + C = \sin^{-1}x + C$

43. Let $x^2 = \tan\theta,\ 0 \le \theta < \frac{\pi}{2},\ 2x\,dx = \sec^2\theta\,d\theta \Rightarrow x\,dx = \frac{1}{2}\sec^2\theta\,d\theta;\ \sqrt{1 + x^4} = \sqrt{1 + \tan^2\theta} = \sec\theta$

$\int \frac{x}{\sqrt{1 + x^4}}\,dx = \frac{1}{2}\int \frac{\sec^2\theta}{\sec\theta}\,d\theta = \frac{1}{2}\int \sec\theta\,d\theta = \frac{1}{2}\ln|\sec\theta + \tan\theta| + C = \frac{1}{2}\ln\left|\sqrt{1 + x^4} + x^2\right| + C$

44. Let $\ln x = \sin \theta$, $-\frac{\pi}{2} \le \theta < 0$ or $0 < \theta \le \frac{\pi}{2}$, $\frac{1}{x}dx = \cos \theta \, d\theta$, $\sqrt{1 - (\ln x)^2} = \cos \theta$

$$\int \frac{\sqrt{1-(\ln x)^2}}{x \ln x}dx = \int \frac{\cos^2 \theta}{\sin \theta}d\theta = \int \frac{1 - \sin^2 \theta}{\sin \theta}d\theta = \int \csc \theta \, d\theta - \int \sin \theta \, d\theta = -\ln|\csc \theta + \cot \theta| + \cos \theta + C$$

$$= -\ln\left|\frac{1}{\ln x} + \frac{\sqrt{1-(\ln x)^2}}{\ln x}\right| + \sqrt{1 - (\ln x)^2} + C = -\ln\left|\frac{1 + \sqrt{1-(\ln x)^2}}{\ln x}\right| + \sqrt{1 - (\ln x)^2} + C$$

45. Let $u = \sqrt{x} \Rightarrow x = u^2 \Rightarrow dx = 2u \, du \Rightarrow \int \sqrt{\frac{4-x}{x}}dx = \int \sqrt{\frac{4-u^2}{u^2}} 2u \, du = 2\int \sqrt{4 - u^2} \, du$;

$u = 2 \sin \theta$, $du = 2 \cos \theta \, d\theta$, $0 < \theta \le \frac{\pi}{2}$, $\sqrt{4 - u^2} = 2 \cos \theta$

$$2\int \sqrt{4 - u^2} \, du = 2\int (2 \cos \theta)(2 \cos \theta) \, d\theta = 8\int \cos^2 \theta \, d\theta = 8\int \frac{1 + \cos 2\theta}{2} \, d\theta = 4\int d\theta + 4\int \cos 2\theta \, d\theta$$

$$= 4\theta + 2 \sin 2\theta + C = 4\theta + 4 \sin \theta \cos \theta + C = 4 \sin^{-1}\left(\frac{u}{2}\right) + 4\left(\frac{u}{2}\right)\left(\frac{\sqrt{4-u^2}}{2}\right) + C = 4 \sin^{-1}\left(\frac{\sqrt{x}}{2}\right) + \sqrt{x}\sqrt{4 - x} + C$$

$$= 4 \sin^{-1}\left(\frac{\sqrt{x}}{2}\right) + \sqrt{4x - x^2} + C$$

46. Let $u = x^{3/2} \Rightarrow x = u^{2/3} \Rightarrow dx = \frac{2}{3}u^{-1/3}du$

$$\int \sqrt{\frac{x}{1-x^3}}dx = \int \sqrt{\frac{u^{2/3}}{1-(u^{2/3})^3}}\left(\frac{2}{3}u^{-1/3}\right)du = \int \frac{u^{1/3}}{\sqrt{1-u^2}}\left(\frac{2}{3u^{1/3}}\right)du = \frac{2}{3}\int \frac{1}{\sqrt{1-u^2}}du = \frac{2}{3}\sin^{-1}u + C = \frac{2}{3}\sin^{-1}\left(x^{3/2}\right) + C$$

47. Let $u = \sqrt{x} \Rightarrow x = u^2 \Rightarrow dx = 2u \, du \Rightarrow \int \sqrt{x}\sqrt{1 - x} \, dx = \int u\sqrt{1 - u^2} 2u \, du = 2\int u^2 \sqrt{1 - u^2} \, du$;

$u = \sin \theta$, $du = \cos \theta \, d\theta$, $-\frac{\pi}{2} < \theta \le \frac{\pi}{2}$, $\sqrt{1 - u^2} = \cos \theta$

$$2\int u^2 \sqrt{1 - u^2} \, du = 2\int \sin^2 \theta \cos \theta \cos \theta \, d\theta = 2\int \sin^2 \theta \cos^2 \theta \, d\theta = \frac{1}{2}\int \sin^2 2\theta \, d\theta = \frac{1}{2}\int \frac{1 - \cos 4\theta}{2} \, d\theta$$

$$= \frac{1}{4}\int d\theta - \frac{1}{4}\int \cos 4\theta \, d\theta = \frac{1}{4}\theta - \frac{1}{16}\sin 4\theta + C = \frac{1}{4}\theta - \frac{1}{8}\sin 2\theta \cos 2\theta + C = \frac{1}{4}\theta - \frac{1}{4}\sin \theta \cos \theta (2\cos^2 \theta - 1) + C$$

$$= \frac{1}{4}\theta - \frac{1}{2}\sin \theta \cos^3 \theta + \frac{1}{4}\sin \theta \cos \theta + C = \frac{1}{4}\sin^{-1}u - \frac{1}{2}u(1 - u^2)^{3/2} - \frac{1}{4}u\sqrt{1 - u^2} + C$$

$$= \frac{1}{4}\sin^{-1}\sqrt{x} - \frac{1}{2}\sqrt{x}(1 - x)^{3/2} - \frac{1}{4}\sqrt{x}\sqrt{1 - x} + C$$

48. Let $w = \sqrt{x - 1} \Rightarrow w^2 = x - 1 \Rightarrow 2w \, dw = dx \Rightarrow \int \frac{\sqrt{x-2}}{\sqrt{x-1}}dx = \int \frac{\sqrt{w^2-1}}{w}2w \, dw = 2\int \sqrt{w^2 - 1} \, dw$

$w = \sec \theta$, $dx = \sec \theta \tan \theta \, d\theta$, $0 < \theta < \frac{\pi}{2}$, $\sqrt{w^2 - 1} = \tan \theta$

$$2\int \sqrt{w^2 - 1} \, dw = 2\int \tan \theta \sec \theta \tan \theta \, d\theta; u = \tan \theta, du = \sec^2 \theta \, d\theta, dv = \sec \theta \tan \theta \, d\theta, v = \sec \theta$$

$$2\int \tan \theta \sec \theta \tan \theta \, d\theta = 2 \sec \theta \tan \theta - 2\int \sec^3 \theta \, d\theta = 2 \sec \theta \tan \theta - 2\int \sec^2 \theta \sec \theta d\theta$$

$$= 2 \sec \theta \tan \theta - 2\int (\tan^2 \theta + 1)\sec \theta \, d\theta = 2 \sec \theta \tan \theta - 2\left(\int \tan^2 \theta \sec \theta \, d\theta + \int \sec \theta \, d\theta\right)$$

$$= 2\sec \theta \tan \theta - 2\ln|\sec \theta + \tan \theta| - 2\int \tan^2 \theta \sec \theta \, d\theta \Rightarrow 2\int \tan^2 \theta \sec \theta \, d\theta = \sec \theta \tan \theta - \ln|\sec \theta + \tan \theta| + C$$

$$= w\sqrt{w^2 - 1} - \ln|w + \sqrt{w^2 - 1}| + C = \sqrt{x - 1}\sqrt{x - 2} - \ln|\sqrt{x - 1} + \sqrt{x - 2}| + C$$

49. $x\frac{dy}{dx} = \sqrt{x^2 - 4}$; $dy = \sqrt{x^2 - 4}\frac{dx}{x}$ ; $y = \int \frac{\sqrt{x^2-4}}{x} \, dx$; $\begin{bmatrix} x = 2 \sec \theta, 0 < \theta < \frac{\pi}{2} \\ dx = 2 \sec \theta \tan \theta \, d\theta \\ \sqrt{x^2 - 4} = 2 \tan \theta \end{bmatrix}$

$$\rightarrow y = \int \frac{(2 \tan \theta)(2 \sec \theta \tan \theta) \, d\theta}{2 \sec \theta} = 2\int \tan^2 \theta \, d\theta = 2\int (\sec^2 \theta - 1) \, d\theta = 2(\tan \theta - \theta) + C$$

$$= 2\left[\frac{\sqrt{x^2-4}}{2} - \sec^{-1}\left(\frac{x}{2}\right)\right] + C; x = 2 \text{ and } y = 0 \Rightarrow 0 = 0 + C \Rightarrow C = 0 \Rightarrow y = 2\left[\frac{\sqrt{x^2-4}}{2} - \sec^{-1}\frac{x}{2}\right]$$

50. $\sqrt{x^2-9}\,\frac{dy}{dx}=1$, $dy=\frac{dx}{\sqrt{x^2-9}}$; $y=\int\frac{dx}{\sqrt{x^2-9}}$; $\begin{bmatrix} x=3\sec\theta, 0<\theta<\frac{\pi}{2} \\ dx=3\sec\theta\tan\theta\,d\theta \\ \sqrt{x^2-9}=3\tan\theta \end{bmatrix} \rightarrow y=\int\frac{3\sec\theta\tan\theta\,d\theta}{3\tan\theta}$

$=\int\sec\theta\,d\theta=\ln|\sec\theta+\tan\theta|+C=\ln\left|\frac{x}{3}+\frac{\sqrt{x^2-9}}{3}\right|+C$; $x=5$ and $y=\ln 3 \Rightarrow \ln 3=\ln 3+C \Rightarrow C=0$

$\Rightarrow y=\ln\left|\frac{x}{3}+\frac{\sqrt{x^2-9}}{3}\right|$

51. $(x^2+4)\frac{dy}{dx}=3$, $dy=\frac{3\,dx}{x^2+4}$; $y=3\int\frac{dx}{x^2+4}=\frac{3}{2}\tan^{-1}\frac{x}{2}+C$; $x=2$ and $y=0 \Rightarrow 0=\frac{3}{2}\tan^{-1}1+C$

$\Rightarrow C=-\frac{3\pi}{8} \Rightarrow y=\frac{3}{2}\tan^{-1}\left(\frac{x}{2}\right)-\frac{3\pi}{8}$

52. $(x^2+1)^2\frac{dy}{dx}=\sqrt{x^2+1}$, $dy=\frac{dx}{(x^2+1)^{3/2}}$; $x=\tan\theta$, $dx=\sec^2\theta\,d\theta$, $(x^2+1)^{3/2}=\sec^3\theta$;

$y=\int\frac{\sec^2\theta\,d\theta}{\sec^3\theta}=\int\cos\theta\,d\theta=\sin\theta+C=\tan\theta\cos\theta+C=\frac{\tan\theta}{\sec\theta}+C=\frac{x}{\sqrt{x^2+1}}+C$; $x=0$ and $y=1$

$\Rightarrow 1=0+C \Rightarrow y=\frac{x}{\sqrt{x^2+1}}+1$

53. $A=\int_0^3\frac{\sqrt{9-x^2}}{3}\,dx$; $x=3\sin\theta, 0\le\theta\le\frac{\pi}{2}$, $dx=3\cos\theta\,d\theta$, $\sqrt{9-x^2}=\sqrt{9-9\sin^2\theta}=3\cos\theta$;

$A=\int_0^{\pi/2}\frac{3\cos\theta\cdot 3\cos\theta\,d\theta}{3}=3\int_0^{\pi/2}\cos^2\theta\,d\theta=\frac{3}{2}[\theta+\sin\theta\cos\theta]_0^{\pi/2}=\frac{3\pi}{4}$

54. $\frac{x^2}{a^2}+\frac{y^2}{b^2}=1 \Rightarrow y=\pm b\sqrt{1-\frac{x^2}{a^2}}$; $A=4\int_0^a b\sqrt{1-\frac{x^2}{a^2}}\,dx=4b\int_0^a\sqrt{1-\frac{x^2}{a^2}}\,dx$

$\begin{bmatrix} x=a\sin\theta, -\frac{\pi}{2}\le\theta\le\frac{\pi}{2}, dx=a\cos\theta\,d\theta, \sqrt{1-\frac{x^2}{a^2}}=\cos\theta, x=0=a\sin\theta \Rightarrow \theta=0, x=a=a\sin\theta \Rightarrow \theta=\frac{\pi}{2} \end{bmatrix}$

$4b\int_0^a\sqrt{1-\frac{x^2}{a^2}}\,dx=4b\int_0^{\pi/2}\cos\theta\,(a\cos\theta)\,d\theta=4ab\int_0^{\pi/2}\cos^2\theta\,d\theta=4ab\int_0^{\pi/2}\frac{1+\cos 2\theta}{2}\,d\theta$

$=2ab\int_0^{\pi/2}d\theta+2ab\int_0^{\pi/2}\cos 2\theta\,d\theta=2ab\left[\theta\right]_0^{\pi/2}+ab\left[\sin 2\theta\right]_0^{\pi/2}=2ab\left(\frac{\pi}{2}-0\right)+ab(\sin\pi-\sin 0)=\pi ab$

55. (a) $A=\int_0^{1/2}\sin^{-1}x\,dx$ $\left[u=\sin^{-1}x, du=\frac{1}{\sqrt{1-x^2}}dx, dv=dx, v=x\right]$

$=\left[x\sin^{-1}x\right]_0^{1/2}-\int_0^{1/2}\frac{x}{\sqrt{1-x^2}}\,dx==\left(\frac{1}{2}\sin^{-1}\frac{1}{2}-0\right)+\left[\sqrt{1-x^2}\right]_0^{1/2}=\frac{\pi+6\sqrt{3}-12}{12}$

(b) $M=\int_0^{1/2}\sin^{-1}x\,dx=\frac{\pi+6\sqrt{3}-12}{12}$; $\bar{x}=\frac{1}{\frac{\pi+6\sqrt{3}-12}{12}}\int_0^{1/2}x\sin^{-1}x\,dx=\frac{12}{\pi+6\sqrt{3}-12}\int_0^{1/2}x\sin^{-1}x\,dx$

$\left[u=\sin^{-1}x, du=\frac{1}{\sqrt{1-x^2}}dx, dv=x\,dx, v=\frac{1}{2}x^2\right]$

$=\frac{12}{\pi+6\sqrt{3}-12}\left(\left[\frac{1}{2}x^2\sin^{-1}x\right]_0^{1/2}-\frac{1}{2}\int_0^{1/2}\frac{x^2}{\sqrt{1-x^2}}\,dx\right)$

$\left[x=\sin\theta, -\frac{\pi}{2}<\theta<\frac{\pi}{2}, dx=\cos\theta\,d\theta, \sqrt{1-x^2}=\cos\theta, x=0=\sin\theta \Rightarrow \theta=0, x=\frac{1}{2}=\sin\theta \Rightarrow \theta=\frac{\pi}{6}\right]$

$=\frac{12}{\pi+6\sqrt{3}-12}\left(\left(\frac{1}{2}\left(\frac{1}{2}\right)^2\sin^{-1}\left(\frac{1}{2}\right)-0\right)-\frac{1}{2}\int_0^{\pi/6}\frac{\sin^2\theta}{\cos\theta}\cos\theta\,d\theta\right)=\frac{12}{\pi+6\sqrt{3}-12}\left(\frac{\pi}{48}-\frac{1}{2}\int_0^{\pi/6}\sin^2\theta\,d\theta\right)$

$=\frac{12}{\pi+6\sqrt{3}-12}\left(\frac{\pi}{48}-\frac{1}{2}\int_0^{\pi/6}\frac{1-\cos 2\theta}{2}\,d\theta\right)=\frac{12}{\pi+6\sqrt{3}-12}\left(\frac{\pi}{48}-\frac{1}{4}\int_0^{\pi/6}d\theta+\frac{1}{4}\int_0^{\pi/6}\cos 2\theta\,d\theta\right)$

$=\frac{12}{\pi+6\sqrt{3}-12}\left(\frac{\pi}{48}+\left[-\frac{\theta}{4}+\frac{1}{8}\sin 2\theta\right]_0^{\pi/6}\right)=\frac{3\sqrt{3}-\pi}{4\left(\pi+6\sqrt{3}-12\right)}$; $\bar{y}=\frac{1}{\frac{\pi+6\sqrt{3}-12}{12}}\int_0^{1/2}\frac{1}{2}(\sin^{-1}x)^2dx$

$\left[u=(\sin^{-1}x)^2, du=\frac{2\sin^{-1}x}{\sqrt{1-x^2}}dx, dv=dx, v=x\right]$

$$= \frac{6}{\pi + 6\sqrt{3} - 12}\left(\left[x(\sin^{-1}x\,dx)^2\right]_0^{1/2} - \int_0^{1/2}\frac{2x\sin^{-1}x}{\sqrt{1-x^2}}dx\right)$$

$$\left[u = \sin^{-1}x, du = \frac{1}{\sqrt{1-x^2}}dx, dv = \frac{2x}{\sqrt{1-x^2}}dx, v = -2\sqrt{1-x^2}\right]$$

$$= \frac{6}{\pi + 6\sqrt{3} - 12}\left(\left(\tfrac{1}{2}\left(\sin^{-1}\left(\tfrac{1}{2}\right)\right)^2 - 0\right) + \left[2\sqrt{1-x^2}\sin^{-1}x\right]_0^{1/2} - \int_0^{1/2}\frac{2\sqrt{1-x^2}}{\sqrt{1-x^2}}dx\right)$$

$$= \frac{6}{\pi + 6\sqrt{3} - 12}\left(\frac{\pi^2}{72} + \left(2\sqrt{1-\left(\tfrac{1}{2}\right)^2}\sin^{-1}\left(\tfrac{1}{2}\right) - 0\right) - [2x]_0^{1/2}\right) = \frac{6}{\pi + 6\sqrt{3} - 12}\left(\frac{\pi^2}{72} + \frac{\pi\sqrt{3}}{6} - 1\right) = \frac{\pi^2 + 12\pi\sqrt{3} - 72}{12\left(\pi + 6\sqrt{3} - 12\right)}$$

56. $V = \int_0^1 \pi\left(\sqrt{x\tan^{-1}x}\right)^2 dx = \pi\int_0^1 x\tan^{-1}x\,dx$ $\qquad \left[u = \tan^{-1}x, du = \frac{1}{1+x^2}dx, dv = x\,dx, v = \tfrac{1}{2}x^2\right]$

$$= \pi\left(\left[\tfrac{1}{2}x^2\tan^{-1}x\right]_0^1 - \tfrac{1}{2}\int_0^1\frac{x^2}{1+x^2}dx\right) = \pi\left(\left(\tfrac{1}{2}\tan^{-1}1 - 0\right) - \tfrac{1}{2}\int_0^1\left(1 - \frac{1}{1+x^2}\right)dx\right) = \pi\left(\frac{\pi}{8} - \tfrac{1}{2}\int_0^1\left(1 - \frac{1}{1+x^2}\right)dx\right)$$

$$= \pi\left(\frac{\pi}{8} - \tfrac{1}{2}\int_0^1 dx + \tfrac{1}{2}\int_0^1\frac{1}{1+x^2}dx\right) = \pi\left(\frac{\pi}{8} + \left[-\tfrac{1}{2}x + \tfrac{1}{2}\tan^{-1}x\right]_0^1\right) = \pi\left(\frac{\pi}{8} + \left(-\tfrac{1}{2} + \tfrac{1}{2}\tan^{-1}1 + 0 - 0\right)\right) = \frac{\pi(\pi - 2)}{4}$$

57. (a) Integration by parts: $u = x^2, du = 2x\,dx, dv = x\sqrt{1-x^2}\,dx, v = -\tfrac{1}{3}(1-x^2)^{3/2}$

$$\int x^3\sqrt{1-x^2}\,dx = -\tfrac{1}{3}x^2(1-x^2)^{3/2} + \tfrac{1}{3}\int(1-x^2)^{3/2}2x\,dx = -\tfrac{1}{3}x^2(1-x^2)^{3/2} - \tfrac{2}{15}(1-x^2)^{5/2} + C$$

(b) Substitution: $u = 1 - x^2 \Rightarrow x^2 = 1 - u \Rightarrow du = -2x\,dx \Rightarrow -\tfrac{1}{2}du = x\,dx$

$$\int x^3\sqrt{1-x^2}\,dx = \int x^2\sqrt{1-x^2}\,x\,dx = -\tfrac{1}{2}\int(1-u)\sqrt{u}\,du = -\tfrac{1}{2}\int\left(\sqrt{u} - u^{3/2}\right)du = -\tfrac{1}{3}u^{3/2} + \tfrac{1}{5}u^{5/2} + C$$

$$= -\tfrac{1}{3}(1-x^2)^{3/2} + \tfrac{1}{5}(1-x^2)^{5/2} + C$$

(c) Trig substitution: $x = \sin\theta,\ \frac{\pi}{2} \le \theta \le \frac{\pi}{2},\ dx = \cos\theta\,d\theta,\ \sqrt{1-x^2} = \cos\theta$

$$\int x^3\sqrt{1-x^2}\,dx = \int\sin^3\theta\cos\theta\cos\theta\,d\theta = \int\sin^2\theta\cos^2\theta\sin\theta\,d\theta = \int(1 - \cos^2\theta)\cos^2\theta\sin\theta\,d\theta$$

$$= \int\cos^2\theta\sin\theta\,d\theta - \int\cos^4\theta\sin\theta\,d\theta = -\tfrac{1}{3}\cos^3\theta + \tfrac{1}{5}\cos^5\theta + C = -\tfrac{1}{3}(1-x^2)^{3/2} + \tfrac{1}{5}(1-x^2)^{5/2} + C$$

58. (a) The slope of the line tangent to $y = f(x)$ is given by $f'(x)$. Consider the triangle whose hypotenuse is the 30 ft rope, the length of the base is x and the height $h = \sqrt{900 - x^2}$. The slope of the tangent line is also $-\frac{\sqrt{900 - x^2}}{x}$, thus $f'(x) = -\frac{\sqrt{900 - x^2}}{x}$.

(b) $f(x) = \int -\frac{\sqrt{900 - x^2}}{x}dx$ $\quad\left[x = 30\sin\theta, 0 < \theta \le \frac{\pi}{2}, dx = 30\cos\theta\,d\theta, \sqrt{900 - x^2} = 30\cos\theta\right]$

$$= -\int\frac{30\cos\theta}{30\sin\theta}30\cos\theta\,d\theta = -30\int\frac{\cos^2\theta}{\sin\theta}d\theta = -30\int\frac{(1 - \sin^2\theta)}{\sin\theta}d\theta = -30\int\csc\theta\,d\theta + 30\int\sin\theta\,d\theta$$

$$= 30\ln|\csc\theta + \cot\theta| - 30\cos\theta + C = 30\ln\left|\frac{30}{x} + \frac{\sqrt{900 - x^2}}{x}\right| - \sqrt{900 - x^2} + C; f(30) = 0$$

$$\Rightarrow 0 = 30\ln\left|\frac{30}{30} + \frac{\sqrt{900 - 30^2}}{30}\right| - \sqrt{900 - 30^2} + C = C \Rightarrow f(x) = 30\ln\left|\frac{30}{x} + \frac{\sqrt{900 - x^2}}{x}\right| - \sqrt{900 - x^2}$$

## 8.4 INTEGRATION OF RATIONAL FUNCTIONS BY PARTIAL FRACTIONS

1. $\frac{5x - 13}{(x - 3)(x - 2)} = \frac{A}{x - 3} + \frac{B}{x - 2} \Rightarrow 5x - 13 = A(x - 2) + B(x - 3) = (A + B)x - (2A + 3B)$

$\Rightarrow \left.\begin{array}{l} A + B = 5 \\ 2A + 3B = 13 \end{array}\right\} \Rightarrow -B = (10 - 13) \Rightarrow B = 3 \Rightarrow A = 2$; thus, $\frac{5x - 13}{(x - 3)(x - 2)} = \frac{2}{x - 3} + \frac{3}{x - 2}$

2. $\frac{5x - 7}{x^2 - 3x + 2} = \frac{5x - 7}{(x - 2)(x - 1)} = \frac{A}{x - 2} + \frac{B}{x - 1} \Rightarrow 5x - 7 = A(x - 1) + B(x - 2) = (A + B)x - (A + 2B)$

$\Rightarrow \left.\begin{array}{l} A + B = 5 \\ A + 2B = 7 \end{array}\right\} \Rightarrow B = 2 \Rightarrow A = 3$; thus, $\frac{5x - 7}{x^2 - 3x + 2} = \frac{3}{x - 2} + \frac{2}{x - 1}$

3. $\frac{x+4}{(x+1)^2} = \frac{A}{x+1} + \frac{B}{(x+1)^2} \Rightarrow x+4 = A(x+1)+B = Ax+(A+B) \Rightarrow \left.\begin{matrix} A=1 \\ A+B=4 \end{matrix}\right\} \Rightarrow A=1$ and $B=3$;

thus, $\frac{x+4}{(x+1)^2} = \frac{1}{x+1} + \frac{3}{(x+1)^2}$

4. $\frac{2x+2}{x^2-2x+1} = \frac{2x+2}{(x-1)^2} = \frac{A}{x-1} + \frac{B}{(x-1)^2} \Rightarrow 2x+2 = A(x-1)+B = Ax+(-A+B) \Rightarrow \left.\begin{matrix} A=2 \\ -A+B=2 \end{matrix}\right\}$

$\Rightarrow A=2$ and $B=4$; thus, $\frac{2x+2}{x^2-2x+1} = \frac{2}{x-1} + \frac{4}{(x-1)^2}$

5. $\frac{z+1}{z^2(z-1)} = \frac{A}{z} + \frac{B}{z^2} + \frac{C}{z-1} \Rightarrow z+1 = Az(z-1)+B(z-1)+Cz^2 \Rightarrow z+1 = (A+C)z^2+(-A+B)z-B$

$\Rightarrow \left.\begin{matrix} A+C=0 \\ -A+B=1 \\ -B=1 \end{matrix}\right\} \Rightarrow B=-1 \Rightarrow A=-2 \Rightarrow C=2$; thus, $\frac{z+1}{z^2(z-1)} = \frac{-2}{z} + \frac{-1}{z^2} + \frac{2}{z-1}$

6. $\frac{z}{z^3-z^2-6z} = \frac{1}{z^2-z-6} = \frac{1}{(z-3)(z+2)} = \frac{A}{z-3} + \frac{B}{z+2} \Rightarrow 1 = A(z+2)+B(z-3) = (A+B)z+(2A-3B)$

$\Rightarrow \left.\begin{matrix} A+B=0 \\ 2A-3B=1 \end{matrix}\right\} \Rightarrow -5B=1 \Rightarrow B=-\frac{1}{5} \Rightarrow A=\frac{1}{5}$; thus, $\frac{z}{z^3-z^2-6z} = \frac{\frac{1}{5}}{z-3} + \frac{-\frac{1}{5}}{z+2}$

7. $\frac{t^2+8}{t^2-5t+6} = 1 + \frac{5t+2}{t^2-5t+6}$ (after long division); $\frac{5t+2}{t^2-5t+6} = \frac{5t+2}{(t-3)(t-2)} = \frac{A}{t-3} + \frac{B}{t-2}$

$\Rightarrow 5t+2 = A(t-2)+B(t-3) = (A+B)t+(-2A-3B) \Rightarrow \left.\begin{matrix} A+B=5 \\ -2A-3B=2 \end{matrix}\right\} \Rightarrow -B=(10+2)=12$

$\Rightarrow B=-12 \Rightarrow A=17$; thus, $\frac{t^2+8}{t^2-5t+6} = 1 + \frac{17}{t-3} + \frac{-12}{t-2}$

8. $\frac{t^4+9}{t^4+9t^2} = 1 + \frac{-9t^2+9}{t^4+9t^2} = 1 + \frac{-9t^2+9}{t^2(t^2+9)}$ (after long division); $\frac{-9t^2+9}{t^2(t^2+9)} = \frac{A}{t} + \frac{B}{t^2} + \frac{Ct+D}{t^2+9}$

$\Rightarrow -9t^2+9 = At(t^2+9)+B(t^2+9)+(Ct+D)t^2 = (A+C)t^3+(B+D)t^2+9At+9B$

$\Rightarrow \left.\begin{matrix} A+C=0 \\ B+D=-9 \\ 9A=0 \\ 9B=9 \end{matrix}\right\} \Rightarrow A=0 \Rightarrow C=0;\ B=1 \Rightarrow D=-10$; thus, $\frac{t^4+9}{t^4+9t^2} = 1 + \frac{1}{t^2} + \frac{-10}{t^2+9}$

9. $\frac{1}{1-x^2} = \frac{A}{1-x} + \frac{B}{1+x} \Rightarrow 1 = A(1+x)+B(1-x);\ x=1 \Rightarrow A=\frac{1}{2};\ x=-1 \Rightarrow B=\frac{1}{2}$;

$\int \frac{dx}{1-x^2} = \frac{1}{2}\int \frac{dx}{1-x} + \frac{1}{2}\int \frac{dx}{1+x} = \frac{1}{2}\left[\ln|1+x| - \ln|1-x|\right] + C$

10. $\frac{1}{x^2+2x} = \frac{A}{x} + \frac{B}{x+2} \Rightarrow 1 = A(x+2)+Bx;\ x=0 \Rightarrow A=\frac{1}{2};\ x=-2 \Rightarrow B=-\frac{1}{2}$;

$\int \frac{dx}{x^2+2x} = \frac{1}{2}\int \frac{dx}{x} - \frac{1}{2}\int \frac{dx}{x+2} = \frac{1}{2}\left[\ln|x| - \ln|x+2|\right] + C$

11. $\frac{x+4}{x^2+5x-6} = \frac{A}{x+6} + \frac{B}{x-1} \Rightarrow x+4 = A(x-1)+B(x+6);\ x=1 \Rightarrow B=\frac{5}{7};\ x=-6 \Rightarrow A=\frac{-2}{-7}=\frac{2}{7}$;

$\int \frac{x+4}{x^2+5x-6}\,dx = \frac{2}{7}\int \frac{dx}{x+6} + \frac{5}{7}\int \frac{dx}{x-1} = \frac{2}{7}\ln|x+6| + \frac{5}{7}\ln|x-1| + C = \frac{1}{7}\ln\left|(x+6)^2(x-1)^5\right| + C$

12. $\frac{2x+1}{x^2-7x+12} = \frac{A}{x-4} + \frac{B}{x-3} \Rightarrow 2x+1 = A(x-3)+B(x-4);\ x=3 \Rightarrow B=\frac{7}{-1}=-7;\ x=4 \Rightarrow A=\frac{9}{1}=9$;

$\int \frac{2x+1}{x^2-7x+12}\,dx = 9\int \frac{dx}{x-4} - 7\int \frac{dx}{x-3} = 9\ln|x-4| - 7\ln|x-3| + C = \ln\left|\frac{(x-4)^9}{(x-3)^7}\right| + C$

13. $\frac{y}{y^2-2y-3} = \frac{A}{y-3} + \frac{B}{y+1} \Rightarrow y = A(y+1)+B(y-3);\ y=-1 \Rightarrow B=\frac{-1}{-4}=\frac{1}{4};\ y=3 \Rightarrow A=\frac{3}{4}$;

$\int_4^8 \frac{y\,dy}{y^2-2y-3} = \frac{3}{4}\int_4^8 \frac{dy}{y-3} + \frac{1}{4}\int_4^8 \frac{dy}{y+1} = \left[\frac{3}{4}\ln|y-3| + \frac{1}{4}\ln|y+1|\right]_4^8 = \left(\frac{3}{4}\ln 5 + \frac{1}{4}\ln 9\right) - \left(\frac{3}{4}\ln 1 + \frac{1}{4}\ln 5\right)$

$= \frac{1}{2}\ln 5 + \frac{1}{2}\ln 3 = \frac{\ln 15}{2}$

14. $\frac{y+4}{y^2+y} = \frac{A}{y} + \frac{B}{y+1} \Rightarrow y+4 = A(y+1) + By;\ y=0 \Rightarrow A=4;\ y=-1 \Rightarrow B=\frac{3}{-1}=-3;$

$\int_{1/2}^{1} \frac{y+4}{y^2+y}\,dy = 4\int_{1/2}^{1}\frac{dy}{y} - 3\int_{1/2}^{1}\frac{dy}{y+1} = [4\ln|y| - 3\ln|y+1|]_{1/2}^{1} = (4\ln 1 - 3\ln 2) - \left(4\ln\frac{1}{2} - 3\ln\frac{3}{2}\right)$

$= \ln\frac{1}{8} - \ln\frac{1}{16} + \ln\frac{27}{8} = \ln\left(\frac{27}{8}\cdot\frac{1}{8}\cdot 16\right) = \ln\frac{27}{4}$

15. $\frac{1}{t^3+t^2-2t} = \frac{A}{t} + \frac{B}{t+2} + \frac{C}{t-1} \Rightarrow 1 = A(t+2)(t-1) + Bt(t-1) + Ct(t+2);\ t=0 \Rightarrow A=-\frac{1}{2};\ t=-2$

$\Rightarrow B=\frac{1}{6};\ t=1 \Rightarrow C=\frac{1}{3};\ \int\frac{dt}{t^3+t^2-2t} = -\frac{1}{2}\int\frac{dt}{t} + \frac{1}{6}\int\frac{dt}{t+2} + \frac{1}{3}\int\frac{dt}{t-1}$

$= -\frac{1}{2}\ln|t| + \frac{1}{6}\ln|t+2| + \frac{1}{3}\ln|t-1| + C$

16. $\frac{x+3}{2x^3-8x} = \frac{A}{x} + \frac{B}{x+2} + \frac{C}{x-2} \Rightarrow \frac{1}{2}(x+3) = A(x+2)(x-2) + Bx(x-2) + Cx(x+2);\ x=0 \Rightarrow A=\frac{3}{-8};\ x=-2$

$\Rightarrow B=\frac{1}{16};\ x=2 \Rightarrow C=\frac{5}{16};\ \int\frac{x+3}{2x^3-8x}\,dx = -\frac{3}{8}\int\frac{dx}{x} + \frac{1}{16}\int\frac{dx}{x+2} + \frac{5}{16}\int\frac{dx}{x-2}$

$= -\frac{3}{8}\ln|x| + \frac{1}{16}\ln|x+2| + \frac{5}{16}\ln|x-2| + C = \frac{1}{16}\ln\left|\frac{(x-2)^5(x+2)}{x^6}\right| + C$

17. $\frac{x^3}{x^2+2x+1} = (x-2) + \frac{3x+2}{(x+1)^2}$ (after long division); $\frac{3x+2}{(x+1)^2} = \frac{A}{x+1} + \frac{B}{(x+1)^2} \Rightarrow 3x+2 = A(x+1) + B$

$= Ax + (A+B) \Rightarrow A=3,\ A+B=2 \Rightarrow A=3,\ B=-1;\ \int_0^1\frac{x^3\,dx}{x^2+2x+1}$

$= \int_0^1(x-2)\,dx + 3\int_0^1\frac{dx}{x+1} - \int_0^1\frac{dx}{(x+1)^2} = \left[\frac{x^2}{2} - 2x + 3\ln|x+1| + \frac{1}{x+1}\right]_0^1$

$= \left(\frac{1}{2} - 2 + 3\ln 2 + \frac{1}{2}\right) - (1) = 3\ln 2 - 2$

18. $\frac{x^3}{x^2-2x+1} = (x+2) + \frac{3x-2}{(x-1)^2}$ (after long division); $\frac{3x-2}{(x-1)^2} = \frac{A}{x-1} + \frac{B}{(x-1)^2} \Rightarrow 3x-2 = A(x-1) + B$

$= Ax + (-A+B) \Rightarrow A=3,\ -A+B=-2 \Rightarrow A=3,\ B=1;\ \int_{-1}^{0}\frac{x^3\,dx}{x^2-2x+1}$

$= \int_{-1}^{0}(x+2)\,dx + 3\int_{-1}^{0}\frac{dx}{x-1} + \int_{-1}^{0}\frac{dx}{(x-1)^2} = \left[\frac{x^2}{2} + 2x + 3\ln|x-1| - \frac{1}{x-1}\right]_{-1}^{0}$

$= \left(0 + 0 + 3\ln 1 - \frac{1}{(-1)}\right) - \left(\frac{1}{2} - 2 + 3\ln 2 - \frac{1}{(-2)}\right) = 2 - 3\ln 2$

19. $\frac{1}{(x^2-1)^2} = \frac{A}{x+1} + \frac{B}{x-1} + \frac{C}{(x+1)^2} + \frac{D}{(x-1)^2} \Rightarrow 1 = A(x+1)(x-1)^2 + B(x-1)(x+1)^2 + C(x-1)^2 + D(x+1)^2;$

$x=-1 \Rightarrow C=\frac{1}{4};\ x=1 \Rightarrow D=\frac{1}{4};$ coefficient of $x^3 = A+B \Rightarrow A+B=0;$ constant $= A-B+C+D$

$\Rightarrow A-B+C+D=1 \Rightarrow A-B=\frac{1}{2};$ thus, $A=\frac{1}{4} \Rightarrow B=-\frac{1}{4};\ \int\frac{dx}{(x^2-1)^2}$

$= \frac{1}{4}\int\frac{dx}{x+1} - \frac{1}{4}\int\frac{dx}{x-1} + \frac{1}{4}\int\frac{dx}{(x+1)^2} + \frac{1}{4}\int\frac{dx}{(x-1)^2} = \frac{1}{4}\ln\left|\frac{x+1}{x-1}\right| - \frac{x}{2(x^2-1)} + C$

20. $\frac{x^2}{(x-1)(x^2+2x+1)} = \frac{A}{x-1} + \frac{B}{x+1} + \frac{C}{(x+1)^2} \Rightarrow x^2 = A(x+1)^2 + B(x-1)(x+1) + C(x-1);\ x=-1$

$\Rightarrow C=-\frac{1}{2};\ x=1 \Rightarrow A=\frac{1}{4};$ coefficient of $x^2 = A+B \Rightarrow A+B=1 \Rightarrow B=\frac{3}{4};\ \int\frac{x^2\,dx}{(x-1)(x^2+2x+1)}$

$= \frac{1}{4}\int\frac{dx}{x-1} + \frac{3}{4}\int\frac{dx}{x+1} - \frac{1}{2}\int\frac{dx}{(x+1)^2} = \frac{1}{4}\ln|x-1| + \frac{3}{4}\ln|x+1| + \frac{1}{2(x+1)} + C = \frac{\ln|(x-1)(x+1)^3|}{4} + \frac{1}{2(x+1)} + C$

21. $\frac{1}{(x+1)(x^2+1)} = \frac{A}{x+1} + \frac{Bx+C}{x^2+1} \Rightarrow 1 = A(x^2+1) + (Bx+C)(x+1);\ x=-1 \Rightarrow A=\frac{1}{2};$ coefficient of $x^2$

$= A+B \Rightarrow A+B=0 \Rightarrow B=-\frac{1}{2};$ constant $= A+C \Rightarrow A+C=1 \Rightarrow C=\frac{1}{2};\ \int_0^1\frac{dx}{(x+1)(x^2+1)}$

$= \frac{1}{2}\int_0^1\frac{dx}{x+1} + \frac{1}{2}\int_0^1\frac{(-x+1)}{x^2+1}\,dx = \left[\frac{1}{2}\ln|x+1| - \frac{1}{4}\ln(x^2+1) + \frac{1}{2}\tan^{-1}x\right]_0^1$

$= \left(\frac{1}{2}\ln 2 - \frac{1}{4}\ln 2 + \frac{1}{2}\tan^{-1}1\right) - \left(\frac{1}{2}\ln 1 - \frac{1}{4}\ln 1 + \frac{1}{2}\tan^{-1}0\right) = \frac{1}{4}\ln 2 + \frac{1}{2}\left(\frac{\pi}{4}\right) = \frac{(\pi + 2\ln 2)}{8}$

22. $\frac{3t^2+t+4}{t^3+t} = \frac{A}{t} + \frac{Bt+C}{t^2+1} \Rightarrow 3t^2+t+4 = A(t^2+1) + (Bt+C)t;\ t=0 \Rightarrow A=4;$ coefficient of $t^2$

$= A+B \Rightarrow A+B=3 \Rightarrow B=-1;$ coefficient of $t = C \Rightarrow C=1;\ \int_1^{\sqrt{3}}\frac{3t^2+t+4}{t^3+1}\,dt$

$$= 4 \int_1^{\sqrt{3}} \tfrac{dt}{t} + \int_1^{\sqrt{3}} \tfrac{(-t+1)}{t^2+1}\, dt = \left[ 4 \ln|t| - \tfrac{1}{2} \ln(t^2+1) + \tan^{-1} t \right]_1^{\sqrt{3}}$$

$$= \left( 4 \ln\sqrt{3} - \tfrac{1}{2}\ln 4 + \tan^{-1}\sqrt{3} \right) - \left( 4\ln 1 - \tfrac{1}{2}\ln 2 + \tan^{-1} 1 \right) \doteq 2\ln 3 - \ln 2 + \tfrac{\pi}{3} + \tfrac{1}{2}\ln 2 - \tfrac{\pi}{4}$$

$$= 2\ln 3 - \tfrac{1}{2}\ln 2 + \tfrac{\pi}{12} = \ln\left( \tfrac{9}{\sqrt{2}} \right) + \tfrac{\pi}{12}$$

23. $\frac{y^2+2y+1}{(y^2+1)^2} = \frac{Ay+B}{y^2+1} + \frac{Cy+D}{(y^2+1)^2} \Rightarrow y^2+2y+1 = (Ay+B)(y^2+1)+Cy+D$

$= Ay^3 + By^2 + (A+C)y + (B+D) \Rightarrow A=0, B=1; A+C=2 \Rightarrow C=2; B+D=1 \Rightarrow D=0;$

$\int \frac{y^2+2y+1}{(y^2+1)^2}\, dy = \int \frac{1}{y^2+1}\, dy + 2\int \frac{y}{(y^2+1)^2}\, dy = \tan^{-1} y - \frac{1}{y^2+1} + C$

24. $\frac{8x^2+8x+2}{(4x^2+1)^2} = \frac{Ax+B}{4x^2+1} + \frac{Cx+D}{(4x^2+1)^2} \Rightarrow 8x^2+8x+2 = (Ax+B)(4x^2+1)+Cx+D$

$= 4Ax^3 + 4Bx^2 + (A+C)x + (B+D); A=0, B=2; A+C=8 \Rightarrow C=8; B+D=2 \Rightarrow D=0;$

$\int \frac{8x^2+8x+2}{(4x^2+1)^2}\, dx = 2\int \frac{dx}{4x^2+1} + 8\int \frac{x\, dx}{(4x^2+1)^2} = \tan^{-1} 2x - \frac{1}{4x^2+1} + C$

25. $\frac{2s+2}{(s^2+1)(s-1)^3} = \frac{As+B}{s^2+1} + \frac{C}{s-1} + \frac{D}{(s-1)^2} + \frac{E}{(s-1)^3} \Rightarrow 2s+2$

$= (As+B)(s-1)^3 + C(s^2+1)(s-1)^2 + D(s^2+1)(s-1) + E(s^2+1)$

$= [As^4 + (-3A+B)s^3 + (3A-3B)s^2 + (-A+3B)s - B] + C(s^4 - 2s^3 + 2s^2 - 2s + 1) + D(s^3 - s^2 + s - 1)$

$\qquad + E(s^2+1)$

$= (A+C)s^4 + (-3A+B-2C+D)s^3 + (3A-3B+2C-D+E)s^2 + (-A+3B-2C+D)s + (-B+C-D+E)$

$\Rightarrow \left. \begin{array}{rl} A \;\;\;\; + C & = 0 \\ -3A + B - 2C + D & = 0 \\ 3A - 3B + 2C - D + E & = 0 \\ -A + 3B - 2C + D & = 2 \\ -B + C - D + E & = 2 \end{array} \right\}$ summing all equations $\Rightarrow 2E = 4 \Rightarrow E = 2;$

summing eqs (2) and (3) $\Rightarrow -2B + 2 = 0 \Rightarrow B = 1;$ summing eqs (3) and (4) $\Rightarrow 2A + 2 = 2 \Rightarrow A = 0; C = 0$
from eq (1); then $-1 + 0 - D + 2 = 2$ from eq (5) $\Rightarrow D = -1;$

$\int \frac{2s+2}{(s^2+1)(s-1)^3}\, ds = \int \frac{ds}{s^2+1} - \int \frac{ds}{(s-1)^2} + 2\int \frac{ds}{(s-1)^3} = -(s-1)^{-2} + (s-1)^{-1} + \tan^{-1} s + C$

26. $\frac{s^4+81}{s(s^2+9)^2} = \frac{A}{s} + \frac{Bs+C}{s^2+9} + \frac{Ds+E}{(s^2+9)^2} \Rightarrow s^4+81 = A(s^2+9)^2 + (Bs+C)s(s^2+9) + (Ds+E)s$

$= A(s^4 + 18s^2 + 81) + (Bs^4 + Cs^3 + 9Bs^2 + 9Cs) + Ds^2 + Es$

$= (A+B)s^4 + Cs^3 + (18A+9B+D)s^2 + (9C+E)s + 81A \Rightarrow 81A = 81 \text{ or } A = 1; A+B = 1 \Rightarrow B = 0;$

$C = 0; 9C+E = 0 \Rightarrow E = 0; 18A+9B+D = 0 \Rightarrow D = -18; \int \frac{s^4+81}{s(s^2+9)^2}\, ds = \int \frac{ds}{s} - 18\int \frac{s\, ds}{(s^2+9)^2}$

$= \ln|s| + \frac{9}{(s^2+9)} + C$

27. $\frac{x^2-x+2}{x^3-1} = \frac{A}{x-1} + \frac{Bx+C}{x^2+x+1} \Rightarrow x^2-x+2 = A(x^2+x+1) + (Bx+C)(x-1) = (A+B)x^2 + (A-B+C)x + (A-C)$

$\Rightarrow A+B = 1, A-B+C = -1, A-C = 2 \Rightarrow$ adding eq(2) and eq(3) $\Rightarrow 2A-B = 1,$ add this equation to eq(1)

$\Rightarrow 3A = 2 \Rightarrow A = \frac{2}{3} \Rightarrow B = 1 - A = \frac{1}{3} \Rightarrow C = -1 - A + B = -\frac{4}{3}; \int \frac{x^2-x+2}{x^3-1}\, dx = \int \left( \frac{2/3}{x-1} + \frac{(1/3)x - 4/3}{x^2+x+1} \right) dx$

$= \frac{2}{3} \int \frac{1}{x-1}\, dx + \frac{1}{3} \int \frac{x-4}{(x+\frac{1}{2})^2 + \frac{3}{4}}\, dx \quad \left[ u = x + \frac{1}{2} \Rightarrow u - \frac{1}{2} = x \Rightarrow du = dx \right]$

$= \frac{2}{3} \int \frac{1}{x-1}\, dx + \frac{1}{3} \int \frac{u - \frac{9}{2}}{u^2 + \frac{3}{4}}\, du = \frac{2}{3} \int \frac{1}{x-1}\, dx + \frac{1}{3} \int \frac{u}{u^2 + \frac{3}{4}}\, du - \frac{3}{2} \int \frac{1}{u^2 + \frac{3}{4}}\, du$

$= \frac{2}{3}\ln|x-1| + \frac{1}{6}\ln\left| \left(x + \frac{1}{2}\right)^2 + \frac{3}{4} \right| - \frac{3}{\sqrt{3}}\tan^{-1}\left( \frac{x + \frac{1}{2}}{\sqrt{3}/2} \right) + C = \frac{2}{3}\ln|x-1| + \frac{1}{6}\ln|x^2+x+1| - \sqrt{3}\tan^{-1}\left( \frac{2x+1}{\sqrt{3}} \right) + C$

**28.** $\frac{1}{x^4+x} = \frac{A}{x} + \frac{B}{x+1} + \frac{Cx+D}{x^2-x+1} \Rightarrow 1 = A(x+1)(x^2-x+1) + Bx(x^2-x+1) + (Cx+D)x(x+1)$

$= (A+B+C)x^3 + (-B+C+D)x^2 + (B+D)x + A \Rightarrow A=1, B+D=0 \Rightarrow D=-B, -B+C+D=0$

$\Rightarrow -2B+C=0 \Rightarrow C=2B, A+B+C=0 \Rightarrow 1+B+2B=0 \Rightarrow B=-\frac{1}{3} \Rightarrow C=-\frac{2}{3} \Rightarrow D=\frac{1}{3};$

$\int \frac{1}{x^4+x}dx = \int \left(\frac{1}{x} - \frac{1/3}{x+1} + \frac{(-2/3)x+1/3}{x^2-x+1}\right)dx = \int \frac{1}{x}dx - \frac{1}{3}\int \frac{1}{x+1}dx - \frac{1}{3}\int \frac{2x-1}{x^2-x+1}dx$

$= \ln|x| - \frac{1}{3}\ln|x+1| - \frac{1}{3}\ln|x^2-x+1| + C$

**29.** $\frac{x^2}{x^4-1} = \frac{A}{x+1} + \frac{B}{x-1} + \frac{Cx+D}{x^2+1} \Rightarrow x^2 = A(x-1)(x^2+1) + B(x+1)(x^2+1) + (Cx+D)(x-1)(x+1)$

$= (A+B+C)x^3 + (-A+B+D)x^2 + (A+B-C)x - A+B-D \Rightarrow A+B+C=0, -A+B+D=1,$

$A+B-C=0, -A+B-D=0 \Rightarrow$ adding eq(1) to eq (3) gives $2A+2B=0$, adding eq(2) to eq(4) gives

$-2A+2B=1$, adding these two equations gives $4B=1 \Rightarrow B=\frac{1}{4}$, using $2A+2B=0 \Rightarrow A=-\frac{1}{4}$, using

$-A+B-D=0 \Rightarrow D=\frac{1}{2}$, and using $A+B-C=0 \Rightarrow C=0; \int \frac{x^2}{x^4-1}dx = \int \left(\frac{-1/4}{x+1} + \frac{1/4}{x-1} + \frac{1/2}{x^2+1}\right)dx$

$= -\frac{1}{4}\int \frac{1}{x+1}dx + \frac{1}{4}\int \frac{1}{x-1}dx + \frac{1}{2}\int \frac{1}{x^2+1}dx = -\frac{1}{4}\ln|x+1| + \frac{1}{4}\ln|x-1| + \frac{1}{2}\tan^{-1}x + C = \frac{1}{4}\ln\left|\frac{x-1}{x+1}\right| + \frac{1}{2}\tan^{-1}x + C$

**30.** $\frac{x^2+x}{x^4-3x^2-4} = \frac{A}{x-2} + \frac{B}{x+2} + \frac{Cx+D}{x^2+1} \Rightarrow x^2+x = A(x+2)(x^2+1) + B(x-2)(x^2+1) + (Cx+D)(x-2)(x+2)$

$= (A+B+C)x^3 + (2A-2B+D)x^2 + (A+B-4C)x + 2A-2B-4D \Rightarrow A+B+C=0, 2A-2B+D=1,$

$A+B-4C=1, 2A-2B-4D=0 \Rightarrow$ subtractin eq(1) from eq (3) gives $-5C=1 \Rightarrow C=-\frac{1}{5}$, subtacting eq(2) from

eq(4) gives $-5D=-1 \Rightarrow D=\frac{1}{5}$, substituting for C in eq(1) gives $A+B=\frac{1}{5}$, and substituting for D in eq(4) gives

$2A-2B=\frac{4}{5} \Rightarrow A-B=\frac{2}{5}$, adding this equation to the previous equatin gives $2A=\frac{3}{5} \Rightarrow A=\frac{3}{10} \Rightarrow B=-\frac{1}{10};$

$\int \frac{x^2+x}{x^4-3x^2-4}dx = \int \left(\frac{3/10}{x-2} - \frac{1/10}{x+2} + \frac{(-1/5)x+1/5}{x^2+1}\right)dx = \frac{3}{10}\int \frac{1}{x-2}dx - \frac{1}{10}\int \frac{1}{x+2}dx - \frac{1}{5}\int \frac{x}{x^2+1}dx + \frac{1}{5}\int \frac{1}{x^2+1}dx$

$\frac{3}{10}\ln|x-2| - \frac{1}{10}\ln|x+2| - \frac{1}{10}\ln|x^2+1| + \frac{1}{5}\tan^{-1}x + C$

**31.** $\frac{2\theta^3+5\theta^2+8\theta+4}{(\theta^2+2\theta+2)^2} = \frac{A\theta+B}{\theta^2+2\theta+2} + \frac{C\theta+D}{(\theta^2+2\theta+2)^2} \Rightarrow 2\theta^3+5\theta^2+8\theta+4 = (A\theta+B)(\theta^2+2\theta+2) + C\theta+D$

$= A\theta^3 + (2A+B)\theta^2 + (2A+2B+C)\theta + (2B+D) \Rightarrow A=2; 2A+B=5 \Rightarrow B=1; 2A+2B+C=8 \Rightarrow C=2;$

$2B+D=4 \Rightarrow D=2; \int \frac{2\theta^3+5\theta^2+8\theta+4}{(\theta^2+2\theta+2)^2}d\theta = \int \frac{2\theta+1}{(\theta^2+2\theta+2)}d\theta + \int \frac{2\theta+2}{(\theta^2+2\theta+2)^2}d\theta$

$= \int \frac{2\theta+2}{\theta^2+2\theta+2}d\theta - \int \frac{d\theta}{\theta^2+2\theta+2} + \int \frac{d(\theta^2+2\theta+2)}{(\theta^2+2\theta+2)^2} = \int \frac{d(\theta^2+2\theta+2)}{\theta^2+2\theta+2} - \int \frac{d\theta}{(\theta+1)^2+1} - \frac{1}{\theta^2+2\theta+2}$

$= \frac{-1}{\theta^2+2\theta+2} + \ln(\theta^2+2\theta+2) - \tan^{-1}(\theta+1) + C$

**32.** $\frac{\theta^4-4\theta^3+2\theta^2-3\theta+1}{(\theta^2+1)^3} = \frac{A\theta+B}{\theta^2+1} + \frac{C\theta+D}{(\theta^2+1)^2} + \frac{E\theta+F}{(\theta^2+1)^3} \Rightarrow \theta^4-4\theta^3+2\theta^2-3\theta+1$

$= (A\theta+B)(\theta^2+1)^2 + (C\theta+D)(\theta^2+1) + E\theta+F = (A\theta+B)(\theta^4+2\theta^2+1) + (C\theta^3+D\theta^2+C\theta+D) + E\theta+F$

$= (A\theta^5+B\theta^4+2A\theta^3+2B\theta^2+A\theta+B) + (C\theta^3+D\theta^2+C\theta+D) + E\theta+F$

$= A\theta^5 + B\theta^4 + (2A+C)\theta^3 + (2B+D)\theta^2 + (A+C+E)\theta + (B+D+F) \Rightarrow A=0; B=1; 2A+C=-4$

$\Rightarrow C=-4; 2B+D=2 \Rightarrow D=0; A+C+E=-3 \Rightarrow E=1; B+D+F=1 \Rightarrow F=0;$

$\int \frac{\theta^4-4\theta^3+2\theta^2-3\theta+1}{(\theta^2+1)^3}d\theta = \int \frac{d\theta}{\theta^2+1} - 4\int \frac{\theta\,d\theta}{(\theta^2+1)^2} + \int \frac{\theta\,d\theta}{(\theta^2+1)^3} = \tan^{-1}\theta + 2(\theta^2+1)^{-1} - \frac{1}{4}(\theta^2+1)^{-2} + C$

**33.** $\frac{2x^3-2x^2+1}{x^2-x} = 2x + \frac{1}{x^2-x} = 2x + \frac{1}{x(x-1)}; \frac{1}{x(x-1)} = \frac{A}{x} + \frac{B}{x-1} \Rightarrow 1 = A(x-1) + Bx; x=0 \Rightarrow A=-1;$

$x=1 \Rightarrow B=1; \int \frac{2x^3-2x^2+1}{x^2-x} = \int 2x\,dx - \int \frac{dx}{x} + \int \frac{dx}{x-1} = x^2 - \ln|x| + \ln|x-1| + C = x^2 + \ln\left|\frac{x-1}{x}\right| + C$

**34.** $\frac{x^4}{x^2-1} = (x^2+1) + \frac{1}{x^2-1} = (x^2+1) + \frac{1}{(x+1)(x-1)}; \frac{1}{(x+1)(x-1)} = \frac{A}{x+1} + \frac{B}{x-1} \Rightarrow 1 = A(x-1) + B(x+1);$

$x=-1 \Rightarrow A=-\frac{1}{2}; x=1 \Rightarrow B=\frac{1}{2}; \int \frac{x^4}{x^2-1}dx = \int (x^2+1)dx - \frac{1}{2}\int \frac{dx}{x+1} + \frac{1}{2}\int \frac{dx}{x-1}$

$= \frac{1}{3}x^3 + x - \frac{1}{2}\ln|x+1| + \frac{1}{2}\ln|x-1| + C = \frac{x^3}{3} + x + \frac{1}{2}\ln\left|\frac{x-1}{x+1}\right| + C$

**35.** $\frac{9x^3 - 3x + 1}{x^3 - x^2} = 9 + \frac{9x^2 - 3x + 1}{x^2(x-1)}$ (after long division); $\frac{9x^2 - 3x + 1}{x^2(x-1)} = \frac{A}{x} + \frac{B}{x^2} + \frac{C}{x-1}$

$\Rightarrow 9x^2 - 3x + 1 = Ax(x-1) + B(x-1) + Cx^2$; $x = 1 \Rightarrow C = 7$; $x = 0 \Rightarrow B = -1$; $A + C = 9 \Rightarrow A = 2$;

$\int \frac{9x^3 - 3x + 1}{x^3 - x^2}\, dx = \int 9\, dx + 2\int \frac{dx}{x} - \int \frac{dx}{x^2} + 7\int \frac{dx}{x-1} = 9x + 2\ln|x| + \frac{1}{x} + 7\ln|x-1| + C$

**36.** $\frac{16x^3}{4x^2 - 4x + 1} = (4x + 4) + \frac{12x - 4}{4x^2 - 4x + 1}$ ; $\frac{12x - 4}{(2x-1)^2} = \frac{A}{2x-1} + \frac{B}{(2x-1)^2} \Rightarrow 12x - 4 = A(2x-1) + B$

$\Rightarrow A = 6; -A + B = -4 \Rightarrow B = 2; \int \frac{16x^3}{4x^2 - 4x + 1}\, dx = 4\int (x+1)\, dx + 6\int \frac{dx}{2x-1} + 2\int \frac{dx}{(2x-1)^2}$

$= 2(x+1)^2 + 3\ln|2x-1| - \frac{1}{2x-1} + C_1 = 2x^2 + 4x + 3\ln|2x-1| - (2x-1)^{-1} + C$, where $C = 2 + C_1$

**37.** $\frac{y^4 + y^2 - 1}{y^3 + y} = y - \frac{1}{y(y^2+1)}$ ; $\frac{1}{y(y^2+1)} = \frac{A}{y} + \frac{By + C}{y^2 + 1} \Rightarrow 1 = A(y^2 + 1) + (By + C)y = (A + B)y^2 + Cy + A$

$7 \Rightarrow A = 1; A + B = 0 \Rightarrow B = -1; C = 0; \int \frac{y^4 + y^2 - 1}{y^3 + y}\, dy = \int y\, dy - \int \frac{dy}{y} + \int \frac{y\, dy}{y^2 + 1}$

$= \frac{y^2}{2} - \ln|y| + \frac{1}{2}\ln(1 + y^2) + C$

**38.** $\frac{2y^4}{y^3 - y^2 + y - 1} = 2y + 2 + \frac{2}{y^3 - y^2 + y - 1}$ ; $\frac{2}{y^3 - y^2 + y - 1} = \frac{2}{(y^2+1)(y-1)} = \frac{A}{y-1} + \frac{By + C}{y^2 + 1}$

$\Rightarrow 2 = A(y^2 + 1) + (By + C)(y - 1) = (Ay^2 + A) + (By^2 + Cy - By - C) = (A + B)y^2 + (-B + C)y + (A - C)$

$\Rightarrow A + B = 0, -B + C = 0$ or $C = B, A - C = A - B = 2 \Rightarrow A = 1, B = -1, C = -1$;

$\int \frac{2y^4}{y^3 - y^2 + y - 1}\, dy = 2\int (y+1)\, dy + \int \frac{dy}{y-1} - \int \frac{y}{y^2+1}\, dy - \int \frac{dy}{y^2 + 1}$

$= (y+1)^2 + \ln|y-1| - \frac{1}{2}\ln(y^2 + 1) - \tan^{-1} y + C_1 = y^2 + 2y + \ln|y-1| - \frac{1}{2}\ln(y^2 + 1) - \tan^{-1} y + C$,

where $C = C_1 + 1$

**39.** $\int \frac{e^t\, dt}{e^{2t} + 3e^t + 2} = [e^t = y]\int \frac{dy}{y^2 + 3y + 2} = \int \frac{dy}{y+1} - \int \frac{dy}{y+2} = \ln\left|\frac{y+1}{y+2}\right| + C = \ln\left(\frac{e^t + 1}{e^t + 2}\right) + C$

**40.** $\int \frac{e^{4t} + 2e^{2t} - e^t}{e^{2t} + 1}\, dt = \int \frac{e^{3t} + 2e^t - e^t}{e^{2t} + 1}e^t dt; \begin{bmatrix} y = e^t \\ dy = e^t\, dt \end{bmatrix} \rightarrow \int \frac{y^3 + 2y - 1}{y^2 + 1}\, dy = \int \left(y + \frac{y-1}{y^2+1}\right) dy = \frac{y^2}{2} + \int \frac{y}{y^2+1}\, dy - \int \frac{dy}{y^2 + 1}$

$= \frac{y^2}{2} + \frac{1}{2}\ln(y^2 + 1) - \tan^{-1} y + C = \frac{1}{2}e^{2t} + \frac{1}{2}\ln(e^{2t} + 1) - \tan^{-1}(e^t) + C$

**41.** $\int \frac{\cos y\, dy}{\sin^2 y + \sin y - 6}; [\sin y = t, \cos y\, dy = dt] \rightarrow \int \frac{dy}{t^2 + t - 6} = \frac{1}{5}\int \left(\frac{1}{t-2} - \frac{1}{t+3}\right) dt = \frac{1}{5}\ln\left|\frac{t-2}{t+3}\right| + C$

$= \frac{1}{5}\ln\left|\frac{\sin y - 2}{\sin y + 3}\right| + C$

**42.** $\int \frac{\sin\theta\, d\theta}{\cos^2\theta + \cos\theta - 2}; [\cos\theta = y] \rightarrow -\int \frac{dy}{y^2 + y - 2} = \frac{1}{3}\int \frac{dy}{y+2} - \frac{1}{3}\int \frac{dy}{y-1} = \frac{1}{3}\ln\left|\frac{y+2}{y-1}\right| + C = \frac{1}{3}\ln\left|\frac{\cos\theta + 2}{\cos\theta - 1}\right| + C$

$= \frac{1}{3}\ln\left|\frac{2 + \cos\theta}{1 - \cos\theta}\right| + C = -\frac{1}{3}\ln\left|\frac{\cos\theta - 1}{\cos\theta + 2}\right| + C$

**43.** $\int \frac{(x-2)^2 \tan^{-1}(2x) - 12x^3 - 3x}{(4x^2 + 1)(x-2)^2}\, dx = \int \frac{\tan^{-1}(2x)}{4x^2 + 1}\, dx - 3\int \frac{x}{(x-2)^2}\, dx$

$= \frac{1}{2}\int \tan^{-1}(2x)\, d(\tan^{-1}(2x)) - 3\int \frac{dx}{x-2} - 6\int \frac{dx}{(x-2)^2} = \frac{(\tan^{-1} 2x)^2}{4} - 3\ln|x-2| + \frac{6}{x-2} + C$

**44.** $\int \frac{(x+1)^2 \tan^{-1}(3x) + 9x^3 + x}{(9x^2 + 1)(x+1)^2}\, dx = \int \frac{\tan^{-1}(3x)}{9x^2 + 1}\, dx + \int \frac{x}{(x+1)^2}\, dx$

$= \frac{1}{3}\int \tan^{-1}(3x)\, d(\tan^{-1}(3x)) + \int \frac{dx}{x+1} - \int \frac{dx}{(x+1)^2} = \frac{(\tan^{-1} 3x)^2}{6} + \ln|x+1| + \frac{1}{x+1} + C$

**45.** $\int \frac{1}{x^{3/2} - \sqrt{x}}\, dx = \int \frac{1}{\sqrt{x}(x-1)}\, dx \left[\text{Let } u = \sqrt{x} \Rightarrow du = \frac{1}{2\sqrt{x}}\, dx \Rightarrow 2\, du = \frac{1}{\sqrt{x}}\, dx\right] \rightarrow \int \frac{2}{u^2 - 1}\, du;$

$\frac{2}{u^2 - 1} = \frac{A}{u+1} + \frac{B}{u-1} \Rightarrow 2 = A(u-1) + B(u+1) = (A + B)u - A + B \Rightarrow A + B = 0, -A + B = 2$

$\Rightarrow B = 1 \Rightarrow A = -1; \int \frac{2}{u^2-1} du = \int \left(\frac{-1}{u+1} + \frac{1}{u-1}\right) du = -\int \frac{1}{u+1} du + \int \frac{1}{u-1} du = -\ln|u+1| + \ln|u-1| + C$

$= \ln\left|\frac{\sqrt{x}-1}{\sqrt{x}+1}\right| + C$

46. $\int \frac{1}{(x^{1/3}-1)\sqrt{x}} dx \left[\text{Let } x = u^6 \Rightarrow dx = 6u^5 du\right] \to \int \frac{1}{(u^2-1)u^3} 6u^5 du = \int \frac{6u^2}{u^2-1} du = \int \left(6 + \frac{6}{u^2-1}\right) du$

$= 6\int du + \int \frac{6}{u^2-1} du; \frac{6}{u^2-1} = \frac{A}{u+1} + \frac{B}{u-1} \Rightarrow 6 = A(u-1) + B(u+1) = (A+B)u - A + B \Rightarrow A + B = 0,$

$-A + B = 6 \Rightarrow B = 3 \Rightarrow A = -3; 6\int du + \int \frac{6}{u^2-1} du = 6u + \int \left(\frac{-3}{u+1} + \frac{3}{u-1}\right) du = 6u - 3\int \frac{1}{u+1} du + 3\int \frac{1}{u-1} du$

$= 6u - 3\ln|u+1| + 3\ln|u-1| + C = 6x^{1/6} + 3\ln\left|\frac{x^{1/6}-1}{x^{1/6}+1}\right| + C$

47. $\int \frac{\sqrt{x+1}}{x} dx \left[\text{Let } x+1 = u^2 \Rightarrow dx = 2u\, du\right] \to \int \frac{u}{u^2-1} 2u\, du = \int \frac{2u^2}{u^2-1} du = \int \left(2 + \frac{2}{u^2-1}\right) du$

$= 2\int du + \int \frac{2}{u^2-1} du; \frac{2}{u^2-1} = \frac{A}{u+1} + \frac{B}{u-1} \Rightarrow 2 = A(u-1) + B(u+1) = (A+B)u - A + B \Rightarrow A + B = 0,$

$-A + B = 2 \Rightarrow B = 1 \Rightarrow A = -1; 2\int du + \int \frac{2}{u^2-1} du = 2u + \int \left(\frac{-1}{u+1} + \frac{1}{u-1}\right) du = 2u - \int \frac{1}{u+1} du + \int \frac{1}{u-1} du$

$= 2u - \ln|u+1| + \ln|u-1| + C = 2\sqrt{x+1} + \ln\left|\frac{\sqrt{x+1}-1}{\sqrt{x+1}+1}\right| + C$

48. $\int \frac{1}{x\sqrt{x+9}} dx \left[\text{Let } x+9 = u^2 \Rightarrow dx = 2u\, du\right] \to \int \frac{1}{(u^2-9)u} 2u\, du = \int \frac{2}{u^2-9} du; \frac{2}{u^2-9} = \frac{A}{u-3} + \frac{B}{u+3}$

$\Rightarrow 2 = A(u+3) + B(u-3) = (A+B)u + 3A - 3B \Rightarrow A + B = 0, 3A - 3B = 2 \Rightarrow A = \frac{1}{3} \Rightarrow B = -\frac{1}{3};$

$\int \frac{2}{u^2-9} du = \int \left(\frac{1/3}{u-3} - \frac{1/3}{u+3}\right) du = \frac{1}{3}\int \frac{1}{u-3} du - \frac{1}{3}\int \frac{1}{u+3} du = \frac{1}{3}\ln|u-3| - \frac{1}{3}\ln|u+3| + C = \frac{1}{3}\ln\left|\frac{\sqrt{x+9}-3}{\sqrt{x+9}+3}\right| + C$

49. $\int \frac{1}{x(x^4+1)} dx = \int \frac{x^3}{x^4(x^4+1)} dx \left[\text{Let } u = x^4 \Rightarrow du = 4x^3 dx\right] \to \frac{1}{4}\int \frac{1}{u(u+1)} du; \frac{1}{u(u+1)} = \frac{A}{u} + \frac{B}{u+1}$

$\Rightarrow 1 = A(u+1) + Bu = (A+B)u + A \Rightarrow A = 1 \Rightarrow B = -1; \frac{1}{4}\int \frac{1}{u(u+1)} du = \frac{1}{4}\int \left(\frac{1}{u} - \frac{1}{u+1}\right) du$

$= \frac{1}{4}\int \frac{1}{u} du - \frac{1}{4}\int \frac{1}{u+1} du = \frac{1}{4}\ln|u| - \frac{1}{4}\ln|u+1| + C = \frac{1}{4}\ln\left(\frac{x^4}{x^4+1}\right) + C$

50. $\int \frac{1}{x^6(x^5+4)} dx = \int \frac{x^4}{x^{10}(x^5+4)} dx = \left[\text{Let } u = x^5 \Rightarrow du = 5x^4 dx\right] \to \frac{1}{5}\int \frac{1}{u^2(u+4)} du; \frac{1}{u^2(u+4)} = \frac{A}{u} + \frac{B}{u^2} + \frac{C}{u+4}$

$\Rightarrow 1 = Au(u+4) + B(u+4) + Cu^2 = (A+C)u^2 + (4A+B)u + 4B \Rightarrow A + C = 0, 4A + B = 0, 4B = 1 \Rightarrow B = \frac{1}{4}$

$\Rightarrow A = -\frac{1}{16} \Rightarrow C = \frac{1}{16}; \frac{1}{5}\int \frac{1}{u^2(u+4)} du = \frac{1}{5}\int \left(-\frac{1/16}{u} + \frac{1/4}{u^2} + \frac{1/16}{u+4}\right) du = -\frac{1}{80}\int \frac{1}{u} du + \frac{1}{20}\int \frac{1}{u^2} du + \frac{1}{80}\int \frac{1}{u+4} du$

$= -\frac{1}{80}\ln|u| - \frac{1}{20u} + \frac{1}{80}\ln|u+4| + C = -\frac{1}{80}\ln|x^5| - \frac{1}{20x^5} + \frac{1}{80}\ln|x^5+4| + C = \frac{1}{80}\ln\left|\frac{x^5+4}{x^5}\right| - \frac{1}{20x^5} + C$

51. $(t^2 - 3t + 2)\frac{dx}{dt} = 1; x = \int \frac{dt}{t^2-3t+2} = \int \frac{dt}{t-2} - \int \frac{dt}{t-1} = \ln\left|\frac{t-2}{t-1}\right| + C; \frac{t-2}{t-1} = Ce^x; t = 3 \text{ and } x = 0$

$\Rightarrow \frac{1}{2} = C \Rightarrow \frac{t-2}{t-1} = \frac{1}{2}e^x \Rightarrow x = \ln\left|2\left(\frac{t-2}{t-1}\right)\right| = \ln|t-2| - \ln|t-1| + \ln 2$

52. $(3t^4 + 4t^2 + 1)\frac{dx}{dt} = 2\sqrt{3}; x = 2\sqrt{3}\int \frac{dt}{3t^4+4t^2+1} = \sqrt{3}\int \frac{dt}{t^2+\frac{1}{3}} - \sqrt{3}\int \frac{dt}{t^2+1}$

$= 3\tan^{-1}\left(\sqrt{3}t\right) - \sqrt{3}\tan^{-1}t + C; t = 1 \text{ and } x = \frac{-\pi\sqrt{3}}{4} \Rightarrow -\frac{\sqrt{3}\pi}{4} = \pi - \frac{\sqrt{3}}{4}\pi + C \Rightarrow C = -\pi$

$\Rightarrow x = 3\tan^{-1}\left(\sqrt{3}t\right) - \sqrt{3}\tan^{-1}t - \pi$

53. $(t^2 + 2t) \frac{dx}{dt} = 2x + 2$; $\frac{1}{2}\int \frac{dx}{x+1} = \int \frac{dt}{t^2+2t}$ $\Rightarrow$ $\frac{1}{2}\ln|x+1| = \frac{1}{2}\int \frac{dt}{t} - \frac{1}{2}\int \frac{dt}{t+2}$ $\Rightarrow$ $\ln|x+1| = \ln\left|\frac{t}{t+2}\right| + C$;

$t = 1$ and $x = 1$ $\Rightarrow$ $\ln 2 = \ln\frac{1}{3} + C$ $\Rightarrow$ $C = \ln 2 + \ln 3 = \ln 6$ $\Rightarrow$ $\ln|x+1| = \ln 6\left|\frac{t}{t+2}\right|$ $\Rightarrow$ $x + 1 = \frac{6t}{t+2}$

$\Rightarrow$ $x = \frac{6t}{t+2} - 1, t > 0$

54. $(t+1)\frac{dx}{dt} = x^2 + 1$ $\Rightarrow$ $\int \frac{dx}{x^2+1} = \int \frac{dt}{t+1}$ $\Rightarrow$ $\tan^{-1}x = \ln|t+1| + C$; $t = 0$ and $x = 0$ $\Rightarrow$ $\tan^{-1}0 = \ln|1| + C$

$\Rightarrow$ $C = \tan^{-1}0 = 0$ $\Rightarrow$ $\tan^{-1}x = \ln|t+1|$ $\Rightarrow$ $x = \tan(\ln(t+1)), t > -1$

55. $V = \pi\int_{0.5}^{2.5} y^2\,dx = \pi\int_{0.5}^{2.5}\frac{9}{3x-x^2}\,dx = 3\pi\left(\int_{0.5}^{2.5}\left(-\frac{1}{x-3} + \frac{1}{x}\right)\right)dx = \left[3\pi\ln\left|\frac{x}{x-3}\right|\right]_{0.5}^{2.5} = 3\pi\ln 25$

56. $V = 2\pi\int_0^1 xy\,dx = 2\pi\int_0^1 \frac{2x}{(x+1)(2-x)}\,dx = 4\pi\int_0^1\left(-\frac{1}{3}\left(\frac{1}{x+1}\right) + \frac{2}{3}\left(\frac{1}{2-x}\right)\right)dx$

$= \left[-\frac{4\pi}{3}\left(\ln|x+1| + 2\ln|2-x|\right)\right]_0^1 = \frac{4\pi}{3}(\ln 2)$

57. $A = \int_0^{\sqrt{3}} \tan^{-1}x\,dx = \left[x\tan^{-1}x\right]_0^{\sqrt{3}} - \int_0^{\sqrt{3}}\frac{x}{1+x^2}\,dx$

$= \frac{\pi\sqrt{3}}{3} - \left[\frac{1}{2}\ln(x^2+1)\right]_0^{\sqrt{3}} = \frac{\pi\sqrt{3}}{3} - \ln 2$;

$\bar{x} = \frac{1}{A}\int_0^{\sqrt{3}} x\tan^{-1}x\,dx$

$= \frac{1}{A}\left(\left[\frac{1}{2}x^2\tan^{-1}x\right]_0^{\sqrt{3}} - \frac{1}{2}\int_0^{\sqrt{3}}\frac{x^2}{1+x^2}\,dx\right)$

$= \frac{1}{A}\left[\frac{\pi}{2} - \left[\frac{1}{2}(x - \tan^{-1}x)\right]_0^{\sqrt{3}}\right]$

$= \frac{1}{A}\left(\frac{\pi}{2} - \frac{\sqrt{3}}{2} + \frac{\pi}{6}\right) = \frac{1}{A}\left(\frac{2\pi}{3} - \frac{\sqrt{3}}{2}\right) \cong 1.10$

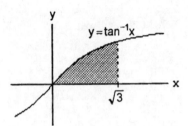

58. $A = \int_3^5 \frac{4x^2 + 13x - 9}{x^3 + 2x^2 - 3x}\,dx = 3\int_3^5\frac{dx}{x} - \int_3^5\frac{dx}{x+3} + 2\int_3^5\frac{dx}{x-1} = \left[3\ln|x| - \ln|x+3| + 2\ln|x-1|\right]_3^5 = \ln\frac{125}{9}$;

$\bar{x} = \frac{1}{A}\int_3^5\frac{x(4x^2+13x-9)}{x^3+2x^2-3x}\,dx = \frac{1}{A}\left(\left[4x\right]_3^5 + 3\int_3^5\frac{dx}{x+3} + 2\int_3^5\frac{dx}{x-1}\right) = \frac{1}{A}(8 + 11\ln 2 - 3\ln 6) \cong 3.90$

59. (a) $\frac{dx}{dt} = kx(N-x)$ $\Rightarrow$ $\int\frac{dx}{x(N-x)} = \int k\,dt$ $\Rightarrow$ $\frac{1}{N}\int\frac{dx}{x} + \frac{1}{N}\int\frac{dx}{N-x} = \int k\,dt$ $\Rightarrow$ $\frac{1}{N}\ln\left|\frac{x}{N-x}\right| = kt + C$;

$k = \frac{1}{250}, N = 1000, t = 0$ and $x = 2$ $\Rightarrow$ $\frac{1}{1000}\ln\left|\frac{2}{998}\right| = C$ $\Rightarrow$ $\frac{1}{1000}\ln\left|\frac{x}{1000-x}\right| = \frac{t}{250} + \frac{1}{1000}\ln\left(\frac{1}{499}\right)$

$\Rightarrow$ $\ln\left|\frac{499x}{1000-x}\right| = 4t$ $\Rightarrow$ $\frac{499x}{1000-x} = e^{4t}$ $\Rightarrow$ $499x = e^{4t}(1000-x)$ $\Rightarrow$ $(499 + e^{4t})x = 1000e^{4t}$ $\Rightarrow$ $x = \frac{1000e^{4t}}{499+e^{4t}}$

(b) $x = \frac{1}{2}N = 500$ $\Rightarrow$ $500 = \frac{1000e^{4t}}{499+e^{4t}}$ $\Rightarrow$ $500 \cdot 499 + 500e^{4t} = 1000e^{4t}$ $\Rightarrow$ $e^{4t} = 499$ $\Rightarrow$ $t = \frac{1}{4}\ln 499 \approx 1.55$ days

60. $\frac{dx}{dt} = k(a-x)(b-x)$ $\Rightarrow$ $\frac{dx}{(a-x)(b-x)} = k\,dt$

(a) $a = b$: $\int\frac{dx}{(a-x)^2} = \int k\,dt$ $\Rightarrow$ $\frac{1}{a-x} = kt + C$; $t = 0$ and $x = 0$ $\Rightarrow$ $\frac{1}{a} = C$ $\Rightarrow$ $\frac{1}{a-x} = kt + \frac{1}{a}$

$\Rightarrow$ $\frac{1}{a-x} = \frac{akt+1}{a}$ $\Rightarrow$ $a - x = \frac{a}{akt+1}$ $\Rightarrow$ $x = a - \frac{a}{akt+1} = \frac{a^2kt}{akt+1}$

(b) $a \neq b$: $\int\frac{dx}{(a-x)(b-x)} = \int k\,dt$ $\Rightarrow$ $\frac{1}{b-a}\int\frac{dx}{a-x} - \frac{1}{b-a}\int\frac{dx}{b-x} = \int k\,dt$ $\Rightarrow$ $\frac{1}{b-a}\ln\left|\frac{b-x}{a-x}\right| = kt + C$;

$t = 0$ and $x = 0$ $\Rightarrow$ $\frac{1}{b-a}\ln\frac{b}{a} = C$ $\Rightarrow$ $\ln\left|\frac{b-x}{a-x}\right| = (b-a)kt + \ln\left(\frac{b}{a}\right)$ $\Rightarrow$ $\frac{b-x}{a-x} = \frac{b}{a}e^{(b-a)kt}$

$\Rightarrow$ $x = \frac{ab\left[1 - e^{(b-a)kt}\right]}{a - be^{(b-a)kt}}$

## 8.5 INTEGRAL TABLES AND COMPUTER ALGEBRA SYSTEMS

1. $\int\frac{dx}{x\sqrt{x-3}} = \frac{2}{\sqrt{3}}\tan^{-1}\sqrt{\frac{x-3}{3}} + C$

(We used FORMULA 13(a) with $a = 1, b = 3$)

2. $\int \frac{dx}{x\sqrt{x+4}} = \frac{1}{\sqrt{4}} \ln \left| \frac{\sqrt{x+4}-\sqrt{4}}{\sqrt{x+4}+\sqrt{4}} \right| + C = \frac{1}{2} \ln \left| \frac{\sqrt{x+4}-2}{\sqrt{x+4}+2} \right| + C$

    (We used FORMULA 13(b) with $a = 1$, $b = 4$)

3. $\int \frac{x\,dx}{\sqrt{x-2}} = \int \frac{(x-2)\,dx}{\sqrt{x-2}} + 2 \int \frac{dx}{\sqrt{x-2}} = \int \left( \sqrt{x-2} \right)^1 dx + 2 \int \left( \sqrt{x-2} \right)^{-1} dx$

    $= \left( \frac{2}{1} \right) \frac{\left( \sqrt{x-2} \right)^3}{3} + 2 \left( \frac{2}{1} \right) \frac{\left( \sqrt{x-2} \right)^1}{1} = \sqrt{x-2} \left[ \frac{2(x-2)}{3} + 4 \right] + C$

    (We used FORMULA 11 with $a = 1$, $b = -2$, $n = 1$ and $a = 1$, $b = -2$, $n = -1$)

4. $\int \frac{x\,dx}{(2x+3)^{3/2}} = \frac{1}{2} \int \frac{(2x+3)\,dx}{(2x+3)^{3/2}} - \frac{3}{2} \int \frac{dx}{(2x+3)^{3/2}} = \frac{1}{2} \int \frac{dx}{\sqrt{2x+3}} - \frac{3}{2} \int \frac{dx}{\left( \sqrt{2x+3} \right)^3}$

    $= \frac{1}{2} \int \left( \sqrt{2x+3} \right)^{-1} dx - \frac{3}{2} \int \left( \sqrt{2x+3} \right)^{-3} dx = \left( \frac{1}{2} \right) \left( \frac{2}{2} \right) \frac{\left( \sqrt{2x+3} \right)^1}{1} - \left( \frac{3}{2} \right) \left( \frac{2}{2} \right) \frac{\left( \sqrt{2x+3} \right)^{-1}}{(-1)} + C$

    $= \frac{1}{2\sqrt{2x+3}} (2x + 3 + 3) + C = \frac{(x+3)}{\sqrt{2x+3}} + C$

    (We used FORMULA 11 with $a = 2$, $b = 3$, $n = -1$ and $a = 2$, $b = 3$, $n = -3$)

5. $\int x\sqrt{2x-3}\,dx = \frac{1}{2} \int (2x-3)\sqrt{2x-3}\,dx + \frac{3}{2} \int \sqrt{2x-3}\,dx = \frac{1}{2} \int \left( \sqrt{2x-3} \right)^3 dx + \frac{3}{2} \int \left( \sqrt{2x-3} \right)^1 dx$

    $= \left( \frac{1}{2} \right) \left( \frac{2}{2} \right) \frac{\left( \sqrt{2x-3} \right)^5}{5} + \left( \frac{3}{2} \right) \left( \frac{2}{2} \right) \frac{\left( \sqrt{2x-3} \right)^3}{3} + C = \frac{(2x-3)^{3/2}}{2} \left[ \frac{2x-3}{5} + 1 \right] + C = \frac{(2x-3)^{3/2}(x+1)}{5} + C$

    (We used FORMULA 11 with $a = 2$, $b = -3$, $n = 3$ and $a = 2$, $b = -3$, $n = 1$)

6. $\int x(7x+5)^{3/2}\,dx = \frac{1}{7} \int (7x+5)(7x+5)^{3/2}\,dx - \frac{5}{7} \int (7x+5)^{3/2}\,dx = \frac{1}{7} \int \left( \sqrt{7x+5} \right)^5 dx - \frac{5}{7} \int \left( \sqrt{7x+5} \right)^3 dx$

    $= \left( \frac{1}{7} \right) \left( \frac{2}{7} \right) \frac{\left( \sqrt{7x+5} \right)^7}{7} - \left( \frac{5}{7} \right) \left( \frac{2}{7} \right) \frac{\left( \sqrt{7x+5} \right)^5}{5} + C = \left[ \frac{(7x+5)^{5/2}}{49} \right] \left[ \frac{2(7x+5)}{7} - 2 \right] + C$

    $= \left[ \frac{(7x+5)^{5/2}}{49} \right] \left( \frac{14x-4}{7} \right) + C$

    (We used FORMULA 11 with $a = 7$, $b = 5$, $n = 5$ and $a = 7$, $b = 5$, $n = 3$)

7. $\int \frac{\sqrt{9-4x}}{x^2}\,dx = -\frac{\sqrt{9-4x}}{x} + \frac{(-4)}{2} \int \frac{dx}{x\sqrt{9-4x}} + C$

    (We used FORMULA 14 with $a = -4$, $b = 9$)

    $= -\frac{\sqrt{9-4x}}{x} - 2 \left( \frac{1}{\sqrt{9}} \right) \ln \left| \frac{\sqrt{9-4x}-\sqrt{9}}{\sqrt{9-4x}+\sqrt{9}} \right| + C$

    (We used FORMULA 13(b) with $a = -4$, $b = 9$)

    $= \frac{-\sqrt{9-4x}}{x} - \frac{2}{3} \ln \left| \frac{\sqrt{9-4x}-3}{\sqrt{9-4x}+3} \right| + C$

8. $\int \frac{dx}{x^2\sqrt{4x-9}} = -\frac{\sqrt{4x-9}}{(-9)x} + \frac{4}{18} \int \frac{dx}{x\sqrt{4x-9}} + C$

    (We used FORMULA 15 with $a = 4$, $b = -9$)

    $= \frac{\sqrt{4x-9}}{9x} + \left( \frac{2}{9} \right) \left( \frac{2}{\sqrt{9}} \right) \tan^{-1} \sqrt{\frac{4x-9}{9}} + C$

    (We used FORMULA 13(a) with $a = 4$, $b = 9$)

    $= \frac{\sqrt{4x-9}}{9x} + \frac{4}{27} \tan^{-1} \sqrt{\frac{4x-9}{9}} + C$

9. $\int x\sqrt{4x-x^2}\,dx = \int x\sqrt{2 \cdot 2x - x^2}\,dx = \frac{(x+2)(2x-3 \cdot 2)\sqrt{2 \cdot 2 \cdot x - x^2}}{6} + \frac{2^3}{2} \sin^{-1} \left( \frac{x-2}{2} \right) + C$

    $= \frac{(x+2)(2x-6)\sqrt{4x-x^2}}{6} + 4 \sin^{-1} \left( \frac{x-2}{2} \right) + C = \frac{(x+2)(x-3)\sqrt{4x-x^2}}{3} + 4 \sin^{-1} \left( \frac{x-2}{2} \right) + C$

    (We used FORMULA 51 with $a = 2$)

10. $\int \frac{\sqrt{x-x^2}}{x}\,dx = \int \frac{\sqrt{2\cdot\frac{1}{2}x-x^2}}{x}\,dx = \sqrt{2\cdot\frac{1}{2}x-x^2} + \frac{1}{2}\sin^{-1}\left(\frac{x-\frac{1}{2}}{\frac{1}{2}}\right) + C = \sqrt{x-x^2} + \frac{1}{2}\sin^{-1}(2x-1) + C$

   (We used FORMULA 52 with $a = \frac{1}{2}$)

11. $\int \frac{dx}{x\sqrt{7+x^2}} = \int \frac{dx}{x\sqrt{\left(\sqrt{7}\right)^2+x^2}} = -\frac{1}{\sqrt{7}}\ln\left|\frac{\sqrt{7}+\sqrt{\left(\sqrt{7}\right)^2+x^2}}{x}\right| + C = -\frac{1}{\sqrt{7}}\ln\left|\frac{\sqrt{7}+\sqrt{7+x^2}}{x}\right| + C$

   $\left(\text{We used FORMULA 26 with } a = \sqrt{7}\right)$

12. $\int \frac{dx}{x\sqrt{7-x^2}} = \int \frac{dx}{x\sqrt{\left(\sqrt{7}\right)^2-x^2}} = -\frac{1}{\sqrt{7}}\ln\left|\frac{\sqrt{7}+\sqrt{\left(\sqrt{7}\right)^2-x^2}}{x}\right| + C = -\frac{1}{\sqrt{7}}\ln\left|\frac{\sqrt{7}+\sqrt{7-x^2}}{x}\right| + C$

   $\left(\text{We used FORMULA 34 with } a = \sqrt{7}\right)$

13. $\int \frac{\sqrt{4-x^2}}{x}\,dx = \int \frac{\sqrt{2^2-x^2}}{x}\,dx = \sqrt{2^2-x^2} - 2\ln\left|\frac{2+\sqrt{2^2-x^2}}{x}\right| + C = \sqrt{4-x^2} - 2\ln\left|\frac{2+\sqrt{4-x^2}}{x}\right| + C$

   (We used FORMULA 31 with $a = 2$)

14. $\int \frac{\sqrt{x^2-4}}{x}\,dx = \int \frac{\sqrt{x^2-2^2}}{x}\,dx = \sqrt{x^2-2^2} - 2\sec^{-1}\left|\frac{x}{2}\right| + C = \sqrt{x^2-4} - 2\sec^{-1}\left|\frac{x}{2}\right| + C$

   (We used FORMULA 42 with $a = 2$)

15. $\int e^{2t}\cos 3t\,dt = \frac{e^{2t}}{2^2+3^2}(2\cos 3t + 3\sin 3t) + C = \frac{e^{2t}}{13}(2\cos 3t + 3\sin 3t) + C$

   (We used FORMULA 108 with $a = 2, b = 3$)

16. $\int e^{-3t}\sin 4t\,dt = \frac{e^{-3t}}{(-3)^2+4^2}(-3\sin 4t - 4\cos 4t) + C = \frac{e^{-3t}}{25}(-3\sin 4t - 4\cos 4t) + C$

   (We used FORMULA 107 with $a = -3, b = 4$)

17. $\int x\cos^{-1}x\,dx = \int x^1\cos^{-1}x\,dx = \frac{x^{1+1}}{1+1}\cos^{-1}x + \frac{1}{1+1}\int\frac{x^{1+1}\,dx}{\sqrt{1-x^2}} = \frac{x^2}{2}\cos^{-1}x + \frac{1}{2}\int\frac{x^2\,dx}{\sqrt{1-x^2}}$

   (We used FORMULA 100 with $a = 1, n = 1$)

   $= \frac{x^2}{2}\cos^{-1}x + \frac{1}{2}\left(\frac{1}{2}\sin^{-1}x\right) - \frac{1}{2}\left(\frac{1}{2}x\sqrt{1-x^2}\right) + C = \frac{x^2}{2}\cos^{-1}x + \frac{1}{4}\sin^{-1}x - \frac{1}{4}x\sqrt{1-x^2} + C$

   (We used FORMULA 33 with $a = 1$)

18. $\int x\tan^{-1}x\,dx = \int x^1\tan^{-1}(1x)\,dx = \frac{x^{1+1}}{1+1}\tan^{-1}(1x) - \frac{1}{1+1}\int\frac{x^{1+1}\,dx}{1+(1)^2x^2} = \frac{x^2}{2}\tan^{-1}x - \frac{1}{2}\int\frac{x^2\,dx}{1+x^2}$

   (We used FORMULA 101 with $a = 1, n = 1$)

   $= \frac{x^2}{2}\tan^{-1}x - \frac{1}{2}\int\left(1-\frac{1}{1+x^2}\right)dx$ (after long division)

   $= \frac{x^2}{2}\tan^{-1}x - \frac{1}{2}\int dx + \frac{1}{2}\int\frac{1}{1+x^2}\,dx = \frac{x^2}{2}\tan^{-1}x - \frac{1}{2}x + \frac{1}{2}\tan^{-1}x + C = \frac{1}{2}((x^2+1)\tan^{-1}x - x) + C$

19. $\int x^2\tan^{-1}x\,dx = \frac{x^{2+1}}{2+1}\tan^{-1}x - \frac{1}{2+1}\int\frac{x^{2+1}}{1+x^2}\,dx = \frac{x^3}{3}\tan^{-1}x - \frac{1}{3}\int\frac{x^3}{1+x^2}\,dx$

   (We used FORMULA 101 with $a = 1, n = 2$);

   $\int\frac{x^3}{1+x^2}\,dx = \int x\,dx - \int\frac{x\,dx}{1+x^2} = \frac{x^2}{2} - \frac{1}{2}\ln(1+x^2) + C \Rightarrow \int x^2\tan^{-1}x\,dx$

   $= \frac{x^3}{3}\tan^{-1}x - \frac{x^2}{6} + \frac{1}{6}\ln(1+x^2) + C$

20. $\int \frac{\tan^{-1}x}{x^2}\,dx = \int x^{-2}\tan^{-1}x\,dx = \frac{x^{(-2+1)}}{(-2+1)}\tan^{-1}x - \frac{1}{(-2+1)}\int \frac{x^{(-2+1)}}{1+x^2}\,dx = \frac{x^{-1}}{(-1)}\tan^{-1}x + \int \frac{x^{-1}}{(1+x^2)}\,dx$

(We used FORMULA 101 with a $= 1$, n $= -2$);

$\int \frac{x^{-1}\,dx}{1+x^2} = \int \frac{dx}{x(1+x^2)} = \int \frac{dx}{x} - \int \frac{x\,dx}{1+x^2} = \ln|x| - \frac{1}{2}\ln(1+x^2) + C$

$\Rightarrow \int \frac{\tan^{-1}x}{x^2}\,dx = -\frac{1}{x}\tan^{-1}x + \ln|x| - \frac{1}{2}\ln(1+x^2) + C$

21. $\int \sin 3x \cos 2x \, dx = -\frac{\cos 5x}{10} - \frac{\cos x}{2} + C$

(We used FORMULA 62(a) with a $= 3$, b $= 2$)

22. $\int \sin 2x \cos 3x \, dx = -\frac{\cos 5x}{10} + \frac{\cos x}{2} + C$

(We used FORMULA 62(a) with a $= 2$, b $= 3$)

23. $\int 8 \sin 4t \sin \frac{t}{2}\,dx = \frac{8}{7}\sin\left(\frac{7t}{2}\right) - \frac{8}{9}\sin\left(\frac{9t}{2}\right) + C = 8\left[\frac{\sin\left(\frac{7t}{2}\right)}{7} - \frac{\sin\left(\frac{9t}{2}\right)}{9}\right] + C$

(We used FORMULA 62(b) with a $= 4$, b $= \frac{1}{2}$)

24. $\int \sin \frac{t}{3} \sin \frac{t}{6}\,dt = 3\sin\left(\frac{t}{6}\right) - \sin\left(\frac{t}{2}\right) + C$

(We used FORMULA 62(b) with a $= \frac{1}{3}$, b $= \frac{1}{6}$)

25. $\int \cos \frac{\theta}{3} \cos \frac{\theta}{4}\,d\theta = 6\sin\left(\frac{\theta}{12}\right) + \frac{6}{7}\sin\left(\frac{7\theta}{12}\right) + C$

(We used FORMULA 62(c) with a $= \frac{1}{3}$, b $= \frac{1}{4}$)

26. $\int \cos \frac{\theta}{2} \cos 7\theta \, d\theta = \frac{1}{13}\sin\left(\frac{13\theta}{2}\right) + \frac{1}{15}\sin\left(\frac{15\theta}{2}\right) + C = \frac{\sin\left(\frac{13\theta}{2}\right)}{13} + \frac{\sin\left(\frac{15\theta}{2}\right)}{15} + C$

(We used FORMULA 62(c) with a $= \frac{1}{2}$, b $= 7$)

27. $\int \frac{x^3+x+1}{(x^2+1)^2}\,dx = \int \frac{x\,dx}{x^2+1} + \int \frac{dx}{(x^2+1)^2} = \frac{1}{2}\int \frac{d(x^2+1)}{x^2+1} + \int \frac{dx}{(x^2+1)^2}$

$= \frac{1}{2}\ln(x^2+1) + \frac{x}{2(1+x^2)} + \frac{1}{2}\tan^{-1}x + C$

(For the second integral we used FORMULA 17 with a $= 1$)

28. $\int \frac{x^2+6x}{(x^2+3)^2}\,dx = \int \frac{dx}{x^2+3} + \int \frac{6x\,dx}{(x^2+3)^2} - \int \frac{3\,dx}{(x^2+3)^2} = \int \frac{dx}{x^2+\left(\sqrt{3}\right)^2} + 3\int \frac{d(x^2+3)}{(x^2+3)^2} - 3\int \frac{dx}{\left[x^2+\left(\sqrt{3}\right)^2\right]^2}$

$= \frac{1}{\sqrt{3}}\tan^{-1}\left(\frac{x}{\sqrt{3}}\right) - \frac{3}{(x^2+3)} - 3\left(\frac{x}{2\left(\sqrt{3}\right)^2\left(\left(\sqrt{3}\right)^2+x^2\right)} + \frac{1}{2\left(\sqrt{3}\right)^3}\tan^{-1}\left(\frac{x}{\sqrt{3}}\right)\right) + C$

$\left(\text{For the first integral we used FORMULA 16 with a} = \sqrt{3}; \text{ for the third integral we used FORMULA 17 with} \right.$

$\left. a = \sqrt{3}\right)$

$= \frac{1}{2\sqrt{3}}\tan^{-1}\left(\frac{x}{\sqrt{3}}\right) - \frac{3}{x^2+3} - \frac{x}{2(x^2+3)} + C$

29. $\int \sin^{-1}\sqrt{x}\,dx; \quad \begin{bmatrix} u = \sqrt{x} \\ x = u^2 \\ dx = 2u\,du \end{bmatrix} \rightarrow 2\int u^1 \sin^{-1}u\,du = 2\left(\frac{u^{1+1}}{1+1}\sin^{-1}u - \frac{1}{1+1}\int \frac{u^{1+1}}{\sqrt{1-u^2}}\,du\right)$

$= u^2 \sin^{-1} u - \int \frac{u^2 \, du}{\sqrt{1-u^2}}$

(We used FORMULA 99 with a = 1, n = 1)

$= u^2 \sin^{-1} u - \left( \frac{1}{2} \sin^{-1} u - \frac{1}{2} u \sqrt{1-u^2} \right) + C = \left( u^2 - \frac{1}{2} \right) \sin^{-1} u + \frac{1}{2} u \sqrt{1-u^2} + C$

(We used FORMULA 33 with a = 1)

$= \left( x - \frac{1}{2} \right) \sin^{-1} \sqrt{x} + \frac{1}{2} \sqrt{x - x^2} + C$

30. $\int \frac{\cos^{-1} \sqrt{x}}{\sqrt{x}} \, dx; \quad \begin{bmatrix} u = \sqrt{x} \\ x = u^2 \\ dx = 2u \, du \end{bmatrix} \to \int \frac{\cos^{-1} u}{u} \cdot 2u \, du = 2 \int \cos^{-1} u \, du = 2 \left( u \cos^{-1} u - \frac{1}{1} \sqrt{1-u^2} \right) + C$

(We used FORMULA 97 with a = 1)

$= 2 \left( \sqrt{x} \cos^{-1} \sqrt{x} - \sqrt{1-x} \right) + C$

31. $\int \frac{\sqrt{x}}{\sqrt{1-x}} \, dx; \quad \begin{bmatrix} u = \sqrt{x} \\ x = u^2 \\ dx = 2u \, du \end{bmatrix} \to \int \frac{u \cdot 2u}{\sqrt{1-u^2}} \, du = 2 \int \frac{u^2}{\sqrt{1-u^2}} \, du = 2 \left( \frac{1}{2} \sin^{-1} u - \frac{1}{2} u \sqrt{1-u^2} \right) + C$

$= \sin^{-1} u - u \sqrt{1-u^2} + C$

(We used FORMULA 33 with a = 1)

$= \sin^{-1} \sqrt{x} - \sqrt{x} \sqrt{1-x} + C = \sin^{-1} \sqrt{x} - \sqrt{x - x^2} + C$

32. $\int \frac{\sqrt{2-x}}{\sqrt{x}} \, dx; \quad \begin{bmatrix} u = \sqrt{x} \\ x = u^2 \\ dx = 2u \, du \end{bmatrix} \to \int \frac{\sqrt{2-u^2}}{u} \cdot 2u \, du = 2 \int \sqrt{\left( \sqrt{2} \right)^2 - u^2} \, du$

$= 2 \left[ \frac{u}{2} \sqrt{\left( \sqrt{2} \right)^2 - u^2} + \frac{\left( \sqrt{2} \right)^2}{2} \sin^{-1} \left( \frac{u}{\sqrt{2}} \right) \right] + C = u \sqrt{2-u^2} + 2 \sin^{-1} \left( \frac{u}{\sqrt{2}} \right) + C$

$\left( \text{We used FORMULA 29 with } a = \sqrt{2} \right)$

$= \sqrt{2x - x^2} + 2 \sin^{-1} \sqrt{\frac{x}{2}} + C$

33. $\int (\cot t) \sqrt{1 - \sin^2 t} \, dt = \int \frac{\sqrt{1 - \sin^2 t} \, (\cos t) \, dt}{\sin t}; \quad \begin{bmatrix} u = \sin t \\ du = \cos t \, dt \end{bmatrix} \to \int \frac{\sqrt{1-u^2} \, du}{u}$

$= \sqrt{1-u^2} - \ln \left| \frac{1 + \sqrt{1-u^2}}{u} \right| + C$

(We used FORMULA 31 with a = 1)

$= \sqrt{1 - \sin^2 t} - \ln \left| \frac{1 + \sqrt{1 - \sin^2 t}}{\sin t} \right| + C$

34. $\int \frac{dt}{(\tan t) \sqrt{4 - \sin^2 t}} = \int \frac{\cos t \, dt}{(\sin t) \sqrt{4 - \sin^2 t}}; \quad \begin{bmatrix} u = \sin t \\ du = \cos t \, dt \end{bmatrix} \to \int \frac{du}{u \sqrt{4 - u^2}} = -\frac{1}{2} \ln \left| \frac{2 + \sqrt{4 - u^2}}{u} \right| + C$

(We used FORMULA 34 with a = 2)

$= -\frac{1}{2} \ln \left| \frac{2 + \sqrt{4 - \sin^2 t}}{\sin t} \right| + C$

35. $\int \frac{dy}{y \sqrt{3 + (\ln y)^2}}; \quad \begin{bmatrix} u = \ln y \\ y = e^u \\ dy = e^u \, du \end{bmatrix} \to \int \frac{e^u \, du}{e^u \sqrt{3 + u^2}} = \int \frac{du}{\sqrt{3 + u^2}} = \ln \left| u + \sqrt{3 + u^2} \right| + C$

$= \ln \left| \ln y + \sqrt{3 + (\ln y)^2} \right| + C$

$\left( \text{We used FORMULA 20 with } a = \sqrt{3} \right)$

36. $\int \tan^{-1} \sqrt{y}\, dy;$ $\begin{bmatrix} t = \sqrt{y} \\ y = t^2 \\ dy = 2t\, dt \end{bmatrix}$ $\rightarrow$ $2\int t \tan^{-1} t\, dt = 2\left[\frac{t^2}{2} \tan^{-1} t - \frac{1}{2}\int \frac{t^2}{1+t^2}\, dt\right] = t^2 \tan^{-1} t - \int \frac{t^2}{1+t^2}\, dt$

(We used FORMULA 101 with n = 1, a = 1)

$= t^2 \tan^{-1} t - \int \frac{t^2+1}{t^2+1}\, dt + \int \frac{dt}{1+t^2} = t^2 \tan^{-1} t - t + \tan^{-1} t + C = y \tan^{-1} \sqrt{y} + \tan^{-1} \sqrt{y} - \sqrt{y} + C$

37. $\int \frac{1}{\sqrt{x^2+2x+5}}\, dx = \int \frac{1}{\sqrt{(x+1)^2+4}}\, dx;$ $\begin{bmatrix} t = x+1 \\ dt = dx \end{bmatrix}$ $\rightarrow \int \frac{1}{\sqrt{t^2+4}}\, dt$

(We used FORMULA 20 with a = 2)

$= \ln\left|t + \sqrt{t^2+4}\right| + C = \ln\left|(x+1) + \sqrt{(x+1)^2+4}\right| + C = \ln\left|(x+1) + \sqrt{x^2+2x+5}\right| + C$

38. $\int \frac{x^2}{\sqrt{x^2-4x+5}}\, dx = \int \frac{x^2}{\sqrt{(x-2)^2+1}}\, dx;$ $\begin{bmatrix} t = x-2 \\ dt = dx \end{bmatrix}$ $\rightarrow \int \frac{(t+2)^2}{\sqrt{t^2+1}}\, dt = \int \frac{t^2+4t+2}{\sqrt{t^2+1}}\, dt = \int \frac{t^2}{\sqrt{t^2+1}}\, dt + \int \frac{4t}{\sqrt{t^2+1}}\, dt + \int \frac{4}{\sqrt{t^2+1}}\, dt$

(We used FORMULA 25 with a = 1)          (We used FORMULA 20 with a = 1)

$= \left[-\frac{1}{2}\ln\left|t + \sqrt{t^2+1}\right| + \frac{t\sqrt{t^2+1}}{2}\right] + 4\sqrt{t^2+1} + \left[4\ln\left|t + \sqrt{t^2+1}\right|\right] + C$

$= -\frac{1}{2}\ln\left|(x-2) + \sqrt{(x-2)^2+1}\right| + \frac{(x-2)\sqrt{(x-2)^2+1}}{2} + 4\sqrt{(x-2)^2+1} + 4\ln\left|(x-2) + \sqrt{(x-2)^2+1}\right| + C$

$= \frac{7}{2}\ln\left|(x-2) + \sqrt{x^2-4x+5}\right| + \frac{(x+6)\sqrt{x^2-4x+5}}{2} + C$

39. $\int \sqrt{5-4x-x^2}\, dx = \int \sqrt{9-(x+2)^2}\, dx;$ $\begin{bmatrix} t = x+2 \\ dt = dx \end{bmatrix}$ $\rightarrow \int \sqrt{9-t^2}\, dt;$

(We used FORMULA 29 with a = 3)

$= \frac{t}{2}\sqrt{9-t^2} + \frac{3^2}{2}\sin^{-1}\left(\frac{t}{3}\right) + C = \frac{x+2}{2}\sqrt{9-(x+2)^2} + \frac{9}{2}\sin^{-1}\left(\frac{x+2}{3}\right) + C = \frac{x+2}{2}\sqrt{5-4x-x^2} + \frac{9}{2}\sin^{-1}\left(\frac{x+2}{3}\right) + C$

40. $\int x^2\sqrt{2x-x^2}\, dx = \int x^2\sqrt{1-(x-1)^2}\, dx;$ $\begin{bmatrix} t = x-1 \\ dt = dx \end{bmatrix}$ $\rightarrow \int (t+1)^2\sqrt{1-t^2}\, dt = \int (t^2+2t+1)\sqrt{1-t^2}\, dt$

$= \int t^2\sqrt{1-t^2}\, dt + \int 2t\sqrt{1-t^2}\, dt + \int \sqrt{1-t^2}\, dt$

(We used FORMULA 30 with a = 1)                    (We used FORMULA 29 with a = 1)

$= \left[\frac{1^4}{8}\sin^{-1}\left(\frac{t}{1}\right) - \frac{1}{8}t\sqrt{1-t^2}(1^2-2t^2)\right] - \frac{2}{3}(1-t^2)^{3/2} + \left[\frac{t}{2}\sqrt{1-t^2} + \frac{1^2}{2}\sin^{-1}\left(\frac{t}{1}\right)\right] + C$

$= \frac{1}{8}\sin^{-1}(x-1) - \frac{1}{8}(x-1)\sqrt{1-(x-1)^2}\left(1^2-2(x-1)^2\right) - \frac{2}{3}\left(1-(x-1)^2\right)^{3/2} + \frac{x-1}{2}\sqrt{1-(x-1)^2}$

$+ \frac{1}{2}\sin^{-1}(x-1) + C = \frac{5}{8}\sin^{-1}(x-1) - \frac{2}{3}(2x-x^2)^{3/2} + \frac{x-1}{8}\sqrt{2x-x^2}(2x^2-4x+5) + C$

41. $\int \sin^5 2x\, dx = -\frac{\sin^4 2x \cos 2x}{5\cdot 2} + \frac{5-1}{5}\int \sin^3 2x\, dx = -\frac{\sin^4 2x \cos 2x}{10} + \frac{4}{5}\left[-\frac{\sin^2 2x \cos 2x}{3\cdot 2} + \frac{3-1}{3}\int \sin 2x\, dx\right]$

(We used FORMULA 60 with a = 2, n = 5 and a = 2, n = 3)

$= -\frac{\sin^4 2x \cos 2x}{10} - \frac{2}{15}\sin^2 2x \cos 2x + \frac{8}{15}\left(-\frac{1}{2}\right)\cos 2x + C = -\frac{\sin^4 2x \cos 2x}{10} - \frac{2\sin^2 2x \cos 2x}{15} - \frac{4\cos 2x}{15} + C$

42. $\int 8\cos^4 2\pi t\, dt = 8\left(\frac{\cos^3 2\pi t \sin 2\pi t}{4\cdot 2\pi} + \frac{4-1}{4}\int \cos^2 2\pi t\, dt\right)$

(We used FORMULA 61 with a = 2π, n = 4)

$= \frac{\cos^3 2\pi t \sin 2\pi t}{\pi} + 6\left[\frac{t}{2} + \frac{\sin(2\cdot 2\pi\cdot t)}{4\cdot 2\pi}\right] + C$

(We used FORMULA 59 with a = 2π)

$= \frac{\cos^3 2\pi t \sin 2\pi t}{\pi} + 3t + \frac{3\sin 4\pi t}{4\pi} + C = \frac{\cos^3 2\pi t \sin 2\pi t}{\pi} + \frac{3\cos 2\pi t \sin 2\pi t}{2\pi} + 3t + C$

43. $\int \sin^2 2\theta \cos^3 2\theta \, d\theta = \frac{\sin^3 2\theta \cos^2 2\theta}{2(2+3)} + \frac{3-1}{3+2} \int \sin^2 2\theta \cos 2\theta \, d\theta$

(We used FORMULA 69 with a = 2, m = 3, n = 2)

$= \frac{\sin^3 2\theta \cos^2 2\theta}{10} + \frac{2}{5} \int \sin^2 2\theta \cos 2\theta \, d\theta = \frac{\sin^3 2\theta \cos^2 2\theta}{10} + \frac{2}{5} \left[ \frac{1}{2} \int \sin^2 2\theta \, d(\sin 2\theta) \right] = \frac{\sin^3 2\theta \cos^2 2\theta}{10} + \frac{\sin^3 2\theta}{15} + C$

44. $\int 2 \sin^2 t \sec^4 t \, dt = \int 2 \sin^2 t \cos^{-4} t \, dt = 2 \left( -\frac{\sin t \cos^{-3} t}{2-4} + \frac{2-1}{2-4} \int \cos^{-4} t \, dt \right)$

(We used FORMULA 68 with a = 1, n = 2, m = −4)

$= \sin t \cos^{-3} t - \int \cos^{-4} t \, dt = \sin t \cos^{-3} t - \int \sec^4 t \, dt = \sin t \cos^{-3} t - \left( \frac{\sec^2 t \tan t}{4-1} + \frac{4-2}{4-1} \int \sec^2 t \, dt \right)$

(We used FORMULA 92 with a = 1, n = 4)

$= \sin t \cos^{-3} t - \left( \frac{\sec^2 t \tan t}{3} \right) - \frac{2}{3} \tan t + C = \frac{2}{3} \sec^2 t \tan t - \frac{2}{3} \tan t + C = \frac{2}{3} \tan t (\sec^2 t - 1) + C$

$= \frac{2}{3} \tan^3 t + C$

An easy way to find the integral using substitution:

$\int 2 \sin^2 t \cos^{-4} t \, dt = \int 2 \tan^2 t \sec^2 t \, dt = \int 2 \tan^2 t \, d(\tan t) = \frac{2}{3} \tan^3 t + C$

45. $\int 4 \tan^3 2x \, dx = 4 \left( \frac{\tan^2 2x}{2 \cdot 2} - \int \tan 2x \, dx \right) = \tan^2 2x - 4 \int \tan 2x \, dx$

(We used FORMULA 86 with n = 3, a = 2)

$= \tan^2 2x - \frac{4}{2} \ln |\sec 2x| + C = \tan^2 2x - 2 \ln |\sec 2x| + C$

46. $\int 8 \cot^4 t \, dt = 8 \left( -\frac{\cot^3 t}{3} - \int \cot^2 t \, dt \right)$

(We used FORMULA 87 with a = 1, n = 4)

$= 8 \left( -\frac{1}{3} \cot^3 t + \cot t + t \right) + C$

(We used FORMULA 85 with a = 1)

47. $\int 2 \sec^3 \pi x \, dx = 2 \left[ \frac{\sec \pi x \tan \pi x}{\pi(3-1)} + \frac{3-2}{3-1} \int \sec \pi x \, dx \right]$

(We used FORMULA 92 with n = 3, a = π)

$= \frac{1}{\pi} \sec \pi x \tan \pi x + \frac{1}{\pi} \ln |\sec \pi x + \tan \pi x| + C$

(We used FORMULA 88 with a = π)

48. $\int 3 \sec^4 3x \, dx = 3 \left[ \frac{\sec^2 3x \tan 3x}{3(4-1)} + \frac{4-2}{4-1} \int \sec^2 3x \, dx \right]$

(We used FORMULA 92 with n = 4, a = 3)

$= \frac{\sec^2 3x \tan 3x}{3} + \frac{2}{3} \tan 3x + C$

(We used FORMULA 90 with a = 3)

49. $\int \csc^5 x \, dx = -\frac{\csc^3 x \cot x}{5-1} + \frac{5-2}{5-1} \int \csc^3 x \, dx = -\frac{\csc^3 x \cot x}{4} + \frac{3}{4} \left( -\frac{\csc x \cot x}{3-1} + \frac{3-2}{3-1} \int \csc x \, dx \right)$

(We used FORMULA 93 with n = 5, a = 1 and n = 3, a = 1)

$= -\frac{1}{4} \csc^3 x \cot x - \frac{3}{8} \csc x \cot x - \frac{3}{8} \ln |\csc x + \cot x| + C$

(We used FORMULA 89 with a = 1)

50. $\int 16 x^3 (\ln x)^2 \, dx = 16 \left[ \frac{x^4 (\ln x)^2}{4} - \frac{2}{4} \int x^3 \ln x \, dx \right] = 16 \left[ \frac{x^4 (\ln x)^2}{4} - \frac{1}{2} \left[ \frac{x^4 (\ln x)}{4} - \frac{1}{4} \int x^3 \, dx \right] \right]$

(We used FORMULA 110 with a = 1, n = 3, m = 2 and a = 1, n = 3, m = 1)

$= 16 \left( \frac{x^4 (\ln x)^2}{4} - \frac{x^4 (\ln x)}{8} + \frac{x^4}{32} \right) + C = 4 x^4 (\ln x)^2 - 2 x^4 \ln x + \frac{x^4}{2} + C$

51. $\int e^t \sec^3(e^t - 1) \, dt;$ $\begin{bmatrix} x = e^t - 1 \\ dx = e^t \, dt \end{bmatrix}$ $\rightarrow$ $\int \sec^3 x \, dx = \frac{\sec x \tan x}{3-1} + \frac{3-2}{3-1} \int \sec x \, dx$

(We used FORMULA 92 with a = 1, n = 3)

$= \frac{\sec x \tan x}{2} + \frac{1}{2} \ln|\sec x + \tan x| + C = \frac{1}{2}[\sec(e^t - 1)\tan(e^t - 1) + \ln|\sec(e^t - 1) + \tan(e^t - 1)|] + C$

52. $\int \frac{\csc^3 \sqrt{\theta}}{\sqrt{\theta}} \, d\theta;$ $\begin{bmatrix} t = \sqrt{\theta} \\ \theta = t^2 \\ d\theta = 2t \, dt \end{bmatrix}$ $\rightarrow$ $2\int \csc^3 t \, dt = 2\left[-\frac{\csc t \cot t}{3-1} + \frac{3-2}{3-1}\int \csc t \, dt\right]$

(We used FORMULA 93 with a = 1, n = 3)

$= 2\left[-\frac{\csc t \cot t}{2} - \frac{1}{2}\ln|\csc t + \cot t|\right] + C = -\csc \sqrt{\theta} \cot \sqrt{\theta} - \ln\left|\csc \sqrt{\theta} + \cot \sqrt{\theta}\right| + C$

53. $\int_0^1 2\sqrt{x^2 + 1} \, dx;$ $[x = \tan t]$ $\rightarrow$ $2\int_0^{\pi/4} \sec t \cdot \sec^2 t \, dt = 2\int_0^{\pi/4} \sec^3 t \, dt = 2\left[\left[\frac{\sec t \cdot \tan t}{3-1}\right]_0^{\pi/4} + \frac{3-2}{3-1}\int_0^{\pi/4} \sec t \, dt\right]$

(We used FORMULA 92 with n = 3, a = 1)

$= [\sec t \cdot \tan t + \ln|\sec t + \tan t|]_0^{\pi/4} = \sqrt{2} + \ln\left(\sqrt{2} + 1\right)$

54. $\int_0^{\sqrt{3}/2} \frac{dy}{(1-y^2)^{5/2}};$ $[y = \sin x]$ $\rightarrow$ $\int_0^{\pi/3} \frac{\cos x \, dx}{\cos^5 x} = \int_0^{\pi/3} \sec^4 x \, dx = \left[\frac{\sec^2 x \tan x}{4-1}\right]_0^{\pi/3} + \frac{4-2}{4-1}\int_0^{\pi/3} \sec^2 x \, dx$

(We used FORMULA 92 with a = 1, n = 4)

$= \left[\frac{\sec^2 x \tan x}{3} + \frac{2}{3}\tan x\right]_0^{\pi/3} = \left(\frac{4}{3}\right)\sqrt{3} + \left(\frac{2}{3}\right)\sqrt{3} = 2\sqrt{3}$

55. $\int_1^2 \frac{(t^2-1)^{3/2}}{r} \, dr;$ $[r = \sec \theta]$ $\rightarrow$ $\int_0^{\pi/3} \frac{\tan^3 \theta}{\sec \theta}(\sec \theta \tan \theta) \, d\theta = \int_0^{\pi/3} \tan^4 \theta \, d\theta = \left[\frac{\tan^3 \theta}{4-1}\right]_0^{\pi/3} - \int_0^{\pi/3} \tan^2 \theta \, d\theta$

$= \left[\frac{\tan^3 \theta}{3} - \tan \theta + \theta\right]_0^{\pi/3} = \frac{3\sqrt{3}}{3} - \sqrt{3} + \frac{\pi}{3} = \frac{\pi}{3}$

(We used FORMULA 86 with a = 1, n = 4 and FORMULA 84 with a = 1)

56. $\int_0^{1/\sqrt{3}} \frac{dt}{(t^2+1)^{7/2}};$ $[t = \tan \theta]$ $\rightarrow$ $\int_0^{\pi/6} \frac{\sec^2 \theta \, d\theta}{\sec^7 \theta} = \int_0^{\pi/6} \cos^5 \theta \, d\theta = \left[\frac{\cos^4 \theta \sin \theta}{5}\right]_0^{\pi/6} + \left(\frac{5-1}{5}\right)\int_0^{\pi/6} \cos^3 \theta \, d\theta$

$= \left[\frac{\cos^4 \theta \sin \theta}{5}\right]_0^{\pi/6} + \frac{4}{5}\left[\left[\frac{\cos^2 \theta \sin \theta}{3}\right]_0^{\pi/6} + \left(\frac{3-1}{3}\right)\int_0^{\pi/6} \cos \theta \, d\theta\right] = \left[\frac{\cos^4 \theta \sin \theta}{5} + \frac{4}{15}\cos^2 \theta \sin \theta + \frac{8}{15}\sin \theta\right]_0^{\pi/6}$

(We used FORMULA 61 with a = 1, n = 5 and a = 1, n = 3)

$= \frac{\left(\frac{\sqrt{3}}{2}\right)^4 \left(\frac{1}{2}\right)}{5} + \left(\frac{4}{15}\right)\left(\frac{\sqrt{3}}{2}\right)^2 \left(\frac{1}{2}\right) + \left(\frac{8}{15}\right)\left(\frac{1}{2}\right) = \frac{9}{160} + \frac{1}{10} + \frac{4}{15} = \frac{3 \cdot 9 + 48 + 32 \cdot 4}{480} = \frac{203}{480}$

57. $S = \int_0^{\sqrt{2}} 2\pi y \sqrt{1 + (y')^2} \, dx$

$= 2\pi \int_0^{\sqrt{2}} \sqrt{x^2 + 2}\sqrt{1 + \frac{x^2}{x^2+2}} \, dx$

$= 2\sqrt{2}\pi \int_0^{\sqrt{2}} \sqrt{x^2 + 1} \, dx$

$= 2\sqrt{2}\pi \left[\frac{x\sqrt{x^2+1}}{2} + \frac{1}{2}\ln\left|x + \sqrt{x^2+1}\right|\right]_0^{\sqrt{2}}$

(We used FORMULA 21 with a = 1)

$= \sqrt{2}\pi\left[\sqrt{6} + \ln\left(\sqrt{2} + \sqrt{3}\right)\right] = 2\pi\sqrt{3} + \pi\sqrt{2}\ln\left(\sqrt{2} + \sqrt{3}\right)$

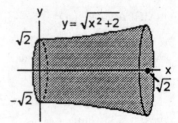

58. $L = \int_0^{\sqrt{3}/2} \sqrt{1 + (2x)^2} \, dx = 2\int_0^{\sqrt{3}/2} \sqrt{\frac{1}{4} + x^2} \, dx = 2\left[\frac{x}{2}\sqrt{\frac{1}{4} + x^2} + \left(\frac{1}{4}\right)\left(\frac{1}{2}\right)\ln\left(x + \sqrt{\frac{1}{4} + x^2}\right)\right]_0^{\sqrt{3}/2}$

(We used FORMULA 2 with a = $\frac{1}{2}$)

$$= \left[\frac{x}{2}\sqrt{1+4x^2} + \frac{1}{4}\ln\left(x+\frac{1}{2}\sqrt{1+4x^2}\right)\right]_0^{\sqrt{3}/2} = \frac{\sqrt{3}}{4}\sqrt{1+4\left(\frac{3}{4}\right)} + \frac{1}{4}\ln\left(\frac{\sqrt{3}}{2}+\frac{1}{2}\sqrt{1+4\left(\frac{3}{4}\right)}\right) - \frac{1}{4}\ln\frac{1}{2}$$

$$= \frac{\sqrt{3}}{4}(2) + \frac{1}{4}\ln\left(\frac{\sqrt{3}}{2}+1\right) + \frac{1}{4}\ln 2 = \frac{\sqrt{3}}{2} + \frac{1}{4}\ln\left(\sqrt{3}+2\right)$$

59. $A = \int_0^3 \frac{dx}{\sqrt{x+1}} = \left[2\sqrt{x+1}\right]_0^3 = 2; \bar{x} = \frac{1}{A}\int_0^3 \frac{x\,dx}{\sqrt{x+1}}$

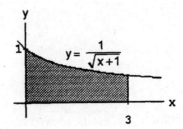

$y = \dfrac{1}{\sqrt{x+1}}$

$$= \frac{1}{A}\int_0^3 \sqrt{x+1}\,dx - \frac{1}{A}\int_0^3 \frac{dx}{\sqrt{x+1}}$$

$$= \frac{1}{2}\cdot\frac{2}{3}\left[(x+1)^{3/2}\right]_0^3 - 1 = \frac{4}{3};$$

(We used FORMULA 11 with a = 1, b = 1, n = 1 and
a = 1, b = 1, n = −1)

$$\bar{y} = \frac{1}{2A}\int_0^3 \frac{dx}{x+1} = \frac{1}{4}\left[\ln(x+1)\right]_0^3 = \frac{1}{4}\ln 4 = \frac{1}{2}\ln 2 = \ln\sqrt{2}$$

60. $M_y = \int_0^3 x\left(\frac{36}{2x+3}\right) dx = 18\int_0^3 \frac{2x+3}{2x+3}\,dx - 54\int_0^3 \frac{dx}{2x+3} = \left[18x - 27\ln|2x+3|\right]_0^3$

$$= 18\cdot 3 - 27\ln 9 - (-27\ln 3) = 54 - 27\cdot 2\ln 3 + 27\ln 3 = 54 - 27\ln 3$$

61. $S = 2\pi\int_{-1}^1 x^2\sqrt{1+4x^2}\,dx$;

$$\begin{bmatrix} u = 2x \\ du = 2\,dx \end{bmatrix} \rightarrow \frac{\pi}{4}\int_{-2}^2 u^2\sqrt{1+u^2}\,du$$

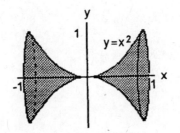

$y = x^2$

$$= \frac{\pi}{4}\left[\frac{u}{8}(1+2u^2)\sqrt{1+u^2} - \frac{1}{8}\ln\left(u+\sqrt{1+u^2}\right)\right]_{-2}^2$$

(We used FORMULA 22 with a = 1)

$$= \frac{\pi}{4}\left[\frac{2}{8}(1+2\cdot 4)\sqrt{1+4} - \frac{1}{8}\ln\left(2+\sqrt{1+4}\right)\right.$$

$$\left. + \frac{2}{8}(1+2\cdot 4)\sqrt{1+4} + \frac{1}{8}\ln\left(-2+\sqrt{1+4}\right)\right]$$

$$= \frac{\pi}{4}\left[\frac{9}{2}\sqrt{5} - \frac{1}{8}\ln\left(\frac{2+\sqrt{5}}{-2+\sqrt{5}}\right)\right] \approx 7.62$$

62. (a) The volume of the filled part equals the length of the
tank times the area of the shaded region shown in the
accompanying figure. Consider a layer of gasoline
of thickness dy located at height y where
−r < y < −r + d. The width of this layer is
$2\sqrt{r^2-y^2}$. Therefore, $A = 2\int_{-r}^{-r+d}\sqrt{r^2-y^2}\,dy$
and $V = L\cdot A = 2L\int_{-r}^{-r+d}\sqrt{r^2-y^2}\,dy$

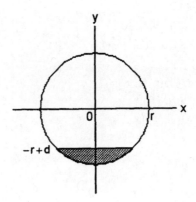

(b) $2L\int_{-r}^{-r+d}\sqrt{r^2-y^2}\,dy = 2L\left[\frac{y\sqrt{r^2-y^2}}{2} + \frac{r^2}{2}\sin^{-1}\frac{y}{r}\right]_{-r}^{-r+d}$

(We used FORMULA 29 with a = r)

$$= 2L\left[\frac{(d-r)}{2}\sqrt{2rd-d^2} + \frac{r^2}{2}\sin^{-1}\left(\frac{d-r}{r}\right) + \frac{r^2}{2}\left(\frac{\pi}{2}\right)\right] = 2L\left[\left(\frac{d-r}{2}\right)\sqrt{2rd-d^2} + \left(\frac{r^2}{2}\right)\left(\sin^{-1}\left(\frac{d-r}{r}\right)+\frac{\pi}{2}\right)\right]$$

63. The integrand $f(x) = \sqrt{x-x^2}$ is nonnegative, so the integral is maximized by integrating over the function's
entire domain, which runs from x = 0 to x = 1

$\Rightarrow \int_0^1 \sqrt{x - x^2}\, dx = \int_0^1 \sqrt{2 \cdot \frac{1}{2} x - x^2}\, dx = \left[ \frac{(x - \frac{1}{2})}{2} \sqrt{2 \cdot \frac{1}{2} x - x^2} + \frac{(\frac{1}{2})^2}{2} \sin^{-1} \left( \frac{x - \frac{1}{2}}{\frac{1}{2}} \right) \right]_0^1$

(We used FORMULA 48 with $a = \frac{1}{2}$)

$= \left[ \frac{(x - \frac{1}{2})}{2} \sqrt{x - x^2} + \frac{1}{8} \sin^{-1} (2x - 1) \right]_0^1 = \frac{1}{8} \cdot \frac{\pi}{2} - \frac{1}{8} \left( -\frac{\pi}{2} \right) = \frac{\pi}{8}$

64. The integrand is maximized by integrating $g(x) = x\sqrt{2x - x^2}$ over the largest domain on which g is nonnegative, namely $[0, 2]$

$\Rightarrow \int_0^2 x\sqrt{2x - x^2}\, dx = \left[ \frac{(x + 1)(2x - 3)\sqrt{2x - x^2}}{6} + \frac{1}{2} \sin^{-1} (x - 1) \right]_0^2$

(We used FORMULA 51 with $a = 1$)

$= \frac{1}{2} \cdot \frac{\pi}{2} - \frac{1}{2} \left( -\frac{\pi}{2} \right) = \frac{\pi}{2}$

CAS EXPLORATIONS

65.     Example CAS commands:

Maple:

```
q1 := Int( x*ln(x), x );                        # (a)
q1 = value( q1 );
q2 := Int( x^2*ln(x), x );                      # (b)
q2 = value( q2 );
q3 := Int( x^3*ln(x), x );                      # (c)
q3 = value( q3 );
q4 := Int( x^4*ln(x), x );                      # (d)
q4 = value( q4 );
q5 := Int( x^n*ln(x), x );                      # (e)
q6 := value( q5 );
q7 := simplify(q6) assuming n::integer;
q5 = collect( factor(q7), ln(x) );
```

66.     Example CAS commands:

Maple:

```
q1 := Int( ln(x)/x, x );                        # (a)
q1 = value( q1 );
q2 := Int( ln(x)/x^2, x );                      # (b)
q2 = value( q2 );
q3 := Int( ln(x)/x^3, x );                      # (c)
q3 = value( q3 );
q4 := Int( ln(x)/x^4, x );                      # (d)
q4 = value( q4 );
q5 := Int( ln(x)/x^n, x );                      # (e)
q6 := value( q5 );
q7 := simplify(q6) assuming n::integer;
q5 = collect( factor(q7), ln(x) );
```

67.        Example CAS commands:

Maple:

```
q := Int( sin(x)^n/(sin(x)^n+cos(x)^n), x=0..Pi/2 );       # (a)
q = value( q );
q1 := eval( q, n=1 ):                                      # (b)
q1 = value( q1 );
for N in [1,2,3,5,7] do
  q1 := eval( q, n=N );
  print( q1 = evalf(q1) );
end do:
qq1 := PDEtools[dchange]( x=Pi/2-u, q, [u] );              # (c)
qq2 := subs( u=x, qq1 );
qq3 := q + q = q + qq2;
qq4 := combine( qq3 );
qq5 := value( qq4 );
simplify( qq5/2 );
```

65-67.   Example CAS commands:

Mathematica: (functions may vary)

In Mathematica, the natural log is denoted by Log rather than Ln, Log base 10 is Log[x,10]

Mathematica does not include an arbitrary constant when computing an indefinite integral,

```
Clear[x, f, n]
f[x_]:=Log[x] / x^n
Integrate[f[x], x]
```

For exercise 67, Mathematica cannot evaluate the integral with arbitrary n. It does evaluate the integral (value is $\pi/4$ in each case) for small values of n, but for large values of n, it identifies this integral as Indeterminate

65. (e) $\int x^n \ln x \, dx = \frac{x^{n+1} \ln x}{n+1} - \frac{1}{n+1} \int x^n \, dx, n \neq -1$

   (We used FORMULA 110 with $a = 1, m = 1$)

   $= \frac{x^{n+1} \ln x}{n+1} - \frac{x^{n+1}}{(n+1)^2} + C = \frac{x^{n+1}}{n+1} \left( \ln x - \frac{1}{n+1} \right) + C$

66. (e) $\int x^{-n} \ln x \, dx = \frac{x^{-n+1} \ln x}{-n+1} - \frac{1}{(-n)+1} \int x^{-n} \, dx, n \neq 1$

   (We used FORMULA 110 with $a = 1, m = 1, n = -n$)

   $= \frac{x^{1-n} \ln x}{1-n} - \frac{1}{1-n} \left( \frac{x^{1-n}}{1-n} \right) + C = \frac{x^{1-n}}{1-n} \left( \ln x - \frac{1}{1-n} \right) + C$

67. (a) Neither MAPLE nor MATHEMATICA can find this integral for arbitrary n.

   (b) MAPLE and MATHEMATICA get stuck at about n = 5.

   (c) Let $x = \frac{\pi}{2} - u \Rightarrow dx = -du; x = 0 \Rightarrow u = \frac{\pi}{2}, x = \frac{\pi}{2} \Rightarrow u = 0;$

   $I = \int_0^{\pi/2} \frac{\sin^n x \, dx}{\sin^n x + \cos^n x} = \int_{\pi/2}^0 \frac{-\sin^n \left( \frac{\pi}{2} - u \right) du}{\sin^n \left( \frac{\pi}{2} - u \right) + \cos^n \left( \frac{\pi}{2} - u \right)} = \int_0^{\pi/2} \frac{\cos^n u \, du}{\cos^n u + \sin^n u} = \int_0^{\pi/2} \frac{\cos^n x \, dx}{\cos^n x + \sin^n x}$

   $\Rightarrow I + I = \int_0^{\pi/2} \left( \frac{\sin^n x + \cos^n x}{\sin^n x + \cos^n x} \right) dx = \int_0^{\pi/2} dx = \frac{\pi}{2} \Rightarrow I = \frac{\pi}{4}$

## 8.6 NUMERICAL INTEGRATION

1. $\int_1^2 x\,dx$

   I.  (a) For $n = 4$, $\Delta x = \frac{b-a}{n} = \frac{2-1}{4} = \frac{1}{4} \Rightarrow \frac{\Delta x}{2} = \frac{1}{8}$;

   $\sum mf(x_i) = 12 \Rightarrow T = \frac{1}{8}(12) = \frac{3}{2}$;

   $f(x) = x \Rightarrow f'(x) = 1 \Rightarrow f'' = 0 \Rightarrow M = 0$

   $\Rightarrow |E_T| = 0$

|       | $x_i$ | $f(x_i)$ | $m$ | $mf(x_i)$ |
|-------|-------|----------|-----|-----------|
| $x_0$ | 1     | 1        | 1   | 1         |
| $x_1$ | 5/4   | 5/4      | 2   | 5/2       |
| $x_2$ | 3/2   | 3/2      | 2   | 3         |
| $x_3$ | 7/4   | 7/4      | 2   | 7/2       |
| $x_4$ | 2     | 2        | 1   | 2         |

   (b) $\int_1^2 x\,dx = \left[\frac{x^2}{2}\right]_1^2 = 2 - \frac{1}{2} = \frac{3}{2} \Rightarrow |E_T| = \int_1^2 x\,dx - T = 0$

   (c) $\frac{|E_T|}{\text{True Value}} \times 100 = 0\%$

   II. (a) For $n = 4$, $\Delta x = \frac{b-a}{n} = \frac{2-1}{4} = \frac{1}{4} \Rightarrow \frac{\Delta x}{3} = \frac{1}{12}$;

   $\sum mf(x_i) = 18 \Rightarrow S = \frac{1}{12}(18) = \frac{3}{2}$;

   $f^{(4)}(x) = 0 \Rightarrow M = 0 \Rightarrow |E_S| = 0$

|       | $x_i$ | $f(x_i)$ | $m$ | $mf(x_i)$ |
|-------|-------|----------|-----|-----------|
| $x_0$ | 1     | 1        | 1   | 1         |
| $x_1$ | 5/4   | 5/4      | 4   | 5         |
| $x_2$ | 3/2   | 3/2      | 2   | 3         |
| $x_3$ | 7/4   | 7/4      | 4   | 7         |
| $x_4$ | 2     | 2        | 1   | 2         |

   (b) $\int_1^2 x\,dx = \frac{3}{2} \Rightarrow |E_S| = \int_1^2 x\,dx - S = \frac{3}{2} - \frac{3}{2} = 0$

   (c) $\frac{|E_S|}{\text{True Value}} \times 100 = 0\%$

2. $\int_1^3 (2x - 1)\,dx$

   I.  (a) For $n = 4$, $\Delta x = \frac{b-a}{n} = \frac{3-1}{4} = \frac{2}{4} = \frac{1}{2} \Rightarrow \frac{\Delta x}{2} = \frac{1}{4}$;

   $\sum mf(x_i) = 24 \Rightarrow T = \frac{1}{4}(24) = 6$;

   $f(x) = 2x - 1 \Rightarrow f'(x) = 2 \Rightarrow f'' = 0 \Rightarrow M = 0$

   $\Rightarrow |E_T| = 0$

|       | $x_i$ | $f(x_i)$ | $m$ | $mf(x_i)$ |
|-------|-------|----------|-----|-----------|
| $x_0$ | 1     | 1        | 1   | 1         |
| $x_1$ | 3/2   | 2        | 2   | 4         |
| $x_2$ | 2     | 3        | 2   | 6         |
| $x_3$ | 5/2   | 4        | 2   | 8         |
| $x_4$ | 3     | 5        | 1   | 5         |

   (b) $\int_1^3 (2x-1)\,dx = [x^2 - x]_1^3 = (9 - 3) - (1 - 1) = 6 \Rightarrow |E_T| = \int_1^3 (2x-1)\,dx - T = 6 - 6 = 0$

   (c) $\frac{|E_T|}{\text{True Value}} \times 100 = 0\%$

   II. (a) For $n = 4$, $\Delta x = \frac{b-a}{n} = \frac{3-1}{4} = \frac{2}{4} = \frac{1}{2} \Rightarrow \frac{\Delta x}{3} = \frac{1}{6}$;

   $\sum mf(x_i) = 36 \Rightarrow S = \frac{1}{6}(36) = 6$;

   $f^{(4)}(x) = 0 \Rightarrow M = 0 \Rightarrow |E_S| = 0$

|       | $x_i$ | $f(x_i)$ | $m$ | $mf(x_i)$ |
|-------|-------|----------|-----|-----------|
| $x_0$ | 1     | 1        | 1   | 1         |
| $x_1$ | 3/2   | 2        | 4   | 8         |
| $x_2$ | 2     | 3        | 2   | 6         |
| $x_3$ | 5/2   | 4        | 4   | 16        |
| $x_4$ | 3     | 5        | 1   | 5         |

   (b) $\int_1^3 (2x-1)\,dx = 6 \Rightarrow |E_S| = \int_1^3 (2x-1)\,dx - S$

   $= 6 - 6 = 0$

   (c) $\frac{|E_S|}{\text{True Value}} \times 100 = 0\%$

3. $\int_{-1}^1 (x^2 + 1)\,dx$

   I.  (a) For $n = 4$, $\Delta x = \frac{b-a}{n} = \frac{1-(-1)}{4} = \frac{2}{4} = \frac{1}{2} \Rightarrow \frac{\Delta x}{2} = \frac{1}{4}$;

   $\sum mf(x_i) = 11 \Rightarrow T = \frac{1}{4}(11) = 2.75$;

   $f(x) = x^2 + 1 \Rightarrow f'(x) = 2x \Rightarrow f''(x) = 2 \Rightarrow M = 2$

   $\Rightarrow |E_T| \le \frac{1-(-1)}{12}\left(\frac{1}{2}\right)^2(2) = \frac{1}{12}$ or $0.08333$

|       | $x_i$ | $f(x_i)$ | $m$ | $mf(x_i)$ |
|-------|-------|----------|-----|-----------|
| $x_0$ | $-1$  | 2        | 1   | 2         |
| $x_1$ | $-1/2$| 5/4      | 2   | 5/2       |
| $x_2$ | 0     | 1        | 2   | 2         |
| $x_3$ | 1/2   | 5/4      | 2   | 5/2       |
| $x_4$ | 1     | 2        | 1   | 2         |

   (b) $\int_{-1}^1 (x^2+1)\,dx = \left[\frac{x^3}{3} + x\right]_{-1}^1 = \left(\frac{1}{3} + 1\right) - \left(-\frac{1}{3} - 1\right) = \frac{8}{3} \Rightarrow E_T = \int_{-1}^1 (x^2+1)\,dx - T = \frac{8}{3} - \frac{11}{4} = -\frac{1}{12}$

   $\Rightarrow |E_T| = \left|-\frac{1}{12}\right| \approx 0.08333$

   (c) $\frac{|E_T|}{\text{True Value}} \times 100 = \left(\frac{\frac{1}{12}}{\frac{8}{3}}\right) \times 100 \approx 3\%$

II. (a) For $n = 4$, $\Delta x = \frac{b-a}{n} = \frac{1-(-1)}{4} = \frac{2}{4} = \frac{1}{2} \Rightarrow \frac{\Delta x}{3} = \frac{1}{6}$;

$\sum mf(x_i) = 16 \Rightarrow S = \frac{1}{6}(16) = \frac{8}{3} = 2.66667$;

$f^{(3)}(x) = 0 \Rightarrow f^{(4)}(x) = 0 \Rightarrow M = 0 \Rightarrow |E_s| = 0$

| | $x_i$ | $f(x_i)$ | $m$ | $mf(x_i)$ |
|---|---|---|---|---|
| $x_0$ | $-1$ | 2 | 1 | 2 |
| $x_1$ | $-1/2$ | $5/4$ | 4 | 5 |
| $x_2$ | 0 | 1 | 2 | 2 |
| $x_3$ | $1/2$ | $5/4$ | 4 | 5 |
| $x_4$ | 1 | 2 | 1 | 2 |

(b) $\int_{-1}^{1}(x^2 + 1)\,dx = \left[\frac{x^3}{3} + x\right]_{-1}^{1} = \frac{8}{3}$

$\Rightarrow |E_s| = \int_{-1}^{1}(x^2 + 1)\,dx - S = \frac{8}{3} - \frac{8}{3} = 0$

(c) $\frac{|E_s|}{\text{True Value}} \times 100 = 0\%$

4. $\int_{-2}^{0}(x^2 - 1)\,dx$

I. (a) For $n = 4$, $\Delta x = \frac{b-a}{n} = \frac{0-(-2)}{4} = \frac{2}{4} = \frac{1}{2} \Rightarrow \frac{\Delta x}{2} = \frac{1}{4}$

$\sum mf(x_i) = 3 \Rightarrow T = \frac{1}{4}(3) = \frac{3}{4}$;

$f(x) = x^2 - 1 \Rightarrow f'(x) = 2x \Rightarrow f''(x) = 2$

$\Rightarrow M = 2 \Rightarrow |E_T| \leq \frac{0-(-2)}{12}\left(\frac{1}{2}\right)^2(2) = \frac{1}{12} = 0.08333$

| | $x_i$ | $f(x_i)$ | $m$ | $mf(x_i)$ |
|---|---|---|---|---|
| $x_0$ | $-2$ | 3 | 1 | 3 |
| $x_1$ | $-3/2$ | $5/4$ | 2 | $5/2$ |
| $x_2$ | $-1$ | 0 | 2 | 0 |
| $x_3$ | $-1/2$ | $-3/4$ | 2 | $-3/2$ |
| $x_4$ | 0 | $-1$ | 1 | $-1$ |

(b) $\int_{-2}^{0}(x^2 - 1)\,dx = \left[\frac{x^3}{3} - x\right]_{-2}^{0} = 0 - \left(-\frac{8}{3} + 2\right) = \frac{2}{3} \Rightarrow E_T = \int_{-2}^{0}(x^2 - 1)\,dx - T = \frac{2}{3} - \frac{3}{4} = -\frac{1}{12}$

$\Rightarrow |E_T| = \frac{1}{12}$

(c) $\frac{|E_T|}{\text{True Value}} \times 100 = \left(\frac{\frac{1}{12}}{\frac{2}{3}}\right) \times 100 \approx 13\%$

II. (a) For $n = 4$, $\Delta x = \frac{b-a}{n} = \frac{0-(-2)}{4} = \frac{2}{4} = \frac{1}{2}$

$\Rightarrow \frac{\Delta x}{3} = \frac{1}{6}$; $\sum mf(x_i) = 4 \Rightarrow S = \frac{1}{6}(4) = \frac{2}{3}$;

$f^{(3)}(x) = 0 \Rightarrow f^{(4)}(x) = 0 \Rightarrow M = 0 \Rightarrow |E_s| = 0$

| | $x_i$ | $f(x_i)$ | $m$ | $mf(x_i)$ |
|---|---|---|---|---|
| $x_0$ | $-2$ | 3 | 1 | 3 |
| $x_1$ | $-3/2$ | $5/4$ | 4 | 5 |
| $x_2$ | $-1$ | 0 | 2 | 0 |
| $x_3$ | $-1/2$ | $-3/4$ | 4 | $-3$ |
| $x_4$ | 0 | $-1$ | 1 | $-1$ |

(b) $\int_{-2}^{0}(x^2 - 1)\,dx = \frac{2}{3} \Rightarrow |E_s| = \int_{-2}^{0}(x^2 - 1)\,dx - S$

$= \frac{2}{3} - \frac{2}{3} = 0$

(c) $\frac{|E_s|}{\text{True Value}} \times 100 = 0\%$

5. $\int_{0}^{2}(t^3 + t)\,dt$

I. (a) For $n = 4$, $\Delta x = \frac{b-a}{n} = \frac{2-0}{4} = \frac{2}{4} = \frac{1}{2}$

$\Rightarrow \frac{\Delta x}{2} = \frac{1}{4}$; $\sum mf(t_i) = 25 \Rightarrow T = \frac{1}{4}(25) = \frac{25}{4}$;

$f(t) = t^3 + t \Rightarrow f'(t) = 3t^2 + 1 \Rightarrow f''(t) = 6t$

$\Rightarrow M = 12 = f''(2) \Rightarrow |E_T| \leq \frac{2-0}{12}\left(\frac{1}{2}\right)^2(12) = \frac{1}{2}$

| | $t_i$ | $f(t_i)$ | $m$ | $mf(t_i)$ |
|---|---|---|---|---|
| $t_0$ | 0 | 0 | 1 | 0 |
| $t_1$ | $1/2$ | $5/8$ | 2 | $5/4$ |
| $t_2$ | 1 | 2 | 2 | 4 |
| $t_3$ | $3/2$ | $39/8$ | 2 | $39/4$ |
| $t_4$ | 2 | 10 | 1 | 10 |

(b) $\int_{0}^{2}(t^3 + t)\,dt = \left[\frac{t^4}{4} + \frac{t^2}{2}\right]_{0}^{2} = \left(\frac{2^4}{4} + \frac{2^2}{2}\right) - 0 = 6 \Rightarrow |E_T| = \int_{0}^{2}(t^3 + t)\,dt - T = 6 - \frac{25}{4} = -\frac{1}{4} \Rightarrow |E_T| = \frac{1}{4}$

(c) $\frac{|E_T|}{\text{True Value}} \times 100 = \frac{\left|-\frac{1}{4}\right|}{6} \times 100 \approx 4\%$

II. (a) For $n = 4$, $\Delta x = \frac{b-a}{n} = \frac{2-0}{4} = \frac{2}{4} = \frac{1}{2} \Rightarrow \frac{\Delta x}{3} = \frac{1}{6}$;

$\sum mf(t_i) = 36 \Rightarrow S = \frac{1}{6}(36) = 6$;

$f^{(3)}(t) = 6 \Rightarrow f^{(4)}(t) = 0 \Rightarrow M = 0 \Rightarrow |E_s| = 0$

| | $t_i$ | $f(t_i)$ | $m$ | $mf(t_i)$ |
|---|---|---|---|---|
| $t_0$ | 0 | 0 | 1 | 0 |
| $t_1$ | $1/2$ | $5/8$ | 4 | $5/2$ |
| $t_2$ | 1 | 2 | 2 | 4 |
| $t_3$ | $3/2$ | $39/8$ | 4 | $39/2$ |
| $t_4$ | 2 | 10 | 1 | 10 |

(b) $\int_{0}^{2}(t^3 + t)\,dt = 6 \Rightarrow |E_s| = \int_{0}^{2}(t^3 + t)\,dt - S$

$= 6 - 6 = 0$

(c) $\frac{|E_s|}{\text{True Value}} \times 100 = 0\%$

6. $\int_{-1}^{1}(t^3+1)\,dt$

I.  (a) For $n=4$, $\Delta x = \frac{b-a}{n} = \frac{1-(-1)}{4} = \frac{2}{4} = \frac{1}{2}$

| | $t_i$ | $f(t_i)$ | $m$ | $mf(t_i)$ |
|---|---|---|---|---|
| $t_0$ | $-1$ | 0 | 1 | 0 |
| $t_1$ | $-1/2$ | 7/8 | 2 | 7/4 |
| $t_2$ | 0 | 1 | 2 | 2 |
| $t_3$ | 1/2 | 9/8 | 2 | 9/4 |
| $t_4$ | 1 | 2 | 1 | 2 |

$\Rightarrow \frac{\Delta x}{2} = \frac{1}{4}$; $\sum mf(t_i) = 8 \Rightarrow T = \frac{1}{4}(8) = 2$;

$f(t) = t^3 + 1 \Rightarrow f'(t) = 3t^2 \Rightarrow f''(t) = 6t$

$\Rightarrow M = 6 = f''(1) \Rightarrow |E_T| \le \frac{1-(-1)}{12}\left(\frac{1}{2}\right)^2(6) = \frac{1}{4}$

(b) $\int_{-1}^{1}(t^3+1)\,dt = \left[\frac{t^4}{4} + t\right]_{-1}^{1} = \left(\frac{1^4}{4} + 1\right) - \left(\frac{(-1)^4}{4} + (-1)\right) = 2 \Rightarrow |E_T| = \int_{-1}^{1}(t^3+1)\,dt - T = 2 - 2 = 0$

(c) $\frac{|E_T|}{\text{True Value}} \times 100 = 0\%$

II.  (a) For $n=4$, $\Delta x = \frac{b-a}{n} = \frac{1-(-1)}{4} = \frac{2}{4} = \frac{1}{2}$

| | $t_i$ | $f(t_i)$ | $m$ | $mf(t_i)$ |
|---|---|---|---|---|
| $t_0$ | $-1$ | 0 | 1 | 0 |
| $t_1$ | $-1/2$ | 7/8 | 4 | 7/2 |
| $t_2$ | 0 | 1 | 2 | 2 |
| $t_3$ | 1/2 | 9/8 | 4 | 9/2 |
| $t_4$ | 1 | 2 | 1 | 2 |

$\Rightarrow \frac{\Delta x}{3} = \frac{1}{6}$; $\sum mf(t_i) = 12 \Rightarrow S = \frac{1}{6}(12) = 2$;

$f^{(3)}(t) = 6 \Rightarrow f^{(4)}(t) = 0 \Rightarrow M = 0 \Rightarrow |E_S| = 0$

(b) $\int_{-1}^{1}(t^3+1)\,dt = 2 \Rightarrow |E_S| = \int_{-1}^{1}(t^3+1)\,dt - S$

$= 2 - 2 = 0$

(c) $\frac{|E_S|}{\text{True Value}} \times 100 = 0\%$

7. $\int_{1}^{2} \frac{1}{s^2}\,ds$

I.  (a) For $n=4$, $\Delta x = \frac{b-a}{n} = \frac{2-1}{4} = \frac{1}{4} \Rightarrow \frac{\Delta x}{2} = \frac{1}{8}$;

| | $s_i$ | $f(s_i)$ | $m$ | $mf(s_i)$ |
|---|---|---|---|---|
| $s_0$ | 1 | 1 | 1 | 1 |
| $s_1$ | 5/4 | 16/25 | 2 | 32/25 |
| $s_2$ | 3/2 | 4/9 | 2 | 8/9 |
| $s_3$ | 7/4 | 16/49 | 2 | 32/49 |
| $s_4$ | 2 | 1/4 | 1 | 1/4 |

$\sum mf(s_i) = \frac{179{,}573}{44{,}100} \Rightarrow T = \frac{1}{8}\left(\frac{179{,}573}{44{,}100}\right) = \frac{179{,}573}{352{,}800}$

$\approx 0.50899; f(s) = \frac{1}{s^2} \Rightarrow f'(s) = -\frac{2}{s^3}$

$\Rightarrow f''(s) = \frac{6}{s^4} \Rightarrow M = 6 = f''(1)$

$\Rightarrow |E_T| \le \frac{2-1}{12}\left(\frac{1}{4}\right)^2(6) = \frac{1}{32} = 0.03125$

(b) $\int_{1}^{2}\frac{1}{s^2}\,ds = \int_{1}^{2}s^{-2}\,ds = \left[-\frac{1}{s}\right]_{1}^{2} = -\frac{1}{2} - \left(-\frac{1}{1}\right) = \frac{1}{2} \Rightarrow E_T = \int_{1}^{2}\frac{1}{s^2}\,ds - T = \frac{1}{2} - 0.50899 = -0.00899$

$\Rightarrow |E_T| = 0.00899$

(c) $\frac{|E_T|}{\text{True Value}} \times 100 = \frac{0.00899}{0.5} \times 100 \approx 2\%$

II.  (a) For $n=4$, $\Delta x = \frac{b-a}{n} = \frac{2-1}{4} = \frac{1}{4} \Rightarrow \frac{\Delta x}{3} = \frac{1}{12}$;

| | $s_i$ | $f(s_i)$ | $m$ | $mf(s_i)$ |
|---|---|---|---|---|
| $s_0$ | 1 | 1 | 1 | 1 |
| $s_1$ | 5/4 | 16/25 | 4 | 64/25 |
| $s_2$ | 3/2 | 4/9 | 2 | 8/9 |
| $s_3$ | 7/4 | 16/49 | 4 | 64/49 |
| $s_4$ | 2 | 1/4 | 1 | 1/4 |

$\sum mf(s_i) = \frac{264{,}821}{44{,}100} \Rightarrow S = \frac{1}{12}\left(\frac{264{,}821}{44{,}100}\right) = \frac{264{,}821}{529{,}200}$

$\approx 0.50042; f^{(3)}(s) = -\frac{24}{s^5} \Rightarrow f^{(4)}(s) = \frac{120}{s^6}$

$\Rightarrow M = 120 \Rightarrow |E_S| \le \left|\frac{2-1}{180}\right|\left(\frac{1}{4}\right)^4(120)$

$= \frac{1}{384} \approx 0.00260$

(b) $\int_{1}^{2}\frac{1}{s^2}\,ds = \frac{1}{2} \Rightarrow E_S = \int_{1}^{2}\frac{1}{s^2}\,ds - S = \frac{1}{2} - 0.50042 = -0.00042 \Rightarrow |E_S| = 0.00042$

(c) $\frac{|E_S|}{\text{True Value}} \times 100 = \frac{0.0004}{0.5} \times 100 \approx 0.08\%$

8. $\int_{2}^{4} \frac{1}{(s-1)^2}\,ds$

I.  (a) For $n=4$, $\Delta x = \frac{b-a}{n} = \frac{4-2}{4} = \frac{1}{2} \Rightarrow \frac{\Delta x}{2} = \frac{1}{4}$;

| | $s_i$ | $f(s_i)$ | $m$ | $mf(s_i)$ |
|---|---|---|---|---|
| $s_0$ | 2 | 1 | 1 | 1 |
| $s_1$ | 5/2 | 4/9 | 2 | 8/9 |
| $s_2$ | 3 | 1/4 | 2 | 1/2 |
| $s_3$ | 7/2 | 4/25 | 2 | 8/25 |
| $s_4$ | 4 | 1/9 | 1 | 1/9 |

$\sum mf(s_i) = \frac{1269}{450}$

$\Rightarrow T = \frac{1}{4}\left(\frac{1269}{450}\right) = \frac{1269}{1800} = 0.70500$;

$f(s) = (s-1)^{-2} \Rightarrow f'(s) = -\frac{2}{(s-1)^3}$

$\Rightarrow f''(s) = \frac{6}{(s-1)^4} \Rightarrow M = 6$

$\Rightarrow |E_T| \le \frac{4-2}{12}\left(\frac{1}{2}\right)^2(6) = \frac{1}{4} = 0.25$

(b) $\int_2^4 \frac{1}{(s-1)^2}\, ds = \left[\frac{-1}{(s-1)}\right]_2^4 = \left(\frac{-1}{4-1}\right) - \left(\frac{-1}{2-1}\right) = \frac{2}{3} \Rightarrow E_T = \int_2^4 \frac{1}{(s-1)^2}\, ds - T = \frac{2}{3} - 0.705 \approx -0.03833$

$\Rightarrow |E_T| \approx 0.03833$

(c) $\frac{|E_T|}{\text{True Value}} \times 100 = \frac{0.03833}{\left(\frac{2}{3}\right)} \times 100 \approx 6\%$

II. (a) For $n = 4$, $\Delta x = \frac{b-a}{n} = \frac{4-2}{4} = \frac{1}{2} \Rightarrow \frac{\Delta x}{3} = \frac{1}{6}$;

$\sum mf(s_i) = \frac{1813}{450}$

$\Rightarrow S = \frac{1}{6}\left(\frac{1813}{450}\right) = \frac{1813}{2700} \approx 0.67148$;

$f^{(3)}(s) = \frac{-24}{(s-1)^5} \Rightarrow f^{(4)}(s) = \frac{120}{(s-1)^6} \Rightarrow M = 120$

$\Rightarrow |E_S| \leq \frac{4-2}{180}\left(\frac{1}{2}\right)^4 (120) = \frac{1}{12} \approx 0.08333$

| | $s_i$ | $f(s_i)$ | m | $mf(s_i)$ |
|---|---|---|---|---|
| $s_0$ | 2 | 1 | 1 | 1 |
| $s_1$ | 5/2 | 4/9 | 4 | 16/9 |
| $s_2$ | 3 | 1/4 | 2 | 1/2 |
| $s_3$ | 7/2 | 4/25 | 4 | 16/25 |
| $s_4$ | 4 | 1/9 | 1 | 1/9 |

(b) $\int_2^4 \frac{1}{(s-1)^2}\, ds = \frac{2}{3} \Rightarrow E_S = \int_2^4 \frac{1}{(s-1)^2}\, ds - S \approx \frac{2}{3} - 0.67148 = -0.00481 \Rightarrow |E_S| \approx 0.00481$

(c) $\frac{|E_S|}{\text{True Value}} \times 100 = \frac{0.00481}{\left(\frac{2}{3}\right)} \times 100 \approx 1\%$

9. $\int_0^\pi \sin t\, dt$

I. (a) For $n = 4$, $\Delta x = \frac{b-a}{n} = \frac{\pi-0}{4} = \frac{\pi}{4} \Rightarrow \frac{\Delta x}{2} = \frac{\pi}{8}$;

$\sum mf(t_i) = 2 + 2\sqrt{2} \approx 4.8284$

$\Rightarrow T = \frac{\pi}{8}\left(2 + 2\sqrt{2}\right) \approx 1.89612$;

$f(t) = \sin t \Rightarrow f'(t) = \cos t \Rightarrow f''(t) = -\sin t$

$\Rightarrow M = 1 \Rightarrow |E_T| \leq \frac{\pi-0}{12}\left(\frac{\pi}{4}\right)^2 (1) = \frac{\pi^3}{192}$

$\approx 0.16149$

| | $t_i$ | $f(t_i)$ | m | $mf(t_i)$ |
|---|---|---|---|---|
| $t_0$ | 0 | 0 | 1 | 0 |
| $t_1$ | $\pi/4$ | $\sqrt{2}/2$ | 2 | $\sqrt{2}$ |
| $t_2$ | $\pi/2$ | 1 | 2 | 2 |
| $t_3$ | $3\pi/4$ | $\sqrt{2}/2$ | 2 | $\sqrt{2}$ |
| $t_4$ | $\pi$ | 0 | 1 | 0 |

(b) $\int_0^\pi \sin t\, dt = [-\cos t]_0^\pi = (-\cos \pi) - (-\cos 0) = 2 \Rightarrow |E_T| = \int_0^\pi \sin t\, dt - T \approx 2 - 1.89612 = 0.10388$

(c) $\frac{|E_T|}{\text{True Value}} \times 100 = \frac{0.10388}{2} \times 100 \approx 5\%$

II. (a) For $n = 4$, $\Delta x = \frac{b-a}{n} = \frac{\pi-0}{4} = \frac{\pi}{4} \Rightarrow \frac{\Delta x}{3} = \frac{\pi}{12}$;

$\sum mf(t_i) = 2 + 4\sqrt{2} \approx 7.6569$

$\Rightarrow S = \frac{\pi}{12}\left(2 + 4\sqrt{2}\right) \approx 2.00456$;

$f^{(3)}(t) = -\cos t \Rightarrow f^{(4)}(t) = \sin t$

$\Rightarrow M = 1 \Rightarrow |E_S| \leq \frac{\pi-0}{180}\left(\frac{\pi}{4}\right)^4 (1) \approx 0.00664$

| | $t_i$ | $f(t_i)$ | m | $mf(t_i)$ |
|---|---|---|---|---|
| $t_0$ | 0 | 0 | 1 | 0 |
| $t_1$ | $\pi/4$ | $\sqrt{2}/2$ | 4 | $2\sqrt{2}$ |
| $t_2$ | $\pi/2$ | 1 | 2 | 2 |
| $t_3$ | $3\pi/4$ | $\sqrt{2}/2$ | 4 | $2\sqrt{2}$ |
| $t_4$ | $\pi$ | 0 | 1 | 0 |

(b) $\int_0^\pi \sin t\, dt = 2 \Rightarrow E_S = \int_0^\pi \sin t\, dt - S \approx 2 - 2.00456 = -0.00456 \Rightarrow |E_S| \approx 0.00456$

(c) $\frac{|E_S|}{\text{True Value}} \times 100 = \frac{0.00456}{2} \times 100 \approx 0\%$

10. $\int_0^1 \sin \pi t\, dt$

I. (a) For $n = 4$, $\Delta x = \frac{b-a}{n} = \frac{1-0}{4} = \frac{1}{4} \Rightarrow \frac{\Delta x}{2} = \frac{1}{8}$;

$\sum mf(t_i) = 2 + 2\sqrt{2} \approx 4.828$

$\Rightarrow T = \frac{1}{8}\left(2 + 2\sqrt{2}\right) \approx 0.60355$; $f(t) = \sin \pi t$

$\Rightarrow f'(t) = \pi \cos \pi t$

$\Rightarrow f''(t) = -\pi^2 \sin \pi t \Rightarrow M = \pi^2$

$\Rightarrow |E_T| \leq \frac{1-0}{12}\left(\frac{1}{4}\right)^2 (\pi^2) \approx 0.05140$

| | $t_i$ | $f(t_i)$ | m | $mf(t_i)$ |
|---|---|---|---|---|
| $t_0$ | 0 | 0 | 1 | 0 |
| $t_1$ | 1/4 | $\sqrt{2}/2$ | 2 | $\sqrt{2}$ |
| $t_2$ | 1/2 | 1 | 2 | 2 |
| $t_3$ | 3/4 | $\sqrt{2}/2$ | 2 | $\sqrt{2}$ |
| $t_4$ | 1 | 0 | 1 | 0 |

(b) $\int_0^1 \sin \pi t\, dt = \left[-\frac{1}{\pi}\cos \pi t\right]_0^1 = \left(-\frac{1}{\pi}\cos \pi\right) - \left(-\frac{1}{\pi}\cos 0\right) = \frac{2}{\pi} \approx 0.63662 \Rightarrow |E_T| = \int_0^1 \sin \pi t\, dt - T$

$\approx \frac{2}{\pi} - 0.60355 = 0.03307$

(c) $\frac{|E_T|}{\text{True Value}} \times 100 = \frac{0.03307}{\left(\frac{2}{\pi}\right)} \times 100 \approx 5\%$

II. (a) For $n = 4$, $\Delta x = \frac{b-a}{n} = \frac{1-0}{4} = \frac{1}{4} \Rightarrow \frac{\Delta x}{3} = \frac{1}{12}$;

$\sum mf(t_i) = 2 + 4\sqrt{2} \approx 7.65685$

$\Rightarrow S = \frac{1}{12}\left(2 + 4\sqrt{2}\right) \approx 0.63807$;

$f^{(3)}(t) = -\pi^3 \cos \pi t \Rightarrow f^{(4)}(t) = \pi^4 \sin \pi t$

$\Rightarrow M = \pi^4 \Rightarrow |E_s| \le \frac{1-0}{180}\left(\frac{1}{4}\right)^4 (\pi^4) \approx 0.00211$

| | $t_i$ | $f(t_i)$ | $m$ | $mf(t_i)$ |
|---|---|---|---|---|
| $t_0$ | 0 | 0 | 1 | 0 |
| $t_1$ | 1/4 | $\sqrt{2}/2$ | 4 | $2\sqrt{2}$ |
| $t_2$ | 1/2 | 1 | 2 | 2 |
| $t_3$ | 3/4 | $\sqrt{2}/2$ | 4 | $2\sqrt{2}$ |
| $t_4$ | 1 | 0 | 1 | 0 |

(b) $\int_0^1 \sin \pi t \, dt = \frac{2}{\pi} \approx 0.63662 \Rightarrow E_s = \int_0^1 \sin \pi t \, dt - S \approx \frac{2}{\pi} - 0.63807 = -0.00145 \Rightarrow |E_s| \approx 0.00145$

(c) $\frac{|E_s|}{\text{True Value}} \times 100 = \frac{0.00145}{\left(\frac{2}{\pi}\right)} \times 100 \approx 0\%$

11. (a) $M = 0$ (see Exercise 1): Then $n = 1 \Rightarrow \Delta x = 1 \Rightarrow |E_T| = \frac{1}{12}(1)^2(0) = 0 < 10^{-4}$

(b) $M = 0$ (see Exercise 1): Then $n = 2$ (n must be even) $\Rightarrow \Delta x = \frac{1}{2} \Rightarrow |E_s| = \frac{1}{180}\left(\frac{1}{2}\right)^4(0) = 0 < 10^{-4}$

12. (a) $M = 0$ (see Exercise 2): Then $n = 1 \Rightarrow \Delta x = 2 \Rightarrow |E_T| = \frac{2}{12}(2)^2(0) = 0 < 10^{-4}$

(b) $M = 0$ (see Exercise 2): Then $n = 2$ (n must be even) $\Rightarrow \Delta x = 1 \Rightarrow |E_s| = \frac{2}{180}(1)^4(0) = 0 < 10^{-4}$

13. (a) $M = 2$ (see Exercise 3): Then $\Delta x = \frac{2}{n} \Rightarrow |E_T| \le \frac{2}{12}\left(\frac{2}{n}\right)^2(2) = \frac{4}{3n^2} < 10^{-4} \Rightarrow n^2 > \frac{4}{3}(10^4) \Rightarrow n > \sqrt{\frac{4}{3}(10^4)}$

$\Rightarrow n > 115.4$, so let $n = 116$

(b) $M = 0$ (see Exercise 3): Then $n = 2$ (n must be even) $\Rightarrow \Delta x = 1 \Rightarrow |E_s| = \frac{2}{180}(1)^4(0) = 0 < 10^{-4}$

14. (a) $M = 2$ (see Exercise 4): Then $\Delta x = \frac{2}{n} \Rightarrow |E_T| \le \frac{2}{12}\left(\frac{2}{n}\right)^2(2) = \frac{4}{3n^2} < 10^{-4} \Rightarrow n^2 > \frac{4}{3}(10^4) \Rightarrow n > \sqrt{\frac{4}{3}(10^4)}$

$\Rightarrow n > 115.4$, so let $n = 116$

(b) $M = 0$ (see Exercise 4): Then $n = 2$ (n must be even) $\Rightarrow \Delta x = 1 \Rightarrow |E_s| = \frac{2}{180}(1)^4(0) = 0 < 10^{-4}$

15. (a) $M = 12$ (see Exercise 5): Then $\Delta x = \frac{2}{n} \Rightarrow |E_T| \le \frac{2}{12}\left(\frac{2}{n}\right)^2(12) = \frac{8}{n^2} < 10^{-4} \Rightarrow n^2 > 8(10^4) \Rightarrow n > \sqrt{8(10^4)}$

$\Rightarrow n > 282.8$, so let $n = 283$

(b) $M = 0$ (see Exercise 5): Then $n = 2$ (n must be even) $\Rightarrow \Delta x = 1 \Rightarrow |E_s| = \frac{2}{180}(1)^4(0) = 0 < 10^{-4}$

16. (a) $M = 6$ (see Exercise 6): Then $\Delta x = \frac{2}{n} \Rightarrow |E_T| \le \frac{2}{12}\left(\frac{2}{n}\right)^2(6) = \frac{4}{n^2} < 10^{-4} \Rightarrow n^2 > 4(10^4) \Rightarrow n > \sqrt{4(10^4)}$

$= 200$, so let $n = 201$

(b) $M = 0$ (see Exercise 6): Then $n = 2$ (n must be even) $\Rightarrow \Delta x = 1 \Rightarrow |E_s| = \frac{2}{180}(1)^4(0) = 0 < 10^{-4}$

17. (a) $M = 6$ (see Exercise 7): Then $\Delta x = \frac{1}{n} \Rightarrow |E_T| \le \frac{1}{12}\left(\frac{1}{n}\right)^2(6) = \frac{1}{2n^2} < 10^{-4} \Rightarrow n^2 > \frac{1}{2}(10^4) \Rightarrow n > \sqrt{\frac{1}{2}(10^4)}$

$\Rightarrow n > 70.7$, so let $n = 71$

(b) $M = 120$ (see Exercise 7): Then $\Delta x = \frac{1}{n} \Rightarrow |E_s| = \frac{1}{180}\left(\frac{1}{n}\right)^4(120) = \frac{2}{3n^4} < 10^{-4} \Rightarrow n^4 > \frac{2}{3}(10^4)$

$\Rightarrow n > \sqrt[4]{\frac{2}{3}(10^4)} \Rightarrow n > 9.04$, so let $n = 10$ (n must be even)

18. (a) $M = 6$ (see Exercise 8): Then $\Delta x = \frac{2}{n} \Rightarrow |E_T| \le \frac{2}{12}\left(\frac{2}{n}\right)^2(6) = \frac{4}{n^2} < 10^{-4} \Rightarrow n^2 > 4(10^4) \Rightarrow n > \sqrt{4(10^4)}$

$\Rightarrow n > 200$, so let $n = 201$

(b) $M = 120$ (see Exercise 8): Then $\Delta x = \frac{2}{n} \Rightarrow |E_s| \le \frac{2}{180}\left(\frac{2}{n}\right)^4(120) = \frac{64}{3n^4} < 10^{-4} \Rightarrow n^4 > \frac{64}{3}(10^4)$

$\Rightarrow n > \sqrt[4]{\frac{64}{3}(10^4)} \Rightarrow n > 21.5$, so let $n = 22$ (n must be even)

19. (a) $f(x) = \sqrt{x+1} \Rightarrow f'(x) = \frac{1}{2}(x+1)^{-1/2} \Rightarrow f''(x) = -\frac{1}{4}(x+1)^{-3/2} = -\frac{1}{4(\sqrt{x+1})^3} \Rightarrow M = \frac{1}{4(\sqrt{1})^3} = \frac{1}{4}$.

Then $\Delta x = \frac{3}{n} \Rightarrow |E_T| \le \frac{3}{12}\left(\frac{3}{n}\right)^2\left(\frac{1}{4}\right) = \frac{9}{16n^2} < 10^{-4} \Rightarrow n^2 > \frac{9}{16}(10^4) \Rightarrow n > \sqrt{\frac{9}{16}(10^4)} \Rightarrow n > 75$,

so let n = 76

(b) $f^{(3)}(x) = \frac{3}{8}(x+1)^{-5/2} \Rightarrow f^{(4)}(x) = -\frac{15}{16}(x+1)^{-7/2} = -\frac{15}{16(\sqrt{x+1})^7} \Rightarrow M = \frac{15}{16(\sqrt{1})^7} = \frac{15}{16}$. Then $\Delta x = \frac{3}{n}$

$\Rightarrow |E_S| \le \frac{3}{180}\left(\frac{3}{n}\right)^4\left(\frac{15}{16}\right) = \frac{3^5(15)}{16(180)n^4} < 10^{-4} \Rightarrow n^4 > \frac{3^5(15)(10^4)}{16(180)} \Rightarrow n > \sqrt[4]{\frac{3^5(15)(10^4)}{16(180)}} \Rightarrow n > 10.6$, so let

n = 12 (n must be even)

20. (a) $f(x) = \frac{1}{\sqrt{x+1}} \Rightarrow f'(x) = -\frac{1}{2}(x+1)^{-3/2} \Rightarrow f''(x) = \frac{3}{4}(x+1)^{-5/2} = \frac{3}{4(\sqrt{x+1})^5} \Rightarrow M = \frac{3}{4(\sqrt{1})^5} = \frac{3}{4}$.

Then $\Delta x = \frac{3}{n} \Rightarrow |E_T| \le \frac{3}{12}\left(\frac{3}{n}\right)^2\left(\frac{3}{4}\right) = \frac{3^4}{48n^2} < 10^{-4} \Rightarrow n^2 > \frac{3^4(10^4)}{48} \Rightarrow n > \sqrt{\frac{3^4(10^4)}{48}} \Rightarrow n > 129.9$, so let n = 130

(b) $f^{(3)}(x) = -\frac{15}{8}(x+1)^{-7/2} \Rightarrow f^{(4)}(x) = \frac{105}{16}(x+1)^{-9/2} = \frac{105}{16(\sqrt{x+1})^9} \Rightarrow M = \frac{105}{16(\sqrt{1})^9} = \frac{105}{16}$. Then $\Delta x = \frac{3}{n}$

$\Rightarrow |E_S| \le \frac{3}{180}\left(\frac{3}{n}\right)^4\left(\frac{105}{16}\right) = \frac{3^5(105)}{16(180)n^4} < 10^{-4} \Rightarrow n^4 > \frac{3^5(105)(10^4)}{16(180)} \Rightarrow n > \sqrt[4]{\frac{3^5(105)(10^4)}{16(180)}} \Rightarrow n > 17.25$, so

let n = 18 (n must be even)

21. (a) $f(x) = \sin(x+1) \Rightarrow f'(x) = \cos(x+1) \Rightarrow f''(x) = -\sin(x+1) \Rightarrow M = 1$. Then $\Delta x = \frac{2}{n} \Rightarrow |E_T| \le \frac{2}{12}\left(\frac{2}{n}\right)^2(1)$

$= \frac{8}{12n^2} < 10^{-4} \Rightarrow n^2 > \frac{8(10^4)}{12} \Rightarrow n > \sqrt{\frac{8(10^4)}{12}} \Rightarrow n > 81.6$, so let n = 82

(b) $f^{(3)}(x) = -\cos(x+1) \Rightarrow f^{(4)}(x) = \sin(x+1) \Rightarrow M = 1$. Then $\Delta x = \frac{2}{n} \Rightarrow |E_S| \le \frac{2}{180}\left(\frac{2}{n}\right)^4(1) = \frac{32}{180n^4} < 10^{-4}$

$\Rightarrow n^4 > \frac{32(10^4)}{180} \Rightarrow n > \sqrt[4]{\frac{32(10^4)}{180}} \Rightarrow n > 6.49$, so let n = 8 (n must be even)

22. (a) $f(x) = \cos(x+\pi) \Rightarrow f'(x) = -\sin(x+\pi) \Rightarrow f''(x) = -\cos(x+\pi) \Rightarrow M = 1$. Then $\Delta x = \frac{2}{n}$

$\Rightarrow |E_T| \le \frac{2}{12}\left(\frac{2}{n}\right)^2(1) = \frac{8}{12n^2} < 10^{-4} \Rightarrow n^2 > \frac{8(10^4)}{12} \Rightarrow n > \sqrt{\frac{8(10^4)}{12}} \Rightarrow n > 81.6$, so let n = 82

(b) $f^{(3)}(x) = \sin(x+\pi) \Rightarrow f^{(4)}(x) = \cos(x+\pi) \Rightarrow M = 1$. Then $\Delta x = \frac{2}{n} \Rightarrow |E_S| \le \frac{2}{180}\left(\frac{2}{n}\right)^4(1) = \frac{32}{180n^4} < 10^{-4}$

$\Rightarrow n^4 > \frac{32(10^4)}{180} \Rightarrow n > \sqrt[4]{\frac{32(10^4)}{180}} \Rightarrow n > 6.49$, so let n = 8 (n must be even)

23. $\frac{5}{2}(6.0 + 2(8.2) + 2(9.1)\ldots + 2(12.7) + 13.0)(30) = 15{,}990$ ft$^3$.

24. Use the conversion 30 mph = 44 fps (ft per sec) since time is measured in seconds. The distance traveled as the car accelerates from, say, 40 mph = 58.67 fps to 50 mph = 73.33 fps in $(4.5 - 3.2) = 1.3$ sec is the area of the trapezoid (see figure) associated with that time interval: $\frac{1}{2}(58.67 + 73.33)(1.3) = 85.8$ ft. The total distance traveled by the Ford Mustang Cobra is the sum of all these eleven trapezoids (using $\frac{\Delta t}{2}$ and the table below):

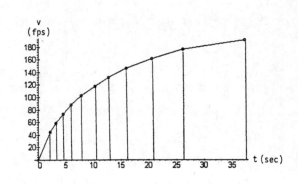

| v (mph) | 0 | 30 | 40 | 50 | 60 | 70 | 80 | 90 | 100 | 110 | 120 | 130 |
|---|---|---|---|---|---|---|---|---|---|---|---|---|
| v (fps) | 0 | 44 | 58.67 | 73.33 | 88 | 102.67 | 117.33 | 132 | 146.67 | 161.33 | 176 | 190.67 |
| t (sec) | 0 | 2.2 | 3.2 | 4.5 | 5.9 | 7.8 | 10.2 | 12.7 | 16 | 20.6 | 26.2 | 37.1 |
| $\Delta t/2$ | 0 | 1.1 | 0.5 | 0.65 | 0.7 | 0.95 | 1.2 | 1.25 | 1.65 | 2.3 | 2.8 | 5.45 |

$s = (44)(1.1) + (102.67)(0.5) + (132)(0.65) + (161.33)(0.7) + (190.67)(0.95) + (220)(1.2) + (249.33)(1.25)$
$\quad + (278.67)(1.65) + (308)(2.3) + (337.33)(2.8) + (366.67)(5.45) = 5166.346 \text{ ft} \approx 0.9785 \text{ mi}$

25. Using Simpson's Rule, $\Delta x = 1 \Rightarrow \frac{\Delta x}{3} = \frac{1}{3}$;

$\sum my_i = 33.6 \Rightarrow$ Cross Section Area $\approx \frac{1}{3}(33.6)$
$= 11.2 \text{ ft}^2$. Let x be the length of the tank. Then the
Volume $V = (\text{Cross Sectional Area}) x = 11.2x$.
Now 5000 lb of gasoline at 42 lb/ft$^3$
$\Rightarrow V = \frac{5000}{42} = 119.05 \text{ ft}^3$
$\Rightarrow 119.05 = 11.2x \Rightarrow x \approx 10.63 \text{ ft}$

|  | $x_i$ | $y_i$ | m | $my_i$ |
|---|---|---|---|---|
| $x_0$ | 0 | 1.5 | 1 | 1.5 |
| $x_1$ | 1 | 1.6 | 4 | 6.4 |
| $x_2$ | 2 | 1.8 | 2 | 3.6 |
| $x_3$ | 3 | 1.9 | 4 | 7.6 |
| $x_4$ | 4 | 2.0 | 2 | 4.0 |
| $x_5$ | 5 | 2.1 | 4 | 8.4 |
| $x_6$ | 6 | 2.1 | 1 | 2.1 |

26. $\frac{24}{2}[0.019 + 2(0.020) + 2(0.021) + \ldots + 2(0.031) + 0.035] = 4.2 \text{ L}$

27. (a) $|E_s| \le \frac{b-a}{180}(\Delta x^4) M; n = 4 \Rightarrow \Delta x = \frac{\frac{\pi}{2}-0}{4} = \frac{\pi}{8}; |f^{(4)}| \le 1 \Rightarrow M = 1 \Rightarrow |E_s| \le \frac{(\frac{\pi}{2}-0)}{180}\left(\frac{\pi}{8}\right)^4 (1) \approx 0.00021$

(b) $\Delta x = \frac{\pi}{8} \Rightarrow \frac{\Delta x}{3} = \frac{\pi}{24}$;

$\sum mf(x_i) = 10.47208705$
$\Rightarrow S = \frac{\pi}{24}(10.47208705) \approx 1.37079$

|  | $x_i$ | $f(x_i)$ | m | $mf(x_{1i})$ |
|---|---|---|---|---|
| $x_0$ | 0 | 1 | 1 | 1 |
| $x_1$ | $\pi/8$ | 0.974495358 | 4 | 3.897981432 |
| $x_2$ | $\pi/4$ | 0.900316316 | 2 | 1.800632632 |
| $x_3$ | $3\pi/8$ | 0.784213303 | 4 | 3.136853212 |
| $x_4$ | $\pi/2$ | 0.636619772 | 1 | 0.636619772 |

(c) $\approx \left(\frac{0.00021}{1.37079}\right) \times 100 \approx 0.015\%$

28. (a) $\Delta x = \frac{b-a}{n} = \frac{1-0}{10} = 0.1 \Rightarrow \text{erf}(1) = \frac{2}{\sqrt{3}}\left(\frac{0.1}{3}\right)(y_0 + 4y_1 + 2y_2 + 4y_3 + \ldots + 4y_9 + y_{10})$

$\frac{2}{30\sqrt{\pi}}(e^0 + 4e^{-0.01} + 2e^{-0.04} + 4e^{-0.09} + \ldots + 4e^{-0.81} + e^{-1}) \approx 0.843$

(b) $|E_s| \le \frac{1-0}{180}(0.1)^4(12) \approx 6.7 \times 10^{-6}$

29. $T = \frac{\Delta x}{2}(y_0 + 2y_1 + 2y_2 + 2y_3 + \ldots + 2y_{n-1} + y_n)$ where $\Delta x = \frac{b-a}{n}$ and f is continuous on [a, b]. So
$T = \frac{b-a}{n}\frac{(y_0 + y_1 + y_1 + y_2 + y_2 + \ldots + y_{n-1} + y_{n-1} + y_n)}{2} = \frac{b-a}{n}\left(\frac{f(x_0) + f(x_1)}{2} + \frac{f(x_1) + f(x_2)}{2} + \ldots + \frac{f(x_{n-1}) + f(x_n)}{2}\right)$.

Since f is continuous on each interval $[x_{k-1}, x_k]$, and $\frac{f(x_{k-1}) + f(x_k)}{2}$ is always between $f(x_{k-1})$ and $f(x_k)$, there is a point $c_k$ in
$[x_{k-1}, x_k]$ with $f(c_k) = \frac{f(x_{k-1}) + f(x_k)}{2}$; this is a consequence of the Intermediate Value Theorem. Thus our sum is
$\sum_{k=1}^{n}\left(\frac{b-a}{n}\right)f(c_k)$ which has the form $\sum_{k=1}^{n}\Delta x_k f(c_k)$ with $\Delta x_k = \frac{b-a}{n}$ for all k. This is a Riemann Sum for f on [a, b].

30. $S = \frac{\Delta x}{3}(y_0 + 4y_1 + 2y_2 + 4y_3 + \ldots + 2y_{n-2} + 4y_{n-1} + y_n)$ where n is even, $\Delta x = \frac{b-a}{n}$ and f is continuous on [a, b]. So
$S = \frac{b-a}{n}\left(\frac{y_0 + 4y_1 + y_2}{3} + \frac{y_2 + 4y_3 + y_4}{3} + \frac{y_4 + 4y_5 + y_6}{3} + \ldots + \frac{y_{n-2} + 4y_{n-1} + y_n}{3}\right)$
$= \frac{b-a}{\frac{n}{2}}\left(\frac{f(x_0) + 4f(x_1) + f(x_2)}{6} + \frac{f(x_2) + 4f(x_3) + f(x_4)}{6} + \frac{f(x_4) + 4f(x_5) + f(x_6)}{6} + \ldots + \frac{f(x_{n-2}) + 4f(x_{n-1}) + f(x_n)}{6}\right)$

$\frac{f(x_{2k}) + 4f(x_{2k+1}) + f(x_{2k+2})}{6}$ is the average of the six values of the continuous function on the interval $[x_{2k}, x_{2k+2}]$, so it is between
the minimum and maximum of f on this interval. By the Extreme Value Theorem for continuous functions, f takes on its
maximum and minimum in this interval, so there are $x_a$ and $x_b$ with $x_{2k} \le x_a$, $x_b \le x_{2k+2}$ and
$f(x_a) \le \frac{f(x_{2k}) + 4f(x_{2k+1}) + f(x_{2k+2})}{6} \le f(x_b)$. By the Intermediate Value Theorem, there is $c_k$ in $[x_{2k}, x_{2k+2}]$ with
$f(c_k) = \frac{f(x_{2k}) + 4f(x_{2k+1}) + f(x_{2k+2})}{6}$. So our sum has the form $\sum_{k=1}^{n/2}\Delta x_k f(c_k)$ with $\Delta x_k = \frac{b-a}{(n/2)}$, a Riemann sum for f on [a, b].

31. (a) $a = 1, e = \frac{1}{2} \Rightarrow$ Length $= 4 \int_0^{\pi/2} \sqrt{1 - \frac{1}{4} \cos^2 t} \, dt$

$= 2 \int_0^{\pi/2} \sqrt{4 - \cos^2 t} \, dt = \int_0^{\pi/2} f(t) \, dt$; use the

Trapezoid Rule with $n = 10 \Rightarrow \Delta t = \frac{b-a}{n} = \frac{\left(\frac{\pi}{2}\right) - 0}{10}$

$= \frac{\pi}{20}$. $\int_0^{\pi/2} \sqrt{4 - \cos^2 t} \, dt \approx \sum_{n=0}^{10} mf(x_n) = 37.3686183$

$\Rightarrow T = \frac{\Delta t}{2}(37.3686183) = \frac{\pi}{40}(37.3686183)$

$\doteq 2.934924419 \Rightarrow$ Length $= 2(2.934924419)$

$\approx 5.870$

(b) $|f''(t)| < 1 \Rightarrow M = 1$

$\Rightarrow |E_T| \leq \frac{b-a}{12}(\Delta t^2 M) \leq \frac{\left(\frac{\pi}{2}\right) - 0}{12}\left(\frac{\pi}{20}\right)^2 1 \leq 0.0032$

|         | $x_i$ | $f(x_i)$ | $m$ | $mf(x_i)$ |
|---------|-------|----------|-----|-----------|
| $x_0$   | 0 | 1.732050808 | 1 | 1.732050808 |
| $x_1$   | $\pi/20$ | 1.739100843 | 2 | 3.478201686 |
| $x_2$   | $\pi/10$ | 1.759400893 | 2 | 3.518801786 |
| $x_3$   | $3\pi/20$ | 1.790560631 | 2 | 3.581121262 |
| $x_4$   | $\pi/5$ | 1.82906848 | 1 | 3.658136959 |
| $x_5$   | $\pi/4$ | 1.870828693 | 1 | 3.741657387 |
| $x_6$   | $3\pi/10$ | 1.911676881 | 2 | 3.823353762 |
| $x_7$   | $7\pi/20$ | 1.947791731 | 2 | 3.895583461 |
| $x_8$   | $2\pi/5$ | 1.975982919 | 2 | 3.951965839 |
| $x_9$   | $9\pi/20$ | 1.993872679 | 2 | 3.987745357 |
| $x_{10}$| $\pi/2$ | 2 | 1 | 2 |

32. $\Delta x = \frac{\pi - 0}{8} = \frac{\pi}{8} \Rightarrow \frac{\Delta x}{3} = \frac{\pi}{24}$; $\sum mf(x_i) = 29.184807792$

$\Rightarrow S = \frac{\pi}{24}(29.18480779) \approx 3.82028$

|         | $x_i$ | $f(x_i)$ | $m$ | $mf(x_i)$ |
|---------|-------|----------|-----|-----------|
| $x_0$   | 0 | 1.414213562 | 1 | 1.414213562 |
| $x_1$   | $\pi/8$ | 1.361452677 | 4 | 5.445810706 |
| $x_2$   | $\pi/4$ | 1.224744871 | 2 | 2.449489743 |
| $x_3$   | $3\pi/8$ | 1.070722471 | 4 | 4.282889883 |
| $x_4$   | $\pi/2$ | 1 | 2 | 2 |
| $x_5$   | $5\pi/8$ | 1.070722471 | 4 | 4.282889883 |
| $x_6$   | $3\pi/4$ | 1.224744871 | 2 | 2.449489743 |
| $x_7$   | $7\pi/8$ | 1.361452677 | 4 | 5.445810706 |
| $x_8$   | $\pi$ | 1.414213562 | 1 | 1.414213562 |

33. The length of the curve $y = \sin\left(\frac{3\pi}{20} x\right)$ from 0 to 20 is: $L = \int_0^{20} \sqrt{1 + \left(\frac{dy}{dx}\right)^2} \, dx$; $\frac{dy}{dx} = \frac{3\pi}{20} \cos\left(\frac{3\pi}{20} x\right) \Rightarrow \left(\frac{dy}{dx}\right)^2$

$= \frac{9\pi^2}{400} \cos^2\left(\frac{3\pi}{20} x\right) \Rightarrow L = \int_0^{20} \sqrt{1 + \frac{9\pi^2}{400} \cos^2\left(\frac{3\pi}{20} x\right)} \, dx$. Using numerical integration we find $L \approx 21.07$ in

34. First, we'll find the length of the cosine curve: $L = \int_{-25}^{25} \sqrt{1 + \left(\frac{dy}{dx}\right)^2} \, dx$; $\frac{dy}{dx} = -\frac{25\pi}{50} \sin\left(\frac{\pi x}{50}\right)$

$\Rightarrow \left(\frac{dy}{dx}\right)^2 = \frac{\pi^2}{4} \sin^2\left(\frac{\pi x}{50}\right) \Rightarrow L = \int_{-25}^{25} \sqrt{1 + \frac{\pi^2}{4} \sin^2\left(\frac{\pi x}{50}\right)} \, dx$. Using a numerical integrator we find

$L \approx 73.1848$ ft. Surface area is: $A = $ length $\cdot$ width $= (73.1848)(300) = 21,955.44$ ft.

Cost $= 1.75A = (1.75)(21,955.44) = \$38,422.02$. Answers may vary slightly, depending on the numerical integration used.

35. $y = \sin x \Rightarrow \frac{dy}{dx} = \cos x \Rightarrow \left(\frac{dy}{dx}\right)^2 = \cos^2 x \Rightarrow S = \int_0^{\pi} 2\pi(\sin x) \sqrt{1 + \cos^2 x} \, dx$; a numerical integration gives

$S \approx 14.4$

36. $y = \frac{x^2}{4} \Rightarrow \frac{dy}{dx} = \frac{x}{2} \Rightarrow \left(\frac{dy}{dx}\right)^2 = \frac{x^2}{4} \Rightarrow S = \int_0^2 2\pi\left(\frac{x^2}{4}\right) \sqrt{1 + \frac{x^2}{4}} \, dx$; a numerical integration gives $S \approx 5.28$

37. A calculator or computer numerical integrator yields $\sin^{-1} 0.6 \approx 0.643501109$.

38. A calculator or computer numerical integrator yields $\pi \approx 3.1415929$.

## 8.7 IMPROPER INTEGRALS

1. $\displaystyle\int_0^\infty \frac{dx}{x^2+1} = \lim_{b\to\infty}\int_0^b \frac{dx}{x^2+1} = \lim_{b\to\infty}\left[\tan^{-1}x\right]_0^b = \lim_{b\to\infty}(\tan^{-1}b - \tan^{-1}0) = \frac{\pi}{2} - 0 = \frac{\pi}{2}$

2. $\displaystyle\int_1^\infty \frac{dx}{x^{1.001}} = \lim_{b\to\infty}\int_1^b \frac{dx}{x^{1.001}} = \lim_{b\to\infty}\left[-1000x^{-0.001}\right]_1^b = \lim_{b\to\infty}\left(\frac{-1000}{b^{0.001}} + 1000\right) = 1000$

3. $\displaystyle\int_0^1 \frac{dx}{\sqrt{x}} = \lim_{b\to 0^+}\int_b^1 x^{-1/2}\,dx = \lim_{b\to 0^+}\left[2x^{1/2}\right]_b^1 = \lim_{b\to 0^+}\left(2 - 2\sqrt{b}\right) = 2 - 0 = 2$

4. $\displaystyle\int_0^4 \frac{dx}{\sqrt{4-x}} = \lim_{b\to 4^-}\int_0^b (4-x)^{-1/2}dx = \lim_{b\to 4^-}\left[-2\sqrt{4-b} - \left(-2\sqrt{4}\right)\right] = 0 + 4 = 4$

5. $\displaystyle\int_{-1}^1 \frac{dx}{x^{2/3}} = \int_{-1}^0 \frac{dx}{x^{2/3}} + \int_0^1 \frac{dx}{x^{2/3}} = \lim_{b\to 0^-}\left[3x^{1/3}\right]_{-1}^b + \lim_{c\to 0^+}\left[3x^{1/3}\right]_c^1$
$= \lim_{b\to 0^-}\left[3b^{1/3} - 3(-1)^{1/3}\right] + \lim_{c\to 0^+}\left[3(1)^{1/3} - 3c^{1/3}\right] = (0+3) + (3-0) = 6$

6. $\displaystyle\int_{-8}^1 \frac{dx}{x^{1/3}} = \int_{-8}^0 \frac{dx}{x^{1/3}} + \int_0^1 \frac{dx}{x^{1/3}} = \lim_{b\to 0^-}\left[\frac{3}{2}x^{2/3}\right]_{-8}^b + \lim_{c\to 0^+}\left[\frac{3}{2}x^{2/3}\right]_c^1$
$= \lim_{b\to 0^-}\left[\frac{3}{2}b^{2/3} - \frac{3}{2}(-8)^{2/3}\right] + \lim_{c\to 0^+}\left[\frac{3}{2}(1)^{2/3} - \frac{3}{2}c^{2/3}\right] = \left[0 - \frac{3}{2}(4)\right] + \left(\frac{3}{2} - 0\right) = -\frac{9}{2}$

7. $\displaystyle\int_0^1 \frac{dx}{\sqrt{1-x^2}} = \lim_{b\to 1^-}\left[\sin^{-1}x\right]_0^b = \lim_{b\to 1^-}(\sin^{-1}b - \sin^{-1}0) = \frac{\pi}{2} - 0 = \frac{\pi}{2}$

8. $\displaystyle\int_0^1 \frac{dr}{r^{0.999}} = \lim_{b\to 0^+}\left[1000r^{0.001}\right]_b^1 = \lim_{b\to 0^+}(1000 - 1000b^{0.001}) = 1000 - 0 = 1000$

9. $\displaystyle\int_{-\infty}^{-2} \frac{2\,dx}{x^2-1} = \int_{-\infty}^{-2}\frac{dx}{x-1} - \int_{-\infty}^{-2}\frac{dx}{x+1} = \lim_{b\to -\infty}\left[\ln|x-1|\right]_b^{-2} - \lim_{b\to -\infty}\left[\ln|x+1|\right]_b^{-2} = \lim_{b\to -\infty}\left[\ln\left|\frac{x-1}{x+1}\right|\right]_b^{-2}$
$= \lim_{b\to -\infty}\left(\ln\left|\frac{-3}{-1}\right| - \ln\left|\frac{b-1}{b+1}\right|\right) = \ln 3 - \ln\left(\lim_{b\to -\infty}\frac{b-1}{b+1}\right) = \ln 3 - \ln 1 = \ln 3$

10. $\displaystyle\int_{-\infty}^2 \frac{2\,dx}{x^2+4} = \lim_{b\to -\infty}\left[\tan^{-1}\frac{x}{2}\right]_b^2 = \lim_{b\to -\infty}\left(\tan^{-1}1 - \tan^{-1}\frac{b}{2}\right) = \frac{\pi}{4} - \left(-\frac{\pi}{2}\right) = \frac{3\pi}{4}$

11. $\displaystyle\int_2^\infty \frac{2\,dv}{v^2-v} = \lim_{b\to\infty}\left[2\ln\left|\frac{v-1}{v}\right|\right]_2^b = \lim_{b\to\infty}\left(2\ln\left|\frac{b-1}{b}\right| - 2\ln\left|\frac{2-1}{2}\right|\right) = 2\ln(1) - 2\ln\left(\frac{1}{2}\right) = 0 + 2\ln 2 = \ln 4$

12. $\displaystyle\int_2^\infty \frac{2\,dt}{t^2-1} = \lim_{b\to\infty}\left[\ln\left|\frac{t-1}{t+1}\right|\right]_2^b = \lim_{b\to\infty}\left(\ln\left|\frac{b-1}{b+1}\right| - \ln\left|\frac{2-1}{2+1}\right|\right) = \ln(1) - \ln\left(\frac{1}{3}\right) = 0 + \ln 3 = \ln 3$

13. $\displaystyle\int_{-\infty}^\infty \frac{2x\,dx}{(x^2+1)^2} = \int_{-\infty}^0 \frac{2x\,dx}{(x^2+1)^2} + \int_0^\infty \frac{2x\,dx}{(x^2+1)^2};\ \begin{bmatrix}u = x^2+1 \\ du = 2x\,dx\end{bmatrix} \to \int_\infty^1 \frac{du}{u^2} + \int_1^\infty \frac{du}{u^2} = \lim_{b\to\infty}\left[-\frac{1}{u}\right]_b^1 + \lim_{c\to\infty}\left[-\frac{1}{u}\right]_1^c$
$= \lim_{b\to\infty}\left(-1 + \frac{1}{b}\right) + \lim_{c\to\infty}\left[-\frac{1}{c} - (-1)\right] = (-1+0) + (0+1) = 0$

14. $\displaystyle\int_{-\infty}^\infty \frac{x\,dx}{(x^2+4)^{3/2}} = \int_{-\infty}^0 \frac{x\,dx}{(x^2+4)^{3/2}} + \int_0^\infty \frac{x\,dx}{(x^2+4)^{3/2}};\ \begin{bmatrix}u = x^2+4 \\ du = 2x\,dx\end{bmatrix} \to \int_\infty^4 \frac{du}{2u^{3/2}} + \int_4^\infty \frac{du}{2u^{3/2}}$
$= \lim_{b\to\infty}\left[-\frac{1}{\sqrt{u}}\right]_b^4 + \lim_{c\to\infty}\left[-\frac{1}{\sqrt{u}}\right]_4^c = \lim_{b\to\infty}\left(-\frac{1}{2} + \frac{1}{\sqrt{b}}\right) + \lim_{c\to\infty}\left(-\frac{1}{\sqrt{c}} + \frac{1}{2}\right) = \left(-\frac{1}{2} + 0\right) + \left(0 + \frac{1}{2}\right) = 0$

15. $\int_0^1 \frac{\theta+1}{\sqrt{\theta^2+2\theta}}\, d\theta;$ $\begin{bmatrix} u = \theta^2 + 2\theta \\ du = 2(\theta+1)\,d\theta \end{bmatrix}$ $\rightarrow \int_0^3 \frac{du}{2\sqrt{u}} = \lim_{b \to 0^+} \int_b^3 \frac{du}{2\sqrt{u}} = \lim_{b \to 0^+} \left[\sqrt{u}\right]_b^3 = \lim_{b \to 0^+} \left(\sqrt{3} - \sqrt{b}\right) = \sqrt{3} - 0$

$= \sqrt{3}$

16. $\int_0^2 \frac{s+1}{\sqrt{4-s^2}}\, ds = \frac{1}{2}\int_0^2 \frac{2s\, ds}{\sqrt{4-s^2}} + \int_0^2 \frac{ds}{\sqrt{4-s^2}};$ $\begin{bmatrix} u = 4 - s^2 \\ du = -2s\, ds \end{bmatrix}$ $\rightarrow -\frac{1}{2}\int_4^0 \frac{du}{\sqrt{u}} + \lim_{c \to 2^-} \int_0^c \frac{ds}{\sqrt{4-s^2}}$

$= \lim_{b \to 0^+} \int_b^4 \frac{du}{2\sqrt{u}} + \lim_{c \to 2^-} \int_0^c \frac{ds}{\sqrt{4-s^2}} = \lim_{b \to 0^+} \left[\sqrt{u}\right]_b^4 + \lim_{c \to 2^-} \left[\sin^{-1}\frac{s}{2}\right]_0^c$

$= \lim_{b \to 0^+} \left(2 - \sqrt{b}\right) + \lim_{c \to 2^-} \left(\sin^{-1}\frac{c}{2} - \sin^{-1} 0\right) = (2 - 0) + \left(\frac{\pi}{2} - 0\right) = \frac{4+\pi}{2}$

17. $\int_0^\infty \frac{dx}{(1+x)\sqrt{x}};$ $\begin{bmatrix} u = \sqrt{x} \\ du = \frac{dx}{2\sqrt{x}} \end{bmatrix}$ $\rightarrow \int_0^\infty \frac{2\, du}{u^2+1} = \lim_{b \to \infty} \int_0^b \frac{2\, du}{u^2+1} = \lim_{b \to \infty} \left[2\tan^{-1} u\right]_0^b$

$= \lim_{b \to \infty} \left(2\tan^{-1} b - 2\tan^{-1} 0\right) = 2\left(\frac{\pi}{2}\right) - 2(0) = \pi$

18. $\int_1^\infty \frac{dx}{x\sqrt{x^2-1}} = \int_1^2 \frac{dx}{x\sqrt{x^2-1}} + \int_2^\infty \frac{dx}{x\sqrt{x^2-1}} = \lim_{b \to 1^+} \int_b^2 \frac{dx}{x\sqrt{x^2-1}} + \lim_{c \to \infty} \int_2^c \frac{dx}{x\sqrt{x^2-1}}$

$= \lim_{b \to 1^+} \left[\sec^{-1}|x|\right]_b^2 + \lim_{c \to \infty} \left[\sec^{-1}|x|\right]_2^c = \lim_{b \to 1^+} \left(\sec^{-1} 2 - \sec^{-1} b\right) + \lim_{c \to \infty} \left(\sec^{-1} c - \sec^{-1} 2\right)$

$= \left(\frac{\pi}{3} - 0\right) + \left(\frac{\pi}{2} - \frac{\pi}{3}\right) = \frac{\pi}{2}$

19. $\int_0^\infty \frac{dv}{(1+v^2)(1+\tan^{-1} v)} = \lim_{b \to \infty} \left[\ln|1+\tan^{-1} v|\right]_0^b = \lim_{b \to \infty} \left[\ln|1+\tan^{-1} b|\right] - \ln|1+\tan^{-1} 0|$

$= \ln\left(1+\frac{\pi}{2}\right) - \ln(1+0) = \ln\left(1+\frac{\pi}{2}\right)$

20. $\int_0^\infty \frac{16\tan^{-1} x}{1+x^2}\, dx = \lim_{b \to \infty} \left[8\left(\tan^{-1} x\right)^2\right]_0^b = \lim_{b \to \infty} \left[8\left(\tan^{-1} b\right)^2\right] - 8\left(\tan^{-1} 0\right)^2 = 8\left(\frac{\pi}{2}\right)^2 - 8(0) = 2\pi^2$

21. $\int_{-\infty}^0 \theta e^\theta\, d\theta = \lim_{b \to -\infty} \left[\theta e^\theta - e^\theta\right]_b^0 = (0 \cdot e^0 - e^0) - \lim_{b \to -\infty} \left[be^b - e^b\right] = -1 - \lim_{b \to -\infty} \left(\frac{b-1}{e^{-b}}\right)$

$= -1 - \lim_{b \to -\infty} \left(\frac{1}{-e^{-b}}\right)$   (l'Hôpital's rule for $\frac{\infty}{\infty}$ form)

$= -1 - 0 = -1$

22. $\int_0^\infty 2e^{-\theta} \sin\theta\, d\theta = \lim_{b \to \infty} \int_0^b 2e^{-\theta} \sin\theta\, d\theta$

$= \lim_{b \to \infty} 2\left[\frac{e^{-\theta}}{1+1}(-\sin\theta - \cos\theta)\right]_0^b$   (FORMULA 107 with $a = -1, b = 1$)

$= \lim_{b \to \infty} \frac{-2(\sin b + \cos b)}{2e^b} + \frac{2(\sin 0 + \cos 0)}{2e^0} = 0 + \frac{2(0+1)}{2} = 1$

23. $\int_{-\infty}^0 e^{-|x|}\, dx = \int_{-\infty}^0 e^x\, dx = \lim_{b \to -\infty} \left[e^x\right]_b^0 = \lim_{b \to -\infty} (1 - e^b) = (1 - 0) = 1$

24. $\int_{-\infty}^\infty 2xe^{-x^2}\, dx = \int_{-\infty}^0 2xe^{-x^2}\, dx + \int_0^\infty 2xe^{-x^2}\, dx = \lim_{b \to -\infty} \left[-e^{-x^2}\right]_b^0 + \lim_{c \to \infty} \left[-e^{-x^2}\right]_0^c$

$= \lim_{b \to -\infty} \left[-1 - (-e^{-b^2})\right] + \lim_{c \to \infty} \left[-e^{-c^2} - (-1)\right] = (-1 - 0) + (0 + 1) = 0$

25. $\int_0^1 x \ln x\, dx = \lim_{b \to 0^+} \left[\frac{x^2}{2}\ln x - \frac{x^2}{4}\right]_b^1 = \left(\frac{1}{2}\ln 1 - \frac{1}{4}\right) - \lim_{b \to 0^+} \left(\frac{b^2}{2}\ln b - \frac{b^2}{4}\right) = -\frac{1}{4} - \lim_{b \to 0^+} \frac{\ln b}{\left(\frac{2}{b^2}\right)} + 0$

$= -\frac{1}{4} - \lim_{b \to 0^+} \frac{\left(\frac{1}{b}\right)}{\left(-\frac{4}{b^3}\right)} = -\frac{1}{4} + \lim_{b \to 0^+} \left(\frac{b^2}{4}\right) = -\frac{1}{4} + 0 = -\frac{1}{4}$

26. $\int_0^1 (-\ln x)\, dx = \lim_{b \to 0^+} [x - x \ln x]_b^1 = [1 - 1 \ln 1] - \lim_{b \to 0^+} [b - b \ln b] = 1 - 0 + \lim_{b \to 0^+} \frac{\ln b}{\left(\frac{1}{b}\right)} = 1 + \lim_{b \to 0^+} \frac{\left(\frac{1}{b}\right)}{\left(-\frac{1}{b^2}\right)}$

$= 1 - \lim_{b \to 0^+} b = 1 - 0 = 1$

27. $\int_0^2 \frac{ds}{\sqrt{4 - s^2}} = \lim_{b \to 2^-} \left[\sin^{-1} \frac{s}{2}\right]_0^b = \lim_{b \to 2^-} \left(\sin^{-1} \frac{b}{2}\right) - \sin^{-1} 0 = \frac{\pi}{2} - 0 = \frac{\pi}{2}$

28. $\int_0^1 \frac{4r\, dr}{\sqrt{1 - r^4}} = \lim_{b \to 1^-} \left[2 \sin^{-1} (r^2)\right]_0^b = \lim_{b \to 1^-} \left[2 \sin^{-1} (b^2)\right] - 2 \sin^{-1} 0 = 2 \cdot \frac{\pi}{2} - 0 = \pi$

29. $\int_1^2 \frac{ds}{s\sqrt{s^2 - 1}} = \lim_{b \to 1^+} \left[\sec^{-1} s\right]_b^2 = \sec^{-1} 2 - \lim_{b \to 1^+} \sec^{-1} b = \frac{\pi}{3} - 0 = \frac{\pi}{3}$

30. $\int_2^4 \frac{dt}{t\sqrt{t^2 - 4}} = \lim_{b \to 2^+} \left[\frac{1}{2} \sec^{-1} \frac{t}{2}\right]_b^4 = \lim_{b \to 2^+} \left[\left(\frac{1}{2} \sec^{-1} \frac{4}{2}\right) - \frac{1}{2} \sec^{-1} \left(\frac{b}{2}\right)\right] = \frac{1}{2} \left(\frac{\pi}{3}\right) - \frac{1}{2} \cdot 0 = \frac{\pi}{6}$

31. $\int_{-1}^4 \frac{dx}{\sqrt{|x|}} = \lim_{b \to 0^-} \int_{-1}^b \frac{dx}{\sqrt{-x}} + \lim_{c \to 0^+} \int_c^4 \frac{dx}{\sqrt{x}} = \lim_{b \to 0^-} \left[-2\sqrt{-x}\right]_{-1}^b + \lim_{c \to 0^+} \left[2\sqrt{x}\right]_c^4$

$= \lim_{b \to 0^-} \left(-2\sqrt{-b}\right) - \left(-2\sqrt{-(-1)}\right) + 2\sqrt{4} - \lim_{c \to 0^+} 2\sqrt{c} = 0 + 2 + 2 \cdot 2 - 0 = 6$

32. $\int_0^2 \frac{dx}{\sqrt{|x - 1|}} = \int_0^1 \frac{dx}{\sqrt{1 - x}} + \int_1^2 \frac{dx}{\sqrt{x - 1}} = \lim_{b \to 1^-} \left[-2\sqrt{1 - x}\right]_0^b + \lim_{c \to 1^+} \left[2\sqrt{x - 1}\right]_c^2$

$= \lim_{b \to 1^-} \left(-2\sqrt{1 - b}\right) - \left(-2\sqrt{1 - 0}\right) + 2\sqrt{2 - 1} - \lim_{c \to 1^+} \left(2\sqrt{c - 1}\right) = 0 + 2 + 2 - 0 = 4$

33. $\int_{-1}^{\infty} \frac{d\theta}{\theta^2 + 5\theta + 6} = \lim_{b \to \infty} \left[\ln \left|\frac{\theta + 2}{\theta + 3}\right|\right]_{-1}^b = \lim_{b \to \infty} \left[\ln \left|\frac{b + 2}{b + 3}\right|\right] - \ln \left|\frac{-1 + 2}{-1 + 3}\right| = 0 - \ln \left(\frac{1}{2}\right) = \ln 2$

34. $\int_0^{\infty} \frac{dx}{(x + 1)(x^2 + 1)} = \lim_{b \to \infty} \left[\frac{1}{2} \ln |x + 1| - \frac{1}{4} \ln (x^2 + 1) + \frac{1}{2} \tan^{-1} x\right]_0^b = \lim_{b \to \infty} \left[\frac{1}{2} \ln \left(\frac{x + 1}{\sqrt{x^2 + 1}}\right) + \frac{1}{2} \tan^{-1} x\right]_0^b$

$= \lim_{b \to \infty} \left[\frac{1}{2} \ln \left(\frac{b + 1}{\sqrt{b^2 + 1}}\right) + \frac{1}{2} \tan^{-1} b\right] - \left[\frac{1}{2} \ln \frac{1}{\sqrt{1}} + \frac{1}{2} \tan^{-1} 0\right] = \frac{1}{2} \ln 1 + \frac{1}{2} \cdot \frac{\pi}{2} - \frac{1}{2} \ln 1 - \frac{1}{2} \cdot 0 = \frac{\pi}{4}$

35. $\int_0^{\pi/2} \tan \theta\, d\theta = \lim_{b \to \frac{\pi}{2}^-} \left[-\ln |\cos \theta|\right]_0^b = \lim_{b \to \frac{\pi}{2}^-} \left[-\ln |\cos b|\right] + \ln 1 = \lim_{b \to \frac{\pi}{2}^-} \left[-\ln |\cos b|\right] = +\infty$, the integral diverges

36. $\int_0^{\pi/2} \cot \theta\, d\theta = \lim_{b \to 0^+} \left[\ln |\sin \theta|\right]_b^{\pi/2} = \ln 1 - \lim_{b \to 0^+} \left[\ln |\sin b|\right] = -\lim_{b \to 0^+} \left[\ln |\sin b|\right] = +\infty$, the integral diverges

37. $\int_0^{\pi} \frac{\sin \theta\, d\theta}{\sqrt{\pi - \theta}}$; $[\pi - \theta = x] \to -\int_{\pi}^0 \frac{\sin x\, dx}{\sqrt{x}} = \int_0^{\pi} \frac{\sin x\, dx}{\sqrt{x}}$. Since $0 \le \frac{\sin x}{\sqrt{x}} \le \frac{1}{\sqrt{x}}$ for all $0 \le x \le \pi$ and $\int_0^{\pi} \frac{dx}{\sqrt{x}}$ converges, then

$\int_0^{\pi} \frac{\sin x}{\sqrt{x}}\, dx$ converges by the Direct Comparison Test.

38. $\int_{-\pi/2}^{\pi/2} \frac{\cos \theta\, d\theta}{(\pi - 2\theta)^{1/3}}$; $\begin{bmatrix} x = \pi - 2\theta \\ \theta = \frac{\pi}{2} - \frac{x}{2} \\ d\theta = -\frac{dx}{2} \end{bmatrix} \to \int_{2\pi}^0 \frac{-\cos \left(\frac{\pi}{2} - \frac{x}{2}\right) dx}{2x^{1/3}} = \int_0^{2\pi} \frac{\sin \left(\frac{x}{2}\right) dx}{2x^{1/3}}$. Since $0 \le \frac{\sin \frac{x}{2}}{2x^{1/3}} \le \frac{1}{2x^{1/3}}$ for all $0 \le x \le 2\pi$ and

$\int_0^{2\pi} \frac{dx}{2x^{1/3}}$ converges, then $\int_0^{2\pi} \frac{\sin \frac{x}{2}\, dx}{2x^{1/3}}$ converges by the Direct Comparison Test.

39. $\int_0^{\ln 2} x^{-2} e^{-1/x}\, dx$; $\left[\frac{1}{x} = y\right] \to \int_{\infty}^{1/\ln 2} \frac{y^2 e^{-y}\, dy}{-y^2} = \int_{1/\ln 2}^{\infty} e^{-y}\, dy = \lim_{b \to \infty} \left[-e^{-y}\right]_{1/\ln 2}^b = \lim_{b \to \infty} \left[-e^{-b}\right] - \left[-e^{-1/\ln 2}\right]$

$= 0 + e^{-1/\ln 2} = e^{-1/\ln 2}$, so the integral converges.

40. $\int_0^1 \frac{e^{-\sqrt{x}}}{\sqrt{x}}\, dx$; $\left[y = \sqrt{x}\right] \;\rightarrow\; 2\int_0^1 e^{-y}\, dy = 2 - \frac{2}{e}$, so the integral converges.

41. $\int_0^\pi \frac{dt}{\sqrt{t + \sin t}}$. Since for $0 \le t \le \pi$, $0 \le \frac{1}{\sqrt{t + \sin t}} \le \frac{1}{\sqrt{t}}$ and $\int_0^\pi \frac{dt}{\sqrt{t}}$ converges, then the original integral converges as well by the Direct Comparison Test.

42. $\int_0^1 \frac{dt}{t - \sin t}$; let $f(t) = \frac{1}{t - \sin t}$ and $g(t) = \frac{1}{t^3}$, then $\lim\limits_{t \to 0} \frac{f(t)}{g(t)} = \lim\limits_{t \to 0} \frac{t^3}{t - \sin t} = \lim\limits_{t \to 0} \frac{3t^2}{1 - \cos t} = \lim\limits_{t \to 0} \frac{6t}{\sin t}$

   $= \lim\limits_{t \to 0} \frac{6}{\cos t} = 6$. Now, $\int_0^1 \frac{dt}{t^3} = \lim\limits_{b \to 0^+} \left[-\frac{1}{2t^2}\right]_b^1 = -\frac{1}{2} - \lim\limits_{b \to 0^+} \left[-\frac{1}{2b^2}\right] = +\infty$, which diverges $\Rightarrow \int_0^1 \frac{dt}{t - \sin t}$ diverges by the Limit Comparison Test.

43. $\int_0^2 \frac{dx}{1 - x^2} = \int_0^1 \frac{dx}{1 - x^2} + \int_1^2 \frac{dx}{1 - x^2}$ and $\int_0^1 \frac{dx}{1 - x^2} = \lim\limits_{b \to 1^-} \left[\frac{1}{2}\ln\left|\frac{1+x}{1-x}\right|\right]_0^b = \lim\limits_{b \to 1^-} \left[\frac{1}{2}\ln\left|\frac{1+b}{1-b}\right|\right] - 0 = \infty$, which

   diverges $\Rightarrow \int_0^2 \frac{dx}{1 - x^2}$ diverges as well.

44. $\int_0^2 \frac{dx}{1 - x} = \int_0^1 \frac{dx}{1 - x} + \int_1^2 \frac{dx}{1 - x}$ and $\int_0^1 \frac{dx}{1 - x} = \lim\limits_{b \to 1^-} \left[-\ln(1 - x)\right]_0^b = \lim\limits_{b \to 1^-} \left[-\ln(1 - b)\right] - 0 = \infty$, which diverges

   $\Rightarrow \int_0^2 \frac{dx}{1 - x}$ diverges as well.

45. $\int_{-1}^1 \ln|x|\, dx = \int_{-1}^0 \ln(-x)\, dx + \int_0^1 \ln x\, dx$; $\int_0^1 \ln x\, dx = \lim\limits_{b \to 0^+} \left[x \ln x - x\right]_b^1 = [1 \cdot 0 - 1] - \lim\limits_{b \to 0^+} [b \ln b - b]$

   $= -1 - 0 = -1$; $\int_{-1}^0 \ln(-x)\, dx = -1 \Rightarrow \int_{-1}^1 \ln|x|\, dx = -2$ converges.

46. $\int_{-1}^1 (-x \ln|x|)\, dx = \int_{-1}^0 [-x \ln(-x)]\, dx + \int_0^1 (-x \ln x)\, dx = \lim\limits_{b \to 0^+} \left[\frac{x^2}{2}\ln x - \frac{x^2}{4}\right]_b^1 - \lim\limits_{c \to 0^+} \left[\frac{x^2}{2}\ln x - \frac{x^2}{4}\right]_c^1$

   $= \left[\frac{1}{2}\ln 1 - \frac{1}{4}\right] - \lim\limits_{b \to 0^+} \left[\frac{b^2}{2}\ln b - \frac{b^2}{4}\right] - \left[\frac{1}{2}\ln 1 - \frac{1}{4}\right] + \lim\limits_{c \to 0^+} \left[\frac{c^2}{2}\ln c - \frac{c^2}{4}\right] = -\frac{1}{4} - 0 + \frac{1}{4} + 0 = 0 \Rightarrow$ the integral

   converges (see Exercise 25 for the limit calculations).

47. $\int_1^\infty \frac{dx}{1 + x^3}$; $0 \le \frac{1}{x^3 + 1} \le \frac{1}{x^3}$ for $1 \le x < \infty$ and $\int_1^\infty \frac{dx}{x^3}$ converges $\Rightarrow \int_1^\infty \frac{dx}{1 + x^3}$ converges by the Direct Comparison Test.

48. $\int_4^\infty \frac{dx}{\sqrt{x - 1}}$; $\lim\limits_{x \to \infty} \frac{\left(\frac{1}{\sqrt{x - 1}}\right)}{\left(\frac{1}{\sqrt{x}}\right)} = \lim\limits_{x \to \infty} \frac{\sqrt{x}}{\sqrt{x - 1}} = \lim\limits_{x \to \infty} \frac{1}{1 - \frac{1}{x}} = \frac{1}{1 - 0} = 1$ and $\int_4^\infty \frac{dx}{\sqrt{x}} = \lim\limits_{b \to \infty} \left[2\sqrt{x}\right]_4^b = \infty$,

   which diverges $\Rightarrow \int_4^\infty \frac{dx}{\sqrt{x - 1}}$ diverges by the Limit Comparison Test.

49. $\int_2^\infty \frac{dv}{\sqrt{v - 1}}$; $\lim\limits_{v \to \infty} \frac{\left(\frac{1}{\sqrt{v - 1}}\right)}{\left(\frac{1}{\sqrt{v}}\right)} = \lim\limits_{v \to \infty} \frac{\sqrt{v}}{\sqrt{v - 1}} = \lim\limits_{v \to \infty} \frac{1}{\sqrt{1 - \frac{1}{v}}} = \frac{1}{\sqrt{1 - 0}} = 1$ and $\int_2^\infty \frac{dv}{\sqrt{v}} = \lim\limits_{b \to \infty} \left[2\sqrt{v}\right]_2^b = \infty$,

   which diverges $\Rightarrow \int_2^\infty \frac{dv}{\sqrt{v - 1}}$ diverges by the Limit Comparison Test.

50. $\int_0^\infty \frac{d\theta}{1 + e^\theta}$; $0 \le \frac{1}{1 + e^\theta} \le \frac{1}{e^\theta}$ for $0 \le \theta < \infty$ and $\int_0^\infty \frac{d\theta}{e^\theta} = \lim\limits_{b \to \infty} \left[-e^{-\theta}\right]_0^b = \lim\limits_{b \to \infty} \left(-e^{-b} + 1\right) = 1 \Rightarrow \int_0^\infty \frac{d\theta}{e^\theta}$ converges

   $\Rightarrow \int_0^\infty \frac{d\theta}{1 + e^\theta}$ converges by the Direct Comparison Test.

51. $\int_0^\infty \frac{dx}{\sqrt{x^6 + 1}} = \int_0^1 \frac{dx}{\sqrt{x^6 + 1}} + \int_1^\infty \frac{dx}{\sqrt{x^6 + 1}} < \int_0^1 \frac{dx}{\sqrt{x^6 + 1}} + \int_1^\infty \frac{dx}{x^3}$ and $\int_1^\infty \frac{dx}{x^3} = \lim\limits_{b \to \infty} \left[-\frac{1}{2x^2}\right]_1^b$

   $= \lim\limits_{b \to \infty} \left(-\frac{1}{2b^2} + \frac{1}{2}\right) = \frac{1}{2} \Rightarrow \int_0^\infty \frac{dx}{\sqrt{x^6 + 1}}$ converges by the Direct Comparison Test.

52. $\int_2^\infty \frac{dx}{\sqrt{x^2-1}}$; $\lim_{x\to\infty} \frac{\left(\frac{1}{\sqrt{x^2-1}}\right)}{\left(\frac{1}{x}\right)} = \lim_{x\to\infty} \frac{x}{\sqrt{x^2-1}} = \lim_{x\to\infty} \frac{1}{\sqrt{1-\frac{1}{x^2}}} = 1$; $\int_2^\infty \frac{1}{x}\,dx = \lim_{b\to\infty} [\ln b]_2^b = \infty$,

which diverges $\Rightarrow \int_2^\infty \frac{dx}{\sqrt{x^2-1}}$ diverges by the Limit Comparison Test.

53. $\int_1^\infty \frac{\sqrt{x+1}}{x^2}\,dx$; $\lim_{x\to\infty} \frac{\left(\frac{\sqrt{x}}{x^2}\right)}{\left(\frac{\sqrt{x+1}}{x^2}\right)} = \lim_{x\to\infty} \frac{\sqrt{x}}{\sqrt{x+1}} = \lim_{x\to\infty} \frac{1}{\sqrt{1+\frac{1}{x}}} = 1$; $\int_1^\infty \frac{\sqrt{x}}{x^2}\,dx = \int_1^\infty \frac{dx}{x^{3/2}}$

$= \lim_{b\to\infty} \left[-2x^{-1/2}\right]_1^b = \lim_{b\to\infty} \left(\frac{-2}{\sqrt{b}}+2\right) = 2 \Rightarrow \int_1^\infty \frac{\sqrt{x+1}}{x^2}\,dx$ converges by the Limit Comparison Test.

54. $\int_2^\infty \frac{x\,dx}{\sqrt{x^4-1}}$; $\lim_{x\to\infty} \frac{\left(\frac{x}{\sqrt{x^4-1}}\right)}{\left(\frac{x}{\sqrt{x^4}}\right)} = \lim_{x\to\infty} \frac{\sqrt{x^4}}{\sqrt{x^4-1}} = \lim_{x\to\infty} \frac{1}{\sqrt{1-\frac{1}{x^4}}} = 1$; $\int_2^\infty \frac{x\,dx}{\sqrt{x^4}} = \int_2^\infty \frac{dx}{x} = \lim_{b\to\infty} [\ln x]_2^b = \infty$,

which diverges $\Rightarrow \int_2^\infty \frac{x\,dx}{\sqrt{x^4-1}}$ diverges by the Limit Comparison Test.

55. $\int_\pi^\infty \frac{2+\cos x}{x}\,dx$; $0 < \frac{1}{x} \le \frac{2+\cos x}{x}$ for $x \ge \pi$ and $\int_\pi^\infty \frac{dx}{x} = \lim_{b\to\infty} [\ln x]_\pi^b = \infty$, which diverges

$\Rightarrow \int_\pi^\infty \frac{2+\cos x}{x}\,dx$ diverges by the Direct Comparison Test.

56. $\int_\pi^\infty \frac{1+\sin x}{x^2}\,dx$; $0 \le \frac{1+\sin x}{x^2} \le \frac{2}{x^2}$ for $x \ge \pi$ and $\int_\pi^\infty \frac{2}{x^2}\,dx = \lim_{b\to\infty} \left[-\frac{2}{x}\right]_\pi^b = \lim_{b\to\infty} \left(-\frac{2}{b}+\frac{2}{\pi}\right) = \frac{2}{\pi}$

$\Rightarrow \int_\pi^\infty \frac{2\,dx}{x^2}$ converges $\Rightarrow \int_\pi^\infty \frac{1+\sin x}{x^2}\,dx$ converges by the Direct Comparison Test.

57. $\int_4^\infty \frac{2\,dt}{t^{3/2}-1}$; $\lim_{t\to\infty} \frac{t^{3/2}}{t^{3/2}-1} = 1$ and $\int_4^\infty \frac{2\,dt}{t^{3/2}} = \lim_{b\to\infty} \left[-4t^{-1/2}\right]_4^b = \lim_{b\to\infty} \left(\frac{-4}{\sqrt{b}}+2\right) = 2 \Rightarrow \int_4^\infty \frac{2\,dt}{t^{3/2}}$ converges

$\Rightarrow \int_4^\infty \frac{2\,dt}{t^{3/2}+1}$ converges by the Limit Comparison Test.

58. $\int_2^\infty \frac{dx}{\ln x}$; $0 < \frac{1}{x} < \frac{1}{\ln x}$ for $x > 2$ and $\int_2^\infty \frac{dx}{x}$ diverges $\Rightarrow \int_2^\infty \frac{dx}{\ln x}$ diverges by the Direct Comparison Test.

59. $\int_1^\infty \frac{e^x}{x}\,dx$; $0 < \frac{1}{x} < \frac{e^x}{x}$ for $x > 1$ and $\int_1^\infty \frac{dx}{x}$ diverges $\Rightarrow \int_1^\infty \frac{e^x\,dx}{x}$ diverges by the Direct Comparison Test.

60. $\int_{e^e}^\infty \ln(\ln x)\,dx$; $[x = e^y] \to \int_e^\infty (\ln y)e^y\,dy$; $0 < \ln y < (\ln y)e^y$ for $y \ge e$ and $\int_e^\infty \ln y\,dy = \lim_{b\to\infty} [y\ln y - y]_e^b = \infty$,

which diverges $\Rightarrow \int_e^\infty \ln e^y\,dy$ diverges $\Rightarrow \int_{e^e}^\infty \ln(\ln x)\,dx$ diverges by the Direct Comparison Test.

61. $\int_1^\infty \frac{dx}{\sqrt{e^x-x}}$; $\lim_{x\to\infty} \frac{\left(\frac{1}{\sqrt{e^x-x}}\right)}{\left(\frac{1}{\sqrt{e^x}}\right)} = \lim_{x\to\infty} \frac{\sqrt{e^x}}{\sqrt{e^x-x}} = \lim_{x\to\infty} \frac{1}{\sqrt{1-\frac{x}{e^x}}} = \frac{1}{\sqrt{1-0}} = 1$; $\int_1^\infty \frac{dx}{\sqrt{e^x}} = \int_1^\infty e^{-x/2}\,dx$

$= \lim_{b\to\infty} \left[-2e^{-x/2}\right]_1^b = \lim_{b\to\infty} \left(-2e^{-b/2}+2e^{-1/2}\right) = \frac{2}{\sqrt{e}} \Rightarrow \int_1^\infty e^{-x/2}\,dx$ converges $\Rightarrow \int_1^\infty \frac{dx}{\sqrt{e^x-x}}$ converges

by the Limit Comparison Test.

62. $\int_1^\infty \frac{dx}{e^x-2^x}$; $\lim_{x\to\infty} \frac{\left(\frac{1}{e^x-2^x}\right)}{\left(\frac{1}{e^x}\right)} = \lim_{x\to\infty} \frac{e^x}{e^x-2^x} = \lim_{x\to\infty} \frac{1}{1-\left(\frac{2}{e}\right)^x} = \frac{1}{1-0} = 1$ and $\int_1^\infty \frac{dx}{e^x} = \lim_{b\to\infty} [-e^{-x}]_1^b$

$= \lim_{b\to\infty} (-e^{-b}+e^{-1}) = \frac{1}{e} \Rightarrow \int_1^\infty \frac{dx}{e^x}$ converges $\Rightarrow \int_1^\infty \frac{dx}{e^x-2^x}$ converges by the Limit Comparison Test.

63. $\int_{-\infty}^\infty \frac{dx}{\sqrt{x^4+1}} = 2\int_0^\infty \frac{dx}{\sqrt{x^4+1}}$; $\int_0^\infty \frac{dx}{\sqrt{x^4+1}} = \int_0^1 \frac{dx}{\sqrt{x^4+1}} + \int_1^\infty \frac{dx}{\sqrt{x^4+1}} < \int_0^1 \frac{dx}{\sqrt{x^4+1}} + \int_1^\infty \frac{dx}{x^2}$ and

$\int_1^\infty \frac{dx}{x^2} = \lim_{b\to\infty} \left[-\frac{1}{x}\right]_1^b = \lim_{b\to\infty} \left(-\frac{1}{b}+1\right) = 1 \Rightarrow \int_{-\infty}^\infty \frac{dx}{\sqrt{x^4+1}}$ converges by the Direct Comparison Test.

64. $\int_{-\infty}^{\infty} \frac{dx}{e^x + e^{-x}} = 2\int_0^{\infty} \frac{dx}{e^x + e^{-x}}$ ; $0 < \frac{1}{e^x + e^{-x}} < \frac{1}{e^x}$ for $x > 0$; $\int_0^{\infty} \frac{dx}{e^x}$ converges $\Rightarrow 2\int_0^{\infty} \frac{dx}{e^x + e^{-x}}$ converges by the
Direct Comparison Test.

65. (a) $\int_1^2 \frac{dx}{x(\ln x)^p}$ ; $[t = \ln x] \rightarrow \int_0^{\ln 2} \frac{dt}{t^p} = \lim_{b \to 0^+} \left[\frac{1}{-p+1} t^{1-p}\right]_b^{\ln 2} = \lim_{b \to 0^+} \frac{b^{1-p}}{p-1} + \frac{1}{1-p}(\ln 2)^{1-p}$
   $\Rightarrow$ the integral converges for $p < 1$ and diverges for $p \geq 1$

   (b) $\int_2^{\infty} \frac{dx}{x(\ln x)^p}$ ; $[t = \ln x] \rightarrow \int_{\ln 2}^{\infty} \frac{dt}{t^p}$ and this integral is essentially the same as in Exercise 65(a): it converges
   for $p > 1$ and diverges for $p \leq 1$

66. $\int_0^{\infty} \frac{2x \, dx}{x^2 + 1} = \lim_{b \to \infty} \left[\ln(x^2 + 1)\right]_0^b = \lim_{b \to \infty} \left[\ln(b^2 + 1)\right] - 0 = \lim_{b \to \infty} \ln(b^2 + 1) = \infty \Rightarrow$ the integral $\int_{-\infty}^{\infty} \frac{2x}{x^2 + 1} \, dx$

   diverges. But $\lim_{b \to \infty} \int_{-b}^b \frac{2x \, dx}{x^2 + 1} = \lim_{b \to \infty} \left[\ln(x^2 + 1)\right]_{-b}^b = \lim_{b \to \infty} \left[\ln(b^2 + 1) - \ln(b^2 + 1)\right] = \lim_{b \to \infty} \ln\left(\frac{b^2 + 1}{b^2 + 1}\right)$

   $= \lim_{b \to \infty} (\ln 1) = 0$

67. $A = \int_0^{\infty} e^{-x} \, dx = \lim_{b \to \infty} \left[-e^{-x}\right]_0^b = \lim_{b \to \infty} (-e^{-b}) - (-e^{-0})$

   $= 0 + 1 = 1$

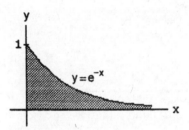

68. $\bar{x} = \frac{1}{A} \int_0^{\infty} xe^{-x} \, dx = \lim_{b \to \infty} \left[-xe^{-x} - e^{-x}\right]_0^b = \lim_{b \to \infty} (-be^{-b} - e^{-b}) - (-0 \cdot e^{-0} - e^{-0}) = 0 + 1 = 1$;

   $\bar{y} = \frac{1}{2A} \int_0^{\infty} (e^{-x})^2 \, dx = \frac{1}{2} \int_0^{\infty} e^{-2x} \, dx = \lim_{b \to \infty} \frac{1}{2}\left[-\frac{1}{2} e^{-2x}\right]_0^b = \lim_{b \to \infty} \frac{1}{2}\left(-\frac{1}{2} e^{-2b}\right) - \frac{1}{2}\left(-\frac{1}{2} e^{-2 \cdot 0}\right) = 0 + \frac{1}{4} = \frac{1}{4}$

69. $V = \int_0^{\infty} 2\pi xe^{-x} \, dx = 2\pi \int_0^{\infty} xe^{-x} \, dx = 2\pi \lim_{b \to \infty} \left[-xe^{-x} - e^{-x}\right]_0^b = 2\pi \left[\lim_{b \to \infty} (-be^{-b} - e^{-b}) - 1\right] = 2\pi$

70. $V = \int_0^{\infty} \pi (e^{-x})^2 \, dx = \pi \int_0^{\infty} e^{-2x} \, dx = \pi \lim_{b \to \infty} \left[-\frac{1}{2} e^{-2x}\right]_0^b = \pi \lim_{b \to \infty} \left(-\frac{1}{2} e^{-2b} + \frac{1}{2}\right) = \frac{\pi}{2}$

71. $A = \int_0^{\pi/2} (\sec x - \tan x) \, dx = \lim_{b \to \frac{\pi}{2}^-} \left[\ln|\sec x + \tan x| - \ln|\sec x|\right]_0^b = \lim_{b \to \frac{\pi}{2}^-} \left(\ln\left|1 + \frac{\tan b}{\sec b}\right| - \ln|1 + 0|\right)$

   $= \lim_{b \to \frac{\pi}{2}^-} \ln|1 + \sin b| = \ln 2$

72. (a) $V = \int_0^{\pi/2} \pi \sec^2 x \, dx - \int_0^{\pi/2} \pi \tan^2 x \, dx = \pi \int_0^{\pi/2} (\sec^2 x - \tan^2 x) \, dx = \int_0^{\pi/2} \pi [\sec^2 x - (\sec^2 x - 1)] \, dx$

   $= \pi \int_0^{\pi/2} dx = \frac{\pi^2}{2}$

   (b) $S_{outer} = \int_0^{\pi/2} 2\pi \sec x\sqrt{1 + \sec^2 x \tan^2 x} \, dx \geq \int_0^{\pi/2} 2\pi \sec x(\sec x \tan x) \, dx = \pi \lim_{b \to \frac{\pi}{2}^-} \left[\tan^2 x\right]_0^b$

   $= \pi \left[\lim_{b \to \frac{\pi}{2}^-} [\tan^2 b] - 0\right] = \pi \lim_{b \to \frac{\pi}{2}^-} (\tan^2 b) = \infty \Rightarrow S_{outer}$ diverges; $S_{inner} = \int_0^{\pi/2} 2\pi \tan x\sqrt{1 + \sec^4 x} \, dx$

   $\geq \int_0^{\pi/2} 2\pi \tan x \sec^2 x \, dx = \pi \lim_{b \to \frac{\pi}{2}^-} [\tan^2 x]_0^b = \pi \left[\lim_{b \to \frac{\pi}{2}^-} [\tan^2 b] - 0\right] = \pi \lim_{b \to \frac{\pi}{2}^-} (\tan^2 b) = \infty$

   $\Rightarrow S_{inner}$ diverges

73. (a) $\int_3^\infty e^{-3x}\, dx = \lim_{b\to\infty}\left[-\tfrac{1}{3}e^{-3x}\right]_3^b = \lim_{b\to\infty}\left(-\tfrac{1}{3}e^{-3b}\right) - \left(-\tfrac{1}{3}e^{-3\cdot 3}\right) = 0 + \tfrac{1}{3}\cdot e^{-9} = \tfrac{1}{3}e^{-9}$

$\approx 0.0000411 < 0.000042$. Since $e^{-x^2} \le e^{-3x}$ for $x > 3$, then $\int_3^\infty e^{-x^2}\, dx < 0.000042$ and therefore

$\int_0^\infty e^{-x^2}\, dx$ can be replaced by $\int_0^3 e^{-x^2}\, dx$ without introducing an error greater than 0.000042.

(b) $\int_0^3 e^{-x^2}\, dx \cong 0.88621$

74. (a) $V = \int_1^\infty \pi\left(\tfrac{1}{x}\right)^2 dx = \pi \lim_{b\to\infty}\left[-\tfrac{1}{x}\right]_1^b = \pi\left[\lim_{b\to\infty}\left(-\tfrac{1}{b}\right) - \left(-\tfrac{1}{1}\right)\right] = \pi(0 + 1) = \pi$

(b) When you take the limit to $\infty$, you are no longer modeling the real world which is finite. The comparison step in the modeling process discussed in Section 4.2 relating the mathematical world to the real world fails to hold.

75. (a)

$Si(x) = \int_0^x \frac{\sin t}{t}\, dt$

(b) > int((sin(t))/t, t=0..infinity);  (answer is $\frac{\pi}{2}$)

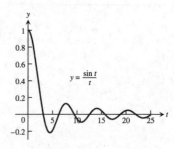

$y = \frac{\sin t}{t}$

76. (a)

$\text{erf}(x) = \int_0^x \frac{2e^{-t^2}}{\sqrt{\pi}}\, dt$

(b) > f:= 2*exp(−t^2)/sqrt(Pi);
> int(f, t=0..infinity);  (answer is 1)

77. (a) $f(x) = \frac{1}{\sqrt{2\pi}}e^{-x^2/2}$

f is increasing on $(-\infty, 0]$. f is decreasing on $[0, \infty)$.

f has a local maximum at $(0, f(0)) = \left(0, \frac{1}{\sqrt{2\pi}}\right)$

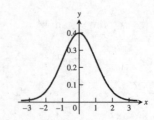

(b)  Maple commands:

>f: = exp(−x^2/2)(sqrt(2*pi));

>int(f, x = −1..1);          ≈ 0.683

>int(f, x = −2..2);          ≈ 0.954

>int(f, x = −3..3);          ≈ 0.997

(c)  Part (b) suggests that as n increases, the integral approaches 1. We can take $\int_{-n}^{n} f(x)\,dx$ as close to 1 as we want by

choosing n > 1 large enough. Also, we can make $\int_{n}^{\infty} f(x)\,dx$ and $\int_{-\infty}^{-n} f(x)\,dx$ as small as we want by choosing n large

enough. This is because $0 < f(x) < e^{-x/2}$ for x > 1. (Likewise, $0 < f(x) < e^{x/2}$ for x < −1.)

Thus, $\int_{n}^{\infty} f(x)\,dx < \int_{n}^{\infty} e^{-x/2}\,dx$.

$\int_{n}^{\infty} e^{-x/2}\,dx = \lim_{c \to \infty} \int_{n}^{c} e^{-x/2}\,dx = \lim_{c \to \infty} \left[ -2e^{-x/2} \right]_{n}^{c} = \lim_{c \to \infty} \left[ -2e^{-c/2} + 2e^{-n/2} \right] = 2e^{-n/2}$

As $n \to \infty$, $2e^{-n/2} \to 0$, for large enough n, $\int_{n}^{\infty} f(x)\,dx$ is as small as we want. Likewise for large enough n,

$\int_{-\infty}^{-n} f(x)\,dx$ is as small as we want.

78.  (a)  The statement is true since $\int_{-\infty}^{b} f(x)\,dx = \int_{-\infty}^{a} f(x)\,dx + \int_{a}^{b} f(x)\,dx$, $\int_{b}^{\infty} f(x)\,dx = \int_{a}^{\infty} f(x)\,dx - \int_{a}^{b} f(x)\,dx$

and $\int_{a}^{b} f(x)\,dx$ exists since f(x) is integrable on every interval [a, b].

(b)  $\int_{-\infty}^{a} f(x)\,dx + \int_{a}^{\infty} f(x)\,dx = \int_{-\infty}^{a} f(x)\,dx + \int_{a}^{b} f(x)\,dx - \int_{a}^{b} f(x)\,dx + \int_{a}^{\infty} f(x)\,dx$

$= \int_{-\infty}^{b} f(x)\,dx + \int_{b}^{a} f(x)\,dx + \int_{a}^{\infty} f(x)\,dx = \int_{-\infty}^{b} f(x)\,dx + \int_{b}^{\infty} f(x)\,dx$

79.    Example CAS commands:

<u>Maple:</u>

```
f := (x,p) -> x^p*ln(x);
domain := 0..exp(1);
fn_list := [seq( f(x,p), p=-2..2 )];
plot( fn_list, x=domain, y=-50..10, color=[red,blue,green,cyan,pink], linestyle=[1,3,4,7,9], thickness=[3,4,1,2,0],
      legend=["p= -2","p = -1","p = 0","p = 1","p = 2"], title="#79 (Section 8.7)" );
q1 := Int( f(x,p), x=domain );
q2 := value( q1 );
q3 := simplify( q2 ) assuming p>-1;
q4 := simplify( q2 ) assuming p<-1;
q5 := value( eval( q1, p=-1 ) );
i1 := q1 = piecewise( p<-1, q4, p=-1, q5, p>-1, q3 );
```

80.    Example CAS commands:

<u>Maple:</u>

```
f := (x,p) -> x^p*ln(x);
domain := exp(1)..infinity;
fn_list := [seq( f(x,p), p=-2..2 )];
plot( fn_list, x=exp(1)..10, y=0..100, color=[red,blue,green,cyan,pink], linestyle=[1,3,4,7,9], thickness=[3,4,1,2,0],
      legend=["p = -2","p = -1","p = 0","p = 1","p = 2"], title="#80 (Section 8.7)" );
q6 := Int( f(x,p), x=domain );
q7 := value( q6 );
q8 := simplify( q7 ) assuming p>-1;
q9 := simplify( q7 ) assuming p<-1;
```

q10 := value( eval( q6, p=-1 ) );

i2 := q6 = piecewise( p<-1, q9, p=-1, q10, p>-1, q8 );

81.    Example CAS commands:

Maple:

f := (x,p) -> x^p*ln(x);

domain := 0..infinity;

fn_list := [seq( f(x,p), p=-2..2 )];

plot( fn_list, x=0..10, y=-50..50, color=[red,blue,green,cyan,pink], linestyle=[1,3,4,7,9], thickness=[3,4,1,2,0],
    legend=["p = -2","p = -1","p = 0","p = 1","p = 2"], title="#81 (Section 8.7)" );

q11 := Int( f(x,p), x=domain ):

q11 = lhs(i1+i2);

`` = rhs(i1+i2);

`` = piecewise( p<-1, q4+q9, p=-1, q5+q10, p>-1, q3+q8 );

`` = piecewise( p<-1, -infinity, p=-1, undefined, p>-1, infinity );

82.    Example CAS commands:

Maple:

f := (x,p) -> x^p*ln(abs(x));

domain := -infinity..infinity;

fn_list := [seq( f(x,p), p=-2..2 )];

plot( fn_list, x=-4..4, y=-20..10, color=[red,blue,green,cyan,pink], linestyle=[1,3,4,7,9],
    legend=["p = -2","p = -1","p = 0","p = 1","p = 2"], title="#82 (Section 8.7)" );

q12 := Int( f(x,p), x=domain );

q12p := Int( f(x,p), x=0..infinity );

q12n := Int( f(x,p), x=-infinity..0 );

q12 = q12p + q12n;

`` = simplify( q12p+q12n );

79-82.    Example CAS commands:

Mathematica: (functions and domains may vary)

Clear[x, f, p]

f[x_]:= x^p Log[Abs[x]]

int = Integrate[f[x], {x, e, 100)]

int /. p → 2.5

In order to plot the function, a value for p must be selected.

p = 3;

Plot[f[x], {x, 2.72, 10}]

## CHAPTER 8 PRACTICE EXERCISES

1.  $u = \ln(x+1)$, $du = \frac{dx}{x+1}$ ; $dv = dx$, $v = x$;

$\int \ln(x+1)\,dx = x\ln(x+1) - \int \frac{x}{x+1}\,dx = x\ln(x+1) - \int dx + \int \frac{dx}{x+1} = x\ln(x+1) - x + \ln(x+1) + C_1$

$= (x+1)\ln(x+1) - x + C_1 = (x+1)\ln(x+1) - (x+1) + C$, where $C = C_1 + 1$

2.  $u = \ln x$, $du = \frac{dx}{x}$ ; $dv = x^2\,dx$, $v = \frac{1}{3}x^3$;

$\int x^2 \ln x\,dx = \frac{1}{3}x^3 \ln x - \int \frac{1}{3}x^3 \left(\frac{1}{x}\right)\,dx = \frac{x^3}{3}\ln x - \frac{x^3}{9} + C$

3. $u = \tan^{-1} 3x$, $du = \frac{3\,dx}{1+9x^2}$; $dv = dx$, $v = x$;

$$\int \tan^{-1} 3x \, dx = x \tan^{-1} 3x - \int \frac{3x\,dx}{1+9x^2} ; \begin{bmatrix} y = 1 + 9x^2 \\ dy = 18x\,dx \end{bmatrix} \to x\tan^{-1} 3x - \frac{1}{6} \int \frac{dy}{y}$$

$$= x \tan^{-1}(3x) - \frac{1}{6} \ln(1 + 9x^2) + C$$

4. $u = \cos^{-1}\left(\frac{x}{2}\right)$, $du = \frac{-dx}{\sqrt{4-x^2}}$; $dv = dx$, $v = x$;

$$\int \cos^{-1}\left(\frac{x}{2}\right) dx = x\cos^{-1}\left(\frac{x}{2}\right) + \int \frac{x\,dx}{\sqrt{4-x^2}}; \begin{bmatrix} y = 4 - x^2 \\ dy = -2x\,dx \end{bmatrix} \to x\cos^{-1}\left(\frac{x}{2}\right) - \frac{1}{2} \int \frac{dy}{\sqrt{y}}$$

$$= x\cos^{-1}\left(\frac{x}{2}\right) - \sqrt{4-x^2} + C = x\cos^{-1}\left(\frac{x}{2}\right) - 2\sqrt{1 - \left(\frac{x}{2}\right)^2} + C$$

5.

$(x+1)^2$  $\xrightarrow{(+)}$  $e^x$

$2(x+1)$  $\xrightarrow{(-)}$  $e^x$

$2$  $\xrightarrow{(+)}$  $e^x$

$0$  $\qquad \Rightarrow \int (x+1)^2 e^x \, dx = \left[(x+1)^2 - 2(x+1) + 2\right] e^x + C$

6.

$\qquad\qquad \sin(1-x)$

$x^2$  $\xrightarrow{(+)}$  $\cos(1-x)$

$2x$  $\xrightarrow{(-)}$  $-\sin(1-x)$

$2$  $\xrightarrow{(+)}$  $-\cos(1-x)$

$0$  $\qquad \Rightarrow \int x^2 \sin(1-x)\,dx = x^2 \cos(1-x) + 2x\sin(1-x) - 2\cos(1-x) + C$

7. $u = \cos 2x$, $du = -2\sin 2x\,dx$; $dv = e^x\,dx$, $v = e^x$;

$I = \int e^x \cos 2x \, dx = e^x \cos 2x + 2 \int e^x \sin 2x \, dx$;

$u = \sin 2x$, $du = 2\cos 2x \, dx$; $dv = e^x \, dx$, $v = e^x$;

$I = e^x \cos 2x + 2\left[ e^x \sin 2x - 2 \int e^x \cos 2x \, dx \right] = e^x \cos 2x + 2e^x \sin 2x - 4I \Rightarrow I = \frac{e^x \cos 2x}{5} + \frac{2e^x \sin 2x}{5} + C$

8. $u = \sin 3x$, $du = 3\cos 3x\,dx$; $dv = e^{-2x}\,dx$, $v = -\frac{1}{2}e^{-2x}$;

$I = \int e^{-2x} \sin 3x \, dx = -\frac{1}{2} e^{-2x} \sin 3x + \frac{3}{2} \int e^{-2x} \cos 3x \, dx$;

$u = \cos 3x$, $du = -3\sin 3x\,dx$; $dv = e^{-2x}\,dx$, $v = -\frac{1}{2}e^{-2x}$;

$I = -\frac{1}{2} e^{-2x} \sin 3x + \frac{3}{2}\left[ -\frac{1}{2} e^{-2x} \cos 3x - \frac{3}{2} \int e^{-2x} \sin 3x \, dx \right] = -\frac{1}{2} e^{-2x} \sin 3x - \frac{3}{4} e^{-2x} \cos 3x - \frac{9}{4} I$

$\Rightarrow I = \frac{4}{13} \left( -\frac{1}{2} e^{-2x} \sin 3x - \frac{3}{4} e^{-2x} \cos 3x \right) + C = -\frac{2}{13} e^{-2x} \sin 3x - \frac{3}{13} e^{-2x} \cos 3x + C$

9. $\int \frac{x\,dx}{x^2 - 3x + 2} = \int \frac{2\,dx}{x-2} - \int \frac{dx}{x-1} = 2\ln|x-2| - \ln|x-1| + C$

10. $\int \frac{x\,dx}{x^2 + 4x + 3} = \frac{3}{2} \int \frac{dx}{x+3} - \frac{1}{2} \int \frac{dx}{x+1} = \frac{3}{2} \ln|x+3| - \frac{1}{2} \ln|x+1| + C$

11. $\int \frac{dx}{x(x+1)^2} = \int \left( \frac{1}{x} - \frac{1}{x+1} + \frac{-1}{(x+1)^2} \right) dx = \ln|x| - \ln|x+1| + \frac{1}{x+1} + C$

12. $\int \frac{x+1}{x^2(x-1)} \, dx = \int \left( \frac{2}{x-1} - \frac{2}{x} - \frac{1}{x^2} \right) dx = 2\ln\left|\frac{x-1}{x}\right| + \frac{1}{x} + C = -2\ln|x| + \frac{1}{x} + 2\ln|x-1| + C$

13. $\int \frac{\sin\theta\, d\theta}{\cos^2\theta + \cos\theta - 2}$ ; $[\cos\theta = y] \;\to\; -\int \frac{dy}{y^2 + y - 2} = -\frac{1}{3}\int \frac{dy}{y-1} + \frac{1}{3}\int \frac{dy}{y+2} = \frac{1}{3}\ln\left|\frac{y+2}{y-1}\right| + C$

$= \frac{1}{3}\ln\left|\frac{\cos\theta + 2}{\cos\theta - 1}\right| + C = -\frac{1}{3}\ln\left|\frac{\cos\theta - 1}{\cos\theta + 2}\right| + C$

14. $\int \frac{\cos\theta\, d\theta}{\sin^2\theta + \sin\theta - 6}$ ; $[\sin\theta = x] \;\to\; \int \frac{dx}{x^2 + x - 6} = \frac{1}{5}\int \frac{dx}{x-2} - \frac{1}{5}\int \frac{dx}{x+3} = \frac{1}{5}\ln\left|\frac{\sin\theta - 2}{\sin\theta + 3}\right| + C$

15. $\int \frac{3x^2 + 4x + 4}{x^3 + x}\, dx = \int \frac{4}{x}\, dx - \int \frac{x-4}{x^2 + 1}\, dx = 4\ln|x| - \frac{1}{2}\ln(x^2 + 1) + 4\tan^{-1}x + C$

16. $\int \frac{4x\, dx}{x^3 + 4x} = \int \frac{4\, dx}{x^2 + 4} = 2\tan^{-1}\left(\frac{x}{2}\right) + C$

17. $\int \frac{(v+3)\, dv}{2v^3 - 8v} = \frac{1}{2}\int\left(-\frac{3}{4v} + \frac{5}{8(v-2)} + \frac{1}{8(v+2)}\right) dv = -\frac{3}{8}\ln|v| + \frac{5}{16}\ln|v-2| + \frac{1}{16}\ln|v+2| + C$

$= \frac{1}{16}\ln\left|\frac{(v-2)^5(v+2)}{v^6}\right| + C$

18. $\int \frac{(3v-7)\, dv}{(v-1)(v-2)(v-3)} = \int \frac{(-2)\, dv}{v-1} + \int \frac{dv}{v-2} + \int \frac{dv}{v-3} = \ln\left|\frac{(v-2)(v-3)}{(v-1)^2}\right| + C$

19. $\int \frac{dt}{t^4 + 4t^2 + 3} = \frac{1}{2}\int \frac{dt}{t^2 + 1} - \frac{1}{2}\int \frac{dt}{t^2 + 3} = \frac{1}{2}\tan^{-1}t - \frac{1}{2\sqrt{3}}\tan^{-1}\left(\frac{t}{\sqrt{3}}\right) + C = \frac{1}{2}\tan^{-1}t - \frac{\sqrt{3}}{6}\tan^{-1}\frac{t}{\sqrt{3}} + C$

20. $\int \frac{t\, dt}{t^4 - t^2 - 2} = \frac{1}{3}\int \frac{t\, dt}{t^2 - 2} - \frac{1}{3}\int \frac{t\, dt}{t^2 + 1} = \frac{1}{6}\ln|t^2 - 2| - \frac{1}{6}\ln(t^2 + 1) + C$

21. $\int \frac{x^3 + x^2}{x^2 + x - 2}\, dx = \int\left(x + \frac{2x}{x^2 + x - 2}\right) dx = \int x\, dx + \frac{2}{3}\int \frac{dx}{x-1} + \frac{4}{3}\int \frac{dx}{x+2} = \frac{x^2}{2} + \frac{4}{3}\ln|x+2| + \frac{2}{3}\ln|x-1| + C$

22. $\int \frac{x^3 + 1}{x^3 - x}\, dx = \int\left(1 + \frac{x+1}{x^3 - x}\right) dx = \int\left[1 + \frac{1}{x(x-1)}\right] dx = \int dx + \int \frac{dx}{x-1} - \int \frac{dx}{x} = x + \ln|x-1| - \ln|x| + C$

23. $\int \frac{x^3 + 4x^2}{x^2 + 4x + 3}\, dx = \int\left(x - \frac{3x}{x^2 + 4x + 3}\right) dx = \int x\, dx + \frac{3}{2}\int \frac{dx}{x+1} - \frac{9}{2}\int \frac{dx}{x+3} = \frac{x^2}{2} - \frac{9}{2}\ln|x+3| + \frac{3}{2}\ln|x+1| + C$

24. $\int \frac{2x^3 + x^2 - 21x + 24}{x^2 + 2x - 8}\, dx = \int\left[(2x - 3) + \frac{x}{x^2 + 2x - 8}\right] dx = \int (2x-3)\, dx + \frac{1}{3}\int \frac{dx}{x-2} + \frac{2}{3}\int \frac{dx}{x+4}$

$= x^2 - 3x + \frac{2}{3}\ln|x+4| + \frac{1}{3}\ln|x-2| + C$

25. $\int \frac{dx}{x\left(3\sqrt{x+1}\right)}$ ; $\begin{bmatrix} u = \sqrt{x+1} \\ du = \frac{dx}{2\sqrt{x+1}} \\ dx = 2u\, du \end{bmatrix} \;\to\; \frac{2}{3}\int \frac{u\, du}{(u^2 - 1)u} = \frac{1}{3}\int \frac{du}{u-1} - \frac{1}{3}\int \frac{du}{u+1} = \frac{1}{3}\ln|u-1| - \frac{1}{3}\ln|u+1| + C$

$= \frac{1}{3}\ln\left|\frac{\sqrt{x+1} - 1}{\sqrt{x+1} + 1}\right| + C$

26. $\int \frac{dx}{x\left(1 + \sqrt[3]{x}\right)}$ ; $\begin{bmatrix} u = \sqrt[3]{x} \\ du = \frac{dx}{3x^{2/3}} \\ dx = 3u^2\, du \end{bmatrix} \;\to\; \int \frac{3u^2\, du}{u^3(1 + u)} = 3\int \frac{du}{u(1 + u)} = 3\ln\left|\frac{u}{u+1}\right| + C = 3\ln\left|\frac{\sqrt[3]{x}}{1 + \sqrt[3]{x}}\right| + C$

27. $\int \frac{ds}{e^s - 1}$ ; $\begin{bmatrix} u = e^s - 1 \\ du = e^s\, ds \\ ds = \frac{du}{u+1} \end{bmatrix} \;\to\; \int \frac{du}{u(u+1)} = -\int \frac{du}{u+1} + \int \frac{du}{u} = \ln\left|\frac{u}{u+1}\right| + C = \ln\left|\frac{e^s - 1}{e^s}\right| + C = \ln|1 - e^{-s}| + C$

28. $\int \frac{ds}{\sqrt{e^s+1}}$ ; $\left[\begin{array}{c} u = \sqrt{e^s+1} \\ du = \frac{e^s\,ds}{2\sqrt{e^s+1}} \\ ds = \frac{2u\,du}{u^2-1} \end{array}\right]$ $\rightarrow \int \frac{2u\,du}{u\,(u^2-1)} = 2\int \frac{du}{(u+1)(u-1)} = \int \frac{du}{u-1} - \int \frac{du}{u+1} = \ln\left|\frac{u-1}{u+1}\right| + C$

$= \ln\left|\frac{\sqrt{e^s+1}-1}{\sqrt{e^s+1}+1}\right| + C$

29. (a) $\int \frac{y\,dy}{\sqrt{16-y^2}} = -\frac{1}{2}\int \frac{d\,(16-y^2)}{\sqrt{16-y^2}} = -\sqrt{16-y^2} + C$

(b) $\int \frac{y\,dy}{\sqrt{16-y^2}}$ ; $[y = 4\sin x] \rightarrow 4\int \frac{\sin x \cos x\,dx}{\cos x} = -4\cos x + C = -\frac{4\sqrt{16-y^2}}{4} + C = -\sqrt{16-y^2} + C$

30. (a) $\int \frac{x\,dx}{\sqrt{4+x^2}} = \frac{1}{2}\int \frac{d\,(4+x^2)}{\sqrt{4+x^2}} = \sqrt{4+x^2} + C$

(b) $\int \frac{x\,dx}{\sqrt{4+x^2}}$ ; $[x = 2\tan y] \rightarrow \int \frac{2\tan y\cdot 2\sec^2 y\,dy}{2\sec y} = 2\int \sec y\tan y\,dy = 2\sec y + C = \sqrt{4+x^2} + C$

31. (a) $\int \frac{x\,dx}{4-x^2} = -\frac{1}{2}\int \frac{d\,(4-x^2)}{4-x^2} = -\frac{1}{2}\ln|4-x^2| + C$

(b) $\int \frac{x\,dx}{4-x^2}$ ; $[x = 2\sin\theta] \rightarrow \int \frac{2\sin\theta\cdot 2\cos\theta\,d\theta}{4\cos^2\theta} = \int \tan\theta\,d\theta = -\ln|\cos\theta| + C = -\ln\left(\frac{\sqrt{4-x^2}}{2}\right) + C$

$= -\frac{1}{2}\ln|4-x^2| + C$

32. (a) $\int \frac{t\,dt}{\sqrt{4t^2-1}} = \frac{1}{8}\int \frac{d\,(4t^2-1)}{\sqrt{4t^2-1}} = \frac{1}{4}\sqrt{4t^2-1} + C$

(b) $\int \frac{t\,dt}{\sqrt{4t^2-1}}$ ; $\left[t = \frac{1}{2}\sec\theta\right] \rightarrow \int \frac{\frac{1}{2}\sec\theta\tan\theta\cdot\frac{1}{2}\sec\theta\,d\theta}{\tan\theta} = \frac{1}{4}\int \sec^2\theta\,d\theta = \frac{\tan\theta}{4} + C = \frac{\sqrt{4t^2-1}}{4} + C$

33. $\int \frac{x\,dx}{9-x^2}$ ; $\left[\begin{array}{c} u = 9-x^2 \\ du = -2x\,dx \end{array}\right] \rightarrow -\frac{1}{2}\int \frac{du}{u} = -\frac{1}{2}\ln|u| + C = \ln\frac{1}{\sqrt{u}} + C = \ln\frac{1}{\sqrt{9-x^2}} + C$

34. $\int \frac{dx}{x\,(9-x^2)} = \frac{1}{9}\int \frac{dx}{x} + \frac{1}{18}\int \frac{dx}{3-x} - \frac{1}{18}\int \frac{dx}{3+x} = \frac{1}{9}\ln|x| - \frac{1}{18}\ln|3-x| - \frac{1}{18}\ln|3+x| + C$

$= \frac{1}{9}\ln|x| - \frac{1}{18}\ln|9-x^2| + C$

35. $\int \frac{dx}{9-x^2} = \frac{1}{6}\int \frac{dx}{3-x} + \frac{1}{6}\int \frac{dx}{3+x} = -\frac{1}{6}\ln|3-x| + \frac{1}{6}\ln|3+x| + C = \frac{1}{6}\ln\left|\frac{x+3}{x-3}\right| + C$

36. $\int \frac{dx}{\sqrt{9-x^2}}$ ; $\left[\begin{array}{c} x = 3\sin\theta \\ dx = 3\cos\theta\,d\theta \end{array}\right] \rightarrow \int \frac{3\cos\theta}{3\cos\theta}\,d\theta = \int d\theta = \theta + C = \sin^{-1}\frac{x}{3} + C$

37. $\int \sin^3 x\cos^4 x\,dx = \int \cos^4 x(1-\cos^2 x)\sin x\,dx = \int \cos^4 x\sin x\,dx - \int \cos^6 x\sin x\,dx = -\frac{\cos^5 x}{5} + \frac{\cos^7 x}{7} + C$

38. $\int \cos^5 x\sin^5 x\,dx = \int \sin^5 x\cos^4 x\cos x\,dx = \int \sin^5 x\,(1-\sin^2 x)^2\cos x\,dx$

$= \int \sin^5 x\cos x\,dx - 2\int \sin^7 x\cos x\,dx + \int \sin^9 x\cos x\,dx = \frac{\sin^6 x}{6} - \frac{2\sin^8 x}{8} + \frac{\sin^{10} x}{10} + C$

39. $\int \tan^4 x\sec^2 x\,dx = \frac{\tan^5 x}{5} + C$

40. $\int \tan^3 x\sec^3 x\,dx = \int (\sec^2 x - 1)\sec^2 x\cdot\sec x\cdot\tan x\,dx = \int \sec^4 x\cdot\sec x\cdot\tan x\,dx - \int \sec^2 x\cdot\sec x\cdot\tan x\,dx$

$= \frac{\sec^5 x}{5} - \frac{\sec^3 x}{3} + C$

41. $\int \sin 5\theta \cos 6\theta \, d\theta = \frac{1}{2} \int (\sin(-\theta) + \sin(11\theta)) \, d\theta = \frac{1}{2} \int \sin(-\theta) \, d\theta + \frac{1}{2} \int \sin(11\theta) \, d\theta = \frac{1}{2} \cos(-\theta) - \frac{1}{22} \cos 11\theta + C$

$= \frac{1}{2} \cos \theta - \frac{1}{22} \cos 11\theta + C$

42. $\int \cos 3\theta \cos 3\theta \, d\theta = \frac{1}{2} \int \left( \cos 0 + \cos 6\theta \right) \, d\theta = \frac{1}{2} \int d\theta + \frac{1}{2} \int \cos 6\theta \, d\theta = \frac{1}{2}\theta + \frac{1}{12} \sin 6\theta + C$

43. $\int \sqrt{1 + \cos\left(\frac{1}{2}\right)} \, dt = \int \sqrt{2} \left| \cos \frac{t}{4} \right| \, dt = 4\sqrt{2} \left| \sin \frac{t}{4} \right| + C$

44. $\int e^t \sqrt{\tan^2 e^t + 1} \, dt = \int \left| \sec e^t \right| e^t \, dt = \ln \left| \sec e^t + \tan e^t \right| + C$

45. $|E_s| \leq \frac{3-1}{180} (\triangle x)^4 \, M$ where $\triangle x = \frac{3-1}{n} = \frac{2}{n}$; $f(x) = \frac{1}{x} = x^{-1} \Rightarrow f'(x) = -x^{-2} \Rightarrow f''(x) = 2x^{-3} \Rightarrow f'''(x) = -6x^{-4}$

$\Rightarrow f^{(4)}(x) = 24x^{-5}$ which is decreasing on $[1, 3] \Rightarrow$ maximum of $f^{(4)}(x)$ on $[1, 3]$ is $f^{(4)}(1) = 24 \Rightarrow M = 24$. Then

$|E_s| \leq 0.0001 \Rightarrow \left( \frac{3-1}{180} \right) \left( \frac{2}{n} \right)^4 (24) \leq 0.0001 \Rightarrow \left( \frac{768}{180} \right) \left( \frac{1}{n^4} \right) \leq 0.0001 \Rightarrow \frac{1}{n^4} \leq (0.0001) \left( \frac{180}{768} \right) \Rightarrow n^4 \geq 10{,}000 \left( \frac{768}{180} \right)$

$\Rightarrow n \geq 14.37 \Rightarrow n \geq 16$ (n must be even)

46. $|E_T| \leq \frac{1-0}{12} (\triangle x)^2 \, M$ where $\triangle x = \frac{1-0}{n} = \frac{1}{n}$; $0 \leq f''(x) \leq 8 \Rightarrow M = 8$. Then $|E_T| \leq 10^{-3} \Rightarrow \frac{1}{12} \left( \frac{1}{n} \right)^2 (8) \leq 10^{-3}$

$\Rightarrow \frac{2}{3n^2} \leq 10^{-3} \Rightarrow \frac{3n^2}{2} \geq 1000 \Rightarrow n^2 \geq \frac{2000}{3} \Rightarrow n \geq 25.82 \Rightarrow n \geq 26$

47. $\triangle x = \frac{b-a}{n} = \frac{\pi - 0}{6} = \frac{\pi}{6} \Rightarrow \frac{\triangle x}{2} = \frac{\pi}{12}$;

$\sum_{i=0}^{6} mf(x_i) = 12 \Rightarrow T = \left( \frac{\pi}{12} \right) (12) = \pi$;

|        | $x_i$ | $f(x_i)$ | m | $mf(x_i)$ |
|--------|-------|----------|---|-----------|
| $x_0$  | 0 | 0 | 1 | 0 |
| $x_1$  | $\pi/6$ | 1/2 | 2 | 1 |
| $x_2$  | $\pi/3$ | 3/2 | 2 | 3 |
| $x_3$  | $\pi/2$ | 2 | 2 | 4 |
| $x_4$  | $2\pi/3$ | 3/2 | 2 | 3 |
| $x_5$  | $5\pi/6$ | 1/2 | 2 | 1 |
| $x_6$  | $\pi$ | 0 | 1 | 0 |

$\sum_{i=0}^{6} mf(x_i) = 18$ and $\frac{\triangle x}{3} = \frac{\pi}{18} \Rightarrow$

$S = \left( \frac{\pi}{18} \right) (18) = \pi$.

|        | $x_i$ | $f(x_i)$ | m | $mf(x_i)$ |
|--------|-------|----------|---|-----------|
| $x_0$  | 0 | 0 | 1 | 0 |
| $x_1$  | $\pi/6$ | 1/2 | 4 | 2 |
| $x_2$  | $\pi/3$ | 3/2 | 2 | 3 |
| $x_3$  | $\pi/2$ | 2 | 4 | 8 |
| $x_4$  | $2\pi/3$ | 3/2 | 2 | 3 |
| $x_5$  | $5\pi/6$ | 1/2 | 4 | 2 |
| $x_6$  | $\pi$ | 0 | 1 | 0 |

48. $\left| f^{(4)}(x) \right| \leq 3 \Rightarrow M = 3$; $\triangle x = \frac{2-1}{n} = \frac{1}{n}$. Hence $|E_s| \leq 10^{-5} \Rightarrow \left( \frac{2-1}{180} \right) \left( \frac{1}{n} \right)^4 (3) \leq 10^{-5} \Rightarrow \frac{1}{60n^4} \leq 10^{-5} \Rightarrow n^4 \geq \frac{10^5}{60}$

$\Rightarrow n \geq 6.38 \Rightarrow n \geq 8$ (n must be even)

49. $y_{av} = \frac{1}{365-0} \int_0^{365} \left[ 37 \sin \left( \frac{2\pi}{365} (x - 101) \right) + 25 \right] \, dx = \frac{1}{365} \left[ -37 \left( \frac{365}{2\pi} \cos \left( \frac{2\pi}{365} (x - 101) \right) + 25x \right) \right]_0^{365}$

$= \frac{1}{365} \left[ \left( -37 \left( \frac{365}{2\pi} \right) \cos \left[ \frac{2\pi}{365} (365 - 101) \right] + 25(365) \right) - \left( -37 \left( \frac{365}{2\pi} \right) \cos \left[ \frac{2\pi}{365} (0 - 101) \right] + 25(0) \right) \right]$

$= -\frac{37}{2\pi} \cos \left( \frac{2\pi}{365} (264) \right) + 25 + \frac{37}{2\pi} \cos \left( \frac{2\pi}{365} (-101) \right) = -\frac{37}{2\pi} \left( \cos \left( \frac{2\pi}{365} (264) \right) - \cos \left( \frac{2\pi}{365} (-101) \right) \right) + 25$

$\approx -\frac{37}{2\pi} (0.16705 - 0.16705) + 25 = 25° \text{F}$

50. $av(C_v) = \frac{1}{675-20} \int_{20}^{675} \left[ 8.27 + 10^{-5} \left( 26T - 1.87T^2 \right) \right] \, dT = \frac{1}{655} \left[ 8.27T + \frac{13}{10^5} T^2 - \frac{0.62333}{10^5} T^3 \right]_{20}^{675}$

$\approx \frac{1}{655} \left[ (5582.25 + 59.23125 - 1917.03194) - (165.4 + 0.052 - 0.04987) \right] \approx 5.434$;

$8.27 + 10^{-5} \left( 26T - 1.87T^2 \right) = 5.434 \Rightarrow 1.87T^2 - 26T - 283{,}600 = 0 \Rightarrow T \approx \frac{26 + \sqrt{676 + 4(1.87)(283{,}600)}}{2(1.87)} \approx 396.45° \text{C}$

51. (a) Each interval is 5 min $= \frac{1}{12}$ hour.

   $\frac{1}{24}[2.5 + 2(2.4) + 2(2.3) + \ldots + 2(2.4) + 2.3] = \frac{29}{12} \approx 2.42$ gal

   (b) $(60 \text{ mph})\left(\frac{12}{29} \text{ hours/gal}\right) \approx 24.83$ mi/gal

52. Using the Simpson's rule, $\triangle x = 15 \Rightarrow \frac{\triangle x}{3} = 5$;

   $\sum mf(x_i) = 1211.8 \Rightarrow \text{Area} \approx (1211.8)(5) = 6059 \text{ ft}^2$;

   The cost is Area $\cdot$ ($2.10/\text{ft}^2) \approx (6059 \text{ ft}^2)($2.10/\text{ft}^2)$

   $= $12,723.90 \Rightarrow$ the job cannot be done for $11,000.

| | $x_i$ | $f(x_i)$ | m | $mf(x_i)$ |
|---|---|---|---|---|
| $x_0$ | 0 | 0 | 1 | 0 |
| $x_1$ | 15 | 36 | 4 | 144 |
| $x_2$ | 30 | 54 | 2 | 108 |
| $x_3$ | 45 | 51 | 4 | 204 |
| $x_4$ | 60 | 49.5 | 2 | 99 |
| $x_5$ | 75 | 54 | 4 | 216 |
| $x_6$ | 90 | 64.4 | 2 | 128.8 |
| $x_7$ | 105 | 67.5 | 4 | 270 |
| $x_8$ | 120 | 42 | 1 | 42 |

53. $\int_0^3 \frac{dx}{\sqrt{9-x^2}} = \lim_{b \to 3^-} \int_0^b \frac{dx}{\sqrt{9-x^2}} = \lim_{b \to 3^-} \left[\sin^{-1}\left(\frac{x}{3}\right)\right]_0^b = \lim_{b \to 3^-} \sin^{-1}\left(\frac{b}{3}\right) - \sin^{-1}\left(\frac{0}{3}\right) = \frac{\pi}{2} - 0 = \frac{\pi}{2}$

54. $\int_0^1 \ln x \, dx = \lim_{b \to 0^+} [x \ln x - x]_b^1 = (1 \cdot \ln 1 - 1) - \lim_{b \to 0^+} [b \ln b - b] = -1 - \lim_{b \to 0^+} \frac{\ln b}{\left(\frac{1}{b}\right)} = -1 - \lim_{b \to 0^+} \frac{\left(\frac{1}{b}\right)}{\left(-\frac{1}{b^2}\right)}$

   $= -1 + 0 = -1$

55. $\int_{-1}^1 \frac{dy}{y^{2/3}} = \int_{-1}^0 \frac{dy}{y^{2/3}} + \int_0^1 \frac{dy}{y^{2/3}} = 2 \int_0^1 \frac{dy}{y^{2/3}} = 2 \cdot 3 \lim_{b \to 0^+} \left[y^{1/3}\right]_b^1 = 6 \left(1 - \lim_{b \to 0^+} b^{1/3}\right) = 6$

56. $\int_{-2}^\infty \frac{d\theta}{(\theta+1)^{3/5}} = \int_{-2}^{-1} \frac{d\theta}{(\theta+1)^{3/5}} + \int_{-1}^2 \frac{d\theta}{(\theta+1)^{3/5}} + \int_2^\infty \frac{d\theta}{(\theta+1)^{3/5}}$ converges if each integral converges, but

   $\lim_{\theta \to \infty} \frac{\theta^{3/5}}{(\theta+1)^{3/5}} = 1$ and $\int_2^\infty \frac{d\theta}{\theta^{3/5}}$ diverges $\Rightarrow \int_{-2}^\infty \frac{d\theta}{(\theta+1)^{3/5}}$ diverges

57. $\int_3^\infty \frac{2 \, du}{u^2 - 2u} = \int_3^\infty \frac{du}{u-2} - \int_3^\infty \frac{du}{u} = \lim_{b \to \infty} \left[\ln \left|\frac{u-2}{u}\right|\right]_3^b = \lim_{b \to \infty} \left[\ln \left|\frac{b-2}{b}\right|\right] - \ln \left|\frac{3-2}{3}\right| = 0 - \ln \left(\frac{1}{3}\right) = \ln 3$

58. $\int_1^\infty \frac{3v-1}{4v^3 - v^2} \, dv = \int_1^\infty \left(\frac{1}{v} + \frac{1}{v^2} - \frac{4}{4v-1}\right) dv = \lim_{b \to \infty} \left[\ln v - \frac{1}{v} - \ln(4v-1)\right]_1^b$

   $= \lim_{b \to \infty} \left[\ln \left(\frac{b}{4b-1}\right) - \frac{1}{b}\right] - (\ln 1 - 1 - \ln 3) = \ln \frac{1}{4} + 1 + \ln 3 = 1 + \ln \frac{3}{4}$

59. $\int_0^\infty x^2 e^{-x} \, dx = \lim_{b \to \infty} \left[-x^2 e^{-x} - 2xe^{-x} - 2e^{-x}\right]_0^b = \lim_{b \to \infty} (-b^2 e^{-b} - 2be^{-b} - 2e^{-b}) - (-2) = 0 + 2 = 2$

60. $\int_{-\infty}^0 xe^{3x} \, dx = \lim_{b \to -\infty} \left[\frac{x}{3} e^{3x} - \frac{1}{9} e^{3x}\right]_b^0 = -\frac{1}{9} - \lim_{b \to -\infty} \left(\frac{b}{3} e^{3b} - \frac{1}{9} e^{3b}\right) = -\frac{1}{9} - 0 = -\frac{1}{9}$

61. $\int_{-\infty}^\infty \frac{dx}{4x^2 + 9} = 2 \int_0^\infty \frac{dx}{4x^2 + 9} = \frac{1}{2} \int_0^\infty \frac{dx}{x^2 + \frac{9}{4}} = \frac{1}{2} \lim_{b \to \infty} \left[\frac{2}{3} \tan^{-1}\left(\frac{2x}{3}\right)\right]_0^b = \frac{1}{2} \lim_{b \to \infty} \left[\frac{2}{3} \tan^{-1}\left(\frac{2b}{3}\right)\right] - \frac{1}{3} \tan^{-1}(0)$

   $= \frac{1}{2} \left(\frac{2}{3} \cdot \frac{\pi}{2}\right) - 0 = \frac{\pi}{6}$

62. $\int_{-\infty}^\infty \frac{4 \, dx}{x^2 + 16} = 2 \int_0^\infty \frac{4 \, dx}{x^2 + 16} = 2 \lim_{b \to \infty} \left[\tan^{-1}\left(\frac{x}{4}\right)\right]_0^b = 2 \left(\lim_{b \to \infty} \left[\tan^{-1}\left(\frac{b}{4}\right)\right] - \tan^{-1}(0)\right) = 2 \left(\frac{\pi}{2}\right) - 0 = \pi$

63. $\lim_{\theta \to \infty} \frac{\theta}{\sqrt{\theta^2 + 1}} = 1$ and $\int_6^\infty \frac{d\theta}{\theta}$ diverges $\Rightarrow \int_6^\infty \frac{d\theta}{\sqrt{\theta^2 + 1}}$ diverges

64. $I = \int_0^\infty e^{-u} \cos u \, du = \lim_{b \to \infty} [-e^{-u} \cos u]_0^b - \int_0^\infty e^{-u} \sin u \, du = 1 + \lim_{b \to \infty} [e^{-u} \sin u]_0^b - \int_0^\infty (e^{-u}) \cos u \, du$

$\Rightarrow I = 1 + 0 - I \Rightarrow 2I = 1 \Rightarrow I = \frac{1}{2}$ converges

65. $\int_1^\infty \frac{\ln z}{z} \, dz = \int_1^e \frac{\ln z}{z} \, dz + \int_e^\infty \frac{\ln z}{z} \, dz = \left[\frac{(\ln z)^2}{2}\right]_1^e + \lim_{b \to \infty} \left[\frac{(\ln z)^2}{2}\right]_e^b = \left(\frac{1^2}{2} - 0\right) + \lim_{b \to \infty} \left[\frac{(\ln b)^2}{2} - \frac{1}{2}\right] = \infty$

$\Rightarrow$ diverges

66. $0 < \frac{e^{-t}}{\sqrt{t}} \le e^{-t}$ for $t \ge 1$ and $\int_1^\infty e^{-t} \, dt$ converges $\Rightarrow \int_1^\infty \frac{e^{-t}}{\sqrt{t}} \, dt$ converges

67. $\int_{-\infty}^\infty \frac{2 \, dx}{e^x + e^{-x}} = 2 \int_0^\infty \frac{2 \, dx}{e^x + e^{-x}} < \int_0^\infty \frac{4 \, dx}{e^x}$ converges $\Rightarrow \int_{-\infty}^\infty \frac{2 \, dx}{e^x + e^{-x}}$ converges

68. $\int_{-\infty}^\infty \frac{dx}{x^2(1 + e^x)} = \int_{-\infty}^{-1} \frac{dx}{x^2(1 + e^x)} + \int_{-1}^0 \frac{dx}{x^2(1 + e^x)} + \int_0^1 \frac{dx}{x^2(1 + e^x)} + \int_1^\infty \frac{dx}{x^2(1 + e^x)}$ ;

$\lim_{x \to 0} \frac{\left(\frac{1}{x^2}\right)}{\left[\frac{1}{x^2(1+e^x)}\right]} = \lim_{x \to 0} \frac{x^2(1 + e^x)}{x^2} = \lim_{x \to 0} (1 + e^x) = 2$ and $\int_0^1 \frac{dx}{x^2}$ diverges $\Rightarrow \int_0^1 \frac{dx}{x^2(1 + e^x)}$ diverges

$\Rightarrow \int_{-\infty}^\infty \frac{dx}{x^2(1 + e^x)}$ diverges

69. $\int \frac{x \, dx}{1 + \sqrt{x}}$ ; $\begin{bmatrix} u = \sqrt{x} \\ du = \frac{dx}{2\sqrt{x}} \end{bmatrix} \to \int \frac{u^2 \cdot 2u \, du}{1 + u} = \int \left(2u^2 - 2u + 2 - \frac{2}{1+u}\right) du = \frac{2}{3}u^3 - u^2 + 2u - 2 \ln|1 + u| + C$

$= \frac{2x^{3/2}}{3} - x + 2\sqrt{x} - 2 \ln(1 + \sqrt{x}) + C$

70. $\int \frac{x^3 + 2}{4 - x^2} \, dx = -\int \left(x + \frac{4x + 2}{x^2 - 4}\right) dx = -\int x \, dx - \frac{3}{2}\int \frac{dx}{x + 2} - \frac{5}{2}\int \frac{dx}{x - 2} = -\frac{x^2}{2} - \frac{3}{2} \ln|x + 2| - \frac{5}{2} \ln|x - 2| + C$

71. $\int \frac{dx}{x(x^2 + 1)^2}$ ; $\begin{bmatrix} x = \tan \theta \\ dx = \sec^2 \theta \, d\theta \end{bmatrix} \to \int \frac{\sec^2 \theta \, d\theta}{\tan \theta \sec^4 \theta} = \int \frac{\cos^3 \theta \, d\theta}{\sin \theta} = \int \left(\frac{1 - \sin^2 \theta}{\sin \theta}\right) d(\sin \theta)$

$= \ln|\sin \theta| - \frac{1}{2} \sin^2 \theta + C = \ln\left|\frac{x}{\sqrt{x^2 + 1}}\right| - \frac{1}{2}\left(\frac{x}{\sqrt{x^2 + 1}}\right)^2 + C$

72. $\int \frac{dx}{\sqrt{-2x - x^2}} = \int \frac{d(x + 1)}{\sqrt{1 - (x + 1)^2}} = \sin^{-1}(x + 1) + C$

73. $\int \frac{2 - \cos x + \sin x}{\sin^2 x} \, dx = \int 2 \csc^2 x \, dx - \int \frac{\cos x \, dx}{\sin^2 x} + \int \csc x \, dx = -2 \cot x + \frac{1}{\sin x} - \ln|\csc x + \cot x| + C$

$= -2 \cot x + \csc x - \ln|\csc x + \cot x| + C$

74. $\int \frac{\sin^2 \theta}{\cos^2 \theta} \, d\theta = \int \frac{1 - \cos^2 \theta}{\cos^2 \theta} \, d\theta = \int \sec^2 \theta \, d\theta - \int d\theta = \tan \theta - \theta + C$

75. $\int \frac{9 \, dv}{81 - v^4} = \frac{1}{2}\int \frac{dv}{v^2 + 9} + \frac{1}{12}\int \frac{dv}{3 - v} + \frac{1}{12}\int \frac{dv}{3 + v} = \frac{1}{12} \ln\left|\frac{3 + v}{3 - v}\right| + \frac{1}{6} \tan^{-1} \frac{v}{3} + C$

76. $\int_2^\infty \frac{dx}{(x - 1)^2} = \lim_{b \to \infty} \left[\frac{1}{1 - x}\right]_2^b = \lim_{b \to \infty} \left[\frac{1}{1 - b} - (-1)\right] = 0 + 1 = 1$

77.

$\qquad\qquad\qquad \cos(2\theta + 1)$

$\theta \ \xrightarrow{\ \ (+)\ \ } \ \frac{1}{2} \sin(2\theta + 1)$

$1 \ \xrightarrow{\ \ (-)\ \ } \ -\frac{1}{4} \cos(2\theta + 1)$

$0 \qquad\qquad\qquad \Rightarrow \int \theta \cos(2\theta + 1) \, d\theta = \frac{\theta}{2} \sin(2\theta + 1) + \frac{1}{4} \cos(2\theta + 1) + C$

78. $\int \frac{x^3\,dx}{x^2-2x+1} = \int \left(x+2+\frac{3x-2}{x^2-2x+1}\right) dx = \int (x+2)\,dx + 3\int \frac{dx}{x-1} + \int \frac{dx}{(x-1)^2}$

$= \frac{x^2}{2} + 2x + 3\ln|x-1| - \frac{1}{x-1} + C$

79. $\int \frac{\sin 2\theta\,d\theta}{(1+\cos 2\theta)^2} = -\frac{1}{2}\int \frac{d(1+\cos 2\theta)}{(1+\cos 2\theta)^2} = \frac{1}{2(1+\cos 2\theta)} + C = \frac{1}{4}\sec^2\theta + C$

80. $\int_{\pi/4}^{\pi/2} \sqrt{1+\cos 4x}\,dx = -\sqrt{2}\int_{\pi/4}^{\pi/2} \cos 2x\,dx = \left[-\frac{\sqrt{2}}{2}\sin 2x\right]_{\pi/4}^{\pi/2} = \frac{\sqrt{2}}{2}$

81. $\int \frac{x\,dx}{\sqrt{2-x}}\,;\ \begin{bmatrix} y=2-x \\ dy=-dx \end{bmatrix} \rightarrow -\int \frac{(2-y)\,dy}{\sqrt{y}} = \frac{2}{3}y^{3/2} - 4y^{1/2} + C = \frac{2}{3}(2-x)^{3/2} - 4(2-x)^{1/2} + C$

$= 2\left[\frac{\left(\sqrt{2-x}\right)^3}{3} - 2\sqrt{2-x}\right] + C$

82. $\int \frac{\sqrt{1-v^2}}{v^2}\,dv;\ [v=\sin\theta] \rightarrow \int \frac{\cos\theta\cdot\cos\theta\,d\theta}{\sin^2\theta} = \int \frac{(1-\sin^2\theta)\,d\theta}{\sin^2\theta} = \int \csc^2\theta\,d\theta - \int d\theta = \cot\theta - \theta + C$

$= -\sin^{-1} v - \frac{\sqrt{1-v^2}}{v} + C$

83. $\int \frac{dy}{y^2-2y+2} = \int \frac{d(y-1)}{(y-1)^2+1} = \tan^{-1}(y-1) + C$

84. $\int \frac{x\,dx}{\sqrt{8-2x^2-x^4}} = \frac{1}{2}\int \frac{d(x^2+1)}{\sqrt{9-(x^2+1)^2}} = \frac{1}{2}\sin^{-1}\left(\frac{x^2+1}{3}\right) + C$

85. $\int \frac{z+1}{z^2(z^2+4)}\,dz = \frac{1}{4}\int \left(\frac{1}{z}+\frac{1}{z^2}-\frac{z+1}{z^2+4}\right) dz = \frac{1}{4}\ln|z| - \frac{1}{4z} - \frac{1}{8}\ln(z^2+4) - \frac{1}{8}\tan^{-1}\frac{z}{2} + C$

86. $\int x^3 e^{x^2}\,dx = \frac{1}{2}\int x^2 e^{x^2}\,d(x^2) = \frac{1}{2}\left(x^2 e^{x^2} - e^{x^2}\right) + C = \frac{(x^2-1)\,e^{x^2}}{2} + C$

87. $\int \frac{t\,dt}{\sqrt{9-4t^2}} = -\frac{1}{8}\int \frac{d(9-4t^2)}{\sqrt{9-4t^2}} = -\frac{1}{4}\sqrt{9-4t^2} + C$

88. $u = \tan^{-1} x,\ du = \frac{dx}{1+x^2}\,;\ dv = \frac{dx}{x^2},\ v = -\frac{1}{x}\,;$

$\int \frac{\tan^{-1}x\,dx}{x^2} = -\frac{1}{x}\tan^{-1}x + \int \frac{dx}{x(1+x^2)} = -\frac{1}{x}\tan^{-1}x + \int \frac{dx}{x} - \int \frac{x\,dx}{1+x^2}$

$= -\frac{1}{x}\tan^{-1}x + \ln|x| - \frac{1}{2}\ln(1+x^2) + C = -\frac{\tan^{-1}x}{x} + \ln|x| - \ln\sqrt{1+x^2} + C$

89. $\int \frac{e^t\,dt}{e^{2t}+3e^t+2}\,;\ [e^t=x] \rightarrow \int \frac{dx}{(x+1)(x+2)} = \int \frac{dx}{x+1} - \int \frac{dx}{x+2} = \ln|x+1| - \ln|x+2| + C = \ln\left|\frac{x+1}{x+2}\right| + C$

$= \ln\left(\frac{e^t+1}{e^t+2}\right) + C$

90. $\int \tan^3 t\,dt = \int (\tan t)(\sec^2 t - 1)\,dt = \frac{\tan^2 t}{2} - \int \tan t\,dt = \frac{\tan^2 t}{2} - \ln|\sec t| + C$

91. $\int_1^\infty \frac{\ln y\,dy}{y^3}\,;\ \begin{bmatrix} x=\ln y \\ dx=\frac{dy}{y} \\ dy=e^x\,dx \end{bmatrix} \rightarrow \int_0^\infty \frac{x\cdot e^x}{e^{3x}}\,dx = \int_0^\infty x e^{-2x}\,dx = \lim_{b\to\infty}\left[-\frac{x}{2}e^{-2x} - \frac{1}{4}e^{-2x}\right]_0^b$

$= \lim_{b\to\infty}\left(\frac{-b}{2e^{2b}} - \frac{1}{4e^{2b}}\right) - \left(0-\frac{1}{4}\right) = \frac{1}{4}$

92. $\int \frac{\cot v\,dv}{\ln(\sin v)} = \int \frac{\cos v\,dv}{(\sin v)\ln(\sin v)}\,;\ \begin{bmatrix} u=\ln(\sin v) \\ du=\frac{\cos v\,dv}{\sin v} \end{bmatrix} \rightarrow \int \frac{du}{u} = \ln|u| + C = \ln|\ln(\sin v)| + C$

93. $\int e^{\ln\sqrt{x}}\, dx = \int \sqrt{x}\, dx = \frac{2}{3}x^{3/2} + C$

94. $\int e^{\theta}\sqrt{3 + 4e^{\theta}}\, d\theta;\ \begin{bmatrix} u = 4e^{\theta} \\ du = 4e^{\theta}\, d\theta \end{bmatrix} \to \frac{1}{4}\int \sqrt{3 + u}\, du = \frac{1}{4}\cdot\frac{2}{3}(3 + u)^{3/2} + C = \frac{1}{6}(3 + 4e^{\theta})^{3/2} + C$

95. $\int \frac{\sin 5t\, dt}{1 + (\cos 5t)^{2}};\ \begin{bmatrix} u = \cos 5t \\ du = -5\sin 5t\, dt \end{bmatrix} \to -\frac{1}{5}\int \frac{du}{1 + u^{2}} = -\frac{1}{5}\tan^{-1}u + C = -\frac{1}{5}\tan^{-1}(\cos 5t) + C$

96. $\int \frac{dv}{\sqrt{e^{2v} - 1}};\ \begin{bmatrix} x = e^{v} \\ dx = e^{v}\, dv \end{bmatrix} \to \int \frac{dx}{x\sqrt{x^{2} - 1}} = \sec^{-1}x + C = \sec^{-1}(e^{v}) + C$

97. $\int \frac{dr}{1 + \sqrt{r}};\ \begin{bmatrix} u = \sqrt{r} \\ du = \frac{dr}{2\sqrt{r}} \end{bmatrix} \to \int \frac{2u\, du}{1 + u} = \int \left(2 - \frac{2}{1 + u}\right) du = 2u - 2\ln|1 + u| + C = 2\sqrt{r} - 2\ln\left(1 + \sqrt{r}\right) + C$

98. $\int \frac{4x^{3} - 20x}{x^{4} - 10x^{2} + 9}\, dx = \int \frac{d\left(x^{4} - 10x^{2} + 9\right)}{x^{4} - 10x^{2} + 9} = \ln|x^{4} - 10x^{2} + 9| + C$

99. $\int \frac{x^{3}}{1 + x^{2}}\, dx = \int \left(x - \frac{x}{1 + x^{2}}\right) dx = \int x\, dx - \frac{1}{2}\int \frac{2x}{1 + x^{2}}\, dx = \frac{1}{2}x^{2} - \frac{1}{2}\ln(1 + x^{2}) + C$

100. $\int \frac{x^{2}}{1 + x^{3}}\, dx = \frac{1}{3}\int \frac{3x^{2}}{1 + x^{3}}\, dx = \frac{1}{3}\ln|1 + x^{3}| + C$

101. $\int \frac{1 + x^{2}}{1 + x^{3}}\, dx;\ \frac{1 + x^{2}}{1 + x^{3}} = \frac{A}{1 + x} + \frac{Bx + C}{1 - x + x^{2}} \Rightarrow 1 + x^{2} = A(1 - x + x^{2}) + (Bx + C)(1 + x)$

$= (A + B)x^{2} + (-A + B + C)x + (A + C) \Rightarrow A + B = 1,\ -A + B + C = 0,\ A + C = 1 \Rightarrow A = \frac{2}{3},\ B = \frac{1}{3},\ C = \frac{1}{3};$

$\int \frac{1 + x^{2}}{1 + x^{3}}\, dx = \int \left(\frac{2/3}{1 + x} + \frac{(1/3)x + 1/3}{1 - x + x^{2}}\right) dx = \frac{2}{3}\int \frac{1}{1 + x}\, dx + \frac{1}{3}\int \frac{x + 1}{1 - x + x^{2}}\, dx = \frac{2}{3}\int \frac{1}{1 + x}\, dx + \frac{1}{3}\int \frac{x + 1}{\frac{3}{4} + \left(x - \frac{1}{2}\right)^{2}}\, dx;$

$\begin{bmatrix} u = x - \frac{1}{2} \\ du = dx \end{bmatrix} \to \frac{1}{3}\int \frac{u + \frac{3}{2}}{\frac{3}{4} + u^{2}}\, du = \frac{1}{3}\int \frac{u}{\frac{3}{4} + u^{2}}\, du + \frac{1}{2}\int \frac{1}{\frac{3}{4} + u^{2}}\, du = \frac{1}{6}\ln\left|\frac{3}{4} + u^{2}\right| + \frac{1}{\sqrt{3}}\tan^{-1}\left(\frac{u}{\sqrt{3}/2}\right)$

$= \frac{1}{6}\ln\left|\frac{3}{4} + \left(x - \frac{1}{2}\right)^{2}\right| + \frac{1}{\sqrt{3}}\tan^{-1}\left(\frac{x - \frac{1}{2}}{\sqrt{3}/2}\right) = \frac{1}{6}\ln|1 - x + x^{2}| + \frac{1}{\sqrt{3}}\tan^{-1}\left(\frac{2x - 1}{\sqrt{3}}\right)$

$\Rightarrow \frac{2}{3}\int \frac{1}{1 + x}\, dx + \frac{1}{3}\int \frac{x + 1}{1 - x + x^{2}}\, dx = \frac{2}{3}\ln|1 + x| + \frac{1}{6}\ln|1 - x + x^{2}| + \frac{1}{\sqrt{3}}\tan^{-1}\left(\frac{2x - 1}{\sqrt{3}}\right) + C$

102. $\int \frac{1 + x^{2}}{(1 + x)^{3}}\, dx;\ \begin{bmatrix} u = 1 + x \\ du = dx \end{bmatrix} \to \int \frac{1 + (u - 1)^{2}}{u^{3}}\, du = \int \frac{u^{2} - 2u + 2}{u^{3}}\, du = \int \frac{1}{u}\, du - \int \frac{2}{u^{2}}\, du + \int \frac{2}{u^{3}}\, du = \ln|u| + \frac{2}{u} - \frac{1}{u^{2}} + C$

$= \ln|1 + x| + \frac{2}{1 + x} - \frac{1}{(1 + x)^{2}} + C$

103. $\int \sqrt{x}\sqrt{1 + \sqrt{x}}\, dx;\ \begin{bmatrix} w = \sqrt{x} \Rightarrow w^{2} = x \\ 2w\, dw = dx \end{bmatrix} \to \int 2w^{2}\sqrt{1 + w}\, dw$

$\sqrt{1 + w}$

$2w^{2} \xrightarrow{\ (+)\ } \frac{2}{3}(1 + w)^{3/2}$

$4w \xrightarrow{\ (-)\ } \frac{4}{15}(1 + w)^{5/2}$

$4 \xrightarrow{\ (+)\ } \frac{8}{105}(1 + w)^{7/2}$

$0 \qquad\qquad \Rightarrow \int 2w^{2}\sqrt{1 + w}\, dw = \frac{4}{3}w^{2}(1 + w)^{3/2} - \frac{16}{15}w(1 + w)^{5/2} + \frac{32}{105}(1 + w)^{7/2} + C$

$= \frac{4}{3}x\left(1 + \sqrt{x}\right)^{3/2} - \frac{16}{15}\sqrt{x}\left(1 + \sqrt{x}\right)^{5/2} + \frac{32}{105}\left(1 + \sqrt{x}\right)^{7/2} + C$

104. $\int \sqrt{1 + \sqrt{1+x}}\, dx;$ $\left[\begin{array}{c} w = \sqrt{1+x} \Rightarrow w^2 = 1+x \\ 2w\, dw = dx \end{array}\right] \rightarrow \int 2w\sqrt{1+w}\, dw;$

$$\left[u = 2w,\ du = 2\, dw,\ dv = \sqrt{1+w}\, dw,\ v = \tfrac{2}{3}(1+w)^{3/2}\right]$$

$\int 2w\sqrt{1+w}\, dw = \tfrac{4}{3}w(1+w)^{3/2} - \int \tfrac{4}{3}(1+w)^{3/2}\, dw = \tfrac{4}{3}w(1+w)^{3/2} - \tfrac{8}{15}(1+w)^{5/2} + C$

$= \tfrac{4}{3}\sqrt{1+x}\left(1 + \sqrt{1+x}\right)^{3/2} - \tfrac{8}{15}\left(1 + \sqrt{1+x}\right)^{5/2} + C$

105. $\int \dfrac{1}{\sqrt{x}\sqrt{1+x}}\, dx;$ $\left[\begin{array}{c} u = \sqrt{x} \Rightarrow u^2 = x \\ 2u\, du = dx \end{array}\right] \rightarrow \int \dfrac{2}{\sqrt{1+u^2}}\, du;$ $\left[u = \tan\theta,\ -\tfrac{\pi}{2} < \theta < \tfrac{\pi}{2},\ du = \sec^2\theta\, d\theta,\ \sqrt{1+u^2} = \sec\theta\right]$

$\int \dfrac{2}{\sqrt{1+u^2}}\, du = \int \dfrac{2\sec^2\theta}{\sec\theta}\, d\theta = \int 2\sec\theta\, d\theta = 2\ln|\sec\theta + \tan\theta| + C = 2\ln\left|\sqrt{1+u^2} + u\right| + C$

$= 2\ln\left|\sqrt{1+x} + \sqrt{x}\right| + C$

106. $\int_0^{1/2} \sqrt{1 + \sqrt{1 - x^2}}\, dx;$

$$\left[x = \sin\theta,\ -\tfrac{\pi}{2} < \theta < \tfrac{\pi}{2},\ dx = \cos\theta\, d\theta,\ \sqrt{1 - x^2} = \cos\theta,\ x = 0 = \sin\theta \Rightarrow \theta = 0,\ x = \tfrac{1}{2} = \sin\theta \Rightarrow \theta = \tfrac{\pi}{6}\right]$$

$\rightarrow \int_0^{\pi/6} \sqrt{1 + \cos\theta}\, \cos\theta\, d\theta = \int_0^{\pi/6} \dfrac{\sqrt{1 - \cos^2\theta}}{\sqrt{1 - \cos\theta}}\, \cos\theta\, d\theta = \int_0^{\pi/6} \dfrac{\sin\theta\cos\theta}{\sqrt{1 - \cos\theta}}\, d\theta = \lim_{c \to 0^+} \int_c^{\pi/6} \dfrac{\sin\theta\cos\theta}{\sqrt{1 - \cos\theta}}\, d\theta;$

$$\left[u = \cos\theta,\ du = -\sin\theta\, d\theta,\ dv = \dfrac{\sin\theta}{\sqrt{1 - \cos\theta}}\, d\theta,\ v = 2(1 - \cos\theta)^{1/2}\right]$$

$= \lim_{c \to 0^+} \left[\left[2\cos\theta\,(1 - \cos\theta)^{1/2}\right]_c^{\pi/6} + \int_c^{\pi/6} 2(1 - \cos\theta)^{1/2}\sin\theta\, d\theta\right]$

$= \lim_{c \to 0^+} \left[\left(2\cos\left(\tfrac{\pi}{6}\right)\left(1 - \cos\left(\tfrac{\pi}{6}\right)\right)^{1/2} - 2\cos c\,(1 - \cos c)^{1/2}\right) + \left[\tfrac{4}{3}(1 - \cos\theta)^{3/2}\right]_c^{\pi/6}\right]$

$= \lim_{c \to 0^+} \left[\sqrt{3}\left(1 - \tfrac{\sqrt{3}}{2}\right)^{1/2} - 2\cos c\,(1 - \cos c)^{1/2} + \left(\tfrac{4}{3}\left(1 - \cos\left(\tfrac{\pi}{6}\right)\right)^{3/2} - \tfrac{4}{3}(1 - \cos c)^{3/2}\right)\right]$

$= \lim_{c \to 0^+} \left[\sqrt{3}\left(1 - \tfrac{\sqrt{3}}{2}\right)^{1/2} - 2\cos c\,(1 - \cos c)^{1/2} + \tfrac{4}{3}\left(1 - \tfrac{\sqrt{3}}{2}\right)^{3/2} - \tfrac{4}{3}(1 - \cos c)^{3/2}\right]$

$= \sqrt{3}\left(1 - \tfrac{\sqrt{3}}{2}\right)^{1/2} + \tfrac{4}{3}\left(1 - \tfrac{\sqrt{3}}{2}\right)^{3/2} = \left(1 - \tfrac{\sqrt{3}}{2}\right)^{1/2}\left(\tfrac{4 + \sqrt{3}}{3}\right) = \dfrac{\left(4 + \sqrt{3}\right)\sqrt{2 - \sqrt{3}}}{3\sqrt{2}}$

107. $\int \dfrac{\ln x}{x + x\ln x}\, dx = \int \dfrac{\ln x}{x(1 + \ln x)}\, dx;$ $\left[\begin{array}{c} u = 1 + \ln x \\ du = \tfrac{1}{x}dx \end{array}\right] \rightarrow \int \dfrac{u - 1}{u}\, du = \int du - \int \tfrac{1}{u}\, du = u - \ln|u| + C$

$= (1 + \ln x) - \ln|1 + \ln x| + C = \ln x - \ln|1 + \ln x| + C$

108. $\int \dfrac{1}{x\ln x\cdot \ln(\ln x)}\, dx;$ $\left[\begin{array}{c} u = \ln(\ln x) \\ du = \tfrac{1}{x\ln x}dx \end{array}\right] \rightarrow \int \tfrac{1}{u}\, du = \ln|u| + C = \ln|\ln(\ln x)| + C$

109. $\int \dfrac{x^{\ln x}\ln x}{x}\, dx;$ $\left[u = x^{\ln x} \Rightarrow \ln u = \ln x^{\ln x} = (\ln x)^2 \Rightarrow \tfrac{1}{u}du = \tfrac{2\ln x}{x}\, dx \Rightarrow du = \tfrac{2u\ln x}{x}\, dx = \tfrac{2x^{\ln x}\ln x}{x}\, dx\right] \rightarrow \tfrac{1}{2}\int du$

$= \tfrac{1}{2}u + C = \tfrac{1}{2}x^{\ln x} + C$

110. $\int (\ln x)^{\ln x}\left[\tfrac{1}{x} + \tfrac{\ln(\ln x)}{x}\right]\, dx;$ $\left[u = (\ln x)^{\ln x} \Rightarrow \ln u = \ln(\ln x)^{\ln x} = (\ln x)\ln(\ln x) \Rightarrow \tfrac{1}{u}du = \left(\tfrac{(\ln x)}{x\ln x} + \tfrac{\ln(\ln x)}{x}\right)dx\right.$

$\left. \Rightarrow du = u\left[\tfrac{1}{x} + \tfrac{\ln(\ln x)}{x}\right]dx = (\ln x)^{\ln x}\left[\tfrac{1}{x} + \tfrac{\ln(\ln x)}{x}\right]dx\right] \rightarrow \int du = u + C = (\ln x)^{\ln x} + C$

111. $\int \frac{1}{x\sqrt{1-x^4}}\,dx = \int \frac{x}{x^2\sqrt{1-x^4}}\,dx; \left[x^2 = \sin\theta, 0 \le \theta < \frac{\pi}{2}, 2x\,dx = \cos\theta\,d\theta, \sqrt{1-x^4} = \cos\theta\right] \to \frac{1}{2}\int \frac{\cos\theta}{\sin\theta\cos\theta}\,d\theta$

$$= \frac{1}{2}\int \csc\theta\,d\theta = -\frac{1}{2}\ln|\csc\theta + \cot\theta| + C = -\frac{1}{2}\ln\left|\frac{1}{x^2} + \frac{\sqrt{1-x^4}}{x^2}\right| + C = -\frac{1}{2}\ln\left|\frac{1+\sqrt{1-x^4}}{x^2}\right| + C$$

112. $\int \frac{\sqrt{1-x}}{x}\,dx; \left[u = \sqrt{1-x} \Rightarrow u^2 = 1-x \Rightarrow 2u\,du = -dx\right] \to \int \frac{-2u^2}{1-u^2}\,du = \int \frac{2u^2}{u^2-1}\,du = \int \left(2 + \frac{2}{u^2-1}\right)du;$

$\frac{2}{u^2-1} = \frac{A}{u-1} + \frac{B}{u+1} \Rightarrow 2 = A(u+1) + B(u-1) = (A+B)u + A - B \Rightarrow A + B = 0, A - B = 2$

$\Rightarrow A = 1 \Rightarrow B = -1; \int \left(2 + \frac{2}{u^2-1}\right)du = \int 2\,du + \int \left(\frac{1}{u-1} - \frac{1}{u+1}\right)du$

$$= 2u + \ln|u-1| - \ln|u+1| + C = 2\sqrt{1-x} + \frac{1}{2}\ln\left|\frac{\sqrt{1-x}-1}{\sqrt{1-x}+1}\right| + C$$

113. (a) $\int_0^a f(a-x)\,dx; \left[u = a - x \Rightarrow du = -dx, x = 0 \Rightarrow u = a, x = a \Rightarrow u = 0\right] \to -\int_a^0 f(u)\,du = \int_0^a f(u)\,du$, which is

the same integral as $\int_0^a f(x)\,dx$.

(b) $\int_0^{\pi/2} \frac{\sin x}{\sin x + \cos x}\,dx = \int_0^{\pi/2} \frac{\sin\left(\frac{\pi}{2}-x\right)}{\sin\left(\frac{\pi}{2}-x\right) + \cos\left(\frac{\pi}{2}-x\right)}\,dx = \int_0^{\pi/2} \frac{\sin\left(\frac{\pi}{2}\right)\cos x - \cos\left(\frac{\pi}{2}\right)\sin x}{\sin\left(\frac{\pi}{2}\right)\cos x - \cos\left(\frac{\pi}{2}\right)\sin x + \cos\left(\frac{\pi}{2}\right)\cos x + \sin\left(\frac{\pi}{2}\right)\sin x}\,dx$

$= \int_0^{\pi/2} \frac{\cos x}{\cos x + \sin x}\,dx \Rightarrow 2\int_0^{\pi/2} \frac{\sin x}{\sin x + \cos x}\,dx = \int_0^{\pi/2} \frac{\sin x}{\sin x + \cos x}\,dx + \int_0^{\pi/2} \frac{\cos x}{\cos x + \sin x}\,dx = \int_0^{\pi/2} \frac{\sin x + \cos x}{\sin x + \cos x}\,dx = \int_0^{\pi/2} dx$

$= \left[x\right]_0^{\pi/2} = \frac{\pi}{2} \Rightarrow 2\int_0^{\pi/2} \frac{\sin x}{\sin x + \cos x}\,dx = \frac{\pi}{2} \Rightarrow \int_0^{\pi/2} \frac{\sin x}{\sin x + \cos x}\,dx = \frac{\pi}{4}$

114. $\int \frac{\sin x}{\sin x + \cos x}\,dx = \int \frac{\sin x + \cos x - \cos x + \sin x - \sin x}{\sin x + \cos x}\,dx = \int \frac{\sin x + \cos x}{\sin x + \cos x}\,dx + \int \frac{-\cos x + \sin x}{\sin x + \cos x}\,dx + \int \frac{-\sin x}{\sin x + \cos x}\,dx$

$= \int dx - \int \frac{\cos x - \sin x}{\sin x + \cos x}\,dx - \int \frac{\sin x}{\sin x + \cos x}\,dx = x - \ln|\sin x + \cos x| - \int \frac{\sin x}{\sin x + \cos x}\,dx$

$\Rightarrow 2\int \frac{\sin x}{\sin x + \cos x}\,dx = x - \ln|\sin x + \cos x| \Rightarrow \int \frac{\sin x}{\sin x + \cos x}\,dx = \frac{x}{2} - \frac{1}{2}\ln|\sin x + \cos x| + C$

115. $\int \frac{\sin^2 x}{1 + \sin^2 x}\,dx = \int \frac{\frac{\sin^2 x}{\cos^2 x}}{\frac{1}{\cos^2 x} + \frac{\sin^2 x}{\cos^2 x}}\,dx = \int \frac{\tan^2 x}{\sec^2 x + \tan^2 x}\,dx = \int \frac{\tan^2 x + \sec^2 x - \sec^2 x}{\sec^2 x + \tan^2 x}\,dx = \int \frac{\tan^2 x + \sec^2 x}{\sec^2 x + \tan^2 x}\,dx - \int \frac{\sec^2 x}{\sec^2 x + \tan^2 x}\,dx$

$= \int dx - \int \frac{\sec^2 x}{1 + 2\tan^2 x}\,dx = x - \frac{1}{\sqrt{2}}\tan^{-1}\left(\sqrt{2}\tan x\right) + C$

116. $\int \frac{1-\cos x}{1+\cos x}\,dx = \int \frac{(1-\cos x)^2}{1-\cos^2 x}\,dx = \int \frac{1 - 2\cos x + \cos^2 x}{\sin^2 x}\,dx = \int \frac{1}{\sin^2 x}\,dx - \int \frac{2\cos x}{\sin^2 x}\,dx + \int \frac{\cos^2 x}{\sin^2 x}\,dx$

$= \int \csc^2 x\,dx - 2\int \csc x \cot x\,dx + \int \cot^2 x\,dx = -\cot x + 2\csc x + \int \left(\csc^2 x - 1\right)dx = = -2\cot x + 2\csc x - x + C$

## CHAPTER 8 ADDITIONAL AND ADVANCED EXERCISES

1. $u = \left(\sin^{-1} x\right)^2, du = \frac{2\sin^{-1}x\,dx}{\sqrt{1-x^2}}; dv = dx, v = x;$

$\int \left(\sin^{-1} x\right)^2 dx = x\left(\sin^{-1} x\right)^2 - \int \frac{2x\sin^{-1}x\,dx}{\sqrt{1-x^2}};$

$u = \sin^{-1} x, du = \frac{dx}{\sqrt{1-x^2}}; dv = -\frac{2x\,dx}{\sqrt{1-x^2}}, v = 2\sqrt{1-x^2};$

$-\int \frac{2x\sin^{-1}x\,dx}{\sqrt{1-x^2}} = 2\left(\sin^{-1} x\right)\sqrt{1-x^2} - \int 2\,dx = 2\left(\sin^{-1} x\right)\sqrt{1-x^2} - 2x + C;$ therefore

$\int \left(\sin^{-1} x\right)^2 dx = x\left(\sin^{-1} x\right)^2 + 2\left(\sin^{-1} x\right)\sqrt{1-x^2} - 2x + C$

2. $\frac{1}{x} = \frac{1}{x},$

$\frac{1}{x(x+1)} = \frac{1}{x} - \frac{1}{x+1},$

$\frac{1}{x(x+1)(x+2)} = \frac{1}{2x} - \frac{1}{x+1} + \frac{1}{2(x+2)},$

$\dfrac{1}{x(x+1)(x+2)(x+3)} = \dfrac{1}{6x} - \dfrac{1}{2(x+1)} + \dfrac{1}{2(x+2)} - \dfrac{1}{6(x+3)}$,

$\dfrac{1}{x(x+1)(x+2)(x+3)(x+4)} = \dfrac{1}{24x} - \dfrac{1}{6(x+1)} + \dfrac{1}{4(x+2)} - \dfrac{1}{6(x+3)} + \dfrac{1}{24(x+4)} \Rightarrow$ the following pattern:

$\dfrac{1}{x(x+1)(x+2)\cdots(x+m)} = \displaystyle\sum_{k=0}^{m} \dfrac{(-1)^k}{(k!)(m-k)!(x+k)}$; therefore $\displaystyle\int \dfrac{dx}{x(x+1)(x+2)\cdots(x+m)}$

$= \displaystyle\sum_{k=0}^{m} \left[ \dfrac{(-1)^k}{(k!)(m-k)!} \ln |x+k| \right] + C$

3.  $u = \sin^{-1} x$, $du = \dfrac{dx}{\sqrt{1-x^2}}$ ; $dv = x \, dx$, $v = \dfrac{x^2}{2}$ ;

$\displaystyle\int x \sin^{-1} x \, dx = \dfrac{x^2}{2} \sin^{-1} x - \int \dfrac{x^2 \, dx}{2\sqrt{1-x^2}}$ ; $\begin{bmatrix} x = \sin\theta \\ dx = \cos\theta \, d\theta \end{bmatrix} \rightarrow \displaystyle\int x \sin^{-1} x \, dx = \dfrac{x^2}{2} \sin^{-1} x - \int \dfrac{\sin^2\theta \cos\theta \, d\theta}{2\cos\theta}$

$= \dfrac{x^2}{2} \sin^{-1} x - \dfrac{1}{2} \displaystyle\int \sin^2\theta \, d\theta = \dfrac{x^2}{2} \sin^{-1} x - \dfrac{1}{2}\left(\dfrac{\theta}{2} - \dfrac{\sin 2\theta}{4}\right) + C = \dfrac{x^2}{2} \sin^{-1} x + \dfrac{\sin\theta\cos\theta - \theta}{4} + C$

$= \dfrac{x^2}{2} \sin^{-1} x + \dfrac{x\sqrt{1-x^2} - \sin^{-1} x}{4} + C$

4.  $\displaystyle\int \sin^{-1} \sqrt{y} \, dy$; $\begin{bmatrix} z = \sqrt{y} \\ dz = \dfrac{dy}{2\sqrt{y}} \end{bmatrix} \rightarrow \displaystyle\int 2z \sin^{-1} z \, dz$; from Exercise 3, $\displaystyle\int z \sin^{-1} z \, dz$

$= \dfrac{z^2 \sin^{-1} z}{2} + \dfrac{z\sqrt{1-z^2} - \sin^{-1} z}{4} + C \Rightarrow \displaystyle\int \sin^{-1}\sqrt{y} \, dy = y \sin^{-1}\sqrt{y} + \dfrac{\sqrt{y}\sqrt{1-y} - \sin^{-1}\sqrt{y}}{2} + C$

$= y \sin^{-1}\sqrt{y} + \dfrac{\sqrt{y - y^2}}{2} - \dfrac{\sin^{-1}\sqrt{y}}{2} + C$

5.  $\displaystyle\int \dfrac{dt}{t - \sqrt{1-t^2}}$ ; $\begin{bmatrix} t = \sin\theta \\ dt = \cos\theta \, d\theta \end{bmatrix} \rightarrow \displaystyle\int \dfrac{\cos\theta \, d\theta}{\sin\theta - \cos\theta} = \int \dfrac{d\theta}{\tan\theta - 1}$ ; $\begin{bmatrix} u = \tan\theta \\ du = \sec^2\theta \, d\theta \\ d\theta = \dfrac{du}{u^2+1} \end{bmatrix} \rightarrow \displaystyle\int \dfrac{du}{(u-1)(u^2+1)}$

$= \dfrac{1}{2}\displaystyle\int \dfrac{du}{u-1} - \dfrac{1}{2}\int \dfrac{du}{u^2+1} - \dfrac{1}{2}\int \dfrac{u\,du}{u^2+1} = \dfrac{1}{2}\ln\left|\dfrac{u-1}{\sqrt{u^2+1}}\right| - \dfrac{1}{2}\tan^{-1} u + C = \dfrac{1}{2}\ln\left|\dfrac{\tan\theta - 1}{\sec\theta}\right| - \dfrac{1}{2}\theta + C$

$= \dfrac{1}{2}\ln\left(t - \sqrt{1-t^2}\right) - \dfrac{1}{2}\sin^{-1} t + C$

6.  $\displaystyle\int \dfrac{1}{x^4+4} \, dx = \int \dfrac{1}{(x^2+2)^2 - 4x^2} \, dx = \int \dfrac{1}{(x^2+2x+2)(x^2-2x+2)} \, dx$

$= \dfrac{1}{16}\displaystyle\int \left[\dfrac{2x+2}{x^2+2x+2} + \dfrac{2}{(x+1)^2+1} - \dfrac{2x-2}{x^2-2x+2} + \dfrac{2}{(x-1)^2+1}\right] dx$

$= \dfrac{1}{16}\ln\left|\dfrac{x^2+2x+2}{x^2-2x+2}\right| + \dfrac{1}{8}\left[\tan^{-1}(x+1) + \tan^{-1}(x-1)\right] + C$

7.  $\displaystyle\lim_{x\to\infty} \int_{-x}^{x} \sin t \, dt = \lim_{x\to\infty} \left[-\cos t\right]_{-x}^{x} = \lim_{x\to\infty} \left[-\cos x + \cos(-x)\right] = \lim_{x\to\infty} \left(-\cos x + \cos x\right) = \lim_{x\to\infty} 0 = 0$

8.  $\displaystyle\lim_{x\to 0^+} \int_x^1 \dfrac{\cos t}{t^2} \, dt$; $\displaystyle\lim_{t\to 0^+} \dfrac{\left(\frac{1}{t^2}\right)}{\left(\frac{\cos t}{t^2}\right)} = \lim_{t\to 0^+} \dfrac{1}{\cos t} = 1 \Rightarrow \lim_{x\to 0^+} \int_x^1 \dfrac{\cos t}{t^2} \, dt$ diverges since $\displaystyle\int_0^1 \dfrac{dt}{t^2}$ diverges; thus

$\displaystyle\lim_{x\to 0^+} x \int_x^1 \dfrac{\cos t}{t^2} \, dt$ is an indeterminate $0 \cdot \infty$ form and we apply l'Hôpital's rule:

$\displaystyle\lim_{x\to 0^+} x \int_x^1 \dfrac{\cos t}{t^2} \, dt = \lim_{x\to 0^+} \dfrac{-\int_1^x \frac{\cos t}{t^2} \, dt}{\frac{1}{x}} = \lim_{x\to 0^+} \dfrac{-\left(\frac{\cos x}{x^2}\right)}{\left(-\frac{1}{x^2}\right)} = \lim_{x\to 0^+} \cos x = 1$

9.  $\displaystyle\lim_{n\to\infty} \sum_{k=1}^{n} \ln \sqrt[n]{1 + \dfrac{k}{n}} = \lim_{n\to\infty} \sum_{k=1}^{n} \ln\left(1 + k\left(\dfrac{1}{n}\right)\right)\left(\dfrac{1}{n}\right) = \int_0^1 \ln(1+x) \, dx$; $\begin{bmatrix} u = 1+x, \; du = dx \\ x = 0 \Rightarrow u = 1, \; x = 1 \Rightarrow u = 2 \end{bmatrix}$

$\rightarrow \displaystyle\int_1^2 \ln u \, du = \left[u \ln u - u\right]_1^2 = (2\ln 2 - 2) - (\ln 1 - 1) = 2\ln 2 - 1 = \ln 4 - 1$

10. $\lim\limits_{n \to \infty} \sum\limits_{k=0}^{n-1} \frac{1}{\sqrt{n^2 - k^2}} = \lim\limits_{n \to \infty} \sum\limits_{k=0}^{n-1} \left( \frac{n}{\sqrt{n^2 - k^2}} \right) \left( \frac{1}{n} \right) = \lim\limits_{n \to \infty} \sum\limits_{k=0}^{n-1} \left( \frac{1}{\sqrt{1 - \left[ k \left( \frac{1}{n} \right) \right]^2}} \right) \left( \frac{1}{n} \right)$

$= \int_0^1 \frac{1}{\sqrt{1 - x^2}} \, dx = \left[ \sin^{-1} x \right]_0^1 = \frac{\pi}{2}$

11. $\frac{dy}{dx} = \sqrt{\cos 2x} \Rightarrow 1 + \left( \frac{dy}{dx} \right)^2 = 1 + \cos 2x = 2 \cos^2 x; \ L = \int_0^{\pi/4} \sqrt{1 + \left( \sqrt{\cos 2t} \right)^2} \, dt = \sqrt{2} \int_0^{\pi/4} \sqrt{\cos^2 t} \, dt$

$= \sqrt{2} \left[ \sin t \right]_0^{\pi/4} = 1$

12. $\frac{dy}{dx} = \frac{-2x}{1 - x^2} \Rightarrow 1 + \left( \frac{dy}{dx} \right)^2 = \frac{(1 - x^2)^2 + 4x^2}{(1 - x^2)^2} = \frac{1 + 2x^2 + x^4}{(1 - x^2)^2} = \left( \frac{1 + x^2}{1 - x^2} \right)^2; \ L = \int_0^{1/2} \sqrt{1 + \left( \frac{dy}{dx} \right)^2} \, dx$

$= \int_0^{1/2} \left( \frac{1 + x^2}{1 - x^2} \right) dx = \int_0^{1/2} \left( -1 + \frac{2}{1 - x^2} \right) dx = \int_0^{1/2} \left( -1 + \frac{1}{1 + x} + \frac{1}{1 - x} \right) dx = \left[ -x + \ln \left| \frac{1 + x}{1 - x} \right| \right]_0^{1/2}$

$= \left( -\frac{1}{2} + \ln 3 \right) - (0 + \ln 1) = \ln 3 - \frac{1}{2}$

13. $V = \int_a^b 2\pi \left( \begin{smallmatrix} \text{shell} \\ \text{radius} \end{smallmatrix} \right) \left( \begin{smallmatrix} \text{shell} \\ \text{height} \end{smallmatrix} \right) dx = \int_0^1 2\pi xy \, dx$

$= 6\pi \int_0^1 x^2 \sqrt{1 - x} \, dx; \ \begin{bmatrix} u = 1 - x \\ du = -dx \\ x^2 = (1 - u)^2 \end{bmatrix}$

$\rightarrow -6\pi \int_1^0 (1 - u)^2 \sqrt{u} \, du$

$= -6\pi \int_1^0 \left( u^{1/2} - 2u^{3/2} + u^{5/2} \right) du$

$= -6\pi \left[ \frac{2}{3} u^{3/2} - \frac{4}{5} u^{5/2} + \frac{2}{7} u^{7/2} \right]_1^0 = 6\pi \left( \frac{2}{3} - \frac{4}{5} + \frac{2}{7} \right)$

$= 6\pi \left( \frac{70 - 84 + 30}{105} \right) = 6\pi \left( \frac{16}{105} \right) = \frac{32\pi}{35}$

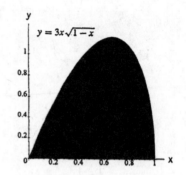

14. $V = \int_a^b \pi y^2 \, dx = \pi \int_1^4 \frac{25 \, dx}{x^2(5 - x)}$

$= \pi \int_1^4 \left( \frac{dx}{x} + \frac{5 \, dx}{x^2} + \frac{dx}{5 - x} \right)$

$= \pi \left[ \ln \left| \frac{x}{5 - x} \right| - \frac{5}{x} \right]_1^4 = \pi \left( \ln 4 - \frac{5}{4} \right) - \pi \left( \ln \frac{1}{4} - 5 \right)$

$= \frac{15\pi}{4} + 2\pi \ln 4$

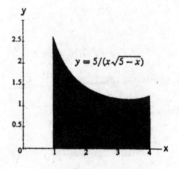

15. $V = \int_a^b 2\pi \left( \begin{smallmatrix} \text{shell} \\ \text{radius} \end{smallmatrix} \right) \left( \begin{smallmatrix} \text{shell} \\ \text{height} \end{smallmatrix} \right) dx = \int_0^1 2\pi x e^x \, dx$

$= 2\pi \left[ x e^x - e^x \right]_0^1 = 2\pi$

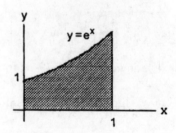

(e) Pick initial condition $y_0 < \frac{a}{b}$. Then, from the figure at right, $f(y_0) < M_y$ implies $\frac{M_y}{M_x} \frac{x^m}{e^{nx}} = \frac{y_0^a}{e^{by_0}} < M_y$ and thus $\frac{x^m}{e^{nx}} < M_x$. From the figure for $g(x)$, there exists a unique $x_0 < \frac{m}{n}$ satisfying $\frac{x^m}{e^{nx}} < M_x$. That is, for each $y < \frac{a}{b}$ there is a unique $x$ satisfying $\frac{y^a}{e^{by}} = \frac{M_y}{M_x} \frac{x^m}{e^{nx}}$. Thus, there can exist only one trajectory solution approaching $\left(\frac{m}{n}, \frac{a}{b}\right)$. (You can think of the point $(x_0, y_0)$ as the initial condition for that trajectory.)

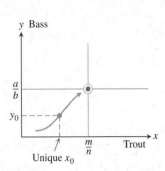

(f) Likewise there exists a unique trajectory when $y_0 > \frac{a}{b}$. Again, $f(y_0) < M_y$ implies $\frac{M_y}{M_x} \frac{x^m}{e^{nx}} = \frac{y_0^a}{e^{by_0}} < M_y$ and thus $\frac{x^m}{e^{nx}} < M_x$. From the figure for $g(x)$, there exists a unique $x_0 > \frac{m}{n}$ satisfying $\frac{x^m}{e^{nx}} < M_x$. That is, for each $y > \frac{a}{b}$ there is a unique $x$ satisfying $\frac{y^a}{e^{by}} = \frac{M_y}{M_x} \frac{x^m}{e^{nx}}$. Thus, there can exist only one trajectory solution approaching $\left(\frac{m}{n}, \frac{a}{b}\right)$.

8. Let $z = y' = \frac{dy}{dx} \Rightarrow \frac{dz}{dx} = z' = y''$, then given the differential equation $y'' = F(x, y, y')$, we can write it as the following system of first order differential equations: $\frac{dy}{dx} = z$

$$\frac{dz}{dx} = F(x, y, z)$$

In general, for the $n^{\text{th}}$ order differential equation given by $y^{(n)} = F\left(x, y, y', y'', \ldots, y^{(n-1)}\right)$, let $z_1 = y' = \frac{dy}{dx}$ $\Rightarrow \frac{dz_1}{dx} = z_1' = y''$, let $z_2 = z_1' = y''$, $\Rightarrow \frac{dz_2}{dx} = z_2' = y'''$, \ldots, let $z_{n-1} = z_{n-2}' = y^{(n-1)} \Rightarrow z_{n-1}' = y^{(n)}$. This gives us the following system of first order differential equations: $\frac{dy}{dx} = z_1$

$$\frac{dz_1}{dx} = z_2$$
$$\frac{dz_2}{dx} = z_3$$
$$\vdots$$
$$\frac{dz_{n-2}}{dx} = z_{n-1}$$
$$\frac{dz_{n-1}}{dx} = F(x, y, z_1, z_2, \ldots, z_{n-1})$$

9. In the absence of foxes $\Rightarrow b = 0 \Rightarrow \frac{dx}{dt} = ax$ and the population of rabbits grows at a rate proportional to the number of rabbits.

10. In the absence of rabbits $\Rightarrow d = 0 \Rightarrow \frac{dy}{dt} = -cy$ and the population of foxes decays (since the foxes have no food source) at a rate proportional to the number of foxes.

11. $\frac{dx}{dt} = (a - by)x = 0 \Rightarrow y = \frac{a}{b}$ or $x = 0$; $\frac{dy}{dt} = (-c + dx)y = 0 \Rightarrow x = \frac{c}{d}$ or $y = 0 \Rightarrow$ equilibrium points at $(0, 0)$ or $\left(\frac{c}{d}, \frac{a}{b}\right)$. For the point $(0, 0)$, there are no rabbits and no foxes. It is an unstable equilibrium point, if there are no foxes, but a few rabbits are introduced, then $\frac{dx}{dt} = a \Rightarrow$ the rabbit population will grow exponentially away from $(0, 0)$

12. Let $x(t)$ and $y(t)$ both be positive and suppose that they satisfy the differential equations $\frac{dx}{dt} = (a - by)x$ and $\frac{dy}{dt} = (-c + dx)y$. Let $C(t) = a \ln y(t) - by(t) - dx(t) + c \ln x(t) \Rightarrow C'(t) = a \frac{y'(t)}{y(t)} - by'(t) - dx'(t) + c \frac{x'(t)}{x(t)}$ $= \left(\frac{a}{y(t)} - b\right)y'(t) + \left(\frac{c}{x(t)} - d\right)x'(t) = \left(\frac{a}{y(t)} - b\right)(-c + dx(t))x(t) + \left(\frac{c}{x(t)} - d\right)(a - by(t))y(t) = 0$ Since $C'(t) = 0 \Rightarrow C(t) = \text{constant}$.

13. Consider a particular trajectory and suppose that $(x_0, y_0)$ is such that $x_0 < \frac{c}{d}$ and $y_0 < \frac{a}{b}$, then $\frac{dx}{dt} > 0$ and $\frac{dy}{dt} < 0 \Rightarrow$ the rabbit population is increasing while the fox population is decreasing, points on the trajectory are moving down and to the right; if $x_0 > \frac{c}{d}$ and $y_0 < \frac{a}{b}$, then $\frac{dx}{dt} > 0$ and $\frac{dy}{dt} > 0 \Rightarrow$ both the rabbit and fox populations are increasing, points on the trajectory are moving up and to the right; if $x_0 > \frac{c}{d}$ and $y_0 > \frac{a}{b}$, then $\frac{dx}{dt} < 0$ and $\frac{dy}{dt} > 0 \Rightarrow$ the rabbit population is decreasing while the fox population is increasing, points on the trajectory are moving up and to the left; and finally if

$x_0 < \frac{c}{d}$ and $y_0 > \frac{a}{b}$, then $\frac{dx}{dt} < 0$ and $\frac{dy}{dt} < 0 \Rightarrow$ both the rabbit and fox populations are decreasing, points on the trajectory are moving down and to the left. Thus, points travel around the trajectory in a counterclockwise direction. Note that we will follow the same trajectory if $(x_0, y_0)$ starts at a different point on the trajectory.

14. There are three possible cases: If the rabbit population begins (before the wolf) and ends (after the wolf) at a value larger than the equilibrium level of $x = \frac{c}{d}$, then the trajectory moves closer to the equilibrium and the maximum value of the foxes is smaller. If the rabbit population begins (before the wolf) and ends (after the wolf) at a value smaller than the equilibrium level of $x = \frac{c}{d}$, but greater than 0, then the trajectory moves further from the equilibrium and the maximum value of the foxes is greater. If the rabbit population begins and ends very near the equilibrium value, then the trajectory will stay near the equilibrium value, since it is a stable equilibrium, and the fox population will remain roughly the same.

## CHAPTER 9 PRACTICE EXERCISES

1. $y' = xe^y \sqrt{x-2} \Rightarrow e^{-y}dy = x\sqrt{x-2}\,dx \Rightarrow -e^{-y} = \frac{2(x-2)^{3/2}(3x+4)}{15} + C \Rightarrow e^{-y} = \frac{-2(x-2)^{3/2}(3x+4)}{15} - C$
   $\Rightarrow -y = \ln\left[\frac{-2(x-2)^{3/2}(3x+4)}{15} - C\right] \Rightarrow y = -\ln\left[\frac{-2(x-2)^{3/2}(3x+4)}{15} - C\right]$

2. $y' = xye^{x^2} \Rightarrow \frac{dy}{y} = e^{x^2}x\,dx \Rightarrow \ln y = \frac{1}{2}e^{x^2} + C$

3. $\sec x\,dy + x\cos^2 y\,dx = 0 \Rightarrow \frac{dy}{\cos^2 y} = -\frac{x\,dx}{\sec x} \Rightarrow \tan y = -\cos x - x\sin x + C$

4. $2x^2dx - 3\sqrt{y}\csc x\,dy = 0 \Rightarrow 3\sqrt{y}\,dy = \frac{2x^2}{\csc x}dx \Rightarrow 2y^{3/2} = 2(2-x^2)\cos x + 4x\sin x + C$
   $\Rightarrow y^{3/2} = (2-x^2)\cos x + 2x\sin x + C_1$

5. $y' = \frac{e^y}{xy} \Rightarrow ye^{-y}dy = \frac{dx}{x} \Rightarrow (y+1)e^{-y} = -\ln|x| + C$

6. $y' = xe^{x-y}\csc y \Rightarrow y' = \frac{xe^x}{e^y}\csc y \Rightarrow \frac{e^y}{\csc y}dy = xe^x dx \Rightarrow \frac{e^y}{2}(\sin y - \cos y) = (x-1)e^x + C$

7. $x(x-1)dy - y\,dx = 0 \Rightarrow x(x-1)dy = y\,dx \Rightarrow \frac{dy}{y} = \frac{dx}{x(x-1)} \Rightarrow \ln y = \ln(x-1) - \ln(x) + C$
   $\Rightarrow \ln y = \ln(x-1) - \ln(x) + \ln C_1 \Rightarrow \ln y = \ln\left(\frac{C_1(x-1)}{x}\right) \Rightarrow y = \frac{C_1(x-1)}{x}$

8. $y' = (y^2-1)(x^{-1}) \Rightarrow \frac{dy}{y^2-1} = \frac{dx}{x} \Rightarrow \frac{\ln\left(\frac{y-1}{y+1}\right)}{2} = \ln x + C \Rightarrow \ln\left(\frac{y-1}{y+1}\right) = 2\ln x + \ln C_1 \Rightarrow \frac{y-1}{y+1} = C_1 x^2$

9. $2y' - y = xe^{x/2} \Rightarrow y' - \frac{1}{2}y = \frac{x}{2}e^{x/2}$.
   $p(x) = -\frac{1}{2}, v(x) = e^{\int(-\frac{1}{2})dx} = e^{-x/2}$.
   $e^{-x/2}y' - \frac{1}{2}e^{-x/2}y = (e^{-x/2})(\frac{x}{2})(e^{x/2}) = \frac{x}{2} \Rightarrow \frac{d}{dx}(e^{-x/2}y) = \frac{x}{2} \Rightarrow e^{-x/2}y = \frac{x^2}{4} + C \Rightarrow y = e^{x/2}\left(\frac{x^2}{4} + C\right)$

10. $\frac{y'}{2} + y = e^{-x}\sin x \Rightarrow y' + 2y = 2e^{-x}\sin x$.
    $p(x) = 2, v(x) = e^{\int 2dx} = e^{2x}$.
    $e^{2x}y' + 2e^{2x}y = 2e^{2x}e^{-x}\sin x = 2e^x\sin x \Rightarrow \frac{d}{dx}(e^{2x}y) = 2e^x\sin x \Rightarrow e^{2x}y = e^x(\sin x - \cos x) + C$
    $\Rightarrow y = e^{-x}(\sin x - \cos x) + Ce^{-2x}$

11. $xy' + 2y = 1 - x^{-1} \Rightarrow y' + \left(\frac{2}{x}\right)y = \frac{1}{x} - \frac{1}{x^2}$.

$v(x) = e^{2\int \frac{dx}{x}} = e^{2\ln x} = e^{\ln x^2} = x^2$.

$x^2y' + 2xy = x - 1 \Rightarrow \frac{d}{dx}(x^2y) = x - 1 \Rightarrow x^2y = \frac{x^2}{2} - x + C \Rightarrow y = \frac{1}{2} - \frac{1}{x} + \frac{C}{x^2}$

12. $xy' - y = 2x \ln x \Rightarrow y' - \left(\frac{1}{x}\right)y = 2\ln x$.

$v(x) = e^{-\int \frac{dx}{x}} = e^{-\ln x} = \frac{1}{x}$. $\left(\frac{1}{x}\right)y' - \left(\frac{1}{x}\right)^2 y = \frac{2}{x}\ln x \Rightarrow$

$\frac{d}{dx}\left(\frac{1}{x} \cdot y\right) = \frac{2}{x}\ln x \Rightarrow \frac{1}{x} \cdot y = [\ln x]^2 + C \Rightarrow y = x[\ln x]^2 + Cx$

13. $(1 + e^x)dy + (ye^x + e^{-x})dx = 0 \Rightarrow (1 + e^x)y' + e^xy = -e^{-x} \Rightarrow y' = \frac{e^x}{1+e^x}y = \frac{-e^{-x}}{(1+e^x)}$.

$v(x) = e^{\int \frac{e^x dx}{(1+e^x)}} = e^{\ln(e^x+1)} = e^x + 1$.

$(e^x + 1)y' + (e^x + 1)\left(\frac{e^x}{1+e^x}\right)y = \frac{-e^{-x}}{(1+e^x)}(e^x + 1) \Rightarrow \frac{d}{dx}[(e^x + 1)y] = -e^{-x} \Rightarrow (e^x + 1)y = e^{-x} + C$

$\Rightarrow y = \frac{e^{-x}+C}{e^x+1} = \frac{e^{-x}+C}{1+e^x}$

14. $e^{-x} dy + (e^{-x} y - 4x)dx = 0 \Rightarrow \frac{dy}{dx} + y = 4x e^x \Rightarrow p(x) = 1, v(x) = e^{\int 1dx} = e^x \Rightarrow e^x \frac{dy}{dx} + y e^x = 4x e^{2x}$

$\Rightarrow \frac{d}{dx}(y e^x) = 4x e^{2x} \Rightarrow y e^x = \int 4x e^{2x} dx \Rightarrow y e^x = 2x e^{2x} - e^{2x} + C \Rightarrow y = 2x e^x - e^x + C e^{-x}$

15. $(x + 3y^2) dy + y dx = 0 \Rightarrow x dy + y dx = -3y^2 dy \Rightarrow \frac{d}{dx}(xy) = -3y^2 dy \Rightarrow xy = -y^3 + C$

16. $x dy + (3y - x^{-2}\cos x) dx = 0 \Rightarrow y' + \left(\frac{3}{x}\right)y = x^{-3}\cos x$. Let $v(y) = e^{\int \frac{3dx}{x}} = e^{3\ln x} = e^{\ln x^3} = x^3$.

Then $x^3 y' + 3x^2 y = \cos x$ and $x^3 y = \int \cos x\, dx = \sin x + C$. So $y = x^{-3}(\sin x + C)$

17. $(x + 1)\frac{dy}{dx} + 2y = x \Rightarrow y' + \left(\frac{2}{x+1}\right)y = \frac{x}{x+1}$. Let $v(x) = e^{\int \frac{2}{x+1}dx} = e^{2\ln(x+1)} = e^{\ln(x+1)^2} = (x + 1)^2$.

So $y'(x + 1)^2 + \frac{2}{(x+1)}(x + 1)^2 y = \frac{x}{(x+1)}(x + 1)^2 \Rightarrow \frac{d}{dx}[y(x + 1)^2] = x(x + 1) \Rightarrow y(x + 1)^2 = \int x(x + 1)dx$

$\Rightarrow y(x + 1)^2 = \frac{x^3}{3} + \frac{x^2}{2} + C \Rightarrow y = (x + 1)^{-2}\left(\frac{x^3}{3} + \frac{x^2}{2} + C\right)$. We have $y(0) = 1 \Rightarrow 1 = C$. So

$y = (x + 1)^{-2}\left(\frac{x^3}{3} + \frac{x^2}{2} + 1\right)$

18. $x\frac{dy}{dx} + 2y = x^2 + 1 \Rightarrow y' + \left(\frac{2}{x}\right)y = x + \frac{1}{x}$. Let $v(x) = e^{\int \left(\frac{2}{x}\right)dx} = e^{\ln x^2} = x^2$. So $x^2y' + 2xy = x^3 + x$

$\Rightarrow \frac{d}{dx}(x^2y) = x^3 + x \Rightarrow x^2y = \frac{x^4}{4} + \frac{x^2}{2} + C \Rightarrow y = \frac{x^2}{4} + \frac{C}{x^2} + \frac{1}{2}$. We have $y(1) = 1 \Rightarrow 1 = \frac{1}{4} + C + \frac{1}{2} \Rightarrow C = \frac{1}{4}$.

So $y = \frac{x^2}{4} + \frac{1}{4x^2} + \frac{1}{2} = \frac{x^4 + 2x^2 + 1}{4x^2}$

19. $\frac{dy}{dx} + 3x^2y = x^2$. Let $v(x) = e^{\int 3x^2dx} = e^{x^3}$. So $e^{x^3}y' + 3x^2e^{x^3}y = x^2e^{x^3} \Rightarrow \frac{d}{dx}\left(e^{x^3}y\right) = x^2e^{x^3} \Rightarrow e^{x^3}y = \frac{1}{3}e^{x^3} + C$.

We have $y(0) = -1 \Rightarrow e^{0^3}(-1) = \frac{1}{3}e^{0^3} + C \Rightarrow -1 = \frac{1}{3} + C \Rightarrow C = -\frac{4}{3}$ and $e^{x^3}y = \frac{1}{3}e^{x^3} - \frac{4}{3} \Rightarrow y = \frac{1}{3} - \frac{4}{3}e^{-x^3}$

20. $xdy + (y - \cos x)dx = 0 \Rightarrow xy' + y - \cos x = 0 \Rightarrow y' + \left(\frac{1}{x}\right)y = \frac{\cos x}{x}$. Let $v(x) = e^{\int \frac{1}{x}dx} = e^{\ln x} = x$.

So $xy' + x\left(\frac{1}{x}\right)y = \cos x \Rightarrow \frac{d}{dx}(xy) = \cos x \Rightarrow xy = \int \cos x\, dx \Rightarrow xy = \sin x + C$. We have $y\left(\frac{\pi}{2}\right) = 0 \Rightarrow \left(\frac{\pi}{2}\right)0 = 1 + C$

$\Rightarrow C = -1$. So $xy = -1 + \sin x \Rightarrow y = \frac{-1+\sin x}{x}$

21. $xy' + (x - 2)y = 3x^3e^{-x} \Rightarrow y' + \left(\frac{x-2}{x}\right)y = 3x^2e^{-x}$. Let $v(x) = e^{\int \left(\frac{x-2}{x}\right)dx} = e^{x-2\ln x} = \frac{e^x}{x^2}$. So

$\frac{e^x}{x^2}y' + \frac{e^x}{x^2}\left(\frac{x-2}{x}\right)y = 3 \Rightarrow \frac{d}{dx}\left(y \cdot \frac{e^x}{x^2}\right) = 3 \Rightarrow y \cdot \frac{e^x}{x^2} = 3x + C$. We have $y(1) = 0 \Rightarrow 0 = 3(1) + C \Rightarrow C = -3$

$\Rightarrow y \cdot \frac{e^x}{x^2} = 3x - 3 \Rightarrow y = x^2e^{-x}(3x - 3)$

22. $y\,dx + (3x - xy + 2)dy = 0 \Rightarrow \frac{dx}{dy} + \frac{3x - xy + 2}{y} = 0 \Rightarrow \frac{dx}{dy} + \frac{3x}{y} - x = -\frac{2}{y} \Rightarrow \frac{dx}{dy} + \left(\frac{3}{y} - 1\right)x = -\frac{2}{y}$.

$P(y) = \frac{3}{y} - 1 \Rightarrow \int P(y)dy = 3\ln y - y \Rightarrow v(y) = e^{3\ln y - y} = y^3 e^{-y}$

$y^3 e^{-y}x' + y^3 e^{-y}\left(\frac{3}{y} - 1\right)x = -2y^2 e^{-y} \Rightarrow y^3 e^{-y}x = \int -2y^2 e^{-y}dy = 2e^{-y}(y^2 + 2y + 2) + C$

$\Rightarrow y^3 = \frac{2(y^2 + 2y + 2) + Ce^y}{x}$. We have $y(2) = -1 \Rightarrow -1 = \frac{2(1 - 2 + 2) + Ce^{-1}}{2} \Rightarrow C = -4e$ and

$\Rightarrow y^3 = \frac{2(y^2 + 2y + 2) - 4e^{y+1}}{x}$

23. To find the approximate values let $y_n = y_{n-1} + (y_{n-1} + \cos x_{n-1})(0.1)$ with $x_0 = 0$, $y_0 = 0$, and 20 steps. Use a spreadsheet, graphing calculator, or CAS to obtain the values in the following table.

| x | y | | x | y |
|---|---|---|---|---|
| 0 | 0 | | 1.1 | 1.6241 |
| 0.1 | 0.1000 | | 1.2 | 1.8319 |
| 0.2 | 0.2095 | | 1.3 | 2.0513 |
| 0.3 | 0.3285 | | 1.4 | 2.2832 |
| 0.4 | 0.4568 | | 1.5 | 2.5285 |
| 0.5 | 0.5946 | | 1.6 | 2.7884 |
| 0.6 | 0.7418 | | 1.7 | 3.0643 |
| 0.7 | 0.8986 | | 1.8 | 3.3579 |
| 0.8 | 1.0649 | | 1.9 | 3.6709 |
| 0.9 | 1.2411 | | 2.0 | 4.0057 |
| 1.0 | 1.4273 | | | |

24. To find the approximate values let $y_n = y_{n-1} + (2 - y_{n-1})(2x_{n-1} + 3)(0.1)$ with $x_0 = -3$, $y_0 = 1$, and 20 steps. Use a spreadsheet, graphing calculator, or CAS to obtain the values in the following table.

| x | y | | x | y |
|---|---|---|---|---|
| −3.0 | 1.0000 | | −1.9 | −5.3172 |
| −2.9 | 0.7000 | | −1.8 | −5.9026 |
| −2.8 | 0.3360 | | −1.7 | −6.3768 |
| −2.7 | −0.0966 | | −1.6 | −6.7119 |
| −2.6 | −0.5998 | | −1.5 | −6.8861 |
| −2.5 | −1.1718 | | −1.4 | −6.8861 |
| −2.4 | −1.8062 | | −1.3 | −6.7084 |
| −2.3 | −2.4913 | | −1.2 | −6.3601 |
| −2.2 | −3.2099 | | −1.1 | −5.8585 |
| −2.1 | −3.9393 | | −1.0 | −5.2298 |
| −2.0 | −4.6520 | | | |

25. To estimate $y(3)$, let $y = y_{n-1} + \left(\frac{x_{n-1} - 2y_{n-1}}{x_{n-1} + 1}\right)(0.05)$ with initial values $x_0 = 0$, $y_0 = 1$, and 60 steps. Use a spreadsheet, graphing calculator, or CAS to obtain $y(3) \approx 0.8981$.

26. To estimate $y(4)$, let $z_n = y_{n-1} + \left(\frac{x_{n-1}^2 - 2y_{n-1} + 1}{x_{n-1}}\right)(0.05)$ with initial values $x_0 = 1$, $y_0 = 1$, and 60 steps. Use a spreadsheet, graphing calculator, or CAS to obtain $y(4) \approx 4.4974$.

27. Let $y_n = y_{n-1} + \left(\frac{1}{e^{x_{n-1} + y_{n-1} + 2}}\right)(dx)$ with starting values $x_0 = 0$ and $y_0 = 2$, and steps of 0.1 and −0.1. Use a spreadsheet, programmable calculator, or CAS to generate the following graphs.

(a)

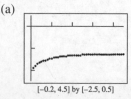

[−0.2, 4.5] by [−2.5, 0.5]

(b) Note that we choose a small interval of x-values because the y-values decrease very rapidly and our calculator cannot handle the calculations for $x \le -1$. (This occurs because the analytic solution is $y = -2 + \ln(2 - e^{-x})$, which has an asymptote at $x = -\ln 2 \approx 0.69$. Obviously, the Euler approximations are misleading for $x \le -0.7$.)

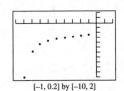

[-1, 0.2] by [-10, 2]

28. Let $y_n = y_{n-1} - \left(\frac{x_{n-1}^2 + y_{n-1}}{e^{y_{n-1}} + x_{n-1}}\right)(dx)$ with starting values $x_0 = 0$ and $y_0 = 0$, and steps of 0.1 and $-0.1$. Use a spreadsheet, programmable calculator, or CAS to generate the following graphs.

(a)

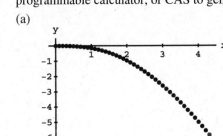

(b)

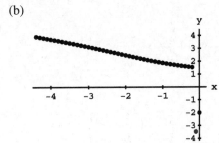

29.

| x | 1 | 1.2 | 1.4 | 1.6 | 1.8 | 2.0 |
|---|---|---|---|---|---|---|
| y | $-1$ | $-0.8$ | $-0.56$ | $-0.28$ | 0.04 | 0.4 |

$\frac{dy}{dx} = x \Rightarrow dy = x\,dx \Rightarrow y = \frac{x^2}{2} + C; x = 1$ and $y = -1$

$\Rightarrow -1 = \frac{1}{2} + C \Rightarrow C = -\frac{3}{2} \Rightarrow y(\text{exact}) = \frac{x^2}{2} - \frac{3}{2}$

$\Rightarrow y(2) = \frac{2^2}{2} - \frac{3}{2} = \frac{1}{2}$ is the exact value.

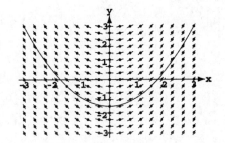

30.

| x | 1 | 1.2 | 1.4 | 1.6 | 1.8 | 2.0 |
|---|---|---|---|---|---|---|
| y | $-1$ | $-0.8$ | $-0.6333$ | $-0.4904$ | $-0.3654$ | $-0.2544$ |

$\frac{dy}{dx} = \frac{1}{x} \Rightarrow dy = \frac{1}{x}dx \Rightarrow y = \ln|x| + C; x = 1$ and $y = -1$

$\Rightarrow -1 = \ln 1 + C \Rightarrow C = -1 \Rightarrow y(\text{exact}) = \ln|x| - 1$

$\Rightarrow y(2) = \ln 2 - 1 \approx -0.3069$ is the exact value.

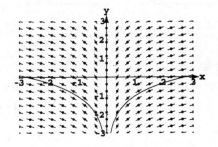

31.

| x | 1 | 1.2 | 1.4 | 1.6 | 1.8 | 2.0 |
|---|---|---|---|---|---|---|
| y | $-1$ | $-1.2$ | $-0.488$ | $-1.9046$ | $-2.5141$ | $-3.4192$ |

$\frac{dy}{dx} = xy \Rightarrow \frac{dy}{y} = x\,dx \Rightarrow \ln|y| = \frac{x^2}{2} + C$

$\Rightarrow y = e^{\frac{x^2}{2}+C} = e^{\frac{x^2}{2}} \cdot e^C = C_1 e^{\frac{x^2}{2}}; x = 1$ and $y = -1$

$\Rightarrow -1 = C_1 e^{1/2} \Rightarrow C_1 = -e^{1/2} y(\text{exact}) = -e^{1/2} \cdot e^{\frac{x^2}{2}}$

$= -e^{(x^2-1)/2} \Rightarrow y(2) = -e^{3/2} \approx -4.4817$ is the exact value.

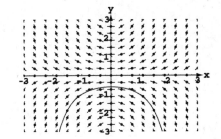

32.

| x | 1 | 1.2 | 1.4 | 1.6 | 1.8 | 2.0 |
|---|---|-----|-----|-----|-----|-----|
| y | −1 | −1.2 | −1.3667 | −1.5130 | −1.6452 | −1.7688 |

$\frac{dy}{dx} = \frac{1}{y} \Rightarrow y\,dy = dx \Rightarrow \frac{y^2}{2} = x + C$; $x = 1$ and $y = -1$

$\frac{1}{2} = 1 + C \Rightarrow C = -\frac{1}{2} \Rightarrow y^2 = 2x - 1$

$\Rightarrow y(\text{exact}) = \sqrt{2x - 1} \Rightarrow y(2) = -\sqrt{3} \approx -1.7321$ is the exact value.

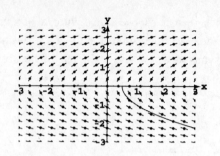

33. $\frac{dy}{dx} = y^2 - 1 \Rightarrow y' = (y+1)(y-1)$. We have $y' = 0 \Rightarrow (y+1) = 0, (y-1) = 0 \Rightarrow y = -1, 1$.

(a) Equilibrium points are $-1$ (stable) and $1$ (unstable)

(b) $y' = y^2 - 1 \Rightarrow y'' = 2yy' \Rightarrow y'' = 2y(y^2 - 1) = 2y(y+1)(y-1)$. So $y'' = 0 \Rightarrow y = 0, y = -1, y = 1$.

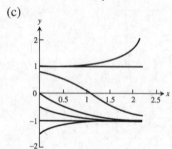

(c)

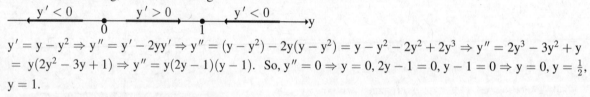

34. $\frac{dy}{dx} = y - y^2 \Rightarrow y' = y(1 - y)$. We have $y' = 0 \Rightarrow y(1-y) = 0 \Rightarrow y = 0, 1 - y = 0 \Rightarrow y = 0, 1$.

(a) The equilibrium points are $0$ and $1$. So, $0$ is unstable and $1$ is stable.

(b) Let $\longrightarrow$ = increasing, $\longleftarrow$ = decreasing.

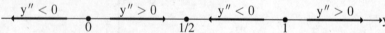

$y' = y - y^2 \Rightarrow y'' = y' - 2yy' \Rightarrow y'' = (y - y^2) - 2y(y - y^2) = y - y^2 - 2y^2 + 2y^3 \Rightarrow y'' = 2y^3 - 3y^2 + y$
$= y(2y^2 - 3y + 1) \Rightarrow y'' = y(2y - 1)(y - 1)$. So, $y'' = 0 \Rightarrow y = 0, 2y - 1 = 0, y - 1 = 0 \Rightarrow y = 0, y = \frac{1}{2}$,
$y = 1$.

Let $\longrightarrow$ = concave up, $\longleftarrow$ = concave down.

(c)

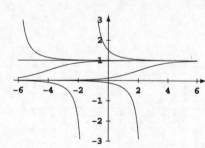

35. (a) Force = Mass times Acceleration (Newton's Second Law) or $F = ma$. Let $a = \frac{dv}{dt} = \frac{dv}{ds} \cdot \frac{ds}{dt} = v\frac{dv}{ds}$. Then

$ma = -mgR^2s^{-2} \Rightarrow a = -gR^2s^{-2} \Rightarrow v\frac{dv}{ds} = -gR^2s^{-2} \Rightarrow v\,dv = -gR^2s^{-2}ds \Rightarrow \int v\,dv = \int -gR^2s^{-2}ds$

$\Rightarrow \frac{v^2}{2} = \frac{gR^2}{s} + C_1 \Rightarrow v^2 = \frac{2gR^2}{s} + 2C_1 = \frac{2gR^2}{s} + C$. When $t = 0$, $v = v_0$ and $s = R \Rightarrow v_0^2 = \frac{2gR^2}{R} + C$

$\Rightarrow C = v_0^2 - 2gR \Rightarrow v^2 = \frac{2gR^2}{s} + v_0^2 - 2gR$

(b) If $v_0 = \sqrt{2gR}$, then $v^2 = \frac{2gR^2}{s} \Rightarrow v = \sqrt{\frac{2gR^2}{s}}$, since $v \geq 0$ if $v_0 \geq \sqrt{2gR}$. Then $\frac{ds}{dt} = \frac{\sqrt{2gR^2}}{\sqrt{s}} \Rightarrow \sqrt{s}\, ds = \sqrt{2gR^2}\, dt$

$\Rightarrow \int s^{1/2} ds = \int \sqrt{2gR^2}\, dt \Rightarrow \frac{2}{3} s^{3/2} = \sqrt{2gR^2}\, t + C_1 \Rightarrow s^{3/2} = \left(\frac{3}{2}\sqrt{2gR^2}\right) t + C; \, t = 0$ and $s = R$

$\Rightarrow R^{3/2} = \left(\frac{3}{2}\sqrt{2gR^2}\right)(0) + C \Rightarrow C = R^{3/2} \Rightarrow s^{3/2} = \left(\frac{3}{2}\sqrt{2gR^2}\right) t + R^{3/2} = \left(\frac{3}{2}R\sqrt{2g}\right) t + R^{3/2}$

$= R^{3/2}\left[\left(\frac{3}{2}R^{-1/2}\sqrt{2g}\right) t + 1\right] = R^{3/2}\left[\left(\frac{3\sqrt{2gR}}{2R}\right) t + 1\right] = R^{3/2}\left[\left(\frac{3v_0}{2R}\right) t + 1\right] \Rightarrow s = R\left[1 + \left(\frac{3v_0}{2R}\right) t\right]^{2/3}$

36. $\frac{v_0 m}{k} = $ coasting distance $\Rightarrow \frac{(0.86)(30.84)}{k} = 0.97 \Rightarrow k \approx 27.343$. $s(t) = \frac{v_0 m}{k}\left(1 - e^{-(k/m)t}\right) \Rightarrow s(t) = 0.97\left(1 - e^{-(27.343/30.84)t}\right)$

$\Rightarrow s(t) = 0.97(1 - e^{-0.8866t})$. A graph of the model is shown superimposed on a graph of the data.

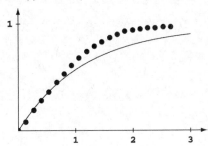

## CHAPTER 9 ADDITIONAL AND ADVANCED EXERCISES

1. (a) $\frac{dy}{dt} = k\frac{A}{V}(c - y) \Rightarrow dy = -k\frac{A}{V}(y - c)dt \Rightarrow \frac{dy}{y-c} = -k\frac{A}{V}dt \Rightarrow \int \frac{dy}{y-c} = -\int k\frac{A}{V}dt \Rightarrow \ln|y - c| = -k\frac{A}{V}t + C_1$

$\Rightarrow y - c = \pm e^{C_1}e^{-k\frac{A}{V}t}$. Apply the initial condition, $y(0) = y_0 \Rightarrow y_0 = c + C \Rightarrow C = y_0 - c$

$\Rightarrow y = c + (y_0 - c)e^{-k\frac{A}{V}t}$.

(b) Steady state solution: $y_\infty = \lim_{t\to\infty} y(t) = \lim_{t\to\infty}\left[c + (y_0 - c)e^{-k\frac{A}{V}t}\right] = c + (y_0 - c)(0) = c$

2. $\frac{d(mv)}{dt} = F + (v + u)\frac{dm}{dt} \Rightarrow F = \frac{d(mv)}{dt} - (v + u)\frac{dm}{dt} \Rightarrow F = m\frac{dv}{dt} + v\frac{dm}{dt} - v\frac{dm}{dt} - u\frac{dm}{dt} \Rightarrow F = m\frac{dv}{dt} - u\frac{dm}{dt}$.

$\frac{dm}{dt} = -b \Rightarrow m = -|b|t + C$. At $t = 0$, $m = m_0$, so $C = m_0$ and $m = m_0 - |b|t$.

Thus, $F = (m_0 - |b|t)\frac{dv}{dt} - u|b| = -(m_0 - |b|t)|g| \Rightarrow \frac{dv}{dt} = -g + \frac{u|b|}{m_0 - |b|t} \Rightarrow v = -gt - u\ln\left(\frac{m_0 - |b|t}{m_0}\right) + C_1$

$v = 0$ at $t = 0 \Rightarrow C_1 = 0$. So $v = -gt - u\ln\left(\frac{m_0 - |b|t}{m_0}\right) = \frac{dy}{dt} \Rightarrow y = \int\left[-gt - u\ln\left(\frac{m_0 - |b|t}{m_0}\right)\right] dt$ and $u = c$, $y = 0$ at

$t = 0 \Rightarrow y = -\frac{1}{2}gt^2 + c\left[t + \left(\frac{m_0 - |b|t}{|b|}\right)\ln\left(\frac{m_0 - |b|t}{m_0}\right)\right]$

3. (a) Let y be any function such that $v(x)y = \int v(x)Q(x)\, dx + C$, $v(x) = e^{\int P(x)\, dx}$. Then

$\frac{d}{dx}(v(x) \cdot y) = v(x) \cdot y' + y \cdot v'(x) = v(x)Q(x)$. We have $v(x) = e^{\int P(x)\, dx} \Rightarrow v'(x) = e^{\int P(x)\, dx}P(x) = v(x)P(x)$.

Thus $v(x) \cdot y' + y \cdot v(x)P(x) = v(x)Q(x) \Rightarrow y' + yP(x) = Q(x) \Rightarrow$ the given y is a solution.

(b) If v and Q are continuous on $[a, b]$ and $x \in (a, b)$, then $\frac{d}{dx}\left[\int_{x_0}^{x} v(t)Q(t)\, dt\right] = v(x)Q(x)$

$\Rightarrow \int_{x_0}^{x} v(t)Q(t)\, dt = \int v(x)Q(x)\, dx$. So $C = y_0 v(x_0) - \int v(x)Q(x)\, dx$. From part (a), $v(x)y = \int v(x)Q(x)\, dx + C$.

Substituting for C: $v(x)y = \int v(x)Q(x)\, dx + y_0 v(x_0) - \int v(x)Q(x)\, dx \Rightarrow v(x)y = y_0 v(x_0)$ when $x = x_0$.

4. (a) $y' + P(x)y = 0$, $y(x_0) = 0$. Use $v(x) = e^{\int P(x)\, dx}$ as an integrating factor. Then $\frac{d}{dx}(v(x)y) = 0 \Rightarrow v(x)y = C$

$\Rightarrow y = Ce^{-\int P(x)\, dx}$ and $y_1 = C_1 e^{-\int P(x)\, dx}$, $y_2 = C_2 e^{-\int P(x)\, dx}$, $y_1(x_0) = y_2(x_0) = 0$, $y_1 - y_2 = (C_1 - C_2)e^{-\int P(x)\, dx}$

$= C_3 e^{-\int P(x)\, dx}$ and $y_1 - y_2 = 0 - 0 = 0$. So $y_1 - y_2$ is a solution to $y' + P(x)y = 0$ with $y(x_0) = 0$.

(b) $\frac{d}{dx}(v(x)[y_1(x) - y_2(x)]) = \frac{d}{dx}\left(e^{\int P(x)\, dx}\left[e^{-\int P(x)\, dx}(C_1 - C_2)\right]\right) = \frac{d}{dx}(C_1 - C_2) = \frac{d}{dx}(C_3) = 0$.

$\int \frac{d}{dx}(v(x)[y_1(x) - y_2(x)])dx = (v(x)[y_1(x) - y_2(x)]) = \int 0\, dx = C$

(c) $y_1 = C_1 e^{-\int P(x)\,dx}$, $y_2 = C_2 e^{-\int P(x)\,dx}$, $y = y_1 - y_2$. So $y(x_0) = 0 \Rightarrow C_1 e^{-\int P(x)\,dx} - C_2 e^{-\int P(x)\,dx} = 0$
$\Rightarrow C_1 - C_2 = 0 \Rightarrow C_1 = C_2 \Rightarrow y_1(x) = y_2(x)$ for $a < x < b$.

5. $(x^2 + y^2)dx + xy\,dy = 0 \Rightarrow \frac{dy}{dx} = \frac{-(x^2+y^2)}{xy} = -\frac{x}{y} - \frac{y}{x} = -\frac{1}{y/x} - \frac{y}{x} = F\left(\frac{y}{x}\right) \Rightarrow F(v) = -\frac{1}{v} - v \Rightarrow \frac{dx}{x} + \frac{dv}{v - F(v)} = 0$

$\Rightarrow \frac{dx}{x} + \frac{dv}{v - \left(-\frac{1}{v} - v\right)} = 0 \Rightarrow \int \frac{dx}{x} + \int \frac{v\,dv}{2v^2 + 1} = C \Rightarrow \ln|x| + \frac{1}{4}\ln|2v^2 + 1| = C \Rightarrow 4\ln|x| + \ln\left|2\left(\frac{y}{x}\right)^2 + 1\right| = C$

$\Rightarrow \ln|x^4| + \ln\left|\frac{2y^2 + x^2}{x^2}\right| = C \Rightarrow \ln\left|x^2(2y^2 + x^2)\right| = C \Rightarrow x^2(2y^2 + x^2) = e^C \Rightarrow x^2(2y^2 + x^2) = C$

6. $x^2\,dy + (y^2 - xy)dx = 0 \Rightarrow \frac{dy}{dx} = \frac{-(y^2 - xy)}{x^2} \Rightarrow \frac{dy}{dx} = -\left(\frac{y}{x}\right)^2 + \frac{y}{x} = F\left(\frac{y}{x}\right) \Rightarrow F(v) = -v^2 + v \Rightarrow \frac{dx}{x} + \frac{dv}{v - (-v^2 + v)} = 0$

$\Rightarrow \int \frac{dx}{x} + \int \frac{dv}{v^2} = C \Rightarrow \ln|x| - \frac{1}{v} = C \Rightarrow \ln|x| - \frac{1}{y/x} = C \Rightarrow \ln|x| - \frac{x}{y} = C$

7. $\left(xe^{y/x} + y\right)dx - x\,dy = 0 \Rightarrow \frac{dy}{dx} = \frac{xe^{y/x} + y}{x} = e^{y/x} + \frac{y}{x} = F\left(\frac{y}{x}\right) \Rightarrow F(v) = e^v + v \Rightarrow \frac{dx}{x} + \frac{dv}{v - (e^v + v)} = 0$

$\Rightarrow \int \frac{dx}{x} - \int \frac{dv}{e^v} = C \Rightarrow \ln|x| + e^{-v} = C \Rightarrow \ln|x| + e^{-y/x} = C$

8. $(x + y)dy + (x - y)dx = 0 \Rightarrow \frac{dy}{dx} = \frac{-(x - y)}{x + y} = \frac{\frac{y}{x} - 1}{1 + \frac{y}{x}} = F\left(\frac{y}{x}\right) \Rightarrow F(v) = \frac{v - 1}{1 + v} \Rightarrow \frac{dx}{x} + \frac{dv}{v - \left(\frac{v-1}{1+v}\right)} = 0$

$\Rightarrow \int \frac{dx}{x} + \int \frac{(1 + v)dv}{v^2 + 1} = 0 \Rightarrow \int \frac{dx}{x} + \int \frac{dv}{v^2 + 1} + \int \frac{v\,dv}{v^2 + 1} = 0 \Rightarrow \ln|x| + \tan^{-1}v + \frac{1}{2}\ln|v^2 + 1| = C$

$\Rightarrow 2\ln|x| + 2\tan^{-1}v + \ln\left|\left(\frac{y}{x}\right)^2 + 1\right| = C \Rightarrow \ln|x^2| + 2\tan^{-1}\left(\frac{y}{x}\right) + \ln\left|\frac{y^2 + x^2}{x^2}\right| = C \Rightarrow 2\tan^{-1}\left(\frac{y}{x}\right) + \ln\left|y^2 + x^2\right| = C$

9. $y' = \frac{y}{x} + \cos\left(\frac{y - x}{x}\right) = \frac{y}{x} + \cos\left(\frac{y}{x} - 1\right) = F\left(\frac{y}{x}\right) \Rightarrow F(v) = v + \cos(v - 1) \Rightarrow \frac{dx}{x} + \frac{dv}{v - (v + \cos(v - 1))} = 0$

$\Rightarrow \int \frac{dx}{x} - \int \sec(v - 1)\,dv = 0 \Rightarrow \ln|x| - \ln|\sec(v - 1) + \tan(v - 1)| = C \Rightarrow \ln|x| - \ln\left|\sec\left(\frac{y}{x} - 1\right) + \tan\left(\frac{y}{x} - 1\right)\right| = C$

10. $\left(x\sin\frac{y}{x} - y\cos\frac{y}{x}\right)dx + x\cos\frac{y}{x}\,dy = 0 \Rightarrow \frac{dy}{dx} = \frac{-\left(x\sin\frac{y}{x} - y\cos\frac{y}{x}\right)}{x\cos\frac{y}{x}} = \frac{y}{x} - \tan\frac{y}{x} = F\left(\frac{y}{x}\right) \Rightarrow F(v) = v - \tan v$

$\Rightarrow \frac{dx}{x} + \frac{dv}{v - (v - \tan v)} = 0 \Rightarrow \int \frac{dx}{x} + \int \cot v\,dv = 0 \Rightarrow \ln|x| + \ln|\sin v| = C \Rightarrow \ln|x| + \ln\left|\sin\frac{y}{x}\right| = C$

# CHAPTER 10  INFINITE SEQUENCES AND SERIES

## 10.1 SEQUENCES

1. $a_1 = \frac{1-1}{1^2} = 0$, $a_2 = \frac{1-2}{2^2} = -\frac{1}{4}$, $a_3 = \frac{1-3}{3^2} = -\frac{2}{9}$, $a_4 = \frac{1-4}{4^2} = -\frac{3}{16}$

2. $a_1 = \frac{1}{1!} = 1$, $a_2 = \frac{1}{2!} = \frac{1}{2}$, $a_3 = \frac{1}{3!} = \frac{1}{6}$, $a_4 = \frac{1}{4!} = \frac{1}{24}$

3. $a_1 = \frac{(-1)^2}{2-1} = 1$, $a_2 = \frac{(-1)^3}{4-1} = -\frac{1}{3}$, $a_3 = \frac{(-1)^4}{6-1} = \frac{1}{5}$, $a_4 = \frac{(-1)^5}{8-1} = -\frac{1}{7}$

4. $a_1 = 2 + (-1)^1 = 1$, $a_2 = 2 + (-1)^2 = 3$, $a_3 = 2 + (-1)^3 = 1$, $a_4 = 2 + (-1)^4 = 3$

5. $a_1 = \frac{2}{2^2} = \frac{1}{2}$, $a_2 = \frac{2^2}{2^3} = \frac{1}{2}$, $a_3 = \frac{2^3}{2^4} = \frac{1}{2}$, $a_4 = \frac{2^4}{2^5} = \frac{1}{2}$

6. $a_1 = \frac{2-1}{2} = \frac{1}{2}$, $a_2 = \frac{2^2-1}{2^2} = \frac{3}{4}$, $a_3 = \frac{2^3-1}{2^3} = \frac{7}{8}$, $a_4 = \frac{2^4-1}{2^4} = \frac{15}{16}$

7. $a_1 = 1$, $a_2 = 1 + \frac{1}{2} = \frac{3}{2}$, $a_3 = \frac{3}{2} + \frac{1}{2^2} = \frac{7}{4}$, $a_4 = \frac{7}{4} + \frac{1}{2^3} = \frac{15}{8}$, $a_5 = \frac{15}{8} + \frac{1}{2^4} = \frac{31}{16}$, $a_6 = \frac{63}{32}$,
   $a_7 = \frac{127}{64}$, $a_8 = \frac{255}{128}$, $a_9 = \frac{511}{256}$, $a_{10} = \frac{1023}{512}$

8. $a_1 = 1$, $a_2 = \frac{1}{2}$, $a_3 = \frac{\left(\frac{1}{2}\right)}{3} = \frac{1}{6}$, $a_4 = \frac{\left(\frac{1}{6}\right)}{4} = \frac{1}{24}$, $a_5 = \frac{\left(\frac{1}{24}\right)}{5} = \frac{1}{120}$, $a_6 = \frac{1}{720}$, $a_7 = \frac{1}{5040}$, $a_8 = \frac{1}{40,320}$,
   $a_9 = \frac{1}{362,880}$, $a_{10} = \frac{1}{3,628,800}$

9. $a_1 = 2$, $a_2 = \frac{(-1)^2(2)}{2} = 1$, $a_3 = \frac{(-1)^3(1)}{2} = -\frac{1}{2}$, $a_4 = \frac{(-1)^4\left(-\frac{1}{2}\right)}{2} = -\frac{1}{4}$, $a_5 = \frac{(-1)^5\left(-\frac{1}{4}\right)}{2} = \frac{1}{8}$,
   $a_6 = \frac{1}{16}$, $a_7 = -\frac{1}{32}$, $a_8 = -\frac{1}{64}$, $a_9 = \frac{1}{128}$, $a_{10} = \frac{1}{256}$

10. $a_1 = -2$, $a_2 = \frac{1\cdot(-2)}{2} = -1$, $a_3 = \frac{2\cdot(-1)}{3} = -\frac{2}{3}$, $a_4 = \frac{3\cdot\left(-\frac{2}{3}\right)}{4} = -\frac{1}{2}$, $a_5 = \frac{4\cdot\left(-\frac{1}{2}\right)}{5} = -\frac{2}{5}$, $a_6 = -\frac{1}{3}$,
   $a_7 = -\frac{2}{7}$, $a_8 = -\frac{1}{4}$, $a_9 = -\frac{2}{9}$, $a_{10} = -\frac{1}{5}$

11. $a_1 = 1$, $a_2 = 1$, $a_3 = 1 + 1 = 2$, $a_4 = 2 + 1 = 3$, $a_5 = 3 + 2 = 5$, $a_6 = 8$, $a_7 = 13$, $a_8 = 21$, $a_9 = 34$, $a_{10} = 55$

12. $a_1 = 2$, $a_2 = -1$, $a_3 = -\frac{1}{2}$, $a_4 = \frac{\left(-\frac{1}{2}\right)}{-1} = \frac{1}{2}$, $a_5 = \frac{\left(\frac{1}{2}\right)}{\left(-\frac{1}{2}\right)} = -1$, $a_6 = -2$, $a_7 = 2$, $a_8 = -1$, $a_9 = -\frac{1}{2}$, $a_{10} = \frac{1}{2}$

13. $a_n = (-1)^{n+1}$, $n = 1, 2, \ldots$

14. $a_n = (-1)^n$, $n = 1, 2, \ldots$

15. $a_n = (-1)^{n+1}n^2$, $n = 1, 2, \ldots$

16. $a_n = \frac{(-1)^{n+1}}{n^2}$, $n = 1, 2, \ldots$

17. $a_n = \frac{2^{n-1}}{3(n+2)}$, $n = 1, 2, \ldots$

18. $a_n = \frac{2n-5}{n(n+1)}$, $n = 1, 2, \ldots$

19. $a_n = n^2 - 1$, $n = 1, 2, \ldots$

20. $a_n = n - 4$, $n = 1, 2, \ldots$

21. $a_n = 4n - 3$, $n = 1, 2, \ldots$

22. $a_n = 4n - 2$, $n = 1, 2, \ldots$

23. $a_n = \frac{3n+2}{n!}$, $n = 1, 2, \ldots$

24. $a_n = \frac{n^3}{5^{n+1}}$, $n = 1, 2, \ldots$

25. $a_n = \frac{1 + (-1)^{n+1}}{2}$, $n = 1, 2, \dots$

26. $a_n = \frac{n - \frac{1}{2} + (-1)^n \left(\frac{1}{2}\right)}{2} = \lfloor \frac{n}{2} \rfloor$, $n = 1, 2, \dots$

27. $\lim\limits_{n \to \infty} 2 + (0.1)^n = 2 \Rightarrow$ converges    (Theorem 5, #4)

28. $\lim\limits_{n \to \infty} \frac{n + (-1)^n}{n} = \lim\limits_{n \to \infty} 1 + \frac{(-1)^n}{n} = 1 \Rightarrow$ converges

29. $\lim\limits_{n \to \infty} \frac{1 - 2n}{1 + 2n} = \lim\limits_{n \to \infty} \frac{\left(\frac{1}{n}\right) - 2}{\left(\frac{1}{n}\right) + 2} = \lim\limits_{n \to \infty} \frac{-2}{2} = -1 \Rightarrow$ converges

30. $\lim\limits_{n \to \infty} \frac{2n + 1}{1 - 3\sqrt{n}} = \lim\limits_{n \to \infty} \frac{2\sqrt{n} + \left(\frac{1}{\sqrt{n}}\right)}{\left(\frac{1}{\sqrt{n}} - 3\right)} = -\infty \Rightarrow$ diverges

31. $\lim\limits_{n \to \infty} \frac{1 - 5n^4}{n^4 + 8n^3} = \lim\limits_{n \to \infty} \frac{\left(\frac{1}{n^4}\right) - 5}{1 + \left(\frac{8}{n}\right)} = -5 \Rightarrow$ converges

32. $\lim\limits_{n \to \infty} \frac{n + 3}{n^2 + 5n + 6} = \lim\limits_{n \to \infty} \frac{n + 3}{(n + 3)(n + 2)} = \lim\limits_{n \to \infty} \frac{1}{n + 2} = 0 \Rightarrow$ converges

33. $\lim\limits_{n \to \infty} \frac{n^2 - 2n + 1}{n - 1} = \lim\limits_{n \to \infty} \frac{(n - 1)(n - 1)}{n - 1} = \lim\limits_{n \to \infty} (n - 1) = \infty \Rightarrow$ diverges

34. $\lim\limits_{n \to \infty} \frac{1 - n^3}{70 - 4n^2} = \lim\limits_{n \to \infty} \frac{\left(\frac{1}{n^2}\right) - n}{\left(\frac{70}{n^2}\right) - 4} = \infty \Rightarrow$ diverges

35. $\lim\limits_{n \to \infty} (1 + (-1)^n)$ does not exist $\Rightarrow$ diverges      36. $\lim\limits_{n \to \infty} (-1)^n \left(1 - \frac{1}{n}\right)$ does not exist $\Rightarrow$ diverges

37. $\lim\limits_{n \to \infty} \left(\frac{n + 1}{2n}\right) \left(1 - \frac{1}{n}\right) = \lim\limits_{n \to \infty} \left(\frac{1}{2} + \frac{1}{2n}\right) \left(1 - \frac{1}{n}\right) = \frac{1}{2} \Rightarrow$ converges

38. $\lim\limits_{n \to \infty} \left(2 - \frac{1}{2^n}\right) \left(3 + \frac{1}{2^n}\right) = 6 \Rightarrow$ converges      39. $\lim\limits_{n \to \infty} \frac{(-1)^{n+1}}{2n - 1} = 0 \Rightarrow$ converges

40. $\lim\limits_{n \to \infty} \left(-\frac{1}{2}\right)^n = \lim\limits_{n \to \infty} \frac{(-1)^n}{2^n} = 0 \Rightarrow$ converges

41. $\lim\limits_{n \to \infty} \sqrt{\frac{2n}{n + 1}} = \sqrt{\lim\limits_{n \to \infty} \frac{2n}{n + 1}} = \sqrt{\lim\limits_{n \to \infty} \left(\frac{2}{1 + \frac{1}{n}}\right)} = \sqrt{2} \Rightarrow$ converges

42. $\lim\limits_{n \to \infty} \frac{1}{(0.9)^n} = \lim\limits_{n \to \infty} \left(\frac{10}{9}\right)^n = \infty \Rightarrow$ diverges

43. $\lim\limits_{n \to \infty} \sin \left(\frac{\pi}{2} + \frac{1}{n}\right) = \sin \left(\lim\limits_{n \to \infty} \left(\frac{\pi}{2} + \frac{1}{n}\right)\right) = \sin \frac{\pi}{2} = 1 \Rightarrow$ converges

44. $\lim\limits_{n \to \infty} n\pi \cos (n\pi) = \lim\limits_{n \to \infty} (n\pi)(-1)^n$ does not exist $\Rightarrow$ diverges

45. $\lim\limits_{n \to \infty} \frac{\sin n}{n} = 0$ because $-\frac{1}{n} \le \frac{\sin n}{n} \le \frac{1}{n} \Rightarrow$ converges by the Sandwich Theorem for sequences

46. $\lim\limits_{n \to \infty} \frac{\sin^2 n}{2^n} = 0$ because $0 \le \frac{\sin^2 n}{2^n} \le \frac{1}{2^n} \Rightarrow$ converges by the Sandwich Theorem for sequences

47. $\lim\limits_{n \to \infty} \frac{n}{2^n} = \lim\limits_{n \to \infty} \frac{1}{2^n \ln 2} = 0 \Rightarrow$ converges (using l'Hôpital's rule)

48. $\lim\limits_{n \to \infty} \frac{3^n}{n^3} = \lim\limits_{n \to \infty} \frac{3^n \ln 3}{3n^2} = \lim\limits_{n \to \infty} \frac{3^n (\ln 3)^2}{6n} = \lim\limits_{n \to \infty} \frac{3^n (\ln 3)^3}{6} = \infty \Rightarrow$ diverges (using l'Hôpital's rule)

49. $\lim\limits_{n \to \infty} \frac{\ln(n+1)}{\sqrt{n}} = \lim\limits_{n \to \infty} \frac{\left(\frac{1}{n+1}\right)}{\left(\frac{1}{2\sqrt{n}}\right)} = \lim\limits_{n \to \infty} \frac{2\sqrt{n}}{n+1} = \lim\limits_{n \to \infty} \frac{\left(\frac{2}{\sqrt{n}}\right)}{1+\left(\frac{1}{n}\right)} = 0 \Rightarrow$ converges

50. $\lim\limits_{n \to \infty} \frac{\ln n}{\ln 2n} = \lim\limits_{n \to \infty} \frac{\left(\frac{1}{n}\right)}{\left(\frac{2}{2n}\right)} = 1 \Rightarrow$ converges

51. $\lim\limits_{n \to \infty} 8^{1/n} = 1 \Rightarrow$ converges       (Theorem 5, #3)

52. $\lim\limits_{n \to \infty} (0.03)^{1/n} = 1 \Rightarrow$ converges       (Theorem 5, #3)

53. $\lim\limits_{n \to \infty} \left(1 + \frac{7}{n}\right)^n = e^7 \Rightarrow$ converges       (Theorem 5, #5)

54. $\lim\limits_{n \to \infty} \left(1 - \frac{1}{n}\right)^n = \lim\limits_{n \to \infty} \left[1 + \frac{(-1)}{n}\right]^n = e^{-1} \Rightarrow$ converges       (Theorem 5, #5)

55. $\lim\limits_{n \to \infty} \sqrt[n]{10n} = \lim\limits_{n \to \infty} 10^{1/n} \cdot n^{1/n} = 1 \cdot 1 = 1 \Rightarrow$ converges       (Theorem 5, #3 and #2)

56. $\lim\limits_{n \to \infty} \sqrt[n]{n^2} = \lim\limits_{n \to \infty} \left(\sqrt[n]{n}\right)^2 = 1^2 = 1 \Rightarrow$ converges       (Theorem 5, #2)

57. $\lim\limits_{n \to \infty} \left(\frac{3}{n}\right)^{1/n} = \frac{\lim\limits_{n \to \infty} 3^{1/n}}{\lim\limits_{n \to \infty} n^{1/n}} = \frac{1}{1} = 1 \Rightarrow$ converges       (Theorem 5, #3 and #2)

58. $\lim\limits_{n \to \infty} (n+4)^{1/(n+4)} = \lim\limits_{x \to \infty} x^{1/x} = 1 \Rightarrow$ converges; (let $x = n+4$, then use Theorem 5, #2)

59. $\lim\limits_{n \to \infty} \frac{\ln n}{n^{1/n}} = \frac{\lim\limits_{n \to \infty} \ln n}{\lim\limits_{n \to \infty} n^{1/n}} = \frac{\infty}{1} = \infty \Rightarrow$ diverges       (Theorem 5, #2)

60. $\lim\limits_{n \to \infty} [\ln n - \ln(n+1)] = \lim\limits_{n \to \infty} \ln\left(\frac{n}{n+1}\right) = \ln\left(\lim\limits_{n \to \infty} \frac{n}{n+1}\right) = \ln 1 = 0 \Rightarrow$ converges

61. $\lim\limits_{n \to \infty} \sqrt[n]{4^n n} = \lim\limits_{n \to \infty} 4 \sqrt[n]{n} = 4 \cdot 1 = 4 \Rightarrow$ converges       (Theorem 5, #2)

62. $\lim\limits_{n \to \infty} \sqrt[n]{3^{2n+1}} = \lim\limits_{n \to \infty} 3^{2+(1/n)} = \lim\limits_{n \to \infty} 3^2 \cdot 3^{1/n} = 9 \cdot 1 = 9 \Rightarrow$ converges       (Theorem 5, #3)

63. $\lim\limits_{n \to \infty} \frac{n!}{n^n} = \lim\limits_{n \to \infty} \frac{1 \cdot 2 \cdot 3 \cdots (n-1)(n)}{n \cdot n \cdot n \cdots n \cdot n} \leq \lim\limits_{n \to \infty} \left(\frac{1}{n}\right) = 0$ and $\frac{n!}{n^n} \geq 0 \Rightarrow \lim\limits_{n \to \infty} \frac{n!}{n^n} = 0 \Rightarrow$ converges

64. $\lim\limits_{n \to \infty} \frac{(-4)^n}{n!} = 0 \Rightarrow$ converges       (Theorem 5, #6)

65. $\lim\limits_{n \to \infty} \frac{n!}{10^{6n}} = \lim\limits_{n \to \infty} \frac{1}{\left(\frac{(10^6)^n}{n!}\right)} = \infty \Rightarrow$ diverges       (Theorem 5, #6)

66. $\lim\limits_{n \to \infty} \frac{n!}{2^n 3^n} = \lim\limits_{n \to \infty} \frac{1}{\left(\frac{6^n}{n!}\right)} = \infty \Rightarrow$ diverges       (Theorem 5, #6)

67. $\lim\limits_{n \to \infty} \left(\frac{1}{n}\right)^{1/(\ln n)} = \lim\limits_{n \to \infty} \exp\left(\frac{1}{\ln n} \ln\left(\frac{1}{n}\right)\right) = \lim\limits_{n \to \infty} \exp\left(\frac{\ln 1 - \ln n}{\ln n}\right) = e^{-1} \Rightarrow$ converges

68. $\lim\limits_{n \to \infty} \ln\left(1 + \frac{1}{n}\right)^n = \ln\left(\lim\limits_{n \to \infty} \left(1 + \frac{1}{n}\right)^n\right) = \ln e = 1 \Rightarrow$ converges    (Theorem 5, #5)

69. $\lim\limits_{n \to \infty} \left(\frac{3n+1}{3n-1}\right)^n = \lim\limits_{n \to \infty} \exp\left(n \ln\left(\frac{3n+1}{3n-1}\right)\right) = \lim\limits_{n \to \infty} \exp\left(\frac{\ln(3n+1) - \ln(3n-1)}{\frac{1}{n}}\right)$

$= \lim\limits_{n \to \infty} \exp\left(\frac{\frac{3}{3n+1} - \frac{3}{3n-1}}{\left(-\frac{1}{n^2}\right)}\right) = \lim\limits_{n \to \infty} \exp\left(\frac{6n^2}{(3n+1)(3n-1)}\right) = \exp\left(\frac{6}{9}\right) = e^{2/3} \Rightarrow$ converges

70. $\lim\limits_{n \to \infty} \left(\frac{n}{n+1}\right)^n = \lim\limits_{n \to \infty} \exp\left(n \ln\left(\frac{n}{n+1}\right)\right) = \lim\limits_{n \to \infty} \exp\left(\frac{\ln n - \ln(n+1)}{\left(\frac{1}{n}\right)}\right) = \lim\limits_{n \to \infty} \exp\left(\frac{\frac{1}{n} - \frac{1}{n+1}}{\left(-\frac{1}{n^2}\right)}\right)$

$= \lim\limits_{n \to \infty} \exp\left(-\frac{n^2}{n(n+1)}\right) = e^{-1} \Rightarrow$ converges

71. $\lim\limits_{n \to \infty} \left(\frac{x^n}{2n+1}\right)^{1/n} = \lim\limits_{n \to \infty} x \left(\frac{1}{2n+1}\right)^{1/n} = x \lim\limits_{n \to \infty} \exp\left(\frac{1}{n} \ln\left(\frac{1}{2n+1}\right)\right) = x \lim\limits_{n \to \infty} \exp\left(\frac{-\ln(2n+1)}{n}\right)$

$= x \lim\limits_{n \to \infty} \exp\left(\frac{-2}{2n+1}\right) = xe^0 = x, x > 0 \Rightarrow$ converges

72. $\lim\limits_{n \to \infty} \left(1 - \frac{1}{n^2}\right)^n = \lim\limits_{n \to \infty} \exp\left(n \ln\left(1 - \frac{1}{n^2}\right)\right) = \lim\limits_{n \to \infty} \exp\left(\frac{\ln\left(1 - \frac{1}{n^2}\right)}{\left(\frac{1}{n}\right)}\right) = \lim\limits_{n \to \infty} \exp\left[\frac{\left(\frac{2}{n^3}\right) / \left(1 - \frac{1}{n^2}\right)}{\left(-\frac{1}{n^2}\right)}\right]$

$= \lim\limits_{n \to \infty} \exp\left(\frac{-2n}{n^2-1}\right) = e^0 = 1 \Rightarrow$ converges

73. $\lim\limits_{n \to \infty} \frac{3^n \cdot 6^n}{2^{-n} \cdot n!} = \lim\limits_{n \to \infty} \frac{36^n}{n!} = 0 \Rightarrow$ converges    (Theorem 5, #6)

74. $\lim\limits_{n \to \infty} \frac{\left(\frac{10}{11}\right)^n}{\left(\frac{9}{10}\right)^n + \left(\frac{11}{12}\right)^n} = \lim\limits_{n \to \infty} \frac{\left(\frac{12}{11}\right)^n \left(\frac{10}{11}\right)^n}{\left(\frac{12}{11}\right)^n \left(\frac{9}{10}\right)^n + \left(\frac{12}{11}\right)^n \left(\frac{11}{12}\right)^n} = \lim\limits_{n \to \infty} \frac{\left(\frac{120}{121}\right)^n}{\left(\frac{108}{110}\right)^n + 1} = 0 \Rightarrow$ converges
    (Theorem 5, #4)

75. $\lim\limits_{n \to \infty} \tanh n = \lim\limits_{n \to \infty} \frac{e^n - e^{-n}}{e^n + e^{-n}} = \lim\limits_{n \to \infty} \frac{e^{2n} - 1}{e^{2n} + 1} = \lim\limits_{n \to \infty} \frac{2e^{2n}}{2e^{2n}} = \lim\limits_{n \to \infty} 1 = 1 \Rightarrow$ converges

76. $\lim\limits_{n \to \infty} \sinh(\ln n) = \lim\limits_{n \to \infty} \frac{e^{\ln n} - e^{-\ln n}}{2} = \lim\limits_{n \to \infty} \frac{n - \left(\frac{1}{n}\right)}{2} = \infty \Rightarrow$ diverges

77. $\lim\limits_{n \to \infty} \frac{n^2 \sin\left(\frac{1}{n}\right)}{2n - 1} = \lim\limits_{n \to \infty} \frac{\sin\left(\frac{1}{n}\right)}{\left(\frac{2}{n} - \frac{1}{n^2}\right)} = \lim\limits_{n \to \infty} \frac{-\left(\cos\left(\frac{1}{n}\right)\right)\left(\frac{1}{n^2}\right)}{\left(-\frac{2}{n^2} + \frac{2}{n^3}\right)} = \lim\limits_{n \to \infty} \frac{-\cos\left(\frac{1}{n}\right)}{-2 + \left(\frac{2}{n}\right)} = \frac{1}{2} \Rightarrow$ converges

78. $\lim\limits_{n \to \infty} n\left(1 - \cos\frac{1}{n}\right) = \lim\limits_{n \to \infty} \frac{\left(1 - \cos\frac{1}{n}\right)}{\left(\frac{1}{n}\right)} = \lim\limits_{n \to \infty} \frac{\left[\sin\left(\frac{1}{n}\right)\right]\left(\frac{1}{n^2}\right)}{\left(\frac{1}{n^2}\right)} = \lim\limits_{n \to \infty} \sin\left(\frac{1}{n}\right) = 0 \Rightarrow$ converges

79. $\lim\limits_{n \to \infty} \sqrt{n} \sin\left(\frac{1}{\sqrt{n}}\right) = \lim\limits_{n \to \infty} \frac{\sin\left(\frac{1}{\sqrt{n}}\right)}{\frac{1}{\sqrt{n}}} = \lim\limits_{n \to \infty} \frac{\cos\left(\frac{1}{\sqrt{n}}\right)\left(-\frac{1}{2n^{3/2}}\right)}{-\frac{1}{2n^{3/2}}} = \lim\limits_{n \to \infty} \cos\left(\frac{1}{\sqrt{n}}\right) = \cos 0 = 1 \Rightarrow$ converges

80. $\lim\limits_{n \to \infty} (3^n + 5^n)^{1/n} = \lim\limits_{n \to \infty} \exp\left[\ln(3^n + 5^n)^{1/n}\right] = \lim\limits_{n \to \infty} \exp\left[\frac{\ln(3^n + 5^n)}{n}\right] = \lim\limits_{n \to \infty} \exp\left[\frac{\frac{3^n \ln 3 + 5^n \ln 5}{3^n + 5^n}}{1}\right]$

$= \lim\limits_{n \to \infty} \exp\left[\frac{\left(\frac{3^n}{5^n}\right)\ln 3 + \ln 5}{\left(\frac{3^n}{5^n}\right) + 1}\right] = \lim\limits_{n \to \infty} \exp\left[\frac{\left(\frac{3}{5}\right)^n \ln 3 + \ln 5}{\left(\frac{3}{5}\right)^n + 1}\right] = \exp(\ln 5) = 5$

81. $\lim\limits_{n \to \infty} \tan^{-1} n = \frac{\pi}{2} \Rightarrow$ converges

82. $\lim\limits_{n \to \infty} \frac{1}{\sqrt{n}} \tan^{-1} n = 0 \cdot \frac{\pi}{2} = 0 \Rightarrow$ converges

83. $\lim\limits_{n \to \infty} \left(\frac{1}{3}\right)^n + \frac{1}{\sqrt{2^n}} = \lim\limits_{n \to \infty} \left(\left(\frac{1}{3}\right)^n + \left(\frac{1}{\sqrt{2}}\right)^n\right) = 0 \Rightarrow$ converges     (Theorem 5, #4)

84. $\lim\limits_{n \to \infty} \sqrt[n]{n^2 + n} = \lim\limits_{n \to \infty} \exp\left[\frac{\ln(n^2+n)}{n}\right] = \lim\limits_{n \to \infty} \exp\left(\frac{2n+1}{n^2+n}\right) = e^0 = 1 \Rightarrow$ converges

85. $\lim\limits_{n \to \infty} \frac{(\ln n)^{200}}{n} = \lim\limits_{n \to \infty} \frac{200(\ln n)^{199}}{n} = \lim\limits_{n \to \infty} \frac{200 \cdot 199(\ln n)^{198}}{n} = \ldots = \lim\limits_{n \to \infty} \frac{200!}{n} = 0 \Rightarrow$ converges

86. $\lim\limits_{n \to \infty} \frac{(\ln n)^5}{\sqrt{n}} = \lim\limits_{n \to \infty} \left[\frac{\left(\frac{5(\ln n)^4}{n}\right)}{\left(\frac{1}{2\sqrt{n}}\right)}\right] = \lim\limits_{n \to \infty} \frac{10(\ln n)^4}{\sqrt{n}} = \lim\limits_{n \to \infty} \frac{80(\ln n)^3}{\sqrt{n}} = \ldots = \lim\limits_{n \to \infty} \frac{3840}{\sqrt{n}} = 0 \Rightarrow$ converges

87. $\lim\limits_{n \to \infty} \left(n - \sqrt{n^2 - n}\right) = \lim\limits_{n \to \infty} \left(n - \sqrt{n^2 - n}\right)\left(\frac{n + \sqrt{n^2 - n}}{n + \sqrt{n^2 - n}}\right) = \lim\limits_{n \to \infty} \frac{n}{n + \sqrt{n^2 - n}} = \lim\limits_{n \to \infty} \frac{1}{1 + \sqrt{1 - \frac{1}{n}}}$
$= \frac{1}{2} \Rightarrow$ converges

88. $\lim\limits_{n \to \infty} \frac{1}{\sqrt{n^2 - 1} - \sqrt{n^2 + n}} = \lim\limits_{n \to \infty} \left(\frac{1}{\sqrt{n^2 - 1} - \sqrt{n^2 + n}}\right)\left(\frac{\sqrt{n^2 - 1} + \sqrt{n^2 + n}}{\sqrt{n^2 - 1} + \sqrt{n^2 + n}}\right) = \lim\limits_{n \to \infty} \frac{\sqrt{n^2 - 1} + \sqrt{n^2 + n}}{-1 - n}$
$= \lim\limits_{n \to \infty} \frac{\sqrt{1 - \frac{1}{n^2}} + \sqrt{1 + \frac{1}{n}}}{\left(-\frac{1}{n} - 1\right)} = -2 \Rightarrow$ converges

89. $\lim\limits_{n \to \infty} \frac{1}{n} \int_1^n \frac{1}{x}\, dx = \lim\limits_{n \to \infty} \frac{\ln n}{n} = \lim\limits_{n \to \infty} \frac{1}{n} = 0 \Rightarrow$ converges     (Theorem 5, #1)

90. $\lim\limits_{n \to \infty} \int_1^n \frac{1}{x^p}\, dx = \lim\limits_{n \to \infty} \left[\frac{1}{1-p}\frac{1}{x^{p-1}}\right]_1^n = \lim\limits_{n \to \infty} \frac{1}{1-p}\left(\frac{1}{n^{p-1}} - 1\right) = \frac{1}{p-1}$ if $p > 1 \Rightarrow$ converges

91. Since $a_n$ converges $\Rightarrow \lim\limits_{n \to \infty} a_n = L \Rightarrow \lim\limits_{n \to \infty} a_{n+1} = \lim\limits_{n \to \infty} \frac{72}{1 + a_n} \Rightarrow L = \frac{72}{1 + L} \Rightarrow L(1 + L) = 72 \Rightarrow L^2 + L - 72 = 0$
$\Rightarrow L = -9$ or $L = 8$; since $a_n > 0$ for $n \geq 1 \Rightarrow L = 8$

92. Since $a_n$ converges $\Rightarrow \lim\limits_{n \to \infty} a_n = L \Rightarrow \lim\limits_{n \to \infty} a_{n+1} = \lim\limits_{n \to \infty} \frac{a_n + 6}{a_n + 2} \Rightarrow L = \frac{L+6}{L+2} \Rightarrow L(L + 2) = L + 6 \Rightarrow L^2 + L - 6 = 0$
$\Rightarrow L = -3$ or $L = 2$; since $a_n > 0$ for $n \geq 2 \Rightarrow L = 2$

93. Since $a_n$ converges $\Rightarrow \lim\limits_{n \to \infty} a_n = L \Rightarrow \lim\limits_{n \to \infty} a_{n+1} = \lim\limits_{n \to \infty} \sqrt{8 + 2a_n} \Rightarrow L = \sqrt{8 + 2L} \Rightarrow L^2 - 2L - 8 = 0 \Rightarrow L = -2$
or $L = 4$; since $a_n > 0$ for $n \geq 3 \Rightarrow L = 4$

94. Since $a_n$ converges $\Rightarrow \lim\limits_{n \to \infty} a_n = L \Rightarrow \lim\limits_{n \to \infty} a_{n+1} = \lim\limits_{n \to \infty} \sqrt{8 + 2a_n} \Rightarrow L = \sqrt{8 + 2L} \Rightarrow L^2 - 2L - 8 = 0 \Rightarrow L = -2$
or $L = 4$; since $a_n > 0$ for $n \geq 2 \Rightarrow L = 4$

95. Since $a_n$ converges $\Rightarrow \lim\limits_{n \to \infty} a_n = L \Rightarrow \lim\limits_{n \to \infty} a_{n+1} = \lim\limits_{n \to \infty} \sqrt{5a_n} \Rightarrow L = \sqrt{5L} \Rightarrow L^2 - 5L = 0 \Rightarrow L = 0$ or $L = 5$; since
$a_n > 0$ for $n \geq 1 \Rightarrow L = 5$

96. Since $a_n$ converges $\Rightarrow \lim\limits_{n \to \infty} a_n = L \Rightarrow \lim\limits_{n \to \infty} a_{n+1} = \lim\limits_{n \to \infty} \left(12 - \sqrt{a_n}\right) \Rightarrow L = \left(12 - \sqrt{L}\right) \Rightarrow L^2 - 25L + 144 = 0$
$\Rightarrow L = 9$ or $L = 16$; since $12 - \sqrt{a_n} < 12$ for $n \geq 1 \Rightarrow L = 9$

97. $a_{n+1} = 2 + \frac{1}{a_n}$, $n \geq 1$, $a_1 = 2$. Since $a_n$ converges $\Rightarrow \lim\limits_{n \to \infty} a_n = L \Rightarrow \lim\limits_{n \to \infty} a_{n+1} = \lim\limits_{n \to \infty} \left(2 + \frac{1}{a_n}\right) \Rightarrow L = 2 + \frac{1}{L}$
$\Rightarrow L^2 - 2L - 1 = 0 \Rightarrow L = 1 \pm \sqrt{2}$; since $a_n > 0$ for $n \geq 1 \Rightarrow L = 1 + \sqrt{2}$

98. $a_{n+1} = \sqrt{1 + a_n}$, $n \geq 1$, $a_1 = \sqrt{1}$. Since $a_n$ converges $\Rightarrow \lim\limits_{n \to \infty} a_n = L \Rightarrow \lim\limits_{n \to \infty} a_{n+1} = \lim\limits_{n \to \infty} \sqrt{1 + a_n} \Rightarrow L = \sqrt{1 + L}$

$\Rightarrow L^2 - L - 1 = 0 \Rightarrow L = \frac{1 \pm \sqrt{5}}{2}$; since $a_n > 0$ for $n \geq 1 \Rightarrow L = \frac{1 + \sqrt{5}}{2}$

99. $1, 1, 2, 4, 8, 16, 32, \ldots = 1, 2^0, 2^1, 2^2, 2^3, 2^4, 2^5, \ldots \Rightarrow x_1 = 1$ and $x_n = 2^{n-2}$ for $n \geq 2$

100. (a) $1^2 - 2(1)^2 = -1$, $3^2 - 2(2)^2 = 1$; let $f(a, b) = (a + 2b)^2 - 2(a + b)^2 = a^2 + 4ab + 4b^2 - 2a^2 - 4ab - 2b^2$

$= 2b^2 - a^2$; $a^2 - 2b^2 = -1 \Rightarrow f(a, b) = 2b^2 - a^2 = 1$; $a^2 - 2b^2 = 1 \Rightarrow f(a, b) = 2b^2 - a^2 = -1$

(b) $r_n^2 - 2 = \left(\frac{a + 2b}{a + b}\right)^2 - 2 = \frac{a^2 + 4ab + 4b^2 - 2a^2 - 4ab - 2b^2}{(a + b)^2} = \frac{-(a^2 - 2b^2)}{(a + b)^2} = \frac{\pm 1}{y_n^2} \Rightarrow r_n = \sqrt{2 \pm \left(\frac{1}{y_n}\right)^2}$

In the first and second fractions, $y_n \geq n$. Let $\frac{a}{b}$ represent the $(n - 1)$th fraction where $\frac{a}{b} \geq 1$ and $b \geq n - 1$

for $n$ a positive integer $\geq 3$. Now the $n$th fraction is $\frac{a + 2b}{a + b}$ and $a + b \geq 2b \geq 2n - 2 \geq n \Rightarrow y_n \geq n$. Thus,

$\lim\limits_{n \to \infty} r_n = \sqrt{2}$.

101. (a) $f(x) = x^2 - 2$; the sequence converges to $1.414213562 \approx \sqrt{2}$

(b) $f(x) = \tan(x) - 1$; the sequence converges to $0.7853981635 \approx \frac{\pi}{4}$

(c) $f(x) = e^x$; the sequence $1, 0, -1, -2, -3, -4, -5, \ldots$ diverges

102. (a) $\lim\limits_{n \to \infty} n f\left(\frac{1}{n}\right) = \lim\limits_{\Delta x \to 0^+} \frac{f(\Delta x)}{\Delta x} = \lim\limits_{\Delta x \to 0^+} \frac{f(0 + \Delta x) - f(0)}{\Delta x} = f'(0)$, where $\Delta x = \frac{1}{n}$

(b) $\lim\limits_{n \to \infty} n \tan^{-1}\left(\frac{1}{n}\right) = f'(0) = \frac{1}{1 + 0^2} = 1$, $f(x) = \tan^{-1} x$

(c) $\lim\limits_{n \to \infty} n \left(e^{1/n} - 1\right) = f'(0) = e^0 = 1$, $f(x) = e^x - 1$

(d) $\lim\limits_{n \to \infty} n \ln\left(1 + \frac{2}{n}\right) = f'(0) = \frac{2}{1 + 2(0)} = 2$, $f(x) = \ln(1 + 2x)$

103. (a) If $a = 2n + 1$, then $b = \lfloor \frac{a^2}{2} \rfloor = \lfloor \frac{4n^2 + 4n + 1}{2} \rfloor = \lfloor 2n^2 + 2n + \frac{1}{2} \rfloor = 2n^2 + 2n$, $c = \lceil \frac{a^2}{2} \rceil = \lceil 2n^2 + 2n + \frac{1}{2} \rceil$

$= 2n^2 + 2n + 1$ and $a^2 + b^2 = (2n + 1)^2 + (2n^2 + 2n)^2 = 4n^2 + 4n + 1 + 4n^4 + 8n^3 + 4n^2$

$= 4n^4 + 8n^3 + 8n^2 + 4n + 1 = (2n^2 + 2n + 1)^2 = c^2$.

(b) $\lim\limits_{a \to \infty} \frac{\lfloor \frac{a^2}{2} \rfloor}{\lceil \frac{a^2}{2} \rceil} = \lim\limits_{a \to \infty} \frac{2n^2 + 2n}{2n^2 + 2n + 1} = 1$ or $\lim\limits_{a \to \infty} \frac{\lfloor \frac{a^2}{2} \rfloor}{\lceil \frac{a^2}{2} \rceil} = \lim\limits_{a \to \infty} \sin \theta = \lim\limits_{\theta \to \pi/2} \sin \theta = 1$

104. (a) $\lim\limits_{n \to \infty} (2n\pi)^{1/(2n)} = \lim\limits_{n \to \infty} \exp\left(\frac{\ln 2n\pi}{2n}\right) = \lim\limits_{n \to \infty} \exp\left(\frac{\left(\frac{2\pi}{2n\pi}\right)}{2}\right) = \lim\limits_{n \to \infty} \exp\left(\frac{1}{2n}\right) = e^0 = 1$;

$n! \approx \left(\frac{n}{e}\right) \sqrt[n]{2n\pi}$, Stirlings approximation $\Rightarrow \sqrt[n]{n!} \approx \left(\frac{n}{e}\right) (2n\pi)^{1/(2n)} \approx \frac{n}{e}$ for large values of $n$

(b)

| n | $\sqrt[n]{n!}$ | $\frac{n}{e}$ |
|---|---|---|
| 40 | 15.76852702 | 14.71517765 |
| 50 | 19.48325423 | 18.39397206 |
| 60 | 23.19189561 | 22.07276647 |

105. (a) $\lim\limits_{n \to \infty} \frac{\ln n}{n^c} = \lim\limits_{n \to \infty} \frac{\left(\frac{1}{n}\right)}{cn^{c-1}} = \lim\limits_{n \to \infty} \frac{1}{cn^c} = 0$

(b) For all $\epsilon > 0$, there exists an $N = e^{-(\ln \epsilon)/c}$ such that $n > e^{-(\ln \epsilon)/c} \Rightarrow \ln n > -\frac{\ln \epsilon}{c} \Rightarrow \ln n^c > \ln\left(\frac{1}{\epsilon}\right)$

$\Rightarrow n^c > \frac{1}{\epsilon} \Rightarrow \frac{1}{n^c} < \epsilon \Rightarrow \left|\frac{1}{n^c} - 0\right| < \epsilon \Rightarrow \lim\limits_{n \to \infty} \frac{1}{n^c} = 0$

106. Let $\{a_n\}$ and $\{b_n\}$ be sequences both converging to L. Define $\{c_n\}$ by $c_{2n} = b_n$ and $c_{2n-1} = a_n$, where

$n = 1, 2, 3, \ldots$. For all $\epsilon > 0$ there exists $N_1$ such that when $n > N_1$ then $|a_n - L| < \epsilon$ and there exists $N_2$

such that when $n > N_2$ then $|b_n - L| < \epsilon$. If $n > 1 + 2\max\{N_1, N_2\}$, then $|c_n - L| < \epsilon$, so $\{c_n\}$ converges to L.

107. $\lim\limits_{n \to \infty} n^{1/n} = \lim\limits_{n \to \infty} \exp\left(\frac{1}{n} \ln n\right) = \lim\limits_{n \to \infty} \exp\left(\frac{1}{n}\right) = e^0 = 1$

108. $\lim\limits_{n \to \infty} x^{1/n} = \lim\limits_{n \to \infty} \exp\left(\frac{1}{n} \ln x\right) = e^0 = 1$, because x remains fixed while n gets large

109. Assume the hypotheses of the theorem and let $\epsilon$ be a positive number. For all $\epsilon$ there exists a $N_1$ such that when $n > N_1$ then $|a_n - L| < \epsilon \Rightarrow -\epsilon < a_n - L < \epsilon \Rightarrow L - \epsilon < a_n$, and there exists a $N_2$ such that when $n > N_2$ then $|c_n - L| < \epsilon \Rightarrow -\epsilon < c_n - L < \epsilon \Rightarrow c_n < L + \epsilon$. If $n > \max\{N_1, N_2\}$, then $L - \epsilon < a_n \le b_n \le c_n < L + \epsilon \Rightarrow |b_n - L| < \epsilon \Rightarrow \lim\limits_{n \to \infty} b_n = L$.

110. Let $\epsilon > 0$. We have f continuous at $L \Rightarrow$ there exists $\delta$ so that $|x - L| < \delta \Rightarrow |f(x) - f(L)| < \epsilon$. Also, $a_n \to L \Rightarrow$ there exists N so that for $n > N$ $|a_n - L| < \delta$. Thus for $n > N$, $|f(a_n) - f(L)| < \epsilon \Rightarrow f(a_n) \to f(L)$.

111. $a_{n+1} \ge a_n \Rightarrow \frac{3(n+1)+1}{(n+1)+1} > \frac{3n+1}{n+1} \Rightarrow \frac{3n+4}{n+2} > \frac{3n+1}{n+1} \Rightarrow 3n^2 + 3n + 4n + 4 > 3n^2 + 6n + n + 2$
$\Rightarrow 4 > 2$; the steps are reversible so the sequence is nondecreasing; $\frac{3n+1}{n+1} < 3 \Rightarrow 3n + 1 < 3n + 3$
$\Rightarrow 1 < 3$; the steps are reversible so the sequence is bounded above by 3

112. $a_{n+1} \ge a_n \Rightarrow \frac{(2(n+1)+3)!}{((n+1)+1)!} > \frac{(2n+3)!}{(n+1)!} \Rightarrow \frac{(2n+5)!}{(n+2)!} > \frac{(2n+3)!}{(n+1)!} \Rightarrow \frac{(2n+5)!}{(2n+3)!} > \frac{(n+2)!}{(n+1)!}$
$\Rightarrow (2n+5)(2n+4) > n+2$; the steps are reversible so the sequence is nondecreasing; the sequence is not bounded since $\frac{(2n+3)!}{(n+1)!} = (2n+3)(2n+2)\cdots(n+2)$ can become as large as we please

113. $a_{n+1} \le a_n \Rightarrow \frac{2^{n+1}3^{n+1}}{(n+1)!} \le \frac{2^n 3^n}{n!} \Rightarrow \frac{2^{n+1}3^{n+1}}{2^n 3^n} \le \frac{(n+1)!}{n!} \Rightarrow 2 \cdot 3 \le n + 1$ which is true for $n \ge 5$; the steps are reversible so the sequence is decreasing after $a_5$, but it is not nondecreasing for all its terms; $a_1 = 6$, $a_2 = 18$, $a_3 = 36$, $a_4 = 54$, $a_5 = \frac{324}{5} = 64.8 \Rightarrow$ the sequence is bounded from above by 64.8

114. $a_{n+1} \ge a_n \Rightarrow 2 - \frac{2}{n+1} - \frac{1}{2^{n+1}} \ge 2 - \frac{2}{n} - \frac{1}{2^n} \Rightarrow \frac{2}{n} - \frac{2}{n+1} \ge \frac{1}{2^{n+1}} - \frac{1}{2^n} \Rightarrow \frac{2}{n(n+1)} \ge -\frac{1}{2^{n+1}}$; the steps are reversible so the sequence is nondecreasing; $2 - \frac{2}{n} - \frac{1}{2^n} \le 2 \Rightarrow$ the sequence is bounded from above

115. $a_n = 1 - \frac{1}{n}$ converges because $\frac{1}{n} \to 0$ by Example 1; also it is a nondecreasing sequence bounded above by 1

116. $a_n = n - \frac{1}{n}$ diverges because $n \to \infty$ and $\frac{1}{n} \to 0$ by Example 1, so the sequence is unbounded

117. $a_n = \frac{2^n - 1}{2^n} = 1 - \frac{1}{2^n}$ and $0 < \frac{1}{2^n} < \frac{1}{n}$; since $\frac{1}{n} \to 0$ (by Example 1) $\Rightarrow \frac{1}{2^n} \to 0$, the sequence converges; also it is a nondecreasing sequence bounded above by 1

118. $a_n = \frac{2^n - 1}{3^n} = \left(\frac{2}{3}\right)^n - \frac{1}{3^n}$; the sequence converges to 0 by Theorem 5, #4

119. $a_n = ((-1)^n + 1)\left(\frac{n+1}{n}\right)$ diverges because $a_n = 0$ for n odd, while for n even $a_n = 2\left(1 + \frac{1}{n}\right)$ converges to 2; it diverges by definition of divergence

120. $x_n = \max\{\cos 1, \cos 2, \cos 3, \ldots, \cos n\}$ and $x_{n+1} = \max\{\cos 1, \cos 2, \cos 3, \ldots, \cos(n+1)\} \ge x_n$ with $x_n \le 1$ so the sequence is nondecreasing and bounded above by 1 $\Rightarrow$ the sequence converges.

121. $a_n \ge a_{n+1} \Leftrightarrow \frac{1+\sqrt{2n}}{\sqrt{n}} \ge \frac{1+\sqrt{2(n+1)}}{\sqrt{n+1}} \Leftrightarrow \sqrt{n+1} + \sqrt{2n^2+2n} \ge \sqrt{n} + \sqrt{2n^2+2n} \Leftrightarrow \sqrt{n+1} \ge \sqrt{n}$ and $\frac{1+\sqrt{2n}}{\sqrt{n}} \ge \sqrt{2}$; thus the sequence is nonincreasing and bounded below by $\sqrt{2} \Rightarrow$ it converges

122. $a_n \geq a_{n+1} \Leftrightarrow \frac{n+1}{n} \geq \frac{(n+1)+1}{n+1} \Leftrightarrow n^2 + 2n + 1 \geq n^2 + 2n \Leftrightarrow 1 \geq 0$ and $\frac{n+1}{n} \geq 1$; thus the sequence is nonincreasing and bounded below by $1 \Rightarrow$ it converges

123. $\frac{4^{n+1} + 3^n}{4^n} = 4 + \left(\frac{3}{4}\right)^n$ so $a_n \geq a_{n+1} \Leftrightarrow 4 + \left(\frac{3}{4}\right)^n \geq 4 + \left(\frac{3}{4}\right)^{n+1} \Leftrightarrow \left(\frac{3}{4}\right)^n \geq \left(\frac{3}{4}\right)^{n+1} \Leftrightarrow 1 \geq \frac{3}{4}$ and $4 + \left(\frac{3}{4}\right)^n \geq 4$; thus the sequence is nonincreasing and bounded below by $4 \Rightarrow$ it converges

124. $a_1 = 1, a_2 = 2 - 3, a_3 = 2(2 - 3) - 3 = 2^2 - (2^2 - 1) \cdot 3, a_4 = 2(2^2 - (2^2 - 1) \cdot 3) - 3 = 2^3 - (2^3 - 1) 3,$
$a_5 = 2[2^3 - (2^3 - 1) 3] - 3 = 2^4 - (2^4 - 1) 3, \ldots, a_n = 2^{n-1} - (2^{n-1} - 1) 3 = 2^{n-1} - 3 \cdot 2^{n-1} + 3$
$= 2^{n-1}(1 - 3) + 3 = -2^n + 3; a_n \geq a_{n+1} \Leftrightarrow -2^n + 3 \geq -2^{n+1} + 3 \Leftrightarrow -2^n \geq -2^{n+1} \Leftrightarrow 1 \leq 2$
so the sequence is nonincreasing but not bounded below and therefore diverges

125. Let $0 < M < 1$ and let N be an integer greater than $\frac{M}{1-M}$. Then $n > N \Rightarrow n > \frac{M}{1-M} \Rightarrow n - nM > M$
$\Rightarrow n > M + nM \Rightarrow n > M(n + 1) \Rightarrow \frac{n}{n+1} > M$.

126. Since $M_1$ is a least upper bound and $M_2$ is an upper bound, $M_1 \leq M_2$. Since $M_2$ is a least upper bound and $M_1$ is an upper bound, $M_2 \leq M_1$. We conclude that $M_1 = M_2$ so the least upper bound is unique.

127. The sequence $a_n = 1 + \frac{(-1)^n}{2}$ is the sequence $\frac{1}{2}, \frac{3}{2}, \frac{1}{2}, \frac{3}{2}, \ldots$. This sequence is bounded above by $\frac{3}{2}$, but it clearly does not converge, by definition of convergence.

128. Let L be the limit of the convergent sequence $\{a_n\}$. Then by definition of convergence, for $\frac{\epsilon}{2}$ there corresponds an N such that for all m and n, $m > N \Rightarrow |a_m - L| < \frac{\epsilon}{2}$ and $n > N \Rightarrow |a_n - L| < \frac{\epsilon}{2}$. Now $|a_m - a_n| = |a_m - L + L - a_n| \leq |a_m - L| + |L - a_n| < \frac{\epsilon}{2} + \frac{\epsilon}{2} = \epsilon$ whenever $m > N$ and $n > N$.

129. Given an $\epsilon > 0$, by definition of convergence there corresponds an N such that for all $n > N$, $|L_1 - a_n| < \epsilon$ and $|L_2 - a_n| < \epsilon$. Now $|L_2 - L_1| = |L_2 - a_n + a_n - L_1| \leq |L_2 - a_n| + |a_n - L_1| < \epsilon + \epsilon = 2\epsilon$. $|L_2 - L_1| < 2\epsilon$ says that the difference between two fixed values is smaller than any positive number $2\epsilon$. The only nonnegative number smaller than every positive number is 0, so $|L_1 - L_2| = 0$ or $L_1 = L_2$.

130. Let $k(n)$ and $i(n)$ be two order-preserving functions whose domains are the set of positive integers and whose ranges are a subset of the positive integers. Consider the two subsequences $a_{k(n)}$ and $a_{i(n)}$, where $a_{k(n)} \to L_1$, $a_{i(n)} \to L_2$ and $L_1 \neq L_2$. Thus $|a_{k(n)} - a_{i(n)}| \to |L_1 - L_2| > 0$. So there does not exist N such that for all $m, n > N$ $\Rightarrow |a_m - a_n| < \epsilon$. So by Exercise 128, the sequence $\{a_n\}$ is not convergent and hence diverges.

131. $a_{2k} \to L \Leftrightarrow$ given an $\epsilon > 0$ there corresponds an $N_1$ such that $[2k > N_1 \Rightarrow |a_{2k} - L| < \epsilon]$. Similarly, $a_{2k+1} \to L \Leftrightarrow [2k + 1 > N_2 \Rightarrow |a_{2k+1} - L| < \epsilon]$. Let $N = \max\{N_1, N_2\}$. Then $n > N \Rightarrow |a_n - L| < \epsilon$ whether n is even or odd, and hence $a_n \to L$.

132. Assume $a_n \to 0$. This implies that given an $\epsilon > 0$ there corresponds an N such that $n > N \Rightarrow |a_n - 0| < \epsilon$ $\Rightarrow |a_n| < \epsilon \Rightarrow ||a_n|| < \epsilon \Rightarrow ||a_n| - 0| < \epsilon \Rightarrow |a_n| \to 0$. On the other hand, assume $|a_n| \to 0$. This implies that given an $\epsilon > 0$ there corresponds an N such that for $n > N$, $||a_n| - 0| < \epsilon \Rightarrow ||a_n|| < \epsilon \Rightarrow |a_n| < \epsilon$ $\Rightarrow |a_n - 0| < \epsilon \Rightarrow a_n \to 0$.

133. (a) $f(x) = x^2 - a \Rightarrow f'(x) = 2x \Rightarrow x_{n+1} = x_n - \frac{x_n^2 - a}{2x_n} \Rightarrow x_{n+1} = \frac{2x_n^2 - (x_n^2 - a)}{2x_n} = \frac{x_n^2 + a}{2x_n} = \frac{\left(x_n + \frac{a}{x_n}\right)}{2}$

(b) $x_1 = 2, x_2 = 1.75, x_3 = 1.732142857, x_4 = 1.73205081, x_5 = 1.732050808$; we are finding the positive number where $x^2 - 3 = 0$; that is, where $x^2 = 3, x > 0$, or where $x = \sqrt{3}$.

134. $x_1 = 1$, $x_2 = 1 + \cos(1) = 1.540302306$, $x_3 = 1.540302306 + \cos(1 + \cos(1)) = 1.570791601$,

$x_4 = 1.570791601 + \cos(1.570791601) = 1.570796327 = \frac{\pi}{2}$ to 9 decimal places. After a few steps, the arc $(x_{n-1})$ and line segment $\cos(x_{n-1})$ are nearly the same as the quarter circle.

135-146. Example CAS Commands:

Mathematica: (sequence functions may vary):

```
Clear[a, n]
a[n_]; = n^(1/n)
first25= Table[N[a[n]],{n, 1, 25}]
Limit[a[n], n → 8]
```

Mathematica: (sequence functions may vary):

```
Clear[a, n]
a[n_]; = n^(1/n)
first25= Table[N[a[n]],{n, 1, 25}]
Limit[a[n], n → 8]
```

The last command (Limit) will not always work in Mathematica. You could also explore the limit by enlarging your table to more than the first 25 values.

If you know the limit (1 in the above example), to determine how far to go to have all further terms within 0.01 of the limit, do the following.

```
Clear[minN, lim]
lim= 1
Do[{diff=Abs[a[n] − lim], If[diff < .01, {minN= n, Abort[]}]}, {n, 2, 1000}]
minN
```

For sequences that are given recursively, the following code is suggested. The portion of the command a[n_]:=a[n] stores the elements of the sequence and helps to streamline computation.

```
Clear[a, n]
a[1]= 1;
a[n_]; = a[n]= a[n − 1] + (1/5)^(n−1)
first25= Table[N[a[n]], {n, 1, 25}]
```

The limit command does not work in this case, but the limit can be observed as 1.25.

```
Clear[minN, lim]
lim= 1.25
Do[{diff=Abs[a[n] − lim], If[diff < .01, {minN= n, Abort[]}]}, {n, 2, 1000}]
minN
```

## 10.2 INFINITE SERIES

1. $s_n = \frac{a(1-r^n)}{(1-r)} = \frac{2\left(1-\left(\frac{1}{3}\right)^n\right)}{1-\left(\frac{1}{3}\right)} \Rightarrow \lim_{n \to \infty} s_n = \frac{2}{1-\left(\frac{1}{3}\right)} = 3$

2. $s_n = \frac{a(1-r^n)}{(1-r)} = \frac{\left(\frac{9}{100}\right)\left(1-\left(\frac{1}{100}\right)^n\right)}{1-\left(\frac{1}{100}\right)} \Rightarrow \lim_{n \to \infty} s_n = \frac{\left(\frac{9}{100}\right)}{1-\left(\frac{1}{100}\right)} = \frac{1}{11}$

3. $s_n = \frac{a(1-r^n)}{(1-r)} = \frac{1-\left(-\frac{1}{2}\right)^n}{1-\left(-\frac{1}{2}\right)} \Rightarrow \lim_{n \to \infty} s_n = \frac{1}{\left(\frac{3}{2}\right)} = \frac{2}{3}$

4. $s_n = \frac{1-(-2)^n}{1-(-2)}$, a geometric series where $|r| > 1 \Rightarrow$ divergence

5. $\frac{1}{(n+1)(n+2)} = \frac{1}{n+1} - \frac{1}{n+2} \Rightarrow s_n = \left(\frac{1}{2} - \frac{1}{3}\right) + \left(\frac{1}{3} - \frac{1}{4}\right) + \ldots + \left(\frac{1}{n+1} - \frac{1}{n+2}\right) = \frac{1}{2} - \frac{1}{n+2} \Rightarrow \lim_{n \to \infty} s_n = \frac{1}{2}$

6. $\frac{5}{n(n+1)} = \frac{5}{n} - \frac{5}{n+1} \Rightarrow s_n = \left(5 - \frac{5}{2}\right) + \left(\frac{5}{2} - \frac{5}{3}\right) + \left(\frac{5}{3} - \frac{5}{4}\right) + \ldots + \left(\frac{5}{n-1} - \frac{5}{n}\right) + \left(\frac{5}{n} - \frac{5}{n+1}\right) = 5 - \frac{5}{n+1}$
   $\Rightarrow \lim\limits_{n \to \infty} s_n = 5$

7. $1 - \frac{1}{4} + \frac{1}{16} - \frac{1}{64} + \ldots$, the sum of this geometric series is $\frac{1}{1-\left(-\frac{1}{4}\right)} = \frac{1}{1+\left(\frac{1}{4}\right)} = \frac{4}{5}$

8. $\frac{1}{16} + \frac{1}{64} + \frac{1}{256} + \ldots$, the sum of this geometric series is $\frac{\left(\frac{1}{16}\right)}{1-\left(\frac{1}{4}\right)} = \frac{1}{12}$

9. $\frac{7}{4} + \frac{7}{16} + \frac{7}{64} + \ldots$, the sum of this geometric series is $\frac{\left(\frac{7}{4}\right)}{1-\left(\frac{1}{4}\right)} = \frac{7}{3}$

10. $5 - \frac{5}{4} + \frac{5}{16} - \frac{5}{64} + \ldots$, the sum of this geometric series is $\frac{5}{1-\left(-\frac{1}{4}\right)} = 4$

11. $(5 + 1) + \left(\frac{5}{2} + \frac{1}{3}\right) + \left(\frac{5}{4} + \frac{1}{9}\right) + \left(\frac{5}{8} + \frac{1}{27}\right) + \ldots$, is the sum of two geometric series; the sum is
    $\frac{5}{1-\left(\frac{1}{2}\right)} + \frac{1}{1-\left(\frac{1}{3}\right)} = 10 + \frac{3}{2} = \frac{23}{2}$

12. $(5 - 1) + \left(\frac{5}{2} - \frac{1}{3}\right) + \left(\frac{5}{4} - \frac{1}{9}\right) + \left(\frac{5}{8} - \frac{1}{27}\right) + \ldots$, is the difference of two geometric series; the sum is
    $\frac{5}{1-\left(\frac{1}{2}\right)} - \frac{1}{1-\left(\frac{1}{3}\right)} = 10 - \frac{3}{2} = \frac{17}{2}$

13. $(1 + 1) + \left(\frac{1}{2} - \frac{1}{5}\right) + \left(\frac{1}{4} + \frac{1}{25}\right) + \left(\frac{1}{8} - \frac{1}{125}\right) + \ldots$, is the sum of two geometric series; the sum is
    $\frac{1}{1-\left(\frac{1}{2}\right)} + \frac{1}{1+\left(\frac{1}{5}\right)} = 2 + \frac{5}{6} = \frac{17}{6}$

14. $2 + \frac{4}{5} + \frac{8}{25} + \frac{16}{125} + \ldots = 2\left(1 + \frac{2}{5} + \frac{4}{25} + \frac{8}{125} + \ldots\right)$; the sum of this geometric series is $2\left(\frac{1}{1-\left(\frac{2}{5}\right)}\right) = \frac{10}{3}$

15. Series is geometric with $r = \frac{2}{5} \Rightarrow \left|\frac{2}{5}\right| < 1 \Rightarrow$ Converges to $\frac{1}{1-\frac{2}{5}} = \frac{5}{3}$

16. Series is geometric with $r = -3 \Rightarrow \left|-3\right| > 1 \Rightarrow$ Diverges

17. Series is geometric with $r = \frac{1}{8} \Rightarrow \left|\frac{1}{8}\right| < 1 \Rightarrow$ Converges to $\frac{\frac{1}{8}}{1-\frac{1}{8}} = \frac{1}{7}$

18. Series is geometric with $r = -\frac{2}{3} \Rightarrow \left|-\frac{2}{3}\right| < 1 \Rightarrow$ Converges to $\frac{-\frac{2}{3}}{1-\left(-\frac{2}{3}\right)} = -\frac{2}{5}$

19. $0.\overline{23} = \sum\limits_{n=0}^{\infty} \frac{23}{100}\left(\frac{1}{10^2}\right)^n = \frac{\left(\frac{23}{100}\right)}{1-\left(\frac{1}{100}\right)} = \frac{23}{99}$    20. $0.\overline{234} = \sum\limits_{n=0}^{\infty} \frac{234}{1000}\left(\frac{1}{10^3}\right)^n = \frac{\left(\frac{234}{1000}\right)}{1-\left(\frac{1}{1000}\right)} = \frac{234}{999}$

21. $0.\overline{7} = \sum\limits_{n=0}^{\infty} \frac{7}{10}\left(\frac{1}{10}\right)^n = \frac{\left(\frac{7}{10}\right)}{1-\left(\frac{1}{10}\right)} = \frac{7}{9}$    22. $0.\overline{d} = \sum\limits_{n=0}^{\infty} \frac{d}{10}\left(\frac{1}{10}\right)^n = \frac{\left(\frac{d}{10}\right)}{1-\left(\frac{1}{10}\right)} = \frac{d}{9}$

23. $0.0\overline{6} = \sum\limits_{n=0}^{\infty} \left(\frac{1}{10}\right)\left(\frac{6}{10}\right)\left(\frac{1}{10}\right)^n = \frac{\left(\frac{6}{100}\right)}{1-\left(\frac{1}{10}\right)} = \frac{6}{90} = \frac{1}{15}$

24. $1.\overline{414} = 1 + \sum\limits_{n=0}^{\infty} \frac{414}{1000}\left(\frac{1}{10^3}\right)^n = 1 + \frac{\left(\frac{414}{1000}\right)}{1-\left(\frac{1}{1000}\right)} = 1 + \frac{414}{999} = \frac{1413}{999}$

25. $1.2\overline{4123} = \frac{124}{100} + \sum\limits_{n=0}^{\infty} \frac{123}{10^5}\left(\frac{1}{10^3}\right)^n = \frac{124}{100} + \frac{\left(\frac{123}{10^5}\right)}{1-\left(\frac{1}{10^3}\right)} = \frac{124}{100} + \frac{123}{10^5-10^2} = \frac{124}{100} + \frac{123}{99,900} = \frac{123,999}{99,900} = \frac{41,333}{33,300}$

26. $3.\overline{142857} = 3 + \sum\limits_{n=0}^{\infty} \frac{142,857}{10^6}\left(\frac{1}{10^6}\right)^n = 3 + \frac{\left(\frac{142,857}{10^6}\right)}{1-\left(\frac{1}{10^6}\right)} = 3 + \frac{142,857}{10^6-1} = \frac{3,142,854}{999,999} = \frac{116,402}{37,037}$

27. $\lim\limits_{n\to\infty} \frac{n}{n+10} = \lim\limits_{n\to\infty} \frac{1}{1} = 1 \neq 0 \Rightarrow$ diverges

28. $\lim\limits_{n\to\infty} \frac{n(n+1)}{(n+2)(n+3)} = \lim\limits_{n\to\infty} \frac{n^2+n}{n^2+5n+6} = \lim\limits_{n\to\infty} \frac{2n+1}{2n+5} = \lim\limits_{n\to\infty} \frac{2}{2} = 1 \neq 0 \Rightarrow$ diverges

29. $\lim\limits_{n\to\infty} \frac{1}{n+4} = 0 \Rightarrow$ test inconclusive

30. $\lim\limits_{n\to\infty} \frac{n}{n^2+3} = \lim\limits_{n\to\infty} \frac{1}{2n} = 0 \Rightarrow$ test inconclusive

31. $\lim\limits_{n\to\infty} \cos\frac{1}{n} = \cos 0 = 1 \neq 0 \Rightarrow$ diverges

32. $\lim\limits_{n\to\infty} \frac{e^n}{e^n+n} = \lim\limits_{n\to\infty} \frac{e^n}{e^n+1} = \lim\limits_{n\to\infty} \frac{e^n}{e^n} = \lim\limits_{n\to\infty} \frac{1}{1} = 1 \neq 0 \Rightarrow$ diverges

33. $\lim\limits_{n\to\infty} \ln\frac{1}{n} = -\infty \neq 0 \Rightarrow$ diverges

34. $\lim\limits_{n\to\infty} \cos n\pi =$ does not exist $\Rightarrow$ diverges

35. $s_k = \left(1-\frac{1}{2}\right) + \left(\frac{1}{2}-\frac{1}{3}\right) + \left(\frac{1}{3}-\frac{1}{4}\right) + \dots + \left(\frac{1}{k-1}-\frac{1}{k}\right) + \left(\frac{1}{k}-\frac{1}{k+1}\right) = 1 - \frac{1}{k+1} \Rightarrow \lim\limits_{k\to\infty} s_k$

    $= \lim\limits_{k\to\infty} \left(1-\frac{1}{k+1}\right) = 1$, series converges to 1

36. $s_k = \left(\frac{3}{1}-\frac{3}{4}\right) + \left(\frac{3}{4}-\frac{3}{9}\right) + \left(\frac{3}{9}-\frac{3}{16}\right) + \dots + \left(\frac{3}{(k-1)^2}-\frac{3}{k^2}\right) + \left(\frac{3}{k^2}-\frac{3}{(k+1)^2}\right) = 3 - \frac{3}{(k+1)^2} \Rightarrow \lim\limits_{k\to\infty} s_k$

    $= \lim\limits_{k\to\infty} \left(3-\frac{3}{(k+1)^2}\right) = 3$, series converges to 3

37. $s_k = \left(\ln\sqrt{2}-\ln\sqrt{1}\right) + \left(\ln\sqrt{3}-\ln\sqrt{2}\right) + \left(\ln\sqrt{4}-\ln\sqrt{3}\right) + \dots + \left(\ln\sqrt{k}-\ln\sqrt{k-1}\right) + \left(\ln\sqrt{k+1}-\ln\sqrt{k}\right)$

    $= \ln\sqrt{k+1} - \ln\sqrt{1} = \ln\sqrt{k+1} \Rightarrow \lim\limits_{k\to\infty} s_k = \lim\limits_{k\to\infty} \ln\sqrt{k+1} = \infty$; series diverges

38. $s_k = (\tan 1 - \tan 0) + (\tan 2 - \tan 1) + (\tan 3 - \tan 2) + \dots + (\tan k - \tan(k-1)) + (\tan(k+1) - \tan k)$

    $= \tan(k+1) - \tan 0 = \tan(k+1) \Rightarrow \lim\limits_{k\to\infty} s_k = \lim\limits_{k\to\infty} \tan(k+1) =$ does not exist; series diverges

39. $s_k = \left(\cos^{-1}\left(\frac{1}{2}\right) - \cos^{-1}\left(\frac{1}{3}\right)\right) + \left(\cos^{-1}\left(\frac{1}{3}\right) - \cos^{-1}\left(\frac{1}{4}\right)\right) + \left(\cos^{-1}\left(\frac{1}{4}\right) - \cos^{-1}\left(\frac{1}{5}\right)\right) + \dots$

    $+ \left(\cos^{-1}\left(\frac{1}{k}\right) - \cos^{-1}\left(\frac{1}{k+1}\right)\right) + \left(\cos^{-1}\left(\frac{1}{k+1}\right) - \cos^{-1}\left(\frac{1}{k+2}\right)\right) = \frac{\pi}{3} - \cos^{-1}\left(\frac{1}{k+2}\right)$

    $\Rightarrow \lim\limits_{k\to\infty} s_k = \lim\limits_{k\to\infty} \left[\frac{\pi}{3} - \cos^{-1}\left(\frac{1}{k+2}\right)\right] = \frac{\pi}{3} - \frac{\pi}{2} = \frac{\pi}{6}$, series converges to $\frac{\pi}{6}$

40. $s_k = \left(\sqrt{5}-\sqrt{4}\right) + \left(\sqrt{6}-\sqrt{5}\right) + \left(\sqrt{7}-\sqrt{6}\right) + \dots + \left(\sqrt{k+3}-\sqrt{k+2}\right) + \left(\sqrt{k+4}-\sqrt{k+3}\right)$

    $= \sqrt{k+4} - 2 \Rightarrow \lim\limits_{k\to\infty} s_k = \lim\limits_{k\to\infty} \left[\sqrt{k+4}-2\right] = \infty$; series diverges

41. $\frac{4}{(4n-3)(4n+1)} = \frac{1}{4n-3} - \frac{1}{4n+1} \Rightarrow s_k = \left(1 - \frac{1}{5}\right) + \left(\frac{1}{5} - \frac{1}{9}\right) + \left(\frac{1}{9} - \frac{1}{13}\right) + \ldots + \left(\frac{1}{4k-7} - \frac{1}{4k-3}\right)$

$+ \left(\frac{1}{4k-3} - \frac{1}{4k+1}\right) = 1 - \frac{1}{4k+1} \Rightarrow \lim\limits_{k \to \infty} s_k = \lim\limits_{k \to \infty} \left(1 - \frac{1}{4k+1}\right) = 1$

42. $\frac{6}{(2n-1)(2n+1)} = \frac{A}{2n-1} + \frac{B}{2n+1} = \frac{A(2n+1) + B(2n-1)}{(2n-1)(2n+1)} \Rightarrow A(2n+1) + B(2n-1) = 6 \Rightarrow (2A+2B)n + (A-B) = 6$

$\Rightarrow \begin{cases} 2A + 2B = 0 \\ A - B = 6 \end{cases} \Rightarrow \begin{cases} A + B = 0 \\ A - B = 6 \end{cases} \Rightarrow 2A = 6 \Rightarrow A = 3 \text{ and } B = -3. \text{ Hence, } \sum\limits_{n=1}^{k} \frac{6}{(2n-1)(2n+1)} = 3 \sum\limits_{n=1}^{k} \left(\frac{1}{2n-1} - \frac{1}{2n+1}\right)$

$= 3\left(\frac{1}{1} - \frac{1}{3} + \frac{1}{3} - \frac{1}{5} + \frac{1}{5} - \frac{1}{7} + \ldots - \frac{1}{2(k-1)+1} + \frac{1}{2k-1} - \frac{1}{2k+1}\right) = 3\left(1 - \frac{1}{2k+1}\right) \Rightarrow \text{the sum is}$

$\lim\limits_{k \to \infty} 3\left(1 - \frac{1}{2k+1}\right) = 3$

43. $\frac{40n}{(2n-1)^2(2n+1)^2} = \frac{A}{(2n-1)} + \frac{B}{(2n-1)^2} + \frac{C}{(2n+1)} + \frac{D}{(2n+1)^2} = \frac{A(2n-1)(2n+1)^2 + B(2n+1)^2 + C(2n+1)(2n-1)^2 + D(2n-1)^2}{(2n-1)^2(2n+1)^2}$

$\Rightarrow A(2n-1)(2n+1)^2 + B(2n+1)^2 + C(2n+1)(2n-1)^2 + D(2n-1)^2 = 40n$

$\Rightarrow A\left(8n^3 + 4n^2 - 2n - 1\right) + B\left(4n^2 + 4n + 1\right) + C\left(8n^3 - 4n^2 - 2n + 1\right) = D\left(4n^2 - 4n + 1\right) = 40n$

$\Rightarrow (8A + 8C)n^3 + (4A + 4B - 4C + 4D)n^2 + (-2A + 4B - 2C - 4D)n + (-A + B + C + D) = 40n$

$\Rightarrow \begin{cases} 8A + 8C = 0 \\ 4A + 4B - 4C + 4D = 0 \\ -2A + 4B - 2C - 4D = 40 \\ -A + B + C + D = 0 \end{cases} \Rightarrow \begin{cases} 8A + 8C = 0 \\ A + B - C + D = 0 \\ -A + 2B - C - 2D = 20 \\ -A + B + C + D = 0 \end{cases} \Rightarrow \begin{cases} B + D = 0 \\ 2B - 2D = 20 \end{cases} \Rightarrow 4B = 20 \Rightarrow B = 5$

and $D = -5 \Rightarrow \begin{cases} A + C = 0 \\ -A + 5 + C - 5 = 0 \end{cases} \Rightarrow C = 0 \text{ and } A = 0. \text{ Hence, } \sum\limits_{n=1}^{k} \left[\frac{40n}{(2n-1)^2(2n+1)^2}\right]$

$= 5 \sum\limits_{n=1}^{k} \left[\frac{1}{(2n-1)^2} - \frac{1}{(2n+1)^2}\right] = 5\left(\frac{1}{1} - \frac{1}{9} + \frac{1}{9} - \frac{1}{25} + \frac{1}{25} - \ldots - \frac{1}{(2(k-1)+1)^2} + \frac{1}{(2k-1)^2} - \frac{1}{(2k+1)^2}\right)$

$= 5\left(1 - \frac{1}{(2k+1)^2}\right) \Rightarrow \text{the sum is } \lim\limits_{n \to \infty} 5\left(1 - \frac{1}{(2k+1)^2}\right) = 5$

44. $\frac{2n+1}{n^2(n+1)^2} = \frac{1}{n^2} - \frac{1}{(n+1)^2} \Rightarrow s_k = \left(1 - \frac{1}{4}\right) + \left(\frac{1}{4} - \frac{1}{9}\right) + \left(\frac{1}{9} - \frac{1}{16}\right) + \ldots + \left[\frac{1}{(k-1)^2} - \frac{1}{k^2}\right] + \left[\frac{1}{k^2} - \frac{1}{(k+1)^2}\right]$

$\Rightarrow \lim\limits_{k \to \infty} s_k = \lim\limits_{k \to \infty} \left[1 - \frac{1}{(k+1)^2}\right] = 1$

45. $s_k = \left(1 - \frac{1}{\sqrt{2}}\right) + \left(\frac{1}{\sqrt{2}} - \frac{1}{\sqrt{3}}\right) + \left(\frac{1}{\sqrt{3}} - \frac{1}{\sqrt{4}}\right) + \ldots + \left(\frac{1}{\sqrt{k-1}} + \frac{1}{\sqrt{k}}\right) + \left(\frac{1}{\sqrt{k}} - \frac{1}{\sqrt{k+1}}\right) = 1 - \frac{1}{\sqrt{k+1}}$

$\Rightarrow \lim\limits_{k \to \infty} s_k = \lim\limits_{k \to \infty} \left(1 - \frac{1}{\sqrt{k+1}}\right) = 1$

46. $s_k = \left(\frac{1}{2} - \frac{1}{2^{1/2}}\right) + \left(\frac{1}{2^{1/2}} - \frac{1}{2^{1/3}}\right) + \left(\frac{1}{2^{1/3}} - \frac{1}{2^{1/4}}\right) + \ldots + \left(\frac{1}{2^{1/(k-1)}} - \frac{1}{2^{1/k}}\right) + \left(\frac{1}{2^{1/k}} - \frac{1}{2^{1/(k+1)}}\right) = \frac{1}{2} - \frac{1}{2^{1/(k+1)}}$

$\Rightarrow \lim\limits_{k \to \infty} s_k = \frac{1}{2} - \frac{1}{1} = -\frac{1}{2}$

47. $s_k = \left(\frac{1}{\ln 3} - \frac{1}{\ln 2}\right) + \left(\frac{1}{\ln 4} - \frac{1}{\ln 3}\right) + \left(\frac{1}{\ln 5} - \frac{1}{\ln 4}\right) + \ldots + \left(\frac{1}{\ln(k+1)} - \frac{1}{\ln k}\right) + \left(\frac{1}{\ln(k+2)} - \frac{1}{\ln(k+1)}\right)$

$= -\frac{1}{\ln 2} + \frac{1}{\ln(k+2)} \Rightarrow \lim\limits_{k \to \infty} s_k = -\frac{1}{\ln 2}$

48. $s_k = [\tan^{-1}(1) - \tan^{-1}(2)] + [\tan^{-1}(2) - \tan^{-1}(3)] + \ldots + [\tan^{-1}(k-1) - \tan^{-1}(k)]$

$+ [\tan^{-1}(k) - \tan^{-1}(k+1)] = \tan^{-1}(1) - \tan^{-1}(k+1) \Rightarrow \lim\limits_{k \to \infty} s_k = \tan^{-1}(1) - \frac{\pi}{2} = \frac{\pi}{4} - \frac{\pi}{2} = -\frac{\pi}{4}$

49. convergent geometric series with sum $\frac{1}{1 - \left(\frac{1}{\sqrt{2}}\right)} = \frac{\sqrt{2}}{\sqrt{2}-1} = 2 + \sqrt{2}$

50. divergent geometric series with $|r| = \sqrt{2} > 1$       51. convergent geometric series with sum $\frac{\left(\frac{3}{2}\right)}{1 - \left(-\frac{1}{2}\right)} = 1$

52. $\lim_{n \to \infty} (-1)^{n+1}n \neq 0 \Rightarrow$ diverges

53. $\lim_{n \to \infty} \cos(n\pi) = \lim_{n \to \infty} (-1)^n \neq 0 \Rightarrow$ diverges

54. $\cos(n\pi) = (-1)^n \Rightarrow$ convergent geometric series with sum $\frac{1}{1-\left(-\frac{1}{5}\right)} = \frac{5}{6}$

55. convergent geometric series with sum $\frac{1}{1-\left(\frac{1}{e^2}\right)} = \frac{e^2}{e^2-1}$

56. $\lim_{n \to \infty} \ln\frac{1}{3^n} = -\infty \neq 0 \Rightarrow$ diverges

57. convergent geometric series with sum $\frac{2}{1-\left(\frac{1}{10}\right)} - 2 = \frac{20}{9} - \frac{18}{9} = \frac{2}{9}$

58. convergent geometric series with sum $\frac{1}{1-\left(\frac{1}{x}\right)} = \frac{x}{x-1}$

59. difference of two geometric series with sum $\frac{1}{1-\left(\frac{2}{3}\right)} - \frac{1}{1-\left(\frac{1}{3}\right)} = 3 - \frac{3}{2} = \frac{3}{2}$

60. $\lim_{n \to \infty} \left(1 - \frac{1}{n}\right)^n = \lim_{n \to \infty} \left(1 + \frac{-1}{n}\right)^n = e^{-1} \neq 0 \Rightarrow$ diverges

61. $\lim_{n \to \infty} \frac{n!}{1000^n} = \infty \neq 0 \Rightarrow$ diverges

62. $\lim_{n \to \infty} \frac{n^n}{n!} = \lim_{n \to \infty} \frac{n \cdot n \cdots n}{1 \cdot 2 \cdots n} > \lim_{n \to \infty} n = \infty \Rightarrow$ diverges

63. $\sum_{n=1}^{\infty} \frac{2^n + 3^n}{4^n} = \sum_{n=1}^{\infty} \frac{2^n}{4^n} + \sum_{n=1}^{\infty} \frac{3^n}{4^n} = \sum_{n=1}^{\infty} \left(\frac{1}{2}\right)^n + \sum_{n=1}^{\infty} \left(\frac{3}{4}\right)^n$; both $= \sum_{n=1}^{\infty} \left(\frac{1}{2}\right)^n$ and $\sum_{n=1}^{\infty} \left(\frac{3}{4}\right)^n$ are geometric series, and both converge

since $r = \frac{1}{2} \Rightarrow \left|\frac{1}{2}\right| < 1$ and $r = \frac{3}{4} \Rightarrow \left|\frac{3}{4}\right| < 1$, respectivley $\Rightarrow \sum_{n=1}^{\infty} \left(\frac{1}{2}\right)^n = \frac{\frac{1}{2}}{1-\frac{1}{2}} = 1$ and $\sum_{n=1}^{\infty} \left(\frac{3}{4}\right)^n = \frac{\frac{3}{4}}{1-\frac{3}{4}} = 3 \Rightarrow$

$\sum_{n=1}^{\infty} \frac{2^n + 3^n}{4^n} = 1 + 3 = 4$ by Theorem 8, part (1)

64. $\lim_{n \to \infty} \frac{2^n + 4^n}{3^n + 4^n} = \lim_{n \to \infty} \frac{\frac{2^n}{4^n} + 1}{\frac{3^n}{4^n} + 1} = \lim_{n \to \infty} \frac{\left(\frac{1}{2}\right)^n + 1}{\left(\frac{3}{4}\right)^n + 1} = \frac{1}{1} = 1 \neq 0 \Rightarrow$ diverges by $n^{th}$ term test for divergence

65. $\sum_{n=1}^{\infty} \ln\left(\frac{n}{n+1}\right) = \sum_{n=1}^{\infty} [\ln(n) - \ln(n+1)] \Rightarrow s_k = [\ln(1) - \ln(2)] + [\ln(2) - \ln(3)] + [\ln(3) - \ln(4)] + \ldots$

$+ [\ln(k-1) - \ln(k)] + [\ln(k) - \ln(k+1)] = -\ln(k+1) \Rightarrow \lim_{k \to \infty} s_k = -\infty, \Rightarrow$ diverges

66. $\lim_{n \to \infty} a_n = \lim_{n \to \infty} \ln\left(\frac{n}{2n+1}\right) = \ln\left(\frac{1}{2}\right) \neq 0 \Rightarrow$ diverges

67. convergent geometric series with sum $\frac{1}{1-\left(\frac{e}{\pi}\right)} = \frac{\pi}{\pi - e}$

68. divergent geometric series with $|r| = \frac{e^\pi}{\pi^e} \approx \frac{23.141}{22.459} > 1$

69. $\sum_{n=0}^{\infty} (-1)^n x^n = \sum_{n=0}^{\infty} (-x)^n$; $a = 1, r = -x$; converges to $\frac{1}{1-(-x)} = \frac{1}{1+x}$ for $|x| < 1$

70. $\sum_{n=0}^{\infty} (-1)^n x^{2n} = \sum_{n=0}^{\infty} (-x^2)^n$; $a = 1, r = -x^2$; converges to $\frac{1}{1+x^2}$ for $|x| < 1$

71. $a = 3, r = \frac{x-1}{2}$ ; converges to $\frac{3}{1-\left(\frac{x-1}{2}\right)} = \frac{6}{3-x}$ for $-1 < \frac{x-1}{2} < 1$ or $-1 < x < 3$

72. $\sum_{n=0}^{\infty} \frac{(-1)^n}{2} \left(\frac{1}{3+\sin x}\right)^n = \sum_{n=0}^{\infty} \frac{1}{2} \left(\frac{-1}{3+\sin x}\right)^n; a = \frac{1}{2}, r = \frac{-1}{3+\sin x}$ ; converges to $\frac{\left(\frac{1}{2}\right)}{1-\left(\frac{-1}{3+\sin x}\right)}$

$= \frac{3+\sin x}{2(4+\sin x)} = \frac{3+\sin x}{8+2\sin x}$ for all x $\left(\text{since } \frac{1}{4} \le \frac{1}{3+\sin x} \le \frac{1}{2} \text{ for all x}\right)$

73. $a = 1, r = 2x$; converges to $\frac{1}{1-2x}$ for $|2x| < 1$ or $|x| < \frac{1}{2}$

74. $a = 1, r = -\frac{1}{x^2}$ ; converges to $\frac{1}{1-\left(\frac{-1}{x^2}\right)} = \frac{x^2}{x^2+1}$ for $\left|\frac{1}{x^2}\right| < 1$ or $|x| > 1.$

75. $a = 1, r = -(x+1)^n$; converges to $\frac{1}{1+(x+1)} = \frac{1}{2+x}$ for $|x+1| < 1$ or $-2 < x < 0$

76. $a = 1, r = \frac{3-x}{2}$ ; converges to $\frac{1}{1-\left(\frac{3-x}{2}\right)} = \frac{2}{x-1}$ for $\left|\frac{3-x}{2}\right| < 1$ or $1 < x < 5$

77. $a = 1, r = \sin x$; converges to $\frac{1}{1-\sin x}$ for $x \ne (2k+1)\frac{\pi}{2}$ , k an integer

78. $a = 1, r = \ln x$; converges to $\frac{1}{1-\ln x}$ for $|\ln x| < 1$ or $e^{-1} < x < e$

79. (a) $\sum_{n=-2}^{\infty} \frac{1}{(n+4)(n+5)}$    (b) $\sum_{n=0}^{\infty} \frac{1}{(n+2)(n+3)}$    (c) $\sum_{n=5}^{\infty} \frac{1}{(n-3)(n-2)}$

80. (a) $\sum_{n=-1}^{\infty} \frac{5}{(n+2)(n+3)}$    (b) $\sum_{n=3}^{\infty} \frac{5}{(n-2)(n-1)}$    (c) $\sum_{n=20}^{\infty} \frac{5}{(n-19)(n-18)}$

81. (a) one example is $\frac{1}{2} + \frac{1}{4} + \frac{1}{8} + \frac{1}{16} + \ldots = \frac{\left(\frac{1}{2}\right)}{1-\left(\frac{1}{2}\right)} = 1$

(b) one example is $-\frac{3}{2} - \frac{3}{4} - \frac{3}{8} - \frac{3}{16} - \ldots = \frac{\left(-\frac{3}{2}\right)}{1-\left(\frac{1}{2}\right)} = -3$

(c) one example is $1 - \frac{1}{2} - \frac{1}{4} - \frac{1}{8} - \frac{1}{16} - \ldots = 1 - \frac{\left(\frac{1}{2}\right)}{1-\left(\frac{1}{2}\right)} = 0.$

82. The series $\sum_{n=0}^{\infty} k\left(\frac{1}{2}\right)^{n+1}$ is a geometric series whose sum is $\frac{\left(\frac{k}{2}\right)}{1-\left(\frac{1}{2}\right)} = k$ where k can be any positive or negative number.

83. Let $a_n = b_n = \left(\frac{1}{2}\right)^n$. Then $\sum_{n=1}^{\infty} a_n = \sum_{n=1}^{\infty} b_n = \sum_{n=1}^{\infty} \left(\frac{1}{2}\right)^n = 1$, while $\sum_{n=1}^{\infty} \left(\frac{a_n}{b_n}\right) = \sum_{n=1}^{\infty} (1)$ diverges.

84. Let $a_n = b_n = \left(\frac{1}{2}\right)^n$. Then $\sum_{n=1}^{\infty} a_n = \sum_{n=1}^{\infty} b_n = \sum_{n=1}^{\infty} \left(\frac{1}{2}\right)^n = 1$, while $\sum_{n=1}^{\infty} (a_n b_n) = \sum_{n=1}^{\infty} \left(\frac{1}{4}\right)^n = \frac{1}{3} \ne AB.$

85. Let $a_n = \left(\frac{1}{4}\right)^n$ and $b_n = \left(\frac{1}{2}\right)^n$. Then $A = \sum_{n=1}^{\infty} a_n = \frac{1}{3}$, $B = \sum_{n=1}^{\infty} b_n = 1$ and $\sum_{n=1}^{\infty} \left(\frac{a_n}{b_n}\right) = \sum_{n=1}^{\infty} \left(\frac{1}{2}\right)^n = 1 \ne \frac{A}{B}.$

86. Yes: $\sum \left(\frac{1}{a_n}\right)$ diverges. The reasoning: $\sum a_n$ converges $\Rightarrow a_n \to 0 \Rightarrow \frac{1}{a_n} \to \infty \Rightarrow \sum \left(\frac{1}{a_n}\right)$ diverges by the nth-Term Test.

87. Since the sum of a finite number of terms is finite, adding or subtracting a finite number of terms from a series that diverges does not change the divergence of the series.

88. Let $A_n = a_1 + a_2 + \ldots + a_n$ and $\lim\limits_{n \to \infty} A_n = A$. Assume $\sum (a_n + b_n)$ converges to S. Let
$S_n = (a_1 + b_1) + (a_2 + b_2) + \ldots + (a_n + b_n) \Rightarrow S_n = (a_1 + a_2 + \ldots + a_n) + (b_1 + b_2 + \ldots + b_n)$
$\Rightarrow b_1 + b_2 + \ldots + b_n = S_n - A_n \Rightarrow \lim\limits_{n \to \infty} (b_1 + b_2 + \ldots + b_n) = S - A \Rightarrow \sum b_n$ converges. This
contradicts the assumption that $\sum b_n$ diverges; therefore, $\sum (a_n + b_n)$ diverges.

89. (a) $\frac{2}{1-r} = 5 \Rightarrow \frac{2}{5} = 1 - r \Rightarrow r = \frac{3}{5}; 2 + 2\left(\frac{3}{5}\right) + 2\left(\frac{3}{5}\right)^2 + \ldots$

   (b) $\frac{\left(\frac{13}{2}\right)}{1-r} = 5 \Rightarrow \frac{13}{10} = 1 - r \Rightarrow r = -\frac{3}{10}; \frac{13}{2} - \frac{13}{2}\left(\frac{3}{10}\right) + \frac{13}{2}\left(\frac{3}{10}\right)^2 - \frac{13}{2}\left(\frac{3}{10}\right)^3 + \ldots$

90. $1 + e^b + e^{2b} + \ldots = \frac{1}{1 - e^b} = 9 \Rightarrow \frac{1}{9} = 1 - e^b \Rightarrow e^b = \frac{8}{9} \Rightarrow b = \ln\left(\frac{8}{9}\right)$

91. $s_n = 1 + 2r + r^2 + 2r^3 + r^4 + 2r^5 + \ldots + r^{2n} + 2r^{2n+1}, n = 0, 1, \ldots$
   $\Rightarrow s_n = (1 + r^2 + r^4 + \ldots + r^{2n}) + (2r + 2r^3 + 2r^5 + \ldots + 2r^{2n+1}) \Rightarrow \lim\limits_{n \to \infty} s_n = \frac{1}{1-r^2} + \frac{2r}{1-r^2}$
   $= \frac{1+2r}{1-r^2}$, if $|r^2| < 1$ or $|r| < 1$

92. $L - s_n = \frac{a}{1-r} - \frac{a(1-r^n)}{1-r} = \frac{ar^n}{1-r}$

93. area $= 2^2 + \left(\sqrt{2}\right)^2 + (1)^2 + \left(\frac{1}{\sqrt{2}}\right)^2 + \ldots = 4 + 2 + 1 + \frac{1}{2} + \ldots = \frac{4}{1 - \frac{1}{2}} = 8$ m$^2$

94. (a) $L_1 = 3, L_2 = 3\left(\frac{4}{3}\right), L_3 = 3\left(\frac{4}{3}\right)^2, \ldots, L_n = 3\left(\frac{4}{3}\right)^{n-1} \Rightarrow \lim\limits_{n \to \infty} L_n = \lim\limits_{n \to \infty} 3\left(\frac{4}{3}\right)^{n-1} = \infty$

   (b) Using the fact that the area of an equilateral triangle of side length s is $\frac{\sqrt{3}}{4}s^2$, we see that $A_1 = \frac{\sqrt{3}}{4}$,
   $A_2 = A_1 + 3\left(\frac{\sqrt{3}}{4}\right)\left(\frac{1}{3}\right)^2 = \frac{\sqrt{3}}{4} + \frac{\sqrt{3}}{12}, A_3 = A_2 + 3(4)\left(\frac{\sqrt{3}}{4}\right)\left(\frac{1}{3^2}\right)^2 = \frac{\sqrt{3}}{4} + \frac{\sqrt{3}}{12} + \frac{\sqrt{3}}{27},$
   $A_4 = A_3 + 3(4)^2\left(\frac{\sqrt{3}}{4}\right)\left(\frac{1}{3^3}\right)^2, A_5 = A_4 + 3(4)^3\left(\frac{\sqrt{3}}{4}\right)\left(\frac{1}{3^4}\right)^2, \ldots,$
   $A_n = \frac{\sqrt{3}}{4} + \sum\limits_{k=2}^{n} 3(4)^{k-2}\left(\frac{\sqrt{3}}{4}\right)\left(\frac{1}{3^2}\right)^{k-1} = \frac{\sqrt{3}}{4} + \sum\limits_{k=2}^{n} 3\sqrt{3}(4)^{k-3}\left(\frac{1}{9}\right)^{k-1} = \frac{\sqrt{3}}{4} + 3\sqrt{3}\left(\sum\limits_{k=2}^{n} \frac{4^{k-3}}{9^{k-1}}\right).$
   $\lim\limits_{n \to \infty} A_n = \lim\limits_{n \to \infty}\left(\frac{\sqrt{3}}{4} + 3\sqrt{3}\left(\sum\limits_{k=2}^{n} \frac{4^{k-3}}{9^{k-1}}\right)\right) = \frac{\sqrt{3}}{4} + 3\sqrt{3}\left(\frac{\frac{1}{36}}{1 - \frac{4}{9}}\right) = \frac{\sqrt{3}}{4} + 3\sqrt{3}\left(\frac{1}{20}\right) = \frac{\sqrt{3}}{4}\left(1 + \frac{3}{5}\right)$
   $= \frac{\sqrt{3}}{4}\left(\frac{8}{5}\right) = \frac{8}{5}A_1$

## 10.3 THE INTEGRAL TEST

1. $f(x) = \frac{1}{x^2}$ is positive, continuous, and decreasing for $x \geq 1$; $\int_1^{\infty} \frac{1}{x^2} dx = \lim\limits_{b \to \infty} \int_1^b \frac{1}{x^2} dx = \lim\limits_{b \to \infty}\left[-\frac{1}{x}\right]_1^b$
   $= \lim\limits_{b \to \infty}\left(-\frac{1}{b} + 1\right) = 1 \Rightarrow \int_1^{\infty} \frac{1}{x^2} dx$ converges $\Rightarrow \sum\limits_{n=1}^{\infty} \frac{1}{n^2}$ converges

2. $f(x) = \frac{1}{x^{0.2}}$ is positive, continuous, and decreasing for $x \geq 1$; $\int_1^{\infty} \frac{1}{x^{0.2}} dx = \lim\limits_{b \to \infty} \int_1^b \frac{1}{x^{0.2}} dx = \lim\limits_{b \to \infty}\left[\frac{5}{4}x^{0.8}\right]_1^b$
   $= \lim\limits_{b \to \infty}\left(\frac{5}{4}b^{0.8} - \frac{5}{4}\right) = \infty \Rightarrow \int_1^{\infty} \frac{1}{x^{0.2}} dx$ diverges $\Rightarrow \sum\limits_{n=1}^{\infty} \frac{1}{n^{0.2}}$ diverges

3. $f(x) = \frac{1}{x^2+4}$ is positive, continuous, and decreasing for $x \geq 1$; $\int_1^\infty \frac{1}{x^2+4}\, dx = \lim_{b \to \infty} \int_1^b \frac{1}{x^2+4}\, dx = \lim_{b \to \infty} \left[ \frac{1}{2}\tan^{-1}\frac{x}{2} \right]_1^b$

$= \lim_{b \to \infty} \left( \frac{1}{2}\tan^{-1}\frac{b}{2} - \frac{1}{2}\tan^{-1}\frac{1}{2} \right) = \frac{\pi}{4} - \frac{1}{2}\tan^{-1}\frac{1}{2} \Rightarrow \int_1^\infty \frac{1}{x^2+4}\, dx$ converges $\Rightarrow \sum_{n=1}^{\infty} \frac{1}{n^2+4}$ converges

4. $f(x) = \frac{1}{x+4}$ is positive, continuous, and decreasing for $x \geq 1$; $\int_1^\infty \frac{1}{x+4}\, dx = \lim_{b \to \infty} \int_1^b \frac{1}{x+4}\, dx = \lim_{b \to \infty} \left[ \ln|x+4| \right]_1^b$

$= \lim_{b \to \infty} \left( \ln|b+4| - \ln 5 \right) = \infty \Rightarrow \int_1^\infty \frac{1}{x+4}\, dx$ diverges $\Rightarrow \sum_{n=1}^{\infty} \frac{1}{n+4}$ diverges

5. $f(x) = e^{-2x}$ is positive, continuous, and decreasing for $x \geq 1$; $\int_1^\infty e^{-2x}\, dx = \lim_{b \to \infty} \int_1^b e^{-2x}\, dx = \lim_{b \to \infty} \left[ -\frac{1}{2}e^{-2x} \right]_1^b$

$= \lim_{b \to \infty} \left( -\frac{1}{2e^{2b}} + \frac{1}{2e^2} \right) = \frac{1}{2e^2} \Rightarrow \int_1^\infty e^{-2x}\, dx$ converges $\Rightarrow \sum_{n=1}^{\infty} e^{-2n}$ converges

6. $f(x) = \frac{1}{x(\ln x)^2}$ is positive, continuous, and decreasing for $x \geq 2$; $\int_2^\infty \frac{1}{x(\ln x)^2}\, dx = \lim_{b \to \infty} \int_2^b \frac{1}{x(\ln x)^2}\, dx = \lim_{b \to \infty} \left[ -\frac{1}{\ln x} \right]_2^b$

$= \lim_{b \to \infty} \left( -\frac{1}{\ln b} + \frac{1}{\ln 2} \right) = \frac{1}{\ln 2} \Rightarrow \int_2^\infty \frac{1}{x(\ln x)^2}\, dx$ converges $\Rightarrow \sum_{n=2}^{\infty} \frac{1}{n(\ln n)^2}$ converges

7. $f(x) = \frac{x}{x^2+4}$ is positive and continuous for $x \geq 1$, $f'(x) = \frac{4-x^2}{(x^2+4)^2} < 0$ for $x > 2$, thus $f$ is decreasing for $x \geq 3$;

$\int_3^\infty \frac{x}{x^2+4}\, dx = \lim_{b \to \infty} \int_3^b \frac{x}{x^2+4}\, dx = \lim_{b \to \infty} \left[ \frac{1}{2}\ln(x^2+4) \right]_3^b = \lim_{b \to \infty} \left( \frac{1}{2}\ln(b^2+4) - \frac{1}{2}\ln(13) \right) = \infty \Rightarrow \int_3^\infty \frac{x}{x^2+4}\, dx$

diverges $\Rightarrow \sum_{n=3}^{\infty} \frac{n}{n^2+4}$ diverges $\Rightarrow \sum_{n=1}^{\infty} \frac{n}{n^2+4} = \frac{1}{5} + \frac{2}{8} + \sum_{n=3}^{\infty} \frac{n}{n^2+4}$ diverges

8. $f(x) = \frac{\ln x^2}{x}$ is positive and continuous for $x \geq 2$, $f'(x) = \frac{2 - \ln x^2}{x^2} < 0$ for $x > e$, thus $f$ is decreasing for $x \geq 3$;

$\int_3^\infty \frac{\ln x^2}{x}\, dx = \lim_{b \to \infty} \int_3^b \frac{\ln x^2}{x}\, dx = \lim_{b \to \infty} \left[ 2(\ln x)^2 \right]_3^b = \lim_{b \to \infty} \left( 2(\ln b)^2 - 2(\ln 3)^2 \right) = \infty \Rightarrow \int_3^\infty \frac{\ln x^2}{x}\, dx$

diverges $\Rightarrow \sum_{n=3}^{\infty} \frac{\ln n^2}{n}$ diverges $\Rightarrow \sum_{n=2}^{\infty} \frac{\ln n^2}{n} = \frac{\ln 4}{2} + \sum_{n=3}^{\infty} \frac{\ln n^2}{n}$ diverges

9. $f(x) = \frac{x^2}{e^{x/3}}$ is positive and continuous for $x \geq 1$, $f'(x) = \frac{-x(x-6)}{3e^{x/3}} < 0$ for $x > 6$, thus $f$ is decreasing for $x \geq 7$;

$\int_7^\infty \frac{x^2}{e^{x/3}}\, dx = \lim_{b \to \infty} \int_7^b \frac{x^2}{e^{x/3}}\, dx = \lim_{b \to \infty} \left[ -\frac{3x^2}{e^{x/3}} - \frac{18x}{e^{x/3}} - \frac{54}{e^{x/3}} \right]_7^b = \lim_{b \to \infty} \left( \frac{-3b^2 - 18b - 54}{e^{b/3}} + \frac{327}{e^{7/3}} \right) =$

$= \lim_{b \to \infty} \left( \frac{3(-6b - 18)}{e^{b/3}} \right) + \frac{327}{e^{7/3}} = \lim_{b \to \infty} \left( \frac{-54}{e^{b/3}} \right) + \frac{327}{e^{7/3}} = \frac{327}{e^{7/3}} \Rightarrow \int_7^\infty \frac{x^2}{e^{x/3}}\, dx$ converges $\Rightarrow \sum_{n=7}^{\infty} \frac{n^2}{e^{n/3}}$ converges

$\Rightarrow \sum_{n=1}^{\infty} \frac{n^2}{e^{n/3}} = \frac{1}{e^{1/3}} + \frac{4}{e^{2/3}} + \frac{9}{e^1} + \frac{16}{e^{4/3}} + \frac{25}{e^{5/3}} + \frac{36}{e^2} + \sum_{n=7}^{\infty} \frac{n^2}{e^{n/3}}$ converges

10. $f(x) = \frac{x-4}{x^2-2x+1} = \frac{x-4}{(x-1)^2}$ is continuous for $x \geq 2$, $f$ is positive for $x > 4$, and $f'(x) = \frac{7-x}{(x-1)^3} < 0$ for $x > 7$, thus $f$ is

decreasing for $x \geq 8$; $\int_8^\infty \frac{x-4}{(x-1)^2}\, dx = \lim_{b \to \infty} \left[ \int_8^b \frac{x-1}{(x-1)^2}\, dx - \int_8^b \frac{3}{(x-1)^2}\, dx \right] = \lim_{b \to \infty} \left[ \int_8^b \frac{1}{x-1}\, dx - \int_8^b \frac{3}{(x-1)^2}\, dx \right]$

$= \lim_{b \to \infty} \left[ \ln|x-1| + \frac{3}{x-1} \right]_8^b = \lim_{b \to \infty} \left( \ln|b-1| + \frac{3}{b-1} - \ln 7 - \frac{3}{7} \right) = \infty \Rightarrow \int_8^\infty \frac{x-4}{(x-1)^2}\, dx$ diverges

$\Rightarrow \sum_{n=8}^{\infty} \frac{n-4}{n^2-2n+1}$ diverges $\Rightarrow \sum_{n=2}^{\infty} \frac{n-4}{n^2-2n+1} = -2 - \frac{1}{4} + 0 + \frac{1}{16} + \frac{2}{25} + \frac{3}{36} + \sum_{n=8}^{\infty} \frac{n-4}{n^2-2n+1}$ diverges

11. converges; a geometric series with $r = \frac{1}{10} < 1$          12. converges; a geometric series with $r = \frac{1}{e} < 1$

13. diverges; by the nth-Term Test for Divergence, $\lim_{n \to \infty} \frac{n}{n+1} = 1 \neq 0$

14. diverges by the Integral Test; $\int_1^n \frac{5}{x+1}\,dx = 5\ln(n+1) - 5\ln 2 \;\Rightarrow\; \int_1^\infty \frac{5}{x+1}\,dx \to \infty$

15. diverges; $\sum\limits_{n=1}^\infty \frac{3}{\sqrt{n}} = 3\sum\limits_{n=1}^\infty \frac{1}{\sqrt{n}}$, which is a divergent p-series ($p = \frac{1}{2}$)

16. converges; $\sum\limits_{n=1}^\infty \frac{-2}{n\sqrt{n}} = -2\sum\limits_{n=1}^\infty \frac{1}{n^{3/2}}$, which is a convergent p-series ($p = \frac{3}{2}$)

17. converges; a geometric series with $r = \frac{1}{8} < 1$

18. diverges; $\sum\limits_{n=1}^\infty \frac{-8}{n} = -8\sum\limits_{n=1}^\infty \frac{1}{n}$ and since $\sum\limits_{n=1}^\infty \frac{1}{n}$ diverges, $-8\sum\limits_{n=1}^\infty \frac{1}{n}$ diverges

19. diverges by the Integral Test: $\int_2^n \frac{\ln x}{x}\,dx = \frac{1}{2}\left(\ln^2 n - \ln 2\right) \;\Rightarrow\; \int_2^\infty \frac{\ln x}{x}\,dx \to \infty$

20. diverges by the Integral Test: $\int_2^\infty \frac{\ln x}{\sqrt{x}}\,dx;\; \begin{bmatrix} t = \ln x \\ dt = \frac{dx}{x} \\ dx = e^t\,dt \end{bmatrix} \to \int_{\ln 2}^\infty t e^{t/2}\,dt = \lim\limits_{b\to\infty}\left[2te^{t/2} - 4e^{t/2}\right]_{\ln 2}^{b}$

$= \lim\limits_{b\to\infty}\left[2e^{b/2}(b-2) - 2e^{(\ln 2)/2}(\ln 2 - 2)\right] = \infty$

21. converges; a geometric series with $r = \frac{2}{3} < 1$

22. diverges; $\lim\limits_{n\to\infty} \frac{5^n}{4^n+3} = \lim\limits_{n\to\infty} \frac{5^n \ln 5}{4^n \ln 4} = \lim\limits_{n\to\infty}\left(\frac{\ln 5}{\ln 4}\right)\left(\frac{5}{4}\right)^n = \infty \neq 0$

23. diverges; $\sum\limits_{n=0}^\infty \frac{-2}{n+1} = -2\sum\limits_{n=0}^\infty \frac{1}{n+1}$, which diverges by the Integral Test

24. diverges by the Integral Test: $\int_1^n \frac{dx}{2x-1} = \frac{1}{2}\ln(2n-1) \to \infty$ as $n \to \infty$

25. diverges; $\lim\limits_{n\to\infty} a_n = \lim\limits_{n\to\infty} \frac{2^n}{n+1} = \lim\limits_{n\to\infty} \frac{2^n \ln 2}{1} = \infty \neq 0$

26. diverges by the Integral Test: $\int_1^n \frac{dx}{\sqrt{x}\,(\sqrt{x}+1)};\; \begin{bmatrix} u = \sqrt{x}+1 \\ du = \frac{dx}{\sqrt{x}} \end{bmatrix} \to \int_2^{\sqrt{n}+1} \frac{du}{u} = \ln\left(\sqrt{n}+1\right) - \ln 2 \to \infty$ as $n \to \infty$

27. diverges; $\lim\limits_{n\to\infty} \frac{\sqrt{n}}{\ln n} = \lim\limits_{n\to\infty} \frac{\left(\frac{1}{2\sqrt{n}}\right)}{\left(\frac{1}{n}\right)} = \lim\limits_{n\to\infty} \frac{\sqrt{n}}{2} = \infty \neq 0$

28. diverges; $\lim\limits_{n\to\infty} a_n = \lim\limits_{n\to\infty} \left(1 + \frac{1}{n}\right)^n = e \neq 0$

29. diverges; a geometric series with $r = \frac{1}{\ln 2} \approx 1.44 > 1$

30. converges; a geometric series with $r = \frac{1}{\ln 3} \approx 0.91 < 1$

31. converges by the Integral Test: $\int_3^\infty \frac{\left(\frac{1}{x}\right)}{(\ln x)\sqrt{(\ln x)^2 - 1}}\,dx;\; \begin{bmatrix} u = \ln x \\ du = \frac{1}{x}\,dx \end{bmatrix} \to \int_{\ln 3}^\infty \frac{1}{u\sqrt{u^2-1}}\,du$

$= \lim\limits_{b \to \infty} [\sec^{-1}|u|]_{\ln 3}^{b} = \lim\limits_{b \to \infty} [\sec^{-1} b - \sec^{-1}(\ln 3)] = \lim\limits_{b \to \infty} [\cos^{-1}(\frac{1}{b}) - \sec^{-1}(\ln 3)]$

$= \cos^{-1}(0) - \sec^{-1}(\ln 3) = \frac{\pi}{2} - \sec^{-1}(\ln 3) \approx 1.1439$

32. converges by the Integral Test: $\int_1^\infty \frac{1}{x(1+\ln^2 x)}\,dx = \int_1^\infty \frac{(\frac{1}{x})}{1+(\ln x)^2}\,dx; \begin{bmatrix} u = \ln x \\ du = \frac{1}{x}\,dx \end{bmatrix} \to \int_0^\infty \frac{1}{1+u^2}\,du$

$= \lim\limits_{b \to \infty} [\tan^{-1} u]_0^b = \lim\limits_{b \to \infty} (\tan^{-1} b - \tan^{-1} 0) = \frac{\pi}{2} - 0 = \frac{\pi}{2}$

33. diverges by the nth-Term Test for divergence; $\lim\limits_{n \to \infty} n \sin(\frac{1}{n}) = \lim\limits_{n \to \infty} \frac{\sin(\frac{1}{n})}{(\frac{1}{n})} = \lim\limits_{x \to 0} \frac{\sin x}{x} = 1 \neq 0$

34. diverges by the nth-Term Test for divergence; $\lim\limits_{n \to \infty} n \tan(\frac{1}{n}) = \lim\limits_{n \to \infty} \frac{\tan(\frac{1}{n})}{(\frac{1}{n})} = \lim\limits_{n \to \infty} \frac{(-\frac{1}{n^2}) \sec^2(\frac{1}{n})}{(-\frac{1}{n^2})}$

$= \lim\limits_{n \to \infty} \sec^2(\frac{1}{n}) = \sec^2 0 = 1 \neq 0$

35. converges by the Integral Test: $\int_1^\infty \frac{e^x}{1+e^{2x}}\,dx; \begin{bmatrix} u = e^x \\ du = e^x\,dx \end{bmatrix} \to \int_e^\infty \frac{1}{1+u^2}\,du = \lim\limits_{n \to \infty} [\tan^{-1} u]_e^b$

$= \lim\limits_{b \to \infty} (\tan^{-1} b - \tan^{-1} e) = \frac{\pi}{2} - \tan^{-1} e \approx 0.35$

36. converges by the Integral Test: $\int_1^\infty \frac{2}{1+e^x}\,dx; \begin{bmatrix} u = e^x \\ du = e^x\,dx \\ dx = \frac{1}{u}\,du \end{bmatrix} \to \int_e^\infty \frac{2}{u(1+u)}\,du = \int_e^\infty (\frac{2}{u} - \frac{2}{u+1})\,du$

$= \lim\limits_{b \to \infty} [2 \ln \frac{u}{u+1}]_e^b = \lim\limits_{b \to \infty} 2 \ln(\frac{b}{b+1}) - 2 \ln(\frac{e}{e+1}) = 2 \ln 1 - 2 \ln(\frac{e}{e+1}) = -2 \ln(\frac{e}{e+1}) \approx 0.63$

37. converges by the Integral Test: $\int_1^\infty \frac{8 \tan^{-1} x}{1+x^2}\,dx; \begin{bmatrix} u = \tan^{-1} x \\ du = \frac{dx}{1+x^2} \end{bmatrix} \to \int_{\pi/4}^{\pi/2} 8u\,du = [4u^2]_{\pi/4}^{\pi/2} = 4(\frac{\pi^2}{4} - \frac{\pi^2}{16}) = \frac{3\pi^2}{4}$

38. diverges by the Integral Test: $\int_1^\infty \frac{x}{x^2+1}\,dx; \begin{bmatrix} u = x^2 + 1 \\ du = 2x\,dx \end{bmatrix} \to \frac{1}{2} \int_2^\infty \frac{du}{4} = \lim\limits_{b \to \infty} [\frac{1}{2} \ln u]_2^b = \lim\limits_{b \to \infty} \frac{1}{2}(\ln b - \ln 2) = \infty$

39. converges by the Integral Test: $\int_1^\infty \text{sech } x\,dx = 2 \lim\limits_{b \to \infty} \int_1^b \frac{e^x}{1+(e^x)^2}\,dx = 2 \lim\limits_{b \to \infty} [\tan^{-1} e^x]_1^b$

$= 2 \lim\limits_{b \to \infty} (\tan^{-1} e^b - \tan^{-1} e) = \pi - 2 \tan^{-1} e \approx 0.71$

40. converges by the Integral Test: $\int_1^\infty \text{sech}^2 x\,dx = \lim\limits_{b \to \infty} \int_1^b \text{sech}^2 x\,dx = \lim\limits_{b \to \infty} [\tanh x]_1^b = \lim\limits_{b \to \infty} (\tanh b - \tanh 1)$

$= 1 - \tanh 1 \approx 0.76$

41. $\int_1^\infty (\frac{a}{x+2} - \frac{1}{x+4})\,dx = \lim\limits_{b \to \infty} [a \ln |x+2| - \ln |x+4|]_1^b = \lim\limits_{b \to \infty} \ln \frac{(b+2)^a}{b+4} - \ln(\frac{3^a}{5})$;

$\lim\limits_{b \to \infty} \frac{(b+2)^a}{b+4} = a \lim\limits_{b \to \infty} (b+2)^{a-1} = \begin{cases} \infty, & a > 1 \\ 1, & a = 1 \end{cases} \Rightarrow$ the series converges to $\ln(\frac{5}{3})$ if $a = 1$ and diverges to $\infty$ if

$a > 1$. If $a < 1$, the terms of the series eventually become negative and the Integral Test does not apply. From that point on, however, the series behaves like a negative multiple of the harmonic series, and so it diverges.

42. $\int_3^\infty (\frac{1}{x-1} - \frac{2a}{x+1})\,dx = \lim\limits_{b \to \infty} [\ln |\frac{x-1}{(x+1)^{2a}}|]_3^b = \lim\limits_{b \to \infty} \ln \frac{b-1}{(b+1)^{2a}} - \ln(\frac{2}{4^{2a}}); \lim\limits_{b \to \infty} \frac{b-1}{(b+1)^{2a}}$

$= \lim\limits_{b \to \infty} \frac{1}{2a(b+1)^{2a-1}} = \begin{cases} 1, & a = \frac{1}{2} \\ \infty, & a < \frac{1}{2} \end{cases} \Rightarrow$ the series converges to $\ln(\frac{4}{2}) = \ln 2$ if $a = \frac{1}{2}$ and diverges to $\infty$ if if $a < \frac{1}{2}$. If $a > \frac{1}{2}$, the terms of the series eventually become negative and the Integral Test does not apply. From that point on, however, the series behaves like a negative multiple of the harmonic series, and so it diverges.

43. (a)

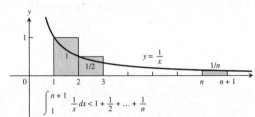 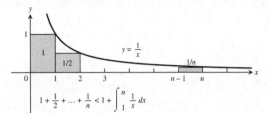

$$\int_1^{n+1} \frac{1}{x} dx < 1 + \frac{1}{2} + \dots + \frac{1}{n} \qquad 1 + \frac{1}{2} + \dots + \frac{1}{n} < 1 + \int_1^n \frac{1}{x} dx$$

(b) There are $(13)(365)(24)(60)(60)\,(10^9)$ seconds in 13 billion years; by part (a) $s_n \leq 1 + \ln n$ where
$n = (13)(365)(24)(60)(60)\,(10^9) \Rightarrow s_n \leq 1 + \ln\left((13)(365)(24)(60)(60)\,(10^9)\right)$
$= 1 + \ln(13) + \ln(365) + \ln(24) + 2\ln(60) + 9\ln(10) \approx 41.55$

44. No, because $\sum_{n=1}^{\infty} \frac{1}{nx} = \frac{1}{x} \sum_{n=1}^{\infty} \frac{1}{n}$ and $\sum_{n=1}^{\infty} \frac{1}{n}$ diverges

45. Yes. If $\sum_{n=1}^{\infty} a_n$ is a divergent series of positive numbers, then $\left(\frac{1}{2}\right) \sum_{n=1}^{\infty} a_n = \sum_{n=1}^{\infty} \left(\frac{a_n}{2}\right)$ also diverges and $\frac{a_n}{2} < a_n$.

There is no "smallest" divergent series of positive numbers: for any divergent series $\sum_{n=1}^{\infty} a_n$ of positive numbers $\sum_{n=1}^{\infty} \left(\frac{a_n}{2}\right)$ has smaller terms and still diverges.

46. No, if $\sum_{n=1}^{\infty} a_n$ is a convergent series of positive numbers, then $2 \sum_{n=1}^{\infty} a_n = \sum_{n=1}^{\infty} 2a_n$ also converges, and $2a_n \geq a_n$.
There is no "largest" convergent series of positive numbers.

47. (a) Both integrals can represent the area under the curve $f(x) = \frac{1}{\sqrt{x+1}}$, and the sum $s_{50}$ can be considered an

approximation of either integral using rectangles with $\Delta x = 1$. The sum $s_{50} = \sum_{n=1}^{50} \frac{1}{\sqrt{n+1}}$ is an overestimate of the

integral $\int_1^{51} \frac{1}{\sqrt{x+1}} dx$. The sum $s_{50}$ represents a left-hand sum (that is, the we are choosing the left-hand endpoint of

each subinterval for $c_i$) and because $f$ is a decreasing function, the value of $f$ is a maximum at the left-hand endpoint of

each sub interval. The area of each rectangle overestimates the true area, thus $\int_1^{51} \frac{1}{\sqrt{x+1}} dx < \sum_{n=1}^{50} \frac{1}{\sqrt{n+1}}$. In a similar

manner, $s_{50}$ underestimates the integral $\int_0^{50} \frac{1}{\sqrt{x+1}} dx$. In this case, the sum $s_{50}$ represents a right-hand sum and because

$f$ is a decreasing function, the value of $f$ is aminimum at the right-hand endpoint of each subinterval. The area of each

rectangle underestimates the true area, thus $\sum_{n=1}^{50} \frac{1}{\sqrt{n+1}} < \int_0^{50} \frac{1}{\sqrt{x+1}} dx$. Evaluating the integrals we find $\int_1^{51} \frac{1}{\sqrt{x+1}} dx$

$= \left[2\sqrt{x+1}\right]_1^{51} = 2\sqrt{52} - 2\sqrt{2} \approx 11.6$ and $\int_0^{50} \frac{1}{\sqrt{x+1}} dx = \left[2\sqrt{x+1}\right]_0^{50} = 2\sqrt{51} - 2\sqrt{1} \approx 12.3$. Thus,

$11.6 < \sum_{n=1}^{50} \frac{1}{\sqrt{n+1}} < 12.3$.

(b) $s_n > 1000 \Rightarrow \int_1^{n+1} \frac{1}{\sqrt{x+1}} dx = \left[2\sqrt{x+1}\right]_1^{n+1} = 2\sqrt{n+1} - 2\sqrt{2} > 1000 \Rightarrow n > \left(500 + 2\sqrt{2}\right)^2 - \approx 251414.2$

$\Rightarrow n \geq 251415$.

48. (a) Since we are using $s_{30} = \sum\limits_{n=1}^{30} \frac{1}{n^4}$ to estimate $\sum\limits_{n=1}^{\infty} \frac{1}{n^4}$, the error is given by $\sum\limits_{n=31}^{\infty} \frac{1}{n^4}$. We can consider this sum as an estimate

of the area under the curve $f(x) = \frac{1}{x^4}$ when $x \geq 30$ using rectangles with $\Delta x = 1$ and $c_i$ is the right-hand endpoint of

each subinterval. Since f is a decreasing function, the value of f is a minimum at the right-hand endpoint of each

subinterval, thus $\sum\limits_{n=31}^{\infty} \frac{1}{n^4} < \int_{30}^{\infty} \frac{1}{x^4} dx = \lim\limits_{b\to\infty} \int_{30}^{b} \frac{1}{x^4} dx = \lim\limits_{b\to\infty} \left[ -\frac{1}{3x^3} \right]_{30}^{b} = \lim\limits_{b\to\infty} \left( -\frac{1}{3b^3} + \frac{1}{3(30)^3} \right) \approx 1.23 \times 10^{-5}$.

Thus the error $< 1.23 \times 10^{-5}$.

(b) We want $S - s_n < 0.000001 \Rightarrow \int_n^{\infty} \frac{1}{x^4} dx < 0.000001 \Rightarrow \int_n^{\infty} \frac{1}{x^4} dx = \lim\limits_{b\to\infty} \int_n^{b} \frac{1}{x^4} dx = \lim\limits_{b\to\infty} \left[ -\frac{1}{3x^3} \right]_n^b$

$= \lim\limits_{b\to\infty} \left( -\frac{1}{3b^3} + \frac{1}{3n^3} \right) = \frac{1}{3n^3} < 0.000001 \Rightarrow n > \sqrt[3]{\frac{1000000}{3}} \approx 69.336 \Rightarrow n \geq 70$.

49. We want $S - s_n < 0.01 \Rightarrow \int_n^{\infty} \frac{1}{x^3} dx < 0.01 \Rightarrow \int_n^{\infty} \frac{1}{x^3} dx = \lim\limits_{b\to\infty} \int_n^b \frac{1}{x^3} dx = \lim\limits_{b\to\infty} \left[ -\frac{1}{2x^2} \right]_n^b = \lim\limits_{b\to\infty} \left( -\frac{1}{2b^2} + \frac{1}{2n^2} \right)$

$= \frac{1}{2n^2} < 0.01 \Rightarrow n > \sqrt{50} \approx 7.071 \Rightarrow n \geq 8 \Rightarrow S \approx s_8 = \sum\limits_{n=1}^{8} \frac{1}{n^3} \approx 1.195$

50. We want $S - s_n < 0.1 \Rightarrow \int_n^{\infty} \frac{1}{x^2+4} dx < 0.1 \Rightarrow \lim\limits_{b\to\infty} \int_n^b \frac{1}{x^2+4} dx = \lim\limits_{b\to\infty} \left[ \frac{1}{2} \tan^{-1}\left(\frac{x}{2}\right) \right]_n^b$

$= \lim\limits_{b\to\infty} \left( \frac{1}{2}\tan^{-1}\left(\frac{b}{2}\right) - \frac{1}{2}\tan^{-1}\left(\frac{n}{2}\right) \right) = \frac{\pi}{4} - \frac{1}{2}\tan^{-1}\left(\frac{n}{2}\right) < 0.1 \Rightarrow n > 2\tan\left(\frac{\pi}{2} - 0.2\right) \approx 9.867 \Rightarrow n \geq 10 \Rightarrow S \approx s_{10}$

$= \sum\limits_{n=1}^{10} \frac{1}{n^2+4} \approx 0.57$

51. $S - s_n < 0.00001 \Rightarrow \int_n^{\infty} \frac{1}{x^{1.1}} dx < 0.00001 \Rightarrow \int_n^{\infty} \frac{1}{x^{1.1}} dx = \lim\limits_{b\to\infty} \int_n^b \frac{1}{x^{1.1}} dx = \lim\limits_{b\to\infty} \left[ -\frac{10}{x^{0.1}} \right]_n^b = \lim\limits_{b\to\infty} \left( -\frac{10}{b^{0.1}} + \frac{10}{n^{0.1}} \right)$

$= \frac{10}{n^{0.1}} < 0.00001 \Rightarrow n > 1000000^{10} \Rightarrow n > 10^{60}$

52. $S - s_n < 0.01 \Rightarrow \int_n^{\infty} \frac{1}{x(\ln x)^3} dx < 0.01 \Rightarrow \int_n^{\infty} \frac{1}{x(\ln x)^3} dx = \lim\limits_{b\to\infty} \int_n^b \frac{1}{x(\ln x)^3} dx = \lim\limits_{b\to\infty} \left[ -\frac{1}{2(\ln x)^2} \right]_n^b$

$= \lim\limits_{b\to\infty} \left( -\frac{1}{2(\ln b)^2} + \frac{1}{2(\ln n)^2} \right) = \frac{1}{2(\ln n)^2} < 0.01 \Rightarrow n > e^{\sqrt{50}} \approx 1177.405 \Rightarrow n \geq 1178$

53. Let $A_n = \sum\limits_{k=1}^{n} a_k$ and $B_n = \sum\limits_{k=1}^{n} 2^k a_{(2^k)}$, where $\{a_k\}$ is a nonincreasing sequence of positive terms converging to

0. Note that $\{A_n\}$ and $\{B_n\}$ are nondecreasing sequences of positive terms. Now,

$B_n = 2a_2 + 4a_4 + 8a_8 + \ldots + 2^n a_{(2^n)} = 2a_2 + (2a_4 + 2a_4) + (2a_8 + 2a_8 + 2a_8 + 2a_8) + \ldots$

$+ \underbrace{\left( 2a_{(2^n)} + 2a_{(2^n)} + \ldots + 2a_{(2^n)} \right)}_{2^{n-1} \text{ terms}} \leq 2a_1 + 2a_2 + (2a_3 + 2a_4) + (2a_5 + 2a_6 + 2a_7 + 2a_8) + \ldots$

$+ \left( 2a_{(2^{n-1})} + 2a_{(2^{n-1}+1)} + \ldots + 2a_{(2^n)} \right) = 2A_{(2^n)} \leq 2\sum\limits_{k=1}^{\infty} a_k$. Therefore if $\sum a_k$ converges,

then $\{B_n\}$ is bounded above $\Rightarrow \sum 2^k a_{(2^k)}$ converges. Conversely,

$A_n = a_1 + (a_2 + a_3) + (a_4 + a_5 + a_6 + a_7) + \ldots + a_n < a_1 + 2a_2 + 4a_4 + \ldots + 2^n a_{(2^n)} = a_1 + B_n < a_1 + \sum\limits_{k=1}^{\infty} 2^k a_{(2^k)}$.

Therefore, if $\sum\limits_{k=1}^{\infty} 2^k a_{(2^k)}$ converges, then $\{A_n\}$ is bounded above and hence converges.

54. (a) $a_{(2^n)} = \frac{1}{2^n \ln (2^n)} = \frac{1}{2^n \cdot n(\ln 2)} \Rightarrow \sum\limits_{n=2}^{\infty} 2^n a_{(2^n)} = \sum\limits_{n=2}^{\infty} 2^n \frac{1}{2^n \cdot n(\ln 2)} = \frac{1}{\ln 2} \sum\limits_{n=2}^{\infty} \frac{1}{n}$, which diverges

$\Rightarrow \sum\limits_{n=2}^{\infty} \frac{1}{n \ln n}$ diverges.

(b) $a_{(2^n)} = \frac{1}{2^{np}} \Rightarrow \sum\limits_{n=1}^{\infty} 2^n a_{(2^n)} = \sum\limits_{n=1}^{\infty} 2^n \cdot \frac{1}{2^{np}} = \sum\limits_{n=1}^{\infty} \frac{1}{(2^n)^{p-1}} = \sum\limits_{n=1}^{\infty} \left(\frac{1}{2^{p-1}}\right)^n$, a geometric series that

converges if $\frac{1}{2^{p-1}} < 1$ or $p > 1$, but diverges if $p \le 1$.

55. (a) $\int_2^{\infty} \frac{dx}{x(\ln x)^p} ; \begin{bmatrix} u = \ln x \\ du = \frac{dx}{x} \end{bmatrix} \to \int_{\ln 2}^{\infty} u^{-p} \, du = \lim\limits_{b \to \infty} \left[\frac{u^{-p+1}}{-p+1}\right]_{\ln 2}^b = \lim\limits_{b \to \infty} \left(\frac{1}{1-p}\right)[b^{-p+1} - (\ln 2)^{-p+1}]$

$= \begin{cases} \frac{1}{p-1}(\ln 2)^{-p+1}, & p > 1 \\ \infty, & p < 1 \end{cases} \Rightarrow$ the improper integral converges if $p > 1$ and diverges if $p < 1$.

For $p = 1$: $\int_2^{\infty} \frac{dx}{x \ln x} = \lim\limits_{b \to \infty} [\ln (\ln x)]_2^b = \lim\limits_{b \to \infty} [\ln (\ln b) - \ln (\ln 2)] = \infty$, so the improper integral diverges if $p = 1$.

(b) Since the series and the integral converge or diverge together, $\sum\limits_{n=2}^{\infty} \frac{1}{n(\ln n)^p}$ converges if and only if $p > 1$.

56. (a) $p = 1 \Rightarrow$ the series diverges

(b) $p = 1.01 \Rightarrow$ the series converges

(c) $\sum\limits_{n=2}^{\infty} \frac{1}{n (\ln n^3)} = \frac{1}{3} \sum\limits_{n=2}^{\infty} \frac{1}{n(\ln n)} ; p = 1 \Rightarrow$ the series diverges

(d) $p = 3 \Rightarrow$ the series converges

57. (a) From Fig. 10.11(a) in the text with $f(x) = \frac{1}{x}$ and $a_k = \frac{1}{k}$, we have $\int_1^{n+1} \frac{1}{x} \, dx \le 1 + \frac{1}{2} + \frac{1}{3} + \ldots + \frac{1}{n}$

$\le 1 + \int_1^n f(x) \, dx \Rightarrow \ln (n + 1) \le 1 + \frac{1}{2} + \frac{1}{3} + \ldots + \frac{1}{n} \le 1 + \ln n \Rightarrow 0 \le \ln (n + 1) - \ln n$

$\le \left(1 + \frac{1}{2} + \frac{1}{3} + \ldots + \frac{1}{n}\right) - \ln n \le 1$. Therefore the sequence $\left\{\left(1 + \frac{1}{2} + \frac{1}{3} + \ldots + \frac{1}{n}\right) - \ln n\right\}$ is bounded above by 1 and below by 0.

(b) From the graph in Fig. 10.11(b) with $f(x) = \frac{1}{x}$, $\frac{1}{n+1} < \int_n^{n+1} \frac{1}{x} \, dx = \ln (n + 1) - \ln n$

$\Rightarrow 0 > \frac{1}{n+1} - [\ln (n + 1) - \ln n] = \left(1 + \frac{1}{2} + \frac{1}{3} + \ldots + \frac{1}{n+1} - \ln (n + 1)\right) - \left(1 + \frac{1}{2} + \frac{1}{3} + \ldots + \frac{1}{n} - \ln n\right)$.

If we define $a_n = 1 + \frac{1}{2} = \frac{1}{3} + \frac{1}{n} - \ln n$, then $0 > a_{n+1} - a_n \Rightarrow a_{n+1} < a_n \Rightarrow \{a_n\}$ is a decreasing sequence of nonnegative terms.

58. $e^{-x^2} \le e^{-x}$ for $x \ge 1$, and $\int_1^{\infty} e^{-x} \, dx = \lim\limits_{b \to \infty} [-e^{-x}]_1^b = \lim\limits_{b \to \infty} (-e^{-b} + e^{-1}) = e^{-1} \Rightarrow \int_1^{\infty} e^{-x^2} \, dx$ converges by

the Comparison Test for improper integrals $\Rightarrow \sum\limits_{n=0}^{\infty} e^{-n^2} = 1 + \sum\limits_{n=1}^{\infty} e^{-n^2}$ converges by the Integral Test.

59. (a) $s_{10} = \sum\limits_{n=1}^{10} \frac{1}{n^3} = 1.97531986; \int_{11}^{\infty} \frac{1}{x^3} \, dx = \lim\limits_{b \to \infty} \int_{11}^b x^{-3} \, dx = \lim\limits_{b \to \infty} \left[-\frac{x^{-2}}{2}\right]_{11}^b = \lim\limits_{b \to \infty} \left(-\frac{1}{2b^2} + \frac{1}{242}\right) = \frac{1}{242}$ and

$\int_{10}^{\infty} \frac{1}{x^3} \, dx = \lim\limits_{b \to \infty} \int_{10}^b x^{-3} \, dx = \lim\limits_{b \to \infty} \left[-\frac{x^{-2}}{2}\right]_{10}^b = \lim\limits_{b \to \infty} \left(-\frac{1}{2b^2} + \frac{1}{200}\right) = \frac{1}{200}$

$\Rightarrow 1.97531986 + \frac{1}{242} < s < 1.97531986 + \frac{1}{200} \Rightarrow 1.20166 < s < 1.20253$

(b) $s = \sum\limits_{n=1}^{\infty} \frac{1}{n^3} \approx \frac{1.20166 + 1.20253}{2} = 1.202095;$ error $\le \frac{1.20253 - 1.20166}{2} = 0.000435$

60. (a) $s_{10} = \sum\limits_{n=1}^{10} \frac{1}{n^4} = 1.082036583; \int_{11}^{\infty} \frac{1}{x^4} \, dx = \lim\limits_{b \to \infty} \int_{11}^b x^{-4} \, dx = \lim\limits_{b \to \infty} \left[-\frac{x^{-3}}{3}\right]_{11}^b = \lim\limits_{b \to \infty} \left(-\frac{1}{3b^3} + \frac{1}{3993}\right) = \frac{1}{3993}$ and

$\int_{10}^{\infty} \frac{1}{x^4} \, dx = \lim\limits_{b \to \infty} \int_{10}^b x^{-4} \, dx = \lim\limits_{b \to \infty} \left[-\frac{x^{-3}}{3}\right]_{10}^b = \lim\limits_{b \to \infty} \left(-\frac{1}{3b^3} + \frac{1}{3000}\right) = \frac{1}{3000}$

$\Rightarrow 1.082036583 + \frac{1}{3993} < s < 1.082036583 + \frac{1}{3000} \Rightarrow 1.08229 < s < 1.08237$

(b) $s = \sum\limits_{n=1}^{\infty} \frac{1}{n^4} \approx \frac{1.08229 + 1.08237}{2} = 1.08233;$ error $\le \frac{1.08237 - 1.08229}{2} = 0.00004$

## 10.4 COMPARISON TESTS

1. Compare with $\sum\limits_{n=1}^{\infty} \frac{1}{n^2}$, which is a convergent p-series, since $p = 2 > 1$. Both series have nonnegative terms for $n \geq 1$. For $n \geq 1$, we have $n^2 \leq n^2 + 30 \Rightarrow \frac{1}{n^2} \geq \frac{1}{n^2+30}$. Then by Comparison Test, $\sum\limits_{n=1}^{\infty} \frac{1}{n^2+30}$ converges.

2. Compare with $\sum\limits_{n=1}^{\infty} \frac{1}{n^3}$, which is a convergent p-series, since $p = 3 > 1$. Both series have nonnegative terms for $n \geq 1$. For $n \geq 1$, we have $n^4 \leq n^4 + 2 \Rightarrow \frac{1}{n^4} \geq \frac{1}{n^4+2} \Rightarrow \frac{n}{n^4} \geq \frac{n}{n^4+2} \Rightarrow \frac{1}{n^3} \geq \frac{n}{n^4+2} \geq \frac{n-1}{n^4+2}$. Then by Comparison Test, $\sum\limits_{n=1}^{\infty} \frac{n-1}{n^4+2}$ converges.

3. Compare with $\sum\limits_{n=2}^{\infty} \frac{1}{\sqrt{n}}$, which is a divergent p-series, since $p = \frac{1}{2} \leq 1$. Both series have nonnegative terms for $n \geq 2$. For $n \geq 2$, we have $\sqrt{n} - 1 \leq \sqrt{n} \Rightarrow \frac{1}{\sqrt{n-1}} \geq \frac{1}{\sqrt{n}}$. Then by Comparison Test, $\sum\limits_{n=2}^{\infty} \frac{1}{\sqrt{n-1}}$ diverges.

4. Compare with $\sum\limits_{n=2}^{\infty} \frac{1}{n}$, which is a divergent p-series, since $p = 1 \leq 1$. Both series have nonnegative terms for $n \geq 2$. For $n \geq 2$, we have $n^2 - n \leq n^2 \Rightarrow \frac{1}{n^2-n} \geq \frac{1}{n^2} \Rightarrow \frac{n}{n^2-n} \geq \frac{n}{n^2} = \frac{1}{n} \Rightarrow \frac{n+2}{n^2-n} \geq \frac{n}{n^2-n} \geq \frac{1}{n}$. Thus $\sum\limits_{n=2}^{\infty} \frac{n+2}{n^2-n}$ diverges.

5. Compare with $\sum\limits_{n=1}^{\infty} \frac{1}{n^{3/2}}$, which is a convergent p-series, since $p = \frac{3}{2} > 1$. Both series have nonnegative terms for $n \geq 1$. For $n \geq 1$, we have $0 \leq \cos^2 n \leq 1 \Rightarrow \frac{\cos^2 n}{n^{3/2}} \leq \frac{1}{n^{3/2}}$. Then by Comparison Test, $\sum\limits_{n=1}^{\infty} \frac{\cos^2 n}{n^{3/2}}$ converges.

6. Compare with $\sum\limits_{n=1}^{\infty} \frac{1}{3^n}$, which is a convergent geometric series, since $|r| = \left|\frac{1}{3}\right| < 1$. Both series have nonnegative terms for $n \geq 1$. For $n \geq 1$, we have $n \cdot 3^n \geq 3^n \Rightarrow \frac{1}{n \cdot 3^n} \leq \frac{1}{3^n}$. Then by Comparison Test, $\sum\limits_{n=1}^{\infty} \frac{1}{n \cdot 3^n}$ converges.

7. Compare with $\sum\limits_{n=1}^{\infty} \frac{\sqrt{5}}{n^{3/2}}$. The series $\sum\limits_{n=1}^{\infty} \frac{1}{n^{3/2}}$ is a convergent p-series, since $p = \frac{3}{2} > 1$, and the series $\sum\limits_{n=1}^{\infty} \frac{\sqrt{5}}{n^{3/2}}$ $= \sqrt{5} \sum\limits_{n=1}^{\infty} \frac{1}{n^{3/2}}$ converges by Theorem 8 part 3. Both series have nonnegative terms for $n \geq 1$. For $n \geq 1$, we have $n^3 \leq n^4 \Rightarrow 4n^3 \leq 4n^4 \Rightarrow n^4 + 4n^3 \leq n^4 + 4n^4 = 5n^4 \Rightarrow n^4 + 4n^3 \leq 5n^4 + 20 = 5(n^4 + 4) \Rightarrow \frac{n^4+4n^3}{n^4+4} \leq 5$. $\Rightarrow \frac{n^3(n+4)}{n^4+4} \leq 5 \Rightarrow \frac{n+4}{n^4+4} \leq \frac{5}{n^3} \Rightarrow \sqrt{\frac{n+4}{n^4+4}} \leq \sqrt{\frac{5}{n^3}} = \frac{\sqrt{5}}{n^{3/2}}$ Then by Comparison Test, $\sum\limits_{n=1}^{\infty} \sqrt{\frac{n+4}{n^4+4}}$ converges.

8. Compare with $\sum\limits_{n=1}^{\infty} \frac{1}{\sqrt{n}}$, which is a divergent p-series, since $p = \frac{1}{2} \leq 1$. Both series have nonnegative terms for $n \geq 1$. For $n \geq 1$, we have $\sqrt{n} \geq 1 \Rightarrow 2\sqrt{n} \geq 2 \Rightarrow 2\sqrt{n} + 1 \geq 3 \Rightarrow n(2\sqrt{n} + 1) \geq 3n \geq 3 \Rightarrow 2n\sqrt{n} + n \geq 3$ $\Rightarrow n^2 + 2n\sqrt{n} + n \geq n^2 + 3 \Rightarrow \frac{n(n+2\sqrt{n}+1)}{n^2+3} \geq 1 \Rightarrow \frac{n+2\sqrt{n}+1}{n^2+3} \geq \frac{1}{n} \Rightarrow \frac{(\sqrt{n}+1)^2}{n^2+3} \geq \frac{1}{n} \Rightarrow \sqrt{\frac{(\sqrt{n}+1)^2}{n^2+3}} \geq \sqrt{\frac{1}{n}}$ $\Rightarrow \frac{\sqrt{n}+1}{\sqrt{n^2+3}} \geq \frac{1}{\sqrt{n}}$. Then by Comparison Test, $\sum\limits_{n=1}^{\infty} \frac{\sqrt{n}+1}{\sqrt{n^2+3}}$ diverges.

9. Compare with $\sum\limits_{n=1}^{\infty} \frac{1}{n^2}$, which is a convergent p-series, since $p = 2 > 1$. Both series have positive terms for $n \geq 1$. $\lim\limits_{n\to\infty} \frac{a_n}{b_n}$

$= \lim\limits_{n\to\infty} \frac{\frac{n-2}{n^3-n^2+3}}{1/n^2} = \lim\limits_{n\to\infty} \frac{n^3-2n^2}{n^3-n^2+3} = \lim\limits_{n\to\infty} \frac{3n^2-4n}{3n^2-2n} = \lim\limits_{n\to\infty} \frac{6n-4}{6n-2} = \lim\limits_{n\to\infty} \frac{6}{6} = 1 > 0$. Then by Limit Comparison Test,

$\sum\limits_{n=1}^{\infty} \frac{n-2}{n^3-n^2+3}$ converges.

10. Compare with $\sum\limits_{n=1}^{\infty} \frac{1}{\sqrt{n}}$, which is a divergent p-series, since $p = \frac{1}{2} \leq 1$. Both series have positive terms for $n \geq 1$. $\lim\limits_{n\to\infty} \frac{a_n}{b_n}$

$= \lim\limits_{n\to\infty} \frac{\sqrt{\frac{n+1}{n^2+2}}}{1/\sqrt{n}} = \lim\limits_{n\to\infty} \sqrt{\frac{n^2+n}{n^2+2}} = \sqrt{\lim\limits_{n\to\infty} \frac{n^2+n}{n^2+2}} = \sqrt{\lim\limits_{n\to\infty} \frac{2n+1}{2n}} = \sqrt{\lim\limits_{n\to\infty} \frac{2}{2}} = \sqrt{1} = 1 > 0$. Then by Limit Comparison

Test, $\sum\limits_{n=1}^{\infty} \sqrt{\frac{n+1}{n^2+2}}$ diverges.

11. Compare with $\sum\limits_{n=2}^{\infty} \frac{1}{n}$, which is a divergent p-series, since $p = 1 \leq 1$. Both series have positive terms for $n \geq 2$. $\lim\limits_{n\to\infty} \frac{a_n}{b_n}$

$= \lim\limits_{n\to\infty} \frac{\frac{n(n+1)}{(n^2+1)(n-1)}}{1/n} = \lim\limits_{n\to\infty} \frac{n^3+n^2}{n^3-n^2+n-1} = \lim\limits_{n\to\infty} \frac{3n^2+2n}{3n^2-2n+1} = \lim\limits_{n\to\infty} \frac{6n+2}{6n-2} = \lim\limits_{n\to\infty} \frac{6}{6} = 1 > 0$. Then by Limit Comparison

Test, $\sum\limits_{n=2}^{\infty} \frac{n(n+1)}{(n^2+1)(n-1)}$ diverges.

12. Compare with $\sum\limits_{n=1}^{\infty} \frac{1}{2^n}$, which is a convergent geometric series, since $|r| = \left|\frac{1}{2}\right| < 1$. Both series have positive terms for

$n \geq 1$. $\lim\limits_{n\to\infty} \frac{a_n}{b_n} = \lim\limits_{n\to\infty} \frac{\frac{2^n}{3+4^n}}{1/2^n} = \lim\limits_{n\to\infty} \frac{4^n}{3+4^n} = \lim\limits_{n\to\infty} \frac{4^n \ln 4}{4^n \ln 4} = 1 > 0$. Then by Limit Comparison Test, $\sum\limits_{n=1}^{\infty} \frac{2^n}{3+4^n}$ converges.

13. Compare with $\sum\limits_{n=1}^{\infty} \frac{1}{\sqrt{n}}$, which is a divergent p-series, since $p = \frac{1}{2} \leq 1$. Both series have positive terms for $n \geq 1$. $\lim\limits_{n\to\infty} \frac{a_n}{b_n}$

$= \lim\limits_{n\to\infty} \frac{\frac{5^n}{\sqrt{n \cdot 4^n}}}{1/\sqrt{n}} = \lim\limits_{n\to\infty} \frac{5^n}{4^n} = \lim\limits_{n\to\infty} \left(\frac{5}{4}\right)^n = \infty$. Then by Limit Comparison Test, $\sum\limits_{n=1}^{\infty} \frac{5^n}{\sqrt{n \cdot 4^n}}$ diverges.

14. Compare with $\sum\limits_{n=1}^{\infty} \left(\frac{2}{5}\right)^n$, which is a convergent geometric series, since $|r| = \left|\frac{2}{5}\right| < 1$. Both series have positive terms for

$n \geq 1$. $\lim\limits_{n\to\infty} \frac{a_n}{b_n} = \lim\limits_{n\to\infty} \frac{\left(\frac{2n+3}{5n+4}\right)^n}{(2/5)^n} = \lim\limits_{n\to\infty} \left(\frac{10n+15}{10n+8}\right)^n = \exp \lim\limits_{n\to\infty} \ln\left(\frac{10n+15}{10n+8}\right)^n = \exp \lim\limits_{n\to\infty} n \ln\left(\frac{10n+15}{10n+8}\right)$

$= \exp \lim\limits_{n\to\infty} \frac{\ln\left(\frac{10n+15}{10n+8}\right)}{1/n} = \exp \lim\limits_{n\to\infty} \frac{\frac{10}{10n+15} - \frac{10}{10n+8}}{-1/n^2} = \exp \lim\limits_{n\to\infty} \frac{70n^2}{(10n+15)(10n+8)} = \exp \lim\limits_{n\to\infty} \frac{70n^2}{100n^2+230n+120}$

$= \exp \lim\limits_{n\to\infty} \frac{140n}{200n+230} = \exp \lim\limits_{n\to\infty} \frac{140}{200} = e^{7/10} > 0$. Then by Limit Comparison Test, $\sum\limits_{n=1}^{\infty} \left(\frac{2n+3}{5n+4}\right)^n$ converges.

15. Compare with $\sum\limits_{n=2}^{\infty} \frac{1}{n}$, which is a divergent p-series, since $p = 1 \leq 1$. Both series have positive terms for $n \geq 2$. $\lim\limits_{n\to\infty} \frac{a_n}{b_n}$

$= \lim\limits_{n\to\infty} \frac{\frac{1}{\ln n}}{1/n} = \lim\limits_{n\to\infty} \frac{n}{\ln n} = \lim\limits_{n\to\infty} \frac{1}{1/n} = \lim\limits_{n\to\infty} n = \infty$. Then by Limit Comparison Test, $\sum\limits_{n=2}^{\infty} \frac{1}{\ln n}$ diverges.

16. Compare with $\sum\limits_{n=1}^{\infty} \frac{1}{n^2}$, which is a convergent p-series, since $p = 2 > 1$. Both series have positive terms for $n \geq 1$. $\lim\limits_{n\to\infty} \frac{a_n}{b_n}$

$= \lim\limits_{n\to\infty} \frac{\ln\left(1+\frac{1}{n^2}\right)}{1/n^2} = \lim\limits_{n\to\infty} \frac{\frac{1}{1+\frac{1}{n^2}}\left(-\frac{2}{n^3}\right)}{\left(-\frac{2}{n^3}\right)} = \lim\limits_{n\to\infty} \frac{1}{1+\frac{1}{n^2}} = 1 > 0$. Then by Limit Comparison Test, $\sum\limits_{n=1}^{\infty} \ln\left(1+\frac{1}{n^2}\right)$ converges.

17. diverges by the Limit Comparison Test (part 1) when compared with $\sum_{n=1}^{\infty} \frac{1}{\sqrt{n}}$, a divergent p-series:

$$\lim_{n \to \infty} \frac{\left(\frac{1}{2\sqrt{n} + \sqrt[3]{n}}\right)}{\left(\frac{1}{\sqrt{n}}\right)} = \lim_{n \to \infty} \frac{\sqrt{n}}{2\sqrt{n} + \sqrt[3]{n}} = \lim_{n \to \infty} \left(\frac{1}{2 + n^{-1/6}}\right) = \frac{1}{2}$$

18. diverges by the Direct Comparison Test since $n + n + n > n + \sqrt{n} + 0 \Rightarrow \frac{3}{n + \sqrt{n}} > \frac{1}{n}$, which is the nth

term of the divergent series $\sum_{n=1}^{\infty} \frac{1}{n}$ or use Limit Comparison Test with $b_n = \frac{1}{n}$

19. converges by the Direct Comparison Test; $\frac{\sin^2 n}{2^n} \leq \frac{1}{2^n}$, which is the nth term of a convergent geometric series

20. converges by the Direct Comparison Test; $\frac{1 + \cos n}{n^2} \leq \frac{2}{n^2}$ and the p-series $\sum \frac{1}{n^2}$ converges

21. diverges since $\lim_{n \to \infty} \frac{2n}{3n - 1} = \frac{2}{3} \neq 0$

22. converges by the Limit Comparison Test (part 1) with $\frac{1}{n^{3/2}}$, the nth term of a convergent p-series:

$$\lim_{n \to \infty} \frac{\left(\frac{n+1}{n^2\sqrt{n}}\right)}{\left(\frac{1}{n^{3/2}}\right)} = \lim_{n \to \infty} \left(\frac{n+1}{n}\right) = 1$$

23. converges by the Limit Comparison Test (part 1) with $\frac{1}{n^2}$, the nth term of a convergent p-series:

$$\lim_{n \to \infty} \frac{\left(\frac{10n+1}{n(n+1)(n+2)}\right)}{\left(\frac{1}{n^2}\right)} = \lim_{n \to \infty} \frac{10n^2 + n}{n^2 + 3n + 2} = \lim_{n \to \infty} \frac{20n + 1}{2n + 3} = \lim_{n \to \infty} \frac{20}{2} = 10$$

24. converges by the Limit Comparison Test (part 1) with $\frac{1}{n^2}$, the nth term of a convergent p-series:

$$\lim_{n \to \infty} \frac{\left(\frac{5n^3 - 3n}{n^2(n-2)(n^2+5)}\right)}{\left(\frac{1}{n^2}\right)} = \lim_{n \to \infty} \frac{5n^3 - 3n}{n^3 - 2n^2 + 5n - 10} = \lim_{n \to \infty} \frac{15n^2 - 3}{3n^2 - 4n + 5} = \lim_{n \to \infty} \frac{30n}{6n - 4} = 5$$

25. converges by the Direct Comparison Test; $\left(\frac{n}{3n+1}\right)^n < \left(\frac{n}{3n}\right)^n = \left(\frac{1}{3}\right)^n$, the nth term of a convergent geometric series

26. converges by the Limit Comparison Test (part 1) with $\frac{1}{n^{3/2}}$, the nth term of a convergent p-series:

$$\lim_{n \to \infty} \frac{\left(\frac{1}{n^{3/2}}\right)}{\left(\frac{1}{\sqrt{n^3 + 2}}\right)} = \lim_{n \to \infty} \sqrt{\frac{n^3 + 2}{n^3}} = \lim_{n \to \infty} \sqrt{1 + \frac{2}{n^3}} = 1$$

27. diverges by the Direct Comparison Test; $n > \ln n \Rightarrow \ln n > \ln \ln n \Rightarrow \frac{1}{n} < \frac{1}{\ln n} < \frac{1}{\ln (\ln n)}$ and $\sum_{n=3}^{\infty} \frac{1}{n}$ diverges

28. converges by the Limit Comparison Test (part 2) when compared with $\sum_{n=1}^{\infty} \frac{1}{n^2}$, a convergent p-series:

$$\lim_{n \to \infty} \frac{\left[\frac{(\ln n)^2}{n^3}\right]}{\left(\frac{1}{n^2}\right)} = \lim_{n \to \infty} \frac{(\ln n)^2}{n} = \lim_{n \to \infty} \frac{2(\ln n)\left(\frac{1}{n}\right)}{1} = 2 \lim_{n \to \infty} \frac{\ln n}{n} = 0$$

29. diverges by the Limit Comparison Test (part 3) with $\frac{1}{n}$, the nth term of the divergent harmonic series:

$$\lim_{n \to \infty} \frac{\left[\frac{1}{\sqrt{n} \ln n}\right]}{\left(\frac{1}{n}\right)} = \lim_{n \to \infty} \frac{\sqrt{n}}{\ln n} = \lim_{n \to \infty} \frac{\left(\frac{1}{2\sqrt{n}}\right)}{\left(\frac{1}{n}\right)} = \lim_{n \to \infty} \frac{\sqrt{n}}{2} = \infty$$

30. converges by the Limit Comparison Test (part 2) with $\frac{1}{n^{5/4}}$, the nth term of a convergent p-series:

$$\lim_{n \to \infty} \frac{\left[\frac{(\ln n)^2}{n^{3/2}}\right]}{\left(\frac{1}{n^{5/4}}\right)} = \lim_{n \to \infty} \frac{(\ln n)^2}{n^{1/4}} = \lim_{n \to \infty} \frac{\left(\frac{2\ln n}{n}\right)}{\left(\frac{1}{4n^{3/4}}\right)} = 8 \lim_{n \to \infty} \frac{\ln n}{n^{1/4}} = 8 \lim_{n \to \infty} \frac{\left(\frac{1}{n}\right)}{\left(\frac{1}{4n^{3/4}}\right)} = 32 \lim_{n \to \infty} \frac{1}{n^{1/4}} = 32 \cdot 0 = 0$$

31. diverges by the Limit Comparison Test (part 3) with $\frac{1}{n}$, the nth term of the divergent harmonic series:

$$\lim_{n \to \infty} \frac{\left(\frac{1}{1+\ln n}\right)}{\left(\frac{1}{n}\right)} = \lim_{n \to \infty} \frac{n}{1 + \ln n} = \lim_{n \to \infty} \frac{1}{\left(\frac{1}{n}\right)} = \lim_{n \to \infty} n = \infty$$

32. diverges by the Integral Test: $\int_2^\infty \frac{\ln(x+1)}{x+1}\, dx = \int_{\ln 3}^\infty u\, du = \lim_{b \to \infty} \left[\frac{1}{2} u^2\right]_{\ln 3}^b = \lim_{b \to \infty} \frac{1}{2}(b^2 - \ln^2 3) = \infty$

33. converges by the Direct Comparison Test with $\frac{1}{n^{3/2}}$, the nth term of a convergent p-series: $n^2 - 1 > n$ for

$n \geq 2 \Rightarrow n^2(n^2 - 1) > n^3 \Rightarrow n\sqrt{n^2 - 1} > n^{3/2} \Rightarrow \frac{1}{n^{3/2}} > \frac{1}{n\sqrt{n^2 - 1}}$ or use Limit Comparison Test with $\frac{1}{n^2}$.

34. converges by the Direct Comparison Test with $\frac{1}{n^{3/2}}$, the nth term of a convergent p-series: $n^2 + 1 > n^2$

$\Rightarrow n^2 + 1 > \sqrt{n}n^{3/2} \Rightarrow \frac{n^2+1}{\sqrt{n}} > n^{3/2} \Rightarrow \frac{\sqrt{n}}{n^2+1} < \frac{1}{n^{3/2}}$ or use Limit Comparison Test with $\frac{1}{n^{3/2}}$.

35. converges because $\sum_{n=1}^\infty \frac{1-n}{n2^n} = \sum_{n=1}^\infty \frac{1}{n2^n} + \sum_{n=1}^\infty \frac{-1}{2^n}$ which is the sum of two convergent series:

$\sum_{n=1}^\infty \frac{1}{n2^n}$ converges by the Direct Comparison Test since $\frac{1}{n2^n} < \frac{1}{2^n}$, and $\sum_{n=1}^\infty \frac{-1}{2^n}$ is a convergent geometric series

36. converges by the Direct Comparison Test: $\sum_{n=1}^\infty \frac{n+2^n}{n^2 2^n} = \sum_{n=1}^\infty \left(\frac{1}{n2^n} + \frac{1}{n^2}\right)$ and $\frac{1}{n2^n} + \frac{1}{n^2} \leq \frac{1}{2^n} + \frac{1}{n^2}$, the sum of

the nth terms of a convergent geometric series and a convergent p-series

37. converges by the Direct Comparison Test: $\frac{1}{3^{n-1}+1} < \frac{1}{3^{n-1}}$, which is the nth term of a convergent geometric series

38. diverges; $\lim_{n \to \infty} \left(\frac{3^{n-1}+1}{3^n}\right) = \lim_{n \to \infty} \left(\frac{1}{3} + \frac{1}{3^n}\right) = \frac{1}{3} \neq 0$

39. converges by Limit Comparison Test: compare with $\sum_{n=1}^\infty \left(\frac{1}{5}\right)^n$, which is a convergent geometric series with $|r| = \frac{1}{5} < 1$,

$$\lim_{n \to \infty} \frac{\left(\frac{n+1}{n^2+3n} \cdot \frac{1}{5^n}\right)}{(1/5)^n} = \lim_{n \to \infty} \frac{n+1}{n^2+3n} = \lim_{n \to \infty} \frac{1}{2n+3} = 0.$$

40. converges by Limit Comparison Test: compare with $\sum_{n=1}^\infty \left(\frac{3}{4}\right)^n$, which is a convergent geometric series with $|r| = \frac{1}{5} < 1$,

$$\lim_{n \to \infty} \frac{\left(\frac{2^n+3^n}{3^n+4^n}\right)}{(3/4)^n} = \lim_{n \to \infty} \frac{8^n + 12^n}{9^n + 12^n} = \lim_{n \to \infty} \frac{\left(\frac{8}{12}\right)^n + 1}{\left(\frac{9}{12}\right)^n + 1} = \frac{1}{1} = 1 > 0.$$

41. diverges by Limit Comparison Test: compare with $\sum_{n=1}^\infty \frac{1}{n}$, which is a divergent p-series, $\lim_{n \to \infty} \frac{\left(\frac{2^n-n}{n\cdot 2^n}\right)}{1/n} = \lim_{n \to \infty} \frac{2^n - n}{2^n}$

$$= \lim_{n \to \infty} \frac{2^n \ln 2 - 1}{2^n \ln 2} = \lim_{n \to \infty} \frac{2^n (\ln 2)^2}{2^n (\ln 2)^2} = 1 > 0.$$

42. diverges by the definition of an infinite series: $\sum_{n=1}^\infty \ln\left(\frac{n}{n+1}\right) = \sum_{n=1}^\infty \left[\ln n - \ln(n+1)\right]$, $s_k = (\ln 1 - \ln 2) + (\ln 2 - \ln 3)$

$+ \ldots + (\ln(k-1) - \ln k) + (\ln k - \ln(k+1)) = -\ln(k+1) \Rightarrow \lim_{k \to \infty} s_k = -\infty$

43. converges by Comparison Test with $\sum\limits_{n=2}^{\infty} \frac{1}{n(n-1)}$ which converges since $\sum\limits_{n=2}^{\infty} \frac{1}{n(n-1)} = \sum\limits_{n=2}^{\infty} \left[ \frac{1}{n-1} - \frac{1}{n} \right]$, and

$s_k = \left( 1 - \frac{1}{2} \right) + \left( \frac{1}{2} - \frac{1}{3} \right) + \dots + \left( \frac{1}{k-2} - \frac{1}{k-1} \right) + \left( \frac{1}{k-1} - \frac{1}{k} \right) = 1 - \frac{1}{k} \Rightarrow \lim\limits_{k \to \infty} s_k = 1$; for $n \geq 2$, $(n-2)! \geq 1$

$\Rightarrow n(n-1)(n-2)! \geq n(n-1) \Rightarrow n! \geq n(n-1) \Rightarrow \frac{1}{n!} \leq \frac{1}{n(n-1)}$

44. converges by Limit Comparison Test: compare with $\sum\limits_{n=1}^{\infty} \frac{1}{n^3}$, which is a convergent p-series, $\lim\limits_{n \to \infty} \frac{\frac{(n-1)!}{(n+2)!}}{1/n^3}$

$= \lim\limits_{n \to \infty} \frac{n^3(n-1)!}{(n+2)(n+1)n(n-1)!} = \lim\limits_{n \to \infty} \frac{n^2}{n^2+3n+2} = \lim\limits_{n \to \infty} \frac{2n}{2n+3} = \lim\limits_{n \to \infty} \frac{2}{2} = 1 > 0$

45. diverges by the Limit Comparison Test (part 1) with $\frac{1}{n}$, the nth term of the divergent harmonic series:

$\lim\limits_{n \to \infty} \frac{\left( \sin \frac{1}{n} \right)}{\left( \frac{1}{n} \right)} = \lim\limits_{x \to 0} \frac{\sin x}{x} = 1$

46. diverges by the Limit Comparison Test (part 1) with $\frac{1}{n}$, the nth term of the divergent harmonic series:

$\lim\limits_{n \to \infty} \frac{\left( \tan \frac{1}{n} \right)}{\left( \frac{1}{n} \right)} = \lim\limits_{n \to \infty} \left( \frac{1}{\cos \frac{1}{n}} \right) \frac{\left( \sin \frac{1}{n} \right)}{\left( \frac{1}{n} \right)} = \lim\limits_{x \to 0} \left( \frac{1}{\cos x} \right) \left( \frac{\sin x}{x} \right) = 1 \cdot 1 = 1$

47. converges by the Direct Comparison Test: $\frac{\tan^{-1} n}{n^{1.1}} < \frac{\frac{\pi}{2}}{n^{1.1}}$ and $\sum\limits_{n=1}^{\infty} \frac{\frac{\pi}{2}}{n^{1.1}} = \frac{\pi}{2} \sum\limits_{n=1}^{\infty} \frac{1}{n^{1.1}}$ is the product of a

convergent p-series and a nonzero constant

48. converges by the Direct Comparison Test: $\sec^{-1} n < \frac{\pi}{2} \Rightarrow \frac{\sec^{-1} n}{n^{1.3}} < \frac{\left( \frac{\pi}{2} \right)}{n^{1.3}}$ and $\sum\limits_{n=1}^{\infty} \frac{\left( \frac{\pi}{2} \right)}{n^{1.3}} = \frac{\pi}{2} \sum\limits_{n=1}^{\infty} \frac{1}{n^{1.3}}$ is the

product of a convergent p-series and a nonzero constant

49. converges by the Limit Comparison Test (part 1) with $\frac{1}{n^2}$ : $\lim\limits_{n \to \infty} \frac{\left( \frac{\coth n}{n^2} \right)}{\left( \frac{1}{n^2} \right)} = \lim\limits_{n \to \infty} \coth n = \lim\limits_{n \to \infty} \frac{e^n + e^{-n}}{e^n - e^{-n}}$

$= \lim\limits_{n \to \infty} \frac{1 + e^{-2n}}{1 - e^{-2n}} = 1$

50. converges by the Limit Comparison Test (part 1) with $\frac{1}{n^2}$ : $\lim\limits_{n \to \infty} \frac{\left( \frac{\tanh n}{n^2} \right)}{\left( \frac{1}{n^2} \right)} = \lim\limits_{n \to \infty} \tanh n = \lim\limits_{n \to \infty} \frac{e^n - e^{-n}}{e^n + e^{-n}}$

$= \lim\limits_{n \to \infty} \frac{1 - e^{-2n}}{1 + e^{-2n}} = 1$

51. diverges by the Limit Comparison Test (part 1) with $\frac{1}{n}$ : $\lim\limits_{n \to \infty} \frac{\left( \frac{1}{n\sqrt[n]{n}} \right)}{\left( \frac{1}{n} \right)} = \lim\limits_{n \to \infty} \frac{1}{\sqrt[n]{n}} = 1$.

52. converges by the Limit Comparison Test (part 1) with $\frac{1}{n^2}$ : $\lim\limits_{n \to \infty} \frac{\left( \frac{\sqrt[n]{n}}{n^2} \right)}{\left( \frac{1}{n^2} \right)} = \lim\limits_{n \to \infty} \sqrt[n]{n} = 1$

53. $\frac{1}{1+2+3+\dots+n} = \frac{1}{\left( \frac{n(n+1)}{2} \right)} = \frac{2}{n(n+1)}$. The series converges by the Limit Comparison Test (part 1) with $\frac{1}{n^2}$ :

$\lim\limits_{n \to \infty} \frac{\left( \frac{2}{n(n+1)} \right)}{\left( \frac{1}{n^2} \right)} = \lim\limits_{n \to \infty} \frac{2n^2}{n^2+n} = \lim\limits_{n \to \infty} \frac{4n}{2n+1} = \lim\limits_{n \to \infty} \frac{4}{2} = 2$.

54. $\frac{1}{1+2^2+3^2+\dots+n^2} = \frac{1}{\frac{n(n+1)(2n+1)}{6}} = \frac{6}{n(n+1)(2n+1)} \leq \frac{6}{n^3} \Rightarrow$ the series converges by the Direct Comparison Test

55. (a) If $\lim\limits_{n \to \infty} \frac{a_n}{b_n} = 0$, then there exists an integer N such that for all $n > N$, $\left| \frac{a_n}{b_n} - 0 \right| < 1 \Rightarrow -1 < \frac{a_n}{b_n} < 1$
$\Rightarrow a_n < b_n$. Thus, if $\sum b_n$ converges, then $\sum a_n$ converges by the Direct Comparison Test.

   (b) If $\lim\limits_{n \to \infty} \frac{a_n}{b_n} = \infty$, then there exists an integer N such that for all $n > N$, $\frac{a_n}{b_n} > 1 \Rightarrow a_n > b_n$. Thus, if
$\sum b_n$ diverges, then $\sum a_n$ diverges by the Direct Comparison Test.

56. Yes, $\sum\limits_{n=1}^{\infty} \frac{a_n}{n}$ converges by the Direct Comparison Test because $\frac{a_n}{n} < a_n$

57. $\lim\limits_{n \to \infty} \frac{a_n}{b_n} = \infty \Rightarrow$ there exists an integer N such that for all $n > N$, $\frac{a_n}{b_n} > 1 \Rightarrow a_n > b_n$. If $\sum a_n$ converges,
then $\sum b_n$ converges by the Direct Comparison Test

58. $\sum a_n$ converges $\Rightarrow \lim\limits_{n \to \infty} a_n = 0 \Rightarrow$ there exists an integer N such that for all $n > N$, $0 \le a_n < 1 \Rightarrow a_n^2 < a_n$
$\Rightarrow \sum a_n^2$ converges by the Direct Comparison Test

59. Since $a_n > 0$ and $\lim\limits_{n \to \infty} a_n = \infty \neq 0$, by $n^{\text{th}}$ term test for divergence, $\sum a_n$ diverges.

60. Since $a_n > 0$ and $\lim\limits_{n \to \infty} \left( n^2 \cdot a_n \right) = 0$, compare $\sum a_n$ with $\sum \frac{1}{n^2}$, which is a convergent p-series; $\lim\limits_{n \to \infty} \frac{a_n}{1/n^2}$
$= \lim\limits_{n \to \infty} \left( n^2 \cdot a_n \right) = 0 \Rightarrow \sum a_n$ converges by Limit Comparison Test

61. Let $-\infty < q < \infty$ and $p > 1$. If $q = 0$, then $\sum\limits_{n=2}^{\infty} \frac{(\ln n)^q}{n^p} = \sum\limits_{n=2}^{\infty} \frac{1}{n^p}$, which is a convergent p-series. If $q \neq 0$, compare with

$\sum\limits_{n=2}^{\infty} \frac{1}{n^r}$ where $1 < r < p$, then $\lim\limits_{n \to \infty} \frac{\frac{(\ln n)^q}{n^p}}{1/n^r} = \lim\limits_{n \to \infty} \frac{(\ln n)^q}{n^{p-r}}$, and $p - r > 0$. If $q < 0 \Rightarrow -q > 0$ and $\lim\limits_{n \to \infty} \frac{(\ln n)^q}{n^{p-r}}$

$= \lim\limits_{n \to \infty} \frac{1}{(\ln n)^{-q} n^{p-r}} = 0$. If $q > 0$, $\lim\limits_{n \to \infty} \frac{(\ln n)^q}{n^{p-r}} = \lim\limits_{n \to \infty} \frac{q(\ln n)^{q-1}\left(\frac{1}{n}\right)}{(p-r)n^{p-r-1}} = \lim\limits_{n \to \infty} \frac{q(\ln n)^{q-1}}{(p-r)n^{p-r}}$. If $q - 1 \le 0 \Rightarrow 1 - q \ge 0$ and

$\lim\limits_{n \to \infty} \frac{q(\ln n)^{q-1}}{(p-r)n^{p-r}} = \lim\limits_{n \to \infty} \frac{q}{(p-r)n^{p-r}(\ln n)^{1-q}} = 0$, otherwise, we apply L'Hopital's Rule again. $\lim\limits_{n \to \infty} \frac{q(q-1)(\ln n)^{q-2}\left(\frac{1}{n}\right)}{(p-r)^2 n^{p-r-1}}$

$= \lim\limits_{n \to \infty} \frac{q(q-1)(\ln n)^{q-2}}{(p-r)^2 n^{p-r}}$. If $q - 2 \le 0 \Rightarrow 2 - q \ge 0$ and $\lim\limits_{n \to \infty} \frac{q(q-1)(\ln n)^{q-2}}{(p-r)^2 n^{p-r}} = \lim\limits_{n \to \infty} \frac{q(q-1)}{(p-r)^2 n^{p-r}(\ln n)^{2-q}} = 0$; otherwise, we

apply L'Hopital's Rule again. Since q is finite, there is a positive integer k such that $q - k \le 0 \Rightarrow k - q \ge 0$. Thus, after k

applications of L'Hopital's Rule we obtain $\lim\limits_{n \to \infty} \frac{q(q-1)\cdots(q-k+1)(\ln n)^{q-k}}{(p-r)^k n^{p-r}} = \lim\limits_{n \to \infty} \frac{q(q-1)\cdots(q-k+1)}{(p-r)^k n^{p-r}(\ln n)^{k-q}} = 0$. Since the limit is

0 in every case, by Limit Comparison Test, the series $\sum\limits_{n=1}^{\infty} \frac{(\ln n)^q}{n^p}$ converges.

62. Let $-\infty < q < \infty$ and $p \le 1$. If $q = 0$, then $\sum\limits_{n=2}^{\infty} \frac{(\ln n)^q}{n^p} = \sum\limits_{n=2}^{\infty} \frac{1}{n^p}$, which is a divergent p-series. If $q > 0$, compare with

$\sum\limits_{n=2}^{\infty} \frac{1}{n^p}$, which is a divergent p-series. Then $\lim\limits_{n \to \infty} \frac{\frac{(\ln n)^q}{n^p}}{1/n^p} = \lim\limits_{n \to \infty} (\ln n)^q = \infty$. If $q < 0 \Rightarrow -q > 0$, compare with $\sum\limits_{n=2}^{\infty} \frac{1}{n^r}$,

where $0 < p < r \le 1$. $\lim\limits_{n \to \infty} \frac{\frac{(\ln n)^q}{n^p}}{1/n^r} = \lim\limits_{n \to \infty} \frac{(\ln n)^q}{n^{p-r}} = \lim\limits_{n \to \infty} \frac{n^{r-p}}{(\ln n)^{-q}}$ since $r - p > 0$. Apply L'Hopital's to obtain

$\lim\limits_{n \to \infty} \frac{(r-p)n^{r-p-1}}{(-q)(\ln n)^{-q-1}\left(\frac{1}{n}\right)} = \lim\limits_{n \to \infty} \frac{(r-p)n^{r-p}}{(-q)(\ln n)^{-q-1}}$. If $-q - 1 \le 0 \Rightarrow q + 1 \ge 0$ and $\lim\limits_{n \to \infty} \frac{(r-p)n^{r-p}(\ln n)^{q+1}}{(-q)} = \infty$,

otherwise, we apply L'Hopital's Rule again to obtain $\lim\limits_{n \to \infty} \frac{(r-p)^2 n^{r-p-1}}{(-q)(-q-1)(\ln n)^{-q-2}\left(\frac{1}{n}\right)} = \lim\limits_{n \to \infty} \frac{(r-p)^2 n^{r-p}}{(-q)(-q-1)(\ln n)^{-q-2}}$. If

$-q - 2 \le 0 \Rightarrow q + 2 \ge 0$ and $\lim\limits_{n \to \infty} \frac{(r-p)^2 n^{r-p}}{(-q)(-q-1)(\ln n)^{-q-2}} = \lim\limits_{n \to \infty} \frac{(r-p)^2 n^{r-p}(\ln n)^{q+2}}{(-q)(-q-1)} = \infty$, otherwise, we

apply L'Hopital's Rule again. Since q is finite, there is a positive integer k such that $-q - k \le 0 \Rightarrow q + k \ge 0$. Thus, after

k applications of L'Hopital's Rule we obtain $\lim\limits_{n \to \infty} \frac{(r-p)^k n^{r-p}}{(-q)(-q-1)\cdots(-q-k+1)(\ln n)^{-q-k}} = \lim\limits_{n \to \infty} \frac{(r-p)^k n^{r-p}(\ln n)^{q+k}}{(-q)(-q-1)\cdots(-q-k+1)} = \infty$.

Since the limit is $\infty$ if $q > 0$ or if $q < 0$ and $p < 1$, by Limit comparison test, the series $\sum\limits_{n=1}^{\infty} \frac{(\ln n)^q}{n^{p-r}}$ diverges. Finally if $q < 0$

and $p = 1$ then $\sum\limits_{n=2}^{\infty} \frac{(\ln n)^q}{n^p} = \sum\limits_{n=2}^{\infty} \frac{(\ln n)^q}{n}$. Compare with $\sum\limits_{n=2}^{\infty} \frac{1}{n}$, which is a divergent p-series. For $n \geq 3$, $\ln n \geq 1$

$\Rightarrow (\ln n)^q \geq 1 \Rightarrow \frac{(\ln n)^q}{n} \geq \frac{1}{n}$. Thus $\sum\limits_{n=2}^{\infty} \frac{(\ln n)^q}{n}$ diverges by Comparison Test. Thus, if $-\infty < q < \infty$ and $p \leq 1$,

the series $\sum\limits_{n=1}^{\infty} \frac{(\ln n)^q}{n^{p-r}}$ diverges.

63. Converges by Exercise 61 with $q = 3$ and $p = 4$.

64. Diverges by Exercise 62 with $q = \frac{1}{2}$ and $p = \frac{1}{2}$.

65. Converges by Exercise 61 with $q = 1000$ and $p = 1.001$.

66. Diverges by Exercise 62 with $q = \frac{1}{5}$ and $p = 0.99$.

67. Converges by Exercise 61 with $q = -3$ and $p = 1.1$.

68. Diverges by Exercise 62 with $q = -\frac{1}{2}$ and $p = \frac{1}{2}$.

69. Example CAS commands:
    Maple:
```
a := n -> 1./n^3/sin(n)^2;
s := k -> sum( a(n), n=1..k );              # (a)]
limit( s(k), k=infinity );
pts := [seq( [k,s(k)], k=1..100 )]:          # (b)
plot( pts, style=point, title="#69(b) (Section 10.4)" );
pts := [seq( [k,s(k)], k=1..200 )]:          # (c)
plot( pts, style=point, title="#69(c) (Section 10.4)" );
pts := [seq( [k,s(k)], k=1..400 )]:          # (d)
plot( pts, style=point, title="#69(d) (Section 10.4)" );
evalf( 355/113 );
```
    Mathematica:
```
Clear[a, n, s, k, p]
a[n_]:= 1 / ( n^3 Sin[n]^2 )
s[k_]= Sum[ a[n], {n, 1, k}]
points[p_]:= Table[{k, N[s[k]]}, {k, 1, p}]
points[100]
ListPlot[points[100]]
points[200]
ListPlot[points[200]]
points[400]
ListPlot[points[400], PlotRange -> All]
```
    To investigate what is happening around k = 355, you could do the following.
```
N[355/113]
N[π - 355/113]
Sin[355]//N
a[355]//N
N[s[354]]
```

N[s[355]]

N[s[356]]

70. (a) Let $S = \sum\limits_{n=1}^{\infty} \frac{1}{n^2}$, which is a convergent p-series. By Example 5 in Section 10.2, $\sum\limits_{n=1}^{\infty} \frac{1}{n(n+1)}$ converges to 1. By Theorem 8,

$$S = \sum_{n=1}^{\infty} \frac{1}{n^2} = \sum_{n=1}^{\infty} \frac{1}{n(n+1)} + \sum_{n=1}^{\infty} \frac{1}{n^2} - \sum_{n=1}^{\infty} \frac{1}{n(n+1)} = \sum_{n=1}^{\infty} \frac{1}{n(n+1)} + \sum_{n=1}^{\infty} \left( \frac{1}{n^2} - \frac{1}{n(n+1)} \right) \text{ also converges.}$$

(b) Since $\sum\limits_{n=1}^{\infty} \frac{1}{n(n+1)}$ converges to 1 (from Example 5 in Section 10.2), $S = 1 + \sum\limits_{n=1}^{\infty} \left( \frac{1}{n^2} - \frac{1}{n(n+1)} \right) = 1 + \sum\limits_{n=1}^{\infty} \frac{1}{n^2(n+1)}$

(c) The new series is comparible to $\sum\limits_{n=1}^{\infty} \frac{1}{n^3}$, so it will converge faster because its terms $\to 0$ faster than the terms of $\sum\limits_{n=1}^{\infty} \frac{1}{n^2}$.

(d) The series $1 + \sum\limits_{n=1}^{1000} \frac{1}{n^2(n+1)}$ gives a better approximation. Using Mathematica, $1 + \sum\limits_{n=1}^{1000} \frac{1}{n^2(n+1)} = 1.644933568$, while

$\sum\limits_{n=1}^{1000000} \frac{1}{n^2} = 1.644933067$. Note that $\frac{\pi^2}{6} = 1.644934067$. The error is $4.99 \times 10^{-7}$ compared with $1 \times 10^{-6}$.

## 10.5 THE RATIO AND ROOT TESTS

1. $\frac{2^n}{n!} > 0$ for all $n \geq 1$; $\lim\limits_{n\to\infty} \left( \frac{\frac{2^{n+1}}{(n+1)!}}{\frac{2^n}{n!}} \right) = \lim\limits_{n\to\infty} \left( \frac{2^n \cdot 2}{(n+1)\cdot n!} \cdot \frac{n!}{2^n} \right) = \lim\limits_{n\to\infty} \left( \frac{2}{n+1} \right) = 0 < 1 \Rightarrow \sum\limits_{n=1}^{\infty} \frac{2^n}{n!}$ converges

2. $\frac{n+2}{3^n} > 0$ for all $n \geq 1$; $\lim\limits_{n\to\infty} \left( \frac{\frac{(n+1)+2}{3^{n+1}}}{\frac{n+2}{3^n}} \right) = \lim\limits_{n\to\infty} \left( \frac{n+3}{3^n \cdot 3} \cdot \frac{3^n}{n+2} \right) = \lim\limits_{n\to\infty} \left( \frac{n+3}{3n+6} \right) = \lim\limits_{n\to\infty} \left( \frac{1}{3} \right) = \frac{1}{3} < 1 \Rightarrow \sum\limits_{n=1}^{\infty} \frac{n+2}{3^n}$ converges

3. $\frac{(n-1)!}{(n+1)^2} > 0$ for all $n \geq 1$; $\lim\limits_{n\to\infty} \left( \frac{\frac{((n+1)-1)!}{((n+1)+1)^2}}{\frac{(n-1)!}{(n+1)^2}} \right) = \lim\limits_{n\to\infty} \left( \frac{n\cdot(n-1)!}{(n+2)^2} \cdot \frac{(n+1)^2}{(n-1)!} \right) = \lim\limits_{n\to\infty} \left( \frac{n^3+2n^2+n}{n^2+4n+4} \right) = \lim\limits_{n\to\infty} \left( \frac{3n^2+4n+1}{2n+4} \right)$

$= \lim\limits_{n\to\infty} \left( \frac{6n+4}{2} \right) = \infty > 1 \Rightarrow \sum\limits_{n=1}^{\infty} \frac{(n-1)!}{(n+1)^2}$ diverges

4. $\frac{2^{n+1}}{n\cdot 3^{n-1}} > 0$ for all $n \geq 1$; $\lim\limits_{n\to\infty} \left( \frac{\frac{2^{(n+1)+1}}{(n+1)\cdot 3^{(n+1)-1}}}{\frac{2^{n+1}}{n\cdot 3^{n-1}}} \right) = \lim\limits_{n\to\infty} \left( \frac{2^{n+1}\cdot 2}{(n+1)\cdot 3^{n-1}\cdot 3} \cdot \frac{n\cdot 3^{n-1}}{2^{n+1}} \right) = \lim\limits_{n\to\infty} \left( \frac{2n}{3n+3} \right) = \lim\limits_{n\to\infty} \left( \frac{2}{3} \right) = \frac{2}{3} < 1$

$\Rightarrow \sum\limits_{n=1}^{\infty} \frac{2^{n+1}}{n\cdot 3^{n-1}}$ converges

5. $\frac{n^4}{4^n} > 0$ for all $n \geq 1$; $\lim\limits_{n\to\infty} \left( \frac{\frac{(n+1)^4}{4^{n+1}}}{\frac{n^4}{4^n}} \right) = \lim\limits_{n\to\infty} \left( \frac{(n+1)^4}{4^n \cdot 4} \cdot \frac{4^n}{n^4} \right) = \lim\limits_{n\to\infty} \left( \frac{n^4+4n^3+6n^2+4n+1}{4n^4} \right)$

$= \lim\limits_{n\to\infty} \left( \frac{1}{4} + \frac{1}{n} + \frac{3}{2n^2} + \frac{1}{n^3} + \frac{1}{4n^4} \right) = \frac{1}{4} < 1 \Rightarrow \sum\limits_{n=1}^{\infty} \frac{n^4}{4^n}$ converges

6. $\frac{3^{n+2}}{\ln n} > 0$ for all $n \geq 2$; $\lim\limits_{n\to\infty} \left( \frac{\frac{3^{(n+1)+2}}{\ln(n+1)}}{\frac{3^{n+2}}{\ln n}} \right) = \lim\limits_{n\to\infty} \left( \frac{3^{n+2}\cdot 3}{\ln(n+1)} \cdot \frac{\ln n}{3^{n+2}} \right) = \lim\limits_{n\to\infty} \left( \frac{3\ln n}{\ln(n+1)} \right) = \lim\limits_{n\to\infty} \left( \frac{3}{\frac{1}{n+1}} \right) = \lim\limits_{n\to\infty} \left( \frac{3n+3}{n} \right)$

$= \lim\limits_{n\to\infty} \left( \frac{3}{1} \right) = 3 > 1 \Rightarrow \sum\limits_{n=2}^{\infty} \frac{3^{n+2}}{\ln n}$ diverges

7. $\frac{n^2(n+2)!}{n!3^{2n}} > 0$ for all $n \geq 1$; $\lim\limits_{n\to\infty} \left( \frac{\frac{(n+1)^2((n+1)+2)!}{(n+1)!3^{2(n+1)}}}{\frac{n^2(n+2)!}{n!3^{2n}}} \right) = \lim\limits_{n\to\infty} \left( \frac{(n+1)^2(n+3)(n+2)!}{(n+1)\cdot n!3^{2n}\cdot 3^2} \cdot \frac{n!3^{2n}}{n^2(n+2)!} \right) = \lim\limits_{n\to\infty} \left( \frac{n^3+5n^2+7n+3}{9n^3+9n^2} \right)$

$= \lim\limits_{n\to\infty} \left( \frac{3n^2+15n+7}{27n^2+18n} \right) = \lim\limits_{n\to\infty} \left( \frac{6n+15}{54n+18} \right) = \lim\limits_{n\to\infty} \left( \frac{6}{54} \right) = \frac{1}{9} < 1 \Rightarrow \sum\limits_{n=1}^{\infty} \frac{n^2(n+2)!}{n!3^{2n}}$ converges

8. $\frac{n \cdot 5^n}{(2n+3)\ln(n+1)} > 0$ for all $n \geq 1$; $\lim\limits_{n\to\infty} \left( \frac{\frac{(n+1)\cdot 5^{n+1}}{(2(n+1)+3)\ln((n+1)+1)}}{\frac{n\cdot 5^n}{(2n+3)\ln(n+1)}} \right) = \lim\limits_{n\to\infty} \left( \frac{(n+1)\cdot 5^n \cdot 5}{(2n+5)\ln(n+2)} \cdot \frac{(2n+3)\ln(n+1)}{n\cdot 5^n} \right)$

$= \lim\limits_{n\to\infty} \left( \frac{5(n+1)\cdot(2n+3)}{n(2n+5)} \cdot \frac{\ln(n+1)}{\ln(n+2)} \right) = \lim\limits_{n\to\infty} \left( \frac{10n^2 + 25n + 15}{2n^2 + 5n} \right) \cdot \lim\limits_{n\to\infty} \left( \frac{\ln(n+1)}{\ln(n+2)} \right) = \lim\limits_{n\to\infty} \left( \frac{20n+25}{4n+5} \right) \cdot \lim\limits_{n\to\infty} \left( \frac{\frac{1}{n+1}}{\frac{1}{n+2}} \right)$

$= \lim\limits_{n\to\infty} \left( \frac{20}{4} \right) \cdot \lim\limits_{n\to\infty} \left( \frac{n+2}{n+1} \right) = 5 \cdot \lim\limits_{n\to\infty} \left( \frac{1}{1} \right) = 5 \cdot 1 = 5 > 1 \Rightarrow \sum\limits_{n=2}^{\infty} \frac{n\cdot 5^n}{(2n+3)\ln(n+1)}$ diverges

9. $\frac{7}{(2n+5)^n} \geq 0$ for all $n \geq 1$; $\lim\limits_{n\to\infty} \sqrt[n]{\frac{7}{(2n+5)^n}} = \lim\limits_{n\to\infty} \left( \frac{\sqrt[n]{7}}{2n+5} \right) = 0 < 1 \Rightarrow \sum\limits_{n=1}^{\infty} \frac{7}{(2n+5)^n}$ converges

10. $\frac{4^n}{(3n)^n} \geq 0$ for all $n \geq 1$; $\lim\limits_{n\to\infty} \sqrt[n]{\frac{4^n}{(3n)^n}} = \lim\limits_{n\to\infty} \left( \frac{4}{3n} \right) = 0 < 1 \Rightarrow \sum\limits_{n=1}^{\infty} \frac{4^n}{(3n)^n}$ converges

11. $\left( \frac{4n+3}{3n-5} \right)^n \geq 0$ for all $n \geq 2$; $\lim\limits_{n\to\infty} \sqrt[n]{\left( \frac{4n+3}{3n-5} \right)^n} = \lim\limits_{n\to\infty} \left( \frac{4n+3}{3n-5} \right) = \lim\limits_{n\to\infty} \left( \frac{4}{3} \right) = \frac{4}{3} > 1 \Rightarrow \sum\limits_{n=1}^{\infty} \left( \frac{4n+3}{3n-5} \right)^n$ diverges

12. $\left[ \ln\left( e^2 + \frac{1}{n} \right) \right]^{n+1} \geq 0$ for all $n \geq 1$; $\lim\limits_{n\to\infty} \sqrt[n]{\left[ \ln\left( e^2 + \frac{1}{n} \right) \right]^{n+1}} = \lim\limits_{n\to\infty} \left[ \ln\left( e^2 + \frac{1}{n} \right) \right]^{1+1/n} = \ln(e^2) = 2 > 1$

$\Rightarrow \sum\limits_{n=1}^{\infty} \left[ \ln\left( e^2 + \frac{1}{n} \right) \right]^{n+1}$ diverges

13. $\frac{8}{\left( 3 + \frac{1}{n} \right)^{2n}} \geq 0$ for all $n \geq 1$; $\lim\limits_{n\to\infty} \sqrt[n]{\frac{8}{\left( 3 + \frac{1}{n} \right)^{2n}}} = \lim\limits_{n\to\infty} \left( \frac{\sqrt[n]{8}}{\left( 3 + \frac{1}{n} \right)^2} \right) = \frac{1}{9} < 1 \Rightarrow \sum\limits_{n=1}^{\infty} \frac{8}{\left( 3 + \frac{1}{n} \right)^{2n}}$ converges

14. $\left[ \sin\left( \frac{1}{\sqrt{n}} \right) \right]^n \geq 0$ for all $n \geq 1$; $\lim\limits_{n\to\infty} \sqrt[n]{\left[ \sin\left( \frac{1}{\sqrt{n}} \right) \right]^n} = \lim\limits_{n\to\infty} \sin\left( \frac{1}{\sqrt{n}} \right) = \sin(0) = 0 < 1 \Rightarrow \sum\limits_{n=1}^{\infty} \left[ \sin\left( \frac{1}{\sqrt{n}} \right) \right]^n$ converges

15. $\left( 1 - \frac{1}{n} \right)^{n^2} \geq 0$ for all $n \geq 1$; $\lim\limits_{n\to\infty} \sqrt[n]{\left( 1 - \frac{1}{n} \right)^{n^2}} = \lim\limits_{n\to\infty} \left( 1 - \frac{1}{n} \right)^n = e^{-1} < 1 \Rightarrow \sum\limits_{n=1}^{\infty} \left( 1 - \frac{1}{n} \right)^{n^2}$ converges

16. $\frac{1}{n^{1+n}} \geq 0$ for all $n \geq 2$; $\lim\limits_{n\to\infty} \sqrt[n]{\frac{1}{n^{1+n}}} = \lim\limits_{n\to\infty} \left( \frac{\sqrt[n]{1}}{n^{1/n+1}} \right) = \lim\limits_{n\to\infty} \left( \frac{\sqrt[n]{1}}{n \sqrt[n]{n}} \right) = 0 < 1 \Rightarrow \sum\limits_{n=2}^{\infty} \frac{1}{n^{1+n}}$ converges

17. converges by the Ratio Test: $\lim\limits_{n\to\infty} \frac{a_{n+1}}{a_n} = \lim\limits_{n\to\infty} \frac{\left[ \frac{(n+1)^{\sqrt{2}}}{2^{n+1}} \right]}{\left[ \frac{n^{\sqrt{2}}}{2^n} \right]} = \lim\limits_{n\to\infty} \frac{(n+1)^{\sqrt{2}}}{2^{n+1}} \cdot \frac{2^n}{n^{\sqrt{2}}} = \lim\limits_{n\to\infty} \left( 1 + \frac{1}{n} \right)^{\sqrt{2}} \left( \frac{1}{2} \right) = \frac{1}{2} < 1$

18. converges by the Ratio Test: $\lim\limits_{n\to\infty} \frac{a_{n+1}}{a_n} = \lim\limits_{n\to\infty} \frac{\left( \frac{(n+1)^2}{e^{n+1}} \right)}{\left( \frac{n^2}{e^n} \right)} = \lim\limits_{n\to\infty} \frac{(n+1)^2}{e^{n+1}} \cdot \frac{e^n}{n^2} = \lim\limits_{n\to\infty} \left( 1 + \frac{1}{n} \right)^2 \left( \frac{1}{e} \right) = \frac{1}{e} < 1$

19. diverges by the Ratio Test: $\lim\limits_{n\to\infty} \frac{a_{n+1}}{a_n} = \lim\limits_{n\to\infty} \frac{\left( \frac{(n+1)!}{e^{n+1}} \right)}{\left( \frac{n!}{e^n} \right)} = \lim\limits_{n\to\infty} \frac{(n+1)!}{e^{n+1}} \cdot \frac{e^n}{n!} = \lim\limits_{n\to\infty} \frac{n+1}{e} = \infty$

20. diverges by the Ratio Test: $\lim\limits_{n\to\infty} \frac{a_{n+1}}{a_n} = \lim\limits_{n\to\infty} \frac{\left( \frac{(n+1)!}{10^{n+1}} \right)}{\left( \frac{n!}{10^n} \right)} = \lim\limits_{n\to\infty} \frac{(n+1)!}{10^{n+1}} \cdot \frac{10^n}{n!} = \lim\limits_{n\to\infty} \frac{n}{10} = \infty$

21. converges by the Ratio Test: $\lim\limits_{n\to\infty} \frac{a_{n+1}}{a_n} = \lim\limits_{n\to\infty} \frac{\left( \frac{(n+1)^{10}}{10^{n+1}} \right)}{\left( \frac{n^{10}}{10^n} \right)} = \lim\limits_{n\to\infty} \frac{(n+1)^{10}}{10^{n+1}} \cdot \frac{10^n}{n^{10}} = \lim\limits_{n\to\infty} \left( 1 + \frac{1}{n} \right)^{10} \left( \frac{1}{10} \right) = \frac{1}{10} < 1$

22. diverges; $\lim\limits_{n \to \infty} a_n = \lim\limits_{n \to \infty} \left(\frac{n-2}{n}\right)^n = \lim\limits_{n \to \infty} \left(1 + \frac{-2}{n}\right)^n = e^{-2} \neq 0$

23. converges by the Direct Comparison Test: $\frac{2+(-1)^n}{(1.25)^n} = \left(\frac{4}{5}\right)^n [2 + (-1)^n] \leq \left(\frac{4}{5}\right)^n (3)$ which is the $n^{\text{th}}$ term of a convergent geometric series

24. converges; a geometric series with $|r| = \left|-\frac{2}{3}\right| < 1$

25. diverges; $\lim\limits_{n \to \infty} a_n = \lim\limits_{n \to \infty} \left(1 - \frac{3}{n}\right)^n = \lim\limits_{n \to \infty} \left(1 + \frac{-3}{n}\right)^n = e^{-3} \approx 0.05 \neq 0$

26. diverges; $\lim\limits_{n \to \infty} a_n = \lim\limits_{n \to \infty} \left(1 - \frac{1}{3n}\right)^n = \lim\limits_{n \to \infty} \left(1 + \frac{\left(-\frac{1}{3}\right)}{n}\right)^n = e^{-1/3} \approx 0.72 \neq 0$

27. converges by the Direct Comparison Test: $\frac{\ln n}{n^3} < \frac{n}{n^3} = \frac{1}{n^2}$ for $n \geq 2$, the $n^{\text{th}}$ term of a convergent p-series.

28. converges by the nth-Root Test: $\lim\limits_{n \to \infty} \sqrt[n]{a_n} = \lim\limits_{n \to \infty} \sqrt[n]{\frac{(\ln n)^n}{n^n}} = \lim\limits_{n \to \infty} \frac{((\ln n)^n)^{1/n}}{(n^n)^{1/n}} = \lim\limits_{n \to \infty} \frac{\ln n}{n} = \lim\limits_{n \to \infty} \frac{\left(\frac{1}{n}\right)}{1} = 0 < 1$

29. diverges by the Direct Comparison Test: $\frac{1}{n} - \frac{1}{n^2} = \frac{n-1}{n^2} > \frac{1}{2}\left(\frac{1}{n}\right)$ for $n > 2$ or by the Limit Comparison Test (part 1) with $\frac{1}{n}$.

30. converges by the nth-Root Test: $\lim\limits_{n \to \infty} \sqrt[n]{a_n} = \lim\limits_{n \to \infty} \sqrt[n]{\left(\frac{1}{n} - \frac{1}{n^2}\right)^n} = \lim\limits_{n \to \infty} \left(\left(\frac{1}{n} - \frac{1}{n^2}\right)^n\right)^{1/n} = \lim\limits_{n \to \infty} \left(\frac{1}{n} - \frac{1}{n^2}\right) = 0 < 1$

31. diverges by the Direct Comparison Test: $\frac{\ln n}{n} > \frac{1}{n}$ for $n \geq 3$

32. converges by the Ratio Test: $\lim\limits_{n \to \infty} \frac{a_{n+1}}{a_n} = \lim\limits_{n \to \infty} \frac{(n+1)\ln(n+1)}{2^{n+1}} \cdot \frac{2^n}{n \ln(n)} = \frac{1}{2} < 1$

33. converges by the Ratio Test: $\lim\limits_{n \to \infty} \frac{a_{n+1}}{a_n} = \lim\limits_{n \to \infty} \frac{(n+2)(n+3)}{(n+1)!} \cdot \frac{n!}{(n+1)(n+2)} = 0 < 1$

34. converges by the Ratio Test: $\lim\limits_{n \to \infty} \frac{a_{n+1}}{a_n} = \lim\limits_{n \to \infty} \frac{(n+1)^3}{e^{n+1}} \cdot \frac{e^n}{n^3} = \frac{1}{e} < 1$

35. converges by the Ratio Test: $\lim\limits_{n \to \infty} \frac{a_{n+1}}{a_n} = \lim\limits_{n \to \infty} \frac{(n+4)!}{3!(n+1)!3^{n+1}} \cdot \frac{3!n!3^n}{(n+3)!} = \lim\limits_{n \to \infty} \frac{n+4}{3(n+1)} = \frac{1}{3} < 1$

36. converges by the Ratio Test: $\lim\limits_{n \to \infty} \frac{a_{n+1}}{a_n} = \lim\limits_{n \to \infty} \frac{(n+1)2^{n+1}(n+2)!}{3^{n+1}(n+1)!} \cdot \frac{3^n n!}{n2^n(n+1)!} = \lim\limits_{n \to \infty} \left(\frac{n+1}{n}\right)\left(\frac{2}{3}\right)\left(\frac{n+2}{n+1}\right) = \frac{2}{3} < 1$

37. converges by the Ratio Test: $\lim\limits_{n \to \infty} \frac{a_{n+1}}{a_n} = \lim\limits_{n \to \infty} \frac{(n+1)!}{(2n+3)!} \cdot \frac{(2n+1)!}{n!} = \lim\limits_{n \to \infty} \frac{n+1}{(2n+3)(2n+2)} = 0 < 1$

38. converges by the Ratio Test: $\lim\limits_{n \to \infty} \frac{a_{n+1}}{a_n} = \lim\limits_{n \to \infty} \frac{(n+1)!}{(n+1)^{n+1}} \cdot \frac{n^n}{n!} = \lim\limits_{n \to \infty} \left(\frac{n}{n+1}\right)^n = \lim\limits_{n \to \infty} \frac{1}{\left(\frac{n+1}{n}\right)^n}$

    $= \lim\limits_{n \to \infty} \frac{1}{\left(1+\frac{1}{n}\right)^n} = \frac{1}{e} < 1$

39. converges by the Root Test: $\lim\limits_{n \to \infty} \sqrt[n]{a_n} = \lim\limits_{n \to \infty} \sqrt[n]{\frac{n}{(\ln n)^n}} = \lim\limits_{n \to \infty} \frac{\sqrt[n]{n}}{\ln n} = \lim\limits_{n \to \infty} \frac{1}{\ln n} = 0 < 1$

40. converges by the Root Test: $\lim\limits_{n\to\infty} \sqrt[n]{a_n} = \lim\limits_{n\to\infty} \sqrt[n]{\frac{n}{(\ln n)^{n/2}}} = \lim\limits_{n\to\infty} \frac{\sqrt[n]{n}}{\sqrt{\ln n}} = \frac{\lim\limits_{n\to\infty} \sqrt[n]{n}}{\lim\limits_{n\to\infty}\sqrt{\ln n}} = 0 < 1$

$\left(\lim\limits_{n\to\infty} \sqrt[n]{n} = 1\right)$

41. converges by the Direct Comparison Test: $\frac{n!\,\ln n}{n(n+2)!} = \frac{\ln n}{n(n+1)(n+2)} < \frac{n}{n(n+1)(n+2)} = \frac{1}{(n+1)(n+2)} < \frac{1}{n^2}$

which is the nth-term of a convergent p-series

42. diverges by the Ratio Test: $\lim\limits_{n\to\infty} \frac{a_{n+1}}{a_n} = \lim\limits_{n\to\infty} \frac{3^{n+1}}{(n+1)^3\,2^{n+1}} \cdot \frac{n^3 2^n}{3^n} = \lim\limits_{n\to\infty} \frac{n^3}{(n+1)^3}\left(\frac{3}{2}\right) = \frac{3}{2} > 1$

43. converges by the Ratio Test: $\lim\limits_{n\to\infty} \frac{a_{n+1}}{a_n} = \lim\limits_{n\to\infty} \frac{[(n+1)!]^2}{[2(n+1)]!} \cdot \frac{(2n)!}{[n!]^2} = \lim\limits_{n\to\infty} \frac{(n+1)^2}{(2n+2)(2n+1)} = \lim\limits_{n\to\infty} \frac{n^2+2n+1}{4n^2+6n+2} = \frac{1}{4} < 1$

44. converges by the Ratio Test: $\lim\limits_{n\to\infty} \frac{a_{n+1}}{a_n} = \lim\limits_{n\to\infty} \frac{(2n+5)(2^{n+1}+3)}{3^{n+1}+2} \cdot \frac{3^n+2}{(2n+3)(2^n+3)} = \lim\limits_{n\to\infty}\left[\frac{2n+5}{2n+3} \cdot \frac{2\cdot6^n+4\cdot2^n+3\cdot3^n+6}{3\cdot6^n+9\cdot3^n+2\cdot2^n+6}\right]$

$= \lim\limits_{n\to\infty}\left[\frac{2n+5}{2n+3}\right] \cdot \lim\limits_{n\to\infty}\left[\frac{2\cdot6^n+4\cdot2^n+3\cdot3^n+6}{3\cdot6^n+9\cdot3^n+2\cdot2^n+6}\right] = 1 \cdot \frac{2}{3} = \frac{2}{3} < 1$

45. converges by the Ratio Test: $\lim\limits_{n\to\infty} \frac{a_{n+1}}{a_n} = \lim\limits_{n\to\infty} \frac{\left(\frac{1+\sin n}{n}\right) a_n}{a_n} = 0 < 1$

46. converges by the Ratio Test: $\lim\limits_{n\to\infty} \frac{a_{n+1}}{a_n} = \lim\limits_{n\to\infty} \frac{\left(\frac{1+\tan^{-1}n}{n}\right) a_n}{a_n} = \lim\limits_{n\to\infty} \frac{1+\tan^{-1}n}{n} = 0$ since the numerator

approaches $1 + \frac{\pi}{2}$ while the denominator tends to $\infty$

47. diverges by the Ratio Test: $\lim\limits_{n\to\infty} \frac{a_{n+1}}{a_n} = \lim\limits_{n\to\infty} \frac{\left(\frac{3n-1}{2n+5}\right) a_n}{a_n} = \lim\limits_{n\to\infty} \frac{3n-1}{2n+5} = \frac{3}{2} > 1$

48. diverges; $a_{n+1} = \frac{n}{n+1} a_n \Rightarrow a_{n+1} = \left(\frac{n}{n+1}\right)\left(\frac{n-1}{n} a_{n-1}\right) \Rightarrow a_{n+1} = \left(\frac{n}{n+1}\right)\left(\frac{n-1}{n}\right)\left(\frac{n-2}{n-1} a_{n-2}\right)$

$\Rightarrow a_{n+1} = \left(\frac{n}{n+1}\right)\left(\frac{n-1}{n}\right)\left(\frac{n-2}{n-1}\right)\cdots\left(\frac{1}{2}\right) a_1 \Rightarrow a_{n+1} = \frac{a_1}{n+1} \Rightarrow a_{n+1} = \frac{3}{n+1}$, which is a constant times the

general term of the diverging harmonic series

49. converges by the Ratio Test: $\lim\limits_{n\to\infty} \frac{a_{n+1}}{a_n} = \lim\limits_{n\to\infty} \frac{\left(\frac{2}{n}\right) a_n}{a_n} = \lim\limits_{n\to\infty} \frac{2}{n} = 0 < 1$

50. converges by the Ratio Test: $\lim\limits_{n\to\infty} \frac{a_{n+1}}{a_n} = \lim\limits_{n\to\infty} \frac{\left(\frac{\sqrt[n]{n}}{2}\right) a_n}{a_n} = \lim\limits_{n\to\infty} \frac{\sqrt[n]{n}}{2} = \frac{1}{2} < 1$

51. converges by the Ratio Test: $\lim\limits_{n\to\infty} \frac{a_{n+1}}{a_n} = \lim\limits_{n\to\infty} \frac{\left(\frac{1+\ln n}{n}\right) a_n}{a_n} = \lim\limits_{n\to\infty} \frac{1+\ln n}{n} = \lim\limits_{n\to\infty} \frac{1}{n} = 0 < 1$

52. $\frac{n+\ln n}{n+10} > 0$ and $a_1 = \frac{1}{2} \Rightarrow a_n > 0$; $\ln n > 10$ for $n > e^{10} \Rightarrow n + \ln n > n + 10 \Rightarrow \frac{n+\ln n}{n+10} > 1$

$\Rightarrow a_{n+1} = \frac{n+\ln n}{n+10} a_n > a_n$; thus $a_{n+1} > a_n \geq \frac{1}{2} \Rightarrow \lim\limits_{n\to\infty} a_n \neq 0$, so the series diverges by the nth-Term Test

53. diverges by the nth-Term Test: $a_1 = \frac{1}{3}$, $a_2 = \sqrt[2]{\frac{1}{3}}$, $a_3 = \sqrt[3]{\sqrt[2]{\frac{1}{3}}} = \sqrt[6]{\frac{1}{3}}$, $a_4 = \sqrt[4]{\sqrt[3]{\sqrt[2]{\frac{1}{3}}}} = \sqrt[4!]{\frac{1}{3}},\ldots$,

$a_n = \sqrt[n!]{\frac{1}{3}} \Rightarrow \lim\limits_{n\to\infty} a_n = 1$ because $\left\{\sqrt[n!]{\frac{1}{3}}\right\}$ is a subsequence of $\left\{\sqrt[n]{\frac{1}{3}}\right\}$ whose limit is 1 by Table 8.1

54. converges by the Direct Comparison Test: $a_1 = \frac{1}{2}$, $a_2 = \left(\frac{1}{2}\right)^2$, $a_3 = \left(\left(\frac{1}{2}\right)^2\right)^3 = \left(\frac{1}{2}\right)^6$, $a_4 = \left(\left(\frac{1}{2}\right)^6\right)^4 = \left(\frac{1}{2}\right)^{24}, \ldots$

$\Rightarrow a_n = \left(\frac{1}{2}\right)^{n!} < \left(\frac{1}{2}\right)^n$ which is the nth-term of a convergent geometric series

55. converges by the Ratio Test: $\lim\limits_{n \to \infty} \frac{a_{n+1}}{a_n} = \lim\limits_{n \to \infty} \frac{2^{n+1}(n+1)!(n+1)!}{(2n+2)!} \cdot \frac{(2n)!}{2^n n! n!} = \lim\limits_{n \to \infty} \frac{2(n+1)(n+1)}{(2n+2)(2n+1)}$

$= \lim\limits_{n \to \infty} \frac{n+1}{2n+1} = \frac{1}{2} < 1$

56. diverges by the Ratio Test: $\lim\limits_{n \to \infty} \frac{a_{n+1}}{a_n} = \lim\limits_{n \to \infty} \frac{(3n+3)!}{(n+1)!(n+2)!(n+3)!} \cdot \frac{n!(n+1)!(n+2)!}{(3n)!}$

$= \lim\limits_{n \to \infty} \frac{(3n+3)(3+2)(3n+1)}{(n+1)(n+2)(n+3)} = \lim\limits_{n \to \infty} 3\left(\frac{3n+2}{n+2}\right)\left(\frac{3n+1}{n+3}\right) = 3 \cdot 3 \cdot 3 = 27 > 1$

57. diverges by the Root Test: $\lim\limits_{n \to \infty} \sqrt[n]{a_n} \equiv \lim\limits_{n \to \infty} \sqrt[n]{\frac{(n!)^n}{(n^n)^2}} = \lim\limits_{n \to \infty} \frac{n!}{n^2} = \infty > 1$

58. converges by the Root Test: $\lim\limits_{n \to \infty} \sqrt[n]{\frac{(n!)^n}{n^{n^2}}} = \lim\limits_{n \to \infty} \sqrt[n]{\frac{(n!)^n}{(n^n)^n}} = \lim\limits_{n \to \infty} \frac{n!}{n^n} = \lim\limits_{n \to \infty} \left(\frac{1}{n}\right)\left(\frac{2}{n}\right)\left(\frac{3}{n}\right) \cdots \left(\frac{n-1}{n}\right)\left(\frac{n}{n}\right)$

$\leq \lim\limits_{n \to \infty} \frac{1}{n} = 0 < 1$

59. converges by the Root Test: $\lim\limits_{n \to \infty} \sqrt[n]{a_n} = \lim\limits_{n \to \infty} \sqrt[n]{\frac{n^n}{2^{n^2}}} = \lim\limits_{n \to \infty} \frac{n}{2^n} = \lim\limits_{n \to \infty} \frac{1}{2^n \ln 2} = 0 < 1$

60. diverges by the Root Test: $\lim\limits_{n \to \infty} \sqrt[n]{a_n} = \lim\limits_{n \to \infty} \sqrt[n]{\frac{n^n}{(2^n)^2}} = \lim\limits_{n \to \infty} \frac{n}{4} = \infty > 1$

61. converges by the Ratio Test: $\lim\limits_{n \to \infty} \frac{a_{n+1}}{a_n} = \lim\limits_{n \to \infty} \frac{1 \cdot 3 \cdot \cdots \cdot (2n-1)(2n+1)}{4^{n+1} 2^{n+1}(n+1)!} \cdot \frac{4^n 2^n n!}{1 \cdot 3 \cdot \cdots \cdot (2n-1)} = \lim\limits_{n \to \infty} \frac{2n+1}{(4 \cdot 2)(n+1)} = \frac{1}{4} < 1$

62. converges by the Ratio Test: $a_n = \frac{1 \cdot 3 \cdots (2n-1)}{(2 \cdot 4 \cdots 2n)(3^n + 1)} = \frac{1 \cdot 2 \cdot 3 \cdot 4 \cdots (2n-1)(2n)}{(2 \cdot 4 \cdots 2n)^2 (3^n + 1)} = \frac{(2n)!}{(2^n n!)^2 (3^n + 1)}$

$\Rightarrow \lim\limits_{n \to \infty} \frac{(2n+2)!}{[2^{n+1}(n+1)!]^2 (3^{n+1} + 1)} \cdot \frac{(2^n n!)^2 (3^n + 1)}{(2n)!} = \lim\limits_{n \to \infty} \frac{(2n+1)(2n+2)(3^n + 1)}{2^2(n+1)^2 (3^{n+1} + 1)}$

$= \lim\limits_{n \to \infty} \left(\frac{4n^2 + 6n + 2}{4n^2 + 8n + 4}\right) \frac{(1 + 3^{-n})}{(3 + 3^{-n})} = 1 \cdot \frac{1}{3} = \frac{1}{3} < 1$

63. Ratio: $\lim\limits_{n \to \infty} \frac{a_{n+1}}{a_n} = \lim\limits_{n \to \infty} \frac{1}{(n+1)^p} \cdot \frac{n^p}{1} = \lim\limits_{n \to \infty} \left(\frac{n}{n+1}\right)^p = 1^p = 1 \Rightarrow$ no conclusion

Root: $\lim\limits_{n \to \infty} \sqrt[n]{a_n} = \lim\limits_{n \to \infty} \sqrt[n]{\frac{1}{n^p}} = \lim\limits_{n \to \infty} \frac{1}{(\sqrt[n]{n})^p} = \frac{1}{(1)^p} = 1 \Rightarrow$ no conclusion

64. Ratio: $\lim\limits_{n \to \infty} \frac{a_{n+1}}{a_n} = \lim\limits_{n \to \infty} \frac{1}{(\ln(n+1))^p} \cdot \frac{(\ln n)^p}{1} = \left[\lim\limits_{n \to \infty} \frac{\ln n}{\ln(n+1)}\right]^p = \left[\lim\limits_{n \to \infty} \frac{\left(\frac{1}{n}\right)}{\left(\frac{1}{n+1}\right)}\right]^p = \left(\lim\limits_{n \to \infty} \frac{n+1}{n}\right)^p$

$= (1)^p = 1 \Rightarrow$ no conclusion

Root: $\lim\limits_{n \to \infty} \sqrt[n]{a_n} = \lim\limits_{n \to \infty} \sqrt[n]{\frac{1}{(\ln n)^p}} = \frac{1}{\left(\lim\limits_{n \to \infty} (\ln n)^{1/n}\right)^p}$; let $f(n) = (\ln n)^{1/n}$, then $\ln f(n) = \frac{\ln(\ln n)}{n}$

$\Rightarrow \lim\limits_{n \to \infty} \ln f(n) = \lim\limits_{n \to \infty} \frac{\ln(\ln n)}{n} = \lim\limits_{n \to \infty} \frac{\left(\frac{1}{n \ln n}\right)}{1} = \lim\limits_{n \to \infty} \frac{1}{n \ln n} = 0 \Rightarrow \lim\limits_{n \to \infty} (\ln n)^{1/n}$

$= \lim\limits_{n \to \infty} e^{\ln f(n)} = e^0 = 1$; therefore $\lim\limits_{n \to \infty} \sqrt[n]{a_n} = \frac{1}{\left(\lim\limits_{n \to \infty} (\ln n)^{1/n}\right)^p} = \frac{1}{(1)^p} = 1 \Rightarrow$ no conclusion

65. $a_n \leq \frac{n}{2^n}$ for every n and the series $\sum\limits_{n=1}^{\infty} \frac{n}{2^n}$ converges by the Ratio Test since $\lim\limits_{n \to \infty} \frac{(n+1)}{2^{n+1}} \cdot \frac{2^n}{n} = \frac{1}{2} < 1$

$\Rightarrow \sum\limits_{n=1}^{\infty} a_n$ converges by the Direct Comparison Test

66. $\frac{2^{n^2}}{n!} > 0$ for all $n \geq 1$; $\lim\limits_{n\to\infty}\left(\frac{\frac{2^{(n+1)^2}}{(n+1)!}}{\frac{2^{n^2}}{n!}}\right) = \lim\limits_{n\to\infty}\left(\frac{2^{n^2+2n+1}}{(n+1)\cdot n!}\cdot\frac{n!}{2^{n^2}}\right) = \lim\limits_{n\to\infty}\left(\frac{2^{2n+1}}{n+1}\right) = \lim\limits_{n\to\infty}\left(\frac{2\cdot 4^n}{n+1}\right) = \lim\limits_{n\to\infty}\left(\frac{2\cdot 4^n\ln 4}{1}\right)$

$= \infty > 1 \Rightarrow \sum\limits_{n=1}^{\infty}\frac{2^{n^2}}{n!}$ diverges

## 10.6 ALTERNATING SERIES, ABSOLUTE AND CONDITIONAL CONVERGENCE

1. converges by the Alternating Convergence Test since: $u_n = \frac{1}{\sqrt{n}} > 0$ for all $n \geq 1$; $n \geq 1 \Rightarrow n+1 \geq n \Rightarrow \sqrt{n+1} \geq \sqrt{n}$

   $\Rightarrow \frac{1}{\sqrt{n+1}} \leq \frac{1}{\sqrt{n}} \Rightarrow u_{n+1} \leq u_n$; $\lim\limits_{n\to\infty} u_n = \lim\limits_{n\to\infty}\frac{1}{\sqrt{n}} = 0$.

2. converges absolutely $\Rightarrow$ converges by the Alternating Convergence Test since $\sum\limits_{n=1}^{\infty}|a_n| = \sum\limits_{n=1}^{\infty}\frac{1}{n^{3/2}}$ which is a

   convergent p-series

3. converges $\Rightarrow$ converges by Alternating Series Test since: $u_n = \frac{1}{n3^n} > 0$ for all $n \geq 1$; $n \geq 1 \Rightarrow n+1 \geq n \Rightarrow 3^{n+1} \geq 3^n$

   $\Rightarrow (n+1)3^{n+1} \geq n\,3^n \Rightarrow \frac{1}{(n+1)3^{n+1}} \leq \frac{1}{n3^n} \Rightarrow u_{n+1} \leq u_n$; $\lim\limits_{n\to\infty} u_n = \lim\limits_{n\to\infty}\frac{1}{n3^n} = 0$.

4. converges $\Rightarrow$ converges by Alternating Series Test since: $u_n = \frac{4}{(\ln n)^2} > 0$ for all $n \geq 2$; $n \geq 2 \Rightarrow n+1 \geq n$

   $\Rightarrow \ln(n+1) \geq \ln n \Rightarrow (\ln(n+1))^2 \geq (\ln n)^2 \Rightarrow \frac{1}{(\ln(n+1))^2} \leq \frac{1}{(\ln n)^2} \Rightarrow \frac{4}{(\ln(n+1))^2} \leq \frac{4}{(\ln n)^2} \Rightarrow u_{n+1} \leq u_n$;

   $\lim\limits_{n\to\infty} u_n = \lim\limits_{n\to\infty}\frac{4}{(\ln n)^2} = 0$.

5. converges $\Rightarrow$ converges by Alternating Series Test since: $u_n = \frac{n}{n^2+1} > 0$ for all $n \geq 1$; $n \geq 1 \Rightarrow 2n^2 + 2n \geq n^2 + n + 1$

   $\Rightarrow n^3 + 2n^2 + 2n \geq n^3 + n^2 + n + 1 \Rightarrow n(n^2 + 2n + 2) \geq n^3 + n^2 + n + 1 \Rightarrow n\big((n+1)^2 + 1\big) \geq (n^2+1)(n+1)$

   $\Rightarrow \frac{n}{n^2+1} \geq \frac{n+1}{(n+1)^2+1} \Rightarrow u_{n+1} \leq u_n$; $\lim\limits_{n\to\infty} u_n = \lim\limits_{n\to\infty}\frac{n}{n^2+1} = 0$.

6. diverges $\Rightarrow$ diverges by $n^{\text{th}}$ Term Test for Divergence since: $\lim\limits_{n\to\infty}\frac{n^2+5}{n^2+4} = 1 \Rightarrow \lim\limits_{n\to\infty}(-1)^{n+1}\frac{n^2+5}{n^2+4} = $ does not exist

7. diverges $\Rightarrow$ diverges by $n^{\text{th}}$ Term Test for Divergence since: $\lim\limits_{n\to\infty}\frac{2^n}{n^2} = \infty \Rightarrow \lim\limits_{n\to\infty}(-1)^{n+1}\frac{2^n}{n^2} = $ does not exist

8. converges absolutely $\Rightarrow$ converges by the Absolute Convergence Test since $\sum\limits_{n=1}^{\infty}|a_n| = \sum\limits_{n=1}^{\infty}\frac{10^n}{(n+1)!}$, which converges by the

   Ratio Test, since $\lim\limits_{n\to\infty}\frac{a_{n+1}}{a_n} = \lim\limits_{n\to\infty}\frac{10}{n+2} = 0 < 1$

9. diverges by the nth-Term Test since for $n > 10 \Rightarrow \frac{n}{10} > 1 \Rightarrow \lim\limits_{n\to\infty}\left(\frac{n}{10}\right)^n \neq 0 \Rightarrow \sum\limits_{n=1}^{\infty}(-1)^{n+1}\left(\frac{n}{10}\right)^n$ diverges

10. converges by the Alternating Series Test because $f(x) = \ln x$ is an increasing function of $x \Rightarrow \frac{1}{\ln x}$ is decreasing

    $\Rightarrow u_n \geq u_{n+1}$ for $n \geq 1$; also $u_n \geq 0$ for $n \geq 1$ and $\lim\limits_{n\to\infty}\frac{1}{\ln n} = 0$

11. converges by the Alternating Series Test since $f(x) = \frac{\ln x}{x} \Rightarrow f'(x) = \frac{1 - \ln x}{x^2} < 0$ when $x > e \Rightarrow f(x)$ is decreasing

    $\Rightarrow u_n \geq u_{n+1}$; also $u_n \geq 0$ for $n \geq 1$ and $\lim\limits_{n\to\infty} u_n = \lim\limits_{n\to\infty}\frac{\ln n}{n} = \lim\limits_{n\to\infty}\frac{\left(\frac{1}{n}\right)}{1} = 0$

12. converges by the Alternating Series Test since $f(x) = \ln(1 + x^{-1}) \Rightarrow f'(x) = \frac{-1}{x(x+1)} < 0$ for $x > 0 \Rightarrow f(x)$ is decreasing

$\Rightarrow u_n \geq u_{n+1}$; also $u_n \geq 0$ for $n \geq 1$ and $\lim_{n \to \infty} u_n = \lim_{n \to \infty} \ln\left(1 + \frac{1}{n}\right) = \ln\left(\lim_{n \to \infty} \left(1 + \frac{1}{n}\right)\right) = \ln 1 = 0$

13. converges by the Alternating Series Test since $f(x) = \frac{\sqrt{x}+1}{x+1} \Rightarrow f'(x) = \frac{1-x-2\sqrt{x}}{2\sqrt{x}(x+1)^2} < 0 \Rightarrow f(x)$ is decreasing

$\Rightarrow u_n \geq u_{n+1}$; also $u_n \geq 0$ for $n \geq 1$ and $\lim_{n \to \infty} u_n = \lim_{n \to \infty} \frac{\sqrt{n}+1}{n+1} = 0$

14. diverges by the nth-Term Test since $\lim_{n \to \infty} \frac{3\sqrt{n+1}}{\sqrt{n+1}} = \lim_{n \to \infty} \frac{3\sqrt{1+\frac{1}{n}}}{1+\left(\frac{1}{\sqrt{n}}\right)} = 3 \neq 0$

15. converges absolutely since $\sum_{n=1}^{\infty} |a_n| = \sum_{n=1}^{\infty} \left(\frac{1}{10}\right)^n$ a convergent geometric series

16. converges absolutely by the Direct Comparison Test since $\left|\frac{(-1)^{n+1}(0.1)^n}{n}\right| = \frac{1}{(10)^n n} < \left(\frac{1}{10}\right)^n$ which is the nth term of a convergent geometric series

17. converges conditionally since $\frac{1}{\sqrt{n}} > \frac{1}{\sqrt{n+1}} > 0$ and $\lim_{n \to \infty} \frac{1}{\sqrt{n}} = 0 \Rightarrow$ convergence; but $\sum_{n=1}^{\infty} |a_n| = \sum_{n=1}^{\infty} \frac{1}{n^{1/2}}$ is a divergent p-series

18. converges conditionally since $\frac{1}{1+\sqrt{n}} > \frac{1}{1+\sqrt{n+1}} > 0$ and $\lim_{n \to \infty} \frac{1}{1+\sqrt{n}} = 0 \Rightarrow$ convergence; but

$\sum_{n=1}^{\infty} |a_n| = \sum_{n=1}^{\infty} \frac{1}{1+\sqrt{n}}$ is a divergent series since $\frac{1}{1+\sqrt{n}} \geq \frac{1}{2\sqrt{n}}$ and $\sum_{n=1}^{\infty} \frac{1}{n^{1/2}}$ is a divergent p-series

19. converges absolutely since $\sum_{n=1}^{\infty} |a_n| = \sum_{n=1}^{\infty} \frac{n}{n^3+1}$ and $\frac{n}{n^3+1} < \frac{1}{n^2}$ which is the nth-term of a converging p-series

20. diverges by the nth-Term Test since $\lim_{n \to \infty} \frac{n!}{2^n} = \infty$

21. converges conditionally since $\frac{1}{n+3} > \frac{1}{(n+1)+3} > 0$ and $\lim_{n \to \infty} \frac{1}{n+3} = 0 \Rightarrow$ convergence; but $\sum_{n=1}^{\infty} |a_n|$

$= \sum_{n=1}^{\infty} \frac{1}{n+3}$ diverges because $\frac{1}{n+3} \geq \frac{1}{4n}$ and $\sum_{n=1}^{\infty} \frac{1}{n}$ is a divergent series

22. converges absolutely because the series $\sum_{n=1}^{\infty} \left|\frac{\sin n}{n^2}\right|$ converges by the Direct Comparison Test since $\left|\frac{\sin n}{n^2}\right| \leq \frac{1}{n^2}$

23. diverges by the nth-Term Test since $\lim_{n \to \infty} \frac{3+n}{5+n} = 1 \neq 0$

24. converges absolutely by the Direct Comparison Test since $\left|\frac{(-2)^{n+1}}{n+5^n}\right| = \frac{2^{n+1}}{n+5^n} < 2\left(\frac{2}{5}\right)^n$ which is the nth term of a convergent geometric series

25. converges conditionally since $f(x) = \frac{1}{x^2} + \frac{1}{x} \Rightarrow f'(x) = -\left(\frac{2}{x^3} + \frac{1}{x^2}\right) < 0 \Rightarrow f(x)$ is decreasing and hence

$u_n > u_{n+1} > 0$ for $n \geq 1$ and $\lim_{n \to \infty} \left(\frac{1}{n^2} + \frac{1}{n}\right) = 0 \Rightarrow$ convergence; but $\sum_{n=1}^{\infty} |a_n| = \sum_{n=1}^{\infty} \frac{1+n}{n^2}$

$= \sum_{n=1}^{\infty} \frac{1}{n^2} + \sum_{n=1}^{\infty} \frac{1}{n}$ is the sum of a convergent and divergent series, and hence diverges

26. diverges by the nth-Term Test since $\lim\limits_{n \to \infty} a_n = \lim\limits_{n \to \infty} 10^{1/n} = 1 \neq 0$

27. converges absolutely by the Ratio Test: $\lim\limits_{n \to \infty} \left( \frac{u_{n+1}}{u_n} \right) = \lim\limits_{n \to \infty} \left[ \frac{(n+1)^2 \left( \frac{2}{3} \right)^{n+1}}{n^2 \left( \frac{2}{3} \right)^n} \right] = \frac{2}{3} < 1$

28. converges conditionally since $f(x) = \frac{1}{x \ln x} \Rightarrow f'(x) = -\frac{[\ln(x) + 1]}{(x \ln x)^2} < 0 \Rightarrow f(x)$ is decreasing

$\Rightarrow u_n > u_{n+1} > 0$ for $n \geq 2$ and $\lim\limits_{n \to \infty} \frac{1}{n \ln n} = 0 \Rightarrow$ convergence; but by the Integral Test,

$\int_2^\infty \frac{dx}{x \ln x} = \lim\limits_{b \to \infty} \int_2^b \left( \frac{\left( \frac{1}{x} \right)}{\ln x} \right) dx = \lim\limits_{b \to \infty} \left[ \ln(\ln x) \right]_2^b = \lim\limits_{b \to \infty} \left[ \ln(\ln b) - \ln(\ln 2) \right] = \infty$

$\Rightarrow \sum\limits_{n=1}^\infty |a_n| = \sum\limits_{n=1}^\infty \frac{1}{n \ln n}$ diverges

29. converges absolutely by the Integral Test since $\int_1^\infty (\tan^{-1} x) \left( \frac{1}{1+x^2} \right) dx = \lim\limits_{b \to \infty} \left[ \frac{(\tan^{-1} x)^2}{2} \right]_1^b$

$= \lim\limits_{b \to \infty} \left[ (\tan^{-1} b)^2 - (\tan^{-1} 1)^2 \right] = \frac{1}{2} \left[ \left( \frac{\pi}{2} \right)^2 - \left( \frac{\pi}{4} \right)^2 \right] = \frac{3\pi^2}{32}$

30. converges conditionally since $f(x) = \frac{\ln x}{x - \ln x} \Rightarrow f'(x) = \frac{\left( \frac{1}{x} \right)(x - \ln x) - (\ln x)\left( 1 - \frac{1}{x} \right)}{(x - \ln x)^2}$

$= \frac{1 - \left( \frac{\ln x}{x} \right) - \ln x + \left( \frac{\ln x}{x} \right)}{(x - \ln x)^2} = \frac{1 - \ln x}{(x - \ln x)^2} < 0 \Rightarrow u_n \geq u_{n+1} > 0$ when $n > e$ and $\lim\limits_{n \to \infty} \frac{\ln n}{n - \ln n}$

$= \lim\limits_{n \to \infty} \frac{\left( \frac{1}{n} \right)}{1 - \left( \frac{1}{n} \right)} = 0 \Rightarrow$ convergence; but $n - \ln n < n \Rightarrow \frac{1}{n - \ln n} > \frac{1}{n} \Rightarrow \frac{\ln n}{n - \ln n} > \frac{1}{n}$ so that

$\sum\limits_{n=1}^\infty |a_n| = \sum\limits_{n=1}^\infty \frac{\ln n}{n - \ln n}$ diverges by the Direct Comparison Test

31. diverges by the nth-Term Test since $\lim\limits_{n \to \infty} \frac{n}{n+1} = 1 \neq 0$

32. converges absolutely since $\sum\limits_{n=1}^\infty |a_n| = \sum\limits_{n=1}^\infty \left( \frac{1}{5} \right)^n$ is a convergent geometric series

33. converges absolutely by the Ratio Test: $\lim\limits_{n \to \infty} \left( \frac{u_{n+1}}{u_n} \right) = \lim\limits_{n \to \infty} \frac{(100)^{n+1}}{(n+1)!} \cdot \frac{n!}{(100)^n} = \lim\limits_{n \to \infty} \frac{100}{n+1} = 0 < 1$

34. converges absolutely by the Direct Comparison Test since $\sum\limits_{n=1}^\infty |a_n| = \sum\limits_{n=1}^\infty \frac{1}{n^2 + 2n + 1}$ and $\frac{1}{n^2 + 2n + 1} < \frac{1}{n^2}$ which is the

nth-term of a convergent p-series

35. converges absolutely since $\sum\limits_{n=1}^\infty |a_n| = \sum\limits_{n=1}^\infty \left| \frac{(-1)^n}{n\sqrt{n}} \right| = \sum\limits_{n=1}^\infty \frac{1}{n^{3/2}}$ is a convergent p-series

36. converges conditionally since $\sum\limits_{n=1}^\infty \frac{\cos n\pi}{n} = \sum\limits_{n=1}^\infty \frac{(-1)^n}{n}$ is the convergent alternating harmonic series, but

$\sum\limits_{n=1}^\infty |a_n| = \sum\limits_{n=1}^\infty \frac{1}{n}$ diverges

37. converges absolutely by the Root Test: $\lim\limits_{n \to \infty} \sqrt[n]{|a_n|} = \lim\limits_{n \to \infty} \left( \frac{(n+1)^n}{(2n)^n} \right)^{1/n} = \lim\limits_{n \to \infty} \frac{n+1}{2n} = \frac{1}{2} < 1$

38. converges absolutely by the Ratio Test: $\lim\limits_{n \to \infty} \left| \frac{a_{n+1}}{a_n} \right| = \lim\limits_{n \to \infty} \frac{((n+1)!)^2}{((2n+2)!)} \cdot \frac{(2n)!}{(n!)^2} = \lim\limits_{n \to \infty} \frac{(n+1)^2}{(2n+2)(2n+1)} = \frac{1}{4} < 1$

39. diverges by the nth-Term Test since $\lim\limits_{n \to \infty} |a_n| = \lim\limits_{n \to \infty} \frac{(2n)!}{2^n n! \, n} = \lim\limits_{n \to \infty} \frac{(n+1)(n+2)\cdots(2n)}{2^n n}$

   $= \lim\limits_{n \to \infty} \frac{(n+1)(n+2)\cdots(n+(n-1))}{2^{n-1}} > \lim\limits_{n \to \infty} \left( \frac{n+1}{2} \right)^{n-1} = \infty \neq 0$

40. converges absolutely by the Ratio Test: $\lim\limits_{n \to \infty} \left| \frac{a_{n+1}}{a_n} \right| = \lim\limits_{n \to \infty} \frac{(n+1)! \, (n+1)! \, 3^{n+1}}{(2n+3)!} \cdot \frac{(2n+1)!}{n! \, n! \, 3^n}$

   $= \lim\limits_{n \to \infty} \frac{(n+1)^2 \, 3}{(2n+2)(2n+3)} = \frac{3}{4} < 1$

41. converges conditionally since $\frac{\sqrt{n+1} - \sqrt{n}}{1} \cdot \frac{\sqrt{n+1} + \sqrt{n}}{\sqrt{n+1} + \sqrt{n}} = \frac{1}{\sqrt{n+1} + \sqrt{n}}$ and $\left\{ \frac{1}{\sqrt{n+1} + \sqrt{n}} \right\}$ is a

   decreasing sequence of positive terms which converges to $0 \Rightarrow \sum\limits_{n=1}^{\infty} \frac{(-1)^n}{\sqrt{n+1} + \sqrt{n}}$ converges; but

   $\sum\limits_{n=1}^{\infty} |a_n| = \sum\limits_{n=1}^{\infty} \frac{1}{\sqrt{n+1} + \sqrt{n}}$ diverges by the Limit Comparison Test (part 1) with $\frac{1}{\sqrt{n}}$; a divergent p-series:

   $\lim\limits_{n \to \infty} \left( \frac{\frac{1}{\sqrt{n+1} + \sqrt{n}}}{\frac{1}{\sqrt{n}}} \right) = \lim\limits_{n \to \infty} \frac{\sqrt{n}}{\sqrt{n+1} + \sqrt{n}} = \lim\limits_{n \to \infty} \frac{1}{\sqrt{1 + \frac{1}{n}} + 1} = \frac{1}{2}$

42. diverges by the nth-Term Test since $\lim\limits_{n \to \infty} \left( \sqrt{n^2 + n} - n \right) = \lim\limits_{n \to \infty} \left( \sqrt{n^2 + n} - n \right) \cdot \left( \frac{\sqrt{n^2 + n} + n}{\sqrt{n^2 + n} + n} \right)$

   $= \lim\limits_{n \to \infty} \frac{n}{\sqrt{n^2 + n} + n} = \lim\limits_{n \to \infty} \frac{1}{\sqrt{1 + \frac{1}{n}} + 1} = \frac{1}{2} \neq 0$

43. diverges by the nth-Term Test since $\lim\limits_{n \to \infty} \left( \sqrt{n + \sqrt{n}} - \sqrt{n} \right) = \lim\limits_{n \to \infty} \left[ \left( \sqrt{n + \sqrt{n}} - \sqrt{n} \right) \left( \frac{\sqrt{n + \sqrt{n}} + \sqrt{n}}{\sqrt{n + \sqrt{n}} + \sqrt{n}} \right) \right]$

   $= \lim\limits_{n \to \infty} \frac{\sqrt{n}}{\sqrt{n + \sqrt{n}} + \sqrt{n}} = \lim\limits_{n \to \infty} \frac{1}{\sqrt{1 + \frac{1}{\sqrt{n}}} + 1} = \frac{1}{2} \neq 0$

44. converges conditionally since $\left\{ \frac{1}{\sqrt{n} + \sqrt{n+1}} \right\}$ is a decreasing sequence of positive terms converging to 0

   $\Rightarrow \sum\limits_{n=1}^{\infty} \frac{(-1)^n}{\sqrt{n} + \sqrt{n+1}}$ converges; but $\lim\limits_{n \to \infty} \frac{\left( \frac{1}{\sqrt{n} + \sqrt{n+1}} \right)}{\left( \frac{1}{\sqrt{n}} \right)} = \lim\limits_{n \to \infty} \frac{\sqrt{n}}{\sqrt{n} + \sqrt{n+1}} = \lim\limits_{n \to \infty} \frac{1}{1 + \sqrt{1 + \frac{1}{n}}} = \frac{1}{2}$

   so that $\sum\limits_{n=1}^{\infty} \frac{1}{\sqrt{n} + \sqrt{n+1}}$ diverges by the Limit Comparison Test with $\sum\limits_{n=1}^{\infty} \frac{1}{\sqrt{n}}$ which is a divergent p-series

45. converges absolutely by the Direct Comparison Test since $\operatorname{sech}(n) = \frac{2}{e^n + e^{-n}} = \frac{2e^n}{e^{2n} + 1} < \frac{2e^n}{e^{2n}} = \frac{2}{e^n}$ which is the

   nth term of a convergent geometric series

46. converges absolutely by the Limit Comparison Test (part 1): $\sum\limits_{n=1}^{\infty} |a_n| = \sum\limits_{n=1}^{\infty} \frac{2}{e^n - e^{-n}}$

   Apply the Limit Comparison Test with $\frac{1}{e^n}$, the n-th term of a convergent geometric series:

   $\lim\limits_{n \to \infty} \left( \frac{\frac{2}{e^n - e^{-n}}}{\frac{1}{e^n}} \right) = \lim\limits_{n \to \infty} \frac{2e^n}{e^n - e^{-n}} = \lim\limits_{n \to \infty} \frac{2}{1 - e^{-2n}} = 2$

47. $\frac{1}{4} - \frac{1}{6} + \frac{1}{8} - \frac{1}{10} + \frac{1}{12} - \frac{1}{14} + \ldots = \sum\limits_{n=1}^{\infty} \frac{(-1)^{n+1}}{2(n+1)}$; converges by Alternating Series Test since: $u_n = \frac{1}{2(n+1)} > 0$ for all $n \geq 1$;

   $n + 2 \geq n + 1 \Rightarrow 2(n+2) \geq 2(n+1) \Rightarrow \frac{1}{2((n+1)+1)} \leq \frac{1}{2(n+1)} \Rightarrow u_{n+1} \leq u_n$; $\lim\limits_{n \to \infty} u_n = \lim\limits_{n \to \infty} \frac{1}{2(n+1)} = 0$.

48. $1 + \frac{1}{4} - \frac{1}{9} - \frac{1}{16} + \frac{1}{25} + \frac{1}{36} - \frac{1}{49} - \frac{1}{64} + \ldots = \sum\limits_{n=1}^{\infty} a_n$; converges by the Absolute Convergence Test since $\sum\limits_{n=1}^{\infty} |a_n| = \sum\limits_{n=1}^{\infty} \frac{1}{n^2}$ which is a convergent p-series

49. $|\text{error}| < \left|(-1)^6 \left(\frac{1}{5}\right)\right| = 0.2$

50. $|\text{error}| < \left|(-1)^6 \left(\frac{1}{10^5}\right)\right| = 0.00001$

51. $|\text{error}| < \left|(-1)^6 \frac{(0.01)^5}{5}\right| = 2 \times 10^{-11}$

52. $|\text{error}| < |(-1)^4 t^4| = t^4 < 1$

53. $|\text{error}| < 0.001 \Rightarrow u_{n+1} < 0.001 \Rightarrow \frac{1}{(n+1)^2 + 3} < 0.001 \Rightarrow (n+1)^2 + 3 > 1000 \Rightarrow n > -1 + \sqrt{997} \approx 30.5753 \Rightarrow n \geq 31$

54. $|\text{error}| < 0.001 \Rightarrow u_{n+1} < 0.001 \Rightarrow \frac{n+1}{(n+1)^2 + 1} < 0.001 \Rightarrow (n+1)^2 + 1 > 1000(n+1) \Rightarrow n > \frac{998 + \sqrt{998^2 + 4(998)}}{2}$

$\approx 998.9999 \Rightarrow n \geq 999$

55. $|\text{error}| < 0.001 \Rightarrow u_{n+1} < 0.001 \Rightarrow \frac{1}{\left((n+1) + 3\sqrt{n+1}\right)^3} < 0.001 \Rightarrow \left((n+1) + 3\sqrt{n+1}\right)^3 > 1000$

$\Rightarrow \left(\sqrt{n+1}\right)^2 + 3\sqrt{n+1} - 10 > 0 \Rightarrow \sqrt{n+1} = -\frac{3 + \sqrt{9+40}}{2} = 2 \Rightarrow n = 3 \Rightarrow n \geq 4$

56. $|\text{error}| < 0.001 \Rightarrow u_{n+1} < 0.001 \Rightarrow \frac{1}{\ln(\ln(n+3))} < 0.001 \Rightarrow \ln(\ln(n+3)) > 1000 \Rightarrow n > -3 + e^{e^{1000}} \approx 5.297 \times 10^{323228467}$

which is the maximum arbitrary-precision number represented by Mathematica on the particular computer solving this problem..

57. $\frac{1}{(2n)!} < \frac{5}{10^6} \Rightarrow (2n)! > \frac{10^6}{5} = 200{,}000 \Rightarrow n \geq 5 \Rightarrow 1 - \frac{1}{2!} + \frac{1}{4!} - \frac{1}{6!} + \frac{1}{8!} \approx 0.54030$

58. $\frac{1}{n!} < \frac{5}{10^6} \Rightarrow \frac{10^6}{5} < n! \Rightarrow n \geq 9 \Rightarrow 1 - 1 + \frac{1}{2!} - \frac{1}{3!} + \frac{1}{4!} - \frac{1}{5!} + \frac{1}{6!} - \frac{1}{7!} + \frac{1}{8!} \approx 0.367881944$

59. (a) $a_n \geq a_{n+1}$ fails since $\frac{1}{3} < \frac{1}{2}$

   (b) Since $\sum\limits_{n=1}^{\infty} |a_n| = \sum\limits_{n=1}^{\infty} \left[\left(\frac{1}{3}\right)^n + \left(\frac{1}{2}\right)^n\right] = \sum\limits_{n=1}^{\infty} \left(\frac{1}{3}\right)^n + \sum\limits_{n=1}^{\infty} \left(\frac{1}{2}\right)^n$ is the sum of two absolutely convergent

   series, we can rearrange the terms of the original series to find its sum:

   $\left(\frac{1}{3} + \frac{1}{9} + \frac{1}{27} + \ldots\right) - \left(\frac{1}{2} + \frac{1}{4} + \frac{1}{8} + \ldots\right) = \frac{\left(\frac{1}{3}\right)}{1 - \left(\frac{1}{3}\right)} - \frac{\left(\frac{1}{2}\right)}{1 - \left(\frac{1}{2}\right)} = \frac{1}{2} - 1 = -\frac{1}{2}$

60. $s_{20} = 1 - \frac{1}{2} + \frac{1}{3} - \frac{1}{4} + \ldots + \frac{1}{19} - \frac{1}{20} \approx 0.6687714032 \Rightarrow s_{20} + \frac{1}{2} \cdot \frac{1}{21} \approx 0.692580927$

61. The unused terms are $\sum\limits_{j=n+1}^{\infty} (-1)^{j+1} a_j = (-1)^{n+1} (a_{n+1} - a_{n+2}) + (-1)^{n+3} (a_{n+3} - a_{n+4}) + \ldots$

   $= (-1)^{n+1} \left[(a_{n+1} - a_{n+2}) + (a_{n+3} - a_{n+4}) + \ldots\right]$. Each grouped term is positive, so the remainder has the same sign as $(-1)^{n+1}$, which is the sign of the first unused term.

62. $s_n = \frac{1}{1 \cdot 2} + \frac{1}{2 \cdot 3} + \frac{1}{3 \cdot 4} + \ldots + \frac{1}{n(n+1)} = \sum\limits_{k=1}^{n} \frac{1}{k(k+1)} = \sum\limits_{k=1}^{n} \left(\frac{1}{k} - \frac{1}{k+1}\right)$

   $= \left(1 - \frac{1}{2}\right) + \left(\frac{1}{2} - \frac{1}{3}\right) + \left(\frac{1}{3} - \frac{1}{4}\right) + \left(\frac{1}{4} - \frac{1}{5}\right) + \ldots + \left(\frac{1}{n} - \frac{1}{n+1}\right)$ which are the first 2n terms of the first series, hence the two series are the same. Yes, for

   $s_n = \sum\limits_{k=1}^{n} \left(\frac{1}{k} - \frac{1}{k+1}\right) = \left(1 - \frac{1}{2}\right) + \left(\frac{1}{2} - \frac{1}{3}\right) + \left(\frac{1}{3} - \frac{1}{4}\right) + \left(\frac{1}{4} - \frac{1}{5}\right) + \ldots + \left(\frac{1}{n-1} - \frac{1}{n}\right) + \left(\frac{1}{n} - \frac{1}{n+1}\right) = 1 - \frac{1}{n+1}$

81. $\lim\limits_{n \to \infty} \left| \frac{2\cdot5\cdot8\cdots(3n-1)(3n+2)x^{n+1}}{2\cdot4\cdot6\cdots(2n)(2n+2)} \cdot \frac{2\cdot4\cdot6\cdots(2n)}{2\cdot5\cdot8\cdots(3n-1)x^n} \right| < 1 \Rightarrow |x| \lim\limits_{n \to \infty} \left| \frac{3n+2}{2n+2} \right| < 1 \Rightarrow |x| < \frac{2}{3}$

$\Rightarrow$ the radius of convergence is $\frac{2}{3}$

82. $\lim\limits_{n \to \infty} \left| \frac{3\cdot5\cdot7\cdots(2n+1)(2n+3)(x-1)^{n+1}}{4\cdot9\cdot14\cdots(5n-1)(5n+4)} \cdot \frac{4\cdot9\cdot14\cdots(5n-1)}{3\cdot5\cdot7\cdots(2n+1)x^n} \right| < 1 \Rightarrow |x| \lim\limits_{n \to \infty} \left| \frac{2n+3}{5n+4} \right| < 1 \Rightarrow |x| < \frac{5}{2}$

$\Rightarrow$ the radius of convergence is $\frac{5}{2}$

83. $\sum\limits_{k=2}^{n} \ln\left(1 - \frac{1}{k^2}\right) = \sum\limits_{k=2}^{n} \left[\ln\left(1 + \frac{1}{k}\right) + \ln\left(1 - \frac{1}{k}\right)\right] = \sum\limits_{k=2}^{n} \left[\ln(k+1) - \ln k + \ln(k-1) - \ln k\right]$

$= [\ln 3 - \ln 2 + \ln 1 - \ln 2] + [\ln 4 - \ln 3 + \ln 2 - \ln 3] + [\ln 5 - \ln 4 + \ln 3 - \ln 4] + [\ln 6 - \ln 5 + \ln 4 - \ln 5]$

$+ \ldots + [\ln(n+1) - \ln n + \ln(n-1) - \ln n] = [\ln 1 - \ln 2] + [\ln(n+1) - \ln n]$    after cancellation

$\Rightarrow \sum\limits_{k=2}^{n} \ln\left(1 - \frac{1}{k^2}\right) = \ln\left(\frac{n+1}{2n}\right) \Rightarrow \sum\limits_{k=2}^{\infty} \ln\left(1 - \frac{1}{k^2}\right) = \lim\limits_{n \to \infty} \ln\left(\frac{n+1}{2n}\right) = \ln\frac{1}{2}$ is the sum

84. $\sum\limits_{k=2}^{n} \frac{1}{k^2-1} = \frac{1}{2} \sum\limits_{k=2}^{n} \left(\frac{1}{k-1} - \frac{1}{k+1}\right) = \frac{1}{2}\left[\left(\frac{1}{1} - \frac{1}{3}\right) + \left(\frac{1}{2} - \frac{1}{4}\right) + \left(\frac{1}{3} - \frac{1}{5}\right) + \left(\frac{1}{4} - \frac{1}{6}\right) + \ldots + \left(\frac{1}{n-2} - \frac{1}{n}\right)\right.$

$\left. + \left(\frac{1}{n-1} - \frac{1}{n+1}\right)\right] = \frac{1}{2}\left(1 + \frac{1}{2} - \frac{1}{n} - \frac{1}{n+1}\right) = \frac{1}{2}\left(\frac{3}{2} - \frac{1}{n} - \frac{1}{n+1}\right) = \frac{1}{2}\left[\frac{3n(n+1) - 2(n+1) - 2n}{2n(n+1)}\right] = \frac{3n^2-n-2}{4n(n+1)}$

$\Rightarrow \sum\limits_{k=2}^{\infty} \frac{1}{k^2-1} = \lim\limits_{n \to \infty} \frac{1}{2}\left(\frac{3}{2} - \frac{1}{n} - \frac{1}{n+1}\right) = \frac{3}{4}$

85. (a) $\lim\limits_{n \to \infty} \left| \frac{1\cdot4\cdot7\cdots(3n-2)(3n+1)x^{3n+3}}{(3n+3)!} \cdot \frac{(3n)!}{1\cdot4\cdot7\cdots(3n-2)x^{3n}} \right| < 1 \Rightarrow |x^3| \lim\limits_{n \to \infty} \frac{(3n+1)}{(3n+1)(3n+2)(3n+3)}$

$= |x^3| \cdot 0 < 1 \Rightarrow$ the radius of convergence is $\infty$

(b) $y = 1 + \sum\limits_{n=1}^{\infty} \frac{1\cdot4\cdot7\cdots(3n-2)}{(3n)!} x^{3n} \Rightarrow \frac{dy}{dx} = \sum\limits_{n=1}^{\infty} \frac{1\cdot4\cdot7\cdots(3n-2)}{(3n-1)!} x^{3n-1}$

$\Rightarrow \frac{d^2y}{dx^2} = \sum\limits_{n=1}^{\infty} \frac{1\cdot4\cdot7\cdots(3n-2)}{(3n-2)!} x^{3n-2} = x + \sum\limits_{n=2}^{\infty} \frac{1\cdot4\cdot7\cdots(3n-5)}{(3n-3)!} x^{3n-2}$

$= x\left(1 + \sum\limits_{n=1}^{\infty} \frac{1\cdot4\cdot7\cdots(3n-2)}{(3n)!} x^{3n}\right) = xy + 0 \Rightarrow a = 1$ and $b = 0$

86. (a) $\frac{x^2}{1+x} = \frac{x^2}{1-(-x)} = x^2 + x^2(-x) + x^2(-x)^2 + x^2(-x)^3 + \ldots = x^2 - x^3 + x^4 - x^5 + \ldots = \sum\limits_{n=2}^{\infty} (-1)^n x^n$ which

converges absolutely for $|x| < 1$

(b) $x = 1 \Rightarrow \sum\limits_{n=2}^{\infty} (-1)^n x^n = \sum\limits_{n=2}^{\infty} (-1)^n$ which diverges

87. Yes, the series $\sum\limits_{n=1}^{\infty} a_n b_n$ converges as we now show. Since $\sum\limits_{n=1}^{\infty} a_n$ converges it follows that $a_n \to 0 \Rightarrow a_n < 1$

for $n >$ some index $N \Rightarrow a_n b_n < b_n$ for $n > N \Rightarrow \sum\limits_{n=1}^{\infty} a_n b_n$ converges by the Direct Comparison Test with $\sum\limits_{n=1}^{\infty} b_n$

88. No, the series $\sum\limits_{n=1}^{\infty} a_n b_n$ might diverge (as it would if $a_n$ and $b_n$ both equaled n) or it might converge (as it would if

$a_n$ and $b_n$ both equaled $\frac{1}{n}$).

89. $\sum\limits_{n=1}^{\infty} (x_{n+1} - x_n) = \lim\limits_{n \to \infty} \sum\limits_{k=1}^{\infty} (x_{k+1} - x_k) = \lim\limits_{n \to \infty} (x_{n+1} - x_1) = \lim\limits_{n \to \infty} (x_{n+1}) - x_1 \Rightarrow$ both the series and

sequence must either converge or diverge.

90. It converges by the Limit Comparison Test since $\lim\limits_{n \to \infty} \dfrac{\left(\frac{a_n}{1+a_n}\right)}{a_n} = \lim\limits_{n \to \infty} \dfrac{1}{1+a_n} = 1$ because $\sum\limits_{n=1}^{\infty} a_n$ converges

and so $a_n \to 0$.

91. $\sum\limits_{n=1}^{\infty} \dfrac{a_n}{n} = a_1 + \dfrac{a_2}{2} + \dfrac{a_3}{3} + \dfrac{a_4}{4} + \ldots \geq a_1 + \left(\dfrac{1}{2}\right) a_2 + \left(\dfrac{1}{3} + \dfrac{1}{4}\right) a_4 + \left(\dfrac{1}{5} + \dfrac{1}{6} + \dfrac{1}{7} + \dfrac{1}{8}\right) a_8$

$+ \left(\dfrac{1}{9} + \dfrac{1}{10} + \dfrac{1}{11} + \ldots + \dfrac{1}{16}\right) a_{16} + \ldots \geq \dfrac{1}{2}\left(a_2 + a_4 + a_8 + a_{16} + \ldots\right)$ which is a divergent series

92. $a_n = \dfrac{1}{\ln n}$ for $n \geq 2 \Rightarrow a_2 \geq a_3 \geq a_4 \geq \ldots$, and $\dfrac{1}{\ln 2} + \dfrac{1}{\ln 4} + \dfrac{1}{\ln 8} + \ldots = \dfrac{1}{\ln 2} + \dfrac{1}{2 \ln 2} + \dfrac{1}{3 \ln 2} + \ldots$

$= \dfrac{1}{\ln 2}\left(1 + \dfrac{1}{2} + \dfrac{1}{3} + \ldots\right)$ which diverges so that $1 + \sum\limits_{n=2}^{\infty} \dfrac{1}{n \ln n}$ diverges by the Integral Test.

## CHAPTER 10 ADDITIONAL AND ADVANCED EXERCISES

1. converges since $\dfrac{1}{(3n-2)^{(2n+1)/2}} < \dfrac{1}{(3n-2)^{3/2}}$ and $\sum\limits_{n=1}^{\infty} \dfrac{1}{(3n-2)^{3/2}}$ converges by the Limit Comparison Test:

$\lim\limits_{n \to \infty} \dfrac{\left(\frac{1}{n^{3/2}}\right)}{\left(\frac{1}{(3n-2)^{3/2}}\right)} = \lim\limits_{n \to \infty} \left(\dfrac{3n-2}{n}\right)^{3/2} = 3^{3/2}$

2. converges by the Integral Test: $\int_1^{\infty} \left(\tan^{-1} x\right)^2 \dfrac{dx}{x^2+1} = \lim\limits_{b \to \infty} \left[\dfrac{\left(\tan^{-1} x\right)^3}{3}\right]_1^b = \lim\limits_{b \to \infty} \left[\dfrac{\left(\tan^{-1} b\right)^3}{3} - \dfrac{\pi^3}{192}\right]$

$= \left(\dfrac{\pi^3}{24} - \dfrac{\pi^3}{192}\right) = \dfrac{7\pi^3}{192}$

3. diverges by the nth-Term Test since $\lim\limits_{n \to \infty} a_n = \lim\limits_{n \to \infty} (-1)^n \tanh n = \lim\limits_{b \to \infty} (-1)^n \left(\dfrac{1-e^{-2n}}{1+e^{-2n}}\right) = \lim\limits_{n \to \infty} (-1)^n$

does not exist

4. converges by the Direct Comparison Test: $n! < n^n \Rightarrow \ln(n!) < n \ln(n) \Rightarrow \dfrac{\ln(n!)}{\ln(n)} < n$

$\Rightarrow \log_n(n!) < n \Rightarrow \dfrac{\log_n(n!)}{n^3} < \dfrac{1}{n^2}$, which is the nth-term of a convergent p-series

5. converges by the Direct Comparison Test: $a_1 = 1 = \dfrac{12}{(1)(3)(2)^2}$, $a_2 = \dfrac{1 \cdot 2}{3 \cdot 4} = \dfrac{12}{(2)(4)(3)^2}$, $a_3 = \left(\dfrac{2 \cdot 3}{4 \cdot 5}\right)\left(\dfrac{1 \cdot 2}{3 \cdot 4}\right)$

$= \dfrac{12}{(3)(5)(4)^2}$, $a_4 = \left(\dfrac{3 \cdot 4}{5 \cdot 6}\right)\left(\dfrac{2 \cdot 3}{4 \cdot 5}\right)\left(\dfrac{1 \cdot 2}{3 \cdot 4}\right) = \dfrac{12}{(4)(6)(5)^2}, \ldots \Rightarrow 1 + \sum\limits_{n=1}^{\infty} \dfrac{12}{(n+1)(n+3)(n+2)^2}$ represents the

given series and $\dfrac{12}{(n+1)(n+3)(n+2)^2} < \dfrac{12}{n^4}$, which is the nth-term of a convergent p-series

6. converges by the Ratio Test: $\lim\limits_{n \to \infty} \dfrac{a_{n+1}}{a_n} = \lim\limits_{n \to \infty} \dfrac{n}{(n-1)(n+1)} = 0 < 1$

7. diverges by the nth-Term Test since if $a_n \to L$ as $n \to \infty$, then $L = \dfrac{1}{1+L} \Rightarrow L^2 + L - 1 = 0 \Rightarrow L = \dfrac{-1 \pm \sqrt{5}}{2} \neq 0$

8. Split the given series into $\sum\limits_{n=1}^{\infty} \dfrac{1}{3^{2n+1}}$ and $\sum\limits_{n=1}^{\infty} \dfrac{2n}{3^{2n}}$; the first subseries is a convergent geometric series and the

second converges by the Root Test: $\lim\limits_{n \to \infty} \sqrt[n]{\dfrac{2n}{3^{2n}}} = \lim\limits_{n \to \infty} \dfrac{\sqrt[n]{2}\,\sqrt[n]{n}}{9} = \dfrac{1 \cdot 1}{9} = \dfrac{1}{9} < 1$

9. $f(x) = \cos x$ with $a = \dfrac{\pi}{3} \Rightarrow f\left(\dfrac{\pi}{3}\right) = 0.5$, $f'\left(\dfrac{\pi}{3}\right) = -\dfrac{\sqrt{3}}{2}$, $f''\left(\dfrac{\pi}{3}\right) = -0.5$, $f'''\left(\dfrac{\pi}{3}\right) = \dfrac{\sqrt{3}}{2}$, $f^{(4)}\left(\dfrac{\pi}{3}\right) = 0.5$;

$\cos x = \dfrac{1}{2} - \dfrac{\sqrt{3}}{2}\left(x - \dfrac{\pi}{3}\right) - \dfrac{1}{4}\left(x - \dfrac{\pi}{3}\right)^2 + \dfrac{\sqrt{3}}{12}\left(x - \dfrac{\pi}{3}\right)^3 + \ldots$

10. $f(x) = \sin x$ with $a = 2\pi \Rightarrow f(2\pi) = 0, f'(2\pi) = 1, f''(2\pi) = 0, f'''(2\pi) = -1, f^{(4)}(2\pi) = 0, f^{(5)}(2\pi) = 1,$
$f^{(6)}(2\pi) = 0, f^{(7)}(2\pi) = -1; \sin x = (x - 2\pi) - \frac{(x-2\pi)^3}{3!} + \frac{(x-2\pi)^5}{5!} - \frac{(x-2\pi)^7}{7!} + \cdots$

11. $e^x = 1 + x + \frac{x^2}{2!} + \frac{x^3}{3!} + \cdots$ with $a = 0$

12. $f(x) = \ln x$ with $a = 1 \Rightarrow f(1) = 0, f'(1) = 1, f''(1) = -1, f'''(1) = 2, f^{(4)}(1) = -6;$
$\ln x = (x - 1) - \frac{(x-1)^2}{2} + \frac{(x-1)^3}{3} - \frac{(x-1)^4}{4} + \cdots$

13. $f(x) = \cos x$ with $a = 22\pi \Rightarrow f(22\pi) = 1, f'(22\pi) = 0, f''(22\pi) = -1, f'''(22\pi) = 0, f^{(4)}(22\pi) = 1,$
$f^{(5)}(22\pi) = 0, f^{(6)}(22\pi) = -1; \cos x = 1 - \frac{1}{2}(x - 22\pi)^2 + \frac{1}{4!}(x - 22\pi)^4 - \frac{1}{6!}(x - 22\pi)^6 + \cdots$

14. $f(x) = \tan^{-1} x$ with $a = 1 \Rightarrow f(1) = \frac{\pi}{4}, f'(1) = \frac{1}{2}, f''(1) = -\frac{1}{2}, f'''(1) = \frac{1}{2};$
$\tan^{-1} x = \frac{\pi}{4} + \frac{(x-1)}{2} - \frac{(x-1)^2}{4} + \frac{(x-1)^3}{12} + \cdots$

15. Yes, the sequence converges: $c_n = (a^n + b^n)^{1/n} \Rightarrow c_n = b\left(\left(\frac{a}{b}\right)^n + 1\right)^{1/n} \Rightarrow \lim_{n \to \infty} c_n = \ln b + \lim_{n \to \infty} \frac{\ln\left(\left(\frac{a}{b}\right)^n + 1\right)}{n}$
$= \ln b + \lim_{n \to \infty} \frac{\left(\frac{a}{b}\right)^n \ln\left(\frac{a}{b}\right)}{\left(\frac{a}{b}\right)^n + 1} = \ln b + \frac{0 \cdot \ln\left(\frac{a}{b}\right)}{0 + 1} = \ln b$ since $0 < a < b$. Thus, $\lim_{n \to \infty} c_n = e^{\ln b} = b.$

16. $1 + \frac{2}{10} + \frac{3}{10^2} + \frac{7}{10^3} + \frac{2}{10^4} + \frac{3}{10^5} + \frac{7}{10^6} + \cdots = 1 + \sum_{n=1}^{\infty} \frac{2}{10^{3n-2}} + \sum_{n=1}^{\infty} \frac{3}{10^{3n-1}} + \sum_{n=1}^{\infty} \frac{7}{10^{3n}}$

$= 1 + \sum_{n=0}^{\infty} \frac{2}{10^{3n+1}} + \sum_{n=0}^{\infty} \frac{3}{10^{3n+2}} + \sum_{n=0}^{\infty} \frac{7}{10^{3n+3}} = 1 + \frac{\left(\frac{2}{10}\right)}{1 - \left(\frac{1}{10}\right)^3} + \frac{\left(\frac{3}{10^2}\right)}{1 - \left(\frac{1}{10}\right)^3} + \frac{\left(\frac{7}{10^3}\right)}{1 - \left(\frac{1}{10}\right)^3}$

$= 1 + \frac{200}{999} + \frac{30}{999} + \frac{7}{999} = \frac{999 + 237}{999} = \frac{412}{333}$

17. $s_n = \sum_{k=0}^{n-1} \int_k^{k+1} \frac{dx}{1 + x^2} \Rightarrow s_n = \int_0^1 \frac{dx}{1 + x^2} + \int_1^2 \frac{dx}{1 + x^2} + \cdots + \int_{n-1}^n \frac{dx}{1 + x^2} \Rightarrow s_n = \int_0^n \frac{dx}{1 + x^2}$
$\Rightarrow \lim_{n \to \infty} s_n = \lim_{n \to \infty} (\tan^{-1} n - \tan^{-1} 0) = \frac{\pi}{2}$

18. $\lim_{n \to \infty} \left| \frac{u_{n+1}}{u_n} \right| = \lim_{n \to \infty} \left| \frac{(n+1)x^{n+1}}{(n+2)(2x+1)^{n+1}} \cdot \frac{(n+1)(2x+1)^n}{nx^n} \right| = \lim_{n \to \infty} \left| \frac{x}{2x+1} \cdot \frac{(n+1)^2}{n(n+2)} \right| = \left| \frac{x}{2x+1} \right| < 1$
$\Rightarrow |x| < |2x + 1|; \text{if } x > 0, |x| < |2x + 1| \Rightarrow x < 2x + 1 \Rightarrow x > -1; \text{if } -\frac{1}{2} < x < 0, |x| < |2x + 1|$
$\Rightarrow -x < 2x + 1 \Rightarrow 3x > -1 \Rightarrow x > -\frac{1}{3}; \text{if } x < -\frac{1}{2}, |x| < |2x + 1| \Rightarrow -x < -2x - 1 \Rightarrow x < -1.$ Therefore,
the series converges absolutely for $x < -1$ and $x > -\frac{1}{3}$.

19. (a) No, the limit does not appear to depend on the value of the constant a
    (b) Yes, the limit depends on the value of b

    (c) $s = \left(1 - \frac{\cos\left(\frac{a}{n}\right)}{n}\right)^n \Rightarrow \ln s = \frac{\ln\left(1 - \frac{\cos\left(\frac{a}{n}\right)}{n}\right)}{\left(\frac{1}{n}\right)} \Rightarrow \lim_{n \to \infty} \ln s = \frac{\left(\frac{1}{1 - \frac{\cos\left(\frac{a}{n}\right)}{n}}\right)\left(\frac{-\frac{a}{n}\sin\left(\frac{a}{n}\right) + \cos\left(\frac{a}{n}\right)}{n^2}\right)}{\left(-\frac{1}{n^2}\right)}$

    $= \lim_{n \to \infty} \frac{\frac{a}{n}\sin\left(\frac{a}{n}\right) - \cos\left(\frac{a}{n}\right)}{1 - \frac{\cos\left(\frac{a}{n}\right)}{n}} = \frac{0 - 1}{1 - 0} = -1 \Rightarrow \lim_{n \to \infty} s = e^{-1} \approx 0.3678794412; \text{similarly,}$

    $\lim_{n \to \infty} \left(1 - \frac{\cos\left(\frac{a}{n}\right)}{bn}\right)^n = e^{-1/b}$

20. $\sum_{n=1}^{\infty} a_n$ converges $\Rightarrow \lim_{n \to \infty} a_n = 0; \lim_{n \to \infty} \left[\left(\frac{1 + \sin a_n}{2}\right)^n\right]^{1/n} = \lim_{n \to \infty} \left(\frac{1 + \sin a_n}{2}\right) = \frac{1 + \sin\left(\lim_{n \to \infty} a_n\right)}{2} = \frac{1 + \sin 0}{2}$
$= \frac{1}{2} \Rightarrow$ the series converges by the nth-Root Test

21. $\lim\limits_{n\to\infty}\left|\frac{u_{n+1}}{u_n}\right|<1 \Rightarrow \lim\limits_{n\to\infty}\left|\frac{b^{n+1}x^{n+1}}{\ln(n+1)}\cdot\frac{\ln n}{b^n x^n}\right|<1 \Rightarrow |bx|<1 \Rightarrow -\frac{1}{b}<x<\frac{1}{b}=5 \Rightarrow b=\pm\frac{1}{5}$

22. A polynomial has only a finite number of nonzero terms in its Taylor series, but the functions sin x, ln x and $e^x$ have infinitely many nonzero terms in their Taylor expansions.

23. $\lim\limits_{x\to0}\frac{\sin(ax)-\sin x-x}{x^3}=\lim\limits_{x\to0}\frac{\left(ax-\frac{a^3x^3}{3!}+\dots\right)-\left(x-\frac{x^3}{3!}+\dots\right)-x}{x^3}=\lim\limits_{x\to0}\left[\frac{a-2}{x^2}-\frac{a^3}{3!}+\frac{1}{3!}-\left(\frac{a^5}{5!}-\frac{1}{5!}\right)x^2+\dots\right]$

    is finite if $a-2=0 \Rightarrow a=2$; $\lim\limits_{x\to0}\frac{\sin 2x-\sin x-x}{x^3}=-\frac{2^3}{3!}+\frac{1}{3!}=-\frac{7}{6}$

24. $\lim\limits_{x\to0}\frac{\cos ax-b}{2x^2}=-1 \Rightarrow \lim\limits_{x\to0}\frac{\left(1-\frac{a^2x^2}{2}+\frac{a^4x^4}{4!}-\dots\right)-b}{2x^2}=-1 \Rightarrow \lim\limits_{x\to0}\left(\frac{1-b}{2x^2}-\frac{a^2}{4}+\frac{a^2x^2}{48}-\dots\right)=-1$

    $\Rightarrow b=1$ and $a=\pm2$

25. (a) $\frac{u_n}{u_{n+1}}=\frac{(n+1)^2}{n^2}=1+\frac{2}{n}+\frac{1}{n^2} \Rightarrow C=2>1$ and $\sum\limits_{n=1}^{\infty}\frac{1}{n^2}$ converges

    (b) $\frac{u_n}{u_{n+1}}=\frac{n+1}{n}=1+\frac{1}{n}+\frac{0}{n^2} \Rightarrow C=1\le1$ and $\sum\limits_{n=1}^{\infty}\frac{1}{n}$ diverges

26. $\frac{u_n}{u_{n+1}}=\frac{2n(2n+1)}{(2n-1)^2}=\frac{4n^2+2n}{4n^2-4n+1}=1+\frac{\left(\frac{6}{4}\right)}{n}+\frac{5}{4n^2-4n+1}=1+\frac{\left(\frac{3}{2}\right)}{n}+\frac{\left[\frac{5n^2}{(4n^2-4n+1)}\right]}{n^2}$ after long division

    $\Rightarrow C=\frac{3}{2}>1$ and $|f(n)|=\frac{5n^2}{4n^2-4n+1}=\frac{5}{\left(4-\frac{4}{n}+\frac{1}{n^2}\right)}\le5 \Rightarrow \sum\limits_{n=1}^{\infty}u_n$ converges by Raabe's Test

27. (a) $\sum\limits_{n=1}^{\infty}a_n=L \Rightarrow a_n^2\le a_n\sum\limits_{n=1}^{\infty}a_n=a_nL \Rightarrow \sum\limits_{n=1}^{\infty}a_n^2$ converges by the Direct Comparison Test

    (b) converges by the Limit Comparison Test: $\lim\limits_{n\to\infty}\frac{\left(\frac{a_n}{1-a_n}\right)}{a_n}=\lim\limits_{n\to\infty}\frac{1}{1-a_n}=1$ since $\sum\limits_{n=1}^{\infty}a_n$ converges and

    therefore $\lim\limits_{x\to\infty}a_n=0$

28. If $0<a_n<1$ then $|\ln(1-a_n)|=-\ln(1-a_n)=a_n+\frac{a_n^2}{2}+\frac{a_n^3}{3}+\dots<a_n+a_n^2+a_n^3+\dots=\frac{a_n}{1-a_n}$,

    a positive term of a convergent series, by the Limit Comparison Test and Exercise 27b

29. $(1-x)^{-1}=1+\sum\limits_{n=1}^{\infty}x^n$ where $|x|<1 \Rightarrow \frac{1}{(1-x)^2}=\frac{d}{dx}(1-x)^{-1}=\sum\limits_{n=1}^{\infty}nx^{n-1}$ and when $x=\frac{1}{2}$ we have

    $4=1+2\left(\frac{1}{2}\right)+3\left(\frac{1}{2}\right)^2+4\left(\frac{1}{2}\right)^3+\dots+n\left(\frac{1}{2}\right)^{n-1}+\dots$

30. (a) $\sum\limits_{n=1}^{\infty}x^{n+1}=\frac{x^2}{1-x} \Rightarrow \sum\limits_{n=1}^{\infty}(n+1)x^n=\frac{2x-x^2}{(1-x)^2} \Rightarrow \sum\limits_{n=1}^{\infty}n(n+1)x^{n-1}=\frac{2}{(1-x)^3} \Rightarrow \sum\limits_{n=1}^{\infty}n(n+1)x^n=\frac{2x}{(1-x)^3}$

    $\Rightarrow \sum\limits_{n=1}^{\infty}\frac{n(n+1)}{x^n}=\frac{\frac{2}{x}}{\left(1-\frac{1}{x}\right)^3}=\frac{2x^2}{(x-1)^3}$, $|x|>1$

    (b) $x=\sum\limits_{n=1}^{\infty}\frac{n(n+1)}{x^n} \Rightarrow x=\frac{2x^2}{(x-1)^3} \Rightarrow x^3-3x^2+x-1=0 \Rightarrow x=1+\left(1+\frac{\sqrt{57}}{9}\right)^{1/3}+\left(1-\frac{\sqrt{57}}{9}\right)^{1/3}$

    $\approx2.769292$, using a CAS or calculator

31. (a) $\frac{1}{(1-x)^2}=\frac{d}{dx}\left(\frac{1}{1-x}\right)=\frac{d}{dx}(1+x+x^2+x^3+\dots)=1+2x+3x^2+4x^3+\dots=\sum\limits_{n=1}^{\infty}nx^{n-1}$

    (b) from part (a) we have $\sum\limits_{n=1}^{\infty}n\left(\frac{5}{6}\right)^{n-1}\left(\frac{1}{6}\right)=\left(\frac{1}{6}\right)\left[\frac{1}{1-\left(\frac{5}{6}\right)}\right]^2=6$

(c) from part (a) we have $\sum\limits_{n=1}^{\infty} np^{n-1}q = \frac{q}{(1-p)^2} = \frac{q}{q^2} = \frac{1}{q}$

32. (a) $\sum\limits_{k=1}^{\infty} p_k = \sum\limits_{k=1}^{\infty} 2^{-k} = \frac{\left(\frac{1}{2}\right)}{1-\left(\frac{1}{2}\right)} = 1$ and $E(x) = \sum\limits_{k=1}^{\infty} kp_k = \sum\limits_{k=1}^{\infty} k2^{-k} = \frac{1}{2} \sum\limits_{k=1}^{\infty} k2^{1-k} = \left(\frac{1}{2}\right) \frac{1}{\left[1-\left(\frac{1}{2}\right)\right]^2} = 2$

by Exercise 31(a)

(b) $\sum\limits_{k=1}^{\infty} p_k = \sum\limits_{k=1}^{\infty} \frac{5^{k-1}}{6^k} = \frac{1}{5} \sum\limits_{k=1}^{\infty} \left(\frac{5}{6}\right)^k = \left(\frac{1}{5}\right) \left[\frac{\left(\frac{5}{6}\right)}{1-\left(\frac{5}{6}\right)}\right] = 1$ and $E(x) = \sum\limits_{k=1}^{\infty} kp_k = \sum\limits_{k=1}^{\infty} k \frac{5^{k-1}}{6^k} = \frac{1}{6} \sum\limits_{k=1}^{\infty} k \left(\frac{5}{6}\right)^{k-1}$

$= \left(\frac{1}{6}\right) \frac{1}{\left[1-\left(\frac{5}{6}\right)\right]^2} = 6$

(c) $\sum\limits_{k=1}^{\infty} p_k = \sum\limits_{k=1}^{\infty} \frac{1}{k(k+1)} = \sum\limits_{k=1}^{\infty} \left(\frac{1}{k} - \frac{1}{k+1}\right) = \lim\limits_{k \to \infty} \left(1 - \frac{1}{k+1}\right) = 1$ and $E(x) = \sum\limits_{k=1}^{\infty} kp_k = \sum\limits_{k=1}^{\infty} k \left(\frac{1}{k(k+1)}\right)$

$= \sum\limits_{k=1}^{\infty} \frac{1}{k+1}$, a divergent series so that $E(x)$ does not exist

33. (a) $R_n = C_0 e^{-kt_0} + C_0 e^{-2kt_0} + \ldots + C_0 e^{-nkt_0} = \frac{C_0 e^{-kt_0}\left(1 - e^{-nkt_0}\right)}{1 - e^{-kt_0}} \Rightarrow R = \lim\limits_{n \to \infty} R_n = \frac{C_0 e^{-kt_0}}{1 - e^{-kt_0}} = \frac{C_0}{e^{kt_0} - 1}$

(b) $R_n = \frac{e^{-1}(1 - e^{-n})}{1 - e^{-1}} \Rightarrow R_1 = e^{-1} \approx 0.36787944$ and $R_{10} = \frac{e^{-1}(1 - e^{-10})}{1 - e^{-1}} \approx 0.58195028$;

$R = \frac{1}{e-1} \approx 0.58197671$; $R - R_{10} \approx 0.00002643 \Rightarrow \frac{R - R_{10}}{R} < 0.0001$

(c) $R_n = \frac{e^{-.1}\left(1 - e^{-.1n}\right)}{1 - e^{-.1}}$, $\frac{R}{2} = \frac{1}{2}\left(\frac{1}{e^{.1} - 1}\right) \approx 4.7541659$; $R_n > \frac{R}{2} \Rightarrow \frac{1 - e^{-.1n}}{e^{.1} - 1} > \left(\frac{1}{2}\right)\left(\frac{1}{e^{.1} - 1}\right)$

$\Rightarrow 1 - e^{-n/10} > \frac{1}{2} \Rightarrow e^{-n/10} < \frac{1}{2} \Rightarrow -\frac{n}{10} < \ln\left(\frac{1}{2}\right) \Rightarrow \frac{n}{10} > -\ln\left(\frac{1}{2}\right) \Rightarrow n > 6.93 \Rightarrow n = 7$

34. (a) $R = \frac{C_0}{e^{kt_0} - 1} \Rightarrow Re^{kt_0} = R + C_0 = C_H \Rightarrow e^{kt_0} = \frac{C_H}{C_L} \Rightarrow t_0 = \frac{1}{k} \ln\left(\frac{C_H}{C_L}\right)$

(b) $t_0 = \frac{1}{0.05} \ln e = 20$ hrs

(c) Give an initial dose that produces a concentration of 2 mg/ml followed every $t_0 = \frac{1}{0.02} \ln\left(\frac{2}{0.5}\right) \approx 69.31$ hrs
by a dose that raises the concentration by 1.5 mg/ml

(d) $t_0 = \frac{1}{0.2} \ln\left(\frac{0.1}{0.03}\right) = 5 \ln\left(\frac{10}{3}\right) \approx 6$ hrs

**NOTES:**

# CHAPTER 11   PARAMETRIC EQUATIONS AND POLAR COORDINATES

## 11.1 PARAMETRIZATIONS OF PLANE CURVES

1. $x = 3t, y = 9t^2, -\infty < t < \infty \Rightarrow y = x^2$

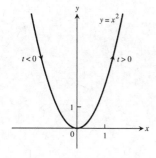

2. $x = -\sqrt{t}, y = t, t \geq 0 \Rightarrow x = -\sqrt{y}$
   or $y = x^2, x \leq 0$

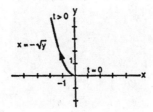

3. $x = 2t - 5, y = 4t - 7, -\infty < t < \infty$
   $\Rightarrow x + 5 = 2t \Rightarrow 2(x + 5) = 4t$
   $\Rightarrow y = 2(x + 5) - 7 \Rightarrow y = 2x + 3$

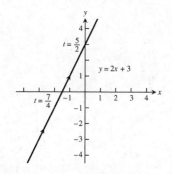

4. $x = 3 - 3t, y = 2t, 0 \leq t \leq 1 \Rightarrow \frac{y}{2} = t$
   $\Rightarrow x = 3 - 3\left(\frac{y}{2}\right) \Rightarrow 2x = 6 - 3y$
   $\Rightarrow y = 2 - \frac{2}{3}x, 0 \leq x \leq 3$

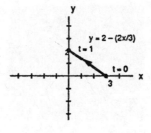

5. $x = \cos 2t, y = \sin 2t, 0 \leq t \leq \pi$
   $\Rightarrow \cos^2 2t + \sin^2 2t = 1 \Rightarrow x^2 + y^2 = 1$

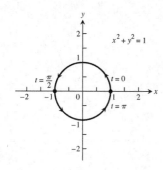

6. $x = \cos(\pi - t), y = \sin(\pi - t), 0 \leq t \leq \pi$
   $\Rightarrow \cos^2(\pi - t) + \sin^2(\pi - t) = 1$
   $\Rightarrow x^2 + y^2 = 1, y \geq 0$

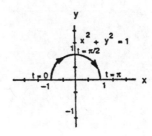

7. $x = 4 \cos t$, $y = 2 \sin t$, $0 \le t \le 2\pi$

$\Rightarrow \frac{16 \cos^2 t}{16} + \frac{4 \sin^2 t}{4} = 1 \Rightarrow \frac{x^2}{16} + \frac{y^2}{4} = 1$

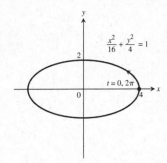

8. $x = 4 \sin t$, $y = 5 \cos t$, $0 \le t \le 2\pi$

$\Rightarrow \frac{16 \sin^2 t}{16} + \frac{25 \cos^2 t}{25} = 1 \Rightarrow \frac{x^2}{16} + \frac{y^2}{25} = 1$

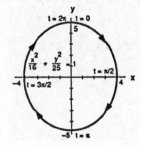

9. $x = \sin t$, $y = \cos 2t$, $-\frac{\pi}{2} \le t \le \frac{\pi}{2}$

$\Rightarrow y = \cos 2t = 1 - 2\sin^2 t \Rightarrow y = 1 - 2x^2$

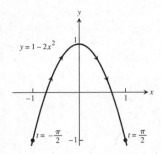

10. $x = 1 + \sin t$, $y = \cos t - 2$, $0 \le t \le \pi$

$\Rightarrow \sin^2 t + \cos^2 t = 1 \Rightarrow (x - 1)^2 + (y + 2)^2 = 1$

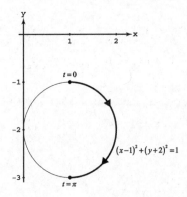

11. $x = t^2$, $y = t^6 - 2t^4$, $-\infty < t < \infty$

$\Rightarrow y = (t^2)^3 - 2(t^2)^2 \Rightarrow y = x^3 - 2x^2$

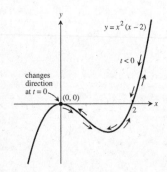

12. $x = \frac{t}{t-1}$, $y = \frac{t-2}{t+1}$, $-1 < t < 1$

$\Rightarrow t = \frac{x}{x-1} \Rightarrow y = \frac{2-x}{2x-1}$

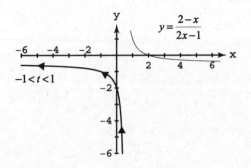

13. $x = t$, $y = \sqrt{1 - t^2}$, $-1 \le t \le 0$

$\Rightarrow y = \sqrt{1 - x^2}$

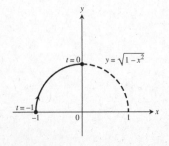

14. $x = \sqrt{t+1}$, $y = \sqrt{t}$, $t \ge 0$

$\Rightarrow y^2 = t \Rightarrow x = \sqrt{y^2 + 1}$, $y \ge 0$

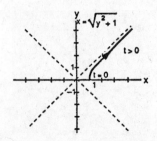

15. $x = \sec^2 t - 1$, $y = \tan t$, $-\frac{\pi}{2} < t < \frac{\pi}{2}$
$\Rightarrow \sec^2 t - 1 = \tan^2 t \Rightarrow x = y^2$

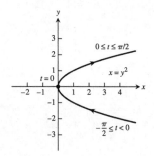

16. $x = -\sec t$, $y = \tan t$, $-\frac{\pi}{2} < t < \frac{\pi}{2}$
$\Rightarrow \sec^2 t - \tan^2 t = 1 \Rightarrow x^2 - y^2 = 1$

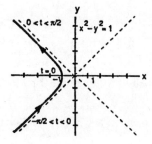

17. $x = -\cosh t$, $y = \sinh t$, $-\infty < 1 < \infty$
$\Rightarrow \cosh^2 t - \sinh^2 t = 1 \Rightarrow x^2 - y^2 = 1$

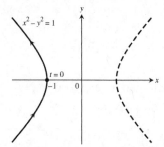

18. $x = 2 \sinh t$, $y = 2 \cosh t$, $-\infty < t < \infty$
$\Rightarrow 4 \cosh^2 t - 4 \sinh^2 t = 4 \Rightarrow y^2 - x^2 = 4$

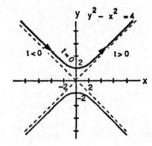

19. (a)  $x = a \cos t$, $y = -a \sin t$, $0 \le t \le 2\pi$
    (b)  $x = a \cos t$, $y = a \sin t$, $0 \le t \le 2\pi$
    (c)  $x = a \cos t$, $y = -a \sin t$, $0 \le t \le 4\pi$
    (d)  $x = a \cos t$, $y = a \sin t$, $0 \le t \le 4\pi$

20. (a)  $x = a \sin t$, $y = b \cos t$, $\frac{\pi}{2} \le t \le \frac{5\pi}{2}$
    (b)  $x = a \cos t$, $y = b \sin t$, $0 \le t \le 2\pi$
    (c)  $x = a \sin t$, $y = b \cos t$, $\frac{\pi}{2} \le t \le \frac{9\pi}{2}$
    (d)  $x = a \cos t$, $y = b \sin t$, $0 \le t \le 4\pi$

21. Using $(-1, -3)$ we create the parametric equations $x = -1 + at$ and $y = -3 + bt$, representing a line which goes through $(-1, -3)$ at $t = 0$. We determine $a$ and $b$ so that the line goes through $(4, 1)$ when $t = 1$. Since $4 = -1 + a \Rightarrow a = 5$. Since $1 = -3 + b \Rightarrow b = 4$. Therefore, one possible parameterization is $x = -1 + 5t$, $y = -3 + 4t$, $0 \le t \le 1$.

22. Using $(-1, 3)$ we create the parametric equations $x = -1 + at$ and $y = 3 + bt$, representing a line which goes through $(-1, 3)$ at $t = 0$. We determine $a$ and $b$ so that the line goes through $(3, -2)$ when $t = 1$. Since $3 = -1 + a \Rightarrow a = 4$. Since $-2 = 3 + b \Rightarrow b = -5$. Therefore, one possible parameterization is $x = -1 + 4t$, $y = 3 - 5t$, $0 \le t \le 1$.

23. The lower half of the parabola is given by $x = y^2 + 1$ for $y \le 0$. Substituting $t$ for $y$, we obtain one possible parameterization $x = t^2 + 1$, $y = t$, $t \le 0$.

24. The vertex of the parabola is at $(-1, -1)$, so the left half of the parabola is given by $y = x^2 + 2x$ for $x \le -1$. Substituting $t$ for $x$, we obtain one possible parametrization: $x = t$, $y = t^2 + 2t$, $t \le -1$.

25. For simplicity, we assume that $x$ and $y$ are linear functions of $t$ and that the point $(x, y)$ starts at $(2, 3)$ for $t = 0$ and passes through $(-1, -1)$ at $t = 1$. Then $x = f(t)$, where $f(0) = 2$ and $f(1) = -1$.
Since slope $= \frac{\Delta x}{\Delta t} = \frac{-1-2}{1-0} = -3$, $x = f(t) = -3t + 2 = 2 - 3t$. Also, $y = g(t)$, where $g(0) = 3$ and $g(1) = -1$.
Since slope $= \frac{\Delta y}{\Delta t} = \frac{-1-3}{1-0} = -4$. $y = g(t) = -4t + 3 = 3 - 4t$.
One possible parameterization is: $x = 2 - 3t$, $y = 3 - 4t$, $t \ge 0$.

26. For simplicity, we assume that x and y are linear functions of t and that the point $(x, y)$ starts at $(-1, 2)$ for $t = 0$ and passes through $(0, 0)$ at $t = 1$. Then $x = f(t)$, where $f(0) = -1$ and $f(1) = 0$.

Since slope $= \frac{\Delta x}{\Delta t} = \frac{0-(-1)}{1-0} = 1$, $x = f(t) = 1t + (-1) = -1 + t$. Also, $y = g(t)$, where $g(0) = 2$ and $g(1) = 0$.

Since slope $= \frac{\Delta y}{\Delta t} = \frac{0-2}{1-0} = -2$. $y = g(t) = -2t + 2 = 2 - 2t$.

One possible parameterization is: $x = -1 + t$, $y = 2 - 2t$, $t \geq 0$.

27. Since we only want the top half of a circle, $y \geq 0$, so let $x = 2\cos t$, $y = 2|\sin t|$, $0 \leq t \leq 4\pi$

28. Since we want x to stay between $-3$ and $3$, let $x = 3\sin t$, then $y = (3\sin t)^2 = 9\sin^2 t$, thus $x = 3\sin t$, $y = 9\sin^2 t$, $0 \leq t < \infty$

29. $x^2 + y^2 = a^2 \Rightarrow 2x + 2y\frac{dy}{dx} = 0 \Rightarrow \frac{dy}{dx} = -\frac{x}{y}$; let $t = \frac{dy}{dx} \Rightarrow -\frac{x}{y} = t \Rightarrow x = -yt$. Substitution yields
$y^2 t^2 + y^2 = a^2 \Rightarrow y = \frac{a}{\sqrt{1+t^2}}$ and $x = \frac{-at}{\sqrt{1+t}}$, $-\infty < t < \infty$

30. In terms of $\theta$, parametric equations for the circle are $x = a\cos\theta$, $y = a\sin\theta$, $0 \leq \theta < 2\pi$. Since $\theta = \frac{s}{a}$, the arc length parametrizations are: $x = a\cos\frac{s}{a}$, $y = a\sin\frac{s}{a}$, and $0 \leq \frac{s}{a} < 2\pi \Rightarrow 0 \leq s \leq 2\pi a$ is the interval for s.

31. Drop a vertical line from the point $(x, y)$ to the x-axis, then $\theta$ is an angle in a right triangle, and from trigonometry we know that $\tan\theta = \frac{y}{x} \Rightarrow y = x\tan\theta$. The equation of the line through $(0, 2)$ and $(4, 0)$ is given by $y = -\frac{1}{2}x + 2$. Thus $x\tan\theta = -\frac{1}{2}x + 2 \Rightarrow x = \frac{4}{2\tan\theta + 1}$ and $y = \frac{4\tan\theta}{2\tan\theta + 1}$ where $0 \leq \theta < \frac{\pi}{2}$.

32. Drop a vertical line from the point $(x, y)$ to the x-axis, then $\theta$ is an angle in a right triangle, and from trigonometry we know that $\tan\theta = \frac{y}{x} \Rightarrow y = x\tan\theta$. Since $y = \sqrt{x} \Rightarrow y^2 = x \Rightarrow (x\tan\theta)^2 = x \Rightarrow x = \cot^2\theta \Rightarrow y = \cot\theta$ where $0 < \theta \leq \frac{\pi}{2}$.

33. The equation of the circle is given by $(x - 2)^2 + y^2 = 1$. Drop a vertical line from the point $(x, y)$ on the circle to the x-axis, then $\theta$ is an angle in a right triangle. So that we can start at $(1, 0)$ and rotate in a clockwise direction, let $x = 2 - \cos\theta$, $y = \sin\theta$, $0 \leq \theta \leq 2\pi$.

34. Drop a vertical line from the point $(x, y)$ to the x-axis, then $\theta$ is an angle in a right triangle, whose height is y and whose base is $x + 2$. By trigonometry we have $\tan\theta = \frac{y}{x+2} \Rightarrow y = (x + 2)\tan\theta$. The equation of the circle is given by $x^2 + y^2 = 1 \Rightarrow x^2 + ((x+2)\tan\theta)^2 = 1 \Rightarrow x^2\sec^2\theta + 4x\tan^2\theta + 4\tan^2\theta - 1 = 0$. Solving for x we obtain

$x = \frac{-4\tan^2\theta \pm \sqrt{(4\tan^2\theta)^2 - 4\sec^2\theta(4\tan^2\theta - 1)}}{2\sec^2\theta} = \frac{-4\tan^2\theta \pm 2\sqrt{1 - 3\tan^2\theta}}{2\sec^2\theta} = -2\sin^2\theta \pm \cos\theta\sqrt{\cos^2\theta - 3\sin^2\theta}$

$= -2 + 2\cos^2\theta \pm \cos\theta\sqrt{4\cos^2\theta - 3}$ and $y = \left(-2 + 2\cos^2\theta \pm \cos\theta\sqrt{4\cos^2\theta - 3} + 2\right)\tan\theta$

$= 2\sin\theta\cos\theta \pm \sin\theta\sqrt{4\cos^2\theta - 3}$. Since we only need to go from $(1, 0)$ to $(0, 1)$, let

$x = -2 + 2\cos^2\theta + \cos\theta\sqrt{4\cos^2\theta - 3}$, $y = 2\sin\theta\cos\theta + \sin\theta\sqrt{4\cos^2\theta - 3}$, $0 \leq \theta \leq \tan^{-1}\left(\frac{1}{2}\right)$.

To obtain the upper limit for $\theta$, note that $x = 0$ and $y = 1$, using $y = (x + 2)\tan\theta \Rightarrow 1 = 2\tan\theta \Rightarrow \theta = \tan^{-1}\left(\frac{1}{2}\right)$.

35. Extend the vertical line through A to the x-axis and let C be the point of intersection. Then $OC = AQ = x$ and $\tan t = \frac{2}{OC} = \frac{2}{x} \Rightarrow x = \frac{2}{\tan t} = 2\cot t$; $\sin t = \frac{2}{OA} \Rightarrow OA = \frac{2}{\sin t}$; and $(AB)(OA) = (AQ)^2 \Rightarrow AB\left(\frac{2}{\sin t}\right) = x^2$
$\Rightarrow AB\left(\frac{2}{\sin t}\right) = \left(\frac{2}{\tan t}\right)^2 \Rightarrow AB = \frac{2\sin t}{\tan^2 t}$. Next $y = 2 - AB\sin t \Rightarrow y = 2 - \left(\frac{2\sin t}{\tan^2 t}\right)\sin t =$
$2 - \frac{2\sin^2 t}{\tan^2 t} = 2 - 2\cos^2 t = 2\sin^2 t$. Therefore let $x = 2\cot t$ and $y = 2\sin^2 t$, $0 < t < \pi$.

36. Arc PF = Arc AF since each is the distance rolled and

$\frac{\text{Arc PF}}{b} = \angle FCP \Rightarrow \text{Arc PF} = b(\angle FCP); \frac{\text{Arc AF}}{a} = \theta$

$\Rightarrow \text{Arc AF} = a\theta \Rightarrow a\theta = b(\angle FCP) \Rightarrow \angle FCP = \frac{a}{b}\theta;$

$\angle OCG = \frac{\pi}{2} - \theta; \angle OCG = \angle OCP + \angle PCE$

$= \angle OCP + \left(\frac{\pi}{2} - \alpha\right)$. Now $\angle OCP = \pi - \angle FCP$

$= \pi - \frac{a}{b}\theta$. Thus $\angle OCG = \pi - \frac{a}{b}\theta + \frac{\pi}{2} - \alpha \Rightarrow \frac{\pi}{2} - \theta$

$= \pi - \frac{a}{b}\theta + \frac{\pi}{2} - \alpha \Rightarrow \alpha = \pi - \frac{a}{b}\theta + \theta = \pi - \left(\frac{a-b}{b}\theta\right)$.

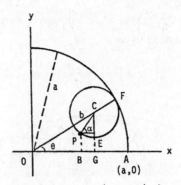

Then $x = OG - BG = OG - PE = (a - b)\cos\theta - b\cos\alpha = (a - b)\cos\theta - b\cos\left(\pi - \frac{a-b}{b}\theta\right)$

$= (a - b)\cos\theta + b\cos\left(\frac{a-b}{b}\theta\right)$. Also $y = EG = CG - CE = (a - b)\sin\theta - b\sin\alpha$

$= (a - b)\sin\theta - b\sin\left(\pi - \frac{a-b}{b}\theta\right) = (a - b)\sin\theta - b\sin\left(\frac{a-b}{b}\theta\right)$. Therefore

$x = (a - b)\cos\theta + b\cos\left(\frac{a-b}{b}\theta\right)$ and $y = (a - b)\sin\theta - b\sin\left(\frac{a-b}{b}\theta\right)$.

If $b = \frac{a}{4}$, then $x = \left(a - \frac{a}{4}\right)\cos\theta + \frac{a}{4}\cos\left(\frac{a - \left(\frac{a}{4}\right)}{\left(\frac{a}{4}\right)}\theta\right)$

$= \frac{3a}{4}\cos\theta + \frac{a}{4}\cos 3\theta = \frac{3a}{4}\cos\theta + \frac{a}{4}(\cos\theta\cos 2\theta - \sin\theta\sin 2\theta)$

$= \frac{3a}{4}\cos\theta + \frac{a}{4}((\cos\theta)(\cos^2\theta - \sin^2\theta) - (\sin\theta)(2\sin\theta\cos\theta))$

$= \frac{3a}{4}\cos\theta + \frac{a}{4}\cos^3\theta - \frac{a}{4}\cos\theta\sin^2\theta - \frac{2a}{4}\sin^2\theta\cos\theta$

$= \frac{3a}{4}\cos\theta + \frac{a}{4}\cos^3\theta - \frac{3a}{4}(\cos\theta)(1 - \cos^2\theta) = a\cos^3\theta;$

$y = \left(a - \frac{a}{4}\right)\sin\theta - \frac{a}{4}\sin\left(\frac{a - \left(\frac{a}{4}\right)}{\left(\frac{a}{4}\right)}\theta\right) = \frac{3a}{4}\sin\theta - \frac{a}{4}\sin 3\theta = \frac{3a}{4}\sin\theta - \frac{a}{4}(\sin\theta\cos 2\theta + \cos\theta\sin 2\theta)$

$= \frac{3a}{4}\sin\theta - \frac{a}{4}((\sin\theta)(\cos^2\theta - \sin^2\theta) + (\cos\theta)(2\sin\theta\cos\theta))$

$= \frac{3a}{4}\sin\theta - \frac{a}{4}\sin\theta\cos^2\theta + \frac{a}{4}\sin^3\theta - \frac{2a}{4}\cos^2\theta\sin\theta$

$= \frac{3a}{4}\sin\theta - \frac{3a}{4}\sin\theta\cos^2\theta + \frac{a}{4}\sin^3\theta$

$= \frac{3a}{4}\sin\theta - \frac{3a}{4}(\sin\theta)(1 - \sin^2\theta) + \frac{a}{4}\sin^3\theta = a\sin^3\theta.$

37. Draw line AM in the figure and note that $\angle AMO$ is a right
angle since it is an inscribed angle which spans the diameter
of a circle. Then $AN^2 = MN^2 + AM^2$. Now, $OA = a$,
$\frac{AN}{a} = \tan t$, and $\frac{AM}{a} = \sin t$. Next $MN = OP$

$\Rightarrow OP^2 = AN^2 - AM^2 = a^2\tan^2 t - a^2\sin^2 t$

$\Rightarrow OP = \sqrt{a^2\tan^2 t - a^2\sin^2 t}$

$= (a\sin t)\sqrt{\sec^2 t - 1} = \frac{a\sin^2 t}{\cos t}$. In triangle BPO,

$x = OP\sin t = \frac{a\sin^3 t}{\cos t} = a\sin^2 t\tan t$ and

$y = OP\cos t = a\sin^2 t \Rightarrow x = a\sin^2 t\tan t$ and $y = a\sin^2 t$.

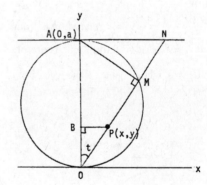

38. Let the x-axis be the line the wheel rolls along with the y-axis through a low point of the trochoid (see the accompanying figure).

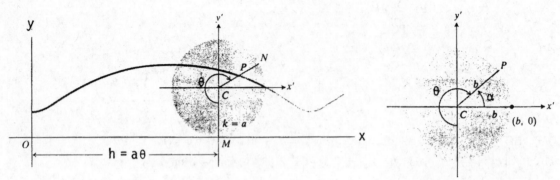

Let $\theta$ denote the angle through which the wheel turns. Then $h = a\theta$ and $k = a$. Next introduce x'y'-axes parallel to the xy-axes and having their origin at the center C of the wheel. Then $x' = b \cos \alpha$ and $y' = b \sin \alpha$, where $\alpha = \frac{3\pi}{2} - \theta$. It follows that $x' = b \cos \left(\frac{3\pi}{2} - \theta\right) = -b \sin \theta$ and $y' = b \sin \left(\frac{3\pi}{2} - \theta\right)$ $= -b \cos \theta \Rightarrow x = h + x' = a\theta - b \sin \theta$ and $y = k + y' = a - b \cos \theta$ are parametric equations of the trochoid.

39. $D = \sqrt{(x-2)^2 + \left(y - \frac{1}{2}\right)^2} \Rightarrow D^2 = (x-2)^2 + \left(y - \frac{1}{2}\right)^2 = (t-2)^2 + \left(t^2 - \frac{1}{2}\right)^2 \Rightarrow D^2 = t^4 - 4t + \frac{17}{4}$

$\Rightarrow \frac{d(D^2)}{dt} = 4t^3 - 4 = 0 \Rightarrow t = 1$. The second derivative is always positive for $t \neq 0 \Rightarrow t = 1$ gives a local minimum for $D^2$ (and hence D) which is an absolute minimum since it is the only extremum $\Rightarrow$ the closest point on the parabola is $(1, 1)$.

40. $D = \sqrt{\left(2 \cos t - \frac{3}{4}\right)^2 + (\sin t - 0)^2} \Rightarrow D^2 = \left(2 \cos t - \frac{3}{4}\right)^2 + \sin^2 t \Rightarrow \frac{d(D^2)}{dt}$

$= 2 \left(2 \cos t - \frac{3}{4}\right)(-2 \sin t) + 2 \sin t \cos t = (-2 \sin t)\left(3 \cos t - \frac{3}{2}\right) = 0 \Rightarrow -2 \sin t = 0$ or $3 \cos t - \frac{3}{2} = 0$

$\Rightarrow t = 0, \pi$ or $t = \frac{\pi}{3}, \frac{5\pi}{3}$. Now $\frac{d^2(D^2)}{dt^2} = -6 \cos^2 t + 3 \cos t + 6 \sin^2 t$ so that $\frac{d^2(D^2)}{dt^2}(0) = -3 \Rightarrow$ relative maximum, $\frac{d^2(D^2)}{dt^2}(\pi) = -9 \Rightarrow$ relative maximum, $\frac{d^2(D^2)}{dt^2}\left(\frac{\pi}{3}\right) = \frac{9}{2} \Rightarrow$ relative minimum, and $\frac{d^2(D^2)}{dt^2}\left(\frac{5\pi}{3}\right) = \frac{9}{2} \Rightarrow$ relative minimum. Therefore both $t = \frac{\pi}{3}$ and $t = \frac{5\pi}{3}$ give points on the ellipse closest to the point $\left(\frac{3}{4}, 0\right) \Rightarrow \left(1, \frac{\sqrt{3}}{2}\right)$ and $\left(1, -\frac{\sqrt{3}}{2}\right)$ are the desired points.

41. (a)                    (b)                    (c)

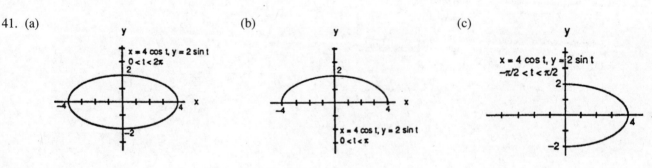

42. (a)                    (b)                    (c)

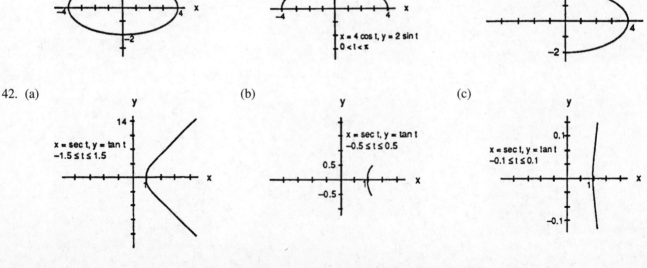

43.

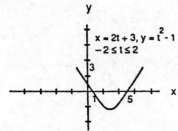

44. (a)

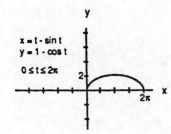

(b)

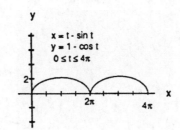

(c)

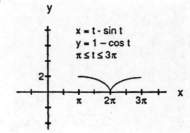

45. (a)

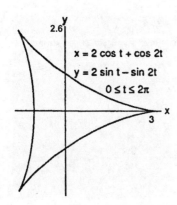

(b)

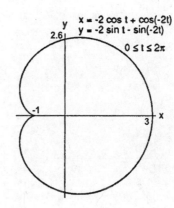

46. (a)

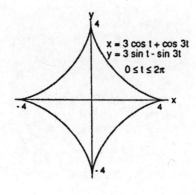

(b)

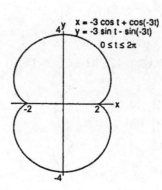

47. (a)

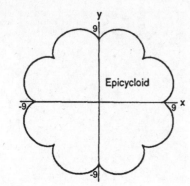

Epicycloid

(b)

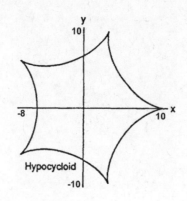

Hypocycloid

(c)

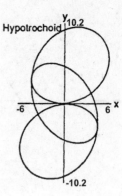

Hypotrochoid

48. (a)

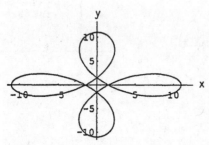

$x = 6 \cos t + 5 \cos 3t, \quad y = 6 \sin t - 5 \sin 3t,$
$0 \le t \le 2\pi$

(b)

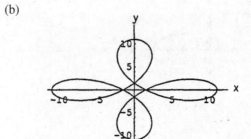

$x = 6 \cos 2t + 5 \cos 6t, \quad y = 6 \sin 2t - 5 \sin 6t,$
$0 \le t \le \pi$

(c)

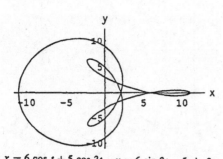

$x = 6 \cos t + 5 \cos 3t, \quad y = 6 \sin 2t - 5 \sin 3t,$
$0 \le t \le 2\pi$

(d)

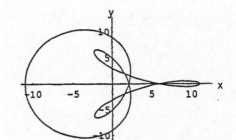

$x = 6 \cos 2t + 5 \cos 6t, \quad y = 6 \sin 4t - 5 \sin 6t,$
$0 \le t \le \pi$

## 11.2 CALCULUS WITH PARAMETRIC CURVES

1. $t = \frac{\pi}{4} \Rightarrow x = 2 \cos \frac{\pi}{4} = \sqrt{2}, y = 2 \sin \frac{\pi}{4} = \sqrt{2}; \frac{dx}{dt} = -2 \sin t, \frac{dy}{dt} = 2 \cos t \Rightarrow \frac{dy}{dx} = \frac{dy/dt}{dx/dt} = \frac{2 \cos t}{-2 \sin t} = -\cot t$

$\Rightarrow \frac{dy}{dx}\Big|_{t=\frac{\pi}{4}} = -\cot \frac{\pi}{4} = -1;$ tangent line is $y - \sqrt{2} = -1\left(x - \sqrt{2}\right)$ or $y = -x + 2\sqrt{2}; \frac{dy'}{dt} = \csc^2 t$

$\Rightarrow \frac{d^2y}{dx^2} = \frac{dy'/dt}{dx/dt} = \frac{\csc^2 t}{-2 \sin t} = -\frac{1}{2 \sin^3 t} \Rightarrow \frac{d^2y}{dx^2}\Big|_{t=\frac{\pi}{4}} = -\sqrt{2}$

2. $t = -\frac{1}{6} \Rightarrow x = \sin\left(2\pi\left(-\frac{1}{6}\right)\right) = \sin\left(-\frac{\pi}{3}\right) = -\frac{\sqrt{3}}{2}, y = \cos\left(2\pi\left(-\frac{1}{6}\right)\right) = \cos\left(-\frac{\pi}{3}\right) = \frac{1}{2}; \frac{dx}{dt} = 2\pi \cos 2\pi t,$

$\frac{dy}{dt} = -2\pi \sin 2\pi t \Rightarrow \frac{dy}{dx} = \frac{-2\pi \sin 2\pi t}{2\pi \cos 2\pi t} = -\tan 2\pi t \Rightarrow \frac{dy}{dx}\Big|_{t=-\frac{1}{6}} = -\tan\left(2\pi\left(-\frac{1}{6}\right)\right) = -\tan\left(-\frac{\pi}{3}\right) = \sqrt{3};$

tangent line is $y - \frac{1}{2} = \sqrt{3}\left[x - \left(-\frac{\sqrt{3}}{2}\right)\right]$ or $y = \sqrt{3}x + 2; \frac{dy'}{dt} = -2\pi \sec^2 2\pi t \Rightarrow \frac{d^2y}{dx^2} = \frac{-2\pi \sec^2 2\pi t}{2\pi \cos 2\pi t}$

$= -\frac{1}{\cos^3 2\pi t} \Rightarrow \frac{d^2y}{dx^2}\Big|_{t=-\frac{1}{6}} = -8$

3.  $t = \frac{\pi}{4} \Rightarrow x = 4 \sin \frac{\pi}{4} = 2\sqrt{2}, y = 2 \cos \frac{\pi}{4} = \sqrt{2}; \frac{dx}{dt} = 4 \cos t, \frac{dy}{dt} = -2 \sin t \Rightarrow \frac{dy}{dx} = \frac{dy/dt}{dx/dt} = \frac{-2 \sin t}{4 \cos t}$

$= -\frac{1}{2} \tan t \Rightarrow \frac{dy}{dx}\Big|_{t=\frac{\pi}{4}} = -\frac{1}{2} \tan \frac{\pi}{4} = -\frac{1}{2}$; tangent line is $y - \sqrt{2} = -\frac{1}{2}\left(x - 2\sqrt{2}\right)$ or $y = -\frac{1}{2}x + 2\sqrt{2}$;

$\frac{dy'}{dt} = -\frac{1}{2} \sec^2 t \Rightarrow \frac{d^2y}{dx^2} = \frac{dy'/dt}{dx/dt} = \frac{-\frac{1}{2} \sec^2 t}{4 \cos t} = -\frac{1}{8 \cos^3 t} \Rightarrow \frac{d^2y}{dx^2}\Big|_{t=\frac{\pi}{4}} = -\frac{\sqrt{2}}{4}$

4.  $t = \frac{2\pi}{3} \Rightarrow x = \cos \frac{2\pi}{3} = -\frac{1}{2}, y = \sqrt{3} \cos \frac{2\pi}{3} = -\frac{\sqrt{3}}{2}; \frac{dx}{dt} = -\sin t, \frac{dy}{dt} = -\sqrt{3} \sin t \Rightarrow \frac{dy}{dx} = \frac{-\sqrt{3} \sin t}{-\sin t} = \sqrt{3}$

$\Rightarrow \frac{dy}{dx}\Big|_{t=\frac{2\pi}{3}} = \sqrt{3}$; tangent line is $y - \left(-\frac{\sqrt{3}}{2}\right) = \sqrt{3}\left[x - \left(-\frac{1}{2}\right)\right]$ or $y = \sqrt{3}x; \frac{dy'}{dt} = 0 \Rightarrow \frac{d^2y}{dx^2} = \frac{0}{-\sin t} = 0$

$\Rightarrow \frac{d^2y}{dx^2}\Big|_{t=\frac{2\pi}{3}} = 0$

5.  $t = \frac{1}{4} \Rightarrow x = \frac{1}{4}, y = \frac{1}{2}; \frac{dx}{dt} = 1, \frac{dy}{dt} = \frac{1}{2\sqrt{t}} \Rightarrow \frac{dy}{dx} = \frac{dy/dt}{dx/dt} = \frac{1}{2\sqrt{t}} \Rightarrow \frac{dy}{dx}\Big|_{t=\frac{1}{4}} = \frac{1}{2\sqrt{\frac{1}{4}}} = 1$; tangent line is

$y - \frac{1}{2} = 1 \cdot \left(x - \frac{1}{4}\right)$ or $y = x + \frac{1}{4}; \frac{dy'}{dt} = -\frac{1}{4} t^{-3/2} \Rightarrow \frac{d^2y}{dx^2} = \frac{dy'/dt}{dx/dt} = -\frac{1}{4} t^{-3/2} \Rightarrow \frac{d^2y}{dx^2}\Big|_{t=\frac{1}{4}} = -2$

6.  $t = -\frac{\pi}{4} \Rightarrow x = \sec^2\left(-\frac{\pi}{4}\right) - 1 = 1, y = \tan\left(-\frac{\pi}{4}\right) = -1; \frac{dx}{dt} = 2 \sec^2 t \tan t, \frac{dy}{dt} = \sec^2 t$

$\Rightarrow \frac{dy}{dx} = \frac{\sec^2 t}{2 \sec^2 t \tan t} = \frac{1}{2 \tan t} = \frac{1}{2} \cot t \Rightarrow \frac{dy}{dx}\Big|_{t=-\frac{\pi}{4}} = \frac{1}{2} \cot\left(-\frac{\pi}{4}\right) = -\frac{1}{2}$; tangent line is

$y - (-1) = -\frac{1}{2}(x - 1)$ or $y = -\frac{1}{2}x - \frac{1}{2}; \frac{dy'}{dt} = -\frac{1}{2} \csc^2 t \Rightarrow \frac{d^2y}{dx^2} = \frac{-\frac{1}{2} \csc^2 t}{2 \sec^2 t \tan t} = -\frac{1}{4} \cot^3 t$

$\Rightarrow \frac{d^2y}{dx^2}\Big|_{t=-\frac{\pi}{4}} = \frac{1}{4}$

7.  $t = \frac{\pi}{6} \Rightarrow x = \sec \frac{\pi}{6} = \frac{2}{\sqrt{3}}, y = \tan \frac{\pi}{6} = \frac{1}{\sqrt{3}}; \frac{dx}{dt} = \sec t \tan t, \frac{dy}{dt} = \sec^2 t \Rightarrow \frac{dy}{dx} = \frac{dy/dt}{dx/dt}$

$= \frac{\sec^2 t}{\sec t \tan t} = \csc t \Rightarrow \frac{dy}{dx}\Big|_{t=\frac{\pi}{6}} = \csc \frac{\pi}{6} = 2$; tangent line is $y - \frac{1}{\sqrt{3}} = 2\left(x - \frac{2}{\sqrt{3}}\right)$ or $y = 2x - \sqrt{3}$;

$\frac{dy'}{dt} = -\csc t \cot t \Rightarrow \frac{d^2y}{dx^2} = \frac{dy'/dt}{dx/dt} = \frac{-\csc t \cot t}{\sec t \tan t} = -\cot^3 t \Rightarrow \frac{d^2y}{dx^2}\Big|_{t=\frac{\pi}{6}} = -3\sqrt{3}$

8.  $t = 3 \Rightarrow x = -\sqrt{3+1} = -2, y = \sqrt{3(3)} = 3; \frac{dx}{dt} = -\frac{1}{2}(t+1)^{-1/2}, \frac{dy}{dt} = \frac{3}{2}(3t)^{-1/2} \Rightarrow \frac{dy}{dx} = \frac{\left(\frac{3}{2}\right)(3t)^{-1/2}}{\left(-\frac{1}{2}\right)(t+1)^{-1/2}}$

$= -\frac{3\sqrt{t+1}}{\sqrt{3t}} = \frac{dy}{dx}\Big|_{t=3} = \frac{-3\sqrt{3+1}}{\sqrt{3(3)}} = -2$; tangent line is $y - 3 = -2[x - (-2)]$ or $y = -2x - 1$;

$\frac{dy'}{dt} = \frac{\sqrt{3t}\left[-\frac{3}{2}(t+1)^{-1/2}\right] + 3\sqrt{t+1}\left[\frac{3}{2}(3t)^{-1/2}\right]}{3t} = \frac{3}{2t\sqrt{3t}\sqrt{t+1}} \Rightarrow \frac{d^2y}{dx^2} = \frac{\left(\frac{3}{2t\sqrt{3t}\sqrt{t+1}}\right)}{\left(\frac{-1}{2\sqrt{t+1}}\right)} = -\frac{3}{t\sqrt{3t}}$

$\Rightarrow \frac{d^2y}{dx^2}\Big|_{t=3} = -\frac{1}{3}$

9.  $t = -1 \Rightarrow x = 5, y = 1; \frac{dx}{dt} = 4t, \frac{dy}{dt} = 4t^3 \Rightarrow \frac{dy}{dx} = \frac{dy/dt}{dx/dt} = \frac{4t^3}{4t} = t^2 \Rightarrow \frac{dy}{dx}\Big|_{t=-1} = (-1)^2 = 1$; tangent line is

$y - 1 = 1 \cdot (x - 5)$ or $y = x - 4; \frac{dy'}{dt} = 2t \Rightarrow \frac{d^2y}{dx^2} = \frac{dy'/dt}{dx/dt} = \frac{2t}{4t} = \frac{1}{2} \Rightarrow \frac{d^2y}{dx^2}\Big|_{t=-1} = \frac{1}{2}$

10. $t = 1 \Rightarrow x = 1, y = -2; \frac{dx}{dt} = -\frac{1}{t^2}, \frac{dy}{dt} = \frac{1}{t} \Rightarrow \frac{dy}{dx} = \frac{\left(\frac{1}{t}\right)}{\left(-\frac{1}{t^2}\right)} = -t \Rightarrow \frac{dy}{dx}\Big|_{t=1} = -1$; tangent line is

$y - (-2) = -1(x - 1)$ or $y = -x - 1; \frac{dy'}{dt} = -1 \Rightarrow \frac{d^2y}{dx^2} = \frac{-1}{\left(-\frac{1}{t^2}\right)} = t^2 \Rightarrow \frac{d^2y}{dx^2}\Big|_{t=1} = 1$

11. $t = \frac{\pi}{3} \Rightarrow x = \frac{\pi}{3} - \sin \frac{\pi}{3} = \frac{\pi}{3} - \frac{\sqrt{3}}{2}, y = 1 - \cos \frac{\pi}{3} = 1 - \frac{1}{2} = \frac{1}{2}; \frac{dx}{dt} = 1 - \cos t, \frac{dy}{dt} = \sin t \Rightarrow \frac{dy}{dx} = \frac{dy/dt}{dx/dt}$

$= \frac{\sin t}{1 - \cos t} \Rightarrow \frac{dy}{dx}\Big|_{t=\frac{\pi}{3}} = \frac{\sin\left(\frac{\pi}{3}\right)}{1 - \cos\left(\frac{\pi}{3}\right)} = \frac{\left(\frac{\sqrt{3}}{2}\right)}{\left(\frac{1}{2}\right)} = \sqrt{3}$; tangent line is $y - \frac{1}{2} = \sqrt{3}\left(x - \frac{\pi}{3} + \frac{\sqrt{3}}{2}\right)$

$\Rightarrow y = \sqrt{3}x - \frac{\pi\sqrt{3}}{3} + 2$; $\frac{dy'}{dt} = \frac{(1-\cos t)(\cos t) - (\sin t)(\sin t)}{(1-\cos t)^2} = \frac{-1}{1-\cos t}$ $\Rightarrow \frac{d^2y}{dx^2} = \frac{dy'/dt}{dx/dt} = \frac{\left(\frac{-1}{1-\cos t}\right)}{1-\cos t}$

$= \frac{-1}{(1-\cos t)^2} \Rightarrow \frac{d^2y}{dx^2}\Big|_{t=\frac{\pi}{3}} = -4$

12. $t = \frac{\pi}{2} \Rightarrow x = \cos\frac{\pi}{2} = 0$, $y = 1 + \sin\frac{\pi}{2} = 2$; $\frac{dx}{dt} = -\sin t$, $\frac{dy}{dt} = \cos t \Rightarrow \frac{dy}{dx} = \frac{\cos t}{-\sin t} = -\cot t$

$\Rightarrow \frac{dy}{dx}\Big|_{t=\frac{\pi}{2}} = -\cot\frac{\pi}{2} = 0$; tangent line is $y = 2$; $\frac{dy'}{dt} = \csc^2 t \Rightarrow \frac{d^2y}{dx^2} = \frac{\csc^2 t}{-\sin t} = -\csc^3 t \Rightarrow \frac{d^2y}{dx^2}\Big|_{t=\frac{\pi}{2}} = -1$

13. $t = 2 \Rightarrow x = \frac{1}{2+1} = \frac{1}{3}$, $y = \frac{2}{2-1} = 2$; $\frac{dx}{dt} = \frac{-1}{(t+1)^2}$, $\frac{dy}{dt} = \frac{-1}{(t-1)^2} \Rightarrow \frac{dy}{dx} = \frac{(t+1)^2}{(t-1)^2} \Rightarrow \frac{dy}{dx}\Big|_{t=2} = \frac{(2+1)^2}{(2-1)^2} = 9$;

tangent line is $y = 9x - 1$; $\frac{dy'}{dt} = -\frac{4(t+1)}{(t-1)^3} \Rightarrow \frac{d^2y}{dx^2} = \frac{4(t+1)^3}{(t-1)^3} \Rightarrow \frac{d^2y}{dx^2}\Big|_{t=2} = \frac{4(2+1)^3}{(2-1)^3} = 108$

14. $t = 0 \Rightarrow x = 0 + e^0 = 1$, $y = 1 - e^0 = 0$; $\frac{dx}{dt} = 1 + e^t$, $\frac{dy}{dt} = -e^t \Rightarrow \frac{dy}{dx} = \frac{-e^t}{1+e^t} \Rightarrow \frac{dy}{dx}\Big|_{t=0} = \frac{-e^0}{1+e^0} = -\frac{1}{2}$;

tangent line is $y = -\frac{1}{2}x + \frac{1}{2}$; $\frac{dy'}{dt} = \frac{-e^t}{(1+e^t)^2} \Rightarrow \frac{d^2y}{dx^2} = \frac{-e^t}{(1+e^t)^3} \Rightarrow \frac{d^2y}{dx^2}\Big|_{t=0} = \frac{-e^0}{(1+e^0)^3} = -\frac{1}{8}$

15. $x^3 + 2t^2 = 9 \Rightarrow 3x^2\frac{dx}{dt} + 4t = 0 \Rightarrow 3x^2\frac{dx}{dt} = -4t \Rightarrow \frac{dx}{dt} = \frac{-4t}{3x^2}$;

$2y^3 - 3t^2 = 4 \Rightarrow 6y^2\frac{dy}{dt} - 6t = 0 \Rightarrow \frac{dy}{dt} = \frac{6t}{6y^2} = \frac{t}{y^2}$; thus $\frac{dy}{dx} = \frac{dy/dt}{dx/dt} = \frac{\left(\frac{t}{y^2}\right)}{\left(\frac{-4t}{3x^2}\right)} = \frac{t(3x^2)}{y^2(-4t)} = \frac{3x^2}{-4y^2}$; $t = 2$

$\Rightarrow x^3 + 2(2)^2 = 9 \Rightarrow x^3 + 8 = 9 \Rightarrow x^3 = 1 \Rightarrow x = 1$; $t = 2 \Rightarrow 2y^3 - 3(2)^2 = 4$

$\Rightarrow 2y^3 = 16 \Rightarrow y^3 = 8 \Rightarrow y = 2$; therefore $\frac{dy}{dx}\Big|_{t=2} = \frac{3(1)^2}{-4(2)^2} = -\frac{3}{16}$

16. $x = \sqrt{5 - \sqrt{t}} \Rightarrow \frac{dx}{dt} = \frac{1}{2}\left(5 - \sqrt{t}\right)^{-1/2}\left(-\frac{1}{2}t^{-1/2}\right) = -\frac{1}{4\sqrt{t}\sqrt{5-\sqrt{t}}}$; $y(t-1) = \sqrt{t} \Rightarrow y + (t-1)\frac{dy}{dt} = \frac{1}{2}t^{-1/2}$

$\Rightarrow (t-1)\frac{dy}{dt} = \frac{1}{2\sqrt{t}} - y \Rightarrow \frac{dy}{dt} = \frac{\frac{1}{2\sqrt{t}} - y}{(t-1)} = \frac{1 - 2y\sqrt{t}}{2t\sqrt{t} - 2\sqrt{t}}$; thus $\frac{dy}{dx} = \frac{\frac{dy}{dt}}{\frac{dx}{dt}} = \frac{\frac{1-2y\sqrt{t}}{2t\sqrt{t}-2\sqrt{t}}}{\frac{-1}{4\sqrt{t}\sqrt{5-\sqrt{t}}}} = \frac{1-2y\sqrt{t}}{2\sqrt{t}(t-1)} \cdot \frac{4\sqrt{t}\sqrt{5-\sqrt{t}}}{-1}$

$= \frac{2(1-2y\sqrt{t})\sqrt{5-\sqrt{t}}}{1-t}$; $t = 4 \Rightarrow x = \sqrt{5-\sqrt{4}} = \sqrt{3}$; $t = 4 \Rightarrow y \cdot 3 = \sqrt{4} \Rightarrow y = \frac{2}{3}$

therefore, $\frac{dy}{dx}\Big|_{t=4} = \frac{2\left(1-2\left(\frac{2}{3}\right)\sqrt{4}\right)\sqrt{5-\sqrt{4}}}{1-4} = \frac{10\sqrt{3}}{9}$

17. $x + 2x^{3/2} = t^2 + t \Rightarrow \frac{dx}{dt} + 3x^{1/2}\frac{dx}{dt} = 2t + 1 \Rightarrow \left(1 + 3x^{1/2}\right)\frac{dx}{dt} = 2t + 1 \Rightarrow \frac{dx}{dt} = \frac{2t+1}{1+3x^{1/2}}$; $y\sqrt{t+1} + 2t\sqrt{y} = 4$

$\Rightarrow \frac{dy}{dt}\sqrt{t+1} + y\left(\frac{1}{2}\right)(t+1)^{-1/2} + 2\sqrt{y} + 2t\left(\frac{1}{2}y^{-1/2}\right)\frac{dy}{dt} = 0 \Rightarrow \frac{dy}{dt}\sqrt{t+1} + \frac{y}{2\sqrt{t+1}} + 2\sqrt{y} + \left(\frac{t}{\sqrt{y}}\right)\frac{dy}{dt} = 0$

$\Rightarrow \left(\sqrt{t+1} + \frac{t}{\sqrt{y}}\right)\frac{dy}{dt} = \frac{-y}{2\sqrt{t+1}} - 2\sqrt{y} \Rightarrow \frac{dy}{dt} = \frac{\left(\frac{-y}{2\sqrt{t+1}} - 2\sqrt{y}\right)}{\left(\sqrt{t+1} + \frac{t}{\sqrt{y}}\right)} = \frac{-y\sqrt{y} - 4y\sqrt{t+1}}{2\sqrt{y}(t+1) + 2t\sqrt{t+1}}$; thus

$\frac{dy}{dx} = \frac{dy/dt}{dx/dt} = \frac{\left(\frac{-y\sqrt{y} - 4y\sqrt{t+1}}{2\sqrt{y}(t+1) + 2t\sqrt{t+1}}\right)}{\left(\frac{2t+1}{1+3x^{1/2}}\right)}$; $t = 0 \Rightarrow x + 2x^{3/2} = 0 \Rightarrow x\left(1 + 2x^{1/2}\right) = 0 \Rightarrow x = 0$; $t = 0$

$\Rightarrow y\sqrt{0+1} + 2(0)\sqrt{y} = 4 \Rightarrow y = 4$; therefore $\frac{dy}{dx}\Big|_{t=0} = \frac{\left(\frac{-4\sqrt{4} - 4(4)\sqrt{0+1}}{2\sqrt{4}(0+1) + 2(0)\sqrt{0+1}}\right)}{\left(\frac{2(0)+1}{1+3(0)^{1/2}}\right)} = -6$

18. $x\sin t + 2x = t \Rightarrow \frac{dx}{dt}\sin t + x\cos t + 2\frac{dx}{dt} = 1 \Rightarrow (\sin t + 2)\frac{dx}{dt} = 1 - x\cos t \Rightarrow \frac{dx}{dt} = \frac{1 - x\cos t}{\sin t + 2}$;

$t\sin t - 2t = y \Rightarrow \sin t + t\cos t - 2 = \frac{dy}{dt}$; thus $\frac{dy}{dx} = \frac{\sin t + t\cos t - 2}{\left(\frac{1-x\cos t}{\sin t+2}\right)}$; $t = \pi \Rightarrow x\sin\pi + 2x = \pi$

$\Rightarrow x = \frac{\pi}{2}$; therefore $\frac{dy}{dx}\Big|_{t=\pi} = \frac{\sin\pi + \pi\cos\pi - 2}{\left[\frac{1 - \left(\frac{\pi}{2}\right)\cos\pi}{\sin\pi + 2}\right]} = \frac{-4\pi - 8}{2 + \pi} = -4$

19. $x = t^3 + t, \ y + 2t^3 = 2x + t^2 \Rightarrow \frac{dx}{dt} = 3t^2 + 1, \ \frac{dy}{dt} + 6t^2 = 2\frac{dx}{dt} + 2t \Rightarrow \frac{dy}{dt} = 2(3t^2 + 1) + 2t - 6t^2 = 2t + 2$

$\Rightarrow \frac{dy}{dx} = \frac{2t+2}{3t^2+1} \Rightarrow \left.\frac{dy}{dx}\right|_{t=1} = \frac{2(1)+2}{3(1)^2+1} = 1$

20. $t = \ln(x - t), \ y = te^t \Rightarrow 1 = \frac{1}{x-t}\left(\frac{dx}{dt} - 1\right) \Rightarrow x - t = \frac{dx}{dt} - 1 \Rightarrow \frac{dx}{dt} = x - t + 1, \ \frac{dy}{dt} = te^t + e^t;$

$\Rightarrow \frac{dy}{dx} = \frac{te^t + e^t}{x - t + 1}; \ t = 0 \Rightarrow 0 = \ln(x - 0) \Rightarrow x = 1 \Rightarrow \left.\frac{dy}{dx}\right|_{t=0} = \frac{(0)e^0 + e^0}{1 - 0 + 1} = \frac{1}{2}$

21. $A = \int_0^{2\pi} y \, dx = \int_0^{2\pi} a(1 - \cos t)a(1 - \cos t)dt = a^2 \int_0^{2\pi} (1 - \cos t)^2 dt = a^2 \int_0^{2\pi} (1 - 2\cos t + \cos^2 t)dt$

$= a^2 \int_0^{2\pi} \left(1 - 2\cos t + \frac{1 + \cos 2t}{2}\right)dt = a^2 \int_0^{2\pi} \left(\frac{3}{2} - 2\cos t + \frac{1}{2}\cos 2t\right)dt = a^2 \left[\frac{3}{2}t - 2\sin t + \frac{1}{4}\sin 2t\right]_0^{2\pi}$

$= a^2(3\pi - 0 + 0) - 0 = 3\pi a^2$

22. $A = \int_0^1 x \, dy = \int_0^1 (t - t^2)(-e^{-t})dt \quad \left[u = t - t^2 \Rightarrow du = (1 - 2t)dt; \ dv = (-e^{-t})dt \Rightarrow v = e^{-t}\right]$

$= e^{-t}(t - t^2)\Big|_0^1 - \int_0^1 e^{-t}(1 - 2t)dt \quad \left[u = 1 - 2t \Rightarrow du = -2dt; \ dv = e^{-t}dt \Rightarrow v = -e^{-t}\right]$

$= e^{-t}(t - t^2)\Big|_0^1 - \left[-e^{-t}(1 - 2t)\Big|_0^1 - \int_0^1 2e^{-t}dt\right] = \left[e^{-t}(t - t^2) + e^{-t}(1 - 2t) - 2e^{-t}\right]\Big|_0^1$

$= (e^{-1}(0) + e^{-1}(-1) - 2e^{-1}) - (e^0(0) + e^0(1) - 2e^0) = 1 - 3e^{-1} = 1 - \frac{3}{e}$

23. $A = 2\int_\pi^0 y \, dx = 2\int_\pi^0 (b\sin t)(-a\sin t)dt = 2ab \int_0^\pi \sin^2 t \, dt = 2ab \int_0^\pi \frac{1 - \cos 2t}{2} \, dt = ab \int_0^\pi (1 - \cos 2t) \, dt$

$= ab\left[t - \frac{1}{2}\sin 2t\right]_0^\pi = ab((\pi - 0) - 0) = \pi ab$

24. (a) $x = t^2, \ y = t^6, \ 0 \le t \le 1 \Rightarrow A = \int_0^1 y \, dx = \int_0^1 (t^6)2t \, dt = \int_0^1 2t^7 \, dt = \left[\frac{1}{4}t^8\right]_0^1 = \frac{1}{4} - 0 = \frac{1}{4}$

(b) $x = t^3, \ y = t^9, \ 0 \le t \le 1 \Rightarrow A = \int_0^1 y \, dx = \int_0^1 (t^9)3t^2 \, dt = \int_0^1 3t^{11} \, dt = \left[\frac{1}{4}t^{12}\right]_0^1 = \frac{1}{4} - 0 = \frac{1}{4}$

25. $\frac{dx}{dt} = -\sin t$ and $\frac{dy}{dt} = 1 + \cos t \Rightarrow \sqrt{\left(\frac{dx}{dt}\right)^2 + \left(\frac{dy}{dt}\right)^2} = \sqrt{(-\sin t)^2 + (1 + \cos t)^2} = \sqrt{2 + 2\cos t}$

$\Rightarrow \text{Length} = \int_0^\pi \sqrt{2 + 2\cos t} \, dt = \sqrt{2}\int_0^\pi \sqrt{\left(\frac{1 - \cos t}{1 - \cos t}\right)(1 + \cos t)} \, dt = \sqrt{2}\int_0^\pi \sqrt{\frac{\sin^2 t}{1 - \cos t}} \, dt$

$= \sqrt{2}\int_0^\pi \frac{\sin t}{\sqrt{1 - \cos t}} \, dt \ (\text{since } \sin t \ge 0 \text{ on } [0, \pi]); \ [u = 1 - \cos t \Rightarrow du = \sin t \, dt; \ t = 0 \Rightarrow u = 0,$

$t = \pi \Rightarrow u = 2] \to \sqrt{2}\int_0^2 u^{-1/2} \, du = \sqrt{2}\left[2u^{1/2}\right]_0^2 = 4$

26. $\frac{dx}{dt} = 3t^2$ and $\frac{dy}{dt} = 3t \Rightarrow \sqrt{\left(\frac{dx}{dt}\right)^2 + \left(\frac{dy}{dt}\right)^2} = \sqrt{(3t^2)^2 + (3t)^2} = \sqrt{9t^4 + 9t^2} = 3t\sqrt{t^2 + 1} \ \left(\text{since } t \ge 0 \text{ on } \left[0, \sqrt{3}\right]\right)$

$\Rightarrow \text{Length} = \int_0^{\sqrt{3}} 3t\sqrt{t^2 + 1} \, dt; \ \left[u = t^2 + 1 \Rightarrow \frac{3}{2}du = 3t \, dt; \ t = 0 \Rightarrow u = 1, t = \sqrt{3} \Rightarrow u = 4\right]$

$\to \int_1^4 \frac{3}{2}u^{1/2} \, du = \left[u^{3/2}\right]_1^4 = (8 - 1) = 7$

27. $\frac{dx}{dt} = t$ and $\frac{dy}{dt} = (2t + 1)^{1/2} \Rightarrow \sqrt{\left(\frac{dx}{dt}\right)^2 + \left(\frac{dy}{dt}\right)^2} = \sqrt{t^2 + (2t + 1)} = \sqrt{(t + 1)^2} = |t + 1| = t + 1 \text{ since } 0 \le t \le 4$

$\Rightarrow \text{Length} = \int_0^4 (t + 1) \, dt = \left[\frac{t^2}{2} + t\right]_0^4 = (8 + 4) = 12$

28. $\frac{dx}{dt} = (2t+3)^{1/2}$ and $\frac{dy}{dt} = 1+t \Rightarrow \sqrt{\left(\frac{dx}{dt}\right)^2 + \left(\frac{dy}{dt}\right)^2} = \sqrt{(2t+3) + (1+t)^2} = \sqrt{t^2 + 4t + 4} = |t+2| = t+2$

since $0 \le t \le 3 \Rightarrow$ Length $= \int_0^3 (t+2)\,dt = \left[\frac{t^2}{2} + 2t\right]_0^3 = \frac{21}{2}$

29. $\frac{dx}{dt} = 8t\cos t$ and $\frac{dy}{dt} = 8t\sin t \Rightarrow \sqrt{\left(\frac{dx}{dt}\right)^2 + \left(\frac{dy}{dt}\right)^2} = \sqrt{(8t\cos t)^2 + (8t\sin t)^2} = \sqrt{64t^2\cos^2 t + 64t^2\sin^2 t}$

$= |8t| = 8t$ since $0 \le t \le \frac{\pi}{2} \Rightarrow$ Length $= \int_0^{\pi/2} 8t\,dt = [4t^2]_0^{\pi/2} = \pi^2$

30. $\frac{dx}{dt} = \left(\frac{1}{\sec t + \tan t}\right)(\sec t \tan t + \sec^2 t) - \cos t = \sec t - \cos t$ and $\frac{dy}{dt} = -\sin t \Rightarrow \sqrt{\left(\frac{dx}{dt}\right)^2 + \left(\frac{dy}{dt}\right)^2}$

$= \sqrt{(\sec t - \cos t)^2 + (-\sin t)^2} = \sqrt{\sec^2 t - 1} = \sqrt{\tan^2 t} = |\tan t| = \tan t$ since $0 \le t \le \frac{\pi}{3}$

$\Rightarrow$ Length $= \int_0^{\pi/3} \tan t\,dt = \int_0^{\pi/3} \frac{\sin t}{\cos t}\,dt = [-\ln|\cos t|]_0^{\pi/3} = -\ln\frac{1}{2} + \ln 1 = \ln 2$

31. $\frac{dx}{dt} = -\sin t$ and $\frac{dy}{dt} = \cos t \Rightarrow \sqrt{\left(\frac{dx}{dt}\right)^2 + \left(\frac{dy}{dt}\right)^2} = \sqrt{(-\sin t)^2 + (\cos t)^2} = 1 \Rightarrow$ Area $= \int 2\pi y\,ds$

$= \int_0^{2\pi} 2\pi(2 + \sin t)(1)dt = 2\pi[2t - \cos t]_0^{2\pi} = 2\pi[(4\pi - 1) - (0 - 1)] = 8\pi^2$

32. $\frac{dx}{dt} = t^{1/2}$ and $\frac{dy}{dt} = t^{-1/2} \Rightarrow \sqrt{\left(\frac{dx}{dt}\right)^2 + \left(\frac{dy}{dt}\right)^2} = \sqrt{t + t^{-1}} = \sqrt{\frac{t^2+1}{t}} \Rightarrow$ Area $= \int 2\pi x\,ds$

$= \int_0^{\sqrt{3}} 2\pi\left(\frac{2}{3}t^{3/2}\right)\sqrt{\frac{t^2+1}{t}}\,dt = \frac{4\pi}{3}\int_0^{\sqrt{3}} t\sqrt{t^2+1}\,dt;\ [u = t^2 + 1 \Rightarrow du = 2t\,dt;\ t = 0 \Rightarrow u = 1,$

$\left[t = \sqrt{3} \Rightarrow u = 4\right] \rightarrow \int_1^4 \frac{2\pi}{3}\sqrt{u}\,du = \left[\frac{4\pi}{9}u^{3/2}\right]_1^4 = \frac{28\pi}{9}$

Note: $\int_0^{\sqrt{3}} 2\pi\left(\frac{2}{3}t^{3/2}\right)\sqrt{\frac{t^2+1}{t}}\,dt$ is an improper integral but $\lim_{t \to 0^+} f(t)$ exists and is equal to 0, where

$f(t) = 2\pi\left(\frac{2}{3}t^{3/2}\right)\sqrt{\frac{t^2+1}{t}}$. Thus the discontinuity is removable: define $F(t) = f(t)$ for $t > 0$ and $F(0) = 0$

$\Rightarrow \int_0^{\sqrt{3}} F(t)\,dt = \frac{28\pi}{9}$.

33. $\frac{dx}{dt} = 1$ and $\frac{dy}{dt} = t + \sqrt{2} \Rightarrow \sqrt{\left(\frac{dx}{dt}\right)^2 + \left(\frac{dy}{dt}\right)^2} = \sqrt{1^2 + \left(t + \sqrt{2}\right)^2} = \sqrt{t^2 + 2\sqrt{2}t + 3} \Rightarrow$ Area $= \int 2\pi x\,ds$

$= \int_{-\sqrt{2}}^{\sqrt{2}} 2\pi\left(t + \sqrt{2}\right)\sqrt{t^2 + 2\sqrt{2}t + 3}\,dt;\ \left[u = t^2 + 2\sqrt{2}t + 3 \Rightarrow du = \left(2t + 2\sqrt{2}\right)dt;\ t = -\sqrt{2} \Rightarrow u = 1,\right.$

$\left[t = \sqrt{2} \Rightarrow u = 9\right] \rightarrow \int_1^9 \pi\sqrt{u}\,du = \left[\frac{2}{3}\pi u^{3/2}\right]_1^9 = \frac{2\pi}{3}(27 - 1) = \frac{52\pi}{3}$

34. From Exercise 30, $\sqrt{\left(\frac{dx}{dt}\right)^2 + \left(\frac{dy}{dt}\right)^2} = \tan t \Rightarrow$ Area $= \int 2\pi y\,ds = \int_0^{\pi/3} 2\pi\cos t\tan t\,dt = 2\pi\int_0^{\pi/3} \sin t\,dt$

$= 2\pi[-\cos t]_0^{\pi/3} = 2\pi\left[-\frac{1}{2} - (-1)\right] = \pi$

35. $\frac{dx}{dt} = 2$ and $\frac{dy}{dt} = 1 \Rightarrow \sqrt{\left(\frac{dx}{dt}\right)^2 + \left(\frac{dy}{dt}\right)^2} = \sqrt{2^2 + 1^2} = \sqrt{5} \Rightarrow$ Area $= \int 2\pi y\,ds = \int_0^1 2\pi(t+1)\sqrt{5}\,dt$

$= 2\pi\sqrt{5}\left[\frac{t^2}{2} + t\right]_0^1 = 3\pi\sqrt{5}$. Check: slant height is $\sqrt{5} \Rightarrow$ Area is $\pi(1+2)\sqrt{5} = 3\pi\sqrt{5}$.

36. $\frac{dx}{dt} = h$ and $\frac{dy}{dt} = r \Rightarrow \sqrt{\left(\frac{dx}{dt}\right)^2 + \left(\frac{dy}{dt}\right)^2} = \sqrt{h^2 + r^2} \Rightarrow$ Area $= \int 2\pi y\, ds = \int_0^1 2\pi rt\sqrt{h^2 + r^2}\, dt$

$= 2\pi r\sqrt{h^2 + r^2} \int_0^1 t\, dt = 2\pi r\sqrt{h^2 + r^2} \left[\frac{t^2}{2}\right]_0^1 = \pi r\sqrt{h^2 + r^2}$. Check: slant height is $\sqrt{h^2 + r^2} \Rightarrow$ Area is

$\pi r\sqrt{h^2 + r^2}$.

37. Let the density be $\delta = 1$. Then $x = \cos t + t\sin t \Rightarrow \frac{dx}{dt} = t\cos t$, and $y = \sin t - t\cos t \Rightarrow \frac{dy}{dt} = t\sin t$

$\Rightarrow dm = 1 \cdot ds = \sqrt{\left(\frac{dx}{dt}\right)^2 + \left(\frac{dy}{dt}\right)^2}\, dt = \sqrt{(t\cos t)^2 + (t\sin t)^2} = |t|\, dt = t\, dt$ since $0 \le t \le \frac{\pi}{2}$. The curve's mass is

$M = \int dm = \int_0^{\pi/2} t\, dt = \frac{\pi^2}{8}$. Also $M_x = \int \tilde{y}\, dm = \int_0^{\pi/2} (\sin t - t\cos t)\, t\, dt = \int_0^{\pi/2} t\sin t\, dt - \int_0^{\pi/2} t^2\cos t\, dt$

$= [\sin t - t\cos t]_0^{\pi/2} - [t^2\sin t - 2\sin t + 2t\cos t]_0^{\pi/2} = 3 - \frac{\pi^2}{4}$, where we integrated by parts. Therefore,

$\bar{y} = \frac{M_x}{M} = \frac{\left(3 - \frac{\pi^2}{4}\right)}{\left(\frac{\pi^2}{8}\right)} = \frac{24}{\pi^2} - 2$. Next, $M_y = \int \tilde{x}\, dm = \int_0^{\pi/2} (\cos t + t\sin t)\, t\, dt = \int_0^{\pi/2} t\cos t\, dt + \int_0^{\pi/2} t^2\sin t\, dt$

$= [\cos t + t\sin t]_0^{\pi/2} + [-t^2\cos t + 2\cos t + 2t\sin t]_0^{\pi/2} = \frac{3\pi}{2} - 3$, again integrating by parts. Hence

$\bar{x} = \frac{M_y}{M} = \frac{\left(\frac{3\pi}{2} - 3\right)}{\left(\frac{\pi^2}{8}\right)} = \frac{12}{\pi} - \frac{24}{\pi^2}$. Therefore $(\bar{x}, \bar{y}) = \left(\frac{12}{\pi} - \frac{24}{\pi^2}, \frac{24}{\pi^2} - 2\right)$.

38. Let the density be $\delta = 1$. Then $x = e^t\cos t \Rightarrow \frac{dx}{dt} = e^t\cos t - e^t\sin t$, and $y = e^t\sin t \Rightarrow \frac{dy}{dt} = e^t\sin t + e^t\cos t$

$\Rightarrow dm = 1 \cdot ds = \sqrt{\left(\frac{dx}{dt}\right)^2 + \left(\frac{dy}{dt}\right)^2}\, dt = \sqrt{(e^t\cos t - e^t\sin t)^2 + (e^t\sin t + e^t\cos t)^2}\, dt = \sqrt{2e^{2t}}\, dt = \sqrt{2}\, e^t\, dt$.

The curve's mass is $M = \int dm = \int_0^\pi \sqrt{2}\, e^t\, dt = \sqrt{2}\, e^\pi - \sqrt{2}$. Also $M_x = \int \tilde{y}\, dm = \int_0^\pi (e^t\sin t)\left(\sqrt{2}\, e^t\right)\, dt$

$= \int_0^\pi \sqrt{2}\, e^{2t}\sin t\, dt = \sqrt{2}\left[\frac{e^{2t}}{5}(2\sin t - \cos t)\right]_0^\pi = \sqrt{2}\left(\frac{e^{2\pi}}{5} + \frac{1}{5}\right) \Rightarrow \bar{y} = \frac{M_x}{M} = \frac{\sqrt{2}\left(\frac{e^{2\pi}}{5} + \frac{1}{5}\right)}{\sqrt{2}\, e^\pi - \sqrt{2}} = \frac{e^{2\pi} + 1}{5(e^\pi - 1)}$.

Next $M_y = \int \tilde{x}\, dm = \int_0^\pi (e^t\cos t)\left(\sqrt{2}\, e^t\right)\, dt = \int_0^\pi \sqrt{2}\, e^{2t}\cos t\, dt = \sqrt{2}\left[\frac{e^{2t}}{5}(2\cos t + \sin t)\right]_0^\pi = -\sqrt{2}\left(\frac{2e^{2\pi}}{5} + \frac{2}{5}\right)$

$\Rightarrow \bar{x} = \frac{M_y}{M} = \frac{-\sqrt{2}\left(\frac{2e^{2\pi}}{5} + \frac{2}{5}\right)}{\sqrt{2}\, e^\pi - \sqrt{2}} = -\frac{2e^{2\pi} + 2}{5(e^\pi - 1)}$. Therefore $(\bar{x}, \bar{y}) = \left(-\frac{2e^{2\pi} + 2}{5(e^\pi - 1)}, \frac{e^{2\pi} + 1}{5(e^\pi - 1)}\right)$.

39. Let the density be $\delta = 1$. Then $x = \cos t \Rightarrow \frac{dx}{dt} = -\sin t$, and $y = t + \sin t \Rightarrow \frac{dy}{dt} = 1 + \cos t$

$\Rightarrow dm = 1 \cdot ds = \sqrt{\left(\frac{dx}{dt}\right)^2 + \left(\frac{dy}{dt}\right)^2}\, dt = \sqrt{(-\sin t)^2 + (1 + \cos t)^2}\, dt = \sqrt{2 + 2\cos t}\, dt$. The curve's mass

is $M = \int dm = \int_0^\pi \sqrt{2 + 2\cos t}\, dt = \sqrt{2}\int_0^\pi \sqrt{1 + \cos t}\, dt = \sqrt{2}\int_0^\pi \sqrt{2\cos^2\left(\frac{t}{2}\right)}\, dt = 2\int_0^\pi \left|\cos\left(\frac{t}{2}\right)\right|\, dt$

$= 2\int_0^\pi \cos\left(\frac{t}{2}\right)\, dt \left(\text{since } 0 \le t \le \pi \Rightarrow 0 \le \frac{t}{2} \le \frac{\pi}{2}\right) = 2\left[2\sin\left(\frac{t}{2}\right)\right]_0^\pi = 4$. Also $M_x = \int \tilde{y}\, dm$

$= \int_0^\pi (t + \sin t)\left(2\cos\frac{t}{2}\right)\, dt = \int_0^\pi 2t\cos\left(\frac{t}{2}\right)\, dt + \int_0^\pi 2\sin t\cos\left(\frac{t}{2}\right)\, dt$

$= 2\left[4\cos\left(\frac{t}{2}\right) + 2t\sin\left(\frac{t}{2}\right)\right]_0^\pi + 2\left[-\frac{1}{3}\cos\left(\frac{3}{2}t\right) - \cos\left(\frac{1}{2}t\right)\right]_0^\pi = 4\pi - \frac{16}{3} \Rightarrow \bar{y} = \frac{M_x}{M} = \frac{\left(4\pi - \frac{16}{3}\right)}{4} = \pi - \frac{4}{3}$.

Next $M_y = \int \tilde{x}\, dm = \int_0^\pi (\cos t)\left(2\cos\frac{t}{2}\right)\, dt = \int_0^\pi \cos t\cos\left(\frac{t}{2}\right)\, dt = 2\left[\sin\left(\frac{t}{2}\right) + \frac{\sin\left(\frac{3}{2}t\right)}{3}\right]_0^\pi = 2 - \frac{2}{3}$

$= \frac{4}{3} \Rightarrow \bar{x} = \frac{M_y}{M} = \frac{\left(\frac{4}{3}\right)}{4} = \frac{1}{3}$. Therefore $(\bar{x}, \bar{y}) = \left(\frac{1}{3}, \pi - \frac{4}{3}\right)$.

40. Let the density be $\delta = 1$. Then $x = t^3 \Rightarrow \frac{dx}{dt} = 3t^2$, and $y = \frac{3t^2}{2} \Rightarrow \frac{dy}{dt} = 3t \Rightarrow dm = 1 \cdot ds$

$= \sqrt{\left(\frac{dx}{dt}\right)^2 + \left(\frac{dy}{dt}\right)^2}\, dt = \sqrt{(3t^2)^2 + (3t)^2}\, dt = 3|t|\sqrt{t^2 + 1}\, dt = 3t\sqrt{t^2 + 1}\, dt$ since $0 \le t \le \sqrt{3}$. The curve's mass

is $M = \int dm = \int_0^{\sqrt{3}} 3t\sqrt{t^2 + 1}\, dt = \left[(t^2 + 1)^{3/2}\right]_0^{\sqrt{3}} = 7$. Also $M_x = \int \tilde{y}\, dm = \int_0^{\sqrt{3}} \frac{3t^2}{2}\left(3t\sqrt{t^2 + 1}\right)\, dt$

$= \frac{9}{2}\int_0^{\sqrt{3}} t^3\sqrt{t^2 + 1}\, dt = \frac{87}{5} = 17.4$ (by computer) $\Rightarrow \bar{y} = \frac{M_x}{M} = \frac{17.4}{7} \approx 2.49$. Next $M_y = \int \tilde{x}\, dm$

$= \int_0^{\sqrt{3}} t^3 \cdot 3t \sqrt{(t^2 + 1)} \, dt = 3 \int_0^{\sqrt{3}} t^4 \sqrt{t^2 + 1} \, dt \approx 16.4849$ (by computer) $\Rightarrow \bar{x} = \frac{M_y}{M} = \frac{16.4849}{7} \approx 2.35$.

Therefore, $(\bar{x}, \bar{y}) \approx (2.35, 2.49)$.

41. (a) $\frac{dx}{dt} = -2 \sin 2t$ and $\frac{dy}{dt} = 2 \cos 2t \Rightarrow \sqrt{\left(\frac{dx}{dt}\right)^2 + \left(\frac{dy}{dt}\right)^2} = \sqrt{(-2 \sin 2t)^2 + (2 \cos 2t)^2} = 2$

$\Rightarrow$ Length $= \int_0^{\pi/2} 2 \, dt = [2t]_0^{\pi/2} = \pi$

(b) $\frac{dx}{dt} = \pi \cos \pi t$ and $\frac{dy}{dt} = -\pi \sin \pi t \Rightarrow \sqrt{\left(\frac{dx}{dt}\right)^2 + \left(\frac{dy}{dt}\right)^2} = \sqrt{(\pi \cos \pi t)^2 + (-\pi \sin \pi t)^2} = \pi$

$\Rightarrow$ Length $= \int_{-1/2}^{1/2} \pi \, dt = [\pi t]_{-1/2}^{1/2} = \pi$

42. (a) $x = g(y)$ has the parametrization $x = g(y)$ and $y = y$ for $c \leq y \leq d \Rightarrow \frac{dx}{dy} = g'(y)$ and $\frac{dy}{dy} = 1$; then

Length $= \int_c^d \sqrt{\left(\frac{dy}{dy}\right)^2 + \left(\frac{dx}{dy}\right)^2} \, dy = \int_c^d \sqrt{1 + \left(\frac{dx}{dy}\right)^2} \, dy = \int_c^d \sqrt{1 + [g'(y)]^2} \, dy$

(b) $x = y^{3/2}, 0 \leq y \leq \frac{4}{3} \Rightarrow \frac{dx}{dy} = \frac{3}{2} y^{1/2} \Rightarrow L = \int_0^{4/3} \sqrt{1 + \left(\frac{3}{2} y^{1/2}\right)^2} \, dy = \int_0^{4/3} \sqrt{1 + \frac{9}{4} y} \, dy = \left[\frac{4}{9} \cdot \frac{2}{3} \left(1 + \frac{9}{4} y\right)^{3/2}\right]_0^{4/3}$

$= \frac{8}{27}(4)^{3/2} - \frac{8}{27}(1)^{3/2} = \frac{56}{27}$

(c) $x = \frac{3}{2} y^{2/3}, 0 \leq y \leq 1 \Rightarrow \frac{dx}{dy} = y^{-1/3} \Rightarrow L = \int_0^1 \sqrt{1 + (y^{-1/3})^2} \, dy = \int_0^1 \sqrt{1 + \frac{1}{y^{2/3}}} \, dy = \lim_{a \to 0^+} \int_a^1 \sqrt{\frac{y^{2/3} + 1}{y^{2/3}}} \, dy$

$= \lim_{a \to 0^+} \frac{3}{2} \int_a^1 (y^{2/3} + 1)^{1/2} \left(\frac{2}{3} y^{-1/3}\right) \, dy = \lim_{a \to 0^+} \left[\frac{3}{2} \cdot \frac{2}{3} (y^{2/3} + 1)^{3/2}\right]_a^1 = \lim_{a \to 0^+} \left((2)^{3/2} - (a^{2/3} + 1)^{3/2}\right) = 2\sqrt{2} - 1$

43. $x = (1 + 2 \sin \theta) \cos \theta, y = (1 + 2 \sin \theta) \sin \theta \Rightarrow \frac{dx}{d\theta} = 2 \cos^2 \theta - \sin \theta (1 + 2 \sin \theta), \frac{dy}{d\theta} = 2 \cos \theta \sin \theta + \cos \theta (1 + 2 \sin \theta)$

$\Rightarrow \frac{dy}{dx} = \frac{2 \cos \theta \sin \theta + \cos \theta (1 + 2 \sin \theta)}{2 \cos^2 \theta - \sin \theta (1 + 2 \sin \theta)} = \frac{4 \cos \theta \sin \theta + \cos \theta}{2 \cos^2 \theta - 2 \sin^2 \theta - \sin \theta} = \frac{2 \sin 2\theta + \cos \theta}{2 \cos 2\theta - \sin \theta}$

(a) $x = (1 + 2 \sin(0)) \cos(0) = 1, y = (1 + 2 \sin(0)) \sin(0) = 0; \left.\frac{dy}{dx}\right|_{\theta=0} = \frac{2 \sin(2(0)) + \cos(0)}{2 \cos(2(0)) - \sin(0)} = \frac{0+1}{2-0} = \frac{1}{2}$

(b) $x = \left(1 + 2 \sin\left(\frac{\pi}{2}\right)\right) \cos\left(\frac{\pi}{2}\right) = 0, y = \left(1 + 2 \sin\left(\frac{\pi}{2}\right)\right) \sin\left(\frac{\pi}{2}\right) = 3; \left.\frac{dy}{dx}\right|_{\theta=\pi/2} = \frac{2 \sin\left(2\left(\frac{\pi}{2}\right)\right) + \cos\left(\frac{\pi}{2}\right)}{2 \cos\left(2\left(\frac{\pi}{2}\right)\right) - \sin\left(\frac{\pi}{2}\right)} = \frac{0+0}{-2-1} = 0$

(c) $x = \left(1 + 2 \sin\left(\frac{4\pi}{3}\right)\right) \cos\left(\frac{4\pi}{3}\right) = \frac{\sqrt{3}-1}{2}, y = \left(1 + 2 \sin\left(\frac{4\pi}{3}\right)\right) \sin\left(\frac{4\pi}{3}\right) = \frac{3-\sqrt{3}}{2}; \left.\frac{dy}{dx}\right|_{\theta=4\pi/3} = \frac{2 \sin\left(2\left(\frac{4\pi}{3}\right)\right) + \cos\left(\frac{4\pi}{3}\right)}{2 \cos\left(2\left(\frac{4\pi}{3}\right)\right) - \sin\left(\frac{4\pi}{3}\right)}$

$= \frac{\sqrt{3} - \frac{1}{2}}{-1 + \frac{\sqrt{3}}{2}} = \frac{2\sqrt{3}-1}{\sqrt{3}-2} = -\left(4 + 3\sqrt{3}\right)$

44. $x = t, y = 1 - \cos t, 0 \leq t \leq 2\pi \Rightarrow \frac{dx}{dt} = 1, \frac{dy}{dt} = \sin t \Rightarrow \frac{dy}{dx} = \frac{\sin t}{1} = \sin t \Rightarrow \frac{d}{dt}\left(\frac{dy}{dx}\right) = \cos t \Rightarrow \frac{d^2y}{dx^2} = \frac{\cos t}{1} = \cos t$. The

maximum and minimum slope will occur at points that maximize/minimize $\frac{dy}{dx}$, in other words, points where $\frac{d^2y}{dx^2} = 0$

$\Rightarrow \cos t = 0 \Rightarrow t = \frac{\pi}{2}$ or $t = \frac{3\pi}{2} \Rightarrow \frac{d^2y}{dx^2} = +++ \left|\begin{array}{c} \\ \pi/2 \end{array}\right. - - - \left|\begin{array}{c} \\ 3\pi/2 \end{array}\right. +++$

(a) the maximum slope is $\left.\frac{dy}{dx}\right|_{t=\pi/2} = \sin\left(\frac{\pi}{2}\right) = 1$, which occurs at $x = \frac{\pi}{2}, y = 1 - \cos\left(\frac{\pi}{2}\right) = 1$

(a) the minimum slope is $\left.\frac{dy}{dx}\right|_{t=3\pi/2} = \sin\left(\frac{3\pi}{2}\right) = -1$, which occurs at $x = \frac{3\pi}{2}, y = 1 - \cos\left(\frac{3\pi}{2}\right) = 1$

45. $\frac{dx}{dt} = \cos t$ and $\frac{dy}{dt} = 2 \cos 2t \Rightarrow \frac{dy}{dx} = \frac{dy/dt}{dx/dt} = \frac{2 \cos 2t}{\cos t} = \frac{2(2 \cos^2 t - 1)}{\cos t}$; then $\frac{dy}{dx} = 0 \Rightarrow \frac{2(2 \cos^2 t - 1)}{\cos t} = 0$

$\Rightarrow 2 \cos^2 t - 1 = 0 \Rightarrow \cos t = \pm \frac{1}{\sqrt{2}} \Rightarrow t = \frac{\pi}{4}, \frac{3\pi}{4}, \frac{5\pi}{4}, \frac{7\pi}{4}$. In the 1st quadrant: $t = \frac{\pi}{4} \Rightarrow x = \sin \frac{\pi}{4} = \frac{\sqrt{2}}{2}$ and

$y = \sin 2\left(\frac{\pi}{4}\right) = 1 \Rightarrow \left(\frac{\sqrt{2}}{2}, 1\right)$ is the point where the tangent line is horizontal. At the origin: $x = 0$ and $y = 0$

$\Rightarrow$ $\sin t = 0$ $\Rightarrow$ $t = 0$ or $t = \pi$ and $\sin 2t = 0$ $\Rightarrow$ $t = 0, \frac{\pi}{2}, \pi, \frac{3\pi}{2}$ ; thus $t = 0$ and $t = \pi$ give the tangent lines at the origin. Tangents at origin: $\frac{dy}{dx}\big|_{t=0} = 2$ $\Rightarrow$ $y = 2x$ and $\frac{dy}{dx}\big|_{t=\pi} = -2$ $\Rightarrow$ $y = -2x$

46. $\frac{dx}{dt} = 2\cos 2t$ and $\frac{dy}{dt} = 3\cos 3t$ $\Rightarrow$ $\frac{dy}{dx} = \frac{dy/dt}{dx/dt} = \frac{3\cos 3t}{2\cos 2t} = \frac{3(\cos 2t \cos t - \sin 2t \sin t)}{2(2\cos^2 t - 1)}$

$= \frac{3[(2\cos^2 t - 1)(\cos t) - 2\sin t \cos t \sin t]}{2(2\cos^2 t - 1)} = \frac{(3\cos t)(2\cos^2 t - 1 - 2\sin^2 t)}{2(2\cos^2 t - 1)} = \frac{(3\cos t)(4\cos^2 t - 3)}{2(2\cos^2 t - 1)}$ ; then

$\frac{dy}{dx} = 0$ $\Rightarrow$ $\frac{(3\cos t)(4\cos^2 t - 3)}{2(2\cos^2 t - 1)} = 0$ $\Rightarrow$ $3\cos t = 0$ or $4\cos^2 t - 3 = 0$: $3\cos t = 0$ $\Rightarrow$ $t = \frac{\pi}{2}, \frac{3\pi}{2}$ and

$4\cos^2 t - 3 = 0$ $\Rightarrow$ $\cos t = \pm\frac{\sqrt{3}}{2}$ $\Rightarrow$ $t = \frac{\pi}{6}, \frac{5\pi}{6}, \frac{7\pi}{6}, \frac{11\pi}{6}$ . In the 1st quadrant: $t = \frac{\pi}{6}$ $\Rightarrow$ $x = \sin 2\left(\frac{\pi}{6}\right) = \frac{\sqrt{3}}{2}$

and $y = \sin 3\left(\frac{\pi}{6}\right) = 1$ $\Rightarrow$ $\left(\frac{\sqrt{3}}{2}, 1\right)$ is the point where the graph has a horizontal tangent. At the origin: $x = 0$

and $y = 0$ $\Rightarrow$ $\sin 2t = 0$ and $\sin 3t = 0$ $\Rightarrow$ $t = 0, \frac{\pi}{2}, \pi, \frac{3\pi}{2}$ and $t = 0, \frac{\pi}{3}, \frac{2\pi}{3}, \pi, \frac{4\pi}{3}, \frac{5\pi}{3}$ $\Rightarrow$ $t = 0$ and $t = \pi$ give

the tangent lines at the origin. Tangents at the origin: $\frac{dy}{dx}\big|_{t=0} = \frac{3\cos 0}{2\cos 0} = \frac{3}{2}$ $\Rightarrow$ $y = \frac{3}{2}x$, and $\frac{dy}{dx}\big|_{t=\pi}$

$= \frac{3\cos(3\pi)}{2\cos(2\pi)} = -\frac{3}{2}$ $\Rightarrow$ $y = -\frac{3}{2}x$

47. (a) $x = a(t - \sin t)$, $y = a(1 - \cos t)$, $0 \le t \le 2\pi$ $\Rightarrow$ $\frac{dx}{dt} = a(1 - \cos t)$, $\frac{dy}{dt} = a\sin t$ $\Rightarrow$ Length

$= \int_0^{2\pi} \sqrt{(a(1 - \cos t))^2 + (a\sin t)^2}\, dt = \int_0^{2\pi} \sqrt{a^2 - 2a^2\cos t + a^2\cos^2 t + a^2\sin^2 t}\, dt$

$= a\sqrt{2} \int_0^{2\pi} \sqrt{1 - \cos t}\, dt = a\sqrt{2} \int_0^{2\pi} \sqrt{2\sin^2\left(\frac{t}{2}\right)}\, dt = 2a \int_0^{2\pi} \sin\left(\frac{t}{2}\right) dt = \left[-4a\cos\left(\frac{t}{2}\right)\right]_0^{2\pi}$

$= -4a\cos \pi + 4a\cos(0) = 8a$

(b) $a = 1$ $\Rightarrow$ $x = t - \sin t$, $y = 1 - \cos t$, $0 \le t \le 2\pi$ $\Rightarrow$ $\frac{dx}{dt} = 1 - \cos t$, $\frac{dy}{dt} = \sin t$ $\Rightarrow$ Surface area $=$

$= \int_0^{2\pi} 2\pi(1 - \cos t)\sqrt{(1 - \cos t)^2 + (\sin t)^2}\, dt = \int_0^{2\pi} 2\pi(1 - \cos t)\sqrt{1 - 2\cos t + \cos^2 t + \sin^2 t}\, dt$

$= 2\pi \int_0^{2\pi} (1 - \cos t)\sqrt{2 - 2\cos t}\, dt = 2\sqrt{2}\pi \int_0^{2\pi} (1 - \cos t)^{3/2}\, dt = 2\sqrt{2}\pi \int_0^{2\pi} \left(1 - \cos\left(2 \cdot \frac{t}{2}\right)\right)^{3/2} dt$

$= 2\sqrt{2}\pi \int_0^{2\pi} \left(2\sin^2\left(\frac{t}{2}\right)\right)^{3/2} dt = 8\pi \int_0^{2\pi} \sin^3\left(\frac{t}{2}\right) dt$

$\left[u = \frac{t}{2} \Rightarrow du = \frac{1}{2}dt \Rightarrow dt = 2\, du; t = 0 \Rightarrow u = 0, t = 2\pi \Rightarrow u = \pi\right]$

$= 16\pi \int_0^\pi \sin^3 u\, du = 16\pi \int_0^\pi \sin^2 u \sin u\, du = 16\pi \int_0^\pi (1 - \cos^2 u)\sin u\, du = 16\pi \int_0^\pi \sin u\, du - 16\pi \int_0^\pi \cos^2 u \sin u\, du$

$= \left[-16\pi\cos u + \frac{16\pi}{3}\cos^3 u\right]_0^\pi = \left(16\pi - \frac{16\pi}{3}\right) - \left(-16\pi + \frac{16\pi}{3}\right) = \frac{64\pi}{3}$

48. $x = t - \sin t$, $y = 1 - \cos t$, $0 \le t \le 2\pi$; Volume $= \int_0^{2\pi} \pi y^2 dx = \int_0^{2\pi} \pi(1 - \cos t)^2(1 - \cos t)dt$

$= \pi \int_0^{2\pi} (1 - 3\cos t + 3\cos^2 t - \cos^3 t)dt = \pi \int_0^{2\pi} \left(1 - 3\cos t + 3\left(\frac{1 + \cos 2t}{2}\right) - \cos^2 t \cos t\right)dt$

$= \pi \int_0^{2\pi} \left(\frac{5}{2} - 3\cos t + \frac{3}{2}\cos 2t - (1 - \sin^2 t)\cos t\right)dt = \pi \int_0^{2\pi} \left(\frac{5}{2} - 4\cos t + \frac{3}{2}\cos 2t + \sin^2 t \cos t\right)dt$

$= \pi \left[\frac{5}{2}t - 4\sin t + \frac{3}{4}\sin 2t + \frac{1}{3}\sin^3 t\right]_0^{2\pi} = \pi(5\pi - 0 + 0 + 0) - 0 = 5\pi^2$

47-50. Example CAS commands:

Maple:

```
with( plots );
with( student );
x := t -> t^3/3;
y := t -> t^2/2;
a := 0;
b := 1;
N := [2, 4, 8 ];
for n in N do
```

```
tt := [seq( a+i*(b-a)/n, i=0..n )];

pts := [seq([x(t),y(t)],t=tt)];

L := simplify(add( student[distance](pts[i+1],pts[i]), i=1..n ));      # (b)

T := sprintf("#47(a) (Section 11.2)\nn=%3d  L=%8.5f\n", n, L );

P[n] := plot( [[x(t),y(t),t=a..b],pts], title=T ):                      # (a)

end do:

display( [seq(P[n],n=N)], insequence=true );

ds := t ->sqrt( simplify(D(x)(t)^2 + D(y)(t)^2) ):                      # (c)

L := Int( ds(t), t=a..b ):

L = evalf(L);
```

## 11.3 POLAR COORDINATES

1.  a, e;  b, g;  c, h;  d, f

2.  a, f;  b, h;  c, g;  d, e

3.  (a)  $\left(2, \frac{\pi}{2} + 2n\pi\right)$ and $\left(-2, \frac{\pi}{2} + (2n+1)\pi\right)$, n an integer

    (b)  $(2, 2n\pi)$ and $(-2, (2n+1)\pi)$, n an integer

    (c)  $\left(2, \frac{3\pi}{2} + 2n\pi\right)$ and $\left(-2, \frac{3\pi}{2} + (2n+1)\pi\right)$, n an integer

    (d)  $(2, (2n+1)\pi)$ and $(-2, 2n\pi)$, n an integer

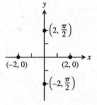

4.  (a)  $\left(3, \frac{\pi}{4} + 2n\pi\right)$ and $\left(-3, \frac{5\pi}{4} + 2n\pi\right)$, n an integer

    (b)  $\left(-3, \frac{\pi}{4} + 2n\pi\right)$ and $\left(3, \frac{5\pi}{4} + 2n\pi\right)$, n an integer

    (c)  $\left(3, -\frac{\pi}{4} + 2n\pi\right)$ and $\left(-3, \frac{3\pi}{4} + 2n\pi\right)$, n an integer

    (d)  $\left(-3, -\frac{\pi}{4} + 2n\pi\right)$ and $\left(3, \frac{3\pi}{4} + 2n\pi\right)$, n an integer

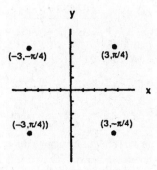

5.  (a)  $x = r\cos\theta = 3\cos 0 = 3$, $y = r\sin\theta = 3\sin 0 = 0$ $\Rightarrow$ Cartesian coordinates are $(3, 0)$

    (b)  $x = r\cos\theta = -3\cos 0 = -3$, $y = r\sin\theta = -3\sin 0 = 0$ $\Rightarrow$ Cartesian coordinates are $(-3, 0)$

    (c)  $x = r\cos\theta = 2\cos\frac{2\pi}{3} = -1$, $y = r\sin\theta = 2\sin\frac{2\pi}{3} = \sqrt{3}$ $\Rightarrow$ Cartesian coordinates are $\left(-1, \sqrt{3}\right)$

    (d)  $x = r\cos\theta = 2\cos\frac{7\pi}{3} = 1$, $y = r\sin\theta = 2\sin\frac{7\pi}{3} = \sqrt{3}$ $\Rightarrow$ Cartesian coordinates are $\left(1, \sqrt{3}\right)$

    (e)  $x = r\cos\theta = -3\cos\pi = 3$, $y = r\sin\theta = -3\sin\pi = 0$ $\Rightarrow$ Cartesian coordinates are $(3, 0)$

    (f)  $x = r\cos\theta = 2\cos\frac{\pi}{3} = 1$, $y = r\sin\theta = 2\sin\frac{\pi}{3} = \sqrt{3}$ $\Rightarrow$ Cartesian coordinates are $\left(1, \sqrt{3}\right)$

    (g)  $x = r\cos\theta = -3\cos 2\pi = -3$, $y = r\sin\theta = -3\sin 2\pi = 0$ $\Rightarrow$ Cartesian coordinates are $(-3, 0)$

    (h)  $x = r\cos\theta = -2\cos\left(-\frac{\pi}{3}\right) = -1$, $y = r\sin\theta = -2\sin\left(-\frac{\pi}{3}\right) = \sqrt{3}$ $\Rightarrow$ Cartesian coordinates are $\left(-1, \sqrt{3}\right)$

6.  (a)  $x = \sqrt{2}\cos\frac{\pi}{4} = 1$, $y = \sqrt{2}\sin\frac{\pi}{4} = 1$ $\Rightarrow$ Cartesian coordinates are $(1, 1)$

    (b)  $x = 1\cos 0 = 1$, $y = 1\sin 0 = 0$ $\Rightarrow$ Cartesian coordinates are $(1, 0)$

    (c)  $x = 0\cos\frac{\pi}{2} = 0$, $y = 0\sin\frac{\pi}{2} = 0$ $\Rightarrow$ Cartesian coordinates are $(0, 0)$

    (d)  $x = -\sqrt{2}\cos\left(\frac{\pi}{4}\right) = -1$, $y = -\sqrt{2}\sin\left(\frac{\pi}{4}\right) = -1$ $\Rightarrow$ Cartesian coordinates are $(-1, -1)$

    (e)  $x = -3\cos\frac{5\pi}{6} = \frac{3\sqrt{3}}{2}$, $y = -3\sin\frac{5\pi}{6} = -\frac{3}{2}$ $\Rightarrow$ Cartesian coordinates are $\left(\frac{3\sqrt{3}}{2}, -\frac{3}{2}\right)$

    (f)  $x = 5\cos\left(\tan^{-1}\frac{4}{3}\right) = 3$, $y = 5\sin\left(\tan^{-1}\frac{4}{3}\right) = 4$ $\Rightarrow$ Cartesian coordinates are $(3, 4)$

(g) $x = -1 \cos 7\pi = 1$, $y = -1 \sin 7\pi = 0$ $\Rightarrow$ Cartesian coordinates are $(1, 0)$

(h) $x = 2\sqrt{3} \cos \frac{2\pi}{3} = -\sqrt{3}$, $y = 2\sqrt{3} \sin \frac{2\pi}{3} = 3$ $\Rightarrow$ Cartesian coordinates are $\left(-\sqrt{3}, 3\right)$

7. (a) $(1, 1) \Rightarrow r = \sqrt{1^2 + 1^2} = \sqrt{2}$, $\sin\theta = \frac{1}{\sqrt{2}}$ and $\cos\theta = \frac{1}{\sqrt{2}}$ $\Rightarrow \theta = \frac{\pi}{4}$ $\Rightarrow$ Polar coordinates are $\left(\sqrt{2}, \frac{\pi}{4}\right)$

(b) $(-3, 0) \Rightarrow r = \sqrt{(-3)^2 + 0^2} = 3$, $\sin\theta = 0$ and $\cos\theta = -1$ $\Rightarrow \theta = \pi$ $\Rightarrow$ Polar coordinates are $(3, \pi)$

(c) $\left(\sqrt{3}, -1\right) \Rightarrow r = \sqrt{\left(\sqrt{3}\right)^2 + (-1)^2} = 2$, $\sin\theta = -\frac{1}{2}$ and $\cos\theta = \frac{\sqrt{3}}{2}$ $\Rightarrow \theta = \frac{11\pi}{6}$ $\Rightarrow$ Polar coordinates are $\left(2, \frac{11\pi}{6}\right)$

(d) $(-3, 4) \Rightarrow r = \sqrt{(-3)^2 + 4^2} = 5$, $\sin\theta = \frac{4}{5}$ and $\cos\theta = -\frac{3}{5}$ $\Rightarrow \theta = \pi - \arctan\left(\frac{4}{3}\right)$ $\Rightarrow$ Polar coordinates are $\left(5, \pi - \arctan\left(\frac{4}{3}\right)\right)$

8. (a) $(-2, -2) \Rightarrow r = \sqrt{(-2)^2 + (-2)^2} = 2\sqrt{2}$, $\sin\theta = -\frac{1}{\sqrt{2}}$ and $\cos\theta = -\frac{1}{\sqrt{2}}$ $\Rightarrow \theta = -\frac{3\pi}{4}$ $\Rightarrow$ Polar coordinates are $\left(2\sqrt{2}, -\frac{3\pi}{4}\right)$

(b) $(0, 3) \Rightarrow r = \sqrt{0^2 + 3^2} = 3$, $\sin\theta = 1$ and $\cos\theta = 0$ $\Rightarrow \theta = \frac{\pi}{2}$ $\Rightarrow$ Polar coordinates are $\left(3, \frac{\pi}{2}\right)$

(c) $\left(-\sqrt{3}, 1\right) \Rightarrow r = \sqrt{\left(-\sqrt{3}\right)^2 + 1^2} = 2$, $\sin\theta = \frac{1}{2}$ and $\cos\theta = -\frac{\sqrt{3}}{2}$ $\Rightarrow \theta = \frac{5\pi}{6}$ $\Rightarrow$ Polar coordinates are $\left(2, \frac{5\pi}{6}\right)$

(d) $(5, -12) \Rightarrow r = \sqrt{5^2 + (-12)^2} = 13$, $\sin\theta = -\frac{12}{13}$ and $\cos\theta = \frac{5}{12}$ $\Rightarrow \theta = -\arctan\left(\frac{12}{5}\right)$ $\Rightarrow$ Polar coordinates are $\left(13, -\arctan\left(\frac{12}{5}\right)\right)$

9. (a) $(3, 3) \Rightarrow r = -\sqrt{3^2 + 3^2} = -3\sqrt{2}$, $\sin\theta = -\frac{1}{\sqrt{2}}$ and $\cos\theta = -\frac{1}{\sqrt{2}}$ $\Rightarrow \theta = \frac{5\pi}{4}$ $\Rightarrow$ Polar coordinates are $\left(-3\sqrt{2}, \frac{5\pi}{4}\right)$

(b) $(-1, 0) \Rightarrow r = -\sqrt{(-1)^2 + 0^2} = -1$, $\sin\theta = 0$ and $\cos\theta = 1$ $\Rightarrow \theta = 0$ $\Rightarrow$ Polar coordinates are $(-1, 0)$

(c) $\left(-1, \sqrt{3}\right) \Rightarrow r = -\sqrt{(-1)^2 + \left(\sqrt{3}\right)^2} = -2$, $\sin\theta = -\frac{\sqrt{3}}{2}$ and $\cos\theta = \frac{1}{2}$ $\Rightarrow \theta = \frac{5\pi}{3}$ $\Rightarrow$ Polar coordinates are $\left(-2, \frac{5\pi}{3}\right)$

(d) $(4, -3) \Rightarrow r = -\sqrt{4^2 + (-3)^2} = -5$, $\sin\theta = \frac{3}{5}$ and $\cos\theta = -\frac{4}{5}$ $\Rightarrow \theta = \pi - \arctan\left(\frac{3}{4}\right)$ $\Rightarrow$ Polar coordinates are $\left(-5, \pi - \arctan\left(\frac{4}{3}\right)\right)$

10. (a) $(-2, 0) \Rightarrow r = -\sqrt{(-2)^2 + 0^2} = -2$, $\sin\theta = 0$ and $\cos\theta = 1$ $\Rightarrow \theta = 0$ $\Rightarrow$ Polar coordinates are $(-2, 0)$

(b) $(1, 0) \Rightarrow r = -\sqrt{1^2 + 0^2} = -1$, $\sin\theta = 0$ and $\cos\theta = -1$ $\Rightarrow \theta = \pi$ or $\theta = -\pi$ $\Rightarrow$ Polar coordinates are $(-1, \pi)$ or $(-1, -\pi)$

(c) $(0, -3) \Rightarrow r = -\sqrt{0^2 + (-3)^2} = -3$, $\sin\theta = 1$ and $\cos\theta = 0$ $\Rightarrow \theta = \frac{\pi}{2}$ $\Rightarrow$ Polar coordinates are $\left(-3, \frac{\pi}{2}\right)$

(d) $\left(\frac{\sqrt{3}}{2}, \frac{1}{2}\right) \Rightarrow r = -\sqrt{\left(\frac{\sqrt{3}}{2}\right)^2 + \left(\frac{1}{2}\right)^2} = -1$, $\sin\theta = -\frac{1}{2}$ and $\cos\theta = -\frac{\sqrt{3}}{2}$ $\Rightarrow \theta = \frac{7\pi}{6}$ or $\theta = -\frac{5\pi}{6}$ $\Rightarrow$ Polar coordinates are $\left(-1, \frac{7\pi}{6}\right)$ or $\left(-1, -\frac{5\pi}{6}\right)$

11.

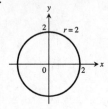

12.

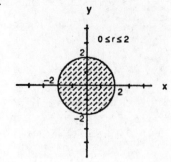

13.

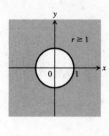

14.

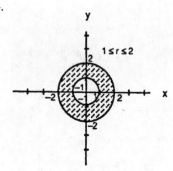

15.

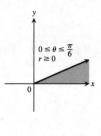

16.

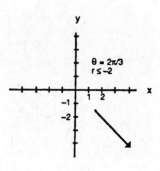

17.

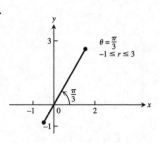

18.

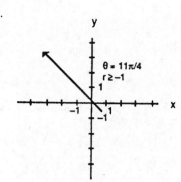

19.

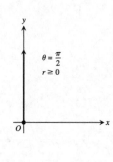

20.

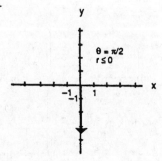

21.

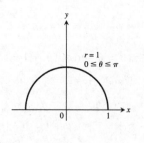

22.

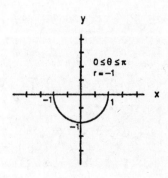

23.

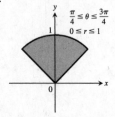

24.

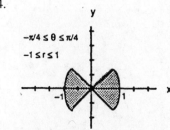

25.

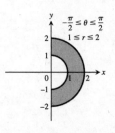

26.

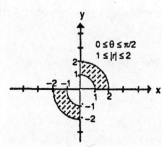

27. $r \cos \theta = 2 \implies x = 2$, vertical line through $(2, 0)$

28. $r \sin \theta = -1 \implies y = -1$, horizontal line through $(0, -1)$

29. $r \sin \theta = 0 \implies y = 0$, the x-axis

30. $r \cos \theta = 0 \implies x = 0$, the y-axis

31. $r = 4 \csc \theta \implies r = \frac{4}{\sin \theta} \implies r \sin \theta = 4 \implies y = 4$, a horizontal line through $(0, 4)$

32. $r = -3 \sec \theta \implies r = \frac{-3}{\cos \theta} \implies r \cos \theta = -3 \implies x = -3$, a vertical line through $(-3, 0)$

33. $r \cos \theta + r \sin \theta = 1 \implies x + y = 1$, line with slope $m = -1$ and intercept $b = 1$

34. $r \sin \theta = r \cos \theta \implies y = x$, line with slope $m = 1$ and intercept $b = 0$

35. $r^2 = 1 \implies x^2 + y^2 = 1$, circle with center $C = (0, 0)$ and radius 1

36. $r^2 = 4r \sin \theta \implies x^2 + y^2 = 4y \implies x^2 + y^2 - 4y + 4 = 4 \implies x^2 + (y - 2)^2 = 4$, circle with center $C = (0, 2)$ and radius 2

37. $r = \frac{5}{\sin \theta - 2 \cos \theta} \implies r \sin \theta - 2r \cos \theta = 5 \implies y - 2x = 5$, line with slope $m = 2$ and intercept $b = 5$

38. $r^2 \sin 2\theta = 2 \implies 2r^2 \sin \theta \cos \theta = 2 \implies (r \sin \theta)(r \cos \theta) = 1 \implies xy = 1$, hyperbola with focal axis $y = x$

39. $r = \cot \theta \csc \theta = \left(\frac{\cos \theta}{\sin \theta}\right)\left(\frac{1}{\sin \theta}\right) \implies r \sin^2 \theta = \cos \theta \implies r^2 \sin^2 \theta = r \cos \theta \implies y^2 = x$, parabola with vertex $(0, 0)$ which opens to the right

40. $r = 4 \tan \theta \sec \theta \implies r = 4 \left(\frac{\sin \theta}{\cos^2 \theta}\right) \implies r \cos^2 \theta = 4 \sin \theta \implies r^2 \cos^2 \theta = 4r \sin \theta \implies x^2 = 4y$, parabola with vertex $= (0, 0)$ which opens upward

41. $r = (\csc \theta) e^{r \cos \theta} \implies r \sin \theta = e^{r \cos \theta} \implies y = e^x$, graph of the natural exponential function

42. $r \sin \theta = \ln r + \ln \cos \theta = \ln (r \cos \theta) \implies y = \ln x$, graph of the natural logarithm function

43. $r^2 + 2r^2 \cos \theta \sin \theta = 1 \implies x^2 + y^2 + 2xy = 1 \implies x^2 + 2xy + y^2 = 1 \implies (x + y)^2 = 1 \implies x + y = \pm 1$, two parallel straight lines of slope $-1$ and y-intercepts $b = \pm 1$

44. $\cos^2 \theta = \sin^2 \theta \implies r^2 \cos^2 \theta = r^2 \sin^2 \theta \implies x^2 = y^2 \implies |x| = |y| \implies \pm x = y$, two perpendicular lines through the origin with slopes 1 and $-1$, respectively.

45. $r^2 = -4r \cos \theta \implies x^2 + y^2 = -4x \implies x^2 + 4x + y^2 = 0 \implies x^2 + 4x + 4 + y^2 = 4 \implies (x + 2)^2 + y^2 = 4$, a circle with center $C(-2, 0)$ and radius 2

46. $r^2 = -6r \sin\theta \implies x^2 + y^2 = -6y \implies x^2 + y^2 + 6y = 0 \implies x^2 + y^2 + 6y + 9 = 9 \implies x^2 + (y+3)^2 = 9$, a circle with center $C(0, -3)$ and radius 3

47. $r = 8\sin\theta \implies r^2 = 8r\sin\theta \implies x^2 + y^2 = 8y \implies x^2 + y^2 - 8y = 0 \implies x^2 + y^2 - 8y + 16 = 16 \implies x^2 + (y-4)^2 = 16$, a circle with center $C(0, 4)$ and radius 4

48. $r = 3\cos\theta \implies r^2 = 3r\cos\theta \implies x^2 + y^2 = 3x \implies x^2 + y^2 - 3x = 0 \implies x^2 - 3x + \frac{9}{4} + y^2 = \frac{9}{4}$
    $\implies \left(x - \frac{3}{2}\right)^2 + y^2 = \frac{9}{4}$, a circle with center $C\left(\frac{3}{2}, 0\right)$ and radius $\frac{3}{2}$

49. $r = 2\cos\theta + 2\sin\theta \implies r^2 = 2r\cos\theta + 2r\sin\theta \implies x^2 + y^2 = 2x + 2y \implies x^2 - 2x + y^2 - 2y = 0$
    $\implies (x-1)^2 + (y-1)^2 = 2$, a circle with center $C(1, 1)$ and radius $\sqrt{2}$

50. $r = 2\cos\theta - \sin\theta \implies r^2 = 2r\cos\theta - r\sin\theta \implies x^2 + y^2 = 2x - y \implies x^2 - 2x + y^2 + y = 0$
    $\implies (x-1)^2 + \left(y + \frac{1}{2}\right)^2 = \frac{5}{4}$, a circle with center $C\left(1, -\frac{1}{2}\right)$ and radius $\frac{\sqrt{5}}{2}$

51. $r\sin\left(\theta + \frac{\pi}{6}\right) = 2 \implies r\left(\sin\theta\cos\frac{\pi}{6} + \cos\theta\sin\frac{\pi}{6}\right) = 2 \implies \frac{\sqrt{3}}{2}r\sin\theta + \frac{1}{2}r\cos\theta = 2 \implies \frac{\sqrt{3}}{2}y + \frac{1}{2}x = 2$
    $\implies \sqrt{3}\,y + x = 4$, line with slope $m = -\frac{1}{\sqrt{3}}$ and intercept $b = \frac{4}{\sqrt{3}}$

52. $r\sin\left(\frac{2\pi}{3} - \theta\right) = 5 \implies r\left(\sin\frac{2\pi}{3}\cos\theta - \cos\frac{2\pi}{3}\sin\theta\right) = 5 \implies \frac{\sqrt{3}}{2}r\cos\theta + \frac{1}{2}r\sin\theta = 5 \implies \frac{\sqrt{3}}{2}x + \frac{1}{2}y = 5$
    $\implies \sqrt{3}\,x + y = 10$, line with slope $m = -\sqrt{3}$ and intercept $b = 10$

53. $x = 7 \implies r\cos\theta = 7$

54. $y = 1 \implies r\sin\theta = 1$

55. $x = y \implies r\cos\theta = r\sin\theta \implies \theta = \frac{\pi}{4}$

56. $x - y = 3 \implies r\cos\theta - r\sin\theta = 3$

57. $x^2 + y^2 = 4 \implies r^2 = 4 \implies r = 2 \text{ or } r = -2$

58. $x^2 - y^2 = 1 \implies r^2\cos^2\theta - r^2\sin^2\theta = 1 \implies r^2(\cos^2\theta - \sin^2\theta) = 1 \implies r^2\cos 2\theta = 1$

59. $\frac{x^2}{9} + \frac{y^2}{4} = 1 \implies 4x^2 + 9y^2 = 36 \implies 4r^2\cos^2\theta + 9r^2\sin^2\theta = 36$

60. $xy = 2 \implies (r\cos\theta)(r\sin\theta) = 2 \implies r^2\cos\theta\sin\theta = 2 \implies 2r^2\cos\theta\sin\theta = 4 \implies r^2\sin 2\theta = 4$

61. $y^2 = 4x \implies r^2\sin^2\theta = 4r\cos\theta \implies r\sin^2\theta = 4\cos\theta$

62. $x^2 + xy + y^2 = 1 \implies x^2 + y^2 + xy = 1 \implies r^2 + r^2\sin\theta\cos\theta = 1 \implies r^2(1 + \sin\theta\cos\theta) = 1$

63. $x^2 + (y-2)^2 = 4 \implies x^2 + y^2 - 4y + 4 = 4 \implies x^2 + y^2 = 4y \implies r^2 = 4r\sin\theta \implies r = 4\sin\theta$

64. $(x-5)^2 + y^2 = 25 \implies x^2 - 10x + 25 + y^2 = 25 \implies x^2 + y^2 = 10x \implies r^2 = 10r\cos\theta \implies r = 10\cos\theta$

65. $(x-3)^2 + (y+1)^2 = 4 \implies x^2 - 6x + 9 + y^2 + 2y + 1 = 4 \implies x^2 + y^2 = 6x - 2y - 6 \implies r^2 = 6r\cos\theta - 2r\sin\theta - 6$

66. $(x+2)^2 + (y-5)^2 = 16 \implies x^2 + 4x + 4 + y^2 - 10y + 25 = 16 \implies x^2 + y^2 = -4x + 10y - 13$
    $\implies r^2 = -4r\cos\theta + 10r\sin\theta - 13$

67. $(0, \theta)$ where $\theta$ is any angle

68. (a) $x = a \Rightarrow r \cos \theta = a \Rightarrow r = \frac{a}{\cos \theta} \Rightarrow r = a \sec \theta$
    (b) $y = b \Rightarrow r \sin \theta = b \Rightarrow r = \frac{b}{\sin \theta} \Rightarrow r = b \csc \theta$

## 11.4 GRAPHING IN POLAR COORDINATES

1. $1 + \cos(-\theta) = 1 + \cos \theta = r \Rightarrow$ symmetric about the
   x-axis; $1 + \cos(-\theta) \neq -r$ and $1 + \cos(\pi - \theta)$
   $= 1 - \cos \theta \neq r \Rightarrow$ not symmetric about the y-axis;
   therefore not symmetric about the origin

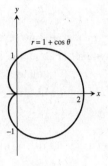

2. $2 - 2 \cos(-\theta) = 2 - 2 \cos \theta = r \Rightarrow$ symmetric about the
   x-axis; $2 - 2 \cos(-\theta) \neq -r$ and $2 - 2 \cos(\pi - \theta)$
   $= 2 + 2 \cos \theta \neq r \Rightarrow$ not symmetric about the y-axis;
   therefore not symmetric about the origin

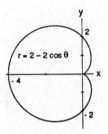

3. $1 - \sin(-\theta) = 1 + \sin \theta \neq r$ and $1 - \sin(\pi - \theta)$
   $= 1 - \sin \theta \neq -r \Rightarrow$ not symmetric about the x-axis;
   $1 - \sin(\pi - \theta) = 1 - \sin \theta = r \Rightarrow$ symmetric about
   the y-axis; therefore not symmetric about the origin

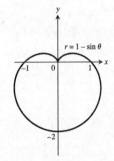

4. $1 + \sin(-\theta) = 1 - \sin \theta \neq r$ and $1 + \sin(\pi - \theta)$
   $= 1 + \sin \theta \neq -r \Rightarrow$ not symmetric about the x-axis;
   $1 + \sin(\pi - \theta) = 1 + \sin \theta = r \Rightarrow$ symmetric about the
   y-axis; therefore not symmetric about the origin

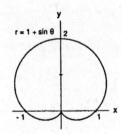

5. $2 + \sin(-\theta) = 2 - \sin\theta \neq r$ and $2 + \sin(\pi - \theta)$
   $= 2 + \sin\theta \neq -r \Rightarrow$ not symmetric about the x-axis;
   $2 + \sin(\pi - \theta) = 2 + \sin\theta = r \Rightarrow$ symmetric about the
   y-axis; therefore not symmetric about the origin

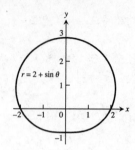

6. $1 + 2\sin(-\theta) = 1 - 2\sin\theta \neq r$ and $1 + 2\sin(\pi - \theta)$
   $= 1 + 2\sin\theta \neq -r \Rightarrow$ not symmetric about the x-axis;
   $1 + 2\sin(\pi - \theta) = 1 + 2\sin\theta = r \Rightarrow$ symmetric about the
   y-axis; therefore not symmetric about the origin

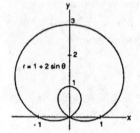

7. $\sin\left(-\frac{\theta}{2}\right) = -\sin\left(\frac{\theta}{2}\right) = -r \Rightarrow$ symmetric about the y-axis;
   $\sin\left(\frac{2\pi-\theta}{2}\right) = \sin\left(\frac{\theta}{2}\right)$, so the graph $\underline{is}$ symmetric about the
   x-axis, and hence the origin.

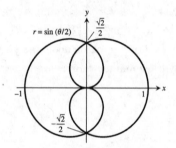

8. $\cos\left(-\frac{\theta}{2}\right) = \cos\left(\frac{\theta}{2}\right) = r \Rightarrow$ symmetric about the x-axis;
   $\cos\left(\frac{2\pi-\theta}{2}\right) = \cos\left(\frac{\theta}{2}\right)$, so the graph $\underline{is}$ symmetric about the
   y-axis, and hence the origin.

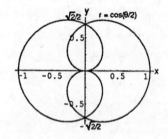

9. $\cos(-\theta) = \cos\theta = r^2 \Rightarrow (r, -\theta)$ and $(-r, -\theta)$ are on the
   graph when $(r, \theta)$ is on the graph $\Rightarrow$ symmetric about the
   x-axis and the y-axis; therefore symmetric about the origin

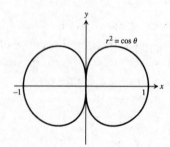

10. $\sin(\pi - \theta) = \sin\theta = r^2 \Rightarrow (r, \pi - \theta)$ and $(-r, \pi - \theta)$ are on the graph when $(r, \theta)$ is on the graph $\Rightarrow$ symmetric about the y-axis and the x-axis; therefore symmetric about the origin

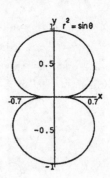

11. $-\sin(\pi - \theta) = -\sin\theta = r^2 \Rightarrow (r, \pi - \theta)$ and $(-r, \pi - \theta)$ are on the graph when $(r, \theta)$ is on the graph $\Rightarrow$ symmetric about the y-axis and the x-axis; therefore symmetric about the origin

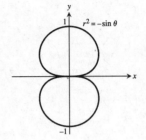

12. $-\cos(-\theta) = -\cos\theta = r^2 \Rightarrow (r, -\theta)$ and $(-r, -\theta)$ are on the graph when $(r, \theta)$ is on the graph $\Rightarrow$ symmetric about the x-axis and the y-axis; therefore symmetric about the origin

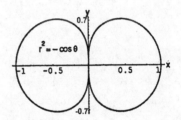

13. Since $(\pm r, -\theta)$ are on the graph when $(r, \theta)$ is on the graph $\left((\pm r)^2 = 4\cos 2(-\theta) \Rightarrow r^2 = 4\cos 2\theta\right)$, the graph is symmetric about the x-axis and the y-axis $\Rightarrow$ the graph is symmetric about the origin

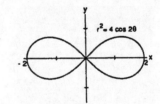

14. Since $(r, \theta)$ on the graph $\Rightarrow (-r, \theta)$ is on the graph $\left((\pm r)^2 = 4\sin 2\theta \Rightarrow r^2 = 4\sin 2\theta\right)$, the graph is symmetric about the origin. But $4\sin 2(-\theta) = -4\sin 2\theta$ $\neq r^2$ and $4\sin 2(\pi - \theta) = 4\sin(2\pi - 2\theta) = 4\sin(-2\theta)$ $= -4\sin 2\theta \neq r^2 \Rightarrow$ the graph is not symmetric about the x-axis; therefore the graph is not symmetric about the y-axis

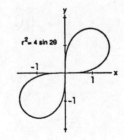

15. Since $(r, \theta)$ on the graph $\Rightarrow (-r, \theta)$ is on the graph $\left((\pm r)^2 = -\sin 2\theta \Rightarrow r^2 = -\sin 2\theta\right)$, the graph is symmetric about the origin. But $-\sin 2(-\theta) = -(-\sin 2\theta)$ $\sin 2\theta \neq r^2$ and $-\sin 2(\pi - \theta) = -\sin(2\pi - 2\theta)$ $= -\sin(-2\theta) = -(-\sin 2\theta) = \sin 2\theta \neq r^2 \Rightarrow$ the graph is not symmetric about the x-axis; therefore the graph is not symmetric about the y-axis

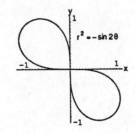

16. Since($\pm$ r, $-\theta$) are on the graph when (r, $\theta$) is on the graph $\left((\pm r)^2 = -\cos 2(-\theta) \Rightarrow r^2 = -\cos 2\theta\right)$, the graph is symmetric about the x-axis and the y-axis $\Rightarrow$ the graph is symmetric about the origin.

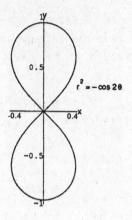

17. $\theta = \frac{\pi}{2} \Rightarrow r = -1 \Rightarrow \left(-1, \frac{\pi}{2}\right)$, and $\theta = -\frac{\pi}{2} \Rightarrow r = -1$
    $\Rightarrow \left(-1, -\frac{\pi}{2}\right); r' = \frac{dr}{d\theta} = -\sin\theta;$ Slope $= \frac{r'\sin\theta + r\cos\theta}{r'\cos\theta - r\sin\theta}$
    $= \frac{-\sin^2\theta + r\cos\theta}{-\sin\theta\cos\theta - r\sin\theta} \Rightarrow$ Slope at $\left(-1, \frac{\pi}{2}\right)$ is
    $\frac{-\sin^2\left(\frac{\pi}{2}\right) + (-1)\cos\frac{\pi}{2}}{-\sin\frac{\pi}{2}\cos\frac{\pi}{2} - (-1)\sin\frac{\pi}{2}} = -1$; Slope at $\left(-1, -\frac{\pi}{2}\right)$ is
    $\frac{-\sin^2\left(-\frac{\pi}{2}\right) + (-1)\cos\left(-\frac{\pi}{2}\right)}{-\sin\left(-\frac{\pi}{2}\right)\cos\left(-\frac{\pi}{2}\right) - (-1)\sin\left(-\frac{\pi}{2}\right)} = 1$

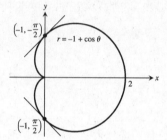

18. $\theta = 0 \Rightarrow r = -1 \Rightarrow (-1, 0)$, and $\theta = \pi \Rightarrow r = -1$
    $\Rightarrow (-1, \pi); r' = \frac{dr}{d\theta} = \cos\theta;$
    Slope $= \frac{r'\sin\theta + r\cos\theta}{r'\cos\theta - r\sin\theta} = \frac{\cos\theta\sin\theta + r\cos\theta}{\cos\theta\cos\theta - r\sin\theta}$
    $= \frac{\cos\theta\sin\theta + r\cos\theta}{\cos^2\theta - r\sin\theta} \Rightarrow$ Slope at $(-1, 0)$ is $\frac{\cos 0\sin 0 + (-1)\cos 0}{\cos^2 0 - (-1)\sin 0}$
    $= -1$; Slope at $(-1, \pi)$ is $\frac{\cos\pi\sin\pi + (-1)\cos\pi}{\cos^2\pi - (-1)\sin\pi} = 1$

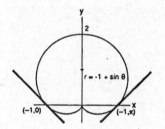

19. $\theta = \frac{\pi}{4} \Rightarrow r = 1 \Rightarrow \left(1, \frac{\pi}{4}\right); \theta = -\frac{\pi}{4} \Rightarrow r = -1$
    $\Rightarrow \left(-1, -\frac{\pi}{4}\right); \theta = \frac{3\pi}{4} \Rightarrow r = -1 \Rightarrow \left(-1, \frac{3\pi}{4}\right);$
    $\theta = -\frac{3\pi}{4} \Rightarrow r = 1 \Rightarrow \left(1, -\frac{3\pi}{4}\right);$
    $r' = \frac{dr}{d\theta} = 2\cos 2\theta;$
    Slope $= \frac{r'\sin\theta + r\cos\theta}{r'\cos\theta - r\sin\theta} = \frac{2\cos 2\theta\sin\theta + r\cos\theta}{2\cos 2\theta\cos\theta - r\sin\theta}$
    $\Rightarrow$ Slope at $\left(1, \frac{\pi}{4}\right)$ is $\frac{2\cos\left(\frac{\pi}{2}\right)\sin\left(\frac{\pi}{4}\right) + (1)\cos\left(\frac{\pi}{4}\right)}{2\cos\left(\frac{\pi}{2}\right)\cos\left(\frac{\pi}{4}\right) - (1)\sin\left(\frac{\pi}{4}\right)} = -1$;

    Slope at $\left(-1, -\frac{\pi}{4}\right)$ is $\frac{2\cos\left(-\frac{\pi}{2}\right)\sin\left(-\frac{\pi}{4}\right) + (-1)\cos\left(-\frac{\pi}{4}\right)}{2\cos\left(-\frac{\pi}{2}\right)\cos\left(-\frac{\pi}{4}\right) - (-1)\sin\left(-\frac{\pi}{4}\right)} = 1$;

    Slope at $\left(-1, \frac{3\pi}{4}\right)$ is $\frac{2\cos\left(\frac{3\pi}{2}\right)\sin\left(\frac{3\pi}{4}\right) + (-1)\cos\left(\frac{3\pi}{4}\right)}{2\cos\left(\frac{3\pi}{2}\right)\cos\left(\frac{3\pi}{4}\right) - (-1)\sin\left(\frac{3\pi}{4}\right)} = 1$;

    Slope at $\left(1, -\frac{3\pi}{4}\right)$ is $\frac{2\cos\left(-\frac{3\pi}{2}\right)\sin\left(-\frac{3\pi}{4}\right) + (1)\cos\left(-\frac{3\pi}{4}\right)}{2\cos\left(-\frac{3\pi}{2}\right)\cos\left(-\frac{3\pi}{4}\right) - (1)\sin\left(-\frac{3\pi}{4}\right)} = -1$

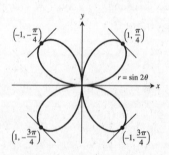

20. $\theta = 0 \Rightarrow r = 1 \Rightarrow (1,0); \theta = \frac{\pi}{2} \Rightarrow r = -1 \Rightarrow \left(-1, \frac{\pi}{2}\right);$

$\theta = -\frac{\pi}{2} \Rightarrow r = -1 \Rightarrow \left(-1, -\frac{\pi}{2}\right); \theta = \pi \Rightarrow r = 1$

$\Rightarrow (1, \pi); r' = \frac{dr}{d\theta} = -2 \sin 2\theta;$

Slope $= \frac{r' \sin \theta + r \cos \theta}{r' \cos \theta - r \sin \theta} = \frac{-2 \sin 2\theta \sin \theta + r \cos \theta}{-2 \sin 2\theta \cos \theta - r \sin \theta}$

$\Rightarrow$ Slope at $(1,0)$ is $\frac{-2 \sin 0 \sin 0 + \cos 0}{-2 \sin 0 \cos 0 - \sin 0}$, which is undefined;

Slope at $\left(-1, \frac{\pi}{2}\right)$ is $\frac{-2 \sin 2\left(\frac{\pi}{2}\right) \sin \left(\frac{\pi}{2}\right) + (-1) \cos \left(\frac{\pi}{2}\right)}{-2 \sin 2\left(\frac{\pi}{2}\right) \cos \left(\frac{\pi}{2}\right) - (-1) \sin \left(\frac{\pi}{2}\right)} = 0;$

Slope at $\left(-1, -\frac{\pi}{2}\right)$ is $\frac{-2 \sin 2\left(-\frac{\pi}{2}\right) \sin \left(-\frac{\pi}{2}\right) + (-1) \cos \left(-\frac{\pi}{2}\right)}{-2 \sin 2\left(-\frac{\pi}{2}\right) \cos \left(-\frac{\pi}{2}\right) - (-1) \sin \left(-\frac{\pi}{2}\right)} = 0;$

Slope at $(1, \pi)$ is $\frac{-2 \sin 2\pi \sin \pi + \cos \pi}{-2 \sin 2\pi \cos \pi - \sin \pi}$, which is undefined

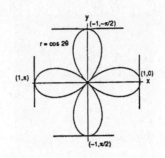

21. (a)

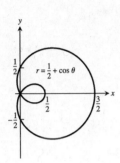

(b)

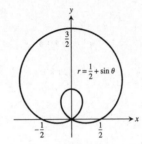

22. (a)

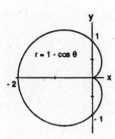

(b)

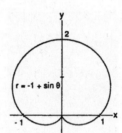

23. (a)

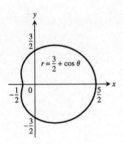

(b)

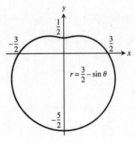

24. (a)

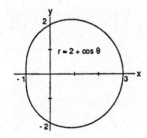

(b)

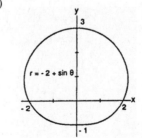

25.

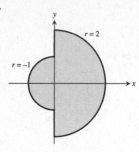

26. $r = 2 \sec \theta \ \Rightarrow \ r = \frac{2}{\cos \theta} \ \Rightarrow \ r \cos \theta = 2 \ \Rightarrow \ x = 2$

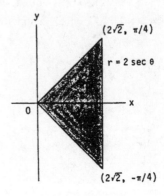

27.

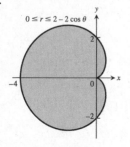

28.

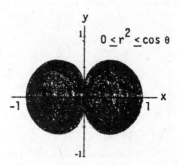

29. Note that $(r, \theta)$ and $(-r, \theta + \pi)$ describe the same point in the plane. Then $r = 1 - \cos \theta \ \Leftrightarrow \ -1 - \cos(\theta + \pi)$
$= -1 - (\cos \theta \cos \pi - \sin \theta \sin \pi) = -1 + \cos \theta = -(1 - \cos \theta) = -r$; therefore $(r, \theta)$ is on the graph of
$r = 1 - \cos \theta \ \Leftrightarrow \ (-r, \theta + \pi)$ is on the graph of $r = -1 - \cos \theta \ \Rightarrow \ $ the answer is (a).

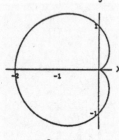

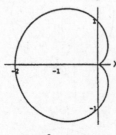

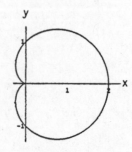

30. Note that $(r, \theta)$ and $(-r, \theta + \pi)$ describe the same point in the plane. Then $r = \cos 2\theta \Leftrightarrow -\sin\left(2(\theta + \pi)\right) + \frac{\pi}{2}$

$= -\sin\left(2\theta + \frac{5\pi}{2}\right) = -\sin(2\theta)\cos\left(\frac{5\pi}{2}\right) - \cos(2\theta)\sin\left(\frac{5\pi}{2}\right) = -\cos 2\theta = -r$; therefore $(r, \theta)$ is on the graph of

$r = -\sin\left(2\theta + \frac{\pi}{2}\right) \Rightarrow$ the answer is (a).

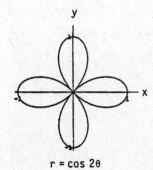

$r = \cos 2\theta$

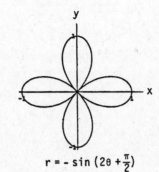

$r = -\sin\left(2\theta + \frac{\pi}{2}\right)$

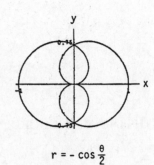

$r = -\cos\frac{\theta}{2}$

31.

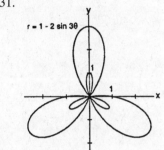

32.

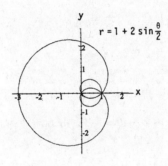

33. (a)

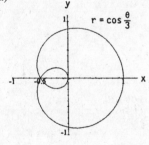

(b)

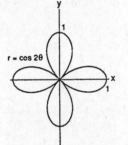

(c)

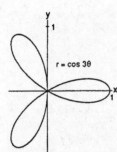

(d)

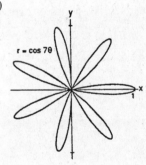

34. (a)

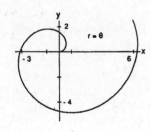

(b)

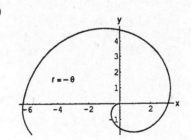

(c)

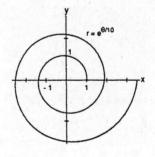

(d)

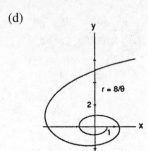

(e)

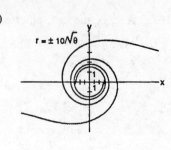

## 11.5 AREA AND LENGTHS IN POLAR COORDINATES

1.  $A = \int_0^\pi \frac{1}{2}\theta^2 \, d\theta = \left[\frac{1}{6}\theta^3\right]_0^\pi = \frac{\pi^3}{6}$

2.  $A = \int_{\pi/4}^{\pi/2} \frac{1}{2}(2\sin\theta)^2 \, d\theta = 2\int_{\pi/4}^{\pi/2} \sin^2\theta \, d\theta = 2\int_{\pi/4}^{\pi/2} \frac{1-\cos 2\theta}{2} \, d\theta = \int_{\pi/4}^{\pi/2}(1-\cos 2\theta)d\theta = \left[\theta - \frac{1}{2}\sin 2\theta\right]_{\pi/4}^{\pi/2}$
    $= \left(\frac{\pi}{2} - 0\right) - \left(\frac{\pi}{4} - \frac{1}{2}\right) = \frac{\pi}{4} + \frac{1}{2}$

3.  $A = \int_0^{2\pi} \frac{1}{2}(4+2\cos\theta)^2 \, d\theta = \int_0^{2\pi} \frac{1}{2}(16+16\cos\theta+4\cos^2\theta) \, d\theta = \int_0^{2\pi}\left[8+8\cos\theta+2\left(\frac{1+\cos 2\theta}{2}\right)\right] d\theta$
    $= \int_0^{2\pi}(9+8\cos\theta+\cos 2\theta) \, d\theta = \left[9\theta + 8\sin\theta + \frac{1}{2}\sin 2\theta\right]_0^{2\pi} = 18\pi$

4.  $A = \int_0^{2\pi} \frac{1}{2}[a(1+\cos\theta)]^2 \, d\theta = \int_0^{2\pi} \frac{1}{2}a^2(1+2\cos\theta+\cos^2\theta) \, d\theta = \frac{1}{2}a^2\int_0^{2\pi}\left(1+2\cos\theta+\frac{1+\cos 2\theta}{2}\right) d\theta$
    $= \frac{1}{2}a^2\int_0^{2\pi}\left(\frac{3}{2}+2\cos\theta+\frac{1}{2}\cos 2\theta\right) d\theta = \frac{1}{2}a^2\left[\frac{3}{2}\theta + 2\sin\theta + \frac{1}{4}\sin 2\theta\right]_0^{2\pi} = \frac{3}{2}\pi a^2$

5.  $A = 2\int_0^{\pi/4} \frac{1}{2}\cos^2 2\theta \, d\theta = \int_0^{\pi/4} \frac{1+\cos 4\theta}{2} \, d\theta = \frac{1}{2}\left[\theta + \frac{\sin 4\theta}{4}\right]_0^{\pi/4} = \frac{\pi}{8}$

6.  $A = \int_{-\pi/6}^{\pi/6} \frac{1}{2}(\cos 3\theta)^2 d\theta = \frac{1}{2}\int_{-\pi/6}^{\pi/6} \cos^2 3\theta \, d\theta = \frac{1}{2}\int_{-\pi/6}^{\pi/6} \frac{1+\cos 6\theta}{2} \, d\theta = \frac{1}{4}\int_{-\pi/6}^{\pi/6}(1+\cos 6\theta) \, d\theta$
    $= \frac{1}{4}\left[\theta + \frac{1}{6}\sin 6\theta\right]_{-\pi/6}^{\pi/6} = \frac{1}{4}\left(\frac{\pi}{6}+0\right) - \frac{1}{4}\left(-\frac{\pi}{6}+0\right) = \frac{\pi}{12}$

7.  $A = \int_0^{\pi/2} \frac{1}{2}(4\sin 2\theta) \, d\theta = \int_0^{\pi/2} 2\sin 2\theta \, d\theta = [-\cos 2\theta]_0^{\pi/2} = 2$

8.  $A = (6)(2)\int_0^{\pi/6} \frac{1}{2}(2\sin 3\theta) \, d\theta = 12\int_0^{\pi/6} \sin 3\theta \, d\theta = 12\left[-\frac{\cos 3\theta}{3}\right]_0^{\pi/6} = 4$

9.  $r = 2\cos\theta$ and $r = 2\sin\theta \Rightarrow 2\cos\theta = 2\sin\theta$
    $\Rightarrow \cos\theta = \sin\theta \Rightarrow \theta = \frac{\pi}{4}$ ; therefore
    $A = 2\int_0^{\pi/4} \frac{1}{2}(2\sin\theta)^2 \, d\theta = \int_0^{\pi/4} 4\sin^2\theta \, d\theta$
    $= \int_0^{\pi/4} 4\left(\frac{1-\cos 2\theta}{2}\right) d\theta = \int_0^{\pi/4}(2-2\cos 2\theta) \, d\theta$
    $= [2\theta - \sin 2\theta]_0^{\pi/4} = \frac{\pi}{2} - 1$

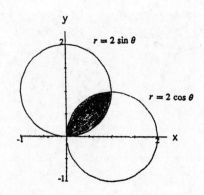

10. $r = 1$ and $r = 2 \sin \theta \Rightarrow 2 \sin \theta = 1 \Rightarrow \sin \theta = \frac{1}{2}$

$\Rightarrow \theta = \frac{\pi}{6}$ or $\frac{5\pi}{6}$ ; therefore

$A = \pi(1)^2 - \int_{\pi/6}^{5\pi/6} \frac{1}{2} [(2 \sin \theta)^2 - 1^2] \, d\theta$

$= \pi - \int_{\pi/6}^{5\pi/6} \left( 2 \sin^2 \theta - \frac{1}{2} \right) d\theta$

$= \pi - \int_{\pi/6}^{5\pi/6} \left( 1 - \cos 2\theta - \frac{1}{2} \right) d\theta$

$= \pi - \int_{\pi/6}^{5\pi/6} \left( \frac{1}{2} - \cos 2\theta \right) d\theta = \pi - \left[ \frac{1}{2} \theta - \frac{\sin 2\theta}{2} \right]_{\pi/6}^{5\pi/6}$

$= \pi - \left( \frac{5\pi}{12} - \frac{1}{2} \sin \frac{5\pi}{3} \right) + \left( \frac{\pi}{12} - \frac{1}{2} \sin \frac{\pi}{3} \right) = \frac{4\pi - 3\sqrt{3}}{6}$

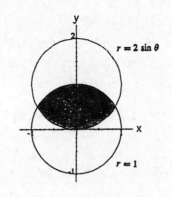

11. $r = 2$ and $r = 2(1 - \cos \theta) \Rightarrow 2 = 2(1 - \cos \theta)$

$\Rightarrow \cos \theta = 0 \Rightarrow \theta = \pm \frac{\pi}{2}$ ; therefore

$A = 2 \int_0^{\pi/2} \frac{1}{2} [2(1 - \cos \theta)]^2 \, d\theta + \frac{1}{2} \text{area of the circle}$

$= \int_0^{\pi/2} 4 (1 - 2 \cos \theta + \cos^2 \theta) \, d\theta + \left( \frac{1}{2} \pi \right) (2)^2$

$= \int_0^{\pi/2} 4 \left( 1 - 2 \cos \theta + \frac{1 + \cos 2\theta}{2} \right) d\theta + 2\pi$

$= \int_0^{\pi/2} (4 - 8 \cos \theta + 2 + 2 \cos 2\theta) \, d\theta + 2\pi$

$= [6\theta - 8 \sin \theta + \sin 2\theta]_0^{\pi/2} + 2\pi = 5\pi - 8$

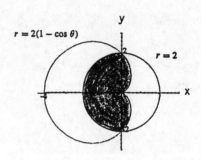

12. $r = 2(1 - \cos \theta)$ and $r = 2(1 + \cos \theta) \Rightarrow 1 - \cos \theta$

$= 1 + \cos \theta \Rightarrow \cos \theta = 0 \Rightarrow \theta = \frac{\pi}{2}$ or $\frac{3\pi}{2}$ ; the graph also

gives the point of intersection $(0, 0)$; therefore

$A = 2 \int_0^{\pi/2} \frac{1}{2} [2(1 - \cos \theta)]^2 \, d\theta + 2 \int_{\pi/2}^{\pi} \frac{1}{2} [2(1 + \cos \theta)]^2 \, d\theta$

$= \int_0^{\pi/2} 4(1 - 2\cos \theta + \cos^2 \theta) d\theta$

$\quad + \int_{\pi/2}^{\pi} 4 (1 + 2 \cos \theta + \cos^2 \theta) d\theta$

$= \int_0^{\pi/2} 4 \left( 1 - 2 \cos \theta + \frac{1 + \cos 2\theta}{2} \right) d\theta + \int_{\pi/2}^{\pi} 4 \left( 1 + 2 \cos \theta + \frac{1 + \cos 2\theta}{2} \right) d\theta$

$= \int_0^{\pi/2} (6 - 8 \cos \theta + 2 \cos 2\theta) \, d\theta + \int_{\pi/2}^{\pi} (6 + 8 \cos \theta + 2 \cos 2\theta) \, d\theta$

$= [6\theta - 8 \sin \theta + \sin 2\theta]_0^{\pi/2} + [6\theta + 8 \sin \theta + \sin 2\theta]_{\pi/2}^{\pi} = 6\pi - 16$

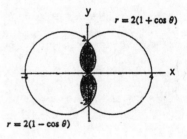

13. $r = \sqrt{3}$ and $r^2 = 6 \cos 2\theta \Rightarrow 3 = 6 \cos 2\theta \Rightarrow \cos 2\theta = \frac{1}{2}$

$\Rightarrow \theta = \frac{\pi}{6}$ (in the 1st quadrant); we use symmetry of the

graph to find the area, so

$A = 4 \int_0^{\pi/6} \left[ \frac{1}{2} (6 \cos 2\theta) - \frac{1}{2} \left( \sqrt{3} \right)^2 \right] d\theta$

$= 2 \int_0^{\pi/6} (6 \cos 2\theta - 3) \, d\theta = 2 [3 \sin 2\theta - 3\theta]_0^{\pi/6}$

$= 3\sqrt{3} - \pi$

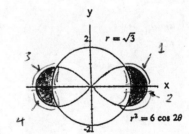

14. $r = 3a \cos \theta$ and $r = a(1 + \cos \theta) \Rightarrow 3a \cos \theta = a(1 + \cos \theta)$

$\Rightarrow 3 \cos \theta = 1 + \cos \theta \Rightarrow \cos \theta = \frac{1}{2} \Rightarrow \theta = \frac{\pi}{3}$ or $-\frac{\pi}{3}$;

the graph also gives the point of intersection $(0, 0)$; therefore

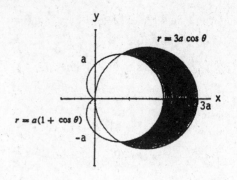

$A = 2 \int_0^{\pi/3} \frac{1}{2} \left[ (3a \cos \theta)^2 - a^2 (1 + \cos \theta)^2 \right] d\theta$

$= \int_0^{\pi/3} (9a^2 \cos^2 \theta - a^2 - 2a^2 \cos \theta - a^2 \cos^2 \theta) \, d\theta$

$= \int_0^{\pi/3} (8a^2 \cos^2 \theta - 2a^2 \cos \theta - a^2) \, d\theta$

$= \int_0^{\pi/3} [4a^2 (1 + \cos 2\theta) - 2a^2 \cos \theta - a^2] \, d\theta$

$= \int_0^{\pi/3} (3a^2 + 4a^2 \cos 2\theta - 2a^2 \cos \theta) \, d\theta$

$= [3a^2 \theta + 2a^2 \sin 2\theta - 2a^2 \sin \theta]_0^{\pi/3} = \pi a^2 + 2a^2 \left( \frac{1}{2} \right) - 2a^2 \left( \frac{\sqrt{3}}{2} \right) = a^2 \left( \pi + 1 - \sqrt{3} \right)$

15. $r = 1$ and $r = -2 \cos \theta \Rightarrow 1 = -2 \cos \theta \Rightarrow \cos \theta = -\frac{1}{2}$

$\Rightarrow \theta = \frac{2\pi}{3}$ in quadrant II; therefore

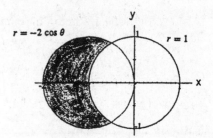

$A = 2 \int_{2\pi/3}^{\pi} \frac{1}{2} \left[ (-2 \cos \theta)^2 - 1^2 \right] d\theta = \int_{2\pi/3}^{\pi} (4 \cos^2 \theta - 1) \, d\theta$

$= \int_{2\pi/3}^{\pi} [2(1 + \cos 2\theta) - 1] \, d\theta = \int_{2\pi/3}^{\pi} (1 + 2 \cos 2\theta) \, d\theta$

$= [\theta + \sin 2\theta]_{2\pi/3}^{\pi} = \frac{\pi}{3} + \frac{\sqrt{3}}{2}$

16. $r = 6$ and $r = 3 \csc \theta \Rightarrow 6 \sin \theta = 3 \Rightarrow \sin \theta = \frac{1}{2}$

$\Rightarrow \theta = \frac{\pi}{6}$ or $\frac{5\pi}{6}$; therefore $A = \int_{\pi/6}^{5\pi/6} \frac{1}{2} (6^2 - 9 \csc^2 \theta) \, d\theta$

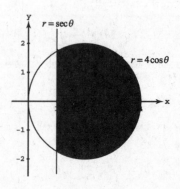

$= \int_{\pi/6}^{5\pi/6} \left( 18 - \frac{9}{2} \csc^2 \theta \right) d\theta = \left[ 18\theta + \frac{9}{2} \cot \theta \right]_{\pi/6}^{5\pi/6}$

$= \left( 15\pi - \frac{9}{2} \sqrt{3} \right) - \left( 3\pi + \frac{9}{2} \sqrt{3} \right) = 12\pi - 9\sqrt{3}$

17. $r = \sec \theta$ and $r = 4 \cos \theta \Rightarrow 4 \cos \theta = \sec \theta \Rightarrow \cos^2 \theta = \frac{1}{4}$

$\Rightarrow \theta = \frac{\pi}{3}, \frac{2\pi}{3}, \frac{4\pi}{3}$, or $\frac{5\pi}{3}$; therefore

$A = 2 \int_0^{\pi/3} \frac{1}{2} (16 \cos^2 \theta - \sec^2 \theta) \, d\theta$

$= \int_0^{\pi/3} (8 + 8 \cos 2\theta - \sec^2 \theta) \, d\theta$

$= [8\theta + 4 \sin 2\theta - \tan \theta]_0^{\pi/3}$

$= \left( \frac{8\pi}{3} + 2\sqrt{3} - \sqrt{3} \right) - (0 + 0 - 0) = \frac{8\pi}{3} + \sqrt{3}$

18. $r = 3\csc\theta$ and $r = 4\sin\theta \Rightarrow 4\sin\theta = 3\csc\theta \Rightarrow \sin^2\theta = \frac{3}{4}$

$\Rightarrow \theta = \frac{\pi}{3}, \frac{2\pi}{3}, \frac{4\pi}{3},$ or $\frac{5\pi}{3}$ ; therefore

$A = 4\pi - 2\int_{\pi/3}^{\pi/2} \frac{1}{2}\left(16\sin^2\theta - 9\csc^2\theta\right) d\theta$

$= 4\pi - \int_{\pi/3}^{\pi/2}\left(8 - 8\cos 2\theta - 9\csc^2\theta\right) d\theta$

$= 4\pi - \left[8\theta - 4\sin 2\theta + 9\cot\theta\right]_{\pi/3}^{\pi/2}$

$= 4\pi - \left[(4\pi - 0 + 0) - \left(\frac{8\pi}{3} - 2\sqrt{3} + 3\sqrt{3}\right)\right]$

$= \frac{8\pi}{3} + \sqrt{3}$

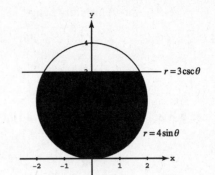

19. (a) $r = \tan\theta$ and $r = \left(\frac{\sqrt{2}}{2}\right)\csc\theta \Rightarrow \tan\theta = \left(\frac{\sqrt{2}}{2}\right)\csc\theta$

$\Rightarrow \sin^2\theta = \left(\frac{\sqrt{2}}{2}\right)\cos\theta \Rightarrow 1 - \cos^2\theta = \left(\frac{\sqrt{2}}{2}\right)\cos\theta$

$\Rightarrow \cos^2\theta + \left(\frac{\sqrt{2}}{2}\right)\cos\theta - 1 = 0 \Rightarrow \cos\theta = -\sqrt{2}$ or

$\frac{\sqrt{2}}{2}$ (use the quadratic formula) $\Rightarrow \theta = \frac{\pi}{4}$ (the solution

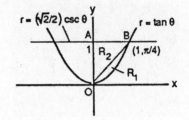

in the first quadrant); therefore the area of $R_1$ is

$A_1 = \int_0^{\pi/4} \frac{1}{2}\tan^2\theta \, d\theta = \frac{1}{2}\int_0^{\pi/4}\left(\sec^2\theta - 1\right) d\theta = \frac{1}{2}\left[\tan\theta - \theta\right]_0^{\pi/4} = \frac{1}{2}\left(\tan\frac{\pi}{4} - \frac{\pi}{4}\right) = \frac{1}{2} - \frac{\pi}{8}; AO = \left(\frac{\sqrt{2}}{2}\right)\csc\frac{\pi}{2}$

$= \frac{\sqrt{2}}{2}$ and $OB = \left(\frac{\sqrt{2}}{2}\right)\csc\frac{\pi}{4} = 1 \Rightarrow AB = \sqrt{1^2 - \left(\frac{\sqrt{2}}{2}\right)^2} = \frac{\sqrt{2}}{2} \Rightarrow$ the area of $R_2$ is $A_2 = \frac{1}{2}\left(\frac{\sqrt{2}}{2}\right)\left(\frac{\sqrt{2}}{2}\right) = \frac{1}{4}$ ;

therefore the area of the region shaded in the text is $2\left(\frac{1}{2} - \frac{\pi}{8} + \frac{1}{4}\right) = \frac{3}{2} - \frac{\pi}{4}$ . Note: The area must be found this way

since no common interval generates the region. For example, the interval $0 \le \theta \le \frac{\pi}{4}$ generates the arc OB of $r = \tan\theta$

but does not generate the segment AB of the line $r = \frac{\sqrt{2}}{2}\csc\theta$. Instead the interval generates the half-line from B to

$+\infty$ on the line $r = \frac{\sqrt{2}}{2}\csc\theta$.

(b) $\lim_{\theta \to \pi/2^-} \tan\theta = \infty$ and the line $x = 1$ is $r = \sec\theta$ in polar coordinates; then $\lim_{\theta \to \pi/2^-} (\tan\theta - \sec\theta)$

$= \lim_{\theta \to \pi/2^-} \left(\frac{\sin\theta}{\cos\theta} - \frac{1}{\cos\theta}\right) = \lim_{\theta \to \pi/2^-} \left(\frac{\sin\theta - 1}{\cos\theta}\right) = \lim_{\theta \to \pi/2^-} \left(\frac{\cos\theta}{-\sin\theta}\right) = 0 \Rightarrow r = \tan\theta$ approaches

$r = \sec\theta$ as $\theta \to \frac{\pi^-}{2} \Rightarrow r = \sec\theta$ (or $x = 1$) is a vertical asymptote of $r = \tan\theta$. Similarly, $r = -\sec\theta$ (or $x = -1$)

is a vertical asymptote of $r = \tan\theta$.

20. It is not because the circle is generated twice from $\theta = 0$ to $2\pi$. The area of the cardioid is

$A = 2\int_0^\pi \frac{1}{2}(\cos\theta + 1)^2 \, d\theta = \int_0^\pi (\cos^2\theta + 2\cos\theta + 1) \, d\theta = \int_0^\pi \left(\frac{1 + \cos 2\theta}{2} + 2\cos\theta + 1\right) d\theta$

$= \left[\frac{3\theta}{2} + \frac{\sin 2\theta}{4} + 2\sin\theta\right]_0^\pi = \frac{3\pi}{2}$ . The area of the circle is $A = \pi\left(\frac{1}{2}\right)^2 = \frac{\pi}{4} \Rightarrow$ the area requested is actually $\frac{3\pi}{2} - \frac{\pi}{4} = \frac{5\pi}{4}$

21. $r = \theta^2, 0 \le \theta \le \sqrt{5} \Rightarrow \frac{dr}{d\theta} = 2\theta$; therefore Length $= \int_0^{\sqrt{5}} \sqrt{(\theta^2)^2 + (2\theta)^2} \, d\theta = \int_0^{\sqrt{5}} \sqrt{\theta^4 + 4\theta^2} \, d\theta$

$= \int_0^{\sqrt{5}} |\theta| \sqrt{\theta^2 + 4} \, d\theta = $ (since $\theta \ge 0$) $\int_0^{\sqrt{5}} \theta\sqrt{\theta^2 + 4} \, d\theta; \left[u = \theta^2 + 4 \Rightarrow \frac{1}{2}\,du = \theta\,d\theta; \theta = 0 \Rightarrow u = 4,\right.$

$\left.\theta = \sqrt{5} \Rightarrow u = 9\right] \to \int_4^9 \frac{1}{2}\sqrt{u}\,du = \frac{1}{2}\left[\frac{2}{3}u^{3/2}\right]_4^9 = \frac{19}{3}$

22. $r = \frac{e^\theta}{\sqrt{2}}, 0 \le \theta \le \pi \Rightarrow \frac{dr}{d\theta} = \frac{e^\theta}{\sqrt{2}}$ ; therefore Length $= \int_0^\pi \sqrt{\left(\frac{e^\theta}{\sqrt{2}}\right)^2 + \left(\frac{e^\theta}{\sqrt{2}}\right)^2} \, d\theta = \int_0^\pi \sqrt{2\left(\frac{e^{2\theta}}{2}\right)} \, d\theta$

$= \int_0^\pi e^\theta \, d\theta = \left[e^\theta\right]_0^\pi = e^\pi - 1$

23. $r = 1 + \cos\theta \Rightarrow \frac{dr}{d\theta} = -\sin\theta$; therefore Length $= \int_0^{2\pi} \sqrt{(1 + \cos\theta)^2 + (-\sin\theta)^2}\, d\theta$

$= 2\int_0^\pi \sqrt{2 + 2\cos\theta}\, d\theta = 2\int_0^\pi \sqrt{\frac{4(1+\cos\theta)}{2}}\, d\theta = 4\int_0^\pi \sqrt{\frac{1+\cos\theta}{2}}\, d\theta = 4\int_0^\pi \cos\left(\frac{\theta}{2}\right) d\theta = 4\left[2\sin\frac{\theta}{2}\right]_0^\pi = 8$

24. $r = a\sin^2\frac{\theta}{2}, 0 \le \theta \le \pi, a > 0 \Rightarrow \frac{dr}{d\theta} = a\sin\frac{\theta}{2}\cos\frac{\theta}{2}$; therefore Length $= \int_0^\pi \sqrt{\left(a\sin^2\frac{\theta}{2}\right)^2 + \left(a\sin\frac{\theta}{2}\cos\frac{\theta}{2}\right)^2}\, d\theta$

$= \int_0^\pi \sqrt{a^2\sin^4\frac{\theta}{2} + a^2\sin^2\frac{\theta}{2}\cos^2\frac{\theta}{2}}\, d\theta = \int_0^\pi a\left|\sin\frac{\theta}{2}\right| \sqrt{\sin^2\frac{\theta}{2} + \cos^2\frac{\theta}{2}}\, d\theta = \text{(since } 0 \le \theta \le \pi\text{) } a\int_0^\pi \sin\left(\frac{\theta}{2}\right) d\theta$

$= \left[-2a\cos\frac{\theta}{2}\right]_0^\pi = 2a$

25. $r = \frac{6}{1+\cos\theta}, 0 \le \theta \le \frac{\pi}{2} \Rightarrow \frac{dr}{d\theta} = \frac{6\sin\theta}{(1+\cos\theta)^2}$; therefore Length $= \int_0^{\pi/2} \sqrt{\left(\frac{6}{1+\cos\theta}\right)^2 + \left(\frac{6\sin\theta}{(1+\cos\theta)^2}\right)^2}\, d\theta$

$= \int_0^{\pi/2} \sqrt{\frac{36}{(1+\cos\theta)^2} + \frac{36\sin^2\theta}{(1+\cos\theta)^4}}\, d\theta = 6\int_0^{\pi/2} \left|\frac{1}{1+\cos\theta}\right| \sqrt{1 + \frac{\sin^2\theta}{(1+\cos\theta)^2}}\, d\theta$

$= \left(\text{since } \frac{1}{1+\cos\theta} > 0 \text{ on } 0 \le \theta \le \frac{\pi}{2}\right) 6\int_0^{\pi/2} \left(\frac{1}{1+\cos\theta}\right) \sqrt{\frac{1 + 2\cos\theta + \cos^2\theta + \sin^2\theta}{(1+\cos\theta)^2}}\, d\theta$

$= 6\int_0^{\pi/2} \left(\frac{1}{1+\cos\theta}\right) \sqrt{\frac{2 + 2\cos\theta}{(1+\cos\theta)^2}}\, d\theta = 6\sqrt{2}\int_0^{\pi/2} \frac{d\theta}{(1+\cos\theta)^{3/2}} = 6\sqrt{2}\int_0^{\pi/2} \frac{d\theta}{\left(2\cos^2\frac{\theta}{2}\right)^{3/2}} = 3\int_0^{\pi/2} \left|\sec^3\frac{\theta}{2}\right| d\theta$

$= 3\int_0^{\pi/2} \sec^3\frac{\theta}{2}\, d\theta = 6\int_0^{\pi/4} \sec^3 u\, du = \text{(use tables) } 6\left(\left[\frac{\sec u\tan u}{2}\right]_0^{\pi/4} + \frac{1}{2}\int_0^{\pi/4} \sec u\, du\right)$

$= 6\left(\frac{1}{\sqrt{2}} + \left[\frac{1}{2}\ln|\sec u + \tan u|\right]_0^{\pi/4}\right) = 3\left[\sqrt{2} + \ln\left(1 + \sqrt{2}\right)\right]$

26. $r = \frac{2}{1-\cos\theta}, \frac{\pi}{2} \le \theta \le \pi \Rightarrow \frac{dr}{d\theta} = \frac{-2\sin\theta}{(1-\cos\theta)^2}$; therefore Length $= \int_{\pi/2}^\pi \sqrt{\left(\frac{2}{1-\cos\theta}\right)^2 + \left(\frac{-2\sin\theta}{(1-\cos\theta)^2}\right)^2}\, d\theta$

$= \int_{\pi/2}^\pi \sqrt{\frac{4}{(1-\cos\theta)^2}\left(1 + \frac{\sin^2\theta}{(1-\cos\theta)^2}\right)}\, d\theta = \int_{\pi/2}^\pi \left|\frac{2}{1-\cos\theta}\right| \sqrt{\frac{(1-\cos\theta)^2 + \sin^2\theta}{(1-\cos\theta)^2}}\, d\theta$

$= \left(\text{since } 1 - \cos\theta \ge 0 \text{ on } \frac{\pi}{2} \le \theta \le \pi\right) 2\int_{\pi/2}^\pi \left(\frac{1}{1-\cos\theta}\right) \sqrt{\frac{1 - 2\cos\theta + \cos^2\theta + \sin^2\theta}{(1-\cos\theta)^2}}\, d\theta$

$= 2\int_{\pi/2}^\pi \left(\frac{1}{1-\cos\theta}\right) \sqrt{\frac{2 - 2\cos\theta}{(1-\cos\theta)^2}}\, d\theta = 2\sqrt{2}\int_{\pi/2}^\pi \frac{d\theta}{(1-\cos\theta)^{3/2}} = 2\sqrt{2}\int_{\pi/2}^\pi \frac{d\theta}{\left(2\sin^2\frac{\theta}{2}\right)^{3/2}} = \int_{\pi/2}^\pi \left|\csc^3\frac{\theta}{2}\right| d\theta$

$= \int_{\pi/2}^\pi \csc^3\left(\frac{\theta}{2}\right) d\theta = \left(\text{since } \csc\frac{\theta}{2} \ge 0 \text{ on } \frac{\pi}{2} \le \theta \le \pi\right) 2\int_{\pi/4}^{\pi/2} \csc^3 u\, du = \text{(use tables)}$

$2\left(\left[-\frac{\csc u\cot u}{2}\right]_{\pi/4}^{\pi/2} + \frac{1}{2}\int_{\pi/4}^{\pi/2} \csc u\, du\right) = 2\left(\frac{1}{\sqrt{2}} - \left[\frac{1}{2}\ln|\csc u + \cot u|\right]_{\pi/4}^{\pi/2}\right) = 2\left[\frac{1}{\sqrt{2}} + \frac{1}{2}\ln\left(\sqrt{2} + 1\right)\right]$

$= \sqrt{2} + \ln\left(1 + \sqrt{2}\right)$

27. $r = \cos^3\frac{\theta}{3} \Rightarrow \frac{dr}{d\theta} = -\sin\frac{\theta}{3}\cos^2\frac{\theta}{3}$; therefore Length $= \int_0^{\pi/4} \sqrt{\left(\cos^3\frac{\theta}{3}\right)^2 + \left(-\sin\frac{\theta}{3}\cos^2\frac{\theta}{3}\right)^2}\, d\theta$

$= \int_0^{\pi/4} \sqrt{\cos^6\left(\frac{\theta}{3}\right) + \sin^2\left(\frac{\theta}{3}\right)\cos^4\left(\frac{\theta}{3}\right)}\, d\theta = \int_0^{\pi/4} \left(\cos^2\frac{\theta}{3}\right) \sqrt{\cos^2\left(\frac{\theta}{3}\right) + \sin^2\left(\frac{\theta}{3}\right)}\, d\theta = \int_0^{\pi/4} \cos^2\left(\frac{\theta}{3}\right) d\theta$

$= \int_0^{\pi/4} \frac{1 + \cos\left(\frac{2\theta}{3}\right)}{2}\, d\theta = \frac{1}{2}\left[\theta + \frac{3}{2}\sin\frac{2\theta}{3}\right]_0^{\pi/4} = \frac{\pi}{8} + \frac{3}{8}$

28. $r = \sqrt{1 + \sin 2\theta}, 0 \le \theta \le \pi\sqrt{2} \Rightarrow \frac{dr}{d\theta} = \frac{1}{2}(1 + \sin 2\theta)^{-1/2}(2\cos 2\theta) = (\cos 2\theta)(1 + \sin 2\theta)^{-1/2}$; therefore

Length $= \int_0^{\pi\sqrt{2}} \sqrt{(1 + \sin 2\theta) + \frac{\cos^2 2\theta}{(1+\sin 2\theta)}}\, d\theta = \int_0^{\pi\sqrt{2}} \sqrt{\frac{1 + 2\sin 2\theta + \sin^2 2\theta + \cos^2 2\theta}{1 + \sin 2\theta}}\, d\theta$

$= \int_0^{\pi\sqrt{2}} \sqrt{\frac{2 + 2\sin 2\theta}{1 + \sin 2\theta}}\, d\theta = \int_0^{\pi\sqrt{2}} \sqrt{2}\, d\theta = \left[\sqrt{2}\,\theta\right]_0^{\pi\sqrt{2}} = 2\pi$

29. Let $r = f(\theta)$. Then $x = f(\theta)\cos\theta \Rightarrow \frac{dx}{d\theta} = f'(\theta)\cos\theta - f(\theta)\sin\theta \Rightarrow \left(\frac{dx}{d\theta}\right)^2 = [f'(\theta)\cos\theta - f(\theta)\sin\theta]^2$

$= [f'(\theta)]^2\cos^2\theta - 2f'(\theta)f(\theta)\sin\theta\cos\theta + [f(\theta)]^2\sin^2\theta$; $y = f(\theta)\sin\theta \Rightarrow \frac{dy}{d\theta} = f'(\theta)\sin\theta + f(\theta)\cos\theta$

$\Rightarrow \left(\frac{dy}{d\theta}\right)^2 = [f'(\theta)\sin\theta + f(\theta)\cos\theta]^2 = [f'(\theta)]^2\sin^2\theta + 2f'(\theta)f(\theta)\sin\theta\cos\theta + [f(\theta)]^2\cos^2\theta$. Therefore

$\left(\frac{dx}{d\theta}\right)^2 + \left(\frac{dy}{d\theta}\right)^2 = [f'(\theta)]^2(\cos^2\theta + \sin^2\theta) + [f(\theta)]^2(\cos^2\theta + \sin^2\theta) = [f'(\theta)]^2 + [f(\theta)]^2 = r^2 + \left(\frac{dr}{d\theta}\right)^2$.

Thus, $L = \int_\alpha^\beta \sqrt{\left(\frac{dx}{d\theta}\right)^2 + \left(\frac{dy}{d\theta}\right)^2}\, d\theta = \int_\alpha^\beta \sqrt{r^2 + \left(\frac{dr}{d\theta}\right)^2}\, d\theta$.

30. (a) $r = a \Rightarrow \frac{dr}{d\theta} = 0$; Length $= \int_0^{2\pi}\sqrt{a^2 + 0^2}\, d\theta = \int_0^{2\pi}|a|\, d\theta = [a\theta]_0^{2\pi} = 2\pi a$

(b) $r = a\cos\theta \Rightarrow \frac{dr}{d\theta} = -a\sin\theta$; Length $= \int_0^\pi \sqrt{(a\cos\theta)^2 + (-a\sin\theta)^2}\, d\theta = \int_0^\pi \sqrt{a^2(\cos^2\theta + \sin^2\theta)}\, d\theta$

$= \int_0^\pi |a|\, d\theta = [a\theta]_0^\pi = \pi a$

(c) $r = a\sin\theta \Rightarrow \frac{dr}{d\theta} = a\cos\theta$; Length $= \int_0^\pi \sqrt{(a\cos\theta)^2 + (a\sin\theta)^2}\, d\theta = \int_0^\pi \sqrt{a^2(\cos^2\theta + \sin^2\theta)}\, d\theta$

$= \int_0^\pi |a|\, d\theta = [a\theta]_0^\pi = \pi a$

31. (a) $r_{av} = \frac{1}{2\pi - 0}\int_0^{2\pi} a(1 - \cos\theta)\, d\theta = \frac{a}{2\pi}[\theta - \sin\theta]_0^{2\pi} = a$

(b) $r_{av} = \frac{1}{2\pi - 0}\int_0^{2\pi} a\, d\theta = \frac{1}{2\pi}[a\theta]_0^{2\pi} = a$

(c) $r_{av} = \frac{1}{\left(\frac{\pi}{2}\right) - \left(-\frac{\pi}{2}\right)}\int_{-\pi/2}^{\pi/2} a\cos\theta\, d\theta = \frac{1}{\pi}[a\sin\theta]_{-\pi/2}^{\pi/2} = \frac{2a}{\pi}$

32. $r = 2f(\theta)$, $\alpha \le \theta \le \beta \Rightarrow \frac{dr}{d\theta} = 2f'(\theta) \Rightarrow r^2 + \left(\frac{dr}{d\theta}\right)^2 = [2f(\theta)]^2 + [2f'(\theta)]^2 \Rightarrow$ Length $= \int_\alpha^\beta \sqrt{4[f(\theta)]^2 + 4[f'(\theta)]^2}\, d\theta$

$= 2\int_\alpha^\beta \sqrt{[f(\theta)]^2 + [f'(\theta)]^2}\, d\theta$ which is twice the length of the curve $r = f(\theta)$ for $\alpha \le \theta \le \beta$.

## 11.6 CONIC SECTIONS

1. $x = \frac{y^2}{8} \Rightarrow 4p = 8 \Rightarrow p = 2$; focus is $(2, 0)$, directrix is $x = -2$

2. $x = -\frac{y^2}{4} \Rightarrow 4p = 4 \Rightarrow p = 1$; focus is $(-1, 0)$, directrix is $x = 1$

3. $y = -\frac{x^2}{6} \Rightarrow 4p = 6 \Rightarrow p = \frac{3}{2}$; focus is $\left(0, -\frac{3}{2}\right)$, directrix is $y = \frac{3}{2}$

4. $y = \frac{x^2}{2} \Rightarrow 4p = 2 \Rightarrow p = \frac{1}{2}$; focus is $\left(0, \frac{1}{2}\right)$, directrix is $y = -\frac{1}{2}$

5. $\frac{x^2}{4} - \frac{y^2}{9} = 1 \Rightarrow c = \sqrt{4 + 9} = \sqrt{13} \Rightarrow$ foci are $\left(\pm\sqrt{13}, 0\right)$; vertices are $(\pm 2, 0)$; asymptotes are $y = \pm\frac{3}{2}x$

6. $\frac{x^2}{4} + \frac{y^2}{9} = 1 \Rightarrow c = \sqrt{9 - 4} = \sqrt{5} \Rightarrow$ foci are $\left(0, \pm\sqrt{5}\right)$; vertices are $(0, \pm 3)$

7. $\frac{x^2}{2} + y^2 = 1 \Rightarrow c = \sqrt{2 - 1} = 1 \Rightarrow$ foci are $(\pm 1, 0)$; vertices are $\left(\pm\sqrt{2}, 0\right)$

8. $\frac{y^2}{4} - x^2 = 1 \Rightarrow c = \sqrt{4 + 1} = \sqrt{5} \Rightarrow$ foci are $\left(0, \pm\sqrt{5}\right)$; vertices are $(0, \pm 2)$; asymptotes are $y = \pm 2x$

9. $y^2 = 12x \Rightarrow x = \frac{y^2}{12} \Rightarrow 4p = 12 \Rightarrow p = 3$;
   focus is $(3, 0)$, directrix is $x = -3$

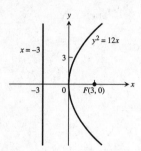

10. $x^2 = 6y \Rightarrow y = \frac{x^2}{6} \Rightarrow 4p = 6 \Rightarrow p = \frac{3}{2}$;
    focus is $\left(0, \frac{3}{2}\right)$, directrix is $y = -\frac{3}{2}$

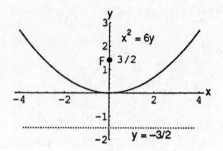

11. $x^2 = -8y \Rightarrow y = \frac{x^2}{-8} \Rightarrow 4p = 8 \Rightarrow p = 2$;
    focus is $(0, -2)$, directrix is $y = 2$

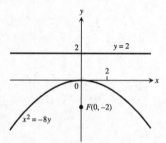

12. $y^2 = -2x \Rightarrow x = \frac{y^2}{-2} \Rightarrow 4p = 2 \Rightarrow p = \frac{1}{2}$;
    focus is $\left(-\frac{1}{2}, 0\right)$, directrix is $x = \frac{1}{2}$

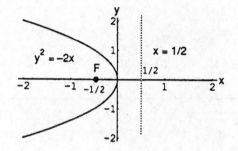

13. $y = 4x^2 \Rightarrow y = \frac{x^2}{\left(\frac{1}{4}\right)} \Rightarrow 4p = \frac{1}{4} \Rightarrow p = \frac{1}{16}$;
    focus is $\left(0, \frac{1}{16}\right)$, directrix is $y = -\frac{1}{16}$

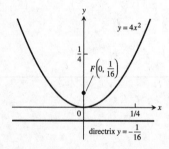

14. $y = -8x^2 \Rightarrow y = -\frac{x^2}{\left(\frac{1}{8}\right)} \Rightarrow 4p = \frac{1}{8} \Rightarrow p = \frac{1}{32}$;
    focus is $\left(0, -\frac{1}{32}\right)$, directrix is $y = \frac{1}{32}$

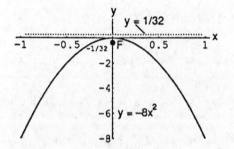

15. $x = -3y^2 \Rightarrow x = -\frac{y^2}{\left(\frac{1}{3}\right)} \Rightarrow 4p = \frac{1}{3} \Rightarrow p = \frac{1}{12}$;
    focus is $\left(-\frac{1}{12}, 0\right)$, directrix is $x = \frac{1}{12}$

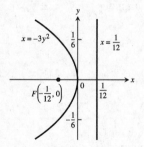

16. $x = 2y^2 \Rightarrow x = \frac{y^2}{\left(\frac{1}{2}\right)} \Rightarrow 4p = \frac{1}{2} \Rightarrow p = \frac{1}{8}$;
    focus is $\left(\frac{1}{8}, 0\right)$, directrix is $x = -\frac{1}{8}$

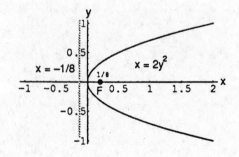

17. $16x^2 + 25y^2 = 400 \Rightarrow \frac{x^2}{25} + \frac{y^2}{16} = 1$
$\Rightarrow c = \sqrt{a^2 - b^2} = \sqrt{25 - 16} = 3$

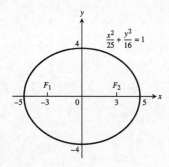

18. $7x^2 + 16y^2 = 112 \Rightarrow \frac{x^2}{16} + \frac{y^2}{7} = 1$
$\Rightarrow c = \sqrt{a^2 - b^2} = \sqrt{16 - 7} = 3$

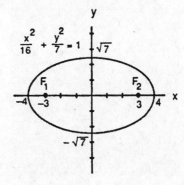

19. $2x^2 + y^2 = 2 \Rightarrow x^2 + \frac{y^2}{2} = 1$
$\Rightarrow c = \sqrt{a^2 - b^2} = \sqrt{2 - 1} = 1$

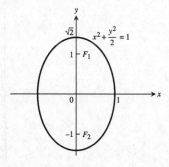

20. $2x^2 + y^2 = 4 \Rightarrow \frac{x^2}{2} + \frac{y^2}{4} = 1$
$\Rightarrow c = \sqrt{a^2 - b^2} = \sqrt{4 - 2} = \sqrt{2}$

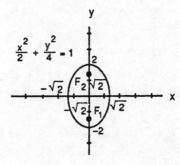

21. $3x^2 + 2y^2 = 6 \Rightarrow \frac{x^2}{2} + \frac{y^2}{3} = 1$
$\Rightarrow c = \sqrt{a^2 - b^2} = \sqrt{3 - 2} = 1$

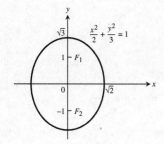

22. $9x^2 + 10y^2 = 90 \Rightarrow \frac{x^2}{10} + \frac{y^2}{9} = 1$
$\Rightarrow c = \sqrt{a^2 - b^2} = \sqrt{10 - 9} = 1$

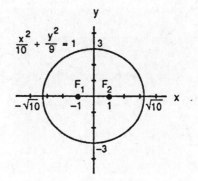

23. $6x^2 + 9y^2 = 54 \Rightarrow \frac{x^2}{9} + \frac{y^2}{6} = 1$
$\Rightarrow c = \sqrt{a^2 - b^2} = \sqrt{9 - 6} = \sqrt{3}$

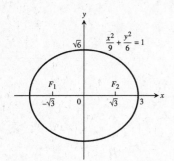

24. $169x^2 + 25y^2 = 4225 \Rightarrow \frac{x^2}{25} + \frac{y^2}{169} = 1$
$\Rightarrow c = \sqrt{a^2 - b^2} = \sqrt{169 - 25} = 12$

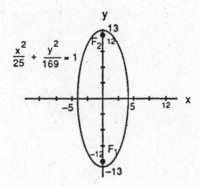

25. Foci: $\left(\pm\sqrt{2}, 0\right)$, Vertices: $(\pm 2, 0) \Rightarrow a = 2, c = \sqrt{2} \Rightarrow b^2 = a^2 - c^2 = 4 - \left(\sqrt{2}\right)^2 = 2 \Rightarrow \frac{x^2}{4} + \frac{y^2}{2} = 1$

26. Foci: $(0, \pm 4)$, Vertices: $(0, \pm 5) \Rightarrow a = 5, c = 4 \Rightarrow b^2 = 25 - 16 = 9 \Rightarrow \frac{x^2}{9} + \frac{y^2}{25} = 1$

27. $x^2 - y^2 = 1 \Rightarrow c = \sqrt{a^2 + b^2} = \sqrt{1 + 1} = \sqrt{2}$;
asymptotes are $y = \pm x$

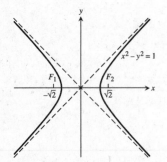

28. $9x^2 - 16y^2 = 144 \Rightarrow \frac{x^2}{16} - \frac{y^2}{9} = 1$
$\Rightarrow c = \sqrt{a^2 + b^2} = \sqrt{16 + 9} = 5$;
asymptotes are $y = \pm \frac{3}{4} x$

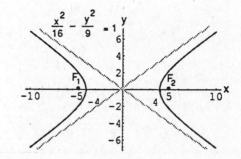

29. $y^2 - x^2 = 8 \Rightarrow \frac{y^2}{8} - \frac{x^2}{8} = 1 \Rightarrow c = \sqrt{a^2 + b^2}$
$= \sqrt{8 + 8} = 4$; asymptotes are $y = \pm x$

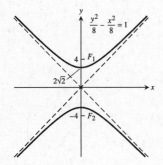

30. $y^2 - x^2 = 4 \Rightarrow \frac{y^2}{4} - \frac{x^2}{4} = 1 \Rightarrow c = \sqrt{a^2 + b^2}$
$= \sqrt{4 + 4} = 2\sqrt{2}$; asymptotes are $y = \pm x$

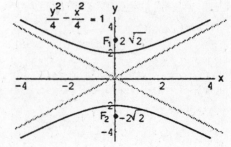

31. $8x^2 - 2y^2 = 16 \Rightarrow \frac{x^2}{2} - \frac{y^2}{8} = 1 \Rightarrow c = \sqrt{a^2 + b^2}$
    $= \sqrt{2 + 8} = \sqrt{10}$; asymptotes are $y = \pm 2x$

32. $y^2 - 3x^2 = 3 \Rightarrow \frac{y^2}{3} - x^2 = 1 \Rightarrow c = \sqrt{a^2 + b^2}$
    $= \sqrt{3 + 1} = 2$; asymptotes are $y = \pm \sqrt{3}x$

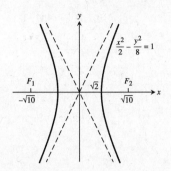

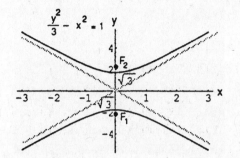

33. $8y^2 - 2x^2 = 16 \Rightarrow \frac{y^2}{2} - \frac{x^2}{8} = 1 \Rightarrow c = \sqrt{a^2 + b^2}$
    $= \sqrt{2 + 8} = \sqrt{10}$; asymptotes are $y = \pm \frac{x}{2}$

34. $64x^2 - 36y^2 = 2304 \Rightarrow \frac{x^2}{36} - \frac{y^2}{64} = 1 \Rightarrow c = \sqrt{a^2 + b^2}$
    $= \sqrt{36 + 64} = 10$; asymptotes are $y = \pm \frac{4}{3}$

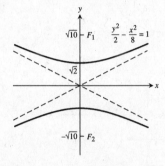

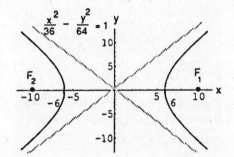

35. Foci: $\left(0, \pm \sqrt{2}\right)$, Asymptotes: $y = \pm x \Rightarrow c = \sqrt{2}$ and $\frac{a}{b} = 1 \Rightarrow a = b \Rightarrow c^2 = a^2 + b^2 = 2a^2 \Rightarrow 2 = 2a^2$
    $\Rightarrow a = 1 \Rightarrow b = 1 \Rightarrow y^2 - x^2 = 1$

36. Foci: $(\pm 2, 0)$, Asymptotes: $y = \pm \frac{1}{\sqrt{3}}x \Rightarrow c = 2$ and $\frac{b}{a} = \frac{1}{\sqrt{3}} \Rightarrow b = \frac{a}{\sqrt{3}} \Rightarrow c^2 = a^2 + b^2 = a^2 + \frac{a^2}{3} = \frac{4a^2}{3}$
    $\Rightarrow 4 = \frac{4a^2}{3} \Rightarrow a^2 = 3 \Rightarrow a = \sqrt{3} \Rightarrow b = 1 \Rightarrow \frac{x^2}{3} - y^2 = 1$

37. Vertices: $(\pm 3, 0)$, Asymptotes: $y = \pm \frac{4}{3}x \Rightarrow a = 3$ and $\frac{b}{a} = \frac{4}{3} \Rightarrow b = \frac{4}{3}(3) = 4 \Rightarrow \frac{x^2}{9} - \frac{y^2}{16} = 1$

38. Vertices: $(0, \pm 2)$, Asymptotes: $y = \pm \frac{1}{2}x \Rightarrow a = 2$ and $\frac{a}{b} = \frac{1}{2} \Rightarrow b = 2(2) = 4 \Rightarrow \frac{y^2}{4} - \frac{x^2}{16} = 1$

39. (a) $y^2 = 8x \Rightarrow 4p = 8 \Rightarrow p = 2 \Rightarrow$ directrix is $x = -2$,
    focus is $(2, 0)$, and vertex is $(0, 0)$; therefore the new
    directrix is $x = -1$, the new focus is $(3, -2)$, and the
    new vertex is $(1, -2)$

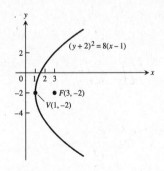

40. (a) $x^2 = -4y \Rightarrow 4p = 4 \Rightarrow p = 1 \Rightarrow$ directrix is $y = 1$,   (b)
    focus is $(0, -1)$, and vertex is $(0, 0)$; therefore the new
    directrix is $y = 4$, the new focus is $(-1, 2)$, and the
    new vertex is $(-1, 3)$

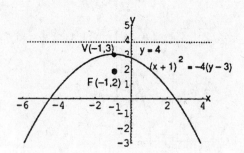

41. (a) $\frac{x^2}{16} + \frac{y^2}{9} = 1 \Rightarrow$ center is $(0, 0)$, vertices are $(-4, 0)$   (b)
    and $(4, 0)$; $c = \sqrt{a^2 - b^2} = \sqrt{7} \Rightarrow$ foci are $\left(\sqrt{7}, 0\right)$
    and $\left(-\sqrt{7}, 0\right)$; therefore the new center is $(4, 3)$, the
    new vertices are $(0, 3)$ and $(8, 3)$, and the new foci are
    $\left(4 \pm \sqrt{7}, 3\right)$

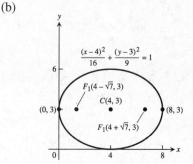

42. (a) $\frac{x^2}{9} + \frac{y^2}{25} = 1 \Rightarrow$ center is $(0, 0)$, vertices are $(0, 5)$   (b)
    and $(0, -5)$; $c = \sqrt{a^2 - b^2} = \sqrt{16} = 4 \Rightarrow$ foci are
    $(0, 4)$ and $(0, -4)$; therefore the new center is $(-3, -2)$,
    the  new vertices are $(-3, 3)$ and $(-3, -7)$, and the new
    foci are $(-3, 2)$ and $(-3, -6)$

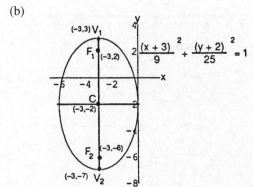

43. (a) $\frac{x^2}{16} - \frac{y^2}{9} = 1 \Rightarrow$ center is $(0, 0)$, vertices are $(-4, 0)$   (b)
    and $(4, 0)$, and the asymptotes are $\frac{x}{4} = \pm \frac{y}{3}$ or
    $y = \pm \frac{3x}{4}$; $c = \sqrt{a^2 + b^2} = \sqrt{25} = 5 \Rightarrow$ foci are
    $(-5, 0)$ and $(5, 0)$; therefore the new center is $(2, 0)$, the
    new vertices are $(-2, 0)$ and $(6, 0)$, the new foci
    are $(-3, 0)$ and $(7, 0)$, and the new asymptotes are
    $y = \pm \frac{3(x - 2)}{4}$

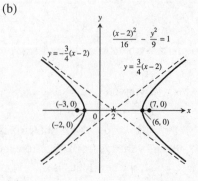

44. (a) $\frac{y^2}{4} - \frac{x^2}{5} = 1 \Rightarrow$ center is $(0,0)$, vertices are $(0,-2)$
and $(0,2)$, and the asymptotes are $\frac{y}{2} = \pm \frac{x}{\sqrt{5}}$ or
$y = \pm \frac{2x}{\sqrt{5}}$; $c = \sqrt{a^2 + b^2} = \sqrt{9} = 3 \Rightarrow$ foci are
$(0,3)$ and $(0,-3)$; therefore the new center is $(0,-2)$,
the new vertices are $(0,-4)$ and $(0,0)$, the new foci
are $(0,1)$ and $(0,-5)$, and the new asymptotes are
$y + 2 = \pm \frac{2x}{\sqrt{5}}$

(b)

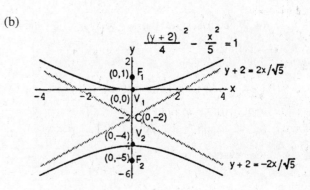

45. $y^2 = 4x \Rightarrow 4p = 4 \Rightarrow p = 1 \Rightarrow$ focus is $(1,0)$, directrix is $x = -1$, and vertex is $(0,0)$; therefore the new
vertex is $(-2,-3)$, the new focus is $(-1,-3)$, and the new directrix is $x = -3$; the new equation is
$(y + 3)^2 = 4(x + 2)$

46. $y^2 = -12x \Rightarrow 4p = 12 \Rightarrow p = 3 \Rightarrow$ focus is $(-3,0)$, directrix is $x = 3$, and vertex is $(0,0)$; therefore the new
vertex is $(4,3)$, the new focus is $(1,3)$, and the new directrix is $x = 7$; the new equation is $(y - 3)^2 = -12(x - 4)$

47. $x^2 = 8y \Rightarrow 4p = 8 \Rightarrow p = 2 \Rightarrow$ focus is $(0,2)$, directrix is $y = -2$, and vertex is $(0,0)$; therefore the new
vertex is $(1,-7)$, the new focus is $(1,-5)$, and the new directrix is $y = -9$; the new equation is
$(x - 1)^2 = 8(y + 7)$

48. $x^2 = 6y \Rightarrow 4p = 6 \Rightarrow p = \frac{3}{2} \Rightarrow$ focus is $\left(0, \frac{3}{2}\right)$, directrix is $y = -\frac{3}{2}$, and vertex is $(0,0)$; therefore the new
vertex is $(-3,-2)$, the new focus is $\left(-3, -\frac{1}{2}\right)$, and the new directrix is $y = -\frac{7}{2}$; the new equation is
$(x + 3)^2 = 6(y + 2)$

49. $\frac{x^2}{6} + \frac{y^2}{9} = 1 \Rightarrow$ center is $(0,0)$, vertices are $(0,3)$ and $(0,-3)$; $c = \sqrt{a^2 - b^2} = \sqrt{9 - 6} = \sqrt{3} \Rightarrow$ foci are $\left(0, \sqrt{3}\right)$
and $\left(0, -\sqrt{3}\right)$; therefore the new center is $(-2,-1)$, the new vertices are $(-2,2)$ and $(-2,-4)$, and the new foci
are $\left(-2, -1 \pm \sqrt{3}\right)$; the new equation is $\frac{(x+2)^2}{6} + \frac{(y+1)^2}{9} = 1$

50. $\frac{x^2}{2} + y^2 = 1 \Rightarrow$ center is $(0,0)$, vertices are $\left(\sqrt{2}, 0\right)$ and $\left(-\sqrt{2}, 0\right)$; $c = \sqrt{a^2 - b^2} = \sqrt{2 - 1} = 1 \Rightarrow$ foci are
$(-1,0)$ and $(1,0)$; therefore the new center is $(3,4)$, the new vertices are $\left(3 \pm \sqrt{2}, 4\right)$, and the new foci are $(2,4)$
and $(4,4)$; the new equation is $\frac{(x-3)^2}{2} + (y-4)^2 = 1$

51. $\frac{x^2}{3} + \frac{y^2}{2} = 1 \Rightarrow$ center is $(0,0)$, vertices are $\left(\sqrt{3}, 0\right)$ and $\left(-\sqrt{3}, 0\right)$; $c = \sqrt{a^2 - b^2} = \sqrt{3 - 2} = 1 \Rightarrow$ foci are
$(-1,0)$ and $(1,0)$; therefore the new center is $(2,3)$, the new vertices are $\left(2 \pm \sqrt{3}, 3\right)$, and the new foci are $(1,3)$
and $(3,3)$; the new equation is $\frac{(x-2)^2}{3} + \frac{(y-3)^2}{2} = 1$

52. $\frac{x^2}{16} + \frac{y^2}{25} = 1 \Rightarrow$ center is $(0,0)$, vertices are $(0,5)$ and $(0,-5)$; $c = \sqrt{a^2 - b^2} = \sqrt{25 - 16} = 3 \Rightarrow$ foci are
$(0,3)$ and $(0,-3)$; therefore the new center is $(-4,-5)$, the new vertices are $(-4,0)$ and $(-4,-10)$, and the new
foci are $(-4,-2)$ and $(-4,-8)$; the new equation is $\frac{(x+4)^2}{16} + \frac{(y+5)^2}{25} = 1$

53. $\frac{x^2}{4} - \frac{y^2}{5} = 1 \Rightarrow$ center is $(0,0)$, vertices are $(2,0)$ and $(-2,0)$; $c = \sqrt{a^2 + b^2} = \sqrt{4 + 5} = 3 \Rightarrow$ foci are $(3,0)$ and
$(-3,0)$; the asymptotes are $\pm \frac{x}{2} = \frac{y}{\sqrt{5}} \Rightarrow y = \pm \frac{\sqrt{5}x}{2}$; therefore the new center is $(2,2)$, the new vertices are

(4, 2) and (0, 2), and the new foci are (5, 2) and (−1, 2); the new asymptotes are $y - 2 = \pm \frac{\sqrt{5}(x-2)}{2}$ ; the new equation is $\frac{(x-2)^2}{4} - \frac{(y-2)^2}{5} = 1$

54. $\frac{x^2}{16} - \frac{y^2}{9} = 1 \Rightarrow$ center is $(0, 0)$, vertices are $(4, 0)$ and $(−4, 0)$; $c = \sqrt{a^2 + b^2} = \sqrt{16 + 9} = 5 \Rightarrow$ foci are $(−5, 0)$ and $(5, 0)$; the asymptotes are $\pm \frac{x}{4} = \frac{y}{3} \Rightarrow y = \pm \frac{3x}{4}$ ; therefore the new center is $(−5, −1)$, the new vertices are $(−1, −1)$ and $(−9, −1)$, and the new foci are $(−10, −1)$ and $(0, −1)$; the new asymptotes are $y + 1 = \pm \frac{3(x+5)}{4}$ ; the new equation is $\frac{(x+5)^2}{16} - \frac{(y+1)^2}{9} = 1$

55. $y^2 - x^2 = 1 \Rightarrow$ center is $(0, 0)$, vertices are $(0, 1)$ and $(0, −1)$; $c = \sqrt{a^2 + b^2} = \sqrt{1 + 1} = \sqrt{2} \Rightarrow$ foci are $\left(0, \pm \sqrt{2}\right)$ ; the asymptotes are $y = \pm x$; therefore the new center is $(−1, −1)$, the new vertices are $(−1, 0)$ and $(−1, −2)$, and the new foci are $\left(−1, −1 \pm \sqrt{2}\right)$ ; the new asymptotes are $y + 1 = \pm (x + 1)$; the new equation is $(y + 1)^2 - (x + 1)^2 = 1$

56. $\frac{y^2}{3} - x^2 = 1 \Rightarrow$ center is $(0, 0)$, vertices are $\left(0, \sqrt{3}\right)$ and $\left(0, −\sqrt{3}\right)$; $c = \sqrt{a^2 + b^2} = \sqrt{3 + 1} = 2 \Rightarrow$ foci are $(0, 2)$ and $(0, −2)$; the asymptotes are $\pm x = \frac{y}{\sqrt{3}} \Rightarrow y = \pm \sqrt{3}x$; therefore the new center is $(1, 3)$, the new vertices are $\left(1, 3 \pm \sqrt{3}\right)$ , and the new foci are $(1, 5)$ and $(1, 1)$; the new asymptotes are $y - 3 = \pm \sqrt{3}(x - 1)$; the new equation is $\frac{(y-3)^2}{3} - (x - 1)^2 = 1$

57. $x^2 + 4x + y^2 = 12 \Rightarrow x^2 + 4x + 4 + y^2 = 12 + 4 \Rightarrow (x + 2)^2 + y^2 = 16$; this is a circle: center at $C(−2, 0)$, $a = 4$

58. $2x^2 + 2y^2 - 28x + 12y + 114 = 0 \Rightarrow x^2 - 14x + 49 + y^2 + 6y + 9 = −57 + 49 + 9 \Rightarrow (x - 7)^2 + (y + 3)^2 = 1$; this is a circle: center at $C(7, −3)$, $a = 1$

59. $x^2 + 2x + 4y - 3 = 0 \Rightarrow x^2 + 2x + 1 = −4y + 3 + 1 \Rightarrow (x + 1)^2 = −4(y - 1)$; this is a parabola: $V(−1, 1)$, $F(−1, 0)$

60. $y^2 - 4y - 8x - 12 = 0 \Rightarrow y^2 - 4y + 4 = 8x + 12 + 4 \Rightarrow (y - 2)^2 = 8(x + 2)$; this is a parabola: $V(−2, 2)$, $F(0, 2)$

61. $x^2 + 5y^2 + 4x = 1 \Rightarrow x^2 + 4x + 4 + 5y^2 = 5 \Rightarrow (x + 2)^2 + 5y^2 = 5 \Rightarrow \frac{(x+2)^2}{5} + y^2 = 1$; this is an ellipse: the center is $(−2, 0)$, the vertices are $\left(−2 \pm \sqrt{5}, 0\right)$ ; $c = \sqrt{a^2 - b^2} = \sqrt{5 - 1} = 2 \Rightarrow$ the foci are $(−4, 0)$ and $(0, 0)$

62. $9x^2 + 6y^2 + 36y = 0 \Rightarrow 9x^2 + 6\left(y^2 + 6y + 9\right) = 54 \Rightarrow 9x^2 + 6(y + 3)^2 = 54 \Rightarrow \frac{x^2}{6} + \frac{(y+3)^2}{9} = 1$; this is an ellipse: the center is $(0, −3)$, the vertices are $(0, 0)$ and $(0, −6)$; $c = \sqrt{a^2 - b^2} = \sqrt{9 - 6} = \sqrt{3} \Rightarrow$ the foci are $\left(0, −3 \pm \sqrt{3}\right)$

63. $x^2 + 2y^2 - 2x - 4y = −1 \Rightarrow x^2 - 2x + 1 + 2\left(y^2 - 2y + 1\right) = 2 \Rightarrow (x - 1)^2 + 2(y - 1)^2 = 2$
$\Rightarrow \frac{(x-1)^2}{2} + (y - 1)^2 = 1$; this is an ellipse: the center is $(1, 1)$, the vertices are $\left(1 \pm \sqrt{2}, 1\right)$ ;
$c = \sqrt{a^2 - b^2} = \sqrt{2 - 1} = 1 \Rightarrow$ the foci are $(2, 1)$ and $(0, 1)$

64. $4x^2 + y^2 + 8x - 2y = −1 \Rightarrow 4\left(x^2 + 2x + 1\right) + y^2 - 2y + 1 = 4 \Rightarrow 4(x + 1)^2 + (y - 1)^2 = 4$
$\Rightarrow (x + 1)^2 + \frac{(y-1)^2}{4} = 1$; this is an ellipse: the center is $(−1, 1)$, the vertices are $(−1, 3)$ and
$(−1, −1)$; $c = \sqrt{a^2 - b^2} = \sqrt{4 - 1} = \sqrt{3} \Rightarrow$ the foci are $\left(−1, 1 \pm \sqrt{3}\right)$

65. $x^2 - y^2 - 2x + 4y = 4 \Rightarrow x^2 - 2x + 1 - (y^2 - 4y + 4) = 1 \Rightarrow (x-1)^2 - (y-2)^2 = 1$; this is a hyperbola: the center is $(1, 2)$, the vertices are $(2, 2)$ and $(0, 2)$; $c = \sqrt{a^2 + b^2} = \sqrt{1+1} = \sqrt{2} \Rightarrow$ the foci are $\left(1 \pm \sqrt{2}, 2\right)$; the asymptotes are $y - 2 = \pm(x - 1)$

66. $x^2 - y^2 + 4x - 6y = 6 \Rightarrow x^2 + 4x + 4 - (y^2 + 6y + 9) = 1 \Rightarrow (x+2)^2 - (y+3)^2 = 1$; this is a hyperbola: the center is $(-2, -3)$, the vertices are $(-1, -3)$ and $(-3, -3)$; $c = \sqrt{a^2 + b^2} = \sqrt{1+1} = \sqrt{2} \Rightarrow$ the foci are $\left(-2 \pm \sqrt{2}, -3\right)$; the asymptotes are $y + 3 = \pm(x + 2)$

67. $2x^2 - y^2 + 6y = 3 \Rightarrow 2x^2 - (y^2 - 6y + 9) = -6 \Rightarrow \frac{(y-3)^2}{6} - \frac{x^2}{3} = 1$; this is a hyperbola: the center is $(0, 3)$, the vertices are $\left(0, 3 \pm \sqrt{6}\right)$; $c = \sqrt{a^2 + b^2} = \sqrt{6+3} = 3 \Rightarrow$ the foci are $(0, 6)$ and $(0, 0)$; the asymptotes are $\frac{y-3}{\sqrt{6}} = \pm \frac{x}{\sqrt{3}} \Rightarrow y = \pm\sqrt{2}x + 3$

68. $y^2 - 4x^2 + 16x = 24 \Rightarrow y^2 - 4(x^2 - 4x + 4) = 8 \Rightarrow \frac{y^2}{8} - \frac{(x-2)^2}{2} = 1$; this is a hyperbola: the center is $(2, 0)$, the vertices are $\left(2, \pm\sqrt{8}\right)$; $c = \sqrt{a^2 + b^2} = \sqrt{8+2} = \sqrt{10} \Rightarrow$ the foci are $\left(2, \pm\sqrt{10}\right)$; the asymptotes are $\frac{y}{\sqrt{8}} = \pm\frac{x-2}{\sqrt{2}} \Rightarrow y = \pm 2(x - 2)$

69. (a) $y^2 = kx \Rightarrow x = \frac{y^2}{k}$; the volume of the solid formed by revolving $R_1$ about the y-axis is $V_1 = \int_0^{\sqrt{kx}} \pi \left(\frac{y^2}{k}\right)^2 dy$

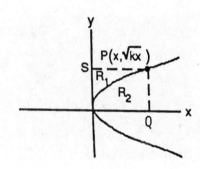

$= \frac{\pi}{k^2} \int_0^{\sqrt{kx}} y^4 \, dy = \frac{\pi x^2 \sqrt{kx}}{5}$; the volume of the right circular cylinder formed by revolving PQ about the y-axis is $V_2 = \pi x^2 \sqrt{kx} \Rightarrow$ the volume of the solid formed by revolving $R_2$ about the y-axis is $V_3 = V_2 - V_1 = \frac{4\pi x^2 \sqrt{kx}}{5}$. Therefore we can see the ratio of $V_3$ to $V_1$ is 4:1.

(b) The volume of the solid formed by revolving $R_2$ about the x-axis is $V_1 = \int_0^x \pi \left(\sqrt{kt}\right)^2 dt = \pi k \int_0^x t \, dt$

$= \frac{\pi k x^2}{2}$. The volume of the right circular cylinder formed by revolving PS about the x-axis is $V_2 = \pi \left(\sqrt{kx}\right)^2 x = \pi k x^2 \Rightarrow$ the volume of the solid formed by revolving $R_1$ about the x-axis is $V_3 = V_2 - V_1 = \pi k x^2 - \frac{\pi k x^2}{2} = \frac{\pi k x^2}{2}$. Therefore the ratio of $V_3$ to $V_1$ is 1:1.

70. $y = \int \frac{w}{H} x \, dx = \frac{w}{H}\left(\frac{x^2}{2}\right) + C = \frac{wx^2}{2H} + C$; $y = 0$ when $x = 0 \Rightarrow 0 = \frac{w(0)^2}{2H} + C \Rightarrow C = 0$; therefore $y = \frac{wx^2}{2H}$ is the equation of the cable's curve

71. $x^2 = 4py$ and $y = p \Rightarrow x^2 = 4p^2 \Rightarrow x = \pm 2p$. Therefore the line $y = p$ cuts the parabola at points $(-2p, p)$ and $(2p, p)$, and these points are $\sqrt{[2p - (-2p)]^2 + (p - p)^2} = 4p$ units apart.

72. $\lim\limits_{x \to \infty} \left(\frac{b}{a}x - \frac{b}{a}\sqrt{x^2 - a^2}\right) = \frac{b}{a}\lim\limits_{x \to \infty}\left(x - \sqrt{x^2 - a^2}\right) = \frac{b}{a}\lim\limits_{x \to \infty}\left[\frac{\left(x - \sqrt{x^2 - a^2}\right)\left(x + \sqrt{x^2 - a^2}\right)}{x + \sqrt{x^2 - a^2}}\right]$

$= \frac{b}{a}\lim\limits_{x \to \infty}\left[\frac{x^2 - (x^2 - a^2)}{x + \sqrt{x^2 - a^2}}\right] = \frac{b}{a}\lim\limits_{x \to \infty}\left[\frac{a^2}{x + \sqrt{x^2 - a^2}}\right] = 0$

73. Let $y = \sqrt{1 - \frac{x^2}{4}}$ on the interval $0 \le x \le 2$. The area of the inscribed rectangle is given by

$A(x) = 2x \left(2\sqrt{1 - \frac{x^2}{4}}\right) = 4x\sqrt{1 - \frac{x^2}{4}}$ (since the length is 2x and the height is 2y)

$\Rightarrow A'(x) = 4\sqrt{1 - \frac{x^2}{4}} - \frac{x^2}{\sqrt{1 - \frac{x^2}{4}}}$. Thus $A'(x) = 0 \Rightarrow 4\sqrt{1 - \frac{x^2}{4}} - \frac{x^2}{\sqrt{1 - \frac{x^2}{4}}} = 0 \Rightarrow 4\left(1 - \frac{x^2}{4}\right) - x^2 = 0 \Rightarrow x^2 = 2$

$\Rightarrow x = \sqrt{2}$ (only the positive square root lies in the interval). Since $A(0) = A(2) = 0$ we have that $A\left(\sqrt{2}\right) = 4$

is the maximum area when the length is $2\sqrt{2}$ and the height is $\sqrt{2}$.

74. (a)  Around the x-axis: $9x^2 + 4y^2 = 36 \Rightarrow y^2 = 9 - \frac{9}{4}x^2 \Rightarrow y = \pm\sqrt{9 - \frac{9}{4}x^2}$ and we use the positive root

$\Rightarrow V = 2\int_0^2 \pi \left(\sqrt{9 - \frac{9}{4}x^2}\right)^2 dx = 2\int_0^2 \pi \left(9 - \frac{9}{4}x^2\right) dx = 2\pi \left[9x - \frac{3}{4}x^3\right]_0^2 = 24\pi$

(b)  Around the y-axis: $9x^2 + 4y^2 = 36 \Rightarrow x^2 = 4 - \frac{4}{9}y^2 \Rightarrow x = \pm\sqrt{4 - \frac{4}{9}y^2}$ and we use the positive root

$\Rightarrow V = 2\int_0^3 \pi \left(\sqrt{4 - \frac{4}{9}y^2}\right)^2 dy = 2\int_0^3 \pi \left(4 - \frac{4}{9}y^2\right) dy = 2\pi \left[4y - \frac{4}{27}y^3\right]_0^3 = 16\pi$

75. $9x^2 - 4y^2 = 36 \Rightarrow y^2 = \frac{9x^2 - 36}{4} \Rightarrow y = \pm\frac{3}{2}\sqrt{x^2 - 4}$ on the interval $2 \le x \le 4 \Rightarrow V = \int_2^4 \pi \left(\frac{3}{2}\sqrt{x^2 - 4}\right)^2 dx$

$= \frac{9\pi}{4}\int_2^4 (x^2 - 4) dx = \frac{9\pi}{4}\left[\frac{x^3}{3} - 4x\right]_2^4 = \frac{9\pi}{4}\left[\left(\frac{64}{3} - 16\right) - \left(\frac{8}{3} - 8\right)\right] = \frac{9\pi}{4}\left(\frac{56}{3} - 8\right) = \frac{3\pi}{4}(56 - 24) = 24\pi$

76. Let $P_1(-p, y_1)$ be any point on $x = -p$, and let $P(x, y)$ be a point where a tangent intersects $y^2 = 4px$. Now

$y^2 = 4px \Rightarrow 2y\frac{dy}{dx} = 4p \Rightarrow \frac{dy}{dx} = \frac{2p}{y}$ ; then the slope of a tangent line from $P_1$ is $\frac{y - y_1}{x - (-p)} = \frac{dy}{dx} = \frac{2p}{y}$

$\Rightarrow y^2 - yy_1 = 2px + 2p^2$. Since $x = \frac{y^2}{4p}$, we have $y^2 - yy_1 = 2p\left(\frac{y^2}{4p}\right) + 2p^2 \Rightarrow y^2 - yy_1 = \frac{1}{2}y^2 + 2p^2$

$\Rightarrow \frac{1}{2}y^2 - yy_1 - 2p^2 = 0 \Rightarrow y = \frac{2y_1 \pm \sqrt{4y_1^2 + 16p^2}}{2} = y_1 \pm \sqrt{y_1^2 + 4p^2}$. Therefore the slopes of the two

tangents from $P_1$ are $m_1 = \frac{2p}{y_1 + \sqrt{y_1^2 + 4p^2}}$ and $m_2 = \frac{2p}{y_1 - \sqrt{y_1^2 + 4p^2}} \Rightarrow m_1m_2 = \frac{4p^2}{y_1^2 - (y_1^2 + 4p^2)} = -1$

$\Rightarrow$ the lines are perpendicular

77. $(x - 2)^2 + (y - 1)^2 = 5 \Rightarrow 2(x - 2) + 2(y - 1)\frac{dy}{dx} = 0 \Rightarrow \frac{dy}{dx} = -\frac{x - 2}{y - 1}$ ; $y = 0 \Rightarrow (x - 2)^2 + (0 - 1)^2 = 5$

$\Rightarrow (x - 2)^2 = 4 \Rightarrow x = 4$ or $x = 0 \Rightarrow$ the circle crosses the x-axis at $(4, 0)$ and $(0, 0)$; $x = 0$

$\Rightarrow (0 - 2)^2 + (y - 1)^2 = 5 \Rightarrow (y - 1)^2 = 1 \Rightarrow y = 2$ or $y = 0 \Rightarrow$ the circle crosses the y-axis at $(0, 2)$ and $(0, 0)$.

At $(4, 0)$: $\frac{dy}{dx} = -\frac{4 - 2}{0 - 1} = 2 \Rightarrow$ the tangent line is $y = 2(x - 4)$ or $y = 2x - 8$

At $(0, 0)$: $\frac{dy}{dx} = -\frac{0 - 2}{0 - 1} = -2 \Rightarrow$ the tangent line is $y = -2x$

At $(0, 2)$: $\frac{dy}{dx} = -\frac{0 - 2}{2 - 1} = 2 \Rightarrow$ the tangent line is $y - 2 = 2x$ or $y = 2x + 2$

78. $x^2 - y^2 = 1 \Rightarrow x = \pm\sqrt{1 + y^2}$ on the interval $-3 \le y \le 3 \Rightarrow V = \int_{-3}^3 \pi \left(\sqrt{1 + y^2}\right)^2 dy = 2\int_0^3 \pi \left(\sqrt{1 + y^2}\right)^2 dy$

$= 2\pi\int_0^3 (1 + y^2) dy = 2\pi \left[y + \frac{y^3}{3}\right]_0^3 = 24\pi$

79. Let $y = \sqrt{16 - \frac{16}{9}x^2}$ on the interval $-3 \le x \le 3$. Since the plate is symmetric about the y-axis, $\bar{x} = 0$. For a

vertical strip: $(\tilde{x}, \tilde{y}) = \left(x, \frac{\sqrt{16 - \frac{16}{9}x^2}}{2}\right)$, length $= \sqrt{16 - \frac{16}{9}x^2}$, width $= dx \Rightarrow$ area $= dA = \sqrt{16 - \frac{16}{9}x^2}\, dx$

$\Rightarrow$ mass $= dm = \delta\, dA = \delta\sqrt{16 - \frac{16}{9}x^2}\, dx$. Moment of the strip about the x-axis:

$\tilde{y}\, dm = \frac{\sqrt{16 - \frac{16}{9}x^2}}{2}\left(\delta\sqrt{16 - \frac{16}{9}x^2}\right) dx = \delta\left(8 - \frac{8}{9}x^2\right) dx$ so the moment of the plate about the x-axis is

$M_x = \int \tilde{y}\, dm = \int_{-3}^{3} \delta\left(8 - \frac{8}{9}x^2\right) dx = \delta\left[8x - \frac{8}{27}x^3\right]_{-3}^{3} = 32\delta$; also the mass of the plate is

$M = \int_{-3}^{3} \delta\sqrt{16 - \frac{16}{9}x^2}\, dx = \int_{-3}^{3} 4\delta\sqrt{1 - \left(\frac{1}{3}x\right)^2}\, dx = 4\delta\int_{-1}^{1} 3\sqrt{1 - u^2}\, du$ where $u = \frac{x}{3} \Rightarrow 3\, du = dx;\ x = -3$

$\Rightarrow u = -1$ and $x = 3 \Rightarrow u = 1$. Hence, $4\delta\int_{-1}^{1} 3\sqrt{1 - u^2}\, du = 12\delta\int_{-1}^{1}\sqrt{1 - u^2}\, du$

$= 12\delta\left[\frac{1}{2}\left(u\sqrt{1 - u^2} + \sin^{-1}u\right)\right]_{-1}^{1} = 6\pi\delta \Rightarrow \bar{y} = \frac{M_x}{M} = \frac{32\delta}{6\pi\delta} = \frac{16}{3\pi}$. Therefore the center of mass is $\left(0, \frac{16}{3\pi}\right)$.

80. $y = \sqrt{x^2 + 1} \Rightarrow \frac{dy}{dx} = \frac{1}{2}(x^2 + 1)^{-1/2}(2x) = \frac{x}{\sqrt{x^2+1}} \Rightarrow \left(\frac{dy}{dx}\right)^2 = \frac{x^2}{x^2+1} \Rightarrow \sqrt{1 + \left(\frac{dy}{dx}\right)^2} = \sqrt{1 + \frac{x^2}{x^2+1}}$

$= \sqrt{\frac{2x^2+1}{x^2+1}} \Rightarrow S = \int_0^{\sqrt{2}} 2\pi y\sqrt{1 + \left(\frac{dy}{dx}\right)^2}\, dx = \int_0^{\sqrt{2}} 2\pi\sqrt{x^2+1}\sqrt{\frac{2x^2+1}{x^2+1}}\, dx = \int_0^{\sqrt{2}} 2\pi\sqrt{2x^2+1}\, dx$;

$\begin{bmatrix} u = \sqrt{2}x \\ du = \sqrt{2}\, dx \end{bmatrix} \rightarrow \frac{2\pi}{\sqrt{2}}\int_0^2 \sqrt{u^2+1}\, du = \frac{2\pi}{\sqrt{2}}\left[\frac{1}{2}\left(u\sqrt{u^2+1} + \ln\left(u + \sqrt{u^2+1}\right)\right)\right]_0^2 = \frac{\pi}{\sqrt{2}}\left[2\sqrt{5} + \ln\left(2 + \sqrt{5}\right)\right]$

81. (a) $\tan\beta = m_L \Rightarrow \tan\beta = f'(x_0)$ where $f(x) = \sqrt{4px}$;

    $f'(x) = \frac{1}{2}(4px)^{-1/2}(4p) = \frac{2p}{\sqrt{4px}} \Rightarrow f'(x_0) = \frac{2p}{\sqrt{4px_0}}$

    $= \frac{2p}{y_0} \Rightarrow \tan\beta = \frac{2p}{y_0}$.

  (b) $\tan\phi = m_{FP} = \frac{y_0 - 0}{x_0 - p} = \frac{y_0}{x_0 - p}$

  (c) $\tan\alpha = \frac{\tan\phi - \tan\beta}{1 + \tan\phi\tan\beta} = \frac{\left(\frac{y_0}{x_0-p} - \frac{2p}{y_0}\right)}{1 + \left(\frac{y_0}{x_0-p}\right)\left(\frac{2p}{y_0}\right)}$

    $= \frac{y_0^2 - 2p(x_0 - p)}{y_0(x_0 - p + 2p)} = \frac{4px_0 - 2px_0 + 2p^2}{y_0(x_0 + p)} = \frac{2p(x_0 + p)}{y_0(x_0 + p)} = \frac{2p}{y_0}$

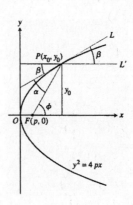

## 11.7 CONICS IN POLAR COORDINATES

1. $16x^2 + 25y^2 = 400 \Rightarrow \frac{x^2}{25} + \frac{y^2}{16} = 1 \Rightarrow c = \sqrt{a^2 - b^2}$

  $= \sqrt{25 - 16} = 3 \Rightarrow e = \frac{c}{a} = \frac{3}{5};\ F(\pm 3, 0)$;

  directrices are $x = 0 \pm \frac{a}{e} = \pm \frac{5}{\left(\frac{3}{5}\right)} = \pm\frac{25}{3}$

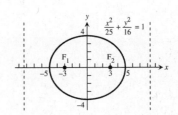

2. $7x^2 + 16y^2 = 112 \Rightarrow \frac{x^2}{16} + \frac{y^2}{7} = 1 \Rightarrow c = \sqrt{a^2 - b^2}$

  $= \sqrt{16 - 7} = 3 \Rightarrow e = \frac{c}{a} = \frac{3}{4};\ F(\pm 3, 0)$;

  directrices are $x = 0 \pm \frac{a}{e} = \pm \frac{4}{\left(\frac{3}{4}\right)} = \pm\frac{16}{3}$

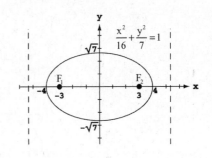

3. $2x^2 + y^2 = 2 \Rightarrow x^2 + \frac{y^2}{2} = 1 \Rightarrow c = \sqrt{a^2 - b^2}$

   $= \sqrt{2 - 1} = 1 \Rightarrow e = \frac{c}{a} = \frac{1}{\sqrt{2}}; F(0, \pm 1);$

   directrices are $y = 0 \pm \frac{a}{e} = \pm \frac{\sqrt{2}}{\left(\frac{1}{\sqrt{2}}\right)} = \pm 2$

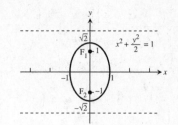

4. $2x^2 + y^2 = 4 \Rightarrow \frac{x^2}{2} + \frac{y^2}{4} = 1 \Rightarrow c = \sqrt{a^2 - b^2}$

   $= \sqrt{4 - 2} = \sqrt{2} \Rightarrow e = \frac{c}{a} = \frac{\sqrt{2}}{2}; F\left(0, \pm \sqrt{2}\right);$

   directrices are $y = 0 \pm \frac{a}{e} = \pm \frac{2}{\left(\frac{\sqrt{2}}{2}\right)} = \pm 2\sqrt{2}$

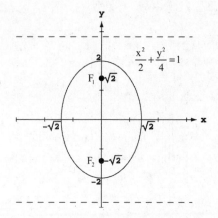

5. $3x^2 + 2y^2 = 6 \Rightarrow \frac{x^2}{2} + \frac{y^2}{3} = 1 \Rightarrow c = \sqrt{a^2 - b^2}$

   $= \sqrt{3 - 2} = 1 \Rightarrow e = \frac{c}{a} = \frac{1}{\sqrt{3}}; F(0, \pm 1);$

   directrices are $y = 0 \pm \frac{a}{e} = \pm \frac{\sqrt{3}}{\left(\frac{1}{\sqrt{3}}\right)} = \pm 3$

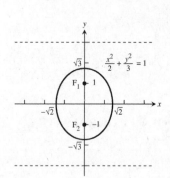

6. $9x^2 + 10y^2 = 90 \Rightarrow \frac{x^2}{10} + \frac{y^2}{9} = 1 \Rightarrow c = \sqrt{a^2 - b^2}$

   $= \sqrt{10 - 9} = 1 \Rightarrow e = \frac{c}{a} = \frac{1}{\sqrt{10}}; F(\pm 1, 0);$

   directrices are $x = 0 \pm \frac{a}{e} = \pm \frac{\sqrt{10}}{\left(\frac{1}{\sqrt{10}}\right)} = \pm 10$

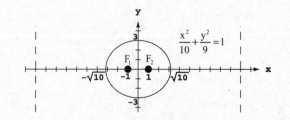

7. $6x^2 + 9y^2 = 54 \Rightarrow \frac{x^2}{9} + \frac{y^2}{6} = 1 \Rightarrow c = \sqrt{a^2 - b^2}$

   $= \sqrt{9 - 6} = \sqrt{3} \Rightarrow e = \frac{c}{a} = \frac{\sqrt{3}}{3}; F\left(\pm \sqrt{3}, 0\right);$

   directrices are $x = 0 \pm \frac{a}{e} = \pm \frac{3}{\left(\frac{\sqrt{3}}{3}\right)} = \pm 3\sqrt{3}$

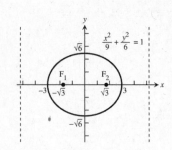

# Chapter 1

# FINANCIAL STATEMENTS
## THE BALANCE SHEET

**NEED FOR AN APPRECIATION OF ACCOUNTING** Corporate financial statements normally include a report or certificate submitted by the public accounting firm employed to examine the statements and to offer an impartial opinion concerning them. When the accountants do not find it necessary to take exception to any accounting treatment, they submit an unqualified certificate to accompany the statements that reads as follows:

> We have examined the balance sheet of _____ Company as of December 31, 19__, and the related statements of income and retained earnings for the year then ended. Our examination was made in accordance with generally accepted auditing standards, and accordingly included such tests of the accounting records and such other auditing procedures as we considered necessary in the circumstances.
>
> In our opinion, the accompanying balance sheet and statements of income and retained earnings present fairly the financial position of _____ Company at December 31, 19__, and the results of its operations for the year then ended, in conformity with generally accepted accounting principles applied on a basis consistent with that of the preceding year.

If a person is to be able to interpret intelligently accounting exhibits and summaries concerning financial position and operating results, he must be familiar with those "generally accepted accounting principles" that are applied in the development of accounting data. If a person is actually to undertake the preparation of financial reports, there is an even greater need for a thorough appreciation of the underlying concepts so that he can assert that such reports "present fairly the financial position ... and the results of ... operations ... in conformity with generally accepted accounting principles." A study of accounting principles and procedures is necessary for all persons who expect to win a responsible place in business. Such a study is equally important for those who are interested in a real understanding of the business enterprise as the fundamental unit in American economic society.

Accounting serves many groups and faces ever-increasing responsibilities. While originally concerned with the demands made by the owners or the creditors of a business for financial data, the accountant now finds a greater number of different groups vitally concerned with

1

his reports. Management, owners, creditors, and employees, as well as the government, trade associations, labor unions, and the public, seek information concerning the financial activities of the business unit. Increasingly the products of accounting are being used as a basis for economic, political, and social policy and action. Modern accounting, thus, is called upon to meet public as well as private responsibilities. Accounting standards and practices represent the response by the profession to the needs and the expectations of the groups calling for financial information. These standards and practices must be widely understood. Financial summaries must be prepared within the framework of such standards with both intelligence and integrity. Only under such circumstances can the products of accounting be received with full appreciation and real confidence by those seeking financial information.

**ACCOUNTING AND THE CORPORATION**    The corporation is the dominant form of large business organization in the United States. Although there exist a greater number of sole proprietorships and partnerships than corporations, the volume of business done by corporations exceeds by far that of the other forms of business organization. Furthermore, the value of properties owned by corporations is greatly in excess of the value of properties belonging to both sole proprietorships and partnerships.

By its very nature the corporate form calls for extended and accurate accounting. In large corporate enterprises the investment and the management groups are separated. Ownership interests are liquid and readily transferable. There are more than 8,500,000 stockholders in the United States today, and bondholders add to the total of the corporate investment group. The number of persons within this group having any first-hand knowledge of the activities of the companies in which they have interests is small. Accounting becomes the only medium for information concerning corporate status and progress for the investor, both present and prospective. Absentee and scattered investment groups must be provided with financial data that tell the business story fully and dependably.

**ACCOUNTING DEFINED**    Transactions relating to the purchase and the sale of goods and services at a price comprise what is known as business and constitute the raw materials of accounting. It is through accounting that the transactions of the business unit are accumulated, summarized, and then communicated to those seeking facts concerning the activities of the business.

The Committee on Terminology of the American Institute of Certified Public Accountants has defined accounting in the following manner:

> Accounting is the art of recording, classifying, and summarizing in a significant manner and in terms of money, transactions and events which are, in part at least, of a financial character, and interpreting the results thereof.[1]

The Committee, faced with the problem of defining accounting as a science or an art, chose the latter to emphasize the knowledge, skill, experience, and constructive efforts that are applied by the accountant in performing a service for society. The inclusion of the interpretive function in the definition of accounting is also worthy of special note. The accountant is in a position to render invaluable service to management by developing significant analyses that interpret the past and provide guides for more effective control and utilization of resources in the future.

**ACCOUNTING STANDARDS**     Definition of accounting as an art does not rule out the fact that the accountant's work is practiced within a framework of fundamental doctrine. This body of doctrine consists of certain standards and practices that have won acceptance within the profession because of their logic as well as their proved usefulness. When reference is made to "accounting principles," it should be understood that the term is used to suggest, not fundamental truths or natural laws of universal applicability, but rather that body of standards that points to what may be considered good accounting practice.

In recent years the accounting profession has applied great effort to a careful re-examination and critical analysis of fundamental theory as well as the practices found in the field of accounting. From such study it has sought to define clearly standards of sound practice in terms of contemporary problems. With agreement as to certain basic standards, the profession encourages the broad application of such theory so that accountants' products may be uniform and comparable and hence can be accepted with confidence.

Several groups have played important roles in the expression and the development of accounting standards. Most prominent among these groups have been the American Institute of Certified Public Accountants, the American Accounting Association, and the Securities and Exchange Commission.

---

[1]*Accounting Terminology Bulletin No. 1*, "Review and Résumé," 1953 (New York: American Institute of Certified Public Accountants), p. 9.

The American Institute of Certified Public Accountants, in coopera-tion with governmental, business, and educational groups, has taken a leading role in this program.[1] Arguments on matters of fundamental accounting theory, as well as the conclusions reached by special research committees of the American Institute of Certified Public Accountants, have been summarized in official pronouncements and bulletins. Since 1939 the Institute has released a series of Accounting Research Bulletins setting forth the recommendations made by its Committee on Account-ing Procedure.[2] The objectives of this program have been to narrow areas of difference and inconsistency in accounting practice and to further the development and recognition of generally accepted account-ing principles. The Institute has also made significant contributions to the ethical standards of the profession.

The American Accounting Association has made important con-tributions to the development of a coordinated body of basic doctrine by continuing studies and the release of official pronouncements.[3] The Executive Committee of this organization issued a summary in 1936 called "A Tentative Statement of Accounting Principles Under-lying Corporate Financial Statements." This statement was revised in 1941 and again in 1948. The study, development, and expression of accounting standards is viewed as a continuing activity, and in 1949 a special Committee on Concepts and Standards Underlying Corporate Financial Statements was appointed for this purpose. This committee has issued a number of statements supplementing the 1948 statement,[4] and in 1957 issued a revision of the 1948 statement under the title, "Accounting and Reporting Standards for Corporate Financial State-ments."

---

[1]The American Institute of Certified Public Accountants is the national organization of certified public accountants and is primarily concerned with professional public ac-counting. The objectives of the Institute are to unite the profession, to advance the interests of public accountants, to set standards for admission into the profession, to advance the art of accounting, and to improve accounting education. The Board of Examiners of the Institute prepares the Uniform Certified Public Accountant Exami-nations, which are now used by all of the states, the District of Columbia, and four territories. The Institute publishes an official monthly journal, *The Journal of Ac-countancy*. The office of the American Institute of Certified Public Accountants is at 270 Madison Avenue, New York 16, New York.

[2]*Accounting Research Bulletin No. 49*, issued in 1958, is the latest in the series at this printing.

[3]The American Accounting Association is the successor organization to the American Association of University Instructors in Accounting established in 1916. The objectives of the organization are to encourage and sponsor accounting research, to develop accounting principles, to promote studies of accounting as an agency of control of business enterprise and of economic affairs, and to improve methods of accounting instruction. The Association publishes an official quarterly magazine, *The Accounting Review*. The office of the Secretary-Treasurer of the American Accounting Association is at the College of Commerce and Administration, The Ohio State University, Columbus 10, Ohio.

[4]*Supplementary Statement No. 8*, issued in 1954, is the latest in the series at this printing.

The Securities and Exchange Commission has made extensive contribution to the development and the expression of standards by issuing rules and regulations relating to the reports to be filed by its registrants and rendering opinions on matters of theory and practice in its official decisions and reports and in its special Accounting Series Releases. The issuance of the series of accounting releases by the Commission was announced as a "program for the publication, from time to time, of opinions on accounting principles for the purpose of contributing to the development of uniform standards and practices in major accounting questions."

It should be observed that the accounting organizations feel that their conclusions should be regarded, not as rigid patterns and restraints, but rather as guides to good practice. The American Institute Committee on Accounting Procedure states with respect to its Accounting Research Bulletins that, in the absence of formal adoption by the Institute membership, "the authority of opinions reached by the committee rests upon their general acceptability." Further, it "recognizes that in extraordinary cases fair presentation and justice to all parties at interest may require exceptional treatment."[1] Adherence to the recommended standards is encouraged; but it is recognized that in the preparation of reports that convey the business story fully, clearly, and honestly, the doors must be left open to the exercise of judgment on the part of the accountant in the determination of the degree of conformity to standards that is proper under different circumstances, as well as the mode of their application. There is also full recognition of the need for the continuous re-examination of accepted standards and rules and their restatement and revision whenever necessary to keep pace with changes in the economic and financial environment.

The progress that has been made in defining the body of doctrine that is applicable to contemporary reporting has been of high service to both the accounting profession and those who look to the services offered by the profession. The practitioner, aware of standards that have general support, is afforded guidance as well as a sense of security in his performance. The product of accounting is improved and at the same time achieves fundamental uniformity and comparability. The reader of the financial report, familiar with the standards that have been applied in its preparation, can view the report with confidence, interpret it properly, and compare it with others prepared within a common framework.

---

[1] *Accounting Research Bulletin No. 43* "Restatement and Revision of Accounting Research Bulletins," 1953 (New York: American Institute of Certified Public Accountants), p. 9.

**THE MATCHING PROCESS**    One of the most important duties of the accountant is to act as historian. It is his function to record, classify, and summarize business activities so that the data can be used in evaluating the past as well as planning the future. In fulfilling the historical function the accountant must be impartial and systematic in seeking out the facts of business. His findings should be objective and verifiable.

Management of the business unit engages in activities directed to the increase of business resources—the production of profits. Recognition of the progress made cannot be delayed until the termination of activities at some unascertainable future date but must be a continuing process. Accordingly, the life of the business unit is broken up into arbitrary segments, and periodic statements of progress are provided. The preparation of statements within a business continuity may be no simple matter and normally involves both estimates and the exercise of judgment. Such statements must be recognized as no more than tentative reports or "test readings," since the full story is yet to be told and the future may modify the inferences made in the periodic analyses.

Business may be considered to consist of two streams of activities. First, there are the regular acquisitions of goods and services required for the performance of its objectives. These activities result in business costs. There follows the accomplishment of the objectives of the business to recover costs as well as profit through the sale of goods and services. These activities are the source of business revenue. The net income from operations for a specified period is determined by matching against the revenues realized within the period those costs that are considered applicable thereto. If incoming revenues exceed outgoing costs, there is an increase in the business net assets accruing to the ownership group; when revenues fail to equal costs, a decrease in net assets identified with the ownership group results. The application of costs against revenues is referred to as the matching process and is fundamental in accounting for the business unit.

Both costs and revenues are expressed in the matching process in terms of the homogeneous qualitative element common to both—a money price. The price for the business effort, or cost, is found in the amount paid for the goods and services at the time these were originally acquired. The price that is assigned to the business accomplishment, or revenue, is the bargained amount arrived at between buyer and seller. As goods and services are acquired, then, their cost is established and recorded. These costs may be marshaled into different combinations where the business unit unites different acquisitions in the development of its services or products. Ultimately such costs, individually or as regrouped, are assigned to the revenue that they have produced.

The use of original historical cost in the matching process is commonly referred to as application of the *cost principle.* Independent buyers and sellers through negotiation reach agreement as to the value of the utility being transferred. This bargained acquisition is the buyer's cost, his investment in the future. It is a value that is immediately available and objective, and is accepted as the starting point in the measurement process.

**FINANCIAL**        It has already been suggested that business
**STATEMENTS**        continuity is broken up into a series of time intervals and that measures of progress and position are developed for each such interval. The reporting period generally selected for a comparison of costs and revenues and their effect upon the business position is one year, either the *calendar year* or some other arbitrarily selected *fiscal year*. At the end of each year two principal financial reports, the *balance sheet* and the *income statement,* are prepared. When the difference in the net assets for the year is not fully explained by the income statement, a third statement is usually provided to supplement profit and loss data and to offer a full reconciliation of the change. This statement is known as the *statement of changes in capital,* or as applied to the corporation, the *retained earnings statement.*

The balance sheet, the income statement, and the statement of changes in capital or the retained earnings statement are referred to as *general purpose statements.* In addition to the general purpose statements, special reports may be prepared in forms that develop certain aspects of position and operations for management or that meet requirements of governmental regulatory bodies, bankers, trade associations, stock exchanges, etc. Such reports are referred to as *special purpose statements*.

**NATURE AND**        The balance sheet, also variously called the
**CONTENT OF THE**    *statement of condition* and the *statement of*
**BALANCE SHEET**      *resources and liabilities,* shows the financial
position of the business unit at a given date. This position results from the effect of transactions of the period just completed upon the financial position of the business at the beginning of the period. More broadly, the financial position is the cumulative result of all transactions of the business from its very start. Since the balance sheet is basically historical, reporting the position growing out of a series of

recorded transactions, only a full understanding of the accounting conventions and practices that are followed in the recording process offers an appreciation of the nature of the end product. Some of the fundamental concepts of balance sheet content, form, and presentation are considered in this chapter. A consideration of the individual balance sheet items in later chapters will serve to develop fully the nature of the balance sheet.

The balance sheet is an expansion of the basic accounting equation, Assets = Liabilities + Proprietorship. The character and the amount of the assets are exhibited. Equities in such assets identified with the creditor and the ownership groups are listed. Such equities normally bear no relationship to specific assets and hence are presented as equities identified with the assets as a whole.

For accounting purposes, assets include not only property rights and values acquired, but also those costs that have not been applied to revenues in the past and are considered to afford utility in the production of revenues in the future. Assets, then, include both money resources — cash, receivables, and marketable securities — and those recorded costs that are recognized as recoverable and hence properly assignable to revenues of future periods — equipment, patents, prepaid rent, etc.[1]

Liabilities measure the equities of the creditor group in the total resources. Such equities arise as the result of contributions by this group as well as the recognition of compensation to this group for its contributions. The method of liability liquidation varies. Claims may call for payment in cash, or they may be liquidated by means of services to be performed or goods to be delivered.

Proprietorship measures the interest of the ownership group in the total resources of the enterprise. Such equities originally arise as the result of contributions by the owners, and the equities change with the change in net assets resulting from operations. An ownership equity does not call for settlement on a maturity date; in the event of business dissolution, it represents a residual equity having a claim on assets only after creditors have been fully satisfied.

---

[1]The American Accounting Association defines assets as "... economic resources devoted to business purposes within a specific accounting entity; they are aggregates of service-potentials available for or beneficial to expected operations" (*Accounting and Reporting Standards for Corporate Financial Statements*). The American Institute of Certified Public Accountants defines an asset as "Something represented by a debit balance that is or would be properly carried forward upon a closing of books of account according to the rules or principles of accounting (provided such a debit balance is not in effect a negative balance applicable to a liability), on the basis that it represents either a property right or value acquired, or an expenditure made which has created a property right or is properly applicable to the future" (*Accounting Terminology Bulletin, No. 1*, "Review and Résumé").

Balance sheet items are normally classified in a manner that will facilitate the analysis and the interpretation of financial data. Information of primary concern to all parties is the business unit's solvency — its ability to meet current obligations. Accordingly, assets and liabilities are generally divided and classified as (1) *current* or *short-term* items and (2) *noncurrent, long-term,* or *fixed* items. Classification of asset and liability balances makes it possible to arrive at a company's *working capital,* the difference between current assets and current liabilities, which is the liquid buffer available in meeting demands and contingencies of the future.[1]

**CURRENT ASSETS AND**    Generally the "current" concept has been
**CURRENT LIABILITIES**    held to mean, with respect to liabilities, those
claims due within the period of one year, and with respect to assets, cash and those assets that are expected to be converted into cash within this same period. This definition would call for the exclusion of inventories and receivables that are not expected to be converted into cash within one year and the exclusion of prepaid expenses that will not produce cash. Liabilities maturing after one year from balance sheet date would likewise be excluded from current reporting. Both the American Institute of Certified Public Accountants and the American Accounting Association, however, have recommended a broadening of the current definition to emphasize a company's ability to meet claims out of proceeds of current operations rather than ability to pay on the assumption of business liquidation. Accordingly, current items are held to embrace those items relating to the particular company's "normal operating cycle." These groups conceive ordinary operations to involve the circulation of capital within the current group. Cash is converted into inventories, inventories into receivables, and receivables ultimately into cash again. Assets falling within this cycle are considered current. Prepaid expenses are considered properly includible in the current grouping since they represent substitutes for expenditures that otherwise would require the use of current resources within the operating cycle. Current liabilities are conceived as those items making claim against assets classified as current, and consist of two basic groups: (1) payables, and (2) prepaid income items.

The position on current assets of the American Institute Committee on Accounting Procedure follows:

> ... For accounting purposes, the term *current assets* is used to designate cash and other assets or resources commonly identified as

---

[1]"Working capital" is used in this text to denote the excess of current assets over current liabilities. Sometimes this excess is referred to as "net working capital," the term "working capital" then being used to denote total current assets.

those which are reasonably expected to be realized in cash or sold or consumed during the normal operating cycle of the business. Thus the term comprehends in general such resources as (a) cash available for current operations and items which are the equivalent of cash; (b) inventories of merchandise, raw materials, goods in process, finished goods, operating supplies, and ordinary maintenance material and parts; (c) trade accounts, notes, and acceptances receivable; (d) receivables from officers, employees, affiliates, and others, if collectible in the ordinary course of business within a year; (e) instalment or deferred accounts and notes receivable if they conform generally to normal trade practices and terms within the business; (f) marketable securities representing the investment of cash available for current operations; and (g) prepaid expenses such as insurance, interest, rents, taxes, unused royalties, current paid advertising service not yet received, and operating supplies. Prepaid expenses are not current assets in the sense that they will be converted into cash but in the sense that, if not paid in advance, they would require the use of current assets during the operating cycle.[1]

The committee further suggests that the one-year period is to be used as a basis for current asset classification in those instances where the average operating cycle is less than twelve months; but where the operating cycle exceeds twelve months, as in the case of the tobacco, distillery, and lumber industries, the longer period is to be used.

In accordance with the foregoing concept of current assets, the bulletin lists the following items as not includible in this category:

(a) Cash and cash claims restricted to use for other than current operations, designated for the acquisition of noncurrent assets, or segregated for the liquidation of noncurrent debts.

(b) Advances or investments in securities, whether marketable or not, made for the purposes of control, affiliation, or other continuing business advantage.

(c) Receivables not expected to be collected within twelve months arising from unusual transactions such as the sale of capital assets or advances to affiliates, officers, or employees.

(d) Cash surrender value of life insurance policies.

(e) Land and other natural resources.

(f) Depreciable assets.

(g) Unamortized costs fairly chargeable to the operations of several years.

Current liabilities are described as follows:

... The term *current liabilities* is used principally to designate obligations whose liquidation is reasonably expected to require the use of existing resources properly classifiable as current assets, or the creation of other current liabilities. As a balance-sheet category, the classification is intended to include obligations for items which have entered

---

[1] *Accounting Research Bulletin No. 43*, "Restatement and Revision of Accounting Research Bulletins," 1953 (New York: American Institute of Certified Public Accountants), p. 20. The American Accounting Association Committee on Concepts and Standards Underlying Corporate Financial Statements endorses the Institute's conclusions on working capital in its *Supplementary Statement No. 3*, "Current Assets and Current Liabilities," 1951.

into the operating cycle, such as payables incurred in the acquisition of materials and supplies to be used in the production of goods or in providing services to be offered for sale; collections received in advance of the delivery of goods or performance of services; and debts which arise from operations directly related to the operating cycle, such as accruals for wages, salaries, commissions, rentals, royalties, and income and other taxes. Other liabilities whose regular and ordinary liquidation is expected to occur within a relatively short period of time, usually twelve months, are also intended for inclusion, such as short-term debts arising from the acquisition of capital assets, serial maturities of long-term obligations, amounts required to be expended within one year under sinking fund provisions, and agency obligations arising from the collection or acceptance of cash or other assets for the account of third persons.[1]

The current liability classification, however, is not intended to include the following items, since these will not require the use of resources classified as current:

(a) Obligations due at an early date that are to be discharged by means of the issuance of new obligations in their places. There should, however, be parenthetical disclosure of the reason for continuing to report such items as noncurrent.

(b) Debts that are to be liquidated from funds that have been accumulated and are reported as noncurrent assets.

(c) Loans on life insurance policies made with the intent that these will not be paid but will be liquidated by deduction from the proceeds of the policies upon their maturity or cancellation.

(d) Obligations for advance collections that involve long-term deferment of the delivery of goods or services.

In practice one still finds a great many accounting statements following the strict "one year" concept in the classification of current items. There has, however, been a steady movement towards acceptance of the Institute's position on current classification since the release of its recommendations in 1947. In view of the sound logic in support of a broader interpretation for current assets and liabilities, illustrations on the following pages are prepared in accordance with Institute recommendations.

Current assets are normally listed on the balance sheet in the order of liquidity. These assets, with the exception of inventories and marketable securities, are usually reported at their estimated realizable values. Thus, current receivable balances are reduced by allowances for estimated bad debts. Both inventories and marketable securities may be reported at cost or on the basis of "cost or market, whichever is lower." The latter method has been supported as a conservative approach to the measurement of working capital position.

Few problems are generally found in the valuation of current liabilities. Amounts payable can usually be determined or accrued ac-

---

[1]*Ibid*, p. 21.

curately. Some items may require estimates as to the amounts ultimately payable. The claim, however determined, if payable currently must be reflected under the current heading.

**NONCURRENT ASSETS AND LIABILITIES**  Assets and liabilities that do not qualify for presentation under the current headings are classified under a number of noncurrent headings. Noncurrent assets are generally listed under separate headings such as Investments, Plant and Equipment, Intangible Assets, Deferred Costs, and Other Assets. Noncurrent liabilities are listed under such headings as Long-Term Debt, Deferred Revenues, and Other Liabilities.

*Investments.* Long-term investments held for periodic income, appreciation, or control purposes are reported under the caption *Investments.* Examples of items properly shown under this heading are long-term stock, bond, and mortgage holdings; securities of affiliated companies as well as advances to such companies; sinking fund assets consisting of cash and securities held for the retirement of bonds, the redemption of stock, the replacement of buildings, or the payment of pensions; investments in plant sites not in current use; and other miscellaneous investments not used directly in the operations of the business. Long-term investments are normally reported at cost.

*Plant and Equipment.* Properties of a tangible and relatively permanent character that are used in the normal business operations are reported under the heading *Plant and Equipment.* Land, buildings, machinery and equipment, furniture and fixtures, and tools are included under this heading. Plant and equipment items are normally reported at original cost less accumulated depreciation.

*Intangibles.* The long-term rights and privileges of an intangible character acquired for use in the normal business operations are reported under the heading *Intangibles.* Included in this class are such items as goodwill, patents, trademarks, franchises, copyrights, formulas, leaseholds, and organization costs. Intangible assets are reported at their costs less amounts that have been written off.

Frequently the term *fixed assets* is used to apply to all of those long-term properties used in the production of goods and services. As thus used, fixed assets would consist of two groups—*fixed tangibles* represented by plant and equipment items and *fixed intangibles* represented by the items named above.

*Deferred Costs or Deferred Charges.* Certain costs are incurred for services or benefits to be realized over a number of periods. Such costs are properly carried forward and assigned to the revenues of the periods that are benefited. Until such services or benefits are realized, the cost balances are properly regarded as assets. Examples of items that call for deferral are bond issuing costs, and developmental and improvement costs. These long-term prepayments are frequently reported on the balance sheet under the heading *Deferred Costs* or *Deferred Charges*.

A deferred costs classification may be considered objectionable on the grounds that such a designation could be applied to all costs assignable to future periods, including those for plant and equipment and intangibles. The deferred costs designation may be avoided by reporting long-term prepayments under separate appropriately descriptive asset headings or within the Other Assets section of the balance sheet.

Supply inventories and short-term prepaid expense items are frequently regarded as noncurrent and are included in the deferred costs category. But, as stated earlier, the trend in recent years has been toward the recognition of these items as current assets in accordance with recommendations made by the American Institute of Certified Public Accountants.

*Other Assets.* Occasionally certain noncurrent items cannot satisfactorily be included under any of the previous classifications and are listed under separate descriptive headings or under the general heading *Other Assets.* The Other Assets designation is used for such assets as cash funds representing miscellaneous deposits received from customers, deposits made with vendors to secure contracts, advances to officers, and construction in progress.

*Contingent Assets.* Circumstances on the balance sheet date may suggest the existence of certain rights or claims that could materialize as valuable property items upon the favorable outcome of certain actions or events. In the absence of a legal right to the properties at this time, these can be viewed only as *contingent assets.* Contingent assets may be reported by means of a parenthetical remark or a special note under a separate contingent assets heading after other asset classifications. Tax claims, insurance claims, and claims against merchandise creditors may warrant such treatment. Reference to contingent assets is relatively infrequent in practice.

*Long-Term Debt.* Long-term notes, bonds, mortgages, and similar obligations that will not require current funds for their retirement are generally reported under the *Long-Term Debt* heading on the balance sheet.

When an amount borrowed is not the same as the amount ultimately required in settlement of the debt, the difference, representing either a debt discount or a debt premium, is properly viewed as a valuation account and is subtracted from or added to the debt stated at its maturity value. However, debt discount is frequently classified as a deferred cost and debt premium as a special long-term debt item or as a deferred revenue. When a note, a bond issue, or a mortgage formerly classified as a long-term obligation becomes due and is to be paid within a year, it should be reclassified and presented as a current liability on the balance sheet.

Frequently the term *fixed liabilities* is used to refer to the long-term obligations.

*Deferred Revenues or Deferred Credits.* Certain revenues give rise to obligations for goods, services, or benefits to be provided in future periods. Such revenues are properly carried forward and assigned to those periods in which the company meets its responsibilities and the revenue is realized. Until responsibilities are met, the revenue balances are unearned and must be regarded as liabilities: certain costs are involved in their liquidation; net income will emerge only to the extent that balances exceed such costs. Examples of revenues that call for deferral and recognition as long-term obligations include leasehold advances and long-term service and insurance contract premiums. These long-term prepayments are normally reported on the balance sheet under the heading of *Deferred Revenues or Deferred Credits*.

A deferred revenues classification may be considered objectionable on the grounds that it fails to suggest the liability character of the items that are listed thereunder. The deferred revenues classification may be avoided by reporting unearned items under separate liability headings or within the Other Liabilities section of the balance sheet.

All unearned revenue items are frequently reported under the deferred revenues heading, including amounts received for goods and services to be provided in the near future. However, classification of an unearned revenue balance as a noncurrent item is appropriate only when the item will make no significant claim upon the current assets reported on the statement. When there are significant costs involved in the course of income realization and these costs are to be met from current assets presently reported, the unearned balance is really a claim against current assets and hence properly reported as a current liability. Unearned subscriptions income, for example, is properly recognized as a current liability in view of the claim that this makes against current assets.

*Other Liabilities.* Occasionally certain noncurrent liabilities cannot satisfactorily be reported under the long-term debt or the deferred revenue headings and are listed under separate descriptive headings or under the general heading *Other Liabilities.* The Other Liabilities designation is used for obligations to customers in the form of long-term refundable deposits, long-term obligations to company officers or affiliated companies, matured but unclaimed bond principal and interest obligations, amounts payable under pension plans, and equities of minority interests in assets reported on the balance sheet.

*Contingent Liabilities.* Past activities or circumstances may have given rise to possible future liabilities, although legal obligations do not exist on the date of the balance sheet. Such possible claims are known as *contingent liabilities* and are normally reported by means of a parenthetical remark or a special note under a separate contingent liability heading after reported liabilities. Possible obligations resulting from the discounting of customers' notes, accommodation endorsements on obligations of other parties, pending lawsuits, taxes and other charges in dispute, and guarantees on goods and services, are examples of items frequently reported as contingent liabilities.

Careful distinction should be made between the contingent liabilities just described and liabilities that exist but that cannot be definitely and finally measured in amount on the balance sheet date. For example, an income tax liability may have accrued although the exact amount of the obligation is not yet determinable; or payments may have to be made ultimately to employees under retirement plans although the costs of such benefits cannot be finally determined. These claims, even though arrived at through estimates, cannot be ignored in setting forth the financial condition. The estimated tax liability is a current item and hence is properly reported under the current heading; the estimated pensions are not currently payable and hence would be reported under a noncurrent heading.

**PROPRIETORSHIP**      In the case of a sole owner, proprietorship is represented by a single capital balance. This is the cumulative result of the owner's investments and withdrawals as well as past profits and losses. In the partnership form of organization, proprietorship is composed of separate capital balances reporting the interests of the several owners. Although the agreement with respect to profit and loss determines how profit and loss is to be divided among individual partners, the capital accounts measure the partners' equities in the assets of the firm. Upon partnership liquidation, firm creditors are paid off and all profits and losses from liquidation are divided among the partners in the profit and loss ratio. Remaining assets are then distributed to partners in accordance with their equities as reported by their respective capital accounts.

In the corporation, proprietorship, commonly referred to as *capital, stockholders' interest,* or *net worth,* is reported in terms of the sources of this interest, consisting of *paid-in capital* and *retained earnings.* In certain instances corporate proprietorship includes *appraisal capital* arising from asset revaluation. Frequently, the term "surplus" is applied to all corporate capital balances other than capital stock. Thus, paid-in capital other than that portion representing capital stock is designated *paid-in surplus,* retained earnings is designated *earned surplus,* and appraisal capital is designated *appraisal surplus.*

*Paid-In Capital.* Paid-in capital reports the invested or contributed portion of the corporate capital. Paid-in capital is normally divided into two parts: (1) *Capital stock* representing that portion of the contribution by stockholders that is assignable to the shares of stock issued; (2) *additional paid-in capital* or *paid-in surplus* representing capital contributions by shareholders in excess of the amounts assignable to capital stock as well as capital contributions other than for shares.

*Capital Stock.* Capital stock outstanding, if it has a par value, is shown on the balance sheet at par. If it is no-par, it is stated at the amount received on its original sale or at some arbitrary value as set by law or as assigned by action of the board of directors of the corporation. When more than a single class of stock has been issued and is outstanding, the stock of each class is reported separately. *Treasury stock,* which is stock issued but subsequently reacquired by the corporation, is a subtraction from the total stock issued or from the sum of the positive capital balances. The capital stock balance is interpreted as the legal capital or permanent capital of the corporation.

*Additional Paid-In Capital or Paid-In Surplus.* A premium received on the sale of par-value stock or the amount received in excess of the value assigned to no-par stock is included as a part of paid-in capital. Capital contributed other than for shares (the donation of assets, for example) and gains resulting from the sale of treasury stock at amounts in excess of cost are also recognized as a part of the paid-in capital. Capital stock and other paid-in capital balances should be totaled so that the full amount of the paid-in capital may be indicated. Sale of stock at less than par calls for the recognition of a capital stock balance at par and a stock discount balance that is reported as a subtraction item in arriving at paid-in capital.

*Retained Earnings or Earned Surplus.* The amount of undistributed earnings of past periods is reported as retained earnings or earned surplus. This balance is reduced by dividends and losses. An excess of dividends and losses over profits results in a negative retained earnings balance called a *deficit*. The balance of retained earnings is added to the paid-in capital total in summarizing the stockholders' interest in the corporation; a deficit would be subtracted from the paid-in capital total.

Portions of retained earnings are sometimes reported as restricted and unavailable as a basis for dividends. Restricted earnings are designated as *appropriations* or *reserves*. Appropriations are frequently made for sinking funds, for plant extension, for contingencies, etc. When appropriations have been made, retained earnings on the balance sheet consist of an amount reported as *Appropriated* and a balance designated as *Unappropriated* or *Free*.

*Appraisal Capital or Appraisal Surplus.* When there has been an independent appraisal of assets and when increases in assets as indicated by the appraisal are recorded in the accounts, such increases in asset values are accompanied by increases in *Appraisal Capital* or *Appraisal Surplus* balances. Appraisal capital is added to paid-in capital and retained earnings balances in arriving at the total corporate capital.

Frequently one finds a *Capital Surplus* balance in the capital section of published statements. This designation may be used to indicate all paid-in capital balances other than those reported as capital stock, or it may be used to embrace both paid-in capital and appraisal capital. Such reporting is unfortunate since use of the catch-all term leaves the reader of the statement uninformed concerning the exact source or sources of the proprietorship item.

**FORM OF THE BALANCE SHEET**  The form of the balance sheet varies in practice. The balance sheet is normally prepared in *account form*, assets being reported on the left-hand side and liabilities and proprietorship on the right-hand side. It may also be prepared in *report form*, with assets, liabilities, and proprietorship elements appearing in vertical arrangement.

The order of asset and liability classifications also varies in practice. For example, where emphasis is placed upon a company's working capital position and liquidity, asset and liability groups, as well as the items within such groups, may be presented in the order of liquidity.

WEBSTER<br>BALANCE<br>DECEMBER

ASSETS

Current assets:

| | | | |
|---|---|---|---|
| Cash in bank and on hand................. | | $ 45,500 | |
| Marketable securities (reported at cost; market value, $71,500)........................ | | 70,000 | |
| Notes receivable, trade debtors*............ | $ 15,000 | | |
| Accounts receivable....................... | 50,000 | | |
| | $ 65,000 | | |
| Less: Allowance for bad debts............. | 5,000 | 60,000 | |
| Creditors' accounts with debit balances....... | | 750 | |
| Advances to employees..................... | | 1,250 | |
| Accrued interest on notes receivable.......... | | 250 | |
| Inventories (at lower of cost or market)...... | | 125,000 | |
| Prepaid expenses: | | | |
| Miscellaneous supplies inventories.......... | $ 3,000 | | |
| Unexpired insurance..................... | 4,250 | 7,250 | $310,000 |

Investments:

| | | | |
|---|---|---|---|
| Preferred stock redemption fund............ | | | 30,000 |

Plant and equipment:

| | Cost | Allowance for Depreciation | Book Value |
|---|---|---|---|
| Equipment..................... | $100,000 | $ 45,000 | $ 55,000 |
| Buildings...................... | 150,000 | 35,000 | 115,000 |
| Land.......................... | 80,000 | | 80,000 |
| | $330,000 | $ 80,000 | 250,000 |

Intangibles:

| | | |
|---|---|---|
| Organization costs........................... | $ 6,500 | |
| Goodwill.................................... | 18,500 | 25,000 |

Deferred costs:

| | |
|---|---|
| Unamortized bond issue costs................ | 5,000 |

Other assets:

| | |
|---|---|
| Advances to officers...................... | 15,000 |

| | |
|---|---|
| Total assets................................ | $635,000 |

*The Company is contingently liable on customers' notes of $5,000 that have been discounted.

**Account Form**

This is the usual presentation for the mercantile unit, and class headings appear as follows:

| | |
|---|---|
| Current Assets | Current Liabilities |
| Investments | Long-Term Debt |
| Plant and Equipment | Deferred Revenues |
| Intangibles | Other Liabilities |
| Deferred Costs | Paid-In Capital |
| Other Assets | Retained Earnings |
| | Appraisal Capital |

A balance sheet in account form with financial data reported in the order of liquidity is illustrated above. When readers of the balance

COMPANY
SHEET
31, 1958

| | | | |
|---|---|---|---|
| LIABILITIES AND CAPITAL | | | |
| LIABILITIES | | | |
| Current liabilities: | | | |
| Notes payable, trade creditors.............. | | $ 14,250 | |
| Accounts payable........................ | | 24,500 | |
| Advances by customers................... | | 5,750 | |
| Estimated income taxes payable........... | | 23,000 | |
| Accrued expenses: | | | |
| Salaries and wages..................... | $ 1,000 | | |
| Taxes................................ | 1,500 | 2,500 | $ 70,000 |
| | | | |
| Long-term debt: | | | |
| 5½% First mortgage bonds due December 31, | | | |
| 1962.................................. | | | 100,000 |
| Deferred revenues: | | | |
| Unearned interest on notes receivable....... | | $    500 | |
| Unearned leasehold income................. | | 14,500 | 15,000 |
| | | | |
| Total liabilities............................ | | | $185,000 |
| CAPITAL | | | |
| Paid-in capital: | | | |
| 6% Preferred stock, par $10, 5,000 shares issued | | | |
| and outstanding...................... | $ 50,000 | | |
| No-par common stock, stated value $5, 40,000 | | | |
| shares issued and outstanding............ | 200,000 | | |
| Paid-in capital from sale of common stock in | | | |
| excess of stated value.................. | 45,000 | $295,000 | |
| | | | |
| Retained earnings.......................... | | 155,000 | |
| | | | |
| Total capital.............................. | | | 450,000 |
| | | | |
| | | | |
| | | | |
| Total liabilities and capital..................... | | | $635,000 |

**Balance Sheet**

sheet are concerned primarily with such factors as total plant and the method of financing such plant, and when a satisfactory condition as to solvency is assumed (as in the case of public utilities, for example), the order of presentation may emphasize plant and methods of financing plant in a manner such as the following:

| | |
|---|---|
| Plant and Equipment | Paid-In Capital |
| Intangibles | Appraisal Capital |
| Investments | Long-Term Debt |
| Current Assets | Other Liabilities |
| Deferred Costs | Current Liabilities |
| Other Assets | Deferred Revenues |
| | Retained Earnings |

When the report form is used, assets are followed by the liability and the proprietorship classifications. Liability and proprietorship totals may be added together to form an amount equal to the asset total. In other instances total liabilities are subtracted from total assets, and proprietorship is offered as the difference. A variation of the report form referred to as the *financial position form* has found wide favor in recent years. This form emphasizes the current position and develops a working capital balance. The financial position form is illustrated below:[1]

WEBSTER COMPANY
BALANCE SHEET
DECEMBER 31, 1958

| | | |
|---|---:|---:|
| Current assets.......................................... | | $310,000 |
| Deduct: Current liabilities............................. | | 70,000 |
| | | |
| Working capital........................................ | | $240,000 |
| Add: | | |
| Investments........................................... | | 30,000 |
| Plant and equipment................................... | | 250,000 |
| Intangibles........................................... | | 25,000 |
| Deferred costs........................................ | | 5,000 |
| Other assets.......................................... | | 15,000 |
| | | |
| | | $565,000 |
| Deduct: | | |
| Long-term debt........................................ | $100,000 | |
| Deferred revenues..................................... | 15,000 | 115,000 |
| | | |
| Stockholders' Equity—Excess of assets over liabilities.... | | $450,000 |
| | | |
| Stockholders' equity derived from: | | |
| Paid-in capital....................................... | | $295,000 |
| Retained earnings..................................... | | 155,000 |
| | | |
| Total equal to excess of assets over liabilities........... | | $450,000 |

**Financial Position Form of Balance Sheet**

Related balance sheet items are frequently combined so that the balance sheet may be prepared in condensed form. For example, for balance sheet presentation, land, buildings, equipment, and furniture may be reported as a single item; raw materials, goods in process, and finished goods inventories may be combined; and investments may be reported in total. Consolidation of similar items within reasonable limits may actually serve to clarify balance sheet position and data relationships. Supporting detail for individual items, when considered of particular significance or when required by law, may be supplied by means of special summaries referred to as *supplementary schedules*.

Balance sheet data are frequently presented in comparative form. With comparative reports for two or more dates, information is made available concerning the nature and the trend of financial changes

---

[1]Individual assets and liabilities have been omitted in the illustration.

taking place within the periods between balance sheets. When a statement is presented in special form, the heading should designate such form, as, for example, "Condensed Balance Sheet," "Comparative Balance Sheet," etc.

**OFFSETS ON**          A number of items are frequently reported
**THE BALANCE SHEET**    at gross amounts that call for the recognition of offset balances in arriving at proper balance sheet valuations. Such offset balances are found in asset, liability, and proprietorship categories. For example, in the case of assets, accounts receivable may be reported at the sum of the customers' accounts less an allowance for bad debts to bring the balance down to the amount estimated to be recoverable; plant and equipment items are usually reported at cost less allowances for depreciation that bring the assets down to the costs yet to be assigned to future periods. In the case of liabilities, available purchases discounts are sometimes subtracted from accounts payable in arriving at the net amount estimated to be paid; bonds payable reacquired by a company but not formally retired are reported as an offset to bonds payable issued in arriving at the bonds outstanding; a bond discount is subtracted from the par value of bonds payable in arriving at the net obligation. In the case of proprietorship, a discount on capital stock is properly reported as an offset from the par value of capital stock in arriving at paid-in capital; a deficit is shown as a subtraction from invested capital in arriving at the net stockholders' interest.

It should be observed that the offsets involved above are required in the proper valuation of a particular balance sheet item. The offset procedure, however, is improper if it is applied to an asset and a liability or to an asset and a capital balance even in cases where some relationship exists between the items. For example, a company may accumulate cash in special funds to discharge certain tax liabilities; but as long as control of the cash is retained and as long as the obligation is still outstanding, the balance sheet should reflect both the asset and the liability. Or a plant may have been purchased, a mortgage note having been issued on the purchase. The business unit has acquired a building and at the same time is obliged to meet the payment requirements of the mortgage. Even though the property might be subject to foreclosure sale by the creditor upon failure to meet the debt, to subtract the liability balance from the property item would be to understate the assets owned by the company as well as the obligations that it must meet. A cash fund may have been accumulated for the purpose of acquiring preferred stock; but until the stock is redeemed, the company continues to control the cash and must meet its responsibilities to holders of the stock. A company may have made advances to certain salesmen and amounts may be owed to others; the company has both a claim against certain individuals and a responsibility to others. A net figure cannot be justified here, just as a net figure cannot be justified for the offset of trade receivables against trade payables.

**BALANCE SHEET TERMINOLOGY**     Recent years have witnessed an attempt on the part of the accounting profession to define the terms used in accounting. Attention has also been directed to those terms that have been subject to misinterpretation because of an accounting use that differs from the sense in which they are popularly used. This study has been accompanied by a movement to modify existing practice where such action might contribute to a better understanding of accounting.

*Net Worth and Surplus.* As early as 1941 the American Institute of Certified Public Accountants raised the question of more informative designations in reporting corporate proprietorship. The use of the heading "net worth" was challenged on the grounds that "a balance sheet does not purport to reflect and could not usefully reflect the value of the enterprise or of equity interests therein." The need for a designation that would emphasize *investment* rather than *value* was recognized. Objection was also made to the use of the term "surplus." The popular meaning for "surplus" is "excess," "overplus," "residue," "that which remains when use or need has been satisfied." As indicated earlier, "surplus" as employed in an accounting sense has been used to suggest investment by owners, as in *paid-in surplus*; accumulated earnings, as in *earned surplus*; and unrealized profits, as in *appraisal surplus*. In order to clarify ownership reporting, the American Institute Committee on Accounting Procedure has recommended the discontinuance of the term "surplus" in the balance sheet presentation of the stockholders equity, and the substitution of terms that clearly point out the sources from which proprietary capital was derived. In fulfilling this objective the committee has recommended that: (1) the capital contributed to the company be divided between capital assigned to shares to the extent of their par and stated value, and capital in excess of such par or stated value including capital received other than for shares; (2) the increase in capital from earnings be designated by such terms as *retained income, retained earnings, accumulated earnings,* or *earnings retained for use in the business;* and (3) any capital from asset appreciation be designated by such terms as *excess of appraised or fair value of fixed assets over cost*, or *appreciation of fixed assets*.[1]

*Reserves*. The use of the term "reserves" and classification problems relating to reserves have been subject to special inquiry and challenge. The term "reserve" is popularly interpreted to mean property that is held or retained for some purpose. For accounting purposes, such property would be referred to as a deposit, a temporary investment, or a sinking fund. The reserve designation, however, is employed in the following conflicting senses on the balance sheet:

(1) As a valuation account—

　　Reserve for Bad Debts, which reduces a receivable balance to the estimated amount collectible.

　　Reserve for Depreciation, which reduces the cost of an asset by the amount already charged to revenues.

(2) As a liability whose amount is uncertain—

　　Reserve for Federal Income Taxes, which indicates the amount of income taxes estimated to be payable.

　　Reserve for Damages, which indicates the probable amount payable in a disputed claim.

(3) As an appropriation of retained earnings—

　　Reserve for Bond Retirement Fund, which represents an appropriation of earnings matching assets that have been segregated and that are to be used for a special purpose.

　　Reserve for Higher Costs of Plant Replacement, which represents an appropriation of earnings so that an unsegregated or undivided portion of net assets may be retained for future plant replacement.

The American Institute Committee on Terminology has recommended certain limitations in the use of the reserve designation. It has pointed out that the term "reserve" is popularly interpreted to mean property that is held or retained for some special purpose. Since the generally accepted meaning of the term "reserve" relates only to appropriations of retained earnings, the committee has recommended that its use be limited to items within this class. The committee has further suggested that asset offsets be referred to as "less estimated losses on collection" and "less accrued depreciation," and that a liability involving an estimate be reported as "estimated liability" or "liability of estimated amount."[2]

[1]See *Accounting Terminology Bulletin No. 1*, "Review and Résumé," 1953 (New York: American Institute of Certified Public Accountants), p. 28–32. It may be observed that the American Institute continues to use the term "surplus" in its pronouncements. The Committee on Accounting Procedure states in its preface to *Accounting Research Bulletin No. 43*, "Although the committee has approved the objective of finding a better term than the word *surplus* for use in published financial statements, it has used *surplus* herein as being a technical term well understood among accountants, to whom its pronouncements are primarily directed."

[2]*Ibid*, pp. 26–28.

The use of "reserve" as a valuation, a liability, and a proprietorship designation is subject to serious criticism. However, the practice of listing such diverse reserve elements under a common heading "Reserves" usually reported between the liabilities and the proprietorship sections on the balance sheet, is thoroughly objectionable. This practice results in a distortion of asset, liability, and capital elements, making necessary a full screening of the reserves and their identification with the appropriate balance sheet section in arriving at a summary of assets and related equities. Further, the use of such titles as "Miscellaneous Reserves," "General Reserves," and "Contingency Reserves" within the reserves section frequently makes identification of the balance sheet element impossible. The American Accounting Association Committee on Concepts and Standards Underlying Corporate Financial Statements has taken a positive stand on this matter and has recommended:

> The "reserve section" in corporate balance sheets should be eliminated and its elements exhibited as deduction-from-asset, or liability, or retained income amounts.[1]

Such terms as "net worth," "surplus," and "reserve" are still widely used in practice, although there is significant movement towards acceptance of the recommendations mentioned. Most of the illustrations in the text employ statement forms and terminology recommended by leading accounting authority. However, alternate forms and terms are referred to and employed in the text questions, exercises, and problems, since such alternates are frequently encountered in practice. It must be pointed out that in communicating the business story, movement towards more readily understood terminology is only one phase of the problem; the reader of the statement must be educated so that he understands the nature of accounting, the service that it can legitimately perform, the limitations to which it is subject, and the kind of analysis and interpretation that is called for under these circumstances.

**THE SIMPLIFIED REPORT** Along with the movement towards more descriptive terminology in accounting has come the attempt to improve the manner of presentation of financial data. Parenthetical remarks and notes are frequently employed to explain or to supplement the basic financial data. Careful classification of items under descriptive headings and the presentation of statements in comparative form provide more meaningful reports. Pres-

---

[1]*Accounting and Reporting Standards for Corporate Financial Statements*, "Reserves and Retained Income," 1957 (Columbus: American Accounting Association), p. 19.

entations in condensed forms and reporting of items to the nearest dollar, cents being omitted, clarify relationships and facilitate analysis.

A number of companies have developed simplified reports that attempt to offer basic financial data in a nontechnical and an explanatory manner. Presentation may compare with standard form, it may take a narrative form, or in some cases it may take a graphic form. The development of original forms by different companies is movement away from an objective of the profession, which is to encourage fundamental uniformity so that statements may be generally comparable. Further, there is a real question as to whether the simplified reports have received more enthusiastic response or have proved to be any more serviceable than reports prepared in the conventional manner.

A variety of different balance sheet forms are found in practice. Several selected statements are given in the Appendix of this textbook. These should be studied carefully, for they offer suggestions as to the varied approaches that may be taken in the development of reports summarizing financial status.

## QUESTIONS

**1.** "From a convenient mechanical device, privately applied to the measurement of the status and results of a business enterprise, it (accounting) has grown into an important medium for the public expression of important facts about our vast and complex commercial and industrial society."

"In America the corporation is the dominant form of enterprise."

Are these two ideas related? Discuss.

**2.** How would you distinguish between accounting "principles" and accounting "methods"?

**3.** (a) What is meant by "the matching process"? (b) What is meant by the "cost principle"?

**4.** Distinguish between general purpose statements and special purpose statements.

**5.** Explain the two positions that have been taken in distinguishing items as current and noncurrent. Which position do you support? Why?

**6.** (a) Give examples of expense prepayments that are properly reported as (1) current items and (2) noncurrent items. What factors govern in the determination of the appropriate classification? (b) Give examples of income prepayments properly reported as (1) current items and (2) noncurrent items. What factors govern here?

**7.** Browne Liquidators, Inc. insists on reporting the cash surrender value of life insurance on company officials as a current asset in view of its immediate convertibility into cash. Do you support this argument?

**8.** What major classifications may be applied to (a) assets, (b) liabilities, and (c) proprietorship items? Indicate the nature of the data that is reported within each classification.

**9.** What two basic sequences may be employed in listing assets, liabilities, and proprietorship on the balance sheet? What factors govern in making a choice between the two?

**10.** (a) Give an example of (1) an asset offset, (2) a liability offset, and (3) a proprietorship offset. (b) When is offset improperly applied?

**11.** Give an example of (a) a contingent asset, (b) a contingent liability, and (c) a contingent proprietorship item.

**12.** Indicate under what circumstances each of the following can be considered noncurrent: (a) cash, (b) receivables, (c) marketable securities, (d) inventories.

**13.** Distinguish between the following: (a) contingent liabilities and estimated liabilities, (b) appropriated retained earnings and free retained earnings, (c) capital surplus and appraisal surplus.

**14.** (a) What objections are raised to the use of the terms (1) reserve, (2) net worth, and (3) surplus? (b) What suggestions have been made with respect to these terms in attempts to improve reporting?

**15.** The Belle Corporation asks you to draw up a balance sheet reporting properties at their present market value to be used as a basis for borrowing cash from the bank. (a) Would you support the preparation of such a statement? (b) If you prepare such a statement, how would you obtain information as to present market values of current and noncurrent assets? (c) What special disclosures, if any, would you make on the statement?

## EXERCISES

**1.** Indicate the balance sheet classification for each of the following accounts. In the case of doubtful items, indicate what further information would be required.

(a) Cash Sinking Fund for Payment of Bonds
(b) Supplies Inventory
(c) Receivables — U. S. Government Contracts
(d) Accrued Interest on Long-Term Investments
(e) Treasury Stock
(f) Retained Earnings
(g) Reserve for Unclaimed Payroll Checks
(h) Allowance for Depreciation
(i) Accrued Interest on Bonds Payable
(j) Dividends Payable on Preferred Stock
(k) Raw Materials Inventory
(l) Unearned Subscription Income

**2.** State how each of the following items should be classified:

(a) Reserve for Patent Amortization
(b) Reserve for Income Taxes
(c) Reserve for Depletion
(d) Reserve for Contingencies
(e) Reserve for Doubtful Accounts
(f) Reserve for Pension Payments
(g) Marketable Securities
(h) Premium on Sale of Stock
(i) Unamortized Bond Issue Costs
(j) Unearned Rental Income
(k) Deficit
(l) Advances to Salesmen
(m) Customers' accounts with credit balances
(n) Creditors' accounts with debit balances
(o) Cash representing miscellaneous refundable deposits
(p) Prepaid Rental Expense

(q) Accrued Interest on Notes Rec.
(r) Subscription Income Received in Advance
(s) Treasury Stock
(t) Factory Supplies
(u) Tools
(v) Postage Stamps
(w) Loans to Officers
(x) Leasehold Improvements
(y) Patents

**3.** Indicate how each of the following items should be classified on the balance sheet:

(a) Cash surrender value of life insurance.
(b) Sinking fund cash for retirement of bonds.
(c) Bonds payable in six months out of sinking fund cash.
(d) Note receivable collectible in 10 annual installments.
(e) Cash deposited with broker on option to buy real estate.
(f) Land held as future plant site.
(g) Warehouse in process of construction.
(h) Cash fund representing customers' deposits on returnable containers.
(i) Cash fund representing sales tax collections.
(j) Advances from customers on orders being produced.

**4.** From the following account balances, select the proprietorship items and list them as they should appear on the balance sheet:

| | | | |
|---|---|---|---|
| Capital stock issued, stated value $5, 10,000 shares. | $ 50,000 | Treasury stock, 1,000 sh. | $ 5,000 |
| Dividends payable....... | 5,000 | Estimated amount payable under pension plan..... | 10,000 |
| Premium on issue of capital stock................ | 120,000 | Appraisal capital........ | 30,000 |
| Undistributed profits..... | 45,000 | Retained earnings appropriated for possible future contingencies...... | 20,000 |
| Sinking fund for bond retirement............. | 40,000 | Estimated amount payable for federal income taxes. | 7,500 |
| Premium on bonds payable | 10,000 | | |

## PROBLEMS

**1-1.** From the account balances given below and at the top of the next page for Cory's, Inc., as of December 31, 1958, prepare a balance sheet with information properly classified:

| | | | |
|---|---|---|---|
| Accounts Payable........ | $40,000 | Common Stock, Stated Value $25.............. | $150,000 |
| Accounts Receivable...... | 77,500 | Discount on Preferred Stock | 4,500 |
| Accrued Interest and Property Taxes......... | 3,050 | Dividends Receivable...... | 1,200 |
| Accrued Salaries......... | 1,400 | Equipment............... | 42,000 |
| Allow. for Bad Accounts... | 3,000 | Estimated Inc. Taxes Pay.. | 6,200 |
| Allowance for Depreciation of Buildings....... | 36,000 | Goodwill................ | 28,800 |
| | | Interest Receivable....... | 1,500 |
| Allowance for Depreciation of Equipment....... | 12,000 | Inventories............... | 142,000 |
| | | Land.................... | 60,000 |
| 6% Bonds Payable due Sept. 30, 1967......... | 100,000 | Land for Future Bldg. Site | 35,000 |
| | | Notes Payable............ | 15,950 |
| Buildings............... | 105,000 | Notes Receivable......... | 30,000 |
| Cash.................... | 30,500 | Paid-In Capital from Sale of Common Stock in Excess of Stated Value........ | 119,500 |
| Cash Dividends Payable... | 16,000 | | |

| | | | |
|---|---|---|---|
| Preferred Stock, par $100... | $120,000 | Temporary Investments in | |
| Preferred Stock Redemption Fund.............. | 40,000 | Marketable Securities.... | $24,000 |
| | | Trade-Marks............. | 10,000 |
| Prepaid Taxes, Insurance, and Interest........... | 2,600 | Treasury Stock, Common, 1,000 shares........... | 25,000 |
| Retained Earnings........ | 44,800 | Unamortized Developmental Costs.............. | 5,400 |
| Supplies Inventory........ | 3,500 | Unearned Int. on Notes Rec. | 600 |

**1-2.** Prepare a properly classified balance sheet for the Abbey Sales Co. from the information that follows as of June 30, 1958:

| | | | |
|---|---|---|---|
| Accounts Payable......... | $30,650 | Misc. Accrued Expenses... | $ 2,100 |
| Accounts Receivable...... | 48,500 | Misc. Prepaid Expenses... | 1,600 |
| Accrued Interest on Notes Receivable............ | 300 | Misc. Supplies Inventories.. | 2,600 |
| | | Notes Payable (short term) | 15,000 |
| Advances from Customers on Uncompleted Contracts.. | 5,000 | Notes Payable (due 1963).. | 20,000 |
| Allowance for Depreciation of Buildings........... | 40,000 | Notes Receivable........ | 10,500 |
| | | Patents................. | 15,000 |
| Allowance for Depreciation of Machinery and Equipment................. | 21,000 | Preferred Stock, $10 par... | 100,000 |
| | | Premium on Issue of Common Stock............ | 40,000 |
| Allowance for Doubtful Notes and Accounts..... | 1,600 | Raw Materials Inventory.. | 26,000 |
| | | Retained Earnings (debit balance).............. | 49,500 |
| Buildings................ | 100,000 | Salaries and Wages Payable | 1,500 |
| Cash in Banks........... | 18,500 | 4% Serial Bonds Payable (due March 31, 1959).... | 5,000 |
| Cash on Hand........... | 500 | | |
| Common Stock, $10 par... | 200,000 | 4% Serial Bonds Payable (due in 1960 and thereafter)................. | 90,000 |
| Dividends Receivable..... | 150 | | |
| Estimated Inc. Taxes Pay.. | 6,000 | | |
| Finished Goods Inventory.. | 19,500 | Temporary Investments in Marketable Securities.... | 15,600 |
| Goods in Process Inventory | 30,000 | | |
| Investment in Subsidiary Company Stocks........ | 85,000 | Tools................... | 6,000 |
| | | Unamortized Bond Issue Costs................. | 5,200 |
| Investment in Undeveloped Properties......... | 30,000 | | |
| Land................... | 50,000 | Unearned Int. on Notes Rec. | 400 |
| Machinery and Equipment | 65,000 | Withholding Taxes Payable | 1,200 |

**1-3.** The following balance sheet is submitted to you for inspection and review. In the course of the review you find the data listed below and on the following page. Using the balance sheet and the information that follows, prepare a corrected balance sheet with items properly classified.

BALANCE SHEET

BANNER DISTRIBUTORS

DECEMBER 31, 1958

| ASSETS | | LIABILITIES AND PROPRIETORSHIP | |
|---|---|---|---|
| Cash........................ | $ 16,500 | Accrued expenses........... | $ 2,500 |
| Accounts receivable......... | 65,000 | Loans payable............. | 20,000 |
| Inventories................ | 80,000 | Accounts payable.......... | 65,000 |
| Unexpired insurance........ | 3,500 | Capital stock.............. | 100,000 |
| Plant and equipment........ | 115,000 | Surplus................... | 92,500 |
| | $280,000 | | $280,000 |

(a) The possibility of bad debt losses on accounts receivable has not been considered. It is estimated that bad debt losses will total $2,000.

(b) $15,000 representing the cost of a large-scale newspaper advertising campaign completed in 1958 has been added to the inventories, since it is believed that this campaign will benefit sales of 1959. It is also found that inventories include merchandise of $6,500 received on December 31 that has not yet been recorded as a purchase.

(c) Unexpired insurance consists of $550, the cost of fire insurance for 1959, and $2,950, the cash surrender value on officers' life insurance policies.

(d) The books show that plant and equipment has a cost of $200,000 with depreciation of $85,000 recognized in prior years. However, these balances include fully depreciated equipment of $15,000 that has been scrapped and is no longer on hand.

(e) Accrued expenses of $2,500 represent accrued salaries of $3,500, less noncurrent advances of $1,000 made to company officials.

(f) Loans were made from the bank, the bank charging interest on the loans in advance. The interest was recorded as an expense. On December 31, the prepaid interest on the loans relating to 1959 was $405.

(g) Tax liabilities not shown are estimated to total $2,200.

(h) Capital stock consists of 6,000 shares of 4% preferred stock, par $10, and 8,000 shares of no-par common stock, stated value $5 per share.

(i) Capital stock had been issued for a total consideration of $185,000, the amount received in excess of the par and stated values of the stock being reported as surplus.

**1-4.** The bookkeeper for the Forrest Corporation submits the following condensed balance sheet. A review of the account balances reveals the data listed below and on the next page. Using the balance sheet and the related data, prepare a balance sheet reporting individual asset, liability, and proprietorship balances correctly stated and properly classified.

BALANCE SHEET

FORREST CORPORATION

JUNE 30, 1958

| | | | | |
|---|---|---|---|---|
| Current assets.............. | $ 55,000 | Current liabilities........... | $ 30,000 |
| Other assets............... | 60,000 | Other liabilities............. | 20,000 |
| | | Net worth ............... | 65,000 |
| | $115,000 | | $115,000 |

An analysis of current assets discloses the following:

| | |
|---|---|
| Cash ......................................... | $ 2,500 |
| Marketable securities................................. | 10,000 |
| Forrest Corporation Preferred Stock, 500 shares......... | 5,000 |
| Trade accounts receivable............................ | 20,000 |
| Inventories, including advertising supplies of $500....... | 17,500 |
| | $55,000 |

Other assets include:

| | |
|---|---:|
| Plant and equipment, cost $65,000, depreciated value..... | $40,000 |
| Deposit with a supplier for merchandise ordered for August delivery........................................... | 5,500 |
| Goodwill recorded on the books to cancel losses incurred by the company in prior years...................... | 14,500 |
| | $60,000 |

Current liabilities include:

| | |
|---|---:|
| Accrued payrolls..................................... | $ 2,500 |
| Accrued taxes....................................... | 2,000 |
| Trade accounts payable, $27,500, less a $2,000 debit balance reported in the account of a vendor to whom merchandise had been returned after the account was paid in full...... | 25,500 |
| | $30,000 |

Other liabilities include:

| | |
|---|---:|
| 5-year 6% mortgage on plant and equipment which falls due on December 31, 1958.......................... | $20,000 |

Net worth includes:

| | |
|---|---:|
| 5,000 shares of preferred stock, par $10................. | $50,000 |
| 10,000 shares of common stock at stated value........... | 15,000 |

Common shares were originally issued at a price of $40,000, but the paid-in capital in excess of the share stated value was applied against losses of the company incurred in past years.

**1-5.** The balance sheet that appears below was prepared by the bookkeeper for David and Green, partners. A review of the books and records discloses the need for a revision of the statement. Using the balance sheet data and the information that follows, prepare a corrected balance sheet with items properly classified.

BALANCE SHEET
DAVID AND GREEN
DECEMBER 31, 1958

| ASSETS | | LIABILITIES AND PROPRIETORSHIP | |
|---|---:|---|---:|
| Cash ..................... | $ 5,250 | Sundry liabilities......... | $ 19,000 |
| Receivables............... | 12,500 | | |
| Inventories............... | 27,000 | Net worth.............. | 47,500 |
| Land and buildings........ | 21,750 | | |
| | $ 66,500 | | $ 66,500 |

(a) The possibility of bad debt losses is not recognized above. It is estimated that bad debts may total $600.

(b) The inventories balance includes the following:

(1) Merchandise of $6,000 acquired by the partnership on a consignment basis. The receipt of the merchandise was never recorded as a purchase, since terms of the consignment provide that the merchandise is to be paid for only if sold; if unsold it can be returned.

(2) Miscellaneous supplies inventories valued at $350.

(c)  The balance of land and buildings was determined as follows:

Land..........................................  $18,500
Buildings.....................................   14,000

$32,500

Deduct depreciation of buildings to Dec. 31, 1958.....      250

$32,250

Deduct mortgage on property, $10,000 and accrued interest, $500 (Mortgage bears interest at 5% and is due January 1, 1962)........................  10,500

Partners' equity in land and buildings..............  $21,750

(d)  Expense prepayments on the balance sheet date were: taxes, $25; insurance, $200.

(e)  The sundry liabilities total was developed as follows:

Accounts payable..............................  $18,400
Less creditors' accounts with debit balances resulting from purchases returns....................      150

$18,250
Accrued salaries...............................      400
Accrued taxes.................................      350

$19,000

(f)  David and Green had started business on March 1, 1958, agreeing to share profits and losses in the ratio of 3 : 2 respectively. Each partner had invested $20,000 on the date of organization. Green had made cash withdrawals of $3,000 during 1958. Net worth represents profits reported for 1958.

**1-6.** Wayne and York formed a partnership at the beginning of 1958. The partners invested cash of $25,000 and $15,000 respectively and agreed to share profits and losses in the ratio of original investments. During the year merchandise was acquired at a cost of $60,000, invoices of $6,500 remaining unpaid on December 31. Sales for the year totaled $100,000, which was 250% of the cost of merchandise sold; collections from customers were $88,500, and the balance of $11,500 is believed fully collectible. During the year furniture and fixtures were acquired for cash at a cost of $8,500; depreciation of this asset for 1958 was calculated as $850.

At the end of the year accrued expenses for taxes and salaries total $550. Prepaid expenses consisting of insurance and supplies inventories total $400. An income statement prepared for the year shows net income of $24,000 accruing to partners. Wayne and York withdrew $8,000 and $4,500 respectively during the year.

*Instructions:* (1) Prepare a balance sheet for the partnership as of December 31, 1958, in classified form and reporting capitals of the individual partners.

(2) Prepare a summary of cash receipts and payments in support of the cash balance reported on the balance sheet.

Chapter **2**

# FINANCIAL STATEMENTS

## THE INCOME AND RETAINED EARNINGS STATEMENTS

**NATURE OF THE INCOME STATEMENT**  The income statement, also variously called the *statement of profit and loss*, the *statement of earnings*, and the *statement of operations*, summarizes revenues and expenses of the period and reports the profit or the loss resulting from the matching process. The statement thus explains the financial progress of the company and accounts for the changes in the net assets and in proprietorship resulting from profit and loss activities.

The importance of the income measurement function of the income statement cannot be overemphasized. Reference is made to this statement in judging business progress for a period. Reference is also made to this statement in arriving at the value of the property owned by a business, for it is business earnings that validate asset values. Owners, both present and prospective, reach estimates of business worth through analyses of earnings and earning potentials. As earnings rise, a higher value is assigned to the source of such earnings; as earnings shrink, the value of the property shrinks accordingly. The income statement, then, assumes broad importance, not only as a report that is used in the analysis of business success, but also as a complement to the balance sheet in the measurement of business worth.

It has already been suggested that a business unit commences activities in the attempt to increase its net assets through profitable operations. Generally, as a first step in this process, cash or other assets are given up in the acquisition of goods or services. Costs are thus incurred. Goods and services may now be sold; this means the acquisition of new assets (or reductions in liabilities) and the realization of revenue. With such realization comes a need for recognizing those costs that have expired. Profit or loss emerges from the comparison of revenue and those costs that are considered to be related to such revenue. Profit or loss of the enterprise from normal and recurring activities may be accompanied by other gains or losses from the sale, exchange, or other conversion of property items, or from the liquidation of debt.

The American Accounting Association in its "Accounting and Reporting Standards for Corporate Financial Statements" defines revenue as " . . . the monetary expression of the aggregate of products or services transferred by an enterprise to its customers during a period of time."[1] Revenue, then, would not be considered to arise from investments by owners, changes in invested capital, gifts, or the appreciation of assets prior to the realization of such increased values through sale. The Association would use the term *expired costs* to indicate costs "having no discernible benefit to future operations." Expired costs are classified as *expense* or *loss* as follows: "Expense is the expired cost, directly or indirectly related to a given fiscal period, of the flow of goods or services into the market and of related operations. Loss is expired cost not beneficial to the revenue producing activities of the enterprise."[2] Expense, then, would include both charges directly identified with revenue of the period, as cost of goods sold, and charges indirectly identified with revenue of the period, as interest, taxes, or rent. Losses would consist of charges which, although not associated with the production of current revenue, must be recognized currently, as losses from fire or flood. Expense or loss would not be considered to result from withdrawals of invested capital or from distributions of retained income.

Revenue is recognized for accounting purposes when a sale of goods is made or when services are performed for customers. In certain instances involving long-term contracts, revenue may be recognized in accordance with the degree of progress made towards contract fulfillment. Cost expiration is recognized under the following circumstances: when an asset is consumed, as in the transfer of merchandise and in the payment of cash for salaries; when there is a decline in the utility represented by an asset, as in equipment that is exhausted through use or destroyed by fire; and when there is the emergence of a liability, as in the case of salary accruals and product guarantees.

**NATURE OF THE RETAINED EARNINGS STATEMENT**   In making available the entire story of activities of the period, there should be an explanation for the change in proprietorship as reflected on beginning and ending balance sheets. The income statement is the vehicle for the revenue and expense summary. The *statement of changes in capital* in the case of the sole proprietorship and the partnership, and the *retained earnings statement* in the case of the

---

[1] *Accounting and Reporting Standards for Corporate Financial Statements*, 1957 (Columbus: American Accounting Association), p. 5.
[2] *Ibid.*, p. 6.

corporation serve as the proprietorship reconciliation device. In the case of the sole proprietorship or the partnership, statements accounting for proprietorship changes consist of opening capital balances, the changes in such balances resulting from owners' investments and withdrawals, the changes resulting from operations as summarized on the income statement, and any other changes in capital not reflected on the income statement and considered as affecting capital directly. In the case of the corporation, the retained earnings statement reports the opening retained earnings balance, the change in this balance resulting from operations as summarized on the income statement, the changes resulting from profit distributions, and any other changes in retained earnings not reflected on the income statement. When, in a corporation, there are changes in the invested capital as a result of the sale of additional shares, a stock dividend, the retirement of shares, etc., a *paid-in capital statement* can be prepared reconciling beginning and ending paid-in capital balances.

**CONTENT OF THE INCOME STATEMENT**    The income statement normally consists of a series of sections that develop the net income for the period. Such sections include (1) sales (or income from services), (2) cost of goods sold (or expenses of providing services), (3) operating expenses, (4) other income and expenses (financial management income and expenses), and (5) income taxes.

(1) *Sales.* The revenue from sales reports the total sales to customers for the period. This total should not include additions that may have been made to billings for sales taxes that the business is required to collect on behalf of the government. Such billing increase is properly recognized as a current liability. Sales returns and allowances are subtractions from gross sales. Sales discounts represent adjustments in the sales price and should be subtracted from gross sales in arriving at a net sales balance. When the sales price is increased to cover the cost of freight to the customer and the customer is billed accordingly, freight charges paid by the company should likewise be considered subtractions from sales in arriving at the net sales revenue.

(2) *Cost of Goods Sold.* When merchandise is acquired from outsiders, the cost of goods relating to sales of the period must be determined. Cost of goods available for sale is first determined. This is the sum of the beginning inventory, purchases, and all other buying, freight, and storage costs relating to acquisitions. A net purchases balance is developed by subtracting purchases returns and allowances as well as purchases discounts from the gross purchases balance. Cost

of goods sold is calculated by subtracting the cost of merchandise on hand at the end of the period from the cost of goods available for sale.

When the goods are manufactured by the seller, the cost of goods manufactured must first be calculated. Cost of goods manufactured then takes the place of purchases in the summary just described. The determination of cost of goods manufactured begins with the cost of goods in process at the beginning of the period. To this is added the cost of materials put into production, the cost of labor applied to material conversions, and all of the other costs for services and facilities utilized in production for the period, including such items as factory superintendence, indirect labor, depreciation and other costs relating to factory buildings and equipment, factory supplies used, patent amortization, and factory light, heat, and power. The total cost as thus obtained represents the cost of both completed work and uncompleted work still in production. The ending goods in process inventory is subtracted from this total in arriving at the cost of the product completed and made available for sale.

(3) *Operating Expenses.* Operating expenses are normally reported in two categories: (1) selling expenses and (2) general and administrative expenses. Selling expenses include such items as salesmen's salaries and commissions and related payroll taxes, advertising and store displays, store supplies used, depreciation of store furniture and equipment, and all expenses relating to the delivery of goods. General and administrative expenses include officers' and office salaries and related payroll taxes, office supplies used, depreciation of office furniture and fixtures, telephone, postage, business licenses and fees, legal and accounting services, contributions, and similar items. Expense items relating to the use of buildings, such as rent, depreciation, taxes, insurance, light, heat, and power, should be allocated in some equitable manner to manufacturing costs and to selling and general and administrative functions. In the case of the trading concern, charges relating to buildings are generally reported in full in the general and administrative category.

(4) *Other Income and Expenses.* Other income and expenses include items identified with financial management and other miscellaneous recurring items not related to the central operations. Other income consists of such items as interest income, dividend income, and miscellaneous income from rentals, royalties, and fees. Other expenses include interest expense and other expenses related to the miscellaneous income items shown. In practice purchases discounts are frequently regarded as

financial management income and are reported as Other Income instead of as a reduction from the purchases balance. When purchases discounts are treated as Other Income, sales discounts are reported as Other Expense.

(5) *Income Taxes.* The government levies a tax on the earnings of the corporate business unit. The portion of income representing federal, state, and other income taxes is summarized and separately reported.

**THE CURRENT OPERA-TING PERFORMANCE VS. THE ALL-INCLUSIVE INCOME STATEMENT** There is general agreement that there should be a clear distinction on the statements summarizing activities between those charges and credits that are considered normal and recurring and those that are considered extraordinary, nonrecurring, and unpredictable. The latter consist of two classes of items: (1) unusual gains and losses and (2) charges and credits arising from the recognition of errors made in reporting the income of prior periods. There has not been full agreement, however, as to how such a distinction should be made. Should the extraordinary items be summarized on the retained earnings statement, the income statement being limited to a presentation of normally recurring profit and loss items, or should the income statement summarize both ordinary and extraordinary items? Limitation of the income statement to normally recurring items, referred to as the *current operating performance* statement, is supported by the American Institute of Certified Public Accountants. The income statement that includes extraordinary items, commonly referred to as the *all-inclusive* statement, has found strong advocates in both the American Accounting Association and the Securities and Exchange Commission. Because extraordinary items are cleared through profit and loss, and surplus or retained earnings is freed of such charges or credits, all-inclusive reporting is commonly referred to as the *clean surplus* approach.

*The Current Operating Performance Statement.* The current operating performance statement finds its support in the following arguments:

(1) The income statement should show as clearly as possible what happened and what the company was able to earn under normal conditions for the period so that sound comparisons may be made with similar summaries for prior periods as well as with summaries of other companies for the current period.

(2) Use of the all-inclusive statement may result in unsound judgment and misleading inferences as to the level of sustained earning power, since many users are unable satisfactorily to analyze the state-

ment and eliminate those items that distort results for their purposes. The reader, unfamiliar with the full story behind the items indicated, is less qualified than the accountant to determine what items cause misleading inferences with respect to the "basic earning power" of the enterprise.

The American Institute of Certified Public Accountants has considered the problems arising in the reporting of normal and extraordinary items on the income and retained earnings statements and has issued a number of pronouncements dealing with this matter. In Bulletin No. 43, the Committee on Accounting Procedure defines "net income" and suggests standards for the determination of extraordinary items that are to be excluded from the net income summary as follows:

> ... it is the opinion of the committee that there should be a general presumption that all items of profit and loss recognized during the period are to be used in determining the figure reported as net income. The only possible exception to this presumption relates to items which in the aggregate are material in relation to the company's net income and are clearly not identifiable with or do not result from the usual or typical business operations of the period. Thus, only extraordinary items such as the following may be excluded from the determination of net income for the year, and they should be excluded when their inclusion would impair the significance of net income so that misleading inferences might be drawn therefrom:
>
>> (a) Material charges or credits (other than ordinary adjustments of a recurring nature) specifically related to operations of prior years, such as the elimination of unused reserves provided in prior years and adjustments of income taxes for prior years;
>> (b) Material charges or credits resulting from unusual sales of assets not acquired for resale and not of the type in which the company generally deals;
>> (c) Material losses of a type not usually insured against, such as those resulting from wars, riots, earthquakes and similar calamities or catastrophes except where such losses are a recurrent hazard of the business;
>> (d) The write-off of a material amount of intangibles;
>> (e) The write-off of material amounts of unamortized bond discount or premium and bond issue expenses at the time of the retirement or refunding of the debt before maturity.[1]

While recommending the exclusion of the above items in the determination of net income, the Institute Committee also expresses a strong preference for reporting these on the retained earnings statement rather than on the income statement. It is of the opinion that even when the latter are listed in a separate section following a net income determination on the income statement, misconceptions are

[1]*Accounting Research Bulletin No. 43*, "Restatement and Revision of Accounting Research Bulletins," 1953 (New York: American Institute of Certified Public Accountants), p. 63.

likely to arise as to whether the earnings for the period are represented by the amount actually designated as net income or by the final and often more prominent amount reported after recognition of the extraordinary items. When reporting is to take the all-inclusive form, the committee cautions that special care be taken to report clearly and unequivocally the net income figure and to describe precisely the final figure on the statement for what it represents, for example, "net income and special items," "net loss and special items," "profit on sale of subsidiary less net loss," etc.[1]

*The All-Inclusive Statement.* Those who favor the all-inclusive statement offer the following arguments in support of their position:

(1) A statement purporting to show operating results for a period should offer the full story of activities so that annual statements since the start of the enterprise will offer the total income history for the life of the enterprise. Whether gain or loss is the product of one year or several years, it deserves appropriate recognition on the income statement as a means of evaluating business and management performance. The all-inclusive statement is simple to prepare, is not subject to variations in judgment as to treatment of special items, is easy to understand and less subject to misunderstandings, and can be accepted with confidence as a full report of the administration of business properties. With all of the operating data made available, a reader of the statement can employ and adjust such data in a manner appropriate to the nature of his analysis.

(2) The current operating performance statement carries with it a number of difficulties and dangers:

(a) The reader of the statement untrained in accounting may be unaware of the fact that an income statement can be prepared in a manner incomplete as to activities of the period, and by failing to analyze the change in retained earnings will not have a full appreciation of current activities as well as the long-run earning capacity of the enterprise.
(b) Permitting the omission of extraordinary items opens the doors to possible manipulation of current earnings by burying significant information in retained earnings.
(c) Use of distortion as criteria for the omission of items means the adoption of standards for normalizing income rather than measuring income.
(d) Differences in judgment will be found with respect to the treatment of borderline cases.

---

[1] *Ibid.*, p. 65. It may be observed that the Committee on Accounting Procedure in 1948 recommended that the income statement be prepared in "current operating performance" form. However, this stand was modified and the "all-inclusive" form was termed "acceptable" in 1951, after the Securities and Exchange Commission in its revised Regulations S-X ruled that items of profit and loss given recognition in the accounts during a period but not included in the determination of net income or loss be reported as additions to or deductions from such net income or loss on the income statement.

(e) The establishment of net income in this form carries with it implications as to future earnings. However, the past is only of limited help in forecasting; furthermore, unusual events are a part of the history of the past and should be considered in estimating the future.

Those supporting the all-inclusive statement would generally use the net income designation for the final effect of all of the items given recognition on the income statement.

*Modified All-Inclusive Form.* There are many who support the inclusion on the income statement of all extraordinary items except those charges and credits representing corrections in profits of prior periods. For this group the income statement should be the vehicle for reporting fully on current transactions involving profit and loss but the retained earnings statement should report changes in retained earnings arising from past accounting failures.[1]

*Combined Income and Retained Earnings Statement.* The preparation of a combined income and retained earnings statement has been encouraged as a means of recognizing both normal and extraordinary items on a single report, while still providing for the classification of the extraordinary items as adjustments in retained earnings. Presentation of normal and extraordinary items on the single report offers a current earnings picture plus an appreciation of the modifications of earnings on a long-term basis. The latter items add emphasis to the income report as a tentative installment in the long-term story of financial progress. A disadvantage of the combined statement is that net income is reported within the body of the statement, and special care must be taken to provide clear and descriptive item and total designations. The combined statement has won wide favor in recent years.[2]

**ALLOCATION OF INCOME TAXES BETWEEN NET INCOME AND EXTRAORDINARY ITEMS** When both normal and extraordinary items enter into the calculation of the income taxes, an allocation of the taxes should be made

---

[1]It may be noted that the American Accounting Association Committee on Accounting Concepts and Standards in its 1957 statement, *Accounting and Reporting Standards for Corporate Financial Statements*, would permit the recognition of corrections of profits of prior periods on the retained earnings statement. The committee states, "Income-determining transactions recognized in the current period but primarily relating to prior activities such as corrections of accruals, should not affect the determination or reporting of realized net income of the period."

[2]The American Institute Committee on Accounting Procedure comments that the preparation of the combined statement will often be found to be convenient and desirable. However it cautions, ". . . The adoption of the combined statement provides no excuse for less care in distinguishing charges and credits to income from charges and credits to surplus than would be required if separate statements of income and surplus were presented. Failure to exercise care in the use of this form of statement would immediately discredit it." *Accounting Research Bulletin No. 43*, "Restatement and Revision of Accounting Research Bulletins," 1953 (New York: American Institute of Certified Public Accountants), p. 18.

between the two classes of items. Both normal activities and extraordinary activities including the income tax consequences emerging from each of these activities can then be fully set forth.

Satisfactory allocation of income taxes is ordinarily achieved by assigning to net income the taxes that would apply to this balance in the absence of any other items and assigning to extraordinary items the difference between the actual taxes and taxes related to normal income. Normal activities, then, neither receive tax benefit nor suffer tax penalty as a result of the extraordinary items; "net income after taxes" is both a meaningful balance and a balance that is comparable with similar presentations of prior periods. Extraordinary activities, in turn, are summarized together with the tax effects emerging from such activities; the real effect that these items have upon proprietorship is thus fully set forth.

When both normal and extraordinary items are positive items contributing to the total income tax payment, the tax allocation involves a division of the total tax and the assignment of this balance to the separate profit sources. When either normal or extraordinary items are negative items serving to reduce the taxes that would otherwise be payable, a tax allocation is still required if the two types of activities are to be satisfactorily presented and evaluated. However, allocation here involves the assignment of a tax charge that is larger than the actual tax payment to the positive or profit item accompanied by a tax credit that counterbalances the excessive tax charge to the negative or loss item. Under these circumstances, favorable activities of the period carry their normal tax burden; unfavorable activities which served to reduce the taxes that otherwise would have been payable are summarized in terms of their net effect upon proprietorship.

When extraordinary items are reported following normal items on the income statement, the tax allocation affects only sections on the income statement. When extraordinary items are reported on the retained earnings statement, the tax allocation involves both the income statement and the retained earnings statement, the tax related to extraordinary items being reported on the latter statement. In either case, it is desirable to report on the income statement the actual amount of the income taxes for the period together with the adjustment made in this total in effecting an allocation of the taxes. The actual taxes and the increase or decrease in this total carried to other sections of the income statement or to the retained earnings statement may be indicated parenthetically, or the two values may be listed in developing the charge made against net income.

The American Institute of Certified Public Accountants has given full support to the allocation of income taxes.[1] However, it should be pointed out that there may be special instances where an allocation procedure is not practical. Furthermore, there are some who prefer to report the actual amount of the income taxes as a single charge at the bottom of the income statement. When taxes are to be reported as a single charge without adjustment on the income statement, it is important that a note or other disclosure be provided to point out the nature of the charge and its implications in the evaluation of net income and extraordinary balances reported on the income and retained earnings statements.

**FORM OF THE INCOME STATEMENT** Many variations in income statement form are found in practice. Data can be presented in account or report form. The account form reports expenses and losses on the left-hand side of the statement, revenues on the right-hand side, and the income or the loss as a balancing figure. The data are presented in report form with various groupings of profit and loss data vertically arranged. An illustration of a statement prepared in report form is found on page 42. This statement is prepared in all-inclusive form. The result of normal activities is first summarized and is designated as net income in accordance with the American Institute view, and this summary is followed by a listing of the extraordinary items. The statement is prepared in *multiple-step* form with groupings of various items in the determination of the profit measurements as follows:

*Gross profit on sales* (or *gross margin*)—the difference between sales and costs related to such sales.
*Net profit from operations*—the gross profit on sales less operating expenses.
*Net income before income taxes*—the net gain on trading activities plus and minus financial management and other miscellaneous income and expense.
*Net income after income taxes*—the net income less the income taxes.
*Net income and extraordinary items*—the net income after income taxes plus and minus extraordinary gains and losses.

There are some who raise objection to the multiple-step income statement. This group points out that the various profit designations may prove a source of confusion to the reader. Furthermore, use of such profit designations in the absence of full statement context may prove ambiguous or actually misleading. These persons would support

---

[1] *Ibid.*, p. 88. It may be observed that the Committee on Accounting Procedure does not contemplate a determination of the tax effect attributable to every separate transaction. In the Committee's view all that is necessary in making an allocation is to consider the effect on taxes of all of those items that are excluded from the net income determination.

## WEBSTER COMPANY
### INCOME STATEMENT
#### FOR YEAR ENDED DECEMBER 31, 1958

| | | | |
|---|---:|---:|---:|
| Revenue from sales: | | | |
| Gross sales................................... | | | $510,000 |
| Less: Sales returns and allowances............. | | $ 7,500 | |
| Sales discounts................................ | | 2,500 | 10,000 |
| Net sales.................................. | | | $500,000 |
| Cost of goods sold: | | | |
| Merchandise inventory, January 1, 1958....... | | $ 95,000 | |
| Add:  Merchandise purchases................. | $320,000 | | |
| Freight in...................... | 15,000 | | |
| Delivered cost of purchases............. | $335,000 | | |
| Less:  Purchases returns and allow- | | | |
| ances.................  $1,000 | | | |
| Purchases discounts.......  4,000 | 5,000 | 330,000 | |
| Merchandise available for sale................. | | $425,000 | |
| Deduct: Merchandise inventory, December 31, 1958 | | 125,000 | |
| Cost of goods sold........................... | | | 300,000 |
| Gross profit on sales........................... | | | $200,000 |
| Operating expenses: | | | |
| Selling expenses: | | | |
| Sales salaries............................. | $ 30,000 | | |
| Advertising............................... | 15,000 | | |
| Depreciation of selling and delivery equipment | 5,000 | | |
| Miscellaneous selling expense.............. | 10,000 | $ 60,000 | |
| General and administrative expenses: | | | |
| Officers and office salaries .................. | $ 45,000 | | |
| Taxes, insurance, etc...................... | 20,000 | | |
| Miscellaneous supplies used................. | 5,000 | | |
| Depreciation of office furniture and fixtures.... | 5,000 | | |
| Miscellaneous general expense.............. | 15,000 | 90,000 | 150,000 |
| Net profit from operations..................... | | | $ 50,000 |
| Other income and expenses: | | | |
| Other income: | | | |
| Interest income...................... | $ 3,500 | | |
| Dividend income..................... | 1,500 | $ 5,000 | |
| Other expenses: | | | |
| Interest expense......................... | | 10,000 | |
| Deduct excess of other expenses over other income . | | | 5,000 |
| Net income before income taxes................. | | | $ 45,000 |
| Income taxes applicable to net income (total tax provision, $23,000, less $5,000 applicable to gain on sale of securities)...................... | | | 18,000 |
| Net income after income taxes.................. | | | $ 27,000 |
| Extraordinary items: | | | |
| Gains, other increases: | | | |
| Gain on sale of securities............................ | | $ 20,000 | |
| Losses, other decreases: | | | |
| Corrections in profits of prior periods—under- | | | |
| statement of depreciation.................. | $ 7,000 | | |
| Income taxes applicable to extraordinary gain.. | 5,000 | 12,000 | |
| Excess of gains and other increases over losses and other decreases............................ | | | 8,000 |
| Net income and extraordinary items............. | | | $ 35,000 |

**All-Inclusive Income Statement**

a *single-step form* that avoids sectional labeling. The single-step form has won wide adoption in recent years and is illustrated below:

WEBSTER COMPANY

CONDENSED INCOME STATEMENT

FOR YEAR ENDED DECEMBER 31, 1958

| | | |
|---|---:|---:|
| Net sales | | $500,000 |
| Other income—interest and dividends | | 5,000 |
| Extraordinary gains, other increases—gain on sale of securities | | 20,000 |
| | | $525,000 |
| Deduct: | | |
| Cost of goods sold | $300,000 | |
| Selling expenses | 60,000 | |
| General and administrative expenses | 90,000 | |
| Other expenses—interest | 10,000 | |
| Extraordinary losses, other decreases—corrections in profits of prior periods—understatement of depreciation | 7,000 | |
| Income taxes | 23,000 | 490,000 |
| Net income and extraordinary items | | $ 35,000 |

**Single-Step Income Statement**

Frequently the income statement prepared for stockholders simply reports totals for certain classes of items, such as cost of goods sold, selling expenses, general expenses, other income, other expenses, and other special items. This plan was followed in the single-step statement just given. Additional detail may be provided by means of supporting schedules.

When goods are manufactured by the seller, the cost of goods manufactured must be determined before the cost of goods sold can be found. If this information is made available with the regular reports, it is generally displayed on a separate schedule supporting the income statement because it involves so much detail. Assuming that the goods available for sale were obtained by manufacture rather than by purchase as in the example on page 42, the cost of goods sold section of the income statement may be prepared in the form shown below. This statement may be supported by the manufacturing schedule on the following page.

| | | |
|---|---:|---:|
| Cost of goods sold: | | |
| Finished goods inventory, January 1, 1958 | | $ 40,000 |
| Add: Cost of goods manufactured per manufacturing schedule | | 310,000 |
| Merchandise available for sale | | $350,000 |
| Deduct: Finished goods inventory, December 31, 1958 | | 50,000 |
| Cost of goods sold | | $300,000 |

**Cost of Goods Sold Section of Income Statement for a Manufacturing Business**

## WEBSTER COMPANY
### Manufacturing Schedule
### To Accompany Income Statement
### For Year Ended December 31, 1958

| | | | |
|---|---|---|---|
| Goods in process inventory, January 1, 1958...... | | | $ 25,000 |
| | | | |
| Raw materials: | | | |
| Inventory, January 1, 1958.................. | | $ 30,000 | |
| Purchases................................. | $105,000 | | |
| Freight in................................. | 10,000 | | |
| Delivered cost of raw materials.............. | $115,000 | | |
| Less: Returns and allowances.......... $1,000 | | | |
| Purchases discounts............. 4,000 | 5,000 | 110,000 | |
| Total cost of raw materials available for use.... | | $140,000 | |
| Less: Inventory, December 31, 1958........... | | 40,000 | |
| Cost of raw materials consumed............... | | | 100,000 |
| Direct labor................................... | | | 140,000 |
| | | | |
| Manufacturing expenses: | | | |
| Indirect labor............................... | | $ 20,000 | |
| Factory superintendence..................... | | 14,500 | |
| Depreciation of factory buildings, machinery and equipment | | 12,000 | |
| Light, heat, and power...................... | | 10,000 | |
| Factory supplies used....................... | | 8,500 | |
| Miscellaneous factory expense................. | | 15,000 | |
| Total manufacturing expenses................ | | | 80,000 |
| | | | |
| Total goods in process during 1958............. | | | $345,000 |
| Deduct: Goods in process inventory, December 31, 1958 | | | 35,000 |
| Cost of goods manufactured................... | | | $310,000 |

**Manufacturing Schedule**

If desired, simply the cost of goods sold total could be reported on the income statement. A supporting cost of goods sold schedule would summarize the cost of goods manufactured as well as the change in finished goods inventories.

**FORM OF THE RETAINED EARNINGS STATEMENT** When the income statement reports extraordinary items, including corrections in profits of prior periods, the retained earnings statement may consist merely of beginning and ending retained earnings balances reconciled by the change in retained earnings as reported by the income statement and decreased by the dividends declared for the period. Such a statement is shown on the following page.

WEBSTER COMPANY
RETAINED EARNINGS STATEMENT
FOR YEAR ENDED DECEMBER 31, 1958

| | |
|---|---:|
| Retained earnings, January 1, 1958.................................... | $140,000 |
| Add: Net income and extraordinary items per income statement........ | 35,000 |
| | $175,000 |
| Deduct: Dividends declared during year............................. | 20,000 |
| Retained earnings, December 31, 1958............................. | $155,000 |

**Retained Earnings Statement to Accompany an All-Inclusive Income Statement**

When the income statement is limited to normally recurring items, the retained earnings statement summarizes extraordinary items. The order of presentation of net income, extraordinary gains and losses, corrections in profits of prior periods, and dividend charges on the retained earnings statement varies. In the form that follows, retained earnings for the beginning of the period is first corrected for past errors. Other increases and decreases follow.

WEBSTER COMPANY
RETAINED EARNINGS STATEMENT
FOR YEAR ENDED DECEMBER 31, 1958

| | | |
|---|---:|---:|
| Balance of retained earnings, January 1, 1958............... | | $140,000 |
| Corrections in retained earnings applicable to prior periods: | | |
| Deduction for understatement of depreciation............ | | 7,000 |
| Corrected balance of retained earnings at beginning of year... | | $133,000 |
| Add: Net income after income taxes per income statement... | $ 27,000 | |
| Extraordinary gains: | | |
| Gain on sale of securities...................... | 20,000 | 47,000 |
| | | $180,000 |
| Deduct: Dividends declared............................ | $ 20,000 | |
| Income taxes applicable to extraordinary gain....... | 5,000 | 25,000 |
| Balance of retained earnings, December 31, 1958........... | | $155,000 |

**Retained Earnings Statement to Accompany a Current Operating Performance
Income Statement**

**FORM OF THE COMBINED
INCOME AND RETAINED
EARNINGS STATEMENT**
A combined income and retained earnings statement may be prepared in various forms. For example, it is possible to present net income data followed by the extraordinary items, thus summarizing the change in retained earnings from the two sources. This total is increased by the retained earnings balance at the beginning of the period, and total retained earnings is then reduced by the dividends declared in arriving at the balance at the end of the period.

The combined statement can also be prepared in a form as follows:

WEBSTER COMPANY

INCOME AND RETAINED EARNINGS STATEMENT

FOR YEAR ENDED DECEMBER 31, 1958

Income from sales:

| | | | |
|---|---|---|---|
| Net income after income taxes per income statement. | | | $ 27,000 |
| Add: Retained earnings, January 1, 1958............ | | | 140,000 |
| | | | $167,000 |
| Extraordinary items: | | | |
| Gains, other increases: | | | |
| Gain on sale of securities.................... | | $20,000 | |
| Losses, other decreases: | | | |
| Correction in profits of prior periods—understatement of depreciation.................. | $7,000 | | |
| Income taxes applicable to extraordinary gain... | 5,000 | 12,000 | |
| Excess of gains and other increases over losses and other decreases............................. | | | 8,000 |
| | | | $175,000 |
| Deduct dividends declared....................... | | | 20,000 |
| Retained earnings, December 31, 1958............ | | | $155,000 |

**Combined Income and Retained Earnings Statement**

The foregoing presentations report dividends on the statement summarizing changes in retained earnings. Some companies prefer to add a section on the income statement that reports the disposition of net income. When such a form is employed, net income or net income and extraordinary items would be followed by a summary of dividends for the period and the resulting change in retained earnings after dividends. Preferred dividends may be listed as a separate item on the income statement to offer data concerning the net income accruing to common stockholders. Sometimes bond interest is excluded in arriving at net income and is reported together with dividends as a disposition of income; emphasis is thus placed on management's success in the use of all business resources — resources contributed by the creditors as well as the owners.

**THE SIMPLIFIED INCOME STATEMENT**    Some companies depart from the conventional forms of the income statement in the attempt to display profit and loss data in simplified or more popular and readable form. Data are frequently presented in narrative or graphic form to help the reader grasp significant relationships. A variety of different forms for the income statement and retained earnings summaries are included in the Appendix of this textbook.

**CERTAIN BASIC CONCEPTS IN THE MEASUREMENT PROCESS**    The measurement process and the nature and form of the statements giving expression to this process have been described in the past pages. There are several general assumptions and practices that are considered basic to accounting. These are considered in the following paragraphs.

**THE BUSINESS ENTITY**    The accountant views the business enterprise as a specific entity separate from its owners. It is this entity and its activities that assume the focus of his attention. This unit has as its objective to make a profit, and periodic reports are means of bringing to the attention of the ownership — whether a single owner, partners, or stockholders — the progress that has been made in this objective within a stated period. Such reports recognize the effects of all of the transactions upon the assets of the entity, as well as the equities that are identified with it.

**OBJECTIVE, VERIFIABLE EVIDENCE**    Accounting seeks to present its findings on a foundation of facts determined objectively and subject to verification. Cash receipts and disbursements can be adequately supported by vouchers, and cash on hand is determined by count; full support and verification for this element and its changes are available. Findings here can be fully objective. Purchases of goods and services as well as sales are also generally well supported by evidence and subject to verification. There are a number of areas in accounting, however, where one must develop conclusions based in certain measure upon judgment, estimate, and subjective factors. The recognition of depreciation is an example of the latter. But the degree of estimate can be minimized by the attempt to secure and develop evidence that will lend objective support to conclusions. Objective determinations to the fullest extent possible are encouraged as a means of closing the doors to possible error, bias, or even intentional fraud, thus achieving an accounting deserving of complete confidence.

**THE GOING CONCERN ASSUMPTION**    When the future is unpredictable, one can only assume a continuity of existence and a business environment to follow that is similar to that in which the enterprise finds itself currently. The business unit, thus, is viewed as a "going concern" in the absence of evidence to the contrary. The concept of continuity is support for the preparation of a balance sheet that reports costs that are assignable to future activities rather than realizable values that would attach to properties in the event of liquidation or forced sale. The concept of continuity calls for the preparation of an income statement that reports only such portions of costs as are allocable to current activities. Obviously, the assumption of a going concern may be invalidated by future experience. Statements, then, should be regarded as of a provisional nature, with support for their conclusions still to be found in the events of the future. In the event business termination was anticipated, a "quitting concern" assumption would have to be adopted; the implications of such change of status would then require recognition.

In applying the assumption of continuity, the intent of management frequently requires recognition in problems of valuation and presentation. For example, if it is the policy of management to trade in automotive equipment at three-year intervals even though such equipment might have a materially longer life, the intent of management would govern the allocation of cost. Or if management has taken steps to replace currently maturing bonds with a new issue, the maturing bonds would continue to be reported on the balance sheet as a noncurrent obligation since they would make no claim on current assets. The balance sheet should reveal, however, the evidence in support of the noncurrent classification.

**THE CONSERVATIVE**     Alternative approaches may frequently be
**APPROACH**             suggested in resolving certain problems relative to the measurement of financial position and progress. When such alternatives are involved, accountants have generally felt that they can serve business best by the adoption of a conservative approach to such problems.

The doctrine of conservatism is illustrated in the application of practices such as the following: increases in the values of assets and anticipated gains are normally ignored until realized by means of sale; declines in asset values and anticipated losses, however, frequently receive full recognition. Marketable securities, for example, are normally valued at cost or market, whichever is lower. A market value in excess of cost is ignored or shown only parenthetically, recognition of the gain awaiting realization through sale. A decrease in market, however, although not yet incurred through sale, is currently recognized. Again, certain expenditures are charged in full against current revenue despite the probability of future benefits. For example, a large-scale advertising campaign may contribute to future sales; however, in view of the indeterminate character of the contribution, conservatism would suggest no deferral of the expenditure but rather the recognition of the entire amount as expense.

It is agreed that a healthy conservatism as applied to the recognition of income is fully laudable. However, the deliberate and arbitrary understatement of asset values or overstatement of liabilities simply to achieve a conservative balance sheet is hardly the appropriate application of this concept. There are instances where, as a means of arriving at conservative appraisals of business worth or business debt-paying ability, inventories have been deliberately understated, plant and intangibles have been reported at nominal amounts, and reserves for possible losses and future contingencies have been established and reported among the liabilities. Conservatism expressed in this manner results in financial statements that no longer serve to report a revenue-cost matching process. The understatement of inventories to achieve a conservative current position carries with it an understatement of current income; the current understatement of inventories further results in the understatement of cost of goods sold and the overstatement of net income in the next period. The arbitrary reduction of plant items in the interest of a conservative asset position results in the understatement of depreciation charges in future periods and the overstatement of net incomes; balance sheet conservatism here has been accompanied by a contrary effect on the income statements. The recognition of fictitious liabilities to achieve a conservative capital results in the misrepresentation of financial condition until such balances are canceled; further, if payment of future expenses is applied against such liability balances, incomes of these periods are overstated. Departures from sound measurement procedures to achieve balance sheet conservatism serve to distort net income as well as net asset and proprietorship measurements.

The concept of balance sheet conservatism carries over from an earlier day when the accounting process was considered to be concerned largely with the development and preparation of a statement of financial condition for creditors and owners. The income statement occupied a supporting role by linking successive balance sheets, income measurement being determined by the values assigned to assets. But with a growing recognition of the importance of earnings both as a progress and a value indicator, the income statement has now become the center of attention. With emphasis upon accuracy in earnings measurement, there has come a regard for the balance sheet as "the connecting link between successive income statements and as the vehicle for the distribution of charges and credits between them."[1] Conservatism is now

---

[1] *Accounting Research Bulletin No. 1* "General Introduction and Rules Formerly Adopted," 1939 (New York: American Institute of Certified Public Accountants), p. 2.

accepted as a moderating and refining influence to be applied to the matching process as a whole.

**CONSISTENCY** In view of such variations as the different methods for cost allocation in arriving at depreciation, the different approaches to the pricing of inventories in arriving at cost of goods sold, and the different forms and classifications for the presentation of operating and financial data, methods that are adopted should be consistently employed if there is to be continuity and comparability in the accounting presentations. In analyzing statements one is constantly making conclusions with respect to trends within the enterprise. Such conclusions are distorted, for example, if straight-line depreciation is applied against the revenue of one year and output depreciation against the revenue of the next year, or if marketable securities are reported under long-term investments in one year and under current assets in the following year.

This is not to suggest that methods once adopted should not be changed. A continuing analysis of the business activities as well as changing conditions may suggest changes in accounting methods and presentations that will lead to more informative statements. Such changes should be incorporated in the accounting system and statements. But the statements should be accompanied by a summary of the changes and their effects, where material, so that one can properly interpret current data and relate these to statements of the past. When comparative statements are presented, it would normally be desirable either (1) to restate the statement for the periods prior to the change in terms of current reporting so that statements are fully comparable, or (2) to offer the statements in noncomparable form but with an accompanying note or exhibit indicating the comparable results that would have been obtained if either the old practice or the new had been used consistently.

It may be further observed that a company may adopt certain practices and apply these consistently. However, alternative practices offering materially different results may be in common use by other companies. Under these circumstances, special disclosure of the method followed and data required in developing such alternate results may well be provided through accompanying notes and exhibits.

**FULL DISCLOSURE** One finds constant reference in accounting literature to the concept of *full disclosure*. It has already been suggested that a great many groups rely on accounting statements as their only source of information concerning the financial progress of an enterprise. The accountant, aware of the needs of these groups, can meet his responsibility to them only by making known all of those facts that are required in reaching informed opinions. These facts are not limited to matters of the past and the present, but, under certain circumstances, include matters relating to the future, either anticipated or actually accomplished.[1]

The concept of full disclosure calls not only for adequate disclosure of all financial facts, but also for the presentation of such facts in a manner that will lead to their proper interpretation. Close care should be taken in developing data classifications, arrangements, and summaries, and in employing supporting schedules and supplementary exhibits.

It should be pointed out that full disclosure calls for setting forth all matters of a material nature, not simply more detail. Excessive detail, descriptions, and qualifications may only serve to obscure certain significant facts and relationships and thus act as an impairment to the appreciation of the full story. The American Accounting Association Committee on Concepts and Standards Underlying Corporate Financial Statements comments on materiality and offers a criterion for judging materiality in the following statement:

> In the selection of classifications, in planning the extent of summarization, in giving emphasis to or omitting information, and in determining periodic net income, materiality is often a deciding factor. Materiality, as used in accounting, may be described as a state of relative importance. The materiality of an item may depend upon its size, its nature, or a combination of both. An item should be regarded as material if there is reason to believe that knowledge of it would influence the decisions of an informed investor.[2]

---

[1]The American Accounting Association Committee on Concepts and Standards Underlying Corporate Financial Statements directs its attention to the basic considerations underlying adequacy of disclosure in *Accounting and Reporting Standards for Corporate Financial Statements*, "Standards of Disclosure for Published Financial Reports," 1957 (Columbus: American Accounting Association), pp. 46–48. It is pointed out that the needs of all of the groups requiring financial data cannot be met equally well by a single set of statements. Under these circumstances the traditional view has been to regard the requirements of stockholders as of primary concern, and the Committee is in accord with such practice. The Committee points out, "The underlying determinant of adequacy of disclosure in published financial reports is their usefulness in making decisions, particularly with respect to investment problems. It is reasonable to assume that any recipient desirous of making effective use of a financial statement must be willing and competent to read it carefully and with discrimination. Such statements should, therefore, be prepared for use by interested persons having a working knowledge of business methods and terminology." The Committee is also of the opinion that at the present time the risk of excessive disclosure is far less than that of inadequate disclosure, and suggests that management in preparing its reports be urged to use "a concept of full rather than minimum disclosure as a point of departure."

[2]*Accounting and Reporting Standards for Corporate Financial Statements and Preceding Statements and Supplements*, 1957 (Columbus: American Accounting Association) p. 8.

Obviously, the goal of full disclosure will continue to be a product of accounting convention and individual judgment on the part of the accountant.

It may be possible to provide all significant financial information within the body of the financial statements through the use of descriptive account titles and supporting data developed in parenthetical form. Frequently, however, certain matters can better be handled by means of (1) special notes to accompany the statements, or (2) explanations in the auditor's report accompanying the statements. Whenever the data are not included on the face of the statements, the statements should make reference to such supporting material as representing an integral part of current reporting.

Matters that should be recognized and developed in some appropriate manner in telling the full financial story include the following:

(1) Methods of arriving at cost and valuation bases for marketable securities and inventories.

(2) Methods of valuation for noncurrent assets, including particulars for any departures from the normal cost and cost allocation procedures.

(3) Material differences between costs reported on the statements and current market values.

(4) Hypothecation, pledge, or mortgage of any asset.

(5) Maturity dates for noncurrent receivables.

(6) Legal aspects of property reported on the statements but not owned.

(7) Long-term leases, including particulars with respect to period covered, annual rental schedule, rental guarantees, and other significant terms involved in the contracts.

(8) Purchase commitments outstanding involving material amounts and significant market price fluctuation.

(9) Policies and procedures employed in consolidating subsidiary companies.

(10) Particulars as to long-term debt, including amounts authorized and outstanding, maturity date or dates for installment obligations, conversion and redemption rights, interest rates, assets securing debt, redemption fund or other requirements, defaults on scheduled redemption fund contributions or principal and interest payments, etc.

(11) Basis for estimating income tax liabilities, including reference to tax audits, tax settlements, taxable years under review by taxing authorities, and the status of any taxes in dispute.

(12) Particulars concerning provisions for retirement, bonus, and separation plans.

(13) Contingent claims, with full analysis of the nature of contingencies, sums of money involved, etc.

(14) Particulars as to classes of stock issued including par or no-par features; amounts authorized, reacquired, and outstanding; dividend preferences, redemption and liquidation values on senior issues; dividends in arrears on cumulative stock; conversion features; stock purchase options outstanding; etc.

(15) Particulars as to special limitations on the use of retained earnings as a basis for dividends, including references to legal requirements, contractual agreements with creditor groups, etc.

(16) Effects on income taxes of extraordinary gains and losses, and also the consequences emerging from differences between financial accounting and tax accounting.

(17) Methods of income measurement where income is recognized at some time other than at time of sale and on a basis other than the conventional accrual basis.

(18) Major accounting policies with respect to depreciation, depletion, and amortization procedures.

(19) Departures from consistency in methods of valuation and presentation, including the effects of such changes in the development of comparative statement values.

(20) Departures from "generally accepted accounting principles" in the development of the financial summaries.

(21) Contemplated future actions of material significance where supporting evidence is adequate to assume such projects will be consummated, including proposed expansion, financing, reorganization, and liquidation.

(22) Occurrences between the end of the previous period and the date of completion of statements that have a material effect upon the company and are of significance in projecting the financial facts disclosed by the statements into the future.    Post-statement disclosures frequently include such items as:

    (a) Financing operations, including long-term debt increase or retirement.
    (b) Changes in the capital structure, including stock issuance, retirement, or conversion.
    (c) Significant changes in the market value of inventories, securities, real property, etc.
    (d) Major property acquisitions or sales.
    (e) Union negotiations and settlements.
    (f) Legal suits filed, appealed, or settled.
    (g) Death, resignation, and appointment of officers and directors.
    (h) Sales, orders, earnings statistics and trends.
    (i) Action taken by the board of directors on major policy.
    (j) Involuntary conversion of property items.
    (k) Significant events that modify inferences that might otherwise be drawn from financial statements.

**ASSUMPTION OF A STABLE MONETARY UNIT**     Business consists of exchange transactions. Contemporary accounting practice calls for the preparation of statements that reflect the dollars originally identified with such exchanges: thus, revenue is the cash received or the cash equivalent of the commodities or services received; cost is the cash outlay made or the cash equivalent of the item given up. Fluctuations in the value of money and differences in purchasing power are ignored; the dollar is assumed to represent a stable unit of value, an acceptable yardstick.

With significant price level changes in recent years, accounting measurements are being challenged. It is charged that the balance

sheet involves assemblies of dollars of different values and that matching of dollars of different purchasing power on the income statement
fails to provide a satisfactory measurement of income. It is further
charged that comparative financial data have lost their validity and
usefulness where money amounts reflect widely different price levels.

Suggestions have been made by responsible groups who use the
product of accounting as well as by accounting authorities that, in
view of marked changes in the price level, accountants must now
assume a new major responsibility, that of making available statements reflecting dollars adjusted for purchasing power.[1] Such "common dollar" statements would offer significant data relating to economic position and progress. They would attempt to report the story
behind the dollars. Proponents of common dollar statements recognize
that the definition of the methods and the procedures for the development of such statements requires considerable study. They are also
aware that the conventional financial statements reflecting historical
dollar reporting are so firmly embedded in law, business relationships,
and general understanding that these will continue to represent the
basic reports and that common dollar reports will assume a position
as interpretive supplements.

There is little question as to the usefulness of supplementary
statements that will make clear the effect of changing dollar values
upon financial position and operating results. It should be observed
that some progress has been made in this direction. Modern corporate
reporting frequently includes supplementary comments and explanations pointing out in varying manner and degree the nature and limitations of conventional reporting together with the modifications that
apply to these data in considering the effects of price changes.

**STATEMENT**
**LIMITATIONS**
The framework for modern reporting has
been suggested in the first two chapters. An
appreciation of what accounting seeks to do also affords an understanding of certain difficulties and limitations identified with this
process. In reading financial statements, one must be aware of the
judgment, opinion, and estimate involved in measurements that represent no more than interim reports in the continuing and indeterminate
life of the business. Furthermore, in the measurement process the use
of different procedures may give rise to different answers, yet each
answer can be supported as the product of "generally accepted prin-

---

[1]*Accounting and Reporting Standards for Corporate Financial Statements and Preceding
Statements and Supplements*, "Price Level Changes and Financial Statements," 1957
(Columbus: American Accounting Association), pp. 23–29.

ciples." One must be familiar with the nature of the values presented and with the need for other approaches to value in using reports for certain specialized purposes. The need for comparative statements in evaluating progress and trend should be recognized. One needs to be aware of the shortcomings and the distortions of a varying standard of measurement—the dollar. Finally, one must recognize that statements fail to give the full story. Certain very real assets never appear on the balance sheet—capable management, the demand for a company's services and products, good management-employee relationships, and other valuable intangibles built up through years of operations. And one must look beyond the statements for certain matters that explain operations and affect the financial position both present and future—the business cycle, war or peace, governmental tax policies, governmental regulatory policies, changes in styles, demand, etc. An appraisal of business position and progress can be obtained only through the intelligent use of basic reports honestly and independently prepared and a full appreciation of the business environment.

## QUESTIONS

**1.** "There has been a shift from the balance sheet to the income statement as the statement of primary accounting importance." What reasons can you offer for the change in emphasis?

**2.** It has been sugggested that the balance sheet is subject to certain "major limitations." It has also been said that the balance sheet is "a statement of non-homogeneous residuals." (a) Give arguments in favor of each of these contentions. (b) In view of these arguments would you suggest that the importance of the balance sheet be discounted in modern accounting?

**3.** How would you define (a) revenue, (b) cost, (c) expense?

**4.** Describe the nature of each of the following: (a) cost of goods manufactured, (b) cost of goods sold, (c) operating expenses, (d) financial management expense, (e) extraordinary losses.

**5.** How would you distinguish between ordinary items and extraordinary items in profit and loss analysis?

**6.** What are the arguments for and against use of: (a) the current operating performance income statement? (b) the all-inclusive income statement?

**7.** (a) What two opinions are held with respect to net income determination? (b) What classes of items may be excluded in the measurement of net income according to the American Institute of Certified Public Accountants?

**8.** What are the advantages and the disadvantages that are found in the use of the combined income and retained earnings statement?

**9.** What two positions are taken with respect to reporting income taxes when these accrue as a result of regular activities and extraordinary activities? What position do you favor?

**10.** What procedures are followed when income taxes are to be allocated between net income reported on the income statement and special items reported on the retained earnings statement?

**11.** The income statement for the Walker Co. reports the following:

| | | |
|---|---|---|
| Net income before income taxes................................ | | $150,000 |
| Income taxes applicable to net income (total tax provision, $60,000, increased by $15,000 credit applicable to fire loss)... | | 75,000 |
| Net income after income taxes............................... | | $ 75,000 |
| Extraordinary items: | | |
| Losses, and other decreases—Loss from fire....... | $30,000 | |
| Less: Income taxes credit applicable to loss....... | 15,000 | 15,000 |
| Net income and extraordinary items...................... | | $ 60,000 |

(a) Explain the nature and purpose of reporting the income taxes as above.
(b) Suggest an alternative method for reporting the income taxes.

**12.** Distinguish between the proper application of accounting conservatism and the improper application of this concept. Give reasons in support of your conclusions.

**13.** (a) What is meant by accounting consistency? (b) Are changes in method ever permissible? (c) How would you develop and present comparative data where changes in accounting methods had been effected?

**14.** (a) What is meant by the concept of full disclosure? (b) Accounting reports have been criticized as affording insufficient disclosure and as offering too much detail. Are these contentions contradictory? Evaluate.

**15.** (a) Give five significant items relating to past or current financial matters that might be reported in the auditor's report or special notes accompanying the statements. (b) Give five significant items relating to prospective financial matters that might be reported in the auditor's report or special notes. (c) Give five significant post-statement occurrences that might be reported in the auditor's report or special notes.

**16.** (a) What is meant by common dollar reports? (b) What advantages are claimed for such reporting? (c) Is such reporting expected to replace conventional procedures?

## EXERCISES

**1.** Complete the following tabulation by giving the missing amount wherever the letter "x" appears:

| | CAPITAL AT BEGINNING OF PERIOD | INVESTMENTS BY PROPRIE- TOR | WITHDRAWALS BY PROPRIE- TOR | CAPITAL AT END OF PERIOD | NET INCOME | NET LOSS |
|---|---|---|---|---|---|---|
| (a) | $15,000 | $2,000 | $ 500 | $20,000 | $ x | $ |
| (b) | 16,000 | | 3,000 | 13,500 | x | |
| (c) | 20,000 | 6,000 | 2,000 | 18,000 | | x |
| (d) | 10,000 | | 2,500 | x | 5,000 | |
| (e) | 15,000 | x | 1,000 | 22,000 | 4,500 | |
| (f) | 22,000 | 3,000 | x | 21,000 | | 2,500 |
| (g) | x | 4,000 | 5,500 | 27,000 | | 2,000 |

**2.** Complete the following tabulation by giving the missing amount wherever the letter "x" appears:

| Sales | Begin-ning In-ventory | Pur-chases | Ending Inven-tory | Cost of Goods Sold | Gross Profit on Sales | Expenses | Net Income or (Loss) |
|---|---|---|---|---|---|---|---|
| (a) $15,000 | $6,000 | $10,000 | $  x | $9,000 | $  x | $4,000 | $  x |
| (b)   x | 8,000 | 10,000 | 6,000 | x | 8,000 | x | (1,000) |
| (c)  14,000 | x | 6,000 | 7,000 | x | 6,000 | x | 2,000 |
| (d)  20,000 | 8,000 | x | 10,000 | x | x | 5,000 | 3,000 |

**3.** List each of the following items as an asset, expense, or extraordinary charge:

(a) Loss on sale of marketable securities.
(b) Loss on sale of securities by security dealer.
(c) Write-off of goodwill and patents in the interest of conservatism.
(d). Installation costs for new machinery.
(e) Payments representing organization costs incurred.
(f) Costs of rehabilitating plant just purchased.
(g) Cost of grading land for construction.
(h) Additional federal tax assessment for prior years.
(i) Landscaping costs upon completion of new building.
(j) Charges on suits arising from breach of contract.
(k) Purchase and retirement of bonds outstanding at an amount in excess of their book value.
(l) Contributions to Community Chest.
(m) Loss from flood.

**4.** Give the section of the income statement in which each of the following items is reported:

(a) Gain on sale of land.
(b) Purchases discounts earned.
(c) Loss from bad debts.
(d) Loss from securities written off as worthless.
(e) Loss from a strike.
(f) Income tax refund.
(g) Loss from inventory price decline.
(h) Depletion.
(i) Sales discounts.
(j) Dividends received on long-term investments.
(k) Income taxes for current period.
(l) Charge for understatement of depreciation in prior periods.

**5.** Indicate which of the following items involves the realization of income and give the reasons for your conclusions.

(a) Land acquired in 1940 at $15,000 is now conservatively appraised at $40,000.

(b) Capital stock acquired at $40 per share now has a market value of $52.

(c) Timberlands show a growth in timber valued at $40,000 for the year.

(d) An addition to a building was self-constructed at a cost of $3,600 after two offers from private contractors for the work at $4,650 and $5,000.

(e) Certain valuable franchise rights were received from a city for payment of annual licensing fees.

(f) A customer owing $4,600, which was delinquent for one year, gave securities valued at $5,000 in settlement of his obligation.

(g) Merchandise, cost $1,000, is sold for $1,600 with a 50% down payment on a conditional sales contract, title to the merchandise being retained by the seller until the full contract price is collected.

(h) Cash is received on the sale of gift certificates redeemable in merchandise in the following period.

**6.** The following accounts, among others, are maintained by The Erman Company. Name the financial statement or schedule and the section in which each account listed below will appear.

Accrued Interest on Notes Payable
Accrued Interest on Notes Receivable
Allowance for Doubtful Accounts
Cash Dividends Payable
Cash Surrender Value of Life Insurance on Company Officers
Claims on U. S. for Income Tax Refunds
Deferred Interest Expense
Deferred Interest Income
Deposits by Customers on Goods in Process of Manufacture
Direct Labor
Estimated Income Taxes Payable
Finished Goods Inventory (ending)
Fund for Pension Payments
Gain on Sale of Securities
Goods in Process Inv. (beginning)
Goodwill
Interest Expense

Investment in Plant Not Being Used
Loans to Officers
Loss from Bad Debts
Loss from Fire
Miscellaneous Factory Expense
Office Supplies
Patents
Petty Cash Fund
Plant and Equipment
Premium on Capital Stock Issued
Prepaid Taxes
Purchases Discounts
Raw Materials Purchases
Reserve for Income Taxes
Reserve for Pension Payments
Retained Earnings
Sales Discounts
Tools
Treasury Stock
Unearned Rental Income

**7.** From the information that appears below for Drake and Kormick, Inc., select those items pertaining to retained earnings and prepare a retained earnings statement for the year ending December 31, 1958.

| | |
|---|---:|
| Retained earnings balance, January 1, 1958................... | $46,500 |
| Net income for 1958........................................ | 26,500 |
| Call premium paid on retirement of bonds before maturity (bondholders were paid $102,000 in paying off bonded debt of $100,000)............................................... | 2,000 |
| Paid-in capital from sale of treasury stock.................... | 15,000 |
| Dividends paid on capital stock outstanding................. | 25,000 |
| Extraordinary loss suffered through fire...................... | 21,600 |
| Premium received on issue of additional stock............... | 6,500 |
| Refund of federal income taxes for prior years............... | 1,650 |
| Loss on write-off of abandoned building no longer usable...... | 14,000 |
| Gift of unimproved land from municipal authority............ | 50,000 |

**8.** E and E, Inc. shows a retained earnings balance on January 1, 1958, of $160,000. For 1958, the net income before income taxes was $40,000. The following extraordinary gains and losses were also recognized during the year:

Gain on sale of long-term investments........................ $14,000
Refund of tax payments by federal government.............. 6,000
Understatement of depreciation charges of prior years......... 10,000
Understatement of accrued expenses at end of 1957.......... 2,000

Income taxes for 1958 were $15,800, of which $3,500 accrued as a result of the gain on the sale of investments. Dividends of $16,000 were declared by the company during the year.

Assuming that the income statement shows extraordinary items and that income taxes are allocated between normal income and extraordinary items, complete the lower section of the income statement, beginning with the item "Net Income before income taxes," and prepare an accompanying retained earnings statement.

**9.** Using the data in Exercise 8, prepare a retained earnings statement for E and E, Inc., assuming that extraordinary items are reported on this statement, only normal operations being reported on the income statement.

**10.** The selling expenses of F and M, Inc. are 10% of sales. General expenses, excluding bad debts, are 15% of sales and 25% of cost of sales. Bad Debts are 2% of sales. The beginning merchandise inventory was $62,000 and it decreased 25% during the year. Net income for the year before income taxes of 40% is $52,000. Prepare an income statement, giving supporting computations.

## PROBLEMS

**2-1.** The following balances are taken from the books of the Parkway Company on December 31, 1958:

| | | | |
|---|---|---|---|
| Corrections in Profits of | | Income Taxes—1958...... | $ 12,000 |
| Prior Years: Understate- | | Income Tax Refunds for | |
| ment of Depreciation... | $ 74,000 | Prior Years............ | 48,000 |
| Cost of Goods Sold....... | 275,000 | Interest Expense......... | 6,350 |
| Dividend Income......... | 1,250 | Interest Income.......... | 3,000 |
| Dividends Paid.......... | 25,000 | Sales.................... | 430,500 |
| General and Admin. Exp.. | 35,000 | Selling Expenses......... | 80,000 |
| Rental Income.......... | 4,800 | | |

The retained earnings balance on January 1, 1958, was $76,400.

*Instructions:* (1) Assuming that the income statement reports ordinary and extraordinary items including corrections in profits of prior periods, prepare an income statement and a retained earnings statement for the year ended December 31, 1958.

(2) Assuming that the income statement reports only normally recurring items, prepare a retained earnings statement for the year ended December 31, 1958.

**2-2.** The Lindy Co. began operations in 1958 with a retained earnings balance of $18,800. Its records for 1958 show the following information:

| | | | |
|---|---|---|---|
| Dividends Declared...... | $ 20,000 | Interest Income.......... | $ 1,200 |
| Dividend Income........ | 2,800 | Loss from Fire........... | 3,600 |
| Gain on Sale of Land...... | 4,500 | Purchases............... | 304,400 |
| General and Admin. Exp.. | 86,600 | Purchases Discounts...... | 4,400 |
| Income Taxes, 1958....... | 12,000 | Sales................... | 482,000 |
| Interest Expense......... | 7,600 | Sales Discounts.......... | 3,200 |

| Sales Returns and Allowances.............. | $14,000 | Selling Expenses......... | $62,500 |
|---|---|---|---|

Merchandise Inventory, Jan. 1, 1958, $115,000; Dec. 31, 1958, $146,500. Overstatement of Income Tax Liability at end of 1957, $1,500.

*Instructions:* (1) Prepare a combined statement of income and retained earnings for the year ended December 31, 1958. (Assume that the full amount of income taxes for 1958 is charged to normal activities.)

(2) Using the same data, prepare an income statement in single-step form and a separate retained earnings statement, assuming that the income statement reports only normal operations, while extraordinary items and corrections are shown on the retained earnings statement.

**2-3.** The Thomas Co. prepares an income statement that summarizes normal operations as well as extraordinary items and corrections in profits of prior periods. The statement is supported by (1) a manufacturing schedule, (2) a selling expense schedule, and (3) a general and administrative expense schedule. Prepare an income statement with supporting schedules and a retained earnings statement for this company using the data for 1958 that is listed below. Retained earnings on January 1, 1958, were $46,400.

Federal income taxes for 1958 were as follows:

| | |
|---|---|
| Applicable to net income......................... | $16,050 |
| Applicable to gains on sale of securities............ | 2,000 |
| Total taxes................................. | $18,050 |

Inventories were as follows:

| | JANUARY 1 | DECEMBER 31 |
|---|---|---|
| Finished goods......................... | $36,500 | $48,600 |
| Goods in process....................... | 21,500 | 26,000 |
| Raw Materials......................... | 16,000 | 19,000 |

Other account balances include the following:

| | | | |
|---|---|---|---|
| Advertising.............. $ | 6,500 | Loss from Bad Debts...... $ | 1,600 |
| Delivery Expense......... | 12,200 | Misc. Factory Expense..... | 6,000 |
| Depreciation of Machinery. | 5,600 | Misc. General Expense..... | 3,200 |
| Direct Labor............. | 76,000 | Misc. Selling Expense...... | 2,150 |
| Dividend Income.......... | 300 | Officers Salaries .......... | 15,200 |
| Dividends Declared....... | 8,500 | Office Salaries............ | 12,000 |
| Factory Heat, Light, Power | 20,100 | Office Supplies Used....... | 2,200 |
| Factory Maintenance...... | 2,600 | Raw Materials Purchases... | 84,000 |
| Factory Superintendence... | 20,000 | Raw Materials Returns.... | 2,000 |
| Factory Supplies Used..... | 4,000 | Royalty Income......... | 2,700 |
| Factory Taxes............ | 14,000 | Sales................... | 374,000 |
| Freight In on Raw Materials | 2,500 | Sales Discounts........... | 4,000 |
| Gain on Sale of Securities... | 8,000 | Sales Returns and Allowances................. | 4,700 |
| Indirect Labor............ | 24,000 | | |
| Interest Expense......... | 10,200 | Sales Salaries............ | 25,000 |
| Interest Income.......... | 650 | | |

**2-4.** The following balances were taken from the books of Midwest Corporation on December 31, 1958:

| | | | |
|---|---|---|---|
| Cash Dividends Declared. | $ 15,000 | Merchandise Purchases... | $ 885,500 |
| General and Administra- | | Purchases Discounts...... | 22,350 |
| tive Expenses......... | 211,250 | Pur. Returns and Allow... | 11,150 |
| Interest Income......... | 13,500 | Sales................... | 1,500,000 |
| Interest Expense........ | 21,250 | Sales Discounts.......... | 28,250 |
| Loss on the Retirement of | | Sales Returns and Allow. | 16,750 |
| Company Bonds....... | 95,500 | Selling Expenses......... | 178,500 |

Income taxes paid for 1958 amounted to $20,500, however, the income taxes applicable to net income, exclusive of the loss on the retirement of the company bonds, amounted to $70,160.

Merchandise Inventory: January 1, 1958................. $210,000
December 31, 1958.............. $150,000
Retained Earnings: January 1, 1958.................... $117,000

*Instructions:* Prepare a combined statement of income and retained earnings for the year ended December 31, 1958.

**2-5.** Data relating to the financial condition and the results from operations for the year ended December 31, 1958, are assembled for Adams-Boone, Inc., as follows:

| | | | |
|---|---|---|---|
| Cash on Hand and in Bank | $49,500 | Land.................... | $ 40,000 |
| Marketable Securities...... | 10,000 | Goodwill................ | 15,000 |
| Notes Receivable......... | 8,000 | Patents................. | 6,000 |
| Accounts Receivable...... | 36,500 | Deferred Bond Issue Costs. | 4,200 |
| Allowance for Doubtful | | Notes Payable........... | 4,000 |
| Notes and Accounts..... | 1,200 | Accounts Payable........ | 14,000 |
| Accrued Int. on Notes Rec. | 150 | Estimated Federal Income | |
| Finished Goods Inventory: | | Taxes Payable......... | 27,050 |
| January 1, 1958......... | 18,500 | Dividends Payable........ | 2,750 |
| December 31, 1958...... | 28,000 | Accrued Taxes and Interest | 2,400 |
| Goods in Process Inventory: | | Long-Term Notes Payable.. | 22,000 |
| January 1, 1958......... | 8,000 | 5% Bonds Payable due 1970 | 60,000 |
| December 31, 1958...... | 19,500 | Preferred Stock, $100 par, | |
| Raw Materials Inventory: | | 500 shares............. | 50,000 |
| January 1, 1958........ | 10,000 | Treasury Stock, Preferred, | |
| December 31, 1958...... | 14,000 | 100 shares............. | 10,000 |
| Factory Supplies Inventory | 500 | Common Stock, 10,000 | |
| Misc. Supplies Inventories. | 350 | shares, $10 stated value.... | 100,000 |
| Prepaid Insurance........ | 700 | Paid-in Capital from Sale of | |
| Misc. Prepaid Expenses... | 850 | Common Stock........ | 47,850 |
| Tools................... | 6,000 | Deficit, January 1, 1958... | 22,150 |
| Patterns and Dies........ | 3,600 | Sales................... | 305,150 |
| Office Equipment........ | 4,000 | Sales Returns and Allow.... | 1,400 |
| Allowance for Depreciation | | Raw Materials Purchases... | 82,000 |
| of Office Equipment..... | 1,200 | Freight In on Raw | |
| Machinery and Equipment | 46,000 | Materials............. | 1,700 |
| Allowance for Depreciation | | Raw Materials Returns and | |
| of Machinery and Equip. | 18,400 | Allowances............ | 1,200 |
| Factory Buildings........ | 75,000 | Direct Labor............ | 76,000 |
| Allowance for Depreciation | | Indirect Labor........... | 14,000 |
| of Factory Buildings..... | 16,000 | Superintendence......... | 12,000 |

| | | | |
|---|---|---|---|
| Heat, Light, and Power.... | $8,800 | Loss from Bad Debts...... | $ 1,800 |
| Taxes on Buildings and Equipment............ | 2,600 | Miscellaneous General and Administrative Expense.. | 5,400 |
| Factory Repairs and Maintenance............... | 1,400 | Dividend Income....... | 800 |
| Tools Expense........... | 1,750 | Interest Income.......... | 300 |
| Depreciation of Buildings and Factory Equipment.. | 6,500 | Interest Expense......... | 5,200 |
| Patents Expense......... | 1,000 | Federal Income Tax—1958 Applicable to Net Income....$24,950 | |
| Factory Supplies Used..... | 2,200 | Applicable to Special Items... 2,100 | |
| Misc. Factory Expense.... | 4,000 | | |
| Advertising............. | 6,000 | | |
| Sales Salaries and Commissions.............. | 12,500 | Total............. | 27,050 |
| Selling Supplies Used...... | 1,000 | Gain on Sale of Marketable Securities.............. | 10,000 |
| Misc. Selling Expense...... | 6,200 | Overstatement of 1957 Federal Tax Liability........ | 600 |
| Officers Salaries ......... | 14,500 | | |
| Office Salaries........... | 4,600 | Loss on Sale of Equipment | 1,600 |
| Office Supplies Used....... | 700 | Dividends Declared....... | 8,000 |

*Instructions:* Using the data above, prepare:

(1) A balance sheet.

(2) An income statement that includes extraordinary items and corrections in profits of prior periods, supported by schedules that show cost of goods manufactured, selling expenses, and general and administrative expenses.

(3) A retained earnings statement.

**2-6.** The Power Electronics Corporation was organized on January 1, 1958, 10,000 shares of no-par stock being issued in exchange for plant and equipment valued at $60,000 and cash of $20,000. Data below summarize activities for the first year of operations:

(a) Net income for the year was $12,000.

(b) Raw materials on hand on December 31 were equal to 25% of raw materials purchased for the year.

(c) Manufacturing expenses for the year were distributed as follows:

Materials used...... 50%

Direct labor........ 30%

Other manufacturing expenses......... 20% (includes depreciation of plant, $2,500)

(d) Goods in process remaining in the factory on December 31 were equal to 33⅓% of the goods finished and transferred to stock.

(e) Finished goods remaining in stock were equal to 25% of the cost of good sold.

(f) Operating expenses were 30% of sales.

(g) Cost of goods sold was 150% of the operating expenses total.

(h) Ninety per cent of sales were collected during the year; the balance was considered collectible in 1959.

(i) Seventy-five per cent of the raw materials purchased were paid for; there were no expense accruals or prepayments at the end of the year.

*Instructions:* (1) Prepare a balance sheet, an income statement, and a supporting manufacturing schedule.

(2) Prepare a summary of cash receipts and disbursements to support the cash balance reported on the balance sheet.

# Chapter 3

# THE RECORDING PROCESS

**PHASES OF THE ACCOUNTING PROCESS** The first two chapters described the nature, the form, and the content of the financial statements, the end product of the accounting function. Attention is now directed to the accounting process that makes possible the preparation of these reports.

The accounting process may be considered to be composed of two parts: (1) the recording phase and (2) the summarizing phase. During the fiscal period it is necessary to engage in a continuing activity— the recording of transactions in the various books of record. At the end of the fiscal period the recorded data are brought up to date and summarized and the financial reports are prepared. The recording phase is described in this chapter, while the activities that comprise the periodic summary are described in the next chapter. The entire accounting process as applied to a particular business unit is then illustrated in Chapter 5.

**RECORDING TRANSACTIONS** Accurate statements can be prepared only if transactions have been properly recorded. A transaction is an action that results in a change in the assets, the liabilities, or the proprietorship of a business. There are two general classes of transactions that require accounting recognition: (1) *business transactions*, or transactions entered into with outsiders; and (2) *internal transactions*, or accountable transfers of costs within the business. Among the latter, for example, are the transfers of costs from raw materials to goods in process and from goods in process to finished goods in manufacturing activities.

**BOOKKEEPING SYSTEMS** The bookkeeping records of a business consist of: (1) the original documents evidencing the transactions, called *business papers or vouchers*; (2) the media for classifying and recording the transactions, known as the *books of original entry or journals*; and (3) the media for summarizing the effects of transactions upon individual asset, liability, and proprietorship items, known as the *ledgers or ledger records*. The bookkeeping records of the business are referred to as its *bookkeeping system*. The various recording routines in such a system are developed to meet the special demands of the business unit with particular regard to its size and the nature of its activities. Recording mechanisms and processes must be designed to serve adequately and efficiently in telling the story of the business.

**BUSINESS PAPERS**  A business paper or voucher is prepared as a first record for each transaction. Such a document offers detailed information concerning the transaction and also fixes responsibility for such information by naming the parties identified with the transaction. The business papers are support for the information that is to be recorded in the books of original entry. Copies of sales invoices or the cash register tapes, for example, are the evidence in support of the sales record; purchases invoices support the purchases or invoice record; debit and credit memorandums support adjustments in debtor and creditor balances; check stubs or duplicate checks provide data concerning cash disbursements; duplicates of receipts issued show cash collections; the corporation minute book supports entries authorized by action of the board of directors; journal vouchers or summaries prepared or approved by appropriate officers are used in support of certain data such as adjustments or corrections that are to be reflected in the accounts.

**BOOKS OF ORIGINAL RECORD**  Transactions are analyzed from the information provided on the business papers. They may then be recorded in chronological order in the appropriate books of original entry. Transactions are analyzed in terms of accounts to be maintained for (1) assets, (2) liabilities, (3) proprietorship, (4) income and gains, and (5) expenses and losses. Classes (4) and (5) are temporary proprietorship accounts summarizing profit and loss data for the current period. The analysis is expressed in terms of *debit* and *credit*. Asset, expense, and loss accounts have left-hand or debit balances and are decreased by entries on the right-hand or credit side. Liabilities, proprietorship, income, and gain accounts have credit balances and are decreased by entries on the debit side.

While it would be possible to record every transaction in a single book of original entry, this is hardly ever done. Whenever a number of transactions of the same character take place, special journals may be designed in which such transactions can be conveniently entered and summarized. Special journals include sales journals, purchases journals, cash receipts and disbursements journals, the voucher register, and various other books of original entry designed to summarize special groups of transactions. Regardless of the number and the nature of the special books of original entry, there are always certain entries that cannot be made in the special journals, and these are recorded in the general journal.

A number of special columns may be provided in the various journals adopted. Special columns facilitate the recording of transactions and also serve to summarize the effects of a number of transactions upon individual account balances. This simplifies the subsequent transfer of information from the books of original entry.

**ACCOUNTS AND THE LEDGER**     Information as reported on a business paper and analyzed, classified, and summarized in terms of debits and credits in the books of original entry is transferred to accounts in the ledger. The accounts summarize the full effects of the transactions upon property and property equities and are used as a basis for the preparation of the financial statements.

Accounts are sometimes referred to as *real* (or *permanent*) accounts and *nominal* (or *temporary*) accounts. The balance sheet accounts are referred to as real accounts; the profit and loss accounts are referred to as nominal accounts. When during the course of the accounting period a balance sheet or a profit and loss account balance represents both real and nominal elements, it may be described as a *mixed account*. The store supplies account, for example, may be considered as composed of two elements: (1) the store supplies used, and (2) the store supplies still on hand. There is no need to analyze mixed accounts for the real and the nominal elements until financial statements are prepared. At this time the real and nominal elements of each mixed account must be determined. The classification of accounts is shown on page 66.

When accounts are set up to record subtractions from related accounts reporting positive balances, such accounts are termed *offset, contra,* or *negative accounts*. Allowance for Bad Debts is an offset to Accounts Receivable and is a negative asset account. Treasury Stock is an offset to Capital Stock and is a negative proprietorship account. Sales Returns and Allowances is an offset to Sales and is a negative income account.

Accounts are commonly set up in the ledger in *T form* or in *balance form*. The two forms are illustrated on page 67. The balance form is more widely used in modern practice.

The real and nominal accounts required by a business unit vary depending upon the nature of the business, its properties and activities, the information to be provided on the financial statements, and the controls to be exercised in carrying out the accounting functions. The

REAL
ACCOUNTS

ASSETS

- Current Assets
- Investments
- Plant and Equipment
- Intangible Assets
- Deferred Costs
- Other Assets

LIABILITIES

- Current Liabilities
- Long-Term Debt
- Deferred Revenues
- Other Liabilities

PROPRIETORSHIP

- (Sole Proprietorship or Partnership)
  - Owners' Capitals
- (Corporation)
  - Capital Stock
  - Additional Paid-In Capital
  - Retained Earnings
  - Appraisal Capital

NOMINAL
ACCOUNTS

INCOMES AND
GAINS

- Sales
- Other Income
- Extraordinary Gains, Other Miscellaneous Credits

EXPENSES AND
LOSSES

- Cost of Goods Sold
- Selling Expenses
- General and Administrative Expenses
- Other Expenses
- Extraordinary Losses, Other Miscellaneous Charges

**Classes of Accounts**

accounts to be maintained by a particular business are usually expressed in the form of a *chart of accounts*. Such a chart lists in systematic form the accounts with identifying numbers or symbols that are to form the framework for all accounting activities.

It is often desirable to establish separate ledgers for detailed information in support of balance sheet or profit and loss items. The *general ledger* then carries summaries of all of the statement items, while separate *subsidiary ledgers* afford additional detail in support of general ledger balances. For example, a single accounts receivable account is usually carried in the general ledger, and individual customers' accounts are shown in a subsidiary *accounts receivable ledger;* the capital stock account is normally supported by individual stockholders' accounts in a subsidiary *stockholders ledger;* selling and general and administrative expenses may be summarized in a single account in the general ledger, individual expenses being carried in a subsidiary

CASH                                                    Account No. 111

| Date | | Description | Post. Ref. | Debit Amount | | Date | | Description | Post. Ref. | Credit Amount | |
|---|---|---|---|---|---|---|---|---|---|---|---|
| 1958 Jan. | 1 | Balance | √ | 4,000 | 00 | 1958 Jan. | 31 | | CP12 | 6,000 | 00 |
| | 31 | | CR9 | 7,500 | 00 | | 31 | Balance | √ | 5,500 | 00 |
| | | | 5,500.00 | 11,500 | 00 | | | | | | |
| | | | | 11,500 | 00 | | | | | 11,500 | 00 |
| Feb. | 1 | Balance | √ | 5,500 | 00 | | | | | | |

**Ledger Account, T Form**

CASH                                                    Account No 111

| Date | | Description | Post. Ref. | Debit | | Credit | | Debit Balance | | Credit Balance | |
|---|---|---|---|---|---|---|---|---|---|---|---|
| 1958 Jan. | 1 | Balance | √ | 4,000 | 00 | | | 4,000 | 00 | | |
| | 31 | | CR9 | 7,500 | 00 | | | 11,500 | 00 | | |
| | 31 | | CP12 | | | 6,000 | 00 | 5,500 | 00 | | |

**Ledger Account, Balance Form**

*expense ledger.* The account in the general ledger that summarizes the detailed information reported elsewhere is known as a *controlling account.*

Whenever possible, individual postings to subsidiary accounts are made directly from the business paper evidencing the transaction. This practice saves time. It also avoids possible inaccuracies that may arise if information is first summarized separately and such summaries are then used as a basis for entries to the subsidiary accounts. A business paper also provides the basis for the journal entry that authorizes the postings to the controlling account in the general ledger. In many instances business papers themselves are used to represent a book of original entry. When this is done, business papers are assembled and summarized, and the summaries are transferred directly to the appropriate controlling accounts as well as to the other accounts affected in the general ledger. Whatever the procedure may be, if postings to the subsidiary records and to the controlling accounts are completed accurately, the sum of the detail in a subsidiary record will agree with the balance as reported in the controlling account. Such a reconciliation of each controlling account and its subsidiary record is made periodically, and any discrepancies disclosed through such comparisons are investigated and corrected.

The use of subsidiary records results in a number of advantages: (1) the number of accounts in the general ledger is reduced, thus making the general ledger more useful as a basis for preparing reports; (2) errors in the general ledger are minimized because of fewer accounts and fewer postings; (3) the accuracy of the posting to a large number of subsidiary accounts may be tested by comparing the total of the balances of the accounts with the balance of one account in the general ledger; (4) totals relating to various items are readily obtained; (5) specialization of bookkeeping duties and individual bookkeeping responsibilities is made possible; and (6) daily posting is facilitated for accounts that must be kept up to date, such as customer and creditor accounts.

Those procedures relating to the recording process that are commonly found in practice are discussed in the remaining pages of this chapter.

**RECORDS FOR SALES AND CASH RECEIPTS** When sales are made on account, the number of such sales is ordinarily large enough to warrant the use of a special sales journal. Sales on account result in subsequent collections on account, and a special journal for cash receipts facilitates the recording of such remittances as well as cash receipts from other sources. Both the particular factors relating to sales and those relating to the receipt of cash must be considered carefully in the development of a set of complementary journals. Several special journal forms are illustrated here to suggest the possibilities in special journal construction, design, and use.

A sales journal and a cash receipts journal may take the following form:

SALES JOURNAL                                                          Page 37

| Date | Invoice Number | Account Debited | Post. Ref. | Amount |
|------|------|------|------|------|
| 1958 Dec. 1 | 1456 | L. S. Carter | √ | 456 00 |
| 1 | 1457 | T. W. Wallace | √ | 138 55 |
| 1 | 1458 | A. M. Boyle | √ | 316 78 |
| 1 | 1459 | C. Y. Young | √ | 39 40 |
| 30 | 1613 | B. F. Myer | √ | 212 80 |
| 31 | 1614 | C. D. Drake | √ | 61 33 |
| 31 | 1615 | P. O. Powell | √ | 27 60 |
| 31 | | Accounts Receivable Dr. — Sales Cr. | 116/41 | 6,318 20 |

| DATE | DESCRIPTION | POST. REF. | GENERAL CR. | SALES CR. | ACCOUNTS RECEIVABLE CR. | SALES DISCOUNTS DR. | CASH DR. |
|---|---|---|---|---|---|---|---|
| 1958 Dec. 1 | Notes Receivable | 113 | 2,000 00 | | | | |
| | Interest Income | 72 | 120 00 | | | | 2,120 00 |
| 1 | R. C. Cole | ✓ | | | 640 00 | 12 80 | 627 20 |
| 1 | Sales | ✓ | | 512 40 | | | 512 40 |
| 31 | Notes Payable | 211 | 5,000 00 | | | | 5,000 00 |
| 31 | Sales | ✓ | | 660 15 | | | 660 15 |
| 31 | Totals | ✓ | 12,656 10 | 15,380 20 | 5,418 12 | 93 00 | 33,361 42 |
| | | | (✓) | (41) | (116) | (81) | (111) |

The pertinent details with respect to each sale on account are entered on a single line in the sales journal. Debits to the individual accounts in the accounts receivable ledger are posted frequently, preferably daily. The accounts in the accounts receivable ledger are arranged alphabetically and are not numbered; therefore, when the debits to the individual accounts in the accounts receivable ledger are posted from the sales journal, a check mark is placed in the Posting Reference column of that journal to indicate that the posting has been completed.

In some instances it is more convenient to post to the accounts receivable ledger directly from duplicate copies of sales invoices. When this plan is followed, a check mark is placed in the Posting Reference column of the sales journal at the time each sale is entered to show that, so far as this journal is concerned, the entry is complete and the item is not to be posted.

When daily sales on account are numerous, copies of the sales invoices for the day may be assembled and totaled, and the total sales on account for the day may be entered on a single line in the sales journal. When this plan is followed, postings to the individual accounts in the accounts receivable ledger are made from the duplicate sales invoices.

At the end of the month the total in the Amount column of the sales journal is posted to the general ledger as a debit to Accounts Receivable and as a credit to Sales. The account numbers to which postings are made are indicated in the Posting Reference column of the journal. The debit to the accounts receivable controlling account will agree with the sum of the debits to subsidiary accounts during the month if individual postings have been properly made.

All cash receipts are recorded in the cash receipts journal. The net amount of cash received is entered in the Cash Debit column, other debits and credits being entered in the other columns provided. Cash sales for each day are summarized and recorded on a single line, the cash sales total being recorded in the Sales Credit column. Reductions in accounts receivable resulting from cash receipts are entered in the Accounts Receivable Credit column, and cash discounts allowed on the collections are recorded in the Sales Discounts Debit column. All receipts of cash resulting in credits to accounts other than Sales or Accounts Receivable are entered separately; the name of the account credited is written in the Description column and the amount of the credit is entered in the General Credit column.

Credits to the individual customers' accounts in the subsidiary accounts receivable ledger may be posted from the cash receipts journal. The completion of the posting is then indicated in the Posting Reference column of the cash receipts journal by a check mark. When there are numerous cash receipts daily, a list of the cash receipts for the day may be prepared and totaled, and the total cash received from customers for the day may be entered on a single line in the cash receipts journal. The posting to the customers' accounts is then completed from the separate list of cash receipts.

Credits in the General Credit column are posted individually to the accounts in the general ledger. At the end of the month the amount columns of the cash receipts journal are totaled and the totals of the special columns are posted; Sales is credited, Accounts Receivable is credited, Sales Discounts is debited, and Cash is debited. The credit to Accounts Receivable will agree with the sum of the credits to subsidiary accounts made during the month if individual postings have been properly made. The balance in the controlling account after posting both debits and credits at the end of the month is compared with the sum of the account balances in the accounts receivable ledger in proving the accuracy of the controlling account balance and the supporting detail in the subsidiary ledger.

Postings of individual amounts in the General Credit column are indicated by writing the account number in the Posting Reference column of the cash receipts journal. The posting of a column total is indicated by writing the account number in parentheses immediately below the total. When the individual items are not posted because they are included in a total to be posted, or when a total is not posted because the individual items are posted, a check mark may be used to show that posting is not required.

More elaborate sales and cash receipts journals may be designed to meet special requirements. To illustrate, assume that (1) sales are to be distinguished as regular or installment sales, (2) receivables are to be distinguished as regular accounts or installment contracts, (3) all sales including cash sales are to be reflected in the sales journal, and (4) a state sales tax charge is made on all sales. Special journals to meet the foregoing conditions follow:

SALES JOURNAL                                                                Page 27

| Cash Dr. | Install- ment Contracts Rec. Dr. | Accts. Rec. Dr. | Invoice No. | Date | Description | P. R. | Sales Cr. | Install- ment Sales Cr. | Sales Taxes Payable Cr. |
|---|---|---|---|---|---|---|---|---|---|
| | | | | 1958 | | | | | |
| | 309 00 | | 1293 | Dec. 1 | R. A. Wylie | √ | | 300 00 | 9 00 |
| | | 66 95 | 1294 | 1 | S. M. Scott | √ | 65 00 | | 1 95 |
| 413 67 | | | | 1 | Cash Sales | √ | 401 10 | | 12 57 |
| 371 40 | | | | 31 | Cash Sales | √ | 360 20 | | 11 20 |
| 12,381 06 | 4,799 80 | 4,441 46 | | 31 | Totals | √ | 16,320 56 | 4,660 00 | 641 76 |
| (√) | (115) | (116) | | | | | (41) | (42) | (216) |

CASH RECEIPTS JOURNAL                                                         Page 89

| Sales Discounts Dr. | Cash Dr. | Date | Description | P. R. | Gen. Cr. | Sales Cr. | Install- ment Contracts Rec. Cr. | Accts. Rec. Cr. |
|---|---|---|---|---|---|---|---|---|
| | | 1958 | | | | | | |
| 1 10 | 53 90 | Dec. 1 | A. M. Nelson | √ | | | | 55 00 |
| | 70 00 | 1 | R. Jennings | √ | | | | 70 00 |
| | 78 75 | 1 | R. A. Wylie | √ | | | 78 75 | |
| | 16 00 | 1 | A. C. Wilson | √ | | | 16 00 | |
| | 757 50 | 1 | Notes Receivable | 113 | 750 00 | | | |
| | | | Interest Income | 72 | 7 50 | | | |
| | 413 67 | 1 | Sales | √ | | 413 67 | | |
| | 371 40 | 31 | Sales | √ | | 371 40 | | |
| 13 04 | 21,460 16 | 31 | Totals | √ | 2,375 00 | 12,381 06 | 3,105 04 | 3,612 10 |
| (81) | (111) | | | | (√) | (√) | (115) | (116) |

Each sale is entered in the sales journal, provision being made for distinguishing between charges to installment contracts and regular accounts as well as credits to the installment sales account and the regular sales account. When there are a number of such sales daily, it is possible to record total sales on account and total sales on the installment contract basis daily, charges to the two subsidiary ledgers being made directly from the supporting vouchers. Cash sales are also recorded in the sales journal, total sales from all sources thus being reported in this record. In the sales journal, cash and receivable columns report total receipts and charges, sales columns report the net sales price, and the Sales Taxes Payable Credit column summarizes tax charges on sales, payable to the state by the retailer.

The cash receipts journal provides for a distinction between collections on installment contracts and regular accounts. Here, too, collections for the day on each of these receivables may be summarized and entered in total, individual credits to the subsidiary ledgers being made directly from business vouchers. A General Credit column shows those credits for which special columns are not provided.

Since cash sales are recorded in both the sales journal and the cash receipts journal, complete posting from both sources would result in duplication. To avoid such duplication, the Cash Debit column in the sales journal is checked and the Sales Credit column in the cash receipts journal is checked. The total cash received is recorded in the cash receipts journal and is posted from this source; total sales are recorded in the sales journal and are posted from this source. Postings at the end of the month, then, result in the following charges and credits:

|  |  | DEBITS | CREDITS |
|---|---|---|---|
| From Sales Journal: | Installment Contracts Receivable... | $ 4,799.80 | |
|  | Accounts Receivable.............. | 4,441.46 | |
|  | Sales........................... | | $16,320.56 |
|  | Installment Sales................. | | 4,660.00 |
|  | Sales Taxes Payable.............. | | 641.76 |
| From Cash Receipts Journal: | Sales Discounts.................. | 13.04 | |
|  | Cash........................... | 21,460.16 | |
|  | Notes Receivable................ | | 750.00 |
|  | Interest Income.................. | | 7.50 |
|  | Other General Credits (Dec. 2–31 not shown)........................ | | 1,617.50 |
|  | Installment Contracts Receivable... | | 3,105.04 |
|  | Accounts Receivable............. | | 3,612.10 |
|  |  | $30,714.46 | $30,714.46 |

The journals just given differ from preceding illustrations in that special columns are provided on both the right and the left sides of each form. Originality may be exercised in designing special journals to serve adequately and efficiently as classifying and summarizing mediums.

**RECORDS FOR
PURCHASES AND
CASH PAYMENTS**
Normally, purchases and cash payments are summarized in special books of original entry.  As in previous illustrations, forms vary depending upon the individual requirements of the particular business.  Purchases and cash payments journals may take the following form:

PURCHASES JOURNAL                                              PAGE 12

| DATE | | PURCHASE No. | ACCOUNT CREDITED | POST. REF. | AMOUNT |
|------|---|---|---|---|---|
| 1958 Dec. | 1 | 466 | J. R. Kirby | √ | 456 10 |
| | 1 | 467 | Brant & Lake | √ | 101 33 |
| | 31 | 493 | Loy Manufacturing Co. | √ | 215 00 |
| | 31 | | Purchases Dr.—Accounts Payable Cr. | 51/213 | 13,164 60 |

CASH PAYMENTS JOURNAL                                          Page 23

| DATE | | CK. No. | DESCRIPTION | POST. REF. | GENERAL Dr. | Cr | ACCTS. PAYABLE Dr. | EXPENSES Dr. | PUR. DIS. Cr. | CASH Cr. |
|------|---|---|---|---|---|---|---|---|---|---|
| 1958 Dec. | 1 | 415 | L. M. Roberts | √ | | | 450 00 | | 9 00 | 441 00 |
| | 1 | 416 | Office Equip. | 122 | 404 00 | | | | | 404 00 |
| | 1 | 417 | Notes Payable | 211 | 2,000 00 | | | | | |
| | | | Interest Expense | 61 | | | | 60 00 | | 2,060 00 |
| | 1 | 418 | Rent | 61 | | | | 650 00 | | 650 00 |
| | 31 | 472-9 | Payroll | 61 | | | | 816 00 | | |
| | | | Employees Inc. Taxes Pay. | 214 | | 76 12 | | | | |
| | | | F.I.C.A. Taxes Payable | 215 | | 18 36 | | | | |
| | | | Hospital Care Payable | 216 | | 11 25 | | | | 710 27 |
| | 31 | | Totals | √ | 6,054 10 | 505 60 | 12,210 20 | 9,950 50 | 120 16 | 27,589 04 |
| | | | | | (√) | (√) | (213) | (√) | (71) | (111) |

In the foregoing illustrations it is assumed that the purchases journal is limited to a record of merchandise purchases.  Further, it is assumed that all daily receipts of cash are deposited in the bank and all cash disbursements are made by means of checks with the exception of relatively small payments that are made from a separate petty cash fund.  The cash payments journal, then, summarizes all checks written.

The cash journals may be used as a check against the bank record of cash.

The pertinent details with respect to each purchase on account are entered on a single line in the purchases journal. When credits to the individual accounts in the accounts payable ledger are posted from the purchases journal, a check mark is placed in the Posting Reference column of that journal to indicate that the posting has been completed.

In some instances it is more convenient to post to the accounts payable ledger directly from duplicate copies of purchases invoices. When this plan is followed, a check mark is placed in the Posting Reference column of the purchases journal at the time each purchase is entered to show that, so far as this journal is concerned, the entry is complete and the item is not to be posted.

When daily purchases on account are numerous, copies of the purchases invoices for the day may be assembled and totaled, and the total purchases on account for the day may be entered on a single line in the purchases journal. When this plan is followed, postings to the individual accounts in the accounts payable ledger are made from the purchases invoices.

At the end of the month the total in the Amount column of the purchases journal is posted to the general ledger as a debit to Purchases and a credit to Accounts Payable.

All payments by check are recorded in the cash payments journal, the net amount paid being recorded in the Cash Credit column and other debits and credits being recorded in the special columns provided. Reductions in accounts payable resulting from cash payments are entered in the Accounts Payable Debit column, and cash discounts received on the payments are recorded in the Purchases Discounts Credit column. Debits to the individual creditors' accounts in the

EXPENSES — SUB-ACCOUNTS

| SALES SALARIES AND COMMISSIONS | ADVERTISING | MISC. SELLING EXPENSES | GEN. AND ADMINISTRATIVE SALARIES | SUPPLIES | RENT | TAXES AND LICENSES | MISC. GENERAL EXPENSES |
|---|---|---|---|---|---|---|---|
| | | | | | | | |
| | | | | | 650 00 | | |
| | | 8 50 | | | | | 8 50 |
| | | | | | | 300 00 | |
| 556 00 | | | 260 00 | | | | |
| 3,060 50 | 1,250 00 | 460 05 | 2,150 40 | 360 00 | 650 00 | 1,200 00 | 657 55 |

subsidiary accounts payable ledger may be posted from the cash payments journal, or the posting may be made directly from duplicate copies of the checks or from the check stubs.

The charges to expenses are reported in the Expenses Debit column and a special analysis ledger form may be used in the general ledger to summarize individual expense charges. Such a form may be designed as illustrated across the double page below.

The last three columns on the right side of the form represent a balance form of ledger account. The left side of the form consists of analysis columns that explain the nature of the charges summarized in the control section at the right. Copies of checks issued or check stubs, together with copies of the paid invoices, are used in posting analysis detail. At the end of the month the analysis columns are added and proved against the total in the Debit Balance column. Additional analysis columns can be inserted on the left-hand side of the form as required.

In making payments to employees, the employer is required to withhold amounts for income taxes under Federal Revenue Acts and for social security taxes under the Federal Insurance Contributions Act (F.I.C.A.). In some cases amounts must be withheld for state unemployment insurance, hospital care, group insurance, union dues, U. S. bond purchases, etc. The amounts withheld represent payables to the required agencies by the employer on behalf of his employees in accordance with the law or the agreement between employer and employee. When the entry is made in the cash payments journal to record the payment of the payroll, the total of the payroll is entered in the Expense Debit column, the amount actually paid is entered in the Cash Credit column, and the various amounts withheld are entered in the General Credit column.

EXPENSES — CONTROL                                                    Account No. 61

| INTEREST EXPENSE | DATE | | DESCRIPTION | POST. REF. | DEBIT | CREDIT | DEBIT BALANCE |
|---|---|---|---|---|---|---|---|
| | 1958 | | | | | | |
| 60 00 | Dec. | 1 | Interest on note | Ck. #417 | 60 00 | | 60 00 |
| | | 1 | Rent for December | #418 | 650 00 | | 710 00 |
| | | 1 | Miscellaneous repairs | #425 | 17 00 | | 727 00 |
| | | 2 | Taxes and licenses | #426 | 300 00 | | 1,027 00 |
| | | 31 | Payroll | #472–479 | 816 00 | | 9,950 50 |
| 162 00 | | 31 | Totals | ✓ | | | |

As the entries in the General columns and the Expenses Debit column of the cash payments journal are posted individually, check marks are placed below these columns to show that the totals are not to be posted. The other column totals are posted, the posting being indicated by the account numbers in parentheses immediately below each total. As a check on the accuracy of the posting to the expenses control account, the total of the Expenses Debit column of the cash payments journal may be compared with the total of the Debit Balance column of the account.

Ordinarily, a payroll record is desirable in accumulating payroll information. A form similar to the following provides the required detail:

PAYROLL RECORD FOR WEEK OF DECEMBER 25–31

| No. | Name | No. of Exemptions | Time in Hrs. | | Regular Rate | Commissions | Total Earned | Deductions | | | | Net Pay | | Account Charged | |
| | | | Regular | Over-Time | | | | Income Tax | F.I.C.A. Taxes | Other | Amount | Ck. No. | Sales Sal. & Comm. | Gen. Adm. Sal. |
| 1 | J. Benson | 2 | | | $60/wk. | 26.00 | 86.00 | 11.65 | 1.94 | | 72.41 | 472 | 86.00 | |
| 2 | V. Dosser | 2 | | | $60/wk. | 14.00 | 74.00 | 9.34 | 1.67 | 3.75HC | 59.24 | 473 | 74.00 | |
| 3 | A. Ernst | 3 | 40 | 14 | $1.20/hr. | | 73.20 | 6.35 | 1.65 | | 65.20 | 474 | 55.20 | 1 |
| 8 | C. Oliver | 2 | | | $55/wk. | | 55.00 | 5.59 | 1.24 | | 48.17 | 479 | | |
| | | | | | | | 816.00 | 76.12 | 18.36 | 11.25HC | 710.27 | | 556.00 | 2( |

OTHER DEDUCTIONS: GI—Group Insurance; HC—Hospital Care; SB—Savings Bonds; UD—Union Dues.

It would be possible to use the payroll record as a book of original entry instead of a supplementary record, columnar totals being posted from this record as follows:

| | DEBITS | CREDITS |
| --- | --- | --- |
| Sales Salaries and Commissions.................... | $556.00 | |
| General and Administrative Salaries............... | 260.00 | |
| Employees Income Taxes Payable................. | | $76.12 |
| F.I.C.A. Taxes Payable.......................... | | 18.36 |
| Hospital Care Payable........................... | | 11.25 |
| Salaries and Commissions Payable................ | | 710.27 |
| | $816.00 | $816.00 |

When this is done, only amounts actually paid to employees are recorded in the cash payments journal. The payroll checks are recorded in the General Debit column as a debit to Salaries and Commissions Payable.

**THE INVOICE RECORD**  Frequently an *invoice record* or *invoice journal* is used in the place of a purchases journal. A record of invoices goes beyond the purchases journal in that it normally summarizes all purchases on a credit basis, including merchandise, supplies, plant and equipment items, and services. The form that such a record may take, together with an accompanying cash payments record, follows:

INVOICE RECORD  Page 35

| DATE | | PURCHASE No. | DESCRIPTION | POST. REF. | GENERAL DR. | GENERAL CR. | EX-PENSES DR. | PUR-CHASES DR. | ACCTS. PAY. CR. |
|---|---|---|---|---|---|---|---|---|---|
| 58 ec. | 1 | 816 | Masters Wholesale Co. | ✓ | | | | 480 00 | 480 00 |
| | 1 | 817 | Notes Payable | 211 | | 1,600 00 | | 1,600 00 | |
| | 1 | 818 | Office Equip. — Loft, Inc. | 122/✓ | 312 00 | | | | 312 00 |
| 31 | | 891 | Merton Auditors | 61/✓ | | | 350 00 | | 350 00 |
| 31 | | | Totals | ✓ | 2,050 00 | 3,100 00 | 640 00 | 10,205 60 | 9,795 60 |
| | | | | | (✓) | (✓) | (✓) | (51) | (213) |

CASH PAYMENTS JOURNAL  Page 63

| DATE | | CHECK No. | DESCRIPTION | POST. REF. | GENERAL DR. | GENERAL CR. | EX-PENSES DR. | ACCTS. PAY. DR. | PUR. DIS. CR. | CASH CR. |
|---|---|---|---|---|---|---|---|---|---|---|
| 58 c. | 1 | 951 | Elson Bros. | ✓ | | | | 310 00 | 6 20 | 303 80 |
| | 1 | 952 | Macy and Stone | ✓ | | | | 600 00 | | 600 00 |
| | 1 | 953-9 | Payroll | 61 | | | 829 80 | | | |
| | | | Emp. Inc. Taxes Pay. | 214 | | 93 53 | | | | |
| | | | F.I.C.A. Taxes Pay. | 215 | | 18 67 | | | | 717 60 |
| 31 | | 1047 | Notes Payable | 211 | 5,000 00 | | | | | |
| | | | Interest Expense | 61 | | | 150 00 | | | 5,150 00 |
| 31 | | | Totals | ✓ | 9,620 10 | 615 60 | 4,410 00 | 7,460 60 | 120 15 | 20,754 95 |
| | | | | | (✓) | (✓) | (✓) | (213) | (71) | (111) |

Each invoice is entered in the invoice record, provision being made in the journal for indicating the charge resulting from the invoice as well as the nature of the payable arising from the transaction. A special column is provided for Accounts Payable, other payables being reported in the General Credit column. Items reported in the General Credit column are posted separately. Special columns are provided for Purchases and for Expenses, other charges being reported in the General Debit column. As previously illustrated, an expense account providing for expense analysis may be maintained in the general ledger, the expense detail being posted to the analysis section from the invoices. Charges reported in the General Debit column are posted separately.

As previously indicated, forms for recording purchases or invoices and for cash payments should be designed to serve the particular business unit. The forms that have been illustrated are representative of the needs of a retail establishment of moderate size.

**THE VOUCHER SYSTEM**  A relatively large organization ordinarily provides for the control of purchases and cash disbursements through adoption of some form of a *voucher system*. With the use of a voucher system, checks may be drawn only upon a written authorization in the form of a voucher approved by some responsible official. A voucher must be prepared, not only in support of payments for purchases of merchandise and services on account, but also for cash purchases, retirement of debt, replenishment of petty cash funds, payrolls, dividends, etc. Vouchers identify the person authorizing the expenditure, explain the nature of the transaction, and name the accounts that are affected by the transaction. Vouchers relating to purchases invoices are normally compared with receiving reports. Upon verification, the voucher and the related business papers in support of the voucher are submitted to the appropriate officer for final approval. Only when the voucher is approved may it be used as the basis for the issue of a check.

Upon approval, vouchers are numbered and recorded in a *voucher register*. Vouchers, together with supporting papers, are then placed in an unpaid vouchers file.

The voucher register is a book of original entry classifying and summarizing the charges on each voucher and reporting the credit to Accounts Payable, or *Vouchers Payable* as the liability is sometimes called. Individual amounts owed need not be posted to an accounts payable ledger, as the unpaid vouchers file serves as a subsidiary record and offers the detail of the individual payables as summarized in the voucher register.

Checks are written in payment of individual vouchers and result in a charge to Accounts Payable, or Vouchers Payable, in a check register. Charges to the various asset, liability, or expense accounts, having been recognized when the payable was recorded in the voucher register, are no longer required in the cash payments record. When a check is issued, payment of the voucher is reported in the voucher register by entering the check number and the payment date. Paid vouchers and invoices are removed from the unpaid vouchers file, marked "Paid," and filed in a separate paid vouchers file. The bal-

ance of the payable account after the credit for total vouchers issued
has been posted from the voucher register and the debit for total
vouchers paid has been posted from the cash payments record should
be equal to the sum of the unpaid vouchers as shown both in the voucher register and in the unpaid vouchers file.

A voucher register and a check register are illustrated below:

VOUCHER REGISTER                                                    Page 51

| | | | PAID | | ACCTS. PAY. CR. | PUR- CHASES DR. | √ | Ex- PENSES DR. | GENERAL | | | |
| DATE | VCHR. No. | NAME | DATE | CK. No. | | | | | ACCOUNT | P. R. | DR. | CR. |
|---|---|---|---|---|---|---|---|---|---|---|---|---|
| 1958 Dec. | 1 | 1216 | R. A. Ross | | | 417 40 | 417 40 | | | | | | |
| | 1 | 1217 | B. L. Belsey | 12/1 | 1009 | 600 00 | | √ | 600 00 | | | | |
| | 1 | 1218 | Parks & Co. | | | 110 00 | | | | Office Equip. | 122 | 110 00 | |
| | 1 | 1219 | State Bank | 12/1 | 1010 | 5075 00 | | √ | 75 00 | Notes Pay. | 211 | 5000 00 | |
| | 31 | 1307 | Payroll | 12/31 | 1093 | 796 66 | | √ | 914 00 | Empl. Inc. Taxes Pay. | 214 | | 96 77 |
| | | | | | | | | | | F.I.C.A. Taxes Pay. | 215 | | 20 57 |
| | 31 | 1308 | Petty Cash | 12/31 | 1094 | 81 14 | | √ | 81 14 | | | | |
| | 31 | | Totals | | | 23129 42 | 8012 02 | | 6389 05 | Totals | √ | 9315 05 | 586 70 |
| | | | | | | (213) | (51) | | (√) | | | (√) | (√) |

CHECK REGISTER                                                     Page 81

| DATE | CHECK No. | PAYEE | VCHR. No. | ACCOUNTS PAYABLE DR. | PURCHASES DISCOUNTS CR. | CASH CR. |
|---|---|---|---|---|---|---|
| 1958 Dec. | 1 | 1008 | L. A. Lee | 1184 | 317 00 | 6 34 | 310 66 |
| | 1 | 1009 | B. L. Belsey | 1217 | 600 00 | | 600 00 |
| | 1 | 1010 | State Bank | 1219 | 5,075 00 | | 5,075 00 |
| | 31 | 1093 | Payroll | 1307 | 796 66 | | 796 66 |
| | 31 | 1094 | Petty Cash | 1308 | 81 14 | | 81 14 |
| | 31 | | Totals | | 21,288 75 | 116 40 | 21,172 35 |
| | | | | | (213) | (71) | (11) |

The total of the Accounts Payable Credit column and the total of
the Purchases Debit column in the voucher register are posted at the
end of the month to the corresponding accounts in the general ledger.
The individual amounts in the Expenses Debit column are posted to the
account, Expenses — Control; the distribution to the analysis columns
of this account is made from the business papers. At the end of the
month the balance of this account is compared with the total of the

Expenses Debit column in the voucher register. The amounts in the General Debit and Credit columns are posted individually to the appropriate accounts in the general ledger. Only column totals are posted from the check register.

**THE GENERAL JOURNAL**    Entries that cannot be recorded in the special journals are recorded in a *general journal*. While the general journal may be set up in two-column form, it is frequently set up in three-column form, with a detail column provided for individual debits and credits to subsidiary records and separate debit and credit columns for entries affecting general ledger accounts. The general journal with a detail column is illustrated below:

GENERAL JOURNAL                                      PAGE 15

| DATE | | DESCRIPTION | POST. REF. | DETAIL | DEBITS | CREDITS |
|---|---|---|---|---|---|---|
| 1958 Dec. | 1 | Notes Receivable | 113 | | 450 00 | |
| | | Accounts Receivable | 116 | | | 450 0 |
| | | A. R. Ross | ✓ | 450 00 | | |

It would be possible to provide additional special debit and credit columns in the general journal. Special columns then summarize the effect of general journal entries for posting purposes.

**RECORDING METHODS: FROM MANUAL OPERATION TO ELECTRONIC DATA-PROCESSING**    As a business grows in size and complexity, the recording process becomes more involved and means are sought for greater efficiency and reduced costs. Some business units may find that a system involving primarily manual operations is adequate in meeting their needs; others may find that their recording requirements can be handled effectively only through the introduction of machines or elaborate electronic data-processing arrangements.

Record-keeping may be carried on by processes frequently classified as follows: (1) manual operation, (2) key-driven operation, (3) punched-card operation and (4) electronic data-processing operation. A description of these processes follows.

*Manual Operation.* Bookkeeping systems may consist of operations that are carried on entirely by hand. Original documents — invoices, checks, and other business papers — are written out, and such source data are transferred by hand to the journals, the ledgers, and the trial balance. Systems involving full manual operation are generally found in small businesses.

_Key-Driven Operation_. Bookkeeping systems frequently employ key-driven equipment for the accomplishment of certain basic and repetitive functions. Typewriters, adding machines, calculators, and bookkeeping machines are employed in certain phases of the recording, classifying, and summarizing functions. Certain machines engaged in a single operation may serve a number of functions. For example, a bookkeeping machine may be used to prepare original papers, journalize, and post in one operation; documents, special journals, and subsidiary account forms are designed and arranged so that recording with the use of carbons meets the different needs.

_Punched-Card Operation._ Mechanical performance of basic functions may be enlarged by the use of punch-card procedures. Here, original documents may be manually or machine prepared, and significant data applied to cards by means of punched holes. Financial data are assembled, sorted, classified, and merged by means of card sorting and collating machines. Electronic calculators may be employed in auxiliary computing functions and printing tabulators employed to provide formal summaries of punch-card data.

_Electronic Data-Processing Operation._ Mechanical operations are accompanied by electronic speed in the electronic data-processing operation. Here, data on original documents are transferred by _input_ preparation equipment to a magnetic tape, paper tape, or punched cards, for electronic processing. Data are applied in terms of a _binary code_ — the language of the electronic system. Input data may now be fed into a central processing unit. In the latter unit, a series of stored instructions, called a _program_, determines the assembling, sorting, classifying, and summarizing operations that are to be automatically performed. Automatic devices prepare in printed form the _output_ data, the product of the processing arrangement.

Obviously, the introduction of machines, punch cards and electronic data-processing units for recording functions results in procedures that are less flexible than those common to the manual operation. Difficulties are encountered in handling special matters. Particular techniques must be developed for checking and verifying recorded data. Arrangements must be made for the elimination of "judgment" and "decision" areas that are not within the capacity of the particular mechanical device. On the other hand, there are significant efficiencies and cost advantages in the mechanized arrangements. Electronic approaches because of their capacities and speed, offer important advantages not only in the field of accounting, but also in areas of management where they can make contributions to production control, inventory control, sales analysis, forecasting, etc.

## QUESTIONS

**1.** Indicate the accounting function supplied by (a) the business paper, (b) the book of original entry, and (c) the ledger.

**2.** Distinguish between: (a) real and nominal accounts, (b) general journal and special journal, (c) general ledger and subsidiary ledger, (d) invoice record and voucher register, (e) T form and balance form of a ledger account.

**3.** Classify the following transactions as (1) business transactions or (2) internal transactions:

    (a) Trade-in of an old asset for a new one.
    (b) Depreciation of building.
    (c) Receipt of 60¢ on the dollar on an account receivable.
    (d) Cash dividend paid.
    (e) Factory supplies used.
    (f) Estimate of bad debts expense.

**4.** What advantages are provided through the use of (a) special journals, (b) subsidiary ledgers, and (c) the voucher system?

**5.** (a) What business papers are used in posting debits and credits to customer and creditor accounts? (b) Would it be better practice to post to these accounts from books of original entry? Explain.

**6.** Describe the use of an expenses control account with sub-account analysis.

**7.** (a) What is the purpose of the payroll record? (b) Explain the use of this form as a supplementary record. (c) Explain the use of this form as a special book of original entry. (d) Explain the use of this form as a subsidiary record for a general ledger account balance.

**8.** The Select Products Co. maintains special books of original entry for sales, invoices, cash receipts, and cash disbursements. State the journal in which each of the following transactions should be recorded:

    (a) Purchased office supplies on account.
    (b) Issued a note to a creditor.
    (c) Wrote off a customer's uncollectible account against the allowance for bad debts.
    (d) Replenished the petty cash fund.
    (e) Recorded a shortage caused by mistakes in making change.
    (f) Traded in delivery equipment for new equipment.
    (g) Sold capital stock for cash.
    (h) Paid the payroll.
    (i) Recorded depreciation for the month.
    (j) Purchased merchandise for cash.

**9.** (a) Describe the nature and the operation of the voucher system. (b) How does the voucher register serve as a combined book of original entry and subsidiary ledger?

**10.** Suggest books of original entry and the form that these might take in designing a bookkeeping system for (a) a theater, (b) a retail grocery store doing a cash business, (c) a gas station offering credit to certain customers, and (d) a retail department store selling furniture, clothing, and dry goods.

## EXERCISES

**1.** Assume the use of sales and cash receipts journal forms as illustrated on pages 68 and 69, together with a general journal. Explain how each of the following transactions would be recorded in these journals:

    (a) A sale on account, $600, is made to A. P. Reeder.
    (b) Reeder makes payment of $300 less 2% cash discount and gives a 60-day note for the $300 balance.
    (c) Cash sales for the day are $950, on which sales taxes of $20 are collected.
    (d) Cash of $990 is received on a 60-day note for $1,000 issued to the bank.
    (e) Furniture and fixtures, cost $800, book value $250, are sold for $100 cash.
    (f) A dividend check for $60 is received on shares of stock owned.

**2.** Assume the use of sales and cash receipts journal forms as illustrated on page 71, together with a general journal. Explain how each of the transactions in Exercise 1 above would be recorded therein.

**3.** Assume the use of purchases and cash payments journal forms as illustrated on page 73, together with a general journal. Explain how each of the following transactions would be recorded in these journals:

    (a) Merchandise is purchased from R. A. Faye, $300.
    (b) Payment is made to R. A. Faye less 2% discount.
    (c) Store supplies are purchased from T. C. Sharpe, $112.
    (d) Payment is made to T. C. Sharpe.
    (e) Payment is made on a $1,000, 60-day, 6% note, $1,010.
    (f) An invoice is received for utilities for the month, $90.
    (g) The invoice received in (f) is paid.
    (h) The payroll for the week is paid, $334, representing salaries, $400, less income taxes withheld, $57, and less F.I.C.A. taxes withheld, $9.
    (i) Store fixtures are purchased at a cost of $1,200, a 25% down payment being made on the purchase.

**4.** Assume the use of invoice record and cash payments journal forms as illustrated on page 77, together with a general journal. Explain how each of the transactions in Exercise 3 above would be recorded therein.

**5.** Assume the use of a voucher register and a check register similar to those illustrated on page 79. Explain (1) how each voucher would be recorded in the voucher register and (2) how the payment of each voucher would be recorded in the check register.

    (a) Voucher No. 1311 for merchandise purchased from A. L. Phillips, $560.
    (b) Voucher No. 1312 for legal services, $75.
    (c) Voucher No. 1313 for factory supplies purchased from Jones Manufacturing Co., $60.
    (d) Voucher No. 1314 for sales salaries of $600, less income taxes withheld, $96.50, and less F.I.C.A. taxes withheld, $13.50.
    (e) Voucher No. 1315 for a note, $2,500, and interest, $25, payable to State National Bank.
    (f) Voucher No. 1316 to set up a petty cash fund, $100.

## PROBLEMS

**3-1.** R. T. Stone began business on July 1. The books of original entry used to record his transactions for July were the same as those illustrated in the text on the following pages:

Sales Journal—page 71          Voucher Register—page 79
Cash Receipts Journal—page 71   Check Register—page 79

All cash receipts are entered in the cash receipts journal and are deposited in the bank. All payments are made by check upon voucher authorization, and checks are recorded in the check register. All sales—including cash, installment, and regular charge sales—are recorded in the sales journal. A 3% sales tax is added to all sales prices. A 2% discount is allowed on regular charge sales (before sales tax) when collection is received within 10 days of sale.

The chart of general ledger accounts required is as follows:

| Acct. No. | Account Title | Acct. No. | Account Title |
|---|---|---|---|
| 111 | Cash | 216 | F.I.C.A. Taxes Payable |
| 115 | Installment Contracts Receivable | 31 | R. T. Stone, Capital |
| | | 41 | Sales |
| 116 | Accounts Receivable | 41.1 | Sales Discounts |
| 118 | Store Supplies | 42 | Installment Sales |
| 119 | Prepaid Insurance | 51 | Purchases |
| 122 | Store Equipment | 51.1 | Purchases Discounts |
| 213 | Accounts Payable | 61 | Expenses |
| 214 | Sales Taxes Payable | | |
| 215 | Employees Income Taxes Payable | | |

The following transactions were completed during July:

July  1. Invested cash in the business, $10,000.

   1. Issued Voucher No. 1 to Lambert Realty Co. for July rent, $325: then issued Check No. 1 in payment of the voucher.

   1. Purchased store equipment on account from Standard Equipment Co., $5,600, terms n/30.

   1. Purchased store supplies from Acme Supply Co. for cash, $350.

   2. Purchased merchandise from Superior Mfg. Co. for cash, $1,200.

   3. Sold merchandise on regular account to Polk & Vance, $516.50, plus sales tax, $15.50.

   3. Purchased merchandise on account from R. J. Brooks, $4,400.

   3. Paid premium for insurance on merchandise and fixtures for one year to Lawton Insurance Agency, $210.

   5. Purchased merchandise on account from P. A. Gale Co., $2,100.

   6. Sold merchandise on regular account to Vernon Co., $475, plus sales tax, $14.25.

   6. Paid the *Daily News* for newspaper advertising, $57.50.

   8. Sold merchandise on regular account to Morse & Co., $615, plus sales tax, $18.45.

July 10. Sold merchandise on the installment contract plan to C. D. Hyde, $185, plus sales tax, $5.55. Received a down payment of $50.

12. Received payment from Polk & Vance for sale of July 3, $521.67.

13. Paid R. J. Brooks invoice of July 3, less 2% discount.

15. Paid the payroll for July 1–15, $550, less income taxes withheld, $78.27, and less F.I.C.A. taxes withheld, $12.38.

15. Paid the P. A. Gale Co. invoice of July 5, less 2% discount.

15. Cash sales for July 1–15 were $3,105, plus sales tax, $93.15.

16. Received payment from Vernon Co. for sale of July 6, $479.75.

17. Sold merchandise on the installment contract plan to Henry Abbott, $395, plus sales tax, $11.85. Received a down payment of $100.

18. Received payment from Morse & Co. for sale of July 8, $621.15.

19. Paid Freeman Bros. for miscellaneous repairs, $47.25.

20. Sold merchandise on regular account to Woodall and Co., $360, plus sales tax, $10.80.

20. Purchased merchandise on account from Stoner Corporation, $1,650.

22. Sold merchandise on regular account to B. A. Bailey, $750, plus sales tax, $22.50.

24. Received the weekly installment payment from Henry Abbott, $10.

26. Purchased merchandise on account from Superior Manufacturing Co., $865.

29. Paid Stoner Corporation invoice of July 20, less 2% discount.

30. Sold merchandise on the installment contract plan to J. S. Snider, $275, plus sales tax, $8.25. Received a down payment of $75.

31. Received the weekly installment payment from Henry Abbott, $10.

31. Paid Standard Equipment Co. invoice of July 1.

31. Paid the payroll for July 16–31, $550, less income taxes withheld, $78.27, and less F.I.C.A. taxes withheld, $12.38.

31. Cash sales for July 16–31 were $3,660, plus sales tax, $109.80.

*Instructions:* (1) Record the transactions for July in the four books of original entry indicated above. Number vouchers, checks, and sales invoices beginning with No. 1 for each classification.

(2) Rule the books of original entry and post to accounts in (a) the general ledger, (b) the subsidiary accounts receivable ledger, and (c) the subsidiary installment contracts receivable ledger. Set up the general ledger accounts in balance form. In this problem you will post the total of the Expenses Dr. column of the voucher register to the expenses control account, but you need not maintain the sub-accounts showing the distribution of expenses. Set up the subsidiary ledger accounts in T form.

(3) Prepare a trial balance of the general ledger and prepare summaries to prove the subsidiary ledgers.

**3-2.** Paul B. McRay began business operations on November 1. The following books of original entry were designed to record his transactions:

SALES JOURNAL

| Cash Dr. | Accounts Receivable Dr. | Date | Invoice No. | Description | Post. Ref. | Sales Taxes Payable Cr. | Sales Cr. |
|---|---|---|---|---|---|---|---|
|  |  |  |  |  |  |  |  |

CASH RECEIPTS JOURNAL

| GENERAL DR. | SALES DISCOUNTS DR. | CASH DR. | DATE | DESCRIPTION | POST. REF. | GENERAL CR. | SALES CR. | ACCOUNTS RECEIVABLE CR. |
|---|---|---|---|---|---|---|---|---|
| | | | | | | | | |

INVOICE RECORD

| GENERAL DR. | EXPENSES DR. | PURCHASES DR. | DATE | DESCRIPTION | POST. REF. | GENERAL CR. | ACCOUNTS PAYABLE CR. |
|---|---|---|---|---|---|---|---|
| | | | | | | | |

RECORD OF CHECKS DRAWN

| GENERAL DR. | EXPENSES DR. | ACCOUNTS PAYABLE DR. | DATE | CHECK NO. | DESCRIPTION | POST. REF. | GENERAL CR. | PURCHASES DISCOUNTS CR. | CASH CR. |
|---|---|---|---|---|---|---|---|---|---|
| | | | | | | | | | |

GENERAL JOURNAL

| ACCOUNTS PAYABLE DR. | GENERAL DR. | DATE | DESCRIPTION | POST. REF. | GENERAL CR. | ACCOUNTS RECEIVABLE CR. |
|---|---|---|---|---|---|---|
| | | | | | | |

All sales, both cash and credit, are to be recorded in the sales journal. All cash receipts are to be entered in the cash receipts journal, and all receipts are to be deposited in the bank. All payments are to be made by check and are to be recorded in the check record. A 3% state sales tax is added to all sales prices. A 2% discount is allowed on charge sales (before sales tax) when collection is received within 10 days of sale.

The chart of general ledger accounts required for the November transactions is as follows:

| ACCT. No. | ACCOUNT TITLE | ACCT. No. | ACCOUNT TITLE |
|---|---|---|---|
| 111 | Cash | 216 | F.I.C.A. Taxes Payable |
| 113 | Notes Receivable | 31 | Paul B. McRay, Capital |
| 115 | Accounts Receivable | 32 | Paul B. McRay, Drawing |
| 117 | Supplies | 41 | Sales |
| 118 | Prepaid Insurance | 042 | Sales Discounts |
| 121 | Store Equipment | 51 | Purchases |
| 211 | Notes Payable | 051 | Purchases Returns and Allowances |
| 213 | Accounts Payable | | |
| 214 | Sales Taxes Payable | 052 | Purchases Discounts |
| 215 | Employees Income Taxes Payable | 61 | Expenses |
| | | 82 | Loss on Sale of Store Equipment |

The following transactions were completed by Mr. McRay during November.

Nov. 1. Invested cash in the business, $12,000.
 1. Paid cash for rent for November, $600.
 1. Purchased store equipment on account from Porter Equipment Co., $4,500.
 1. Purchased store supplies for cash, $120.
 2. Purchased merchandise on account from Stabler Co., $3,200.

2. Purchased merchandise for cash, $1,200.
2. Paid for insurance on merchandise and fixtures for one year, $180.
4. Purchased merchandise on account from Phillips Products, $1,750.
8. Sold merchandise on account to Paul, Inc., $510, plus sales tax, $15.30.
9. Purchased merchandise from Belsey, Inc., $2,750, terms 60-day, 6% note. Sent note to Belsey, Inc.
10. Paid Porter Equipment Co.
12. Paid Phillips Products invoice of November 4, less 2% discount.
15. Cash sales for November 1-15 were $2,095, plus sales tax collections, $62.85.
15. Paid the payroll for November 1-15, $450, less income taxes withheld, $57.12, and less F.I.C.A. taxes withheld, $10.13.
15. Withdrew cash for personal use, $250.
17. Sold merchandise on account to R & S Co., $800, plus sales tax, $24. Received a 2-month, 6% note in settlement.
18. Received a credit memorandum from Stabler Co. for merchandise returned, $120.
18. Received payment from Paul, Inc. for sale of November 8, $515.10.
21. Purchased merchandise on account from Phillips Products, $1,600.
23. Sold merchandise on account to R & S Co., $150, plus sales tax, $4.50.
25. Received a credit memorandum from Phillips Products for merchandise returned, $36.50.
26. Purchased store equipment for cash, $600, and paid an additional $50 to install the equipment. Sold equipment purchased on November 1 that was inadequate, cost $350, for $250.
29. Issued a 30-day, non-interest-bearing note to Stabler Co. for the balance due, $3,080.
30. Received an invoice from Lang Bros. for miscellaneous repairs, $65.
30. Paid the payroll for November 16-30, $515, less income taxes withheld, $68.74, and less F.I.C.A. taxes withheld, $11.59.
30. Cash sales for November 16-30 were $2,518, plus sales tax collections, $75.54.

*Instructions:* (1) Record the transactions for November in the five books of original entry shown above. Number checks and sales beginning with No. 1 for each classification.

(2) Rule the books of original entry and post to accounts in (a) the general ledger, (b) the subsidiary accounts receivable ledger, and (c) the subsidiary accounts payable ledger. Set up the general ledger accounts in balance form. In this problem you will post the totals of the Expenses Dr. columns in the invoice record and in the record of checks drawn to the expenses control account, but you need not maintain the sub-accounts showing the distribution of expenses. Set up the subsidiary ledger accounts in T form.

(3) Prepare a trial balance of the general ledger and prepare summaries to prove the subsidiary ledgers.

**3-3.** The account balances in the general ledger of the Moreno Machine Company as of November 30 are shown in the trial balance on the following page. Books of original entry as summarized for the month of December follow the trial balance.

## MORENO MACHINE COMPANY
### TRIAL BALANCE
### NOVEMBER 30, 19--

| | | |
|---|---:|---:|
| Allstate Bank | $ 38,650 | |
| Petty Cash | 250 | |
| Notes Receivable | 9,500 | |
| Accounts Receivable | 56,500 | |
| Allowance for Bad Debts | | $ 1,000 |
| Finished Goods Inventory | 38,000 | |
| Goods in Process Inventory | 22,600 | |
| Raw Materials Inventory | 18,200 | |
| Investment in Bailey Co. Common Stock | 24,000 | |
| Tools | 12,000 | |
| Delivery Equipment | 10,000 | |
| Allowance for Depreciation of Delivery Equipment | | 3,500 |
| Office Furniture and Fixtures | 6,000 | |
| Allowance for Depreciation of Furniture and Fixtures | | 1,600 |
| Machinery and Equipment | 61,550 | |
| Allowance for Depreciation of Machinery and Equip. | | 12,200 |
| Buildings | 72,000 | |
| Allowance for Depreciation of Buildings | | 8,400 |
| Land | 40,000 | |
| Patents | 7,500 | |
| Goodwill | 25,000 | |
| Notes Payable | | 20,800 |
| Accounts Payable | | 29,700 |
| F.I.C.A. Taxes Payable | | 800 |
| Employees Income Taxes Payable | | 1,350 |
| State Unemployment Taxes Payable | | 750 |
| Federal Unemployment Taxes Payable | | 450 |
| 6% First Mortgage Payable, due 1972 | | 100,000 |
| Common Stock, Stated Value $1 | | 214,600 |
| Treasury Stock, 10,000 Shares at Cost | 16,000 | |
| Retained Earnings | | 28,000 |
| Sales | | 388,400 |
| Sales Returns and Allowances | 6,000 | |
| Sales Discounts | 4,000 | |
| Raw Materials Purchases | 86,000 | |
| Freight In | 4,400 | |
| Raw Materials Purchases Returns | | 2,000 |
| Purchases Discounts | | 2,700 |
| Direct Labor | 69,500 | |
| Indirect Labor | 26,400 | |
| Factory Superintendence | 22,000 | |
| Building Maintenance | 3,200 | |
| Factory Heat, Light, Power | 21,000 | |
| Factory Supplies Used | 6,000 | |
| Taxes | 16,400 | |
| Miscellaneous Factory Expense | 3,200 | |
| Sales Salaries | 24,100 | |
| Advertising | 8,000 | |
| Miscellaneous Selling Expense | 1,700 | |
| Delivery Salaries | 9,200 | |
| Miscellaneous Delivery Expense | 2,200 | |

| | | |
|---|---|---|
| Officers Salaries.............................. | 15,400 | |
| Office Salaries................................ | 12,000 | |
| Office Supplies Used.......................... | 2,800 | |
| Insurance..................................... | 6,000 | |
| Miscellaneous General Expense................. | 2,600 | |
| Interest Income............................... | | 1,200 |
| Dividend Income.............................. | | 400 |
| Interest Expense.............................. | 8,000 | |
| | $817,850 | $817,850 |

The sales journal summarized both cash sales and sales on account and was as follows:

SALES JOURNAL

| Allstate Bank Dr. | Accounts Receivable Dr. | Post. Ref. | Date | Description | Sales Cr. | Sales Taxes Payable Cr. |
|---|---|---|---|---|---|---|
| 8,600 | 35,500 | | | | 43,600 | 500 |
| (✓) | | | | | | |

The cash receipts journal reported all cash received and was as follows:

CASH RECEIPTS JOURNAL

| General Dr. | Sales Discounts Dr. | Allstate Bank Dr. | Date | Description | Post. Ref. | General Cr. | Sales Cr. | Accounts Receivable Cr. |
|---|---|---|---|---|---|---|---|---|
| 2,400 | 700 | 68,700 | | | | 32,400 | 8,600 | 30,800 |
| | | | | | | (✓) | | |

General Debits and Credits recorded in the cash receipts journal were:

| DEBITS | | CREDITS | |
|---|---|---|---|
| Loss on Sale of Bailey Co. | | Notes Receivable......... | $ 8,000 |
| Common Stock.......... | $2,400 | Interest Income........ | 400 |
| | | Investment in Bailey Co. | |
| | | Common Stock...... | 24,000 |

Checks are written only upon authorization in the form of a voucher. The voucher register follows:

VOUCHER REGISTER

| Date | Vchr. No. | Name | Paid Date | Ck. No. | Accounts Payable Cr. | Raw Materials Purchases Dr. | Expenses Dr. | General Account | P. R. | Dr. | Cr. |
|---|---|---|---|---|---|---|---|---|---|---|---|
| | | | | | 54,875 | 12,000 | 28,600 | | | 16,100 | 1,825 |

An analysis of expense vouchers showed the following distribution:

| | | | |
|---|---:|---|---:|
| Direct Labor | $8,000 | Factory Supplies Used | $ 700 |
| Indirect Labor | 2,600 | Taxes | 2,100 |
| Factory Superintendence | 2,400 | Misc. Factory Expense | 400 |
| Sales Salaries | 2,700 | Advertising | 500 |
| Delivery Salaries | 1,000 | Misc. Selling Expense | 200 |
| Officers Salaries | 1,600 | Misc. Delivery Expense | 300 |
| Office Salaries | 1,500 | Office Supplies Used | 400 |
| Freight In | 400 | Misc. General Expense | 200 |
| Building Maintenance | 600 | Interest Expense | 600 |
| Factory Heat, Light, Power | 2,400 | | |

General Debits and Credits reported in the voucher register were as follows:

| DEBITS | | CREDITS | |
|---|---:|---|---:|
| Tools | $ 800 | Employees Income Taxes | |
| Office Furniture and Fixtures | 500 | Payable | $1,400 |
| Machinery and Equipment | 250 | F.I.C.A. Taxes Payable | 425 |
| Notes Payable | 12,000 | | |
| Sales Returns and Allowances | 400 | | |
| Employees Income Taxes Payable | 1,350 | | |
| F.I.C.A. Taxes Payable | 800 | | |

The cash payments journal summarized all checks drawn and appeared as follows:

CASH PAYMENTS JOURNAL

| DATE | CHECK No. | VCHR. No. | PAYEE | ACCOUNTS PAYABLE DR. | PURCHASES DISCOUNTS CR. | ALLSTATE BANK CR. |
|---|---|---|---|---:|---:|---:|
| | | | | 41,775 | 300 | 41,475 |

General journal entries in December were:

| | | |
|---|---:|---:|
| Notes Receivable | 2,500 | |
| Accounts Receivable | | 2,500 |
| Allowance for Bad Debts | 400 | |
| Accounts Receivable | | 400 |
| Accounts Payable | 1,000 | |
| Raw Materials Purchases Returns | | 1,000 |
| Taxes | 650 | |
| F.I.C.A. Taxes Payable | | 425 |
| State Unemployment Taxes Payable | | 200 |
| Federal Unemployment Taxes Payable | | 25 |

*Instructions:* (1) Set up T accounts and record the balances reported as of November 30.

(2) Record directly in the accounts the transactions for the month of December as reported in the books of original entry.

(3) Prepare a trial balance as of December 31.

# Chapter 4

# THE PERIODIC SUMMARY

The accounting routine at the close of the fiscal period is frequently referred to as the *periodic summary* and normally consists of the following steps:

(1) *A trial balance of the accounts in the ledger is taken.* The trial balance offers a summary of the information as classified and summarized in the ledger, as well as a check on the accuracy of the recording process.

(2) *The data required to bring the accounts up to date are compiled.* Before financial statements can be prepared, all of the accountable information that has not been recorded must be determined.

(3) *A work sheet is prepared.* By means of the work sheet, data in steps (1) and (2) are summarized and classified.

(4) *Financial statements are prepared from the work sheet.* Statements that summarize operations and that show the financial condition are prepared from the information supplied on the work sheet.

(5) *Accounts are adjusted and closed.* Accounts in the ledger are brought up to date. Balances in nominal accounts are then closed, and the profit and loss detail is summarized in appropriate summary accounts. The result from operations as calculated in summary accounts is finally transferred to the appropriate proprietorship account.

(6) *A post-closing trial balance is taken.* A trial balance is taken to check the equality of the debits and credits after posting the adjusting and closing entries.

(7) *Accounts are reversed.* Accrued and prepaid balances that were established by adjusting entries are returned to the nominal accounts that are to be used in accounting for activities involving these items in the new period.

**ADJUSTING THE
ACCOUNTS** The division of the life of a business into periods of arbitrary length creates many important problems for the accountant who must measure the financial progress for a certain period and report on the financial position at the end of this period. Transactions of the period have been recorded in balance sheet and profit and loss accounts. At the end of the period, mixed accounts require adjustment. At this time, too, other financial data not recognized currently must be entered in the accounts in bringing the books up to date. Attention is directed in this chapter to the special problems that arise in bringing the accounts up to date and summarizing their effects. The adjustment of accounts is considered under the following headings:

| | |
|---|---|
| Asset Depreciation and Cost Amortization | Prepaid Expenses |
| Probable Uncollectible Accounts | Prepaid Incomes |
| Accrued Expenses | Inventories |
| Accrued Incomes | |

It should be observed that while the discussion of adjustments is based upon their treatment in the books of account during the adjusting and closing phase of the accounting process, each adjustment would first appear on the work sheet.

**ASSET DEPRECIATION AND COST AMORTIZATION** The charge to operations for the use of plant and equipment items during a period must be calculated and recorded at the end of the period. In recognizing depreciation on an asset, operations are charged with a portion of the cost of the asset, the carrying value of the asset being reduced by this amount. The asset account may be credited directly for the cost assigned to the current operating period. However, when it is desired that both original cost and the amount of the cost already charged to operations be shown, a valuation account is credited. In determining the charge to be made to current operations, the cost of the asset less any estimated residual value is divided by the estimated useful life of the asset. To illustrate this procedure, assume the use of the following asset:

> Store equipment; cost, $50,000; estimated useful life, 10 years; estimated salvage value at the end of that time, $2,500.

The entry to record the depreciation of store equipment for a year follows:

> Depreciation of Store Equipment.................. 4,750
>    Allowance for Depreciation of Store Equipment.....      4,750

**PROBABLE UNCOLLECTIBLE ACCOUNTS** Provision is ordinarily made for the probable loss that will result from failure to collect receivables created by sales of the current period. In recognizing the probable loss arising from the policy of granting credit to customers, operations are charged with the estimated loss, and receivables are reduced by means of a valuation account. When receivables actually prove uncollectible, they are charged against the valuation account balance. To illustrate the nature of the adjustment to be made for probable uncollectibles, assume that losses of $5,000 are expected on accounts arising from sales of the current period. The adjustment at the end of the period is:

> Loss from Bad Debts............................. 5,000
>    Allowance for Bad Debts........................      5,000

**ACCRUED EXPENSES**     During the period, certain expenses may have been incurred although payment is not to be made until a subsequent period. At the end of the current period, it is necessary to determine and record the expenses that have not yet been recognized. In recording an accrued expense, an expense account is debited and an accrued liability account is credited.

At the start of the new period, the balance in the accrued liability account may be transferred to the credit side of the appropriate expense account by means of a reversing entry. The reversing entry makes it possible for the bookkeeper to record the expense payments in the new period in the usual manner. The expense account is debited for the full expense payments, the entry on the credit side of the account absorbing that part of the payments recognized as expense in the prior period. If reversing entries are not made for accrued expenses, expense payments will have to be analyzed as to (1) the amount representing payment of an accrued liability balance, and (2) the amount representing expense of the current period. Reversing entries are normally made for accrued expenses in order to avoid the need for such analysis.

*Accounting for Accrued Expense Illustrated.* To illustrate accounting for an accrued expense (1) when reversing entries are made and (2) when reversing entries are not made, assume that on December 31 accrued salaries are $350. Payment of salaries for the week ending January 4 is $1,000. Adjustments are made and the books are closed annually on December 31. Entries would be made as follows:

|  | (1) Assuming Accrued Liability Account Is Reversed | (2) Assuming Accrued Liability Account Is Not Reversed |
|---|---|---|
| December 31<br>Adjusting entry to record accrued salaries. | Salaries.........350<br>    Salaries Payable     350 | Salaries..........350<br>    Salaries Payable.     350 |
| December 31<br>Closing entry to transfer expense to the profit and loss account. | Profit and Loss...xxx<br>    Salaries........     xxx | Profit and Loss....xxx<br>    Salaries........     xxx |
| January 1<br>Reversing entry to transfer balance to the account that will be charged when payment is made. | Salaries Payable..350<br>    Salaries........     350 | No entry |
| January 4<br>Payment of salaries for week ending January 4. | Salaries.......1,000<br>    Cash.......     1,000 | Salaries Payable.350<br>Salaries.........650<br>    Cash.........     1,000 |

**ACCRUED INCOMES**      During the period, certain amounts may have been earned although collection is not to be made until a subsequent period. At the end of the period, then, it is necessary to determine and record the earnings that have not yet been recognized. In recording accrued income, an accrued asset account is debited and an income account is credited.

At the start of the new period, the balance in the accrued asset account may be transferred to the debit side of the appropriate income account by means of a reversing entry. The reversing entry makes it possible for the bookkeeper to record the receipt of income in the new period in the usual manner. The income account is credited for the full receipts, the entry on the debit side of the account absorbing that part of the receipts which was recognized as income of the prior period. If reversing entries are not made for accrued incomes, income receipts will have to be analyzed as to (1) the amount representing collection of an accrued income balance as of the end of the preceding period, and (2) the amount representing earnings of the current period.

*Accounting for Accrued Income Illustrated.* To illustrate accounting for accrued income (1) when reversing entries are made and (2) when reversing entries are not made, assume that on December 31, interest for 2 months is accrued on $10,000 of 6% bonds held as an investment. Interest on bonds is received semiannually. Adjustments are made and the books are closed annually on December 31. Entries would be made as follows:

|  | (1) Assuming Accrued Asset Account Is Reversed | (2) Assuming Accrued Asset Account is Not Reversed |
|---|---|---|
| December 31<br>Adjusting entry to record accrued interest. | Accrued Interest on Investment in Bonds......... 100<br>   Interest Income     100 | Accrued Interest on Investment in Bonds.......... 100<br>   Interest Income     100 |
| December 31<br>Closing entry to transfer income to the profit and loss account. | Interest Income. xxx<br>   Profit and Loss     xxx | Interest Income.. xxx<br>   Profit and Loss.     xxx |
| January 1<br>Reversing entry to transfer balance to the account that will be credited when collection is made. | Interest Income. 100<br>   Accrued Interest on Investment in Bonds.....     100 | No entry |
| April 30<br>Collection of interest for six-month period. | Cash.......... 300<br>   Interest Income     300 | Cash........... 300<br>   Accrued Interest on Investment in Bonds......     100<br>   Interest Income     200 |

**PREPAID EXPENSES**     During the period, charges may have been recorded on the books for services or commodities that are not to be received or used up in the current period. At the end of the period it is necessary to determine and record the portions of such charges that are prepaid and are applicable to subsequent periods. Such charges are to be reported as assets.

The method of adjusting for a prepaid expense depends upon how the expenditure was originally entered in the accounts. The charge for the commodity or service may have been recorded as a debit to (1) an expense account or (2) an asset account.

*Original Debit to an Expense Account.* If an expense account was originally debited, an appropriate asset account is debited for the expense applicable to a future period and the expense account is credited. The expense account then remains with a debit balance representing the amount applicable to the current accounting period.

The asset account balance is ordinarily returned to the expense account at the start of the next period by a reversing entry.  This is desirable, since further expenditures of the same character will continue to be recorded in the expense account, and the expense account at the end of the next fiscal period should show all of the relevant data for purposes of determining and recording the required adjustment at that time.

*Original Debit to an Asset Account.* If an asset account was originally debited, an appropriate expense account is debited for the expense portion applicable to the current period and the asset account is credited. The asset account remains with a debit balance that shows the amount applicable to future periods. In this instance, no transfer of the asset balance to an expense account at the start of the new period is made, since subsequent expenditures for the same purpose will continue to be recorded in the asset account.

*Accounting for Prepaid Expense Illustrated.* To illustrate the two methods of accounting, assume that a 3-year insurance policy, dated July 1, is purchased for $900. Adjustments are made and the books are closed annually on December 31. The required entries are given at the top of the following page.

**PREPAID INCOMES**     During the period, incomes may have been recorded on the books in advance of fulfillment of obligations in the form of services or commodities. At the end of the period, it is necessary to determine and record the amounts of such incomes that are unearned and applicable to future periods. Such credits are to be reported as liabilities.

|  | (1) Assuming that the Charge Is Made to an Expense Account | (2) Assuming that the Charge Is Made to an Asset Account |
|---|---|---|
| **July 1**<br>Payment of premium. | Insurance.......900<br>   Cash..........     900 | Unexpired<br>Insurance.......900<br>   Cash..........     900 |
| **December 31**<br>Adjusting entry to record:<br>(1) unexpired portion.<br>(2) expired portion. | Unexpired<br>Insurance.......750<br>   Insurance.....     750 | Insurance.......150<br>   Unexpired<br>   Insurance.....     150 |
| **December 31**<br>Closing entry to transfer expense to the profit and loss account. | Profit and Loss...150<br>   Insurance.....     150 | Profit and Loss...150<br>   Insurance.....     150 |
| **January 1**<br>Reversing entry to transfer balance to the account that will be charged with subsequent expenditures. | Insurance.......750<br>   Unexpired<br>   Insurance......     750 | No entry |

The method of adjusting for a prepaid income item depends upon how the income was originally entered in the accounts. The income may have been recorded as a credit to (1) an income account or (2) a liability account.

*Original Credit to an Income Account.* If an income account was originally credited, this account is debited and an appropriate liability account is credited for the income applicable to a future period. The income account remains with a credit balance representing the earnings applicable to the current accounting period.

 The unearned balance in the liability account is ordinarily returned to the income account at the start of the next period by means of a reversing entry. This is desirable, since further income of the same character will continue to be recorded in the income account, and the income account at the end of the next fiscal period should show all of the relevant data for purposes of determining and recording the required adjustment at that time.

*Original Credit to a Liability Account.* If a liability account was originally credited, this account is debited and an appropriate income account is credited for the portion of the income that is applicable to the current period. The liability account remains with a credit balance that shows the amount applicable to future periods. In this instance, no transfer of the liability balance to an income account is made, since subsequent income of the same character will continue to be recorded in the liability account.

*Accounting for Prepaid Income Illustrated.* To illustrate the two methods of accounting, assume that on October 1, $600 is collected representing rental income for a period of one year from this date. Adjustments are made and the books are closed annually on December 31. The required entries are as follows:

| | (1) Assuming that the Credit Is Made to an Income Account | (2) Assuming that the Credit Is Made to a Liability Account |
|---|---|---|
| **October 1** Collection of rent. | Cash............600    Rental Income.    600 | Cash............600    Unearned    Rental Income.    600 |
| **December 31** Adjusting entry to record: (1) unearned portion. (2) earned portion. | Rental Income...450    Unearned    Rental Income..    450 | Unearned    Rental Income...150    Rental Income.    150 |
| **December 31** Closing entry to transfer income to the profit and loss account. | Rental Income...150    Profit and Loss.    150 | Rental Income...150    Profit and Loss.    150 |
| **January 1** Reversing entry to transfer balance to the account that will be credited with subsequent income. | Unearned    Rental Income...450    Rental Income.    · 450 | No entry |

**INVENTORIES**   When perpetual or book inventory records are not maintained, physical inventories must be taken at the end of the period to determine the inventory amount to be reported on the balance sheet and the cost of goods sold amount to be reported on the income statement. When perpetual or book inventories are maintained, the ending inventory balance and the cost of goods sold balance appear in the ledger and no adjustment is required. The two practices are described for trading and manufacturing concerns in the following paragraphs.

*Physical Inventories — The Trading Enterprise.* In a trading concern, the beginning inventory and the balance in the purchases account may be closed into the profit and loss account. The ending inventory is then recorded by a debit to the inventory account and a credit to the profit and loss account. The asset account now reflects the inventory balance at the end of the period; the profit and loss account shows the cost of goods sold. To illustrate, assume the following facts: merchandise on hand, January 1, 1958, $95,000; purchases, 1958, $330,000; merchandise on hand, December 31, 1958, $125,000. The entries to close the beginning balance and to record the ending inventory follow:

| To close the beginning | Profit and Loss................. | 95,000 | |
| inventory balance: | Merchandise Inventory...... | | 95,000 |
| To record the ending | Merchandise Inventory......... | 125,000 | |
| inventory balance: | Profit and Loss.............. | | 125,000 |

After Purchases has been closed into Profit and Loss, the inventory and profit and loss accounts appear as follows:

### MERCHANDISE INVENTORY

| Beginning Inventory | 95,000 | To Profit and Loss | 95,000 |
|---|---|---|---|
| Ending Inventory | 125,000 | | |

### PROFIT AND LOSS

| Beginning Inventory | 95,000 | Ending Inventory | 125,000 |
|---|---|---|---|
| Purchases | 330,000 | | |

(Balance, $300,000, Cost of Goods Sold)

*Physical Inventories — The Manufacturing Enterprise.* In a manufacturing organization, three inventories are recognized: raw materials, goods in process, and finished goods. If the cost of goods manufactured is to be summarized separately, beginning and ending raw materials and goods in process inventories are recorded in a manufacturing account, and beginning and ending finished goods inventories are recorded in the profit and loss account. To illustrate the entries to close beginning inventories and to record ending balances, assume the following data:

Inventories, January 1, 1958: Raw Materials, $30,000; Goods in Process, $25,000; Finished Goods, $40,000.

Charges incurred during 1958: Raw Materials Purchases, $110,000; Direct Labor, $140,000; Manufacturing Expenses, $80,000.

Inventories, December 31, 1958: Raw Materials, $40,000; Goods in Process, $35,000; Finished Goods, $50,000.

The entries to close the beginning inventories and to record the ending inventories follow:

| To close the beginning | Manufacturing................ | 30,000 | |
| inventory balances: | Raw Materials Inventory..... | | 30,000 |
| | Manufacturing................ | 25,000 | |
| | Goods in Process Inventory... | | 25,000 |
| | Profit and Loss................ | 40,000 | |
| | Finished Goods Inventory.... | | 40,000 |
| To record the ending | Raw Materials Inventory....... | 40,000 | |
| inventory balances: | Manufacturing............. | | 40,000 |
| | Goods in Process Inventory..... | 35,000 | |
| | Manufacturing............. | | 35,000 |
| | Finished Goods Inventory...... | 50,000 | |
| | Profit and Loss.............. | | 50,000 |

After manufacturing costs are closed into the manufacturing account, the inventory and summary accounts are as follows:

RAW MATERIALS INVENTORY

| | | | |
|---|---|---|---|
| Beginning Inventory | 30,000 | To Manufacturing | 30,000 |
| Ending Inventory | 40,000 | | |

GOODS IN PROCESS INVENTORY

| | | | |
|---|---|---|---|
| Beginning Inventory | 25,000 | To Manufacturing | 25,000 |
| Ending Inventory | 35,000 | | |

FINISHED GOODS INVENTORY

| | | | |
|---|---|---|---|
| Beginning Inventory | 40,000 | To Profit and Loss | 40,000 |
| Ending Inventory | 50,000 | | |

MANUFACTURING

| | | | |
|---|---|---|---|
| Beginning Raw Materials Inventory | 30,000 | Ending Raw Materials Inventory | 40,000 |
| Beginning Goods in Process Inventory | 25,000 | Ending Goods in Process Inventory | 35,000 |
| Raw Materials Purchases | 110,000 | | |
| Direct Labor | 140,000 | | |
| Manufacturing Expenses | 80,000 | | |

(Balance, $310,000, Cost of Goods Manufactured)

PROFIT AND LOSS

| | | | |
|---|---|---|---|
| Beginning Finished Goods Inventory | 40,000 | Ending Finished Goods Inventory | 50,000 |

In closing the accounts, the balance in the manufacturing account representing the cost of goods manufactured is transferred to the profit and loss account; the latter account then shows the cost of goods sold.

MANUFACTURING

| | | | |
|---|---|---|---|
| Beginning Raw Materials Inventory | 30,000 | Ending Raw Materials Inventory | 40,000 |
| Beginning Goods in Process Inventory | 25,000 | Ending Goods in Process Inventory | 35,000 |
| Raw Materials Purchases | 110,000 | Cost of Goods Manufactured to Profit and Loss | 310,000 |
| Direct Labor | 140,000 | | |
| Manufacturing Expenses | 80,000 | | |
| | 385,000 | | 385,000 |

PROFIT AND LOSS

| Beginning Finished Goods Inventory | 40,000 | Ending Finished Goods Inventory | 50,000 |
| Cost of Goods Manufactured | 310,000 | | |

(Balance, $300,000, Cost of Goods Sold)

*Perpetual Inventories — The Trading Enterprise.* When the perpetual inventory plan is maintained, the inventory account instead of Purchases is debited upon the acquisition of merchandise. When a sale takes place, two entries are required: (1) the sale is recorded in the usual manner, and (2) the merchandise removed from stock is recorded by a debit to Cost of Goods Sold and a credit to the inventory account. Subsidiary records for inventory items are normally maintained. Detailed increases and decreases in the various inventory items are reported in the subsidiary accounts, and the costs of goods purchased and sold are summarized in the merchandise controlling account. Physical counts of the merchandise are made at regular intervals during the period to check on the accuracy of the book record. In the event of discrepancies between the book record and actual amounts on hand, appropriate adjustments are made to bring the book record into agreement with the amounts determined by physical count. At the end of the period, the inventory account reflects the inventory on hand; the cost of goods sold account is closed into Profit and Loss. These accounts appear as follows:

MERCHANDISE INVENTORY

| Beginning Inventory | 95,000 | To Cost of Goods Sold | 300,000 |
| Purchases | 330,000 | | |

(Balance, $125,000, Ending Inventory)

COST OF GOODS SOLD

| Cost of Goods Sold | 300,000 | To Profit and Loss | 300,000 |

PROFIT AND LOSS

| Cost of Goods Sold | 300,000 | |

Even where the cost of goods sold is obtained by means of physical inventories, one may prefer to follow a closing procedure similar to the foregoing. The purchases account is closed into the merchandise inventory account. The merchandise inventory account is then reduced to the ending inventory figure, a cost of goods sold account being opened and charged with the inventory decrease. Cost of Goods Sold is then closed into Profit and Loss as above.

*Perpetual Inventories — The Manufacturing Enterprise.*  When perpetual inventories are maintained by a manufacturing enterprise, raw materials purchases are recorded by charges to Raw Materials Inventory.  Materials removed from stores for processing result in a charge to Goods in Process Inventory and a credit to Raw Materials Inventory.  Labor and manufacturing costs, likewise, are charged to Goods in Process Inventory.  Finished Goods Inventory is debited and the goods in process inventory account is credited for the cost of goods completed and transferred into the finished goods stock from factory processing centers.  The entry to record a sale is accompanied by an entry to record the cost of goods sold, Cost of Goods Sold being debited and Finished Goods Inventory credited.  At the end of the period, inventory accounts reflect ending balances; the cost of goods sold account is closed into Profit and Loss.  Normally, the raw materials, goods in process, and finished goods inventory accounts are controlling accounts, individual increases and decreases in the various inventory items being reported in the respective subsidiary ledgers.  Frequently, such procedures are maintained as a part of a cost system designed to offer detailed information concerning job order or process costs.  Perpetual inventory accounts and the cost of goods sold account, together with the other accounts affected in the closing process, will appear as follows:

RAW MATERIALS INVENTORY

| | | | |
|---|---|---|---|
| Beginning Inventory | 30,000 | Materials Used in Proc- | |
| Raw Materials Pur- | | essing to Goods in | |
|     chases | 110,000 | Process Inventory | 100,000 |

(Balance, $40,000, Ending Inventory)

GOODS IN PROCESS INVENTORY

| | | | |
|---|---|---|---|
| Beginning Inventory | 25,000 | Cost of Goods Manufac- | |
| Materials Used in Proc- | | tured to Finished | |
|     essing | 100,000 | Goods Inventory | 310,000 |
| Direct Labor | 140,000 | | |
| Manufacturing Expenses | 80,000 | | |

(Balance, $35,000, Ending Inventory)

FINISHED GOODS INVENTORY

| | | | |
|---|---|---|---|
| Beginning Inventory | 40,000 | To Cost of Goods Sold | 300,000 |
| Cost of Goods Manu- | | | |
|     factured | 310,000 | | |

(Balance, $50,000, Ending Inventory)

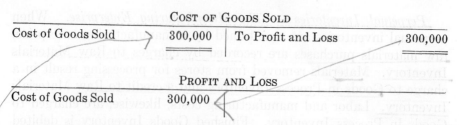

Even when cost of goods sold for a manufacturing enterprise is to be obtained by means of physical inventories, one may prefer to follow a closing procedure similar to the foregoing. The raw materials purchases account is closed into the raw materials inventory account. The inventory account is then reduced to the ending inventory balance, Goods in Process Inventory being charged with the decrease in raw materials. Direct labor and manufacturing expense accounts are closed into Goods in Process Inventory. Goods in Process Inventory is then reduced to the ending inventory figure, Finished Goods Inventory being debited. Finished Goods Inventory is finally reduced to its ending balance, a cost of goods sold account being opened and charged with the inventory decrease. Cost of Goods Sold is closed into Profit and Loss as shown.

**CLOSING THE ACCOUNTS WITH PROVISION FOR INCOME TAXES** After the accounts have been adjusted and the ending inventories recorded, nominal accounts are closed into the profit and loss account. In the case of the sole proprietorship and partnership, the balance in the profit and loss account is transferred to appropriate capital accounts. In the case of the corporation, provision must be made for income taxes before activities can be summarized and the result of activities transferred to Retained Earnings.

When nominal accounts include extraordinary gains and losses that are to be reported on the income statement and the provision for income taxes is to be allocated between net income and extraordinary items, separate nominal accounts may be established to report the income taxes applicable to net income and the income taxes applicable to the special items. When extraordinary items have been reported directly in the retained earnings account and are to be reflected on the retained earnings statement, the taxes related to net income are reported in a nominal account and taxes related to the special items are recorded directly in Retained Earnings. The entries that follow illustrate the allocation of taxes between net income and extraordinary items under circumstances involving (a) an extraordinary gain, and (b) an extraordinary loss. It is assumed in the examples that the tax rate is 50%, and that the special items are fully recognized in the calculation of the tax as would be the case, for example, in a gain resulting from the retirement of bonds at less than their book value, or in a loss from fire.

| Summary of Transactions for Year | Entries to Record Tax Provision Assuming Extraordinary Items are Reported on the Income Statement | Entries to Record Tax Provision Assuming Extraordinary Items are Reported on the Retained Earnings Statement |
|---|---|---|
| (a) Net income......... $100,000<br>　　Extraordinary gains..　50,000<br>　　　　　　　　　　　$150,000<br>　　Income tax rate.....　50%<br><br>　　Estimated income tax<br>　　　liability.......... $ 75,000 | Income Taxes Applicable to Net Income .. 50,000<br>Income Taxes Applicable to Extraordinary Gains........... 25,000<br>　Estimated Income<br>　Taxes Payable...... 75,000 | Income Taxes Applicable to Net Income. 50,000<br>Retained Earnings... 25,000<br>　Estimated Income<br>　Taxes Payable......　75,000 |
| (b) Net income......... $100,000<br>　　Extraordinary losses..　50,000<br>　　　　　　　　　　　$ 50,000<br>　　Income tax rate......　50%<br><br>　　Estimated income tax<br>　　　liability.......... $ 25,000 | Income Taxes Applicable to Net Income. 50,000<br>Income Tax Credit Applicable to Extraordinary Losses. 25,000<br>　Estimated Income<br>　Taxes Payable.... 25,000 | Income Taxes Applicable to Net Income. 50,000<br>Retained Earnings.　25,000<br>　Estimated Income<br>　Taxes Payable......　25,000 |

To illustrate the application of the foregoing procedures in the accounts at the end of the period, assume that nominal accounts after adjustment report the following balances:

| Debits | | Credits | |
|---|---|---|---|
| Cost of Goods Sold | $300,000 | Sales | $500,000 |
| Operating Expenses | 150,000 | Other Income | 5,000 |
| Other Expenses | 10,000 | Extraordinary Gain | 20,000 |
| Corrections in Profits of Prior Periods | 7,000 | | |

The total income tax liability on the total taxable income of $65,000 ($525,000 less $460,000) is estimated at $23,000. However, assume that the ordinary income and the extraordinary gain are not taxed at the same rates, the special item qualifying as a "long-term capital gain" with the tax limited to an effective rate of 25% of the gain, or $5,000. Estimated Income Taxes Payable is credited for $23,000 and charges are made to Income Taxes Applicable to Net Income, $18,000, and Income Taxes Applicable to Extraordinary Gain, $5,000.

When the tax provision has been recorded, nominal accounts may be closed into Profit and Loss, and Profit and Loss closed into Retained Earnings. These accounts will appear as follows after closing is completed:

### PROFIT AND LOSS

| | | | |
|---|---:|---|---:|
| Cost of Goods Sold | 300,000 | Sales | 500,000 |
| Operating Expenses | 150,000 | Other Income | 5,000 |
| Other Expenses | 10,000 | Extraordinary Gains | 20,000 |
| Corrections in Profits of Prior Periods | 7,000 | | |
| Income Taxes Applicable to Net Income | 18,000 | | |
| Income Taxes Applicable to Extraordinary Gain | 5,000 | | |
| Balance to Retained Earnings | 35,000 | | |
| | 525,000 | | 525,000 |

### ESTIMATED INCOME TAXES PAYABLE

| | |
|---|---:|
| Estimated Income Taxes | 23,000 |

### RETAINED EARNINGS

| | |
|---|---:|
| Increase for Period | 35,000 |

**FINANCIAL REPORTS ON CASH VERSUS ACCRUAL BASIS** In the preceding pages of this chapter, adjustments were made at the end of the period in the attempt to measure accurately income and expenses of the fiscal period. Income *earned* rather than income *collected*, and expenses *incurred* rather than expenses *paid* were considered and given effect in the measurement of profit and loss. Statements recognizing income in the period when earned and expenses in the period when incurred are said to be prepared on the *accrual basis*. For most businesses, satisfactory measurement of operating results can be achieved only through use of the accrual basis of accounting.

Statements are said to be prepared on a *cash basis* when income and expenses are recognized only upon the receipt and the disbursement of cash. In the case of a pure cash basis, income from the sale of goods and services is recognized only when collections from customers are made; expenses are recognized only when payments are made for depreciable assets, goods, services, and other operating costs. There is no recognition of a bad debt loss, since revenue is recognized only when cash is received; there is no recognition of depreciation, since the entire cost of the plant and equipment item is recognized as expense at the time of payment.

The federal government permits the filing of tax returns on the accrual basis or on the cash basis. But the cash basis for tax purposes is defined as a combination cash-accrual basis, since it is recognized that the application of a strict cash approach as suggested above might result in serious distortions in net income measurement; furthermore, a strictly cash approach would offer a means of shifting significant amounts of income from one year to another by control of cash receipts and disbursements. For tax purposes, the following requirements must be observed:

(1) When goods are sold, income from sales must include full recognition of sales on account, and cost of goods sold must include full recognition of purchases on account and inventories, even though the cash basis for reporting income is adopted. In the case of trading or manufacturing companies, then, the gross profit on sales is the same regardless of cash or accrual reporting. But professional men or companies who sell their services, in adopting the cash basis, should disregard receivables from clients for services rendered and should recognize as income only those amounts actually collected from clients during the period for services of the past or present or for services to be rendered in the future.

(2) When income from receivables must be recognized, the taxpayer is given the option of recognizing as a loss from bad debts either (a) those amounts actually written off as uncollectible during the period or (b) the amount anticipated to be uncollectible established through satisfactory valuation procedures.

(3) In the case of acquisitions of plant and equipment, deductions from income are allowed only to the extent of the depreciation or amortization allocable to the current period regardless of the basis of accounting adopted.

(4) The policy that is adopted for reporting must be employed consistently each period.

Use of the cash basis, then, generally means the use of a hybrid system, with sales, purchases, depreciation, and bad debts being reported as on the accrual basis, but with the remaining income and expense items being measured on a cash basis without regard to accrued and prepaid items. The cash basis offers certain advantages in the form of simpler and more economical bookkeeping. A summary of operations prepared on this basis may be acceptable when failure to recognize accruals and prepayments results in relatively minor misstatements of a compensating nature with no material effect upon the periodic profit or loss figures. When accruals and prepayments are significant in amount and vary from period to period, however, satisfactory income measurement would call for the appropriate recognition of these items by the adoption of the accrual basis.

**FROM TRANSACTIONS TO STATEMENTS**  Preceding pages have stressed the importance of financial reports in modern economic society. The standard procedures used in recording transactions and events incident to the preparation of such reports have been briefly reviewed. The treatment applied to these transactions and events is called the *accounting process*.

The accounting process includes the entire field of analyzing, classifying, recording, and summarizing as practiced by accountants. It includes the successive steps that constitute the bookkeeping or accounting cycle. It starts with the first written record of the transactions of the business unit and concludes with the final summarized financial statements.

The significance of the accounting process and its applicability to every unit of whatever size in our economic society must be appreciated. While the process may be modified to suit conditions peculiar to the economic unit, procedures that have been reviewed here are basic in accounting for every business unit.

## QUESTIONS

**1.** List and describe the steps in the periodic summary. State why each step is necessary.

**2.** Distinguish between a pre-closing trial balance and a post-closing trial balance.

**3.** Explain the nature and the purpose of (a) adjusting entries, (b) closing entries, and (c) reversing entries.

**4.** (a) State a general rule that may be applied in the determination of when to reverse adjusting entries. (b) Give examples for both accrued income and accrued expense items where exceptions to the rule can be supported.

**5.** A member of the board of directors of the Monarch Co. suggests that depreciation be reported following the net income determination inasmuch as the depreciation did not cost the company anything currently. What reply would you make?

6. Payment of insurance in advance may be recorded in either an expense account or an asset account. Which method would you recommend? What periodic entries are required under each method?

7. The receipt of rentals in advance may be recorded in either an income account or a liability account. Which method would you recommend? What periodic entries would be required under each of these methods?

8. The bookkeeper for the Walls Co. does not reverse accrued and prepaid balances at the beginning of the period. At the end of the period he charges or credits these accounts to bring them to the appropriate balances as of the end of the fiscal period, and the offsetting debits and credits are made to the related income and expense accounts. Income and expense accounts at the end of the year thus report receipts and disbursements and the adjustments resulting from variations in the accrued and prepaid balances. Evaluate this procedure.

9. (a) Distinguish between physical and perpetual inventory methods. (b) Does a perpetual inventory method eliminate the need for physical counts of merchandise on hand?

10. Upon inspecting the books for Wiggins, Inc., you find that the beginning inventory was raised to the ending balance and the profit and loss account was credited for the variation between beginning and ending inventories in adjusting the accounts. Furthermore, in the preparation of the income statement, the inventory increase was subtracted from the purchases balance in calculating cost of goods sold. Evaluate these procedures.

11. Describe the entries that would be made in recognizing the income taxes for the period in each case below, assuming that taxes are to be allocated between net income and extraordinary items:

(a) There is a profit from normal activities and a loss that is less than such profit from extraordinary sources, the latter being reported on the income statement.
(b) There is a profit from normal activities and a gain from extraordinary sources, the latter being reported on the retained earnings statement.
(c) There is a loss from normal activities and a gain in excess of such loss from extraordinary sources, the extraordinary gain being reported on the income statement.

12. Distinguish between accounting on a cash basis and accounting on an accrual basis.

13. Use of the cash basis generally means something less than full cash basis reporting. Explain.

## EXERCISES

**1.** D. A. Reed had his own $1,000, 6-month note discounted at the bank on October 31. The entry to record the transaction was:

| | | |
|---|---|---|
| Cash. . . . . . . . . . . . . . . . . . . . . . . . . . . . . | 970 | |
| Prepaid Interest Expense. . . . . . . . . . . | 30 | |
| Notes Payable. . . . . . . . . . . . . . . . . . | | 1,000 |

(a) What adjustment is required on December 31? What reversing entry, if any, is required?  (b) What nominal account could be debited instead of Prepaid Interest Expense? What adjustment would then be necessary? What reversing entry, if any, would be necessary?

**2.** Reed received rent of $1,800 for 1 year on January 31. He recorded the transaction as follows:

| | | |
|---|---|---|
| Cash. . . . . . . . . . . . . . . . . . . . . . . . . . . . . . . . . . . . . . . . . . . . . | 1,800 | |
| Unearned Rental Income. . . . . . . . . . . . . . . . . . . . . . | | 1,800 |

(a) What adjustment is required on December 31? What reversing entry, if any, is required?  (b) What nominal account could have been credited instead of Unearned Rental Income? What adjustment would then be necessary? What reversing entry, if any, would be necessary?

**3.** In analyzing the accounts of L. S. Stone, the adjusting data listed below are determined on December 31, the end of an annual fiscal period. (a) What adjusting entry would be made for each item?  (b) What reversing entry would be made for each item?  (c) What sources would provide the information for each adjustment?

(1) The unexpired insurance account shows a debit of $450, representing the cost of a 3-year fire insurance policy dated September 1.

(2) On November 1, Rental Income was credited for $600, representing income from a subrental for a 3-month period beginning on that date.

(3) Purchase of advertising materials for $400 during the year was recorded in the advertising expense account. On December 31 advertising materials of $60 are on hand.

(4) On August 1, $750 was paid as rent for a 6-month period beginning on that date. The expense account, Rent, was debited.

(5) Miscellaneous Office Expense was debited for office supplies of $860 purchased during the year. On December 31 office supplies of $280 are on hand.

(6) Interest expense includes a note discount charge of $4 applicable to January of the following year.

(7) Interest of $12 is accrued on notes payable.

**4.** In analyzing the accounts for the W. D. Arnold Sales Corp., you find the following data. Give any entries that are required to correct and bring the books up to date on December 31, 1958. State which entries require reversing at the beginning of the new fiscal period.

(1) The rental income account had been credited for rental receipts of $3,600. On December 31, $400 is unearned. In addition it is found that certain property was rented on November 1, 1958, at $150 per month, but the rent for November and December will not be received until February 1, 1959.

(2) Advertising expense was debited for $800, the cost of advertising materials purchased. There are advertising materials of $120 on hand. In addition, a contract for radio advertising for 1 year beginning December 1, 1958, was made. The rate is $120 for a 3-month period payable at the end of each such period.

(3) It is found that the following adjustments were overlooked in closing the books on December 31, 1957:
   (a) Depreciation on store equipment, $50.
   (b) Accrued interest on notes payable, $60.
   (c) Interest received in advance on notes receivable, $25.
   (d) Insurance paid in advance, $40 (Miscellaneous Expense was debited for insurance payments).

**5.** Upon inspecting the accounts for the Proctor Co. before they are closed at the end of 1958, you find the following data. What entries are required to correct the accounts?

(a) A sale of merchandise for $600 had been made on December 31, 1957. The merchandise, cost $450, was delivered to the customer on this date and was not included in the ending inventory. However, the sale was not recorded until remittance was received on January 10, 1958.

(b) 50 shares of X Company stock were sold at $60 per share on July 8, 1958. The bookkeeper debited Cash and credited the investment account for proceeds from the sale, $3,000. The investment account shows that 100 shares of this stock were originally acquired at a cost of $7,500.

(c) Raw materials, cost $400, received on December 31, 1957, had been included in the inventory of raw materials taken on that date. However, the materials were recorded as a purchase on January 4, 1958, when the invoice was received.

(d) Equipment, cost $6,000, acquired on July 1, 1954, depreciated on a 5-year basis, was destroyed by fire on May 1, 1958. Cash was debited and Equipment was credited for $800, the proceeds from an insurance policy.

**6.** Some of the accounts that appear in the ledger of the Mills Manufacturing Co. on November 30, the end of an annual fiscal period, follow:

| | | | |
|---|---|---|---|
| Raw Materials Inventory.. | $ 60,000 | Direct Labor............ | $130,000 |
| Goods in Process Inventory | 50,000 | Manufacturing Expenses.. | 100,000 |
| Finished Goods Inventory. | 70,000 | Sales.................... | 800,000 |
| Raw Materials Purchases.. | 340,000 | Operating Expenses....... | 150,000 |

Physical inventories on November 30 are: Raw Materials, $80,000; Goods in Process, $60,000; Finished Goods, $60,000. The federal income tax liability is estimated at $46,500.

Assuming no further adjustments, give the entries required to adjust and close the accounts according to two different methods.

**7.** The Weber Co. reported for 1957 taxable net income of $160,000 and a fully taxable special gain of $40,000 from the retirement of bonds outstanding at less than book value. Special items are recorded directly in the retained earnings account. Income tax rates for 1957 were: 30% on the first $25,000 of taxable income; 52% on taxable income in excess of $25,000. The Weber Co. allocates the provision for income taxes between net income and special items. (a) Give the entry that would be made in recording the tax provision for 1957. (b) Assuming that the bond retirement had resulted in a fully deductible loss of $40,000, what entry would be made?

**8.** Accounts for the Barlow Co. show a taxable net income for 1957 of $160,000, a fire loss that is deductible from other income for tax purposes of $20,000, and taxable gains from the sales of investments during the year of $45,000. Income taxes for 1957 are calculated at $78,550; in analyzing the tax provision, the company determines that the fire loss resulted in a tax savings of $10,400 while the sale of securities resulted in additional taxes of $11,250. (a) Give the entry that is required in recording the tax allocation, assuming that the company reports the special gains and losses on the income statement. (b) Give the entry that would be required if the company reports the special gains and losses directly in Retained Earnings.

**9.** Reiss and Taylor, attorneys, summarize income on a cash basis. Their net income for 1958 is calculated at $14,600. What income would they have shown for the year if income had been calculated on the accrual basis and the following adjusting data were recognized?

|                                   | JAN. 1, 1958 | DEC. 31, 1958 |
|-----------------------------------|-------------|---------------|
| Receivables from clients          | $12,000     | $10,600       |
| Office supplies on hand           | 310         | 360           |
| Unearned retainer income          | 1,600       | 3,000         |
| Miscellaneous accrued expenses    | 450         | 300           |

**10.** The income statement for the Blaine Co. for 1958 shows: interest income, $805; interest expense, $1,240. A comparative balance sheet at the end of 1958 reports:

|                               | JAN. 1, 1958 | DEC. 31, 1958 |
|-------------------------------|-------------|---------------|
| Accrued interest receivable   | $140        | $305          |
| Prepaid interest income       | 200         | 160           |
| Accrued interest payable      | 125         | 540           |
| Prepaid interest expense      | 150         | 300           |

What were the amounts of interest received and paid in 1958?

## PROBLEMS

**4-1.** The trial balance of the Lester Company shows among other items the following balances on December 31, 1958, the end of a fiscal year:

| | |
|---|---:|
| Accounts Receivable............................... | $35,000 |
| Allowance for Doubtful Accounts...................... | $ 430 |
| 3½% Bonds of Sands, Inc........................ | 30,000 |
| Buildings......................................... | 95,000 |
| Allowance for Depreciation of Buildings................. | 1,500 |
| Unexpired Insurance.............................. | 430 |
| Notes Payable.................................... | 7,500 |
| Unearned Rental Income........................... | 1,400 |
| Advertising Expense............................... | 3,000 |
| Interest Income.................................. | 360 |

The following facts are ascertained on this date upon inspection of the records of the company:

(a) After careful examination of the accounts receivable, it was estimated that the Allowance for Doubtful Accounts should be brought up to 2% of the accounts receivable.

(b) Interest on the bonds of Sands, Inc. is collected semiannually on March 1 and September 1.

(c) Buildings are depreciated at 3% per year; however, there were building additions during the year costing $15,000. The company computes depreciation on asset acquisitions during the year at one half the annual rate.

(d) The $7,500 note was issued on August 31, 1958, and accrues interest at 6%, which is payable upon maturity of the note, August 31, 1959.

(e) Payments for insurance coverage were made as follows:

| POLICY DATES | COVERAGE (YEARS) | PREMIUM |
|---|:---:|---:|
| May 1, 1957 | 3 | $180 |
| Sept. 30, 1958 | 1 | 140 |
| Nov. 30, 1958 | 1 | 150 |

(f) The unearned rental income account was credited for $1,400 on August 1, 1958, representing rental from August 1, 1958, to April 1, 1959.

(g) Advertising materials of $900 were purchased from January 1 to December 31 and were charged to the advertising expense account. No materials were on hand on January 1, 1958. Approximately two thirds of the materials purchased had been used up by December 31, 1958.

(h) It is determined that $35 of the $360 interest income balance is unearned on December 31, 1958.

*Instructions:* (1) Prepare the journal entries to adjust the books on December 31, 1958.

(2) Prepare the reversing entries that would be made on January 1, 1959.

**4-2.** The trial balance of the Rand Corporation shows among other items the following balances on December 31, 1958, the end of a fiscal year:

| | | |
|---|---:|---:|
| Accounts Receivable | $48,000 | |
| 4½% Park Corporation Bonds | 25,000 | |
| Buildings | 90,000 | |
| Allowance for Depreciation of Buildings | | $14,000 |
| Land | 100,000 | |
| 5% First Mortgage Bonds Payable | | 100,000 |
| Rental Income | | 26,000 |
| Office Expense | 800 | |

The following facts are ascertained on this date upon inspection of the records of the company:

(a) It is estimated that approximately 4% of accounts receivable may prove uncollectible.

(b) Interest is receivable semiannually on the Park Corporation Bonds on March 1 and September 1.

(c) Buildings are depreciated at 2½% a year; however, there were building additions of $20,000 during the year. The company computes depreciation on asset acquisitions during the year at one half the annual rate.

(d) Interest on the first mortgage bonds is payable semiannually on February 1 and August 1.

(e) Rental income includes $1,800 that was received on October 1, representing rent on part of the buildings for the period October 1, 1958, to September 30, 1959.

(f) Office supplies of $350 are on hand on December 31. Purchases of office supplies were charged to the office expense account.

*Instructions:* (1) Prepare the journal entries to adjust the books on December 31, 1958.

(2) Give the reversing entries that would be made at the beginning of 1959.

**4-3.** The following facts are ascertained from the books and records of Todd, Inc., at the end of the first year of operations:

(a) On December 21, 1958, $9,000 was borrowed from the First State Bank on a 30-day note. The bank deducted interest of $45 in advance on the loan and a nominal account was charged for the discount.

(b) On September 1, 1958, $1,500 was collected for one year's rent beginning on that date. The credit was made to a balance sheet account.

(c) $15,000 of 4½% bonds of the Mason Co. were purchased on March 15, 1958. Interest on the bonds is receivable semiannually on May 1 and November 1.

(d) A truck was acquired on August 1, 1958, for $4,000. The estimated life is 6 years, with a trade-in value of $400.

(e) A 45-day, non-interest-bearing note was received on December 16, 1958. A discount of $75 was deducted and credited to a nominal account.

(f) A real account was debited on October 20, 1958, for $162, representing the payment of the premium on a 3-year fire insurance policy dated October 1, 1958.

(g) On December 31, 1958, the allowance for bad debts account has a debit balance of $125. The account is to be maintained at 3% of accounts receivable. Accounts receivable on December 31, 1958, are $12,500.

(h) The payroll for the week ending January 4, 1959, will be $1,400. Of this amount $600 had been earned by the employees during the period December 29–31. (No accrual of payroll taxes is required.)

*Instructions:* (1) Give the adjusting entries on December 31, 1958.
(2) List the letters of those entries that should be reversed.

**4-4.** The following information is available with respect to transactions of the Peters Publishing Company, which began operations in 1958:

(a) Cash collections on annual subscriptions to their monthly magazine during the last six months of 1958 were as follows:

| | | | |
|---|---|---|---|
| July | $12,000 | October | $ 6,500 |
| August | 8,000 | November | 7,500 |
| September | 6,200 | December | 10,000 |

The subscriptions are effective as of the start of the month following receipt of the subscription.

(b) Payments for insurance coverage were made as follows:

| POLICY DATE | COVERAGE (YEARS) | PREMIUM |
|---|---|---|
| July 1 | 3 | $ 75 |
| Sept. 30 | 1 | 90 |
| Oct. 1 | 3 | 450 |
| Nov. 30 | 1 | 45 |

(c) The annual real and personal property tax paid on December 5, 1958, was $520. The bill covers the city's fiscal year beginning July 1, 1958.

(d) Advertising materials of $750 were purchased from July 1 to December 31. No materials were on hand on July 1. Approximately one third of the materials purchased remains on hand on December 31.

*Instructions:* (1) Assuming that original entries for expense or income items in each of the above transactions were made to real accounts, give the necessary adjusting entries at the end of the 6-month period. (Give schedules following journal entries to show how the amounts were calculated.)

(2) Assuming that original entries for expense or income items in each of the above transactions were made to nominal accounts, give the necessary adjusting entries.

(3) State which of the entries in parts (1) and (2) require reversing at the beginning of 1959.

**4-5.** The bookkeeper for the Bell Co. has submitted an income statement for the year ended December 31, 1957, with results as follows:

| | |
|---|---|
| Net income from operations | $ 88,500 |
| Gain on sale of securities | 12,000 |
| Net income and extraordinary items | $100,500 |

Accounts have not yet been closed, and a review of the books discloses the need for the following additional adjustments:

(a) The account Office Expense shows the cost of all purchases of office supplies for the year. At the end of 1957 there are supplies of $450 on hand.

(b) The allowance for bad debts account shows a debit balance of $350. It is estimated that 4% of the accounts receivable as of December 31 will prove uncollectible. The accounts receivable balance on this date is $22,500.

(c) The ledger shows a balance for accrued salaries and wages of $1,200 as of December 31, 1956, which was left unadjusted during 1957. No recognition was made in the accounts at the end of 1957 for accrued salaries and wages which amounted to $1,350.

(d) The ledger shows a balance for accrued interest on investments of $375 as of December 31, 1956, which was left unchanged during 1957. No recognition was made in the accounts at the end of 1957 for accrued interest on investments which amounted to $325.

(e) The account Unexpired Insurance was debited during the year for amounts paid for insurance and shows a balance of $1,550 at the end of 1957. The unexpired portions of the policies on December 31, 1957, total $350.

(f) A portion of a building was subleased for 3 months, November 1, 1957, to Feburary 1, 1958. Unearned Rental Income was credited for $900 and no adjustment was made in this account at the end of 1957.

(g) The account Interest Expense was charged for all interest charges incurred during the year and shows a balance of $2,050. However, of this amount, $250 represents charges applicable to 1958.

(h) Provision for income taxes for 1957 is to be made at the following rates: 30% on taxable income up to $25,000; 52% on taxable income in excess of $25,000. However, the income taxes applicable to the sale of securities is limited to 25% of the gain. Income taxes are to be allocated in the accounts between net income and special items.

*Instructions:* (1) Give the entries that are required on December 31, 1957, to bring the books up to date.

(2) Prepare a revised summary of the results from 1957 activities with a supporting schedule showing how the corrected net income figure is determined.

**4-6.** The bookkeeper for the Franklin Corp. submits an income statement for the year ended December 31, 1957, which reports the following:

| | |
|---|---:|
| Net income from normal activities. . . . . . . . . . . . . . . . . . . . . . | $44,100 |
| Deduct extraordinary loss resulting from fire. . . . . . . . . . . . . | 18,500 |
| Net income and extraordinary items. . . . . . . . . . . . . . . . . . . . | $25,600 |

An inspection of the books before they are closed reveals the following accounting failures:

(a) A balance of $1,200 for accrued salaries established at the end of 1956 was left unchanged during 1957, with no recognition of accrued salaries as of December 31, 1957, which totaled $1,475.

(b) A balance of $350 for accrued interest on customer notes established at the end of 1956 was left unchanged during 1957, with no recognition of accrued interest as of December 31, 1957, which amounted to $275.

(c) Prepaid insurance was debited for insurance premiums paid during 1957 and was left at the end of 1957 with a balance of $660. The unexpired insurance balance at the end of 1957 was $210.

(d) On December 1, 1957, part of a building was sublet by the company for 6 months; $1,200 was collected and was recorded as Rental Income. No adjustment was made in this balance at the end of 1957.

(e) On November 1, 1957, the company borrowed cash on a $7,500 one-year non-interest-bearing note. The note was discounted by the bank at 6%. The discount was reported as Interest Expense. No adjustment was made for this item at the end of 1957.

(f) Bonds of $100,000 are outstanding. Interest at 4½% is payable semiannually on Feburary 1 and August 1. No entry was made for accrued interest as of December 31, 1957.

(g) Income taxes for 1957 are to be calculated at the following rates: 30% on taxable income up to $25,000; 52% on all income in excess of $25,000. (The fire loss is fully deductible from other taxable income in arriving at the net income subject to tax.) Income taxes are to be allocated in the accounts between net income and special items.

*Instructions:* (1) Give the entries that are required on December 31, 1957, to bring the books up to date.

(2) Prepare a revised summary of the results from 1957 activities with a supporting schedule showing how the corrected net income figure is determined.

**4-7.** A balance sheet for the Chandler Sales Company on January 1, 1958, reports the following balances:

| | | | | | |
|---|---|---|---|---|---|
| Cash............. | | $ 6,550 | Accounts Payable......... | | $ 9,300 |
| Accounts Receivable $6,000 | | | Salaries Payable.......... | | 200 |
| Less: Allowance for | | | Taxes Payable............ | | 150 |
| Bad Debts...... | 350 | 5,650 | A. B. Chandler, Capital.... | | 20,150 |
| Inventories............. | | 14,500 | | | |
| Unexpired Insurance | | 100 | | | |
| Furniture........ | $3,600 | | | | |
| Less: Allowance | | | | | |
| for Depreciation | 600 | 3,000 | | | |
| | | $29,800 | | | $29,800 |

Transactions for 1958 are summarized below:

| | |
|---|---|
| Sales on account...................................... | $102,000 |
| Purchases on account................................. | 67,500 |
| Sales returns (credits were made to customers' accounts)............................................ | 1,500 |
| Cash collected on accounts receivable.................... | 97,000 |
| Discounts allowed on accounts collected................. | 1,200 |
| Uncollectible accounts written off against allowance........ | 300 |

| Cash paid on accounts payable. | | $64,000 |
| Discounts taken on accounts paid. | | 800 |
| Operating expenses paid. | | 24,000 |
| Withdrawals for personal use: | | |
| Merchandise (cost). | $ 2,000 | |
| Cash. | 16,000 | 18,000 |

Cash received on issuance to bank of a $6,000,
6-month note on November 1, on which bank
deducted interest in advance............................ 5,820

In addition to the foregoing information, the following data are to be considered on December 31: inventories, $18,000; unexpired insurance, $250; accrued salaries, $300; and accrued taxes, $200. Depreciation of furniture for the year is $300. The balance in the allowance for bad debts account is increased by $150.

*Instructions:* Prepare an income statement, a balance sheet, and a statement of changes in the owner's capital account for the year ended December 31, 1958. (T accounts or working papers should be used in developing statement data.)

**4-8.** The Miracle Sales Co. is organized on January 1, 1958, selling its total authorized stock of 7,500 shares for cash at par, $75,000. Transactions for the next six months follow:

| Payments for equipment. | $ 20,000 |
| Sales on account. | 142,000 |
| Purchases on account. | 166,000 |
| Cash borrowed on long-term notes. | 40,000 |
| Operating expenses paid. | 42,000 |
| Purchases returns and allowances (charges were made to | |
| creditors' accounts). | 2,000 |

A cash dividend of $2,000 is declared in June, payable July 15. On June 30, there are accounts of trade debtors of $40,000 that have not been collected; sales discounts of $1,200 were allowed on accounts collected. On June 30, there are also accounts of trade creditors of $30,000 that have not been paid. An allowance for bad debts of $650 is to be established on accounts receivable on hand. The merchandise inventory on this date is $76,500. Depreciation for the six months is estimated at $600. In addition, adjustments are to be made for the following prepaid and accrued items as of June 30:

| Unexpired insurance. | $500 |
| Advances to employees. | 550 |
| (Insurance and advances were recorded as operating expenses | |
| during the period.) | |
| Accrued interest on notes payable. | 750 |
| Accrued salaries. | 350 |
| Accrued payroll and property taxes. | 400 |

The income taxes for 1958 are estimated at 40% of the net income.

*Instructions:* Prepare an income statement, a balance sheet, and retained earnings statement for the six-month period ended June 30, 1958. (T accounts or working papers should be used in developing statement data.)

# Chapter 5

# THE ACCOUNTING
# PROCESS ILLUSTRATED

**STEPS IN THE ACCOUNTING PROCESS** The accounting process as described in the preceding chapters is composed of a number of steps in well-defined sequence. To review, these steps consist of:

(1) The entry of the transactions in chronological order in the books of original entry.

(2) The transfer of transactions as classified and summarized in the journals to the appropriate accounts in the ledgers.

(3) The preparation of a trial balance of the accounts in the general ledger and the reconciliation of supporting data in the subsidiary ledgers with respective controlling accounts.

(4) The compilation of the data required in bringing the accounts up to date.

(5) Preparation of the work sheet.

(6) Preparation of the financial statements and supporting schedules.

(7) The adjustment of accounts and the closing of all nominal account balances.

(8) The preparation of a post-closing trial balance.

(9) The reversal of entries that were made to establish accrued and prepaid income and expense balances.

The entire course of the accounting process is illustrated in the example that appears on the following pages. The books of original entry for a hypothetical company, the Martin Manufacturing Company, are described. Data in the journals are transferred to the ledger, and the work involved in the periodic summary at the end of a fiscal year is then illustrated.

**BOOKS OF ORIGINAL ENTRY** The Martin Manufacturing Company maintains the following books of original entry: a sales journal, a sales returns and allowances journal, a cash receipts journal, a voucher register, a cash payments journal, and a general journal.

*Sales Journal.* The sales journal maintained by the Martin Manufacturing Company for the month of December as summarized at the end of the month is shown on the following page.

SALES JOURNAL

| Cash Dr. | Accounts Receivable Dr. | Date | Description | Sales Cr. | Sales Taxes Payable Cr. |
|---|---|---|---|---|---|
| | 816 00 | 31 | Sales on account for day | 800 00 | 16 00 |
| 245 00 | | 31 | Cash sales for day...... | 240 00 | 5 00 |
| 8,150 00 | 24,500 00 | 31 | Totals................ | 32,000 00 | 650 00 |
| (✓) | (116) | | | (41) | (218) |

One entry is made to record the sales on account for each day. Accounts Receivable is debited for the total of the sales on account, including the amount of the sales taxes; Sales and Sales Taxes Payable are credited. Debits are posted to the individual customers' accounts in the accounts receivable ledger directly from the sales invoices.

One entry is also made for the cash sales for each day. Cash is debited and Sales and Sales Taxes Payable are credited.

*Sales Returns and Allowances Journal.* The sales returns and allowances journal maintained by the Martin Manufacturing Company is illustrated below:

SALES RETURNS AND ALLOWANCES JOURNAL

| Date | Description | Accounts Receivable Cr. | Sales Returns and Allowances Dr. | Sales Taxes Payable Dr. |
|---|---|---|---|---|
| 31 | Sales returns and allowances for day........... | 51 00 | 50 00 | 1 00 |
| 31 | Totals................. | 490 00 | 480 00 | 10 00 |
| | | (116) | (041) | (218) |

One entry is made to record the sales returns and allowances for each day. Sales Returns and Allowances and Sales Taxes Payable are debited; Accounts Receivable is credited. Credits are posted to the individual customers' accounts in the accounts receivable ledger directly from the credit memorandums.

*Cash Receipts Journal.* The cash receipts journal maintained by the Martin Manufacturing Company is shown on the opposite page.

One entry is made each day for the total amount collected on accounts receivable. In this entry Cash and Sales Discounts are debited and Accounts Receivable is credited. Credits are posted to the individual customers' accounts in the accounts receivable ledger from a separate list of receipts on account maintained by the cashier.

CASH RECEIPTS JOURNAL

| CASH DR. | SALES DISCOUNTS DR. | DATE | DESCRIPTION | POST. REF. | GENERAL CR. | SALES CR. | ACCOUNTS RECEIVABLE CR. |
|---|---|---|---|---|---|---|---|
| 6,565 00 | | 31 | Notes Receivable....... | 113 | 6,500 00 | | |
| | | | Interest Income . | 72 | 65 00 | | |
| 10,000 00 | | 31 | Note Payable... | 211 | 10,000 00 | | |
| 1,050 00 | 10 00 | 31 | S. G. Selby..... | ✓ | | | 1,060 00 |
| 245 00 | | 31 | Sales.......... | ✓ | | 245 00 | |
| 47,810 00 | 255 00 | 31 | Totals......... | ✓ | 16,565 00 | 8,150 00 | 23,350 00 |
| (111) | (81) | | | | (✓) | (✓) | (116) |

In order to maintain the cash receipts journal as a complete record of all cash received, an entry for cash sales is made each day. This entry is also made in the sales journal so that that journal will have a complete record of sales. To avoid double posting of the transaction, the total of the Cash Dr. column in the sales journal and the total of the Sales Cr. column in the cash receipts journal are checked and are not posted. As a result, the debit to Cash for cash sales is posted from the cash receipts journal as a part of the total of the Cash Dr. column, and the credit to Sales for cash sales is posted from the sales journal as a part of the total of the Sales Cr. column.

*Voucher Register.* The voucher register maintained by the Martin Manufacturing Company appears across the top of pages 120 and 121.

The Martin Manufacturing Company does not maintain an expenses control account and therefore has a number of separate columns for expenses in its voucher register. The total of each amount column is posted to the corresponding account, with the exception of the Payroll Dr. column and the General Dr. and Cr. columns.

The debits to the various accounts for salaries and wages are posted directly from the payroll records. The total of the amounts thus posted must equal the total of the Payroll Dr. column in the voucher register.

The debits posted from the payroll records to the various salaries and wages accounts for the month of December are given below:

| | |
|---|---:|
| Direct Labor.... | $ 6,500 |
| Indirect Labor.... | 1,900 |
| Sales Salaries and Commissions.... | 2,100 |
| Delivery Salaries.... | 800 |
| Factory Superintendence.... | 1,700 |
| Officers Salaries.... | 1,400 |
| Office Salaries.... | 900 |
| | $15,300 |

VOUCHER REGISTER

| | DATE | VCHR. No. | NAME | PAID DATE | CHK. No. | ACCOUNTS PAYABLE CR. | RAW MATERIALS PURCHASES DR. | FREIGHT IN DR. | PAYROLL DR. | |
|---|---|---|---|---|---|---|---|---|---|---|
| 21 | 31 | 5154 | J. Harvey | 12/31 | 4207 | 8,120 | | | | 21 |
| 22 | | | | | | | | | | 22 |
| 23 | 31 | 5155 | Payroll | 12/31 | 4208 | 1,780 | | | 2,000 | 23 |
| 24 | | | | | | | | | | 24 |
| 25 | 31 | 5156 | Columbia G. & E. | | | 1,700 | | | | 25 |
| 26 | 31 | 5157 | Jackson Hardware | | | 300 | | | | 26 |
| 27 | 31 | 5158 | Williams Supply | | | 1,200 | 1,200 | | | 27 |
| 28 | 31 | 5159 | Petty Cash | 12/31 | 4210 | 160 | | | | 28 |
| 29 | 31 | | Totals | | | 37,020 | 6,800 | 400 | 15,300 | 29 |
| | | | | | | (213) | (51) | (52) | Posted to accounts as indicated by payroll records | |

One payroll record is kept for direct labor, indirect labor, sales salaries and commissions, and delivery salaries; another, for factory superintendence, officers salaries, and office salaries. The first group is paid weekly; the second, semimonthly. The entry for the payroll on December 31 in the voucher register across the double page above is for the second group only.

General debits reported in the voucher register for December total $14,010 and are composed of the following items (the first five items represent vouchers recorded prior to December 31 and are not shown in the partial record):

| | |
|---|---|
| Employees Income Taxes Payable (November) | $ 2,000 |
| F.I.C.A. Taxes Payable (November) | 440 |
| Sales Taxes Payable (November) | 720 |
| Prepaid Insurance | 250 |
| Building Maintenance and Repair | 480 |
| Notes Payable | 8,000 |
| Interest Expense—Other | 120 |
| Factory Heat, Light, and Power | 1,700 |
| Tools | 300 |
| | $14,010 |

General credits reported in the voucher register for December represent payroll income tax and federal social security tax withholdings. These are summarized for the month as follows:

| | |
|---|---|
| Employees Income Taxes Payable | $ 2,130 |
| F.I.C.A. Taxes Payable | 210 |
| | $ 2,340 |

*Cash Payments Journal.* The cash payments journal maintained by the Martin Manufacturing Company is illustrated on the opposite page:

For Month of December, 1958

| | Misc. | | Misc. | Misc. | | Misc. | General | | | | |
|---|---|---|---|---|---|---|---|---|---|---|---|
| Factory Supplies Dr. | Factory Expense Dr. | Adver- tising Dr. | Selling Expense Dr. | Del. Expense Dr. | Office Supplies Dr. | Gen. Exp. Dr. | Account | P. R. | Amount Dr. | Cr. | |
| 21 | | | | | | | Notes Payable | 211 | 8,000 | | 21 |
| 22 | | | | | | | Interest Expense — Other | 83 | 120 | | 22 |
| 23 | | | | | | | Emp. Income Taxes Pay. | 214 | | 200 | 23 |
| 24 | | | | | | | F.I.C.A. Taxes Pay. | 215 | | 20 | 24 |
| 25 | | | | | | | Factory Ht., Lt., & Power | 624 | 1,700 | | 25 |
| 26 | | | | | | | Tools | 131 | 300 | | 26 |
| 27 | | | | | | | | | | | 27 |
| 28 | | 20 | | 60 | | 80 | | | | | 28 |
| 29 | 400 | 300 | 800 | 200 | 180 | 750 | 220 | Totals | | 14,010 | 2,340 | 29 |
| | (1110) | (626) | (632) | (633) | (642) | (1111) | (653) | | | (√) | (√) | |

Cash Payments Journal

| Date | Check No. | Description | Vchr. No. | Accounts Payable Dr. | Purchases Discounts Cr. | Cash Cr. |
|---|---|---|---|---|---|---|
| 31 | 4207 | J. Harvey......... | 5154 | 8,120 00 | | 8,120 00 |
| 31 | 4208 | Payroll........... | 5155 | 1,780 00 | | 1,780 00 |
| 31 | 4209 | R. A. Westmore.... | 5006 | 2,000 00 | 20 00 | 1,980 00 |
| 31 | 4210 | Petty Cash....... | 5159 | 160 00 | | 160 00 |
| 31 | | Totals........... | | 29,480 00 | 160 00 | 29,320 00 |
| | | | | (213) | (71) | (111) |

*General Journal.* The general journal for the Martin Manufacturing Company on page 122 shows the entries for the month of December.

**POSTING; PREPARATION OF TRIAL BALANCE** Data in the journals are transferred to the accounts in the ledger at the end of December, and a trial balance is then taken. In order to conserve space here, the complete ledger of the Martin Manufacturing Company is not reproduced. Instead, the information that would appear in the ledger has been summarized in tabular form on page 123. The tabulation shows: (1) the trial balance of the Martin Manufacturing Company taken from its ledger on November 30, (2) the effects upon account balances of the information transferred from the books of original entry for the month of December, and (3) a trial balance as of December 31 formed by combining the transactions for December with the trial balance of November 30.

The letters in the parentheses preceding each amount in the transactions columns of the tabulation refer to the books of original entry on the previous pages from which the information was obtained. The

GENERAL JOURNAL

| DATE | DESCRIPTION | POST. REF. | DETAIL | DEBITS | CREDITS |
|------|-------------|-----------|--------|--------|---------|
| 1958 Dec. | 1 Notes Receivable.................... | 113 | | 6,000 00 | |
| | Accounts Receivable.............. | 116 | | | 6,000 00 |
| | H. A. Malley.................... | AR | 6,000 00 | | |
| | Received note from customer....... | | | | |
| | 5 Notes Receivable Discounted........ | 114 | | 4,500 00 | |
| | Notes Receivable................. | 113 | | | 4,500 00 |
| | Note discounted at bank paid by maker on its due date.......... | | | | |
| | 12 Allowance for Bad Debts............ | 0116 | | 120 00 | |
| | Accounts Receivable.............. | 116 | | | 120 00 |
| | Arthur R. Jordan................ | AR | 120 00 | | |
| | To write off uncollectible customer's account...................... | | | | |
| | 22 Accounts Payable................... | 213 | | 200 00 | |
| | Rodger L. Welson................. | AP | 200 00 | | |
| | Raw Materials Returns and Allow. | 051 | | | 200 00 |
| | Materials returned to supplier.... | | | | |
| | 31 Taxes........................... | 625 | | 210 00 | |
| | F.I.C.A. Taxes Payable........... | 215 | | | 210 00 |
| | To record employer's F.I.C.A. taxes payable for month............. | | | | |
| | 31 Taxes........................... | 625 | | 200 00 | |
| | State Unemployment Taxes Payable | 216 | | | 200 00 |
| | To record employer's state unemployment taxes payable for month...................... | | | | |
| | 31 Taxes............................. | 625 | | 30 00 | |
| | Federal Unemployment Taxes Pay.. | 217 | | | 30 00 |
| | To record employer's federal unemployment taxes payable for year. | | | | |

identification letters used follow: VR, Voucher Register; CR, Cash Receipts Journal; CP, Cash Payments Journal; S, Sales Journal; P, Purchases Journal; SR, Sales Returns and Allowances Journal; and J, General Journal. These are the letters that are customarily used in the ledger to indicate the sources of information posted to the accounts.

**COMPILATION OF ADJUSTING DATA**      In considering the adjustments to be applied to the trial balance in the preparation of the statements at the end of 1958, it is found that the accounts do not reflect the following information:[1]

---

[1]The adjusting data are numbered to correspond to the numbers given the adjustments on the work sheet on pages 126 to 129. Numbers (3), (4), and (5) do not appear in this list because the data for these adjustments, representing transfers of beginning inventories, already appear on the work sheet trial balance.

| Accounts | Trial Balance November 30, 1958 | | Transactions December, 1958 | | Trial Balance December 31, 1958 | |
|---|---|---|---|---|---|---|
| | Dr. | Cr. | Dr. | Cr. | Dr. | Cr. |
| Cash.......................... | 23,420 | | (CR) 47,810 | (CP) 29,320 | 41,910 | |
| Petty Cash................... | 200 | | | | 200 | |
| Notes Receivable............. | 21,000 | | (J) 6,000 | (CR) 6,500 | 16,000 | |
| | | | | (J) 4,500 | | |
| Notes Receivable Discounted... | | 14,500 | (J) 4,500 | | | 10,000 |
| Accounts Receivable........... | 57,460 | | (S) 24,500 | (SR) 490 | 52,000 | |
| | | | | (CR) 23,350 | | |
| | | | | (J) 6,000 | | |
| | | | | (J) 120 | | |
| Allowance for Bad Debts....... | | 730 | (J) 120 | | | 610 |
| Finished Goods Inventory...... | 36,000 | | | | 36,000 | |
| Goods in Process Inventory.... | 21,000 | | | | 21,000 | |
| Raw Materials Inventory....... | 17,000 | | | | 17,000 | |
| Factory Supplies.............. | 5,100 | | (VR) 400 | | 5,500 | |
| Office Supplies............... | 2,050 | | (VR) 750 | | 2,800 | |
| Prepaid Insurance............. | 4,750 | | (VR) 250 | | 5,000 | |
| Burton Co. Common Stock....... | 24,300 | | | | 24,300 | |
| Tools........................ | 9,700 | | (VR) 300 | | 10,000 | |
| Delivery Equipment............ | 8,000 | | | | 8,000 | |
| Allowance for Depreciation of Delivery Equip... | | 3,600 | | | | 3,600 |
| Office Furniture and Fixtures.... | 5,000 | | | | 5,000 | |
| Allowance for Depreciation of Office Furniture and Fixtures............... | | 1,600 | | | | 1,600 |
| Machinery and Equipment....... | 64,000 | | | | 64,000 | |
| Allowance for Depreciation of Machinery and Equipment............... | | 9,300 | | | | 9,300 |
| Buildings..................... | 42,500 | | | | 42,500 | |
| Allowance for Depreciation of Buildings........ | | 6,800 | | | | 6,800 |
| Land......................... | 40,000 | | | | 40,000 | |
| Patents...................... | 6,500 | | | | 6,500 | |
| Goodwill..................... | 40,000 | | | | 40,000 | |
| Notes Payable................ | | 18,000 | (VR) 8,000 | (CR) 10,000 | | 20,000 |
| Accounts Payable............. | | 21,010 | (CP) 29,480 | (VR) 37,020 | | 28,350 |
| | | | (J) 200 | | | |
| Employees Income Taxes Payable............ | | 2,000 | (VR) 2,000 | (VR) 2,130 | | 2,130 |
| F.I.C.A. Taxes Payable........ | | 440 | (VR) 440 | (VR) 210 | | 420 |
| | | | | (J) 210 | | |
| State Unemployment Taxes Payable......... | | 530 | | (J) 200 | | 730 |
| Federal Unemployment Taxes Payable....... | | 250 | | (J) 30 | | 280 |
| Sales Taxes Payable.......... | | 720 | (VR) 720 | (S) 650 | | 640 |
| | | | (SR) 10 | | | |
| 6% First Mortgage Bonds........ | | 100,000 | | | | 100,000 |
| 6% Preferred Stock, $100 par........ | | 50,000 | | | | 50,000 |
| Common Stock, $20 par........ | | 150,000 | | | | 150,000 |
| Treasury Stock — Common....... | 30,000 | | | | 30,000 | |
| Paid-in Capital—Premium on Preferred Stock.. | | 2,000 | | | | 2,000 |
| Retained Earnings............. | | 50,450 | | | | 50,450 |
| Sales........................ | | 333,000 | | (S) 32,000 | | 365,000 |
| Sales Returns and Allowances............. | 4,520 | | (SR) 480 | | 5,000 | |
| Sales Discounts.............. | 2,845 | | (CR) 255 | | 3,100 | |
| Raw Materials Purchases...... | 78,600 | | (VR) 6,800 | | 85,400 | |
| Raw Materials Returns and Allowances........ | | 1,900 | | (J) 200 | | 2,100 |
| Purchases Discounts.......... | | 2,020 | | (CP) 160 | | 2,180 |
| Freight In................... | 4,300 | | (VR) 400 | | 4,700 | |
| Direct Labor................. | 69,700 | | (VR) 6,500 | | 76,200 | |
| Indirect Labor............... | 20,700 | | (VR) 1,900 | | 22,600 | |
| Factory Superintendence...... | 18,300 | | (VR) 1,700 | | 20,000 | |
| Building Maintenance and Repairs........... | 2,520 | | (VR) 480 | | 3,000 | |
| Factory Heat, Light, and Power............. | 18,780 | | (VR) 1,700 | | 20,480 | |
| Taxes........................ | 15,960 | | (J) 210 | | 16,400 | |
| | | | (J) 200 | | | |
| | | | (J) 30 | | | |
| Miscellaneous Factory Expense.............. | 3,000 | | (VR) 300 | | 3,300 | |
| Sales Salaries and Commissions............. | 21,900 | | (VR) 2,100 | | 24,000 | |
| Advertising.................. | 7,300 | | (VR) 800 | | 8,100 | |
| Miscellaneous Selling Expense............... | 2,000 | | (VR) 200 | | 2,200 | |
| Delivery Salaries............ | 8,200 | | (VR) 800 | | 9,000 | |
| Miscellaneous Delivery Expense............. | 1,920 | | (VR) 180 | | 2,100 | |
| Officers Salaries............ | 14,600 | | (VR) 1,400 | | 16,000 | |
| Office Salaries.............. | 9,100 | | (VR) 900 | | 10,000 | |
| Miscellaneous General Expense............... | 2,080 | | (VR) 220 | | 2,300 | |
| Interest Income.............. | | 635 | | (CR) 65 | | 700 |
| Dividend Income.............. | | 300 | | | | 300 |
| Interest Expense — Bonds.................. | 5,000 | | | | 5,000 | |
| Interest Expense — Other.............. | 480 | | (VR) 120 | | 600 | |
| | 769,785 | 769,785 | 153,155 | 153,155 | 807,190 | 807,190 |

(1) A dividend of $1.50 per share, payable January 15 to stockholders of record December 31, has been declared on Burton Co. common stock. The Martin Manufacturing Company owns 200 shares of Burton Co. common stock as a long-term investment.

(2) Dividends on the Martin Manufacturing Company's stock have been declared and are payable on January 10 to stockholders of record December 26 as follows:

> Regular quarterly dividend of $1.50 on 500 shares of 6% preferred stock outstanding, par $100.
>
> Forty cents per share on 6,000 shares of common stock outstanding, par $20 (7,500 shares of stock were originally issued, 1,500 shares being reacquired and held as treasury stock.)

The following adjusting data as of December 31, 1958, were compiled upon thorough examination of the company's books and records:

*Physical Inventories:*

(6) Finished Goods Inventory, $49,000.
(7) Goods in Process Inventory, $28,000.
(8) Raw Materials Inventory, $20,000.
(9) Factory Supplies, $1,200.
(10) Office Supplies, $700.

*Bad Debts:*

(11) The allowance for bad debts is to be increased by $1,800

*Depreciation and amortization:*

(12) Tools on hand are valued at $7,500.
(13) Delivery equipment depreciation, 20% a year.
(14) Office furniture and fixtures depreciation, 10% a year.
(15) Machinery and equipment depreciation, 5% a year.
(16) Buildings depreciation, 4% a year.
(17) Patents are to be reduced by $500, the amortization for the year.

*Accrued Expenses:*

(18) Salaries and wages:
    Direct Labor, $1,400.
    Indirect Labor, $300.
    Sales Salaries and Commissions, $400.
    Delivery Salaries, $200.
(19) Interest accrued on bonds payable, $1,000.
(20) Interest accrued on notes payable, $600.

*Prepaid Expenses:*

(21) Prepaid insurance, $2,600.
(22) Prepaid interest on notes payable, $300.

*Accrued Income:*

(23) Accrued interest on notes receivable, $200.

*Prepaid Income:*

(24) Unearned interest on notes receivable, $100.

*Income Taxes:*

(25) Provision is to be made for federal and state income taxes at $12,000.

Building expenses, expired insurance, and taxes are to be distributed as follows:  to manufacturing operations, 85%; to general and administrative operations, 15%.

Retained earnings of the company were $52,700 on January 1, 1958, and have been affected only by dividends declared on preferred stock prior to recording the foregoing data.

**PREPARATION OF
THE WORK SHEET**          The next step in the accounting process is to combine the adjusting data with the information on the trial balance in order to bring the accounts up to date. This is done and the financial statements are developed through the preparation of a work sheet.  In the construction of the work sheet, trial balance data are listed in the first two amount columns.  The adjusting entries are listed in the second pair of columns.  Sometimes a third pair of columns is included to show the trial balance after adjustment.  Account balances as adjusted are carried to the appropriate statement columns and serve as the basis for the preparation of the financial statements.  A work sheet for a manufacturing concern usually includes a pair of columns for (a) manufacturing accounts, (b) profit and loss accounts, and (c) balance sheet accounts.  A similar work-sheet form would be used for a trading concern except for the absence of manufacturing columns.

The work sheet for the Martin Manufacturing Co. is shown on pages 126 to 129.

The adjustments to the inventory accounts should be particularly noted.  Items (4) and (5) are entered as debits to Manufacturing and as credits to Goods in Process Inventory and Raw Materials Inventory respectively.  The purpose of these entries is to transfer the beginning inventory costs to the manufacturing account.

Entries (7) and (8) are debits to Goods in Process Inventory and Raw Materials Inventory respectively and credits to Manufacturing. The purpose of these entries is to record the goods in process and raw material inventories at the end of the fiscal period and to reduce manufacturing costs by the ending inventories.

Both the debit and the credit amounts in the manufacturing account are carried to the manufacturing columns.  This is done in order that the manufacturing columns may include all the information that is required in preparing the manufacturing schedule.

Adjustment (3) is a debit to Profit and Loss and a credit to Finished Goods Inventory, while adjustment (6) is a debit to Finished Goods Inventory and a credit to Profit and Loss.  Entry (3) transfers

MARTIN MANUFAC-
WORK
FOR YEAR ENDED          DECEMBER

| | NAME OF ACCOUNT | TRIAL BALANCE | | ADJUSTMENTS | | |
|---|---|---|---|---|---|---|
| | | DR. | CR. | DR. | CR. | |
| 1 | Cash | 41,910 | | | | 1 |
| 2 | Petty Cash | 200 | | | | 2 |
| 3 | Notes Receivable | 16,000 | | | | 3 |
| 4 | Notes Receivable Discounted | | 10,000 | | | 4 |
| 5 | Accounts Receivable | 52,000 | | | | 5 |
| 6 | Allowance for Bad Debts | | 610 | | (11)  1,800 | 6 |
| 7 | Finished Goods Inventory | 36,000 | | (6)  49,000 | (3)  36,000 | 7 |
| 8 | Goods in Process Inventory | 21,000 | | (7)  28,000 | (4)  21,000 | 8 |
| 9 | Raw Materials Inventory | 17,000 | | (8)  20,000 | (5)  17,000 | 9 |
| 10 | Factory Supplies | 5,500 | | | (9)  4,300 | 10 |
| 11 | Office Supplies | 2,800 | | | (10)  2,100 | 11 |
| 12 | Prepaid Insurance | 5,000 | | | (21)  2,400 | 12 |
| 13 | Burton Co. Common Stock | 24,300 | | | | 13 |
| 14 | Tools | 10,000 | | | (12)  2,500 | 14 |
| 15 | Delivery Equipment | 8,000 | | | | 15 |
| 16 | Allow. for Depr. of Del. Equip. | | 3,600 | | (13)  1,600 | 16 |
| 17 | Office Furniture and Fixtures | 5,000 | | | | 17 |
| 18 | Allowance for Depreciation of Office Furniture and Fixtures | | 1,600 | | (14)  500 | 18 |
| 19 | Machinery and Equipment | 64,000 | | | | 19 |
| 20 | Allowance for Depreciation of Machinery and Equipment | | 9,300 | | (15)  3,200 | 20 |
| 21 | Buildings | 42,500 | | | | 21 |
| 22 | Allow. for Depr. of Buildings | | 6,800 | | (16)  1,700 | 22 |
| 23 | Land | 40,000 | | | | 23 |
| 24 | Patents | 6,500 | | | (17)  500 | 24 |
| 25 | Goodwill | 40,000 | | | | 25 |
| 26 | Notes Payable | | 20,000 | | | 26 |
| 27 | Accounts Payable | | 28,350 | | | 27 |
| 28 | Employees Income Taxes Pay. | | 2,130 | | | 28 |
| 29 | F.I.C.A. Taxes Payable | | 420 | | | 29 |
| 30 | State Unemployment Taxes Pay. | | 730 | | | 30 |
| 31 | Fed. Unemployment Taxes Pay. | | 280 | | | 31 |
| 32 | Sales Taxes Payable | | 640 | | | 32 |
| 33 | 6% First Mortgage Bonds | | 100,000 | | | 33 |
| 34 | 6% Preferred Stock, $100 par | | 50,000 | | | 34 |
| 35 | Common Stock, $20 par | | 150,000 | | | 35 |
| 36 | Treasury Stock — Common | 30,000 | | | | 36 |
| 37 | Paid-in Capital—Premium on Pre-ferred Stock | | 2,000 | | | 37 |
| 38 | Retained Earnings | | 50,450 | (2)  3,150 | | 38 |
| 39 | Sales | | 365,000 | | | 39 |
| 40 | Sales Returns and Allowances | 5,000 | | | | 40 |
| 41 | Sales Discounts | 3,100 | | | | 41 |
| 42 | Raw Materials Purchases | 85,400 | | | | 42 |
| 43 | Raw Mat. Returns and Allow. | | 2,100 | | | 43 |
| 44 | Purchases Discounts | | 2,180 | | | 44 |
| 45 | Freight In | 4,700 | | | | 45 |
| 46 | Direct Labor | 76,200 | | (18)  1,400 | | 46 |
| 47 | Indirect Labor | 22,600 | | (18)  300 | | 47 |
| 48 | Factory Superintendence | 20,000 | | | | 48 |
| 49 | Bldg. Maintenance & Repairs | 3,000 | | | | 49 |
| 50 | Factory Heat, Light, and Power | 20,480 | | | | 50 |
| 51 | Taxes | 16,400 | | | | 51 |
| 52 | Miscellaneous Factory Expense | 3,300 | | | | 52 |
| 53 | Sales Salaries and Commissions | 24,000 | | (18)  400 | | 53 |
| 54 | Advertising | 8,100 | | | | 54 |
| 55 | Miscellaneous Selling Expense | 2,200 | | | | 55 |
| 56 | Delivery Salaries | 9,000 | | (18)  200 | | 56 |

TURING COMPANY
SHEET
31, 1958

| # | Manufacturing Dr. | Manufacturing Cr. | Profit and Loss Dr. | Profit and Loss Cr. | Balance Sheet Dr. | Balance Sheet Cr. |
|---|---|---|---|---|---|---|
| 1 | | | | | 41,910 | |
| 2 | | | | | 200 | |
| 3 | | | | | 16,000 | |
| 4 | | | | | | 10,000 |
| 5 | | | | | 52,000 | |
| 6 | | | | | | 2,410 |
| 7 | | | | | 49,000 | |
| 8 | | | | | 28,000 | |
| 9 | | | | | 20,000 | |
| 10 | | | | | 1,200 | |
| 11 | | | | | 700 | |
| 12 | | | | | 2,600 | |
| 13 | | | | | 24,300 | |
| 14 | | | | | 7,500 | |
| 15 | | | | | 8,000 | |
| 16 | | | | | | 5,200 |
| 17 | | | | | 5,000 | |
| 18 | | | | | | 2,100 |
| 19 | | | | | 64,000 | |
| 20 | | | | | | 12,500 |
| 21 | | | | | 42,500 | |
| 22 | | | | | | 8,500 |
| 23 | | | | | 40,000 | |
| 24 | | | | | 6,000 | |
| 25 | | | | | 40,000 | |
| 26 | | | | | | 20,000 |
| 27 | | | | | | 28,350 |
| 28 | | | | | | 2,130 |
| 29 | | | | | | 420 |
| 30 | | | | | | 730 |
| 31 | | | | | | 280 |
| 32 | | | | | | 640 |
| 33 | | | | | | 100,000 |
| 34 | | | | | | 50,000 |
| 35 | | | | | | 150,000 |
| 36 | | | | | 30,000 | |
| 37 | | | | | | 2,000 |
| 38 | | | | | | 47,300 |
| 39 | | | | 365,000 | | |
| 40 | | | 5,000 | | | |
| 41 | | | 3,100 | | | |
| 42 | 85,400 | | | | | |
| 43 | | 2,100 | | | | |
| 44 | | 2,180 | | | | |
| 45 | 4,700 | | | | | |
| 46 | 77,600 | | | | | |
| 47 | 22,900 | | | | | |
| 48 | 20,000 | | | | | |
| 49 | 2,550 | | 450 | | | |
| 50 | 20,480 | | | | | |
| 51 | 13,940 | | 2,460 | | | |
| 52 | 3,300 | | | | | |
| 53 | | | 24,400 | | | |
| 54 | | | 8,100 | | | |
| 55 | | | 2,200 | | | |
| 56 | | | 9,200 | | | |

WORK SHEET (Continued)

| | NAME OF ACCOUNT | TRIAL BALANCE | | ADJUSTMENTS | | |
|---|---|---|---|---|---|---|
| | | DR. | CR. | DR. | CR. | |
| 57 | Miscellaneous Delivery Expense. | 2,100 | ........ | ........... | ............ | 57 |
| 58 | Officers Salaries............... | 16,000 | ........ | ........... | ............ | 58 |
| 59 | Office Salaries.................. | 10,000 | ........ | ........... | ............ | 59 |
| 60 | Miscellaneous General Expense.. | 2,300 | ........ | ........... | ............ | 60 |
| 61 | Interest Income................. | ........ | 700 | (24) 100 | (23) 200 | 61 |
| 62 | Dividend Income................ | | 300 | ........... | (1) 300 | 62 |
| 63 | Interest Expense — Bonds...... | 5,000 | ........ | (19) 1,000 | ............ | 63 |
| 64 | Interest Expense — Other...... | 600 | ........ | (20) 600 | (22) 300 | 64 |
| 65 | | 807,190 | 807,190 | ........... | ............ | 65 |
| 66 | Dividends Receivable.......... | ........... | ........... | (1) 300 | ........... | 66 |
| 67 | Div. Pay. on Preferred Stock.... | ........... | ........... | ........... | (2) 750 | 67 |
| 68 | Div. Pay. on Common Stock.... | ........... | ........... | ........... | (2) 2,400 | 68 |
| 69 | Profit and Loss................. | ........... | ........... | (3) 36,000 | (6) 49,000 | 69 |
| 70 | Manufacturing.................. | ........... | ........... | {(4) 21,000 | (7) 28,000 | 70 |
| 71 | ............................... | ........... | ........... | {(5) 17,000 | (8) 20,000 | 71 |
| 72 | Factory Supplies Used......... | ........... | ........... | (9) 4,300 | ........... | 72 |
| 73 | Office Supplies Used........... | ........... | ........... | (10) 2,100 | ........... | 73 |
| 74 | Loss from Bad Debts........... | ........... | ........... | (11) 1,800 | ........... | 74 |
| 75 | Tools Expense.................. | ........... | ........... | (12) 2,500 | ........... | 75 |
| 76 | Depreciation of Delivery Equip.. | ........... | ........... | (13) 1,600 | ........... | 76 |
| 77 | Depr. of Office Fur. and Fix..... | ........... | ........... | (14) 500 | ........... | 77 |
| 78 | Depr. of Machinery and Equip... | ........... | ........... | (15) 3,200 | ........... | 78 |
| 79 | Depreciation of Buildings....... | ........... | ........... | (16) 1,700 | ........... | 79 |
| 80 | Patents Expense................ | ........... | ........... | (17) 500 | ........... | 80 |
| 81 | Accrued Salaries and Wages..... | ........... | ........... | ........... | (18) 2,300 | 81 |
| 82 | Accrued Interest on Bonds Pay.. | ........... | ........... | ........... | (19) 1,000 | 82 |
| 83 | Accrued Interest on Notes Pay... | ........... | ........... | ........... | (20) 600 | 83 |
| 84 | Insurance...................... | ........... | ........... | (21) 2,400 | ........... | 84 |
| 85 | Prepaid Interest on Notes Pay... | ........... | ........... | (22) 300 | ........... | 85 |
| 86 | Accrued Interest on Notes Rec... | ........... | ........... | (23) 200 | ........... | 86 |
| 87 | Unearned Interest on Notes Rec. | ........... | ........... | ........... | (24) 100 | 87 |
| 88 | Income Taxes.................. | ........... | ........... | (25) 12,000 | ........... | 88 |
| 89 | Estimated Income Taxes Pay.... | ........... | ........... | ........... | (25) 12,000 | 89 |
| 90 | | | | 211,550 | 211,550 | 90 |
| 91 | Cost of Goods Manufactured.... | ........ | ........ | ........... | ........... | 91 |
| 92 | | | | | | 92 |
| 93 | ............................... | ........ | ........ | ........... | ........... | 93 |
| 94 | Net Income after Income Taxes.. | ........ | ........ | ........... | ........... | 94 |
| 95 | | | | | | 95 |

the beginning inventory of finished goods to profit and loss, while entry (6) records the ending inventory of finished goods and reports this item as a deduction from costs.

In carrying the profit and loss adjustments to the profit and loss columns, both debit and credit amounts are shown. This is done so

WORK SHEET (Continued)

| | MANUFACTURING | | PROFIT AND LOSS | | BALANCE SHEET | | |
|---|---|---|---|---|---|---|---|
| | DR. | CR. | DR. | CR. | DR. | CR. | |
| 57 | | | 2,100 | | | | 57 |
| 58 | | | 16,000 | | | | 58 |
| 59 | | | 10,000 | | | | 59 |
| 60 | | | 2,300 | | | | 60 |
| 61 | | | | 800 | | | 61 |
| 62 | | | | 600 | | | 62 |
| 63 | | | 6,000 | | | | 63 |
| 64 | | | 900 | | | | 64 |
| 65 | | | | | | | 65 |
| 66 | | | | | 300 | | 66 |
| 67 | | | | | | 750 | 67 |
| 68 | | | | | | 2,400 | 68 |
| 69 | | | 36,000 | 49,000 | | | 69 |
| 70 | 21,000 | 28,000 | | | | | 70 |
| 71 | 17,000 | 20,000 | | | | | 71 |
| 72 | 4,300 | | | | | | 72 |
| 73 | | | 2,100 | | | | 73 |
| 74 | | | 1,800 | | | | 74 |
| 75 | 2,500 | | | | | | 75 |
| 76 | | | 1,600 | | | | 76 |
| 77 | | | 500 | | | | 77 |
| 78 | 3,200 | | | | | | 78 |
| 79 | 1,445 | | 255 | | | | 79 |
| 80 | 500 | | | | | | 80 |
| 81 | | | | | | 2,300 | 81 |
| 82 | | | | | | 1,000 | 82 |
| 83 | | | | | | 600 | 83 |
| 84 | 2,040 | | 360 | | | | 84 |
| 85 | | | | | 300 | | 85 |
| 86 | | | | | 200 | | 86 |
| 87 | | | | | | 100 | 87 |
| 88 | | | 12,000 | | | | 88 |
| 89 | | | | | | 12,000 | 89 |
| 90 | 302,855 | 52,280 | | | | | 90 |
| 91 | | 250,575 | 250,575 | | | | 91 |
| 92 | 302,855 | 302,855 | | | | | 92 |
| 93 | | | 397,400 | 415,400 | 479,710 | 461,710 | 93 |
| 94 | | | 18,000 | | | 18,000 | 94 |
| 95 | | | 415,400 | 415,400 | 479,710 | 479,710 | 95 |

that the profit and loss columns may show all the information that is required in the development of the cost of goods sold section of the income statement.

A number of different methods may be used in recording inventory data on the work sheet. A simple procedure would be the following:

| NAME OF ACCOUNT | TRIAL BALANCE | | ADJUSTMENTS | | MANUFACTURING | | PROFIT AND LOSS | | BALANCE SHEET | |
|---|---|---|---|---|---|---|---|---|---|---|
| | DR. | CR. | DR. | CR. | DR. | CR. | DR. | CR. | DR. | CR. |
| Finished Goods Inventory 1/1, 1958 | 36,000 | | | | | | 36,000 | | | |
| Goods in Process Inventory 1/1, 1958 | 21,000 | | | | 21,000 | | | | | |
| Raw Materials Inventory 1/1, 1958 | 17,000 | | | | 17,000 | | | | | |
| Finished Goods Inventory 12/31, 1958 | | | | | | | | 49,000 | 49,000 | |
| Goods in Process Inventory 12/31, 1958 | | | | | | 28,000 | | | 28,000 | |
| Raw Materials Inventory 12/31, 1958 | | | | | | 20,000 | | | 20,000 | |

In the foregoing example, beginning inventories in the trial balance are carried to the manufacturing and the profit and loss columns; ending inventories are listed below the trial balance and are reported

MARTIN MANUFACTURING
BALANCE
DECEMBER

ASSETS

Current assets:
Cash on hand and in bank.......................... $42,110
Notes receivable...........................$16,000
Less: Notes receivable discounted.......... 10,000    6,000
Accounts receivable.........................$52,000
Less: Allowance for bad debts............ 2,410    49,590
Accrued interest and dividends receivable..............    500
Inventories:
Finished goods..........................$49,000
Goods in process........................ 28,000
Raw materials.......................... 20,000
Factory supplies........................ 1,200    98,200
Prepaid expenses:
Office supplies, prepaid insurance, and interest........    3,600
Total current assets...............................    $200,000

Investments:
Burton Co. common stock ...........................    24,300

Plant and equipment:

| | Cost | Allowance for Depreciation | Book Value |
|---|---|---|---|
| Tools...................... | $ 7,500 | — | $ 7,500 |
| Delivery equipment.............. | 8,000 | $ 5,200 | 2,800 |
| Office furniture and fixtures....... | 5,000 | 2,100 | 2,900 |
| Machinery and equipment....... | 64,000 | 12,500 | 51,500 |
| Buildings..................... | 42,500 | 8,500 | 34,000 |
| Land...................... | 40,000 | — | 40,000 |
| Total plant and equipment..... | $167,000 | $28,300 | 138,700 |

Intangible assets:
Patents....................................... $ 6,000
Goodwill...................................... 40,000
Total intangible assets.............................    46,000
Total assets.......................................    $409,000

directly as credits in the manufacturing and the profit and loss columns and as debits in the balance sheet columns without their prior inclusion in the adjustments columns. An even simpler procedure would be to report the ending inventory balances in a similar manner but on the same lines used for beginning inventories; beginning balances would then be carried as debits to the manufacturing and the profit and loss columns, while ending balances would be entered directly as credits in the manufacturing columns and as debits in the balance sheet columns on the same lines. While the procedures described, as well as other similar procedures for recording adjustments directly in the statement columns, are acceptable, adjusting entries are still required in the journal and in the ledger to bring accounts up to date and to transfer profit and loss data to the appropriate summary account. Normally

COMPANY — EXHIBIT A
SHEET
31, 1958

| LIABILITIES AND CAPITAL | | |
|---|---:|---:|
| Current liabilities: | | |
| Notes payable................................... | $20,000 | |
| Accounts payable............................... | 28,350 | |
| Estimated income taxes payable...................... | 12,000 | |
| Misc. sales, payroll, and withholding taxes payable....... | 4,200 | |
| Accrued salaries and wages......................... | 2,300 | |
| Accrued interest on notes and bonds payable............ | 1,600 | |
| Dividends payable on preferred and common stock....... | 3,150 | |
| Total current liabilities............................. | | $71,600 |
| Long-term debt: | | |
| 6% First mortgage bonds, due Nov. 1, 1967 ........... | | 100,000 |
| Deferred revenues: | | |
| Unearned interest on notes receivable................. | | 100 |
| Total liabilities.................................. | | $171,700 |
| CAPITAL | | |
| Paid-in capital: | | |
| Capital stock: | | |
| 6% Preferred stock, $100 par, 500 shares issued and outstanding................. $50,000 | | |
| Common stock, $20 par (7,500 shares issued)................ $150,000 | | |
| Less: Treasury stock (1,500 shares reacquired)........... 30,000 | | |
| Common stock, 6,000 shares outstanding.. 120,000 | | |
| Paid-in capital — premium on preferred stock.. 2,000 | | |
| Total paid-in capital............................... | $172,000 | |
| Retained earnings.................................... | 65,300 | |
| Total capital....................................... | | 237,300 |
| Total liabilities and capital........................... | | $409,000 |

it is desirable to assemble all adjusting data and to summarize this data in informal journal form for subsequent formal restatement on the books. When such a procedure is followed, it may prove convenient to apply these adjusting entries to the working papers in exactly the same form that is to be followed in formally recognizing the adjustments in the journal and the ledger. This procedure was followed in the adjustments columns of the work sheet on pages 126 and 128 even though this involves more detail than a direct method of adjustment on the work sheet as suggested above.

It was indicated earlier that building expenses, expired insurance, and taxes are allocated 85% to manufacturing activities and 15% to general and administrative activities. The percentage used in the distribution of the charges resulted from an analysis of expenses during the course of the fiscal period. The building maintenance and repair account is shown on the trial balance at $3,000. Of this amount, 85% or $2,550 is entered in the manufacturing columns and 15% or $450 is entered in the profit and loss columns. The charges for taxes, depreciation of buildings, and expired insurance are similarly distributed on the work sheet.

**PREPARATION OF FINANCIAL STATEMENTS**

*Balance Sheet.* The balance sheet of the Martin Manufacturing Company, shown at the bottom of pages 130 and 131, is prepared from the balance sheet columns of the work sheet. A number of items reported in the balance sheet columns of the work sheet have been combined for purposes of balance sheet presentation. Such a procedure may be followed when items can be combined under some descriptive summary title and when amounts involved for the individual items are not material and hence are not considered to require separate disclosure. Items that have been combined on the statement include: accrued interest and dividends receivable; office supplies, prepaid insurance, and prepaid interest on notes payable; employees income taxes withheld, federal insurance contributions taxes, state unemployment taxes, federal unemployment taxes, and state sales taxes; accrued interest on notes and bonds payable; and dividends payable on preferred and common stock. Retained earnings as shown on the balance sheet are composed of retained earnings as reported in the trial balance columns, minus the charge for dividends as shown in the adjustments column, and plus the net income after deduction for estimated income taxes as reported in summarizing the work sheet. The net income after income taxes is shown at the bottom of the work sheet as a balancing item for the profit and loss and the balance sheet columns. When extraordinary gains or losses are reported in the profit and loss columns, the balancing item after taxes may be designated "Net Income and Extraordinary Items."

*Income Statement.* The amounts on the income statement are taken directly from the profit and loss columns in the work sheet. The statement is shown below:

MARTIN MANUFACTURING COMPANY — EXHIBIT B

INCOME STATEMENT

FOR YEAR ENDED DECEMBER 31, 1958

| | | | |
|---|---:|---:|---:|
| Income from sales: | | | |
| Gross sales | | $365,000 | |
| Less: Sales returns and allowances | $5,000 | | |
| Sales discounts | 3,100 | 8,100 | |
| Net sales | | | $356,900 |
| Cost of goods sold: | | | |
| Finished goods inventory, January 1, 1958 | | $ 36,000 | |
| Cost of goods manufactured (Schedule No. 1) | | 250,575 | |
| Total cost of finished goods available for sale | | $286,575 | |
| Less: Finished goods inventory, December 31, 1958 | | 49,000 | |
| Cost of goods sold | | | 237,575 |
| Gross profit on sales | | | $119,325 |
| Operating expenses: | | | |
| Selling expenses: | | | |
| Sales salaries and commissions | $24,400 | | |
| Advertising | 8,100 | | |
| Miscellaneous selling expense | 2,200 | | |
| Delivery salaries | 9,200 | | |
| Depreciation of delivery equipment | 1,600 | | |
| Miscellaneous delivery expense | 2,100 | $47,600 | |
| General and administrative expenses: | | | |
| Officers salaries | $16,000 | | |
| Office salaries | 10,000 | | |
| Office supplies used | 2,100 | | |
| Loss from bad debts | 1,800 | | |
| Depr. of office furniture and fixtures | 500 | | |
| Depreciation of buildings | 255 | | |
| Insurance | 360 | | |
| Building maintenance and repairs | 450 | | |
| Taxes | 2,460 | | |
| Miscellaneous general expense | 2,300 | 36,225 | |
| Total operating expenses | | | 83,825 |
| Net profit from operations | | | $35,500 |
| Other income and expenses: | | | |
| Other income: | | | |
| Interest income | $800 | | |
| Dividend income | 600 | $1,400 | |
| Other expenses: | | | |
| Interest expense — bonds | $6,000 | | |
| Interest expense — other | 900 | 6,900 | |
| Deduct excess of other expenses over other income | | | 5,500 |
| Net income before income taxes | | | $30,000 |
| Income taxes | | | 12,000 |
| Net income after income taxes | | | $18,000 |

*Manufacturing Schedule.* The manufacturing schedule shows in detail the costs involved in completing goods during the period. The information shown on the schedule below is taken directly from the manufacturing columns of the work sheet.

MARTIN MANUFACTURING COMPANY — SCHEDULE No. 1
MANUFACTURING SCHEDULE
TO ACCOMPANY INCOME STATEMENT
FOR YEAR ENDED DECEMBER 31, 1958

| | | | |
|---|---:|---:|---:|
| Goods in process inventory, January 1, 1958 . . . . . . . . . . | | | $21,000 |
| Raw materials: | | | |
|   Raw materials inventory, January 1, 1958 . . . . . . . . . | $17,000 | | |
|   Raw materials purchases . . . . . . . . $85,400 | | | |
|   Freight in . . . . . . . . . . . . . . . . . . . 4,700 $90,100 | | | |
|   Less: Raw materials returns and | | | |
|      allowances . . . . . . . . . . . . . . . . $2,100 | | | |
|      Purchases discounts . . . . . . . . 2,180 4,280 | 85,820 | | |
| Total cost of raw materials available for use . . . . . . . . . | $102,820 | | |
| Less: Raw materials inventory, December 31, 1958 . . . | 20,000 | | |
| Cost of raw materials consumed . . . . . . . . . . . . . . . . . . . . | $82,820 | | |
| Direct labor . . . . . . . . . . . . . . . . . . . . . . . . . . . . . . . . . . . . | 77,600 | | |
| Manufacturing expenses: | | | |
|   Indirect labor . . . . . . . . . . . . . . . . . . . . . . . . $22,900 | | | |
|   Factory superintendence . . . . . . . . . . . . . . . . 20,000 | | | |
|   Building maintenance and repairs . . . . . . . . 2,550 | | | |
|   Factory heat, light, and power . . . . . . . . . . 20,480 | | | |
|   Taxes . . . . . . . . . . . . . . . . . . . . . . . . . . . . . . 13,940 | | | |
|   Factory supplies used . . . . . . . . . . . . . . . . . . 4,300 | | | |
|   Tools expense . . . . . . . . . . . . . . . . . . . . . . . . 2,500 | | | |
|   Depr. of machinery and equipment . . . . . . . 3,200 | | | |
|   Depreciation of buildings . . . . . . . . . . . . . . . 1,445 | | | |
|   Patents expense . . . . . . . . . . . . . . . . . . . . . . 500 | | | |
|   Expired insurance . . . . . . . . . . . . . . . . . . . . . 2,040 | | | |
|   Miscellaneous factory expense . . . . . . . . . . . 3,300 | 97,155 | 257,575 | |
| Total goods in process during period . . . . . . . . . . . . . . . | | | $278,575 |
| Less: Goods in process inventory, December 31, 1958 . . | | | 28,000 |
| Cost of goods manufactured . . . . . . . . . . . . . . . . . . . . . . | | | $250,575 |

*Retained Earnings Statements.* The retained earnings statement below summarizes the changes in retained earnings for the year:

MARTIN MANUFACTURING COMPANY — EXHIBIT C
RETAINED EARNINGS STATEMENT
FOR YEAR ENDED DECEMBER 31, 1958

| | | |
|---|---:|---:|
| Balance of retained earnings, January 1, 1958 . . . . . . . . | | $52,700 |
| Add: Net income per income statement . . . . . . . . . . . . . | | 18,000 |
| | | $70,700 |
| Deduct: Dividends on preferred stock . . . . . . . . . . . . . . | $3,000 | |
|        Dividends on common stock . . . . . . . . . . . . . . | 2,400 | 5,400 |
| Balance of retained earnings, December 31, 1958 . . . . . . | | $65,300 |

**ADJUSTING AND CLOSING ACCOUNTS**        Upon completion of the work sheet and statements, the entries to bring the accounts up to date and to close the accounts are recorded in the journal. Before closing the accounts, any current, correcting, and adjusting entries are recorded. While such entries may first have been prepared in informal form in connection with the preparation of the work sheet, these are now entered formally in the journal. Closing entries may be conveniently prepared by using as a basis for the entries the balances as shown in the manufacturing and profit and loss columns of the work sheet. The following current entries are required for the Martin Manufacturing Company:

December 31

| | | |
|---|---|---|
| (1) Dividends Receivable.......................... | 300 | |
| Dividend Income............................ | | 300 |
| To record announcement of $1.50 dividend on 200 shares of Burton Co. common stock owned. | | |

31

| | | |
|---|---|---|
| (2) Retained Earnings............................ | 3,150 | |
| Dividends Payable on Preferred Stock......... | | 750 |
| Dividends Payable on Common Stock......... | | 2,400 |
| To record declaration of dividends payable on January 10 to stockholders of record December 26. | | |

Adjustments may now be recorded. These follow:

31

| | | |
|---|---|---|
| (3) Profit and Loss.............................. | 36,000 | |
| Finished Goods Inventory.................... | | 36,000 |
| To transfer beginning finished goods inventory to profit and loss. | | |

31

| | | |
|---|---|---|
| (4) Manufacturing...... ........................ | 21,000 | |
| Goods in Process Inventory.................. | | 21,000 |
| To transfer the beginning goods in process inventory to manufacturing. | | |

31

| | | |
|---|---|---|
| (5) Manufacturing.............................. | 17,000 | |
| Raw Materials Inventory.................... | | 17,000 |
| To transfer the beginning raw materials inventory to manufacturing. | | |

31

| | | |
|---|---|---|
| (6) Finished Goods Inventory..................... | 49,000 | |
| Profit and Loss............................. | | 49,000 |
| To record ending finished goods inventory. | | |

                                   31
(7) Goods in Process Inventory.................... 28,000
        Manufacturing...............................          28,000
            To record ending goods in process
            inventory.

                                   31
(8) Raw Materials Inventory...................... 20,000
        Manufacturing...............................          20,000
            To record ending raw materials
            inventory.

                                   31
(9) Factory Supplies Used........................ 4,300
        Factory Supplies............................          4,300
            To record cost of factory supplies
            used.

                                   31
(10) Office Supplies Used.......................... 2,100
        Office Supplies..............................          2,100
            To record cost of office supplies used.

                                   31
(11) Loss from Bad Debts.......................... 1,800
        Allowance for Bad Debts.....................          1,800
            To provide for estimated loss from
            bad debts.
                                   31
(12) Tools Expense................................ 2,500
        Tools.......................................          2,500
            To record tools expense for the year.

                                   31
(13) Depreciation of Delivery Equipment............ 1,600
        Allowance for Depreciation of Delivery Equipment      1,600
            To record estimated depreciation of
            delivery equipment.
                                   31
(14) Depreciation of Office Furniture and Fixtures..... 500
        Allowance for Depreciation of Office Furniture
        and Fixtures...............................          500
            To record estimated depreciation of
            office furniture and fixtures.
                                   31
(15) Depreciation of Machinery and Equipment....... 3,200
        Allowance for Depreciation of Machinery and
        Equipment..................................          3,200
            To record estimated depreciation of
            machinery and equipment.

                                   31
(16) Depreciation of Buildings...................... 1,700
        Allowance for Depreciation of Buildings........          1,700
            To record estimated depreciation of
            buildings.

31
| (17) Patents Expense.............................. | 500 | |
| Patents................................... | | 500 |

To record amortization of patents.

31
| (18) Direct Labor................................ | 1,400 | |
| Indirect Labor............................... | 300 | |
| Sales Salaries and Commissions................. | 400 | |
| Delivery Salaries............................. | 200 | |
| Accrued Salaries and Wages.................. | | 2,300 |

To record accrued salaries and wages.

31
| (19) Interest Expense—Bonds...................... | 1,000 | |
| Accrued Interest on Bonds Payable............ | | 1,000 |

To record accrued interest on bonds.

31
| (20) Interest Expense—Other...................... | 600 | |
| Accrued Interest on Notes Payable............ | | 600 |

To record accrued interest on notes payable.

31
| (21) Insurance................................... | 2,400 | |
| Prepaid Insurance........................... | | 2,400 |

To record expired insurance.

31
| (22) Prepaid Interest on Notes Payable............. | 300 | |
| Interest Expense........................... | | 300 |

To record prepaid interest on notes payable.

31
| (23) Accrued Interest on Notes Receivable........... | 200 | |
| Interest Income............................. | | 200 |

To record accrued interest on notes
receivable.

31
| (24) Interest Income............................. | 100 | |
| Unearned Interest on Notes Receivable........ | | 100 |

To record unearned interest on
notes receivable.

| (25) Income Taxes................................ | 12,000 | |
| Estimated Income Taxes Payable............. | | 12,000 |

To record estimated income taxes.

The adjusting entries are followed by those that close all of the nominal accounts. The closing entries are:

31
| Manufacturing................................... | 260,575 | |
| Raw Materials Returns and Allowances............. | 2,100 | |
| Purchases Discounts............................. | 2,180 | |
| Raw Materials Purchases...................... | | 85,400 |
| Freight In................................... | | 4,700 |

| | | |
|---|---|---|
| Direct Labor.................................. | | 77,600 |
| Indirect Labor................................ | | 22,900 |
| Factory Superintendence....................... | | 20,000 |
| Building Maintenance and Repairs.............. | | 2,550 |
| Factory Heat, Light, and Power............... | | 20,480 |
| Taxes........................................ | | 13,940 |
| Factory Supplies Used........................ | | 4,300 |
| Tools Expense................................ | | 2,500 |
| Depreciation of Machinery and Equipment....... | | 3,200 |
| Depreciation of Buildings.................... | | 1,445 |
| Patents Expense.............................. | | 500 |
| Insurance.................................... | | 2,040 |
| Miscellaneous Factory Expense................. | | 3,300 |

To close manufacturing accounts into Manufacturing.

31

| | | |
|---|---|---|
| Sales........................................ | 365,000 | |
| Interest Income.............................. | 800 | |
| Dividend Income.............................. | 600 | |
| Profit and Loss.............................. | | 366,400 |

To close income accounts into Profit and Loss.

31

| | | |
|---|---|---|
| Profit and Loss.............................. | 361,400 | |
| Manufacturing............................... | | 250,575 |
| Sales Returns and Allowances................. | | 5,000 |
| Sales Discounts.............................. | | 3,100 |
| Sales Salaries and Commissions............... | | 24,400 |
| Advertising.................................. | | 8,100 |
| Miscellaneous Selling Expense................ | | 2,200 |
| Delivery Salaries............................ | | 9,200 |
| Depreciation of Delivery Equipment........... | | 1,600 |
| Miscellaneous Delivery Expense............... | | 2,100 |
| Officers Salaries............................ | | 16,000 |
| Office Salaries.............................. | | 10,000 |
| Office Supplies Used......................... | | 2,100 |
| Loss from Bad Debts.......................... | | 1,800 |
| Depreciation of Office Furniture and Fixtures...... | | 500 |
| Depreciation of Buildings.................... | | 255 |
| Insurance.................................... | | 360 |
| Building Maintenance and Repairs............. | | 450 |
| Taxes........................................ | | 2,460 |
| Miscellaneous General Expense................ | | 2,300 |
| Interest Expense—Bonds....................... | | 6,000 |
| Interest Expense—Other....................... | | 900 |
| Income Taxes................................. | | 12,000 |

To close expense accounts into Profit and Loss.

31

| | | |
|---|---|---|
| Profit and Loss.............................. | 18,000 | |
| Retained Earnings............................ | | 18,000 |

To transfer the balance in Profit and Loss after income taxes to Retained Earnings.

**PREPARATION OF POST-CLOSING TRIAL BALANCE**    After the adjusting and closing entries are posted, the post-closing trial balance, which appears below, is prepared to verify the equality of the debits and credits.

MARTIN MANUFACTURING COMPANY

POST-CLOSING TRIAL BALANCE

DECEMBER 31, 1958

| | | |
|---|---:|---:|
| Cash | 41,910 | |
| Petty Cash | 200 | |
| Notes Receivable | 16,000 | |
| Notes Receivable Discounted | | 10,000 |
| Accounts Receivable | 52,000 | |
| Allowance for Bad Debts | | 2,410 |
| Dividends Receivable | 300 | |
| Accrued Interest on Notes Receivable | 200 | |
| Finished Goods Inventory | 49,000 | |
| Goods in Process Inventory | 28,000 | |
| Raw Materials Inventory | 20,000 | |
| Factory Supplies | 1,200 | |
| Office Supplies | 700 | |
| Prepaid Insurance | 2,600 | |
| Prepaid Interest on Notes Payable | 300 | |
| Burton Co. Common Stock | 24,300 | |
| Tools | 7,500 | |
| Delivery Equipment | 8,000 | |
| Allowance for Depreciation of Delivery Equipment | | 5,200 |
| Office Furniture and Fixtures | 5,000 | |
| Allowance for Depreciation of Office Furniture and Fixtures | | 2,100 |
| Machinery and Equipment | 64,000 | |
| Allowance for Depreciation of Machinery and Equipment | | 12,500 |
| Buildings | 42,500 | |
| Allowance for Depreciation of Buildings | | 8,500 |
| Land | 40,000 | |
| Patents | 6,000 | |
| Goodwill | 40,000 | |
| Notes Payable | | 20,000 |
| Accounts Payable | | 28,350 |
| Employees Income Taxes Payable | | 2,130 |
| F.I.C.A. Taxes Payable | | 420 |
| State Unemployment Taxes Payable | | 730 |
| Federal Unemployment Taxes Payable | | 280 |
| Sales Taxes Payable | | 640 |
| Estimated Income Taxes Payable | | 12,000 |
| Accrued Salaries and Wages | | 2,300 |
| Accrued Interest on Bonds Payable | | 1,000 |
| Accrued Interest on Notes Payable | | 600 |
| Dividends Payable on Preferred Stock | | 750 |
| Dividends Payable on Common Stock | | 2,400 |
| 6% First Mortgage Bonds | | 100,000 |
| Unearned Interest on Notes Receivable | | 100 |
| 6% Preferred Stock, $100 par | | 50,000 |
| Common Stock, $20 par | | 150,000 |
| Treasury Stock — Common | 30,000 | |
| Paid-in Capital — Premium on Preferred Stock | | 2,000 |
| Retained Earnings | | 65,300 |
| | 479,710 | 479,710 |

**REVERSING THE ACCOUNTS**    The accrued and prepaid balances established in adjusting the accounts may now be reversed. The reversing entries follow:

January 1

| | | |
|---|---|---|
| Accrued Salaries and Wages....................... | 2,300 | |
| Direct Labor.................................... | | 1,400 |
| Indirect Labor................................. | | 300 |
| Sales Salaries and Commissions.................. | | 400 |
| Delivery Salaries............................... | | 200 |

1

| | | |
|---|---|---|
| Accrued Interest on Bonds Payable................ | 1,000 | |
| Interest Expense—Bonds....................... | | 1,000 |

1

| | | |
|---|---|---|
| Accrued Interest on Notes Payable................ | 600 | |
| Interest Expense—Other....................... | | 600 |

1

| | | |
|---|---|---|
| Interest Expense............................... | 300 | |
| Prepaid Interest on Notes Payable............... | | 300 |

1

| | | |
|---|---|---|
| Interest Income................................ | 200 | |
| Accrued Interest on Notes Receivable............. | | 200 |

1

| | | |
|---|---|---|
| Unearned Interest on Notes Receivable............. | 100 | |
| Interest Income................................ | | 100 |

The post-closing trial balance is frequently prepared only after the reversing entries have been posted. When such practice is followed, a check is offered on the accuracy in posting reversing data.

**INTERIM STATEMENTS**    Statements are prepared at least once a year, and at that time the accounts in the ledger are adjusted and closed. Many business units, however, require statements during the fiscal year at one-month, three-month, or six-month intervals. Such statements may be prepared only for management and internal use, or they may be prepared and made available to stockholders as a means of keeping this group fully informed on financial progress during the course of the year.

When interim statements are desired, they are prepared by means of a work sheet. The accounts in the ledger may be adjusted but they would not be closed. In preparing the work sheet, balances in the ledger are first listed in trial balance form. Because accounts have not been closed since the end of the previous year, nominal accounts reflect balances to date. Adjustments are listed on the work sheet to bring the account balances up to date, and adjusted balances are carried to the appropriate statement columns. Financial statements are then prepared from the work sheet data.

For example, in preparing the interim statements at the end of March, the adjusting data are reported on the working papers just as though the fiscal period were one quarter. Inventories and accrued and prepaid items as of March 31 are recorded. Amortization and depreciation are stated for a three-month period. The balance sheet prepared from the work sheet shows the financial position as of March 31; the income statement reports cumulative results for the three months ended March 31. To obtain an income statement covering operations for the month of March alone, it is necessary to subtract income and expense balances on the income statement for the two-month period ended February 28 from similar cumulative balances on the statement for the three-month period ended March 31. Inventory figures as of February 28 and March 31 are reported, and a statement showing the net income for the month of March is then available. By following the procedure just outlined, monthly statements, as well as cumulative income statements showing progress for the year to date, may be obtained.

## QUESTIONS

**1.** The Medwick Co. maintains a sales journal, a sales returns and allowances journal, a voucher register, a cash payments journal, and a general journal. For each account listed below indicate the possible sources of charges and credits:

| | |
|---|---|
| Cash | Capital Stock |
| Marketable Securities | Retained Earnings |
| Notes Receivable | Sales |
| Accounts Receivable | Sales Returns and Allowances |
| Allowance for Bad Debts | Sales Discounts |
| Merchandise Inventory | Purchases |
| Land and Buildings | Freight In |
| Allowance for Depreciation | Purchases Returns and Allowances |
| Notes Payable | Purchases Discounts |
| Vouchers Payable | Salaries |
| Accrued Expenses | Depreciation |

**2.** Describe the kind of work sheet that would be employed for:

(a) A trading concern.
(b) A manufacturing concern.
(c) A departmentalized business, the gross profit to be ascertained for each department.
(d) A manufacturing organization with departmentalized retail sales departments, a net operating profit to be determined for each department.

**3.** When would you recommend the preparation of working papers with a pair of columns reporting an adjusted trial balance?

**4.** Describe two methods that may be followed in adjusting the accounts for the ending inventories on the work sheet of a manufacturing company.

**5.** The bookkeeper for the Miller Co. in adjusting the accounts on the working papers charges or credits the beginning inventory to adjust it to the ending balance, with an offsetting credit or charge to an inventory variation balance. The inventory as adjusted is carried to the balance sheet column and the variation balance is carried to the appropriate profit and loss column. Appraise this procedure.

**6.** The bookkeeper for the Folsom Trading Co., after completing all adjustments except those for the merchandise inventories, makes the entry reported below to close the beginning inventory, to set up the ending inventory, to close all nominal accounts, and to report the net result of operations in the capital account.

| | | |
|---|---:|---:|
| Merchandise Inventory, December 31, 1958 | 18,000 | |
| Sales | 200,000 | |
| Purchases Discounts | 2,000 | |
| Merchandise Inventory, January 1, 1958 | | 20,000 |
| Purchases | | 140,000 |
| Selling Expenses | | 20,000 |
| General and Administrative Expenses | | 15,000 |
| Interest Expense | | 1,500 |
| R. C. Folsom, Capital | | 23,500 |

(a) Appraise the foregoing procedure.

(b) What alternate procedure could be followed in adjusting and closing the accounts?

**7.** The Beverly Corporation prepares financial statements and adjusts and closes the accounts at the end of each month. The Burke Corporation prepares financial statements monthly, but adjusts and closes the accounts only at the end of each year.

(a) Will the reports of each company be the same?

(b) Can a cumulative "year-to-date" income statement be made available for the Beverly Corporation? How?

(c) Can income statements covering single months be made available for the Burke Corporation? How?

(d) Which procedure, monthly or annual closing, do you consider preferable? Why?

**8.** State the effect upon the balance sheet and the income statement of each of the following errors:

(a) Accrued expenses are overstated at the end of the period.

(b) Prepaid incomes are understated at the end of the period.

(c) Prepaid expenses are understated at the end of the period.

(d) Accrued incomes are overstated at the end of the period.

(e) The inventory is understated at the end of the period.

(f) Depreciation on an equipment item is overstated at the end of the period.

## EXERCISES

**1.** Give the account balances to be shown on an income statement for P. A. Jones for the month of June calculated from the following cumulative data:

|  | JANUARY 1 TO MAY 31 | JANUARY 1 TO JUNE 30 |
|---|---|---|
| Income from Sales: |  |  |
| Sales.................................. | $66,000 | $76,000 |
| Sales Returns......................... | $ 1,500 | $ 1,800 |
| Sales Discounts....................... | 1,200 | 1,450 |
|  | $ 2,700 | $ 3,250 |
| Net Sales............................. | $63,300 | $72,750 |
| Cost of Goods Sold: |  |  |
| Merchandise Inventory, January 1........ | $14,000 | $14,000 |
| Purchases............................ | $36,000 | $44,000 |
| Purchases Discounts.................. | 700 | 850 |
|  | $35,300 | $43,150 |
| Merchandise Available for Sale.......... | $49,300 | $57,150 |
| Merchandise Inventory at End of Period.. | 16,000 | 18,500 |
| Cost of Goods Sold.................... | $33,300 | $38,650 |
| Gross Profit on Sales.................... | $30,000 | $34,100 |
| Operating Expenses: |  |  |
| Selling Expenses....................... | $10,500 | $12,800 |
| General and Administrative Expenses..... | 6,800 | 8,200 |
| Total Operating Expenses.............. | $17,300 | $21,000 |
| Net Profit from Operations............... | $12,700 | $13,100 |
| Financial Management Income: |  |  |
| Interest Income....................... | 350 | 400 |
|  | $13,050 | $13,500 |
| Financial Management Expense: |  |  |
| Interest Expense...................... | 250 | 250 |
| Net Income............................ | $12,800 | $13,250 |
| Gain from Sale of Securities.............. |  | 2,500 |
| Net Income and Extraordinary Items....... | $12,800 | $15,750 |

**2.** The data listed below and on the next page are assembled for use in preparing a work sheet and financial statements. Give the adjustments that are required on December 31 assuming that (1) accounts in the ledger are adjusted, closed, and reversed monthly, and (2) accounts in the ledger are adjusted, closed, and reversed only at the end of the year.

(a) On September 1, $600 was collected as subscription income for one year. A nominal account was credited for the income.

(b) On October 1, insurance of $180 was paid on a policy covering a 3-year period from this date. A real account was debited for the cost.

(c) On February 1, $40,000 was borrowed on a 3-year mortgage note, interest at 6% to be paid at quarterly intervals from this date.

(d) On May 1, 4% bonds of $5,000 were acquired, interest receivable semi-annually on April 1 and October 1.

**3.** Accounts of Super Products Co. at the end of the first year of operations show the following balances:

| | | |
|---|---:|---:|
| Cash | $13,200 | |
| Investments | 20,000 | |
| Machinery | 50,000 | |
| Factory Buildings | 80,000 | |
| Land | 40,000 | |
| Accounts Payable | | $ 30,000 |
| Capital Stock | | 200,000 |
| Paid-in Capital — Premium on Stock | | 40,000 |
| Sales | | 300,000 |
| Raw Materials Purchases | 140,000 | |
| Direct Labor | 100,000 | |
| Manufacturing Expenses | 75,500 | |
| Operating Expenses | 52,000 | |
| Income on Investments | | 700 |
| | $570,700 | $570,700 |

At the end of the year physical inventories are: raw materials, $40,000; goods in process, $30,000; finished goods, $30,000. Prepaid operating expenses are $1,500 and accrued manufacturing expenses are $500. Accrued income on investments is $300. Depreciation for the year on buildings is $2,000, apportioned $1,500 to the factory and $500 to general operations. Depreciation of machinery is $2,500. The tax liability for the year is estimated at $10,000.

Give the entries to adjust and close the books.

**4.** E. S. Barnett fails to adjust the accounts for the following items in closing the books on December 31, 1958. Assume that the omissions are never discovered but that adjustments are properly made at the end of 1959. What effect does each omission have on the profits for 1958 and 1959?

(a) Sales salaries accrued, $30.
(b) Prepaid advertising, $200. Advertising Expense was debited for advertising payments.
(c) Depreciation of office machine, $100.
(d) Accrued interest on notes receivable, $20.
(e) Office supplies inventory, $100. Office Supplies, an asset account, was charged for purchases and has a balance of $300.

**5.** Upon inspecting the books and records for the Melcombe Manufacturing Co. for the year ended December 31, 1958, you find the following data. What entries are required to bring the accounts up to date?

(a) A receivable of $150 from L. A. Case is determined to be uncollectible. The company maintains no allowance for such losses.

(b) A creditor, the Williams Co., has just been awarded damages of $2,200 as a result of breach of contract by Melcombe Manufacturing Co. Nothing appears on the books in connection with this matter.

(c) Furniture and fixtures, cost $12,000, book value, $1,800, had been sold for salvage of $250, the salvage proceeds being credited to Miscellaneous Income.

(d) Advances of $1,500 to salesmen have been recorded as Sales Salaries.

(e) Machinery at the end of the year shows a balance of $24,500. It is discovered that additions to this account during the year totaled $6,000, but of this amount $2,500 should have been recorded as expense. Depreciation is to be recorded at 10% on machinery owned throughout the year; at one half this rate on machinery purchased during the year.

**6.** The Waring Sales Co. shows a credit balance in the profit and loss account of $16,600 after the income and expense items have been transferred to this account at the end of a fiscal year. Give the remaining entries to close the books, assuming:

(a) The business is a sole proprietorship; the owner, A. C. Waring, has made withdrawals of $12,000 during the year and this is reported in a drawing account.

(b) The business is a partnership; the owners, A. C. Waring and P. H. Waring, share profits 5:3; they have made withdrawals of $15,000 and $5,000 respectively and these amounts are reported in drawing accounts.

(c) The business is a corporation; the ledger reports additional paid-in capital, $150,000, and retained earnings, $15,000; dividends during the year of $18,000 were charged to a dividends paid account.

**7.** A. L. James began operations in 1958 with cash of $15,000. During the year his sales were $50,000, $36,000 being collected from customers during the year. Accounts receivable on December 31 are believed fully collectible. Purchases for the year were $40,000, payments of $27,500 being made on account. All sales were made at double the cost of the merchandise. Operating expenses were all paid in cash. The income statement reported a profit for 1958 of $6,500. (a) Prepare a balance sheet as of December 31, 1958. (b) Submit a summary of cash in support of the balance reported on the balance sheet.

**8.** Sales for the Parallel Products Co. were $150,000 for 1958. The beginning inventory was 30% of the cost of goods sold. The ending inventory was 50% of the beginning inventory. Selling expenses were 10% of sales and absorbed 30% of the gross profit on sales. Net income before income taxes was 12% of sales. Income taxes were 30% of net income before taxes. Prepare an income statement for 1958.

## PROBLEMS

**5-1.** The following cumulative income statements have been prepared for the Hoffman Company in 1958:

| | Five Months Ended May 31 | Six Months Ended June 30 | Seven Months Ended July 31 |
|---|---|---|---|
| Income from sales: | | | |
| Sales................................. | $175,200 | $219,750 | $258,900 |
| Sales returns and allowances......... | $  2,500 | $  3,750 | $  5,200 |
| Sales discounts...................... | 2,200 | 2,650 | 3,100 |
| | $  4,700 | $  6,400 | $  8,300 |
| Net sales........................... | $170,500 | $213,350 | $250,600 |
| Cost of goods sold: | | | |
| Inventory, January 1................ | $ 40,000 | $ 40,000 | $ 40,000 |
| Purchases........................... | 117,000 | 153,000 | 185,000 |
| Freight in.......................... | 2,540 | 3,060 | 3,600 |
| | $159,540 | $196,060 | $228,600 |
| Purchases returns.................... | ........ | ........ | $    250 |
| Merchandise available for sale....... | $159,540 | $196,060 | $228,350 |
| Inventory, end of period............. | 28,000 | 34,000 | 44,350 |
| Cost of goods sold.................. | $131,540 | $162,060 | $184,000 |
| Gross profit on sales................. | $ 38,960 | $ 51,290 | $ 66,600 |
| Operating expenses: | | | |
| Selling expenses: | | | |
| Advertising...................... | $ 12,000 | $ 17,300 | $ 19,700 |
| Sales salaries.................... | 15,000 | 20,000 | 24,750 |
| Delivery expense................. | 2,300 | 2,900 | 3,500 |
| Sales contest bonuses............. | | 1,000 | 1,000 |
| Depreciation of store equipment.... | 2,000 | 2,500 | 3,100 |
| Total selling expenses............. | $ 31,300 | $ 43,700 | $ 52,050 |
| General and administrative expenses: | | | |
| Depreciation of buildings.......... | $  6,000 | $  7,500 | $  9,000 |
| General and administrative salaries | 7,700 | 9,500 | 11,000 |
| Legal expense..................... | | | 2,000 |
| Total general expenses............. | $ 13,700 | $ 17,000 | $ 22,000 |
| Total operating expenses........... | $ 45,000 | $ 60,700 | $ 74,050 |
| Net loss from operations.............. | $  6,040 | $  9,410 | $  7,450 |
| Other income: | | | |
| Interest income.................... | $    440 | $    525 | $    700 |
| | $  5,600 | $  8,885 | $  6,750 |
| Other expense: | | | |
| Interest expense................... | $    320 | $    735 | $    940 |
| Net loss............................. | $  5,920 | $  9,620 | $  7,690 |

*Instructions:* Prepare an income statement in comparative form showing profit and loss data for the month of June and for the month of July.

**5-2.** The data that follow are compiled from the books and records of the Pendleton Company:

   (1) On October 1, 1958, $3,000 was collected for one-year subscriptions beginning on that date. A balance sheet account was credited for the amount collected.

   (2) The First State Bank deducted $96 from a 60-day, non-interest-bearing note payable issued and dated November 10, 1958. An entry in a nominal account was made for the interest deducted in advance.

   (3) $2,500 was borrowed from the bank on July 31, 1958, a 6-month note accruing interest at 6% being issued to the bank.

   (4) The company received a 60-day, non-interest-bearing note dated November 20, 1958, from a customer, and credited the customer's account for the face value of the note less $72 for interest on the obligation. The interest was recorded in a nominal account.

   (5) On September 1, 1958, a real account was debited for $108 for the premium on a 3-year fire insurance policy beginning on that date.

   (6) The company owns a $5,000, 6% note dated October 31, 1958, and due on October 31, 1959.

The company follows the practice of reversing adjustments for all prepaid items originally entered in nominal accounts and for all accrued items.

*Instructions:* (1) Give adjusting journal entries as of November 30, 1958, assuming that the books are adjusted and closed *monthly.*

(2) Give adjusting journal entries as of December 31, 1958, assuming that the books are adjusted and closed *monthly.*

(3) Give adjusting journal entries as of December 31, 1958, assuming that the books are adjusted and closed only at the end of each calendar year.

**5-3.** The following data are compiled from the books and records of the Stoner Company:

   (1) $2,500 was borrowed from the bank on October 31, 1958. A note was issued, the principal sum and interest at 6% becoming payable on October 31, 1959.

   (2) On August 1, 1958, a real account was debited for $144 for the premium on a fire insurance policy covering a 3-year period from that date.

   (3) On September 1, 1958, $750 was collected, representing rental income for one year beginning on that date. A balance sheet account was credited for the amount collected.

   (4) The company owns bonds of $10,000 on which interest at 4% is paid semiannually on April 1 and October 1.

   (5) The First National Bank deducted $24 from cash borrowed on a 60-day, non-interest-bearing note payable issued and dated November 8, 1958. An entry in a nominal account was made for the interest paid in advance.

   (6) The company received a 90-day, non-interest-bearing note dated October 23, 1958, from a customer and credited the customer's account for the face value of the note less $45, representing interest on the obligation. The interest was recorded in a nominal account.

The company follows the practice of reversing adjustments for all prepaid items originally entered in nominal accounts and for all accrued items.

*Instructions:* (1) Give adjusting entries as of November 30, 1958, assuming that the books are adjusted and closed *monthly.*

(2) Give adjusting journal entries as of December 31, 1958, assuming the books are adjusted and closed *monthly.*

(3) Give adjusting journal entries as of December 31, 1958, assuming that the books are adjusted and closed only at the end of each calendar year.

**5-4.** The account balances taken from the ledger of P. R. Larson on January 31, 1958, are given below:

| | | | |
|---|---:|---|---:|
| Cash....................... | $ 2,520 | Withholding Taxes Payable | $ 160 |
| Notes Receivable.......... | 1,500 | Sales Tax Payable......... | 515 |
| Notes Rec. Discounted..... | 1,200 | P. R. Larson, Capital...... | 9,800 |
| Accounts Receivable....... | 3,840 | P. R. Larson, Drawing..... | 400 |
| Allowance for Bad Debts.... | 50 | Sales..................... | 27,760 |
| Merchandise Inventory, | | Sales Discounts........... | 125 |
| January 1, 1958......... | 6,500 | Purchases................ | 19,000 |
| Office Equipment.......... | 1,600 | Purchases Discounts....... | 165 |
| Allowance for Depreciation | | Freight In................ | 340 |
| of Office Equipment...... | 660 | Advertising Expense....... | 110 |
| Store Equipment.......... | 3,600 | Delivery Expense.......... | 230 |
| Allowance for Depreciation | | Sales Salaries............ | 1,800 |
| of Store Equipment...... | 1,350 | Office Expense............ | 2,000 |
| Unexpired Insurance....... | 80 | Rent..................... | 360 |
| Notes Payable............ | 1,200 | Taxes, Payroll, and Other.. | 285 |
| Accounts Payable......... | 980 | Interest Income........... | 30 |
| Accrued Property and Payroll Taxes.............. | 440 | Interest Expense.......... | 20 |

Data for adjustments for the month ended January 31, 1958, follow:

(a) The allowance for bad debts is to be increased to $150.

(b) Depreciation of office equipment is $7\frac{1}{2}\%$ a year.

(c) Depreciation of store equipment is $10\%$ a year.

(d) Insurance to be deferred amounts to $45.

(e) Accrued taxes covering property and payrolls are to be increased to $490.

(f) Accrued advertising amounts to $40.

(g) Sales salaries accrued are $250.

(h) Office supplies on hand total $400.

(i) Of the $30 reported as interest income, $10 is unearned.

(j) Interest of $15 has accrued on notes receivable.

(k) Interest of $30 has accrued on notes payable.

(l) Of the $20 reported as interest expense, $5 represents a prepayment for the month of February.

(m) The merchandise inventory on January 31, 1958, is $2,250.

*Instructions:* (1) Prepare an eight-column work sheet.

(2) Prepare an income statement and a balance sheet.

(3) Assuming that adjusting entries have been prepared as reported on the work sheet, give in compound form only those entries required to close the books on January 31.

(4) List the letters for those adjustments that should be reversed as of February 1.

**5-5.** The account balances taken from the ledger of W. W. Hammet and R. T. Wilkins at the end of the first year's operations on December 31, 1958, and the data for adjustments are given below:

| | | | |
|---|---|---|---|
| Cash.................... | $ 4,500 | R. T. Wilkins, Personal (dr.) | $   900 |
| Notes Receivable.......... | 3,600 | Sales..................... | 64,850 |
| Notes Receivable | | Purchases............... | 67,000 |
| Discounted............. | 2,000 | Purchases Returns and Al- | |
| Accounts Receivable....... | 2,500 | lowances.............. | 1,650 |
| Store Furniture........... | 3,700 | Purchases Discounts....... | 2,300 |
| Store Supplies............ | 600 | Sales Salaries............ | 8,000 |
| Notes Payable............ | 6,000 | Taxes.................... | 600 |
| Accounts Payable......... | 12,600 | Miscellaneous General Ex- | |
| W. W. Hammet, Capital... | 10,000 | pense.................. | 12,600 |
| R. T. Wilkins, Capital..... | 7,350 | Interest Income........... | 150 |
| W. W. Hammet, Personal | | Interest Expense.......... | 500 |
| (dr.)................... | 2,400 | | |

Data for adjustments, year ended December 31, 1958:

(a) Inventories: merchandise, $23,600; store supplies, $280.
(b) Depreciation of store furniture, 10% a year. Additions to store furniture were made on March 1 costing $900.
(c) Accrued advertising, $65.
(d) Taxes paid in advance, $100.
(e) Accrued taxes, $215.
(f) Prepaid interest on notes payable, $60.
(g) Accrued interest on notes payable, $30.
(h) Accrued interest on notes receivable, $35.
(i) Unearned interest income, $45.
(j) 5% of the accounts receivable are expected to prove uncollectible.
(k) Hammet and Wilkins divide profits and losses in the ratio 3:2.

*Instructions:* (1) Prepare an eight-column work sheet.
(2) Prepare an income statement, a statement of changes in partners' capital accounts, and a balance sheet.
(3) Prepare the required adjusting, closing, and reversing entries.

**5-6.** The following account balances are taken from the books of the Marks Manufacturing Co. on December 31, 1958, the end of the first year of operations:

| | | | |
|---|---|---|---|
| Cash..................... | $38,000 | Indirect Labor............ | $25,500 |
| Accounts Receivable....... | 92,800 | Heat, Light, and Power.... | 9,000 |
| Factory Supplies.......... | 1,200 | Maintenance and Repairs... | 5,000 |
| Office Supplies............ | 700 | Miscellaneous Factory | |
| Plant and Equipment...... | 205,000 | Expense................ | 3,500 |
| Accounts Payable......... | 77,200 | Sales Salaries and Commis- | |
| 4½% Bonds Payable........ | 150,000 | sions................... | 24,000 |
| Capital Stock (par $20).... | 100,000 | Advertising.............. | 15,000 |
| Sales..................... | 470,000 | Miscellaneous Selling Ex- | |
| Sales of Raw Materials (at | | pense.................. | 20,000 |
| cost)................... | 26,100 | Office Salaries............ | 17,000 |
| Raw Materials Purchases... | 247,100 | Miscellaneous General and | |
| Freight In............... | 7,000 | Administrative Expense... | 4,125 |
| Direct Labor............. | 105,000 | Interest Expense — Bonds... | 3,375 |

The following adjustments are to be made on December 31:

(a) Inventories:
Finished Goods, $18,000
Goods in Process, $14,000
Raw Materials, $20,000
Factory Supplies, $500
Office Supplies, $250

(b) Provision for loss from bad debts, 1% of sales of finished product.

(c) Depreciation, 8%, chargeable ¾ to manufacturing, ⅛ to selling, ⅛ to office.

(d) Accrued Salaries and Wages:

| | | |
|---|---|---|
| Direct Labor | $2,200 | |
| Indirect Labor | 500 | |
| Sales Salaries | 300 | $3,000 |

(e) A dividend of $1 per share had been declared December 28 and is payable January 10, 1959.

(f) Bond interest payment dates are March 1 and September 1.

(g) Provision of $10,000 is to be made for income taxes for 1958.

*Instructions:* (1) Prepare a ten-column work sheet.

(2) Prepare a balance sheet, an income statement and a manufacturing schedule, and a retained earnings statement.

(3) Prepare the necessary adjusting, closing, and reversing entries.

**5-7.** The following account balances are taken from the general ledger of the Carter Manufacturing Co. on December 31, 1958, the end of a fiscal year. The corporation was organized January 2, 1952.

| | | | |
|---|---|---|---|
| Cash on Hand and in Banks. | $19,500 | Allowance for Depreciation of Office Furniture and Fixtures | $ 9,000 |
| Notes Receivable | 18,500 | | |
| Accounts Receivable | 56,000 | | |
| Allowance for Doubtful Accounts | 650 | Machinery and Equipment. | 160,000 |
| Finished Goods Inventory January 1, 1958 | 40,500 | Allowance for Depreciation of Machinery and Equipment | 30,000 |
| Goods in Process Inventory, January 1, 1958 | 42,000 | Buildings | 125,000 |
| Raw Materials Inventory, January 1, 1958 | 24,000 | Allowance for Depreciation of Buildings | 18,000 |
| | | Land | 20,000 |
| Factory Supplies | 12,500 | Patents | 27,500 |
| Shipping Supplies | 8,500 | Notes Payable | 23,000 |
| Office Supplies | 6,200 | Accounts Payable | 45,700 |
| Tools | 10,000 | 4½% First Mortgage Bonds. | 100,000 |
| Patterns and Dies | 20,000 | 6% Preferred Stock (Par $100) | 100,000 |
| Shipping Department Equipment | 12,000 | Common Stock (Par $100) | 100,000 |
| Allowance for Depreciation of Shipping Equipment | 7,200 | Paid-In Capital — Premium on Common Stock. | 10,000 |
| Office Furniture and Fixtures | 15,000 | Retained Earnings | 105,875 |
| | | Sales | 520,000 |

| | | | |
|---|---|---|---|
| Sales Returns and Allowances | $ 10,000 | Sundry Factory Expense | $ 3,600 |
| Sales Discounts | 6,500 | Sales Salaries | 30,000 |
| Raw Materials Purchases | 110,200 | Sales Commissions | 12,300 |
| Freight and Cartage In | 8,800 | Traveling Expense | 8,500 |
| Purchase Returns and Allowances | 3,000 | Advertising Expense | 24,000 |
| Purchases Discounts | 3,400 | Shipping Department Salaries | 6,000 |
| Direct Labor | 103,700 | Sundry Shipping Department Expenses | 1,000 |
| Indirect Labor | 24,000 | Officers Salaries | 30,000 |
| Plant Superintendence | 20,000 | Office Salaries | 14,000 |
| Maintenance and Repairs of Buildings | 6,300 | Insurance | 8,500 |
| Maintenance and Repairs of Machinery | 4,500 | Postage, Telephone, and Telegraph | 1,400 |
| Heat, Light, and Power (Factory) | 11,000 | Sundry Office Expense | 1,500 |
| Taxes | 10,200 | Interest Income | 800 |
| | | Interest Expense—Bonds | 2,625 |
| | | Interest Expense—Other | 800 |

The following adjustments are to be made on December 31, 1958, before the books are closed:

(a) Inventories:

Finished Goods, $49,500; Goods in Process, $55,200; Raw Materials, $36,600; Factory Supplies, $2,700; Shipping Supplies, $1,800; Office Supplies, $1,000.

(b) Depreciation and Amortization:

Shipping department equipment, $12\frac{1}{2}\%$.

Office furniture and fixtures, $10\%$.

Machinery and equipment, $5\%$. New machinery and equipment costing $60,000 was installed on March 1, 1958.

Buildings, $4\%$. Additions to the buildings costing $50,000 were completed June 30, 1958.

Patents were acquired January 2, 1952. They are being reduced by $\frac{1}{17}$ of cost each year.

Patterns and dies are reduced by $15\%$ of the balance in the account.

Tools are reduced by $20\%$ of the balance in the account.

(c) The allowance for doubtful accounts is to be increased to a balance of $3,200.

(d) Accrued Expenses:

Salaries and wages: direct labor, $1,400; indirect labor, $300; sales salaries, $400; shipping department salaries, $100.

Interest on bonds is payable semiannually on February 1 and August 1.

Interest on notes payable, $50.

Property taxes, $2,000.

(e) Prepaid Expenses:

Insurance, $2,500.

Interest on notes payable, $100.

(f) Accrued Income: Interest on notes receivable, $200.

(g) The following information is also to be recorded:

(1) It is discovered that sales commissions of $1,200 were charged in error to the account Shipping Department Salaries.

(2) On December 30 the board of directors declared a quarterly dividend on preferred stock and a dividend of $1.50 on common stock, payable January 25, 1959, to stockholders of record Jan. 15, 1959.

(3) Provision is to be made for income taxes for 1958 at 40% of net income.

Taxes, expired insurance, and building expenses are to be distributed as follows: to manufacturing operations, 70%; to selling operations, 20%; to general operations, 10%.

The only charges to retained earnings during the year resulted from the declaration of the regular quarterly dividends on preferred stock. The balance of Retained Earnings on January 1, 1958, was $110,375.

*Instructions:* (1) Prepare a ten-column work sheet. There should be a pair of columns for trial balance, adjustments, manufacturing, profit and loss, and balance sheet.

(2) Prepare (a) a balance sheet, (b) an income statement supported by schedules showing the cost of goods manufactured, selling expenses, and general and administrative expenses, and (c) a retained earnings statement.

(3) Draft all of the journal entries necessary to give effect to the foregoing information and to adjust and close the books of the corporation.

(4) Draft the necessary reversing entries as of January 1, 1959.

**5-8.** The Crandall Trading Co. maintains two sales departments, Department A and Department B. A factory division of this company manufactures merchandise that is sold only in Department A. Below is given a complete list of the account balances taken from the company's general ledger on December 31, 1958, the end of a fiscal year.

| | | | |
|---|---|---|---|
| Cash | $18,750 | Allowance for Depreciation of Store Building | $ 2,800 |
| Notes Receivable | 11,400 | Factory Building | 40,000 |
| Notes Receivable Discounted | 2,500 | Allowance for Depreciation of Factory Building | 4,900 |
| Accounts Receivable | 33,300 | Store Fixtures | 10,000 |
| Allowance for Bad Debts | 450 | Allowance for Depreciation of Store Fixtures | 4,200 |
| Merchandise Inventory, Dept. A | 14,800 | Machinery and Equipment | 50,000 |
| Merchandise Inventory, Dept. B | 12,200 | Allowance for Depreciation of Machinery and Equipment | 14,000 |
| Finished Goods Inventory | 5,400 | Land | 40,000 |
| Goods in Process Inventory | 11,800 | Tools | 8,500 |
| Raw Materials Inventory | 10,000 | Patterns and Dies | 6,000 |
| Factory Supplies | 4,100 | Goodwill | 20,000 |
| Store Supplies, Dept. A | 2,100 | Notes Payable | 6,000 |
| Store Supplies, Dept. B | 1,800 | Accounts Payable | 23,000 |
| Unexpired Insurance | 7,000 | 6% First Mortgage Bonds | 50,000 |
| Store Building | 20,000 | Common Stock ($100 par) | 100,000 |

| | | | |
|---|---|---|---|
| Treasury Stock (Common, 150 shares)............. | $ 15,000 | Factory Maintenance and Repairs................ | $ 1,500 |
| 7% Cumulative Preferred Stock ($100 par)....... | 50,000 | Factory Heat, Light, and Power................ | 14,000 |
| Retained Earnings........ | 26,205 | Taxes................... | 7,200 |
| Sales, Department A....... | 262,400 | Miscellaneous Factory Expense.............. | 2,100 |
| Sales, Department B...... | 101,000 | Sales Salaries, Dept. A..... | 13,000 |
| Sales Returns and Allowances Department A..... | 5,400 | Sales Salaries, Dept. B..... | 6,500 |
| Sales Returns and Allowances, Department B.... | 2,000 | Advertising............. | 8,400 |
| Merchandise Purchases, Dept. A.............. | 24,000 | Miscellaneous Store Expense................. | 1,500 |
| | | Officers Salaries ......... | 17,400 |
| Merchandise Purchases, Dept. B.............. | 66,000 | Postage, Telephone, and Telegraph.............. | 300 |
| Freight in — Mdse. Purchases................ | 3,000 | Miscellaneous Office Expense................. | 1,800 |
| Raw Materials Purchases... | 41,400 | Interest Income.......... | 545 |
| Direct Labor............. | 50,400 | Rental Income........... | 2,000 |
| Indirect Labor........... | 26,900 | Interest Expense — Bonds | 2,000 |
| Factory Superintendence... | 12,000 | Interest Expense — Other.. | 1,050 |

The following information is to be considered in adjusting and closing the books on December 31, 1958:

(a) Inventories:

| | | | |
|---|---|---|---|
| Mdse. Inventory, Dept. A........ | $15,800 | Raw Materials Inventory ................. | $8,600 |
| Mdse. Inventory, Dept. B........ | 11,500 | Store Supplies Inventory, Dept. A............... | 430 |
| Finished Goods Inventory........ | 7,600 | Store Supplies Inventory, Dept. B.............. | 275 |
| Goods in Process Inventory...... | 12,000 | Factory Supplies......... | 875 |

(b) Depreciation and Amortization:

Store and factory buildings, 4%. An extension to the factory building, costing $5,000, was completed October 1, 1958.
Store fixtures, 20%.
Machinery and equipment, 10%.
Tools of $3,000 are to be written off to expense.
Patterns and dies of $2,100 are to be written off to expense.

(c) Bad Debts:

Each department is to be charged with $\frac{1}{2}$ of 1% of its net sales, and the allowance for bad debts is to be credited for this total.

(d) Accrued Expenses:

Advertising, $1,500.
Wages and Salaries:

| | | | |
|---|---|---|---|
| Direct Labor............$800 | | Sales Salaries, Dept. A.....$250 | |
| Indirect Labor.......... 450 | | Sales Salaries, Dept. B..... 200 | |

Interest: Interest on the first mortgage bonds is payable semiannually on March 1 and September 1.

(e) Prepaid Expenses:
Insurance prepaid on December 31, $4,200.
Taxes prepaid on December 31, $650.
Interest prepaid on notes payable, $150.

(f) Accrued Income:
Accrued interest on notes receivable, $85.

(g) The following information is also to be recorded:
(1) In December the board of directors declared a regular quarterly dividend on preferred stock and a $6 dividend on common stock, dividends payable January 20, 1959. It was also decided to write off goodwill against Retained Earnings at the end of the year.
(2) Provision is to be made for income taxes for 1958 at 40% of the net income.

(h) Expenses are to be distributed to departments as indicated below:

|  | Factory | Dept. A | Dept. B |
|---|---|---|---|
| Taxes and expired insurance...... | 50% | 30% | 20% |
| Selling and general expenses that cannot be identified with departments...................... |  | 70% | 30% |

Freight in on merchandise purchases is chargeable to departments on basis of purchases.

*Instructions:* (1) Prepare a 14-column work sheet with columns as follows:
Two columns for trial balance.
Two columns for adjustments.
Two columns in which will be summarized the cost of goods manufactured and transferred to Dept. A (finished goods remain in the factory until requisitioned by Dept. A).
Two columns for income and expense of Department A.
Two columns for income and expense of Department B.
Two columns for nondepartmental income and expense (interest and discount items). Departmental profits and losses are carried to this pair of columns so that a balance may be determined here that shows the profit and loss for operations as a whole.
Two columns for balance sheet items.

(2) Prepare (a) a balance sheet; (b) an income statement showing results of operations for Department A, Department B, and for the business as a whole; (c) a schedule supporting the income statement to show the cost of goods manufactured and transferred to Department A; and (d) a retained earnings statement (assume that retained earnings were affected only by regular quarterly preferred dividends in 1958 prior to December 31).

(3) Draft all of the journal entries necessary to give effect to the foregoing information and to close the books.

(4) Draft the necessary reversing entries as of January 1, 1959.

**5-9.** The Forbes Company commenced operations on July 1, 1958. The following shows the gross debits and credits in each account of the ledger as of December 31, 1958 except for work in process and finished goods inventory accounts. The company uses a cost system for its manufacturing operations.

TRIAL BALANCE AT DECEMBER 31, 1958

| | Transactions | | Balance | |
|---|---|---|---|---|
| | Dr. | Cr. | Dr. | Cr. |
| Cash.......................... | $464,000 | $370,000 | $ 94,000 | |
| Notes receivable.............. | 20,000 | 12,000 | 8,000 | |
| Accounts receivable........... | 340,000 | 302,000 | 38,000 | |
| Raw materials................. | 125,000 | 118,000 | 7,000 | |
| Finished goods................ | compute | compute | 30,000 | |
| Work in process............... | compute | compute | 14,000 | |
| Supplies...................... | 18,000 | 14,000 | 4,000 | |
| Prepaid insurance............. | 1,900 | 1,500 | 400 | |
| Plant and equipment........... | 95,000 | 0 | 95,000 | |
| Mortgage payable.............. | 0 | 50,000 | | $ 50,000 |
| Accrued mortgage interest...... | 0 | 750 | | 750 |
| Accrued wages................. | 145,100 | 147,000 | | 1,900 |
| Capital stock................. | 0 | 150,000 | | 150,000 |
| Vouchers payable.............. | 325,000 | 365,500 | | 40,500 |
| Sales......................... | 0 | 360,000 | | 360,000 |
| Cost of goods sold............ | 250,000 | 0 | 250,000 | |
| Selling expense............... | 27,500 | 0 | 27,500 | |
| Administrative expense........ | 29,000 | 0 | 29,000 | |
| Financial expense............. | 6,250 | 0 | 6,250 | |
| | | | $603,150 | $603,150 |

You are also given the following information:

**a.** The ending work in process inventory consists of the following: Materials—$6,000; Direct labor—$4,500; and Manufacturing expense—$3,500.

**b.** Insurance premiums apply two-thirds to the plant and one-third to the office.

**c.** The cost of the finished product is made up of: Materials 40%, Labor 40% and Manufacturing expense 20%.

*Instructions:* Set up skeleton ledger "T" accounts. Show therein the entries making up the transactions included in the figures shown on the trial balance. Key each entry (debit and offsetting credit) by use of a number, and on a separate sheet give an explanation and support for each entry.

(A.I.C.P.A. adapted)

# Chapter 6

## CASH AND TEMPORARY INVESTMENTS

**IMPORTANCE OF WORKING CAPITAL** The nature of working capital and the importance that attaches to a satisfactory working capital position have already been mentioned. A business cannot survive in the absence of a satisfactory ratio between current assets and current liabilities. Furthermore, its ability to prosper will be largely determined by the composition of the current asset pool. There must be a healthy balance between liquid capital, in the form of cash and temporary investments, and receivables and inventories. Activities of the business center around these items. Cash and temporary investments, representing purchasing power immediately available, are used to meet current claims and purchasing, payroll, and expense requirements; receivables are the outgrowth of sales effort and are a source of cash in the course of operations; merchandise is also a source of cash as well as the means of achieving a profit. Management in setting policies with respect to general operations, purchasing, financing, expansion, and dividends must work within the limitations set by the company's working capital position. This and the succeeding five chapters direct attention to the current asset and current liability items and the problems of income measurement related thereto.

**NATURE OF CASH** Cash is the most active item on the accounting statements. The movement of cash completes almost all purchases and sales transactions. Purchases of goods or services normally result in cash payments; sales normally result in cash receipts. Cash, more often than any other asset, is the item involved in business transactions. This is due to the nature of the business transactions, which include a price and conditions calling for settlement in terms of the medium of exchange.

In striking contrast to the activity of cash is its unproductive nature. Since cash is the measure of value, it cannot expand or grow unless it is converted into other properties. Large balances of cash on hand are often referred to as "idle cash." To be most useful to a business enterprise, cash must be kept moving.

**COMPOSITION OF CASH**      Cash is represented by those monetary as well as nonmonetary items that are immediately available and are acceptable in the liquidation of obligations. Cash includes commercial and saving deposits in banks and elsewhere that are available upon demand, and those money items on hand that can be used as a medium of exchange or that are acceptable for deposit by a bank at face value. Cash on hand would include petty cash funds, change funds, and other regularly used and unexpended monetary funds, together with nonmonetary items consisting of personal checks, travelers' checks, cashiers' checks, bank drafts, and money orders.

"Acceptance at face value on deposit" is a satisfactory test in classifying as cash the items that may be found in the cash drawer. It is assumed that deposits in a bank are made regularly, and such deposits become the basis for disbursements by the debtor. Although postage stamps may in some instances pass for mail payments of small amounts, they are not accepted for deposit and should be classified as office supplies rather than as cash. Post-dated checks should not be recognized as cash until the time when they can be deposited. Cash-due memorandums for money advanced to officers and employees represent receivable items, in some instances less satisfactory receivables than those of trade customers. Paper left at a bank for collection represents a receivable until collection is made and the amount is added to the depositor's account. Stocks, bonds, and United States securities, although immediately convertible into cash, cannot be used as a means for making payments, hence do not constitute cash and should be reported under appropriately descriptive titles on the balance sheet.

Certain cash items that are specifically designated for certain purposes may be separately reported. But those cash balances that are to be applied to some current purpose or current obligation are properly reported in the current section on the balance sheet. For example, cash funds for employees' travel, for payment of current interest and dividends, or for payment of certain obligations included in the current liabilities may be separately reported but are still classified as current.

Cash restricted as to use by agreement should be separately designated and reported. Such cash would be reported as a current item only if applicable to some current purpose or obligation. Cash representing refundable deposits collected from customers, for example, requires separate reporting. Classification of the item as current or noncurrent should parallel the classification applied to the liability balance.

Cash items not freely available for current disbursements require separate designation and classification under a noncurrent heading on the balance sheet. The noncurrent classification applies to items such as the following: time deposits not currently available as a result of withdrawal restrictions; cash in foreign banks blocked or otherwise restricted as to withdrawals; cash deposits on bids or options that may be applied to the acquisition of noncurrent assets; cash funds held by trustees for plant acquisitions, bond retirement, and pension payments; and cash balances in closed banks.

Since the concept of cash embodies the standard of value, no valuation problem is encountered in reporting this item on the balance sheet.

**CONTROL OF CASH** Because of the characteristics of cash — its small bulk, its lack of owner identification, and its immediate transferability — it is the asset most subject to misappropriation. Losses can be avoided or minimized only by careful control of the movement of this item from the time it is received until the time it is expended.

A satisfactory system of internal control affords safeguards against practices resulting in the misappropriation of cash. When persons have access to cash and also to the business records, the business becomes vulnerable to a great number of fraudulent practices. The following are only a few of the practices that have been found under such conditions: (1) cash receipts from sales, from recoveries of accounts previously written off, and from other income sources are understated, the unrecorded cash being pocketed; (2) refunds collected as a result of invoice overpayments or deposits are not recorded and the cash is withheld; (3) receivables are not entered on the books and cash collected on such receivables is withheld; (4) a part of a customer's remittance is misappropriated, Sales Discounts or Sales Returns and Allowances being charged for the cash withheld; (5) a customer's remittance is misappropriated and Loss from Bad Debts or Allowance for Bad Debts is charged for the sum misappropriated; (6) vouchers once approved and paid are used in support of further reimbursements; (7) checks for personal purposes are charged to business expense; (8) invoices, vouchers, receipts, or payroll records are supplied in support of fictitious charges, and checks issued in payment of such charges are subsequently forged; (9) purchases discounts or purchases returns and allowances are omitted or understated, Cash being credited for an excessive amount and cash misappropriated equal to the fictitious credit; (10) the cash balance is understated by erroneous footings in the cash receipts and disbursement records, cash equivalent to the understatement being withheld.

Two additional practices, "check kiting" and "lapping," are found when those who handle cash also maintain the cash records of the business.

"Check kiting" occurs when at the end of a month a transfer of funds is made by check from one bank to another to cover a cash shortage, and the entry to record the issue of the check is held over until the beginning of the new period. A cash increase in the customer's balance is recognized by the second bank in the current month as a result of the receipt of the check but a corresponding decrease in the customer's balance is not recognized by the first bank in the absence of current clearance of the check affecting the transfer. When the bank statements are received, the balance in the bank in which the check was deposited shows an increase. At the same time, the balance shown in the bank on which the check was drawn remains unchanged, because the check has not yet been presented to that bank for payment. A cash shortage is thus temporarily concealed.

"Lapping" occurs when a customer's remittance is misappropriated, the customer's account being credited when cash is collected from another customer at a later date. This process may be continued with further misappropriations and increasing delays in postings. To illustrate lapping, assume that in successive days, cash is received from customers A, B, and C in amounts of $75, $125, and $120. A's payment is misappropriated. A is subsequently credited with $75 out of B's payment and the difference, $50, is misappropriated. B is credited for $125 upon C's $120 payment and $5 is returned on the amounts originally "borrowed." The shortage at this point is $120, the unrecorded credit to C's account. This procedure can be continued with but slight delay in recording any customer's payment. The embezzler usually intends to return the money and avoid the strain of "lapping" after he has made a "profit on his investments." Unable to make restitution, he may resort to a fictitious entry whereby Loss from Bad Debts or some other expense account is charged, and the customers' balances are brought up to date.

A system of internal control over cash funds should operate to disclose cash discrepancies as well as to fix responsibility for any possible misappropriations or mistakes in handling and recording cash. Where misuse of funds or errors are indicated, it is only fair to members of an organization that the causes be determined and the responsibility be fixed so that innocent parties may be spared any embarrassment.

Responsibilities for the handling and recording functions should be specifically defined and scrupulously observed and carried out.

The system of internal control must be adapted to the particular business that it is to serve. It is not feasible to attempt to describe all of the features and techniques that might be employed in businesses of various kinds and sizes. In general, however, systems of internal control deny access to the records to those who handle cash. This reduces the possibility of improper entries to conceal the misuse of cash receipts and cash payments. The misappropriation of cash is greatly reduced if two or more employees must conspire in the embezzlement. Further, the system normally provides for separation of the receiving and paying functions. The basic characteristics of a system of internal check are listed and described below:

(1) Separation of handling and recording cash receipts.
(2) Daily deposit of all cash received.
(3) Internal audit at irregular intervals.
(4) Voucher system to control cash payments.

*Separation of Handling and Recording Cash Receipts.* Normally an adequate system would require that sales receipts and cash remittances from customers be made available directly to the treasurer or the cashier for deposit, while records supporting such transactions as well as records supporting bank deposits be made available directly to the bookkeeping division. At regular intervals comparisons of bank deposits with the book records of cash are made by a third party who has engaged in neither the cash handling nor the cash recording functions. Frequently, for example, a clerk opens the mail, prepares lists of remittances in duplicate, and then sends the cash and one copy of the list of remittances to the cashier and the second copy of the list to the bookkeeping division. Entries in the books of original entry and postings to customers' accounts are made directly from this list. Readings of cash registers are made by some responsible individual other than the cashier at the end of the day. The cash together with a summary of the receipts is sent to the cashier; a summary of the receipts is also sent to the bookkeeping division to be used in recording the day's activities. While deposits in the bank are made by the cashier or treasurer, entries on the books are made from lists of remittances and register readings prepared by individuals not otherwise involved in handling or recording cash. Members of the accounting or auditing staff compare periodic bank statements with related data on the books to determine whether the data are in agreement. If customers' remittances are not listed and the cash is misused, statements to customers will report excessive amounts and protests will lead to sources of the discrepancies; if cash receipts listed are not deposited properly, the bank record will not agree with cash records.

_Daily Deposit of All Cash Received._ The daily deposit of all cash received prevents sums of cash from lying around the office and being used for other than business purposes. Officers and employees have less opportunity to borrow on I.O.U.'s. Both the temptation for misappropriation of cash and the risk of theft of this item are avoided. The bank now protects company funds and releases these only upon proper company authorization. When the full receipts are deposited daily, the bank's record of deposits must agree with the depositor's record of cash receipts. This double record of cash provides an automatic check over cash receipts.

_Internal Audit at Irregular Intervals._ A system of internal audit at irregular and unannounced intervals may be made a part of the system of internal control. A member of the internal auditing staff verifies the records and checks upon the activities of those employees handling cash to make sure that the provisions of the system are being carried out. Such control is particularly desirable over petty cash and other cash funds where cash handling and bookkeeping are generally combined.

_Voucher System to Control Cash Payments._ The use of the voucher system to control cash payments is a desirable feature of cash control. Vouchers authorizing disbursements of cash by check are made at the time goods or services are received and found acceptable. Entries in the voucher register recording the expenditure and the authorization for payment are accomplished by the bookkeeping division. Checks are also prepared here and are sent, together with the documents supporting the disbursements, to the person specifically authorized to make payment, normally the official designated as treasurer. This party signs and issues checks only after careful inspection of the vouchers supporting and authorizing payments. The bookkeeping department, upon notification of the issuance of checks, makes appropriate records of this fact. Receiving and paying functions of the business are maintained as two separate systems. In each instance cash and recording activities are exercised by different parties which makes misappropriation of funds difficult without the collusion of two or more persons. The voucher system offers control over cash disbursements. It also provides for the immediate recognition of every liability incurred. Vouchers filed according to discount date or due date provide financial officers with significant data concerning future demands upon cash.

**DOUBLE RECORD OF CASH**    The preceding section listed the daily deposit of all cash received as an important factor in the control of cash. If all cash receipts are deposited daily, then the bank record of deposits follows the depositor's record of cash receipts. As a complementary device, all cash payments should be made by check, the bank then maintaining a record for checks that follows the depositor's record of cash payments. Two complete cash summaries are thus available, one in the cash account and the other on the monthly bank statement. In addition to the advantages resulting from organized and consistent routines applied to cash receipts and disbursements, a duplicate record of cash maintained by an outside agency is made available as a check upon the accuracy of the records kept by the company.

Maintenance of the double record of cash involves two special business and accounting procedures described in the following sections: (1) the adoption of a system of cash disbursements from a petty cash fund, and (2) reconciliation of the bank balance with the cash account balance at regular intervals.

**IMPREST SYSTEM OF CASH FUNDS**    Immediate cash payments and payments that are too small to be made by check may be made from a petty cash fund. Under the *imprest system* the petty cash fund is created by drawing a check to Petty Cash for the amount of the fund to be established. The cash is then turned over to a cashier or some person who is to be responsible for payments made out of the fund. The cashier generally requires a signed receipt for all payments made. Such receipts may be printed in prenumbered form. Frequently, a bill or other memorandum is submitted together with the receipt in support of a payment. A record of petty cash payments may be kept in a *petty cash journal*.

Whenever the amount of cash remaining in the fund runs low and also at the end of each fiscal period, the fund is replenished by writing a check to Petty Cash equal to the payments that have been made from the fund. Replenishment is necessary whenever statements are to be prepared, since petty cash disbursements are recognized on the books only when the fund is replenished.

The request for cash to replenish the fund is supported by a summary and analysis of the signed receipts that were required at the time of the payments from the fund. This analysis is the basis for charges to the proper accounts for the amount of the replenishing check. The signed receipts, together with appropriate supporting documents, are filed as evidence supporting these entries.

The cashier of the petty cash fund is held accountable for the total amount of the fund in his care. He must have on hand at all times cash and signed receipts equal in amount to the original balance of the fund. The practice of cashing employees' checks from petty cash or otherwise engaging in a banking function should be discouraged. If such a function is to be undertaken, it should represent a separate activity with a fund established for this purpose. Inasmuch as the cashier normally keeps the petty cash records, the rule of separating the recording and handling of cash is not here enforced. To assure that the operation is properly handled and controlled, unannounced audits of petty cash should be made by internal auditors or other company officials.

To illustrate the accounting procedures involved in the use of a petty cash fund, assume that on May 1, Martin Motors, Inc., sets up a petty cash fund of $200; on May 23, the fund is replenished by $192.47; on May 31, the end of the period, the fund is replenished by $135.18. The following entries are required in recording the establishment and the replenishment of the fund:

| | | |
|---|---|---|
| May 1 Petty Cash Fund...................... | 200.00 | |
| Cash............................... | | 200.00 |
| To set up a petty cash fund. | | |
| | | |
| May 23 Various Expense, Asset, or Other Accounts | 192.47 | |
| Cash............................ | | 192.47 |
| To replenish the petty cash fund for disbursements, May 1–23, as shown by receipts 1–43. | | |
| | | |
| May 31 Various Expense, Asset, or Other Accounts | 135.18 | |
| Cash............................ | | 135.18 |
| To replenish the petty cash fund at the end of the month for disbursements, May 24–31, as shown by receipts 44–63. | | |

If the business uses the voucher system, establishing and replenishing the fund requires the preparation of vouchers and entries in the voucher register. Charges in the voucher register are made to the accounts indicated above, but credits are made to Accounts Payable. When checks are issued, they are recorded as charges to Accounts Payable and credits to Cash. The net effect in the accounts is exactly the same as illustrated above.

Methods other than the imprest system are sometimes employed in handling petty cash. These may provide for checks of fixed amounts to be given to the petty cashier upon his request. Replenishing checks would not have to agree with the disbursements. Records of petty cash payments may be used as books of original entry for posting purposes. Expenses are charged and Petty Cash is credited for cash disbursements. Petty Cash is debited and Cash is credited for cash transfers to the petty cash fund. Such procedures are sometimes called the *fluctuating fund method* to distinguish them from the imprest system that provides for a nonfluctuating fund.

The imprest system may be employed not only for petty cash but also for other funds in a large organization. For example, a branch office or agency may be allowed a fund that is subsequently replenished for amounts equal to disbursements out of the fund. Evidence concerning payments out of the fund is submitted with the request for replenishment, and fund disbursements are recorded on the books at the time of fund replenishment.

The petty cash operation should be maintained apart from other cash funds employed for particular business purposes. For example, a business may require funds for making change. Certain sums of coins and currency are withheld from deposit at the end of each day to be carried forward as the change funds for the beginning of business on the next day. A separate account in the ledger should be established to report such cash supply always retained on hand. Also, special funds or bank accounts may be established for payrolls, dividend distributions, and bond interest payments. Each fund would call for a separate accounting.

**RECONCILIATION OF BANK BALANCES**     When daily receipts are deposited and payments other than those from petty cash are made by check, the bank's account of its transactions with the depositor provides a record that may be compared with the record of cash on the depositor's books. A comparison of the bank balance with the balance reported on the books is usually made monthly by means of a summary known as a *bank reconciliation statement*. The reconciliation statement is prepared to disclose any errors or irregularities existing in either the bank's records or those maintained by the business unit. It is developed in a form that points out the reasons for discrepancies in the two balances. It should be prepared by an individual not otherwise engaged in handling or recording cash, and any discrepancies should be brought to the attention of appropriate company officials.

An understanding of the reciprocal relationship that exists between the records of the bank and the depositor is necessary in the preparation of the reconciliation statement. All debit entries on the books of the bank should be matched by credit entries on the books of the company; all credit entries on the books of the bank should be matched by debit entries on the books of the company. For example, a deposit is a debit to the bank on the depositor's records, a credit to the depositor's account on the bank's records. A check drawn by a depositor is a credit to the bank on the depositor's books and a debit to the depositor's account on the bank's records.

When the two records are compared, certain items may appear on one record and not on the other, resulting in a discrepancy in the two balances. For example, checks may have been entered in the cash records but may not yet have been presented for payment at the depositor's bank. The subtraction then appears on the depositor's books but not on the bank statement. In another instance, receipts of cash shown in the cash receipts book may not be deposited until the following day; the bank statement balance, therefore, will not show the addition for receipts of the last day of the period covered. Other items resulting in discrepancies in the two records may include charges and credits made by the bank such as collection and protest fees charged by the bank to the depositor, various service and interest charges made by the bank, and credits for drafts and notes collected by the bank on behalf of the depositor. The depositor may be unaware of these charges and credits until the bank statement is received. If, after considering the items mentioned, the bank statement and the book balances cannot be reconciled, a detailed analysis of both the bank's records and the depositor's books may be necessary to determine whether errors or other irregularities exist on the records of either party.

The bank reconciliation, then, is a means of determining the accuracy of the cash records as they stand, as well as a basis for bringing the depositor's books up to date. In view of the reciprocal nature of the depositor's and the bank's books, required adjustments in the two balances, apart from any corrections for errors that may be required, fall under one of four headings as follows:

| BANK'S BOOKS | | DEPOSITOR'S BOOKS | |
| Mason, Inc., Depositor | | Cash (First National Bank) | |
| Balance per statement | | Balance per account | |
| 2,979.72 | | 2,552.49 | |
| (1) Credits on depositor's records not shown above. | (2) Debits on depositor's records not shown above. | (3) Credits on bank statement not shown above. | (4) Debits on bank statement not shown above. |

Examples of each of the four types of adjustments are listed on the following page:

(1) Outstanding checks not yet cleared by the bank.
(2) Deposits entered on the books of the depositor but not yet deposited in the bank.
(3) Collection of a note for the depositor by the bank, credited to the depositor's account and reported to him on his monthly statement.
(4) Bank service charges charged to the depositor's account and reported to him on his monthly statement.

There are two forms of the reconciliation statement. One form requires that both the bank and the company balances be brought to the same corrected balance by adjustments for all information not yet reflected on the respective books. Another form begins with the bank balance and reports the adjustments that must be applied to this balance to obtain a reconciliation with the cash balance as shown on the depositor's books. The first form is illustrated below; the second, on page 167.

MASON, INC.

BANK RECONCILIATION STATEMENT

November 30, 1958

| | | |
|---|---:|---:|
| Balance per bank statement, November 30, 1958.............. | | $2,979.72 |
| Add: Receipts for November 30 not yet deposited.. | $658.50 | |
| Charge for interest made to depositor's account by bank in error....................... | 12.50 | 671.00 |
| | | $3,650.72 |
| Deduct: Outstanding checks: | | |
| No. 1125............................. | $ 58.16 | |
| No. 1138............................. | 100.00 | |
| No. 1152............................. | 98.60 | |
| No. 1154............................. | 255.00 | |
| No. 1155............................. | 192.07 | 703.83 |
| Corrected bank balance................................ | | $2,946.89 |
| Balance per books, November 30, 1958..................... | | $2,552.49 |
| Add: Proceeds of draft collected by bank November 30 ($500 face less $1.50 bank charges)... | $498.50 | |
| Check No. 1116 for $46 recorded by depositor as $64 in error......................... | 18.00 | 516.50 |
| | | $3,068.99 |
| Deduct: Service charges........................ | $ 3.16 | |
| Customer's check deposited November 29 found to be uncollectible.............. | 118.94 | 122.10 |
| Corrected book balance................................. | | $2,946.89 |

Reconciliation of Bank and Book Balances to Corrected Cash Balance

## MASON, INC.
### BANK RECONCILIATION STATEMENT
November 30, 1958

| | | |
|---|---:|---:|
| Balance per bank statement, November 30, 1958 . . . . . . . . . . . . . . . | | $2,979.72 |
| Add: Receipts for November 30 deposited on December 1 . . . . . . . . . . . . . . . . . . . . . . . . . . . . . . . . . | $658.50 | |
| Service charges . . . . . . . . . . . . . . . . . . . . . . . . . . . . | 3.16 | |
| Charge for interest made to depositor's account by bank in error . . . . . . . . . . . . . . . . . . . . . . | 12.50 | |
| Customer's check deposited November 29 found to be uncollectible . . . . . . . . . . . . . . . . | 118.94 | 793.10 |
| | | $3,772.82 |

| | | | |
|---|---:|---:|---:|
| Deduct: Outstanding checks: | | | |
| No. 1125 . . . . . . . . . . . . . . . . . . . | $ 58.16 | | |
| No. 1138 . . . . . . . . . . . . . . . . . . . | 100.00 | | |
| No. 1152 . . . . . . . . . . . . . . . . . . . | 98.60 | | |
| No. 1154 . . . . . . . . . . . . . . . . . . . | 255.00 | | |
| No. 1155 . . . . . . . . . . . . . . . . . | 192.07 | $703.83 | |
| Check No. 1116 for $46 recorded by depositor at $64 in error . . . . . . . . . . . . . . . . | | 18.00 | |
| Proceeds of draft collected by bank on November 30 . . . . . . . . . . . . . . . . . . . . . . . | | 498.50 | $1,220.33 |
| Balance per books, November 30, 1958 . . . . . . . . . . . . . . . . . . . . . | | | $2,552.49 |

**Reconciliation of Bank Balance to Book Balance**

The first form brings both figures to the corrected cash balance for statement purposes. It is set up in two sections, the bank statement balance being adjusted in the first section and the book balance being adjusted in the second section. The first section contains items (1) and (2) listed on page 166 that the bank has not yet recognized with respect to the depositor, as well as any corrections for errors that may have been made by the bank. The second section contains items (3) and (4) that the depositor has not yet recognized with respect to the bank, as well as any corrections for errors that may have been made by the depositor. The second reconciliation form simply reports the reasons for the discrepancy between the bank and book balances.

Although the first form of reconciliation of cash may be considered preferable because it develops a corrected cash figure and shows separately all of the items requiring adjustment on the depositor's books, some accountants prefer to use the second form, which is consistent with the nature of the analysis that is required in many other accounting situations.

After preparing the reconciliation, the depositor should record any items appearing on the bank statement and requiring recognition on his books, as well as any corrections for errors discovered on his own books. The bank should be notified immediately of any errors that the bank has made as disclosed in the course of reconciling the balances. The following entries are required on the books of Mason, Inc., as a result of the reconciliation just made:

| | | |
|---|---:|---:|
| Cash........................................... | 498.50 | |
| Miscellaneous General Expense................. | 1.50 | |
|     Notes Receivable........................... | | 500.00 |
|         To record collection of a $500 time draft by the bank on which bank charges were $1.50. | | |
| | | |
| Cash........................................... | 18.00 | |
|     Advertising................................ | | 18.00 |
|         To record correction for check in payment of advertising that was recorded as $64 instead of the actual amount, $46. | | |
| | | |
| Accounts Receivable........................... | 118.94 | |
| Miscellaneous General Expense................. | 3.16 | |
|     Cash....................................... | | 122.10 |
|         To record (1) customer's uncollectible check and (2) bank charges for November. | | |

After these entries are posted, the cash account will show a balance of $2,946.89, the amount reportable on the balance sheet.

**CASH SHORTAGES**    When, during the course of the day, cash records and summaries report a total of cash that is different from the amount available for deposit and it is assumed that cash has been lost or errors have been made in making change, an adjustment is made to a cash short and over account. The net balance in this account may be reported as a financial management item in summarizing profit and loss. A cash shortage resulting from employee defalcation, however, should be charged to an account with the employee or the bonding company liable for such losses. Failure to recover the shortage would call for the recognition of an extraordinary loss.

**MISREPRESENTATION OF**    Although a system of internal check may pro-
**CURRENT CONDITION**    vide for the effective control of cash, careful analysis is still necessary at the end of the accounting period to determine whether transactions are recorded so as to present the cash and current position of the business properly. Certain practices designed to present a more favorable current condition than is actually the case may be encountered. Such practices are sometimes referred to as "window dressing." For example, cash records may be kept open for a

few days beyond the end of the fiscal period. Cash received from customers during this period is reported as cash receipts of the preceding period. A more liquid current position is thus reported. If this cash is then used to pay off creditors and such payments are predated, the ratio of current assets to current liabilities may actually be improved. For example, if the current ratio is 1.5 to 1 with current assets of $30,000 and current liabilities of $20,000, recording payment to creditors of $10,000 will make current assets $20,000 and current liabilities $10,000, a current ratio of 2 to 1. Such misstatement of the current ratio is also possible by writing checks at the end of the period in payment of obligations and entering them on the books but withholding the actual mailing of such checks until some later date. Or misrepresentation of both current position and net income is accomplished by predating sales made at the beginning of the new period. A careful examination of the accounting records is necessary to determine whether any practices that result in a misrepresentation of the current condition have been employed. Where such practices are discovered, corrections must be made if the balance sheet is to present financial condition fairly.

**CASH OVERDRAFTS**    A credit balance in the cash account resulting from the issuance of checks in excess of the amount deposited and available for payment of such checks is known as a *cash overdraft* and should be reported as a current liability. The existence of an overdraft may not necessarily occasion any embarrassment to the company if a number of checks are outstanding and deposits are made before checks are actually cleared. When a company has several balances with a single bank, an overdraft may be offset against a positive bank balance for balance sheet purposes. Opinion is divided as to the procedure that should be followed when there is an overdraft in one bank along with a positive balance in another. Some suggest that offset is proper in view of the possibility of clearing the overdraft by the transfer of cash from the positive balance to the account that is overdrawn. A stronger case, however, can be made for the recognition of both an asset and a liability balance: the business has a claim against one party and an obligation to another. If the reporting of an overdraft is to be avoided on the financial statements, an actual transfer of cash should be effected.

**THE CASH BUDGET**    Successful business operations call for intelligent planning and control of activities. The instrument that sets the standards for the future and offers guides and controls in achieving such standards is the business *budget*. A comprehensive operating budget offers an integrated and detailed plan for the future. Standards are set for sales, production, and expense. The inflow and outgo of cash is planned. Statements are prepared reporting the estimated earnings and financial position in terms of projected operations, financing, and earnings distributions. With a well-organized master plan for integrated and coordinated action by all parts of the organization, operations may be channeled toward achievement of individual and collective goals. Continuous comparisons are made between the standards that have been set by the budget and the results actually achieved through operations. Variations between budgetary standards and actual results are evaluated, and adjustment and revision of the standards are made when appropriate.

An important part of any budget is the forecast and planning of cash. Cash is the beginning and the end of all business activity, and any plans for the future must be directly related to the cash picture. Even in the absence of a comprehensive budgetary program, attention must be directed to cash, its expected movement, and methods for its proper utilization and control, if financial chaos is to be avoided. Cash must be readily available for all business needs; any cash in excess of current needs and reasonable reserves must be profitably employed. Satisfactory cash management calls for planning by means of a *cash budget*.

The preparation of a cash budget requires estimates of future cash receipts and cash disbursements. In projecting the cash picture, it is necessary to refer to other business plans — budgets for sales, raw materials acquisitions, operational costs, and plant and equipment acquisitions. Appropriate consideration must also be given to commitments with creditors and owners and probable actions of the board of directors that will affect the cash position.

Cash receipts and disbursements may not be matched in the months to come as the result of a number of factors, the most important of which are the following:

(1) Purchases and payments to creditors predate sales and collections from customers. Cyclical factors call for heavy seasonal expenditures that are recovered only at some later date.

(2) Acquisition of plant and equipment items are made at various intervals.

(3) Long-term debt is retired at various intervals.

With a full consideration of these factors, plans may be set for the establishment and the maintenance of a satisfactory cash balance. In meeting the requirements of (1) above, steps may be taken to provide for a supply of cash through short-term borrowing or through the conversion of marketable securities held for such purposes. Upon the recovery of cash through sales, excess cash can be applied to the payment of loans, to the acquisition of marketable securities, to the increase of the cash balance, or to the payment of dividends. In meeting the requirements of (2) and (3) on the opposite page, planning is directed towards the acquisition of cash through long-term borrowing, through the issuance of additional stock, or through the accumulation of cash from the operations of the business unit.

The development of a cash budget is illustrated on the next page. The illustration covers only a part of a year. Ordinarily a cash budget would be developed for a period of a year. The budget may be developed on a monthly basis as in the illustration, or it may be broken down into weeks or even days when such practice would be useful.

The first section of the budget is used to summarize the monthly cash receipts and disbursements originating from normal business operations. The monthly changes in cash are then applied to the opening balances. The additional sources and applications of cash are reported in arriving at the estimated cash balance on hand at the end of the month. The cash budget is usually accompanied by schedules that offer detailed support for the various data summarized thereon. Although the cash budget in the example makes reference to a number of schedules, only the schedules in support of collections on trade accounts receivable and payments on trade accounts payable are illustrated. The schedules follow the illustration of the budget.

**NATURE OF TEM-**     A company with an excess of available cash
**PORARY INVESTMENTS**     may deposit such funds as a time deposit or
under a certificate of deposit at a bank, or it may purchase securities. Income will thus be produced that would not be available if cash were left idle. Investments made during seasonal periods of low activity can be converted into cash in periods of expanding operations. Asset items arising from temporary conversions of cash are commonly reported in the current asset section of the balance sheet under the heading, Temporary Investments. Temporary investments are frequently limited to only marketable securities.

Securities that are purchased as temporary investments should actually be marketable on short notice. There should be a day-to-day market for them, and the volume of trading in the securities should be sufficient to absorb a company's holdings without considerably affecting the market price. While there may be no definite assurance that

## CARVER CO.
### CASH BUDGET
### FOR THREE MONTHS ENDING DECEMBER 31, 1958

|  | OCTOBER | NOVEMBER | DECEMBER |
|---|---|---|---|
| Cash sales................................... | 10,000 | 15,000 | 25,000 |
| Collections on accounts receivable (see schedule) | 50,000 | 61,000 | 80,500 |
| Other receipts (interest and dividend income, see schedule)................................... | 2,500 | 2,000 | 3,000 |
|  | 62,500 | 78,000 | 108,500 |
| Merchandise payments (see schedule)........... | 68,600 | 44,100 | 19,600 |
| Expense payments (see schedule)............... | 25,000 | 27,500 | 30,000 |
| Other payments (acquisition of furniture and equipment, see schedule)................. | 7,500 | | |
|  | 101,100 | 71,600 | 49,600 |
| Cash increase, decrease* for month............ | 38,600* | 6,400 | 58,900 |
| Cash balance at beginning of month........... | 16,500 | 7,900 | 14,300 |
| Cash requirements: | | | |
|    Obtained through loans.................... | 10,000 | | |
|    Obtained through sale of marketable securities. | 20,000 | | |
|  | 7,900 | 14,300 | 73,200 |
| Cash applications: | | | |
|    To payment of loans...................... | | | 25,000 |
|    To purchase of marketable securities........ | | | 35,000 |
| Net cash carried into succeeding month........ | 7,900 | 14,300 | 13,200 |

### CASH BUDGET
### SCHEDULE REPORTING COLLECTIONS ON ACCOUNTS RECEIVABLE*
### FOR THREE MONTHS ENDING DECEMBER 31, 1958

|  | ESTIMATED SALES | OCTOBER | NOVEMBER | DECEMBER |
|---|---|---|---|---|
| August......................... | 40,000 | 4,000 | | |
| September...................... | 50,000 | 40,000 | 5,000 | |
| October........................ | 60,000 | 6,000 | 48,000 | 6,000 |
| November....................... | 80,000 | | 8,000 | 64,000 |
| December....................... | 105,000 | | | 10,500 |
| Total monthly collections........ | .......... | 50,000 | 61,000 | 80,500 |

*Terms of sale — no cash discounts, payments due by the tenth of the month following sale. It is assumed that collections on charge sales will be made as follows:

Month of sale..................................... 10%
First month following sale.......................... 80%
Second month following sale........................ 10%

### CASH BUDGET
### SCHEDULE REPORTING PAYMENTS ON ACCOUNTS PAYABLE*
### FOR THREE MONTHS ENDING DECEMBER 31, 1958

|  | ESTIMATED PURCHASES | PURCHASES DISCOUNTS | NET PURCHASES | OCTOBER | NOVEMBER | DECEMBER |
|---|---|---|---|---|---|---|
| September. | 60,000 | 1,200 | 58,800 | 19,600 | | |
| October... | 75,000 | 1,500 | 73,500 | 49,000 | 24,500 | |
| November. | 30,000 | 600 | 29,400 | | 19,600 | 9,800 |
| December. | 15,000 | 300 | 14,700 | | | 9,800 |
| Total monthly payments......... | .......... | | | 68,600 | 44,100 | 19,600 |

*A 2% cash discount is allowed by vendors on payments made within 10 days from date of purchase. It is assumed that discounts will be taken on all purchases, payments to be made as follows:

Month of purchase.................................. 66⅔%
Month following purchase (first 10 days)........... 33⅓%

the securities will be disposed of without loss, it is essential that any possible loss resulting from such disposal be kept at a minimum. Securities that have a limited market and fluctuate widely in price are not suitable for temporary investments. The prices of United States government securities tend to be relatively stable and the market for these securities is quite broad. Because of these factors, short-term government securities are particularly favored despite their relatively low interest rates.

**COMPOSITION OF TEM-** Investments qualify for reporting as tempo-
**PORARY INVESTMENTS** rary investments as long as (1) they are readily available for conversion into cash and (2) it is management's intent to sell them to take care of cash requirements. Such investments may be converted into cash within a relatively short period after being acquired, or they may be carried for some time. In either case, however, since they represent a ready source of cash, they are properly shown under the current heading. The following types of investments do not qualify as marketable securities, and should not be included in the current section: (a) reacquired shares of the company's own stock, (b) securities held in subsidiary companies, (c) securities held for maintenance of business relations, and (d) other securities that cannot be used or are not intended to be used as a ready source of cash.

**RECORDING PURCHASE** Stocks and bonds acquired as temporary
**AND SALE OF MAR-** investments are recorded at cost, which in-
**KETABLE SECURITIES** cludes brokers' fees, taxes, and other charges relating to the purchases. When bonds are acquired between interest payment dates, the bond price is increased by a charge for accrued interest to the date of purchase. Such a charge should not be reported as part of investment cost. Two assets have been acquired — bonds and accrued interest — and the purchase price may be reported in two separate asset accounts. Upon the receipt of bond interest, the accrued interest account is closed and Interest Income is credited for the cash received in excess of the amount originally paid for accrued interest. One may prefer to charge Interest Income for the accrued interest paid. The subsequent collection of interest would then be credited in full to Interest Income. The latter procedure is usually more convenient and is employed in the text illustrations. Upon the sale of the bonds, the difference between the cost and the sales price is reported as the gain or loss on the sale.

The entries that are required for a temporary investment in bonds are illustrated in the example on page 174.

It should be observed that bonds are normally issued in $1,000 denominations, and purchase at $104\frac{1}{4}$ indicates payment at the rate of $104.25 per $100, or $1,042.50 per $1,000 bond. Bonds with a face value of $100,000, then, cost $104,250. In the calculation of accrued interest on the purchase and the sale of bonds other than obligations of the United States, each month is considered to have 30 days. Accrued

| Transaction | Entry | |
|---|---|---|
| **April 1, 1958** Purchased $100,000 National Corporation Bonds at $104\frac{1}{4}$. Interest at 6% is payable semiannually on June 1 and December 1. Payment was made as follows:<br>Bonds of $100,000 at $104\frac{1}{4}$...$104,250<br>Costs incident to purchase................ 120<br>Interest Dec. 1–Apr. 1...... 2,000<br><br>　Total amount paid......$106,370 | Marketable Securities— Investment in National Corporation 6's....... 104,370<br>Interest Income... 2,000<br>　Cash.......... | 106,370 |
| **June 1, 1958** Received semiannual interest on National Corporation 6's. | Cash............ 3,000<br>　Interest Income.. | 3,000 |
| **September 1, 1958** Sold $100,000 National Corporation bonds at $102\frac{7}{8}$. Cash proceeds were as follows:<br>Bonds of $100,000 at $102\frac{7}{8}$... $102,875<br>Interest June 1–September 1　1,500<br>———<br>　　　　　　$104,375<br>Less costs incident to<br>　sale.................. 100<br>———<br>　Net amount received.....$104,275 | Cash............ 104,275<br>Loss on Sale of Marketable Securities.......... 1,595<br>　Interest Income.. <br>　Marketable Securities — Investment in National Corporation 6's............ | 1,500<br><br><br>104,370 |

interest on the purchase for four months in the above example is computed for 120/360 of a year. If the purchase were made on April 12 instead of April 1, interest would be calculated for four months and eleven days or 131/360 of a year. In the case of obligations of the federal government, the exact number of days is determined and the year is considered to have 365 days in calculating the fractional part of the annual interest that is accrued.

The employment of cash for five months in the above example produced a net income of $905, the difference between interest income of $2,500 and the loss on the sale of $1,595. A decrease in the market price of the bonds of $2\frac{3}{8}$ points in place of the $1\frac{3}{8}$ points decline shown ($104\frac{1}{4} - 102\frac{7}{8}$) would have made the investment unprofitable to the corporation.

Entries to illustrate investments in stock are shown below.

| Transaction | Entry | | |
|---|---|---|---|
| **April 1, 1958** Purchased 100 shares of Wilson Co. 5% Preferred, par $100, at $103\frac{1}{8}$. Payment was made as follows: <br> 100 shares at $103\frac{1}{8}$ . . . . . . . $10,312.50 <br> Costs incident to purchase . . . . . . . . . . . . . . 50.00 <br><br> Total amount paid . . . . $10,362.50 | Marketable Securities — Wilson Co. 5% Preferred . . . . . . 10,362.50 <br> Cash . . . . . . . . | | 10,362.50 |
| **June 1, 1958** Purchased 100 shares of Wilson Co. 5% Preferred at $109\frac{3}{4}$. Payment was made as follows: <br> 100 shares at $109\frac{3}{4}$ . . . . . . . $10,975.00 <br> Costs incident to purchase . . . . . . . . . . . . . . 50.00 <br><br> Total amount paid . . . . $11,025.00 | Marketable Securities — Wilson Co. 5% Preferred . . . . . . 11,025.00 <br> Cash . . . . . . . . | | 11,025.00 |
| **July 1, 1958** Received semiannual dividends on Wilson Co. 5% Preferred. | Cash . . . . . . . . . . 500.00 <br> Dividend Income . . . . . . . | | 500.00 |
| **November 1, 1958** Sold 100 shares of Wilson Co. 5% Preferred at 108. Cash proceeds were as follows: <br> 100 shares at 108 . . . . . . . $10,800.00 <br> Less costs incident to sale 40.00 <br><br> Net amount received . . $10,760.00 | Cash . . . . . . . . . . 10,760.00 <br> Marketable Securities — Wilson Co. 5% Preferred. <br> Gain on Sale of Marketable Securities . . . . | | 10,362.50 <br><br><br> 397.50 |

When an investment in securities consists of several purchases and a part of the holdings is sold, a question arises as to what part of the total cost is to be related to the sale in calculating the gain or the loss on the sale. Federal income tax regulations do not permit the use of an average cost, but provide that when a lot sold cannot be related to a specific purchase, cost is determined on a first-in, first-out basis. Ordinarily, security investment accounts are maintained in accordance with the tax law requirements so that analyses and adjustments will not be required in converting accounting data for tax return purposes.

It is assumed in the example for stock that the sale was made of the first lot acquired, resulting in a gain of $397.50. The balance of the investment account is $11,025, the cost of the second purchase. If the second lot of stock instead of the first lot had been sold, a loss of $265 would have resulted, but the cost of the remaining asset for subsequent accounting and tax purposes would then have been $10,362.50.

It should be observed that for federal income tax purposes sale of an investment gives rise to a *capital gain* or *capital loss*. The holding period of the investment must be ascertained in reporting the capital gain or loss on the tax return. If the period from the date of acquisition of the investment to the date of sale does not exceed six months, a *short-term* gain or loss is recognized; if the holding period is more than six months a *long-term* gain or loss is recognized. Certain tax advantages are granted to taxpayers with an excess of long-term capital gains over capital losses: (1) only 50% of such excess is included in gross income subject to tax; (2) the tax rate applicable to this portion of income is limited to 50%. Taxes on an excess of long-term capital gains are thus limited to 25% of such amounts.

**ACQUISITION OF U. S. TREASURY BILLS — TAX ANTICIPATION SERIES** Special mention needs to be made of the practice by corporations of acquiring certain Tax Anticipation Series of United States Treasury Bills. Corporations whose federal income tax liability is not in excess of $100,000 are permitted to pay the entire tax in the year following its accrual. Corporations whose taxes are in excess of $100,000 are required to pay a portion of such excess in the year in which the tax accrues and the balance of the tax in the following year.[1] As part of a "tax saving plan," the United States Treasury at different intervals sells Treasury Bills that may be applied in payment of income tax indebtedness to the United States Government. Such different series are sold at a discount and are applicable to income tax indebtedness at par at stated tax payment dates, the difference between the discounted prices and par values at maturity representing interest income to the investor.

---

[1] In 1957 30% of a corporation's estimated income taxes in excess of $100,000 was payable in two equal installments in the taxable year and the balance in two equal installments in the following year. For example, a company with a calendar year fiscal period estimating its tax for 1957 at $200,000, was required to make payments on September 15, 1957, and December 15, 1957, of $15,000 each ($\frac{1}{2} \times 30\% \times [\$200,000 - \$100,000]$). Assuming that taxes for 1957 actually proved to be $190,000, the company would then make payments on March 15, 1958, and June 15, 1958, of $80,000 each ($\frac{1}{2} \times [\$190,000 - \$30,000]$). Pay-as-you-go percentage payments were scheduled to increase from the 30% rate in 1957 to 40% in 1958 and 50% in 1959 and thereafter.

Tax anticipation bills are negotiable, and in the event they are not used for tax payments at their respective maturities are redeemable in cash at par. Such bills, then, may be regarded as temporary investments and are properly reported as current assets. However, since Treasury Bills, by their terms, may be applied to the discharge of tax liabilities, it is considered proper to accumulate discount on these and report accumulated values as subtractions from the income tax liability. The purchase of the bills is thus recognized as, in effect, an advance payment of taxes. This position has received the full sanction of the Committee on Accounting Procedure of the American Institute of Certified Public Accountants. However, the treatment that is permitted in this particular instance is not to be interpreted as a relaxation of the general rule against the offsetting of asset and liability balances except where a legal right of set-off exists.[1]

**VALUATION OF MARKETABLE SECURITIES**     There has been support for the valuation of marketable securities by three different methods: (1) cost, (2) cost or market, whichever is lower, and (3) market.

*Cost.* Marketable securities held as temporary investments are frequently carried at cost. The recognition of gains or losses is deferred until the asset is sold, at which time investment cost is matched against investment proceeds. Disclosure of the market value of securities is made parenthetically or otherwise on the balance sheet so that the immediate current position can be recognized for analysis purposes. The cost basis finds support as an extension of the matching process. It is consistent with tax requirements. The reader of the statement has information concerning investment costs of the marketable securities on hand as well as current realizable values.

*Cost or Market, Whichever is Lower.* Cost or market, whichever is lower, is the procedure most commonly applied in the valuation of marketable securities. This valuation procedure calls for the recognition of decreases in the values of securities prior to their sale. Such

---

[1]*Accounting Research Bulletin No. 43,* "Restatement and Revision of Accounting Research Bulletins," 1953 (New York: American Institute of Certified Public Accountants), p. 26. It may be observed that some companies have adopted the policy of acquiring various issues of U. S. securities and reporting these as deductions from the tax liability even though such issues are not acceptable for the liquidation of tax liability. In commenting on this practice, the Committee on Accounting Procedure is of the opinion that, "the extension of the practice to include the offset of other types of United States government securities, although a deviation from the general rule against offsets, is not so significant a deviation as to call for an exception in an accountant's report on the financial statements." Nevertheless, the committee cautions that the offset of cash or any other assets against the income tax liability or other amounts owed to the government would not be regarded as acceptable practice.

practice is supported on the grounds that current quoted values offer an objective appraisal of the future worth of these assets. To continue to report securities at cost when market values are less than cost is to misrepresent the working capital measurement as well as total assets and hence the owners' capital. Although value decreases are recognized, this method calls for no recognition of value increases. Refusal to recognize increases represents the application of the conservative doctrine that calls for the recognition of losses though unrealized but for no anticipation of gains. Valuation at the lower of cost or market is also favored because it is consistent with the valuation method that is so widely employed for inventories.

The American Institute Committee on Accounting Procedure is in support of the use of a lower market in the valuation of marketable securities. The Committee states:

> In the case of marketable securities where market value is less than cost by a substantial amount and it is evident that the decline in market value is not due to a mere temporary condition, the amount to be included as a current asset should not exceed the market value.[1]

The lower of cost or market rule may be employed in two ways: (1) it may be applied to securities in the aggregate or (2) it may be applied to the individual items. To illustrate, assume investments with costs and market values on December 31, 1958, as follows:

|  | Cost | Market | Lower of Cost or Market on Individual Basis |
|---|---|---|---|
| 1,000 shares of Carter Co. Common................. | $20,000 | $16,000 | $16,000 |
| $25,000 Emerson Co. 5% Bonds.. | 25,000 | 26,500 | 25,000 |
| $10,000 Gardner Co. 4% Bonds... | 9,000 | 8,500 | 8,500 |
|  | $54,000 | $51,000 | $49,500 |

The lower of cost or market value on an aggregate basis above is $51,000; on an individual basis, $49,500. It would appear that sufficient conservatism is exercised in reporting securities at $51,000, the amount that would become available upon conversion of the securities in the aggregate.

Recognition of the value decline on the books calls for the reduction of the asset and a charge to a loss account; however, for tax purposes the loss cannot be recognized and the basis of the securities for measurement of gain or loss upon subsequent sale continues to be original cost.

---

[1] *Accounting Research Bulletin No. 43*, "Restatement and Revision of Accounting Research Bulletins," 1953 (New York: American Institute of Certified Public Accountants), p. 23.

Security costs can be preserved on the books by the use of a valuation account to reduce the securities to market. The following entry may be made to recognize the market fluctuation in the example above:

| | | |
|---|---|---|
| Recognized Decline in Value of Marketable Securities...................................................... | 3,000 | |
| Allowance for Decline in Value of Marketable Securities................................................. | | **3,000** |

The balance sheet would show:

| | | |
|---|---|---|
| Marketable securities, at cost..................... | $54,000 | |
| Less: Allowance for decline in value of marketable securities............................................... | 3,000 | |
| Securities at market value, December 31, 1958.... | | $51,000 |

This information could also be reported:

| | |
|---|---|
| Marketable securities at market (cost $54,000).... | $51,000 |

The $3,000 loss may be reported on the income statement as a financial management expense or as an extraordinary loss, whichever may be considered appropriate.

Assuming in the example above that the securities are sold in 1959, for $51,500, an entry is made as follows:

| | | |
|---|---|---|
| Cash........................................... | 51,500 | |
| Allowance for Decline in Value of Marketable Securities................................................. | 3,000 | |
| Marketable Securities—Carter Common......... | | 20,000 |
| Marketable Securities—Emerson Co. 5% Bonds. | | 25,000 |
| Marketable Securities—Gardner Co. 4% Bonds.. | | 9,000 |
| Gain on Sale of Marketable Securities........... | | 500 |

Neither the $3,000 loss nor the $500 gain is recognized for tax purposes; instead, a $2,500 loss is reported on the tax return for 1959 when securities that cost $54,000 are sold for $51,500.

When securities have been reduced to a basis of cost or market, whichever is lower, adjustments are normally considered to be necessary in future periods only in the event of further declines. Having established a lower basis, this may be considered as replacing cost for further comparisons with market. A market in excess of such substitutes for cost is thus ignored until sale of the asset takes place.

*Market.* There is some support for reporting marketable securities at current market values, whether higher or lower than cost. Those supporting this position maintain that, with definite evidence as to market values available, one would be derelict in failing to incorporate the full effect of such evidence in a statement that purports to disclose working capital and the over-all financial position. Further, it is maintained that the recognition of losses is generally accepted and justified; consistency would call for similar recognition to be accorded to gains. The arguments in support of the consistent use of market are not without merit. The objectives of such an approach can be met without distorting profit or loss measurements by applying appraisal accounting procedures. For example, assume that securities costing $50,000 have quoted values of $60,000 on December 31. Securities are sold for $62,000 in March of the following year. An unrealized gain may be reported on December 31. This is canceled when the securities are sold and the effect of the sale is reported in profit and loss. The following entries may be made:

| | | |
|---|---:|---:|
| Dec. 31, 1958 Marketable Securities.................... | 10,000 | |
| Appraisal Capital—Increase in Marketable Securities to Current Value........ | | 10,000 |
| March 5, 1959 Cash................................... | 62,000 | |
| Appraisal Capital—Increase in Marketable Securities to Current Value.............. | 10,000 | |
| Marketable Securities.................. | | 60,000 |
| Gain on Sale of Marketable Securities... | | 12,000 |

Such periodic revaluations would have to be disregarded for general income tax purposes. However, regulations do permit recognized dealers in securities to use market values for periodic security "inventories" in arriving at taxable net income. Dealers may choose to value securities at (1) cost, (2) cost or market, whichever is lower, or (3) market. The valuation procedure that is adopted must be applied consistently in successive tax reportings.

The importance of information concerning market values for items included in the working capital pool is obvious. It should be emphasized that when market values are not actually introduced into the accounts, this information should be incorporated by parenthetical remark, footnote, or other appropriate manner in the interest of full disclosure. The Securities and Exchange Commission requires that the following rules be applied in reporting securities as a current asset in statements that are filed with the Commission:

> Include only securities having a ready market .... State the basis of determining the amount at which carried. The aggregate cost, and aggregate amount on the basis of current market quotations, shall be stated parenthetically or otherwise.[1]

[1] Regulation S-X (as amended March 19, 1951). This regulation is issued by the Securities and Exchange Commission and states the basic rules as to form and content that are to be observed in the preparation of reports that are required to be filed with the Commission under federal laws. The Commission has released a number of other instruction books and regulations that give the different rules and procedures adopted by the Commission.

**PRESENTATION OF CASH AND TEMPO-RARY INVESTMENTS ON THE BALANCE SHEET** For statement purposes, cash may be reported as a single item or it may be summarized under several appropriate headings, such as cash on hand, commercial deposits, and savings deposits. Since current assets are normally reported in the order of their liquidity, cash would be the first item listed, followed by temporary investments, receivables, and inventories. When temporary investments are pledged for some particular purpose, the nature and the purpose of such a pledge should be disclosed parenthetically or in some other appropriate manner.

Cash and temporary investments, as these might be reported on the balance sheet, are shown below:

| | | | |
|---|---|---|---|
| Current assets: | | | |
| Cash on hand and demand deposits in banks. | | | $ 46,000 |
| Special cash deposits (to pay accrued interest and dividends)...................... | | | 24,000 |
| Temporary investments: | | | |
| Time deposits in banks............... | | $100,000 | |
| Marketable securities: | | | |
| U. S. Government obligations, at cost, which is approximate market value ($50,000 in bonds has been pledged as security on short-term bank loan) | $150,000 | | |
| Other stocks and bonds (quoted market value $44,200).................... | 35,000 | 185,000 | |
| Total temporary investments............ | | | 285,000 |

## QUESTIONS

**1.** State how each of the following items should be reported on the balance sheet: (a) demand deposits with bank, (b) blocked cash deposits in foreign banks, (c) payroll fund to pay off accrued salaries, (d) change funds on hand, (e) cash on deposit in escrow on purchase of property, (f) cash in a special cash account to be used currently for the construction of a new building.

**2.** (a) Define internal control. (b) Suggest the different techniques that might be employed in adopting a system of internal control for cash.

**3.** (a) Explain "check kiting" and "lapping." (b) Mention at least six other practices that result in misappropriation of cash in the absence of an adequate system of internal control.

**4.** (a) What two methods may be employed in the establishment of a petty cash fund? (b) Which would you recommend? Why?

**5.** (a) What two methods may be employed in reconciling the bank and the cash balances? (b) Which would you recommend? Why? (c) Name at least two other circumstances that call for the preparation of reconciliations.

**6.** The following items were found in the cash drawer on June 30, and had been included as Cash on the balance sheet for the Mitchell Co. How should each of the items have been reported?

    (a) Customer's check for $200 returned by the bank marked "Not Sufficient Funds."

    (b) Customer's check for $150 dated July 5.

    (c) Cashier's note for $100 with no due date.

    (d) Postage stamps received with box tops for merchandise, $9.83.

    (e) Postal money orders from customers awaiting deposit, $45.

    (f) Receipt for expense advances to buyers, $175.

    (g) Change fund, $100 in coins.

**7.** The Kern Co. engaged in the following practices at the end of a fiscal year:

    (a) Sales on account from January 1–January 5 were predated as of the month of December.

    (b) Checks in payment of accounts were prepared on December 31 and were entered on the books, but they were placed in the safe awaiting instructions for mailing.

    (c) Customers' checks returned by the bank and marked "Not Sufficient Funds" were ignored for statement purposes.

Explain what is wrong with each of the practices mentioned and indicate the entries that are required to correct the accounts.

**8.** (a) What is the nature of a budget?  (b) What is a cash budget? (c) Describe the preparation of the cash budget and the nature of the problems encountered in maintaining a healthy cash status.

**9.** On reconciling the cash account with the bank statement, it is found that the general cash fund is overdrawn $436 but that the bond redemption account has a balance of $5,400. The treasurer wishes to show cash as a current asset at $4,964. Discuss.

**10.** Define temporary investments. Distinguish between temporary investments and marketable securities.

**11.** (a) What theories are held with respect to the valuation of marketable securities?  (b) What arguments can be advanced in support of each and which position do you feel has greatest merit?

**12.** Hanson Products Co. acquired marketable securities in 1957 for $60,000. In June, 1958, these securities have a market value of $85,000. The treasurer insists that the balance sheet as of June 30 should show the securities at $85,000, since they were "just as good as cash." Comment on this proposal.

**13.** State two methods for reporting Tax Anticipation Series of United States Treasury Bills and give arguments in support of each.

**14.** The accountant for the Goodwin Co. in preparing a balance sheet has made certain offsets as follows:

United States Treasury Tax Anticipation Bills, $14,000, have been offset against Estimated Federal Income Taxes Payable, $20,000.

An overdraft of $120 in the Payroll Fund kept with the Second National Bank has been offset against the general cash balance kept with the same bank.

Advances of $500 to buyers have been offset against accrued sales salaries of $1,200.

$1,000 receivable from Jones Wholesalers has been offset against a note payable of $1,200 that was sent to Jones Wholesalers as a result of a previous purchase.

Comment on the foregoing practices.

**15.** Stanley, Inc. posted from all of its books of original entry except the cash book on June 30. The bookkeeper kept the cash book open until July 10 in order to show cash collections of $10,000 and payments to short-term creditors of $10,000. (a) Do you approve? (b) If the balance sheet showed a current ratio of 2 to 1 with current assets of $20,000 and current liabilities of $10,000, what was the correct current ratio?

## EXERCISES

**1.** An examination on the morning of January 2 by the auditor for the Davis Manufacturing Company shows the following items in the petty cash drawer:

| | | |
|---|---|---|
| Currency and coin.......................................... | | $ 12.56 |
| IOU's from members of the office staff........................ | | 60.00 |
| An envelope containing collections for a football pool, with office staff names attached.................................... | | 10.00 |
| Petty cash vouchers for: | | |
| Typewriter repairs............................... | $2.50 | |
| Stamps........................................ | 5.00 | |
| Telegram charges................................ | 6.50 | 14.00 |
| Employee's check postdated January 15..................... | | 50.00 |
| Employee's check marked "N.S.F.".......................... | | 70.00 |
| Check drawn by Davis Manufacturing Company to Petty Cash.. | | 92.00 |
| | | $308.56 |

The ledger account shows a $300 balance for Petty Cash. (a) What adjustments should be made on the auditor's working papers in order that petty cash may be correctly stated on the balance sheet? (b) What is the correct amount of petty cash for the balance sheet? (c) How could the practice of borrowing by employees from the fund be discouraged?

**2.** In auditing the books of McDonald, Inc. for 1958, you find that a petty cash fund of $250 is maintained on the imprest basis, but the company has failed to replenish the fund on December 31. Replenishment was made and recorded on January 15, 1959, when a check for $185 was drawn to petty cash for expenses paid. Your analysis discloses that $125 had been spent out of petty cash in 1958. What entry would be made in correcting the records, assuming that the books for 1958 have been closed?

**3.** The Wilson Co. receives its bank statement for the month ending June 30 on July 2. The bank statement shows a balance of $231. The cash account as of the close of business on June 30 shows a credit balance of $123. In reconciling the balances, the auditor discovers the following:

Receipts of June 30, $1,860, were not deposited until July 1.
Checks outstanding on June 30 were $2,215.
The bank has charged the depositor for overdrafts, $10.
A canceled check to S. S. Dohr for $56 was entered in cash payments in error as $65.

Prepare a bank reconciliation statement. (Use the form that reconciles bank and depositor figures to corrected cash balances.)

**4.** The following data are assembled in the course of reconciling the bank balance as of December 31, 1958, for A. P. Moore Co. What cash balance will be found on the company books, assuming no errors on the part of the bank and the depositor?

| | |
|---|---:|
| Balance per bank statement............................. | $1,512.60 |
| Checks outstanding...................................... | 1,805.00 |
| December 31 receipts recorded but not deposited........... | 320.00 |
| Bank charges for December not recognized on books........ | 7.50 |
| Draft collected by bank but not recognized on books........ | 615.00 |

**5.** Sales on account for the Meadows Company for March amount to $10,000 and they are estimated to increase by $3,000 in each succeeding month. Terms of the sales are 2/10, E.O.M. It is estimated that no collections will be made in the month of the sale, 80% will be collected within the discount period, 10% after the discount period in the month following the sale, and 8% in the second month following the sale. What are the estimated cash collections from customers for the month of July?

**6.** The Warren Co. completed the transactions in marketable securities listed below during 1958. What are the entries to record the transactions? (Commissions and other charges are omitted.)

(a) Purchased $10,000 Martin & Co. $5\frac{1}{2}\%$ bonds paying $96\frac{1}{2}$ plus accrued interest of $40.
(b) Purchased 200 shares of Scoville Co. common stock at 19.
(c) Purchased 300 shares of Scoville Co. common stock at 21.
(d) Received semiannual interest on Martin & Co. bonds.
(e) Sold the 300 share lot of Scoville Co. common at $22\frac{1}{2}$.
(f) Sold $5,000 Martin & Co. bonds at 95 plus accrued interest of $15.

**7.** The Westlake Co. acquired 3,000 shares of Nelson Corporation common in three 1,000-share lots at costs of 10, $12\frac{1}{4}$, and 17 respectively. One thousand shares of the stock are sold in 1958 at $16\frac{1}{2}$. (a) What is the entry to record the sale? (b) Assuming that operations for 1958 are profitable and that the Westlake Co. would like to avoid recognizing a profit on this security in 1958, what recommendations would you make?

8. An examination of marketable securities on hand for the Cross Corporation on December 31 discloses the following cost and market values:

| | Total Cost | Market Quotations on Dec. 31 |
|---|---|---|
| 500 shares of Sailyers Co. Common........ | $12,000 | $16\frac{1}{4}$ |
| $60,000 Randall Co. First Mortgage 5's.... | 61,000 | $102\frac{1}{2}$ |

Show how this information would be presented on the balance sheet following three different valuation procedures that might be employed.

## PROBLEMS

**6-1.** The cash account of L. M. Long Co. showed a balance of $4,321.65 on April 30, 1958. The bank statement as of April 30 showed a balance of $3,575.00. Upon comparing the statement with the cash records, it was found that: (1) Long's account had been charged for a customer's uncollectible check amounting to $407.20 on April 26; (2) a two-month, 6%, $1,000 customer's note dated February 25, discounted on April 12, had been protested April 26, protest fees, $2.90; (3) a customer's check for $90 had been entered as $70 both by the depositor and the bank but was later corrected by the bank; (4) check No. 742 for $392 had been entered in the cashbook as $329, and check No. 747 for $42.10 had been entered as $421; (5) there was a bank service charge for the month of March amounting to $9.72; (6) a bank memo stated that A. M. Case's note for $600 had been collected April 29 (the note had been sent to the bank for collection on April 27 but no entry had been made at that time); (7) receipts of April 30 for $1,640 were not deposited until May 2.

The following checks were outstanding on April 30:

| No. 712 | $113.46 | No. 785 | $112.00 |
|---|---|---|---|
| 740 | 43.20 | 786 | 150.00 |
| 782 | 135.00 | 787 | 139.43 |
| 784 | 381.50 | 788 | 312.68 |

*Instructions:* (1) Construct a bank reconciliation statement, using the form where both bank and book balances are brought to a corrected cash balance (the form illustrated on page 166).

(2) Give the journal entries required as a result of the information given above. (Assume that the company makes use of the voucher system.)

**6-2.** Meyers, Inc. received its bank statement for the month ending June 30, 1958. The auditor, in attempting to reconcile the statement with the books, discovered the following:

The cashier, who was also the bookkeeper, had misappropriated $145 by "lapping" and an additional $205 by passing a noncash credit through the sales returns and allowances account.

The bank had charged the depositor with: protest fee, $2.50; collection charges, $3.49; and telegram, $1.60.

A check made payable to C. H. Clawson in payment of an account for $30 was incorrectly recorded as $20.

Outstanding checks were as follows:

| No. 112 | $ 74.25 | | No. 153 | $ 104.69 |
| 138 | 325.00 | | 154 | 532.23 |
| 152 | 85.07 | | 155 | 1,225.50 |

Receipts of June 30 for $1,154.63 were not deposited until July 1.

The balance on the bank statement was $924.36. The cash account showed an overdraft of $250.16.

*Instructions:* (1) Prepare a bank reconciliation statement, using the form where the bank balance is reconciled with the cash balance per books (the form illustrated on page 167).

(2) Give all of the required journal entries indicated by the preceding.

**6-3.** A bank statement for the Roxbury Co. shows a balance as of December 31 of $1,592.95. The cash account for the company as of this date shows an overdraft of $246.05. In reconciling the statement with the books, the following items are discovered:

(1) The cash balance includes $200 representing change cash on hand. When the cash on hand is counted, only $192.50 is found.

(2) The cash balance includes $300 representing a petty cash fund. Inspection of the petty cash fund reveals cash of $210 on hand and a replenishing check drawn on December 31 for $90.

(3) Proceeds from cash sales of $580 for December 27 were stolen. The company expects to recover this amount from the insurance company and has made no entry for the loss.

(4) The bank statement shows the depositor charged with a customer's N.S.F. check for $75, bank service charges of $21.50, and a check for $86 drawn by Roxy, Inc. and incorrectly cleared through this account.

(5) The bank statement does not show receipts of December 31 of $1,214, which were deposited on January 2.

(6) Checks outstanding were found to be $4,315.50. This includes the check transferred to the petty cash fund and also two checks for $110 each payable to F. R. Miles. Miles had notified the company that he had lost the original check and had been sent a second one, the company stopping payment on the first check. Among the checks outstanding, one for $60 has been outstanding for fourteen months, and it is decided to cancel this item since the payee cannot be found and payment may never be claimed.

*Instructions:* (1) Prepare a bank reconciliation statement, using the form where both bank and book balances are brought to a corrected cash balance (form illustrated on page 166).

(2) Give the correcting entries required by the foregoing.

(3) List the cash items as they should appear on the balance sheet on December 31.

**6-4.** Lang, Inc. shows the following information relating to marketable securities on its balance sheet on December 31, 1957:

| | |
|---|---:|
| Fuller $3 Preferred, 500 shares (no par) .................... | $ 9,530.00 |
| Forrest Manufacturing Common, 100 shares................ | 2,050.00 |
| Calway 4% Preferred, 100 shares ($20 par) ................ | 1,680.50 |
| Mason Co. First Mortgage 4½% Bonds (face $10,000)........ | 9,495.00 |
| Total Marketable Securities (current market value, $26,600).... | $22,755.50 |
| Accrued Interest on Mason Co. Bonds..................... | 112.50 |
| | $22,868.00 |

Purchases and sales of securities during 1958 follow.

Jan. 15. Purchased 100 shares of Forrest Manufacturing Common at 18½ plus costs of $25.

Jan. 20. Received quarterly dividend on Fuller Preferred.

Mar. 15. Sold holdings in Fuller Preferred and Calway Preferred at 21¾ and 24 respectively. Costs of $100 and $60 respectively were incurred on the sales.

Mar. 25. Sold Forrest Manufacturing Common (acquired on January 15) at 16½ less costs of $30.

Apr. 1. Received semiannual interest on Mason Co. First Mortgage Bonds.

May 1. Sold Mason Co. First Mortgage Bonds at 102¾ plus accrued interest, less costs of $150.

Dec. 11. Purchased $10,000 Wakefield Co. 5% bonds at 95 plus accrued interest and additional costs of $100. Interest on bonds is payable on May 1 and November 1.

Dec. 15. Purchased 100 shares of Ross Co. 6% Preferred ($100 par) at 105 plus costs of $90.

On December 31, market quotations of securities owned were as follows: Forrest Manufacturing Common, 15¼; Wakefield Co. bonds, 94¼; Ross Co. Preferred, 101½. It is decided to reduce the securities to current market value for balance sheet purposes by means of a valuation account.

*Instructions:* (1) Journalize the foregoing, including any adjustments required on December 31, 1958.

(2) Show the information relating to marketable securities as it would appear on the balance sheet prepared on December 31, 1958.

**6-5.** The balance sheet of Johnson and Marshall, Inc. shows the following current assets as of December 31, 1958:

| | |
|---|---:|
| Current assets: | |
| Cash......................................... | $103,820.35 |
| Temporary investments ......................... | 203,060.00 |
| Total current assets.............................. | $306,880.35 |

In examining the books, the following information is revealed with respect to the current assets:

Cash includes a demand deposit of $24,132.35 at the First National Bank; a time deposit of $12,000 that may not be withdrawn until after

April 1, 1960; customers' checks not yet deposited, $600, and customers' returned N.S.F. checks, $200; a demand deposit of $12,170, which is unavailable, being in a bank in a foreign country at war; an overdraft of $340 in the Second National Bank; a time deposit of $8,000 in a building and loan savings association that is closed; advances of $2,000 to officers; sinking fund cash of $19,758; a pension fund of $25,000 for employees; and a petty cash fund of $300, of which $75 is cash, $60 is in the form of employees' I.O.U.'s, and $165 is supported by the receipts for expenses paid out of the fund.

The following securities have been included under the temporary investments heading:

| | Cost | Market Value (Including Accrued Int.) |
|---|---|---|
| Johnson and Marshall, Inc., Treasury Stock......$ | 7,550.00 | $ 7,325.00 |
| Stock of Eastern Corporation (temporary holding) | 4,455.00 | 4,010.00 |
| Merry Company, 6% bonds (interest payable March 1 and Sept. 1). Face value, $7,000. Acquired on Sept. 1, 1958 (temporary holding).. | 7,210.00 | 7,225.00 |
| 3% United States Treasury Bonds (interest payable on March 1 and September 1). Face value, $20,000. Purchased with pension sinking fund cash. Acquired on September 1, 1958........ | 20,400.00 | 20,500.00 |
| Packard Co. Stock (temporary holding)......... | 4,012.00 | 3,750.00 |
| Nash Co. Stock (stock of subsidiary company).... | 152,750.00 | 151,950.00 |
| Lowry Corp. Stock (temporary holding)......... | 8,100.00 | 8,300.00 |

*Instructions:* Show cash and temporary investments as these items should properly appear in the current assets section of the balance sheet. Provide schedules to show how foregoing balances are determined and what disposition is to be made of items not appropriately shown under the cash and temporary investment headings. Assume that marketable securities are valued at cost or market, whichever is lower, by means of a valuation account.

**6-6.** The Green Novelty Co. asks the controller to prepare a cash forecast for the first three months of 1959. The following information is assembled in developing the forecast.

| Sales: | January | $55,000 |
|---|---|---|
| | February | 60,000 |
| | March | 75,000 |

All sales are made on a credit basis as follows: 2% cash discount if paid by the tenth of the month following the sale; credit period 30 days from end of month in which sale is made. Past experience has shown that 70% of the billings are collected within the first ten days of the month following the sale and are credited with the discount, 20% of the billings are collected during the remainder of the month following sale, and 10% are collected in the second month following sale.

| Purchases: | January | $36,000 |
|---|---|---|
| | February | 42,000 |
| | March | 30,000 |

All purchases are made on terms of 2/10, n/30, and the company follows the practice of taking all discounts on the tenth day following the invoice date. It is assumed that purchases will be distributed evenly throughout the month, purchases for the last third of the month being paid in the first third of the succeeding month.

Selling and general and administrative expenses, excluding depreciation, will be paid as incurred and are anticipated as follows: fixed costs, $5,000 per month; variable costs, $12\frac{1}{2}\%$ of gross sales.

The following balances taken from a trial balance on December 31 are to be considered in developing the cash summary:

| | | |
|---|---:|---:|
| Cash........................................ | | $ 1,500 |
| Accounts receivable: | | |
| November.............................. | $ 8,000 | |
| December ............................. | 90,000 | 98,000 |
| Accounts payable: | | |
| December.............................. | | 15,000 |
| Bank loan due January 15, 1959................. | | 15,000 |
| Estimated federal income tax for 1958 ( the company expects to make payment in two installments of $16,250 on 3/15/59 and 6/15/59).............. | | 32,500 |

*Instructions:* Prepare a forecast of the cash position by months supported by receipts and payments schedules in forms similar to those illustrated on page 172.

**6-7.** The AB Trading Company wishes to prepare a monthly cash budget. The following information is available:

The AB Trading Company purchases merchandise on terms of 2/10, n/60 and regularly takes discounts on the tenth day after the invoice date. It may be assumed that one third of the purchases of any month are due for discount and are paid for in the following month.

The company's sales terms are 2/10, n/30, E. O. M. It has been the company's experience that discounts on 80% of billings have been allowed and that, of the remainder, one half have been paid during the month following billing and the balance during the second following month.

The average rate of gross profit, based on sales price, is 25%. Total sales for the company's fiscal year ending June 30, 1959, have been estimated at 80,000 units, distributed monthly as follows:

| | | | | | | | |
|---|---|---|---|---|---|---|---|
| July........ | 9% | October... | 9% | January.... | 3% | April...... | 7% |
| August..... | 10% | November. | 10% | February... | 5% | May....... | 6% |
| September... | 12% | December.. | 15% | March..... | 6% | June....... | 8% |

To insure prompt delivery of merchandise, inventories are maintained during January and February at 6% of the number of units estimated to be sold throughout the year, while during the rest of the year they are maintained at 10% of that number. The inventories at December 31 and February 28 should be at the levels intended to be maintained during the respective ensuing seasons.

Total budgeted selling and administrative and general expenses for the fiscal year ending June 30, 1959, are estimated at $312,000, of which

$120,000 are fixed expenses (inclusive of $24,000 annual depreciation). These fixed expenses are incurred uniformly throughout the year. The other selling and administrative and general expenses vary with sales. In total, these expenses amount to $192,000, or 12% of total sales for the year. Expenses are paid as incurred, without discounts.

It is assumed that at January 1, 1959, merchandise inventory, at the 6% level, will consist of 4,800 units, to cost $72,000, before discount, and the cash balance will be $112,000.

*Instructions:* From the information given above, prepare a monthly cash budget for the three months ending March 31, 1959. (A.I.C.P.A. adapted)

**6-8.** The Larchmont Company had poor internal control over its cash transactions. Facts about its cash position at November 30, 1958, were as follows:

The cash books showed a balance of $18,901.62, which included cash on hand. A credit of $100 on the bank's records did not appear on the books of the company. The balance per the bank statement was $15,550, and outstanding checks were #62 for $116.25, #183 for $150, #284 for $253.25, #8621 for $190.71, #8623 for $206.80 and #8632 for $145.28.

The cashier removed all of the cash on hand in excess of $3,794.41 and then prepared the following reconciliation:

| | | |
|---|---:|---:|
| Balance per books, Nov. 30, 1958 | | $18,901.62 |
| Add—Outstanding checks: | | |
| #8621 | $190.71 | |
| #8623 | 206.80 | |
| #8632 | 145.28 | 442.79 |
| | | $19,344.41 |
| Deduct—Cash on hand | | 3,794.41 |
| Balance per bank, Nov. 30, 1958 | | $15,550.00 |
| Deduct—Unrecorded credit | | 100.00 |
| True cash, Nov. 30, 1958 | | $15,450.00 |

*Instructions:* (1) How much did the cashier remove and how did he attempt to conceal his theft?

(2) Taking only the information given, name two specific features of internal control which were apparently missing. (A.I.C.P.A. adapted)

**6-9.** In auditing the Howell Company, you obtain directly from its bank the bank statement, the canceled checks, and other memoranda that relate to the company's bank account for December, 1958. In reconciling the bank balance at December 31, 1958, with that shown on the company's books, you observe the facts set forth on the following page.

(1)  Balance per bank statement, 12/31/58................ $88,489.12
(2)  Balance per books, 12/31/58......................... 58,983.46
(3)  Outstanding checks 12/31/58 ........................ 32,108.42
(4)  Receipts of 12/31/58, deposited 1/2/59............... 5,317.20
(5)  Service charge for November, 1958, per bank memo of
     12/15/58............................................ 3.85
(6)  Proceeds of bank loan, 12/15/58, discounted for 3 months
     at 5% per annum, omitted from company books........ $9,875.00
(7)  Deposit of 12/23/58 omitted from bank statement...... 2,892.41
(8)  Check of Rome Products Co. charged back on 12/22/58 for
     absence of countersignature and redeposited with complete
     signature on 1/5/59, no entry on the books having been
     made for the chargeback or the redeposit............. 417.50
(9)  Error on bank statement in entering deposit of 12/16/58:
     Correct amount....................... $3,182.40
     Entered in statement.................. 3,181.40          1.00

(10) Check No. 3917 of Powell Manufacturing Co., charged by
     bank in error to company's account................... 2,690.00
(11) Proceeds of note of J. Somers & Co. collected by bank,
     12/10/58, not entered in cash book:

     Principal........................... $2,000.00
     Interest............................     20.00
                                          _____
                                          $2,020.00
     Less collection charge..............      5.00      2,015.00

(12) Erroneous debit memo 12/23/58, to charge company's
     account with settlement of bank loan, which was paid by
     check No. 8714 on same date.......................... 5,000.00
(13) Error on bank statement in entering deposit of 12/4/58:
     Entered as.......................... $4,817.10
     Correct amount......................  4,807.10         10.00

(14) Deposit of Powell Manufacturing Co. of 12/6/58 credited
     in error to this company............................. 1,819.20

*Instructions:* (1) Prepare a reconciliation of the Howell Company's bank account at December 31, 1958.

(2) Prepare one or more journal entries to adjust the Howell Company's books to reflect the correct bank balance at December 31, 1958. (A.I.C.P.A. adapted)

**6-10.** You have been engaged to review the tax return of John Smith for 1958 and to determine whether the net income as reported was correct. You proceed as follows:

1. You scan the return and note that Smith's only income is derived from a business which he operates as a sole proprietorship.
2. You compare his gross profit percentage with those of comparable businesses and find it is lower than average.
3. You go to his place of business and find he keeps no records, except a check book and data on accounts payable. All sales are for cash. A physical inventory is taken annually. He has not made any investment in the business during 1958.

4. You find a discrepancy in the information shown by his tax return and his records. In the absence of a satisfactory explanation by Smith, you conclude that the gross receipts of the business may be misstated.

The tax return and information developed from the records are as follows:

### JOHN SMITH TAX RETURN
SCHEDULE OF BUSINESS INCOME
Year 1958

| | |
|---|---:|
| 1. Total business receipts.................................... | $68,000 |
| 2. Inventory at beginning of year........................... | $ 9,500 |
| 3. Purchases.............................................. | 51,400 |
| 4. Cost of labor.......................................... | — |
| 5. Materials and supplies.................................. | — |
| 6. Other costs............................................ | — |
| 7. Total................................................. | $60,900 |
| 8. Less—Inventory at end of year.......................... | 8,800 |
| 9. Cost of goods sold..................................... | $52,100 |
| 10. Gross profit........................................... | $15,900 |
| 11. Salaries and wages not included in line 4.............. | $ 2,600 |
| 12. Rent on business property.............................. | 1,500 |
| 13. Interest on business indebtedness...................... | — |
| 14. Taxes on business and business property................ | 800 |
| 15. Bad debts............................................. | — |
| 16. Depreciation.......................................... | 800 |
| 17. Repairs............................................... | 260 |
| 18. Depletion............................................. | — |
| 19. Other business expenses................................ | 4,160 |
| 20. Total................................................. | $10,120 |
| 21. Net profit or (loss).................................... | $ 5,780 |

Information gained from review of Smith's check book:

| | |
|---|---:|
| Cash balance, January 1, 1958.................... | $4,470 |
| Cash balance, December 31, 1958................. | 7,020 |
| Purchases of fixtures during 1958................. | 1,050 |
| Purchase of delivery truck during 1958............ | 2,400 |
| Smith's drawings during 1958.................... | 4,800 |

Other information:

| | |
|---|---:|
| Liabilities, January 1, 1958..................... | $4,500 |
| Liabilities, December 31, 1958.................... | 3,900 |

*Instructions:* Using the available data, prepare a schedule showing computation of the amount of the apparent discrepancy.

(A.I.C.P.A. adapted)

# Chapter 7

# RECEIVABLES

**NATURE OF RECEIVABLES** In its broadest sense, the term *receivables* is applicable to all claims against others, whether these be claims for money, for goods, or for services. For accounting purposes, however, the term is employed in a narrower sense to designate claims that will be settled by the receipt of money.

Usually, the chief source of receivables is found in the normal activities of the operating cycle of the business. Business today is largely based on credit. Goods and services are sold on account, the collection of the accounts following some time after the sales. In the meantime, the seller has claims against the buyers. Other receivables arise as a result of such diverse activities as advances made by a company, the sale of plant and equipment items, and the sale of capital stock.

**COMPOSITION OF RECEIVABLES** Receivables are composed of two classes: (1) those supported by formal promises to pay in the form of notes, referred to as *notes receivable*, and (2) those not so supported, referred to as *accounts receivable*. Accounts receivable may be divided into groupings as follows: (1) receivables from customers, (2) receivables from others, and (3) accrued receivables. Receivables should be established in the accounts only when supportable claims exist, and it can be assumed that the claims will be realized.

**NOTES RECEIVABLE** A note is an unconditional written promise by one party to another to pay a certain sum of money at a specified date. The note may be negotiable or nonnegotiable. It is negotiable or legally transferable by endorsement and delivery only if it provides for payment to the order of the second party or bearer. Such notes are commonly accepted by commercial banks for discount; hence they are considered more liquid than are other classes of receivables.

The term "notes" is commonly used in accounting to include not only promissory notes but also time drafts and trade acceptances. If the time drafts and the trade acceptances are significant in amount, they may be summarized separately.

The notes receivable designation for reporting purposes should be limited to negotiable short-term instruments that are acquired from trade debtors and that are not yet due. When a written instrument fails to meet these requirements, it should be reported separately under an appropriately descriptive title. Notes arising from loans to customers, officers, employees, and affiliated companies, for example, should be separately reported.

**ACCOUNTS RECEIVABLE**   As previously indicated, accounts receivable broadly include all receivables other than those supported by some form of commercial paper. While it would be appropriate to refer to receivables arising from the sale of goods and services as "Trade Debtors" or "Customer Receivables" to distinguish these from other receivables, it has become established practice to use the designation "Accounts Receivable" to represent these claims. Accounts Receivable for reporting purposes should be limited to trade accounts that are expected to be converted into cash in the regular course of business. This balance, for example, should not include receivables arising from customer container charges that will be liquidated by the return of containers.

Normally, the trade account is recognized only upon the legal passing of title of goods to a buyer or upon the performance of services. There is no basis for the recognition of a receivable upon shipments "on approval" where the shipper retains title to the goods until there is an acceptance, or upon shipments "on consignment" where the consignor retains title to the goods until their sale by the consignee. Under these circumstances only a memorandum entry is appropriate until title to goods passes. Ordinarily, detailed records of customer transactions and customers' balances are carried in subsidiary records, an accounts receivable controlling account in the general ledger summarizing subsidiary account balances.

Nontrade receivables should be summarized in appropriately titled accounts and should be reported separately. The following are examples of the special receivables that are separately carried: claims arising from the sale of securities or property other than goods or services; claims on uncompleted contracts; advances to officers, agencies, and affiliated companies; deposits with creditors and other agencies; purchase prepayments; deposits to guarantee contract performance or expense payment; claims against transportation companies or insurance companies for losses or damages; claims for rebates and tax refunds; claims upon subscribers to capital stock; and dividends receivable on investments in stock.

Certain revenues for services or goods accrue with the passage of time and are most conveniently recognized upon collection. At the end of the period, in order to report fully on position and the results of operations, it is necessary to calculate the amounts accrued since the last receipts and to establish appropriate accrued receivables. Accrued interest is recognized on assets in the form of bank deposits, notes, bonds, annuities, etc. Rentals may accrue on real estate holdings. Royalties and patent fees may accrue on certain rights and properties. Salaries and commissions may accrue as a result of services. For some business units accrued receivables may be small in total; for others — banks, utilities, etc. — they may represent a very important asset.

It was indicated in an earlier chapter that the current asset classification as broadly conceived comprehends all receivables identified with the normal operating cycle. Installment and other deferred collection contracts are fully included regardless of their terms. But receivables arising outside of the inventory-to-cash cycle qualify as current only if they are expected to be collected within one year. For balance sheet classification purposes, then, each nontrade item requires separate analysis to determine whether there is reasonable certainty that it will be collected currently. Noncurrent receivables are reported under the Investments or Other Assets caption, whichever may be considered appropriate.

Amounts due from officers, directors, and major stockholders arising out of sales and subject to the usual credit terms are normally considered current; however, when claims have arisen from transactions other than sales and current recovery is not assured, such items are appropriately regarded as noncurrent. Sales to affiliated companies give rise to current claims, but advances to such companies are generally regarded as of a long-term nature. Deposits on materials and merchandise ordered will soon represent inventories and hence are reported as current, whereas deposits on utility contracts may be considered long-term. Deposits for machinery and equipment ordered are noncurrent in view of the ultimate application of the deposit. Claims arising from the sale of assets other than goods or services and calling for collections over a period in excess of one year require special analysis to determine the portion of the claim to be reported as current and the portion to be reported as noncurrent.

Subscriptions to capital stock are current only as long as it is assumed that they are currently collectible; when current collection is not probable or when payments may be deferred indefinitely, such balances are reported as noncurrent assets or in some instances more appropriately as subtractions from capital balances so that no more than the amount actually paid in by stockholders and subscribers is reported as invested capital.

When income tax refund claims or other claims have been granted and collection is expected within one year, they qualify for current presentation. When claims are still being processed and recovery is assured although the period required for such processing is uncertain, claims are shown under a noncurrent heading. Certain claims may be in dispute. When a claim does not involve a material amount and there is little likelihood of recovery, no reference needs to be made to it on the balance sheet pending settlement. On the other hand, if a material amount is involved and there is prospect of a favorable settlement, the claim is properly viewed as a contingent receivable and deserves recognition. Disclosure may be made by a parenthetical remark in the asset section of the balance sheet, by a statement or note, or by an appropriate comment under a separate contingent asset heading. If a contingent receivable becomes an actual receivable, it is recognized as such at the later date, and a gain account or Retained Earnings is credited.

Creditor and customer accounts with contra balances require special attention. These balances are found by an analysis of subsidiary ledger detail. For example, assume that the accounts payable controlling account reports a balance of $10,000. Inspection of subsidiary account detail reveals accounts with credit balances totaling $10,500 together with accounts with debit balances of $500. The nature of the debit balances should be investigated. If the debit balances have arisen as a result of overpayments or returns and allowances after payment, they are reportable as current assets in view of the claims that they represent for cash or merchandise from vendors. Such balances are properly reported under a title such as "Creditors' Accounts with Debit Balances" or "Sundry Claims." If debit balances have resulted from advance raw material or merchandise purchase payments by the company, these, too, represent a current asset reportable under some descriptive title such as "Advances on Purchase Contracts." In either case, Accounts Payable is reported at $10,500. Although both an asset and a liability are reported, no adjustment to the controlling account or the subsidiary ledger detail is required. Debit balances in the subsidiary ledger are carried forward and are ultimately canceled by further purchase billings or cash settlement.

Customer ledger detail needs similar analysis. Customers' accounts with credit balances may result from overpayments, from customer returns after full payment, or from advance payments by customers.

Such credits qualify as current liabilities and should be reported accordingly. Accounts receivable, then, are reported at the sum of the debit balances reported in the subsidiary ledger.

It may be pointed out that when contra balances in customer and creditor accounts are relatively insignificant in amount, they are frequently disregarded and only the net receivable or payable balance as shown by the controlling account is reported on the balance sheet.

**VALUATION OF**           Theoretically, receivables should be carried
**RECEIVABLES**            at their cash value. Receivables, thus, are
properly reported at their present discounted values — claim balances reduced by the application of a discount rate for the period from the balance sheet date to the date of expected collection. Such adjustments are normally small and are generally ignored in practice. Notes re-receivable are usually reported at their face value. Thus, non-interest-bearing notes are shown at face values although, theoretically, not worth face values until their maturity dates. Accounts receivable are usually reported at the amounts collectible according to the terms of the sale even though such collections may not be made for some time. Interest-bearing receivables call for the recognition of accrued interest on the balance sheet date.

Almost invariably some of the accounts receivable arising from sales will prove uncollectible. This makes it desirable to anticipate the loss on accounts so that the loss may be related to the period of the sale, and the asset arising from sales may be stated at its estimated realizable amount.

Recognition of a probable loss on receivable collections, as explained in an earlier chapter, is accomplished by a charge to Loss from Bad Debts and a credit to Allowance for Bad Debts. The bad debts charge may be treated as a deduction from sales on the theory that it is net sales — sales after such bad debts shrinkage — that must cover current charges and yield a profit. Instead of being treated as a contra-sales balance, however, the bad debts item is usually regarded as emerging from a failure of management and, hence, is reported as a selling, general and administrative, or financial charge, depending upon the division that is held responsible for controlling such losses. The allowance account is reported as a subtraction from accounts receivable. Use of the allowance account avoids premature adjustments to individual receivable accounts while making possible a continuing control of subsidiary ledger detail by accounts receivable in the general ledger. When positive evidence is available concerning the partial or complete worthlessness of an account, a charge is made to the allowance and the receivable is credited. Positive evidence of a loss would be found in the bankruptcy, death, or disappearance of a debtor, failure to legally enforce collection, and a barring of collection by the statute of limitations.

**BASES FOR ESTIMATE OF BAD DEBT LOSSES** The estimate for bad debt losses may be based upon (1) the amount of sales or (2) the amount of receivables. When sales are used as the basis for calculation, the problem of estimating losses is viewed as one involving primarily the accurate measurement of income. Basing the adjustment on receivables considers the problem from the point of view of proper asset valuation. A description of the methods employed under each of these bases is described in the paragraphs that follow.

**BAD DEBTS ADJUSTMENT BASED ON SALES** Bad debt losses of recent periods are related to corresponding sales in developing a percentage of losses to sales. This percentage may be modified by expectations in the light of current experience. Since bad debts occur only on credit sales, it would seem logical to develop a percentage of losses to charge sales of the past. This would be applied to charge sales of the current period. However, since extra work may be required in maintaining records of cash and credit sales or in analyzing sales data, the percentage is frequently developed in terms of total sales. Unless there is considerable fluctuation in the proportion of cash and credit sales periodically, the total sales method will give satisfactory results.

The sales percentage method for anticipating losses is widely used in practice because of its soundness in theory and simplicity in application. Although normally offering a satisfactory approach to income measurement by providing equitable charges to periodic revenue, the method may not offer a "cash realizable" valuation for receivables such as would be obtained when an allowance is established in terms of the receivables base. The latter shortcoming can be overcome by analyzing receivables at different intervals and correcting the allowance balance for any significant excess or deficiency.

**BAD DEBTS ADJUSTMENT BASED ON RECEIVABLES** There are three methods of establishing and maintaining an allowance for bad debts when receivables are used as the base for the adjustment:

(1) The allowance is raised to a certain percentage of receivables.

(2) The allowance is increased by a certain percentage of receivables.

(3) The allowance is raised to an amount determined by analyzing the accounts.

*Raising Allowance to a Certain Percentage of Receivables.* This method calls for relating the bad debts experience of recent periods to accounts outstanding in such periods, together with a consideration of special current conditions. An estimate of the probable losses to be suffered in the realization of receivables on hand is developed in terms of this information. Loss from Bad Debts is charged and Allowance for Bad Debts is credited for an amount that will bring the allowance to the desired balance. To illustrate, assume receivables of $60,000 at the end of a period, a credit balance of $200 in the allowance account, and an estimated bad debt loss factor of 2% of accounts receivable. The allowance in this case should be stated at $1,200. The following entry brings the allowance to the desired amount:

Loss from Bad Debts .......................... 1,000
  Allowance for Bad Debts....................... 1,000

This method is simple in application. Although offering a satisfactory approach to the measurement of receivables, it may fail to provide equitable periodic charges to revenue. This is particularly true in view of the irregular determinations of bad debt losses as well as the lag in their recognition. After the first year, periodic bad debt provisions are directly affected by the current reductions in the allowance resulting from a recognition of bad accounts originating in prior periods.

*Increasing Allowance by a Certain Percentage of Receivables.* This method also calls for the development of a rate after appropriate analysis of loss experience. The accepted rate is then applied to the balance of accounts receivable on hand in arriving at the charge for bad debts and allowance increase. This method is a simple one to apply, and it is not subject to the shortcomings of the previous method. The application of this method, however, results in recurring charges for those accounts on hand at the end of successive periods unless the account balances are analyzed and appropriate adjustment is made to avoid a duplication of loss provisions. This factor must be considered, particularly when interim statements are prepared.

*Raising Allowance to an Amount Determined by Analyzing the Accounts.* Perhaps the most satisfactory of the methods wherein receivables are used as the adjustment base is the one commonly called *aging receivables.* Individual accounts receivable are reviewed to determine those that are past-due. Accounts determined to be past-due are analyzed in terms of the length of the period past-due, and are classified in terms of such aging. For purposes of classification, an analysis sheet may be used and past-due balances listed and carried across into a series of columns that show the period past due. An illustration of such an analysis is shown below:

### PARKER AND POPE
#### ANALYSIS OF PAST-DUE RECEIVABLES — DECEMBER 31, 1958

| CUSTOMER | AMOUNT | NOT MORE THAN 30 DAYS PAST DUE | 31–60 DAYS PAST DUE | 61–90 DAYS PAST DUE | 91–180 DAYS PAST DUE | 181–365 DAYS PAST DUE | MORE THAN 1 YEAR PAST DUE |
|---|---|---|---|---|---|---|---|
| A. B. Andrews.... | 450 | | 450 | | | | |
| B. T. Brooks...... | 300 | | | 100 | 200 | | |
| B. Bryant........ | 200 | 200 | | | | | |
| L. B. Devine...... | 100 | 100 | | | | | |
| K. Flood......... | 200 | | | | | | 200 |
| M. A. Young..... | 400 | 100 | | 300 | | | |
| Total........... | 7,550 | 3,000 | 1,200 | 650 | 500 | 800 | 1,400 |

It is desirable to review each overdue balance with some appropriate company official and to arrive at estimates concerning the degree of collectibility of each item listed. An alternative procedure is to develop a series of estimated loss percentages and to apply these to the different receivable classifications. The calculation of the allowance on the latter basis is illustrated below:

### PARKER AND POPE
#### ESTIMATED AMOUNT OF UNCOLLECTIBLE ACCOUNTS — DECEMBER 31, 1958

| CLASSIFICATION | BALANCES | BAD DEBT EXPERIENCE PERCENTAGE | ESTIMATED AMOUNT OF UNCOLLECTIBLES |
|---|---|---|---|
| Not yet due..................... | $40,000 | 2% | $ 800 |
| Not more than 30 days past due. | 3,000 | 5% | 150 |
| 31–60 days past due............ | 1,200 | 10% | 120 |
| 61–90 days past due............ | 650 | 20% | 130 |
| 91–180 days past due........... | 500 | 30% | 150 |
| 181–365 days past due.......... | 800 | 50% | 400 |
| More than one year past due...... | 1,400 | 80% | 1,120 |
| | $47,550 | | $2,870 |

Loss from Bad Debts is now debited and Allowance for Bad Debts is credited for an amount that will bring the allowance account up to the required balance. Assuming that the allowance account shows a credit balance of $620 before adjustment and a loss of $2,870 is indicated as shown in the tabulation, the following entry is made to raise the allowance to the required amount:

| Loss from Bad Debts............................. | 2,250 | |
| Allowance for Bad Debts......................... | | 2,250 |

The aging method provides the most satisfactory approach to the valuation of receivables at their cash realizable amounts.  However, application of this method may require considerable time and may prove expensive when a great many accounts are involved.  The method still involves estimates, and the added refinement that is achieved by the aging process may not warrant the additional effort.  It should be pointed out, too, that the adoption of the asset valuation approach, here as in the other instances, may fail to provide equitable periodic charges to profit and loss, since charges are not coordinated with sales but are made when there is a recognizable impairment of asset values.

**CORRECTIONS IN ALLOWANCE FOR BAD DEBTS**     As indicated in the previous paragraphs, the allowance for bad debts balance is established and maintained by means of adjusting entries at the close of each accounting period.  If the allowance provisions are too large, the allowance account balance will be unnecessarily inflated and profits will be understated; if the allowance provisions are too small, the allowance account balance will be inadequate and profits will be overstated.

Care must be taken to see that the allowance balance follows the credit experience of the particular business.  The process of aging receivables may be employed as a means of checking the allowance balance at different intervals to be certain that it is being maintained satisfactorily.  Such periodic reviews may suggest the need for a correction in the allowance as well as a change in the rate to be applied or a change in method.

When the bad debt experience approximates the anticipation of such losses, even though there is not an exact correspondence between bad debts and the balance allowed therefor, the allowance procedure may be considered satisfactory and no adjustment is called for.  When it appears that there has been a failure to estimate losses satisfactorily in prior periods resulting in an allowance balance that is clearly inadequate or excessive, a correcting entry is in order.  When correction of a material amount to the allowance account is involved, the corresponding charge or credit should be made to a special account disclosing the correction in profits of prior periods or to Retained Earnings, whichever is appropriate.

The recognition of current period receivables as bad debt losses by charges to the allowance may result in a debit balance in the allowance account.  A debit balance arising in this manner does not prove that the allowance is inadequate.  Here charges to the allowance simply predate the current loss provision, and the adjustment at the end of the period should cover losses already determined as well as those yet to be recognized.

Occasionally, accounts that have been charged off as worthless are unexpectedly collected. The original entry whereby the customer's account was written off against the allowance should be reversed, inasmuch as the collection shows the write-off to have been made in error. The receipt of cash is then recorded in the usual manner.

**BAD DEBTS RECOGNI-** In the case of many small businesses and in
**TION AT TIME OF LOSS** certain instances where estimated losses on
accounts receivable cannot be reliably determined, no provision is made at the end of the period in anticipation of bad debt losses. Instead, bad debt losses are recognized in the periods in which the accounts are determined to be uncollectible. When bad debts are not anticipated by the establishment of an allowance, accounts found to be bad are written off by a charge to Loss from Bad Debts and a credit to the customer's account. If an account written off is unexpectedly recovered in the same period, the entry to record the loss may be reversed and the collection recorded in the usual manner. If recovery is made in a subsequent period, it is necessary to restore the receivable balance and to credit a nominal account such as Recoveries of Accounts Written Off in Prior Periods; the collection of the receivable is then recorded in the usual manner. The balance of the account Recoveries of Accounts Written Off in Prior Periods may be reported as a subtraction from Loss from Bad Debts in arriving at the net charge for bad debts made currently, or it may be reported separately as an extraordinary item.

While theory supports the anticipation of uncollectibles so that revenue may carry its full burden of expenses, the identification of the charge with the period of its discovery is frequently practiced because of its simplicity and convenience. It has already been suggested that for income tax purposes the use of either method is acceptable. The method adopted, however, must be employed consistently on successive tax returns. The two methods are compared at the top of the following page.

**ANTICIPATION OF DIS-** The foregoing discussion has been restricted
**COUNTS AND OTHER** to the concepts governing the provision for
**CHARGES IN VALUA-**
**TION OF RECEIVABLES** uncollectible items. Conditions of sales and
collections may suggest the anticipation of other charges that will

| Transaction | Entry | |
|---|---|---|
| | Assuming that bad debts are charged to an allowance account set up in anticipation of such losses | Assuming that bad debts are charged to operations in the period in which the losses are determined |
| To increase allowance for bad debts at the end of the period. | Loss from Bad Debts. . 1,200 Allowance for Bad Debts... 1,200 | |
| To write off customers' accounts assumed to be worthless. | Allowance for Bad Debts..... 850 Accounts Receivable.... 850 | Loss from Bad Debts.......... 850 Accounts Receivable.... 850 |
| To restore customer's account previously written off but now determined to be collectible, | | |
| (a) assuming determination is made in period of write-off. | Accounts Receivable...... 100 Allowance for Bad Debts... 100 | Accounts Receivable...... 100 Loss from Bad Debts........ 100 |
| (b) assuming determination is made in subsequent period. | Accounts Receivable...... 100 Allowance for Bad Debts.... 100 | Accounts Receivable...... 100 Recoveries of Accounts Written Off in Prior Periods...... 100 |
| To record collection of customer's account. | Cash.......... 100 Accounts Receivable.... 100 | Cash.......... 100 Accounts Receivable.... 100 |

emerge in the realization of accounts receivable and hence are properly matched against current revenue.

For example, if customers generally take cash discounts in making remittance, it may be argued that reporting receivables and income in terms of customer billings involves some overstatement of these items. Under such circumstances, it may be desirable to anticipate discounts by a charge to Sales Discounts and a credit to Allowance for Sales Discounts. Allowance for Sales Discounts would be subtracted from Accounts Receivable so that receivables are reflected at their estimated cash realizable value. Discounts on the collection of old accounts in the new period may be charged against the allowance account. It would, however, be more convenient to transfer the allowance to the sales discounts account by a reversing entry at the beginning of the new period. All discounts can then be reported in the sales discounts account, the credit balance in this account serving to absorb that portion of sales discounts already charged against profits of the prior period.

Similar recognition may be suggested for probable allowances yet to be made to customers relative to shipment shortages and defects, price adjustments, etc., and for probable losses to be sustained on sales returns. Claims that customers may make for freight charges that they pay on the receipt of goods or on the return of goods may call for consideration. Future costs of billing, collection activities, and attorneys' efforts involved in the realization of accounts may likewise warrant consideration. It may be pointed out that the refinement in measurement available through the establishment of allowances for the classes of items just mentioned is seldom found in practice. When allowances are not established and the volume of activities and experiences with respect to such charges does not vary materially from period to period, the recognition of such charges in the period in which they are finally determined will have little effect upon periodic profit and loss, although asset balances may include some minor overstatement.

The preceding discussion has considered the anticipation of charges relating to the realization of accounts receivable. The realization of notes receivable may involve similar charges. When sales are used as a basis for estimating future charges, allowances may be considered applicable to accounts receivable and also to notes receivable accepted in liquidation of accounts. When accounts receivable are analyzed and used as a base for developing related allowances, notes receivable would require similar analysis in the development of allowances to absorb charges involved in their realization.

**USE OF RECEIVABLES FOR PROCUREMENT OF CASH**    A business frequently requires cash for current purposes in excess of the amount on hand and the amount to become available in the normal course of operations. The business may use accounts receivable or notes receivable as a basis for a cash advance from a bank or a finance company. These procedures are described in the sections that follow.

**ASSIGNMENT OF ACCOUNTS RECEIVABLE**    In order to obtain immediate cash, accounts receivable owned by the business may be (1) pledged, (2) assigned, or (3) sold.

*Pledge of Accounts Receivable.* Advances are frequently obtained from banks or other lending institutions by pledging accounts receivable as security on the loan. Ordinarily, collections are made by the borrower, who is required to use this cash in meeting his obligation to the lender. The lender, in such instances, may be given access to the borrower's records to determine whether remittances are being properly made on pledged accounts.

*Assignment of Accounts Receivable.* Certain finance companies advance cash upon the assignment to them of a given amount of accounts receivable. Such assignments carry a guarantee on the part of the assignor that he will make up any deficiency in the event the accounts fail to realize the expected amount. Assignments thus represent, in effect, sale of accounts on a *recourse* basis. The total of accounts assigned normally exceeds the cash advanced by an amount considered adequate to cover uncollectible items, returns, offsets, and amounts subject to dispute. When amounts actually recovered on assigned accounts exceed the sum of the advance and the finance company's charges, such excess accrues to the assignor. Charges made by the finance company usually consist of a service charge based upon the face amount of the advance, plus interest upon the actual unrecovered balance computed on a daily basis. Collections on the accounts receivable may be made by the borrower who turns the cash over to the assignee, or they may be made by the finance company.

*Sale of Accounts Receivable.* Certain dealers or finance companies purchase accounts receivable outright on a *without recourse* basis. This is known as accounts receivable *factoring,* and the purchaser is referred to as a *factor.* Customers are notified that their bills are payable to the factor, and this party assumes the burden of billing and collecting accounts. In many instances, factoring may involve more than simply the purchase and collection of accounts receivable. Modern factoring frequently involves a continuing agreement whereby a financing institution assumes the credit function as well as the collection function. Under such an arrangement, the factor grants or denies credit, handles the accounts receivable bookkeeping, sends out billings, and makes collections. The business unit is relieved of all of the activities relating to credit and collection. The sale of goods provides immediate cash for business use. Because the factor may assume certain credit, bookkeeping, and collection routines and also absorb the losses from bad accounts, the charge that he makes exceeds the interest charge involved in borrowing cash from a bank or the service and interest charges involved in the assignment of receivables.

*Accounting Procedures for Accounts Receivable Financing.* No special accounting problems are encountered in the pledge or the sale of receivables. When receivables are pledged, the books simply report the loan and the subsequent settlement. Disclosure should be made on the balance sheet by parenthetical comment or note of the receivables pledged to secure the obligation to the lending agency. When receivables are sold outright, Cash is debited, receivables and related allowance balances are closed, and an expense account is charged for factoring costs. No further entries are required.

The assignment of accounts calls for special accounting procedures. Although the assignment of accounts receivable is comparable to the discounting of customers' notes and similar accounting may be employed, it is simpler practice to treat the relationship with the finance company as a loan secured by specific assets that will be used to liquidate the loan. Two entries are made at the time the advance is received and the accounts receivable are assigned: one entry records the obligation to the finance company for the advance and the flat charge; the second entry sets apart under separate control those accounts whose proceeds will be applied to payment of the loan.

To illustrate accounting for the assignment of accounts receivable following the procedure just explained, assume that the Masters Company on March 1 assigns accounts receivable of $24,000 to the Jones Finance Corporation and receives $19,500 in cash, a service charge of $500 being made for the advance. The entries on the books of the Masters Company are:

| Transaction | Entry on Borrower's Books | | |
|---|---|---|---|
| Mar.  1 Assigned accounts receivable of $24,000 to Jones Finance Corp., receiving $19,500 representing $20,000 less a charge of 2½% on the advance. | Accounts Receivable Assigned............ | 24,000 | |
| | Accounts Receivable. | | 24,000 |
| | Cash................ | 19,500 | |
| | Assignment Expense... | 500 | |
| | Jones Finance Corp.. | | 20,000 |
| Mar. 31 Collections for March, $15,000. Remitted this amount to finance company to apply on advance together with interest at 6% for one month on this amount. | Cash................ | 15,000 | |
| | Accounts Receivable Assigned.......... | | 15,000 |
| | Jones Finance Corp.... | 15,000 | |
| | Interest Expense...... | 75 | |
| | Cash............. | | 15,075 |
| Apr. 30 Collections for April, $7,500. Remitted balance owed to finance company, $5,000, together with interest at 6% for two months on this amount. | Cash................. | 7,500 | |
| | Accounts Receivable Assigned ........... | | 7,500 |
| | Jones Finance Corp...... | 5,000 | |
| | Interest Expense........ | 50 | |
| | Cash.............. | | 5,050 |
| Returned remaining assigned accounts to unassigned accounts control. | Accounts Receivable..... | 1,500 | |
| | Accounts Receivable Assigned ........... | | 1,500 |

If a balance sheet is prepared before the finance company has received full payment, the total of accounts assigned less the portion required to cover the claim of the finance company is reported as an asset. A statement is also made concerning the contingent liability on the part of the company to meet the obligation in the event that assigned accounts do not realize enough to liquidate the loan. To illustrate, if in the preceding example a balance sheet is prepared on March 31, accounts receivable and information relating to assigned accounts may be reported as follows:

Current assets:
| | | |
|---|---|---|
| Accounts receivable........................................ | | $50,000 |
| Company's interest in assigned accounts receivable: | | |
| Assigned accounts.................... | $9,000 | |
| Less interest of Jones Finance Corp. in assigned accounts (company is contingently liable as guarantors of assigned accounts)......................... | 5,000 | 4,000 |
| Total accounts receivable ........................... | | $54,000 |

When collections are made by the finance company, a procedure similar to that illustrated can still be employed. In such instances, however, entries are made when information is received from the finance company concerning collections, interest charges, and the return of accounts in excess of claims.

A business may resort to accounts receivable financing as a temporary and emergency matter after exhausting the limited line of unsecured credit that may be available from a lending institution. On the other hand, a business may engage in such financing as a continuing policy. Recent years have witnessed an increasing number of factoring arrangements involving the full delegation of credit and collection responsibilities to specialists. Financial assistance to business through the factoring of open accounts presently runs into billions of dollars.

**DISCOUNTING CUSTOMERS' NOTES**    Cash may be obtained by having customers' notes discounted by the bank or some other agency willing to accept such instruments. If a customer's note is non-interest-bearing, cash is received for the face value of the note less a charge for interest, known as *discount*, for the period from the date the note is discounted to the date of its maturity. If the note is interest-bearing, the maturity value of the note is first determined. The amount that is received from the bank is the maturity value of the note less discount calculated on this maturity value from the date the note is discounted to its maturity. In calculating the interest charge for short-term notes, it is the usual practice to use the exact number of days from the date of discount to the due date of the note.

To illustrate, assume that a customer's $1,000, 2-month note dated December 1 is discounted on December 11 at 6%. In figuring time, the wording on the note is followed. The above note is due two months hence, or on February 1. If it were a 60-day note, it would be due on January 30 (30 days remaining in December and 30 days in January). The discount period is calculated as follows:

| | |
|---|---:|
| December 11–31 | 20 days |
| January | 31 days |
| February 1 (due date) | 1 day |
| Total | 52 days |

Assuming that the note is non-interest-bearing, the cash proceeds on discounting the note are calculated as follows:

| | |
|---|---:|
| Maturity value of note | $1,000.00 |
| Discount on $1,000 for 52 days at 6% | 8.67 |
| Discounted value of note | $ 991.33 |

The following entry is made:

| | | |
|---|---:|---:|
| Cash | 991.33 | |
| Interest Expense | 8.67 | |
| Notes Receivable | | 1,000.00 |

The discount of $8.67 may be calculated as follows:

Principal × Rate × Time = Interest

$$\$1,000 \times \frac{6}{100} \times \frac{52}{360} = \$8.67$$

It should be observed that in interest calculations involving short-term notes, 360 days rather than 365 days are generally used as the equivalent of a year. When this is the case, the "6% method" may prove convenient in calculating interest. Inasmuch as the year is considered to consist of 360 days, interest at 6% for 60 days is one sixth of a full year's interest, or 1%. Interest at 6% for 30 days is one half of that for 60 days; interest for 6 days is one tenth of that for 60 days. By using such simple combinations, the interest at 6% on any amount can be readily determined. In discounting the note above, the discount is calculated as follows:

| | | |
|---|---:|---:|
| (a) Interest on $1,000 for 60 days at 6% (.01 of principal) | | $10.00 |
| (b) Less: interest on $1,000 for 6 days at 6% (.001 of principal) | $1.00 | |
| (c) interest on $1,000 for 2 days at 6% ($\frac{1}{3}$ of [b]). | .33 | 1.33 |
| (d) Interest on $1,000 for 52 days at 6% | | $ 8.67 |

If the interest rate above were more or less than 6%, the interest at 6% can be computed first and then increased or decreased according to the relationship that the given rate bears to the 6% base figure. For example, if the interest rate is 7%, the interest amount at 6% is multiplied by $\frac{7}{6}$ or raised by $\frac{1}{6}$; if the interest rate is 4%, the interest amount at 6% is multiplied by $\frac{4}{6}$ or reduced by $\frac{1}{3}$.

Assume that the note previously mentioned provides for payment of principal plus interest at 6% at maturity, and that it is discounted at 6%. Determination of the cash proceeds is as follows:

| | |
|---|---:|
| Principal of note............................................. | $1,000.00 |
| Interest to maturity (60 days at 6%)........................ | 10.00 |
| Maturity value of note...................................... | $1,010.00 |
| Discount on $1,010 for 52 days at 6%....................... | 8.75 |
| Discounted value of note.................................... | $1,001.25 |

The following entry is made:

| | | |
|---|---:|---:|
| Cash..................................................... | 1,001.25 | |
| Notes Receivable............................... | | 1,000.00 |
| Interest Income............................... | | 1.25 |

When a person endorses a note "without recourse," he is relieved of any liability on the inability of the maker of the note or any prior endorser to make settlement of the note upon its maturity. When he endorses a note without making any qualification, however, he becomes liable to subsequent holders of the note for its full payment in the event it is not paid at maturity. An endorser who is held liable on an instrument has the right to recover such payment from the maker of the note who failed to comply with its terms.

Normally, endorsement without qualification is required in discounting a note, and the endorser becomes contingently liable on the paper. The possibility that the endorser will be obliged to make payment on a note that is discounted may be indicated in the accounts by a credit to Notes Receivable Discounted instead of Notes Receivable at the time the note is discounted. Notes Receivable Discounted then reports the contingent liability arising through the note transfer; Notes Receivable remains open pending final settlement of the obligation. When the person who holds the note at maturity receives payment from the maker, the contingent liability on the part of an endorsee is ended. The latter party can now apply the notes receivable discounted balance against Notes Receivable.

In preparing statements, Notes Receivable Discounted should be reported as a subtraction from Notes Receivable. This procedure serves to reduce notes to the balance actually held while at the same time showing the contingent liability arising from the transfer of notes.

The use of the notes receivable discounted account gives the same final result as that obtained when Notes Receivable is credited for each note that is discounted. Since data concerning the contingent liability are of concern only on the balance sheet date and these can be determined readily at the end of the period from an examination of the detailed record of notes transferred, the extra work involved in maintaining a notes receivable discounted account may not be warranted. When the notes receivable discounted account is not used, information concerning the contingent liability can be provided on the balance sheet by means of a parenthetical remark, an accompanying note, or a comment under a separate contingent liabilities heading.

If a note is not paid when it is due, the holder of the note must give the endorser prompt notice of such dishonor. The endorser is then required to make payment to the holder. Payment consists of the face value of the note plus interest and plus any fees and costs relating to collection. The full amount paid is recoverable from the maker of the note, and Accounts Receivable, Notes Receivable Dishonored, or Notes Receivable Past-Due is charged. If Notes Receivable Discounted was credited at the time the note was discounted, this balance, together with the original notes receivable balance, should be canceled.

Assuming that collection of the claim on the dishonored note plus additional interest for the overdue period is made at a later date, Cash is debited and the maker's account and Interest Income are credited. Interest for the overdue period is computed according to the terms of the note or at the legal rate as required by the laws of the particular state. If part or all of the debtor's balance proves uncollectible, the unpaid balance is written off as a loss or a charge against an allowance for uncollectibles, whichever is appropriate.

Two sets of illustrations will be offered: (1) discounting a customer's non-interest-bearing note, and (2) discounting a customer's interest-bearing note.

(1) Assume that J. P. Phillips gives S. R. Turner a $1,000, 2-month, non-interest-bearing note dated December 1 in payment of an account. The note is discounted by Turner on December 11 at 6%, and the contingent liability is recorded. The note is paid at maturity.

(2) Assume the facts in the preceding paragraph except that (a) the note bears interest at the rate of 6% and (b) Phillips does not pay the note until 90 days after it is due. Interest for the overdue period is computed on the face of the note at 6%.

Entries for these two illustrations are given on pages 212 and 213.

**PRESENTATION OF RECEIVABLES ON THE BALANCE SHEET** Normally the receivables that qualify as current items are grouped for presentation in the following classes: (1) notes—trade debtors, (2) accounts — trade debtors, (3) other receivables, and (4) accrued receivables. Reporting should disclose notes that are nonnegotiable. The detail reported for other and accrued receivables depends upon the relative significance of the various items included. When trade accounts or installment contracts are properly reported as current but involve collections beyond one year, particulars of such deferred collections should be provided. Valuation accounts are deducted from the individual receivable balance or combined balances to which they relate. Notes receivable may be reported gross with notes receivable discounted shown as a deduction from this balance, or notes may be reported net with the contingent liability being separately mentioned. Accounts receivable assigned may be reported gross with the interest of the assignee in such accounts shown as a subtraction item, or the company's interest in receivables may be reported net with appropriate reference to the contingent liability involved. When receivables have been mortgaged, pledged, or otherwise hypothecated, this should be fully disclosed, together with reference to the obligation that is thus secured.

Current receivable items as they might appear on the balance sheet are shown below:

Receivables:

| | | |
|---|---:|---:|
| Trade notes and drafts receivable(notes of $20,000 have been pledged to secure bank borrowing) | | $ 38,000 |
| Trade accounts receivable (including installment contracts not due for 12–18 months of approximately $30,000)..................... | $112,000 | |
| Less: Allowance for losses on repossessions and bad debts......................... | 2,500 | 109,500 |
| Miscellaneous notes and accounts, including short-term loans to employees of $6,500...... | | 12,000 |
| Accrued receivables........................ | | 4,500 |
| Total receivables............................. | | $164,000 |

*Illustration 1. Discounting a customer's non-interest-bearing note:*

| Transactions | Entries on Books of Phillips, the Customer | | |
|---|---|---|---|
| December 1: Issuance of 2-month, non-interest-bearing note. | Accounts Payable — S.R. Turner ....... Notes Payable ... | 1,000.00 | 1,000.00 |
| December 11: Note discounted for 52 days at 6%. | | | |
| December 31: Adjustment at end of annual fiscal period to record prepaid interest for 32 days. | | | |
| January 1: Reversing entry. | | | |
| February 1: Payment of note. | Notes Payable ..... Cash .......... | 1,000.00 | 1,000.00 |

*Illustration 2. Discounting a customer's interest-bearing note:*

| Transactions | Entries on Books of Phillips, the Customer | | |
|---|---|---|---|
| December 1: Issuance of 2-month, 6% note. | Accounts Payable — S. R. Turner ....... Notes Payable ... | 1,000.00 | 1,000.00 |
| December 11: Note discounted for 52 days at 6%. | | | |
| December 31: Adjustment at end of annual fiscal period to record accrued interest for 30 days. | Interest Expense ... Accrued Interest on Notes Payable .......... | 5.00 | 5.00 |
| January 1: Reversing entry. | Accrued Interest on Notes Payable ..... Interest Expense .. | 5.00 | 5.00 |
| February 1: Failure to pay by maker; payment of note by endorser including interest, $10, and protest fee, $2. | | | |
| May 2: Payment by maker of note, including interest, protest fee, and interest on $1,000 for overdue period at 6%. | Notes Payable ..... Interest Expense ... Miscellaneous Expense .......... Cash .......... | 1,000.00 25.00 2.00 | 1,027.00 |

| Entries on Books of Turner, the Seller | | Entries on Books of Party Discounting Note | |
|---|---|---|---|
| Notes Receivable.... | 1,000.00 | | |
| Accounts Receivable — J.P.Phillips | 1,000.00 | | |
| Cash............ | 991.33 | Notes Receivable... | 1,000.00 |
| Interest Expense... | 8.67 | Cash........... | 991.33 |
| Notes Receivable Discounted...... | 1,000.00 | Interest Income.. | 8.67 |
| Prepaid Interest Expense.......... | 5.33 | Interest Income.... | 5.33 |
| Interest Expense. | 5.33 | Unearned Interest Income........ | 5.33 |
| Interest Expense... | 5.33 | Unearned Interest Income.......... | 5.33 |
| Prepaid Interest Expense........ | 5.33 | Interest Income.. | 5.33 |
| Notes Receivable Discounted........ | 1,000.00 | Cash.... ......... | 1,000.00 |
| Notes Receivable. | 1,000.00 | Notes Receivable. | 1,000.00 |

| Entries on Books of Turner, the Seller | | Entries on Books of Party Discounting Note | |
|---|---|---|---|
| Notes Receivable... | 1,000.00 | | |
| Accounts Receivable — J. P. Phillips | 1,000.00 | | |
| Cash............ | 1,001.25 | Notes Receivable.... | 1,000.00 |
| Notes Receivable Discounted...... | 1,000.00 | Interest Income.... | 1.25 |
| Interest Income.. | 1.25 | Cash........... | 1,001.25 |
| | | Accrued Interest on Notes Receivable... | 5.00 |
| | | Interest Income.. | 5.00 |
| | | Interest Income.... | 5.00 |
| | | Accrued Interest on Notes Receivable.......... | 5.00 |
| Accounts Receivable — J. P. Phillips | 1,012.00 | Cash............. | 1,012.00 |
| Cash.......... | 1,012.00 | Notes Receivable.. | 1,000.00 |
| | | Interest Income.. | 10.00 |
| | | Protest Fees..... | 2.00 |
| Notes Receivable Discounted........ | 1,000.00 | | |
| Notes Receivable | 1,000.00 | | |
| Cash............ | 1,027.00 | | |
| Accounts Receivable—J.P. Phillips | 1,012.00 | | |
| Interest Income.. | 15.00 | | |

## QUESTIONS

**1.** The balance sheet for the Waring Co. shows:

| | | |
|---|---:|---:|
| Notes receivable | $150,000 | |
| Accounts receivable | 300,000 | |
| | $450,000 | |
| Less: Allowances | 120,000 | $330,000 |

What comments would you make on this presentation?

**2.** The Proctor Corporation shows on its balance sheet one receivable balance that includes the following items: (a) advances to officers, (b) deposits on machinery and equipment being produced by various companies for the Proctor Corporation, (c) traveling expense advances to salesmen, (d) damage claims against transportation companies approved by such companies, (e) estimated federal income tax refunds, (f) accrued interest on notes receivable, (g) United States Treasury Tax Anticipation Bills, (h) overdue notes, (i) receivables from a foreign subsidiary company, (j) subscriptions receivable on a new bond issue, (k) customer container deposits, and (l) creditor overpayments. Suggest the proper treatment of each item.

**3.** The Workman Co. includes installment receivables not maturing within one year among its current trade receivables; the Williams Co. reports similar installment receivables under a separate title outside of the current asset group. Which procedure would you support?

**4.** The Burton Corporation summarizes amounts due from affiliates, officers, and employees as a result of sales and loans, etc., under a single heading under current assets. Comment on this practice.

**5.** Soon after C. & R., Inc. had mailed statements to customers on the first of the month, three complaints were received stating that credit had not been given for checks mailed at least a week before the end of the previous month. Upon investigating the complaints, the proper credits were found to have been made to the customers' accounts as of the second and third of the current month. Is there need for any further investigation?

**6.** The Beller Co. includes in its current receivable total an investment in a joint venture with the Carter Corporation. Officials of the Beller Co. justify this practice on the grounds that the assets of the joint venture are all in current form. Comment on this practice.

**7.** (a) Give several examples of items that might qualify for disclosure as contingent assets. (b) What entry would you make in each case, assuming these items finally materialize as assets of value to the business?

**8.** The Baker Manufacturing Co. ships merchandise on a consignment basis to customers, title to such goods passing only at the time the goods are sold by the consignees. The Baker Manufacturing Co. charges accounts receivable for the cost of the goods shipped until sales are reported, when it increases the receivable accounts with the consignee to the regular billing price. Goods on consignment appear on the balance sheet as receivables. (a) Would you approve such practice? (b) Suggest an alternate procedure.

**9.** Suggest several methods for reporting income tax refund claims approved or under review and the circumstances supporting the appropriate use of each method.

**10.** An analysis of the accounts receivable balance of $8,702 on the books of Burke, Inc. on December 31 reveals the following:

| | |
|---|---:|
| Accounts from sales of last three months (appear to be fully collectible)..... | $7,460 |
| Accounts from sales prior to October 1 (of doubtful value)...... | 1,312 |
| Accounts known to be worthless..... | 320 |
| Dishonored notes charged back to customers' accounts........ | 800 |
| Credit balances in customers' accounts..... | 1,190 |

(a) What adjustments are required? (b) How should the various balances be shown on the balance sheet?

**11.** (a) Give four methods for the establishment and the maintenance of an allowance for bad debts. (b) What are the advantages and the disadvantages of each method? (c) Which do you feel is the preferable method?

**12.** The bookkeeper for Wells, Inc. believes he can show a more accurate valuation of notes and accounts receivable by aging the notes and accounts and establishing an allowance on this basis than he can by crediting the allowance account with a percentage of net sales on account. Do you agree? Give the advantages of each procedure.

**13.** Explain what procedure you would recommend in the development of comparative statements in a year in which a company changed its policy from recognition of losses in the period in which they are determinable to that of anticipation of losses by means of an allowance.

**14.** List and explain the nature of at least four deductions that may be applied under certain circumstances in the valuation of accounts receivable.

**15.** In what section of the income statement would you report (a) bad debts, (b) sales discounts, (c) recovery of accounts written off in prior periods?

**16.** (a) Distinguish between the practices of (1) pledging, (2) assigning, and (3) selling accounts receivable. (b) Describe the accounting procedure to be followed in each instance.

**17.** The Parker Co. enters into a continuing agreement with Mercantile Finance, Inc., whereby the latter company buys without recourse all of the trade receivables as they arise and assumes all credit and collection functions. Describe the advantages that may accrue to the Parker Co. as a result of the factoring agreement.

**18.** The Securities and Exchange Commission has rejected as deficient certain financial statements that failed to disclose pledges of certain receivables as security on loans. What reasons can you offer in support of such rejection?

**19.** B. M. Lowell, who has been recording his contingent liability on notes receivable discounted, has noticed that he has been held liable on nearly as many customers' checks as he has on notes. He suggests setting up a "checks endorsed" account to show his contingent liability on checks. Is this advisable? Why?

**20.** Indicate several methods for presenting information on the balance sheet relating to (a) notes receivable discounted, and (b) accounts receivable assigned.

## EXERCISES

**1.** The accounts receivable controlling account for the Armour Co. shows a debit balance of $34,550; the allowance for bad debts account shows a credit balance of $600. Subsidiary ledger detail reveals the following:

| | |
|---|---:|
| Trade accounts receivable in 30 days.......................... | $12,000 |
| Installment receivables, due 1 month–18 months hence.......... | 3,500 |
| Trade receivables from officers, due currently................. | 1,250 |
| Customers' accounts reporting credit balances arising from sales returns..................................................... | 150 |
| Advance payments to creditors on purchase orders............. | 3,000 |
| Advance payments to creditors on orders for machinery........ | 5,000 |
| Customers' accounts reporting credit balances arising from advance payments........................................... | 1,000 |
| Accounts known to be worthless.............................. | 450 |
| Accounts on which post-dated checks are held (no entries were made on receipt of checks)..................................... | 500 |
| Advances to affiliated companies............................. | 10,000 |

Show how this information would be reported on the balance sheet.

**2.** The trial balance before adjustment for the Moore Sales Co. shows the following balances:

| | DR. | CR. |
|---|---:|---:|
| Accounts Receivable............................ | $26,000 | |
| Allowance for Bad Debts........................ | 150 | |
| Sales.......................................... | | $215,000 |
| Sales Returns and Allowances................... | 1,000 | |

Give the adjustment for estimated bad debts, assuming:

(a) The allowance is maintained at 2% of accounts receivable.
(b) The allowance is to provide for losses of $680 arrived at by aging accounts.
(c) The allowance is to be increased by ½ of 1% of net sales.

**3.** The Barnett Co. decides to employ accounts receivable as a basis for financing. Its current position at this time is as follows:

| | | | |
|---|---|---|---|
| Accounts Receivable....... | $30,000 | Cash Overdraft.......... | $  .750 |
| Inventories.............. | 45,000 | Accounts Payable........ | 32,000 |

Prepare a statement of its current position, assuming that cash is obtained as indicated in each case below:

(a) Cash of $20,000 is borrowed on short-term notes and $18,500 is applied to the payment of creditors; accounts of $25,000 are pledged to secure the loan.
(b) Cash of $20,000 is advanced to the company by Wells Finance Co., the advance representing 75% of accounts assigned to it; assignment is made on a "with recourse" basis, and amounts collected in excess of the loan balance and charges accrue to the Barnett Co.
(c) Cash of $20,000 is received on the sale of accounts receivable of $22,500 on a "no recourse" basis.

**4.** Best Dealers, Inc. assigns accounts of $80,000 to the Ace Finance Co. guaranteeing these accounts and receiving an 80% advance less a flat commission of 5% on the amount of the advance. Accounts of $60,000 are collected and remittance is made to the finance company; the remaining accounts are written off against an allowance for bad accounts. Additional accounts of $20,000 are assigned, and $8,000 is collected on these accounts. Settlement is made with the finance company, including payment of $1,200 for interest. What entries are required on the books of Best Dealers, Inc. to record the assignment and the subsequent transactions?

**5.** On September 15 each of the following notes is discounted by the bank at 6% for M. C. Felter. Give the cash proceeds on each note:

(a) Felter's own 30-day, $750 note.
(b) Customer's 60-day, $1,000, non-interest-bearing note dated August 15.
(c) Customer's 60-day, $1,500, 6% note dated August 31.
(d) Customer's 90-day, $1,276.20, 5% note dated September 10.
(e) Customer's 90-day, $1,512, 7½% note dated August 1.

**6.** Joe Burk received from John Carl a 60-day, 6% note for $3,000, dated November 6, 1958. On December 6, Burk had Carl's note discounted at 6% and recorded the contingent liability. The bank protested non-payment of the note and charged the endorser with protest fees of $2.75 in addition to the amount of the note. On January 29, 1959, the note was collected with interest at 8% from the maturity date on the face value of the note. What entries would appear on Burk's, Carl's, and the bank's books as a result of the foregoing?

## PROBLEMS

**7-1.** The balance sheet for the Winslow Co. on December 31, 1957, shows the following current receivable balances:

| | | |
|---|---:|---:|
| Notes receivable including accrued interest of $150..... | $16,800 | |
| Less: Notes receivable discounted.................. | 12,000 | $ 4,800 |
| | | |
| Accounts receivable............................... | $45,200 | |
| Less: Allowance for bad debts..................... | 1,800 | 43,400 |

Transactions during 1958 included the following:

(a) Sales on account were $320,000.

(b) Cash collected on accounts totaled $212,000, which included accounts of $46,500 on which cash discounts of 2% were allowed.

(c) Notes received in payment of accounts totaled $83,500.

(d) Notes receivable discounted as of December 31, 1957, were paid at maturity with the exception of one $2,500 note on which the company has to pay $2,528, which included interest and protest fees. It is expected that recovery will be made on this note in 1959.

(e) Customers' notes of $50,000 were discounted during the year, proceeds from their sale being $49,200. Of this total, $34,500 matured during the year without notice of protest.

(f) Customers' accounts of $2,750 were written off during the year as worthless.

(g) Recoveries of bad debts written off in prior years were $550.

(h) Notes receivable collected during the year totaled $12,500 and interest collected was $850.

(i) On December 31, accrued interest on notes receivable is $180.

(j) Aging the accounts on December 31, 1958, reveals the need for an allowance for bad debts of $2,850.

(k) Cash of $15,000 was borrowed from the bank, accounts receivable of $20,000 being pledged on the loan. Collections of $12,500 had been made on these receivables (included in the total given in transaction [b]) and this amount was applied on December 31, 1958, to payment of accrued interest on the loan of $225, and the balance to partial payment of the loan.

*Instructions:* (1) Prepare journal entries summarizing the transactions and information given above.

(2) Prepare a summary of current receivables for balance sheet presentation.

**7-2.** Current assets for the Thompson Company are listed as follows on the balance sheet prepared on December 31, 1958:

Current assets:

| | |
|---|---:|
| Cash........................................................ | $ 9,150 |
| Marketable securities....................................... | 26,220 |
| Notes receivable........................................... | 21,450 |
| Accounts receivable........................................ | 75,560 |
| Merchandise inventory..................................... | 82,500 |
| | $214,880 |

An examination of the books revealed the following information concerning the current assets:

Cash included:

| | |
|---|---:|
| Petty cash funds (of which $250 is cash, $120 is in the form of employees' I.O.U.'s, and $30 is in the form of postage stamps) . | $    400 |
| Customers' checks not yet deposited...................... | 1,150 |
| Demand deposit at the First National Bank................. | 7,450 |
| An overdraft at the Central City Bank.................... | (450) |
| Customer's non-interest bearing note (due January 2, 1959) deposited at the First National Bank for collection......... | 600 |
| | $ 9,150 |

Marketable securities included:

| | |
|---|---:|
| Glendale Company Common (a subsidiary company), reported at cost......................................... | $16,500 |
| Thompson Company Preferred (treasury stock), reported at cost | 6,500 |
| 6% Hamilton Company Bonds (interest payable Jan. 1 and July 1), $3,000 face value, purchased Sept. 1, 1958 as a temporary investment, reported at cost plus accrued interest to date of purchase........................... | 3,220 |
| | $26,220 |

Notes receivable included:

| | |
|---|---:|
| Customers' notes (due in 1959)........................... | $ 8,750 |
| Glendale Company note (due March 1, 1959)............... | 12,500 |
| Note receivable from sale of equipment (due July 1, 1960).... | 5,700 |
| Notes receivable discounted (customers' notes)............. | (5,500) |
| | $21,450 |

Accounts receivable included:

| | |
|---|---:|
| Creditors' accounts with debit balances..................... | $    525 |
| Customers' accounts (regular)........................... | 37,070 |
| Dividends receivable on investments...................... | 500 |
| Deposit on equipment (ordered for delivery in December, 1960) | 2,000 |
| Installment accounts receivable ($16,200 due in 1959; $7,800 due in 1960)........................................ | 24,000 |
| Interest receivable on bond investment.................... | 60 |
| Interest receivable on notes............................ | 330 |
| Receivables from consignees (representing the merchandise at cost transferred to consignees and still unsold on December 31, 1958)............................................. | 3,600 |
| Refundable income taxes of prior periods (believed to be collectible in 1959)....................................... | 2,500 |
| Salary advances to employees........................... | 975 |
| Subscriptions receivable on capital stock (due in 1960)........ | 6,000 |
| Allowance for bad debts (on regular and installment accounts). | (2,000) |
| | $75,560 |

| | |
|---|---:|
| Merchandise inventory (representing a physical count of goods on hand) at cost........................................ | $82,500 |

*Instructions:* Revise the current asset section of the balance sheet presenting individual items appropriately included therein in a proper manner. Prepare schedules stating what disposition was made of those items excluded in the revised presentation.

**7-3.** The following post-closing trial balance is taken from the books of the Lawrence Co. on December 31, 1958:

LAWRENCE CO.

POST-CLOSING TRIAL BALANCE

DECEMBER 31, 1958

| | | |
|---|---:|---:|
| Cash............................................... | $  7,290 | |
| Marketable securities............................. | 22,775 | |
| Notes receivable................................. | 24,000 | |
| Accounts receivable, net.......................... | 41,000 | |
| Merchandise inventory........................... | 30,000 | |
| Supplies.......................................... | 900 | |
| Equipment....................................... | 55,000 | |
| Allowance for depreciation of equipment........... | | $  5,500 |
| Buildings......................................... | 60,000 | |
| Allowance for depreciation of buildings............ | | 8,000 |
| Land............................................. | 33,000 | |
| Notes payable.................................... | | 22,000 |
| Accounts payable................................. | | 49,900 |
| Capital stock, $10 par............................ | | 150,000 |
| Retained earnings................................ | | 38,565 |
| | $273,965 | $273,965 |

An examination of the composition of the cash account reveals the following:

| | | |
|---|---:|---:|
| Petty cash fund: | | |
|    Cash........................................... | $ 40 | |
|    Expense vouchers.............................. | 180 | |
|    Postage stamps................................ | 30 | $   250 |
| Cash on hand awaiting deposit....................... | | 840 |
| Checking account with California Bank (overdrawn)........... | | (1,800) |
| Employees benefit fund with California Bank................. | | 5,000 |
| Deposit on merchandise ordered from Hall and Hall and to be completed by March 1, 1959.............................. | | 3,000 |
| | | $7,290 |

The following items are shown under marketable securities:

| | |
|---|---:|
| 6% Baldwin Co. Bonds (interest payable May 1 and Nov. 1), $3,000 face, purchased Dec. 1, 1958, at cost plus accrued interest for....................................... | $ 3,115 |
| (Market value of these bonds on December 31, 1958, was $3,120 and accrued interest.) | |
| Stock of Westwood Supply, Inc., (purchased in order to secure a valuable long-term business contract) at cost.............. | 10,000 |
| (Market value of this stock on December 31, 1958, was $12,000) | |
| Stock of Anderson's Motor Co. acquired as a temporary investment, at cost....................................... | 3,375 |
| (Market value of this stock on December 31, 1958, was $3,500) | |
| Cash surrender value of life insurance policies on the principal officers......................................... | 6,285 |
| | $22,775 |

The notes receivable were as follows:

| | |
|---|---:|
| Notes receivable, customers................................. | $15,200 |
| Notes receivable, officers (current)......................... | 4,600 |
| Notes receivable from sale of equipment, due March 1, 1960..... | 4,000 |
| Accrued interest on notes ................................. | 200 |
| | $24,000 |

Customers' notes of $8,000 that were discounted have not yet matured. Notes Receivable was credited when the notes were discounted.

The following is a summary of the accounts receivable:

| | |
|---|---:|
| Customers' accounts....................................... | $33,500 |
| Employees' accounts (current)............................... | 6,000 |
| Acknowledged claim for damages against Eastern Railroad..... | 1,500 |
| Refundable federal income taxes of prior years (current)........ | 2,300 |
| Cash advanced to salesmen for traveling expenses.............. | 1,200 |
| | $44,500 |
| Less: Allowance for doubtful accounts........................ | 3,500 |
| | $41,000 |

The balance of the allowance for doubtful accounts is considered adequate.

*Instructions:* Prepare a balance sheet showing asset and liability items properly classified.

**7-4.** Maltby, Inc. assigned $52,000 in accounts to the Apex Finance Co. on March 1. Seventy-five per cent of this amount was advanced, less a 2% commission charged by the finance company. Interest on the amount paid back is to be figured at 8%. The assignor continues to make collections on the accounts and makes monthly remittances of amounts collected.

Collections of $27,500 were made in March, remittance for this amount being made on March 31 plus the charge for interest.

Collections of $9,500 were made in April, remittance being made on April 30 of collections and interest.

Accounts of $1,200 were written off against an allowance for bad debts in May, collections were made on the balance of accounts, and settlement was made with the finance company on May 30.

*Instructions:* Give the entries on the books of the assignor and the assignee to record the foregoing transactions.

**7-5.** Hat Box, Inc. assigns certain accounts receivable to the Hayman Finance Co. on the following basis: 80% is advanced, a charge of 5% being made on the amount advanced, and interest at 6% is charged on the amount owed; the finance company makes collections, the assignor guaranteeing all accounts. Transactions in March and April follow:

Mar.  1.  Received remittance upon the assignment of $42,500 in accounts to the finance company.

Mar. 31. Received notice that accounts of $30,000 were collected and that $130 was due for interest. Sent check to Hayman Finance Co. for interest charge.

Apr. 30. Received check in settlement from finance company, together with a summary reporting that all accounts were collected with the exception of one from G. E. Brolin for $650 that was being returned. In making settlement, the Hayman Finance Co. deducted $60 as its charge for interest.

*Instructions:* Give the entries that would appear on the books of Hat Box, Inc.

**7-6.** W. C. Turk completes the following transactions, among others:

Oct. 1. Received a $1,500, 60-day, 6% note dated October 1 from H. L. Harris, a customer.

5. Had own $3,000, 90-day note discounted at the bank at 6%.

20. Received a $1,000, 60-day, non-interest-bearing note dated October 19 from F. C. Hamilton, a customer.

21. Had Harris' note discounted at the bank at 6%.

Nov. 4. Had Hamilton's note discounted at the bank at 6%.

12. Issued a $1,400, 60-day, 7% note to W. R. Usher in payment of account.

18. Had own $5,000, 60-day note discounted at the bank at 6%.

21. Received from B. C. Marshall, a customer, a $2,500, 90-day, 6% note dated November 1, payable to Marshall and signed by the Young Corporation. Upon endorsement, gave the customer credit for the maturity value of the note less discount at 7%.

25. Received a $1,000, 60-day, 6% note dated November 24 from G. H. Robbins, a customer.

Dec. 1. Received notice from the bank that Harris' note was not paid at maturity. Protest fees of $2.50 were charged by the bank.

16. Received payment from Harris on his dishonored note, including interest at 8% on the face value of the note from the maturity date.

*Instructions:* (1) Give the journal entries to record the above transactions, showing contingent liabilities in the accounts. (Show data used in calculations with each entry.)

(2) Give the adjusting entries that would be necessary on December 31, including the release of contingent liability on discounted notes paid by makers.

(3) Indicate the adjusting entries that should be reversed.

**7-7.** The following are some of the transactions completed by J. H. Richards over a three-month period:

Oct. 5. Had own $2,000, 90-day note discounted at the bank at 6%.

10. Received from A. C. Kean, a customer, a $1,500, 60-day, 7% note dated October 9.

11. Received from D. A. Hart on account, a $3,000, 60-day, 7% note dated October 10.

13. Had Kean's note discounted at the bank at 6%.

20. Issued a $2,500, 90-day, 6% note dated October 20 to L. M. Horton in payment of account.

27. Had Hart's note discounted at the bank at 6%.

Nov. 3. Received a $650, 90-day, non-interest-bearing note dated November 1 from R. J. Martin, crediting the customer's account at face value.

Nov.  7. Had Martin's note discounted at the bank at 6%.

   28. Received from M. L. Wade, a customer, a $300, 60-day, 6% note dated November 14 and made by the Miles Company. Gave the customer credit for the maturity value of the note less discount at 6%.

   29. Received a $1,650, 15-day, 7% note dated November 29 from B. Sharp, a customer.

Dec. 10. Received notice from the bank that Kean's note was not paid at maturity. Protest fees of $2.50 were charged by the bank.

   27. Received payment on Sharp's note, including interest at 8%, the legal rate, on the face value from the maturity date.

*Instructions:* (1) Prepare the entries to record the above transactions showing the contingent liabilities in the accounts. (Show data used in calculations with each entry.)

(2) Give the necessary adjusting entries on December 31.

(3) Indicate the adjusting entries that should be reversed.

**7-8.** On December 31, the A. R. Nichols Company has the following notes receivable on hand:

(a) A $4,000, 90-day, 7% note of the Hayes Company, dated October 26.

(b) A $1,500, 90-day, 6% note of the Shay Corporation, dated October 11, that had been received on November 5 from K. H. Collins, a customer. Collins was credited for the maturity value of the note less discount at 7%.

(c) A $5,000, 2-month, non-interest-bearing note of the Woods Company, dated November 16. The customer was given credit for the face value of the note less discount at 7% on November 16.

(d) A $900, 90-day, 7% note of S. H. Evans, dated November 14, that had been received from V. R. Davis, a customer. The customer was credited for the maturity value of the note less discount at 7%.

Notes payable outstanding on December 31 were as follows:

(a) A $7,500, 60-day, 6% note, dated November 10.

(b) A $5,000, 60-day, non-interest-bearing note that was discounted by the bank on December 8 at 6%.

*Instructions:* (1) Prepare the necessary adjusting entries as of December 31, giving an analysis of the adjustment totals in the explanation for each entry.

(2) Indicate the adjusting entries that should be reversed.

**7-9.** The Eastern Gas Company follows the practice of cycle billing in order to minimize peak work loads for its clerical employees. All customers are billed monthly on various dates, except in those cases when the meter readers are unable to enter the premises to obtain a reading.

The following information for the year ended September 30, 1958 is presented by the Company:

| CYCLE | BILLING PERIOD | CUSTOMERS BILLED NUMBER | CUSTOMERS BILLED AMOUNT | CUSTOMERS NOT BILLED |
|---|---|---|---|---|
| 1 | Aug.  7–Sept.  5 (inclusive)... | 2760 | $13,800.00 | 324 |
| 2 | Aug. 12–Sept. 10 (inclusive)... | 3426 | 13,704.00 | 411 |
| 3 | Aug. 17–Sept. 15 (inclusive)... | 3265 | 14,692.50 | 335 |
| 4 | Aug. 22–Sept. 20 (inclusive)... | 2630 | 12,492.50 | 370 |
| 5 | Aug. 27–Sept. 25 (inclusive)... | 3132 | 13,311.00 | 468 |

You are further advised that all customers have been billed for prior periods and that the Company's experience shows that charges for those customers whose meters were not read average the same amount as the charges for the customers billed in their cycle. In addition, the Company assumes that the customers usage will be uniform from month to month.

*Instructions:* Compute the unbilled revenues of the Company as of September 30, 1958 arising from cycles No. 1 and No. 3. (*Do not* compute revenues from cycles 2, 4 and 5.) (A.I.C.P.A. adapted)

**7-10.** You are given the following trial balances of The Becker Company. The trial balance as of December 31, 1958, was taken on a gross basis; that is, the totals of the debits and of the credits in each of the ledger accounts, including any balance from the post-closing trial balance at June 30, 1958, rather than the final balance, have been included. You are advised that the company records disbursements for expense items through liability accounts prior to making payment.

The books are not available. Since the trial balance is out of balance by $270, shown as Unlocated Difference, you attempt to locate the probable source of this difference. You are told that Cash in Bank of $28,044 has been verified.

### THE BECKER COMPANY

#### TRIAL BALANCES

| ACCOUNT | JUNE 30, 1958 | | DECEMBER 31, 1958 | |
|---|---|---|---|---|
| Cash in Bank................ | $ 21,849 | | $ 275,016 | $ 246,972 |
| Investments................. | 30,500 | | 40,712 | 5,000 |
| Accounts Receivable......... | 47,420 | | 301,425 | 248,979 |
| Merchandise Inventory....... | 55,542 | | 208,856 | 153,495 |
| Office Furniture & Fixtures.... | 8,663 | | 11,164 | 635 |
| Allowance for Depreciation.... | | $ 4,967 | 176 | 5,940 |
| Bank Loans................. | | 30,000 | 10,000 | 30,000 |
| Accounts Payable............ | | 15,879 | 211,658 | 233,986 |
| Accrued Income Tax......... | | 7,350 | 5,658 | 11,050 |
| Capital Stock............... | | 50,000 | | 50,000 |
| Earned Surplus.............. | | 55,778 | 10,000 | 55,778 |
| Sales....................... | | | 481 | 254,005 |
| Cost of Sales................ | | | 151,914 | |
| Executive Salaries........... | | | 15,500 | |
| Other Administrative Expense. | | | 21,567 | |
| Selling Expense.............. | | | 25,348 | |
| Bad Debt Losses............. | | | 665 | |
| Writedown of Obsolete Merchandise................. | | | 1,025 | |
| Profit on Sale of Investments.. | | | | 168 |
| Loss on Sale of Fixtures...... | | | 23 | |
| Interest Expense............. | | | 850 | |
| Income Tax Expense......... | | | 3,700 | |
| Unlocated Difference......... | | | 270 | |
| | $163,974 | $163,974 | $1,296,008 | $1,296,008 |

*Instructions:* Reconstruct the ledger accounts as they probably appear. Record the transactions for the period in journal form and in skeleton ledger accounts keyed to the journal entries. You need not prepare financial statements, but you should state where you think the error occurred in the books and give reasons to support your conclusion. (A.I.C.P.A. adapted)

**7-11.** Allen, a sole proprietor, intends to form a partnership with Benson. Because of Allen's failure to keep records, however, he cannot furnish to Benson statements indicative of financial position and earnings to serve as a basis for determining the respective capital interests of the prospective partners and for reaching agreement on other financial matters. Accordingly, it is agreed between Allen and Benson that Allen should continue operating as a sole proprietor for a six-month period ending May 31, 1959, and to keep proper accounting records to serve as a basis for the drafting of a satisfactory partnership agreement.

On December 10, 1958, you are engaged by Allen to establish a starting point in the bookkeeping retroactive to December 1. You ascertain the following facts with respect to balances on pertinent dates and transactions during the ten-day period:

(1)  Available data as of December 1, 1958:

Cash:

| | |
|---|---:|
| Bank balance at Nov. 30, 1958, per bank statement. . | $3,070 |

Outstanding checks ascertained from checkbook:

| | |
|---|---:|
| No. 971. . . . . . . . . . . . . . . . . . . . . . . . . . . . . . . . . . . . . . | $120 |
| 978. . . . . . . . . . . . . . . . . . . . . . . . . . . . . . . . . . . . . . . | 145 |
| 984. . . . . . . . . . . . . . . . . . . . . . . . . . . . . . . . . . . . . . . | 170 |
| 992. . . . . . . . . . . . . . . . . . . . . . . . . . . . . . . . . . . . . . . | 180 |

| | |
|---|---:|
| Furniture and fixtures (appraised value). . . . . . . . . . . . | 2,200 |

Receivables (per billing slips):

| | |
|---|---:|
| Myers. . . . . . . . . . . . . . . . . . . . . . . . . . . . . . . . . . . . . . | 800 |
| Nolan. . . . . . . . . . . . . . . . . . . . . . . . . . . . . . . . . . . . . . | 500 |
| Peters. . . . . . . . . . . . . . . . . . . . . . . . . . . . . . . . . . . . . . | 600 |

Payables (per monthly creditors' statements):

| | |
|---|---:|
| Carlson . . . . . . . . . . . . . . . . . . . . . . . . . . . . . . . . . . . . . | 350 |
| Dent. . . . . . . . . . . . . . . . . . . . . . . . . . . . . . . . . . . . . . . | 620 |
| Ferguson. . . . . . . . . . . . . . . . . . . . . . . . . . . . . . . . . . . . | 820 |
| Gates. . . . . . . . . . . . . . . . . . . . . . . . . . . . . . . . . . . . . . . | 100 |

(2)  Transactions, December 1 to December 10:

(a)  Sales on account:

| | |
|---|---:|
| To: Ryan, goods costing $94 delivered Dec. 4. . | 140 |
| Quinn, goods costing $178 delivered Dec. 7. | 250 |
| Young, goods costing $180 delivered Dec. 12 (merchandise purchased from Ferguson below) . . . . . . . . . . . . . . . . . . . . . . . . . . . . . . . | 320 |

(b) Purchases on account:

| | |
|---|---|
| From: Carlson, goods ordered Dec. 1, received Dec. 2........................... | 400 |
| Ferguson, goods ordered Dec. 2, received Dec. 5........................... | 192 |
| Gates, goods ordered Dec. 4, received Dec. 8........................... | 300 |
| Ivers, goods ordered Dec. 10, received Dec. 13........................... | 250 |

(c) Cash receipts:

| | |
|---|---|
| Dec. 2. Cash sales (cost, $634)................ | 860 |
| 5. Myers........................... | 400 |
| 7. Cash sales (cost, $326)................ | 485 |
| 9. Nolan........................... | 300 |
| 10. Peters........................... | 600* |

(d) Cash disbursements:

| | |
|---|---|
| Dec. 2. Check No. 993, supplies ............. | 25 |
| 4. Check No. 994, December rent........ | 175 |
| 5. Check No. 995, Dent................ | 490** |
| 9. Check No. 996, Ferguson ............. | 500 |
| 9. Check No. 997, withdrawal by Allen, proprietor........................ | 200 |

(e)

| | |
|---|---|
| Dec. 4. Receipt of credit memorandum for return of goods to Dent originally received on Nov. 28 and returned Nov. 30... | 120 |
| Dec. 9. Allowance on goods purchased by Nolan, Nov. 24 (error in pricing).......... | 80 |

(3) Balances, December 10, 1958:

Cash:

| | | |
|---|---|---|
| Balance per bank statement, Dec. 10, 1958........ | | $3,780 |
| Outstanding checks: | | |
| No. 984................................... | $170 | |
| 996................................... | 500 | |
| Merchandise inventory (per physical count stated at cost)........................................ | | 3,000 |
| Furniture and fixtures........................... | | 2,200 |

Assume that:

(1) Rent and supplies are fully chargeable to the Dec. 1–10 period.
(2) The sale of merchandise to Young is to be recognized in the Dec. 1–10 period, although shipment is not made until Dec. 12.
(3) Goods ordered from Ivers are not recognized as purchases until the merchandise is received.

*Instructions:* Prepare from the data given above a statement of net assets for Allen as of December 1 and December 10, 1958, and an income statement for the period, ended December 10, 1958. (A.I.C.P.A. adapted)

*Deposited in bank, December 11, 1958.
**After deduction of 2% cash discount.

# Chapter 8

# INVENTORIES

## COST PROCEDURES

*Clyde A. Kile*
2105 Univ.

**NATURE OF INVENTORIES**     The term _inventories is_ an asset designation for those goods that are held for sale in the normal course of business, as well as those goods that are in production or are awaiting such utilization. Practically all tangible items fall into this classification at one time or another. Gasoline, oil, and automotive supplies are included in the inventory of a service station; crops and livestock are included in the inventory of a farmer; machinery and equipment are included in the inventory of a manufacturer producing such items for sale. It is the sale of inventories at more than cost of purchase or manufacture that normally provides a business with its chief source of revenue.

Inventories represent one of the most active elements in business operations, being continuously acquired, converted, and resold. A large part of a company's resources is frequently tied up in inventory procurement or manufacture. Inventory costs must be recorded, grouped, and summarized during the period. At the end of the period, an allocation of costs chargeable to current activities and to future activities must be made. Such allocation normally occupies a central role in the measurement of periodic operating results as well as in the determination of a business unit's financial condition. Failure to allocate costs properly can result in serious distortions of financial position and progress.

Accounting for inventory costs presents a number of serious problems. A great deal of thought has been directed by the accounting profession to these problems in recent years. This and the two chapters that follow consider the special problems relating to inventories.

**CLASSES OF INVENTORIES**     The term _merchandise inventory_ is generally applied to goods held by a trading concern, either wholesale or retail, when such goods have been acquired in a condition for resale. The terms _raw materials, goods in process,_ and _finished goods_ refer to the inventories of a manufacturing concern. The latter items require description.

_Raw Materials._ Raw materials are those tangible goods that are used in the productive process. Raw materials may be obtained directly from natural sources. Ordinarily, however, raw materials are acquired from other companies and represent the finished products of the companies from which they were purchased. For example, newsprint is the finished product of the paper mill but represents raw material to the printer who acquires it.

While the term _raw materials_ can be used broadly to cover all of the materials used in manufacturing, this designation is frequently restricted to materials that will be physically incorporated in the products being manufactured. The term _factory supplies_ or _manufacturing supplies_ is then used to refer to auxiliary materials, that is, materials that while necessary to the productive process are not directly incorporated in the products. Oils, fuels, cleaning materials, etc., would fall into this grouping since these items are not incorporated in a product but simply facilitate production as a whole; paints, nails, bolts, etc., while physically embodied in the final product, are normally of such minor significance as to warrant inclusion within the auxiliary grouping. Materials directly employed in the production of certain goods are frequently referred to as _direct materials_; factory supplies are referred to as _indirect materials_.

Although factory supplies may be summarized separately, they should be reported as a part of the company's inventories in view of their ultimate application to the productive process. Factory supplies should be distinguished from other supplies that make contributions to the delivery, sales, and general administrative functions of the enterprise. Such other supplies should not be reported as part of the company's inventories but rather call for classification as prepaid expenses.

_Goods in Process._ Goods in process, alternately referred to as work in process, consist of materials partly processed and requiring further work before they can be made available for sale. This inventory is considered to be made up of three cost elements: (1) _direct materials_, (2) _direct labor_, and (3) _factory overhead_ or _burden_. The cost of materials identified with the goods in production is included under (1). The cost of labor identified with goods in production is included under (2). The portion of factory overhead considered properly assignable to goods still in production forms the third element in cost. Factory overhead consists of all manufacturing costs other than direct materials and direct labor. It includes factory materials and labor not directly identified with the production of specific products. It also includes such general factory costs as depreciation, repairs, taxes, and insurance, as well as a reasonable share of the managerial costs other than those relating solely to the sales or administrative functions of the business. Overhead may be designated as _fixed_, _variable_, and _semi-_

*variable.* Overhead charges that remain constant in amount regardless of the volume of production are referred to as fixed. Depreciation, insurance and rent normally fall into this category. Charges that fluctuate in proportion to the volume of production are called variable. Indirect materials, power, and supplies vary with production. Some charges vary, but the variations are not in direct proportion to the volume. These charges have both fixed and variable components and are designated as semivariable items. Factory supervision is an example of a semivariable item when it is fixed within a certain range of production but may require significant changes when the production is not within this range.

*Finished Goods.* Finished goods are the completed products awaiting sale. The cost of the finished product consists of the costs of materials, labor, and overhead assigned to it. Finished parts that were purchased and that are to be used in the production of the finished product are normally classed as raw materials; finished parts that are held for purposes of sale may be considered finished goods.

**INVENTORIES IN THE MEASUREMENT OF INCOME**    When goods that are purchased or manufactured are all sold within a fiscal period, the determination of the gross profit on sales is a simple matter. The total cost of goods purchased or manufactured is also the cost of goods sold that is properly chargeable to revenue. The problem of an inventory value to be carried into the new period does not arise. Such a situation, however, is seldom found in practice. Normally, a part of the goods acquired remains on hand at the end of the period. A value must be assigned to such goods. This value is subtracted from the total merchandise acquisition costs of the current period and is carried into the subsequent period to be charged against future revenue. Adequate records are required for the maintenance of inventory cost data. Such records are also required for the proper control of a constantly moving stock.

Two classes of problems arise in the determination of the inventory to be reported on the statements: (1) what items are properly included in the inventory? and (2) what values are to be assigned to such items?

**INVENTORY METHODS**    Quantities of inventories on hand are ascertained either through a *periodic system* that calls for *physical inventories* at the end of each period, or a *perpetual system* that involves *perpetual* or *book inventories.*

When the periodic system is employed, a physical inventory of goods on hand is taken periodically to arrive at the portion of recorded costs to be carried forward. Physical inventories involve counting, measuring, or weighing the units on hand at the end of the period.

The perpetual inventory system requires the maintenance of records that offer a running summary of inventory items on hand. When perpetual inventory records are maintained, individual accounts are kept for each class of goods on hand. Increases in inventory items are recorded by debits, and decreases are recorded by credits; the resulting balances represent the amounts on hand. In the manufacturing organization, a perpetual system applied to inventories calls for recording the full movement of goods through individual accounts maintained for raw materials, goods in process, and finished goods. Perpetual records may be kept in terms of quantities only or in terms of both quantities and costs.

When the perpetual system is employed, physical counts of the units on hand should be made at least once a year, and preferably at more frequent intervals to confirm the book record and provide for its correction. The frequency of physical inventories will vary depending upon the nature of the goods as well as their rate of movement. A plan of continuous checking of inventory items on a rotation basis is frequently employed in practice. Variations between the book record and the amounts actually on hand resulting from errors in recording, shrinkage, breakage, theft, and other causes should be recognized and the book inventories brought into agreement with the physical count. An inventory adjustment account is debited and the book inventory is credited when the actual inventory is found to be less than the book figure; the inventory adjustment account is credited and the book inventory is debited when the actual inventory exceeds the book figure. The source of the discrepancy will suggest whether the adjustment balance should be regarded as an adjustment to cost of goods sold or as an operating expense or loss on the income statement. The inventory adjustment account balance is closed into the profit and loss account at the end of the period.

Practically all large trading and manufacturing enterprises, as well as many relatively small organizations, have adopted the perpetual inventory system as an integral part of their record keeping and internal control. This system offers a continuous check and control over inventories, as well as immediate data concerning inventory position. Purchases and production planning are facilitated, adequate supplies on hand are assured, and losses through damage and theft are fully disclosed. The additional costs of maintaining such a system are usually well repaid by the services provided to management through its adoption.

**ITEMS TO BE INCLUDED IN INVENTORY** As a general rule, goods should be included <u>in the inventory of the party holding title.</u> The "passage of title" is a legal term designating the point at which ownership changes. There are instances where the legal rule may be waived for practical reasons or because of certain limitations that are found in its application. When the circumstances are such that the rule of passing of title does not need to be observed, there should be appropriate disclosure on the statements of the special practice that is followed and the factors that support such special practice. Application of the legal test under a number of special circumstances is described in the following paragraphs.

*Goods in Transit.* When terms of sale are <u>"f.o.b. shipping point,"</u> title passes to the buyer with the loading of goods at the point of shipment. Application of the legal rule to year-end shipments calls for recognition of a sale on the books of the seller. On the other hand, the buyer should recognize such goods in transit as a purchase and an accompanying inventory increase even though there is no physical possession at this time. A determination of the goods in transit as of the year-end is made by a review of the incoming orders during the early part of the new period. The purchases records may be kept open beyond the fiscal period to permit the recognition of goods in transit as of the end of the period, or goods in transit may be recorded by means of an adjusting entry. While no objection to the application of the legal rule can be raised by a seller, the buyer, in the interests of expediency, may prefer to ignore such rule and employ "receipt" as a basis for the recognition of a purchase and the related inventory increase. The latter approach is not objectionable when amounts in transit are not material, when readers of the statements may be expected to assume that there is a regular and continuous flow of goods inward, when goods are subject to rejection, and when the inclusion of such items before their receipt and acceptance offers real practical difficulties.

When terms of a sale are <u>"f.o.b. destination,"</u> application of the legal test calls for no recognition of the transaction by either party until goods are received by the buyer. In this case, it is the seller who may prefer to ignore the legal rule and employ "shipment" as a basis for booking a sale and accompanying inventory decrease. In view of the practical difficulties involved in ascertaining whether goods have reached their destination at year-end, application of a "shipment" rule may not be objectionable under normal circumstances.

*Segregated Goods.* When goods are prepared on special order and segregated for shipment, title may pass with such segregation. When goods are segregated at the end of the period and title has passed, the vendor may properly recognize a sale and exclude segregated goods from his inventory, while the vendee may properly recognize both a purchase and an inventory increase. Frequently, one encounters serious practical problems in arriving at the portion of the inventory that is segregated as well as perplexing legal problems in defining the precise status of such goods. Such difficulties normally lead to the adoption of a policy whereby entries for both sale and purchase await formal shipment of goods by the vendor.

*Goods on Consignment.* Goods are frequently transferred to dealers on a consignment basis, the consignor retaining title to such goods until their sale by the consignee. Until the goods are sold and cash or a receivable can be recognized, the consignor should continue to report consigned goods as a part of his inventory. Consigned goods are properly reported at the sum of their cost and the handling and shipping costs involved in their transfer to the consignee. The goods may be separately designated on the balance sheet as "Merchandise on Consignment." The consignee does not own the consigned goods; hence he reports neither consigned goods nor an obligation for such goods on his statements. Other merchandise owned by a business but in the possession of others, such as goods in the hands of salesmen and agencies and goods held by customers on approval, should also be shown as a part of the ending inventories.

*Conditional and Installment Sales.* Conditional sales and installment sales contracts may provide for a retention of title by the seller until the sales price is fully recovered. Under such circumstances, it would be possible for the seller to continue to show the goods to which he has title, reduced by the buyer's equity in such goods as established by collections from the latter; the buyer, in turn, can report an equity in the goods accruing through payments that have already been made. Ordinarily, however, in circumstances of this kind and particularly where the possibilities of returns and default are negligible, the test of passing of title is relinquished and the transaction is recorded in terms of the expected outcome: the seller, anticipating completion of the contract and the ultimate passing of title, recognizes the transaction as a regular sale involving deferred collections; the buyer, fully intending to comply with the contract and acquire title, recognizes the transfer as a regular purchase.

**INVENTORY
VALUATION**            In viewing the inventory in its dual position as (1) a value that is reported on the operating statement in developing costs properly applicable to current revenue and (2) a value reported on the balance sheet that represents the

charge that is properly assignable to future periods, cost must be accepted as the primary basis for inventory valuation. When there has been a marked change in the value of the inventory between the purchase date and the date of inventory, the question arises as to whether some recognition should be given to current inventory replacement values. With a decline in prices, practice has generally answered this question in the affirmative by applying the valuation method of "cost or market, whichever is lower." Special conditions may suggest the use of valuation methods other than cost or market, whichever is lower. For example, under certain circumstances practice has sanctioned the full departure from cost and the use of a sales price or a modified sales price basis.

Income measurement rather than balance sheet valuation has been accepted in recent years as the major criterion in accounting for inventories. The American Institute adopts such emphasis. The Institute also holds that while inventories should be reported at cost in keeping with the principle that accounting is based on cost, modifications in cost may be appropriate under certain circumstances. The Committee on Accounting Procedure, in discussing inventory pricing, states:

> In accounting for the goods in the inventory at any point of time, the major objective is the matching of appropriate costs against revenues in order that there may be a proper determination of the realized income. Thus, the inventory at any given date is the balance of costs applicable to goods on hand remaining after the matching of absorbed costs with concurrent revenues. This balance is appropriately carried to future periods provided it does not exceed an amount properly chargeable against the revenues expected to be obtained from ultimate disposition of the goods carried forward.[1]

The principal inventory valuation methods and their special applicabilities will be considered in detail. Attention is directed in this chapter to the measurement of cost when cost is required for inventory valuation as well as when cost is to be used as the first step in the development of a lower of cost or market value.

**INVENTORY COST**        The determination of the cost of the inventory may be no simple matter. First, it involves a determination of the expenditures that actually enter into the cost of the goods that are acquired. Second, it involves the application of a method for relating the different costs of the goods acquired to periodic revenue.

---

[1] *Accounting Research Bulletin No. 43*, "Restatement and Revision of Accounting Research Bulletins," 1953 (New York: American Institute of Certified Public Accountants), p. 28.

Inventory costs consist of all expenditures, both direct and indirect, relating to inventory acquisition, preparation, and placement for sale. In the case of raw materials or goods acquired for resale, cost includes all expenditures involved in the acquisition of the goods, including buying costs, freight in, duties, taxes, insurance, and storage. Certain expenditures can be traced to specific acquisitions or can be apportioned to inventory items in some equitable manner. Other expenditures may be relatively small and may be difficult to allocate in some satisfactory manner to the goods acquired. Such items are normally excluded in the calculation of inventory costs and are treated as expenses of the period.

The elements involved in the cost of manufactured products have already been mentioned. Proper accounting for materials, labor, and overhead items and their identification with goods in process and finished goods inventories may be best achieved through adoption of a cost accounting system designed to meet the special requirements of the business unit. Overhead at a predetermined rate may be assigned to goods being produced during the period. At the end of the period, when the actual overhead is known, appropriate adjustments will be made for any under- or over-applied overhead amount. Certain costs relating to the acquisition or the manufacture of goods may be considered of an abnormal nature and may be excluded in arriving at inventory cost. For example, charges arising from idle capacity, excessive spoilage, and reprocessing are normally considered extraordinary items chargeable in total to current revenue. Only that portion of general and administrative costs that is clearly related to procurement or production should be included in inventory costing; selling expenses should be excluded.

**DISCOUNTS AS REDUCTIONS IN COST**   Discounts that are treated as a reduction of cost in recording the acquisition of goods should likewise be treated as a reduction in the cost assigned to the inventory. *Trade discounts* are discounts that convert a printed price list to the prices actually to be charged to the particular buyer. Cost to the buyer, then, is list price less the discount; purchases, here, should be reported at such cost with no accounting recognition given to the discount, and the inventory stated on an equivalent basis. *Cash discounts* are reductions in prices allowed only upon payment of invoices within a limited period. Inventory treatment depends upon whether cash discounts are regarded as a reduction in cost or as a source of income. If cash discounts are treated as a subtraction from purchases, the inventory balance should be correspondingly reduced; if cash discounts are reported as other income, inventories should be reported at invoice cost without reference to such discounts.

Treatment of purchases discounts as income is frequently found in practice and is defended on the grounds that the buyer takes special measures in liquidating a claim in advance of its due date to secure such discounts. There may be expenses attached to raising capital for the advance liquidation of debts. Financial management is charged with such expenses; discounts earned, then, may be properly credited to financial management and matched against such expenses.

Serious objection, however, can be taken to the foregoing practice. Treatment of purchases discounts as income means that a gain is recognized from the act of buying. Sound accounting provides for the recognition of gain from the sale of goods or services, not from their purchase. The buyer is offered goods at a net or cash price, and no more than this actually needs to be paid. Settlement is almost invariably made on a cash basis in view of the difference between the cash discount and the cost of borrowing money for such a discount period. In fact, when settlement is not made within the discount period, a failure on the part of financial management is indicated either through carelessness in considering payment alternatives or through financial inability to avoid the extra charge. The arguments raised in connection with the treatment of purchases discounts by the buyer have their counterpart in the treatment of sales discounts by the seller.

Treatment of purchases discounts taken as a subtraction from purchases is recognition of such discounts as an adjustment in purchase price. But this practice offers only partial recognition of the cost view just developed. Full agreement with the preceding analysis is obtained by reporting purchases net and recording any amounts paid in excess of these amounts as Purchases Discounts Lost, a financial management expense item. When such a practice is to be followed, two methods may be employed: (1) accounts payable may be reported net or (2) accounts payable may be reported at the gross invoice price with a payable offset balance or liability valuation account reporting the purchases discounts available. The two methods are illustrated on the next page.

Although the recording of purchases net and the recognition of cash discounts lost as an expense is of obvious merit, it has failed to obtain wide adoption. Chief objection has been made on practical grounds. Use of this method calls for the conversion of gross amounts as stated by invoices into net amounts relating to individual acquisitions and the subsequent application of such converted values throughout the accounting for inventories. This is normally less convenient than accounting in terms of gross invoice charges.

| Transaction | Accounts Payable Reported Net | Accounts Payable Reported Gross |
|---|---|---|
| Purchase of merchandise priced at $1,000 less trade discount of 30%—20% and a cash discount of 2%:<br><br>$1,000 less 30% = $700<br>$  700 less 20% = $560<br>$  560 less 2% = $548.80 | Purchases (or Inventory)...548.80<br> Accounts Payable..548.80 | Purchases (or Inventory)...548.80<br>Allowance for Purchases Discounts...... 11.20<br> Accounts Payable ........ 560.00 |
| (a) Payment of invoice, assuming payment within discount period. | Accounts Payable .... 548.80<br> Cash ........... 548.80 | Accounts Payable...... 560.00<br> Allowance for Purchases Discounts........ 11.20<br> Cash ........... 548.80 |
| (b) Payment of invoice, assuming payment after discount period. | Accounts Payable...... 548.80<br>Purchases Discounts Lost..... .....11.20<br> Cash ........... 560.00 | Accounts Payable...... 560.00<br> Cash ........... 560.00<br>Purchases Discounts Lost......... 11.20<br> Allowance for Purchases Discounts........11.20 |

**SPECIFIC IDENTIFICA-TION OF COSTS WITH INVENTORY ITEMS**   Revenue may be charged for goods sold on the basis of identified costs of the specific items sold. Such practice calls for the identification of a cost with each item acquired. When perpetual inventories are maintained, the sale of goods calls for the transfer of articles and their identified costs to cost of goods sold. When a system of physical inventories is maintained, goods on hand require identification with specific invoices for cost valuation. In each instance, costs related to units sold are reported as cost of goods sold and costs identified with goods on hand remain to be reported as the ending inventory. Income is the difference between amounts received on the sale of specific units and the amounts paid in their acquisition.

While such identification procedure may be considered a highly satisfactory approach to the revenue-cost matching process under normal circumstances in view of its objectivity and adherence to empirical fact, the practice may be difficult or impossible to apply or may be considered inadequate in view of special existing conditions. When an inventory is composed of a great many items, some being similar items acquired at different times and at different prices, cost identification procedures may prove to be slow, burdensome, and costly. When identical items have been acquired at different times, their identity may be lost and cost identification thus denied. Furthermore, when units are identical and interchangeable, the method opens the doors to possible profit manipulation through the choice of particular units for delivery. Finally, marked changes in costs during a period may suggest charges to revenue on a basis other than past identified costs.

When specific identification procedures are considered inappropriate, it is necessary to adopt some assumption with respect to the flow of costs that is to be associated with the movement of goods. Three methods, each with a different assumption as to an orderly flow of costs, have achieved widest application. These are: (1) *first-in, first-out,* (2) *weighted average,* and (3) *last-in, first-out.*

**FIRST-IN, FIRST-OUT METHOD**    The first-in, first-out method (*fifo* method) is based on the assumption that costs should be charged out in the order in which incurred. Inventories are thus stated in terms of most recent costs. To illustrate the application of this method, assume the following data for a certain commodity:

| January | 1 | Inventory | 200 units at $10 | $ 2,000 |
|---|---|---|---|---|
| | 12 | Purchase | 400 units at 12 | 4,800 |
| | 24 | Purchase | 300 units at 11 | 3,300 |
| | 30 | Purchase | 100 units at 12 | 1,200 |
| | | Totals | 1,000 | $11,300 |

A physical inventory on January 31 shows 300 units on hand. The inventory would be considered to be composed of the most recent costs as follows:

| | | |
|---|---|---|
| Most recent purchase, January 30 | 100 units at $12 | $1,200 |
| Next most recent purchase, Jan. 24 | 200 units at 11 | 2,200 |
| Totals | 300 | $3,400 |

If the ending inventory is recorded at a cost of $3,400, cost of goods sold is $7,900 ($11,300 – $3,400), and revenue is charged with the earliest costs.

When perpetual inventory accounts are maintained, a form similar to that illustrated below is kept to record the cost of units issued and the cost relating to the goods on hand. The first column is used for memorandum entries reporting amounts ordered. Remaining columns show the quantities and values relating to goods acquired, goods issued, and balances on hand. It should be observed that fifo applied to perpetual inventories gives identical inventory values as when it is applied to a periodic inventory.

COMMODITY X (FIFO)

| ORDERED | DATE | RECEIVED | | ISSUED | | BALANCE | |
|---|---|---|---|---|---|---|---|
| MEMO- | Jan.  1 | | | | | 200 at $10 | 2,000 |
| RANDUM | 12 | 400 at $12 | 4,800 | | | 200 at $10<br>400 at $12 | 2,000<br>4,800 |
| ENTRIES | 16 | | | 200 at $10<br>300 at $12 | 2,000<br>3,600 | 100 at $12 | 1,200 |
| | 26 | 300 at $11 | 3,300 | | | 100 at $12<br>300 at $11 | 1,200<br>3,300 |
| | 29 | | | 100 at $12<br>100 at $11 | 1,200<br>1,100 | 200 at $11 | 2,200 |
| | 30 | 100 at $12 | 1,200 | | | 200 at $11<br>100 at $12 | 2,200<br>1,200 |

**WEIGHTED AVERAGE METHOD**     The weighted average method is based on the assumption that goods should be charged out at an average cost, such average being influenced by the number of units acquired at each price. Inventories would be stated at the same weighted average cost. Assuming the cost data in the preceding section, the weighted average cost of a physical inventory of 300 units on January 31 would be as follows:

| January | 1 | Inventory | 200 units at $10 | $ 2,000 |
|---|---|---|---|---|
| | 12 | Purchase | 400 units at  12 | 4,800 |
| | 24 | Purchase | 300 units at  11 | 3,300 |
| | 30 | Purchase | 100 units at  12 | 1,200 |
| | | Totals | 1,000 | $11,300 |

$$\text{Weighted average cost} = \frac{\$11,300}{1,000} = \$11.30$$

Ending inventory: 300 units at $11.30 = $3,390.

If the ending inventory is recorded at a cost of $3,390, cost of goods sold is $7,910 ($11,300 − $3,390), and revenue is charged with a weighted average cost.

Calculations above were made for costs of one month. Calculations could be developed in terms of data for a quarter or for a year.

When perpetual inventories are maintained but the costs of units issued are not recorded until the end of a period, a weighted average cost for the period may be calculated at that time and the accounts may be credited for the cost of total units issued. Frequently, however, costs relating to issues are recorded currently, and it is necessary to calculate costs on the basis of the weighted average on the date of issue. This requires the calculation of a new weighted average cost immediately after the receipt of each additional lot of merchandise. This method, which involves successive average recalculations, is referred to as a *moving average method.*

The use of the moving average method is illustrated below:

COMMODITY X (MOVING AVERAGE)

| ORDERED | DATE | RECEIVED | | ISSUED | | BALANCE | |
|---|---|---|---|---|---|---|---|
| MEMO- | Jan. 1 | | | | | 200 at $10.00 | 2,000 |
| RANDUM | 12 | 400 at $12 | 4,800 | | | 600 at $11.33 | 6,800 |
| ENTRIES | 16 | | | 500 at $11.33 | 5,665 | 100 at $11.35 | 1,135 |
| | 26 | 300 at $11 | 3,300 | | | 400 at $11.09 | 4,435 |
| | 29 | | | 200 at $11.09 | 2,218 | 200 at $11.09 | 2,217 |
| | 30 | 100 at $12 | 1,200 | | | 300 at $11.39 | 3,417 |

On January 12 the new unit cost of $11.33 was found by dividing $6,800, the total cost, by 600, the number of units on hand. On January 16, the dollar balance, $1,135, represented the previous balance, $6,800, less $5,665, the cost assigned to the 500 units issued on this date. New unit costs were calculated on January 26 and 30 when additional units were acquired.

**LAST-IN, FIRST-OUT METHOD**    The last-in, first-out method (*lifo* method) is based on the assumption that the latest costs should be the first that are charged out. Inventories are thus stated in terms of earliest costs. Assuming the cost data in the preceding section, a physical inventory of 300 units on January 31 would have a cost as follows:

| | | |
|---|---|---|
| Earliest costs relating to goods, January 1 | 200 units at $10 | $2,000 |
| Next cost, January 12 | 100 units at $12 | 1,200 |
| Totals | 300 | $3,200 |

If the ending inventory is recorded at a cost of $3,200, cost of goods sold is $8,100 ($11,300–$3,200), and revenue is charged with the latest costs.

When perpetual inventories are maintained but the cost of units issued is not recorded until the end of the period, the most recent costs relating to the total units issued may be determined and the account credited for this cost. Cost, then, is the same as reported above. Frequently, however, costs relating to issues are recorded currently, and it is necessary to calculate costs on a last-in, first-out basis using the cost data as shown on the date of issue. This is illustrated below.

COMMODITY X (LIFO)

| Ordered | Date | Received | | Issued | | Balance | |
|---------|------|----------|---|--------|---|---------|---|
| MEMO- | Jan. 1 | | | | | 200 at $10 | 2,000 |
| RANDUM | 12 | 400 at $12 | 4,800 | | | 200 at $10<br>400 at $12 | 2,000<br>4,800 |
| ENTRIES | 16 | | | 400 at $12<br>100 at $10 | 4,800<br>1,000 | 100 at $10 | 1,000 |
| | 26 | 300 at $11 | 3,300 | | | 100 at $10<br>300 at $11 | 1,000<br>3,300 |
| | 29 | | | 200 at $11 | 2,200 | 100 at $10<br>100 at $11 | 1,000<br>1,100 |
| | 30 | 100 at $12 | 1,200 | | | 100 at $10<br>100 at $11<br>100 at $12 | 1,000<br>1,100<br>1,200 |

It should be noted that lifo applied to perpetual inventories does not offer the same results as when applied to a periodic inventory. In the example, a cost of $3,200 was obtained for the periodic inventory, whereas $3,300 was obtained when costs were calculated as goods were issued. This difference is due to the fact that it was necessary to charge out 100 units at $10 in the issue of January 16. The ending inventory thus reflects only 100 units of the beginning inventory. When units were not charged out currently, the ending inventory was considered to consist of the cost of the 200 units reflected in the beginning inventory plus 100 units at the earliest acquisition cost of the current period.[1]

**EFFECTS OF COST FLOW PROCEDURES COMPARED**     In the absence of significant price-fluctuation in the merchandise acquired, use of any of the three methods just illustrated leads to approximately the same result. In the examples given, where costs

---

[1] It may be noted that certain modifications in the standard lifo procedure as illustrated are recognized for purposes of federal income tax reporting. The taxpayer may use actual, most recent, or average costs in valuing the quantity increase in a lifo inventory. He is also permitted to apply price indexes to inventories reported at year-end prices in arriving at inventory quantity changes. Application of the latter procedure, known as the "dollar value" approach, makes unnecessary the clerical procedures that would normally be involved in a full lifo accounting for all of the individual items that are found in the inventory.

fluctuated from $10 to $12 per unit, inventory costs differed to some degree, ranging from $3,200 to $3,417, as follows:

|  | PHYSICAL INVENTORY | PERPETUAL INVENTORY |
|---|---|---|
| First-in, first-out | $3,400 | $3,400 |
| Weighted average | 3,390 | 3,417 |
| Last-in, first-out | 3,200 | 3,300 |

Assuming that inventories are recorded at cost, variations between costs obtained through use of the first-in, first-out and the last-in, first-out methods may become relatively significant in a period of steadily rising or falling prices. [Use of the first-in, first-out method results in inventories being reported near or at current costs, while use of the last-in, first-out method results in inventories being reported at a more or less fixed amount.]

The effect upon the net profit is of even greater significance. Use of first-in, first-out in a period of rising prices matches oldest low-cost inventory with rising sales prices, thus expanding the gross margin on sales. In a period of declining prices, oldest high-cost inventory is matched with declining sales prices, thus narrowing the margin on sales. On the other hand, use of last-in, first-out in a period of rising prices relates current high costs of acquiring merchandise with rising sales prices, and in a period of falling prices, low costs of acquiring merchandise with declining sales prices. The weighted average method recognizes both past and present costs in the inventory. Ordinarily, however, results will closely parallel first-in, first-out costs since purchases during the period are generally several times the inventory balance carried into the period, and average costs forming the ending inventory valuation will thus approach current costs.

The illustration on page 242 demonstrates the results obtained from inventory valuation at cost with the use of the three methods in periods of rising and falling prices. Assume that the Wilcox Sales Co. sells its goods at 50 per cent in excess of current prevailing costs from 1955 to 1958. It sells out and winds up activities at the end of 1958. Sales, costs, and gross profits using each of the three methods are shown.

Although the total cost of goods sold and the total gross profit on sales are the same for the four-year period under each of the methods used, use of first-in, first-out resulted in increased gross profit margins in periods of rising prices and a contraction of margins in a period of falling prices, while last-in, first-out resulted in relatively steady gross profit percentages in spite of fluctuating prices. The weighted average method, on the other hand, offered results closely comparable to those

|  | FIFO | | | WEIGHTED AVERAGE | | | LIFO¹ | | |
|---|---|---|---|---|---|---|---|---|---|
|  | Amounts | | | Amounts | | | Amounts | | |
| **1955:** | | | | | | | | | |
| Sales, 500 units @ $9 | | | 4,500 | | | 4,500 | | | 4,500 |
| Inventory, 200 units | @ $5 | 1,000 | | 200 @ $5 | 1,000 | | 200 @ $5 | 1,000 | |
| Purchases, 500 units | @ $6 | 3,000 | | 500 @ $6 | 3,000 | | 500 @ $6 | 3,000 | |
|  | | 4,000 | | | 4,000 | | | 4,000 | |
| Ending Inv., 200 units | @ $6 | 1,200 | 2,800 | 200 @ $5.71 ($4,000÷700) | 1,142 | 2,858 | 200 @ $5 | 1,000 | 3,000 |
| Gross Profit on Sales | | | 1,700 | | | 1,642 | | | 1,500 |
| **1956:** | | | | | | | | | |
| Sales, 450 units @ $12 | | | 5,400 | | | 5,400 | | | 5,400 |
| Inventory, 200 units | @ $6 | 1,200 | | 200 @ $5.71 | 1,142 | | 200 @ $5 | 1,000 | |
| Purchases, 500 units | @ $8 | 4,000 | | 500 @ $8 | 4,000 | | 500 @ $8 | 4,000 | |
|  | | 5,200 | | | 5,142 | | | 5,000 | |
| Ending Inv., 250 units | @ $8 | 2,000 | 3,200 | 250 @ $7.35 ($5,142÷700) | 1,838 | 3,304 | 200 @ $5 / 50 @ $8 | 1,400 | 3,600 |
| Gross Profit on Sales | | | 2,200 | | | 2,096 | | | 1,800 |
| **1957:** | | | | | | | | | |
| Sales, 475 units @ $10.50 | | | 4,988 | | | 4,988 | | | 4,988 |
| Inventory, 250 units | @ $8 | 2,000 | | 250 @ $7.35 | 1,838 | | 200 @ $5 / 50 @ $8 | 1,400 | |
| Purchases, 450 units | @ $7 | 3,150 | | 450 @ $7 | 3,150 | | 450 @ $7 | 3,150 | |
|  | | 5,150 | | | 4,988 | | | 4,550 | |
| Ending Inv., 225 units | @ $7 | 1,575 | 3,575 | 225 @ $7.13 ($4,988÷700) | 1,604 | 3,384 | 200 @ $5 / 25 @ $8 | 1,200 | 3,350 |
| Gross Profit on Sales | | | 1,413 | | | 1,604 | | | 1,638 |
| **1958:** | | | | | | | | | |
| Sales, 525 units @ $7.50 | | | 3,938 | | | 3,938 | | | 3,938 |
| Inventory, 225 units | @ $7 | 1,575 | | 225 @ $7.13 | 1,604 | | 200 @ $5 / 25 @ $8 | 1,200 | |
| Purchases, 300 units | @ $5 | 1,500 | 3,075 | 300 @ $5 | 1,500 | 3,104 | 300 @ $5 | 1,500 | 2,700 |
| Gross Profit on Sales | | | 863 | | | 834 | | | 1,238 |

## The foregoing transactions are summarized below:

|  |  | FIFO | | | WEIGHTED AVERAGE | | | LIFO | | |
|---|---|---|---|---|---|---|---|---|---|---|
| Year | Sales | Cost of Sales | Gross Profit on Sales | Gross Profit % to Sales | Cost of Sales | Gross Profit on Sales | Gross Profit % to Sales | Cost of Sales | Gross Profit on Sales | Gross Profit % to Sales |
| 1955 | 4,500 | 2,800 | 1,700 | 37.8 | 2,858 | 1,642 | 36.5 | 3,000 | 1,500 | 33.3 |
| 1956 | 5,400 | 3,200 | 2,200 | 40.7 | 3,304 | 2,096 | 38.8 | 3,600 | 1,800 | 33.3 |
| 1957 | 4,988 | 3,575 | 1,413 | 28.3 | 3,384 | 1,604 | 32.2 | 3,350 | 1,638 | 32.8 |
| 1958 | 3,938 | 3,075 | 863 | 21.9 | 3,104 | 834 | 21.2 | 2,700 | 1,238 | 31.4 |
|  | 18,826 | 12,650 | 6,176 | 32.8% | 12,650 | 6,176 | 32.8% | 12,650 | 6,176 | 32.8% |

obtained by first-in, first-out. Assuming operating expenses at 30 per cent of sales, a profit would be reported for each year with the use of last-in, first-out; larger profits would be reported for 1955 and 1956 with the use of first-in, first-out, but 1957 and 1958 would prove loss years. Inventory valuation on the last-in, first-out basis thus tends to smooth off the peaks and fill in the troughs of the business cycle.

¹Totals in the illustration are calculated to the nearest dollar.

It may be observed that the foregoing examples provided for a relatively close correspondence between periodic unit sales and unit acquisitions. If the lifo method is employed and there should be the liquidation of a significant part or the whole of an inventory carried at costs that are materially different from current costs, the lifo gross profit would not be the steady percentage offered by the recurring application of current costs to current revenue but could be a highly distorted value emerging from the need for charging off original inventory costs.

**EVALUATION OF COST FLOW PROCEDURES**  Fifo assumes a procession of costs that are assignable to revenue in exactly the same order in which they were incurred. The average method assumes a complete commingling of costs for units acquired with costs for units on hand, such commingled costs being assignable to revenue. Lifo assumes that first costs are identified with the inventory, subsequent costs by-passing the inventory and being assignable to revenue.

The fifo method can be supported as a logical and realistic approach to the flow of costs when it is impractical or impossible to achieve cost identification with goods as these move forward. An assumed cost flow is achieved which normally parallels closely the actual physical flow of goods. Revenue is charged with costs considered applicable to those goods involved in revenue realization; ending inventories are reported in terms of most recent costs — costs that fairly present the latest acquisition and that may equitably be assigned to revenues of the subsequent period.

The average cost approach, too, can be supported as realistic and as paralleling the actual physical flow of goods, particularly where there is an intermingling of identical inventory units. Limitations ascribed to this method are inventory values that perpetually contain to some minor degree the influence of earliest costs, and inventory values that may lag significantly behind current prices in periods of rising or falling markets.

The cost assignment resulting from the application of lifo cannot normally be considered in harmony with a movement of goods through the business. One would seldom encounter a practice of priorities for the use or transfer of goods representing latest acquisitions. Sequences involved in the physical movement of goods are disregarded so that charges may be made to revenue in terms of most-current costs, that is, costs that are more nearly representative of the cost of replacing the gap in the inventory occasioned by the transfer out.[1]

---

[1]It may be noted that some accountants would go beyond lifo by charging revenue with the replacement cost of goods sold (next-in, first-out, or *nifo*) rather than with latest acquisition costs.

The adoption of lifo and the assignment to revenue of current costs, it is argued, offers a more accurate statement of earnings accruing to the ownership group than alternate methods. When fifo is used in a period of rising prices, for example, a profit is reported that is not fully available to owners but rather must be applied in part or in whole to higher-cost inventory replacement; in a period of falling prices, a profit is reported that fails to show the full resources accruing to owners from sales activities plus the amounts made available through lower cost inventory replacement. Lifo, on the other hand, by charging revenue with latest costs, avoids the recognition of "paper profit or loss" on an inventory that the company must continue to hold as long as it operates as a going concern. This aspect of the measurement process may be illustrated as follows:

| | Inventory Cost | Sales Price | Latest Purchase Price | Fifo "Profit" | Lifo "Profit" | Dollar Gain After Unit Replacement |
|---|---|---|---|---|---|---|
| With rising prices: | $10 | $15 | $12 | $5 | $3 | $3 |
| With falling prices: | $10 | $12 | $8 | $2 | $4 | $4 |

Under lifo, gains that are not recognized in a period of rising prices when inventory is replaced at higher costs receive recognition in a period of falling prices when inventory is replaced at lower costs.

While arguments for lifo as a means of achieving adequate income measurement are impressive, one must consider the deficiencies of this method as applied to the recognition of inventory position for balance sheet purposes. The lifo inventory value consists of an assembly of congealed costs or cost layers dating back to original acquisitions — values that may differ materially from current costs. Such inventory values enter into the determination of working capital and may seriously distort this measurement. Inventory position is also a determinant of total assets and capital. Adoption of lifo in a period of rising prices results in inventory understatement, a practice that is normally rationalized as acceptable on conservative grounds; adoption in a period of falling prices results in the overstatement of inventories, and special action would normally follow to write down inventory balances to replacement cost.

Last-in, first-out has been widely adopted in recent years, largely because of its ability to smooth the profit curve as well as its tax advantages in a period of steadily rising prices. However, it is not the effects of a procedure but its merit as a means of sound measurement that should determine its acceptance for general accounting purposes. Depreciation, for example, could be recorded in accordance with the ability of revenue to absorb such a charge in smoothing the profit curve.

Reserves could be established to "equalize" profits. Such practices would not lead to measurements of what actually took place; they would serve to obscure measurements and thus contradict the chief aim of accounting — to report faithfully what actually took place.

It is interesting to note that the American Institute and the American Accounting Association differ in the criteria that each would consider in the choice of method for assigning costs. The American Institute views income measurement as the primary factor in making a choice. The Committee on Accounting Procedure has stated:

> Cost for inventory purposes may be determined under any one of several assumptions as to the flow of cost factors (such as first-in first-out, average, and last-in first-out); the major objective in selecting a method should be to choose the one which, under the circumstances, most clearly reflects periodic income.[1]

The American Accounting Association, however, questions the adoption of a cost flow assumption that is unrelated to the actual movement of goods. Its Committee on Concepts and Standards Underlying Corporate Financial Statements has made the following statement:

> (1) Ideally, the measurement of accounting profit involves the matching precisely of the identified costs of specific units of product with the sales revenues derived therefrom.
>
> (2) Where conditions are such that precise matching of identified costs with revenues is impractical, identified cost matching may be simulated by the adoption of an assumed flow of costs.
>
> (3) A flow assumption can be *realistic*, in that it reflects the dominant characteristics of the actual flow of goods; thus it may reflect the actual dominance of first-in, first-out (FIFO), average, or last-in, first-out (LIFO) movement. A flow assumption can be *artificial*, on the other hand, in that it premises a flow of costs that is clearly in contrast with actual physical movement.
>
> (4) The LIFO flow assumption now has wide usage although in very few, if any, instances of its application can the assumption be justified on the ground that it corresponds even approximately with the actual flow of goods. *Artificial LIFO* has appeal to some during periods of markedly changing price levels as a means of approaching a matching of current cost (dollar costs adjusted to reflect changes in the general purchasing power of the monetary unit) with current revenues; however, grave doubt exists as to whether the accuracy of such artificial matching is sufficient to justify the resultant departure from realism ) . . .[2]

[1] *Accounting Research Bulletin No. 43*, "Restatement and Revision of Accounting Research Bulletins," 1953 (New York: American Institute of Certified Public Accountants). p. 29.

[2] *Accounting and Reporting Standards for Corporate Financial Statements and Preceding Statements and Supplements*, "Inventory Pricing and Changes in the Price Levels," 1957 (Columbus: American Accounting Association), pp. 36–37.

Support for lifo will have to be found in its merit as a means of charging current revenue with current costs. Such a current-cost concept of income could conceivably be extended to other income statement charges in developing fully a "real income" measurement. However, those in support of the alternate methods described insist that it is actual historical costs, as best determined, that should be applied for goods sold as well as for the other sacrifices made by the business. Net income emerges from a comparison of revenues with those actual costs that made such revenues possible. This group admits that such accounting may need to be supplemented by special analyses in arriving at conclusions concerning economic gain, changes in resources, and the availability of resources for continued operations and for distribution to owners.

**OTHER COST PROCEDURES** While the methods previously described for arriving at cost are those most widely used, several other procedures are sometimes encountered and deserve mention.

**COST OF LATEST PURCHASES** Sometimes merchandise on hand is valued at cost of the latest purchase of each item regardless of quantities on hand. When the inventory consists largely of recent purchases, this method may give results closely approximating those obtained through specific cost identification or first-in, first-out procedures, and such results are available with considerably less work. However, when major price changes have taken place and the quantities of goods on hand are significantly in excess of the latest quantities purchased, use of latest costs may result in serious cost misstatement.

**SIMPLE AVERAGE OF COSTS** Classes of goods are sometimes valued at a simple average of all of the costs for the period without regard to the number of units acquired on each purchase. With significant differences in quantities acquired, the disregard of the weight factors may result in the development of unrepresentative costs.

**BASE STOCK METHOD** Some companies employ what is known as the *base stock* or *normal stock* method. This method assumes that a minimum stock is a requirement of the business; current purchases are means of satisfying current sales requirements, and hence their cost is properly applicable to revenues. The minimum or normal inventory is considered as a permanent element to be valued at a constant figure, frequently the lowest cost experienced for the stock. At the end of the period the quantity of goods on hand is determined. The base stock quantity is valued at the original base cost. An amount in excess of the base stock quantity is regarded as a temporary inventory accretion and is usually priced at current costs, applied on a first-in, first-out, average, or other basis. A shortage in the base stock quantity is viewed as an amount temporarily "borrowed" to meet sales requirements, the amount borrowed to be charged to sales at current replacement value in view of the cost to be incurred in restoring the inventory deficiency. To illustrate, assume a base stock of 100,000 units at $1 that has increased to a total of 120,000 units. If the current cost for the inventory is $1.60 per unit, the inventory would be valued as follows:

| | | |
|---|---|---|
| Base stock | 100,000 units @ $1.00...... | $100,000 |
| Add base stock increase at current cost....... | 20,000 units @ $1.60 ..... | 32,000 |
| Inventory value.......120,000 units ............ | | $132,000 |

Assuming an inventory of only 90,000 units, and a current cost for units of $1.60, the inventory would be valued as follows:

| | | |
|---|---|---|
| Base stock | 100,000 units @ $1.00...... | $100,000 |
| Deduct inventory deficiency at current cost. | 10,000 units @ $1.60...... | 16,000 |
| Inventory value...... 90,000 units ............ | | $ 84,000 |

The base stock is thus regarded as the equivalent of a permanent asset; operations are charged with the costs of replenishing and maintaining the normal stock. Results obtained through the base stock method are closely comparable with those obtained by the last-in, first-out method. Charges to revenue are those costs currently experienced. The inventory, normally reported at the lowest value in the experience of the organization, may be materially understated in terms of current market. Use of the base stock method is not permitted for income tax purposes.

**STANDARD COSTS**          Manufacturing inventories are frequently reported at *standard costs*, which are representative, normal, or ideal costs relating to the material, labor, and overhead elements under assumed conditions. Differences between actual costs and standard costs that arise from extraordinary items, such as waste, inefficiencies, and idle time, are charged to revenue and absorbed currently. Standard costs are developed by careful analysis of production factors and experience. Standards should be reviewed at frequent intervals to determine whether they still offer reliable evaluations of manufacturing costs. Changes in current conditions will call for adjustment in the standards.

**COST APPORTION- MENT BY RELATIVE SALES VALUE METHOD**
Mention needs to be made of a special accounting problem that arises when different commodities are purchased for one lump sum. Such purchase calls for the apportionment of the single cost to the units in some equitable manner. This cost apportionment should recognize the utility made available by the different units. Ordinarily, the estimated sales value of the different units provides the best measure of respective utilities, and accordingly cost is allocated on the basis of such estimated sales value. Such cost allocation is referred to as valuation by the *relative sales value method*. Costs derived through apportionment in terms of sales price are charged to revenue as units are sold. To illustrate this procedure, assume the purchase by a realty company of 60 acres of land for $220,000. The costs of grading, landscaping, streets, walks, water mains, lighting, and other improvements total $300,000. The property is divided into three groups of lots as follows: Class A, 100 lots to sell for $2,000 each; Class B, 200 lots to sell for $2,500 each; and Class C, 20 lots to sell for $5,000 each.

The total cost of the property, $520,000, is to be apportioned to the lots on the basis of their relative sales values. The cost allocation is made as follows:

| | |
|---|---|
| Class A lots, 100 at $2,000 | $200,000 |
| Class B lots, 200 at $2,500 | 500,000 |
| Class C lots, 20 at $5,000 | 100,000 |
| Total sales value of Class A, B, and C lots | $800,000 |

| | TOTAL | No. OF LOTS | COST ASSIGNED TO EACH LOT |
|---|---|---|---|
| Cost apportioned to Class A lots: $\frac{200,000}{800,000} \times \$520,000 = \$130,000$ | | 100 | $1,300 |
| Cost apportioned to Class B lots: $\frac{500,000}{800,000} \times \$520,000 =$ 325,000 | | 200 | $1,625 |
| Cost apportioned to Class C lots: $\frac{100,000}{800,000} \times \$520,000 =$ 65,000 | | 20 | $3,250 |
| Total | $520,000 | | |

The sale of a lot of any class results in a constant gross profit of 35% of sales.[1] Sale of a Class A lot would be recorded as follows:

| | | |
|---|---|---|
| Contracts Receivable.......................... | 2,000 | |
| Real Estate — Lot A-56.................... | | 1,300 |
| Gross Profit on Sale of Real Estate........... | | 700 |

When, in certain manufacturing organizations, accurate costs cannot be found for certain *joint products*, products that are produced simultaneously by a common process, it may be considered appropriate to assign joint costs to the products in a manner similar to that just illustrated. The sales value of each product is determined, and the total production cost is then allocated according to the relative sales values of the respective products. For example, assume that the Adams Manufacturing Co. produces Products M and N jointly in one of its processing departments and cannot identify costs with individual products. A summary of manufacturing costs, units finished, and units sold during a period follows:

| Costs | | Units Completed | | Units Sold |
|---|---|---|---|---|
| Material Cost — A..... | $15,000 | Product M | 10,000 | 6,000 @ $4.00 |
| Material Cost — B..... | 22,000 | Product N | 8,000 | 5,000 @ 8.50 |
| Labor............... | 26,000 | | | |
| Manufacturing Expense. | 12,600 | | | |
| | $75,600 | | | |

Cost apportionment is made on the basis of relative sale value of products as follows:

| | |
|---|---|
| Product M, 10,000 units @ $4.00...................... | $ 40,000 |
| Product N,  8,000 units @  8.50...................... | 68,000 |
| Total market value of Products M and N.............. | $108,000 |

| | Total | Units | Unit Cost |
|---|---|---|---|
| Cost apportioned to Product A: | | | |
| $\frac{40,000}{108,000} \times \$75,600$ | $28,000 | 10,000 | $2.80 |
| Cost apportioned to Product B: | | | |
| $\frac{68,000}{108,000} \times \$75,600$ | 47,600 | 8,000 | $5.95 |
| | $75,600 | | |

---

[1]The same cost allocation can be developed by calculating the percentage of total cost to total estimated sales value, and applying such percentage to the sales price for the individual unit. In the example, cost is 65% of the total estimated sales value of the properties (520,000 ÷ 800,000). Each lot, then, is assigned a cost equal to 65% of its sales value: Class A lots have a cost of 65% of $2,000, or $1,300; Class B lots a cost of 65% of $2,500, or $1,625; Class C lots a cost of 65% of $5,000, or $3,250.

Cost of goods sold and ending inventory costs for the two products would be as follows:

| | COMPLETED | | | COST OF GOODS SOLD | | | ENDING INVENTORY BALANCE | |
|---|---|---|---|---|---|---|---|---|
| Product M | 10,000 units @ $2.80 | $28,000 | | 6,000 units @ $2.80 | $16,800 | | 4,000 units @ $2.80 | $11,200 |
| Product N | 8,000 units @ 5.95 | 47,600 | | 5,000 units @ 5.95 | 29,750 | | 3,000 units @ 5.95 | 17,850 |
| | | $75,600 | | | $46,550 | | | $29,050 |

A joint product of relatively little value is referred to as a *by-product*. By-products are frequently valued at their sales prices less expenses of disposal, costs identified with the main products being reduced by the amounts assigned to the by-products.

**EFFECTS OF ERRORS IN RECORDING INVENTORY POSITION** Failure to report the inventory position accurately through errors in count, pricing, or inclusion results in misstatements on both the balance sheet and the income statement. The effects of inventory errors on the financial statements prepared at the end of the fiscal period are indicated in the summary that follows.

(a) Overstatement of the ending inventory through errors in the count of goods on hand, pricing, inclusion in inventory of goods not owned or goods already sold, etc.:

Current year:
    Income statement — overstatement of the ending inventory will cause the cost of goods sold to be understated and the net income to be overstated.
    Balance sheet — the inventory will be overstated and the capital will be overstated.

Succeeding year:
    Income statement — overstatement of the beginning inventory will cause the cost of goods sold to be overstated and the net income to be understated.
    Balance sheet — the error of the previous year will have been counterbalanced on the succeeding income statement and the balance sheet will be correctly stated.

(b) Understatement of ending inventory through errors in the count of goods on hand, pricing, failure to include goods purchased, or goods transferred but not yet sold, etc.:

Misstatements indicated in (a) above are reversed.

(c) Overstatement of ending inventory accompanied by failure to recognize sales and corresponding receivables at end of period:

Current year:
    Income statement — sales are understated by the sales price of the goods and cost of goods sold is understated by the cost of the

goods relating to the sales; gross profit and net income are thus understated by the gross profit on the sales.

Balance sheet — receivables are understated by the sales price of the goods and the inventory is overstated by the cost of the goods that were sold; current assets and capital are thus understated by the gross profit on the sales.

Succeeding year:

Income statement — sales of the preceding year are recognized here in sales and cost of sales; gross profit and net income, therefore, are overstated by the gross profit on such sales.

Balance sheet — the error of the previous year is counterbalanced on the succeeding income statement and the balance sheet will be correctly stated.

(d) Understatement of ending inventory accompanied by failure to recognize purchases and corresponding payables at end of period:

Current year:

Income statement — purchases are understated, but this is counterbalanced by the understatement of the ending inventory; gross profit and net income are correctly stated as a result of the counterbalancing effect of the error.

Balance sheet — while capital is reported correctly, both current assets and current liabilities are understated; when current assets exceed liabilities, such understatements by the same amount result in a ratio of current assets to current liabilities that is more favorable than is actually the case.

Succeeding year:

Income statement—the beginning inventory is understated, but this is counterbalanced by an overstatement of purchases, as purchases at the end of the prior year are recognized currently; gross profit and net income are correctly stated as a result of the counterbalancing effect of the error.

Balance sheet — the error of the previous year no longer affects balance sheet data.

Discoveries of inventory errors call for careful analyses of the effects of such errors and the preparation of entries to correct real and nominal accounts so that current and future activities may be accurately expressed in the accounts.

## QUESTIONS

**1.** (a) Why is so much importance attached to the satisfactory valuation of inventories? (b) What criteria might be adopted for inventory valuation? What criterion would you support?

**2.** (a) What distinction is usually made between raw materials and factory supplies? (b) How would you recommend that these be reported on the balance sheet?

**3.** (a) What are the three cost elements entering into goods in process and finished goods? (b) What items enter into factory overhead? (c) Define fixed overhead, variable overhead, and semivariable overhead and give an example of each.

**4.** (a) Describe the nature of a perpetual inventory system. (b) What purposes are served by such a system? (c) Does this system eliminate the need for physical inventories? Explain.

**5.** (a) What items may be considered to compose the cost of raw material acquisitions? (b) Which of these items are normally included as a part of raw material cost for stores purposes? (c) Which of these are normally excluded? Why? What disposition would be made of such items?

**6.** Distinguish between: (a) direct materials and indirect materials; (b) physical inventory and book inventory; (c) manufacturing direct costs and burden; (d) inventory valuation by fifo and lifo.

**7.** (a) How does title passing affect the current sections of a balance sheet? (b) Distinguish between a purchase "f.o.b. destination" and a purchase "f.o.b. shipping point." (c) What circumstances would suggest that exception be made from the legal rule of "passing title?"

**8.** How would you suggest that each of the following items be reported on the financial statements:

    (a) Manufacturing supplies.
    (b) Goods on hand received on a consignment basis.
    (c) Materials of a customer held for processing.
    (d) Goods received but without an accompanying invoice.
    (e) Goods in stock to be delivered to customers in subsequent periods.
    (f) Goods in hands of agents and consignees.
    (g) Deposits with vendors for merchandise to be delivered next period.
    (h) Goods in hands of customers on approval.

**9.** The Alpha Co. records purchases discounts taken as income. The Beta Co. records purchases discounts lost as expense. (a) How does the accounting for purchases for each company differ? (b) What are the arguments in favor of each practice? (c) Which practice do you favor? Why?

**10.** What objections can be raised to inventory valuation by specific cost identification procedures?

**11.** Describe and give the arguments in support of each of the following inventory cost methods: (a) fifo, (b) average, (c) lifo.

**12.** Compare the positions that are taken by the A.I.C.P.A. and the A.A.A. relative to cost flow assumptions that may be considered valid in arriving at inventory cost determinations.

**13.** Compare the effects of the use of fifo and lifo upon inventory valuation and upon net income measurement in a period of rapidly rising prices.

**14.** Your client, R. J. Anderson, wishes to change from fifo to lifo, having heard that the latter method results in a lower profit figure for income tax purposes. What is your comment and recommendation?

**15.** (a) Describe the base stock method. (b) How does this method differ from inventory valuation by lifo?

**16.** (a) Describe the valuation of inventories in terms of standard costs. (b) What precautions are necessary in the use of standard costs?

**17.** Describe cost apportionment by the relative sales method.

**18.** Distinguish between joint-products and by-products and suggest methods for the valuation of each.

**19.** State the effects of each of the following errors upon the financial statements prepared for the current period and those prepared for the succeeding fiscal period:

(a) Understatement of ending inventory through a miscount of goods on hand.

(b) Understatement of ending inventory accompanied by failure to record a purchase of goods on which title has passed.

(c) Understatement of ending inventory accompanied by recognition of a transfer of goods to a consignee as a sale. (Goods remain unsold in the hands of the consignee at the end of each period.)

**20.** State the effect of each of the following errors made by Fields, Inc., upon the balance sheet and the income statement (1) of the current period and (2) of the succeeding period:

(a) The company fails to record a sale of merchandise on account; goods sold are excluded in recording the ending inventory.

(b) The company fails to record a sale of merchandise on account; the goods sold are included, however, in recording the ending inventory.

(c) The company fails to record a purchase of merchandise on account; goods purchased are included in recording the ending inventory.

(d) The company fails to record a purchase of merchandise on account; goods purchased are not recognized in recording the ending inventory.

(e) The ending inventory is understated as the result of a miscount of goods on hand.

(f) The ending inventory is overstated as the result of inclusion of goods held on a consignment basis and never recognized as a purchase.

## EXERCISES

**1.** Perpetual inventory records of the Wallace Co. show 1,000 units of Commodity A on hand at a cost of $1.15. An actual count of the units discloses only 850 on hand. (a) List possible reasons for the discrepancy. (b) Give the entry that should be made to record the discrepancy.

**2.** The following errors are discovered at the beginning of 1959 in auditing the accounts of the Marshall Sales Corporation. Give the entry to correct each of the following errors, assuming that perpetual inventory records are not maintained:

(a) The company failed to record a sale on account of $210 at the end of 1958. The merchandise had been shipped and was not included in the ending inventory. The sale was recorded in 1959 when cash was collected from the customer.

(b) The company failed to recognize $400 due from a consignee as a result of goods sold by this party at the end of 1958. The consignee had failed to report the sale of consigned goods and the company included their cost of $260 in inventory as Goods on Consignment.

(c) The company failed to recognize a purchase on account of $1,350 at the end of 1958 and also failed to include the goods purchased in the ending inventory. The purchase was recorded when payment was made to the creditor in 1959.

(d) The company failed to make an entry for a purchase on account of $60 at the end of 1958, although it included this merchandise in the inventory count. The purchase was recorded when payment was made to the creditor in 1959.

(e) The company overlooked goods of $360 in the physical count of goods at the end of 1958.

**3.** The Whittier Co. buys all of its merchandise from the Elson Manufacturing Co. and is allowed a trade discount of 15%—10%—10% and a cash discount of 2%. Purchases during January are $60,000 before discounts. Two thirds of the merchandise acquired is sold in January. At what value should the ending inventory be reported if the cash discount is treated as: (a) a reduction in purchases? (b) other income?

**4.** Transactions of the Barlow Co. relating to goods purchased during December are summarized below:

> Purchases were $10,000, terms 2/10, n/30.
> Accounts of $8,500 were paid, including accounts of $8,000 paid within the discount period on which discounts of $160 were received.

Give the entries to record purchases and invoice payments in December, assuming that:

(a) Accounts payable are recorded at invoice price and purchases discounts earned are summarized in the accounts.

(b) Accounts payable are recorded net and purchases discounts lost are summarized in the accounts.

(c) Accounts payable are recorded at invoice price and purchases discounts lost are summarized in the accounts.

**5.** The Wilson Manufacturing Company record for Material No. 25A follows:

| | | | |
|---|---|---|---|
| Sept. 1 | Balance | 100 units at $10.................... | $1,000 |
| 10 | Received | 200 units at 9.................... | 1,800 |
| 20 | Received | 50 units at 12.................... | 600 |
| 28 | Received | 100 units at 11.................... | 1,100 |

At the end of the month, 150 units are on hand. Give the cost of the ending inventory, assuming that it is calculated by each of the following methods: (a) first-in, first-out, (b) weighted average, (c) last-in, first-out, (d) cost of latest purchases, (e) simple average of costs.

**6.** Changes in Commodity X during January are:

| | | | |
|---|---|---|---|
| Jan. 1 | Balance | 400 units @ $5 | Jan. 10  Sale 300 units @ $10 |
| 12 | Purchase | 200 units @ 6 | Jan. 30  Sale 200 units @ 12 |
| 28 | Purchase | 200 units @ 7 | |

(a) Assuming that perpetual inventories are maintained and that accounts are kept up to date currently, what is the cost of the ending inventory for Commodity X using: (1) fifo; (2) lifo; (3) average?

(b) Assuming that perpetual inventories are not maintained and that a physical count at the end of the month shows 300 units to be on hand, what is the cost of the ending inventory using each of the three methods listed in part (a)?

**7.** Nelson, Inc., uses the base stock method for inventory valuation. The base stock quantity and value for Commodity A is: 1,000,000 lbs. at $.05.

(a) The inventory on December 31, 1957, consists of 1,150,000 lbs., and the replacement cost per lb. is $.0625. What value should be assigned to the inventory?

(b) The inventory on December 31, 1958, consists of 910,000 lbs. and the replacement cost per lb. at this time is $.07. What value should be assigned to the inventory?

**8.** The Graham Development Company offers for sale lots in a tract of land that cost the company $50,000. Lots are classified as follows:

| Class | No. of Lots | Sales Price Per Lot |
|-------|-------------|---------------------|
| Class A | 10 | $2,500 |
| Class B | 20 | 1,500 |
| Class C | 25 | 1,000 |

One Class A lot and one Class C lot are sold. What entries would be made to record the sales if cost is determined by relative sales values?

**9.** R. T. Roper, a dry goods dealer, purchased a job lot of 6,200 yards of bolt goods for $600. Upon receipt of the goods, he selected the 1,600 yards of best quality and priced them at 25c per yard; 3,000 yards of average grade were priced at 15c per yard; 1,000 yards of the lowest grade were priced at 12c per yard; and the remaining 600 yards of small remnants were marked at 5c per yard. The next periodic inventory showed 400 yards of the 25c goods and 2,000 yards of the 15c goods on hand; all other goods had been sold. At what cost should the inventory be shown?

## PROBLEMS

**8-1.** The Harvey Corp. record of merchandise follows:

| December | 1 | (Inventory) | 1,000 units @ $5.50 |
|----------|---|-------------|---------------------|
| | 7 | Purchase | 3,000 units @ 6.50 |
| | 15 | Purchase | 5,000 units @ 7.20 |
| | 21 | Purchase | 4,000 units @ 7.50 |
| | 30 | Purchase | 1,500 units @ 7.00 |

Sales for December totaled 12,000 units.

*Instructions:* Calculate the cost to be assigned to the ending inventory by each of the following methods: (a) fifo; (b) lifo; (c) weighted average.

**8-2.** The record of Commodity Z for the Andrews Manufacturing Co. shows:

| | | | |
|---|---|---|---|
| Balance: | January | 1 | 350 units at $20.50 |
| Purchases: | January | 3 | 400 units at 21.00 |
| | | 12 | 200 units at 22.00 |
| | | 24 | 100 units at 21.50 |
| Sales: | January | 2 | 300 units at 28.00 |
| | | 18 | 200 units at 28.50 |
| | | 29 | 150 units at 29.00 |

*Instructions:* Calculate the inventory balance and the gross profit on sales for the month on each of the following bases:

(1) First-in, first-out. Perpetual inventories are maintained and costs are charged out currently.
(2) First-in, first-out. No book inventory is maintained.
(3) Last-in, first-out. Perpetual inventories are maintained and costs are charged out currently.
(4) Last-in, first-out. No book inventory is maintained.
(5) Moving average. Perpetual inventories are maintained.
(6) Weighted average.

**8-3.** The Clawson Co. records report sales and purchases of Article M as follows:

| | Purchases | | Sales |
|---|---|---|---|
| | Units | Unit Cost | Units |
| January 6.......... | | | 150 |
| January 7.......... | 250 | $ 4.25 | |
| January 10......... | | | 150 |
| January 12......... | 150 | 4.35 | |
| January 15......... | | | 250 |
| January 20......... | 300 | 4.50 | |
| January 27......... | | | 250 |

Article M inventory on hand on January 1 consisted of 350 units that cost $1,435.

*Instructions:* Calculate the cost of goods sold for January and the cost of the ending inventory balance assuming use of:

(1) The first-in, first-out basis.
(2) The last-in, first-out basis, costs calculated at time of sale.
(3) The last-in, first-out basis, costs calculated at end of month.
(4) Moving average basis, costs calculated at time of sale.
(5) Weighted average basis, costs calculated at end of month.

**8-4.** Evanston, Inc. sells a single commodity. Purchases, sales, and expenses for January, February, and March are summarized below:

| | | Purchases | |
|---|---|---|---|
| | | Units | Cost Per Unit |
| January | 1–15................................... | 1,000 | $ 5.00 |
| | 16–31................................... | 2,000 | 5.75 |
| February | 1–15................................... | 1,000 | 6.00 |
| | 16–28................................... | 1,500 | 6.50 |
| March | 1–15................................... | — | — |
| | 16–31................................... | 1,000 | 5.75 |

|            | Sales | | Operating Expenses |
|------------|-------|---------------|--------------------|
|            | Units | Sales Price Per Unit | |
| January......................... | 1,500 | $ 8.75 | $ 4,025 |
| February........................ | 2,400 | 9.50 | 6,050 |
| March.......................... | 1,500 | 9.50 | 3,600 |

*Instructions:* Prepare a comparative income statement summarizing operations for the months of January, February, and March for each case below:

(1) Assume that monthly inventories are calculated at cost on a first-in, first-out basis.

(2) Assume that monthly inventories are calculated at cost on a last-in, first-out basis.

(3) Assume that monthly inventories are calculated at cost on a weighted average basis. (Unit costs are calculated to the nearest cent.)

**8-5.** The Rosen Manufacturing Co. manufactures a single commodity. A summary of its activities for 1958 follows:

|            | No. of Units | Amount |
|------------|--------------|--------|
| Sales................................. | 40,000 | $ 232,000 |
| Raw Materials Inventory 1/1.......... |  | 20,000 |
| Goods in Process Inventory 1/1........ |  | 25,000 |
| Finished Goods Inventory 1/1......... | 10,000 | 40,000 |
| Raw Materials Inventory 12/31........ |  | 15,000 |
| Goods in Process Inventory 12/31...... |  | 30,000 |
| Finished Goods Inventory 12/31....... | 12,000 | —— |
| Raw Materials Purchases.............. |  | 85,000 |
| Direct Labor........................ |  | 59,000 |
| Manufacturing Expenses.............. |  | 45,000 |
| Selling, General, and Administrative Expenses........................ |  | 26,000 |

*Instructions:* (1) Prepare a schedule summarizing the cost of goods manufactured for the year. Indicate on the schedule the number of units completed for the year and the cost per unit of goods finished.

(2) Prepare an income statement for the year on each of the following assumptions relating to the transfer of cost from finished goods to cost of goods sold: (a) first-in, first-out, (b) last-in, first-out, (c) weighted average (to three decimal places).

**8-6.** The Reardon Co. adjusted and closed its books at the end of 1958, the summary of 1958 activities showing a loss of $2,420. The following errors relating to 1958 are discovered upon an audit of the books of the company made in March, 1959:

(a) Merchandise, cost $1,485, was recorded as a purchase at the end of 1958 but was not included in the ending inventory since it was received on January 9, 1959.

(b) Merchandise, cost $315, was received in 1958 and included in the ending inventory; however, the entry recording the purchase was made on January 4, 1959, when the invoice was received.

(c) 600 units of Commodity Z, costing $4.25 per unit, were recorded at a per unit cost of $2.45 in summarizing the ending inventory.

(d) Goods in the hands of a consignee costing $6,000 were included in the inventory; however, $1,450 of such goods had been sold as of December 31, and the sale was not recorded until January 31 when the consignee made a remittance of $1,750 on this item.

(e) Merchandise, cost $368, sold at $490 and shipped on December 31, 1958, was not included in the ending inventory; however, the sale was not recorded until January 12, 1959, when the customer made payment on the sale.

*Instructions:* (1) Calculate the corrected profit or loss for 1958.

(2) Give the entries that are required in 1959 in correcting the accounts.

**8-7.** The Bell Manufacturing Co. produces and sells a single product. The corporation's condensed income statement for 1958 follows:

| | | |
|---|---:|---:|
| Sales (30,000 units) | | $450,000 |
| Returns, allowances, and discounts | | 13,500 |
| Net sales | | $436,500 |
| Cost of goods sold | | 306,000 |
| Gross profit on sales | | $130,500 |
| Selling expenses | $ 60,000 | |
| Administrative expenses | 30,000 | 90,000 |
| Net income (before income taxes) | | $ 40,500 |

The budget committee has estimated the following changes in income and costs for 1959:

30% increase in number of units sold.

20% increase in material unit cost.

15% increase in direct labor cost per unit.

10% increase in production overhead cost per unit.

14% increase in selling expenses, arising from increased volume as well as from a higher price level.

7% increase in administrative expenses, reflecting anticipated higher wage and supply price levels. Any changes in administrative expenses caused solely by increased sales volume are considered immaterial for the purpose of this budget.

As inventory quantities remain fairly constant, the committee considered that, for budget purposes, any change in inventory valuation can be ignored. The composition of the cost of a unit of finished product during 1958 for materials, direct labor and production overhead, respectively, was in the ratio of 3 to 2 to 1. No changes in production methods or credit policies were contemplated for 1959.

*Instructions:* From the foregoing data, compute the *unit sales price* (adjusted to the nearest full cent) at which the company must sell its only product in 1959 in order to earn a budgeted profit (before income taxes) of $60,000. (A.I.C.P.A. adapted)

8-8. The Erdman Manufacturing Company produces one principal product. The income from sales of this product for the year 1958 is expected to be $200,000. Cost of goods sold will be as follows:

| | |
|---|---:|
| Materials used................................................. | $ 40,000 |
| Direct labor................................................... | 60,000 |
| Fixed overhead................................................ | 20,000 |
| Variable overhead............................................. | 30,000 |

The company realizes that it is facing rising costs and in December is attempting to plan its operations for the year 1959. It is believed that if the product is not redesigned, the following results will be obtained:

Material prices will average 5% higher and rates for direct labor will average 10% higher. Variable overhead will vary in proportion to direct labor costs. If the sale price is increased to produce the same rate of gross profit as the 1958 rate, there will be a 10% decrease in the number of units sold in 1959.

If the product is redesigned according to suggestions offered by the sales manager, it is expected that a 10% increase can be obtained in the number of units sold with a 15% increase in sale price per unit. However, a change in the product would involve several changes in cost.

A different grade of material would be used, but 10% more of it would be required for each unit. The price of this proposed grade of material has averaged 5% below the price of the material now being used, and that 5% difference in price is expected to continue for the year 1959. Redesign would permit a change in processing method enabling the company to use less-skilled workmen. It is believed that the average pay rate for 1959 would be 10% below the average for 1958 because of that change. However, about 20% more labor per unit would be required than was needed in 1958. Variable overhead is incurred directly in relation to production; it is expected to increase 10% because of price changes and to increase an additional amount in proportion to the change in labor hours.

*Instructions:* Assuming the accuracy of these estimates, prepare statements showing the prospective gross profit if:

(1) The same product is continued for 1959.
(2) The product is redesigned for 1959. (A.I.C.P.A. adapted)

8-9. You are engaged to audit the Owl Company and its subsidiary, Owl Sales Co., as of December 31, 1958. During the course of the audit you discover the balances of the intercompany accounts do not agree.

The Owl Company manufactures fountain pens which it sells to its subsidiary at cost plus 20%. The subsidiary then sells the fountain pens to jewelry stores.

Following is a copy of part of the intercompany account ledger sheets:

## ACCOUNT IN THE OWL COMPANY GENERAL LEDGER

### INTERCOMPANY ACCOUNT — OWL SALES CO.

| DATE | REFERENCE | AMOUNT | DATE | REFERENCE | AMOUNT |
|---|---|---|---|---|---|
| | Total forwarded | $178,683.00 | | Total forwarded | $123,867.00 |
| Dec. 26 | SR 17877 | 1,950.00 | Dec. 26 | CR | 3,567.00 |
| 27 | SR 17878 | 1,194.00 | 29 | CR | 31,127.00 |
| 28 | SR 17879 | 2,183.00 | 31 | Balance | 28,189.00 |
| 29 | SR 17880 | 849.00 | | | |
| 31 | SR 17882 | 1,891.00 | | | |
| | | $186,750.00 | | | $186,750.00 |

## ACCOUNT IN THE OWL SALES CO. GENERAL LEDGER

### INTERCOMPANY ACCOUNT — OWL COMPANY

| DATE | REFERENCE | AMOUNT | DATE | REFERENCE | AMOUNT |
|---|---|---|---|---|---|
| | Total forwarded | $127,434.00 | | Total forwarded | $176,508.00 |
| Dec. 28 | CD | 31,127.00 | Dec. 26 | VR 34333-17876 | 2,175.00 |
| 31 | CD | 19,777.00 | 28 | VR 34334-17877 | 1,950.00 |
| 31 | RG 74 | 2,329.00 | 29 | VR 34335-17878 | 1,194.00 |
| 31 | Balance | 6,318.00 | 31 | VR 34336-17881 | 3,647.00 |
| | | | 31 | VR 34340-17883 | 1,511.00 |
| | | $186,985.00 | | | $186,985.00 |

Discussion with company employees developed the following explanation of references found on the ledger accounts:

SR — Sales register and invoice number.

CR — Cash receipts book.

CD — Cash disbursements book.

VR — Voucher register, receiving report number and Owl Company invoice number.

RG — Returned goods register and debit memo number.

A review of the inventory observation working papers discloses the following information:

*Observation at Owl Company on December 31, 1958:*

(1) Last shipment prior to the physical inventory was billed on invoice number 17882 dated December 31, 1958.

(2) No returned merchandise was received from the Owl Sales Co. during the month of December 1958.

(3) The last receiving report used in December, 1958 was number 59742 dated December 30, 1958.

*Observation at Owl Sales Co. on December 31, 1958:*

(1) Last shipment prior to the physical invent ory was billed on invoice number 77843 dated December 31, 1958.

(2) The last shipment of merchandise returned to the Owl Company in December, 1958 was entered on debit memo number 74 dated December 31, 1958.

(3) The last receiving report used in December, 1958 was number 34337 dated December 31, 1958 for merchandise billed on Owl invoice 17879.

*Instructions:* (1) Prepare a reconciliation of the intercompany accounts.

(2) Give the journal entries required by each company to adjust the intercompany accounts.

(3) Give the adjustments to the inventories which are based on physical inventories taken December 31, 1958 and valued by each of the two companies at its cost. (A.I.C.P.A. adapted)

**8-10.** During a certain period, the Perfect Plate Glass Co. cast and rolled about 850,000 square feet of glass. The product, after cutting up in order to eliminate defects, was priced for sale as follows:

| | |
|---|---|
| Size No. 1 | 28 cents per square foot |
| Size No. 2 | 24 cents per square foot |
| Size No. 3 | 22 cents per square foot |
| Size No. 4 | 20 cents per square foot |
| Size No. 5 | 14 cents per square foot |
| Size No. 6 | 5 cents per square foot |

Any product below No. 6 was returned to process and remelted.

As may be seen, the selling price for a given quality varied with the size, the largest perfect sheets selling for the highest price per square foot.

The total cost of materials, manufacture, grinding, polishing, cutting, and sorting, including factory expense, was $120,807.

The inventories, in square feet, were:

| | Opening | Closing |
|---|---|---|
| Size No. 1 | 10,000 | 12,860 |
| Size No. 2 | | 11,000 |
| Size No. 3 | 10,000 | 23,000 |
| Size No. 4 | | 6,000 |
| Size No. 5 | | |
| Size No. 6 | | 2,000 |

The sales, at list selling prices, were:

| | |
|---|---|
| Size No. 1 | $ 30,240 |
| Size No. 2 | 36,480 |
| Size No. 3 | 35,376 |
| Size No. 4 | 21,100 |
| Size No. 5 | 9,030 |
| Size No. 6 | 2,300 |

*Instructions:* Calculate in detail and in total the value of the ending inventory. Assume that manufacturing costs are assigned to products according to their relative sales value. (A.I.C.P.A. adapted)

# Chapter 9

## INVENTORIES

### SPECIAL VALUATION PROCEDURES

**INVENTORY VALUA-
TION AT COST OR
MARKET, WHICHEVER
IS LOWER** Changes in the market may result in a current productive or replacement cost for inventories that is less than original acquisition
cost and may suggest sales prices that are less than those that were
anticipated on the original purchase of goods. Such circumstances are
considered to justify departure from cost and the use of lower market
values in inventory valuation. Recognition of an inventory decline
identifies the loss with the period in which it was incurred; goods are
reported at an amount that measures the contribution carried into the
next period. This practice is referred to as valuation at "cost or market,
whichever is lower," or valuation at "the lower of cost or market."

Replacement cost or market is generally interpreted to be the present expenditure required for the acquisition or the reproduction of the
goods. Federal Income Tax Regulations offer the following definition:
"Under ordinary circumstances and for normal goods in an inventory,
'market' means the current bid price prevailing at the date of the inventory for the particular merchandise in the volume in which usually
purchased by the taxpayer. . . ."[1]

**MODIFICATION IN THE
COST OR MARKET RULE** The rule of valuation at the lower of cost or
market as originally applied stemmed from
the objective of achieving "balance sheet conservatism" and called for
the inventory write-down to a lower market or replacement cost under
all circumstances. In recent years, however, with emphasis shifting
from the balance sheet to the income statement, authorities have taken
the view that departures from inventory cost are appropriate only
when costs have lost a portion of their usefulness and future revenue
should be freed from such burden. Support for an inventory cost reduction, thus, must be found in achieving appropriate charges to the revenue of subsequent periods and not in the establishment of conservative
balance sheet values.

Authorities do not agree on the procedure to be followed in achieving the foregoing objective. The American Institute of Certified Public

---

[1]Regulations, Sec. 39.22 (c)-4.

262

Accountants would apply certain significant limitations in the application of the conventional cost or market rule. The American Institute defines "market" as follows:

As used in the phrase *lower of cost or market,* the term *market* means current replacement cost (by purchase or by reproduction, as the case may be) except that:

(1) Market should not exceed the net realizable value (i.e., estimated selling price in the ordinary course of business less reasonably predictable costs of completion and disposal); and

(2) Market should not be less than net realizable value reduced by an allowance for an approximately normal profit margin.[1]

The foregoing sets a ceiling for the market value at sales price less costs of completion and disposal, and a floor for such market at sales price less both the costs of completion and disposal and the normal profit margin. The ceiling limitation is necessary because, regardless of the apparent replacement cost, the inventory should not be valued at more than its net realizable value, that is, the estimated selling price less the cost of completion and disposal; failure to observe such limitation would result in charges to future periods in excess of the utility carried forward and ultimate loss on the sale of the inventory. The floor limitation is necessary because, regardless of the apparent replacement cost, there is no need to value an inventory at less than the net realizable value minus a normal profit; valuation at the floor still assures the recognition of a normal profit on the sale of the inventory in future periods.

To illustrate the application of the foregoing, assume the following for the sale of a certain commodity: selling expense, $20; normal profit, $15.

Assuming estimated sales price, actual cost, and replacement cost as indicated below, the lower of cost or market as limited by the foregoing concepts is found in each case as follows:

| | ESTIMATED SALES PRICE | COST | MARKET | | | LOWER OF COST OR MARKET* |
| | | | FLOOR (Estimated Sales Price Less Selling Expenses and Normal Profit) | CEILING (Estimated Sales Price Less Selling Expenses) | REPLACEMENT COST | |
|---|---|---|---|---|---|---|
| (a) | 75 | 50 | 40 | 55 | 60 | 50 |
| (b) | 75 | 50 | 40 | 55 | 45 | 45 |
| (c) | 75 | 50 | 40 | 55 | 35 | 40 |
| (d) | 65 | 50 | 30 | 45 | 55 | 45 |
| (e) | 65 | 50 | 30 | 45 | 40 | 40 |
| (f) | 65 | 50 | 30 | 45 | 25 | 30 |

*The value underlined is the value that is applicable for purposes of the cost or market determination.

[1] *Accounting Research Bulletin No. 43,* "Restatement and Revision of Accounting Research Bulletins," 1953 (New York: American Institute of Certified Public Accountants), p. 31.

(a) The cost is less than the replacement cost; it is also less than the net realizable value $(75 − $20); therefore the cost price is used.

(b) The replacement cost is less than the cost; also the replacement cost is less than the realizable value ($75 − $20) and is more than the realizable value minus a normal profit margin ($75 − $20 − $15); therefore the replacement cost is used.

(c) The replacement cost is less than the cost; but the replacement cost is also less than the realizable value minus the normal profit margin ($75 − $20 − $15); therefore the market value is considered to be $40, the realizable value less the normal profit margin. The replacement cost of $35 is actually less than the known value of the asset to the business, hence the higher value is used.

(d) The net realizable value ($65 − $20) is less than either the replacement cost or the cost. As the market value should not be considered more than the net realizable value, this value is used.

(e) and (f) These cases are the same as (b) and (c) respectively.

The American Accounting Association also views inventory valuation as a function of the income measurement problem but recommends the following procedure:

> The residual cost should be carried forward in the balance sheet for assignment in future periods except when it is evident that the cost of an item of inventory cannot be recovered, whether from damage, deterioration, obsolescence, style change, over-supply, reduction in price levels, or other cause. In such event the inventory item should be stated at the estimated amount of sales proceeds less direct expense of completion and disposal.[1]

"Market" is abandoned as a test of subsequent utility in the above. Also, an inventory decline is ignored as long as cost is recoverable.

It may be observed that both authorities modify the "lower of cost or market" rule to a "lower of cost or residual useful cost" approach. However, although the American Accounting Association would set a single criterion — sales proceeds less cost to complete and dispose — as a means for arriving at a residual cost to be carried forward and assigned to future revenue, the American Institute would retain reference to market but would establish significant limitations in its application.

**METHODS OF APPLY-ING LOWER OF COST OR MARKET PRO-CEDURE**    The rule of the lower of cost or market is normally applied to each inventory item in arriving at the inventory valuation. Under certain circumstances, application of this rule to major inventory groupings or to the inventory as a whole may be considered to offer sufficiently conservative valuation. For example, assume that balanced stocks of raw materials are on hand, some of which have gone down and others

---

[1] *Accounting and Reporting Standards for Corporate Financial Statements and Preceding Statements and Supplements*, "Inventory Pricing and Changes in Price Levels," 1957 (Columbus: American Accounting Association), p. 36.

up. When such raw materials are used as components of a single finished product, a loss in the value of certain materials may be considered to be counterbalanced by the gains that are found in other materials, and the lower of cost or market as applied to this category as a whole may provide an adequate measure of the utility of the goods. The illustration below shows the use of the valuation procedure of cost or market, whichever is lower, as applied to (1) individual inventory items, (2) independent sections of the inventory, and (3) inventory as a whole.

| | Quan- tities | Unit Cost | Market | Totals | | Cost or Market, Whichever Is Lower | | |
| | | | | Cost | Market | (1) If Applied to Indi- vidual In- ventory Items | (2) If Applied to Inven- tory Sections | (3) If Applied to Inven- tory as a Whole |
|---|---|---|---|---|---|---|---|---|
| Material A........ | 4,000 | $1.20 | $1.10 | $ 4,800 | $ 4,400 | $ 4,400 | | |
| Material B........ | 5,000 | .50 | .40 | 2,500 | 2,000 | 2,000 | | |
| Material C........ | 2,000 | 1.00 | 1.10 | 2,000 | 2,200 | 2,000 | | |
| | | | | $ 9,300 | $ 8,600 | | $ 8,600 | |
| Goods in Process A.. | 10,000 | 1.60 | 1.40 | $16,000 | $14,000 | 14,000 | | |
| Goods in Process B.. | 12,000 | 1.00 | 1.20 | 12,000 | 14,400 | 12,000 | | |
| | | | | $28,000 | $28,400 | | 28,000 | |
| Finished Goods A... | 3,000 | 2.00 | 1.70 | $ 6,000 | $ 5,100 | 5,100 | | |
| Finished Goods B... | 2,000 | 1.50 | 1.60 | 3,000 | 3,200 | 3,000 | | |
| | | | | $ 9,000 | $ 8,300 | | 8,300 | |
| | | | | $46,300 | $45,300 | | | $45,300 |
| Inventory valuation | | | | | | $42,500 | $44,900 | $45,300 |

In valuing manufacturing inventories, raw materials declines are applicable to the raw materials inventory and also to raw material costs found in goods in process and finished goods. Goods in process and finished goods valuations are also affected by declines in labor and overhead costs; but declines in the latter costs when relatively minor are usually ignored.

The method that is chosen for application of the rule of cost or market, whichever is lower, should be applied consistently in successive inventory valuations. A reduced market value assigned to goods at the end of a period is considered to be its cost for purposes of inventory valuation in subsequent periods; cost reductions, thus, would not be restored in subsequent inventory determinations.

It may be observed that the taxpayer, for federal income tax purposes, may elect to use for inventory valuation either (1) cost, or (2) cost or market, whichever is lower. If cost or market, whichever is lower, is elected, this procedure must be applied to each item in the inventory. The method adopted must be applied in successive returns.

**EVALUATION OF LOWER OF COST OR MARKET PROCEDURE**  Inventory valuation at the lower of cost or market has been widely applied in practice. There has, however, been considerable criticism of this valuation procedure. It has been charged that such valuation produces inconsistencies in the measurements of both the position and the progress of the enterprise: market decreases are recognized; increases are not. Furthermore, with changes in the direction of market prices, a cost or market valuation at the end of one year may be followed by a strictly cost valuation the next. It has also been pointed out that serious income distortions may emerge from assumptions as to a lower future market that fail to materialize. To illustrate, assume that activities summarized in terms of cost would provide the following results over a three-year period:

| | 1956 | | 1957 | | 1958 | |
|---|---|---|---|---|---|---|
| Sales................... | $200,000 | | $225,000 | | $250,000 | |
| Cost of goods sold: | | | | | | |
| Beginning inventory....... | $ 60,000 | | $ 80,000 | | $127,500 | |
| Purchases............... | 120,000 | | 160,000 | | 90,000 | |
| | $180,000 | | $240,000 | | $217,500 | |
| Less ending inventory...... | 80,000 | 100,000 | 127,500 | 112,500 | 92,500 | 125,000 |
| Gross profit on sales........ | | $100,000 | | $112,500 | | $125,000 |
| Expenses................. | | 80,000 | | 90,000 | | 100,000 |
| Net income............... | | $ 20,000 | | $ 22,500 | | $ 25,000 |
| Rate of income to sales....... | | 10% | | 10% | | 10% |

Assume, now, that estimates as to the future utility of ending inventories suggested market values as follows:

| 1956 | 1957 | 1958 |
|---|---|---|
| $75,000 | $110,000 | $92,500 |

Use of the lower of cost or market for inventory valuation would provide the following periodic results:

| | 1956 | | 1957 | | 1958 | |
|---|---|---|---|---|---|---|
| Sales................... | $200,000 | | $225,000 | | $250,000 | |
| Cost of goods sold: | | | | | | |
| Beginning inventory....... | $ 60,000 | | $ 75,000 | | $110,000 | |
| Purchases............... | 120,000 | | 160,000 | | 90,000 | |
| | $180,000 | | $235,000 | | $200,000 | |
| Less ending inventory...... | 75,000 | 105,000 | 110,000 | 125,000 | 92,500 | 107,500 |
| Gross profit on sales........ | | $ 95,000 | | $100,000 | | $142,500 |
| Expenses................. | | 80,000 | | 90,000 | | 100,000 |
| Net income............... | | $ 15,000 | | $ 10,000 | | $ 42,500 |
| Rate of income to sales....... | | 7.5% | | 4.4% | | 17.0% |

Reduction of inventories below cost reduces the net income of the period in which the reduction is made and increases the net income of the subsequent period. In the examples just given, total net income for the three-year period is the same under either set of calculations. But the reduction of inventories to lower market values as a result of lower sales prices anticipated for 1957 and 1958 served to reduce the incomes for 1956 and 1957 and to increase the income for 1958. The fact that inventory cost reductions were not followed by decreases in the sales prices resulted in profit determinations that varied considerably from those that might reasonably have been expected from a trend of increasing sales and costs that normally vary with sales volume. Application of the valuation procedure of cost or market, whichever is lower, calls for analysis of underlying conditions and care in the determination of the values to be used.

**APPLICATION OF LOWER OF COST OR MARKET IN THE ACCOUNTS**  If beginning and ending inventories are reported on the income statement at amounts that are less than cost as a result of inventory pricing at the lower of cost or market, the cost of goods sold determination will reflect both the cost of goods sold and the effects of the recognition of fluctuations in inventory replacement values. With substantial and unusual adjustments resulting from application of the cost or market rule, it is normally desirable to show these separately on the income statement so that the statement reader may be fully informed on these matters and so that appropriate comparisons can be made of operating results, both normal and abnormal, for succeeding periods. The adjustment item should be excluded from the cost of sales section and reported as an operating item or extraordinary item, whichever may be deemed appropriate under the circumstances. Two procedures are available in developing operating data so that the effects of market fluctuations in inventory values may be separately set forth. One procedure calls for the periodic recognition of the effect upon incomes of an ending inventory reduced to a lower valuation. A second procedure calls for the periodic recognition of the effect upon incomes of both beginning and ending inventories stated on a basis that is less than cost. The illustration that follows shows the effects of failure to distinguish between operating and market factors as compared with use of the alternate procedures indicated above. Assume the following inventories.

|  | December 31, 1957 | December 31, 1958 |
|---|---|---|
| Cost | $60,000 | $75,000 |
| Lower of cost or market | 52,000 | 70,000 |

| | | | |
|---|---|---|---|
| December 31, 1957:<br>Entries to record ending inventory. | Merchandise Inventory.....<br>Profit and Loss........ | 52,000 | 52,000 |

Income statement for year 1957:

| | | | |
|---|---|---|---|
| Sales | | | 240,000 |
| Cost of goods sold: | | | |
| Beginning inventory | | 50,000 | |
| Purchases | | 130,000 | |
| Cost of goods available for sale | | 180,000 | |
| Deduct: Ending inventory | (lower of cost or market)... | 52,000 | 128,000 |
| Gross profit on sales | | | 112,000 |
| Operating expenses | | | 100,000 |
| Deduct: Loss on reduction of inventory to market | | | |
| Net income | | | 12,000 |

| | | | |
|---|---|---|---|
| December 31, 1958:<br>Entries to close opening inventory. | Profit and Loss...........<br>Merchandise Inventory... | 52,000 | 52,000 |
| Entries to record ending inventory. | Merchandise Inventory.....<br>Profit and Loss........ | 70,000 | 70,000 |

Income statement for year 1958:

| | | | |
|---|---|---|---|
| Sales | | | 280,000 |
| Cost of goods sold: | | | |
| Beginning inventory | (lower of cost or market)... | 52,000 | |
| Purchases | | 163,000 | |
| Cost of goods available for sale | | 215,000 | |
| Deduct: Ending inventory | (lower of cost or market)... | 70,000 | 145,000 |
| Gross profit on sales | | | 135,000 |
| Operating expenses | | | 100,000 |
| Deduct: Loss on reduction of inventory to market | | | |
| Add: Gain arising from adjustment in inventory allowance to report inventory at lower of cost or market | | | |
| Net income | | | 35,000 |

### Separate Recognition of Inventory Fluctuations

| (2) Recognition of Loss in Ending Inventory | (3) Recognition of Effect of Fluctuations on Beginning and Ending Inventories |
|---|---|
| Merchandise Inventory.... 52,000<br>Loss on Reduction of Inventory to Market........ 8,000<br>Profit and Loss........ 60,000 | Merchandise Inventory..... 60,000<br>Profit and Loss........ 60,000<br>Loss on Reduction of Inventory to Market........ 8,000<br>Allowance for Inventory Decline to Market....... 8,000 |
| 240,000 | 240,000 |
| 50,000<br>130,000<br>180,000<br>(cost) 60,000   120,000 | 50,000<br>130,000<br>180,000<br>(cost) 60,000   120,000 |
| 120,000<br>100,000<br>20,000 | 120,000<br>100,000<br>20,000 |
| 8,000<br>12,000 | 8,000<br>12,000 |
| Profit and Loss........... 52,000<br>Merchandise Inventory... 52,000<br><br>Merchandise Inventory..... 70,000<br>Loss on Reduction of Inventory to Market........ 5,000<br>Profit and Loss........ 75,000 | Profit and Loss........... 60,000<br>Merchandise Inventory... 60,000<br><br>Merchandise Inventory..... 75,000<br>Profit and Loss........ 75,000<br><br>Allowance for Inventory Decline to Market........ 3,000<br>Gain Arising from Decrease in Allowance Requirement Reducing Inventory to Lower of Cost or Market.............. 3,000 |
| 280,000 | 280,000 |
| (lower of cost or market)... 52,000<br>163,000<br>215,000<br>(cost) 75,000   140,000 | (cost) 60,000<br>163,000<br>223,000<br>(cost) 75,000   148,000 |
| 140,000<br>100,000<br>40,000 | 132,000<br>100,000<br>32,000 |
| 5,000 | |
| | 3,000 |
| 35,000 | 35,000 |

In the first example, cost of goods sold each year reflects both goods sold and the effects of inventory declines. In the second example, the ending inventory for each year is reported on the basis of cost, and the decline identified with this balance receives separate recognition. Beginning inventories are reported in terms of the inventory cost utility carried into the current period, a lower of cost or market value for a preceding period thus being used as the beginning cost in measuring cost of goods sold. In the third case above, cost of goods sold is reported in terms of original cost. Inventory fluctuations are screened out of this section and the net effect of such fluctuations in beginning and ending inventories is reported separately as a loss or a gain. An inventory valuation account is adjusted periodically to the balance that is required in bringing the ending inventory down to a lower of cost or market basis. Declines in an ending inventory that exceed those identified with a beginning balance call for an increase in the valuation account and a charge to a loss account; declines in an ending inventory that are less than those identified with a beginning balance call for a decrease in the valuation account and the recognition of a gain.

One frequently finds inventories valued at the lower of cost or market with no separate analysis of the effect of inventory fluctuations in the accounts as in (1) above. Such practice, while it may involve some distortion, is normally the most convenient procedure. Periodic recognition of the loss on the ending inventory as in (2) above offers a satisfactory approach to matching sales with the costs that may be considered applicable thereto while providing a separate analysis of current market declines. The allowance procedure with recognition of the net effect of inventory price fluctuations, method (3) above, finds support on the following grounds:

(1) Price fluctuations relating to the inventory of both the prior year and the current year are fully removed from the cost of goods sold section. This may be considered of particular favor when reductions in inventory replacement values are not necessarily followed by reductions in inventory sales prices; sales is charged with a beginning inventory at cost.

(2) When a system of perpetual inventories is maintained, recognition of only the net periodic fluctuations and their reflection through the valuation account avoids the need for detailed changes in subsidiary inventory records.

**DETERIORATED GOODS, TRADE-INS, REPOSSESSIONS**    A decline in market conditions may not be the only factor suggesting the use of values that are less than cost for inventories. There may be merchandise items that are deteriorated, obsolete, damaged, or shopworn. In arriving at a value for such goods, the lower of cost or market criterion might be applied. Employing the definition of market as advanced by the American Institute, goods would be reported within a ceiling set by their net realizable value, that is, their estimated sales value less the costs to be incurred in their sale, and a floor represented by such realizable value reduced by a normal profit margin. When inventory cost shrinkages are significant, they should not be buried in cost of goods sold but preferably should be reported under appropriate expense or loss headings. Thus, physical deterioration of inventories that emerges from normal activities would be reported as a special cost of goods sold item or selling expense, whichever may be appropriate; physical deterioration that results from some management failure would call for recognition as a special loss.

When goods are acquired in secondhand condition as a result of repossessions and trade-ins, they should be recorded at their estimated "cash purchase price." However, when this is difficult or impossible to define, the consistent application of a "floor" value — amounts which after increase by reconditioning charges will permit the recognition of a normal profit — would normally be indicated. Sales effort attaches to the sale of repossessions and trade-ins just as it does to the sale of new items; recording the goods at a floor value will permit the recognition of a normal profit through such effort.

**LOSSES ON PURCHASE COMMITMENTS**   Commitments are frequently made for the future purchase of goods at fixed prices. When price declines take place subsequent to such commitments, it is considered appropriate to recognize such losses currently in the same manner as losses related to goods on hand.[1] Losses are thus assigned to the period in which the decline takes place, and future periods are charged with no more than the utility of the goods they receive. Current loss recognition would not be appropriate when commitments can be canceled, when they provide for price adjustments, when hedging transactions serve to prevent possible losses, or when declines do not suggest corresponding sales price reductions.

**VALUATION AT SALES PRICE**   There is support for reporting an inventory in special instances at sales price less costs to be incurred in its sale even though such value may exceed cost. Such

---

[1]The Institute Committee on Accounting Procedure states (*Accounting Research Bulletin No. 43*, "Restatement and Revision of Accounting Research Bulletins," p. 34): "Accrued net losses on firm purchase commitments for goods for inventory, measured in the same way as are inventory losses, should, if material, be recognized in the accounts and the amounts thereof separately disclosed in the income statement."

valuation must be regarded as exceptional treatment since profits are anticipated prior to time of sale. Valuation at sales price less selling costs can be justified only when it is a regular trade practice and arises from either (1) assured market conditions that make possible the immediate sale of inventories at a fixed price, or (2) a standard product, a ready market, plus the inability to arrive at reasonable assignments of costs. Inventories such as gold, silver, and certain other metals may be accorded this exceptional treatment in view of their immediate marketability at a fixed sales price. Similar treatment may be accorded a farmer's inventory in view of the difficulty of arriving at a satisfactory cost. When inventories are reported at more than cost, full disclosure of the basis for valuation should be offered on the statements.

The Committee on Accounting Procedure of the American Institute sanctions the departure from cost and the recognition of realizable values in the accounts under the circumstances mentioned.[1] Departures from cost are also accepted for tax purposes in special cases. Dealers in securities and in cotton, grain, and other commodities have been permitted to report inventories at cost, the lower of cost or market, or at market value. The method elected must be used each period. Farmers have been permitted to use an inventory procedure known as the *farm-price method* for tax purposes. This method provides for inventory valuation in terms of current market price less direct costs of marketing. If the farm-price method is adopted, it must be applied consistently to the entire inventory with the exception of livestock. Livestock may be valued under either the farm-price method or the *unit-livestock-price method*. The latter is an adaptation of the standard cost method, providing for a classification of animals and the application to animals within each class of standard unit prices representing the normal costs of production. For example, a cattle raiser may estimate a cost of $75 to produce a calf and $50 a year to raise the calf to maturity. Animals would be classified and valued as follows: calves, $75; yearlings, $125; two-year olds, $175; mature animals, $225.

**UNCOMPLETED CONTRACTS—PROFIT RECOGNITION BASED ON DEGREE OF COMPLETION**    A special valuation problem is encountered in those instances where a contractor engages in certain construction work requiring months or perhaps years for completion and the projects are found in various degrees of completion at the end of the contractor's fiscal period.

---

[1] *Accounting Research Bulletin No. 43*, "Restatement and Revision of Accounting Bulletins," 1953 (New York: American Institute of Certified Public Accountants), p. 34.

It is possible for a contractor engaged in a long-term project to carry such "work in process" at cost until it is completed, accepted by the purchaser, and the full profit can be calculated. This practice, referred to as the *completed-contract method*, is in conformity with the concept that revenue cannot be considered to be realized until there is a completed sale involving the formal recognition by the seller of new assets. Profit emerges from sales, not production.

However, the application of a sales basis concept of revenue for long-term contracts may lead to serious distortions of periodic achievement. If profit recognition is to await completion, the year in which a project is completed will receive full recognition of the profit even though only a small part of the earnings may be attributable to productive effort in this period. Previous periods receive no credit for their productive efforts; as a matter of fact, they may have been penalized through the absorption of selling, general and administrative, and other overhead costs relating to construction in progress but not considered chargeable to the construction inventory. Authorities are in general agreement that circumstances such as those described may justify departure from the sales standard as a basis for the recognition of revenue. Accordingly, they would support a valuation procedure that provides for an accrual of profit over the life of the contract in some equitable and systematic manner.

The American Institute Committee on Accounting Procedure comments on the point at which profit should be recognized as follows:

> It is recognized that income should be recorded and stated in accordance with certain accounting principles as to time and amount; that profit is deemed to be realized when a sale in the ordinary course of business is effected unless the circumstances are such that collection of the sales price is not reasonably assured; and that delivery of goods sold under contract is normally regarded as the test of realization of profit and loss.

> It is, however, a generally accepted accounting procedure to accrue revenues under certain types of contracts and thereby recognize profits, on the basis of partial performance, where the circumstances are such that total profit can be estimated with reasonable accuracy and ultimate realization is reasonably assured.[1]

A satisfactory approach to periodic profit recognition on long-term construction contracts may be achieved by use of the *percentage-of-completion* method. Use of the percentage-of-completion method calls for the selection of either of the following approaches: (1) The degree of completion is developed by comparing costs already incurred with

---

[1] *Accounting Research Bulletin No. 43*, "Restatement and Revision of Accounting Research Bulletins," 1953 (New York: American Institute of Certified Public Accountants), p. 95.

the most recent estimates as to total estimated costs to complete the project. The percentage that costs incurred bear to total estimated costs is applied to the estimated net profit on the project in arriving at the profit to date. Profit is thus recognized in terms of a *percentage-of-cost-completion.* (2) Estimates of the progress of a project in terms of the work performed are obtained from qualified engineers and architects. Such estimates are applied to total contract price, and costs incurred to date are subtracted from estimated revenue in arriving at current earnings.

To illustrate the application of the percentage-of-completion method as found in the first approach above, assume that a dam is to be constructed over a two-year period commencing in September, 1956, at a contract price of $750,000. Summaries of construction progress and the estimated profit calculated on a degree of completion basis for each year follow:

| | | | |
|---|---|---:|---:|
| 1956: | Contract price | | $750,000 |
| | Less estimated cost: | | |
| | Cost to date | $ 50,000 | |
| | Anticipated cost to complete project | 550,000 | 600,000 |
| | Estimated profit | | $150,000 |
| | Estimated profit—1956: | | |
| | 50,000/600,000 × $150,000 | | $ 12,500[1] |
| 1957: | Contract price | | $750,000 |
| | Less estimated cost: | | |
| | Cost to date | $450,000 | |
| | Anticipated cost to complete | 175,000 | 625,000 |
| | Estimated profit | | $125,000 |
| | Estimated profit to date: | | |
| | 450,000/625,000 × $125,000 | | $ 90,000 |
| | Less profit recognized in 1956 | | 12,500 |
| | Estimated profit—1957 | | $ 77,500 |

[1]The same estimated profit is developed if the relationship of costs incurred to total estimated costs is applied to the total contract price in arriving at the contract price considered earned, and this balance is then reduced by costs incurred to date. Calculations in the example would be:

| | |
|---|---:|
| Contract price considered earned: 50,000/600,000 × $750,000 | $62,500 |
| Cost to date | 50,000 |
| Estimated profit — 1956 | $12,500 |

| | | |
|---|---|---:|
| 1958: | Contract price.......................... | $ 750,000 |
| | Less total cost: | |
| | Cost of prior periods.................. $ 450,000 | |
| | Current cost to complete............. 167,500 | 617,500 |
| | Profit on construction.................. | $ 132,500 |
| | Less profits recognized to date ($12,500 + $77,500)............................ | 90,000 |
| | Estimated profit—1958................ | $  42,500 |

In the above example, the deferral of profit recognition until project completion would have resulted in a profit of $132,500 in 1958. Recognition of profits on the basis of degree of completion is compared with recognition of profits only upon project completion in the series of entries below based upon the facts in the example just given.

| Transaction | Profit Recognition by Percentage-of-Completion Method | | Profit Recognition by Completed-Contract Method | |
|---|---|---|---|---|
| 1956: Costs of construction. | Construction in Process...... 50,000 Materials, Cash, etc..... | 50,000 | Construction in Process...... 50,000 Materials, Cash, etc..... | 50,000 |
| Advances from customer on contract. | Cash.......... 60,000 Customer Advances..... | 60,000 | Cash.......... 60,000 Customer Advances..... | 60,000 |
| Recognition of profit for year. | Construction in Process...... 12,500 Recognized Profit on Long-Term Construction.... | 12,500 | | |
| 1957: Costs of construction. | Construction in Process...... 400,000 Materials, Cash, etc..... | 400,000 | Construction in Process...... 400,000 Materials, Cash, etc..... | 400,000 |
| Advances from customer on contract. | Cash.......... 425,000 Customer Advances..... | 425,000 | Cash.......... 425,000 Customer Advances..... | 425,000 |
| Recognition of profit for year. | Construction in Process...... 77,500 Recognized Profit on Long-Term Construction..... | 77,500 | | |
| 1958: Costs of construction in completing contract. | Construction in Process...... 167,500 Materials, Cash, etc.... | 167,500 | Construction in Process...... 167,500 Materials, Cash, etc..... | 167,500 |

| Transaction | Profit Recognition by Percent-age-of-Completion Method | | Profit Recognition by Com-pleted-Contract Method | |
| --- | --- | --- | --- | --- |
| Completion of contract:<br>(a) Recognition of profit for year. | Construction in Process......  42,500<br>Recognized Profit on Long-Term Con-struction..... | 42,500 | Construction in Process......  132,500<br>Profit on Construction.. | 132,500 |
| (b) Advances in-cluding payment in settlement. | Cash..........  265,000<br>Customer Advances..... | 265,000 | Cash..........  265,000<br>Customer Advances..... | 265,000 |
| (c) Approval of completed projects by customer. | Customer Advances.......  750,000<br>Construction in Process.... | 750,000 | Customer Advances.......  750,000<br>Construction in Process.... | 750,000 |

It should be observed that the practice of recognizing a profit on a job still in process is a departure from standard inventory valuation procedures and should be applied only when all of the circumstances are considered to warrant such exceptional treatment. Estimates of the costs to complete a project or the degree of project completion should be developed from data supplied by qualified architects and engineers. When reliable estimates cannot be obtained or when possible future contingencies may operate to eliminate what appear to be accruing profits, conservatism would require the deferral of profit recognition until project completion.[1]

Whatever method is employed in the accounts, full disclosure should be made on the statements of the method of valuation employed as well as the full implications of such valuation. When sales or trans-fers of partnership interests or of capital stock are involved, the status of contracts in progress and the degree of recognition of profits on such contracts in the asset and the capital sections assume vital significance.

When a contractor does not have title to buildings, improvements, etc., in progress, these items, while not qualifying as inventory, nevertheless call for the use of valuation procedures as described and presentation as assets under appropriately descriptive headings until settlement is made with the customer upon contract completion.

When a building, installation, or construction contract covers more than one year, federal income tax requirements permit the tax-

---

[1]The American Institute Committee on Accounting Procedure makes the following statement relative to the method to be employed: "The committee believes that in general when estimates of costs to complete and extent of progress toward com-pletion of long-term contracts are reasonably dependable, the percentage-of-completion method is preferable. When lack of dependable estimates or inherent hazards cause forecasts to be doubtful, the completed-contract method is preferable." *Accounting Research Bulletin No. 45*, "Long-term Construction-type Contracts," 1955 (New York: American Institute of Certified Public Accountants), p. 7.

payer to elect to recognize profits in terms of percentage of completion over the life of the project or to recognize profits on the entire job in the year when the contract is completed and accepted. Salaries, taxes, and other expenses not directly attributable to the contract must be deducted in the year in which incurred. Consistent application of the method of accounting chosen is required for tax purposes, a change from the percentage-of-completion basis to the completed-contract basis, or *vice versa*, requiring special permission.

## QUESTIONS

**1.** Define "market" for purposes of inventory valuation at "cost or market, whichever is lower."

**2.** Objection has been raised to the use of the term "market" in the phrase "cost or market, whichever is lower." Can you suggest a more satisfactory term?

**3.** Describe how one would arrive at market ceiling and floor in developing a lower of cost or market value.

**4.** Distinguish between the approaches that are adopted by the American Institute and the American Accounting Association in arriving at a lower than cost basis for inventory valuation? Which do you support? Why?

**5.** (a) Describe the application of the lower of cost or market valuation to (1) each inventory item, (2) inventory sections, (3) the inventory as a whole. (b) State the conditions that would suggest the use of each of these methods.

**6.** What conditions might suggest caution in the application of the rule of cost or market, whichever is lower? Why?

**7.** (a) State two procedures that might be used in the accounts for the separate recognition of inventory fluctuations arising from inventory valuation at the lower of cost or market. (b) What is the alternative to such separate recognition? (c) Would you recommend such special procedures in the accounts? Why?

**8.** What treatment would you recommend when serious loss seems to be indicated in connection with certain purchase commitments outstanding at the end of the period? Give reasons for your answer.

**9.** What factors might suggest inventory valuation at amounts in excess of cost?

**10.** At the end of the fiscal period, the inventory of Western Products Co. includes a number of special orders in process being produced on a cost-plus basis. Would you permit the recognition of any profit on such goods? If so, how would you arrive at the profit to be recognized and what procedure would you follow in the accounts?

**11.** How would you suggest that repossessed goods be valued? Give reasons for your proposal.

**12.** (a) Describe inventory valuation for crops by the farm-price method. (b) Describe inventory valuation for livestock by the unit-livestock price method.

**13.** (a) Describe the percentage-of-completion method for recognition of profits on long-term construction contracts. (b) What problems are involved in the application of this method?

**14.** The Hauser Construction Co. engages in a variety of construction work as an independent contractor. Profit is recognized as cash is received from customers by an entry as follows:

```
Cash.........................................  100,000
    Customer Advances............................           70,000
    Profit on Construction.......................           30,000
```

Comment on this procedure.

## EXERCISES

**1.** The Martin Supply Store uses the first-in, first-out method in calculating cost of goods sold for the three products that it handles. Inventories and purchases of these products during January and the market price of these products on January 31 are as follows:

|  | Commodity A | Commodity B | Commodity C |
|---|---|---|---|
| Inventory, Jan. 1......1,000 units @ $6.00 | 3,000 units @ $10.00 | 4,500 units @ $1.00 |
| Purchases, Jan. 1–15...3,000 units @ 6.50 | 5,000 units @ 10.50 | 2,000 units @ 1.20 |
| Jan. 16–31..1,000 units @ 7.00 | | |
| Inventory, Jan. 31.....2,000 units | 3,000 units | 4,000 units |
| Market, Jan. 31.....$7.50 per unit | $10.00 per unit | $1.15 per unit |

Determine: (a) the cost of goods sold for January; (b) the cost of the inventory at the end of January; (c) the balance to be provided by means of a valuation allowance to reduce the inventory as of January 31 to a basis of cost or market, whichever is lower as applied to individual items.

**2.** The Barstow Company has 10,000 units of Commodity C on hand. The commodity has a cost per unit of $60; selling expenses per unit are $20; the normal profit on the sale of a unit is $15. Give the inventory value in terms of lower of cost or market for each set of assumptions listed; floor and ceiling limitations are to be applied in arriving at market.

| | Estimated Sales Price | Current Replacement Cost | | Estimated Sales Price | Current Replacement Cost |
|---|---|---|---|---|---|
| (a) | $90 | $75 | (f) | $85 | $45 |
| (b) | 90 | 65 | (g) | 75 | 55 |
| (c) | 90 | 50 | (h) | 75 | 50 |
| (d) | 85 | 70 | (i) | 75 | 35 |
| (e) | 85 | 55 | | | |

**3.** The Morse Company summarizes inventory data at the end of 1957 and 1958 as follows:

| | 1957 | 1958 |
|---|---|---|
| Invoice cost.................................. | $26,000 | $30,000 |
| Lower of cost or market...................... | 23,500 | 28,000 |

What entries are required (a) at the end of 1957 in recording the ending inventory and (b) at the end of 1958 in closing the beginning inventory and recording the ending inventory, assuming each of the following accounting procedures:

(1) The company calculates cost of goods sold in terms of inventories at the lower of cost or market without separate recognition of the effect of inventory market fluctuations.

(2) The company makes periodic recognition of the loss in the ending inventory resulting from valuation at the lower of cost or market.

(3) The company makes periodic recognition of the effects of market fluctuation identified with beginning and ending inventories through valuation at the lower of cost or market.

**4.** Phillip Motor Company records automobiles that are repossessed at a value that will permit the company to show a 25% gross profit on cost upon their resale. In January an automobile was repossessed that had an estimated resale value of $1,000 after reconditioning costs estimated at $150. At what value should the automobile be taken into the inventory?

**5.** The Whitney Construction Company recognizes profits on long-term construction periodically in the proportion that annual costs bear to total estimated costs of the project. Costs incurred on project #18–56 and remaining costs estimated to complete the project as summarized at the end of each year are listed below. The contract price of the project is $250,000.

|            | Costs     | Estimated Remaining Costs |
|------------|-----------|---------------------------|
| 1956       | $ 60,000  | $140,000                  |
| 1957       | 120,000   | 45,000                    |
| 1958       | 47,500    | —                         |

What profit would be recognized by the Whitney Construction Company each year?

**6.** The Allen Manufacturing Co. has the following items in its inventory on December 31, 1958:

|                     | QUANTITIES | UNIT COST | MARKET |
|---------------------|------------|-----------|--------|
| Raw Material A      | 2,000      | $1.10     | $1.00  |
| Raw Material B      | 7,000      | 2.40      | 2.50   |
| Raw Material C      | 5,000      | 3.00      | 3.20   |
| Goods in Process 1  | 8,000      | 3.75      | 3.80   |
| Goods in Process 2  | 6,000      | 5.00      | 5.10   |
| Finished Goods X    | 4,000      | 7.00      | 7.20   |
| Finished Goods Y    | 2,500      | 8.00      | 7.50   |

Calculate the value of the company's inventory using cost or market, whichever is lower, assuming that this valuation procedure is applied:

(a) To individual inventory items.
(b) To each section of inventory.
(c) To the inventory as a whole.

## PROBLEMS

**9-1.** Nelson Distributors carries five products. Units on hand, costs, and market prices of these products on January 31, 1958, are as follows:

| | Units | Cost Per Unit | Current Market Price Per Unit |
|---|---|---|---|
| Product A | 6,000 units | $2.65 | $2.30 |
| B | 1,200 units | 5.60 | 6.25 |
| C | 3,500 units | 4.20 | 4.75 |
| D | 2,200 units | 3.80 | 3.50 |
| E | 5,600 units | 1.85 | 1.80 |

*Instructions:* Prepare a statement to show the calculation of the inventory for statement purposes on the basis of cost or market, whichever is lower.

**9-2.** The inventory in Department #1 of Jack and Associates, at cost using first-in, first-out, and at market is as follows:

| | Units and Costs | Current Market Price, Per Unit |
|---|---|---|
| Article A | 2,200 @ $1.55<br>500 @ 1.70 | $1.60 |
| B | 600 @ 1.95 | 1.80 |
| C | 2,500 @ 1.90<br>1,000 @ 2.00 | 2.20 |
| D | 3,000 @ .80 | .65 |
| E | 400 @ .80<br>600 @ .70 | .75 |
| F | 500 @ 1.00 | 1.25 |
| G | 1,000 @ 1.20<br>1,200 @ 1.30 | 1.30 |

*Instructions:* Calculate the value of the inventory, assuming valuation on the basis of (1) cost, and (2) cost or market, whichever is lower, applied to individual inventory items.

**9-3.** Nichols and Williams, Inc. sells three products. Inventories and purchases during January and the market prices of these goods on January 31 are as follows:

| | Commodity A | Commodity B | Commodity C |
|---|---|---|---|
| Inventory, Jan. 1 | 200 units @ $65 | 200 units @ $110 | 60 units @ $150 |
| Purchases, Jan. 1–31 | 50 units @ 55 | 120 units @ 100 | 50 units @ 135 |
| Total Available for Sale | 250 | 320 | 110 |
| Sales, Jan. 1–31 | 30 units @ 90<br>150 units @ 85 | 50 units @ 125<br>80 units @ 160 | 30 units @ 250<br>20 units @ 220 |
| Total Sales | 180 | 130 | 50 |
| Units on Hand, Jan. 31 | 70 | 190 | 60 |
| Market values per unit, Jan. 31 | $55 | $90 | $140 |

Operating expenses for January were $13,500.

*Instructions:* (1) Prepare an income statement for January, assuming that the ending inventory is valued at cost on a first-in, first-out basis.

(2) Prepare an income statement for January, assuming that the inventory is reduced to cost or market, whichever is lower, applied to individual items, and the inventory loss is reported separately on the income statement.

**9-4.** Johnson Products Co. carries three classes of inventory items. Inventory data as of December 31, 1958, are summarized below:

| | | Per Unit | |
| --- | --- | --- | --- |
| | Quantity | Cost | Replacement Cost |
| **Class A Items** | | | |
| #1. . . . . . . . . . . . . . . | 200 | $11.25 | $10.85 |
| #2. . . . . . . . . . . . . . | 375 | 7.60 | 5.20 |
| #3. . . . . . . . . . . . . . | 300 | 14.50 | 15.65 |
| #4. . . . . . . . . . . . . . | 125 | 10.00 | 8.40 |
| #5. . . . . . . . . . . . . . | 615 | 5.00 | 4.20 |
| **Class B Items** | | | |
| #1. . . . . . . . . . . . . . . | 100 | 15.50 | 14.50 |
| #2. . . . . . . . . . . . . . | 305 | 10.00 | 9.80 |
| #3. . . . . . . . . . . . . . | 150 | 3.20 | 3.30 |
| **Class C Items** | | | |
| #1. . . . . . . . . . . . . . . | 4,500 | 4.10 | 4.50 |
| #2. . . . . . . . . . . . . . | 3,200 | 3.10 | 3.25 |
| #3. . . . . . . . . . . . . . | 1,500 | 2.00 | 2.20 |
| #4. . . . . . . . . . . . . . | 7,800 | 1.50 | 1.40 |

*Instructions:* Prepare summaries to develop inventory valuation at the lower of cost or market, assuming this valuation procedure is applied:

(1) To individual inventory items.
(2) To separate inventory classes.
(3) To the inventory as a whole.

**9-5.** The inventory for Foreign Imports, Inc. at the end of 1958 is to be recorded at the lower of cost or replacement value; however, replacement is not to exceed net realizable value nor is it to be less than net realizable value reduced by the normal profit on sale. Ending inventory data are summarized below:

| | | | UNIT | | | |
| --- | --- | --- | --- | --- | --- | --- |
| | Number of Units | Cost | Replacement | Estimated Sales Price | Cost to Sell | Normal Profit |
| Commodity A. . . . . . . | 1,100 | $ 6.25 | $ 6.50 | $ 9.25 | $ 1.25 | $ 2.00 |
| B. . . . . . . | 1,500 | 4.75 | 4.50 | 7.00 | 1.00 | 1.50 |
| C. . . . . . . | 1,000 | 7.50 | 7.75 | 8.50 | 1.25 | 2.00 |
| D. . . . . . . | 800 | 8.00 | 5.50 | 8.50 | 1.25 | 2.00 |
| E. . . . . . . | 1,250 | 10.00 | 9.25 | 14.00 | 1.50 | 2.50 |
| F. . . . . . . | 1,000 | 8.50 | 7.00 | 10.50 | 1.25 | 2.00 |
| G. . . . . . . | 200 | 6.00 | 2.25 | 3.50 | 1.00 | 1.00 |

*Instructions:* Develop a schedule summarizing the value of the ending inventory at cost or market values, the valuation procedure being applied to the individual items comprising the inventory.

**9-6.** Comparative income summaries for McDonald, Inc. appear below. Inventories have been reflected periodically at cost.

|  | 1956 | | 1957 | | 1958 | |
|---|---|---|---|---|---|---|
| Sales.................... | | $55,000 | | $70,000 | | $75,000 |
| Cost of goods sold: | | | | | | |
|   Beginning inventory....... | $10,000 | | $15,000 | | $16,000 | |
|   Purchases................ | 40,000 | | 46,000 | | 50,000 | |
| | $50,000 | | $61,000 | | $66,000 | |
|   Less: Ending inventory.... | 15,000 | 35,000 | 16,000 | 45,000 | 19,000 | 47,000 |
| Gross profit on sales......... | | $20,000 | | $25,000 | | $28,000 |
| Selling and general expenses... | | 12,000 | | 15,500 | | 17,000 |
| Net income................ | | $ 8,000 | | $ 9,500 | | $11,000 |

An analysis discloses that replacement costs for inventories on hand at the end of each year had been as follows:

|  | 1956 | 1957 | 1958 |
|---|---|---|---|
| Inventory at market............... | $12,500 | $14,500 | $19,500 |

*Instructions:* Prepare a set of comparative income statements on each of the following assumptions:

(1) Inventories are recorded in the cost of goods sold section on the basis of cost or market, whichever is lower.

(2) Inventories are recorded at cost in the cost of goods sold section but at the lower of cost or market for balance sheet purposes, a charge being reported periodically on the income statement reporting the loss identified with the ending inventory.

(3) Inventories are recorded at cost in the cost of goods sold section but at the lower of cost or market for balance sheet purposes, the effect of fluctuations in price on beginning and ending inventories being reflected as a special item on the income statement.

**9-7.** The Chase Engineering Company undertakes the construction of a bridge at a contract price of $900,000. Construction begins in 1956 and is completed in 1958. Construction transactions are summarized below:

1956:   Construction costs incurred total $125,000; remaining costs to complete the project are estimated at $625,000. Collections from the public authority ordering such construction are $100,000.

1957:   Construction costs for the year total $495,000; remaining costs to complete the project are estimated at $155,000. Collections from the public authority are $625,000.

1958:   Construction costs in completing the project total $145,000. Collections are made from the public authority for the balance owed.

*Instructions:* (1) Give the entries for each year that would appear on the books of the company assuming that construction profit is recognized only when the project is completed and full settlement is made.

(2) Give the entries for each year that would appear on the books of the company assuming that construction profit is recognized periodically in the proportion that costs to date bear to the total estimated cost of the project.

**9-8.** Rand Corp. began the manufacture of a single standard product in 1958 and at the end of the first year of operations prepared an income statement as follows:

| | | | |
|---|---|---:|---:|
| Sales................................. | | | $400,000 |
| Cost of goods sold: | | | |
| Materials used: | | | |
| Materials purchased................ | $450,000 | | |
| Less: Ending inventory............ | 90,000 | $360,000 | |
| | | | |
| Direct labor........................ | | 150,000 | |
| Overhead........................... | | 90,000 | |
| | | | |
| Total manufacturing costs........... | | $600,000 | |
| Deduct: Goods in process inventory: | | | |
| Estimated 25% completed as to materials and processing costs........ | | 150,000 | |
| | | | |
| | | $450,000 | |
| Deduct: Finished goods inventory...... | | 110,000 | |
| | | | |
| Cost of goods sold.................. | | | 340,000 |
| | | | |
| Gross profit on sales.................. | | | $ 60,000 |
| Expenses............................ | | | 40,000 |
| | | | |
| Net income.......................... | | | $ 20,000 |

You find that a severe decline in the price of raw materials took place at the end of 1958. In recognition of the decline, the raw materials inventory that cost $150,000 was reported at $90,000, its market value on December 31, and goods in process and finished goods inventory costs were developed in terms of materials charged to production on the above basis.

*Instructions:* (1) Revise the income statement to reflect actual inventory costs, the raw materials decline being recognized separately as a loss.

(2) Give the inventory values that would be reported for raw materials, goods in process, and finished goods on the balance sheet.

**9-9.** The Robertson Construction Company engages in construction work at a fixed contract price. Since the gross profit on contracts has been relatively stable, the company in 1956 began accruing income on the basis of percentage of completion. The percentage of completion on a contract is obtained by comparing the cost incurred on a contract with total estimated cost. Customers are billed as work progresses, the credit being made to Billed Revenue. Costs are accumulated in a construction costs account, which is closed at the end of the period in determining net income.

A trial balance prepared for the Robertson Construction Company on December 31, 1958, is as follows:

|  | DR. | CR. |
|---|---|---|
| Cash | $ 30,000 | |
| Accounts receivable | 740,000 | |
| Prepaid expenses | 12,000 | |
| Land for future building site | 24,000 | |
| Tools | 30,000 | |
| Machinery | 870,000 | |
| Allowance for depreciation of machinery | | $395,000 |
| Buildings | 126,000 | |
| Allowance for depreciation of buildings | | 55,000 |
| Land | 38,000 | |
| 6% Bank loan, due August 1, 1959 | | 500,000 |
| Note receivable | 225,000 | |
| Accounts payable | | 255,000 |
| Reserve for injury claims (estimated current liability) | | 10,000 |
| Purchase money mortgage payable May 1, 1960 | | 200,000 |
| Common stock, stated value $100 | | 400,000 |
| Additional paid-in capital | | 40,000 |
| Retained earnings, January 1, 1958 | | 341,000 |
| Billed revenue | | 1,537,000 |
| Construction costs | 1,381,000 | |
| General and administrative expenses | 257,000 | |
| | $3,733,000 | $3,733,000 |

Information required in the preparation of statements at the end of 1958 is summarized below:

(1) During the year work was done on contracts as follows:

| Contract | Contract Price | Total Estimated Cost | Cost Incurred in 1957 | Cost Incurred in 1958 |
|---|---|---|---|---|
| A | $ 750,000 | $ 600,000 | $ 270,000 | $ 320,000 |
| B | 350,000 | 250,000 | 50,000 | 125,000 |
| C | 600,000 | 450,000 | 180,000 | 265,000 |
| D | 240,000 | 175,000 | —— | 177,000 |
| E | 360,000 | 260,000 | —— | 264,000 |
| F | 960,000 | 720,000 | —— | 230,000 |
| | $3,260,000 | $2,455,000 | $ 500,000 | $1,381,000 |

Contracts B and F are uncompleted as of the end of the year.

(2) The bank loan was made on August 1, 1958, and interest has not been recognized to date.

(3) A bill for $18,000 was received from an engineering firm for services rendered during December and has not yet been recorded; $10,000

of this amount was applicable to Contract F and the balance to Contract G, which is still being negotiated.

(4) Accrued office salaries of $1,500 are not shown in the accounts.

(5) The note receivable of $225,000 is non-interest-bearing and proceeds from its maturity in March, 1959, are to be used to purchase additional equipment.

(6) Assume corporate income taxes to be 40% of net income.

*Instructions:* (1) Prepare working papers for financial statements as of December 31, 1958.

(2) Prepare an income statement for 1958 with a supporting schedule reporting development of gross profit earned for 1958.

(3) Prepare a balance sheet as of December 31, 1958.

**9-10.** On the petition of the principal creditors, receivers in bankruptcy were appointed for the Wilson Sales Company on September 30, 1958. Appraisers appointed by the court took a physical inventory on the morning of October 1, 1958, finding the following merchandise on the premises:

|  | No. of Units |
|---|---|
| Commodity A: | |
| DeLuxe Brand | 40 |
| Special Brand | 10 |
| Standard Brand | 5 |
| Commodity B | 20 |
| Commodity C | 60 |

Accountants appointed by the receivers on October 1, 1958, found that the books had not been posted since September 15, 1958, when accounts had been prepared for the purpose of obtaining a bank loan. The trial balance on that date was as follows:

|  | DR. | CR. |
|---|---|---|
| Cash in bank | $    500.00 | |
| Petty cash | 100.00 | |
| Accounts receivable | 7,609.66 | |
| Accounts receivable—assigned | 12,000.50 | |
| Notes receivable | 190.00 | |
| Notes receivable—officer | 300.00 | |
| Advances to salesmen | 6,000.00 | |
| Inventories: | | |
| Commodity A | 3,180.00 | |
| Commodity B | 360.00 | |
| Commodity C | 375.00 | |
| Inventories—assigned | 10,006.54 | |
| Insurance, taxes, and rent prepaid to Sept. 30, 1958. | 1,866.66 | |
| Life insurance policy | 4,000.00 | |
| Notes payable—president | | $  2,000.00 |
| Accounts payable | | 55,100.90 |
| Accrued sales taxes | | 900.12 |
| Capital stock | | 10,000.00 |
| Deficit | 21,512.66 | |
| | $68,001.02 | $68,001.02 |

On the basis of these accounts a loan of $5,000 was obtained from the bank on the agreement that accounts receivable collections (after September 15) be deposited in a special account at the bank, amounts to be withdrawn therefrom only as approved by the bank.

Cash transactions from September 15 to 30, 1958, were as follows:

Collections:

| | |
|---|---:|
| Accounts receivable deposited in special bank account..... | $ 2,005.00 |
| Accounts receivable—assigned—deposited in special bank account......................................... | 12,000.50 |
| Note receivable.................................... | 190.00 |
| From salesmen (to be applied against advances)........ | 500.00 |
| Proceeds of bank loan of $5,000...................... | 4,900.00 |
| Total...................................... | $19,595.50 |

Disbursements:

| | |
|---|---:|
| President's note payable............................. | $ 2,000.00 |
| Accounts payable................................... | 5,000.00 |
| Sales license for year to September 30, 1959............. | 1,000.00 |
| Advances to salesmen................................ | 1,000.00 |
| Petty expenses (paid from petty cash)................. | 100.00 |
| Total...................................... | $9,100.00 |

An amount of $7,000 had been transferred from the special account to the regular drawing account as approved by the bank.

There were no purchases during the period from September 15 to September 30, 1958. Verified sales during the period, all on credit, were as follows:

| | No. of Units | Price per Unit Net | Total |
|---|---:|---:|---:|
| Commodity A: | | | |
| DeLuxe Brand................... | 10 | $30 | $300 |
| Special Brand................... | 5 | 20 | 100 |
| Standard Brand................. | 5 | 12 | 60 |
| Commodity B...................... | 10 | 15 | 150 |
| Commodity C...................... | 40 | 2 | 80 |
| Total......................... | | | $690 |

The company is liable for a 2% sales tax on the sales listed above.

The perpetual stock records showed the following goods on hand at the close of business September 15:

| | No. of Units | Cost per Unit |
|---|---:|---:|
| Commodity A: | | |
| DeLuxe Brand......................... | 100 | $24.00 |
| Special Brand......................... | 40 | 18.00 |
| Standard Brand....................... | 10 | 6.00 |
| Commodity B.......................... | 30 | 12.00 |
| Commodity C.......................... | 250 | 1.50 |

Among the accounts payable of September 15, 1958, is a debt of $21,007.04 to a supplier, representing two successive shipments of $11,000.50 and $10,006.54. The first shipment had been sold for $12,000.50 and the customer's account pledged to the supplier as security. The second shipment had been stored in a warehouse, but the title to the goods was passed back to the supplier on September 28, 1958.

The life insurance policy (surrender value at September 15, 1958, $2,500) was on the life of the president of the company, but it had been assigned to his wife some years ago.

The receivers expect that the bank will attempt to attach all balances at September 30, 1958, and that other creditors will assert that their claims are preferential.

*Instructions:* The attorneys appointed by the receivers request that you prepare at once a balance sheet as of September 15, 1958, on a going-concern basis, and a tentative balance sheet as of September 30, 1958, for purposes of a discussion on October 2, 1958. A report or memorandum containing full notes should accompany the balance sheets so that the attorneys may be informed as to the facts so far determined. (A.I.C.P.A. adapted)

**9-11.** The Ray Construction Company was incorporated during the month of December, 1955 with an authorized capital stock of 50,000 shares of $100 par value each, all of which were purchased at that time for cash.

On January 1, 1956 the Company entered into a contract for the construction of a power dam. The contract price for the project is $25,000,000, with payment to be received on the basis of approved engineering estimates of percentage of completion. The contract calls for the retention of 10% of each payment prior to final acceptance of the completed dam.

Funds have been received in connection with the contract as follows:

| | |
|---|---:|
| Advance for preparatory work......................... | $ 2,500,000 |
| Payment for work completed at November 30, 1958 (less 10% retained, and less repayment of a portion of amount advanced for preparatory work — equivalent to 10% of gross amount of completed work).................... | 14,000,000 |
| Total cash received................................ | $16,500,000 |

As of December 31, 1958, the work was considered to be 80% completed.

Direct costs to December 31, 1958 amount to $10,150,350.

The cost of plant facilities (buildings, cement mixers, rock crushers, trucks and cranes, etc.) amounting to $4,050,000 less estimated salvage of $810,000 (20% of cost), are amortized on the basis of percentage of completion.

Other expenses are applicable to work completed. These costs are as follows:

| | |
|---|---:|
| Administrative and general expenses.................... | $1,525,000 |
| Maintenance of plant facilities........................ | 1,270,500 |

Operation of plant facilities............................          775,250

Total............................................          $3,570,750

In addition to these costs, provision has been made for Federal and State income taxes amounting to $2,300,000, which you may consider as being correct.

On December 30, 1958 certain of the plant facilities having a cost of $875,000, were sold for $600,000 cash. On the same date a dividend of $20 per share of capital stock was paid in cash.

Additional information as of December 31, 1958, follows:

Cash on hand and in banks amounted to.................          $2,309,050

Inventories — not yet charged to construction costs were as
    follows:
    Work in progress.................................          $   185,625
    Materials and supplies............................             230,250

    Total........................................          $   415,875

The current liabilities consisted of:
    Accounts payable to trade creditors..................          $   125,750
    Accrued payroll....................................              27,200
    Income taxes.......................................           1,500,000
    Social security taxes...............................              20,325
    Income taxes withheld from compensation of employees..              22,750

    Total........................................          $1,696,025

*Instructions:* Prepare in good form with necessary supporting schedules:
(1) A balance sheet as of December 31, 1958.
(2) A statement of income for the three-year period.
(3) A statement of retained earnings for the three-year period. (A.I.C.P.A. adapted)

# Chapter 10

# INVENTORIES
## ESTIMATING PROCEDURES IN VALUATION

**ESTIMATED COSTS**     In the previous chapters the valuation procedures as applied to inventories were described. The methods of arriving at cost and the procedures involved in developing a lower of cost or market value were considered. Frequently, in arriving at an inventory valuation, estimates as to inventory quantities and costs are involved. Certain widely used estimating procedures are described in this chapter. Conditions in a merchandising concern calling for estimates of inventory position, together with the procedures that are applicable under the circumstances, are discussed under (1) the gross profit method and (2) the retail inventory method. The discussion of the estimating procedures for inventories of the merchandising concern is followed by a consideration of the estimating procedures for inventories of the manufacturing unit.

**GROSS PROFIT**     Estimates of merchandise on hand may be
**METHOD**     developed by means of the *gross profit method*. Application of the gross profit method involves the reduction of sales to a cost basis through use of the company's gross profit percentage. Cost of goods sold as calculated is subtracted from the cost of goods available for sale in arriving at an estimated inventory balance.

The gross profit method of arriving at an inventory is applicable in the following instances:

(1) When an inventory has been destroyed by fire or other causes and the specific data required for its valuation are not available.
(2) When inventories are required for interim statements, or for the determination of the week-to-week or month-to-month inventory position, and the cost of taking inventories would be excessive for such purposes.
(3) When it is desired to test or check on the validity of inventory figures determined by other means. Such application is referred to as the *gross profit test*.

The gross profit percentage to be used in reducing sales to a cost of goods sold balance must be a reliable measure of current sales experience. In developing a reliable rate, reference is usually made to past gross profit rates and these are adjusted for variations that are considered to exist currently. The determination of the cost of goods sold depends upon whether the gross profit percentage is developed and stated in terms of sales or in terms of cost. The procedure to be followed in each case is illustrated in the following examples.

*Example 1—Given: Gross Profit as a Percentage of Sales.* Assume: sales are $100,000; goods are sold at a gross profit of 40% of sales.

If gross profit is 40% of sales, then cost of goods sold must be 60% of sales:

| | | | | |
|---|---|---|---|---|
| Sales................... | 100% | | Sales.................... | 100% |
| Cost of goods sold....... | ? | = | Cost of goods sold........ | 60% |
| Gross profit............. | 40% | | Gross profit............. | 40% |

Cost of goods sold, then, is 60% of $100,000, or $60,000. Goods available for sale less the estimated cost of goods sold gives the estimated cost of the remaining inventory. Assuming that the cost of goods available for sale is $85,000 as summarized below, this balance less the estimated cost of goods sold, $60,000, gives an estimated inventory of $25,000:

| Cost of goods available for sale: | | | |
|---|---|---|---|
| Beginning inventory....................... | | | $16,000 |
| Purchases.............................. | | $ 67,800 | |
| Freight in............................... | | 1,500 | |
| Gross purchases.......................... | | $ 69,300 | |
| Less: Purchases returns and allowances....... | | 300 | 69,000 |
| Cost of goods available for sale.............. | | | $85,000 |
| Deduct estimated cost of goods sold: | | | |
| Gross sales.............................. | | $100,800 | |
| Less: Sales returns....................... | | 800 | |
| | | $100,000 | |
| Cost percentage (100% − 40%)............. | | 60% | |
| Estimated cost of goods sold............... | | | 60,000 |
| Ending inventory at estimated cost............. | | | $25,000 |

*Example 2—Given: Gross Profit as a Percentage of Cost.* Assume: sales are $100,000; goods are sold at a gross profit that is 60% of their cost.

(a) If sales are made at a gross profit of 60% of cost, then sales must be equal to the sum of cost, considered 100%, and the gross profit on cost, 60%. Sales, then, are 160% of cost:

| | | | | |
|---|---|---|---|---|
| Sales................... | ? | | Sales.................... | 160% |
| Cost of goods sold....... | 100% | = | Cost of goods sold......... | 100% |
| Gross profit............. | 60% | | Gross profit.............. | 60% |

To find cost, or 100%, sales may be divided by 160 and multiplied by 100, or sales may simply be divided by 1.60 Cost of goods sold, then, is

$100,000 ÷ 1.60, or $62,500. This amount is subtracted from the cost of goods available for sale in arriving at the estimated inventory as illustrated in Example 1 above.

(b) The cost of goods sold can be developed through an alternate calculation. If sales are 60% above cost, then the cost relationship to sales must be 100/160, or 62.5%.

| Sales............ | 160% | But in terms | | Sales............ | 100.0% | |
|---|---|---|---|---|---|---|
| Cost of goods sold | 100% | of sales as | = | Cost of goods sold | 62.5% | (100/160) |
| | | 100% | | | | |
| Gross profit...... | 60% | | | Gross profit...... | 37.5% | (60/160) |

Cost of goods sold, then, is 62.5% of $100,000, or $62,500.

*Example 3—Given: Sales as a Percentage Increase Above Cost.* Assume: sales are $100,000; goods are sold at 20% above cost. This is the same as saying that the gross profit is 20% of cost, and the answer would be developed as in Example 2 above. Sales, then, would be divided by 1.20, as in (a) above, or multiplied by .83⅓ (100/120), as in (b) above, in arriving at the estimated cost of goods sold.

The following cases review the application of the procedures described. Assume sales of $100,000.

| Gross Profit | Cost of Goods Sold | |
|---|---|---|
| Gross profit on sales, 52% | $100,000 × .48 (cost percentage) | $48,000 |
| Gross profit on cost, 150% | $100,000 ÷ 2.50 (cost + percentage markup on cost) <br> or <br> $100,000 × 100/250 (relationship of cost to sales) | $40,000 |
| Goods marked up 100% above cost | $100,000 ÷ 2.00 (cost + percentage markup on cost) <br> or <br> $100,000 × 100/200 (relationship of cost to sales) | $50,000 |

When a business carries a number of different lines of merchandise with different gross profit margins, it may be possible to develop a reliable inventory total only through the separate calculation of the different parts of the inventory. Under such circumstances, it would be necessary to develop summaries of sales, goods available, and gross profit data in terms of the different lines of merchandise that are carried by the business.

The development of a series of cost of goods sold balances and resulting inventory values may be required for various purposes. For example, assume that the merchandise turnover is to be calculated for a retail store whose gross profit calculation is shown at the top of the following page.

| | |
|---|---:|
| Sales............................................... | $500,000 |
| Cost of goods sold: | |
|     Inventory, January 1................... $ 20,000 | |
|     Purchases........................... 310,000 | |
|     Cost of goods available for sale........... $330,000 | |
|     Inventory, December 31................. 30,000 | |
|     Cost of goods sold..................... | 300,000 |
| Gross profit on sales....................... | $200,000 |

If only these data are available, the average inventory is $25,000, the sum of the beginning and ending inventory balances divided by 2. The merchandise turnover, that is, the number of times the average inventory has been replenished during the fiscal period, is then found to be 12 times a year by the following calculation:

$$\frac{\text{Cost of goods sold}}{\text{Average inventory (using year-end balances)}} = \frac{\$300,000}{\$25,000} = 12 \text{ times}$$

A more representative average inventory and therefore a more accurate turnover analysis may be obtained from an analysis of sales and purchases and the calculation of monthly inventory balances by the gross profits method. These calculations follow:

| | A PURCHASES | B SALES | COST OF GOODS SOLD | | | E INVENTORY INCREASE OR DECREASE* (A−D) | F INVENTORY (F+E) |
|---|---|---|---|---|---|---|---|
| | | | C COST PERCENTAGE | D COST OF GOODS SOLD (B×C) | | | |
| January 1 | | | | | | | $ 20,000 |
| January | $ 20,000 | $ 30,000 | 60% | $ 18,000 | | $ 2,000 | 22,000 |
| February | 20,000 | 30,000 | 60 | 18,000 | | 2,000 | 24,000 |
| March | 20,000 | 30,000 | 60 | 18,000 | | 2,000 | 26,000 |
| April | 20,000 | 30,000 | 60 | 18,000 | | 2,000 | 28,000 |
| May | 30,000 | 40,000 | 60 | 24,000 | | 6,000 | 34,000 |
| June | 30,000 | 40,000 | 60 | 24,000 | | 6,000 | 40,000 |
| July | 30,000 | 60,000 | 60 | 36,000 | | 6,000* | 34,000 |
| August | 30,000 | 40,000 | 60 | 24,000 | | 6,000 | 40,000 |
| September | 40,000 | 40,000 | 60 | 24,000 | | 16,000 | 56,000 |
| October | 40,000 | 50,000 | 60 | 30,000 | | 10,000 | 66,000 |
| November | 20,000 | 50,000 | 60 | 30,000 | | 10,000* | 56,000 |
| December | 10,000 | 60,000 | 60 | 36,000 | | 26,000* | 30,000 |
| | $310,000 | $500,000 | 60% | $300,000 | | $10,000 | $476,000 |

The average inventory and the merchandise turnover for the year may now be calculated as follows:

$$\frac{\text{Total of inventories}}{\text{Number of inventories}} = \frac{\$476,000}{13} = \$36,615, \text{ the average inventory}$$

$$\frac{\text{Cost of goods sold}}{\text{Average inventory (using monthly balances)}} = \frac{\$300,000}{\$36,615} = 8.2 \text{ times}$$

This figure is more accurate than the turnover developed on the basis of the year-end inventories, which were unusually low and unrepresentative.

**RETAIL INVENTORY METHOD**     The *retail inventory method* has been widely employed by retail concerns, particularly by department stores, as a means of obtaining, whenever desired, reliable estimates of the business unit's inventory position. When this method is employed, records of goods placed in stock are maintained in terms of costs and also at marked retail prices. The merchandise on hand may be calculated at any time at its retail price by subtracting sales for the period at retail from the total goods available for sale at retail. Cost and retail pricings of goods available for sale are used in developing the percentage that cost bears to retail, and this percentage is applied to the ending inventory at retail in arriving at an estimated inventory cost.

The determination of the estimated cost of the inventory at the end of a month by using the procedure described follows:

|  | AT RETAIL | AT COST |
|---|---|---|
| Inventory, January 1 | $45,000 | $30,000 |
| Purchases in January | 35,000 | 20,000 |
| Goods available for sale | $80,000 | $50,000 |
| Deduct sales for January at retail | 25,000 | |
| Inventory, January 31, at retail sales price | $55,000 | |
| Inventory, January 31, at estimated cost: $55,000 × 62½% (percentage of cost to sales price, $50,000 ÷ $80,000)[1] | | $34,375 |

Use of the retail inventory method offers the following advantages:

(1) Estimated interim inventories may be obtained without a physical count.
(2) Where a physical inventory is actually taken for periodic statement purposes, it may be taken at retail and then converted to cost without reference to individual costs and invoices, thus saving considerable time and expense.
(3) A check is afforded on the movement of merchandise, since a physical count of the inventory at retail should compare closely with the inventory as calculated at retail.

---

[1] Instead of calculating the percentage that total cost bears to total retail price and then applying this percentage to the ending inventory at retail, it is possible to compute the cost of the inventory by one arithmetical calculation as follows:

$$\frac{50,000}{80,000} \times \$55,000 = \$34,375.$$

A physical inventory of goods on hand is required at least once a year in support of the inventory balance to be reported on the annual statements. Relatively significant discrepancies between a physical inventory and the inventory position as derived from book calculations should be investigated. Such inquiry may lead to sources of inventory misappropriations. Retail inventory summaries should be adjusted appropriately for variations as shown by the physical count so that summaries reflect the actual status of the inventory for purposes of future inventory estimates and control.

The foregoing inventory calculation assumed that, after the goods were originally marked at retail prices, no further changes in such prices were made. Frequently, however, because of changes in the price level, changes in consumer demand, or various other reasons, original retail prices are increased or decreased. The following items must ordinarily be considered in arriving at the goods available for sale and the goods remaining on hand in the form of inventory at retail:

(1) *Original sales price*—the established sales price, including the original increase over cost variously referred to as the *markon* or *initial markup*.

(2) *Additional markup*—an increase above the original sales price.

(3) *Markup cancellation*—a reduction in the additional markup that does not decrease the sales price below the original sales price.

(4) *Markdown*—a reduction below the original sales price.

(5) *Markdown cancellation*—a reduction in the markdown that does not increase the sales price above the original sales price.

The difference between cost and retail price as adjusted for any of the changes described above is sometimes referred to as the *maintained markup*.

To illustrate the use of the data listed, assume that goods originally placed for sale are marked at 50% above cost. Certain merchandise costing $4 a unit, then, is marked at $6, which is termed the original sales price. This increase in cost is variously referred to as a "50% markon on cost" or a "$33\frac{1}{3}$% markon on sales price." In anticipation of a heavy demand for the article, the goods are subsequently increased to $7.50. This represents an additional markup of $1.50. At a later date the goods are reduced to $7. This is a markup cancellation of 50 cents and not a markdown, since the retail price has not been reduced below the original sales price. But assume that goods originally marked to sell at $6 are subsequently marked down to $5. This represents a markdown of $1. At a later date the goods are marked to sell at $5.25. This is a markdown cancellation of 25 cents and not a markup, since the retail price does not exceed the original sales price.

In determining the merchandise on hand at retail sales price without a physical inventory, a record of each of the foregoing adjustments is required, and the following summary is prepared:

| | | |
|---|---|---|
| Beginning inventory at retail sales price................ | | xxxx |
| Add: Purchases at original sales price.................. | xxxx | |
| Net additional markups (additional markups less markup cancellations)........................ | xxx | xxx |
| Goods available for sale............................. | | xxxx |
| Deduct: Sales at retail sales prices.................... | xxx | |
| Net markdowns (markdowns less markdown.. cancellations) plus any employees' discounts, in-.. ventory shortages, spoilage, losses, etc........... | xxx | xxx |
| Ending inventory at retail sales price................. | | xxxx |

The ending inventory at retail as thus calculated is multiplied by the percentage representing the relationship of cost to retail in arriving at the ending inventory at cost.

In obtaining the cost percentage, the cost of goods available for sale is normally related to the original sales price plus the net markups, without taking into account the net markdowns. Calculation of ending inventory by the retail inventory method in this manner is illustrated below.

| | At Retail | At Cost |
|---|---|---|
| Beginning inventory......................... | $ 14,000 | $ 8,600 |
| Add: Purchases............................. | 110,000 | 69,000 |
| Freight in............................... | | 3,100 |
| Net markups: | | |
| Additional markups............ $13,000 | | |
| Less: Markup cancellations...... 2,500 | 10,500 | |
| Goods available for sale.................... | $134,500 | $80,700 |
| Deduct: Sales at retail.................$108,000 | | |
| Net markdowns: | | |
| Markdowns......... $4,800 | | |
| Less: Markdown cancellations ...... 800 | 4,000   112,000 | |
| Ending inventory at retail sales price........... | $ 22,500 | |
| Ending inventory at estimated cost: | | |
| $22,500×60% (percentage of cost to sales price before markdowns, $80,700÷$134,500)........ | | $13,500 |

Failure to consider markdowns in calculating the cost percentage results in a lower cost percentage and consequently gives a more conservative inventory figure than would otherwise be obtained. Markdowns may represent changes in price for special sales or clearance purposes, or they may arise from market fluctuations and a decline in the replacement cost of goods. In either case failure to consider markdowns in calculating the cost percentage is justified. This is illustrated in the two examples that follow:

*Example 1 — Markdowns for Special Sales Purposes:* Assume that merchandise which cost $50,000 is marked to sell for $100,000. To dispose of part of the goods immediately, one fourth of the stock is marked down $5,000 and is sold. The cost of the ending inventory is calculated in the following manner:

|  |  | AT RETAIL | AT COST |
|---|---|---|---|
| Purchases................................... |  | $100,000 | $50,000 |
| Deduct: Sales....................... | $20,000 |  |  |
| Markdowns.................. | 5,000 | 25,000 |  |
| Ending inventory at retail sales price........... |  | $ 75,000 |  |
| Ending inventory at estimated cost: |  |  |  |
| $75,000×50% (percentage of cost to sales price before markdowns, $50,000÷$100,000)................. |  |  | $37,500 |

If cost, $50,000, had been related to sales price after markdowns, $95,000, a cost percentage of 52.6 per cent would have been obtained, and the ending inventory, which is three fourths of the merchandise originally acquired, would have been reported at 52.6 per cent of $75,000, or $39,450. The ending inventory would thus be overstated and cost of goods sold understated. A markdown relating to goods no longer on hand would have been recognized in the development of a cost percentage to be applied to the ending inventory. Reductions in the goods available at sales price resulting from shortages, damaged goods, departmental transfers, or employees' discounts should likewise be disregarded in calculating the cost percentage.

*Example 2 — Markdowns as a Result of Market Declines:* Assume that merchandise which cost $50,000 is marked to sell for $100,000. With a drop in replacement cost of the merchandise to $40,000, sales prices are marked down to $80,000. One half of the merchandise is sold. The cost of the ending inventory is calculated in the following manner:

| | | AT RETAIL | AT COST |
|---|---|---|---|
| Purchases.................................... | | $100,000 | $50,000 |
| Deduct: Sales ...................... | $40,000 | | |
| Markdowns .................. | 20,000 | 60,000 | |
| Ending inventory at retail sales price............ | | $ 40,000 | |

Ending inventory at estimated cost:
$40,000×50% (percentage of cost to sales price
before markdowns, $50,000÷$100,000)................. $20,000

Here, if cost, $50,000, had been related to sales price after mark-downs, $80,000, a cost percentage of 62.5 per cent would have been obtained and the ending inventory would have been reported at 62.5 per cent of $40,000, or $25,000. While this procedure reduces the in-ventory to a cost basis, ignoring markdowns results in a cost percentage that reduces the inventory to a basis of cost or market, whichever is lower. Thus, the use of the 50 per cent cost percentage in the example reduces the inventory to $20,000, or to a lower of cost or market basis in view of the company's policy of selling merchandise at a 50 per cent gross profit.

The advantages relating to the retail inventory method have already been described. It should be pointed out, however, that the application of a cost percentage for all of the goods handled to an ending inventory in approximating its cost is valid only when goods in the ending inven-tory may be viewed as a representative slice of the total goods handled. Varying markon percentages and the sale of high and low-margin items in proportions that differ from acquisitions will suggest the maintenance of separate records and the development of separate cost percentages for the different classes of merchandise. In some cases the subdivision of the inventory by departments and by lines within such departments will be necessary.

It may be noted that the retail method may be used for income tax purposes. However, a taxpayer with an inventory composed of different classes of goods with different cost percentages would be required to apply such different rates to the respective inventory sections in arriving at an estimated inventory value.[1]

**INVENTORY VALUATION IN A MANUFACTURING CONCERN**   When a manufacturing organization does not maintain a cost accounting system and accurate costs of various commodities in process and in a finished state are not available, it becomes necessary to estimate the costs of these inventories at the end of the fiscal period. The illustrations that follow assume the manufacture of a single product. If more than one product is manufactured, the procedures to be followed are similar, although estimates would be involved to an even greater degree.

Costs of manufacturing are summarized in materials, labor, and other manufacturing expense accounts. These costs must be allocated to the goods that remain uncompleted at the end of the period and to goods that were completed and placed in stock during the period. After a cost is assigned to goods completed during the period, it is necessary to allocate this cost to finished goods that remain on hand at the end of the period and to goods that were sold during the period.

In the manufacture of certain commodities, the raw materials required in their production must be added at various stages during the course of processing. In the manufacture of other commodities, all of the required raw materials are put in at the very beginning of the production process. In allocating manufacturing costs between goods remaining in process at the end of the period and goods completed during the period, information or estimates concerning two factors, then, must be available:

(1) The degree to which total *material* requirements are met in the goods in process inventory, and

(2) The degree to which total *processing costs*, consisting of labor and overhead, are met in the goods in process inventory.

The accounting problems that arise in the allocation of costs will be illustrated by means of two examples: the first assumes that materials are added uniformly throughout the period of production; the

---

[1] In recent years, tax authorities have approved the use of a *retail-lifo* approach under specified circumstances. Retail price indexes are applied to the ending inventory at retail to convert the inventory to a retail balance comparable with the base period inventory. The retail inventory is then divided into layers — a base year total and accessions for subsequent periods. The base-year inventory is converted to a base-year cost and subsequent additions are converted to accession costs in arriving at a last-in, first-out valuation.

second assumes that all of the required materials are put into process at the beginning of production.

*Example 1: Materials are added uniformly throughout the period of production.*

Assume the following inventories on December 31:

Finished Goods — 1,000 units, cost $2.50 per unit, or $2,500.
Goods in Process — 800 units, estimated one fourth completed, cost $500.

During January, 2,000 units were completed in the factory and placed in finished stock. On January 31 there are 900 units in process that are estimated to be two thirds completed. Fourteen hundred units were shipped to customers, 1,600 remaining in stock at the end of the period. Manufacturing costs were $5,400, distributed as follows: materials, $600; direct labor, $3,500; and other manufacturing expenses, $1,300.

The estimates of the degree of completion of goods in process in beginning and ending inventories express the estimated quantity of all of the elements of manufacturing cost — raw materials and processing costs — required in the final product.

It is first necessary to calculate actual productive effort in the form of equivalent number of whole units of work performed in the factory during the month. This may be done as follows:

| | |
|---|---:|
| Number of units completed in January...................... | 2,000 |
| Deduct equivalent whole units in process on January 1, 800 units estimated ¼ completed, or ...................... | 200 |
| | 1,800 |
| Add equivalent whole units in process on January 31, 900 units estimated ⅔ completed, or.............................. | 600 |
| Equivalent whole units of work performed in January....... | 2,400[1] |

Manufacturing cost in January, $5,400, divided by the number of units of work performed, 2,400, gives $2.25, the cost for each unit of

---

[1]Equivalent units performed for the month may be calculated in an alternate manner as follows:

| | |
|---|---:|
| Equivalent whole units of work done on units in process on January 1, 800 units, ¾ completed........................................ | 600 |
| Units started and completed during January, 2,000 units transferred out less 800 units above........................................ | 1,200 |
| Equivalent whole units of work done on units in process on January 31, 900 units, ⅔ completed........................................ | 600 |
| Equivalent whole units of work performed in January............. | 2,400 |

work performed. Using the first-in, first-out method, costs of goods completed, goods in process inventory, goods sold, and finished goods inventory may be calculated as follows:

COST OF GOODS COMPLETED AND TRANSFERRED FROM FACTORY TO STOCK:

$$
\left.
\begin{array}{l}
\left.
\begin{array}{l}
\frac{1}{4} \text{ completed in December, cost} \dots\dots\dots \ \$\ 500 \\
\frac{3}{4} \text{ completed in January, cost} = \$2.25 \times 600 \\
\quad \text{equivalent units } (800 \times \frac{3}{4}) \dots\dots\dots\dots \quad 1{,}350 \\
\hline
\text{Total cost of first 800 units completed} \\
\quad (\$2.3125 \text{ per unit}) \dots\dots\dots\dots\dots\dots\dots \ \$1{,}850 \\
1{,}200 \text{ started and completed in January, cost } \$2.25 \text{ per unit.} \quad 2{,}700 \\
\hline
\qquad\qquad\qquad \text{Total} \qquad\qquad\qquad\qquad \$4{,}550
\end{array}
\right.
\end{array}
\right.
$$

| | |
|---|---|
| | $ 500 |
| 800 | 1,350 |
| 2,000 units | $1,850 |
| | 2,700 |
| | $4,550 |

COST OF GOODS IN PROCESS INVENTORY:

900 units, $\frac{2}{3}$ completed in January, cost $2.25 $\times$ 600 equivalent units ($900 \times \frac{2}{3}$) ........................................................... $1,350

COST OF GOODS SOLD:

1,400 units
- 1,000 units on hand, December 31, cost $2.50 per unit..... $2,500
- 400 completed in January, cost $2.3125 per unit....... 925

Total .................................................. $3,425

COST OF FINISHED GOODS INVENTORY:

1,600 units
- 400 completed in January, cost $2.3125 per unit....... $ 925
- 1,200 completed in January, cost $2.25 per unit........ 2,700

Total .................................................. $3,625

Assume that, in adjusting and closing the accounts at the end of the period, the cost of goods manufactured is summarized in a manufacturing account and cost of goods sold in the profit and loss account. The inventory, manufacturing, and profit and loss accounts will appear as follows after the goods in process and finished goods inventories as estimated above are recorded:

GOODS IN PROCESS

| | | | | |
|---|---|---|---|---|
| Dec. 31 Bal., 800 units, ¼ completed | 500 | Jan. 31 To Manufacturing | | 500 |
| Jan. 31 Bal., 900 units, ⅔ completed | 1,350 | | | |

FINISHED GOODS

| | | | | |
|---|---|---|---|---|
| Dec. 31 Bal., 1,000 units | 2,500 | Jan. 31 To Profit and Loss | | 2,500 |
| Jan. 31 Bal., 1,600 units | 3,625 | | | |

MANUFACTURING

| | | | |
|---|---|---|---|
| Jan. 31 Beginning Goods in Process Inventory, 800 units, ¼ completed | 500 | Jan. 31 Ending Goods in Process Inventory, 900 units, ⅔ completed | 1,350 |
| 31 Raw Materials Used | 600 | 31 Completed, 2,000 units to Profit and Loss | 4,550 |
| 31 Direct Labor | 3,500 | | |
| 31 Other Manufacturing Expenses | 1,300 | | |
| | 5,900 | | 5,900 |

PROFIT AND LOSS

| | | | |
|---|---|---|---|
| Jan. 31 Beginning Finished Goods Inventory, 1,000 units | 2,500 | Jan. 31 Ending Finished Goods Inventory, 1,600 units | 3,625 |
| 31 Finished Goods from Manufacturing, 2,000 units | 4,550 | | |

The balance in the profit and loss account at this point reflects the cost of goods sold, $3,425. After remaining income and expense accounts are closed into the profit and loss account, the net profit or loss as summarized here is transferred to the appropriate proprietorship account.

As suggested in Chapter 4, the manufacturing concern may close its accounts by summarizing manufacturing costs in the goods in process account, transferring the cost of goods completed from goods in process to finished goods, and then transferring the cost of goods sold from finished goods to a separate cost of goods sold account. If this procedure is followed, goods in process, finished goods, and cost of goods sold accounts will appear as follows:

GOODS IN PROCESS

| | | | |
|---|---|---|---|
| Dec. 31 Bal., 800 units, ¼ completed | 500 | Jan. 31 Cost of Goods Completed, 2,000 units | 4,550 |
| Jan. 31 Raw Materials Used | 600 | | |
| 31 Direct Labor | 3,500 | | |
| 31 Other Manufacturing Expenses | 1,300 | | |

(Balance in the account at the end of the month, $1,350, represents the cost of 900 units of goods in process inventory, ⅔ completed.)

FINISHED GOODS

| | | | |
|---|---|---|---|
| Dec. 31 Bal., 1,000 units | 2,500 | Jan. 31 Cost of Goods Sold, 1,400 units | 3,425 |
| Jan. 31 Cost of Goods Completed, 2,000 units, from Goods in Process | 4,550 | | |

(Balance in the account at the end of the month, $3,625, represents the cost of 1,600 units of finished goods inventory.)

COST OF GOODS SOLD

| | |
|---|---|
| Jan. 31 Cost of Goods Sold,<br>1,400 units      3,425 | |

(Balance in this account is to be transferred to the profit and loss account in summarizing operations for the period.)

*Example 2: Materials are put into process at the beginning of production.*

In the example to follow, material and processing costs must be calculated separately. It is also assumed that goods are transferred from one process to another; hence inventory valuations must be assigned to goods within each process at the end of the period.

Assume the following inventories on December 31:

Finished Goods, 1,000 units, cost $25 per unit, or $25,000.
Goods in Process — Process C, 400 units, $\frac{3}{4}$ completed, cost, $9,000.

The goods in process inventory is made up of the following costs:

| | |
|---|---:|
| Materials cost (goods from Process B) at $15 per unit.......... | $6,000 |
| Processing cost in Process C, $10 \times 300$ equivalent units (400 units in process, $\frac{3}{4}$ completed)................................. | 3,000 |
| Total | $9,000 |

During January, 3,000 units enter Process C from Process B at a finished cost in Process B of $14 per unit. The labor and overhead costs charged to Process C are $24,300. On January 31, 600 units remain on hand in Process C estimated to be $\frac{1}{3}$ completed in this process. Remaining units, 2,800, have been completed and removed to stock. Shipments to customers for January amounted to 2,500 units. Materials are put into process in the first phase of production. The estimates of degree of completion of goods in process thus express only the estimated quantity of processing costs required in the final product.

The equivalent whole units of work performed in Process C during January are calculated as follows:

| | |
|---|---:|
| Number of units completed in January....................... | 2,800 |
| Deduct number of equivalent whole units in process on December 31, 400 units estimated $\frac{3}{4}$ completed.................... | 300 |
| | 2,500 |
| Add equivalent whole units in process on January 31, 600 units estimated $\frac{1}{3}$ completed.................................. | 200 |
| Equivalent whole units of work performed in January.......... | 2,700 |

Processing costs, $24,300, divided by the unit performance for the month, 2,700, gives $9, the cost per unit for work performed. Using the first-in, first-out method, costs for goods completed, goods in process inventory — Process C, goods sold, and finished goods inventory, are calculated as follows:

COST OF GOODS COMPLETED IN PROCESS C AND TRANSFERRED TO STOCK:

|  |  |  |  |
|---|---|---|---|
| | | Material cost (cost from Process B in December), $15 per unit.............. | $ 6,000 |
| | 400 units in process Jan. 1 | Processing cost: $\frac{3}{4}$ completed in December, cost: $10× 300 equivalent units (400×$\frac{3}{4}$)....... | 3,000 |
| | | $\frac{1}{4}$ completed in January, cost: $9×100 equivalent units (400×$\frac{1}{4}$).......... | 900 |
| 2,800 units | | Total cost of first 400 units completed ($24.75 per unit)............................ | $ 9,900 |
| | 2,400 units started and completed in January | Material cost (cost from Process B in January), $14 per unit.............. $33,600 Processing cost in January, $9 per unit.. 21,600 | |
| | | Total cost of additional 2,400 units completed ($23 per unit).................... | 55,200 |
| | | Total | $65,100 |

COST OF GOODS IN PROCESS C INVENTORY:

|  |  |  |
|---|---|---|
| 600 units | Material cost (cost from Process B in January), $14 per unit........................................ | $ 8,400 |
| | Processing $\frac{1}{3}$ completed in January, cost: $9×200 equivalent units (600×$\frac{1}{3}$)............................. | 1,800 |
| | Total | $10,200 |

COST OF GOODS SOLD:

|  |  |  |
|---|---|---|
| 2,500 units | 1,000 units on hand December 31, cost $25 per unit...... | $25,000 |
| | 400 units completed in January, cost $24.75 per unit... | 9,900 |
| | 1,100 units completed in January, cost $23 per unit...... | 25,300 |
| | Total | $60,200 |

COST OF FINISHED GOODS INVENTORY:

1,300 units completed in January, cost $23 per unit.............. $29,900

The accounts in the ledger affected by the foregoing will appear as follows:

PROCESS B

| | | | | |
|---|---|---|---|---|
| Dec. 31 | Balance | xxx | Jan. 31 Completed, to Process C, | |
| Jan. | Materials | xxx | 3,000 units | 42,000 |
| Jan. | Processing costs | xxx | | |

PROCESS C

| | | | |
|---|---|---|---|
| Dec. 31 Balance, 400 units | 9,000 | Jan. 31 Cost of goods completed, | |
| Jan. 31 Material cost (from Process B) 3,000 units | 42,000 | 2,800 units | 65,100 |
| 31 Processing costs | 24,300 | | |

(Balance in the account at the end of the month, $10,200, represents the cost of 600 units of goods in Process C inventory, ⅓ completed.)

FINISHED GOODS

| | | | |
|---|---|---|---|
| Dec. 31 Balance, 1,000 units | 25,000 | Jan. 31 Cost of goods sold, 2,500 | |
| 31 Cost of goods completed, 2,800 units from | | units | 60,200 |
| Process C | 65,100 | | |

(Balance in the account at the end of the month, $29,900, represents the cost of 1,300 units of finished goods inventory.)

COST OF GOODS SOLD

| | |
|---|---|
| Jan. 31 Cost of goods sold, 2,500 units | 60,200 |

(Balance in this account is to be transferred to the profit and loss account in summarizing operations for the period.)

**INVENTORIES ON THE BALANCE SHEET**　　It is customary for business units to report trading as well as manufacturing inventories as current assets, even though it is recognized in some instances that it may take considerable time before parts of such inventories are realized in the form of cash. Among the items that are generally reported separately under the inventories heading are merchandise inventory or finished goods, goods in process, raw materials, factory supplies, goods and materials in transit, goods on consignment, and goods in the hands of agents and salesmen. Normally inventories are listed in the order of their liquidity.

Purchase orders should not be treated as additions to inventories, nor should sales orders be treated as deductions as long as title to goods has not passed. When goods have been formally set aside and the title is transferred, purchases or sales may be recognized with proper recognition of the effect of such transactions on the inventory position. Advance payment on a purchase commitment should not be included in inventories but should be reported separately. Such advances are preferably listed after inventories in the current asset section since they still await entry into the inventory phase of the operating cycle.

A number of parenthetical remarks or notes may be required to afford full disclosure concerning the inventory valuation procedures employed. The basis of valuation (cost, lower of cost or market, etc.), together with the method of arriving at cost (lifo, fifo, average, or other method), should be fully indicated. The reader of a statement may assume that the valuation procedures indicated have been consistently applied. If this is not the case, the change in the method of valuation of inventories in developing balance sheet and income statement data should be explained by means of a special note so that the effects of the change can be fully appreciated. Such a note should also report net income developed in accordance with practices of prior years so that the reader of the statement may make intelligent comparisons of current operating results with those of previous periods. If such data are to be made available, inventory valuations in terms of the old procedures as well as the new will be required in the year in which a change is adopted.

When the inventory costing method offers values that are materially less than current replacement costs, parenthetical disclosure of such current values should be provided on the balance sheet. The use of lifo and base stock methods, for example, may result in serious distortions of working capital measurements. Supplementary data concerning market should be provided if the reader of the statement is to be adequately informed concerning financial position.

When an inventory is reduced to the lower of cost or market by means of a valuation allowance, such an allowance is properly reported as a subtraction from the inventory at cost. However, if retained earnings have been appropriated to preserve earnings within the business for possible future market decline in the inventory value, such an appropriation is reported as a part of the company's capital. If the decline fails to materialize, the appropriation balance is no longer required and is returned to the retained earnings account. If the decline does materialize, the inventory loss is reported on the income statement in the year in which it takes place and the appropriation is still returned to Retained Earnings, where it will absorb the inventory loss that is ultimately carried to the latter account.

If significant inventory price declines take place between the balance sheet date and the date the statement is actually prepared, mention of such declines should be made by parenthetical remark or note. When relatively large orders for merchandise have been placed in a period of widely fluctuating prices but the title to such goods has not yet passed, an explanation should be provided concerning such commitments. Information should also be provided concerning any contingent losses on such purchase commitments. Similar information may be appropriate with respect to sales commitments.

When inventories or sections of an inventory have been pledged as security on certain loan contracts, such pledges should be mentioned parenthetically in the inventory section.

Inventory items, as these might appear on a balance sheet, are shown below:

Inventories (valuation on the basis of cost or market,
    whichever is lower, cost being obtained by the
    first-in, first-out method):

| | | |
|---|---:|---:|
| Finished goods: | | |
| On hand (goods of $100,000 have been pledged as security on loan of $75,000 from First State Bank). | $300,000 | |
| On consignment | 15,000 | $315,000 |
| Finished parts | | 25,000 |
| Goods in process | | 300,000 |
| Raw materials: | | |
| On hand | $210,000 | |
| In transit from suppliers | 30,000 | 240,000 |
| Factory supplies | | 12,000 |
| Total inventories | | $892,000 |

**PREPAID EXPENSES** It has already been suggested that the current assets classification is composed of: (1) monetary assets — cash, temporary investments, and receivables; and (2) non-monetary assets — inventories and prepaid expenses. Prepaid expenses representing rights to services have sometimes been referred to as "service receivables." However, these cannot be classed with receivables for they will not be converted into cash but rather will be applied to revenue of the operating cycle. This quality would suggest a closer relationship to inventories and a more satisfactory designation as "service inventories." But prepaid expenses do not qualify as "items of tangible property held for sale" and hence cannot be included as a part of a company's inventories. Prepaid expenses should be separately shown, normally following inventories on the balance sheet.

Prepayments may be found for such items as insurance, rents, taxes, advertising, royalties, and supply items. When payment is made in advance of the receipt of a service or when supplies are acquired and not fully utilized, recognition of a prepayment is in order. Such prepayment should be assigned to future revenue in accordance with the expiration of the service or the consumption of the supplies. Consideration will be given here to several prepayments commonly found.

*Prepaid Insurance.* Payments in advance are frequently made for insurance against fire and other hazards. Whenever statements are prepared, analysis of the insurance premiums is required to determine the portions identified with future periods and to be reported as prepaid or unexpired and the portions that are chargeable to current revenue. With the maintenance of a number of insurance policies, a special record referred to as an *insurance register* may be maintained to offer full detail relative to insurance coverage, premiums, periods covered, periodic charges, etc.

*Prepaid Rent.* Rents for land, buildings, and for the use of motor vehicles and equipment are frequently paid in advance. Periodically, determinations must be made of the service costs that have expired and the portions of rents that are assignable to future revenue. The basis for the original charges — time, utilization, or other factors — should be used in establishing the prepaid balances.

*Prepaid Taxes, Licenses, and Fees.* Prepayments are frequently involved in taxes, licenses, and fees. Such charges should normally be spread over the periods of their applicabilities as indicated by the governmental authority.

*Operating Supplies.* A business unit frequently acquires office, store, advertising, shipping, and other miscellaneous supplies. These should be reported as assets to the extent that they remain on hand and are usable in subsequent periods. The same procedures that are applied for the control, accounting, and valuation of a company's inventories may be applied to the supplies that it carries when these are found in large quantities and involve relatively significant costs.

## QUESTIONS

**1.** Give certain instances in which estimates of inventory costs are necessary or appropriate and state what procedure would be followed in developing satisfactory estimates of such costs.

**2.** Distinguish between: (a) gross profit as a percentage of cost and gross profit as a percentage of sales; (b) markup cancellation and markdown; (c) the gross profit method of calculating estimated inventory cost and the retail inventory method of calculating estimated inventory cost.

**3.** What is your understanding of the meaning of the "gross profit test"?

**4.** Define (a) initial markup, (b) additional markup, (c) markup cancellation, (d) markdown, (e) markdown cancellation, and (f) maintained markup.

**5.** What are the advantages of the retail inventory method?

**6.** (a) Does the retail inventory method eliminate the need for physical inventory procedures? (b) What procedure would you recommend when a physical inventory at retail offers an inventory balance that differs from inventory records maintained at retail?

**7.** At what point should the cost percentage be calculated in the retail inventory method in order to find the most conservative new inventory figure? Why?

**8.** A merchant taking inventory by the retail method maintains no separate record of markup cancellations and markdown cancellations. Instead he includes the former in markdowns and the latter in markups, as "these represent price decreases and increases respectively." How will this procedure affect his inventory at (a) retail? (b) cost?

**9.** (a) What is meant by the term "equivalent units"? (b) Does this term apply only to processing costs or is it applicable to raw material costs as well?

**10.** How would you recommend that the following items be reported on the balance sheet:

    (a) Unsold goods in the hands of consignees.
    (b) Purchase orders outstanding.
    (c) Advance payments on purchase commitments.
    (d) Raw materials pledged by means of warehouse receipts on notes payable to bank.
    (e) Raw materials in transit from suppliers.
    (f) An allowance to reduce the inventory cost to market.
    (g) A reserve for possible future inventory declines.
    (h) Materials received from a customer for processing.
    (i) Merchandise produced by special order and set aside to be picked up by customer.
    (j) Raw materials set aside and to be used in connection with plant rehabilitation activities.
    (k) Finished parts to be used in the assembly of final products.

**11.** The McArthur Co. changes from fifo to lifo for inventory valuation in 1958. How should this change be accomplished on the statements prepared at the end of 1958?

## EXERCISES

**1.** (a) What is the percentage of profit on the basis of cost price when the gross profit margin is 25% of selling price? 50% of selling price? 60% of selling price?

(b) What is the percentage of profit on the basis of sales price when the gross profit percentage is 25% of cost? $33\frac{1}{3}$% of cost? 50% of cost? 100% of cost?

**2.** (a) What percentage markon on cost is required to produce a 20% gross profit on sales? a 25% gross profit on sales? a 40% gross profit on sales?

(b) What is the gross profit on sales if goods are marked up 20% above cost? 50% above cost? 60% above cost?

**3.** Assume sales for a period of $100,000. What is the cost of goods sold under each assumption below:

(a) Gross profit on sales is 25%.
(b) Gross profit on cost of sales is 60%.
(c) Goods are marked up $\frac{1}{5}$ above cost.
(d) Gross profit on cost of sales is 200%.
(e) Goods are marked up 150% above cost.
(f) Gross profit on sales is 18%.
(g) Gross profit on cost is 18%.

**4.** R. I. Kelly requires an estimate of the cost of merchandise lost by fire on March 7. Merchandise inventory on January 1 was $40,000. Purchases since January 1 were $35,000; freight in, $3,000; purchases returns and allowances, $2,000. Sales are made at 25% above cost and totaled $42,000 to March 7. (a) What was the cost of merchandise destroyed? (b) What would your answer be if sales are made at a gross profit of 25% of sales?

**5.** P. L. Warner takes an inventory at cost on January 15, 1959, which is $18,000. His statements are based on the calendar year, so you find it necessary to establish an inventory figure as of December 31, 1958. You find that during the period January 2–15, sales were $60,000; sales returns, $1,500; goods purchased and placed in stock, $54,000; goods removed from stock and returned to vendors, $2,000; freight in, $500. Calculate an inventory cost as of December 31 assuming that goods are marked to sell at 30% above cost.

**6.** The profit and loss data for the Ernst Co. follows:

|  | SALES | PURCHASES |
|---|---|---|
| January | $50,000 | $40,000 |
| February | 60,000 | 40,000 |
| March | 65,000 | 50,000 |

The merchandise inventory at cost on January 1 was $20,000. Goods are sold at a gross profit of 20% on sales. Compute the monthly inventory balances for interim statement purposes.

**7.** The income statement for P. A. Brock for the year ended December 31, 1958, shows the following:

| | | |
|---|---:|---:|
| Sales.................................... | | $100,000 |
| Cost of goods sold: | | |
|     Beginning inventory.................... | $16,000 | |
|     Purchases........................... | 80,000 | |
| | $96,000 | |
|     Less: Ending inventory................. | 33,500 | 62,500 |
| Gross profit on sales........................ | | $37,500 |

Quarterly sales and purchases during 1958 were as follows:

| | SALES | PURCHASES | | SALES | PURCHASES |
|---|---|---|---|---|---|
| 1st quarter.. | $15,000 | $10,000 | 3rd quarter.. | $30,000 | $35,000 |
| 2nd quarter. | 20,000 | 20,000 | 4th quarter.. | 35,000 | 15,000 |

Assuming that the rate of gross profit on sales was constant during the year and operating expenses were 40% of gross profit, develop:

(a) Quarterly summaries of operating data.

(b) Merchandise turnover rate for the year using beginning and ending inventory balances.

(c) Merchandise turnover rate for the year using quarterly inventory balances as developed in (a).

**8.** A merchandise inventory calculated by the retail inventory method is $64,000. A physical count of the stock on hand shows merchandise at a retail value of $58,000. (a) Suggest possible reasons for the discrepancy. (b) What accounting treatment would be called for in each instance?

**9.** Records for the Brooks Dept. Store disclose the following data:

| | AT RETAIL | AT COST |
|---|---|---|
| Merchandise Inventory, Jan. 1......... | $ 60,000 | $ 40,000 |
| Purchases, Jan. 1–Dec. 31 ............. | | 160,000 |
| Sales, Jan. 1–Dec. 31 ................. | 205,000 | |
| Sales Returns, Jan. 1–Dec. 31 ......... | 5,000 | |

Inventory taken on Dec. 31 shows merchandise on hand valued at retail at $120,000. From the foregoing information calculate the estimated cost of the ending inventory.

**10.** From the records kept by the Lovett Department Store, the following information is available for the month of January:

| | AT SELLING PRICE | AT COST |
|---|---|---|
| Inventory, January 1................... | $12,000 | $ 8,400 |
| Purchases........................... | 80,000 | 48,810 |
| Freight in............................ | | 2,000 |
| Additional markups.................... | 4,300 | |
| Markup cancellations.................. | 800 | |
| Markdowns.......................... | 6,600 | |
| Markdown cancellations............... | 200 | |
| Sales............................... | 72,600 | |

(1) Calculate the inventory on January 31 at (a) the sales price and (b) a conservative cost figure.

(2) Assuming that a physical count on January 31 shows inventory at retail of $15,500, how would this be explained and what effect does this have on the calculation of the ending inventory?

**11.** The Standard Manufacturing Company had 300 units, $\frac{1}{3}$ finished, on hand on January 1; during the month 3,000 units were finished; on January 31 there were 400 units, $\frac{3}{4}$ finished, on hand. How much work, expressed in equivalent whole units, was performed during the month of January?

**12.** On September 1 Moore Manufacturers had 800 units, $\frac{1}{4}$ finished, in Process No. 2; during September, 2,000 units entered into Process No. 2 from Process No. 1; on September 30 there were 900 units, $\frac{2}{3}$ finished, in Process No. 2. (a) How many equivalent whole units of work were performed in Process No. 2 during September? (b) How many units were completed and transferred out of Process No. 2 during the month of September?

**13.** The Paul Manufacturing Co. produces a single product. During December materials of $18,000 were requisitioned for use in the factory. Other manufacturing costs in December were: labor, $30,000; overhead $12,000. During December 12,000 units were completed and transferred to finished stock. On December 1 there were 6,000 units in process in the factory, estimated $\frac{1}{3}$ completed, estimated cost, $7,200. On December 31 there were 8,000 units in process, estimated $\frac{3}{4}$ completed. Degree of completion indicates the estimated portion of the total necessary cost to produce. What is the cost of goods completed in December and the ending goods in process inventory? Assume that the first-in, first-out method is used in calculating inventory costs.

**14.** The Lloyd Co. produces Product X by a continuous processing procedure. On November 30 the Process C account shows the following information:

PROCESS C

| | | |
|---|---|---|
| Nov. 1 Bal., 8,000 lbs. (goods from Process B at 60¢; labor and overhead, processing $\frac{1}{4}$ completed, at 20¢) | 6,400 | Nov. 30 16,000 lbs. to Process D |
| 1–30 From Process B, 20,000 lbs. at 70¢ | 14,000 | Nov. 30 Bal. (12,000 lbs., processing $\frac{1}{2}$ completed) |
| Labor | 12,000 | |
| Overhead | 6,000 | |

What is the cost of the 16,000 lbs. of mix leaving Process C in November and the cost of the 12,000 lbs. remaining in process on November 30? Assume that the first-in, first-out method is used in calculating the cost of the inventory.

# PROBLEMS

**10-1.** All of the merchandise of the Maple Shop is destroyed by fire on March 15, 1958. Sales and merchandise data for the year to date of fire were as follows:

| | |
|---|---:|
| Sales | $70,000 |
| Sales returns | 3,000 |
| Merchandise inventory, January 1 | 25,000 |
| Freight in | 600 |
| Purchases | 40,000 |
| Purchases returns | 1,600 |

*Instructions:* (1) Prepare a schedule to show the estimated fire loss, assuming that merchandise is sold at 60% above cost.

(2) Prepare a schedule to show the estimated fire loss, assuming that merchandise is sold at a gross profit that is 60% of sales price.

**10-2.** The Jensen Dept. Store takes a physical inventory on March 31, 1958, and summarizes operations for the first quarter as follows:

## JENSEN DEPT. STORE

### INCOME STATEMENT

#### FOR THREE MONTHS ENDED MARCH 31, 1958

| | | |
|---|---:|---:|
| Sales | | $150,000 |
| Cost of goods sold: | | |
| Inventory, January 1 | $ 40,000 | |
| Purchases | 170,000 | |
| | $210,000 | |
| Inventory, March 31 | 90,000 | 120,000 |
| Gross profit on sales | | $ 30,000 |
| Expenses | | 10,000 |
| Net income before income taxes | | $ 20,000 |
| Less: Income taxes (30%) | | 6,000 |
| Net income after income taxes | | $ 14,000 |

In analyzing sales, purchases, and expenses, the following monthly totals are available:

| | Sales | Purchases | Expenses |
|---|---:|---:|---:|
| January | $ 40,000 | $ 70,000 | $ 2,000 |
| February | 52,000 | 48,000 | 3,000 |
| March | 58,000 | 52,000 | 5,000 |
| | $150,000 | $170,000 | $10,000 |

*Instructions:* Prepare a comparative income statement showing operating detail for each of the three months. In computing the monthly inventories, assume that the gross profit margin remained constant throughout the three-month period.

**10-3.** Quarterly purchases and sales for Wetherby Products, Inc. for 1958 are listed below. The corporation began 1958 with a merchandise inventory of $31,515. Goods have been sold at a uniform markup of 66 2/3%.

|  | Purchases | Sales |
|---|---|---|
| January 1 — March 31..................... | $36,300 | $43,150 |
| April 1 — June 30........................ | 27,900 | 51,620 |
| July 1 — September 30.................... | 43,815 | 66,550 |
| October 1 — December 31................. | 27,000 | 72,275 |

*Instructions:* (1) Calculate the inventory for the end of each quarter. (2) Calculate the merchandise turnover rate for the year based upon quarterly data.

**10-4.** The records of Whitcomb's Dept. Store show the following data for the month of March:

| Sales................. | $170,000 | Purchases (at sales price) | $ 80,000 |
|---|---|---|---|
| Additional markups..... | 12,000 | Markup cancellations.... | 2,000 |
| Markdowns........... | 30,000 | Beginning inventory (at | |
| Markdown cancellations. | 5,000 | cost price)........... | 105,000 |
| Freight in on purchases.. | 2,000 | Beginning inventory (at | |
| Purchases (at cost price) | 50,000 | sales price).......... | 160,000 |

*Instructions:* (1) Calculate the inventory at retail price.     55,000
(2) Calculate the inventory at a conservative cost price using the retail inventory method.     34,540

**10-5.** The following information is found in the records of Department No. 31 of the Hobby Shop at the end of January: sales, $36,000; beginning inventory, at cost, $31,505; beginning inventory, at selling price, $44,000; purchases, at cost, $9,050; purchases, at selling price, $15,000; freight in, $600; purchases returns, at selling price, $800; purchases returns, at cost price, $520; additional markups, $2,500; markup cancellations, $500; markdowns, $4,200; markdown cancellations, $750; employee discounts, $200; estimated loss from spoilage, breakage, etc., at retail, $300.

*Instructions:* (1) Calculate the inventory at sales price.
(2) Calculate the inventory at a conservative cost price using the retail inventory method.

**10-6.** The Dandridge Corporation engages in the production of a standard type of electric motor. Manufacturing costs for the month of November were $66,000. At the beginning of the month, company inventories were as follows:

Motors in production, estimated 80% completed   2,500 units, $32,000
Motors on hand, 100% completed                  1,200 units, $19,200

During the month 5,500 completed units left the factory and were put into stock. At the end of the month, inventories were as follows:

Motors in production, estimated 50% completed   1,000 units
Motors on hand, 100% completed                  1,400 units

*Instructions:* Assuming valuation on the basis of first-in, first-out, calculate: (1) the cost of the ending work in process and finished goods inventories and (2) the cost of goods sold.

**10-7.** On July 1 the finished goods inventory account on the books of Montgomery Processors has a balance of $12,000 and the goods in process inventory account has a balance of $15,000. There were 400 units of finished product on hand and 750 units in process, averaging $\frac{2}{3}$ completed. During July the total materials cost used in production was $9,600; labor was $8,500; other manufacturing expenses were $6,500. During July 1,100 units were completed and placed in stock, and on July 31 there were 800 units $\frac{1}{4}$ completed in the factory. On July 31 there were 400 finished units in stock after shipments to customers. The degree of completion of goods in process indicates the estimated portion of the total necessary cost to produce. The first-in, first-out method is used in calculating cost.

*Instructions:* Prepare summaries to show:
(1) Equivalent number of whole units of work performed.
(2) Cost of goods completed and transferred to finished stock.
(3) Cost of goods in process inventory.
(4) Cost of finished goods inventory.
(5) Cost of goods sold.

**10-8.** The Bramlett Co. has three processes in its factory. The following charges appear in the Process #2 account for the month of October:

Process #2

| | |
|---|---|
| Oct. 1, Inventory, 200 units, 40% completed.. | 2,160 |
| 1–31, 2,500 units from Process #1............ | 25,625 |
| Labor.............. | 3,800 |
| Other factory expenses. | 2,200 |

In October, 2,400 units were completed and transferred to Process #3. The units remaining in process on October 31 are 60% completed. The degree of completion refers to processing costs only.

*Instructions:* (1) Calculate the number of equivalent whole units of work performed in Process #2.

(2) Calculate the total costs and the costs per unit for goods transferred to Process #3 and for goods remaining in Process #2. The first-in, first-out method is used in calculating costs.

**10-9.** A goods in process account on the books of Crawford Mfg. Co. appears as indicated below. Materials are received from Process A and the degree of completion refers only to processing costs as applied to such materials.

Process B

| | | | |
|---|---|---|---|
| May 1, Inventory,   800 units, $\frac{1}{4}$ completed | 4,400 | May 1–31, 1,900 units to Finished Goods | |
| 1–31, 2,000 units from Process A . . . . . . | 10,000 | 31, Inventory,   900 units, 2/3 completed | |
| Processing costs. | 16,100 | | |

*Instructions:* (1) Calculate the number of equivalent whole units of work performed in Process B.

(2) Determine the total costs and the costs per unit for goods completed and for goods in process. The first-in, first-out method is used in calculating costs.

**10-10.** United Producers, Inc. produces a single product. On December 1, 1958, inventories of the company were:

| | |
|---|---|
| Raw Materials. . . . . . . . . . . . . . . . . . . . . . . . . . . . . . . . . . . . . . . . . | $12,500 |
| Goods in Process (1,000 units, approximately 50% completed). . . | 21,250 |
| Finished Goods (300 units). . . . . . . . . . . . . . . . . . . . . . . . . . . . . . | 12,600 |

During December materials of $14,000 were purchased and materials of $16,830 were requisitioned for use in the factory. Costs during December were: labor, $25,780; other manufacturing costs, $12,000. During the month of December, 1,200 units were placed in finished stock and 1,150 units were sold at $56 per unit. At the end of the month, 1,900 units were in process, approximately 30% completed. Selling, general, and administrative expenses for the month were $9,200. Degree of completion indicates the estimated portion of the total necessary cost to produce. The first-in, first-out method is used in calculating cost.

*Instructions:* Prepare an income statement accompanied by a manufacturing schedule. Provide summaries in support of inventory values used.

**10-11.** In June 1958 the Pioneer Co. sold 50 air conditioning units for $200 each. Costs included material costs of $50 a unit and direct labor costs of $30 a unit. Overhead was computed at 100% of direct labor cost. Interest expense on a 4% bank loan was equivalent to $1.00 a unit. Federal income tax at a 30% rate was equivalent to $15 a unit.

Effective July 1, 1958 material costs decreased 5% and direct labor costs increased 20%. Also effective July 1, 1958 the interest rate on the bank loan increased from 4% per annum to 5% per annum.

*Instructions:* (1) Assuming no change in the rate of overhead in relation to direct labor costs, compute the sales price per unit that will produce the same ratio of gross profit.

(2) Assuming that $10 of the overhead consists of fixed costs, compute the sales price per unit that will produce the same ratio of gross profit. (A.I.C.P.A. adapted)

**10-12.** The operations of a department of a retail store that uses the retail method of inventory determination are given in the figures presented below:

| | |
|---|---:|
| Opening inventory—cost | $14,250 |
| Opening inventory—sales price | 19,105 |
| Purchases—cost | 33,771 |
| Purchases—sales price | 46,312 |
| Purchases allowance | 1,093 |
| Freight in | 845 |
| Departmental transfers (debit)—cost | 100 |
| Departmental transfers (debit)—sales price | 140 |
| Additional markups | 1,207 |
| Markup cancellations | 274 |
| Inventory shortage—sales price | 704 |
| Sales (including sales of $4,460 of items that were marked down from $5,920) | 37,246 |

*Instructions:* Set up a computation showing the ending inventory at sales price and at cost as determined by the retail method. (A.I.C.P.A. adapted)

**10-13.** On July 1, 1958, the merchandise inventory of the glove department of a department store aggregated $90,600 at retail and $54,360 at cost. During the following six months, the purchases and the sales were as follows:

PURCHASES

| | Cost | Retail Price | Original Markup | Net Sales |
|---|---:|---:|---:|---:|
| July | $ 24,300 | $ 40,200 | $ 15,900 | $ 24,900 |
| August | 31,500 | 55,800 | 24,300 | 30,500 |
| September | 43,000 | 75,900 | 32,900 | 38,200 |
| October | 35,200 | 60,000 | 24,800 | 55,300 |
| November | 17,300 | 30,300 | 13,000 | 58,700 |
| December | 9,500 | 15,700 | 6,200 | 60,900 |
| | $160,800 | $277,900 | $117,100 | $268,500 |

During these six months the following reductions were made in the retail prices:

| | |
|---|---:|
| (a) To facilitate disposal of overstock | $ 4,000 |
| (b) In connection with odd lots | 2,500 |
| (c) To meet competitive prices | 3,000 |
| (d) Miscellaneous | 2,000 |
| | $11,500 |

In addition to the above markdowns, the selling price of certain merchandise was reduced in connection with a special store-wide sale held annually in October of each year.  For the duration of the sale, the selling price of a lot of merchandise consisting of 300 dozen pairs of a nationally advertised brand of gloves was reduced from $5 per pair to $4.25 per pair.  At the conclusion of the special sales period it was found that 26 dozen pair remained unsold and the selling price thereof was restored to $5 per pair.

During the season the selling price of a special lot of imported gloves that proved to be unusually popular was increased from the original selling price of $6 per pair to $7.50 per pair.  This additional markup applied to 500 dozen pairs of gloves.  Later in this season the additional markup of $1.50 was canceled on 75 dozen pairs of gloves of a certain color that were not moving as fast as the remainder of the line and the price was reduced to the original price of $6 per pair.

A physical inventory taken at the close of business December 31, 1958, aggregated $94,500 at retail.  The physical inventory at retail was found to be unusually close to the book inventory and did not show the normal expected shrinkage.  Investigation revealed that a lot of 50 dozen pairs of gloves received in the last few days of the year had not been included in the purchases recorded in the stock record because the invoice had not been received until after the close of the year.  This lot of 50 dozen pairs of gloves was purchased at a cost of $3.75 per pair and was marked to sell at $6 per pair.  Some of the gloves included in this lot had been sold before the close of the year and were not included in the inventory.

*Instructions:* From the above information compute the following by use of the retail inventory method, carrying percentages to two decimal places.

(1)  The amount of the stock shortage at retail.

(2)  The value at which the closing inventory of the glove department should be carried on the balance sheet.

(3)  The cost of sales for the six months ended December 31, 1958. (A.I.C.P.A. adapted)

**10-14.**  The Berney Chemical Co. has perfected a process for producing from three raw materials, A, B and C, two chemical compounds, Y and Z.

The following diagram illustrates the manufacturing process:

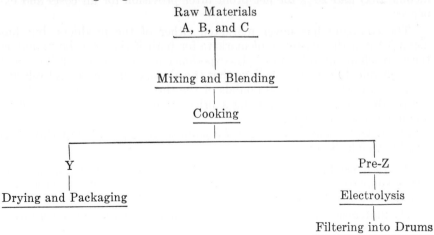

Raw Materials
A, B, and C

Mixing and Blending

Cooking

Y                                        Pre-Z

Drying and Packaging                    Electrolysis

Filtering into Drums

The raw materials are required in the following proportions by weight:

A............................ 3 parts
B............................ 5 parts
C............................ 2 parts
                             ────
                             10 parts
                             ════

One hundred thousand (100,000) pounds of raw material will be processed. The unit costs of the three raw materials are as follows:

A.................................................. $ 2.00 per pound
B.................................................. $50.00 per ton
C..(8 lbs. per gallon)............................. $ 4.00 per gallon

Other costs of production are estimated to be:

Mixing, blending and cooking............................. $16,090
Additional costs applicable to Y:
    Drying and packaging................................    4,660
Additional costs applicable to Z:
    Electrolysis and filtering to drums..................    6,920

The cooking process reduces the weight of the combined raw materials by 40%.

Out of 100,000 pounds of original raw materials, 20,000 pounds of
pre-Z are obtained. Of the pre-Z electrolyzed, 25% becomes a non-
marketable precipitate; the remainder, a liquid, is filtered into 50-gallon
drums without further attention.

The cost of drums, which are returnable and for which customers are
to be charged specifically, is not to be included in either the cost or the
price of Z.

Each product is to be sold on the basis of a list price, less 35% and
10%. Of the net selling price of each product, 25% is to be allowed for
selling, administrative, and general expenses (including provision for
income tax) and 20% for net profit after provision for all costs and expenses.

The company has never marketed either of the products, but has
demonstrated the existence of markets for both if they can be manufactured to sell at suitable prices. Its experience in producing both these and
other chemicals leads it to believe that the above estimates of cost relative
to the processing of 100,000 pounds of the three raw materials combined
are reliable as a basis for setting a price for each of the products to be
manufactured therefrom.

Note: One gallon of Z weighs 7.5 pounds and one gallon of Raw Material C weighs 8 pounds.

*Instructions:* From the information above, prepare the following statements, supported by whatever explanatory schedules you consider necessary.
(Except for unit costs, carry computations to the nearest dollar only.)

(1) Statement to show at what list price and at what net price per pound
Y should be sold.

(2) Statement to show at what list price and at what net price per gallon Z should be sold.

(3) Condensed income statement to show, separately and combined, the results of operations in Y and Z, on the assumption that the entire quantity of each product manufactured will be sold at the respective prices indicated in the statements prepared in (1) and in (2) above, and that selling, administrative, and general expenses are to be included at the same estimate as is allowed in setting such prices. (A.I.C.P.A. adapted)

**10-15.** You have been retained by a fire insurance adjustor to examine the records salvaged from a fire which almost completely destroyed the office and warehouse of A, B and C, partners in a wholesale jobbing business.

Your report, directed to the adjustor, must include an estimate of the inventory value as of the date of the fire, January 2, 1959.

The merchandise handled by the firm is divided into three lines or classes of goods, designated as X, Y and Z. Classes X and Y each consist of a number of items which are bought and sold without change of form; Class Z consists of one item only for which raw material is bought and put through a manufacturing process.

The following records and data are found to be available:

1. Duplicate sales invoices and credit memos, the totals of which are as follows:

|  | Sales | Credit Memos |
|---|---|---|
| Year 1956 | $122,785 | $6,585 |
| Year 1957 | 110,942 | 7,582 |
| Year 1958 | 87,451 | 4,160 |

A check of the numbers discloses that approximately 9% of the duplicate sales invoices for 1958 are missing.

2. Duplicate bank deposit slips without any missing dates:

| | |
|---|---|
| Year 1956 | $108,066 |
| Year 1957 | 96,008 |
| Year 1958 | 91,150 |

Duplicate bank deposit slips were found to represent receipts from accounts receivable and cash sales only. You learn on inquiry that the partnership has made a practice of paying some expenses out of cash receipts not deposited. The amount of such payments cannot be determined.

3. Purchase invoice files, accompanied by adding machine tapes purporting to show the total purchases for each year, with totals as follows:

| | |
|---|---|
| Year 1956 | $131,616 |
| Year 1957 | 117,935 |
| Year 1958 | 76,158 |

4. Inventory sheets, taken by the management as of January 1, 1956:

| | |
|---|---|
| Class X | $ 58,500 |
| Class Y | 28,080 |
| Class Z — raw materials | 17,550 |
| — finished, 4/7 of which is raw material | 16,380 |

The management stated that about 17% was added to the cost of merchandise and raw materials in the 1956 inventory to cover freight and handling. A comparison of some of the inventory prices with purchase invoices at about the date of the inventory confirmed this statement. You find, however, that 2% of *net purchases* is sufficient to cover freight and handling into the warehouse and allow this percentage in *all cost computations*.

You ascertain also that 17% has been added to the cost of direct labor and overhead in the January 1, 1956 finished goods inventory, and that the overhead is 50% of the direct labor.

5. Upon examination of the contents of the purchase invoice files you find that credit memos representing allowances on purchases have been listed on the adding machine tapes as invoices and included in the totals, as follows:

Year 1956............................ $ 7,548
Year 1957............................ 7,225
Year 1958............................ 6,120

All suppliers of merchandise and materials are circularized with a request for an itemized statement of account for the last three years, and these statements show additional credit memos in the following amounts:

Year 1956............................ $ 1,751
Year 1957............................ 3,128
Year 1958............................ 5,610

6. Raw materials for Class Z are purchased in carload lots, and the invoices for the three years show total purchases of $33,000. You find that the shop foreman has kept a record showing that raw materials, of which the invoice cost was $34,000, have been put in process in the three years, and that the proportions of direct labor and overhead to material cost have been approximately maintained.

7. Analysis of a considerable number of sales invoices, selected in such a way as to give a fair sample of the entire file, and comparison with the computed cost of each item, give results which are summarized as follows:

|  | Per Cent of Net Sales | Per Cent of Gross Profit to Net Sales |
|---|---|---|
| Class X............................ | 45% | 10% |
| Class Y............................ | 26% | 15% |
| Class Z............................ | 29% | 21% |

*Instructions:* Prepare computation of approximate inventory at January 2, 1959, including a schedule showing separately the raw materials and finished goods in Class Z. (Do not carry out any computations farther than the nearest dollar.) (A.I.C.P.A. adapted)

# Chapter 11

# CURRENT LIABILITIES

**NATURE OF**　　　　　In an economic system based so largely on
**LIABILITIES**　　　　 credit, one finds many evidences of credit on
the balance sheet. Most goods and services are purchased on account.
Funds are borrowed from commercial banks for working capital purposes. Large sums are provided by bond issues to finance new buildings
and machinery. During the lives of such obligations, interest accrues
as an additional liability. Taxes accrued but not yet due appear as
liabilities until paid. Employees working for the enterprise are creditors
until paid for their services.

Obligations of the business unit must be fully recognized and
properly measured on the balance sheet if both the creditors' equity
and the residual owners' equity in business assets are to be reported
accurately. Appropriate distinction in liability presentation between
current and noncurrent items is necessary if the company's working
capital position is to be accurately defined.

Full recognition on the balance sheet of contingent claims, those
liabilities that may materialize as a result of certain acts or circumstances, is also essential. If contingent claims materialize as actual
claims, creditor and ownership equities will change. Current payment
will normally be called for with a change in the status of the claim.
Contingent claims, therefore, must be considered along with presently
existing claims in arriving at conclusions concerning a company's
ability to meet debt requirements.

This chapter considers the problems relating to determination,
measurement, and presentation of current and contingent liabilities.
The problems relating to long-term obligations are considered in
Chapter 19.

**CURRENT LIABILITIES**　　　It was suggested in Chapter 1 that current
　　　　　　　　　　　　　liabilities may be broadly defined to include
(1) all obligations arising from operations related to the operating cycle
and payable within the course of such a cycle and (2) all other obligations that are to be liquidated within a year. These current liabilities
make a claim against resources classified as current. Current liabilities
are subtracted from current assets in arriving at the company's working
capital.

Items entering into the current liability grouping may be classed under the following headings: (1) notes and accounts currently payable, (2) current maturities of long-term obligations, (3) cash dividends payable, (4) deposits and agency obligations, (5) accrued expenses, and (6) prepaid income items including customers' advances making claims upon current assets. These classes are described in the following paragraphs.

**NOTES AND ACCOUNTS CURRENTLY PAYABLE**  Both notes and accounts that are currently payable originate from the purchase of goods and services and from short-term borrowings. Notes currently payable may include the following: notes issued to trade creditors for the purchase of goods and services; notes issued to banks for loans; notes issued to officers, stockholders, and employees for advances; and notes issued to others for the purchase of equipment, etc. Accounts currently payable may consist of a wide variety of items, such as: obligations to trade creditors for the purchase of goods and services; obligations for the purchase of property items and securities; credit balances in customers' accounts; customers' refundable deposits; advances from officers, stockholders, and employees; and guaranteed interest and dividends on securities of affiliated companies.

In the presentation of current payables for statement purposes, it is normally desirable to classify notes and accounts in terms of the special origins of these items. Such a presentation affords information concerning the sources of business indebtedness as well as the extent to which the business has relied upon such sources in financing its activities.

In arriving at the total amount owed trade creditors, particular attention must be given to the purchase of goods and services at the end of the period. Both the goods and the services acquired, as well as the accompanying obligations, must be reflected on the statements even though invoices evidencing the charges are not received until the following period.

Individual notes and accounts are frequently secured by the pledge of certain assets. Assets pledged may consist of marketable securities, notes receivable, accounts receivable, inventories, or plant and equipment items. The pledge of an asset limits the use or the disposition of the asset or its proceeds until the related obligation is liquidated. In the event of bankruptcy, the cash that is realized on an asset that has been pledged must first be applied to the satisfaction of the related debt. An obligation is *partly secured* or *fully secured* depending upon whether the value of the pledged property is less than the amount of the claim or whether such value is equal to or in excess of the claim. It has already been suggested that reference is made to a lien on an asset by parenthetical remark in the asset section. It is also desirable to provide in connection with the liability item a parenthetical comment or note that identifies the asset pledged and indicates its present market value. Those using the balance sheet are thus informed concerning obligations that make special claims on specific property items.

**CURRENT MATURITIES OF LONG-TERM OBLIGATIONS**    Bonds, mortgage notes, and other long-term indebtedness are reported as current liabilities if they are to be paid within twelve months from the date of the balance sheet. When only a part of a long-term obligation is to be paid currently, as in the case of bonds that are payable in a series of annual installments, the maturing portion of the debt is reported as current, the balance as noncurrent. But, if the maturing obligation is payable out of a special retirement fund or if it is to be retired from the proceeds of a new bond issue or by an exchange for stock, the obligation will not call for the use of current funds and hence should continue to be listed as noncurrent. Appropriate reference to the plan for liquidation should be made parenthetically or by note.

**DIVIDENDS PAYABLE**    A cash dividend that is declared by appropriate action of the board of directors is recorded by a charge to Retained Earnings and a credit to Cash Dividends Payable. The latter balance is reported as a current liability. The declaration of a dividend payable in the form of additional shares of stock is recorded by a charge to Retained Earnings and a credit to Stock Dividends Distributable. The latter balance does not appear in the liabilities section of the balance sheet; instead it is reported in the capital section, since it represents Retained Earnings in the process of transfer to Capital Stock.

A company with cumulative preferred stock outstanding may have sufficient retained earnings for the legal declaration of a dividend but may fail to declare a dividend in order to retain working capital for other purposes. A liability is not recognized here, for dividends are not payable until formal action is taken by the corporate board of directors authorizing the distribution of earnings; nevertheless, the amount of cumulative dividends unpaid should be reported on the balance sheet. This amount may be shown parenthetically in the capital section following a description of the stock or it may be reported by a special note. Readers of the statement are entitled to full information regarding any cumulative dividends in arrears.

**DEPOSITS AND AGENCY OBLIGATIONS**  Current resources of a company may include monies deposited with it and returnable to depositors, or monies that have been collected or otherwise accumulated and that are to be paid to third parties. A company may have received deposits as guarantees of contract performance; here a current liability needs to be recognized until the deposits are returned. In other instances, companies will make payroll deductions for employees' income taxes, payroll taxes, hospital protection, saving plans, etc.; here current liability balances to the third parties need to be recognized until payment is made and the company has fulfilled its agency responsibilities.

**ACCRUED LIABILITIES**  A subsection under current liabilities may be devoted to those liabilities that have accrued as of the balance sheet date. An examination of the expense accounts as well as of the obligations that are interest-bearing is required in determining the accrued liabilities. Some of the most common accrued items include those for sales and use taxes; payroll taxes; salaries, wages, and bonuses; licenses and fees; and interest.

**SALES AND USE TAXES**  With the passage of sales and use tax laws by state and local governments, new duties are required of the business unit. Laws generally provide that the business unit must act as an agent for the governmental authority in the collection from customers of *sales taxes* on the transfers of tangible personal properties. Laws may also provide that the business unit is additionally liable for *use taxes* on goods that it buys for its own use. Use taxes are applied against the vendee because the vendor is outside of the tax authority's jurisdiction. Provision must be made in the accounting records for determining the liability of the business to the government for amounts collected from customers and for additional amounts that the business must absorb.

*Sales Tax Collections Included in Sales Balance.* The sales taxes payable are generally a stated percentage of sales. When the sales tax collections as well as sales are recorded in total in the sales account, it becomes necessary to divide this amount into its component parts, Sales and Sales Taxes Payable. For example, if the sales tax is 3% of sales, then the amount recorded in the sales account is equal to sales + .03 of sales, or 1.03 times the sales total. The amount of sales is obtained by dividing the sales account balance by 1.03, and 3% of the sales amount as thus derived is the tax liability. To illustrate, assume that the sales account balance is $100,000, which includes sales taxes of 3%. Sales, then, are $100,000 ÷ 1.03, or $97,087.38. The sales tax liability is then 3% of $97,087.38 or $2,912.62. The liability can also be determined by subtracting the sales figure, $97,087.38, from $100,000.00. Entries for the period would appear as follows:

| | | |
|---|---|---|
| Cash (or Accounts Receivable)............. | 100,000.00 | |
|     Sales................................ | | 100,000.00 |
|         To record the sales for the period including sales taxes. | | |
| Sales................................... | 2,912.62 | |
|     Sales Taxes Payable................... | | 2,912.62 |
|         To record the sales tax liability for the period. | | |

*Sales Tax Collections Recorded Separately.* Frequently the actual sales total and the sales tax collections are recorded separately at the time of sale. The sales taxes payable account then accumulates the sales tax liability. If sales tax collections are not exactly equal to the sales tax liability for the period as computed under the law, the sales taxes payable account will require adjustment to bring it to the balance due. In making this adjustment a gain or a loss on sales tax collections is recognized, and this balance is ultimately closed into profit and loss.

*Accrual of Use Taxes.* Accrual of use taxes by the business should be accompanied by charges to expense accounts or to plant and equipment balances that record the original purchase. For example, use taxes on the purchase of supplies that are consumed during the period are charged to the supplies expense account; use taxes on the purchase of furniture and fixtures are added to the cost of this asset.

**PAYROLL TAXES AND INCOME TAX WITHHOLDINGS**
Social security and income tax legislation impose four taxes based upon payrolls:

(1) *Federal Old-Age and Survivor Insurance.* The Federal Insurance Contributions Act, generally referred to as the federal old-age retirement legislation, provides for an equal tax on employer and employee to provide funds for federal old-age and survivor insurance benefits for certain individuals and members of their families. At one time only employees were covered by this legislation; however, coverage in recent years has been broadened to include most of those who are self-employed.

As originally enacted, the legislation provided for a tax of 1% on employer and employee to begin on January 1, 1937, with increases in rates to take effect in later years. Beginning January 1, 1957, the rate was set at $2\frac{1}{4}$%. Under current legislation, an employee contributes $2\frac{1}{4}$% on wages up to $4,200 a year received from any number of employers, although he will be entitled to a refund of the taxes he has paid on wages that exceed $4,200 received from two or more employers. An employee filing an income tax return must claim credit for the refund against his income tax. The employer pays the same rate on wages up to $4,200 paid to each employee during the year.[1] An employer is entitled to no refund.

Employers of one or more persons, with certain exceptions, come under the law. The amount of the employee's tax is withheld from the wage payment by the employer. The employer remits this amount together with his own tax to the Director of Internal Revenue. The employer is required to maintain full records and submit detailed support for the tax remittance. He is responsible for the full amount of the tax even when he fails to withhold from employees amounts representing their contributions.

Since 1951 a tax has been levied on self-employed persons who carry on a trade or business as sole proprietors or partners or render services as independent contractors. Certain services, however, are specifically excluded from coverage. The tax rate on the self-employed is one and one-half times the rate on employers and their employees (or ¾ of the combined amount) and is applicable only when self-employment income is at least $400; the rate is applied to a maximum of $4,200 of self-employment income.

(2) *Federal Unemployment Insurance.* The Federal Social Security Act and the Federal Unemployment Tax Act provide for the establishment of unemployment insurance plans. Employers of 4 or more persons with certain exceptions are affected.

Under the law, the federal government taxes eligible employers at 3% on the first $3,000 paid to every employee during the calendar year less a credit of up to 90% of this amount for taxes paid under state unemployment compensation laws. No tax is levied on the employee by the federal government. When an employer is subject to a tax of 2.7% or more as a result of state unemployment legislation, the federal unemployment tax, then, is .3 of 1% of the wages. Payment to the federal government is made on or before January 31 following the taxable calendar year. The actual unemployment benefits are provided by the systems created by the individual states. Revenues of the federal government under the acts are used to meet the cost of administering state and federal unemployment plans.

(3) *State Unemployment Insurance.* State unemployment compensation laws are not the same in all states. In most states laws provide for taxes only on employers; but in a few states taxes are

---

[1] In January, 1958, the rate on employee and employer was still 2¼%. The rate on both employee and employer is scheduled to rise to 2¾% on January 1,1960, and to rise at intervals thereafter until it reaches a maximum of 4¼% in 1975. However, Congress may act to modify the rate schedule as it has done in the past.

applied on both employers and employees. Each state law specifies the classes of employees that are exempt, the number of employees that are required or the amount of wages that must be paid before the tax is applicable, and the contributions that are to be made by employers and employees. In a number of states the tax is applicable only when 4 or more persons are employed, as in the case of the federal legislation; in other states the tax applies when there are one or more employees. Exemptions are normally similar to those under the federal act. Tax payment is normally required on or before the last day of the month following each calendar quarter.

While the normal tax on employers may be 2.7%, states have merit rating or experience plans that provide for lower rates based upon employers' individual experience histories. Thus employers with stable employment records are taxed at a rate in keeping with the limited amount of benefits required for their employees; employers with less satisfactory employment records contribute at a rate more nearly approaching 2.7% in view of the greater amount of benefits paid to their employees. Savings under state merit systems are allowed as credits in the calculation of the federal contribution, so that the federal tax does not exceed .3 of 1% even though payment of less than 2.7% is made by an employer entitled to a lower rate under the merit rating system.

(4) *Income Tax Withholding.* Since 1943 federal income taxes on individuals have been collected at the time income is earned instead of in the calendar year following the earnings. With the change to the "pay-as-you-go" plan, employers were required to withhold income taxes from wages paid to their employees. Withholding is required not only of employers engaged in a trade or business, but also of religious and charitable organizations, educational institutions, social organizations, and governments of the United States, the states, the territories, and their agencies, instrumentalities, and political subdivisions. Certain classes of wage payments are exempt from withholding, although these still represent income subject to income taxes to the recipients.

An employer must meet withholding requirements under the law even if wages of no more than one employee are subject to such action. The amounts to be withheld by the employer are developed from formulas provided by the law or from tax withholding tables made available by the government. Withholding is based upon the length of the payroll period, the amount earned, and the number of family exemptions to which the employee is entitled. The employer reports information concerning the amounts withheld and makes payment to the Director of Internal Revenue. When federal insurance contributions (both employees' and employer's portions) and income tax withholdings for a month do not exceed $100, such amount is accumulated to be paid on a quarterly basis. Payment is required on or before the last day of the month following the calendar quarter. When the total taxes in a month exceed $100, this total must be deposited in an authorized bank prior to the fifteenth of the following month. A Federal Depositary Receipt is validated by the bank and is attached to the quarterly return. The employer is also required to give employees withholding tax statements on or before January 31, summarizing wages paid and income and social security taxes withheld in the preceding calendar year. The employer must also submit copies of such forms to the Director of Internal Revenue.

Employees subject to income tax withholding must still prepare individual income tax returns at the end of the year. In calculating the income tax liability for the year, it is determined whether any additional tax payment is due or whether amounts withheld exceed the amount due, thus calling for a refund from the government.

When income from salaries and wages exceeds a certain amount or when income in excess of $100 is received from sources not subject to withholding, such as business profits, rentals, and dividends, an individual is required to estimate in advance his income tax liability for the current year and to make quarterly payments on such estimates. A tax return is still prepared at the end of the year summarizing actual income and the tax liability; this return operates as a basis for an additional tax payment or as a claim for a tax refund.

**ACCOUNTING FOR PAYROLL TAXES AND INCOME TAX WITHHOLDINGS** To illustrate the accounting procedure for payroll taxes and income tax withholdings, assume that salaries in January, 1958, for a retail store with 7 employees are $3,000. The state unemployment compensation law provides for a tax on employers of 2.7%. Income tax withholdings for the month are $420.

Entries for the payroll and the employer's payroll taxes follow:

| | | |
|---|---|---|
| Salaries and Wages | 3,000 | |
| F.I.C.A. Taxes Payable | | 67.50 |
| Employees Income Taxes Payable | | 420.00 |
| Cash | | 2,512.50 |

> To record payment of payroll of $3,000 after deduction of 2¼% for employees' contribution for federal old-age benefits and $420 for employees' tax withholdings.

| Payroll Taxes...................................... | 157.50 | |
| State Unemployment Taxes Payable.............. | | 81.00 |
| Federal Unemployment Taxes Payable............ | | 9.00 |
| F.I.C.A. Taxes Payable........................ | | 67.50 |

To record the payroll tax liability of the employer:

(1) State unemployment contributions — 2.7% of $3,000, or $81.

(2) Federal unemployment tax — .3% (3% less credit of 90%, or 2.7%) of $3,000, or $9.

(3) Federal insurance contributions tax — $2\frac{1}{4}$% of $3,000, or $67.50.

When tax payments are made to the proper agencies, the tax liability accounts are debited and Cash is credited.

The employer's payroll taxes, as well as the taxes withheld from employees, are based upon amounts paid to employees during the period regardless of the basis employed for measuring income. When financial reports are prepared on the accrual basis, the employer will have to recognize both accrued payroll and the employer's payroll taxes relating thereto by adjustments at the end of the accounting period. In adjusting the accounts for accrued payroll, however, recognition of the amounts to be withheld for employees' taxes may be ignored. The entries recording the accrued payroll and the employer's payroll taxes are reversed at the start of the new period. The next regular payment of wages is recorded in the usual manner, giving recognition to the employees' taxes based upon the entire payroll and the residual amounts payable to employees; a second entry is made at this time recording the accrual of the employer's payroll taxes based upon the full amount of the payroll. The accrual of payroll and taxes at the end of the period as indicated provides accurate statements while deferring the analysis of payroll as to amounts payable to the government and to employees until the wage payment date.

Agreements with employees may provide for payroll deductions and employer contributions for such other items as group insurance plans, pension plans, savings bonds purchases, union dues, etc. The accounting procedures that are followed in these instances are similar to those already described for payroll taxes and income tax withholdings.

**LIABILITY UNDER BONUS AGREEMENTS** Bonuses accruing to officers, managers, or employees at the end of a period are recorded by a charge to an expense account and a credit to an accrued liability account. Such employee bonuses, even though they may be defined as a sharing of profits with an employee, are deductible expenses for income tax purposes.

Special problems frequently arise in the calculation of the amount of the bonus accruing to personnel. An agreement may provide for bonus calculation on the basis of gross revenue or sales, or on the basis of profit from business operations. When business profit is to be used, the calculation will depend upon whether the bonus is based on: (1) profit before deductions for bonus or income taxes, (2) profit after deduction for income taxes but before deduction for bonus, or (3) profit after deductions for both bonus and income taxes. To illustrate the calculations required in each of the three instances, assume the following facts: Parker Sales, Inc., gives the sales managers of its individual stores a bonus of 10% of store profit. Profit for Store No. 1 for 1958 before any charges for bonus or income taxes was $100,000. Income taxes were 40% of net profit.

Let B = Bonus
T = Income Taxes

(1) *Assuming that the bonus is based on profit before deductions for bonus or income taxes:*

$$B = .10 \times \$100,000$$
$$B = \$10,000$$

(2) *Assuming that the bonus is based on profit after deduction for income taxes but before deduction for bonus:*

$$B = .10 \ (\$100,000 - T)$$
$$T = .40 \ (\$100,000 - B)$$

Substituting for T in the first equation and solving for B:

$$B = .10 \ [\$100,000 - .40 \ (\$100,000 - B)]$$
$$B = .10 \ (\$100,000 - \$40,000 + .40B)$$
$$B = \$10,000 - \$4,000 + .04B$$
$$B - .04B = \$6,000$$
$$.96B = \$6,000$$
$$B = \$6,250$$

Substituting for B in the second equation and solving for T:

$$T = .40 \ (\$100,000 - \$6,250)$$
$$T = .40 \times \$93,750$$
$$T = \$37,500$$

Calculation of the bonus may be proved as follows:

| | |
|---|---:|
| Profit before bonus and income taxes | $100,000 |
| Deduct income taxes | 37,500 |
| Profit after income taxes | $ 62,500 |
| Bonus applied to profit after income taxes | 10% |
| Bonus | $ 6,250 |

(3) *Assuming that the bonus is based on profit after deductions for bonus and income taxes:*

$$B = .10 \ (\$100,000 - B - T)$$
$$T = .40 \ (\$100,000 - B)$$

Substituting for T in the first equation and solving for **B**:

$$B = .10 \ [\$100,000 - B - .40 \ (\$100,000 - B)]$$
$$B = .10 \ (\$100,000 - B - \$40,000 + .40B)$$
$$B = \$10,000 - .1B - \$4,000 + .04B$$
$$B + .1B - .04B = \$10,000 - \$4,000$$
$$1.06B = \$6,000$$
$$B = \$5,660.38$$

Substituting for B in the second equation and solving for **T**:

$$T = .40 \ (\$100,000 - \$5,660.38)$$
$$T = .40 \times \$94,339.62$$
$$T = \$37,735.85$$

Calculation of the bonus is proved in the following summary:

| | | |
|---|---:|---:|
| Profit before bonus and income taxes | | $100,000.00 |
| Deduct: Bonus | $ 5,660.38 | |
| Income taxes | 37,735.85 | 43,396.23 |
| Profit after bonus and income taxes | | $ 56,603.77 |
| Bonus applied to profit after bonus and income taxes. | | 10% |
| Bonus | | $ 5,660.38 |

## LIABILITY UNDER PENSION PLANS

Plans for the payment of employee retirement benefits have been widely adopted in recent years. Great variation is found in the provisions of the plans and in the financial arrangements that are made for the payment of pensions.

A distinction should be made between *informal arrangements* wherein payments are determined at the time of retirement and are subject to change or discontinuance at the option of the employer, and *formal arrangements* that involve commitments for payments of fixed sums to be determined by formulas based upon past service and earnings.

Payments under the various arrangements may be made by means of direct cash outlay, by the operation of self-administered funds, or by the payment of premiums to an insurance company or other agency that assumes full pension plan responsibility. In accounting for the plan, consideration must be given to (1) the nature of the arrangement, whether informal or formal, and (2) the payment or funding plan that is employed.

*Informal Arrangements.* In the absence of definite commitments on the part of the employer for the payment of fixed retirement amounts, entries to record pension costs can be made as monies are applied to this purpose; accounting then is on a cash basis. Direct payments to employees are recorded by charges to expense and credits to Cash; similar entries are made if payments are made to an outside agency for the purchase of employee benefits. It would be possible, however, to employ an accrual method for recording the pension costs when these can be estimated with reasonable accuracy and it can be assumed that certain arrangements will be carried out even though the business is not legally required to do so.

*Formal Arrangements.* When formal commitments have been made relative to retirement benefits, it is generally agreed that the costs of providing such benefits for employees should be systematically accrued over the working lives of such employees. It may be impossible to arrive at an exact determination of periodic charges that will cover the sums ultimately payable. Estimates and assumptions, together with actuarial applications, will have to be employed in arriving at such periodic charges.[1]

When a pension plan is self-administered, the company normally recognizes the accrual of the pension obligations in the accounts and at the same time establishes a special trust fund to meet such obligations. The periodic recognition of the pension benefits accruing to employees calls for a debit to a pension expense account and a credit to a pension liability account; the transfer of cash to the pension fund calls for a debit to a pension fund cash account and a credit to Cash. The subsequent payment of pensions is recorded by a debit to the liability account and a credit to the pension fund cash account. The pensions expense should be reported on the income statement in the sections in which the related salaries and wages are shown. The pension fund should be appropriately designated and reported in the investments section of the balance sheet. The liability account may be labeled Estimated Amounts Payable under Employee Retirement System in view of the assumptions and estimates involved in its determination, and it should be reported as a noncurrent liability when pension fund cash will be applied to its satisfaction. In the absence of a pension fund, the amount of the pensions payable within one year would be reported as a current liability and the remaining payable as a noncurrent liability.

---

[1] The Committee on Accounting Procedure of the American Institute of Certified Public Accountants in considering the problem of anticipating pension costs points out, "There are other business costs for which it is necessary to make periodic provisions in the accounts based upon assumptions and estimates. The committee believes that the uncertainties relating to the determination of pension costs are not so pronounced as to preclude similar treatment." *Accounting Research Bulletin No. 47*, "Accounting for Costs of Pensions Plans," 1956 (New York: American Institute of Certified Public Accountants), p. 15.

A company that pays for a pension plan to be administered by an outside agency requires neither a trust fund nor the recognition of a liability for accrued pensions on its books. Premiums under the pension plan are based upon the number of employees, their ages, and the benefits to be provided upon their retirement. Entries are made charging an expense account and crediting a liability account for the accrual of periodic premiums. Payments to the outside agency are charged against the accrued liability; at the end of the fiscal period any premium accrued but unpaid is reported as a current liability.

A special accounting problem arises when a company in establishing a pension plan wishes to recognize past services of employees. Special costs are involved if benefits to be paid to retiring employees are to provide for recognition of services rendered prior to the date the pension plan is adopted. Here, the company is faced with two possibilities as to the accounting treatment of the special costs attributable to past services: (1) Shall these costs be regarded as an extraordinary item or a direct subtraction from retained earnings on the theory that they are related to the revenue of preceding years? (2) Shall these costs be identified with revenues of the present and future periods on the theory that they are related to current and future benefits accruing to the organization? The Committee on Accounting Procedure of the American Institute of Certified Public Accountants has taken the latter position. The Committee states that costs based on past services as well as those based on present and future services ". . . . . are costs of doing business, incurred in contemplation of present and future benefits, as are other employment costs such as wages, salaries, and social security taxes." The Committee would distinguish, however, between such special costs incurred at the inception of a plan and those incurred in the course of an existing plan when charges for past services have been inadequate or have been ignored. The Committee would regard as appropriate a charge to retained earnings for the amount that should have been accumulated by charges to income since inception of the plan.[1]

Following the recommendations of the Institute Committee, the costs that arise from the recognition of past services are chargeable to revenue. These costs should be written off over some reasonable term, the allocation to be made on a systematic and rational basis and without distorting the operating results of any one year. Charges are accompanied by credits to the pension liability account if the plan is to be self-administered and to cash when payment to an outside agency is involved.

---

[1] *Ibid.*, p. 14.

It may be observed that for income tax purposes, pension costs are deductible periodically provided contributions are funded and the plan "qualifies" under the requirements of the Internal Revenue Code. When costs are incurred in recognizing past services, an annual charge that cannot exceed 10% of such costs as of the date of adoption of the plan is allowed until the full amount has been deducted. This charge may be added to the "normal cost of the plan," which is the cost of the actual pension credit arising out of the current year's active employment. For "nonqualifying" plans, the income tax deduction must await contributions that are actually paid to employees or that result in unforfeitable employee pension rights.

Present day pension arrangements involve significant sums. The impact that such plans have on present and future earnings and financial position is highly important. Many companies follow "cash basis" or "tax basis" methods in the accounts that may fail to recognize adequately the obligations that have been assumed under pension plans. Such circumstances require that financial statements offer full disclosure as to the characteristics and the implications of the plans. The Securities and Exchange Commission in Regulation S-X calls for the following to be provided with the balance sheet:

1. A brief description of the essential provisions of any employee pension or retirement plan.

2. The estimated cost of the plan.

3. If the plan has not been funded, or otherwise provided for, the estimated amount that would be necessary to fund or otherwise provide for the past service cost.

The American Institute Committee on Accounting Procedure makes the following statement relative to matters calling for disclosure:

> ... The committee believes that the costs of many pension plans are so material that the fact of adoption of a plan or an important amendment to it constitutes significant information in financial statements. When a plan involving material costs is adopted, there should be a footnote to the financial statements for the year in which this occurs, stating the important features of the plan, the proposed method of funding or paying, the estimated annual charge to operations, and the basis on which such annual charge is determined. When an existing plan is amended to a material extent, there should be similar disclosure of the pertinent features of the amendment. When there is a change in the accounting procedure which materially affects the results of operations, there should be appropriate indication thereof. If there are costs of material amount based on past or current services for which reasonable provision has not been, or is not being, made in the accounts, appropriate disclosure should be made in a footnote to the financial statements as long as this situation exists.[1]

[1] *Ibid.*, p. 17.

**PREPAID INCOME ITEMS MAKING CLAIM ON CURRENT ASSETS** Amounts received from customers for goods and services to be provided in the future are recorded as prepaid income items. When there are significant costs involved in the course of the realization of the income and such costs are to be met from resources classified as current assets, the prepaid item is properly shown as a current liability. Fees received in advance by a school and subscriptions received in advance by a publisher are current liabilities; advances received from customers on purchase orders are likewise current. When the services or the goods are applied to liquidation of the obligation, profit or loss emerges for the difference between the income item that has now been realized and the costs that have been incurred in its realization.

**ESTIMATED LIABILITIES** The valuation problem is generally a relatively minor one in the case of liabilities, since the amounts of the obligations are normally established by contract or accrue at a definite rate. But there are instances when the amount to be paid in the ultimate liquidation of an existing obligation is not definitely measurable when statements are prepared. The fact that the amount to be paid is not certain does not mean that the liability can be ignored or even given a "contingent" status. Such claim must be estimated from whatever data may be available. The amount to be paid in the form of income taxes, for example, must be estimated in the preparation of interim statements, or at the end of the period if the tax return has not yet been prepared. While the exact amount ultimately payable is not known, the obligation is unquestioned and requires recognition. Expenditures to emerge from current activities and the realization of current income, as, for example, the cost of meeting guarantees for servicing and repairs on goods sold, call for estimates. Here the amount of the expenditures cannot be finally determined nor can the parties involved in the claims be identified; but the fact that there are charges yet to be absorbed is certain. Liabilities established to meet estimated charges arising from current activities are often referred to as *operating reserves*. These liabilities generally call for current liquidation and hence are classified under the current heading.

Certain long-term liabilities also call for estimates. A self-administered pension plan calls for estimates as to the amount ultimately payable in the form of pensions. Long-term guarantees and agreements calling for severance payments to employees also involve estimates.

Liabilities definite in existence but estimated in amount are commonly termed "reserves." However, it was suggested in an earlier chapter that this practice should be discouraged and account titles should be used that indicate the exact nature of the item. "Estimated Income Taxes Payable" is preferable to "Reserve for Income Taxes"; "Estimated Amounts Payable under Retirement Plans" is preferable to "Reserve for Retirement Plans." It may be noted that there has been significant progress in this direction since 1949 when the American Institute recommended limitation of the reserve designation to appropriations of retained earnings.

When a separate "Reserves" heading is found in the liability section of a balance sheet, it is important to determine the nature of the practice that has been followed with respect to presentation of items under this heading. Sometimes such diverse items as asset valuation accounts, short and long-term liabilities, and proprietorship reserves are found under this heading. When this practice is encountered, special attention must be directed to the individual items within this category if the balance sheet position is to be properly interpreted. Special investigation is necessary when in a "Reserves" section on a balance sheet are found such account titles as "General Reserve," "Special Reserve," and "Contingency Reserve." Such designations offer no information as to the real nature of the account.

Representative of short-term estimated liabilities that are frequently found on financial statements are the following:

*Estimated Taxes Payable*, reporting the estimated income, state franchise, and other tax obligations.

*Estimated Premium Claims Outstanding*, reporting the estimated value of prizes or premiums that are to be distributed as a result of past sales or sales promotion activities.

*Estimated Claims under Guarantees for Service and Replacements*, reporting the estimated future claims as a result of past guarantees of articles sold or service commitments.

*Estimated Claims on Tokens, Tickets, and Gift Certificates Outstanding*, reporting the estimated obligations in the form of merchandise or services arising from the receipt of cash in past periods.

Some of the problems arising in the development of the balances to be reported for these items are described in the sections that follow.

**ESTIMATED TAX LIABILITIES**　　Estimates are required for all taxes that are related to current activities but that are not finally known at the time statements are prepared. Estimates may thus be called for in the case of federal income taxes, state income or franchise taxes, real and personal property taxes, and various other licenses and fees. Tax rates may vary from year to year. Normally, the best guide as to current tax rates is found in rates that were applicable in the preceding period. When legislative bodies are considering revisions in tax rates and their application, such available evidence should be used in developing estimates. Not only may rates have to be estimated, but also the base to which such rates are applicable may require estimate. In the case of real and personal property taxes, for example, the valuation to be assigned to properties owned may have to be estimated in arriving at an estimated tax liability prior to receipt of the tax bills. In the case of income taxes, estimates of the income subject to taxes are required unless tax data are fully compiled before the financial statements are drawn up.

Estimated taxes are recorded by a charge to an expense account and a credit to a liability account. When the actual obligation is paid, the accrued balance is canceled. Any difference between the amount paid and the obligation originally recognized, if of relatively minor amount, may be reported as an operating item of the current period; if the difference is material, it should be recognized as an extraordinary item or as an adjustment to retained earnings.

Special problems frequently arise in reporting real and personal property taxes and also income taxes on the financial statements. A consideration of these problems follows.

**REAL AND PERSONAL**     Real and personal property taxes are based
**PROPERTY TAXES**        upon the assessed valuation of properties as
of a given date. This has given rise to the view held by courts and others that taxes accrue as of a given date. Generally the date of accrual has been held to be the date of property assessment. However, accounting treatment, in general, has been to charge taxes ratably over a tax year rather than to recognize these at the time the legal obligation emerges.

Real and personal property taxes have been charged against the income of various periods, including (1) the year in which paid (cash basis), (2) the year beginning on the assessment or lien date, (3) the year ending on the assessment or lien date, (4) the year prior to the assessment or lien date, (5) the period that includes the assessment or lien date, (6) the period prior to the payment date, (7) the year that appears on the tax bill, and (8) the fiscal period of the governing body that levies the tax.

The Committee on Accounting Procedure of the American Institute of Certified Public Accountants in a consideration of the various alternatives for tax accounting suggests, "Generally the most acceptable basis of providing for property taxes is monthly accrual on the taxpayers books during the fiscal period of the taxing authority for which the taxes are levied." However, the Committee indicates that special circumstances may suggest the use of alternative periods for accrual, and it concludes, "Consistency of application from year to year is the important consideration and selection of any of the periods mentioned is a matter for individual judgment."[1]

Accounting for taxes when accrual is made over the fiscal period of the taxing authority is illustrated in the example that follows. Assume that the fiscal period for the Baldwin Co. is the calendar year. The fiscal period for the city in which this company is located begins on July 1 and ends on the following June 30. Real and personal property taxes are assessed in March, but bills are sent out in November covering the year ending June 30 of the following year. Tax payments in equal installments are due on December 5 and the following April 20. The Baldwin Co. accrues taxes on its books monthly in terms of the fiscal period of the governmental unit.

On July 1, 1957, the Baldwin Co. estimated total property taxes for the year July 1, 1957–June 30, 1958 at $1,800. On November 4 the company received a tax bill for 1957–58 of $1,842. Entries to record the monthly tax charges and tax payments follow:

| Transaction | Entry |
|---|---|
| AT THE END OF JULY, AUGUST, SEPTEMBER, OCTOBER:<br>Estimated taxes for 1957–58, $1,800. Monthly accrual, $\frac{1}{12} \times $1,800$, or $150. | Property Taxes...... 150.00<br>  Property Taxes<br>  Payable.......... 150.00 |
| AT THE END OF NOVEMBER:<br>Amount of taxes for year...$1,842.00<br><br>Amount chargeable to date<br>4×$153.50 ($1,842÷12)...$ 614.00<br>Accrual recognized to date<br>4×$150.00.............. 600.00<br><br>Tax deficiency — prior<br>periods................$ 14.00<br>Add accrual for November.. 153.50<br><br>Total charge............$ 167.50 | Property Taxes...... 167.50<br>  Property Taxes<br>  Payable.......... 167.50 |

[1] *Accounting Research Bulletin No. 43*, "Restatement and Revision of Accounting Research Bulletins," 1953 (New York: American Institute of Certified Public Accountants), pp. 83 and 84.

| Transaction | Entry |
|---|---|
| DECEMBER 5:<br>Payment of first installment, 50% of $1,842, or $921, chargeable as follows:<br>July–November (accrued)....$767.50<br>December (current period)... 153.50 | Property Taxes<br>Payable........... 767.50<br>Property Taxes ..... 153.50<br>Cash ...........     921.00 |
| AT THE END OF JANUARY, FEBRUARY, MARCH:<br>Monthly accrual. | Property Taxes...... 153.50<br>Property Taxes<br>Payable........     153.50 |
| APRIL 20<br>Payment of second installment, 50% of $1,842, or $921, chargeable as follows:<br>January–March (accrued). ...$460.50<br>April (current period)....... 153.50<br>May and June (prepaid)..... 307.00 | Property Taxes<br>Payable........... 460.50<br>Property Taxes...... 153.50<br>Prepaid Property<br>Taxes............. 307.00<br>Cash...........     921.00 |
| AT THE END OF MAY, JUNE:<br>Monthly amortization of prepaid amount. | Property Taxes...... 153.50<br>Prepaid Property<br>Taxes...........     153.50 |

It should be noted that when the actual tax charge became known in November, a correction was indicated for charges of previous months. As the correction was not material, it was charged to the expense of November rather than being identified with prior periods.

**INTER-PERIOD ALLOCATIONS OF INCOME TAXES**    It has already been suggested that when income taxes apply to both ordinary and extraordinary activities, allocation of such taxes between the two profit and loss sources is appropriate. Such allocations were limited to the statements for a single period and involved the assignment of taxes to separate sections on the income statement or to the income statement and the retained earnings statement. Allocation resulted in a full matching of revenue, expense, and income tax elements and provided summaries that were meaningful and directly comparable with similar summaries of the past.

In recent years, there has been strong support for an extension of the allocation procedure to include successive financial statements when profit and loss as reported on financial statements is not similarly expressed on the tax returns covering the same periods. To illustrate the nature of inter-period tax allocations, assume that a company collects rents on certain property for a three-year period and properly credits a deferred revenue balance; however, for income tax purposes the company is required to pay taxes on such income in the year of its collection. If taxes are recognized on the income statement in the period of their payment, the current period is penalized by a charge for taxes on income not currently reported, and subsequent periods are correspondingly favored by the absence of taxes on the income that emerges from the balance originally deferred. Here, it is suggested, the current period should be relieved of taxes on income not currently recognized; the portion of the tax payment relating to the income deferred on the books would be reported as a deferred cost and would be recognized as a tax charge in future periods concurrent with the recognition of the deferred revenue item as income. Again, assume that a company engages in a long-term construction contract requiring three years for its completion and for statement purposes recognizes income on a percentage-of-completion basis; for income tax purposes, however, the company elects to report the full contract profit and pay income taxes in the year of the contract completion. If taxes are recognized on the income statement in the period of their payment, periods in which the contract is still in progress and in which portions of the profit are recognized benefit through the absence of income taxes on such accrued profits, and the period in which the contract is completed is correspondingly penalized by income taxes on the entire contract profit. Under these circumstances, it is suggested that an accrual of income taxes should accompany the accrual of income; as profit is recognized on the partial completion of a contract, then, incomes taxes applicable to such profit would likewise be recognized, and the taxes assignable to the period in which the contract is completed would be limited to the amount applicable to the earnings recognized in the period of completion.

Differences between financial reporting and tax reporting suggesting tax allocation procedures may be classified as follows:

(1) Net income before taxes is less than taxable net income, because:

    (a) Certain credits are deferred for book purposes but receive current recognition for tax purposes,

    (b) Certain charges are currently recognized for book purposes but recognition is deferred for tax purposes.

(2) Net income before taxes is more than taxable net income, because:

    (a) Certain credits are currently recognized for book purposes but recognition is deferred for tax purposes,

(b) Certain charges are deferred for book purposes but receive current recognition for tax purposes.

When circumstances involve factors summarized in (1) above, inter-period tax allocation calls for the recognition of deferred taxes to be assigned to later periods when book income before taxes will exceed taxable income. When circumstances involve factors such as those summarized in (2), allocation calls for the recognition of accrued taxes that will relieve tax charges of later periods when taxable income will exceed book income before taxes.

The procedures that may be employed are illustrated below.

*When net income before taxes is less than taxable net income:*

Assume book and taxable incomes as follows for a three-year period, a taxable income excess in the first year being counterbalanced by an equal amount in the second and third years.

|  | Net income before income taxes per books | Net income per tax return |
|---|---|---|
| 1958........ | $15,000 | $25,000 |
| 1959........ | 15,000 | 10,000 |
| 1960........ | 20,000 | 15,000 |
|  | $50,000 | $50,000 |

Further, assume an income tax rate of 30% applicable to the full taxable income each year. Entries to record the taxes to be paid each year as well as the allocation of taxes between periods are listed below:

1958: To record accrued taxes, 30% of $25,000, net income per tax return.

Income Taxes........... 7,500
    Income Taxes Payable    7,500

To defer portion of income taxes estimated to be applicable to subsequent periods, 30% of $10,000, taxable income in excess of book income.

Deferred Income Taxes.. 3,000
    Income Taxes........    3,000

1959: To record accrued taxes, 30% of $10,000, net income per tax return.

Income Taxes........... 3,000
    Income Taxes Payable    3,000

To recognize portion of tax deferral as an addition to current tax charge, 30% of $5,000, book income in excess of taxable income.

Income Taxes........... 1,500
    Deferred Income Taxes    1,500

1960: To record accrued taxes, 30% of $15,000, net income per tax return.

Income Taxes........... 4,500
    Income Taxes Payable    4,500

To recognize balance of tax deferral as addition to current tax charge, 30% of $5,000, book income in excess of taxable income.

Income Taxes........... 1,500
    Deferred Income Taxes    1,500

A comparison of book results in the absence of the adjustments for differences between financial reporting and tax reporting with results when adjustments are made is given below:

|  | Book results unadjusted | | | Book results adjusted | | |
|---|---|---|---|---|---|---|
|  | Net Inc. before Inc. Taxes | Income Taxes Paid | Net Inc. after Inc. Taxes | Net Inc. before Inc. Taxes | Inc. Taxes Charged to Inc. | Net Inc. after Inc. Taxes |
| 1958.. | $15,000 | $ 7,500 | $ 7,500 | $15,000 | $ 4,500 | $10,500 |
| 1959.. | 15,000 | 3,000 | 12,000 | 15,000 | 4,500 | 10,500 |
| 1960.. | 20,000 | 4,500 | 15,500 | 20,000 | 6,000 | 14,000 |
|  | $50,000 | $15,000 | $35,000 | $50,000 | $15,000 | $35,000 |

*When net income before taxes is more than taxable net income:*

Assume book and taxable incomes as follows for a three-year period, a book income excess in the first year being counterbalanced by an equal amount in the second and third years.

|  | Net income before income taxes per books | Net income per tax return |
|---|---|---|
| 1958........ | $15,000 | $ 5,000 |
| 1959........ | 15,000 | 20,000 |
| 1960........ | 20,000 | 25,000 |
|  | $50,000 | $50,000 |

Assume again an income tax rate of 30% applicable to the full taxable income each year. Entries to record the taxes to be paid each year as well as the allocation of taxes between periods are listed below:

1958: To record accrued taxes, 30% of $5,000, net income per tax return.

Income Taxes.......... 1,500
    Income Taxes Payable      1,500

To accrue income taxes estimated to be applicable to income not currently reported, 30% of $10,000, book income in excess of taxable income.

Income Taxes.......... 3,000
    Income Taxes Payable
    in Subsequent Periods.      3,000

1959: To record accrued taxes, 30% of $20,000, net income per tax return.

Income Taxes.......... 6,000
    Income Taxes Payable      6,000

To apply portion of tax accrual as a reduction in current tax charge, 30% of $5,000, taxable income in excess of book income.

Income Taxes Payable in
Subsequent Periods...... 1,500
    Income Taxes.......      1,500

1960: To record accrued taxes, 30% of $25,000, net income per tax return.

Income Taxes.......... 7,500
    Income Taxes Payable      7,500

To apply balance of tax accrual as reduction in current tax charge, 30% of $5,000, taxable income in excess of book income.

Income Taxes Payable in Subsequent Periods...... 1,500
Income Taxes.......                    1,500

A comparison of book results in the absence of tax adjustments with results when adjustments are made is given below:

| | Book results unadjusted | | | Book results adjusted | | |
|---|---|---|---|---|---|---|
| | Net Inc. before Inc. Taxes | Income Taxes Paid | Net Inc. after Inc. Taxes | Net Inc. before Inc. Taxes | Inc. Taxes Charged to Inc. | Net Inc. after Inc. Taxes |
| 1958.. | $15,000 | $ 1,500 | $13,500 | $15,000 | $ 4,500 | $10,500 |
| 1959.. | 15,000 | 6,000 | 9,000 | 15,000 | 4,500 | 10,500 |
| 1960.. | 20,000 | 7,500 | 12,500 | 20,000 | 6,000 | 14,000 |
| | $50,000 | $15,000 | $35,000 | $50,000 | $15,000 | $35,000 |

Those who support inter-period tax allocation admit that such procedures may involve difficulties and give rise to special problems. They are faced with such questions as: How can the allocation procedures and the recognition of a tax charge that is more or less than that actually paid be made fully comprehensible to the statement reader? What theoretical support can be offered for the recognition of tax prepayments and tax accruals as assets and liabilities in the conventional sense? Furthermore, what tax accruals and deferrals are appropriate in view of unknown future tax rates as well as uncertain future business profits or losses that will determine future taxes?

The American Institute of Certified Public Accountants is in support of tax allocation procedures under circumstances involving material differences between book income and taxable income. The Institute Committee on Accounting Procedure has stated:

> ...Financial statements are based on allocations of receipts, payments, accruals, and various other items. Many of the allocations are necessarily based on assumptions, but no one suggests that allocations based on imperfect criteria should be abandoned in respect of expenses other than income taxes, or even that the method of allocation should always be indicated. Income taxes are an expense that should be allocated, when necessary and practicable, to income and other accounts, as other expenses are allocated. What the income statement should reflect under this head, as under any other head, is the expense properly allocable to the income included in the income statement for the year.[1]

---

[1] *Accounting Research Bulletin No. 43*, "Restatement and Revision of Accounting Research Bulletins," 1953 (New York: American Institute of Certified Public Accountants), p. 88.

In commenting on the use of an estimated future rate for purposes of inter-period allocations, the Committee suggests:

> The estimated rate should be based upon normal and surtax rates in effect during the period covered by the income statement with such changes therein as can be reasonably anticipated at the time the estimate is made.[1]

Some authorities, while supporting the recognition on the financial statements of material differences in business income and taxable income, feel that such recognition should take the form of supplementary presentations accompanying the financial statements rather than incorporation in the account structure. Supplementary remarks would offer a description of the causes for differences in financial and tax reporting and the full implications of such differences on net income after taxes. The American Accounting Association is in support of disclosure by explanatory means, and it comments on tax allocation procedures as follows:

> Disclosure is sometimes accomplished by recording the differences as prepayments (given an expectation of future tax savings) or accruals (given the opposing prospect). However, these items do not present the usual characteristics of assets or liabilities; the possible future offsets are often subject to unusual uncertainties; and treatment on an accrual basis is in many cases unduly complicated. Consequently, disclosure by accrual may be more confusing than enlightening and is therefore undesirable.[2]

**ESTIMATED LIABILITY ON CUSTOMER PREMIUM OFFERS** Many companies offer special premiums to those purchasing their products. Such offers to stimulate the regular purchase of certain products may be open for a limited time or they may be of a continuing nature. The premium is normally made available when the customer submits the required number of product labels, box tops, wrappers, or certificates. In certain instances the premium offer may be an optional cash remittance.

If a premium offer expires at the end of the company's fiscal period, adjustments in the accounts are not required. Premium requirements are fully met and the premium expense account summarizes the full charge for the period. However, when a premium offer is continuing, accounts at the end of the period must be adjusted to reflect the claim for premiums that is estimated outstanding as of this date. Premium Expense is debited and an appropriate liability account is credited;

---

[1] *Ibid.*, p. 89.

[2] *Accounting and Reporting Standards for Corporate Financial Statements and Preceding Statements and Supplements*, 1957 (Columbus: American Accounting Association), p. 6.

the expense is thus charged to the period that benefits from the premium plan and current liabilities reflect the claim for premiums outstanding. If premium distributions are charged to expense, the liability balance may be reversed at the start of the new period.

To illustrate the accounting for a premium offer, assume the following: Walker Foods offers a set of breakfast bowls upon the receipt of ten certificates, one certificate being included in each large-size package of the cereal distributed by this company. The cost of each set of bowls to the company is $1. It is estimated that 40% of the coupons will be redeemed. Transactions and entries are as follows:

| Transaction | Entry |
|---|---|
| **1957**<br>Premium purchases:<br>  10,000 sets @ $1 | Premiums—<br>Bowl Sets ......... 10,000<br>    Cash .... .......            10,000 |
| Sales — large-size packages:<br>  200,000 @ $.60 | Cash............. 120,000<br>    Sales...........        120,000 |
| Premium redemptions:<br>  60,000 certificates, or 6,000 sets<br>    @ $1 | Premium Expense... 6,000<br>  Premiums —<br>    Bowl Sets........      6,000 |
| **DECEMBER 31, 1957**<br>Coupons estimated redeemable in future periods:<br>  Total estimated redemptions — 40% of 200,000.... 80,000<br>  Redemptions in 1957...... 60,000<br>  Estimated future redemptions................... 20,000<br>  Estimated claim outstanding: 2,000 sets @ $1.......$ 2,000 | Premium Expense... 2,000<br>  Estimated Premium<br>  Claims Outstanding     2,000 |
| **JANUARY 1, 1958**<br>Reversal of accrued liability balance. | Estimated Premium<br>Claims Outstanding. 2,000<br>  Premium Expense.      2,000 |

The balance sheet at the end of 1957 will show premiums of $4,000 as a current asset and estimated premium claims outstanding of $2,000 as a current liability; the income statement for 1957 will show premium expense of $8,000 as a selling expense.

Experience that indicates a redemption percentage that differs from the assumed rate will call for appropriate corrections and the revision of future redemption estimates.

Many organizations have adopted plans for the issue to customers of trading stamps, cash register tapes, or other media redeemable in merchandise, premiums, and in some cases in cash. The accounting that is followed will depend upon the special nature of the plan that is adopted. A business may establish its own plan, prepare its own stamps or other trading media, and assume redemption responsibilities itself. Under these circumstances, the accounting would parallel that just illustrated for specific premium offers. On the other hand, the business unit may enter into an agreement for a stamp plan with a trading stamp company. The latter normally assumes full responsibility for the redemption of stamps and sells the trading stamps for a flat fee whether they are ever redeemed or not. The business would report stamps purchased as an asset and stamps issued as a selling expense; the stamp trading company would recognize on its books the sale of stamps, acquisition of premiums, distributions of premiums, and the estimated redemptions identified with stamps outstanding.

**ESTIMATED LIABILITY UNDER GUARANTEES FOR SERVICE AND REPLACEMENTS**  Some companies agree to provide free service on units that fail to perform satisfactorily or to replace goods that prove defective. When agreements are considered to involve only minor costs, it may be decided to recognize such costs in the periods in which they emerge. When agreements involve significant future costs, estimates of such costs are in order. Such estimates are recorded by a charge to an appropriate expense account and a credit to an appropriate liability account. Subsequent costs of fulfilling guarantees are charged to the liability account. The anticipation of costs results in charges to the period that is credited for the revenue and the recognition of the obligation that is outstanding.

In certain cases customers are charged special fees for a service or replacement guarantee covering a specific period. In such cases, a prepaid income account is credited for the amount of the fees. Expenses and losses in meeting contract requirements are charged to expense, while the prepaid income balance is recognized as income over the guarantee period. Recognition of income in excess of expenses indicates a net profit on such service contracts; income that is less than expenses indicates a net loss from such contracts. The prepaid income balance is properly shown within the current liability classification in view of the claim that it makes upon current assets.

**ESTIMATED LIABILITY ON TICKETS, TOKENS, AND GIFT CERTIFICATES OUTSTANDING** Many companies sell tickets, tokens, certificates, etc., that entitle the owner to services or goods. For example, railroads issue tickets that are used for travel; local transit companies issue tokens that are good for fares; department stores sell gift certificates that are redeemable in merchandise by bearers.

When instruments redeemable in services or goods are outstanding at the end of the period, accounts should be adjusted to reflect such claims. The form of the adjustment will depend upon the entries that were originally made in recording the sale of the instruments.

Ordinarily, the sale of instruments redeemable in services or goods is recorded by a debit to Cash and a credit to a liability account. As instruments are redeemed, the liability balance is debited and Sales or an appropriate income account is credited. Certain claims may be rendered void by lapse of time or for some other reason as defined by the sales agreement. In addition, experience may indicate that a certain percentage of outstanding claims will never be presented for redemption. These factors require consideration at the end of the period. At this time, the liability balance is reduced to the balance of the claim estimated to be outstanding and an income account is credited for the gain that is indicated from forfeitures. If Sales or a special income account is originally credited on the sale of the redemption instrument, the adjustment at the end of the period calls for a charge to the income account and a credit to a liability for the claim estimated still outstanding.

**CONTINGENT LIABILITIES** Contingent liabilities represent liabilities that may arise as a result of past activities or cirumstances. The determination as to whether a liability is contingent or actual is not related to whether it involves an amount that is determinable or indeterminable; a determinable amount may be involved, yet if the claim is uncertain, it is recognized as a contingent liability; an indeterminable amount may be involved, but if the claim is certain, an actual liability, though estimated in amount, must be reported. While a contingent liability involves no legal obligation on the date of the balance sheet, reference must be made to the possibility of such claims materializing in the future if the company's financial condition is to be fully shown. If a contingent liability should become an actual liability, it is recognized in the accounts as such at the later date, and an asset account, loss account, or Retained Earnings, whichever is appropriate, is debited.

Some of the contingent liabilities that are frequently encountered and that call for recognition on the balance sheet are described in the following paragraphs.

*Notes Receivable Discounted and Accounts Receivable Assigned.* The discounting of customers' notes and the assignment of customers' accounts involves a liability on the part of the transferor for payment of the claim in the event that the original debtor fails to make settlement. In the event that a liability ultimately materializes and requires payment, such a payment gives rise to a claim against the original debtor. The emergence of an obligation thus creates a receivable. Subsequent recovery of such a claim will be compensation for the required payment; failure to recover such a claim calls for the recognition of a loss.

*Accommodation Endorsements.* A party may become an accommodation endorser on a note by endorsing it for purposes of transfer. Such an endorsement creates a contingent liability as in the preceding discussion, and any ultimate payment on such an instrument should be treated as described above. If a person signs an accommodation note as maker, an entry should be made charging the party accommodated and crediting Notes Payable. These balances are closed if the accommodated party makes proper settlement on the note at maturity; if the accommodation maker is required to make settlement on the note, he will attempt to recover from the party originally accommodated.

*Lawsuits Pending.* When there are lawsuits pending relative to such matters as patent, copyright, trade-mark infringement, breach of contract, and additional tax obligations, and advice of legal counsel indicates doubt as to the outcome of such suits, these may be regarded as contingent liabilities. If the counsel is of the opinion that certain suits will ultimately result in judgments against the company, an estimate of the amounts payable should be made. The estimated liability is recorded by a debit to a nominal account reporting such a charge or to Retained Earnings and a credit to a liability account.

*Additional Taxes.* Certain tax items may be under review by tax authorities, giving rise to the possibility of additional tax assessments. Additional assessments, if incurred, are recorded by a debit to a nominal account reporting such a charge or to Retained Earnings.

*Guarantee of Debt Service of Affiliated Companies.* A company may guarantee the payment of interest and principal on long-term debt of related companies. If this contingency materializes and payments are required, such obligations will be accompanied by claims against the company whose obligations were assumed.

*Customer Service Guarantees.* In many instances, service or replacement guarantees may be considered of a contingent nature rather than calling for the recognition of a liability of a stated amount. In the event that such charges are subsequently incurred, expense or Retained Earnings is debited.

*Customer Guarantees Against Price Declines.* Guarantees may be made to customers for refunds on goods purchased in the event of price declines or other named contingencies. When conditions develop that call for customer reimbursement, a nominal account or Retained Earnings is charged and customers' accounts are credited.

**CONTINGENT CLAIMS CALLING FOR RETAINED EARNINGS APPROPRIATIONS**  When a liability is certain and of a definite amount, it is presented as a part of the creditors' equity. When it is certain but of an indefinite amount, it is still presented as a part of the creditors' equity, although it is designated as an estimate. When the liability is uncertain, it is reported as a contingent liability. In the latter instance, management may authorize an appropriation of retained earnings. Such action will preserve earnings within the business to absorb the loss if it develops. An appropriation to cover possible losses arising in connection with contingent claims is frequently designated as an appropriation for contingencies. This balance remains a part of the corporate capital as long as the liability item to which it relates is only of a contingent nature. If the liability fails to materialize, the appropriated balance is returned to Retained Earnings. If the liability does materialize, the loss should be charged to a nominal account or to Retained Earnings. The appropriated balance is then returned to Retained Earnings where it will serve to offset the loss. The direct application of the loss against the appropriated balance would not be proper; such action would serve to bury the loss without recognition on either the income statement or the retained earnings statement.

**CURRENT AND CONTINGENT LIABILITIES ON THE BALANCE SHEET**  The nature of the detail to be presented for current liabilities depends upon the use that is to be made of the statement. A balance sheet prepared for stockholders might report little detail; on the other hand, creditors may insist on full information concerning current debt.

Current assets are normally recorded in the order of their liquidity, and consistency would suggest that liabilities be reported in the order of their maturity. The latter practice may be followed only to the extent that it is practical; observance of such procedure would require an analysis of the various classes of current claims and separate reporting of elements with varying maturity dates. A bank overdraft is normally listed first in view of the immediate demand that it makes on cash. In some cases a distinction is made between liabilities that have matured and are presently payable and others that have not matured though they are current.

Current liabilities should not be reduced by assets that are to be applied to their liquidation, except for the reduction of the federal income tax liability balance by U. S. treasury tax-anticipation bills; however, disclosure as to future debt liquidation may be provided by appropriate parenthetical reference or remark. Disclosure by similar means is made of liabilities that are secured by certain assets.

Contingent liabilities are generally reported on the balance sheet by means of (1) parenthetical remarks, (2) accompanying notes, or (3) descriptions under a special contingent liabilities heading. When the third method is used and amounts are indicated, the amounts are reported "short," that is, they are not included in the totals on the liability side since they have not been established as obligations on the balance sheet date. Contingent liabilities presented in a separate section of the balance sheet are preferably reported immediately after the current liabilities since these will normally require current liquidation if they materialize. When a lengthy explanation is required in fully defining the contingent claim, such an explanation is best provided by the second method above.

Foregoing discussions dealt with liabilities as of the balance sheet date, both current and contingent. When business commitments have been made that will result in liabilities in succeeding periods that are material in amount, some brief reference to such future claims should be made. Commitments for the purchase of goods, services, and equipment, and for the construction, purchase, or lease of properties, for example, may warrant disclosure by appropriate note accompanying the statement.

Current and contingent liabilities sections on a balance sheet prepared on December 31, 1958, might appear as shown below:

LIABILITIES

Current liabilities:
  Notes payable:

| | | |
|---|---:|---:|
| Issued to trade creditors..................... | $12,000 | |
| Issued to banks (secured by assignment of moneys to become due under certain contracts totaling $36,000 included in asset section)..... | 20,000 | |
| Issued to officers........................... | 10,000 | |
| Other....................................... | 2,500 | $44,500 |

Accounts payable:

| | | |
|---|---:|---:|
| Trade creditors............................ | $30,500 | |
| Credit balances in customers' accounts......... | 1,250 | |
| Miscellaneous............................. | 3,500 | 35,250 |
| Long-term debt installments due in 1959......... | | 10,000 |
| Cash dividends payable....................... | | 4,500 |
| Estimated federal income taxes payable.......... | $16,000 | |
| Less U. S. Treasury tax anticipation bills...... | 10,000 | 6,000 |

Accrued expenses:

| | | |
|---|---:|---:|
| Salaries and wages......................... | $ 1,250 | |
| Real and personal property taxes............. | 1,550 | |
| Miscellaneous accruals...................... | 1,400 | 4,200 |

Other:

| | | |
|---|---:|---:|
| Customer advances......................... | $ 7,500 | |
| Estimated cost of guaranteed services on machines sold............................. | 2,500 | 10,000 |
| Total current liabilities....................... | | $114,450 |

Contingent liabilities:

| | | |
|---|---:|---:|
| Guarantors on employees' loans................ | $ 7,500 | |
| Customers' drafts discounted.................. | 12,000 | |
| Additional income tax assessments proposed by the Treasury Department for 1956 that are being protested by the company.............. | 4,500 | |
| Total contingent liabilities.................... | $24,000 | |

## QUESTIONS

**1.** (a) Distinguish between current and noncurrent liabilities. (b) Suggest the major classifications for current liabilities.

**2.** "Contingent claims require careful consideration in the evaluation of a company's current position." Explain.

**3.** (a) What are the rates that are currently effective on employer and employee in connection with federal old-age and survivor insurance? (b) What are the rates that are currently effective on employer and employee in connection with unemployment insurance? (c) How many employees are required for purposes of the foregoing taxes?

**4.** The sales manager for the Midwest Sales Co. is entitled to a bonus of "$12\frac{1}{2}\%$ of profits." What difficulties may arise in the interpretation of this profit-sharing agreement?

**5.** The Wyoming Co. and union officials agree to the establishment of a pension plan that will recognize past services of all personnel currently employed. What are the possible treatments in the accounts for the special pension costs attributable to such past services? Give reasons in support of each of the treatments suggested.

**6.** What accounting differences would be suggested by informal pension arrangements involving voluntary payments as compared with formal arrangements involving commitments for the payment of fixed amounts?

**7.** The SEC and the A.I.C.P.A. have recommended extensive disclosures relative to pension plans on the balance sheet. What disclosures have been recommended and why is so much emphasis placed on this matter?

**8.** Give five examples of prepaid income items properly reported as current liabilities.

**9.** Give three examples of estimated liabilities of a short-term character and three examples of estimated liabilities of a long-term character.

**10.** What is an operating reserve? Give an example of an operating reserve and give the entries required in its establishment and in its use.

**11.** The American Accounting Association has recommended that the balance sheet should contain no special section for reserves, and that each reserve should be reported as a valuation account, as a liability, or as a subdivision of retained income. What arguments can you give for and against this recommendation?

**12.** (a) What factors suggest the desirability for income tax allocations within a single set of statements? What factors suggest the desirability of income tax allocations affecting successive periodic statements? (b) What are the arguments pro and con for inter-period income tax allocations? (c) What is the alternative to such inter-period allocations?

**13.** (a) What accounting procedures would you recommend for a bus system that sells coupon books and tokens that are used for travel? (b) How would you take care of the problem of unpresented coupons and tokens?

**14.** (a) Define contingent liabilities. (b) Give five examples of contingent liabilities. (c) Indicate for each example in (b) the accounting treatment to be followed in the event that a real liability emerges from the item previously considered of a contingent nature.

**15.** What methods may be employed on the balance sheet for disclosure of contingent liabilities?

**16.** When in your opinion would a contingent liability suggest appropriation of retained earnings?

**17.** (a) When in your opinion would commitments for future expenditures call for special disclosure? (b) How would you recommend that such disclosure be made?

**18.** Where would each of the following items be reported on the balance sheet?

    (a) Bank overdraft.
    (b) Cash dividends declared.
    (c) Dividends in arrears on preferred stock.
    (d) Estimated income taxes.
    (e) Insurance premiums received in advance for a 5-year period by an insurance company.

(f) Stamps that were issued and that are redeemable by customers for certain premiums.

(g) Deposits received in connection with meter installations by a public utility.

(h) Personal injury claim pending.

(i) Notes receivable discounted.

(j) Current maturities of a serial bond issue.

(k) Customer accounts with credit balances.

(l) Purchase money obligation maturing in five annual installments.

(m) Gift certificates sold to customers but not yet presented for redemption.

(n) Service guarantees on equipment sales.

(o) Accommodation endorsement on a note issued by an affiliated company.

(p) Contract entered into with contractors for the construction of a new building.

(q) Stock dividend payable.

## EXERCISES

**1.** During the first quarter of 1958 the Monarch Retail Company sold merchandise on account for $38,500, to which were added sales taxes totaling $1,150. The total cash sales were $27,833, on which sales tax collections were $858. What entries would be made (a) to record the sales and (b) to adjust the sales tax liability account to 3% of sales at the end of the quarter?

**2.** Richard Rice, public accountant, has 3 employees. The weekly payroll is $400. Give the entries to record payment of the salaries if: (a) the employer is responsible for remitting $4\frac{1}{2}\%$ quarterly to the Federal Government for federal insurance contributions, $2\frac{1}{4}\%$ being deducted from employees' salaries and $2\frac{1}{4}\%$ representing the employer's contribution; (b) the employer is responsible for remitting a total of 3.7% to the State of California quarterly, 1% being deducted from employees' salaries and 2.7% representing the employer's contribution; and (c) income tax withholdings are calculated at $85.

**3.** The Armstrong Shop paid $1,885.50 cash to its 4 employees for services rendered in January, 1958. Assuming that the income tax withholdings were $265 for the entire payroll and that the only other deductions were for federal insurance contributions taxes, give the journal entries to record the payroll data for January.

**4.** The Jensen Co. has an agreement with its sales manager whereby the latter is entitled to 5% of company profits as a bonus. Company profit for a calendar year before bonus and income taxes is $60,000. Income taxes are 40% of profit. What is the amount of the bonus under each of the conditions below:

(a) The bonus is calculated on profit before deductions for bonus and income taxes?

(b) The bonus is calculated on profit after deduction for income taxes but before deduction for bonus?

(c) The bonus is calculated on profit after deductions for both bonus and income taxes?

**5.** The Walsh Co. is advised by insurance company representatives at the beginning of 1958 that the cost of establishing a certain pension plan with full recognition of past services of all present employees is $450,000. Pension premium costs for 1958 will be $40,000. Give all of the journal entries that will appear on the books of the Walsh Co. in 1958, assuming that:

(a) The full cost of the pension plan is paid in 1958, but costs recognizing past services are considered chargeable in equal installments over a 10-year period.

(b) The cost of recognizing past services is to be paid to the insurance company in 10 equal annual installments, and the company wishes to show the full amount payable on the plan as a liability on the balance sheet.

**6.** The Burton Corporation accrues income on its books in 1956 and 1957 of $4,500 and $5,500 respectively, but such income is not taxable for income tax purposes until 1958. Financial earnings and taxable income for the three year period, then, are as follows:

|  | Income per Books | Income subject to Tax |
|---|---|---|
| 1956 | $14,000 | $ 9,500 |
| 1957 | 16,500 | 11,000 |
| 1958 | 15,000 | 25,000 |

Assume that the rate that is applicable to taxable income is 30%. What entries would be made for each year to recognize the tax liability and to provide for a proper allocation of taxes in view of the differences in book and taxable earnings.

**7.** The Master Service Station sells for $12.50 a book that contains 10 coupons, each coupon being good for one automobile lubrication job. During 1958, 400 such books were sold. During the year, 3,250 coupons were collected by the station for work done. (a) What entries would be made to record the foregoing? (b) What data would appear on the balance sheet and the income statement prepared at the end of 1958?

**8.** The Wakefield Co. includes 1 coupon in each box of soap powder that it packs, 10 coupons being redeemable for a premium consisting of a kitchen utensil. In 1958, the Wakefield Co. purchases 5,000 premiums at 65 cents, and sells 80,000 boxes of soap powder. 15,000 coupons are presented for redemption. It is estimated that 60% of the coupons issued will be presented for redemption. What entries would be made relating to the premium plan in 1958?

**9.** Prepare the current liabilities section of the balance sheet on December 31, 1958, from the information that appears below:

Notes payable: arising from loans from banks, $15,000, on which marketable securities valued at $19,500 have been pledged as security; arising from purchases of goods, $28,500; arising from advances by officers, $10,000. Accounts payable: arising from purchases of goods, $22,000.

Cash balance with Farmers Bank, $6,500; cash overdraft with Merchants Bank, $8,750.

Dividends in arrears on preferred stock, $12,000.

Income tax withholdings payable, $650.

First-mortgage serial bonds, $100,000, payable in semiannual installments of $5,000 due on March 1 and September 1 of each year.

Advances received from customers on purchase orders, $1,500.

Customers' accounts with credit balances arising from purchases returns, $900.

Estimated damages to be paid as a result of unsatisfactory performance on a contract, $1,200.

Estimated costs of meeting guarantee for service requirements on goods sold, $3,600.

## PROBLEMS

**11-1.** The Peters Co. shows financial and taxable earnings as follows for 1956 and 1957:

|        | Financial Earnings | Taxable Earnings |
|--------|--------------------|------------------|
| 1956... | $62,200           | $87,400          |
| 1957... | 104,000           | 98,400           |

The reason for the discrepancies is found in the fact that the company, organized in the middle of 1956, wrote off against revenue of that year organization costs totaling $28,000. For federal income tax purposes, however, the organization costs can be written off if this is done ratably over a period of not less than 60 months. For tax purposes, then, the company deducted 6/60 of the costs in 1956 and 12/60 of the costs in 1957. Corporate tax rates in 1956 and 1957 were 30% on all taxable income and an additional 22% on taxable income in excess of $25,000.

*Instructions:* Give the entries that would be made on the books for the company at the end of 1956 and 1957 to recognize the federal tax liability and to provide for a proper allocation of taxes in view of the differences in financial and tax reporting.

**11-2.** Clark Bros., Inc., was incorporated at the beginning of 1956. The books of the company for 1956 and 1957 reported net incomes of $200,000 and $300,000 respectively. In arriving at net income each year, the company charged revenue and credited a liability account for costs estimated to be incurred in the following year as a result of guarantees on products sold. At the end of 1956, the liability was reported at $15,000; at the end of 1957, the liability balance was $22,000. For income tax purposes, charges for guarantees cannot be anticipated but must be recognized in the year that they are incurred. Corporate income tax rates for 1956 and 1957 were 30% on all taxable income and an additional 22% on taxable income in excess of $25,000.

*Instructions:* Give the entries that would be made on the books for the company at the end of 1956 and 1957 to recognize the tax liability and to provide for a proper allocation of taxes in view of the differences in financial and tax reporting.

**11-3.** The Grayson Manufacturing Company manufactures a cake mix flour that is packaged and sold. A cake knife is offered to customers sending in 2 box tops from these packages accompanied by a remittance of 50 cents. Data with respect to the premium offer are summarized below:

|  | 1957 | 1958 |
|---|---|---|
| Cake mix sales (65¢ per package）.............. | $162,500 | $195,000 |
| Cake knife purchases (75¢ per knife)............ | $ 10,125 | $ 9,000 |
| Number of knives distributed as premiums....... | 10,000 | 14,500 |
| Estimated number of knives to be distributed in subsequent periods........................ | 2,000 | 4,000 |

*Instructions:* (1) Give the entries that would be made in 1957 and 1958 to record product sales, premium purchases and redemptions, and year-end adjustments.

(2) List the account balances that will appear on the balance sheet and the income statement at the end of 1957 and 1958 as a result of the foregoing.

**11-4.** Superior Appliance Co. sells a television warranty policy covering all parts and labor for $50 per year. Warranties begin as of the first of the month following issuance of the policy. Policies were first issued in September, 1957. In reviewing the records before closing the accounts for 1958, you find that income and expenses on such contracts have been recognized in 1957 and 1958 on the cash basis. The accounts show income and expenses for the two years as follows:

|  | INCOME | | EXPENSES | |
|---|---|---|---|---|
|  | 1957 | 1958 | 1957 | 1958 |
| January................ |  | $ 4,950 |  | $ 1,625 |
| February............... |  | 4,800 |  | 1,875 |
| March.................. |  | 4,350 |  | 1,900 |
| April.................. |  | 4,200 |  | 2,350 |
| May................... |  | 4,800 |  | 2,700 |
| June.................. |  | 3,300 |  | 2,800 |
| July.................. |  | 3,000 |  | 2,950 |
| August................ |  | 2,850 |  | 3,000 |
| September............. | $ 1,500 | 3,000 |  | 3,050 |
| October............... | 2,250 | 3,450 | $ 375 | 3,250 |
| November.............. | 3,000 | 3,600 | 850 | 3,075 |
| December............. | 3,450 | 3,600 | 1,225 | 2,975 |
|  | $10,200 | $45,900 | $ 2,450 | $31,550 |

*Instructions:* (1) List monthly income, expenses, and net income balances for 1957 and 1958, assuming that proper recognition is given to prepaid income on the service policies. (Submit working paper summaries that show calculation of the monthly income figures listed.)

(2) Assuming that financial statements are to be prepared for 1958 that report the earnings with appropriate recognition of prepaid income

at the beginning and the end of the period, give (a) the correcting entry to be made in recognition of the prepaid income balance at the beginning of the year and (b) the adjusting entry to be made in recognition of the prepaid income balance at the end of the year.

**11-5.** Rhodes, Inc. has an agreement with its sales manager whereby the latter is entitled to 20% of the company profit as an annual bonus. Company profit for a calendar year before calculating the bonus and the income taxes is $70,000. Income taxes are 40% of the profits after bonus.

*Instructions:* Calculate the amount of the bonus and the income taxes, assuming each of the conditions stated below:
   (1) The bonus is calculated on the profit before deductions for bonus and income taxes.
   (2) The bonus is calculated on the profit after deduction for income taxes but before deduction for bonus. Prove your answer.
   (3) The bonus is calculated on the profit after deductions for both bonus and income taxes. Prove your answer.

**11-6.** The real and personal property taxes paid by the Sanford Corp. 1956–1957 were $1,085. The taxes cover the city and county's fiscal year period, July 1, 1956–June 30, 1957, and the company follows the policy of accruing taxes over the fiscal period of the tax authority. The company has made property improvements and estimates the tax for 1957–1958 at $1,500. On October 15, 1957, the company receives its tax bill reporting a liability of $1,680. The assessment is protested. The company pays 50% of the tax bill on December 5, 1957. On March 20, 1958, the company is advised that its tax liability for 1957–1958 was reduced to $1,530. The balance of the amount due, $690, is paid on April 20.

*Instructions:* Give the entries relating to the property taxes that will appear on the books of the Sanford Corp. over the period July 1, 1957–June 30, 1958, including monthly adjustments that are required for the preparation of monthly financial statements.

**11-7.** The following data are made available for purposes of stating the financial position of the Fullerton Corp. on December 31, 1958.

| | |
|---|---:|
| Cash in bank....................................................... | $24,750 |
| Petty cash, which includes IOU's of employees totaling $250 that are to be repaid to petty cash...................... | 750 |
| Marketable securities, valued at $43,250, securities valued at $12,500 having been pledged on a note payable to the bank for $10,000, reported on books at cost................... | 41,125 |
| Notes receivable, which have been reduced by notes discounted of $12,000 that are not yet due and on which the company is contingently liable....................... | 14,500 |
| Accounts receivable, which include accounts with credit balances of $250 and past-due accounts of $3,250 on which a loss of 50% is anticipated........................... | 30,500 |
| Merchandise inventory, which includes goods held on a consignment basis, $3,600, and goods received on December 31, $2,150, neither of these items having been recorded as a purchase..................................................... | 26,600 |

Prepaid insurance, which includes cash surrender value on
life insurance policies on officers of $6,500................. $ 7,250

Prepaid interest expense.............................. 200

Furniture and fixtures, which include fixtures that were fully
depreciated and that have just been scrapped, $3,600

Cost.............................................$12,500

Allowance for depreciation.................... 8,250 4,250

Notes payable, which are trade notes with the exception of a
6-month, $10,000 note discounted at the bank on Novem-
ber 1 at 6%........................................ 25,800

Accounts payable, which include accounts with debit balances
of $425........................................... 27,400

Miscellaneous accrued expenses, which include $3,500 repre-
senting estimated costs of premiums in connection with a
special sales offer made in December.................. 9,150

Long-term notes, which are payable in annual installments of
$2,500 on February 1 of each year.................... 7,500

6% cumulative preferred stock, $10 par, on which dividends
for 3 years are in arrears............................ 50,000

No-par common stock, 40,000 shares authorized and outstanding........................................... 40,000

Retained earnings (debit balance)...................... 9,925

The following data are not reflected in the above account balances:

(1) A suit has been filed against the company for $50,000; legal counsel
has informed the company that while it is probable that the company
will lose the suit, the award for damages will not be in excess of $15,000.

(2) There are replacement guarantees outstanding that are estimated to
result in costs to the company of $5,000.

*Instructions:* Prepare a classified balance sheet, including whatever notes
are appropriate in support of balance sheet data.

**11-8.** The trial balance of the Edgewood Corporation on December 31,
1958, before adjustments, is at the top of the opposite page.

On December 31, 1958, the following facts are determined from the
records:

(1) The mortgage is secured by the land and buildings and is due on
February 1, 1959. Interest is payable annually on February 1.

(2) Bond interest is payable semiannually on March 1 and September 1.

(3) The preferred stock is cumulative, and no dividends have been declared for 1956, 1957, and 1958.

(4) Selling Expenses include salaries and wages of $17,000. General
Expenses include salaries and wages of $16,000. During 1958 the
salaries paid in each quarter of the year were as follows:

| | JAN. 1–<br>MAR. 31 | APRIL 1–<br>JUNE 30 | JULY 1–<br>SEPT. 30 | OCT. 1–<br>DEC. 31 |
|---|---|---|---|---|
| Selling Expense...... | $3,000 | $4,000 | $4,000 | $6,000 |
| General Expense..... | 4,000 | 4,000 | 4,000 | 4,000 |

|                                               | Dr.       | Cr.       |
|-----------------------------------------------|-----------|-----------|
| Cash.........................................  |           | $ 1,025   |
| Notes Receivable..............................| $ 13,500  |           |
| Accounts Receivable...........................| 42,000    |           |
| Merchandise Inventory, January 1, 1958........| 31,000    |           |
| Selling Supplies..............................| 600       |           |
| Prepaid Insurance.............................| 650       |           |
| Fixtures......................................| 12,000    |           |
| Buildings.....................................| 50,000    |           |
| Allowance for Depreciation of Buildings.......|           | 6,000     |
| Land..........................................| 30,000    |           |
| Accounts Payable..............................|           | 12,750    |
| Payroll Taxes Payable.........................|           | 325       |
| Employees Income Taxes Payable................|           | 500       |
| 5% Mortgage Payable...........................|           | 12,000    |
| 6% Bonds Payable (due 1971)...................|           | 20,000    |
| 7% Preferred Stock............................|           | 50,000    |
| Common Stock..................................|           | 50,000    |
| Retained Earnings, January 1, 1958............|           | 3,976     |
| Sales.........................................|           | 164,000   |
| Sales Discounts...............................| 1,050     |           |
| Rental Income.................................|           | 6,000     |
| Purchases.....................................| 95,000    |           |
| Purchases Discounts...........................|           | 1,700     |
| Selling Expenses..............................| 28,000    |           |
| General Expenses..............................| 24,000    |           |
| Interest Expense..............................| 1,000     |           |
| Interest Income...............................|           | 524       |
|                                               | $328,800  | $328,800  |

Federal insurance contributions taxes of $2\frac{1}{4}\%$ and state unemployment compensation taxes of 2.7% were paid during the first three quarters of the year. The account Payroll Taxes Payable was credited for the deductions from employees' wages (deductions of $2\frac{1}{4}\%$ for federal insurance contributions taxes and 1% for state unemployment taxes were made). The employer's liability under federal insurance contributions and state unemployment legislation for the last quarter has not been recorded; the employer's liability for the federal unemployment taxes for the entire year has not been recorded.

(5) The state in which the Edgewood Corporation is located has a sales tax of 3% of sales, which is to be remitted by the retailer within a month following collections. During December, Sales was credited for $12,875, which included sales tax collections.

(6) The notes receivable accrue interest at 6% at their maturity on June 30, 1959, and were received on June 30, 1958.

(7) The fixtures were purchased on January 2, 1958, on a conditional sales contract. The amount of fixtures purchased was $25,000; $13,000 is unpaid, of which $6,500 will be due on July 1, 1959, and $6,500 on July 1, 1960.

(8) Rental Income shows the amount received for the rental of a department in the store for a 2-year period beginning October 1, 1958.

(9) Accounts receivable are analyzed and it is decided to set up an allowance for $820, the estimated loss from bad debts.

(10) When property taxes of $1,400 were paid during 1958, Selling Expenses and General Expenses were charged with equal amounts. These taxes cover the year July 1, 1958, to June 30, 1959.

(11) Depreciation of fixtures is 10% annually (chargeable ½ to Selling Expenses and ½ to General Expenses).

(12) Depreciation of buildings is 4% annually (chargeable ½ to Selling Expenses and ½ to General Expenses).

(13) Merchandise inventory on December 31, 1958, is $27,000. This amount includes merchandise of $2,000 for which an invoice has not been received and no entry has been made.

(14) An examination of the insurance policies shows that the amount prepaid is $350 (expense is chargeable ½ to Selling Expenses and ½ to General Expenses).

(15) Selling supplies of $200 are on hand.

(16) Provision is to be made for income taxes at 40% of net income.

*Instructions:* (1) Prepare an eight-column work sheet, providing a pair of columns for (a) the trial balance before adjustments, (b) correcting and adjusting data, (c) profit and loss data, and (d) balance sheet data.

(2) Prepare an income statement and a balance sheet.

**11-9.** The Miracle Radio Corporation, a client, requests that you compute the appropriate balance for its *Reserve for product warranty* for a statement as of June 30, 1958.

The Miracle Radio Corporation manufactures television tubes and sells them with a six-months' guarantee under which defective tubes will be replaced without a charge. On December 31, 1957, the *Reserve for product warranty* had a balance of $510,000. By June 30, 1958, this reserve had been reduced to $80,250 by charges for estimated net cost of tubes returned which had been sold in 1957.

The company started out in 1958 expecting 8% of the dollar volume of sales to be returned. However, due to the introduction of new models during the year, this estimated percentage of returns was increased to 10% on May 1. It is assumed that no tubes sold during a given month are returned in that month. Each tube is stamped with a date at time of sale so that the warranty may be properly administered. The following table of percentages indicates the likely pattern of sales returns during the six-month period of the warranty, starting with the month following the sale of tubes.

| Month following sale | Percentage of total returns expected |
|---|---|
| First | 20 |
| Second | 30 |
| Third | 20 |
| Fourth through sixth — | |
| 10 per cent each month | 30 |
| Total | 100 |

Gross sales of tubes were as follows for the first six months of 1958:

| Month | Amount | Month | Amount |
|-------|--------|-------|--------|
| January | $3,600,000 | April | $2,850,000 |
| February | 3,300,000 | May | 2,000,000 |
| March | 4,100,000 | June | 1,800,000 |

The company's warranty also covers the payment of freight cost on defective tubes returned and on new tubes sent out as replacements. This freight cost runs approximately 10% of the sales price of the tubes returned. The manufacturing cost of the tubes is roughly 80% of the sales price, and the salvage value of returned tubes averages 15% of their sales price. Returned tubes on hand at December 31, 1957, were thus valued in inventory at 15% of their original sales price.

*Instructions:* Using the data given, draw up a suitable working-paper schedule for arriving at the balance of the reserve for product warranty and give the proposed adjusting entry. Assume that proper recognition of costs for financial accounting will be allowed for income tax purposes. (A.I.C.P.A. adapted)

**11-10.** The Lido Restaurant, an individual proprietorship, keeps no accounting records except a checkbook. You are engaged to prepare financial statements for the month of January, 1958, reflecting the operating results and financial position as completely as possible.

Your analysis of the checkbook reveals the following:

| | | |
|---|--:|--:|
| Balance — January 1, 1958 | | $1,016.52 |
| Receipts: | | |
|   Meals | $4,112.30 | |
|   Catering services | 190.00 | |
|   Candy, tobacco, etc. | 123.45 | |
|   Miscellaneous | 8.25 | 4,434.00 |
| | | $5,450.52 |
| Disbursements: | | |
|   Employees salaries (less income taxes withheld amounting to $68.50 and federal insurance contributions taxes) | $ 909.00 | |
|   Food, tobacco, candy, etc. | 2,847.50 | |
|   Rent | 125.00 | |
|   Gas, electricity, and water | 106.00 | |
|   Laundry | 45.50 | |
|   Tables and chairs | 350.00 | |
|   Printing | 23.25 | |
|   Owner's salary | 250.00 | |
|   Annual license for 1957 | 100.00 | |
|   Social security taxes (O.A.B. and unemployment) | 117.00 | |
|   Income taxes withheld | 232.50 | 5,105.75 |
| Balance — January 31, 1958 | | $ 344.77 |

Your reconciliation of the bank account as of January 31, 1958, shows:

| | | |
|---|---:|---:|
| Balance per bank........................................ | | $ 625.77 |
| Deduct — outstanding checks...................... | $ 271.00 | |
| Error occurring prior to January, 1958............ | 18.00 | 289.00 |
| | | $ 336.77 |
| Add — bank service charges: | | |
| For December, 1957..................... | $ 4.08 | |
| For January, 1958...................... | 3.92 | 8.00 |
| Balance per books............................. | | $ 344.77 |

The balance sheet that your client had as of December 31, 1957, was as follows:

### ASSETS

| | | |
|---|---:|---:|
| Cash............................................... | | $1,016.52 |
| Furniture & fixtures............................. | $2,025.00 | |
| Less — reserve for depreciation.................. | 202.50 | 1,822.50 |
| | | $2,839.02 |

### LIABILITIES

| | |
|---|---:|
| Accounts payable — food purchases......................... | $ 510.25 |
| Accrued 1957 personal property taxes — estimated............ | 24.00 |
| Accrued 1957 O.A.B. and unemployment taxes.............. | 117.00 |
| Income taxes withheld..................................... | 232.50 |
| Accrued 1957 annual license............................... | 100.00 |
| Proprietor's capital....................................... | 1,855.27 |
| | $2,839.02 |

Your investigation reveals that accounts payable should have been $81.50 larger than stated on December 31, 1957, and that as of January 31, 1958, they amount to $703.50. You also discover that as of January 31, 1958, there is a receivable for catering service amounting to $75. There is an inventory of tobacco and candy at January 31, 1958, of $130. The proprietor has no record of the inventory as of December 31, 1957, but is of the opinion that it was about $75. He expects to take monthly inventory hereafter.

You find that the business was opened on January 1, 1957, and that all of the December 31, 1957, balance of furniture and fixtures was purchased at that time.

*Instructions:* (1) Prepare an eight-column work sheet, providing a pair of columns for (a) the trial balance before adjustments, (b) correcting and adjusting data, (c) profit and loss data, and (d) balance sheet data.

(2) Prepare an income statement and a balance sheet. (A.I.C.P.A. adapted)

# Chapter 12

# INVESTMENTS

## STOCKS

**NATURE OF INVESTMENTS**    A company must invest funds in inventories, receivables, plant and equipment, and other assets in order to engage in the sale of goods and services. But a portion of its available funds may be applied to assets not directly identified with primary activities. Assets that occupy an auxiliary relationship to central activities are referred to as *investments*. Investments are expected to contribute to the success of the business either by exercising certain favorable effects upon sales and operations generally, or by making an independent contribution to business profits.

**CLASSIFICATION OF INVESTMENTS**    From the standpoint of the owner, investments are either temporary or long-term. As suggested earlier, investments are classified as current only where they are readily marketable and it is management's intent to use them to meet current cash requirements. Investments that do not meet these tests are considered *long-term* or *permanent investments* and are reported on the balance sheet under a separate noncurrent heading. The purpose that is to be served by the investment governs its classification.

**COMPOSITION OF LONG-TERM INVESTMENTS**    Long-term or permanent investments include a variety of items. For discussion purposes, long-term investments will be classified in four groupings as follows: (1) investments in stocks, both preferred and common; (2) investments in bonds and other similar debt instruments; (3) funds for bond retirement, stock redemption, and other special purposes; and (4) miscellaneous investments including investments in real estate, advances to affiliates, interests in life insurance contracts, ownership equities in partnerships, and interests in trusts and estates. The accounting problems relating to long-term investments in stocks are considered in this chapter; those relating to the remaining long-term investments, in the next two chapters.

**INVESTMENTS IN STOCK**    Long-term investments may be made in corporate stock. While such investments may involve the risk of price decline, they may afford significant rewards in the form of periodic income and price appreciation. Frequently investments in stock are made to secure certain continuing business advantages. For example, stock ownership may be a means of obtaining suppliers for required materials and services or outlets for sales products. Here the income factor is only incidental to the other considerations involved in the investment. Again, ownership of a controlling interest in the voting stock of a company may be sought. With control, activities of the related companies may be integrated towards the achievement of greater profits. A company exercising control over another through majority ownership of its voting stock is called a *holding* or *parent company;* the company controlled is referred to as a *subsidiary company.*

Investments may be made in preferred or common stock. Preferred stock has certain preferences as to dividends and frequently as to assets upon dissolution. Sometimes preferred stock is convertible into some other security, usually common stock, at the option of the stockholder. When this is the case, the preferred stock maintains its preference as to dividends and is exchangeable into common stock should corporate activities prove sufficiently profitable to make the common stock the more attractive equity.

The accounting procedures relative to long-term investments in stock may be considered equally applicable to short-term or temporary investments except where variations in treatment are indicated. Furthermore, the procedures outlined are normally applicable in the case of an individual investor with a single holding in stock as well as in the case of investment companies, insurance companies, or other financial enterprises with large stock holdings.

**STOCK ACQUISITION** Shares of stock may be acquired on the New York Stock Exchange, the American Stock Exchange, and other exchanges in the different regions of the country. Stock that is not listed on the exchanges is acquired "over the counter" through brokers. Stock may also be acquired directly from an issuing company or from a private investor.

When stock is purchased for cash, it is recorded at original cost, including brokerage, taxes, and other fees incidental to the purchase. When stock is acquired "on margin," the stock should be recorded at its full cost and a liability should be recognized for the unpaid balance; to report only the amount invested would be, in effect, to offset the obligation to the broker against the investment account. An agreement or *subscription* entered into with a corporation for the purchase of shares gives rise to an asset representing the security to be received and a liability for the balance to be paid. Interest paid on a stock contract obligation should be reported as expense. When stock is acquired in exchange for properties or services, the fair market value of such considerations or the value at which the stock is currently selling, whichever may be more clearly ascertainable, should be used as a basis for recording the investment. In the absence of clearly defined values identified with assets or services exchanged, or market quotations for the security acquired, the booking of the investment may raise perplexing problems as to valuation that may be resolved only by appraisals and estimates.

Although dividends on preferred stock do not legally accrue, the buyer of a new offering of preferred stock may be charged for so-called "accrued dividends." Such a charge should not be recorded as a part of the cost of the preferred stock but should appear as a deduction from the dividend to be received. To illustrate, assume that 100 shares of $100 par 6 per cent preferred stock are purchased on March 1 at a cost of $10,600, which includes fees, taxes, and a charge for accrued dividends from January 1 to March 1. A semiannual dividend is declared on June 10, payable July 1. Entries are made as follows:

| | | | | |
|---|---|---|---|---|
| March 1 | Investment in 6% Preferred Stock......... | 10,500 | |
| | Dividend Income...................... | 100 | |
| | Cash................................ | | 10,600 |
| July 1 | Cash................................ | 300 | |
| | Dividend Income...................... | | 300 |

When two or more securities are acquired for one lump-sum price, this cost should be allocated in some equitable manner to the different acquisitions. When independent market values are available for each security, cost may be apportioned on the basis of the relative values. When there is a market value for one security but not for the other, it may be reasonable to assign the market value to the one and the cost excess to the other. If no separate values are available, it may be necessary to delay cost apportionment until such time when support for an equitable division of cost is available. In certain instances it may be desirable to carry the two securities in a single account and to treat the proceeds from the sale of one as a subtraction from total cost, the residual cost then to be identified with the other. To illustrate the foregoing procedures, assume the purchase of 100 units of preferred and common stock at $75 per unit; each unit consists of one share of preferred and two shares of common. Assuming independent quoted prices of $60 and $10 per share for preferred and common shares respectively, the investment cost is recorded in terms of the relative values of the securities acquired as follows:

Investment in Preferred Stock...................... 5,625
Investment in Common Stock...................... 1,875
  Cash......................................... 7,500

| Value of preferred: | $100 \times \$60$ | $6,000 |
| Value of common: | $200 \times \$10$ | 2,000 |
| | | $8,000 |

Cost assigned to preferred: $\dfrac{6,000}{8,000} \times \$7,500 = \$5,625$ (cost per share: \$5,625 $\div$ 100, or \$56.25)

Cost assigned to common: $\dfrac{2,000}{8,000} \times \$7,500 = \$1,875$ (cost per share: \$1,875 $\div$ 200, or \$9.375)

If only a value for preferred of \$60 is available, the investment cost is recorded as follows:

Investment in Preferred Stock...................... 6,000
Investment in Common Stock...................... 1,500
  Cash......................................... 7,500

Cost of preferred and common. .\$7,500
Cost identified with preferred
  (market).................... 6,000 (cost per share: \$60.00)

Remaining cost identified with
  common....................\$1,500 (cost per share: \$1,500 $\div$ 200, or \$7.50)

If the division of cost must be deferred, the following entry is made:

Investment in Preferred and Common Stock....... 7,500
  Cash......................................... 7,500

The joint investment balance may be closed when a basis for apportionment is established and costs can be assigned to individual issues.

When stock is subject to special calls or assessments, and such payments are made to the corporation, these are recorded as additions to the costs of the holdings. Prorata contributions by the stockholders to the corporation to enable it to eliminate a deficit, to retire bonds, or to effect a reorganization, are likewise treated as additions to investment cost.

When there are several acquisitions of the same security, care should be taken to preserve costs of the individual purchases in the accounts. As indicated in the discussion of marketable securities, when there is a sale of part of the holdings, cost is normally arrived at by reference to costs of specific shares sold, or in the absence of such identification, by application of the first-in, first-out rule. This costing procedure is required by income tax laws and is also a satisfactory method from an accounting standpoint.

**STOCK VALUATION**    Reference was made in an earlier chapter to the market values of temporary investments. Management's intent to use these assets as a source of cash gives support to the recognition of current market values. But when management intends to hold securities, market values do not assume the significance that they have in the case of temporary investments. As in the case of other long-term assets, cost may be accepted as a primary basis for the valuation of securities acquired as a long-term investment. Cost valuation may be supplemented by parenthetical disclosure of the market values when such data are available. This practice makes the financial statements more informative.

With a significant and apparently permanent decline in the value of long-term securities, departure from cost and the recognition of the loss that has taken place is necessary if financial position is not to be misrepresented. For example, assume that investments are held in companies that have discontinued dividends or that are facing the possibility of creditor control as a result of continued losses, or assume investments in companies in foreign countries and the outbreak of war in such countries. Cost can no longer be considered as recoverable in future periods; the serious impairment of asset values cannot be overlooked. When the investment is to be written down, this is preferably accomplished by a valuation account so that the record of cost is preserved for tax accounting. Special valuation procedures may be employed when a long-term investment represents a controlling interest in the stock of another company. These are described later in this chapter.

**DIVIDENDS**    The receipt of cash dividends is recorded by a debit to Cash and a credit to Dividend Income. When an earnings distribution is made in the form of assets other than cash, the property received should be recorded at its fair market value and Dividend Income credited.

Three dates are generally included in the formal dividend announcement: (1) date of declaration, (2) record date, and (3) date of payment. The formal dividend announcement may read somewhat as follows: "The Board of Directors at their meeting on November 5, 1958, declared a regular quarterly dividend on outstanding common stock of 50 cents per share payable on January 15, 1959, to stockholders of record at the close of business, December 29, 1958." The stockholder becomes aware of the dividend action upon its announcement. But if he sells his holdings and a new owner is recognized by the corporation prior to the record date, the dividend is paid to the new owner. If the stockholder retains his holdings until the record date, he will be entitled to the dividends when paid. After the record date, then, stock no longer carries the dividend right and sells "ex-dividend."[1] Accordingly, a stockholder is justified in recognizing the corporate dividend action on the record date. At this time a receivable account may be debited and Dividend Income credited. Upon receipt of the dividend, Cash is debited and the receivable credited.

There are some who would accrue dividends in the same manner as interest when the declaration of a regular dividend at a certain date is virtually assured by the nature of the security, the position and earnings of the company, and the policies of the board of directors. The recognition of accrued dividends under such circumstances is not objectionable if disclosure is made on the statements of dividend recognition in advance of declaration.

Federal income tax regulations provide that dividends are taxable only when unqualifiedly made subject to the demand of the stockholder. Hence, even though preparing the tax return on an accrual basis, the taxpayer recognizes dividends as income only when these become available. Ordinarily the taxpayer maintains his books in accordance with this tax rule and recognizes income at the time the dividend check is received. It may be further observed that the individual is entitled to exclude from taxable income the first $50 of dividends received during the year from taxable domestic corporations. In addition he is allowed a credit against the final tax equal to 4% of the dividends included in taxable income. A corporation in computing taxable income is entitled to a special deduction equal to 85% of dividends received from domestic corporations. A corporation thus pays income tax on only 15% of the dividends that it receives.

**STOCK DIVIDENDS**          A company may distribute to its stockholders a dividend in the form of additional shares that are the same as those held. Such a dividend does not affect company assets but simply results in the transfer of retained earnings to capital stock. The increase in total shares outstanding is distributed prorata to individual stockholders. The receipt of additional shares by stockholders leaves their respective equities exactly as they were; although the number of shares held by individual stockholders has gone up, there are now a greater number of shares outstanding and proportionate interests remain unchanged. The division of interests into a greater number of parts cannot be regarded as giving rise to income.

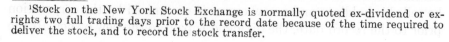

[1]Stock on the New York Stock Exchange is normally quoted ex-dividend or ex-rights two full trading days prior to the record date because of the time required to deliver the stock, and to record the stock transfer.

Only a memorandum entry needs to be made in recognizing the receipt
of additional shares. Original investment cost applies to a greater
number of shares, and this cost is divided by the total shares now held
in arriving at the cost per share to be used upon subsequent disposition
of holdings. The new per-share cost basis is indicated in the memorandum entry.

It may be noted that market recognition of the stock dividend will
result in a similar restatement of the market value of the security. For
example, assume that shares sell for $45 just before the record date for
a 50 per cent stock dividend. Such shares would be expected to sell at a
lower market in view of the dividend that now puts into the hands of
stockholders 50 per cent more shares with no increase in company assets. After the dividend, $1\frac{1}{2}$ shares carry the book value and represent
the equity previously attached to a single share; $1\frac{1}{2}$ shares are now
worth $45, or each share has a value of $30 ($45 ÷ 1.5).

When purchases of shares are made at different costs, the stock
dividend will have to be related to such different purchases. Adjusted
costs for shares comprising each lot held can then be developed. To
illustrate, assume that H. C. Smith owns stock of the Banner Corporation acquired as follows:

| | Shares | Cost per Share | Total Cost |
|---|---|---|---|
| Lot #1........ | 50 | $120 | $6,000 |
| Lot #2........ | 30 | 90 | 2,700 |
| | | | $8,700 |

A stock dividend of 1 share for every 2 held is distributed by the
Banner Corporation. A memorandum entry on Smith's books to report
the number of shares now held and the cost per share within each lot
follows:

Received 40 shares of Banner Corporation stock, representing a
50% stock dividend on 80 shares held. Number of shares held and
costs assigned to shares are now as follows:

| | Shares | Cost per Share | Total Cost |
|---|---|---|---|
| Lot #1........ | 75 (50 + 25) | $80 ($6,000 ÷ 75) | $6,000 |
| Lot #2........ | 45 (30 + 15) | 60 ($2,700 ÷ 45) | 2,700 |
| | | | $8,700 |

These costs assume significance upon the sale of shares. The
sale of the 75 shares comprising Lot 1, for example, would be charged
with a cost of $6,000. The sale of only part of the shares identified
with this lot would call for use of a cost of $80 per share. If shares

sold are identified as those of Lot 2, cost would be figured at $60 per share. Assuming that 100 shares are sold at $100 and stock is unidentified as to lot, the following entry is made in giving effect to cost calculation on the first-in, first-out basis:

| | | |
|---|---|---|
| Cash.......................................... | 10,000 | |
| Investment in Banner Corporation Stock.......... | | 7,500 |
| Gain on Sale of Banner Corporation Stock......... | | 2,500 |
| Sold 100 shares, cost calculated on | | |
| the first-in, first-out basis as follows: | | |
| 75 shares at $80................ | $6,000 | |
| 25 shares at $60................ | 1,500 | |
| Total cost assigned to sale........ | $7,500 | |

The foregoing analyses assume maintenance of cost data in the investment accounts in accordance with income tax requirements. The use of an average cost on the books would result in a charge of $72.50 for each share sold ($8,700 ÷ 120). However, $72.50 cannot be used for tax purposes, and analysis by lots as illustrated would still be required in calculating the taxable gain or loss on share dispositions.

When a stock of a class different from that held is received as a stock dividend, such a dividend, too, should not be regarded as income. As in the case of a like dividend, a portion of the retained earnings relating to the original holdings has now been formally labeled capital stock. All owners of the stock on which the dividend is declared participate prorata in the distribution. The respective equity of each owner in the corporate capital remains unchanged, although it is now composed of two classes of stock instead of a single class. While there is now a book value identified with the new stock, this is accompanied by a corresponding decrease in the book value identified with original holdings. A similar position can be taken when an investor receives dividends in the form of bonds or other contractual obligations of the corporation.

One difference between the receipt of stock of the same class and securities of a different class needs to be noted. When common stock is received on common, all shares are alike and original cost may be equitably assigned in terms of the total number of units held after the dividend. When different securities are received whose value is not the same as that of the shares originally held, it would not be proper to assign an equal amount of original cost to both old and new units. Instead, equitable apportionment of cost would suggest use of the relative sales values of the two classes of securities. To illustrate, assume the ownership of 100 shares of Bell Co. common stock acquired at $100 per share. A stock dividend of 50 shares of $25 par preferred stock is received as a dividend. At this time the common stock is selling for

$65 and the preferred stock for $20. The receipt of the dividend and the cost apportionment is recorded as follows:

Investment in Bell Co. Preferred Stock........  1,333.33
  Investment in Bell Co. Common Stock......        1,333.33
      Received 50 shares of preferred stock as dividend
      on 100 shares of common. Cost of common apportioned
      to common and preferred shares on basis of relative
      sales values:

      Value of Preferred  50×$20................  $1,000
      Value of Common 100×$65................   6,500
                                    $7,500

Cost assigned to preferred: $\frac{1,000}{7,500} \times \$10,000 = \$1,333.33$ (cost per share: $1,333.33 ÷ 50, or $26.67)

Cost assigned to common: $\frac{6,500}{7,500} \times \$10,000 = \$8,666.67$ (cost per share: $8,666.67 ÷ 100, or $86.67)

The receipt by a stockholder of stock of any kind, common or preferred, as a stock dividend is nontaxable for federal income tax purposes except when the distribution is made in lieu of cash. The distribution is regarded as having been made in lieu of cash if (1) it is made in discharge of preference dividends for the current or preceding taxable year, or (2) the stockholder is given the option of receiving cash or other property instead of stock. When a stockholder receives a nontaxable stock dividend of the same class as shares held, the basis for calculating future gain and loss on share dispositions for both new and old shares is original cost divided by the total number of shares now held; when a nontaxable stock dividend is of a different class or preference than shares held, cost allocation is required in terms of the relative values of the two kinds of stock as of the time of the dividend. In measuring the holding period upon the subsequent disposal of stock received as a nontaxable stock dividend, acquisition date of the new stock would be regarded the same as that of the old stock that formed the basis for its cost. When a stock dividend is taxable, the new stock is reported as income at its fair market value when received, and this value becomes its basis; the old stock retains its original basis. When the income tax view is maintained in the accounts, the new security is recorded at its market value and Dividend Income is credited. The acquisition date for stock received as a taxable stock dividend is the date of its receipt.

**STOCK SPLIT-UPS**     A corporation may effect a *stock split-up* by reducing the par or the stated value of capital stock and increasing the number of shares outstanding accordingly.

Capital stock and retained earnings balances remain unchanged on the corporate books; however, the stockholders' ledger is revised to show the increased number of shares identified with each stockholder. A split-up leaves stockholders' respective interests in the corporation exactly as they were.

To illustrate, assume that a company effects a 3-for-1 split of its shares. Each stockholder acquires 3 shares for every 1 held, but each share now represents only one third of the interest previously represented in view of the increase in total shares outstanding. Furthermore, stock can be expected to sell for only one third of its previous value as a result of the split. No income can be recognized on the division of holdings into a greater number of shares; however, with the increase in shares, each new share now carries one third of the original cost. A memorandum entry is made to report the increase in the number of shares and the allocation of original cost to the shares now held.

Accounting for stock split-ups, then, follows that described for a stock dividend of common on common. Tax requirements for a split-up agree with the foregoing.

**STOCK RIGHTS**     A corporation that wishes to raise cash by the sale of additional stock must first offer existing stockholders the right to subscribe to the new stock. This privilege attaching to stock is called the *pre-emptive right* and is designed to enable a stockholder to retain his respective interest in the corporation. For example, assume that a stockholder owns 50 per cent of a company's outstanding stock. If the stock is doubled and the additional shares are offered and sold to other parties, his interest in the company would drop to 25 per cent. With the right to subscribe to his prorata share of any new offering, the stockholder can maintain his proportionate interest in the corporation. It should be noted, however, that pre-emptive rights generally apply only to the issue of the same kind of stock held by the stockholders. The statutes of some states allow the corporation to limit stockholders' pre-emptive rights by suitable provisions in the corporate charter.

Because of the possibility of failure to dispose of an entire new offering by sale to existing stockholders, many corporations follow the policy of having the offering underwritten by an investment house. Under this arrangement, the underwriting house contracts to purchase at an agreed price all of the shares that are not sold to existing stockholders.

In order to make subscription privileges attractive and to insure sale of the stock, it is customary for corporations to offer the additional issues to its stockholders at less than the market price of the stock.

Certificates known as *warrants* or *rights* are issued to each stockholder enabling him to subscribe for stock in proportion to the holdings on which they are issued. One right is offered for each share held. But more than one right may be required for the subscription to one share. Rights may be sold by the stockholder if he does not care to exercise them.

As in the case of cash and other dividends, the board of directors in declaring rights to subscribe for additional shares designates a record date that follows the declaration date. All stockholders of the corporation on the record date are entitled to the rights. Stock is sold "rights-on" up to the record date, since the party who acquires the stock will receive the rights when they are issued. After the record date, the stock sells "ex-rights," and the rights may be sold separately by those who own the rights as of the record date. A date on which the rights expire if they are not exercised is also designated at the time the rights are declared. Rights are worthless beyond the expiration date.

**ACCOUNTING FOR STOCK RIGHTS**　　　　The receipt of stock rights is comparable to the receipt of a stock dividend. The corporation has made no asset distribution; stockholders equities remain unchanged. However, upon the receipt of rights the stockholders' investment is evidenced by shares originally acquired and rights which have an independent value of their own in view of the privilege that they offer of acquiring shares at less than market price. These circumstances call for an allocation of cost between original shares and the rights. Since shares and rights have different values, apportionment should be made in terms of relative market values. A separate accounting for each class of security is subsequently followed. The accounting for stock rights is illustrated in the example that follows.

Assume that in 1956 W. C. Warner acquires 100 shares of Superior Products Common, par $100, at $180 per share. In 1958 the corporation issues rights to purchase 1 share of common at par for every 5 shares owned. Warner thus receives 100 rights—one right for each share owned. However, since 5 rights are required for the acquisition of a single share, the 100 rights enable Warner to subscribe for only 20 new shares. Warner's original investment of $18,000 now applies to two assets, the shares and the rights. A cost apportionment is made on the basis of the relative market values of each security as of the date that the rights are issued. The cost allocation may be expressed as follows:

$$\text{Cost assigned to rights:} \quad \frac{\text{Market Value of Rights}}{\text{Market Value of Stock Ex-Rights} + \text{Market Value of Rights}} \times \begin{matrix}\text{Original}\\ \text{Cost of}\\ \text{Stock}\end{matrix}$$

Cost assigned to stock: $\dfrac{\text{Market Value of Stock Ex-Rights}}{\text{Market Value of Stock Ex-Rights} + \text{Market Value of Rights}} \times \dfrac{\text{Original Cost of Stock}}{}$

Calculation of the cost assigned to stock by the application of the formula above is not actually required; original cost less the cost assigned to rights gives the cost allocable to the original holdings.

Assume that Superior Products Common is selling ex-rights at $121 per share and rights are selling at $4 each. The cost allocation is made as follows:

Cost assigned to rights: $\dfrac{4}{121 + 4} \times \$18,000 = \$576$ ($\$576 \div 100 = \$5.76$, cost per right)

Cost assigned to stock (balance): $\$18,000 - \$576 = \$17,424$ ($\$17,424 \div 100 = \$174.24$, cost per share)

The following entry may be made at this time:

Superior Products Stock Rights...................... 576
    Investment in Superior Products Common............       576
        Received 100 rights permitting the purchase of 20 shares at par. Cost of stock was apportioned on the basis of the relative market values of stock and rights on the date of issue of the rights.

A corporation issuing rights generally notifies individual stockholders of the portion of cost to be applied to rights. While stockholders' cost assignments to rights will vary as a result of the different amounts paid for the stock originally acquired, the cost apportionment formula is the same in each case. Instead of notifying stockholders of an assignment of $4/125$ of the original cost to rights, as above, the corporate notice would normally instruct stockholders to calculate rights cost at 3.2% of their respective investment cost ($4 \div 125$).

The cost apportioned to the rights is used in determining the gain or the loss arising from the sale of rights. Assume that the rights in the preceding example are sold at $4\frac{1}{2}$. The following entry would be made:

Cash........................................................ 450
Loss on Sale of Superior Products Stock Rights.......... 126
    Superior Products Stock Rights........................       576
        Sold 100 rights at $4\frac{1}{2}$.

If the rights are exercised, the cost of the new shares acquired consists of the cost assigned to such rights plus the cash that is paid in the exercise of the rights. Assume that, instead of selling the rights, Warner exercises his privilege to purchase 20 additional shares at par. The following entry is made:

| | | |
|---|---:|---:|
| Investment in Superior Products Common........... | 2,576 | |
| Superior Products Stock Rights................. | | 576 |
| Cash....................................... | | 2,000 |

Exercised rights acquiring 20 shares at par, $100.

Assuming the exercise of rights, Warner's records show an investment balance of $20,000 consisting of two lots of stock as follows:

Lot 1 (1956 acquisition) 100 shares ($17,424 ÷ 100 = $174.24, cost
                 per share as adjusted)........ $17,424
Lot 2 (1958 acquisition)  20 shares ($2,576 ÷ 20 = $128.80, cost per
                 share acquired through rights)   2,576

                                                              $20,000

These costs provide the basis for calculating gains or losses upon subsequent sales of the stock.

When rights are received as a result of the ownership of stock that was acquired through several purchases at different costs, special care is required in tracing costs. Rights must be related to the different stock lots owned. Cost of each lot is then allocated between the stock and the rights emerging from the ownership of the particular lot. These costs are used in the future sale or exercise of the various lots of stock rights. If all of the rights are exercised, newly acquired stock would be considered to consist of a number of lots at different costs depending upon the cost of the rights exercised in their respective acquisitions.

Frequently the receipt of rights includes one or more rights that cannot be used in the purchase of a whole share. For example, assume that the owner of 100 shares receives 100 rights that permit him to subscribe to 1 share for every 6 rights held. Here the holder uses 96 rights in subscribing to 16 shares. He may allow the remaining 4 rights to lapse, sell these and report a gain or a loss on such sale, or supplement these by the purchase of 2 more rights, making possible the purchase of an additional share of stock.

If the owner of valuable rights allows them to lapse, it would appear that the cost assigned to such rights should be written off as a loss. Support for such action is based on the theory that the issuance of stock by the corporation at less than current market price results in some dilution in the equities identified with original holdings. However, when changes in the market price of the stock make the exercise of rights unattractive and the rights cannot be sold, any cost of rights reported separately should be returned to the investment account.

Frequently, in practice, no entry is made upon acquisition of rights; but appropriate reduction in the cost attaching to the original investment is made at the time of the sale or the exercise of rights. While the transfer of cost through a stock rights account is not shown, investment balances would be the same after the sale or the exercise of rights.

For income tax purposes the procedures that have been illustrated are not applicable under all circumstances. When the fair market value of rights is less than 15% of the fair market value of the old stock, the basis of the rights is considered to be zero and the old shares retain their original cost unless the taxpayer formally elects to apportion original cost between the two securities. In the absence of such election, then, sale of rights would give rise to taxable gain for the full sales price; exercise of rights would result in a basis for the new stock of no more than the purchase price. When the taxpayer elects apportionment or when the value of the rights is 15% or more of the market value of the old stock, the stock cost must be allocated between original stock and rights according to relative market values. Tax accounting for stock and rights under these circumstances would follow procedures previously illustrated. The holding period for stock acquired through rights starts from the date that the rights are exercised. It may be further observed that for tax purposes a loss cannot be claimed when rights are allowed to lapse; stock investment cost remains unchanged in the absence of sale or exercise of rights.

**THEORETICAL VALUE OF STOCK RIGHTS**    Reference is frequently made to the *theoretical value* of stock rights. This is the value at which it is expected rights will sell on the market. The theoretical value may be calculated (1) when stock is still selling rights-on or (2) after the date rights have accrued to owners and stock sells ex-rights.

*Calculation of Theoretical Value of Rights When Stock Sells Rights-On.* The theoretical value may be calculated by the following formula:

$$\frac{\text{Value of Stock Rights-On Minus Subscription Price}}{\text{Number of Rights Required to Purchase 1 Share Plus 1}} = \text{Value of 1 Right}[1]$$

---

[1]The derivation of this formula may be observed from the following: Assume that the common stock of Superior Products sells rights-on at $125, but that it later can be purchased at $100 plus 5 rights.

| | |
|---|---|
| Before rights sell separately: | 1 share +1 right = $125 |
| After rights sell separately: | 1 share = $100 +5 rights |
| | |
| The first equation is | 1 share +1 right = $125 |
| After transposition, the second equation is | 1 share −5 rights = $100 |
| | |
| By subtracting the second equation from the first | 6 rights = $25 |
| Then | 1 right  = $4⅙ |

Assume that in the preceding example the common stock of Superior Products sells rights-on at $125 and that after the rights are sold separately a share can be bought for $100 plus 5 rights. By the use of the foregoing formula, the theoretical value of the rights is found as follows:

$$\frac{\$125 - \$100}{5 + 1} = \$4\tfrac{1}{6}, \text{ theoretical value of 1 right}$$

The theoretical value of the stock, or the value at which the stock is expected to sell ex-rights, is $125 − $4⅙, or $120⅚. The foregoing values would result in similar costs for the purchase of rights and the payment of the exercise price ($100 + [5 × $4⅙]) as for the purchase of shares outright ($120⅚). However, market forces may fail to provide such close cost correspondence when the stock and the rights are first quoted separately. In the example on page 374 it was assumed that the stock opened at $121 ex-rights, while rights sold for $4.

*Calculation of Theoretical Value of Rights After Stock Sells Ex-Rights.* When stock sells ex-rights, the difference between the market value of the stock and the amount at which the stock can be acquired from the company through exercise of rights is the value attached to the number of rights required for such exercise. The theoretical value of the rights when the stock sells ex-rights may be expressed in formula form as follows:

$$\frac{\text{Value of Stock Ex-Rights Minus Subscription Price}}{\text{Number of Rights Required to Purchase 1 Share}} = \text{Value of 1 Right}$$

Assuming that the stock previously mentioned drops from $121 to $115, one would expect the rights to move correspondingly from $4 to $3 as follows:

$$\frac{\$115 - \$100}{5} = \$3$$

**LIQUIDATING DIVIDENDS**  When a company consumes natural resources in its operations, sales revenue includes earnings as well as a recovery of the cost of such natural resources. When natural resources are limited and irreplaceable, the company may choose to distribute full proceeds becoming available from operations. Dividends paid, then, represent in part a distribution of earnings and in part a distribution of invested capital. Distributions involving both earnings and invested capital may also be found when a company makes full distribution of the proceeds from the sale of certain properties such as land or securities, or when a distribution represents the proceeds from business liquidation. Dividends that represent in part or in whole a return of invested capital are known as *liquidating dividends.*

In recording a liquidating dividend on the books of the stockholder, income is credited for the amount representing a distribution of earnings, and the investment account is credited for the return of capital. For example, assume that Lucky Mines, Inc., pays a dividend of $50,000, 60% representing a distribution of earnings and 40% representing a distribution of the cost recovery of certain wasting assets. A stockholder receiving a dividend of $1,200 makes the following entry:

| | | |
|---|---|---|
| Cash | 1,200 | |
| Dividend Income | | 720 |
| Investment in Lucky Mines, Inc. Stock | | 480 |

Information regarding the portion of dividends representing earnings and the portion representing invested capital is reported to the stockholder by the corporation making the distribution. This report may not accompany each dividend check but instead may cover the total of dividend checks paid during the year. If dividends have been recorded on the books as income during the year, the income account is charged and the investment account is credited when notification is received at year-end concerning the amount that is to be recognized as a distribution of invested capital.

When liquidating dividends exceed investment cost, excess distributions are reported in the accounts as a gain from the investment. If liquidation is completed and the investment cost is not fully recovered, the balance of the investment account should be written off as a loss.

**SALE OF STOCK** When stock is sold, the investment account should be credited for the carrying value of the shares which is original cost adjusted for any past stock assessments, liquidating dividends, stock dividends, splits, rights, etc. If stock transactions have been properly recorded in the past, adjusted cost is readily available; if there have been past accounting failures, appropriate account correction will be required. The difference between cash or the fair market value of other assets received and the adjusted cost of the shares is reported as a gain or loss on the sale.

**REDEMPTION OF STOCK** Stock, particularly preferred issues, may be called in for redemption and cancellation by the corporation under conditions set by the issue. The call price is ordinarily set at a figure higher than the price at which the stock was originally issued, but this call price may be more or less than the cost to the holder who acquired the stock from another person after its original issue. When stock is surrendered to the corporation, an entry is made recording the cash received on redemption. The difference between the cash proceeds and the investment cost is recorded as a gain or a loss. For example, assume that an investor acquires 100 shares of Z Co. 6 per cent preferred stock, par $100, at 97. These shares are later called in at 105. The redemption is recorded on the books of the stockholder as follows:

| | | |
|---|---:|---:|
| Cash.............................................. | 10,500 | |
| Investment in Z Co. 6% Preferred................. | | 9,700 |
| Gain on Redemption of Z Co. Preferred............ | | 800 |
| Received $10,500 on call of Z Co. preferred stock, cost $9,700. | | |

**EXCHANGE OF STOCK**     When shares of stock are exchanged for other securities, the investor opens an account for the newly acquired security and closes the account of the security originally held. The new securities should be recorded at their fair market value or at the fair market value of the shares given up, whichever may be most clearly determinable, and a gain or loss recognized on the exchange determined by the difference between the value assigned to the securities acquired and the carrying value of the shares given up. In the absence of a market value for either old or new securities, the carrying value of the shares exchanged will have to be recognized as the cost of the new securities. To illustrate, assume that the Y Co. offers its preferred stockholders two shares of no-par common stock in exchange for each share of $100 par preferred. An investor exchanges 100 shares of preferred stock carried at a cost of $10,000 for 200 shares of common stock. Common shares are quoted on the market at the time of exchange at $65. The exchange is recorded on the books of the stockholder by the following entry:

| | | |
|---|---:|---:|
| Y Co. Common Stock............................. | 13,000 | |
| Y Co. Preferred Stock.......................... | | 10,000 |
| Gain on Conversion of Y Co. Preferred........... | | 3,000 |
| Acquired 200 shares of common stock valued at $65 in exchange for 100 shares of preferred stock costing $100. | | |

Recognition of a gain or a loss on a security exchange can be supported on the grounds that the exchange closes the transaction cycle relating to the original asset and opens a new cycle, the newly acquired asset requiring valuation in terms of current market. However, there are some who object to the recognition of gain or loss on the exchange of stock for other securities. These hold that there is no actual realization of gain or loss as there would be upon the outright sale of stock; here an asset has been replaced by a similar asset, such exchange simply calling for a transfer of cost from the asset originally held to the newly acquired asset.

It may be observed that under federal income tax laws an exchange, whether in the form of securities or other properties, gives rise to a taxable gain or loss. But exceptions are made to this general rule and no profit or loss is recognized under circumstances that suggest that the new property is substantially a continuation of the old investment. In the case of exchanges of securities, the following exceptions are made: the exchange of common for common and preferred for preferred of the same corporation; the exchange of preferred for common pursuant to a conversion privilege in the preferred; and exchanges in a statutory corporate reorganization. Although no gain or loss is recognized in these instances, neither is a change in basis recognized; the cost or other basis of the old security becomes the basis for the new. The acquisition date of the old security also becomes the acquisition date of the new. Other exchanges of securities are taxable, including stock for bonds, preferred for common (except under the condition above), common for preferred, bonds for bonds (unless of the same corporation and substantially identical), or common of one corporation for common of another. A gain or loss is established by the difference between the fair market value of the security received on the date of the exchange and the basis of the security exchanged. The basis of the new security is the fair market value recognized on the exchange; the acquisition date for the new security is the date of the exchange.

**OWNERSHIP OF CONTROLLING INTEREST IN STOCK** The acquisition of a majority interest in the stock of another company raises the question of whether such a relationship calls for special accounting in view of the control that is exercised and the effects that favorable and unfavorable operations have upon the welfare of the parent. There are two positions that are taken with respect to carrying investments in subsidiaries: (1) investments may be carried on a cost or a modified cost basis, comparable to investments in companies not so controlled, and (2) investments may be carried in a manner that reflects the degree of success or failure of the controlled unit. The first method emphasizes the legal factors of the relationship by recognizing only investment cost and is referred to as the *cost method;* the second method emphasizes the economic factors involved in the relationship by recognizing changes in the parent's equity in the subsidiary and is referred to as the *equity method.*

*Cost Method.* When the cost method is used, the investment account reports the original cost of the investment in the subsidiary. Increases and decreases in the capital of the subsidiary resulting from profit and loss are disregarded on the books of the parent. Dividends representing distributions of subsidiary earnings are recorded by credits to Dividend Income. Profits of a subsidiary, then, are recognized only as these are distributed in the form of dividends.

The foregoing practices are normally subject to two important modifications representing departures from a strictly legal approach:

(1) Dividends that represent distributions of subsidiary earnings accumulated prior to the date on which the parent company acquired control are recorded by the parent not as dividend income but as reductions in the investment balance. Such dividends represent, in effect, a partial return of investment or the equivalent of a liquidating dividend, since the asset transfer is accompanied by the shrinkage of subsidiary net asset and capital balances below acquisition amounts. The source of dividends, whether out of earnings accumulated prior to stock acquisition or after stock acquisition, could be ignored when holdings were small, all dividend receipts being recognized as income; but when holdings in stock are significant, it becomes important that dividends that impair the values in support of the investment balance be recognized as such.

(2) Subsidiary losses that reduce subsidiary capital substantially below acquisition amounts may be reflected in the parent's books as reductions in its investment balance and retained earnings. Such writedowns may be considered appropriate when unsuccessful operations of the subsidiary have seriously and presumably permanently impaired the value of the investment.

*Equity Method.* The equity method brings on the books of the parent a recognition of the changes in its equity in the subsidiary as a result of subsidiary profit and loss. The subsidiary is viewed as though it were a branch. When the subsidiary announces a profit, the parent debits the investment account and credits a capital account; when a loss is announced, the investment account is credited and the capital account is debited.

Since profits of a subsidiary from a legal point of view are not realized profits until they are made available to the parent in the form of dividends, the capital credit should be made originally to an appraisal capital account. Losses would be recorded as decreases in such a balance. When dividends are received, two entries are called for: (1) the receipt of cash is recorded by a debit to Cash and a credit to the investment account, the increase in the subsidiary equity previously recognized now becoming available in the form of cash, and (2) appraisal capital equal to the amount of the dividend may now be recognized as Dividend Income, subsidiary earnings previously recognized as appraisal capital now having become available to the parent. Dividend Income is closed into Profit and Loss at the end of the period and is ultimately reflected as an increase in Retained Earnings. The equity method thus consists of the periodic recognition of subsidiary success or failure by the application of appraisal accounting. An increase in subsidiary net assets is followed on the books of the parent by a revaluation of the investment balance upward and an increase in appraisal capital; a decrease in subsidiary net assets is followed on the books of the parent by a revaluation of the investment account downward and a decrease in appraisal capital.

The cost method and the equity method of accounting for a controlling interest in the stock of a subsidiary are illustrated in the following example:

| Transaction | Cost Method of Carrying Investment | | Equity Method of Carrying Investment | |
|---|---|---|---|---|
| Jan. 1, 1958 Investment in 80,000 shares of Co. S stock at $5, Co. S having 100,000 shares outstanding. | Investment in Co. S. Stock.... 400,000 Cash...... | 400,000 | Investment in Co. S Stock.... 400,000 Cash........ | 400,000 |
| June 30, 1958 Announcement by Co. S of net income of $30,000 for six-month period. (Parent's share of profits, 80% of $30,000.) | No entry | | Investment in Co. S. Stock... 24,000 Appraisal Capital from Recognition of Undistributed Profits of Co. S. | 24,000 |
| Dec. 10, 1958 Payment of dividend by Co. S, $10,000. (Parent's share of dividend, 80% of $10,000.) | Cash.......... 8,000 Dividend Income....... | 8,000 | Cash......... 8,000 Investment in Co. S. Stock. 8,000 Appraisal Capital from Recognition of Undistributed Profits of Co. S 8,000 Dividend Income....... | 8,000 |
| Dec. 31, 1958 Announcement by Co. S of net loss of $5,000 for six-month period. (Parent's share of loss, 80% of $5,000.) | No entry | | Appraisal Capital from Recognition of Undistributed Profits of Co. S 4,000 Investment in Co. S Stock.. | 4,000 |

The effect of subsidiary operations upon parent company profit and loss in each case above is the same. In each instance the parent recognizes income and a retained earnings increase of $8,000. However, when the cost method is used, the investment account remains unchanged at $400,000. When the equity method is used, the investment balance is $412,000, reflecting the net increase that has taken place in the parent's equity in the subsidiary as a result of the recognition of undistributed earnings of the subsidiary since date of acquisition, 80% of $15,000, or $12,000. The $12,000 increase in the investment balance is matched by a similar balance in the appraisal capital account.

If both the legal and the economic aspects of the relationship are to be disclosed on the statements of the parent company, cost method accounting should be accompanied by data provided in parenthetical or other appropriate form concerning net changes in the parent's equity in subsidiary earnings since control of the subsidiary was achieved; equity method accounting should be accompanied by data concerning original investment cost. Investment data might be shown on the balance sheet as follows:

(Cost Method)

Investment in Subsidiary Co. S
   (Investment is carried at original cost of 80,000 shares representing an 80% interest. The company's equity in undistributed profits of Co. S since date of acquisition, Jan. 1, 1958, not included in the accounts, is 80% of $15,000, or $12,000.) . . . . . . . . . . . . . . . . . . . . . . . . . . . . . . . . . . . . . . . . . . $ 400,000

(Equity Method)

Investment in Subsidiary Co. S
   (Investment is carried at cost of 80,000 shares representing an 80% interest, $400,000, increased by the company's equity in undistributed profits of Co. S since date of acquisition, Jan. 1, 1958, 80% of $15,000, or $12,000.) . . . . . . . . . . . . . . . . . . . . . . . . . . . . . . . . . . . . . . . . . . . . . . . . . . $ 412,000

The use of the equity method calling for an investment balance that follows changes in subsidiary capital brings an economic interpretation of the relationship between parent and subsidiary into the separate accounts of the parent. However, the full economic implications to the parent of subsidiary ownership and operations can be presented only through the preparation of consolidated statements. Assets and liabilities of the subsidiary replace the investment account and are combined with assets and liabilities of the parent and increases or decreases in retained earnings of the subsidiary are combined with retained earnings of the parent in developing a consolidated balance sheet; income and expense balances of the subsidiary are combined with similar balances of the parent in developing a consolidated income statement. Statements are prepared as though parent and subsidiary were a single entity. Financial position and progress are reported for affiliated units from an over-all economic point of view, and the legal realities underlying the relationships are disregarded.

Frequently, only consolidated statements are made available by parent companies to their stockholders; but in a number of cases both individual and consolidated statements are made available. The detailed problems involved in the development of such statements are beyond the scope of this discussion.

**INVESTMENTS AND TAX ACCOUNTING**　　Previous discussions have suggested that federal income tax laws may call for the use of a certain method when a number of methods, including the one prescribed, may be considered theoretically sound from an accounting point of view. In other instances tax laws call for the use of certain arbitrary methods that differ from those that might warrant application on theoretical grounds. Normally, the procedures that are to be used in the calculation of taxable income are actually applied by the taxpayer in the accounts so that analysis of income and its restatement for tax purposes may be avoided. Such practice may be supportable when the tax methods are fully acceptable, or when their applications offer measurements that do not differ materially from those that would be obtained through the use of alternative methods considered more acceptable under the circumstances. But the use in the books of tax methods that are considered to result in significant misstatements in costs and revenues cannot be supported. In the event of conflict between acceptable accounting procedures and tax procedures, financial statements should be developed in terms of the former, while supplementary records may be maintained to report the data required for tax reporting. Financial statements, then, properly summarize financial activities, while tax returns can be satisfactorily prepared and supported through the use of book figures and supplementary records maintained for such purpose.

## QUESTIONS

**1.** Distinguish between temporary investments and long-term investments.

**2.** State how each of the following would be classified on the balance sheet:

(a) Stock held for purposes of controlling the activities of a subsidiary.
(b) Listed stock rights that are to be sold.

(c) Stock that is intended to be transferred to a supplier in cancellation of an amount owed.

**3.** How would you record an investment in stock when it is acquired: (a) by exchange for assets whose value is known; (b) by exchange for assets whose value is not known, stock for patents, for example?

**4.** The Parker Co. accepts 2,000 shares of Murdock Common stock in full payment of a claim of $12,000 against the latter company. State how this transaction would be recorded on the books of the Parker Co., assuming that (a) Murdock stock is closely held and no market value is available; (b) Murdock stock is quoted on the market at $5; (c) Murdock stock is quoted on the market at $6.50 bid, $7.50 asked.

**5.** Explain how you would record the purchase of stock and bond units acquired for one lump sum when (a) only one of the securities is quoted on the market, (b) both securities are quoted, (c) neither security is quoted.

**6.** R. S. Doug purchases 1,000 shares of Abbott Motors at $90 a share in November, paying his broker $65,000. The market value of the stock on December 31 is $125 a share; Doug has made no further payment to his broker. On this date he shows on his balance sheet Abbott Motors Stock, $100,000, the difference between market value and the unpaid balance to the broker. Do you approve of this report? Explain.

**7.** Jackson Parks insists that accounting consistency would require that the valuation procedure applied to permanent investments should be the same as that applied to temporary investments. Do you agree? Give reasons in support of your position.

**8.** (a) Describe stock rights, stock dividends, and stock splits. (b) Distinguish between stock sold rights-on and stock sold ex-rights.

**9.** Give the formula for calculating the theoretical value of a stock right (a) before rights are issued, (b) after rights are issued.

**10.** Warren Phillips receives stock rights on an investment and a notice from the corporation indicating that 2.6135% of the cost of his investment is to be applied to the rights. Explain how the corporation arrived at this percentage and the use that Phillips is to make of this information.

**11.** B. A. Beard receives $400 representing a $4.00 dividend from Atlas Securities Co. accompanied by a statement that $1.56 represents a distribution of income and $2.44 represents a dividend in partial liquidation. (a) What is the meaning of this statement? (b) What entry would Beard make in recording the dividend?

**12.** How should each of the following situations be treated on the books and on the income tax return:

(a) Announcement of dividends on stock and arrival of "record" date.
(b) Sale of part of security holdings acquired in three lots.
(c) Receipt of stock dividend of common on common.

(d) Receipt of stock dividend of preferred stock on common.
(e) Exchange of 1 share of common for 3 shares in a stock split-up.
(f) Receipt of stock rights and their sale.
(g) Surrender of preferred stock at a redemption price that is less than cost.
(h) Receipt of dividends from a subsidiary company 90% owned.

**13.** (a) Define: (1) parent company, (2) subsidiary company. (b) How much stock ownership is required to exercise control?

**14.** (a) Explain the two methods that may be employed in carrying investments in subsidiary companies and indicate how they differ. (b) What arguments can you give pro and con for each method?

## EXERCISES

**1.** R. T. Welding acquired 100 shares of Walsh Co. stock at 15. At a later date he received a stock dividend of 25 shares, which he sold at 12. Proceeds from the sale were recorded as income. What correction in the accounts would you make assuming: (a) the transaction took place currently and accounts are still open; (b) the transaction was recorded in the previous period and accounts are closed?

**2.** The Billings Co. holds stock of Willsie acquired as follows:

| 1955 | 100 shares | $6,200 |
|------|-----------|--------|
| 1956 | 100 shares | 4,750 |
| 1957 | 50 shares | 2,200 |

Give the entries that would be made upon the sale of 150 shares in 1958 at $56 per share assuming that cost is determined by (a) the first-in, first-out method, (b) the weighted average cost, (c) identification of lots sold as 1956 and 1957 purchases.

**3.** A. C. Wilson purchased 1,000 shares of Michigan Motors on April 6 at 65¼. The brokerage cost was $240. On March 15 Michigan Motors had declared a $1.50 cash dividend payable on May 1 to stockholders of record on April 15. Give the journal entry for (a) the purchase of the stock on April 6 and (b) the receipt of the cash dividend on May 1.

**4.** M. A. Parks holds stock of A-B Trading Co. acquired as follows:

| Jan. 2, 1956 | 100 shares at $40 | $4,000 |
|-------------|-------------------|--------|
| Mar. 30, 1957 | 100 shares at $46 | 4,600 |

In 1958 Parks receives a 50% stock dividend. He then sells 150 shares at 34½. What entry would be made to record the sale?

**5.** Bill Beck owns 100 shares of common acquired at $60 per share. What is the cost basis per share for his investment holdings assuming that:

(a) He receives a common stock dividend of 1 for 4.
(b) Common stock is exchanged in a 5-for-1 split.

(c) He receives a preferred stock dividend of 1 share for every 2 held; common is selling ex-dividend at $50; preferred is selling at $50.

**6.** On July 10 the Atlantic Co. declares stock rights to be made available to stockholders of record July 25, the rights to expire on August 15. The rights permit the purchase of 1 share of stock at $100 for every 4 shares held. The stock is sold on July 24 rights-on at $120. (a) What should be the theoretical value of each right when these are sold separately on July 25? (b) What is the significance of each of the dates indicated?

**7.** The Davis Co. issues rights to subscribe to its stock, the ownership of 5 shares entitling the stockholder to subscribe for 1 share at par, $10. (a) Assuming that stock is quoted rights-on at $12.50, what is the theoretical value of a right? (b) Assuming that stock is quoted ex-rights at $12.50, what is the theoretical value of a right?

**8.** The Drucker Manufacturing Co. wishes to finance an expansion program through the issue of new stock. Accordingly it offers its stockholders the opportunity to subscribe to new stock at $135 per share up to 50% of their holdings. The value of the stock on July 1 is $150 per share. Stock goes ex-rights on the market on July 2. A. L. Wesley owns 100 shares of Drucker Manufacturing Co. stock acquired at a cost of $6,000. (a) What is the theoretical value of Wesley's rights when these are received? (b) Assuming that the theoretical value is used as a basis for cost apportionment, what entry would be made if Wesley sells his rights for $380? (c) What entry would be made if Wesley exercises his rights?

**9.** On April 1, N. N. Andrews purchased 1,000 shares of Doyle Corp. common stock, par $5, at 24. On July 7 Andrews received a stock dividend of 1 share for every 5 owned. On September 10 he received a cash dividend of 60 cents on the stock and was granted the right to purchase 1 share at $10 for every 4 shares held. On this date stock had a market value ex-rights of $15, and each right had a value of $1; stock cost was allocated on this basis. On December 12 Andrews sold 400 rights at $1\frac{1}{8}$ and exercised the remaining rights. What entries will appear on Andrews' books as a result of the foregoing?

**10.** Journalize the following transactions for S. R. Shore for 1958:

(a) On June 15 purchased 300 shares of O'Connor Company common stock, par $10, at 60.

(b) On July 10 received a $33\frac{1}{3}\%$ stock dividend.

(c) On September 10 received a $1 cash dividend on stock and was granted the right to purchase 1 share at $50 for every 4 shares held. Stock had a market value ex-rights of $58 and each right had a value of $2; cost of stock was allocated on this basis.

(d) On September 20 acquired 40 shares of stock by exercise of rights and sold remaining rights at $1\frac{3}{4}$.

**11.** A. M. Peet owns 100 shares in Fabulous Prospectors, Inc., acquired in 1950 at a cost of $5 per share. Beginning in 1954, Peet received dividends of $2 per share each year, the corporation notifying him that a portion of this amount represented earnings and the balance a liquidating dividend, the allocation to be made as follows:

|  | Income | Depletion Proceeds—Liquidating |
|---|---|---|
| 1954 | $ .728 | $1.272 |
| 1955 | .68 | 1.32 |
| 1956 | .642 | 1.358 |
| 1957 | .44 | 1.56 |
| 1958 | .61 | 1.39 |

(a) What entries should Peet have made each year in recording the dividends? (b) How would you report the investment on Peet's balance sheet at the end of 1958?

**12.** The Wharton Co. acquires 425,000 shares of Bagby, Inc. in 1957 at a total cost of $1,600,000. Bagby, Inc. has 500,000 shares outstanding. What entries would be made by the Wharton Co. in 1958 for the following data, assuming the investment account is carried on (a) the cost basis, (b) the equity basis:

(1) Bagby, Inc. announces a profit of $80,000 for the first six months and pays a cash dividend of 10 cents per share.

(2) Bagby, Inc. announces a loss of $15,000 for the second six months and distributes a 5% stock dividend.

(3) The Wharton Co. acquires an additional 26,250 shares of Bagby, Inc. stock at 4.

## PROBLEMS

**12-1.** Henry R. Farr holds shares of Eastman Ltd. acquired as follows:

| | | |
|---|---|---|
| 1954 | 300 shares | $10,800 |
| 1956 | 150 shares | 6,750 |

In 1958 the following takes place with respect to these holdings:

April 5. Received a 20% stock dividend.

July 1. Received a $1 dividend, and also rights to subscribe for additional shares as follows: 1 share could be purchased at par, $50, for every 5 shares held. On the date of rights issue, stock was selling ex-rights for 62½; rights were selling for 2½; stock cost was apportioned on this basis.

July 15. Farr purchased 36 shares exercising rights identified with the 1954 stock purchase and sold remaining rights at 2¼.

Dec. 10. Farr sold 100 shares acquired in 1954 at 42⅝.

*Instructions:* (1) Give journal entries to record the foregoing transactions. (Give computations in support of your entries.)

(2) Give the investment account balance on December 31 and the shares and costs making up this balance.

**12-2.** M. O. Marlow owns 400 shares of Detroit Motors, Inc. on January 1, 1958, acquired on May 1, 1955, for $24,000.

During 1958 the following takes place with respect to this investment:

March 1. Received cash dividend of fifty cents and stock dividend of 20%.

15. Received stock rights offering the purchase of 1 share at 80 for

$$\frac{5}{100} \times 14000 = 1200$$

every 3 shares held. At this time stock was quoted ex-rights at 95 and rights were quoted at 5; and stock cost was apportioned on this basis. Rights were exercised.

Sept.  1.    Received a cash dividend of 50 cents and a stock dividend of 20%.
Dec.   5.    Received stock rights offering the purchase of 1 share at 80 for every 3 shares held. At this time stock was quoted ex-rights at 86 and rights were quoted at 2. Rights were sold at this price.

*Instructions:* (1) Give journal entries to record the foregoing transactions.

(2) Give the investment account balance as of December 31, 1958, including shares and costs in support of this balance.

**12-3.** The Truman Corp. has the following securities on hand on January 1, 1958:

Investment in Greely Co. 5% Preferred, par $50, 200 shares..    $ 9,200
Investment in Manhattan Steel Common, 500 shares........    $30,250

During 1958 the following transactions were completed relative to investments:

Jan.   15.   Purchased 150 shares of United Harvester Co. Common at 72½.
March   1.   Received a cash dividend of 50 cents and stock dividend of 10% on Manhattan Steel Common.
April  12.   Purchased 250 shares of United Harvester Co. Common at 74.
May    10.   Received the semiannual dividend on Greely Co. 5% Preferred.
July    1.   United Harvester Co. Common was split on a 2-for-1 basis.
Sept.   1.   Received a dividend of $1 on United Harvester Co. Common.
        1.   Received a cash dividend of 50 cents and a stock dividend of 10% on Manhattan Steel Common.
Oct.   10.   Sold 200 shares of United Harvester Co. Common at 41½, and also sold 200 shares of Greely Co. 5% Preferred at 52.
Nov.   28.   Received rights on United Harvester Co. Common to subscribe for additional shares as follows: 1 share could be acquired at $35 for every 8 shares held. On this date stock was selling for 39½ and rights were selling at ½; stock cost was apportioned on this basis.
Dec.    1.   Sold all of the United Harvester Co. rights at ⅞.
       20.   Received a special year-end dividend on Manhattan Steel Common of $1.50.

*Instructions:* (1) Assuming the use of first-in, first-out in assigning costs to sales, give journal entries to record the foregoing transactions. (Give calculations in support of your entries.)

(2) Give the investment account balances as of December 31, 1958, including the number of shares and costs comprising such balances.

**12-4.** The following balances appeared in the ledger of the Hughes Company on December 31, 1955:

Investment in Marshall Co. Common, par $100, 200 shares ...    $19,500
Investment in Marshall Co. 5% Preferred, par $100, 100 shares.    $ 9,850

The preferred stock had conversion privileges of one share of Marshall Co. Common for each share of Marshall Co. 5% Preferred. The Hughes Company used the first-in, first-out method in accounting for stock transactions. In 1956, 1957 and 1958 the following transactions took place relative to the above investments:

Jan. 10, 1956 Converted the 100 shares of Marshall Co. 5% Preferred. As of that date the common stock had a fair market value of $103.50 per share.

Dec. 31, 1956 Received cash dividends of $2 per share on Marshall Co. Common.

June 30, 1957 Received additional shares of Marshall Co. Common in a 2-for-1 stock split. (Par value of common was reduced to $50.)

Dec. 31, 1957 Exercised option to receive one share of Marshall Co. Common for each 20 shares held in lieu of a cash dividend of $2.40 per share held. Fair market value of Marshall Co. Common on the date of distribution was $50 per share. Dividend income was recognized.

July 1, 1958 Received a stock dividend equal to 20% of common shares held.

Sept. 15, 1958 Received warrants representing right to purchase at par 1 share of Marshall Co. Common for every 4 shares held. On date of warrants issue, the market value of shares ex-rights was $60, and of rights was $2.50; cost of the stock was allocated on this basis.

Sept. 30, 1958 Exercised 400 rights identified with the first lot of stock acquired and sold remaining rights at $2 per right.

Dec. 31, 1958 Sold 300 shares of Marshall Co. Common at $52 per share.

*Instructions:* (1) Prepare journal entries to record the transactions in Marshall Co. Common.

(2) Prepare a schedule showing the balance of Marshall Co. Common held by Hughes Company on December 31, 1958.

**12-5.** You have instructed the bookkeeper for World Imports, Inc., to record all proceeds from security transactions directly in the investment accounts so that all of this data will be summarized there and will be available for analysis and proper disposition at the time of your audit. You find the following data in the account summarizing the investment with American Petroleum Common:

American Petroleum Common

| | | |
|---|---|---|
| 1/12/57 Purchased 100 shares at 40 . . . . . . . . . . . . 4,000 | 2/15/58 Cash dividend . . . . . . 160 | |
| 7/15/57 Purchased 100 shares at 44 . . . . . . . . . . . . 4,400 | 3/25/58 Proceeds from sale of 50 rights at 3 . . . . . . . 150 | |
| 3/20/58 Payment on purchase of 50 shares through exercise of 150 rights 2,500 | 12/20/58 Proceeds from sale of 100 shares at 60 . . . . . 6,000 | |

Further analysis discloses that rights were received in March permitting the purchase of 1 share of stock at $50 for every 3 shares held. In May the company was informed that 5.125% of original stock cost was applicable to the rights.

*Instructions:* (1) Assuming the use of first-in, first-out in calculating cost on sales, give individual entries for each correction required in the investment account on December 31, 1958.

(2) Give the corrected balance for the investment account on December 31 and the shares and costs making up this balance.

**12-6.** The Wrigley and Yale Corporations each have 10,000 shares of no-par stock outstanding. Merrick, Inc. acquired 8,000 shares of Wrigley stock and 9,000 shares of Yale stock in 1950. Changes in retained earnings for Wrigley and Yale for 1957 and 1958 are as follows:

|  | Wrigley Corporation | Yale Corporation |
|---|---|---|
| Retained earnings or deficit* balance, January 1, 1957 . . . . . . . . . . . . . . . . | $40,000 | $15,000* |
| Dividends paid in 1957 . . . . . . . . . . . | 15,000 |  |
|  | $25,000 | $15,000* |
| Profit or Loss* for 1957 . . . . . . . . . . . | 10,000* | 40,000 |
|  | $15,000 | $25,000 |
| Dividends paid in 1958 . . . . . . . . . . . |  | 5,000 |
|  | $15,000 | $20,000 |
| Profit or Loss* for 1958 . . . . . . . . . . . | 10,000 | 5,000* |
|  | $25,000 | $15,000 |

*Instructions:* (1) Give any entries required on the books of Merrick, Inc. for 1957 and 1958, assuming that investments in subsidiaries are carried at cost.

(2) Give any entries required on the books of the parent for 1957 and 1958, assuming that investments in subsidiaries are carried on the equity basis.

**12-7.** David Conley had the following transactions in the stock of the Leigh Corporation:

(a) January 7, 1951, purchased 200 shares of $100 par value common stock at $110 per share.

(b) The corporation was expanding and, as of March 1, 1952, issued to Mr. Conley 200 rights, each permitting him to purchase ¼ share of common stock at par. The bid price of the stock on March 1, 1952, was $140. There was no quoted price for the rights.

(c) Mr. Conley was advised that he would "lose out on his other stock if he did not pay in the money for the rights." He therefore paid for the new shares on April 1, 1952, charging the payment to his investment account. Since he felt that he had been assessed by the company, he credited the dividends (10% in December of each year) to the investment account until the debit was fully offset.

(d) In December, 1956, Mr. Conley received a 50% stock dividend from the company. He made no entry for this dividend because he expected to sell the shares received. He did sell them in January, 1957, for $160 per share. He credited income with the proceeds.

(e) In December, 1957, the stock was split on a 2-for-1 basis and the new shares were issued as no-par shares. Mr. Conley found that each new share was worth $5 more than the $110 per share that he paid for his original stock, so he debited the investment account with the additional shares received at $110 per share and credited income.

(f) In June, 1958, Mr. Conley sold one half of his stock at $92 per share. He credited the proceeds to the investment account.

*Instructions:* (1) Set up the investment account as it was kept by Mr. Conley.

(2) Prepare a schedule showing an analysis of the account as the transactions should have been recorded, using the average cost method for recording stock sold.

(3) Prepare the entries that would be necessary to correct the income of each of the years in which Mr. Conley held the stock. (A.I.C.P.A. adapted.)

**12-8.** Raymond Black, whose fiscal year for accounting purposes ends on March 31 each year, holds common stock of the Ryan Corporation. A summary of transactions concerning these holdings is given below. (Several cash dividend transactions are omitted, and the problem requirements relate only to the data given.) Mr. Black uses the specific identification method in accounting for his stock transactions.

### Transactions

June 12, 1952   Purchased 50 shares of Ryan Common ($100 par) at a total cost of $4,600.

Dec. 15, 1952   Paid assessment of $5 per share to Ryan Corporation.

April 15, 1955   Converted 50 shares of Ryan Preferred into the same number of common shares in accordance with conversion privilege. The preferred shares had cost $4,900 and their market value was $96 per share. Market value of common was $101 at that time.

Nov. 2, 1956   Received cash dividend of $.50 per share on Ryan Common.

May 7, 1957   Received additional shares of Ryan Common in a 2-for-1 stock split. (Par value reduced to $50.)

June 2, 1957   Purchased 100 shares of Ryan Common at a total cost of $5,300.

Nov. 4, 1957   Exercised option to receive one share of common for each 10 shares held in lieu of a cash dividend of $5.40 per share held. The fair market value of a share was $54.

Nov. 2, 1958   Received ordinary stock dividend equal to 20% of common shares held.

Jan. 4, 1959   Received warrants representing right to purchase at par 1 share of Ryan Common for each 10 shares of common held. On date of issue of warrants, market price of shares ex-rights was $58 and of rights, $2.

Jan. 15, 1959   Exercised 100 rights applicable to the block of shares purchased on June 2, 1957 and sold all remaining rights. Net proceeds from sale of rights amounted to $1.80 per right.

Mar. 12, 1959   Sold 60 shares of Ryan Common for $3,240 net proceeds. Shares were identified as 50 of those purchased on June 2, 1957 and 10 purchased on January 15, 1959.

*Instructions:* Prepare a schedule (or schedules) showing clearly the computation of:

(1) The remaining cost of Ryan Corporation common shares held by Mr. Black on March 31, 1959.

(2) The total dividend income from date of acquisition of the first block of shares through March 31, 1959.

(3) The gain or loss on sales made of Ryan Corporation securities. (A.I.C.P.A. adapted)

# Chapter 13

# INVESTMENTS
## BONDS

**INVESTMENTS
IN BONDS**
Bonds and related securities such as long-term notes and mortgages represent means of raising capital by trading, manufacturing, transportation, real estate, and utility enterprises as well as by the various governmental units — federal, state, and local. Investments in such securities are made by the individual investor. Business units acquire securities of this class both for short-term and long-term investment purposes. Large blocks of such securities are held by insurance companies, banks, trust companies, various investment organizations, and educational and charitable institutions. Such securities also make up a large part of the holdings of pension, bond retirement, and other funds maintained by a corporation. Bonds and long-term notes provide for the payment of interest at periodic intervals and principal sums at stated maturity dates. The probability of fluctuation in price during the time these securities are held is generally less than that in the case of stock, and the receipt of income is more regular and assured.

**KINDS OF BONDS**
A bond issue arises from a group contract known as an *indenture* between the borrowing corporation and investors. The bond issue is usually divided into a number of individual bonds of $1,000 denomination or par value. Bond interest payments are usually made at semiannual intervals by the corporation or by an agent designated by the company. When all of the bonds mature on a single date, they are called *term bonds*; when bonds mature in installments, they are known as *serial bonds*.

Bonds issued by private corporations are classified as *secured* or *unsecured*. Secured bonds provide protection to the investor in the form of a mortgage covering the company's real estate and perhaps other property, or a pledge in the form of certain collateral. A *first-mortgage bond* represents a first claim against the property of a corporation in the event of the company's inability to meet bond interest and principal payments. A *second-mortgage bond* is a weaker claim ranking only after the claim of the first-mortgage bonds or senior issue has been completely satisfied. A *collateral trust bond* is usually secured by stocks and bonds of other corporations owned by the issuing company. Such securities are generally transferred to a trustee who holds them as collateral on behalf of the bondholders and, if necessary, will sell them to satisfy the bondholders' claim.

Bonds that offer no security are frequently termed *debenture bonds*. Holders of debenture bonds have no claim on any particular asset of the issuing company, but simply rank as general creditors with other unsecured parties. The risk involved in such securities varies with the strength of the debtor. Debentures issued by a strong company may involve little risk; debentures issued by a weak company whose properties are already mortgaged may involve considerable risk.

When another party promises to make payment on bonds in the event of failure by the issuing company to do so, bonds are referred to as *guaranteed bonds*. A parent company, for example, may guarantee payment of the bonds issued by its subsidiaries.

Obligations known as *income bonds* have been issued when business failure has resulted in corporate reorganization. Such bonds require the payment of interest only to the extent of a company's current earnings.

The investor in acquiring governmental obligations looks to the taxing authority of the issuing unit for the measure of its ability to raise money to meet debt service requirements. Certain government obligations are identified with government-owned enterprises, and principal and income payments are made from the revenues accruing from such operations. These are known as *revenue bonds*.

Bonds may provide for their conversion into some other security at the option of the bondholder. Such bonds are known as *convertible bonds*. The conversion feature generally permits the owner of bonds to exchange his holdings into common stock. The bondholder is thus able to exchange his claim into an ownership interest if corporate operations prove successful and conversion becomes attractive; in the meantime he maintains the special rights of a creditor.

Other bond features may serve the issuer's interests. For example, bond indentures frequently give the issuing company the right to call and retire the bonds prior to their maturity. Such bonds are termed *callable bonds*. When a corporation wishes to reduce its outstanding indebtedness, bondholders are notified of the portion of the issue to be surrendered, and they are paid in accordance with call provisions. Interest does not accrue after the call date.

Bonds may be classified in terms of their form of issuance as (1) *registered bonds* and (2) *bearer* or *coupon bonds*. Registered bonds call for the registry of the name of the bond owner on the books of the corporation. Transfer of bond ownership is similar to that for stock. When a bond previously issued is sold by the holder, the corporate transfer agent cancels the bond certificate surrendered by the seller and issues a new certificate to the buyer. Interest checks are mailed periodically to the bondholders of record. Bearer or coupon bonds are not recorded in the name of the owner. Title to such bonds passes with delivery. Each bond is accompanied by coupons for individual interest payments covering the life of the issue. Coupons are clipped by the owner of the bond and presented to the bank for deposit or collection. The issue of bearer bonds eliminates the work of recording bond ownership changes and preparing and mailing periodic interest checks. But coupon bonds fail to offer the bondholder the protection found in registered bonds in the event bonds are lost or stolen. In some cases bonds provide interest coupons but require registry as to principal. Here, ownership safeguards are afforded while the routines involved in making interest payments are avoided.

**BOND YIELD**   The yield that is offered on the purchase of bonds varies with the safety of the investment. When the financial condition and earnings of a corporation are such that payment of interest and principal on bonded indebtedness is assured, the interest rate that the company must offer to dispose of a bond issue is relatively low. As the risk factor increases, a higher interest return is necessary to attract investors. The interest rate stated on the bonds is known as the *contract rate* or *nominal rate*. While bonds provide for the payment of interest at a certain rate, this rate may not be the same as the prevailing or *market rate* for bonds of similar quality at the time the issue is sold. Furthermore, the market rate constantly fluctuates. It is these factors that result in the difference between bond face values and the prices at which they sell on the market.

The purchase of bonds at face value implies agreement between the bond rate of interest and the prevailing market rate of interest. If the bond rate exceeds the market rate, then bonds will sell at a premium; if the bond rate is less than the market rate, the bonds will sell at a discount. The premium or the discount is the discounted value of the difference between the contract rate and the market rate of the series of interest payments. A declining market rate of interest subsequent to issuance of the bonds results in a rise in market value; a rising market rate of interest results in a decrease in market value. The nominal rate corrected for the premium or the discount on the purchase gives the actual yield on the bonds, known as the *effective rate.*

Extended bond tables are available in determining the price to be paid for bonds if they are to provide a certain yield. A part of such a table is illustrated on the following page.

VALUES TO THE NEAREST CENT OF 5% BOND FOR $1,000,000,
INTEREST PAYABLE SEMIANNUALLY

| Yield | 8 Years | 8½ Years | 9 Years | 9½ Years | 10 Years |
|---|---|---|---|---|---|
| 4 00 | 1 067 888 55 | 1 071 459 36 | 1 074 960 16 | 1 078 392 31 | 1 081 757 17 |
| 4 25 | 1 050 415 84 | 1 053 038 76 | 1 055 607 11 | 1 058 122 02 | 1 060 584 60 |
| 4 50 | 1 033 281 58 | 1 034 994 21 | 1 036 669 15 | 1 038 307 24 | 1 039 909 28 |
| 4 75 | 1 016 478 63 | 1 017 317 34 | 1 018 136 60 | 1 018 936 85 | 1 019 718 53 |
| 5 00 | 1 000 000 00 | 1 000 000 00 | 1 000 000 00 | 1 000 000 00 | 1 000 000 00 |
| 5 25 | 983 838 87 | 983 034 22 | 982 250 16 | 981 486 14 | 980 741 68 |
| 5 50 | 967 988 57 | 966 412 23 | 964 878 08 | 963 385 00 | 961 931 87 |
| 5 75 | 952 442 57 | 950 126 43 | 947 875 02 | 945 686 54 | 943 559 21 |
| 6 00 | 937 194 49 | 934 169 41 | 931 232 43 | 928 381 00 | 925 612 63 |
| 6 25 | 922 238 11 | 918 533 92 | 914 941 98 | 911 458 89 | 908 081 35 |
| 6 50 | 907 567 32 | 903 212 90 | 898 995 54 | 894 910 94 | 890 954 90 |
| 6 75 | 893 176 17 | 888 199 44 | 883 385 19 | 878 728 11 | 874 223 08 |
| 7 00 | 879 058 83 | 873 486 79 | 868 103 18 | 862 901 63 | 857 875 97 |

Assume, for example, that a $1,000, 10-year, 5% bond, interest payable, semiannually, is bought to yield 4.50%. Reference to the column, "10 years" and the required yield line, "4.50%," shows the value to be $1,039.91; if the bond is bought to yield 5.50%, it would be worth only $961.93.

This table can also be used to determine the effective rate on a bond acquired at a certain price. To illustrate, assume that a $1,000, 5% bond due in 10 years is selling at $975. Reference to the column "10 years" shows that a return of 5.50% is provided on an investment of $961.93, while a return of 5.25% is provided on an investment of $980.74. The exact yield can be calculated by interpolation. An interest decrease of .25% is found in the price increase of $18.81 ($961.93 to $980.74). Payment of $975.00, or $13.07 in excess of $961.93, reduces the 5.50% earnings rate by 13.07/18.81 of .25%, or .174%. The effective yield, then, is 5.50% − .174%, or 5.326%.

**BOND ACQUISITION** Bonds may be acquired directly from the issuer or they may be purchased on the open market through securities exchanges or investment bankers.

An investment in bonds, whether short-term or long-term, is initially recorded at cost, which includes brokerage fees and any other costs incident to the purchase. Bonds acquired in exchange for assets or services are recorded at the fair market value of such considerations. When bonds and other securities are acquired for one lump sum, equitable apportionment of such cost among the securities is required. Purchase on a deferred payment basis calls for recognition of both asset and liability balances. Payment for accrued interest as of the date of purchase requires separate recording; the amount paid for accrued interest must be subtracted from subsequent interest collections in measuring interest income.

**AMORTIZATION AND ACCUMULATION PROCEDURES**    When bonds are acquired as a temporary investment, investment cost is maintained in the accounts without adjustment. Interest is reported at amounts actually received. Upon disposition of the bonds, original cost is applied against net sales proceeds in arriving at the gain or the loss on the sale.    If a similar procedure were to be followed on long-term bonds and these were held until maturity, a loss would emerge if bonds had been acquired at a premium and a gain if bonds had been acquired at a discount. But such "gains" and "losses" are in effect adjustments in interest of prior periods. Bonds are acquired at a premium in recognition of an interest rate that exceeds the rate prevailing at the time of bond purchase; hence interest income is properly viewed as consisting of the interest received less the portion of the receipt that may be considered to be a recovery of the premium originally paid. Bonds are acquired at a discount in view of an interest rate that is less than the prevailing rate; here interest income is properly viewed as interest received increased by a portion of the bond discount that will be realized at bond maturity.    While the attempt to refine income measurement by considering the change in bond value over its life is not warranted in the case of bonds acquired as a temporary investment, systematic adjustment for this factor is desirable when bonds are acquired as long-term holdings.

*Bond Premium Amortization.*    A premium on bonds acquired is charged against interest received over the life of the bonds. The bond account is credited and Interest Income is charged each period for the part of the premium that is written off. The investment, then, moves towards its maturity value, and interest is reported periodically at the amount actually earned — the interest collected decreased by that part of the premium considered to have been recovered. The reduction of bonds to par by periodic charges to income is referred to as *bond premium amortization.*

*Bond Discount Accumulation.*    A discount on bonds acquired is added to bond interest received over the life of the bonds. The bond account is charged and Interest Income is credited each period for the part of the discount that is accumulated. Here, too, the investment moves towards its maturity value, and interest is reported periodically at the amount actually earned — the interest collected increased by that part of the discount considered realized.    Increase of bonds to par by periodic credits to income is called *bond discount accumulation.*

**METHODS OF AMORTIZATION AND ACCUMULATION** The *straight-line* method of amortization or accumulation provides for the recognition of an equal amount of premium or discount each period. Use of the *compound-interest* or *scientific* method requires that the effective earning rate on the purchase of the bonds first be determined; interest income is then reported periodically at the effective rate, the difference between the amount earned and the amount actually received being recognized as an adjustment to the investment account. To illustrate, assume the purchase of 5-year bonds of $100,000, interest at 6% payable semiannually, at a price of 104⅜. Reference to bond tables indicates a yield of approximately 5% at this price. The following tabulations show the differences in use of the two methods:

### AMORTIZATION OF PREMIUM — STRAIGHT-LINE METHOD
$100,000 5-Year Bonds, Interest at 6% Payable Semiannually, Purchased at $104,375

| INTEREST PAYMENT | A INTEREST (3% OF FACE VALUE) | B PREMIUM AMORTIZATION (1/10 ×$4,375) | C EFFECTIVE INTEREST (A − B) | D BOND CARRYING VALUE (D − B) |
|---|---|---|---|---|
| | | | | $104,375.00 |
| 1 | $3,000.00 | $437.50 | $2,562.50 | 103,937.50 |
| 2 | 3,000.00 | 437.50 | 2,562.50 | 103,500.00 |
| 3 | 3,000.00 | 437.50 | 2,562.50 | 103,062.50 |
| 4 | 3,000.00 | 437.50 | 2,562.50 | 102,625.00 |
| 5 | 3,000.00 | 437.50 | 2,562.50 | 102,187.50 |
| 6 | 3,000.00 | 437.50 | 2,562.50 | 101,750.00 |
| 7 | 3,000.00 | 437.50 | 2,562.50 | 101,312.50 |
| 8 | 3,000.00 | 437.50 | 2,562.50 | 100,875.00 |
| 9 | 3,000.00 | 437.50 | 2,562.50 | 100,437.50 |
| 10 | 3,000.00 | 437.50 | 2,562.50 | 100,000.00 |

### AMORTIZATION OF PREMIUM — COMPOUND-INTEREST METHOD
$100,000 5-Year Bonds, Interest at 6% Payable Semiannually, Purchased at $104,375 To Yield Approximately 5%

| INTEREST PAYMENT | A INTEREST (3% OF FACE VALUE) | B EFFECTIVE INTEREST (2½% OF BOND CARRYING VALUE) | C PREMIUM AMORTIZATION (A − B) | D BOND CARRYING VALUE (D − C) |
|---|---|---|---|---|
| | | | | $104,375.00 |
| 1 | $3,000.00 | $2,609.38 (2½% of $104,375.00) | $390.62 | 103,984.38 |
| 2 | 3,000.00 | 2,599.61 (2½% of $103,984.38) | 400.39 | 103,583.99 |
| 3 | 3,000.00 | 2,589.60 (2½% of $103,583.99) | 410.40 | 103,173.59 |
| 4 | 3,000.00 | 2,579.34 (2½% of $103,173.59) | 420.66 | 102,752.93 |
| 5 | 3,000.00 | 2,568.82 (2½% of $102,752.93) | 431.18 | 102,321.75 |
| 6 | 3,000.00 | 2,558.04 (2½% of $102,321.75) | 441.96 | 101,879.79 |
| 7 | 3,000.00 | 2,547.00 (2½% of $101,879.79) | 453.00 | 101,426.79 |
| 8 | 3,000.00 | 2,535.67 (2½% of $101,426.79) | 464.33 | 100,962.46 |
| 9 | 3,000.00 | 2,524.06 (2½% of $100,962.46) | 475.94 | 100,486.52 |
| 10 | 3,000.00 | 2,513.48 ($3,000 − $486.52)[1] | 486.52 | 100,000.00 |

[1] 2½% of $100,486.52 would be $2,512.16. However, use of 5% when the effective rate was not exactly 5% has resulted in a small discrepancy that requires compensation upon recording the final receipt of interest. The bond account is reduced to face value, interest income being reduced by the premium balance at the time of bond maturity.

The straight-line method of amortization offers a uniform interest amount for each period. The compound-interest method affords a uniform earnings rate based upon a declining investment balance; since each interest payment represents a partial return of the premium, the investment is reduced each period and earnings, in turn, are correspondingly less.

The use of the two methods when bonds are acquired at a discount is illustrated in the tables that follow. Here it is assumed that 5-year bonds of $100,000, interest at 4% payable semiannually, are purchased to yield 5%, or at a price as shown by bond tables of $95,623.93.

### ACCUMULATION OF DISCOUNT — STRAIGHT-LINE METHOD
$100,000 5-Year Bonds, Interest at 4% Payable Semiannually, Purchased at $95,623.93

| INTEREST PAYMENT | A INTEREST (2% OF FACE VALUE) | B DISCOUNT ACCUMULATION (1/10 × $4,376.07) | C EFFECTIVE INTEREST (A+B) | D BOND CARRIYNG VALUE (D+B) |
|---|---|---|---|---|
|  |  |  |  | $ 95,623.93 |
| 1 | $2,000.00 | $437.61 | $2,437.61 | 96,061.54 |
| 2 | 2,000.00 | 437.61 | 2,437.61 | 96,499.15 |
| 3 | 2,000.00 | 437.61 | 2,437.61 | 96,936.76 |
| 4 | 2,000.00 | 437.61 | 2,437.61 | 97,374.37 |
| 5 | 2,000.00 | 437.61 | 2,437.61 | 97,811.98 |
| 6 | 2,000.00 | 437.61 | 2,437.61 | 98,249.59 |
| 7 | 2,000.00 | 437.61 | 2,437.61 | 98,687.20 |
| 8 | 2,000.00 | 437.60 | 2,437.60 | 99,124.80 |
| 9 | 2,000.00 | 437.60 | 2,437.60 | 99,562.40 |
| 10 | 2,000.00 | 437.60 | 2,437.60 | 100,000.00 |

### ACCUMULATION OF DISCOUNT — COMPOUND-INTEREST METHOD
$100,000 5-Year Bonds, Interest at 4% Payable Semiannually, Purchased at $95,623.93
To Yield 5%

| INTEREST PAYMENT | A INTEREST (2% OF FACE VALUE) | B EFFECTIVE INTEREST (2½% OF BOND CARRYING VALUE) | C DISCOUNT ACCUMULATION (B−A) | D BOND CARRYING VALUE (D+C) |
|---|---|---|---|---|
|  |  |  |  | $ 95,623.93 |
| 1 | $2,000.00 | $2,390.60 (2½% of $95,623.93) | $390.60 | 96,014.53 |
| 2 | 2,000.00 | 2,400.36 (2½% of $96,014.53) | 400.36 | 96,414.89 |
| 3 | 2,000.00 | 2,410.37 (2½% of $96,414.89) | 410.37 | 96,825.26 |
| 4 | 2,000.00 | 2,420.63 (2½% of $96,825.26) | 420.63 | 97,245.89 |
| 5 | 2,000.00 | 2,431.15 (2½% of $97,245.89) | 431.15 | 97,677.04 |
| 6 | 2,000.00 | 2,441.93 (2½% of $97,677.04) | 441.93 | 98,118.97 |
| 7 | 2,000.00 | 2,452.97 (2½% of $98,118.97) | 452.97 | 98,571.94 |
| 8 | 2,000.00 | 2,464.30 (2½% of $98,571.94) | 464.30 | 99,036.24 |
| 9 | 2,000.00 | 2,475.91 (2½% of $99,036.24) | 475.91 | 99,512.15 |
| 10 | 2,000.00 | 2,487.85 ($2,000 + $487.85)[1] | 487.85 | 100,000.00 |

[1] 2½% of $99,512.15 would be $2,487.80. By earlier computations to the nearest cent, an element of error was introduced. Compensation for the error is made when the final receipt of interest is recorded. The bond account is raised to face value, interest income being increased by the discount balance at the time of bond maturity.

In the latter instance the compound-interest method offers a uniform earnings rate based upon a successively higher investment balance. Periodic earnings are composed of the cash received plus the increase that is considered to have taken place in the investment balance. As the investment balance goes up each period, earnings are correspondingly greater.

The compound-interest method may be favored over the straight-line method because of the accuracy that it affords in income measurement. However, the straight-line procedure is normally preferred because of its simplicity, except in those instances where large blocks of bonds are acquired at substantial premiums or discounts and use of this method would give results materially different from the scientific procedures. Straight-line amortization is accepted for income tax purposes. Use of the straight-line method is assumed in the remaining illustrations of this chapter.

**ACCOUNTING FOR LONG-TERM INVESTMENTS IN BONDS**
The entries for a long-term investment in bonds are illustrated in the example that follows. Assume that an investor acquires 6% bonds, face value $100,000, for $107,000, with interest payable semiannually on April 1 and October 1. Bonds are acquired on July 1, 1957, and mature on April 1, 1966. Books are to be adjusted and closed at the end of each calendar year.

A schedule may be prepared by the investor to summarize premium amortization and earnings over the period the bonds are to be held. This schedule can then be used in making periodic adjustments. The bond premium is to be spread over the period that bonds will be earning interest, July 1, 1957, to April 1, 1966, or 105 months. An amortization schedule is prepared as follows:

AMORTIZATION SCHEDULE — STRAIGHT-LINE METHOD

| Period | A Interest Received (Including Adjustments for Accruals) | Number of Months | B Fraction of Premium to be Amortized | C Amount of Premium Amortization (B×$7,000) | D Effective Interest (A−C) | E Bond Carrying Value (E−C) |
|---|---|---|---|---|---|---|
| | | | | | | $107,000 |
| July 1 (acquisition date) to Dec. 31, 1957 | $3,000 | 6 | 6/105 | $ 400 | $2,600 | 106,600 |
| Year Ended Dec. 31, 1958 | 6,000 | 12 | 12/105 | 800 | 5,200 | 105,800 |
| Year Ended Dec. 31, 1959 | 6,000 | 12 | 12/105 | 800 | 5,200 | 105,000 |
| Year Ended Dec. 31, 1960 | 6,000 | 12 | 12/105 | 800 | 5,200 | 104,200 |
| Year Ended Dec. 31, 1961 | 6,000 | 12 | 12/105 | 800 | 5,200 | 103,400 |
| Year Ended Dec. 31, 1962 | 6,000 | 12 | 12/105 | 800 | 5,200 | 102,600 |
| Year Ended Dec. 31, 1963 | 6,000 | 12 | 12/105 | 800 | 5,200 | 101,800 |
| Year Ended Dec. 31, 1964 | 6,000 | 12 | 12/105 | 800 | 5,200 | 101,000 |
| Year Ended Dec. 31, 1965 | 6,000 | 12 | 12/105 | 800 | 5,200 | 100,200 |
| Jan. 1 to Apr. 1, 1966 (maturity date) | 1,500 | 3 | 3/105 | 200 | 1,300 | 100,000 |
| | | 105 | 105/105 | $7,000 | | |

Entries for bond ownership in 1957 and 1958 appear below:

| Transaction | Entry |
|---|---|
| **JULY 1, 1957**<br>Purchased 100, $1,000, 6% bonds of Hope Corp. at 106¾, bonds maturing on April 1, 1966. Interest is payable semiannually on April 1 and October 1. Payment was made as follows:<br>Bonds of $100,000 at 106¾... $106,750<br>Costs of purchase......... 250<br>Accrued interest, April 1–<br>July 1................. 1,500<br>$108,500 | Investment in Hope<br>Corp. 6's............ 107,000<br>Interest Income....... 1,500[1]<br>Cash.............. 108,500 |
| **OCTOBER 1, 1957**<br>Received semiannual interest. | Cash................. 3,000<br>Interest Income..... 3,000 |
| **DECEMBER 31, 1957**<br>(a) To record accrued interest for 3 months, and (b) to amortize bond premium applicable to current year. Amortization: period held in current year, 6 months; total life of bond issue, 8¾ years or 105 months; current amortization, $\frac{6}{105} \times \$7,000$, or $400 (or $6 \times \$66.66\frac{2}{3}$, monthly amortization = $400). | (a) Accrued Interest on<br>Investment in<br>Bonds........... 1,500<br>Interest Income.. 1,500<br><br>(b) Interest Income ... 400<br>Investment in<br>Hope Corp. 6's... 400 |
| **JANUARY 1, 1958**<br>To reverse 1957 accrued interest. | Interest Income....... 1,500<br>Accrued Interest on<br>Investment in Bonds. 1,500 |
| **APRIL 1, 1958**<br>Received semiannual interest. | Cash................. 3,000<br>Interest Income..... 3,000 |
| **OCTOBER 1, 1958**<br>Received semiannual interest. | Cash................. 3,000<br>Interest Income..... 3,000 |
| **DECEMBER 31, 1958**<br>(a) To record accrued interest for 3 months, and (b) to amortize bond premium applicable to current year, $\frac{12}{105} \times \$7,000$, or $800 (or $12 \times \$66.66\frac{2}{3}$, monthly amortization = $800). | (a) Accrued Interest<br>on Investment in<br>Bonds........... 1,500<br>Interest Income.. 1,500<br>(b) Interest Income.... 800<br>Investment in<br>Hope Corp. 6's .. 800 |

[1]As indicated in Chapter 6, payment for accrued interest can be recorded by a charge to an accrued receivable balance; this account would be closed when interest is collected.

Entries similar to those for 1958 will be made until 1966. The reversing entry required on January 1, 1966, and the entries on April 1, 1966, when the last interest payment is received, will be as follows:

| Transaction | Entry |
|---|---|
| **JANUARY 1, 1966**<br>To reverse 1965 accrued interest. | Interest Income...... 1,500<br>Accrued Interest on<br>Investment in Bonds 1,500 |

| Transaction | Entry |
|---|---|
| APRIL 1, 1966<br>(a) To record amortization for last 3-month period, $\frac{3}{105} \times \$7,000$, or \$200 (or $3 \times \$66.66\frac{2}{3}$, monthly amortization = \$200), and (b) to record receipt of semiannual interest and principal amount. | (a) Interest Income...    200<br>    Investment in<br>    Hope Corp. 6's...        200<br><br>(b) Cash............ 103,000<br>    Investment in<br>    Hope Corp. 6's ..     100,000<br>    Interest Income .      3,000 |

When bonds are acquired at a discount, the investment account is raised to par by the process of bond discount accumulation as illustrated below:

| Transaction | Entry |
|---|---|
| OCTOBER 11, 1957<br>Purchased 100, \$1,000, $5\frac{1}{4}\%$ bonds of Atlas, Inc. at $96\frac{1}{2}$, bonds maturing on March 1, 1963. Interest is payable semiannually on March 1 and September 1.<br>Payment was made as follows:<br>Bonds of \$100,000 at $96\frac{1}{2}$.....\$96,500.00<br>Costs of purchase ...........   250.00<br>Interest, Sept. 1–Oct. 11, 40<br>  days, at $5\frac{1}{4}\%$.............   583.33<br><br>               \$97,333.33 | Investment in Atlas,<br>  Inc. $5\frac{1}{4}$'s........... 96,750.00<br>Interest Income....   583.33<br>  Cash............        97,333.33 |
| DECEMBER 31, 1957<br>(a) To record accrued interest for 4 months, and (b) to accumulate bond discount applicable to current year. Accumulation: period held in current year, 3 months; total life of bond issue, $5\frac{5}{12}$ years, or 65 months; current accumulation $\frac{3}{65} \times$ \$3,250, or \$150 (or $3 \times \$50$, monthly accumulation = \$150). | (a) Accrued Interest<br>    on Investment<br>    in Bonds....... 1,750.00<br>      Interest Income........      1,750.00<br>(b) Investment in<br>    Atlas, Inc. $5\frac{1}{4}$'s .   150.00<br>      Interest Income.......      150.00 |
| JANUARY 1, 1958<br>To reverse 1957 accrued income. | Interest Income.... 1,750.00<br>  Accrued Interest<br>  on Investment in<br>  Bonds..........      1,750.00 |
| MARCH 1, 1958<br>Received semiannual interest. | Cash............. 2,625.00<br>  Interest Income..      2,625.00 |
| SEPTEMBER 1, 1958<br>Received semiannual interest. | Cash............. 2,625.00<br>  Interest Income..      2,625.00 |
| DECEMBER 31, 1958<br>(a) To record accrued interest for 4 months, and (b) to accumulate bond discount applicable to current year, $\frac{12}{65} \times$ \$3,250, or \$600 (or $12 \times$ monthly accumulation, \$50 = \$600). | (a) Accrued Interest<br>    on Investment<br>    in Bonds....... 1,750.00<br>      Interest Income.......      1,750.00<br>(b) Investment in<br>    Atlas, Inc. $5\frac{1}{4}$'s..   600.00<br>      Interest Income.......      600.00 |

It is necessary to set some arbitrary minimum time unit in the amortization of bond premium or the accumulation of bond discount. The month is used in the text as the minimum unit. Transactions occurring during the first half of the month are treated as though they were made at the beginning of the month; transactions occurring during the second half are treated as though made at the start of the following month. Use of a longer term, such as the quarter or half year, is possible, although this offers less accuracy than the use of a shorter time unit.

Amortization of bond premium and accumulation of bond discount are recognized in the foregoing examples at the end of the investor's fiscal period and also at the time of bond redemption or sale. It would be possible to recognize amortization or accumulation whenever interest is received. But it would still be necessary to bring the amortization or the accumulation up to date at the end of the year when accrued interest is recognized. Instead of making the adjustment several times a year and for fractional periods, the adjustment is more conveniently made for a full year at the end of each fiscal year, except for the first and last years when fractional parts of a year are involved.

**SALE OF BONDS PRIOR TO MATURITY** Sometimes bonds held as a long-term investment are sold prior to their maturity. Since the carrying value of the investment has been adjusted during the period of bond ownership, it is evident that the basis for calculating gain or loss cannot be original cost. The book value of the bonds must be determined as of date of sale. This requires bond premium or discount adjustment to date of sale. The difference between the book value on the date of sale and the cash proceeds from the sale represents the net gain or loss. To illustrate a sale, assume that the bonds of Atlas, Inc. in the previous example are not held until maturity, but are sold at 97 plus accrued interest on February 1, 1959. Entries in 1959 are:

| Transaction | Entry | | |
|---|---|---|---|
| **JANUARY 1, 1959**<br>To reverse 1958 accrued interest. | Interest Income....<br>    Accrued Interest<br>    on Investment in<br>    Bonds......... | 1,750.00 | 1,750.00 |
| **FEBRUARY 1, 1959**<br>To record accumulation of discount to date of sale:<br>    $1/65 \times \$3,250$, or \$50.<br>To record sale of bonds:<br>(a) Accrued interest,<br>    September 1–February 1.. $2,187.50 | Investment in Atlas<br>Inc. $5\frac{1}{4}$'s..........<br>    Interest Income..<br><br>(a) Cash..........<br>        Interest In-<br>        come........ | 50.00<br><br><br>2,187.50 | 50.00<br><br><br>2,187.50 |

| Transaction | Entry |
|---|---|
| (b) Book value of bonds: <br> Cost.............  $96,750.00 <br> Plus discount accumulation to date of sale: <br>     1957   $150.00 <br>     1958   600.00 <br>     1959    50.00    800.00 <br>                      $97,550.00 <br> Sales proceeds   $97,000.00 <br> Less costs of sale    200.00 <br>                      96,800.00 <br> Net loss.............. $   750.00 | (b) Cash..........96,800.00 <br>    Loss on Sale of <br>     Atlas, Inc. 5¼'s..   750.00 <br>      Investment in <br>      Atlas, Inc. 5¼'s.       97,550.00 |

The two cash entries given may be combined as a single compound entry. The bond interest income for January, 1959, is $487.50, consisting of interest received, $2,187.50, decreased by the interest relating to 1958, $1,750.00, and increased by discount accumulation for the current period, $50. This is the same as the monthly interest recognized in 1957 and 1958.

When bonds are acquired at a premium and bond interest is subject to federal income tax, the bondholder is permitted to report as income (1) the actual amount received or (2) the amount received less the amortization of bond premium. If the actual amount received is reported as income, the bondholder must use the original cost of the bonds as a basis for calculating the taxable gain or loss arising from the subsequent sale or redemption of the bonds; if income is reduced by amortization, bond cost less the amount of amortization becomes the basis for calculation of gain or loss on the ultimate disposal of the bond. In the case of state and municipal bonds whose income is wholly tax exempt, federal tax laws require the amortization of any premium. Since the interest is nontaxable, the deduction for the amortization is not reflected on the return; however, the basis of the bonds is reduced by the premium amortization in calculating the gain or the loss on the sale of the bonds.[1]

When bonds are acquired at a discount, the bondholder must report as income for tax purposes the interest actually received. Upon disposal of the bonds, he reports the difference between proceeds and cost as taxable gain or loss. Realization of a discount is thus recognized as a gain from the disposal of bonds rather than as interest income related to the holding period. Exception to this treatment is required for bonds

---

[1]Interest on certain classes of government bonds is only partially tax-exempt (interest is subject to surtax rates only). In these instances, premium amortization is mandatory as to a corporate owner but elective as to all other owners.

issued after December 31, 1954, at a discount that aggregates ¼ of 1% or more per year on the redemption price; full or partial recovery of original issue discount on such issues is taxed as ordinary income. A further exception is made in the case of United States savings bonds issued at a discount; realization of the discount is taxed as ordinary income, with the taxpayer allowed the option of recognizing such discount as income in the year of bond redemption or in annual increments according to bond redemption values.

When an investment in bonds consists of several purchases, and certain holdings are sold, tax laws call for the same rules that apply on the sale of stocks. Unless the bonds can be identified as to lot and related cost, cost must be determined by the first-in, first-out rule, earliest costs thus being applied to sales proceeds in calculating the taxable gain or loss.

**BOND REDEMPTION PRIOR TO MATURITY**    Bonds that are callable by the issuer prior to their maturity generally provide for the payment of a premium to the holder in the event this option is exercised. To illustrate, bonds issued on January 1, 1956, and due on January 1, 1976, may provide a table of redemption values as follows:

Redeemable January 1, 1961, to December 31, 1965, at 105
Redeemable January 1, 1966, to December 31, 1970, at 103
Redeemable January 1, 1971, to December 31, 1975, at 101

When bonds are acquired at a premium, conservatism calls for an amortization policy that will prevent the bonds from being reported at more than their redemption values at the various call dates. For example, assume in the example above that bonds of $10,000 are acquired for $10,800 on January 1, 1958. Regular premium amortization and accelerated amortization based upon bond redemption values of $10,500, $10,300 and $10,100 are compared below:

| REGULAR AMORTIZATION | ACCELERATED AMORTIZATION |
|---|---|
| $800 ÷ 18 years = $44.44 per year (1958–1976) | ($10,800 − $10,500) ÷ 3 years (1958–1960) = $100.00 per year |
| | ($10,500 − $10,300) ÷ 5 years (1961–1965) = $ 40.00 per year |
| | ($10,300 − $10,100) ÷ 5 years (1966–1970) = $ 40.00 per year |
| | ($10,100 − $10,000) ÷ 5 years (1971–1975) = $ 20.00 per year |

If regular amortization procedures are followed on the books of the investor, bond redemption prior to maturity will result in a recovery of cash that is less than bond carrying value and will require recognition of a loss that nullifies in part the earnings recognized in the past. Accelerated amortization reduces the investment to its redemption value; bond redemption values are used for income measurement purposes and the need for recognition of a loss upon redemption is avoided. Obviously, bonds reported at a discount or bonds reported at a premium reduced by normal amortization to an amount not greater than redemption value require no special treatment.

When bonds are called, cash is debited for the call price received, the investment balance is credited for the book value of the bonds called, and a gain or loss is reported for the difference. The contract with bondholders normally provides for the payment of accrued interest to the bond call date. When bonds are called on a regular interest payment date, the bondholder will receive the call price plus interest for a full period. Interest income is credited for the interest received.

**BOND CONVERSION** When bonds are converted into another security, accounts are opened for the newly acquired security and the bond investment balance is closed. The procedures that are followed by the investor are similar to those previously described for the exchange of stock for other securities. The newly acquired security is recorded at its market value, and the difference between this value and the book value of the bonds surrendered is reported as gain or loss. Before an exchange is recorded, the investment account should be brought up to date for discount accumulation or premium amortization. Interest collected at the time of the exchange is reported as interest income.

To illustrate bond conversion, assume that the Carl Co. offers bondholders 40 shares of Carl Co. common stock, par $25, in exchange for each $1,000 5% bond that they hold. An investor exchanges bonds of $10,000, book value as brought up to date, $9,850, for 400 shares of common stock that are quoted on the market at the time of exchange at $26 per share. The exchange is completed three months after an interest payment date. The exchange is recorded as follows:

| | | |
|---|---:|---:|
| Cash......................................................... | 125 | |
| Investment in Carl Co. Common Stock.............. | 10,400 | |
| Investment in Carl Co. 5% Bonds................ | | 9,850 |
| Gain on Exchange of Carl Co. Bonds............. | | 550 |
| Interest Income..................................... | | 125 |

For federal income tax purposes the exchange of bonds for other securities or property results in gain or loss except for the following that are recognized as nontaxable: the exchange of bonds for other bonds of the same company that are considered substantially the same, and the conversion of bonds into stock in accordance with provisions of the bond indenture.

**BOND VALUATION** The market value of bonds varies with changes in the financial strength of the issuing company, changes in the level of interest rates, and shrinkage in the remaining life of the issue. In the absence of material price declines, bonds held as long-term investments may be reported on the balance sheet at book value. This book value approaches par as the bonds move closer to maturity. To this extent, then, the accounting can be considered to follow a similar change that is taking place on the market as the bond life is reduced and a correspondingly lower valuation is attached to the difference between the actual rate and the market rate for remaining interest payments. Although investments are properly reflected at book value, parenthetical disclosure of market value of the securities is desirable as a means of making the statements more informative.

A serious decline in bond value, however, as a result of unfavorable developments relating to the issuer cannot be ignored. Assume, for example, that the issuing company has found it impossible to meet redemption fund requirements, which suggests that it may have difficulties in paying off the obligation at its maturity. Even more serious, assume that there has been default on bond interest payments. When significant investment loss is indicated, entries to record the loss should be made. Such loss may be established through reference to current market quotations, investigation of prices at which other bonds can be sold, or special appraisal of those assets that are pledged as security on the bonded indebtedness.

When bonds are purchased *flat*, that is, when interest on bonds is in arrears and one price is paid for the bonds together with all accrued and unpaid interest, this price is recorded as the bond investment cost. Any amounts subsequently received on the bonds, whether designated as payments of principal or defaulted interest, should be treated as a recovery of investment cost as long as there is uncertainty of ultimate gain on the investment. No interest should be accrued on the bonds until solvency of the debtor is restored and the regular receipt of interest is assured. Such bonds are reported at their unrecovered cost with full information as to the nature of the investment.

**INVESTMENT IN U. S. SAVINGS BONDS**　　A number of long-term savings bonds are made available to investors by the United States Government. These vary as to denominations, yield, life, and redemption values, and contain specific limitations as to availability to certain classes of purchasers, maximum annual purchases, transferability, redemption, etc. Special accounting problems arise with respect to such savings bonds.

*Bonds Providing for No Interest Payments but Acquired at a Discount (Series E, F, J).* Certain U. S. savings bonds provide for no periodic interest payments but are sold at a discount that represents full compensation for holding the bonds. Interest accrues on the bonds through increases in redemption values, the bonds becoming increasingly more valuable as they approach maturity. To encourage the investor to hold the bonds until maturity, bond value increments are set so that the rate earned on the bonds increases with the length of time held.

To illustrate the accounting problems for an investment in this class, assume the following: Series E bonds calling for payment of $10,000 after 8 years and 11 months are acquired at $7,500 in 1957. The nominal interest rate here is zero; sale at the discount provides effective interest, assuming semiannual compounding, of approximately 3.25% if bonds are held for their full 8 year and 11 month life.[1] Four possibilities are open to the investor in recognizing earnings on his investment:

(1) The bonds may be carried at original cost, no income being recognized until bond maturity when the investment is raised to the full redemption value and income is credited for this increase. This procedure provides for income recognition on a cash basis.

(2) The discount may be accumulated according to the scheduled increases as stated on the bond, the bond account being charged and income credited periodically. This method emphasizes cash realizable values and results in increased earnings as bonds approach maturity.

(3) The discount may be accumulated on a straight-line basis, the bond account being charged and income credited periodically. This method provides for accumulation of discount in terms of equal periodic amounts over the life of the issue without regard to realizable values.

(4) The discount may be accumulated in terms of the effective earnings rate, the bond account being charged and income credited periodically. This method provides for accumulation of discount in terms of an equal periodic yield over the life of the issue without regard to realizable values.

Income recognition and increases in Series E bond values are compared on the following page.

---

[1]Series E bonds were originally issued in 1941 at amounts equal to 75% of their maturity values; such bonds matured ten years from issue date providing an effective yield of approximately 2.90 per cent if held to maturity. New Series E bonds were issued in 1952 with similar issue and maturity values, but with a maturity of 9 years and 8 months from issue date that resulted in an effective yield of approximately 3.00 per cent. It was also provided that Series E bonds could be held beyond their maturity date for an additional ten year period with interest at a rate equal to or slightly in excess of their original rate. In 1957 another Series E issue was made available with a maturity of 8 years and 11 months to provide an effective yield of approximately 3.25 per cent.

| END OF | 1<br>INCOME<br>RECOGNITION<br>AT MATURITY | 2<br>INCOME RECOGNITION<br>ACCORDING TO<br>REDEMPTION VALUES | 3<br>INCOME RECOGNITION<br>ON STRAIGHT-LINE<br>BASIS[1] | 4<br>INCOME RECOGNITION<br>ON COMPOUND-<br>INTEREST BASIS[2] |
|---|---|---|---|---|
| 1st year |  | $ 172.00 | $ 280.37 | $ 245.74 |
| 2nd year |  | 252.00 | 280.37 | 253.78 |
| 3rd year |  | 276.00 | 280.37 | 262.09 |
| 4th year |  | 284.00 | 280.37 | 270.68 |
| 5th year |  | 292.00 | 280.37 | 279.55 |
| 6th year |  | 296.00 | 280.37 | 288.72 |
| 7th year |  | 304.00 | 280.37 | 298.17 |
| 8th year |  | 312.00 | 280.37 | 307.94 |
| 8th year,<br>11th month | $2,500.00 | 312.00 | 257.04 | 293.33 |
|  | $2,500.00 | $2,500.00 | $2,500.00 | $2,500.00 |

[1]First through eighth year: 12/107 x $2,500.00 (12 months held, 107 month bond life); ninth year, 11/107 x $2,500.

[2]Effective yield assumes semiannual compounding; interest for the first year, then, is calculated as follows:

| | |
|---|---|
| First six months, 1.625% of $7,500.00 . . . . . . . . . . . . . . . . . . . . . . . . . . . | $121.88 |
| Second six months, 1.625% of $7,621.88 ($7,500.00+$121.88) . . . . . . . | 123.86 |
| Interest for first year, 3.25% compounded semiannually . . . . . . . . . . | $245.74 |

Interest for subsequent years is similarly calculated in terms of increasing investment balance. Use of 3.25% compounded semiannually when the effective rate is not exactly 3.25% results in a small discrepancy that requires compensation in the last period; the bond account is raised to maturity value and interest income credited for this increase in the last period.

When the investor expects to hold the bonds until maturity, the compound-interest basis provides for the accurate recognition of income. However, for tax purposes the holder must elect one of the following methods: (1) recognition of full interest income upon redemption or bond maturity or (2) recognition of interest periodically according to the redemption value increases.

*Bonds Providing for Fixed Interest Payments but with Varying Redemption Values (Series G and K).* Certain U. S. bonds are sold at par and provide for periodic interest payments at a certain rate. But such a rate is effective only if bonds are held for their full life. To achieve this, bonds provide for successively decreasing redemption values for a number of years, whereupon values successively rise until full value is reached once more at maturity.

For example, a $1,000 Series K 2.76% bond provides for interest payments of $13.80 semiannually. The bond is acquired at par but the value of the bond for redemption purposes shrinks to a value of $966 at the end of the fourth year. From this point, the bond value rises until par is reached at bond maturity, 12 years after the issue date. Redemption before maturity, then, results in loss of a part of the interest previously received and a reduction in the effective earnings below the 2.76% rate. Redemption values when considered together with interest receipts provide for a gradually increasing yield over the life of the issue until maturity is reached and bonds realize par value; the 2.76% yield is fully confirmed at this point.

Since such bonds are acquired as long-term holdings, it is normally acceptable to recognize the full amounts received as income without adjustments to the investment account to reflect changes in redemption values. If investments are carried at cost, appropriate disclosure should be made on the financial statements concerning current redemption values and the implications of redemption prior to maturity.

*Bonds Providing for Varying Interest Payments but with Fixed Re-demption Values (Series H).* A series of U. S. savings bonds is issued at par and is redeemable at this value throughout the bond life, with interest paid at increasing rates over the bond life. The full yield relating to such bonds is achieved only if they are held until maturity. For example, Series H bonds issued in 1957 pay interest at 1.60% for the first 6 months, 2.90% for the next six months, and 3.38% per year for the remaining nine years, providing a yield of approximately 3.25% if held until maturity, but a lower yield if redeemed prior to maturity. When the investor intends to hold the bonds until maturity and wishes to show the yield on the investment in terms of the full bond life, it would be possible to show an accrual of interest in early years for the difference between amounts collected and amounts earned. Amounts collected in excess of the effective yield in later years would be reported as a reduction in the accrued interest balance.

**LONG-TERM NOTES AND MORTGAGES** Investments in long-term notes and mort-gages have many characteristics in common with bond investments. During their lives they provide interest, and at their maturities they call for specified cash payments. Long-term notes and mortgages should be recorded at cost, or at their fair market value when acquired in connection with a sale of property. Any difference between an acquisition value and a maturity value calls for adjustments to income over the life of the investment. A note or mortgage may be acquired at a considerable discount when it involves a relatively large risk element. Such acquisition raises the question of possible failure to recover the full amount of the obligation at maturity. When this possibility is foreseen, the investor may choose to carry the investment without accumulating the discount. If full payment is received at maturity, the discount would be recognized as income at that time. Notes and mortgages should be analyzed in terms of installment maturities; the part that is due within one year is reported as a current asset, the balance as a long-term investment.

## QUESTIONS

**1.** Distinguish between (a) secured and unsecured bonds, (b) collateral trust and debenture bonds, (c) guaranteed bonds and income bonds, (d) convertible bonds and callable bonds, and (e) coupon bonds and registered bonds.

**2.** What is meant by bond market rate, nominal rate, and effective rate? Which of these rates changes during the lifetime of the bond issue?

**3.** Distinguish between the valuation standards applied to long-term and to short-term investments in bonds. What reasons can you offer for any differences?

**4.** Distinguish between straight-line and compound-interest methods of bond premium amortization. What arguments can be offered in support of each method?

**5.** (a) What is meant by purchase of bonds "flat"? (b) What special accounting procedure should be followed for such an investment?

**6.** (a) What special amortization problem is faced when bonds are acquired at a premium and such bonds are subject to redemption at less than the amount paid? (b) Will the same problem arise when bonds are acquired at a discount?

**7.** P. A. Ward acquires U. S. savings bonds. These bonds pay no interest but provide for increasing redemption values. Ward feels that there is no need to recognize any gain on the holdings until redemption. (a) What arguments can be raised in support of the practice advocated by Ward? (b) What arguments can be raised in support of the periodic recognition of income on the investment?

**8.** An investor makes a significant investment in U. S. Series E savings bonds. He wishes to recognize income on the bonds through the accumulation of the discount periodically. (a) What three methods of discount accumulation can be employed? (b) What are the advantages of each method and which method in your opinion is preferred?

**9.** When bonds are converted into another security, how should the exchange be recorded, assuming that (a) the new security acquired has a known market value, (b) the security acquired does not have a market value?

**10.** A. C. McArthur acquires a second-mortgage note, face value $10,000, for $6,000. McArthur feels that in view of the risks involved on this paper, any future collections of both principal and interest should be treated as reductions in the investment balance until he has recovered $6,000. Thereafter, any collections of principal and interest can be regarded as earnings on the investment. What would be your comment on McArthur's stand?

## EXERCISES

**1.** A $1,000, 5% bond, interest payable semiannually, was acquired on January 1, 1958. The bond matures on January 1, 1967. Using the bond table on page 396, determine the price to be paid for the bond assuming it is purchased on a basis to yield (a) 4%, (b) 6%.

**2.** Investment is made in a $1,000 bond, interest at 5%, payable semiannually, maturing 8 years from date of purchase. Using the bond table on page 396, calculate the exact yield on the bond assuming that it is purchased for (a) $1,020, (b) $975.

**3.** A $1,000 bond maturing in 3 years, interest at 5% payable semiannually, is purchased for $1,028. It is determined that this price will produce a yield of 4%. Prepare a bond amortization table using (a) straight-line amortization, (b) scientific amortization.

**4.** The Stewart Corporation acquires $100,000 of 3½% bonds of Western Stores, Inc. on a basis to yield 3.8% paying $97,523.45. Interest is payable semiannually and the bonds mature in 10 years.

(a) What entries would be made for the receipt of the first two interest payments, assuming discount accumulation on each interest date by (1) the straight-line method and (2) the compound-interest method?

(b) Assuming that the purchase was made on a 2.75% basis, $106,518.28 being paid, what entries would be made upon receipt of the first two interest payments, assuming premium amortization on each interest date by (1) the straight-line method and (2) the compound-interest method?

**5.** Bonds of $10,000 due in 5 years and paying interest semiannually at 6%, were purchased at $10,438, a price to yield 5% on the investment. Give the entries for the bond purchase, the semiannual interest receipts, and the premium amortization for the first two years of bond ownership, assuming earnings are recognized at 5%.

**6.** On June 1, 1958, Arthur Welk purchases Rupp Company bonds, face value $10,000, for $10,500, plus accrued interest. Bonds pay interest at the rate of 4½% semiannually on April 1 and October 1, and they mature on October 1, 1966. What are the entries that will be made on Welk's books to record (a) purchase of the bonds on June 1, (b) receipt of interest on October 1, and (c) the adjustment for accrued interest at the end of the fiscal period, December 31, 1958? (Assume amortization for bond premium by the straight-line method.)

**7.** F. A. Peterson acquired $15,000 of Murphy Motors 4% bonds on July 1, 1956. Bonds were acquired at 95; they pay interest semiannually on April 1 and October 1, and they mature on April 1, 1960. The fiscal period for Peterson is the calendar year; discount is accumulated on the bonds by the straight-line method. On March 1, 1959, Peterson sold the bonds for 98½ plus accrued interest. Give the entry to record the sale of the bonds on this date.

**8.** On January 1, 1958, Morris Mason purchases $10,000 of Armstrong Company 5% bonds at 106. Bonds are due on January 1, 1973, but may be redeemed by the company at earlier dates at premium values as follows:

January 1, 1961, to December 31, 1964, at 105
January 1, 1965, to December 31, 1968, at 103
January 1, 1969, to December 31, 1972, at 101

What amortization amounts do you recommend that Mason recognize over the life of the bond issue?

**9.** Burton Rhodes shows Broyles Corp. bonds of $5,000 on his books at a book value of $4,650 on July 1, 1958. Each $1,000 bond is convertible into 20 shares of the issuing company's common stock, and Rhodes exchanges the bonds for stock on this date. Stock on the date of conversion is quoted at 49⅛; accrued interest on bonds of $41.67 is received together with the stock. What entry is made to record the exchange?

**10.** Arthur Bailey acquires new Series E bonds on January 1, 1958. Bonds of $1,500 are acquired for $1,125, a price that results in a yield of 3.25% compounded semiannually if bonds are held until maturity. Redemption values for each $100 value are listed on the bonds as follows:

| | | |
|---|---|---|
| 0 to ½ year | | $75.00 |
| ½ to 1 year | | 75.60 |
| 1 to 1½ years | | 76.72 |
| 1½ to 2 years | | 77.92 |

What interest will Bailey show for 1958 and for 1959 if income is to be recognized by accumulation of bond discount (a) in terms of bond redemption values, (b) by use of the straight-line method, (c) by use of the compound-interest method?

**11.** On March 1, 1958, Lyle Moorhouse acquired $10,000 of 4½% bonds of the Magnolia Corporation in exchange for land that he had acquired several years ago at a cost of $4,800. Bonds were quoted on the market on that date at 94½. Interest on the bonds was payable on April 1 and October 1; the bonds mature on October 1, 1962.

(a) What entries would be made by Moorhouse in 1958 to record (1) the acquisition of the bonds, (2) the receipt of interest on April 1 and October 1, and (3) the accrual of interest and the accumulation of discount on December 31?

(b) Assume that Moorhouse made the following entry in recording the bonds in 1958:

| | | |
|---|---|---|
| Mar. 1 Magnolia Corporation Bonds | 10,000 | |
| Land | | 4,800 |
| Gain on Sale of Land | | 5,200 |

Interest receipts in 1958 were recorded as credits to income; no entry for accrued interest was made on December 31. Give any correcting entries that should be made at the beginning of 1959 so that the accounts may reflect balances as would be obtained in (a) above.

## PROBLEMS

**13-1.** The Firestone Co. acquired $10,000 of Champion Motors 5% bonds, interest payable semiannually, bonds maturing in 5 years. The bonds were acquired at $10,450, a price to yield approximately 4% on the investment.

*Instructions:* (1) Prepare tables to show the periodic adjustments to the investment account and the annual bond earnings, assuming adjustment by each of the following methods: (a) the straight-line method and (b) the compound-interest method.

(2) Give entries for the interest receipts and adjustment for the first year of bond ownership, assuming use of (a) the straight-line method, and (b) the compound-interest method.

**13-2.** The Belmont Corporation acquired $10,000 of Disney, Inc. 4½% bonds, interest payable semiannually, bonds maturing in 5 years. Bonds were acquired at $9,360, a price to yield approximately 6% on the investment.

*Instructions:* (1) Prepare tables to show the periodic adjustments to the investment account and the annual bond earnings, assuming adjustment by each of the following methods: (a) the straight-line method, and (b) the compound-interest method.

(2) Give entries for the interest receipts and adjustments for the first year of bond ownership, assuming use of (a) the straight-line method, and (b) the compound-interest method.

**13-3.** The Keystone Investment Co. acquired $150,000 of Western Co. 5% bonds, interest payable semiannually, at a price to yield 5½%. The bonds have a remaining life of 10 years.

*Instructions*: (1) Using the bond table on page 396, determine the amount paid for the bonds.

(2) Prepare a table of discount accumulation by the compound-interest method for the first two years of ownership.

(3) Give the entries to be made by the investor for the bond purchase, the semiannual interest receipts, and the discount accumulation for the two-year period.

**13-4.** The Kingston Investment Co. acquires $50,000 of Maxwell Corp., 5% bonds, interest payable semiannually, at a price to yield 4½%. The bonds have a remaining life of 8 years.

*Instructions:* (1) Using the bond table on page 396, determine the amount paid for the bonds.

(2) Prepare a table of premium amortization by the compound-interest method for the first two years of ownership.

(3) Give the entries to be made by the investor for the bond purchase, the semiannual interest receipts, and the premium amortization for the two-year period.

**13-5.** On May 1, 1955, the Fulton Co. acquired $20,000 of Melville Corp. 5% bonds at 98½ plus accrued interest. Interest on bonds is payable semiannually on March 1 and September 1, and bonds mature on September 1, 1958.

On May 1, 1956, the Fulton Co. sells bonds of $5,000 for 100¾ plus accrued interest.

On July 1, 1957, $5,000 of bonds are exchanged for 1,000 shares of Melville Corp. no-par common, quoted on the market on this date at 5⅛. Interest is received on bonds to date of exchange.

On September 1, 1958, remaining bonds are redeemed.

*Instructions:* Give journal entries for 1955-1958 to record the foregoing transactions on the books of the Fulton Co. including any adjustments that are required at the end of each fiscal year ending on December 31. (Show all calculations.)

**13-6.** On July 1, 1956, Crawford Investors acquired $200,000 of Westwood Co. 5% bonds at 98½ plus accrued interest. Interest on bonds is payable semiannually on February 1 and August 1, and bonds mature on August 1, 1958.

On August 1, 1957, the Westwood Co. offers additional common stock for sale at par, $100, and offers bondholders the privilege of exchanging $1,000 bonds for 10 shares of stock. Crawford Investors exchange $100,000 in bonds for 1,000 shares of common on this date. Interest is received on bonds to date of exchange.

On April 1, 1958, bonds of $40,000 are sold at 99¾ plus accrued interest.

On August 1, 1958 bonds mature and collection is made on those held.

*Instructions:* Give journal entries for 1956-1958 to record the foregoing transactions on the books of Crawford Investors, including any adjustments that are required at the end of each fiscal year ending on December 31. (Show all calculations.)

**13-7.** Belle, Inc. completes the following transactions, among others, during 1958:

Mar.   1. Purchased $100,000 of Marin Sales Corporation First Mortgage bonds, maturity date August 1, 1963, interest of 5% payable semiannually on February 1 and August 1, at 94½ plus brokerage of $300 and accrued interest.

April  5. Purchased 800 shares of Wood Motors, Inc. common, par $50, for $45,500.

May    2. Received a common stock dividend on Wood Motors, Inc. common of 1 share for every 4 shares held.

July  15. Was granted the right to purchase 1 share of stock at par for every 5 shares of Wood Motors, Inc. stock held, the option expiring August 15. Stock had a market value of $62.50 ex-rights, and each right had a value of $2.50 on the date the rights were issued.

Aug.   1. Received semiannual interest on bonds held. (Bond discount accumulation by the straight-line method is recorded at the time interest is received.)

Aug.  11. Sold Marin Sales Corporation bonds of $20,000 at 97½ and accrued interest, less fees of sale, $50; also exercised option on stock rights on this date.

Oct.   1. Sold 300 shares of Wood Motors, Inc. for $16,800. (The first-in, first-out method is used in calculating the cost of shares sold.)

Dec.  31. Adjusted the accounts relative to the foregoing.

*Instructions:* Journalize the foregoing transactions. (Show calculations.)

**13-8.** Information relative to the A. M. Abbott Company's investments during 1958 follows:

Jan.   6.  Purchased 200 shares of Ace common stock, $50 par, for $17,700.

Feb.  11.  Purchased as a long-term investment $50,000 of Baldwin First Mortgage Bonds, maturity date October 1, 1962, interest of 6% payable semiannually on April 1 and October 1, at 105 plus brokerage of $160 and accrued interest.

Mar.  15.  Received a cash dividend of 75 cents and stock dividend of 1 share for every 4 held on Ace common stock.

April  1.  Received semiannual interest on bonds held. (Bond premium amortization by the straight-line method is recorded at the time interest is received.)

June  15.  Received a cash dividend of 75 cents on Ace common stock. Also was granted the right to purchase 1 share of stock at 54 for every 5 shares held, the option expiring July 1. Stock had a market value of $59 ex-rights, and each stock right had a market value of $1 on the date the rights were issued.

June  30.  Sold 100 rights at 1½ and exercised option on remaining rights.

July  18.  Purchased 100 shares of Ace common stock at 55.

Sept. 12.  Sold $10,000 of Baldwin bonds at 104 and accrued interest less brokerage fees of $40.

Sept. 15.  Received a cash dividend of 75 cents on Ace common stock.

Oct.   1.  Received semiannual interest on bonds held.

Dec.  15.  Received a regular cash dividend of 75 cents and an extra dividend of 25 cents on Ace common stock.

Dec.  28.  Sold 300 shares of Ace common stock for $16,440. (The first-in, first-out method is used in calculating the cost of shares sold.)

Dec.  31.  Adjusted the accounts relative to the foregoing.

*Instructions:* Journalize the foregoing transactions. (Show calculations.)

**13-9.** In auditing the books for the Dalton Corporation as of December 31, 1958, before the accounts are closed, you find the following long-term investment account balance:

INVESTMENT IN BEVERLY CORP.   6's   (Maturity Date, May 1, 1964)

| | |
|---|---|
| January 22, 1958<br>Bonds, $50,000 par, acquired<br>at 102¼ plus accrued interest.. 51,800 | March 10, 1958<br>Proceeds from sale of bonds,<br>$10,000 par and accrued interest..................... 10,650 |
| | May 1<br>Interest received.......... 1,200 |
| | November 1<br>Amount received on call of<br>bonds, $10,000 par, at 102½<br>and accrued interest........ 11,450 |

*Instructions:* (1) Give the entries that should have been made relative to the investment in bonds, including any adjusting entries that would be made on December 31, the end of the fiscal year. (Assume bond premium amortization by the straight-line method.

(2) Give the journal entries required at the end of 1958 to correct and bring the accounts up to date in view of the entries that were actually made.

# Chapter 14

## INVESTMENTS

## FUNDS AND MISCELLANEOUS ITEMS

**KINDS OF FUNDS** Cash and other assets set apart for certain common purposes are called *funds, sinking funds,* or *redemption funds.* Some funds are appropriately reported as current assets, since they are to be used for specified current purposes such as operating expenses and the discharge of current obligations. Examples of these are petty cash funds; payroll funds; withholding tax, social security, and other tax funds; interest funds; and dividend funds. Other funds consisting of cash and investments accumulated over a long term for such purposes as the acquisition or the replacement of properties, the retirement of long-term indebtedness, the redemption of capital stock, or provision for possible future contingencies are properly considered noncurrent and are reported under the investment heading. Example of these are bond retirement funds; preferred stock redemption funds; pension funds; funds for accidents, fires, and other contingencies; and funds for the expansion of plant and equipment.

A fund may be voluntarily created by management or it may be required by contract. It may arise from a single deposit or from a series of deposits, or it may be composed of the sum of the deposits plus the earnings identified with such deposits. The fund may be used for a single purpose, such as the retirement of bonds at maturity, or it may be used for several related purposes, such as the periodic payment of interest on bonds, the retirement of bonds at various intervals, and the ultimate retirement of the remaining bonded indebtedness.

When a fund is created by management, control of the fund and its disposition is an arbitrary matter depending upon the wishes of management. When a fund is created through some legal requirement, it must be administered and applied in accordance therewith. Such a fund is generally administered by one or more trustees under a trust agreement known as a *trust indenture.*

Although a trustee may be in control of assets that he is ultimately to apply to the retirement of debt, such a fund should not be viewed as a reduction in debt unless it has been specifically agreed that payment to the trustee frees the transferor from any further obligation. Normally, the trustee plan is simply an arrangement for debt liquidation, and losses from fund misappropriation or from declines in the values of fund assets do not relieve the corporation of responsibility for full payment. Under such circumstances a fund under the control of a trustee calls for the same accounting that would be followed for a fund accumulated and controlled by its owner.

**FUND ACCUMULATION** When a corporation is required by agreement to establish a fund for a certain purpose, such as to insure payment of bonds or to redeem preferred stock, the agreement generally provides that (1) fund deposits shall be arbitrary amounts or shall vary according to gross income, net income, or units of product sold, or (2) deposits shall be equal periodic sums, such deposits plus earnings on the fund balance to accumulate to the desired amount at some future date. The latter arrangement is based on compound-interest factors, and compound-interest tables are used in determining the equal periodic deposits. Use of such a table, for example, indicates that a fund of $100,000, to be produced by a series of 5 equal annual deposits at 4% compounded annually, requires periodic deposits of $18,462.71. A schedule can be developed to show the hypothetical fund accumulation through deposits and earnings. Such a schedule is illustrated below:

FUND ACCUMULATION SCHEDULE

| YEAR | EARNINGS ON BALANCE OF FUND FOR PERIOD | AMOUNT DEPOSITED IN FUND | TOTAL INCREASE IN FUND FOR PERIOD | ACCUMULATED TOTAL ON DEPOSIT |
|------|------|------|------|------|
| 1 |  | $18,462.71 | $18,462.71 | $18,462.71 |
| 2 | $  738.51 | 18,462.71 | 19,201.22 | 37,663.93 |
| 3 | 1,506.56 | 18,462.71 | 19,969.27 | 57,633.20 |
| 4 | 2,305.33 | 18,462.71 | 20,768.04 | 78,401.24 |
| 5 | 3,136.05 | 18,462.71 | 21,598.76 | 100,000.00 |

Assuming deposits at the end of each year, the table shows $18,462.71 in the fund at the end of the first year as a result of the first deposit. At the end of the second year the fund is increased by (1) earnings at 4% on the investment in the fund during the year, $738.51, and (2) the second deposit to the fund, $18,462.71. The total in the fund at this time is $37,663.93. Fund earnings in the following year are based on a total investment of $37,663.93 as of the beginning of the year.

Although the schedule is set up on the assumption of an annual 4% return, various factors, such as fluctuations in the earning rate and gains and losses on investments, may result in earnings that differ from the assumed amounts. If the fund is to be maintained in accordance with the accumulation schedule, deposits may be adjusted periodically to bring the fund to the required accumulation. Annual fund income in excess of the assumed rate will make possible a smaller deposit; annual earnings that fail to meet the assumed rate will make necessary a larger deposit.

**ACCOUNTING FOR FUNDS**     Fund transactions involving investments in stocks and bonds call for recording and valuation procedures as described in the preceding pages. When a fund is set up on a voluntary basis and is administered by the company, fund transactions may be recorded currently on the company records. When fund deposits are administered by a trustee, the trustee submits periodic reports summarizing fund activities to the company. The summary of fund activities for the period can then be recorded on the company books. The trustee will have to maintain adequate records so that he will be able to report on fund stewardship. Such records are best kept in double-entry form.

The example on page 420 illustrates the accounting that may be followed for a fund when (1) information is recorded on the company's books currently and (2) information is summarized on the company's books from summaries provided by a separate set of books maintained by a fund trustee. The example assumes the establishment of a fund for the retirement of bonds and gives the entries for the fund accumulation for the first year and the entries for debt retirement in the last year.

It should be observed that when separate books are maintained by a trustee, assets are balanced by an account with the company summarizing the trustee's accountability. This account is credited for assets received from the company as well as for the increase in assets resulting from earnings; it is charged for assets applied to the purpose for which the fund was established as well as for assets returned to the company. The fund account on the company's books, in turn, reports the company's investment in fund assets. This account is charged for assets transferred to the trustee and for the increase in assets resulting from fund earnings; it is credited for assets applied to the purpose for which the fund was established and for the individual assets transferred to the company by the trustee. The company account on the trustee's books and the fund account on the company's books are *reciprocal accounts,* since the credit balance in the company account is equal to the debit balance in the fund account when both sets of books are up to date. When a company administers a fund and desires to remove fund detail from the general ledger, a separate ledger can be provided in a form similar to that employed by the trustee in the example.

| Transaction | Fund Transactions Recorded Currently on Company's Books |
|---|---|
| | Entry |
| *1958:*<br>JUNE 30, 1958<br>The Powell Corporation made the first of a series of 20 equal semiannual deposits of $40,000 to bond retirement fund. | Bond Retirement Fund Cash........ 40,000<br>  Cash ..........     40,000 |
| JULY 6, 1958<br>Purchased bond retirement fund securities for $35,725, which includes accrued interest of $125. | Bond Retirement Fund Securities..... 35,600<br>Bond Retirement Fund Income — Interest ............ 125<br>  Bond Retirement Fund Cash......     35,725 |
| DECEMBER 1, 1958<br>Received interest on bond retirement fund securities, $750. | Bond Retirement Fund Cash........ 750<br>  Bond Retirement Fund Inc. — Int.     750 |
| DECEMBER 31, 1958<br>Paid bond retirement fund custodian fees, $200. | Bond Retirement Fund Expenses — Fees.............. 200<br>  Bond Retirement Fund Cash......     200 |
| Made second deposit of $40,000 to bond retirement fund. | Bond Retirement Fund Cash........ 40,000<br>  Cash..........     40,000 |
| To record accrued interest on bond retirement fund securities and cash deposits, $160. | Accrued Interest on Bond Retirement Fund Securities..... 160<br>  Bond Retirement Fund Inc. — Int.     160 |
| To record amortization of premium on bond retirement fund securities, $100. | Bond Retirement Fund Inc. — Int... 100<br>  Bond Retirement Fund Securities...     100 |
| (a) To recognize bond retirement fund income and expense.<br>(b) To close bond retirement fund income and expense balances. | (b) Bond Retirement Fund Income — Interest....... 685<br>  Bond Retirement Fund Expenses — Fees     200<br>  Profit and Loss..     485 |
| *1967:*<br>DECEMBER 31, 1967<br>Sold bond retirement fund securities, book value after amortization entries, $1,060,000, for $1,100,000, including accrued interest, $8,000, total proceeds being added to bond retirement fund cash on hand on this date of $15,000. | Bond Retirement Fund Cash........ 1,100,000<br>  Bond Retirement Fund Securities...     1,060,000<br>  Bond Retirement Fund Inc. — Int.     8,000<br>  Gain on Sale of Bond Retirement Fund Securities...     32,000 |

Fund Transactions Recorded Currently on Trustee's Books

| Entry on Corporation's Books | Entry on Trustee's Books |
|---|---|
| Bond Retirement Fund—<br>A.G. Shaw, Trustee...... 40,000<br>   Cash............... 40,000 | Cash............. 40,000<br>   The Powell Cor-<br>   poration........ 40,000 |
| | Investments in<br>Securities......... 35,600<br>Interest Income.... 125<br>   Cash.......... 35,725 |
| | Cash............. 750<br>   Interest Income.. 750 |
| | Expenses......... 200<br>   Cash.......... 200 |
| Bond Retirement Fund—<br>A.G. Shaw, Trustee...... 40,000<br>   Cash............... 40,000 | Cash............. 40,000<br>   The Powell Cor-<br>   poration........ 40,000 |
| | Accrued Interest<br>on Securities...... 160<br>   Interest Income.. 160 |
| | Interest Income.... 100<br>   Investments in<br>   Securities........ 100 |
| (a) Bond Retirement Fund<br>   —A.G. Shaw, Trustee. 485<br>   Bond Retirement Fund<br>   Expenses—Fees...... 200<br>      Bond Retirement<br>      Fund Inc. — Interest 685<br>(b) Bond Retirement Fund<br>   Income—Interest.... 685<br>      Bond Retirement<br>      Fund Exp. — Fees.. 200<br>      Profit and Loss.... 485 | Interest Income.... 685<br>   Expenses........ 200<br>   The Powell Cor-<br>   poration........ 485 |
| | Cash............. 1,100,000<br>   Investments in<br>   Securities...... 1,060,000<br>   Interest Income.. 8,000<br>   Gain on Sale of<br>   Bond Retirement<br>   Fund Securities... 32,000 |

| Transaction | Fund Transactions Recorded Currently on Company's Books |
|---|---|
| | Entry |
| Paid bonded indebtedness from bond retirement fund cash, $1,000,000 | Bonds Payable..... 1,000,000<br>  Bond Retirement<br>  Fund Cash......      1,000,000 |
| Transferred bond retirement fund cash on hand after payment of bonds to cash account. | Cash............. 115,000<br>  Bond Retirement<br>  Fund Cash......      115,000 |
| (a) To recognize bond retirement fund income and expense.<br>(b) To close nominal accounts relating to bond retirement fund activities. | (b) Bond Retirement<br>    Fund Income—<br>    Interest.......  8,000<br>    Gain on Sale of<br>    Bond Retirement<br>    Fund Securities.. 32,000<br>      Profit and Loss     40,000 |

In the example, bond retirement fund assets as shown on the company's books or as reported to the company by the trustee are as follows at the end of 1958:

| | |
|---|---:|
| Bond Retirement Fund Cash.......................... | $44,825 |
| Bond Retirement Fund Securities...................... | 35,500 |
| Accrued Interest on Bond Retirement Fund Securities..... | 160 |
| Total............................................ | $80,485 |

Bond retirement fund income for 1958 is $685 and bond retirement fund expense is $200; the difference, $485, represents the net fund increase from earnings. This amount is reported on the income statement as Other Income. A gain or a loss on the sale of fund securities would be recognized as an extraordinary item. The individual assets in the fund would be reported under the investments heading on the balance sheet.

The foregoing illustration assumed purchase of securities other than bonds originally issued by the company. Bond retirement fund cash is commonly used to purchase a company's own bonds. Use of the fund for bond purchases frequently operates to support a firm market price for the issue, since the company can enter the market whenever the market price makes retirement of the company's bonds attractive.

When a company acquires its own bonds through bond retirement fund cash and retires them, the liability is canceled, the fund cash account is credited, and a loss or gain on the retirement is recorded. For

Fund Transactions Recorded Currently on Trustee's Books

| Entry on Corporation's Books | Entry on Trustee's Books |
|---|---|
| Bonds Payable..... 1,000,000<br>  Bond Retirement<br>  Fund—A.G. Shaw,<br>  Trustee.........          1,000,000 | The Powell Cor-<br>poration......... 1,000,000<br>  Cash..........            1,000,000 |
| Cash............    115,000<br>  Bond Retirement<br>  Fund—A. G.<br>  Shaw, Trustee...        115,000 | The Powell Cor-<br>poration......... 115,000<br>  Cash..........            115,000 |
| (a) Bond Retirement<br>    Fund—A. G.<br>    Shaw, Trustee..  40,000<br>    Interest Income       8,000<br>    Gain on Sale<br>    of Bond Re-<br>    tirement Fund<br>    Securities....        32,000<br>(b) Interest Income.  8,000<br>  Gain on Sale of<br>  Bond Retire-<br>  ment Fund Se-<br>  curities........  32,000<br>    Profit and Loss       40,000 | Interest Income....    8,000<br>Gain on Sale of Bond<br>Retirement Fund Se-<br>curities............  32,000<br>  The Powell Cor-<br>  poration........        40,000 |

example, assume that the books of a company show bonds of $100,000 outstanding with an unamortized bond discount balance relating to this issue of $3,500. The company acquires and formally retires bonds with a face value of $10,000 at a cost of $9,800. The entry to record the bond retirement follows:

| | | |
|---|---|---|
| 5% Bonds Payable.............................. | 10,000 | |
| Loss on Bond Retirement......................... | 150 | |
|   Bond Retirement Fund Cash................... | | 9,800 |
|   Unamortized Bond Discount................... | | 350 |

To record bond retirement at a loss as follows:

| | | |
|---|---|---|
| Amount paid on retirement..... | | $9,800 |
| Book value of bonds retired: | | |
|   Face value................. | $10,000 | |
|   Less unamortized discount ap-<br>  plicable to bonds......... | 350 | 9,650 |
| Loss on retirement............ | | $ 150 |

When bonds are acquired by a trustee and kept "alive," such bonds are sometimes carried on the books the same as any other investment. The trustee records the bonds at cost, collects interest on the bonds and records collections as income, applies accumulation and amortization procedures in calculating effective earnings, and reports a gain or a loss on the resale of bonds to outsiders. The treatment of reacquired bonds as an investment results in periodic cash transfers to the trustee representing bond interest and permits a cash accumulation in accordance with scheduled requirements. Interest paid by the corporation on its own bonds is counterbalanced by interest received by the trustee. Any difference between the liability book value and the amount paid upon bond reacquisition is deferred and recognized over the remaining life of the bond issue through the discount and premium amortization entries made by the corporation and the trustee on bonds issued and bonds held respectively.

The treatment of bond reacquisition as an investment is not supportable in theory. Reacquired bonds, even though in the hands of a corporate agent, cannot be considered an asset by the corporation. Such bonds are, in effect, evidence of debt retirement. Reacquired bonds may be sold and thus provide additional cash, but this is also true of unissued bonds; both reacquired and unissued bonds must be viewed as no more than instruments that may be used in future borrowing.

The treatment of bond reacquisition as a retirement by an entry similar to that on page 423 may call for an increase in the deposit schedule to compensate for the loss of interest in the fund accumulation. The larger deposit transfers are accompanied by reduced interest payments in the absence of interest accruals on bonds reacquired by the trustee. If bond reissue takes place, the sale is treated the same as sale of an original issue, any premium or discount on the reissue being identified with the remaining life of the bond lot resold. The treatment of bond reacquisitions as bond retirement should be followed even though this calls for adjustments in a plan for systematic fund accumulation.

The accounting procedures described for the bond retirement fund are applicable for other investment funds mentioned earlier.

**PREFERRED STOCK REDEMPTION FUNDS**  Funds are frequently established for the acquisition and the retirement of preferred stock. Such funds may be required by the terms of the preferred stock issue or they may be voluntarily established by the corporation. The preferred stock contract may indicate a stated redemption value or a scale of redemption values related to specified periods when the preferred stock may be called in for redemption.

The transfer of cash to the stock redemption fund increases the balance in the fund; the reacquisition of the company's stock reduces this balance. The amount paid on the redemption of preferred stock may be more or less than the amount received on the original sale of the stock.

*Amount Paid on Stock Redemption Less than Original Investment by Stockholders.* When the amount paid on stock redemption is less than the amount received on the original issue of the stock, there is general agreement that the part of the original investment retained by the company should continue to maintain its original status as paid-in capital. In recording the transaction, original paid-in capital accounts are eliminated, and a new paid-in capital balance is recognized for the paid-in capital retained. For example, assume that 1,000 shares of $50 par preferred stock, originally issued at $55, are reacquired at $53. The stock redemption is recorded as follows:

| | | |
|---|---|---|
| Preferred Stock.................................. | 50,000 | |
| Premium on Preferred Stock..................... | 5,000 | |
| Preferred Stock Redemption Fund Cash.......... | | 53,000 |
| Paid-in Capital — From Preferred Stock Redemption...................................... | | 2,000 |

*Amount Paid on Stock Redemption in Excess of Original Investment by Stockholders.* When the amount paid on stock redemption exceeds the amount received on the original issue of the stock, there is general agreement that such excess should be viewed as a distribution of retained earnings in settlement of the retiring equity. Retained Earnings, then, is charged for the difference between the cash payment and the paid-in capital elimination. To illustrate, assume that 1,000 shares of $50 par preferred stock, originally issued at $51, are reacquired at $54. The entry to record the stock redemption is:

| | | |
|---|---|---|
| Preferred Stock.................................. | 50,000 | |
| Premium on Preferred Stock..................... | 1,000 | |
| Retained Earnings .............................. | 3,000 | |
| Preferred Stock Redemption Fund Cash.......... | | 54,000 |

The subject of stock redemption and retirement is further discussed in Chapter 21.

**FUNDS AND RETAINED EARNINGS APPROPRIATIONS**  The creation of a fund is frequently accompanied by an appropriation of retained earnings. While the two operations may be related, one should distinguish between the nature and purpose of the fund and of the appropriation. The establishment of a fund insures the availability of assets for a specific purpose; the appropriation of retained earnings makes a portion of past earnings temporarily unavailable as a basis for dividend declaration. The latter action prevents working capital from being depleted through both fund accumulations and dividend payments.

The following entries report the transfer of cash to the plant expansion fund and the appropriation of retained earnings.

| | | |
|---|---|---|
| Plant Expansion Fund Cash | 50,000 | |
| Cash | | 50,000 |
| Retained Earnings | 50,000 | |
| Retained Earnings Appropriated for Plant Expansion Fund | | 50,000 |

Fund accumulation accompanied by periodic appropriations of retained earnings and the limitation of dividends may be required by the terms of the contract with the creditor group. On the other hand, such actions may be voluntarily authorized by management.

**MISCELLANEOUS INVESTMENTS**    A great many assets could be named that are of an auxiliary character so far as the main business activities are concerned and that are properly reportable under the investments heading. If such assets do not produce current interest, dividends, or other income, it is expected by management that they will ultimately have a favorable business effect in some other way. For example, a purchase of adjoining property is made in advance of needs because it is felt that such acquisition in the future will be possible only at materially higher costs. Or a long-term loan is made to an old customer because it is believed that the loan will carry him through a financial crisis and he will continue as a profitable customer after the present strain has passed. Several investment items and the related accounting problems commonly found are considered in the remaining sections of this chapter.

**CASH SURRENDER VALUE OF LIFE INSURANCE**    Many business enterprises carry life insurance policies on the lives of their executives. It is recognized that the corporation has a very definite stake in the continuing services of its officers, and the insurance plan affords a financial cushion in the event of the loss of such personnel. Insurance premiums that exceed basic insurance charges produce a *cash surrender value* that is payable in the event of policy cancellation. If this cash surrender value belongs to the corporation, it should be reported as an investment.

The actual insurance expense for a fiscal period is the difference between the amount of the insurance payment and the increase in the cash surrender value for the period. The increase in the cash surrender value is ordinarily relatively uniform after the first year of the policy. At the end of the first year there may be no cash surrender value, or, if there is such a value, it may be quite low, because the insurance company must recover certain costs in connection with selling and initiating the policy. The cost of life insurance to the business, then, may be considered correspondingly high during the first year of the policy because of the starting costs involved.

An insurance policy with a cash surrender value also has a *loan value*; this is the amount that the insurance company will permit the insured to borrow on the policy. When the insured uses the policy as a basis for a loan, the amount borrowed should be recorded as a liability and not as a reduction in the cash value. Such loans may be liquidated by the insured by payments of principal together with a required rate of interest; or the loans may be continuing, to be applied against the insurance proceeds upon policy cancellation or ultimate settlement.

The loan that an insurance company will make on a policy is normally limited to the policy cash surrender value at the end of the policy year less discount from the loan date to the cash surrender value date. For example, assume a cash surrender value of $3,000 at the end of a fifth policy year. The maximum loan value on the policy at the beginning of the fifth policy year, assuming that the insurance premium for the fifth year is paid, is $3,000 discounted for one year. If the discount rate applied by the insurance company is 5%, the policy loan value is calculated as follows: $3,000 ÷ 1.05 = $2,857.14.

Although it would be possible to recognize policy loan values instead of cash surrender values, the latter practice is generally followed.

The insured may authorize the insurance company to apply any dividends that may be declared upon insurance policies to the reduction of the annual premium payment or to the increase in insurance cash surrender value, or he may collect such dividends in cash. Dividends should be viewed as a reduction in the cost of carrying insurance rather than as a source of supplementary income. Hence, if dividends are applied to the reduction of the annual premium, Insurance Expense is simply debited for the net amount paid. If the dividend is applied to the increase in the policy cash surrender value or if it is collected in cash, it should still be treated as an offset to the periodic expense of carrying the policy; the policy cash surrender value or Cash, then, is charged and Insurance Expense is credited. After a number of years, the periodic dividends plus increases in the cash surrender value may exceed the premium payments, thus producing an income balance rather than an expense balance on policy holdings.

Collection of a policy calls for a cancellation of any investment balance. Collection of a policy as a result of the death of the insured requires the recognition of an increase in capital represented by the difference between the insurance proceeds and the balances relating to the insurance policy. The nature of the insurance policies carried and their coverage should be disclosed by appropriate comment on the balance sheet.

For income tax purposes no deduction may be taken by an employer for the payment of life insurance premiums on officers or employees when the employer is directly or indirectly the beneficiary thereof. The amount recovered on the surrender of an insurance contract represents taxable income to the extent that this exceeds total policy payments; the policy here is viewed as an investment that has realized an amount exceeding its cost. Amounts collected on a policy by reason of the death of the insured, however, are free from income tax.

The entries to be made for an insurance contract are illustrated in the example that follows. The Andrews Manufacturing Company insured the life of its president, W. E. Andrews, on October 1, 1956. The amount of the policy was $50,000; the annual premiums were $2,100. The following table gives for each of the first three policy years the gross premium, the dividend, the net premium, the increase in cash value, and the net expense for the insurance.

| Year | Gross Premium | Dividend | Net Premium | Increase in Cash Value | Insurance Expense for Year |
|------|------|------|------|------|------|
| 1 | $2,100 | $ — | $2,100 | $ — | $2,100 |
| 2 | 2,100 | — | 2,100 | 1,150 | 950 |
| 3 | 2,100 | 272 | 1,828 | 1,300 | 528 |

The fiscal period for the company was the calendar year. Mr. Andrews died on July 1, 1959. The entries made in recording transactions relating to the insurance contract follow:

| Transaction | Entry | | |
|---|---|---|---|
| **OCTOBER 1, 1956** <br> Paid first annual premium, $2,100. | Prepaid Insurance... <br> Cash........... | 2,100.00 | 2,100.00 |
| **DECEMBER 31, 1956** <br> To record insurance expense for Oct. 1–Dec. 31: <br> ¼ × $2,100, or $525. | Life Insurance Expense............. <br> Prepaid Insurance | 525.00 | 525.00 |
| **OCTOBER 1, 1957** <br> Paid second annual premium, $2,100. <br> Premium............ $2,100 <br> Less cash surrender value............... 1,150 <br> Net insurance charge... $ 950 | Cash Surrender Value of Life Insurance (as of 10/1/58). <br> Prepaid Insurance.. <br> Cash........... | 1,150.00 <br> 950.00 | 2,100.00 |
| **DECEMBER 31, 1957** <br> To record insurance expense for the year: <br> ¾ × $2,100 (Jan. 1–Sept. 30) $1,575.00 <br> ¼ × $950 (Oct. 1–Dec. 31) 237.50 <br> $1,812.50 | Life Insurance Expense............. <br> Prepaid Insurance | 1,812.50 | 1,812.50 |

| Transaction | Entry | | |
|---|---|---|---|
| **OCTOBER 1, 1958** | Cash Surrender | | |
| Paid third annual premium, $2,100. | Value of Life Insur- | | |
|   Premium . . . . . . . . . . . . . $2,100 | ance (as of 10/1/59) . | 1,300.00 | |
|   Less: Cash surrender | Prepaid Insurance . . | 528.00 | |
|       value credit . . . . . . $1,300 | Cash . . . . . . . . . . . | | 1,828.00 |
|       Dividend credit . . .  272  1,572 | | | |
|   Net insurance charge . . . . . . . . . $ 528 | | | |
| **DECEMBER 31, 1958** | Life Insurance Ex- | | |
| To record insurance expense for the year: | pense . . . . . . . . . . . . | 844.50 | |
|   ¾×$950 (Jan. 1–Sept. 30) . . . $712.50 |   Prepaid Insurance | | 844.50 |
|   ¼×$528 (Oct. 1–Dec. 31) . . .  132.00 | | | |
|                      $844.50 | | | |
| **JULY 1, 1959** | Life Insurance Ex- | | |
| To record insurance expense for Jan. 1– | pense . . . . . . . . . . . . | 264.00 | |
| July 1: |   Prepaid Insurance | | 264.00 |
|   ½×$528, or $264. | | | |
| **JULY 1, 1959** | Receivable from In- | | |
| To record cancellation of policy upon | surance Company . . . | 50,735.00 | |
| death of insured: |   Cash Surrender | | |
|   Amount recoverable on policy: |   Value of Life In- | | |
|     Face of policy . . . . . . . . . . . $50,000 |   surance Policy . . . . | | 2,450.00 |
|     Premium rebate for period |   Prepaid Insurance | | 132.00 |
|     July 1–Oct. 1 and current |   Gain on Settle- | | |
|     year dividend . . . . . . . . . . . .  735 |   ment of Life Insur- | | |
|                   $50,735 |   ance Policy . . . . . . | | 48,153.00 |
|   Cancellation of asset values: | | | |
|     Cash surrender value . . . . . . $ 2,450 | | | |
|     Prepaid insurance . . . . . . . .  132 | | | |
|                 $ 2,582 | | | |
|   Gain on policy settlement . . . . $48,153 | | | |

It should be observed in the example that cash surrender value increases are recognized on the books whenever a premium is paid. The periodic insurance premium includes a charge for the increase in the policy cash surrender value but such increase actually becomes effective only as of the end of the policy year. Hence, anticipation of the cash surrender value on the date of the premium payment needs to be accompanied by a notation as to the effective date of such value. Anticipation of the cash surrender value should also be disclosed in presenting this asset on the balance sheet. If loan values instead of cash surrender values were recognized, no notation would be required since the loan values become effective immediately upon meeting premium requirements for the policy year. Dividends in the example reduce the insurance charge of the period in which they are applied against a premium. Actually the dividend applied against the premium for the third year accrues at the end of the second year and could be considered as a correction in the expense of the second year. Dividends received in the period of policy termination are recognized as a part of policy proceeds in final settlement rather than as a correction of insurance expense. The procedures that are illustrated while involving certain concessions in theoretical accuracy are normally preferred because of their practicality.

**INTERESTS IN REAL ESTATE**  Improved property purchased for supplementary income and for possible price appreciation or future use is shown under the investment heading. The expenses relating to such holdings should be deducted from any revenue produced by the property. Unimproved property is frequently acquired for possible future use or for sale. Land while unused makes no contribution to the annual income. This would suggest that any costs incident to its holding need not be deducted from current earnings but may be added to the investment balance. When the land is used for construction purposes or is sold, its cost will include all expenditures incident to its acquisition and holding.

**ADVANCES**  Advances to subsidiaries are normally considered long-term investments in the absence of definite information that amounts advanced will be collected currently. Such advances are sometimes presented on the balance sheet as additions to the investment in stock. But advances should be reported separately, since they represent claims against the subsidiary, while the investment in stock reflects an ownership interest. Advances of a long-term character to other parties are also classified as investments.

**DEPOSITS**  Deposits to guarantee contract performance, to maintain various memberships, or to secure certain privileges or services, if not to be recovered currently, are usually reported as investment items.

**INTERESTS IN PARTNERSHIPS**  Interests in partnerships or joint ventures should be shown as investments on the books of the individual partners. An investment account is charged for the contribution made by the individual to the partnership. This account is charged for any further contributions and for any profits of the partnership increasing the partner's individual interest; it is credited for any withdrawals and for any losses decreasing his interest.

The reciprocal nature of the investment balance on the partner's own books and the related interest on the partnership books is illustrated in the example that follows:

| Transactions | Separate<br>Books of Partner A | | Partnership Books<br>Firm of A and B | |
|---|---|---|---|---|
| Cash invested by partners:<br>A............ $20,000<br>B............ 25,000<br>———<br>$45,000 | Investment in<br>Firm of A and<br>B.......... 20,000<br>Cash...... | <br><br><br>20,000 | Cash........ 45,000<br>A, Capital...... 20,000<br>B, Capital...... 25,000 | |
| Cash withdrawals by part-<br>ners for period:<br>A............ $ 2,500<br>B............ 4,000<br>———<br>$ 6,500 | Cash........ 2,500<br>Investment<br>in Firm of<br>A and B... 2,500 | | A, Capital. 2,500<br>B, Capital. 4,000<br>Cash...... 6,500 | |
| Profit for partnership for<br>period, $12,000, divided be-<br>tween A and B in profit and<br>loss ratio of 2:3:<br><br>A, $\frac{2}{5} \times$ $12,000.. $ 4,800<br><br>B, $\frac{3}{5} \times$ $12,000.. 7,200<br>———<br>$12,000 | Investment in<br>Firm of A and<br>B.......... 4,800<br>Income<br>from Part-<br>nership.... 4,800 | | Profit and<br>Loss........ 12,000<br>A, Capital. 4,800<br>B, Capital. 7,200 | |

At the end of the period, the partnership books report net assets and equities as follows:

| | | | |
|---|---|---|---|
| Assets.................. | $50,500 | A, Capital.............. | $22,300 |
| | | B, Capital.............. | 28,200 |
| | $50,500 | | $50,500 |

The books of A follow changes in the interest of A in partnership assets and report an investment balance in the partnership of $22,300.

**INTERESTS IN TRUSTS AND ESTATES**    When a party acquires an interest in a trust or an estate, such interest should be recorded as an investment on the beneficiary's books. The investment account is charged for any increases in this interest resulting from income and gains and is credited for any decreases resulting from expenses, losses, or from asset distributions made to the beneficiary. Accounting for an interest in a trust or an estate, then, is similar to that for an interest in a partnership.

**INVESTMENTS ON THE BALANCE SHEET**    The investment classification on the balance sheet generally follows the current asset classification. The investment section should not include temporary investments held as a ready source of cash. The different investment catagories should be individually listed with appropriate detail provided in separate supporting schedules. Investment costs should be supplemented by market quotations offered in parenthetical or note form. Any investment pledges should be fully disclosed. When investments include funds that are to be applied to specific purposes or paid to specific parties, disclosure should be made by special note as to the conditions relative to their establishment and ultimate application. Offset of a fund balance against a liability item is proper only when an asset transfer to a trustee is irrevocable and actually serves to discharge the obligation.

The investment section of a balance sheet might appear as follows:

Investments:

Affiliated companies:
| | | |
|---|---:|---:|
| Investment in Wilson Co., not consolidated, representing 90% interest (90,000 shares reported at cost on date of acquisition, July 1, 1956; retained earnings of subsidiary since date of acquisition have increased by $120,000, $108,000 being identified with parent's equity)................... | $1,500,000 | |
| Advances to Wilson Co................... | 115,000 | $1,615,000 |
| Miscellaneous stock investments (reported at cost, market value $112,000; securities have been deposited as security on bank loan — refer to notes payable, contra)............. | | 100,000 |
| Bond retirement fund in hands of trustee, composed of: | | |
| Cash.................... | $ 15,000 | |
| Stocks and bonds (market value, $420,000), at cost.................... | 410,500 | |
| Dividends and interest receivable........... | 4,500 | 430,000 |
| Investment in land and unused facilities......... | | 65,000 |
| Cash surrender value of insurance carried on officers' lives............. | | 12,500 |
| Total investments.................... | | $2,222,500 |

## QUESTIONS

**1.** Name at least ten items that are properly reported under the investment heading on the balance sheet.

**2.** Name and describe five funds that would be listed as current assets and five that would be listed as investments.

**3.** Give the general ledger entries that would be made for each of the transactions below, assuming that fund transactions are summarized (1) in the general ledger and (2) in a separate ledger.
  (a) Cash is transferred to the bond retirement fund.
  (b) Fund cash is invested in securities of other companies.
  (c) Income is received on fund securities.
  (d) Fund securities are sold at a profit.
  (e) Fund cash is used to redeem bonds outstanding.
  (f) Fund cash not required for bond redemption is transferred to the general cash account.

**4.** (a) What alternative treatments can be employed in accounting for a company's own bonds purchased from bond retirement fund cash and kept alive in the fund? (b) Which do you favor? Why?

**5.** The Marshall Co. reports "Bond redemption fund, $200,000," on its balance sheet. You find that the fund consists of the following:

| | |
|---|---:|
| Marshall Co. common stock, at cost..................... | $ 30,000 |
| Stocks and bonds of other companies, at cost, which exceeds | |
| market on the balance sheet date by $15,000............ | 140,000 |
| Cash in bank........................................ | 25,000 |
| Dividends declared and interest accrued on fund securities... | 5,000 |

What changes in presentation should be made? Explain.

**6.** Upon inspecting the books of the Norman Corporation, you find two credits in Retained Earnings for 1958: Retained Earnings was credited for a $3,000 gain arising from the retirement at $47,000 of bonds of $50,000 originally issued at par; Retained Earnings was also credited for $4,500 arising from the redemption at $47,500 of 1,000 shares of preferred stock originally issued at $52,000. What changes, if any, would you suggest?

**7.** (a) Distinguish between a fund and a fund appropriation out of retained earnings. (b) Would you normally recommend an appropriation of retained earnings in fulfilling the objectives of a fund? Explain.

**8.** (a) Distinguish between life insurance cash surrender value and loan value. (b) How is the loan value on a life insurance policy calculated?

**9.** The Melville Company collects in cash the dividends on the life insurance policies that it carries; the Nielson Company uses dividend credits to reduce the life insurance premiums that it pays; The Otto Corporation authorizes the insurance companies to apply dividend credits to the increase of policy cash surrender values. What entries will each company make in recognizing dividends?

**10.** Explain the accounting that is followed on an individual's books in recording the changes in his interest in a partnership as a result of: (a) additional capital contributions, (b) withdrawals, (c) profits, and (d) losses.

**11.** How would you recommend that advances to a subsidiary company be reported on a parent's balance sheet?

**12.** Indicate the balance sheet classification for each of the following:

(a) Land used as parking area for customers.
(b) United States Treasury Bills, to provide income for otherwise idle cash during the slack season.
(c) Land to provide for expansion program at least five years hence.
(d) A company's own bonds in a bond retirement fund.
(e) Accrued interest on company's own bonds in bond retirement fund.
(f) Advance to subsidiary company.
(g) Cash surrender value of insurance policy.
(h) A fund to be used to pay current bond interest.
(i) A preferred stock redemption fund.

## EXERCISES

**1.** Sinking fund tables show that 5 annual deposits of $18,097.48 accruing interest at 5% compounded annually will result in a total accumulation of $100,000 immediately after the fifth payment. Prepare a fund accumulation schedule showing the theoretical growth of the fund over the 5-year period.

**2.** Sinking fund tables show that 10 equal annual deposits of $87,230.51 will produce a fund of $1,000,000 on a 3% basis. Give the entries required for the first three deposits at the beginning of 1958, 1959, and 1960 and for the increases in the bond retirement fund balance for earnings at 3% at the end of 1958, 1959, and 1960.

**3.** The Bronson Company has accumulated a bond retirement fund that shows the following balances on September 1, 1958:

| | | |
|---|---:|---:|
| Cash..................................... | $ 110,000 | |
| Securities............................... | 904,000 | $1,014,000 |

On this date securities are sold for $926,500 plus accrued interest, $10,250. Retirement fund cash is then applied to the retirement of bonds of $1,000,000 maturing on this date and accrued interest on the bonds of $22,500. The balance of the bond retirement fund cash is transferred to the cash account. Give the entries to record the above transactions.

**4.** Give the entries that would be made for each of the following bond retirement fund transactions, assuming that (1) transactions are recorded only on the books of the corporation, and (2) the transactions are recorded on self-balancing books maintained by the trustee and are summarized on the books of the corporation.

  (a) Cash is transferred to the bond retirement fund trustee, $95,000.
  (b) Securities are purchased out of bond retirement fund cash, $85,000.
  (c) Income is collected on bond retirement fund securities, $6,600.
  (d) Expenses are paid out of bond retirement fund cash, $400.
  (e) All of the bond retirement fund securities are sold for $91,000.
  (f) Bonds are redeemed at maturity date out of bond retirement fund cash, $100,000.
  (g) Remaining cash in bond retirement fund is deposited in general cash account.
  (h) Nominal accounts are closed.

**5.** On April 1, 1958, the Rodd Riggs Corporation invested plant expansion fund cash in bonds of the local municipality. The corporation paid $9,500 for ten $1,000, 5% bonds due in 10 years. Interest is payable semiannually on April 1 and October 1. (a) Give all of the entries that would appear on the company's books in 1958 as a result of the investment. (b) How would the bonds appear on the corporation's balance sheet at the end of 1958?

**6.** Peters Sales Co. maintains a fund for the retirement of bonds. Bonds of $1,000,000, paying interest at 5% semiannually on January 1 and July 1 and maturing in 10 years, had been issued at 90 at the beginning of 1950. Cash is paid out of the fund in 1958 as follows:

  March 1 — Bonds of $20,000 were acquired at 97½ plus accrued interest.
  October 1 — Bonds of $5,000 were acquired at 99 plus accrued interest.

Give the entries that would be made in 1958 for bond retirements, periodic interest payments, and bond discount amortization, assuming that the entire bond issue was outstanding at the beginning of the year.

**7.** Biliky, Inc. maintains a fund for the acquisition and the retirement of preferred stock outstanding. At the beginning of 1955, 1,000 shares of 6% preferred stock, par $100, had been issued at 90. Fund disbursements in 1958 are as follows:

April 1 — Stock, par value $10,000, is acquired at 88.
November 1 — Stock, par value $5,000, is acquired at 95½.

Give the entries to record the acquisition and the retirement of preferred stock in 1958.

**8.** The Benjamin Corporation insures the life of its president for $50,000. The policy is effective on January 1, 1955, and premiums are payable on the first of each year beginning on this date. The following table gives the data for the policy for the first four years:

| Year | Gross Premium | Dividend | Net Premium | Increase in Cash Value | Net Cost for Year |
|------|------|------|------|------|------|
| 1 | $2,000 | $— | $2,000 | $ — | $2,000 |
| 2 | 2,000 | — | 2,000 | 1,100 | 900 |
| 3 | 2,000 | 266 | 1,734 | 1,250 | 484 |
| 4 | 2,000 | 266 | 1,734 | 1,350 | 384 |

The fiscal period for the company is the calendar year. The Benjamin Corporation pays the insurance premiums at the beginning of 1955, 1956, 1957, and 1958. The president of the company dies on July 1, 1958, and the face value of the policy and also $1,130 representing premium refund and current year dividend become recoverable as of this date. Give all of the journal entries, including the periodic adjustments, that would appear on the books of the company relative to the above data for the period 1955–1958.

**9.** Aaron and Burke join in a partnership in January, 1958, and agree to share profits and losses in the ratio of 5:3. Changes in their equities during 1958 are summarized below. What entries would be made on the individual books of Aaron and Burke for the following changes in their respective equities in the firm?

Jan. 15. Cash invested in the firm by Aaron and Burke was $50,000 and $25,000 respectively.
Mar. 10. Aaron withdrew cash of $1,500 from the firm.
June 30. Partnership activities for the period January 15-June 30 were summarized and disclosed a net loss of $5,000.
July 15. Burke invested additional cash of $7,500 in the firm.
Dec. 31. Partnership activities for the period July 1-December 31 were summarized and disclosed a net profit of $15,000.

**10.** In 1948 the C. E. Griff Corporation purchased for $50,000 ten acres adjoining its manufacturing plant to provide for possible future expansion. From 1948–1958 the company paid $20,000 in taxes and $30,000 in special assessments. In 1958 it sold one half of its holdings for $75,000 and erected a building at a cost of $300,000 on the other half. The corporation's books on December 31, 1958, show a "plant" account with a balance of $325,000. Journalize the necessary corrections.

## PROBLEMS

**14-1.** The McKenney Corporation wishes to accumulate a fund of $100,000 over a 5-year period. Ten equal deposits are to be made at semi-annual intervals, beginning on June 30, 1958, to accumulate to the desired balance after the deposit on December 31, 1962. It is assumed that the fund will earn 5% compounded semiannually (2½% each six-month period). Fund tables show that deposits of $8,925.88 are required to provide the desired fund.

*Instructions:* (1) Prepare a table similar to that illustrated on page 418 to show the theoretical growth of the fund over the 5-year period.

(2) Give the entries to record the fund increases for deposits and for interest for the years 1958 and 1959.

**14-2.** On January 1, 1958, the books of the Holland Corporation show a balance in a bond retirement fund of $204,000. Books of Clyde T. Suttle trustee in charge of the bond retirement fund for the Holland Corporation, show account balances as follows:

| | | |
|---|---:|---:|
| Cash........................................ | $ 6,550 | |
| Securities.................................. | 196,300 | |
| Accrued Interest on fund securities............ | 1,150 | |
| The Holland Corporation..................... | | $204,000 |
| | $204,000 | $204,000 |

The following transactions take place in 1958:

(a) A deposit of $39,950 was made with the trustee.
(b) Securities were acquired at a cost of $42,500 that included accrued interest of $1,600.
(c) Interest of $10,800 was collected on interest dates on investments.
(d) Trustee's fees and other miscellaneous expenses paid were $850.
(e) Bond retirement fund securities were sold for $240,500 that included accrued interest of $3,200.
(f) Bonds of $250,000 were retired on their maturity date and remaining cash was returned by the trustee to the corporation.

*Instructions:* (1) Give the entries required on the separate books of the trustee to record the foregoing and to close the books upon termination of the trusteeship.

(2) Give any entries that would be made on the corporation books as a result of the foregoing.

**14-3.** The Beecher Corporation maintains a bond redemption and interest fund. Bonds acquired by the trustee of the fund are immediately canceled. Five per cent bonds of $1,000,000, interest payable semiannually on January 1 and July 1, were originally issued at face value. Bonds of $200,000 were retired prior to 1958. The bond fund on January 1, 1958, has a balance of $65,000, and transactions affecting the fund in 1958 are reported below. The trustee keeps no separate books, all fund transactions being reported on the company books.

Jan. 3. A deposit of $50,000 is made to the bond fund.
Feb. 16. Bonds of $50,000 are called at 101 plus accrued interest.

June 30. Interest checks for 6 months ending July 1 are mailed to bond-holders.

July   1. A deposit of $50,000 is made to the bond fund.

Oct.   1. Bonds of $50,000 are purchased on the open market at 99½ plus accrued interest.

Nov.   1. Bonds of $30,000 are purchased at 99¾ plus accrued interest.

Dec. 31. Interest checks for 6 months ending January 1 are mailed to bond-holders.

Dec. 31. Trustee's fees and bond fund expenses of $3,600 for the year are paid.

*Instructions:* Journalize the foregoing transactions.

**14-4.** The Standard Co. has established a pension plan for employees. At the end of each period, Pensions Expense is debited and Estimated Amounts Payable under Pension Plan is credited for the estimated pension requirements. A pension fund is also maintained and is increased by semiannual deposits. Pension payments are recorded by charges to Estimated Amounts Payable under Pension Plan and credits to Pension Fund Cash. The balance in the pension fund and changes in the fund for 1958 follow:

Fund balance, January 1:

| | |
|---|---:|
| Cash............................................................. | $ 15,000 |
| U. S. Treasury 3's, interest payable May 1 and November 1, due May 1, 1970 (acquired at face value)............... | 100,000 |
| Harding Co. 1st Mortgage 5's, interest payable January 1 and July 1, due January 1, 1970 (face $80,000)......... | 82,400 |
| Accrued interest on U. S. Treasury 3's................. | 500 |

The pension fund transactions for 1958 are as follows:

Jan. 15. Cash of $50,000 was transferred to the pension fund.

Feb.   7. Purchased $50,000 of Lakeview County 3% bonds, interest payable April 1 and October 1, at 96½ plus accrued interest. Bonds mature on April 1, 1962.

April  1. Received semiannual interest on Lakeview County 3's.

May    2. Received semiannual interest on U. S. Treasury 3's.

June 30. Pension payments for 6 months were $14,400.

July   1. Received semiannual interest on Harding Co. 5's.

July  15. Cash of $50,000 was transferred to pension fund.

Aug.   1. Purchased $50,000 additional Lakeview County 3's, 1962 series, at 97½ plus accrued interest.

Oct.   1. Received semiannual interest on Lakeview County 3's.

Nov.   1. Received semiannual interest on U. S. Treasury 3's.

Nov.  25. Sold $20,000 of Harding Co. 5's for $21,250, which includes accrued interest on the bonds to this date.

Dec. 31. Pension payments for 6 months amounted to $15,800.

      31. The balance of Estimated Amounts Payable under Pension Plan was increased by $100,000 for the year.

      31. Received semiannual interest on Harding Co. 5's.

*Instructions:* Give the entries required for 1958 as a result of the above, including any adjustments that would be necessary at the end of the year. (Assume that straight-line accumulation and amortization procedures are followed with respect to all bonds in the pension fund, entries being made at the end of the year.)

**14-5.** On September 1, 1954, the Bell Company insured the life of its president, D. V. Call, for $100,000. The policy was dated September 1,

1954; the annual premium was $4,800. Total cash surrender values on the policy were stated as follows: at end of second policy year, $2,400; at end of third policy year, $5,400; at end of fourth policy year, $8,700.

The fiscal period for the company was the calendar year. Premium payments on the insurance policy were made by the company annually on September 1, 1954 through 1957. Dividend credits were applied against premiums as follows: September 1, 1956, $600; September 1, 1957, $606. Mr. Call died on July 1, 1958, and collection of the face value of the policy as well as a premium refund and dividends totaling $1,300 was made on July 22.

*Instructions:* Give all of the journal entries, including the periodic adjustments, that would appear on the books of the company relative to the above data for the years 1954 to 1958.

**14-6.** On March 1, 1956, Smith & Statler, Inc. insured the lives of its officers, E. A. Smith and J. L. Statler, for $50,000 each. A policy for $50,000 was taken out on each officer effective March 1, 1956; the annual premium on each policy was $1,680. Total cash surrender values for each policy were stated as follows: at end of second policy year, $840; at end of third policy year, $1,920.

The fiscal period for the company was the calendar year. Premium payments on the insurance policies were made by the company annually on March 1, 1956 through 1958. Dividend credits were applied against premium payments on each policy on March 1, 1958, of $240. Mr. Smith died on September 1, 1958, and collection was made by the company of the face value of his policy together with a premium refund and dividends totaling $960.

*Instructions:* Give all of the journal entries, including the periodic adjustments, that would appear on the books of the company relative to the above data for the years 1956 to 1958.

**14-7.** The Diamond Coal Company issued $50,000 worth of 4-year, first-mortgage, sinking-fund, 6% bonds dated July 1, 1954. The bonds were sold on September 1, 1954 (with accrued interest) at 103.59, a price at which they were advertised to yield 5% (semiannual coupons are payable June 30 and December 31).

The bond indenture provided (1) that 25 cents per ton mined would be deposited on June 30 of each year with the Central Trust Company for sinking-fund purposes and (2) that a sinking-fund reserve would be set aside on a straight-line basis.

The production of coal was as follows:

| | |
|---|---|
| Year ended June 30, 1955 | 42,000 tons |
| Year ended June 30, 1956 | 56,000 tons |
| Year ended June 30, 1957 | 50,000 tons |
| Year ended June 30, 1958 | 58,000 tons |

The sinking fund earned 4% the first year and 5% thereafter.

*Instructions:* Submit all journal entries necessary to express all these particulars, including periodic adjustments, on the books of the company. Assume that the company's fiscal period is the calendar year. (Income is not to be accrued on the sinking fund but is to be recognized only on June 30 of each year.) (A.I.C.P.A. adapted)

# Chapter 15

# PLANT AND EQUIPMENT

## ACQUISITION, USE, AND RETIREMENT

**NATURE OF PLANT AND EQUIPMENT** The term *plant and equipment* is a classification heading for those tangible properties of a relatively permanent character that are used in the normal conduct of a business. Under the plant and equipment heading are included such items as land, buildings, machinery, equipment, tools, and furniture and fixtures. The term *fixed assets* is frequently used to designate plant properties. It has already been observed, however, that this term may be used in a broader sense to apply to both tangible and intangible properties used in a business. The tendency in present practice to classify noncurrent items under separate titles that describe the specific nature of the assets is to be encouraged.

As in the case of other noncurrent assets, plant and equipment items do not turn over with the speed of current assets. The number of transactions in plant and equipment is relatively small, and the items involved in the transactions are carried over in successive balance sheets. Plant items are acquired, used, and retired. While plant and equipment as a class remains as long as the business continues, the individual items, with the exception of land, have a limited productive life. The cost of plant items is assigned to operations by means of periodic depreciation charges. When an item is entirely used up, its cost should have been deducted from periodic revenues. If operations are to continue, a new asset is substituted for the one retired.

**COMPOSITION OF PLANT AND EQUIPMENT** It is customary to classify plant and equipment items in three principal groups: (1) *land,* (2) *buildings,* and (3) *machinery and equipment.* Land refers to earth surface and includes building sites, parking areas, and yards. Buildings refer to improvements permanently affixed to land and include not only structures but also structure appurtenances such as heating systems, lighting systems, sewers, sidewalks and driveways. Land and its improvements are frequently referred to as *realty.* Machinery and equipment includes such assets as factory machines, hand and machine tools, patterns and dies, store and office equipment, motor vehicles and other transport equipment, and returnable containers.

**CAPITAL AND REVENUE EXPENDITURES** The proper treatment of expenditures incident to the acquisition and use of plant items presents important accounting problems. Plant and equipment expenditures are made for their favorable effect upon operations. In recording such expenditures, it must be determined whether benefits accrue to the present period alone or whether they extend into future periods. An expenditure that benefits only operations of the current period is called a *revenue expenditure* and is recorded as an expense. An expenditure that benefits operations beyond the current period is called a *capital expenditure* and is recorded as an asset. A revenue expenditure is disposed of currently; a capital expenditure is related to the revenue of more than one period by periodic depreciation charges. An expenditure that is recorded as an asset is said to be *capitalized*.

Income cannot be accurately measured unless expenditures relating to plant assets are properly identified and recorded as capital or revenue charges. An incorrect charge to an equipment item instead of to expense, for example, results in the current overstatement of income on the income statement and the overstatement of assets and capital on the balance sheet. As the charge is assigned to operations in future periods, incomes of such periods will be understated; assets and capital on the successive balance sheets will continue to be overstated, although by lesser amounts each year, until the item is entirely written off and the original error has been fully counterbalanced. An incorrect charge to expense instead of to an equipment item, on the other hand, results in the current understatement of income on the income statement and the understatement of both assets and capital on the balance sheet. Income of subsequent periods will be overstated in the absence of charges for asset depreciation; assets and capital on the successive balance sheets will continue to be understated, although by lesser amounts each year, until the original error has been counterbalanced.

Companies frequently adopt an arbitrary practice of charging to expense all plant expenditures of a relatively small amount, perhaps expenditures not exceeding $50 or $100. Such practice is adopted for the sake of expediency; the special analysis of small expenditures, as well as the development and the application of depreciation plans for those that may qualify as capital items, is thus avoided. Normally, adherence to such an arbitrary rule will result in no significant misstatement of plant and equipment costs and periodic income.

**VALUATION OF PLANT AND EQUIPMENT** Land that has an unlimited life is normally reported on the balance sheet at original cost. Other plant items with limited lives are normally shown at cost less that portion of the cost allocated to past operations.  The rule for valuation is frequently described as *cost less accrued depreciation*.  By *accrued depreciation* is meant the sum of the periodic depreciation charges since the asset was acquired.  The cost of an asset less its depreciation to date is known as its *book value*.  Ordinarily no reference to the market values or the replacement values is made in presenting plant and equipment on the balance sheet.  Plant and equipment items are not intended for conversion into cash; accounting for these assets involves the accumulation of their costs and the appropriate assignment of such costs to the revenues emerging from their use.

Cost of a plant item is usually interpreted to mean the minimum cash outlay necessary in its acquisition.  When the plant item is acquired for consideration other than cash, it is the fair market value of the noncash consideration that determines cost; in the absence of such a measure, the plant item is recorded at its fair market value.

The cost of a plant item ordinarily includes all expenditures up to the time it is usable for the purpose for which it was acquired.  All outlays incident to purchase, freight and cartage in, installation, etc., are properly added to the purchase price of the asset in arriving at its accounting cost.

**ACQUISITION OF PLANT AND EQUIPMENT**    There are a number of different ways in which plant and equipment items are acquired.  These need to be considered, since each method of acquisition raises special accounting problems relating to asset cost.  The acquisition of plant properties is discussed under the following headings: (1) purchase for cash, (2) purchase on deferred payment plan, (3) exchange, (4) issuance of securities, (5) self-construction, and (6) gift or discovery.

**PURCHASE FOR CASH**    A plant and equipment item that is acquired for cash is recorded at the amount of the cash outlay.  Incidental outlays relating to its purchase or to its preparation for use are added to the original cost.  Consideration of the special costs on particular asset acquisitions is covered in a later section.

It was suggested in an earlier chapter that sound theory requires that discounts on purchases be regarded as reductions in costs; income should emerge from the process of selling, not buying.  In accordance with such theory, plant items should be recorded at no more than their cash price, any available discounts being treated as reductions in asset cost.  Charges resulting from failure to take such discounts should be reported in a discounts lost account.

A number of property items may be acquired for a lump sum. Some of the items may be depreciable, others nondepreciable. Asset lives may differ; ultimate disposal dates may be different. If there is to be an accountability for the assets on an individual basis, the purchase price must be allocated to the individual assets. Appraisal values, reproduction costs reduced to present depreciated values, or other appropriate evidence is used to support an equitable allocation of the purchase price. To illustrate such an allocation, assume that land, buildings, and equipment are acquired for $80,000. Assume further that assessed values for the individual assets as reported on the property tax bill provide a satisfactory basis for apportionment of the purchase price. The apportionment is summarized below:

| | Tax Assess- ment | Cost Apportionment According to Relative Assessed Values | Cost Assigned to Individual Assets |
|---|---|---|---|
| Real Properties: Land..................... | $14,000 | $\dfrac{14,000}{50,000} \times \$80,000$ | $22,400 |
| Improvements (Building).... | 30,000 | $\dfrac{30,000}{50,000} \times \$80,000$ | 48,000 |
| Personal Property (Equipment) | 6,000 | $\dfrac{6,000}{50,000} \times \$80,000$ | 9,600 |
| | $50,000 | | $80,000 |

When the price paid for assets of a going business exceeds the value that can be identified with the tangible assets acquired, the excess is recognized as payment for goodwill or other intangibles.

A plant item acquired in secondhand or used condition should be set up at actual cost rather than at its original cost to the seller less an allowance for depreciation on such cost. Expenditures to repair, recondition, or improve such items should be added to the purchase price. It must be assumed that the buyer was aware of such additional expenditures in making the purchase.

**PURCHASE ON DEFERRED PAYMENT PLAN**　　　When an asset is acquired on a deferred payment plan and interest payments are made in the liquidation of the contract, Interest Expense is charged for the amounts paid as interest. When a contract does not provide a specific charge for interest but calls for a total charge that exceeds the price on a cash basis, such excess should be regarded as the charge for deferring payment. The purchase, then, is recorded by a charge to the asset at its cash price, a charge to interest expense for the financing charge, and a credit to the payable for the full contract amount. When a cash price is not quoted, the contract price on a deferred payment plan may still be considered to include a financing charge. In such a case the difference between the contract price and an assumed cash price, regarded as the future payments discounted at a going interest rate, is treated as interest expense. Recognition of interest expense under such circumstances is rarely found in practice; however, special analysis and recognition of this factor are warranted when financing charges are implicit in the contract price.

When a plant and equipment item is acquired on a conditional sales basis in which title to the asset does not pass until payments on the contract are completed, the legal rule is waived and both asset and liability balances are recognized in the accounts as long as it is the intent of the purchaser to complete the contract. The nature of the contract and the fact that default on the obligation will result in failure to acquire title should be disclosed on the balance sheet.

**ACQUISITION BY EXCHANGE**   When one asset is traded for another, the new asset should be recorded at its market value; the difference between the value assigned to the new asset and the book value of the old should be recognized as a gain or loss on the exchange. When a cash payment is required on the acquisition, the new asset should be recorded at the sum of the cash paid and the market value of the asset exchanged; any difference between the market value of the asset given up and its book value should be recognized as a gain or loss. Any trade-in allowance should be carefully examined to determine whether it fairly measures the value of the asset exchanged. The use of an allowance that includes a price concession will result in an overstatement of the newly acquired asset as well as overstatement of subsequent depreciation charges. The newly acquired asset should be recorded at no more than the price that would be paid in the absence of a trade-in.

To illustrate the accounting for a trade, assume that machinery with an original cost of $5,000 and a book value of $2,000 is accepted at $1,600 in part payment on new machinery priced at $6,000. The following entry is made:

| | | |
|---|---:|---:|
| Machinery | 6,000 | |
| Allowance for Depreciation of Machinery | 3,000 | |
| Loss on Trade of Machinery | 400 | |
| Machinery | | 5,000 |
| Cash | | 4,400 |

If, in the preceding example, the machinery could have been acquired at a cash price of $5,600, this value should be used in recording the asset. While the allowance on the old machinery was stated at $1,600, the asset had an actual worth of no more than $1,200; the loss on the exchange is $800, the difference between the actual value of the asset given up, $1,200, and its book value, $2,000. The loss on exchange may be interpreted as an extraordinary loss arising from failure to recognize adequate depreciation in prior years or as an extraordinary loss arising from the decision to trade the asset at this particular time.

In the preceding example, it was assumed that the asset was exchanged at the beginning of a fiscal period. When depreciable assets are exchanged within a fiscal period, depreciation should be recognized to the time of the exchange. The book value at the time of the exchange is then used in recording the exchange. For example, assume that the transaction above did not occur until the middle of the year. The annual depreciation charge is $1,000. Depreciation for one-half year is recorded, and this is followed by the entry to record the exchange. These entries are:

| | | |
|---|---|---|
| Depreciation of Machinery............................ | 500 | |
|    Allowance for Depreciation of Machinery.......... | | 500 |
| Machinery........................................ | 6,000 | |
| Allowance for Depreciation of Machinery............ | 3,500 | |
|    Machinery..................................... | | 5,000 |
|    Cash.......................................... | | 4,400 |
|    Gain on Trade of Machinery..................... | | 100 |

The foregoing may be combined in the form of a single compound entry as follows:

| | | |
|---|---|---|
| Machinery........................................ | 6,000 | |
| Depreciation of Machinery.......................... | 500 | |
| Allowance for Depreciation of Machinery............ | 3,000 | |
|    Machinery..................................... | | 5,000 |
|    Cash.......................................... | | 4,400 |
|    Gain on Trade of Machinery..................... | | 100 |

In the absence of adequate evidence that the depreciation rate used in previous periods was inaccurate, the depreciation rate for the current period would be the same as that used in the past.

For federal income tax purposes, no gain or loss is recognized on the exchange of property held for productive use or investment solely for property of a like kind.[1] The tax basis of the new asset is measured by the book value of the asset given up increased by any cash paid on the trade. To illustrate, in the first example on page 443, the loss of $400 cannot be recognized for tax purposes; instead the cost of the

---

[1] This rule does not cover stock in trade or stocks, bonds, or other evidences of indebtedness or interest.

asset is regarded as $6,400, composed of the book value of the asset exchanged, $2,000, and the cash paid, $4,400. In calculating taxable income, depreciation on the new asset is computed on a cost of $6,400. Assuming straight-line depreciation and a 5-year life, depreciation of $1,280 is allowed annually. The loss on the old asset is thus recovered for tax purposes in the form of additional depreciation charges over the life of the new asset. Assuming trade of the asset as in the second example on page 444, there would be no gain of $100 for income tax purposes; the asset cost here would be $5,900, the sum of the book value of the asset, $1,500, and the cash paid, $4,400.

The income tax method for reporting an asset acquired in an exchange cannot be supported in theory. The life cycle of an old asset has ended and the accounts should reflect the full effects of its cost, use, and disposition; a new asset has been acquired and future periods should be charged with neither more nor less than its actual cost. The tax method is frequently applied in the accounts so that analysis and restatement of account balances may be avoided in the preparation of income tax returns. When gains and losses on exchanges are relatively insignificant, use of this method is not objectionable. However, its use cannot be defended when it leads to the significant misstatement of assets as well as periodic income.

A loss or a gain would be recognized for tax purposes as well as for accounting purposes when old equipment is sold and new equipment acquired as two independent transactions.

**ACQUISITION BY ISSUANCE OF SECURITIES**   A company may acquire assets in exchange for its own stocks or bonds. When the value of the securities is determinable, such value is assigned to the assets acquired; in the absence of a market value for the securities, the market value of the assets acquired would be sought.

Assets are properly valued at the par value of securities only when the market value of securities is equal to par. If stocks or bonds are selling at a discount, the assets should be reported at such current cash value, a stock discount or bond discount account being debited for the discount and Capital Stock or Bonds Payable being credited at par. For example, assume that a company's stock, par $10, is currently selling on the market at $8\frac{1}{2}$. The company gives 10,000 shares of its stock in payment for machinery. An entry should be made as follows:

| | | |
|---|---:|---:|
| Machinery................................... | 85,000 | |
| Discount on Common Stock..................... | 15,000 | |
| Common Stock................................ | | 100,000 |

If the discount were buried in the cost assigned to machinery, both assets and capital would be overstated; this in turn would lead to misstatement of periodic depreciation and net income summaries during the life of the asset.

If a company's own stocks or bonds are selling at a premium, the assets should likewise be reported at the current market value of the security; Capital Stock or Bonds Payable is credited at par and a stock premium or bond premium account is credited for the excess. It is important to note that the securities should be valued at a price that is established by transactions on the securities markets or by transactions involving independent third parties. Amounts assigned to assets and capital must represent accurate expressions of underlying values.

When a company's securities do not have an established market value and these are issued in payment for assets, appraisal of the assets by independent authority may be required in arriving at an objective determination of their fair market value. Both assets acquired and securities issued may then be recorded at values arrived at by appraisal. If a satisfactory market value is obtainable neither for securities issued nor assets acquired, values as established by the board of directors will have to be accepted for accounting purposes. For example, assume that a corporation issues 10,000 shares of stock in payment for certain mining property. A market value cannot be established for the stock, and there are no means of arriving at a fair value for the property received. If the board of directors values the property at $80,000, the property value and the issuing price of the stock are thereby set at this figure. The assignment of values by the board of directors is normally not subject to challenge, unless it can be shown that the board has acted fraudulently.

When a purchase price is made up of cash and securities, similar standards for valuing properties apply. Any security discounts or premiums should be accounted for separately. When an asset is purchased for a given down payment plus a series of non-interest-bearing notes whose face values provide for the interest charges, the asset cost should not include such interest.

**ACQUISITION BY SELF-CONSTRUCTION**      Sometimes a plant and equipment item is constructed by the party who is to make use of it. This may be done because it is believed that the cost will be less than if the asset were acquired from outsiders. It may also be done in order that idle facilities of the plant may be utilized or in order that a higher quality of construction may be achieved. When such construction takes place, a number of problems arise in arriving at a cost for the project that will become the basis for subsequent accounting.

*Overhead Chargeable to Self-Construction.* All construction costs are charged to the assets under construction. There is usually little or no question concerning such items as materials and labor that are directly attributable to the new construction. However, the question of inclusion of overhead in construction costs has brought forth conflicting opinions. There are some who claim that general factory overhead should be assigned to special construction activities just as it is assigned to normal activities. Others would insist that only the increase in general factory overhead specifically incurred as a result of construction activities is properly chargeable to construction.

Those taking the position that construction should carry a fair share of overhead claim that this must be done if constructed assets are to be presented at their actual cost; self-constructed plant and equipment items are entitled to no special favors. This practice should be followed even though general manufacturing activities are relieved of a portion of overhead that they would normally carry; since overhead has served a double purpose during the construction period, this is accurately reflected in below-normal factory costs. Those who support charges to construction for only the increase in general overhead claim that the cost of construction is actually no more than the extra costs involved. It is the normal manufacturing activities that should receive no special favors as a result of the construction. Management is aware of the cost of normal activities, and makes the decision to engage in construction in terms of the special added costs involved.

It is essential to note that the reduction of general factory overhead otherwise chargeable to factory activities by allocation to construction activities will increase income during the construction period. The recognition of a portion of overhead is postponed, such overhead being related to subsequent periods through charges in the form of depreciation.

While there is theoretical support for the use of either position suggested, practice on the whole has leaned to the assignment to construction of only the increase in general factory overhead. Balance sheet conservatism is the major factor for this choice.

*Saving or Loss on Self-Construction.* When the cost of self-construction of a plant and equipment item is less than its cost to acquire through purchase or construction by others, such difference is not a profit but a *saving*. A profit emerges from a sale, not from expenditures incurred in work done for one's self. The construction is properly reported at its cost. The saving will emerge as profits over the life of the asset as lower depreciation is charged against periodic revenue.

When the cost of constructing an asset proves to be more than the price at which it could have been acquired from outsiders, it would be conservative to record the asset at the lower value and to recognize an extraordinary loss in the period of its completion. In following such practice, the asset is reported at no more than its sound value; future periods are not burdened with depreciation on excess cost that could have been avoided.

**ACQUISITION BY GIFT OR DISCOVERY** When property is received as a gift, there is no cost that can be used as a basis for its valuation. Even though certain expenditures may have to be made incident to the gift, these are generally far less than the value of the property. Cost, here, obviously fails to provide a satisfactory basis for asset accountability as well as for income measurement. Under such circumstances, appraisal of the property is appropriate, and appraised value becomes the basis for a charge to the asset account and a credit to capital. A donation is the source of the capital increase, hence a donated capital balance, regarded as a part of paid-in capital, is credited. To illustrate, if the Beverly Hills Chamber of Commerce donated land and buildings appraised at $50,000 and $150,000 respectively, the entry on the books of the party receiving the gift would be:

```
Land.........................................    50,000
Buildings....................................   150,000
    Paid-in Capital—Donation of Land and Buildings    200,000
```

Depreciation of an asset acquired by gift should be recorded in the usual manner, the value assigned to the asset providing the basis for the depreciation charge.

If a gift is contingent upon some act to be performed by the donee, the contingent nature of the asset as well as the capital item should be indicated in the account titles. Account balances should be reported "short" or by special note on the balance sheet.

Occasionally valuable natural resources are discovered on property. The presence of valuable resources, not previously known, materially enhances the value of the property. As in the case of a gift, cost fails to provide a satisfactory basis for asset valuation and income measurement. Here, too, an appraisal of the property is appropriate, and the property is reported at a figure based upon the estimated value of the discovered resources. In this case, an appraisal is the source of the capital increase; hence appraisal capital is credited.

**INTEREST DURING PERIOD OF CONSTRUCTION**   The practice has developed in public utility accounting of regarding interest during a period of asset construction as a part of asset cost. Instead of reporting interest as an expense during a construction period, such interest is treated as cost of plant and emerges as a charge for depreciation in the periods in which the properties are income-producing. Service rates established by governmental regulatory bodies are based upon current charges and thus recognize and provide for a recovery of past interest. Similar grounds for interest capitalization cannot be claimed in accounting for the industrial unit; nevertheless, the practice of capitalizing interest as a cost of building construction has been carried into the industrial field. When interest payments are capitalized, it follows that similar treatment would be applied to adjustments to interest for debt discount and premium amortization.

**OTHER EXPENDITURES DURING PERIOD OF ORGANIZATION AND CONSTRUCTION**   There has been some support for capitalizing expenditures for interest, taxes, general and administrative services, etc., during a period of organization and construction. Support for such procedure is based on the theory that future periods are benefited by necessary initial costs and that it is unreasonable to assume that losses have been incurred before sales activities actually begin. However, it would seem that a stronger case can be made for the recognition of such items as expenses even though these give rise to a deficit. Adequate disclosure can be made by means of statement notes of the special nature of the measurement problem during the initial period of organization. If the practice of capitalizing initial expenditures is to be followed, such expenditures should be reported as a deferred cost in an appropriately titled account and then should be written off in some systematic manner. Description of the policy followed with respect to such initial costs should be provided by special note. Initial costs should not be reported as plant and equipment. To add such costs to plant and equipment would be to misstate the property items as well as periodic depreciation charges.

**SPECIAL PROBLEMS RELATING TO ASSET ACQUISITIONS**   Special accounting problems arise in the acquisition of certain plant and equipment items. Attention is directed in the sections that follow to specific assets and the special problems relating thereto.

**LAND**   The cost of land includes the negotiated price at which it is acquired increased by brokers' commissions, legal fees, title and escrow fees, surveying fees, etc. Any obligations for taxes or interest assumed by the buyer are additions to cost.

Costs of clearing, grading, subdividing, or otherwise improving the land after its acquisition should be treated as increases in the cost of land. When a site secured for a new plant is already occupied by a building that must be torn down, the cost of dismantling and removing the old structure, less any recovery from salvage, is a proper addition to land cost. If salvage exceeds the cost of razing buildings, such excess may be considered a reduction in land cost. Special assessments for certain local area improvements, such as streets, lighting, and sewage systems, may be regarded as costs augmenting the value of the land and thus chargeable to this asset. When expenditures are incurred for land improvements that have a limited life and require ultimate replacement, as, for example, paving, sidewalks, fencing, and water and sewage systems, such items should be summarized in an account entitled Land Improvements and depreciated over their estimated useful lives. The estimated useful lives of certain land improvements may be limited to the life of the buildings on the property; other improvements may have independent lives.

Land qualifies for presentation in the plant and equipment category only when it is being used in the normal activities of the business. Land held for future use, for example, should be reported under the investments heading; land held for current sale should be reported as a current asset. Parcels of land not used in normal operations should be distinguished from the land in use by descriptive account titles.

When land is acquired and held for future use or as a speculative venture for purposes of resale, a special problem arises as to the treatment of the charges in carrying such property. Should expenditures for taxes and interest on mortgages, for example, be charged to periodic revenue or should these be added to the cost of the land? There is some support for adding such charges to land cost. The buyer is aware of the fact that costs will be involved in holding the land before it is applied to the specific purpose for which it is acquired. The purchase is made with the expectation that the investment will yield benefits exceeding both the original cost and carrying charges. When carrying charges are capitalized, the full cost of the investment can be assigned to the purpose for which it is ultimately applied.

To illustrate, assume that a company acquired land for expansion purposes in 1950, although such expansion is not expected to take place until 1960. Cost of the land is $40,000; taxes and other carrying charges are estimated at $20,000 for the ten-year period. Under these circumstances, the company has actually made a decision to invest $60,000 in land instead of delaying action until some later date when efforts towards expansion might find circumstances less favorable. Or assume that land is acquired as a speculative investment in 1950 for $40,000 and that it is ultimately sold in 1960 for $75,000, carrying charges during the ten-year period having totaled $20,000. Here, too, the investment in land may be regarded as $60,000 and the profit as $15,000. The land, in effect, represented "goods in process" during the holding period; $75,000 was realized on an investment totaling $60,000. If carrying charges had been assigned to the revenue of each year, income during the ten-year holding period would have been reduced by $20,000 and a gain of $35,000 would be reported on the ultimate sale of the property. The latter treatment fails to offer a satisfactory accounting for income from normal activities as well as for the gain emerging from the investment in land.

It would be difficult to support the capitalization of expenditures for carrying assets when market values fail to confirm an increasing property value; here conservatism would require the treatment of such expenditures as charges to periodic revenues. The capitalization procedure would likewise be inappropriate when land is used for rental purposes, crops, etc. and is income producing; expenditures under these circumstances should be treated as deductions from revenue.

Carrying charges on investments in land are frequently recorded as expenses as a conservative measure. In reporting land as investment on the balance sheet, it is desirable to provide data in parenthetical or note form indicating the cost procedure employed for the asset as well as its current market value.

For federal income tax purposes, taxes, interest on mortgages, and other carrying charges on unimproved and unproductive real property may be treated as tax deductions or added to the cost of the property. The taxpayer may elect to capitalize carrying charges even though he has deducted such items in the past, and such election is not binding on future expenditures.

**BUILDINGS**   A cost for both land and buildings must be allocated between the two assets. Allocable cost consists of the purchase price plus those charges incident to the purchase, such as brokers' commissions, legal fees, and title and escrow fees. The cost allocated to buildings is increased by reconditioning and repair costs incurred in readying the buildings for use as well as any costs for building alterations, improvements, and additions.

When buildings are constructed, their cost consists of material, labor, and overhead identified with construction. Excavation costs that are related to buildings rather than to making land usable are charged to buildings. Charges relating to construction, architects' fees, building permits and fees, workmen's compensation and accident insurance, fire insurance, and temporary buildings used in connection with construction activities, form part of the total building cost. Taxes on improved property during the period of construction as well as financing costs during a period of construction are frequently capitalized as a cost of buildings.

It was suggested earlier that when land and buildings are acquired and buildings are immediately demolished, the cost of demolishment is added to land as a cost of preparing land for its intended use. However, the cost of demolishing buildings that have been previously occupied by the company requires different treatment. This is a cost that should be identified with the original life of the buildings. A salvage value serves to reduce the cost arising from the use of an asset and is frequently anticipated in developing the periodic charge for use of the asset; a retirement cost, however, serves to increase the cost arising from asset use but is seldom anticipated in developing periodic charges. When asset retirement costs have not been anticipated, they require recognition as an extraordinary item by a charge to a nominal account or to retained earnings.

Expenditures for the purchase and the installation of equipment items relating to buildings, such as boilers, lighting fixtures, and elevator systems, are separately recorded as Building Equipment or Building Improvements. Certain equipment items may be affixed as a permanent part of buildings; other items may be removable. Building equipment items are depreciated over the life of the buildings, except for those units that have a shorter life and will require replacement. Since building equipment items may have varying lives, detailed records must be maintained in support of the balance reported in a building equipment account.

**MACHINERY AND EQUIPMENT**   Machinery and equipment covers a wide range of items that vary with the particular enterprise and its activities. For the manufacturing concern machinery and equipment would include such items as lathes, stamping machines, ovens, and conveyor systems. Machinery and equipment is charged for all expenditures identified with the acquisition and the preparation for use of plant machines and equipment items. Machinery and equipment cost includes the purchase price, taxes on purchase, freight and drayage charges, insurance charges while in transit, installation charges, and expenditures for testing and final preparation for use.

**TOOLS**    Two classes of tools are employed in productive activities: (1) machine tools representing detachable parts of a machine, such as dies, drills, and punches; and (2) hand tools such as hammers, wrenches, and screwdrivers. Both classes of tools are normally of small individual cost and are relatively short-lived as a result of wear, breakage, and loss. Such factors generally suggest that these items be accounted for as a single asset.

**PATTERNS AND DIES**    Patterns and dies are acquired for designing, stamping, cutting, or forging out a particular object. The cost of patterns and dies is either a purchase cost or a development cost consisting of labor, material, and overhead. When patterns and dies are used in normal productive activities, their cost is reported as an asset and this asset is depreciated over its useful life. When such items are limited to use in the manufacture of a special job order, their cost is recognized as a part of the cost of the order.

**FURNITURE AND FIXTURES**    Furniture and fixtures include such items as desks, chairs, carpets, showcases, and window fixtures. Acquisitions should be identified with productive, selling, and general and administrative functions. When furniture and fixtures are thus classified, depreciation of furniture and fixtures can be accurately assigned to production, selling, and general and administrative activities. Furniture and fixtures are recorded at cost, which includes purchase prices, taxes, and freight charges.

**MOTOR VEHICLES**    Automobile and truck acquisitions should be identified with procurement, production, selling and delivery, and general and administrative functions. Depreciation can then be accurately related to the different business activities. Automotive equipment is recorded at its purchase price, increased by any sales and excise taxes and delivery charges paid. When an amount paid for equipment includes charges for such items as current license fees, personal property taxes, and insurance, these should not be recorded as asset cost but should be recognized separately as expenses relating to the current use of the equipment.

**RETURNABLE CONTAINERS**    Goods are frequently sold in containers that are to be returned by customers so that they may be reused. Returnable containers consist of such items as steel tanks, drums, barrels, bottles, and sacks. Containers are depreciable assets used in the business and qualify for inclusion in the plant and equipment asset group.

**PLANT ASSET RECORDS** Since accounting for plant and equipment requires information concerning individual units, it is desirable to have detailed records that may be systematically and efficiently maintained. Such records are variously termed "Unit Plant Records," "Plant Ledger," and "Fixed Asset Control." They usually involve the controlling account principle, plant and equipment items being summarized in the general ledger and detail being recorded in subsidiary ledger form. Subsidiary ledger records are constructed to provide the significant data for each plant and equipment unit.

Subsidiary records are commonly found in one of two forms: (1) a plant and equipment register or (2) a card or sheet file. When a plant register is used, sections are usually assigned to the assets of each department in order that depreciation charges may be accumulated departmentally. One line is provided for each asset, and columns provide space for significant information regarding the asset. The use of cards or separate sheets provides a more flexible record, since the items may be arranged in an order other than date of acquisition. One card or one sheet is provided for each item, and all information with respect to the asset is written or typed thereon or shown by means of punch holes. This information usually includes the name of the asset, location, name of vendor, insurance carried, date acquired, original cost, transportation charges, installation cost, estimated life, depreciation rate, periodic depreciation recorded to date, major maintenance and betterment expenditures, and proceeds from final disposal.

**EXPENDITURES INCURRED IN USE OF PLANT AND EQUIPMENT ITEMS** During the life of plant and equipment, expenditures relating to the use of these properties must be accounted for accurately. Property items call for regular maintenance and repairs, and at different intervals, for betterments and additions. These charges are described in the sections that follow.

*Maintenance.* Certain expenditures are incurred to maintain assets in fit condition to perform their work. Among these are expenditures for painting, lubricating, and adjusting equipment. Such expenditures are referred to as *maintenance.* Maintenance items are recurring and benefit current operations; hence they are recognized as expenses.

*Repairs.* Expenditures are incurred to restore assets to a fit condition upon their breakdown or to restore and replace broken parts. Such expenditures are referred to as *repairs.* When these expenditures are ordinary and recurring, they are charged to expense. When these are of an extraordinary nature and serve to prolong the life of the asset, they may be charged to the allowance for depreciation and the depreciation rate then redetermined in view of changes in the asset book value and estimated life.

Repairs involving the overhauling of certain assets are frequently referred to as *renewals*. Substitutions of parts or entire units are referred to as *replacements*. Minor renewals or part replacements may be regarded as ordinary repairs; major renewals or part replacements fall into the category of extraordinary repairs. When the component parts of an asset have different lives and are carried on the books separately, a part replacement would call for entries to retire the old part and to establish the new. Replacement of an entire unit would call for similar entries.

Repairs arising from flood, fire, or other casualty require special analysis. The cost of restoring an asset to its previous condition should be reported as a loss from casualties. Any cost that improves or enlarges an asset should be added to the asset balance; any cost that prolongs the original life of an asset should be treated as a reduction in the allowance for depreciation account.

*Betterments and Improvements.* Asset replacements providing for increased or improved services are referred to as *betterments or improvements*. Replacements of lighting systems, heating systems, sanitary systems, etc., with improved facilities represent such betterments. Minor expenditures for betterments may be recorded as ordinary repairs. Major expenditures call for entries that establish a new asset and retire an old, or entries that reduce the allowance for depreciation on the original asset.

*Additions.* Enlargements and extensions of existing facilities are referred to as *additions*. A new plant wing, additional loading docks, or the expansion of a paved parking lot, represent additions. An addition is capitalized and depreciated over its service life, which may be limited to that of the original property item to which it is related.

**ESTABLISHMENT OF ALLOWANCE FOR MAINTENANCE AND REPAIRS**

When certain relatively large maintenance and repair charges are expected at irregular intervals during the life of an asset, provision may be made to charge operations not only with a share of the original cost of the asset but also with a share of the total maintenance and repair charges that are anticipated over the life of the asset. An expense account may be charged periodically for the estimated maintenance and repairs, and a maintenance and repairs allowance account credited. If this is done, maintenance expenditures, when incurred, are properly chargeable against the allowance. To illustrate, the cost of repainting buildings does not increase the original estimated service of the buildings, but it may represent a relatively heavy expense charge against the operations of a certain fiscal period. If an allowance for maintenance and repairs has been set up by a periodic charge to operations, the expenditure for repainting buildings can be charged against this allowance. Charges of this kind are thus equalized among the fiscal periods, and an unreasonably large charge against the income of a single period is avoided. A credit balance in the allowance account at the end of a fiscal period is subtracted from the property to which it relates; plant and equipment balances are thus reduced by both accrued depreciation and accrued repairs and maintenance. On the other hand, a debit balance in the allowance account resulting from expenditures that have not yet been assigned to operations through regular maintenance charges would be regarded as a temporary addition to plant and equipment.

If a business has a great many plant items of varying ages in service, it is not likely that the total maintenance and repairs charges will vary to any great extent from period to period. Experience will indicate whether the establishment of an allowance is warranted. Charges to establish an allowance in anticipation of repairs and maintenance items would not be deductible for income tax purposes; repairs and maintenance items are recognized for tax purposes only when the expenditures are made.

**PLANT AND EQUIPMENT RETIREMENTS** Properties may be retired by trade, sale, scrapping and removal, or abandonment. When an asset is retired, depreciation on the item should be recognized to the date of retirement. Entries for the disposal of an asset by trade were described earlier. When cash is received upon the retirement of a property item, Cash is debited, both the asset and the related depreciation allowance balances are closed, and the difference between the cash and the asset book value is recognized as a gain or loss on the retirement.

To illustrate, assume that at the beginning of September, 1958, the McCoy Corporation sells for $750 certain machinery that it no longer needs. The asset was originally acquired in the middle of 1950 for $5,000; depreciation was recorded on the asset at 10% per year. The entries to record the depreciation for 1958 and the sale of the property item follow:

| | | | | |
|---|---|---|---|---|
| Depreciation of Machinery...................... | | 333.33 | | |
| Allowance for Depreciation of Machinery....... | | | 333.33 | |

To record depreciation for eight mon ,hs in 1958:
$5,000×10%×8/12, or $333.33.

| | | | | |
|---|---|---|---|---|
| Cash........................................ | | 750.00 | | |
| Allowance for Depreciation of Machinery.......... | | 4,083.33 | | |
| Loss on Sale of Machinery..................... | | 166.67 | | |
| Machinery................................... | | | 5,000.00 | |

To record sale of machinery:

| | | | |
|---|---|---|---|
| Proceeds from sale ....................... | | $750.00 | |
| Book value of asset: | | | |
| Cost................... ...... | $5,000.00 | | |
| Depreciation to date of sale: | | | |
| July 1950–Dec. 31, 1957 | | | |
| (10% for 7½ years).... | $3,750.00 | | |
| Jan. 1, 1958–Sept. 1, 1958 | | | |
| (10% for ⅔ year)...... | 333.33 | 4,083.33 | 916.67 |
| Loss on sale ................... .... | | $166.67 | |

The above entries could be combined in the form of a single compound entry.

When an asset is scrapped or abandoned and there is no cash recovery, asset and allowance balances are closed and a loss reported equal to the asset book value; if the full cost of the asset has been depreciated, the allowance account is simply offset against the asset balance.

**PROPERTY DAMAGE OR DESTRUCTION**   Special accounting problems arise when property is damaged or destroyed as a result of fire, flood, storm, or other casualty. When a company owns many properties and these are widely distributed, the company itself may assume the risk of loss. However, companies ordinarily carry insurance for casualities that may involve serious loss.

When uninsured property items are damaged and expenditures are incurred in their restoration, such expenditures should be reported as an extraordinary loss. When uninsured assets are partly or wholly destroyed, property book values should be reduced or canceled and an extraordinary loss recorded for such reductions. When property items are insured and these are damaged or destroyed, entries on the books must be made to report asset losses and also the insurance claims that arise from such losses.

The most common casualty loss incurred by a business is that from fire. Of all of the various types of protection offered by insurance, fire is the risk that is most widely covered. Because of the importance of fire insurance in business and because of the special accounting problems that arise in the event of fire, the remaining pages of this chapter are devoted to a detailed discussion of this matter.

**FIRE INSURANCE**          Fire insurance policies are usually written in $100 or $1,000 units for a period of 1, 3, or 5 years. Insurance premiums are normally paid in advance. The amount of the premium is determined by the conditions in each particular case. Some of the factors considered in setting a premium rate are type, location, use, and protection afforded the property being insured. By type is meant the material used in the construction of the property. In location, the surroundings, such as the distance between properties and the general hazards of the area, are considered. Use refers to the nature of the work being carried on. Protection includes consideration of the safety devices available, such as automatic sprinklers and the proximity and efficiency of the fire-fighting equipment.

The insurance contract may be canceled by either the insurer or the insured. If it is canceled by the insurance company, a refund is made on a prorata basis. When the policyholder cancels the policy, a refund may be made on what is known as a "short-rate" basis that provides for a higher insurance rate for the shorter period of coverage.

**COINSURANCE**          A *coinsurance clause* is frequently written into a policy by the insurance companies to offset the tendency on the part of those buying insurance protection to purchase only the estimated minimum coverage. A business with assets that are worth $100,000, for example, may estimate that any single loss could not destroy more than one half of these assets. On the basis of this estimate, the business might consider itself adequately protected by insurance of $50,000. With an 80% coinsurance clause, however, it would be necessary for the business to carry insurance up to 80% of the value of the property, or $80,000, if any loss up to the face of the policy is to be fully paid by the insurance company.

The standard coinsurance clause form reads as follows:

> It is expressly stipulated and made a condition of the contract that, in event of loss, this company shall be liable for no greater proportion thereof than the amount hereby insured bears to ___ per cent of the actual value of the property described herein at the time when such loss shall happen, nor for more than the proportion which this policy bears to the total insurance thereon.

In attaching this clause to an insurance policy, the agreed percentage is inserted in the blank space provided. Assuming that 80% is inserted in the clause, this indicates that the insurance company will pay the full amount of a claim, up to the face of the policy, only if the insurance coverage equals 80% of the value of the property at the time of the loss. When less than the stipulated percentage of insurance is carried, the insured shares in the risk along with the insurance company.

To illustrate the calculation of the amount to be paid on a claim arising under a policy that does not meet the coinsurance requirement, assume the following: assets are insured for $70,000 under a policy containing an 80% coinsurance clause. On the date of a fire, assets have a fair market value of $100,000. Since the policy does not meet the coinsurance requirement, any loss will be borne $\frac{7}{8}$ by the insurance company and $\frac{1}{8}$ by the policyholder; however, the total loss to be absorbed by the insurance company is limited in any case to $70,000, the face of the policy. A fire loss of $48,000, for example, would be divided as follows:

(a) $70,000 = face value of the insurance policy.
(b) $80,000 = coinsurance requirement (80% of the value of assets of $100,000).
(c) $10,000 = difference between the face value of the policy and the coinsurance requirement.

Share of loss to be borne by the insurance company: $\frac{70,000}{80,000} \times \$48,000 = \$42,000$

Share of loss to be borne by the policyholder: $\frac{10,000}{80,000} \times \$48,000 = \underline{\phantom{0}6,000}$

Total loss $\overline{\$48,000}$

The same principles may be applied to a loss greater than $70,000, the face of the policy. Assume the same facts as above but a $75,000 loss. Application of the formula results in the following:

Share of loss to be borne by the insurance company: $\frac{70,000}{80,000} \times \$75,000 = \$65,625$

Share of loss to be borne by the policyholder: $\frac{10,000}{80,000} \times \$75,000 = \underline{\phantom{0}9,375}$

Total loss $\overline{\$75,000}$

In the above example the formula results in a correct allocation, since the company's share is still less than the face of the policy. However, assume a loss of $90,000. The following calculations are made:

$$\frac{70,000}{80,000} \times \$90,000 = \$78,750$$

$$\frac{10,000}{80,000} \times \$90,000 = \underline{\phantom{0}11,250}$$

Total loss $\overline{\$90,000}$

In this case the insurance company does not pay the amount determined by the allocation, since its risk is limited to $70,000, the face value of the policy. The division of the loss, then, is as follows:

| | |
|---|---:|
| Share of loss to be borne by insurance company.......... | $70,000 |
| Share of loss to be borne by policyholder............... | 20,000 |
| Total loss........................................ | $90,000 |

When the insurance coverage is equal to or greater than the percentage required by the coinsurance clause, the formula need not be applied, since any loss is paid in full up to the face value of the policy. It is important to note that coinsurance requirements are based not on the cost or book value of the insured property but upon the actual market value of the property on the date of a fire. If coinsurance requirements are to be maintained, a rise in the value of insured assets requires that increased insurance coverage be acquired.

The following general rule may be stated with respect to fire insurance: The amount of the loss to be paid by the insurance company will be the *lowest* of the following amounts:

(1) The amount allocable to the insurance company as a result of the application of the coinsurance formula to the fire loss.
(2) The face value of the policy.
(3) The actual amount of the loss.

When several policies cover a single piece of property, recovery of a portion of the loss is made under each policy. Collections on each policy are made in accordance with the part that the policy represents of the total insurance carried or of the total insurance requirements per policy, whichever is higher. To illustrate, assume a fire loss of $20,000 on buildings valued at $100,000. Insurance policies are carried as follows: with Co. A, $60,000; with Co. B, $15,000.

(a) Assuming that policies have no coinsurance clauses:
   Recoverable from:

$$\text{Co. A} - \frac{60,000 \text{ (policy)}}{75,000 \text{ (total policies)}} \times \$20,000 \text{ (loss)} \qquad = \$16,000$$

$$\text{Co. B} - \frac{15,000 \text{ (policy)}}{75,000 \text{ (total policies)}} \times \$20,000 \text{ (loss)} \qquad = \underline{\phantom{\$1}4,000}$$

$$\$20,000$$

(b) Assuming that each policy includes an 80% coinsurance clause:
   Recoverable from:

$$\text{Co. A} - \frac{60,000 \text{ (policy)}}{80,000 \text{ (coinsurance requirement)}} \times \$20,000 \text{ (loss)} = \$15,000$$

$$\text{Co. B} - \frac{15,000 \text{ (policy)}}{80,000 \text{ (coinsurance requirement)}} \times \$20,000 \text{ (loss)} = \underline{\phantom{\$1}3,750}$$

$$\$18,750$$

(c) Assuming that coinsurance clauses are as follows: Co. A, 90%; Co. B, 80%:
Recoverable from:

Co. A — $\dfrac{60,000 \text{ (policy)}}{90,000 \text{ (coinsurance requirement)}}$ × \$20,000 (loss)   =   \$13,333

Co. B — $\dfrac{15,000 \text{ (policy)}}{80,000 \text{ (coinsurance requirement)}}$ × \$20,000 (loss)   =   3,750

$\overline{\hspace{4cm}\$17,083}$

**ACCOUNTING FOR FIRE LOSSES**   In the event that a fire occurs and journal and ledger records are destroyed, account balances to the date of the fire will have to be reconstructed by means of the best available evidence. As the first step in summarizing the fire loss, books as maintained or as reconstructed are adjusted as of the date of the fire. With accounts brought up to date, the loss may now be summarized in a fire loss account. The fire loss account is debited for the adjusted book value of property destroyed; it is credited for (1) amounts recoverable from insurance companies and (2) amounts recoverable from any salvage. The balance of the account is recognized as an extraordinary loss and is closed into the profit and loss account or directly to retained earnings at the end of the period.

A number of special problems are encountered in arriving at the charges to be made to the fire loss account. When depreciable assets are destroyed, the book values of the properties are brought up to date and these balances in total or in part are then transferred to the fire loss account. When merchandise is destroyed by fire, the estimated cost of the merchandise on hand at the time of the fire must be determined. If perpetual inventory records are available, the goods on hand may be obtained from this source. In the absence of such records, the inventory balance is generally arrived at by the gross profit method. Sales to the date of the fire are reduced to cost of goods sold by subtracting the estimated gross profit on sales; the sum of beginning inventory and purchases (the goods available for sale) less the estimated cost of goods sold gives the estimated inventory on the date of the fire. This balance may be set up by a charge to the inventory and a credit to the profit and loss account. The inventory total or portion destroyed by fire may now be transferred to the fire loss account.

Insurance expired to the date of the fire is recorded as an expense of normal operations. The balance in the prepaid insurance account after this adjustment is carried forward when policies continue in force and offer original protection on rehabilitated properties or newly-acquired replacements. If a business does not plan to repair or replace the assets, it may cancel a part or all of a policy and receive cash for it on a short-rate basis. The difference between the book value of the prepaid insurance and the amount received on the short-rate basis is a loss from insurance cancellation brought about by the fire, and is recorded as an addition to the fire loss balance.[1]

To illustrate the accounting for a fire loss, assume the facts that follow. J. J. Bailey, a retailer, suffers a fire loss after the close of business on March 31, 1958. Assets destroyed and amounts recoverable from insurance and salvage are summarized below:

| Item | Loss — Book Values | | Amounts Recoverable | |
|---|---|---|---|---|
| Inventory | Entire inventory, estimated to have a cost of $18,000 | | Salvage goods valued at. | $ 1,400 |
| | | | Policy carried.......... | 12,500 |
| | | | Amount recoverable from insurance company: | |
| | | | full amount of policy.... | 12,500 |
| Equipment | One third of equipment: | | Policy carried.......... | $ 6,000 |
| | Cost of equipment... | $15,000 | Value of equipment, date of fire, as agreed by insured and insurer...... | 7,800 |
| | Allowance for depr., 1/1/58 $9,000 | | | |
| | Add depr. at 10% for 3 mo.   375 | 9,375 | Amount recoverable from insurance company: | |
| | | $ 5,625 | ⅓ x $7,800............. | 2,600 |
| | Book value of portion lost: | | | |
| | Cost: ⅓ x $15,000.... | $ 5,000 | | |
| | Allowance: ⅓ x $9,375 | 3,125 | | |
| | Fire loss: asset book value............. | $ 1,875 | | |
| Buildings | One fourth of buildings: | | Policy carried.......... | $35,000 |
| | Cost of buildings.... | $32,000 | Value of buildings, date of fire, as agreed by insured and insurer...... | 32,000 |
| | Allow. for depreciation, 1/1/58...... $4,000 | | Amount recoverable from insurance company: | |
| | Add depreciation at 2½% for 3 months.   200 | 4,200 | ¼ x $32,000............ | 8,000 |
| | | $27,800 | | |
| | Book value of portion lost: | | | |
| | Cost: ¼ x $32,000..... | $ 8,000 | | |
| | Allowance ¼ x $4,200. | 1,050 | | |
| | Fire loss: asset book value............. | $ 6,950 | | |

[1]Under policies written in some states, payment of a policy may serve to cancel that portion of the policy paid on the theory that the insurance company has met such claim obligations on the policy. When this is the case, any unexpired insurance balance applicable to the portion of the policy collected should be written off as an addition to the fire loss account.

Entries for the fire loss are given below and on the next page. These are given in three groups: (1) entries that bring asset book values up to date so that the loss by fire may be determined, (2) entries that record the assets lost, and (3) entries that record the amounts recoverable from salvage and from the insurance companies. Explanations are not shown with the journal entries to save space; each entry in the journal, however, requires appropriate explanation, together with data used in arriving at amounts reported.

Entries to adjust the accounts and to record the fire loss may be transferred to the ledger, but nominal accounts may be left open and transactions for the remainder of the fiscal period recorded therein. At the end of the period, then, nominal accounts will reflect activities for the entire fiscal period and statements can be prepared summarizing activities in the usual manner. Any differences that are found during the period between amounts originally stated to be recoverable from insurance and amounts actually recovered should be charged or credited to the fire loss account, thus correcting this balance to the loss actually sustained.

(1) ENTRIES TO BRING ASSET BOOK VALUES UP TO DATE

(a) Profit and Loss.............................. 12,250
     Inventory[1]................................ 12,250

(b) Inventory.................................. 18,000
     Profit and Loss........................... 18,000

(c) Depreciation of Equipment.................. 375
     Allowance for Depreciation of Equipment.... 375

(d) Depreciation of Buildings................... 200
     Allowance for Depreciation of Buildings...... 200

(2) ENTRIES TO RECORD ASSETS LOST BY FIRE

(e) Fire Loss................................... 18,000
     Inventory................................ 18,000

(f) Fire Loss.................................. 1,875
     Allowance for Depreciation of Equipment...... 3,125
     Equipment............................... 5,000

(g) Fire Loss.................................. 6,950
     Allowance for Depreciation of Buildings........ 1,050
     Buildings ................................ 8,000

---

[1] It is assumed that the opening inventory balance is $12,250; this balance is closed to Profit and Loss. The inventory on the date of the fire is recorded in entry (b) by a charge to the asset and a credit to Profit and Loss; the latter credit represents a subtraction item from goods available for the period in arriving at the cost of goods sold. The inventory account as of the date of the fire is transferred to the fire loss account in entry (e).

(3) Entries to Record Amounts
Recoverable from Salvage and from Insurance Companies

(h) Salvage Goods ............................... 1,400
     Fire Loss.................................. 1,400

(i) Estimated Amount Recoverable from Insurance
    Companies.................................. 12,500
     Fire Loss.................................. 12,500

(j) Estimated Amount Recoverable from Insurance
    Companies.................................. 2,600
     Fire Loss.................................. 2,600

(k) Estimated Amount Recoverable from Insurance
    Companies.................................. 8,000
     Fire Loss.................................. 8,000

The amount recoverable from the insurance companies is \$23,100 and this balance would be reported as a current asset if current settlement can be assumed. The fire loss account reports a debit balance of \$2,325 (book value of assets lost, \$26,825, offset by estimated insurance recoveries and salvage, \$24,500); this is the "Loss from Fire". A credit excess in the fire loss account may be designated for reporting purposes, "Excess of Insurance and Salvage Proceeds over Book Value of Assets Lost by Fire".

## QUESTIONS

**1.** Distinguish between fixed tangibles and fixed intangibles.

**2.** (a) Define asset *cost*. (b) How does one arrive at cost when the consideration is other than cash? (c) What is asset *book value*?

**3.** (a) Distinguish between a capital expenditure and a revenue expenditure. (b) Give five examples of each.

**4.** Which of the following items would be treated as a revenue expenditure and which as a capital expenditure?

  (a) Cost of installing machinery.
  (b) Cost of moving and reinstalling machinery.
  (c) Extensive repairs as a result of fire.
  (d) Cost of grading land.
  (e) Insurance on machinery in transit.
  (f) Bond discount amortization during construction period.
  (g) Cost of major overhaul on machinery.
  (h) New safety guards on machinery.
  (i) Commission on purchase of real estate.
  (j) Special tax assessment for street improvements.

**5.** Indicate the effects on the balance sheet and the income statement in the current year and in succeeding years of the following errors:

  (a) The cost of a depreciable asset is incorrectly recorded as a revenue expenditure.
  (b) A revenue expenditure is incorrectly recorded as a charge to a depreciable asset.

**6.** The controller for the Weston Co. insists that, since discounts received on merchandise purchases are treated as income, consistency requires that a similar practice be followed for discounts received on plant and equipment acquisitions. Evaluate the controller's position.

**7.** A number of plant and equipment items are acquired for a single lump sum. Explain how the purchase price may be allocated to the different assets acquired.

**8.** The Wallace Co. trades an asset for a similar new one, the trade-in value of the old asset being less than its book value. (a) What is the disposition of this difference for tax purposes? (b) Would you recommend similar treatment in the accounts? Explain.

**9.** The Warner Co. acquires land and buildings in exchange for its own stock. How should the property be valued for accounting purposes?

**10.** The Whitehaven Co. decides to construct a building for itself and plans to use whatever plant facilities it has to further such construction. (a) What costs will enter into the cost of construction? (b) What two positions can the company take with respect to general overhead allocation during the period of construction? Evaluate each position and indicate your preference.

**11.** What positions can be taken with respect to interest charges during a period of plant construction? Evaluate each position and state your preference.

**12.** When the Bowman Corporation finds that the lowest bid it can get on the construction of an addition to its plant is $40,000, it proceeds to erect the building with its own workmen and equipment at a cost of $35,000. (a) How will the $5,000 saving be treated? (b) Assuming a cost of $50,000, how would you suggest that the excess cost be treated?

**13.** (a) What entry should be made upon an unconditional donation of land by a municipality to a corporation? (b) What entry should be made for the donation if it is contingent upon the employment of a certain number of persons by the corporation for a 10-year period? (c) What methods may be used in reporting the donation on the balance sheet?

**14.** What items are generally found in addition to the original purchase price in the cost of (a) land, (b) buildings, and (c) machinery and equipment?

**15.** Distinguish between (a) maintenance and repairs, (b) ordinary repairs and extraordinary repairs, (c) betterments and additions.

**16.** (a) What is meant by a "short rate" on a fire insurance policy? (b) Who elects to cancel the policy when the short rate is applied?

**17.** (a) What is a coinsurance clause and why is it found in policies? (b) Prepare a formula, accompanied by a rule or explanation, for determining the liability of an insurance company when a coinsurance clause is included.

**18.** Indicate the charges and the credits that will appear in the fire loss account.

## EXERCISES

**1.** Boyer, Inc. acquires a machine that is priced at $1,800. Payment of this amount may be made within 60 days; a 3% discount is allowed if cash is paid at time of purchase. Give the entry to record the acquisition, assuming:

(a) Cash is paid at time of purchase.

(b) Payment is to be made at the end of 60 days.

(c) A deferred payment plan is agreed upon whereby a down payment of $200 is made with 12 payments of $150 to be made at monthly intervals thereafter.

**2.** The Belmont Co. on July 1, 1958, acquired plant and equipment items at a lump-sum price of $60,000. An appraisal of the assets acquired disclosed the following values:

| | |
|---|---:|
| Land. | $15,000 |
| Buildings. | 30,000 |
| Machinery and Equipment. | 35,000 |

What cost should be assigned to each asset?

**3.** On November 1, 1958, the Parker Corporation trades machinery acquired on January 5, 1955, for new machinery. The old machinery had a cost of $12,000 and had been depreciated on a 10-year life. The new machinery costs $8,000; $5,000 is allowed on the old machinery, the balance being paid in cash. What entry is required to record the transaction? What is the value of the new machine for income tax purposes?

**4.** Marshall Stores acquires a delivery truck, making payment of $1,781.46, the payment being analyzed as follows:

| | |
|---|---:|
| Price of truck. | $2,208.00 |
| Charges for extra equipment. | 124.00 |
| State sales tax, 3% of $2,332.00. | 69.96 |
| Insurance for one year. | 88.00 |
| License and tax for remainder of 1958. | 41.50 |
| | $2,531.46 |
| Less trade-in allowed on old truck. | 750.00 |
| Cash paid. | $1,781.46 |

The old truck cost $1,800 and had a book value of $450 on the date of the trade. Give the entry to be made by Marshall Stores to record the exchange, assuming each of the following procedures:

(a) Any difference between the book value of the asset traded in and the trade-in allowance is to be recognized as an extraordinary gain or loss.

(b) Any difference between the book value of the asset traded in and the trade-in allowance is to be recognized as an adjustment in the basis of the new asset in accordance with income tax requirements.

**5.** The Boston Company acquires land for $75,000 to be paid for by issuance of 5,000 shares of its common stock, par $10, and cash of $25,000.

The accountant ascertains that the company's stock is selling on the market at $6\frac{1}{2}$ when the purchase is made. What entry should be made upon acquisition of the asset?

**6.** The Swisher Co. enters into a contract with the Westlake Construction Co. for construction of an office building at a cost of $425,000. Upon completion of construction, the Westlake Construction Co. agrees to accept in full payment of the contract price Swisher Co. 6% bonds with a par value of $200,000 and common stock with a par value of $200,000. Swisher Co. bonds are selling on the market at this time at 95. How would you recommend that the building acquisition be recorded?

**7.** The McCoy Corporation summarizes manufacturing and construction activities for 1958 as follows:

|  | ON PRODUCT MANUFACTURE | ON PLANT WING CONSTRUCTION |
|---|---|---|
| Materials................. | $120,000 | $16,000 |
| Direct Labor.............. | 105,000 | 20,000 |

Overhead for 1957 was 80% of the direct labor cost. Overhead in 1958 related to both product manufacture and construction activities totaled $91,500.

(a) Calculate the cost of the plant addition, assuming that manufacturing activities are to be charged with overhead at the rate experienced in 1957 and that construction activities are to be charged with the excess.

(b) Calculate the cost of the addition if manufacturing and construction activities are to be charged with overhead at the same rate.

**8.** Following are expenditures paid out during erection of a building: fees for search of title on land purchased, $350; building permit, $100; temporary quarters for construction crews, $1,500; payment to old tenants for vacating premises, $2,000; razing of old building, $1,250; excavation for basement, $5,000; taxes on land, $2,000; dividends, $5,000; damages awarded for injuries sustained in construction, $3,500 (no insurance was carried; the cost of insurance would have been $200); interest on first mortgage bonds, $3,000; costs of construction $100,000; cost of paving parking lot adjoining building, $2,500. What is the cost of land and the cost of the building?

**9.** The Eastern Motors Corp. acquired land and old buildings at a cost of $40,000. Delinquent taxes of $6,000 were paid, as well as attorney's fees of $1,500 for title search, etc., in connection with the purchase of the property. Buildings were removed at a cost of $1,500, but $300 was realized from the sale of salvaged materials. From January 1 to April 1 buildings were constructed at a cost of $80,000. Buildings were occupied on April 1. Insurance on buildings taken out on January 1 was $2,400 for a 3-year period. How would land and buildings be carried on the books at the end of the year?

**10.** A fire insurance policy on buildings has a face value of $90,000 and an 80% coinsurance clause. Assuming that buildings have a fair value of $150,000 on the date of a fire, what amount will be recovered if the fire loss totals are: (a) $60,000; (b) $110,000; (c) $140,000?

**11.** The York Company purchased a building for $80,000 on August 1, 1950. Depreciation was recorded at 3% a year. On October 31, 1958, 50% of the building was destroyed. On this date the building had a fair market value of $100,000. A policy for $60,000 was carried on the building, the policy containing a 75% coinsurance clause. What entries would be made to record (a) the loss from destruction of the building, and (b) the probable collectible amount on the insurance? (Assume that the company's fiscal period is the calendar year.)

**12.** Part of the buildings owned by the Morris Manufacturing Co. are destroyed by fire. Buildings are carried on the books at a value of $60,000; their sound value on the date of the fire is established at $120,000. Assuming that insurance policies contain an 80% coinsurance clause, give the amounts recoverable from each insurance company, assuming fire loss and policies as follows.

(a) One half of buildings are destroyed.
Policies are carried as follows: with A Co.............. $50,000
with B Co.............. 30,000

(b) Buildings are wholly destroyed.
Policies are carried as follows: with A Co.............. $75,000
with B Co.............. 50,000

(c) Buildings are wholly destroyed; recoverable salvage is estimated at $12,000.
Policies are carried as follows: with A Co.............. $60,000
with B Co.............. 40,000

## PROBLEMS

**15-1.** An escrow statement received by A. C. Mitchell Co. in connection with the purchase of land and buildings on September 15, 1958, shows the following:

*Charges:*

| | |
|---|---|
| Purchase price................................... | $18,500 |
| Real estate taxes (paid by vendor and covering tax period, September 15, 1958–June 30, 1959)........... | 416 |
| Fire insurance (paid by vendor and covering insurance period, September 15, 1958–Jan. 1, 1960)........... | 309 |
| Special assessment for street lighting (paid by vendor and covering tax period, September 15, 1958–June 30, 1959)........................................ | 15 |
| Termite inspection fees (fees were $130; ½ of fees were charged to vendee, as agreed)..................... | 65 |
| | $19,305 |

*Credits:*

| | |
|---|---:|
| Rentals on property (retained by vendor and covering rental period, September 15–December 1, 1958)...... | $    315 |
| Lease prepayment (retained by vendor and representing rental for month of December, 1959)............... | 150 |
| First mortgage note signed by vendee................ | 8,500 |
| Cash deposited by vendee in escrow................. | 10,340 |
| | $19,305 |

*Instructions:* Give the entry that would be made by the A. C. Mitchell Co. to summarize the purchase of land and buildings as reported above. Assume that cost is apportioned to land and buildings in the ratio of assessed values as reported by the property tax bill, which are: land, $3,600; improvements, $5,650.

**15-2.** The following transactions were completed by the Parrish Corp. in 1958:

**Mar. 1.**  Purchased land and buildings. The sum paid on the purchase was $55,125, which included a charge of $675 representing property taxes for March 1–June 30 that had been prepaid by the vendor. Twenty per cent of the purchase price is deemed applicable to land and the balance to buildings.

**Mar. 5–30.**  Previous owners had failed to take care of normal maintenance and repairs requirements on the building during the last five years, necessitating current reconditioning at a cost of $5,700.

**Apr. 1–May 15.**  Garages in the rear of the buildings were demolished, $300 being recovered on the lumber salvage. The company itself proceeded to construct a warehouse at a cost of $8,500. This cost was almost exactly the same as bids made on the construction by independent contractors. Upon completion of construction, city inspectors ordered extensive modifications in the buildings as a result of failure on the part of the company to comply with the Building Safety Code. Such modifications that could have been avoided cost an additional $1,800.

**Nov. 5–20.**  A fire of unknown origin destroyed the building show windows and entrance. The amount of the fire loss was estimated at $3,600, which included display merchandise of $600 and fixtures of $400, and the full amount of the loss was recovered from the insurance company. A new entrance and windows of modern design were completed at a cost of $6,500.

**Dec. 30–31.**  The business was closed to permit taking the year-end inventory. During this period, required redecorating and repairs were completed at a cost of $275.

*Instructions:* Give journal entries to record the preceding transactions. (Disregard depreciation.)

**15-3.** The Pat K. Company was organized on January 1, 1958, but it did not begin manufacturing activities until buildings were completed on August 1, 1958. At the beginning of 1959, in reviewing the books and records preparatory to drawing up statements for 1958, the auditor found the following account:

LAND AND BUILDINGS

| 1958 | | | 1958 | | |
|---|---|---|---|---|---|
| Jan. | 5 | Land and buildings. 96,000 | Dec. 31 | Depreciation for 1958 (2%)........ 4,989 | |
| | 15 | Cost of removing old buildings...... 2,000 | | | |
| | 26 | Construction contract...........100,000 | | | |
| Feb. | 20 | Legal fees........ 6,500 | | | |
| May | 1 | Insurance........ 1,200 | | | |
| Aug. | 1 | General and administrative expenses......... 15,000 | | | |
| Sept. | 1 | Semiannual bond interest......... 2,250 | | | |
| Nov. | 15 | County special assessment tax.... 1,500 | | | |
| Dec. | 31 | Asset write-up.... 25,000 | | | |
| | | 249,450 | | | |

An examination of the records discloses the following information relating to the land and buildings account:

(1) On January 5, preparatory to erecting a new building, the corporation acquired land, together with an old warehouse, for $46,000 plus 1,000 shares of the company's preferred stock. (The company was authorized to issue 10,000 shares of preferred stock, par $50, and has received subscriptions on the balance of preferred authorized at $42 per share.)

(2) The old warehouse was razed at a cost of $3,500. Proceeds from salvage, however, amounted to $1,500.

(3) $100,000 worth of 4½% bonds were issued at par on March 1, and proceeds were applied in payment of construction of buildings. Interest during the construction period is to be capitalized as a part of the buildings cost.

(4) Legal fees were incurred incident to: (a) organization of the corporation, $4,000; (b) purchase of land, $1,500; and (c) preparation and execution of contracts relating to construction, $1,000.

(5) Insurance premiums on buildings, $1,200, represent payment for a 3-year period beginning May 1, 1958.

(6) General and administrative expenses, January 1 to August 1, included officers' salaries, $10,000; superintendent's salary, $5,000. Officers were not connected with construction aside from viewing plans. The superintendent supervised construction.

(7) The county special assessment tax represented a charge for district street improvements.

(8) Company officials were advised by the contractor completing the construction that costs had been underestimated and that, as a consequence, he had lost money on the contract; that a fair charge for the project would have been $125,000. As a result of this information, officials raised the carrying value of the asset and increased Retained Earnings by $25,000.

(9) Buildings are estimated to have a 50-year life, and 2% of the balance in the asset account was written off at the end of 1958.

*Instructions:* (1) Prepare any required correcting entries as a result of information disclosed above. (Assume that the books for 1958 have not yet been closed.)

(2) How should the building and land accounts appear on the balance sheet on December 31, 1958?

**15-4.** On December 31, 1958, the Central Co. shows the following account for machinery that it had assembled for its own use during 1958:

MACHINERY (ORDER #560)

| | | | |
|---|---|---|---|
| Cost of dismantling old machine | 650 | Cash proceeds from sale of old machine | 200 |
| Raw materials used in construction of new machine | 11,000 | Depreciation for 1958, 10% of $35,000 | 3,500 |
| Labor in construction of new machine | 10,200 | | |
| Cost of installation of machine | 1,600 | | |
| Materials spoiled in machine trial runs | 750 | | |
| Gain on construction | 8,500 | | |
| Purchase of machine tools | 1,500 | | |

An analysis of the detail in the account discloses the following:

(1) The old machine, which was removed in the installation of the new one, had been fully depreciated.

(2) Cash discounts received on the payments for raw materials used in construction totaled $150 and these were reported in the purchases discount account.

(3) The factory overhead account shows a balance of $42,600 for the year ended December 31, 1958; this balance exceeds normal overhead on regular plant activities by approximately $3,600.

(4) Profit and Loss was credited for the gain that was recognized on construction, the gain being measured by the difference between costs incurred and the price at which the machine could have been acquired through purchase.

(5) Machine tools have an estimated life of 2 years; machinery has an estimated life of 10 years. The machinery was used for production beginning on September 1, 1958.

*Instructions:* (1) Set up property and valuation accounts for the machinery acquisition as they should appear at the end of 1958.

(2) Give the journal entries that are necessary in correcting the accounts in the ledger as of December 31, 1958, assuming that the accounts are still open.

**15-5.** A building with a fair market value of $200,000 is insured under a policy containing a coinsurance clause. Determine the amount that is recoverable from the insurance company under each of the following assumptions:

| | AMOUNT OF LOSS | FACE OF POLICY | PERCENTAGE COINSURANCE CLAUSE |
|---|---|---|---|
| (a) | $100,000 | $160,000 | 75% |
| (b) | 165,000 | 160,000 | 80% |
| (c) | 60,000 | 105,000 | 70% |
| (d) | 140,000 | 80,000 | 50% |
| (e) | 150,000 | 120,000 | 70% |
| (f) | 150,000 | 120,000 | 80% |
| (g) | 190,000 | 150,000 | 90% |
| (h) | 200,000 | 250,000 | 80% |

**15-6.** On March 1, 1956, the Williams Company took out a $70,000, 3-year fire insurance policy on a building that was completed at a cost of $150,000 at the end of June, 1940. The insurance policy contains an 80% coinsurance clause. Depreciation is calculated at 2½% annually. On April 1, 1958, the building was 50% destroyed by fire. The insurance company accepts a sound value for the property of $120,000 and agrees to make settlement on this basis. The fiscal period for the Williams Company is the calendar year.

*Instructions:* Prepare the journal entries necessary as of April 1, 1958, to summarize the foregoing information in the fire loss account and to close this account to Profit and Loss.

**15-7.** The insurance register of the Bell Company shows the following data:

| KIND OF PROPERTY COVERED | POLICY DATE | INSURANCE TERM | AMOUNT OF COVERAGE | TOTAL PREMIUM PAID |
|---|---|---|---|---|
| Store Equipment | Nov. 1, 1956 | 3 years | $40,000 | $450 |
| Merchandise | Feb. 1, 1958 | 1 year | 6,000 | 120 |
| Building | Nov. 1, 1956 | 3 years | 65,000 | 540* |

*This policy contains an 80% coinsurance clause.

On May 1, 1958, a fire destroyed 80% of the store equipment, all of the merchandise, and 60% of the building. An appraiser determined that the fair values as of May 1, 1958, of the store equipment and the building were $50,000 and $110,000 respectively. Since perpetual inventory records were not kept, the value of the merchandise destroyed was estimated on the assumption that sales to date were made at 35% above cost.

A trial balance taken as of May 1, 1958, before adjustments, includes the balances shown on the following page. Depreciation of store equipment is 10% annually; of buildings, 2½% annually. Books were last closed on December 31, 1957.

| | | |
|---|---:|---:|
| Merchandise Inventory, January 1, 1958 | $ 11,000 | |
| Store Equipment | 60,000 | |
| Allowance for Depreciation of Store Equipment | | $ 10,000 |
| Building | 150,000 | |
| Allowance for Depreciation of Building | | 92,000 |
| Sales | | 130,900 |
| Sales Returns and Allowances | 4,000 | |
| Purchases | 94,000 | |
| Purchases Returns and Allowances | | 4,000 |
| Freight In | 2,000 | |

*Instructions:* (1) Determine the estimated inventory balance at the time of the fire.

(2) Give the entries to bring the accounts up to date and to summarize the fire loss.

(3) Give the entry that would be made to close the fire loss account into Profit and Loss.

**15-8.** On September 1, 1958, a fire destroyed a portion of the assets of Sherman Sales Co. Immediately after the fire the trial balance at the top of the following page was obtained.

The fire destroyed one half of the buildings, three fourths of the furniture and fixtures, and all of the merchandise on hand.

The insurance company appraised the property and found that furniture and fixtures had a value of $24,000 and buildings a value of $125,000 on the date of the fire. The merchandise destroyed is to be estimated on the assumption that the gross profit percentage on sales in 1957 was maintained in 1958. Sales in 1957 were $320,000; the January 1, 1957, inventory was $21,000; and the purchases in 1957 were $236,000. It is also estimated that store supplies of $120 and office supplies of $205 were on hand and were destroyed at the time of the fire.

The insurance register disclosed the following information:

| PROPERTY COVERED | POLICY DATE | TERMS | COVERAGE | PREMIUM PAID |
|---|---|---|---|---|
| Furniture and Fixtures | July 1, 1956 | 3 years | $15,000 | $360 |
| Buildings | Jan. 1, 1957 | 3 years | 80,000 | 720* |
| Merchandise | Jan. 1, 1958 | 1 year | 20,000 | 345 |

*This policy contains an 80% coinsurance clause.

Depreciation rates are: furniture and fixtures, 10% a year; buildings, 3% a year.

On September 1 there is accrued interest on notes receivable of $200, accrued interest on notes and bonds payable of $410, and accrued selling expenses of $250.

*Instructions:* (1) Prepare a work sheet with pairs of columns for: (a) account balances as of September 1, 1958, (b) the adjustments necessary to bring the accounts up to date, (c) the adjustments necessary to record the fire loss, (d) profit and loss information (including regular activities and fire

## SHERMAN SALES CO.
TRIAL BALANCE
SEPTEMBER 1, 1958

| | | |
|---|---:|---:|
| Cash.......................................... | $ 16,850 | |
| Notes Receivable................................ | 25,800 | |
| Accounts Receivable............................. | 29,005 | |
| Merchandise Inventory, January 1, 1958............. | 24,200 | |
| Store Supplies.................................. | 410 | |
| Office Supplies................................. | 600 | |
| Unexpired Insurance............................ | 1,005 | |
| Furniture and Fixtures.......................... | 30,000 | |
| Allowance for Depreciation of Furniture and Fixtures.... | | $ 8,900 |
| Buildings...................................... | 120,000 | |
| Allowance for Depreciation of Buildings............. | | 26,400 |
| Land.......................................... | 30,000 | |
| Notes Payable.................................. | | 10,000 |
| Accounts Payable............................... | | 15,440 |
| 6% Bonds Payable............................... | | 50,000 |
| Capital Stock.................................. | | 100,000 |
| Retained Earnings.............................. | | 30,990 |
| Sales.......................................... | | 250,200 |
| Sales Returns.................................. | 2,200 | |
| Purchases...................................... | 169,550 | |
| Freight In..................................... | 3,100 | |
| Purchases Returns.............................. | | 2,410 |
| Selling Expenses................................ | 28,930 | |
| General and Administrative Expenses............... | 11,905 | |
| Rental Income................................. | | 2,260 |
| Interest Income................................ | | 505 |
| Interest Expense................................ | 3,550 | |
| | $497,105 | $497,105 |

loss data) for the period January 1–September 1, and (e) balance sheet data on September 1. (All operating expenses are summarized in selling expense and general and administrative expense controlling accounts; depreciation of buildings, depreciation of furniture and fixtures, and insurance are regarded as general and administrative expenses.)

(2) Prepare an income statement and a balance sheet.

(3) Give the entries to bring the accounts up to date and to close the accounts.

**15-9.** A fire at the Roseville plant of Rose Distributors, Inc., completely destroyed a building on July 1, 1958. The company had insured the building against fire with two companies under the following three-year policies:

| COMPANY | FACE | CO-INSURANCE CLAUSE | UNEXPIRED PREMIUM 1/1/58 | DATE OF EXPIRATION |
|:---:|:---:|:---:|:---:|:---:|
| X | $ 80,000 | 80 % | $ 800 | 8/31/58 |
| Y | 120,000 | 80 % | 1,200 | 8/31/58 |

An umpire set the insurable value at date of the fire at $260,000 and the loss at $255,000. In spite of this ruling, there proved to be no net salvage value recoverable from the building. The building was carried on the books of the corporation at a cost of $200,000 less accumulated depreciation charged to operations to date of fire of $40,000.

*Instructions:* (1) Compute the amount recoverable under each insurance policy and the total amount recoverable. You *must* set forth the formula which you use in making your computation.

(2) Compute the balance of the *Fire Loss* account after such of the above data as affect it have been recorded. Label clearly the various elements entering into your computation. (A.I.C.P.A. adapted)

**15-10.** The Drake Company had a fire at their Los Angeles plant on July 15, 1958 which destroyed part of their inventory of finished goods. The company carries fire insurance on inventories in the amount of $120,000, and the policy has an 80% coinsurance clause. The value of the inventories not destroyed was found to be $85,000 on July 15, 1958.

An analysis of some of the general ledger accounts indicates these balances:

|  | JULY 15, 1958 | DECEMBER 31, 1957 |
| --- | --- | --- |
| Cash.............................. | $118,250 | $110,000 |
| Accounts receivable—customers....... | 125,000 | 125,000 |
| Inventories....................... | 165,000 | 155,000 |
| Machinery and equipment—factory.... | 40,000 | 40,000 |
| Allow. for deprec.—mach. and equip.... | (28,000) | (25,000) |
| Accounts payable—trade............. | (85,000) | (75,000) |
| Capital stock...................... | (100,000) | (100,000) |
| Retained earnings.................. | (238,800) | (236,000) |
| Administration expense............. | 4,000 | 8,200 |
| Depreciation—mach. and equip........ | 3,000 | 5,000 |
| Direct labor—factory............... | 111,000 | 120,000 |
| Factory supplies................... | 200 | 2,500 |
| Freight in........................ | 6,400 | 18,000 |
| Freight out....................... | 2,275 | 20,000 |
| Interest income.................... | (175) | (200) |
| Miscellaneous manufacturing expenses.. | 1,200 | 6,300 |
| Payroll taxes—factory.............. | 1,650 | 2,200 |
| Purchases of materials.............. | 126,500 | 280,000 |
| Purchase discounts................. | (6,000) | (8,000) |
| Sales............................. | (275,000) | (500,000) |
| Sales commissions.................. | 5,000 | 25,000 |
| Sales returns and allowances......... | 12,000 | 25,000 |
| Small tools expense................ | 1,500 | 2,000 |

An inventory of materials, work in process and finished goods is taken annually at the close of the calendar year. At December 31, 1956, the amount of the inventory was $155,000; at December 31, 1957 the amount was $165,000. An analysis of the trial balance accounts at July 15, 1958 indicated the following: (1) Material in transit in the amount of $5,000 had not been recorded in any of the accounts. (2) The company had been billed for $4,010 of material that had not been received, although the entire amount was recorded in purchases.

*Instructions:* (1) On the basis of the preceding information, determine the amount of inventory on hand at July 15, 1958.

(2) Compute the amount of money the company would receive from the insurance company as a result of the loss. (A.I.C.P.A. adapted)

**15-11.** Boyle & Hancock, retail dry goods merchants, operated a cash store, no credit being extended to customers. The business was conducted as a partnership in which Boyle had a two-thirds interest and Hancock a one-third interest (capital as well as profits). The accounts were currently kept on a cash basis, but at the end of each year they were adjusted to the accrual basis. At that time the profits were divided in the above ratio and were credited to the partners' capital accounts.

Life insurance was carried in the amount of $10,000, payable to the partnership upon the death of either member. The premiums paid were charged to expense; as the policies were for term insurance, there were no surrender values.

The stock of merchandise was insured for $45,500 and the store and office fixtures for $9,500. The two policies were carried with different companies, and both were written with an 80% coinsurance clause.

A fire occurred in the early morning hours of February 1, 1959, in which Mr. Boyle lost his life. The fixtures were a total loss, but part of the merchandise was salvaged and was agreed with the adjusters to be worth $17,000. A few days after the settlement it was sold for $17,500.

The books of account had been saved and were used as an aid in arriving at a settlement of the fire loss. The following trial balance was drawn off before any adjustments had been made:

| | | |
|---|---:|---:|
| Cash. | $ 20,256.57 | |
| Inventory, December 31, 1958. | 61,328.20 | |
| Store and office fixtures. | 18,000.00 | |
| Reserve for depreciation. | | $ 7,230.00 |
| Unexpired insurance. | 280.00 | |
| Accounts payable. | | 7,928.75 |
| Boyle, capital. | | 58,475.78 |
| Hancock, capital | | 29,237.89 |
| Sales. | | 15,320.50 |
| Purchases. | 14,396.15 | |
| Expenses. | 3,932.00 | |
| | $118,192.92 | $118,192.92 |

The books showed that 30% gross profit had been made in the preceding two years, and this percentage was agreed upon with the adjusters as a basis for calculating the value of the inventory. It was also agreed to accept the depreciated book value of the fixtures as their value at the time of the fire.

There had been no capital expenditure in 1959, and depreciation had been provided at the rate of 8% per annum to December 31, 1958.

The item of unexpired insurance was carried forward from December 31, 1958, being applicable to the succeeding eight months. The short-rate cash value of $210 was recovered on the fire insurance policy. The balance of the unexpired insurance was recorded as a fire loss. All liabilities outstanding on January 31, 1959, had been recorded.

The fire loss was determined on the basis of the foregoing data and in accordance with the terms of the policies, and the entire amount thus agreed upon was collected in February. Also the life insurance was promptly settled in that month.

The firm then paid its liabilities and dissolved after dividing the cash — its only remaining asset — between the two owning interests.

*Instructions:* Prepare a columnar work sheet, clearly showing the adjustment of the above trial balance in accordance with the data given, the operating results in the month of January as distinct from the fire loss, the amount of the fire loss, and the final liquidation of assets and liabilities other than cash, thus leaving on the books only the cash and the two capital accounts. Submit calculations of the inventory value on the date of the fire and amounts recoverable as a result of the fire loss. (A.I.C.P.A. adapted)

**15-12.** The retail store of James Cox was destroyed by fire on March 20, 1959, and only relatively few items were salvaged. From the general ledger, the one book of account saved, the following figures were abstracted as of February 28:

| | | |
|---|---:|---:|
| Cash in Bank | $ 5,285.01 | |
| Petty Cash | 250.00 | |
| Accounts Receivable | 53,483.82 | |
| Merchandise | 106,836.38 | |
| Fixtures | 10,543.26 | |
| Allowance for Depreciation of Fixtures | | $ 8,672.77 |
| Bank Loan Payable | | 10,000.00 |
| James Cox, Capital | | 130,251.20 |
| Sales | | 59,977.39 |
| Expenses | 32,502.89 | |

The last fiscal closing was October 31, 1958.

Correspondence with creditors revealed unrecorded obligations to wholesale houses as of March 20 amounting to $17,100.60, and an inspection of checks returned from the bank at the end of March, $22,924.83, indicated cash purchases of merchandise from March 1–20 of $15,267.82, the balance representing cash withdrawals by Mr. Cox. Merchandise in transit on March 20 was recovered by suppliers and not billed. Bank deposits during that period, as shown by the bank statement, amounted to $20,929.64 and, with the exception of a refund of $200.25 on March 2 from a merchandise creditor, which Mr. Cox recalls that he deposited shortly thereafter, these may be assumed to be payments on account by customers. Indebtedness acknowledged by customers totaled $52,876.45, but it is estimated that $10,000 more that is due from them will never be acknowledged or recovered. Of the acknowledged indebtedness, $1,000 will probably be uncollectible. Returns to suppliers, not yet accounted for by them, amounted to $2,503.72, of which it is estimated that, in line with similar claims in the past, no more than half will ultimately be allowed.

The merchandise stock was insured for $50,000. An agreement has been reached with the insurer whereby the claim of the insured (a) will be based on the assumption that the arithmetical average of the two gross-profit ratios for the fiscal years ended October 31, 1957 and 1958, was in effect during the 4⅔ months ended March 20, 1959, and (b) will be paid, up to the face value of the policy, in accordance with your computation of the cost of the merchandise destroyed. The inventories on October 31, 1956, 1957, and 1958, were $69,250, $70,485, and $57,611 respectively; the net purchases for the two fiscal years ended in 1957 and 1958 were $89,510 and $74,030; and the net sales were $160,500 and $170,400.

Additions to the fixtures account during the current fiscal year have been $300; depreciation at the rate of 10% per year (5% per year on additions) should be allowed for the current fractional year. (For depreciation purposes, the fractional year is assumed to be 5 months.)

Salvaged items were:
  (a) Fixtures, sold to secondhand dealer with the approval of the insurer, for $200; these fixtures were insured for $500, which will be collected in full.
  (b) Petty cash box containing cash and stamps amounting to $103.
  (c) Merchandise: sold to a dealer in salvage stocks, $5,264.53; sold at auction, $12,821.17.

The balance in the proprietor's account on October 31, 1958, was $140,716.38.

*Instructions:* (1) Calculate the amount of the inventory loss resulting from the fire.

(2) Prepare the journal entries necessary to reflect the transactions, etc. that took place between February 28 and March 20, 1959, distinguishing carefully between ordinary operations and the losses occasioned by the fire.

(3) Prepare a work sheet with pairs of columns for: (a) the general ledger account balances as of February 28, 1959, (b) the adjustments necessary to bring the accounts up to date, (c) the adjustments necessary to record the fire loss, (d) the profit and loss figures (including regular activities and fire loss data) for the period November 1–March 20, and (e) balance sheet data on March 20.

(4) Prepare a statement of the proprietor's equity as of March 20, 1959. (A.I.C.P.A. adapted)

# Chapter 16

# PLANT AND EQUIPMENT
## DEPRECIATION AND DEPLETION

**NATURE OF DEPRECIATION**    In spite of expenditures for maintenance and repairs, the time ultimately comes when all plant and equipment items other than land can no longer make a contribution to business activities and must be retired. The costs that are identified with such assets must be allocated to those periods that benefit from asset use.

The Committee on Terminology of the American Institute of Certified Public Accountants defines depreciation accounting as follows:

> *Depreciation accounting* is a system of accounting which aims to distribute the cost or other basic value of tangible capital assets, less salvage (if any), over the estimated useful life of the unit (which may be a group of assets) in a systematic and rational manner. It is a process of allocation, not of valuation. *Depreciation for the year* is the portion of the total charge under such a system that is allocated to the year. Although the allocation may properly take into account occurrences during the year, it is not intended to be a measurement of the effect of all such occurrences.[1]

It will be noted that the term *depreciation* is used in a specialized sense in accounting. It is the process of cost allocation in recognition of the exhaustion of asset life; it is applicable only to those tangible assets that are used by the business. Depreciation is not used to imply a decline in value as the term is popularly employed. It is not used to designate the charge for consumption of wasting assets, which is termed as *depletion*, or the allocation of costs arising from the use of intangibles, which is termed *amortization*. Depreciation does not refer to a decrease in the value assigned to marketable securities as a result of market decline or a decrease in value assigned to inventories as a result of their obsolescence, spoilage, or other deterioration. The suggestion is frequently made that the accountant should consider the use of some term such as "property cost allocation" in place of "depreciation" to avoid any misinterpretation of the nature of the charge implied thereby.

**CAUSES OF DEPRECIATION**    Plant and equipment items have a limited useful life as a result of the operation of certain *physical* and *functional* factors. The physical factors that

---

[1] *Accounting Terminology Bulletin No. 1,* "Review and Résumé," 1953 (New York: American Institute of Certified Public Accountants), p. 25.

move a property item towards its ultimate retirement are (1) *wear and tear*, (2) *deterioration and decay*, and (3) *damage or destruction*. Everyone is familiar with the processes of wear and tear that render an automobile, a typewriter, a chair, or a book no longer usable. The deterioration and the decay of an asset through aging is equally well known; all classes of plant and equipment are subject to physical decay in time whether used or not. Finally, fire, flood, earthquake, or accident arising from careless or improper use will reduce or terminate the life of an asset.

The functional factors that limit the life of a property item are (1) *inadequacy* and (2) *obsolescence*. An asset may lose its usefulness when, as a result of altered business requirements, it can no longer carry the productive load and requires replacement. Although the asset is still usable, its inadequacy for present purposes has cut short its service life. An asset may also lose its usefulness as a result of consumer demand for new and different products or services, or as a result of technical progress and the availability of other assets that can be more economically applied to the fulfillment of business requirements. Here, obsolescence is the factor that operates to limit the service life of the property item.

Depreciation accounting calls for the recognition of both the physical and functional factors that limit asset life. Physical factors are the more readily apparent in predicting the useful life of an asset. But, when certain functional factors are considered to hasten the retirement of an asset, these must receive appropriate recognition in viewing its useful life. Both physical and functional factors may operate gradually or may emerge in sudden fashion. Recognition of depreciation is usually limited to the conditions that operate in gradual fashion and that are reasonably foreseeable. For example, a sudden change in demand for a certain product may make a plant item worthless, or an accident may destroy a plant item; these are unforeseeable contingencies that call for extraordinary charges in the event that they materialize.

Since the movement of an asset to ultimate exhaustion may be canceled in part or retarded through current maintenance and repairs, the policy that is to be operative with respect to these matters must be considered in estimating the useful life of the asset; low standards of maintenance and repair keep these charges at a minimum but call for the recognition of higher-than-normal allocations for depreciation; high standards of maintenance and repairs will mean higher charges for these items, but depreciation allocations may be reduced to a minimum amount. Depreciation is the charge arising from the impairment of the asset that is not restored by current maintenance and repairs.

It should be emphasized that depreciation must be recognized on properties in use whether operations are profitable or not. The charge for the use of properties is essential even though a rise in property replacement costs may be indicated. Costs have been incurred for benefits to be made available through the use of property items; these costs must be applied against the revenues to which they contribute.

**FACTORS IN ARRIVING AT PERIODIC COST ALLOCATION** Three factors are considered in arriving at the periodic charge for the use of a depreciable property item. These factors are: (1) asset cost, (2) estimated salvage value, (3) estimated useful life.

*Asset Cost.* The cost of a property item includes all of the expenditures relating to its acquisition and preparation for use. Expenditures considered to be related to revenues of future periods are capitalized and form the base for depreciation charges. These expenditures were considered in the preceding chapter.

*Estimated Salvage Value.* The salvage value of a depreciable item is its estimated sale, trade-in, scrap, or junk value when no longer serviceable, less costs involved in such realization. In some cases the cost of dismantling and removing assets may equal or exceed the residual value. From a theoretical point of view, any estimated salvage value should be subtracted from cost in arriving at the depreciable cost of the asset; on the other hand, dismantling and removal costs that may be expected to exceed ultimate salvage values should properly be added to cost in arriving at the depreciable cost. In practice both salvage values and dismantling and removal costs are frequently ignored in the development of the depreciation charge. Disregard of these items is not objectionable when they are relatively small and not subject to precise measurement, and when it is doubtful whether any accuracy will be gained through such a refinement of the depreciation estimate.

*Estimated Useful Life.* The life of a property item may be expressed in terms of either an estimated time factor or an estimated use or output factor. The time factor may be a period of months or years; the use factor may be a number of hours of use or a number of units of output. The cost of the property item flows into production in accordance with the lapse of time or in accordance with measured use. The rate of cost flow may be modified by other factors, but basically depreciation must be measured on a time or use basis.[1]

---

[1]The Internal Revenue Service in Bulletin "F" has offered a compilation of different assets and their probable useful lives on a time basis as found by normal experiences in various industries. The compilation stated probable useful lives for individual assets as well as for composite and group accounts. The compilation was

**RECORDING DEPRECIATION** It would be possible to charge expense and credit the property item for periodic depreciation. Such practice would be consistent with that normally employed in the recognition of periodic charges for intangibles and deferred costs. However, it is customary to report the reduction in a depreciable asset in a separate valuation account. This account is frequently titled Reserve for Depreciation, although, as indicated in an earlier chapter, it is better designated Allowance for Depreciation, Accrued Depreciation, or Depreciation Allocated to Past Operations. The reserve title has suggested to some statement readers the existence of a fund available for asset replacement; such an implication is not found in the other titles indicated. When cost allocation is reported in a separate valuation account, original cost as well as that part of the cost already allocated to revenues may be reported on the balance sheet. The reader of the statement is informed concerning original cost as well as the estimated degree of utilization still recoverable from such properties. This practice also serves to emphasize the estimated character of the allocation process.

A separate valuation account is maintained for each asset or class of assets that requires the use of a separate depreciation rate. When subsidiary ledger support is maintained for plant and equipment, such records normally provide for the accumulation of depreciation allocations on the individual assets. Separate charges relating to individual property items in the subsidiary plant ledger form the support for the balance reported in the general ledger account Plant and Equipment; separate credits representing individual property item cost allocations in the subsidiary plant ledger form the support for the balance reported in the general ledger account Allowance for Depreciation of Plant and Equipment. The periodic recognition of depreciation for the individual property items in the subsidiary records is accompanied by a charge to the depreciation account and a credit to the allowance for depreciation account in the general ledger. When plant and equipment items serve manufacturing, selling, and general functions, subsidiary records facilitate the assignment of depreciation to the various activities. Disposal of an asset calls for the cancellation of both asset cost and the accumulated depreciation balances.

---

put forth as no more than a general guide for taxpayers; individual conditions and accounting policies still needed to be considered in arriving at probable lives and depreciation rates that were appropriate under the circumstances. The Internal Revenue Service pointed out, "A reasonable rate for depreciation is dependent not only on the prospective useful life of the property when acquired, but also on the particular conditions under which the property is used as reflected in the taxpayer's operating policy and the accounting policy followed with respect to repairs, maintenance, replacements, charges to the capital asset account and to the depreciation reserve."

When a certain plant item consists of several major units or structural elements with varying lives, separate recording of such different units and the recognition of depreciation in terms of the respective lives of such different units is appropriate. Retirement of an individual unit and its replacement by a new unit requires the cancellation of cost and allowance balances related to the unit disposed of and the recognition of the new unit.

**METHODS FOR COST ALLOCATION**    There are a number of different methods for allocating plant and equipment costs. As previously indicated, methods are based on time or use factors. Each method attempts to arrive at an equitable assignment of costs in view of the special conditions relating to the asset and its use. The method that is to be used in any specific instance should be selected only after a thorough study of the various factors that relate to the property item. The methods listed below are described in the following pages.

(1) Straight-line method.
(2) Service-hours method.
(3) Productive-output method.
(4) Reducing-charge methods:
    (a) Declining balance method.
    (b) Sum of years'-digits method.

Two other methods, the *annuity method* and the *sinking fund method*, call for the application of compound interest calculations that are beyond the scope of the present discussion. These methods are rarely encountered in practice.

The examples that follow assume the acquisition of a machine at a cost of $10,000 with an estimated salvage value at the end of its useful life of $2,500. The following symbols are employed in the formulas for the development of depreciation rates:

$C$ = Asset cost.
$S$ = Estimated salvage value upon termination of estimated life.
$n$ = Estimated life in years, hours of output, or units of output.
$r$ = Depreciation per year, per hour of output, or per unit of output.

**STRAIGHT-LINE METHOD**    The straight-line method relates depreciation to the passage of time and calls for the recognition of equal periodic charges over the life of the asset. The depreciation charge is not affected by asset age, efficiency, or degree of use. In developing the periodic charge, an estimate is required of the useful life of the asset in terms of months or years. The difference between cost and any estimated salvage value is divided by the estimated life of the asset in arriving at the cost to be assigned to each time unit.

Using data for the asset named earlier and assuming a 5-year life, annual depreciation is calculated as follows:

$$\frac{C - S}{n} = r, \text{ or } \frac{\$10,000 - \$2,500}{5} = \$1,500 \text{ per year}$$

Ordinarily depreciation is expressed as a percentage to be applied periodically to asset cost. Depreciation expressed as a percentage for the facts above would be developed as follows:

$$\frac{100\% - 25\%}{5} = 15\%$$

Fifteen per cent applied to cost annually gives a depreciation charge of $1,500. A table to summarize the process of cost allocation for the preceding example follows:

ASSET COST ALLOCATION — STRAIGHT-LINE METHOD

| END OF YEAR | DEBIT TO DEPRECIATION | CREDIT TO ALLOWANCE FOR DEPRECIATION | BALANCE OF ALLOWANCE FOR DEPRECIATION | ASSET BOOK VALUE |
|---|---|---|---|---|
| | | | | $10,000 |
| 1 | $1,500 | $1,500 | $1,500 | 8,500 |
| 2 | 1,500 | 1,500 | 3,000 | 7,000 |
| 3 | 1,500 | 1,500 | 4,500 | 5,500 |
| 4 | 1,500 | 1,500 | 6,000 | 4,000 |
| 5 | 1,500 | 1,500 | 7,500 | 2,500 |
| | $7,500 | $7,500 | | |

A significant change in the conditions of asset use may justify a change in the depreciation rate. For example, assume that estimates in the preceding example were based on use of the machine at the rate of 8 hours a day; after 2 years, a change in operations takes place and the machine is used for two 8-hour shifts daily. It is assumed that increased production will reduce the life of the asset by 1 year. Here accelerated depreciation should be recognized. Periodic depreciation for the remaining life of the asset would be computed as follows:

| | | | |
|---|---|---|---|
| Asset cost. . . . . . . . . . . . . . . . . . . . . . . . . . . . . . . . . . . . . | | | $10,000 |
| Deduct: | | | |
| Salvage value. . . . . . . . . . . . . . . . . . . . . . . . . . . . . . . . | $2,500 | | |
| Depreciation recognized to date: 2-years @ $1,500 ($7,500÷5). . . . . . . . . . . . . . . . . . . . . . . . . . . | 3,000 | 5,500 | |
| Depreciable cost for remaining life of asset. . . . . . . . | | | $ 4,500 |

Annual depreciation over remaining life of asset
($4,500 ÷ 2)............................................    $ 2,250

Straight-line depreciation is the method most widely used. It is readily understood and frequently parallels observable asset deterioration. It has the advantage of simplicity and under normal plant conditions offers a satisfactory means of cost allocation. By normal plant conditions is meant (1) a supply of properties accumulated over a period of years so that the total of depreciation plus maintenance is comparatively even, and (2) approximately equal output from year to year so that the depreciation related to each unit produced does not fluctuate materially. The absence of either of these conditions may suggest the use of some other method.

In recording straight-line depreciation, it is ordinarily desirable to take an arbitrary position with respect to assets acquired and disposed of during the year. Since depreciation is at best an estimate, it is hardly advisable to calculate it on as short a period as a day or a week. For purposes of this chapter, depreciation is recognized to the nearest month: no charge is made for use of an asset for less than one half of a month; more than one half of a month is recognized as a full month. For example, if an asset is acquired on March 10, a charge would be made for depreciation for the full month of March; if an asset is disposed of on March 10, no charge would be made for depreciation for March. In practice, depreciation to the nearest quarter, half year, or even full year may be appropriate when amounts involved are relatively small.

**SERVICE-HOURS METHOD**    The service-hours method is based on the theory that purchase of an asset is purchase of a number of hours of direct service and that charges should be made for depreciation in recognition of the degree of such service. Instead of being estimated in terms of months or years, the life of the plant item is estimated in terms of available service hours. Depreciable cost is divided by service hours in arriving at the depreciation rate to be assigned for each hour of asset use. The use of the asset during the period is measured, and the number of hours of service is multiplied by the depreciation rate in arriving at the depreciation charge. Depreciation charges fluctuate periodically according to the contribution that the asset makes in service hours.

Using asset data previously given and an estimated service life of 6,000 hours, the rate to be applied for each service hour is calculated as follows:

$$\frac{C - S}{n} = r, \text{ or } \frac{\$10,000 - \$2,500}{6,000} = \$1.25 \text{ per hour}$$

Allocation of asset cost in terms of service hours is summarized in the table below:

ASSET COST ALLOCATION — SERVICE-HOURS METHOD

| END OF YEAR | SERVICE HOURS | DEBIT TO DEPRECIATION | | CREDIT TO ALLOWANCE FOR DEPRECIATION | BALANCE OF ALLOWANCE FOR DEPRECIATION | ASSET BOOK VALUE |
|---|---|---|---|---|---|---|
| | | | | | | $10,000 |
| 1 | 1,000 | (1,000×$1.25) | $1,250 | $1,250 | $1,250 | 8,750 |
| 2 | 1,500 | (1,500×$1.25) | 1,875 | 1,875 | 3,125 | 6,875 |
| 3 | 2,000 | (2,000×$1.25) | 2,500 | 2,500 | 5,625 | 4,375 |
| 4 | 1,000 | (1,000×$1.25) | 1,250 | 1,250 | 6,875 | 3,125 |
| 5 | 500 | ( 500×$1.25) | 625 | 625 | 7,500 | 2,500 |
| | 6,000 | | $7,500 | $7,500 | | |

It is assumed above that the original estimate of service is confirmed in use, and that the asset is retired after 6,000 hours which is reached in the fifth year.

It should be observed that straight-line depreciation resulted in an annual charge of $1,500 regardless of fluctuations in productive activity. When assets are considered to wear out as a direct result of performance or use and when there are significant fluctuations in such use in successive periods, the service-hours method, which recognizes "hours used" instead of "hours available for use" normally provides the more equitable charge to operations.

**PRODUCTIVE-OUTPUT METHOD**    The productive-output method is based on the theory that an asset is acquired for production output and that charges should be made for depreciation in recognition of volume of output. This method requires an estimate of the total productive output of the property item. Depreciable cost divided by the estimated output gives the equal depreciation charge to be assigned for each unit of output. The measured production for a period multiplied by the depreciation charge per unit gives the charge to be made for depreciation. Depreciation charges fluctuate periodically according to the contribution that the asset makes in unit output.

Using the previous asset data and an estimated productive life of 800,000 units, the rate to be applied for each unit produced is calculated as follows:

$$\frac{C - S}{n} = r, \text{ or } \frac{\$10,000 - \$2,500}{800,000} = \$.009375 \text{ per unit (or } \$9.375 \text{ per thousand)}$$

Cost allocation in terms of units produced is summarized in the tabulation below:

ASSET COST ALLOCATION — PRODUCTIVE-OUTPUT METHOD

| END OF YEAR | UNIT OUTPUT | DEBIT TO DEPRECIATION | | CREDIT TO ALLOW- ANCE FOR DEPRE- CIATION | BALANCE OF ALLOW- ANCE FOR DEPRE- CIATION | ASSET BOOK VALUE |
|---|---|---|---|---|---|---|
| | | | | | | $10,000.00 |
| 1 | 100,000 | (100×$9.375) | $ 937.50 | $ 937.50 | $ 937.50 | 9,062.50 |
| 2 | 200,000 | (200×$9.375) | 1,875.00 | 1,875.00 | 2,812.50 | 7,187.50 |
| 3 | 350,000 | (350×$9.375) | 3,281.25 | 3,281.25 | 6,093.75 | 3,906.25 |
| 4 | 100,000 | (100×$9.375) | 937.50 | 937.50 | 7,031.25 | 2,968.75 |
| 5 | 50,000 | ( 50×$9.375) | 468.75 | 468.75 | 7,500.00 | 2,500.00 |
| | 800,000 | | $7,500.00 | $7,500.00 | | |

When quantitative uses of depreciable properties can be reasonably estimated and are readily measurable, the productive-output method provides a highly satisfactory approach to asset cost allocation. Depreciation is a variable charge that tends to follow the revenue curve: periods of high activity are assigned correspondingly high depreciation charges; periods of low activity are assigned correspondingly low depreciation charges. However, certain limitations in the use of the productive-output method need to be pointed out. Asset performance in terms of productive output may be difficult to estimate. Furthermore, measurement solely in terms of output will fail to recognize special conditions that may be operative, such as increasing maintenance and repair costs, as well as possible inadequacy and obsolescence factors.

**REDUCING-CHARGE METHODS**    Reducing-charge methods provide for the highest depreciation charge in the first year of asset use and steadily declining depreciation charges in successive years. Such plans are based on the theory that the sum of depreciation and maintenance and repair charges involved in the use of a property item should be relatively even from year to year. Over the life of the asset, therefore, as maintenance and repair charges rise, depreciation charges go down.

*Declining Balance Method.* Decreasing depreciation charges are provided by the *declining balance method* by applying a fixed percentage rate to a declining asset book value. The rate to be applied to the declining book value that will produce the estimated salvage value at the end of the useful life of the asset is calculated by the following formula:

$$1 - \sqrt[n]{S \div C} = r$$

Using the previous asset data and assuming a 5-year asset life, the depreciation rate is calculated as follows:

$$1 - \sqrt[5]{2,500 \div 10,000} = 1 - \sqrt[5]{.25} = 1 - .757858 = .242142, \text{ or } 24.2142\%$$

Dividing the estimated salvage value by cost in the formula above gives .25, the percentage that the salvage value at the end of 5 years should bear to cost. The fifth root of this percentage is calculated at .757858. Multiplying cost and the successive declining book values by .757858 five times will reduce the asset to .25 of its original balance. The difference between 1 and .757858, or .242142, then, is the rate of decrease to be applied successively in bringing the asset down to .25 of its original balance. A salvage value is required in the use of the above formula. In the absence of an expected salvage value, a nominal amount of $1 can be employed for purposes of the formula.

Depreciation calculated by application of the 24.2142% rate to the declining book value is summarized in the table below:

ASSET COST ALLOCATION — DECLINING BALANCE METHOD

| END OF YEAR | DEBIT TO DEPRECIATION | | CREDIT TO ALLOWANCE FOR DEPRECIATION | BALANCE OF ALLOWANCE FOR DEPRECIATION | ASSET BOOK VALUE |
|---|---|---|---|---|---|
| | | | | | $10,000.00 |
| 1 | (24.2142% of $10,000.00) | $2,421.42 | $2,421.42 | $2,421.42 | 7,578.58 |
| 2 | (24.2142% of $ 7,578.58) | 1,835.09 | 1,835.09 | 4,256.51 | 5,743.49 |
| 3 | (24.2142% of $ 5,743.49) | 1,390.74 | 1,390.74 | 5,647.25 | 4,352.75 |
| 4 | (24.2142% of $ 4,352.75) | 1,053.98 | 1,053.98 | 6,701.23 | 3,298.77 |
| 5 | (24.2142% of $ 3,298.77) | 798.77 | 798.77 | 7,500.00 | 2,500.00 |
| | | | $7,500.00 | $7,500.00 | |

Instead of developing a rate that is refined to produce a salvage value of exactly $2,500, it will usually prove more convenient to approximate a rate that will provide satisfactory cost allocation; since depreciation involves estimates, there is little assurance that rate refinement will produce more accurate results. In the previous example, for instance, a depreciation rate of 25% provides a more convenient basis for recording depreciation than the use of 24.2142%; differences resulting from the use of the 25% rate are not material.[1]

*Sum of Years'-Digits Method.* Decreasing depreciation charges are provided by the *sum of years'-digits method* by applying a series of fractions, each of a smaller value, to original asset cost less salvage over the life of the asset. Fractions are developed in terms of the sum of the asset life periods. Assuming the asset previously described and an estimated 5-year life, periodic charges are developed by the sum of years'-digits method as follows:

|  | REDUCING WEIGHTS | REDUCING FRACTIONS |
|---|---|---|
| First Year | 5 | 5/15 |
| Second Year | 4 | 4/15 |
| Third Year | 3 | 3/15 |
| Fourth Year | 2 | 2/15 |
| Fifth Year | 1 | 1/15 |
|  | 15 | 15/15 |

Weights for purposes of developing reducing fractions are the years'-digits listed in inverse order. The denominator for the fraction is obtained by adding these weights; the numerator is the weight assigned to the specific year.[2] Depreciation calculated by application of the reducing fractions above to depreciable cost is summarized in the table that follows:

ASSET COST ALLOCATION — SUM OF YEARS'-DIGITS METHOD

| END OF YEAR | DEBIT TO DEPRECIATION | | CREDIT TO ALLOWANCE FOR DE- PRECIATION | BALANCE OF ALLOWANCE FOR DE- PRECIATION | ASSET BOOK VALUE |
|---|---|---|---|---|---|
|  |  |  |  |  | $10,000 |
| 1 | (5/15×$7,500) | $2,500 | $2,500 | $2,500 | 7,500 |
| 2 | (4/15×$7,500) | 2,000 | 2,000 | 4,500 | 5,500 |
| 3 | (3/15×$7,500) | 1,500 | 1,500 | 6,000 | 4,000 |
| 4 | (2/15×$7,500) | 1,000 | 1,000 | 7,000 | 3,000 |
| 5 | (1/15×$7,500) | 500 | 500 | 7,500 | 2,500 |
|  |  | $7,500 | $7,500 |  |  |

[1]In practice one frequently finds the declining-balance method employed with a rate that is double the appropriate straight-line rate computed without adjustment for salvage. Such depreciation may be claimed for tax purposes, and when it fairly reflects the cost of asset use may properly be employed in the accounts.

[2]The fraction denominator can be obtained by dividing the sum of the digits for the first and last year by 2 and multiplying this value by the number of years. In the example, calculation of the denominator is possible as follows: $\frac{5+1}{2} \times 5 = 15$.

If the sum of the years'-digits method results in excessive variations between early and late years, the method may be modified to provide smaller variations by raising the weight assigned to the last year and adjusting the remaining weights correspondingly. For example, allowing a weight of 10 for the fifth year and raising preceding weights by 1, reducing fractions and periodic charges may be developed as follows:

| | REDUCING WEIGHTS | REDUCING FRACTIONS APPLIED TO DEPRECIABLE COST | PERIODIC DEPRECIATION |
|---|---|---|---|
| First Year | 14 | 14/60×$7,500 | $1,750 |
| Second Year | 13 | 13/60×$7,500 | 1,625 |
| Third Year | 12 | 12/60×$7,500 | 1,500 |
| Fourth Year | 11 | 11/60×$7,500 | 1,375 |
| Fifth Year | 10 | 10/60×$7,500 | 1,250 |
| | 60 | 60/60 | $7,500 |

*Evaluation of Reducing-Charge Methods.* When the use of a property item calls for increased maintenance and repair costs periodically, a reducing-charge method makes possible an equitable assignment of the combined costs of depreciation and maintenance and repairs to revenue. For example, assume that maintenance and repairs on the asset previously described are expected to be $500 the first year and to rise by approximately $125 a year thereafter. Use of the reducing-charge method illustrated above is compared with the straight-line method in the tabulation below:

| | DEPRECIATION CHARGE | | ESTIMATED MAINTENANCE AND REPAIRS | SUM OF DEPRECIATION AND MAINTENANCE AND REPAIRS | |
|---|---|---|---|---|---|
| YEAR | STRAIGHT-LINE | REDUCING-FRACTION | | STRAIGHT-LINE DEPRECIATION | REDUCING-FRACTION DEPRECIATION |
| 1 | $1,500 | $1,750 | $ 500 | $ 2,000 | $ 2,250 |
| 2 | 1,500 | 1,625 | 625 | 2,125 | 2,250 |
| 3 | 1,500 | 1,500 | 750 | 2,250 | 2,250 |
| 4 | 1,500 | 1,375 | 875 | 2,375 | 2,250 |
| 5 | 1,500 | 1,250 | 1,000 | 2,500 | 2,250 |
| | $7,500 | $7,500 | $3,750 | $11,250 | $11,250 |

The reducing-fraction method above provides equal combined charges periodically, while straight-line depreciation results in higher combined costs as the asset grows older. The illustration assumes a regular increase in maintenance and repairs. Obviously such regularity would not be achieved in practice; hence a reducing-charge method will not provide the uniformity reported above. However, when it is known that maintenance and repairs will show a regular increase in successive years, use of a reducing-charge method will tend to equalize periodic charges for the use of the asset.

Other factors may suggest use of a reducing-charge method: (1) The anticipation of a significant immediate contribution to be realized on the asset acquisition with the extent of the contribution to be realized in later periods less definite suggests highest depreciation rates for the periods in which assets are acquired. (2) The expectation of a shrinkage in asset efficiency or asset output as the asset becomes worn offers support for decreasing depreciation charges. (3) The possibility that inadequacy or obsolescence may result in premature retirement of the asset offers support for a method that will produce decreasing book values that parallel decreases taking place in the market, sales, or trade-in value of the asset; in the event of premature asset retirement, depreciation charges will have absorbed what would otherwise require recognition as an extraordinary loss. Reducing-charge methods are supported as conservative approaches to the cost allotment problem.[1]

**COMPOSITE RATE AND GROUP RATE METHODS** In the previous discussion it was assumed that depreciation is calculated on each individual plant item. There has been no suggestion of averaging the rates and applying a single rate to the total of the plant account or to all departmental properties. The application of average rates are referred to as *composite-rate* or *group-rate methods*.

A composite rate is set by estimate or by an analysis of the various assets or classes of assets in use. The development of a composite rate based upon an analysis of the properties employed by a business unit is illustrated in the example that follows:

| ASSETS | COST | SALVAGE VALUE | DEPRECIABLE COST | ESTIMATED LIFE IN YEARS | ANNUAL DEPRECIATION |
|--------|------|---------------|------------------|-------------------------|---------------------|
| A | $ 2,500 | $ 100 | $ 2,400 | 4 | $ 600 |
| B | 6,000 | 400 | 5,600 | 5 | 1,120 |
| C | 10,000 | 500 | 9,500 | 10 | 950 |
| | $18,500 | $1,000 | $17,500 | | $2,670 |

Composite depreciation rate applied to cost: $2,670 \div \$18,500 = 14.43\%$.
Composite life of business assets: $17,500 \div \$2,670 = 6.55$ years.

---

[1]The American Institute Committee on Accounting Procedure in *Accounting Research Bulletin No. 44*, "Declining-balance Depreciation" (1954), states, "The declining-balance method is one of those which meets the requirements of being 'systematic and rational.' In those cases where the expected productivity or revenue-earning power of the asset is relatively greater during the earlier years of its life, or where maintenance charges tend to increase during the later years, the declining-balance method may well provide the most satisfactory allocation of cost." The Committee would apply these conclusions to other methods, including the sum of the years'-digits method, that produce similar results.

It will be observed that a rate of 14.43% applied to the cost of the assets, $18,500, results in annual depreciation of $2,670. Annual depreciation charges of $2,670 reach the total depreciable cost of $17,500 in 6.55 years; hence 6.55 years may be considered to be the composite or average life of the business assets. Composite depreciation would be reported in a single valuation account.

After a composite rate has been set, it is ordinarily continued in the absence of significant changes in the lives of assets or asset additions and retirements that have a material effect upon the rate. It is assumed in the example above that assets A and B are replaced with similar assets at the end of 4 and 5 years respectively. If the assets are not replaced, obviously a continuation of the depreciation rate of 14.43% will result in overstatements of depreciation charges. Upon individual asset retirement, the asset account is closed and that portion of the valuation account balance that relates to the retired asset is canceled.

When a business owns a great many assets, and these differ in functions, lives, etc., assets may be segregated into a number of homogeneous groupings and depreciation rates developed that are appropriate to each group. Such procedure will call for the establishment of separate allowances for each asset group and subsequent accounting in terms of the different groups. Group rates normally provide more reliable charges for depreciation than the application of a single rate to all of the properties.

Composite-rate and group-rate depreciation represent application of the straight-line procedure to groups of properties. The averaging technique that is substituted for individual calculations results in significant savings in time and clerical efforts. But the accuracy that is achieved by unit depreciation is not available when average rates are applied to group totals.

**APPRAISAL, RETIREMENT, AND REPLACEMENT SYSTEMS** The charge to operations for plant and equipment use may be made on a basis other than cost allocation. Other systems that are sometimes used in establishing such charges are mentioned below:

*Appraisal Systems.* Asset accounts are charged for all asset acquisitions; assets are appraised periodically and the asset balances are reduced to the appraised values, such reduction being recognized as a charge to operations.

*Retirement Systems.* Asset accounts are charged for all asset acquisitions; at the end of the period, assets are credited for the full cost of those assets retired within the period and expense is charged for this amount.

*Replacement Systems.* Asset accounts are charged for original asset acquisitions; charges to expense are recognized in the future for all replacements in the original supply, no charge being made for asset retirements.

Systems such as the foregoing can be considered acceptable only when the use of standard depreciation accounting involves certain practical difficulties. The use of the above systems would be suggested for the ownership of tools of relatively small cost and large number. These systems may likewise be applicable in such instances as accounting for poles and related equipment for an electric utility, railroad ties in the case of a railway, and dishes and silverware in the case of a restaurant.

**ALLOWABLE DEPRECIA- TION FOR FEDERAL IN- COME TAX PURPOSES** Significant changes in allowable depreciation for federal income tax purposes were made in the 1954 Revenue Code. The Code provides that a taxpayer shall be entitled to a reasonable allowance for the exhaustion, wear, and tear of property held for trade or business or for the production of income. The Code further specifically names the following as methods that it will accept:

(1) The straight-line method,

(2) The declining-balance method, using an annual rate limited to double the rate that would be applicable for straight-line depreciation,

(3) The sum of years'-digits method,

(4) Any other consistent method, providing accumulated depreciation over the first two-thirds of the useful life of the property does not exceed that obtainable in (2) above.

Methods (2), (3), and (4) can be applied only to properties with lives of three years or more acquired after December 31, 1953.

The federal income tax laws allow depreciation on an individual unit basis or on a composite or group basis. If the latter basis is to be employed, assets may be combined in the following manners: "group" accounts may be established for assets with approximately the same life; "classified" accounts may be established for assets with similar uses; a "composite" account may be established for all of the assets used in a business. A depreciation rate must be applied separately to each account; the rate may be the average expected useful life of all of the assets in the account or the maximum expected useful life of the longest-lived asset in the account.

**DEPRECIATION ACCOUNTING AND PROPERTY REPLACEMENT**

There has been a tendency on the part of many readers of financial statements to interpret depreciation accounting as somehow related to the accumulation of a fund for asset replacement. The use of such terms as provision for depreciation on the income statement and reserve for depreciation on the balance sheet have contributed to such misinterpretation.

It has been pointed out that the charge for depreciation originates from the recognition of the movement of a property item towards ultimate exhaustion; the nature of this charge is no different from those that are made to recognize the expiration of insurance premiums or the expiration of patent rights. It is true that revenue equal to or in excess of expenses for a period results in a recovery of such expenses; salary expense is thus recovered by revenue, as is insurance expense, patent amortization, and charges for depreciation. This does not suggest, however, that cash equivalent to the recorded depreciation will be available to meet the cost of property item replacement. Resources from revenues may be applied to many uses: to the increase in receivables, inventories, or other working capital items; to the acquisition of plant or other noncurrent items; to the retirement of debt or the redemption of stock; and to the payment of dividends. The *statement of application of funds*, which is described in Chapter 28, traces the employment of resources that are made available by operations of the business. If a fund is to be available for the replacement of property items, this calls for special action — the transfer of cash to the particular fund. Depreciation accounting does not serve such a function.

**DEPLETION**

Natural resources, also called *wasting assets*, move towards exhaustion as the physical units that comprise such resources are removed and sold. The withdrawal of oil or gas, the cutting of timber, and the mining of coal, sulphur, iron, copper, or silver ore are examples of processes leading to the exhaustion of natural resources. The reduction in the cost or value of natural resources as a result of the withdrawal of such resources is referred to as *depletion.*

Depletion may be distinguished from depreciation in the following respects:

(1) Depletion is recognition of the quantitative exhaustion taking place in the case of a natural resource, while depreciation is recognition of the service exhaustion taking place in a plant and equipment item.

(2) Depletion involves a distinctive asset that cannot be directly replaced in kind upon its exhaustion; depreciation involves assets that are generally replaced upon their exhaustion.

(3) Depletion is recognition of the direct conversion of a natural resource into a commodity that is to be sold; depreciation is an allocation of a cost to current revenue for a service function, except when assets are used in manufacturing activities and depreciation is related to the conversion of raw materials into finished goods.

The measurement of net income calls for the recognition of depletion. If the natural resource is sold directly upon its emergence or withdrawal, the recognition of depletion is, in effect, the recognition of a cost of goods sold; if the natural resource is processed and stored before sale, the depletion charge becomes a part of the inventory cost until it emerges as a cost of goods sold.

**RECORDING DEPLETION**     Three factors are considered in arriving at the charge to be made for depletion:

(1) Property cost, including all developmental costs identified with preparation of the property for exploitation.

(2) Estimated residual value of the property upon exhaustion of natural resources.

(3) Estimated supply of units that can be profitably removed from the property.

Cost of the property less the estimated residual value gives the total amount to be recognized as depletion. This value divided by the estimated unit output gives the charge to be recognized for each unit removed from the property, or the *depletion unit charge.* Depletion for the period is the measured number of units removed during the period multiplied by the depletion unit charge.

To illustrate, assume the following facts: land containing natural resources is purchased at a cost of $5,500,000; the land value after resource exploitation is estimated at $250,000; the natural resource supply is estimated at 1,000,000 tons. The depletion unit charge and the charge for the first year, assuming the withdrawal of 80,000 tons, are calculated as follows:

Depletion unit charge: ($5,500,000 − $250,000) ÷ 1,000,000 = $5.25 per ton.

Depletion charge for the first year: 80,000 tons @ $5.25 = $420,000.

If developmental costs are involved in the exploitation of the resource, such costs should be added to the original cost of the property in arriving at the total cost subject to depletion. These costs may be incurred before normal activities begin. On the other hand, such costs may be continuing and hence may call for estimates in arriving at a depletion charge that is to be used uniformly for all recoverable units. Developmental costs of $500,000 would raise the depletion unit charge in the example to $5.75 per ton.

Assuming a depletion charge for the year $420,000 as calculated above, an entry is made as follows:

Depletion.......................................... 420,000
    Allowance for Depletion......................... 420,000

The charge for depletion, increased by labor and overhead relating to removal and processing, is recognized in the cost of goods sold section of the income statement. If all of the units represented by the depletion charge are sold, depletion, labor, and overhead costs measure the cost of goods sold to be applied against revenue in arriving at gross profit on sales; if some of the units remain on hand, their cost should be determined by considering depletion, labor, and overhead charges, and this figure should be subtracted from the total cost of making the resources available in arriving at cost of goods sold. Depletion, therefore, is comparable to raw materials purchases in summarizing the results of operations. The allowance for depletion is subtracted from the property account on the balance sheet in arriving at the cost of the asset assignable to future revenues.

Revisions in the depletion unit charge often become necessary. Revisions are necessary when developmental costs during the period of unit extraction differ significantly from original estimates. Revisions are also necessary when estimates of the available unit supply change as a result of additional evidence or further discoveries or as a result of revised or new extraction processess. When it can be determined that past depletion charges have been in error, corrections may be made in the accounts and current and future charges made in accordance with revised data. But when circumstances suggest that adjustments in cost and modification of estimates of recoverable supplies may be necessary at different future intervals, an alternate procedure may be followed providing for varying depletion charges based upon the latest evidence of each year. In applying such procedure, past charges would be allowed to stand; a current charge would be established by dividing the resource cost balance as found at the end of the year by the estimated remaining recoverable units as of the beginning of the year (units recovered during the year increased by the estimated recoverable supply at the end of the year). To illustrate, assume in the preceding example that additional developmental costs of $500,000 are incurred in the second year and recoverable units are estimated at 950,000 tons, after second year withdrawals of 100,000 tons. The depletion charge for the second year is calculated as follows:

Cost to be assigned to recoverable tons as of the beginning of the second year:

| | | |
|---|---:|---:|
| Original costs applicable to land and resources............ | | $5,500,000 |
| Deduct: Residual land value.................... | $250,000 | |
| Depletion charge for first year......... | 420,000 | 670,000 |
| | | $4,830,000 |
| Add: Additional costs incurred in second year........... | | 500,000 |
| Balance subject to depletion........................... | | $5,330,000 |

Estimated recoverable tons as of the beginning of the second year:

| | |
|---|---:|
| Number of tons withdrawn in second year............. | 100,000 |
| Estimated recoverable tons at end of second year........ | 950,000 |
| Total recoverable tons at the beginning of second year.... | 1,050,000 |

Depletion unit charge for second year: $5,330,000 ÷ 1,050,000, or $5.0762 per ton.

Depletion charge for second year: 100,000 × $5.0762, or $507,620.

When certain buildings and improvements are constructed in connection with ventures involving the exploitation of natural resources and the usefulness of such assets will be limited to the duration of the project, it is reasonable to assign the costs of these assets to revenue in the same manner as that employed for the natural resources themselves. For example, assume that buildings are constructed at a cost of $250,000; the useful life of the buildings will terminate upon exhaustion of the natural resource, the buildings thus servicing operations during the removal of 1,000,000 units. Under such circumstances, a depreciation charge of $.25 ($250,000 ÷ 1,000,000) should accompany the depletion charge that is made for each unit. When improvements provide benefits that are expected to terminate prior to the exhaustion of the natural resource, the cost of such improvements may be allocated on the basis of the units to be removed during the life of the improvements or on a time basis, whichever may be considered more appropriate.

Depletion for tax purposes may differ from the amount reported on the books. Federal income tax laws permit the taxpayer to deduct annually a flat percentage of gross income for depletion of oil and gas wells and minerals. Such *percentage or statutory depletion* is deducted when this exceeds *cost depletion*. The depletion rate for oil and gas wells is 27½% of gross income and varies on minerals from 5% to 23% of gross income, but such deduction cannot exceed 50% of the taxable income from the property calculated without regard to the charge for depletion. The taxpayer is permitted to take percentage depletion as long as properties are income producing; there is no limitation on the total allowable depletion, and the sum of periodic depletion deductions may ultimately far exceed property cost.

**DIVIDENDS REPRESENT- ING PROCEEDS FROM WASTING ASSETS** When a company's stock in trade is its wasting assets, revenue represents a recovery of the cost of such wasting assets charged to operations, a recovery of other expenses, and a net income. When natural resources are not to be replaced and operations are to cease upon exhaustion of the resources, dividends need not be limited to net income but may be paid in amounts equal to such net income increased by the amount charged against revenue as depletion. To limit dividends to net income would be to retain the amount recovered from wasting assets within the business, possibly in unproductive form, until such time as the business is liquidated. In the absence of effective utilization of revenue proceeds for new properties or other productive purposes, such assets should be made available to stockholders. Amounts received by stockholders, then, are in part a distribution of earnings and in part a return of invested capital no longer required by the company.

To illustrate the nature of the foregoing, assume that the Midas Mines Co. in 1958 issues $100,000 in capital stock in exchange for certain wasting assets. During the course of the fiscal period, natural resources that cost $25,000 are sold for $50,000 and operating expenses of $10,000 are incurred. At the end of the period, the balance sheet reports the following:

MIDAS MINES CO.
BALANCE SHEET
DECEMBER 31, 1958

| | | | | |
|---|---|---|---|---|
| Cash................. | | $ 35,000 | Liabilities.............. | $ 5,000 |
| Receivables........... | | 10,000 | Capital stock........... | 100,000 |
| Wasting assets .. | $100,000 | | Retained earnings....... | 15,000 |
| Less: Allowance for depletion.... | 25,000 | 75,000 | | |
| Total assets........... | | $120,000 | Total liabilities and capital | $120,000 |

Management, here, does not need to limit dividends to the balance of retained earnings, $15,000, but may consider the limitation to be $40,000, that is, $15,000 increased by the recovery of the asset depletion,

$25,000. Under the circumstances above, since revenue has not been fully realized in cash, and since some cash is required for a continuation of operations, dividends of a lesser amount would be in order. A dividend of $28,000 would be regarded as representing first a distribution of earnings, the balance a return to owners of invested capital. The return of invested capital is reported by a charge to a capital stock offset balance rather than by a charge to capital stock. The entry to record the $28,000 distribution may be made as follows:

| | | |
|---|---:|---:|
| Retained Earnings............................ | 15,000 | |
| Capital Distributions to Stockholders.............. | 13,000 | |
| Cash....................................... | | 28,000 |

A balance sheet prepared after the distribution will appear as follows:

MIDAS MINES CO.
BALANCE SHEET
DECEMBER 31, 1958

| | | | | | | |
|---|---:|---:|---|---:|---:|---:|
| Cash................. | | $ 7,000 | Liabilities.............. | | | $ 5,000 |
| Receivables........... | | 10,000 | Capital stock.... | $100,000 | | |
| Wasting assets... | $100,000 | | Less: Capital | | | |
| Less: Allowance | | | distributions to | | | |
| for depletion.... | 25,000 | 75,000 | stockholders..... | | 13,000 | 87,000 |
| Total assets........... | | $92,000 | Total liabilities and capital. | | | $92,000 |

The distribution to stockholders of amounts equal to net income increased by the depletion charge is permitted by state laws; such action is sanctioned on the theory that creditors are aware of the shrinking investment requirements that are peculiar to operations involving wasting assets not subject to replacement. As already indicated in an earlier chapter, when dividends are distributed that are in part liquidating, stockholders should be informed by the corporation of the portion of the dividend that represents corporate earnings and of the portion that represents invested capital.

## QUESTIONS

**1.** "Depreciation is an optional charge that the manufacturer may or may not include in finished goods cost." Do you believe this statement to be correct? Discuss.

**2.** Explain the meaning of depreciation accounting.

**3.** "The recognition of depreciation has no essential relation to the problem of replacement." Do you agree? Discuss.

**4.** Distinguish between functional depreciation and physical depreciation.

**5.** Distinguish between inadequacy and obsolescence.

**6.** The president of the Hathaway Co. recommends that no depreciation be recorded for 1958 since the depreciation rate is 5% per year and indexes show that prices during the year have risen by more than this figure. Evaluate this argument.

**7.** The policy of the Burke Co. is to recondition its plant each year so that it may be maintained in perfect repair. In view of the extensive periodic costs involved in keeping the plant in such condition, officials of the company feel that the need for recognizing depreciation is eliminated. Evaluate this argument.

**8.** The board of directors of Chambers, Inc. believes that it is proper to provide for depreciation when determining the results of operations. Because depreciation does not affect the cash position of the company, however, the board believes it can be disregarded in determining the amount of net income available for dividends. To what condition might such a policy lead?

**9.** Describe the calculation of periodic depreciation under each of the following methods:
  (a) Straight-line.
  (b) Service-hours.
  (c) Productive-output.
  (d) Declining balance.
  (e) Sum of years'-digits.

**10.** Evaluate each method listed in Question 9 above, indicating the circumstances under which the method would be particularly appropriate and the advantages found in its use.

**11.** The Heslip Co. has written down its plant and equipment account to $1. It defends this treatment on the grounds that it had adequate retained earnings to accomplish the write-down, and such practice is desirable in the interest of "accounting conservatism." Comment on this practice.

**12.** Phillip Grover, president of the R-X Corp., upon inspecting the financial statements for the first year of operations objects to the use of straight-line depreciation on the grounds that the loss in value of the assets the first year is actually greater than that in subsequent years. What is your answer?

**13.** Would you recommend the use of a reducing-charge method for recording depreciation or the use of straight-line depreciation with a separate allowance for maintenance when maintenance costs are expected to increase over the life of the asset? Give your reasons.

**14.** When, in your opinion, would the use of a composite depreciation rate be appropriate?

**15.** (a) Describe the assignment of plant charges to operations under (1) the appraisal system (2) the retirement system, and (3) the replacement system. (b) Do you recommend the use of such procedures?

**16.** (a) Define wasting assets. (b) Give five examples of wasting assets.

**17.** (a) Define depletion. (b) What distinctions can be made between depletion and depreciation?

**18.** What special problems are involved in recording depreciation on plant and equipment items that are used in connection with the exploitation of natural resources?

**19.** Justify the practice, followed in the case of a company with wasting assets, of adding the charge for depletion to net income in arriving at the amount available for dividends.

## EXERCISES

**1.** The Jones Company has a certain machine costing $50,000 with a useful life of 5 years and salvage value of $2,000. The estimated operating life of the machine is 20,000 hours. In 1957 total hours amounted to 3,000; in 1958, 5,000. Compare depreciation charges for both years, using the straight-line, productive-hours, and sum of years'-digits methods.

**2.** Wesley Sales acquires machinery at a cost of $10,000. The estimated life of the asset is 5 years, and it is believed that the asset will have to be scrapped at the end of this time with a value of approximately $100. Prepare a table of depreciation charges for the 5-year period if depreciation is recorded at a fixed percentage on the diminishing book value of the asset. (The fifth root of .01 = .398.)

**3.** The McArthur Manufacturing Co. acquires a machine at a cost of $18,600 on March 1, 1952. The machine is estimated to have a life of 10 years except for a special unit that will require replacement at the end of 6 years. The asset is recorded in two accounts, $3,600 being assigned to the special unit, the balance of the cost to the main unit. Depreciation is recorded by the straight-line method, salvage values being disregarded. On March 1, 1958, the special unit is scrapped and is replaced with a similar unit; the cost of the replacement at this time is $4,800, and it is estimated that the unit will have a salvage value of approximately 25% of cost at the end of the useful life of the main unit. What are the depreciation charges to be recognized for the years 1952, 1958, and 1959?

**4.** The Winter Co. acquired a machine on October 1, 1948, at a cost of $10,500. The machine was estimated to have a life of 10 years and a scrap value at the end of that time of $500. At the beginning of April, 1950, adjustments were made to the machine increasing its operating capacity 25%; the cost of such work was $1,700. The machine was sold on January 5, 1958, for cash of $550. The fiscal period for the Winter Co. is the calendar year. (a) What entries would be made to record depreciation at the end of 1948, 1949, and 1950? (b) What entry would be made to record the disposal of the machine in 1958?

**5.** The Marshall Co. acquires machinery on January 1, 1958, at a cost of $8,000; the estimated salvage on the machinery is $250 at the end of a 10-year life. The machinery is guaranteed to perform satisfactorily for a 3-year period; it is estimated that repairs for the first year following the guarantee period will amount to $150 and that repairs will increase by approximately $100 per year thereafter until the machinery is scrapped. Prepare a table, similar to the one illustrated on page 490 of the text, reporting periodic depreciation charges for the 10-year period, assuming depreciation is to be recorded at amounts that will result in the same amount for the sum of depreciation and repairs over the life of the asset.

**6.** The Warner Co. records show the following assets:

| | Acquired | Cost | Salvage Value | Estimated Useful Life |
|---|---|---|---|---|
| Machinery | 7/1/57 | $65,000 | $5,000 | 10 years |
| Equipment | 1/1/58 | 25,000 | 1,000 | 6 years |
| Fixtures | 1/1/58 | 15,000 | 3,000 | 4 years |

What is (a) the composite life of the assets and (b) the composite depreciation rate on assets?

**7.** The Barton Co. obtains a lease for 25 years on a piece of land upon which it erects a building at a cost of $25,000 with an estimated life of 30 years. Buildings belong to the lessor at the end of the lease period. It also leases another piece of land for 20 years and erects a factory at a cost of $18,000 with an estimated life of 15 years. What is the annual depreciation charge on each piece of property?

**8.** The Grand Island Trucking Company replaces worn dump bodies on ten of its trucks with new type bodies at a cost of $500 per truck. Bodies similar to the old types used would have cost only $300, but it is estimated that the additional cost will be justified by larger loading facilities. (a) How should the purchase be recorded? (b) How should subsequent depreciation on the trucks be calculated?

**9.** A paving contractor purchases a pavement-breaking outfit, including air compressor and hammers, at a cost of $2,400. The outfit has an estimated life of 12 years with the exception of the air hammers, which replace equipment every 2 years at a cost of $600. What adjusting entry should be made at the end of the first year?

**10.** Whitehaven Construction Company purchases for $50,000 a property with a gravel deposit estimated at 1,000,000 cubic yards. During the first year of operations 50,000 cubic yards of gravel are removed. How is depletion recorded at the end of the year?

## PROBLEMS

**16-1.** The cost of a machine purchased by Cushman Inc. on March 1, 1958, is $16,600. It is estimated that the machine will have a $1,000 trade-in value at the end of its service life. Its life is estimated at 6 years; its working hours are estimated at 25,000; its production is estimated at 375,000 units. During 1958, the machine was operated 5,400 hours and produced 68,000 units.

*Instructions:* Compute the depreciation on the machine for 1958 by: (1) the straight-line method, (2) the productive-hours method, (3) the output method, (4) the sum of years'-digits method, and (5) the declining balance method using an annual rate of 35%.

**16-2.** Hillcrest Parts, Inc. installs a processing line on November 1, 1957, at a cost of $60,000. It is estimated that the machinery will have an 8-year life, and that the cost of removing machinery at the end of this time will be equal to its scrap value. It is estimated that the machine will process 200,000,000 units during its useful life. During 1957 and 1958, 2,400,000 units and 18,000,000 units respectively were produced.

*Instructions:* Compute the depreciation on the machinery for the years ended December 31, 1957 and 1958, using (1) the straight-line method, (2) the output method, and (3) the sum of years'-digits method.

**16-3.** A delivery truck was acquired by Hall, Inc. for $3,000 on January 1, 1958. The truck was estimated to have a 5-year life and a trade-in value at the end of that time of $300. Prepare tables reporting periodic depreciation over the 5-year period, similar to those illustrated in the text, for each assumption below:

  (1) Depreciation is to be calculated by the straight-line method.
  (2) Depreciation is to be calculated by the sum of years'-digits method.
  (3) Depreciation is to be calculated by applying a fixed percentage to the diminishing book value of the asset. (The fifth root of $.10 = .631$)
  (4) Repair charges are estimated at $50 for the first year and are estimated to increase by $50 in each succeeding year; depreciation charges are to be made on a diminishing scale so that the sum of depreciation and estimated repairs is the same over the life of the asset.

**16-4.** The Rio Rita Company had the following property transactions during the first two years of its operation:

| YEAR | PROPERTY ACQUIRED | PROPERTY SOLD | ESTIMATED LIFE |
|------|-------------------|---------------|----------------|
| 1957 | $150,000 | | 12 years |
| 1958 | 80,000 | $60,000 | 12 years |

Depreciation was recorded on the books of the company at one-half of the full year's depreciation in the year of asset acquisition and at a full year's depreciation in the year of asset disposal. No scrap value was considered.

*Instructions:* Based upon the above information show in T-account form the entries that would appear at the end of the two year period in the allowance for depreciation assuming that depreciation is calculated by each of the following methods (show all calculations):

(1) Depreciation for the first one-third of life is to be recorded at one and one-half times the straight-line rate, for the second one-third, at the straight-line rate, and for the last one-third, at one-half of the straight-line rate.

(2) Depreciation is to be recorded on the asset declining balance at a rate that is double the straight-line rate.

**16-5.** Information relating to the equipment owned by Jenson Bros. follows:

|  | COST | ESTIMATED SALVAGE VALUE | ESTIMATED LIFE IN YEARS |
|---|---|---|---|
| Store Equipment | $10,000 | $ 500 | 10 |
| Office Equipment | 6,500 | 500 | 5 |
| Factory Equipment | 40,000 | 2,500 | 10 |
| Delivery Equipment | 16,000 | 4,000 | 4 |

*Instructions:* Calculate (1) a composite depreciation rate and (2) the composite life for the equipment owned.

**16-6.** Equipment items are acquired by the Wilbur Co. on March 1, 1958, as follows:

|  | COST | ESTIMATED SALVAGE VALUE | ESTIMATED LIFE IN YEARS |
|---|---|---|---|
| Equipment Item A | $21,500 | $5,000 | 6 |
| B | 7,500 | 500 | 8 |
| C | 10,000 | 1,500 | 8 |
| D | 6,500 | 3,000 | 4 |
| E | 3,000 | 1,500 | 4 |

*Instructions:* (1) Calculate a composite depreciation rate for this group of equipment items.

(2) Calculate the average life in years for the group.

(3) Give the entry to record the depreciation for the year ending December 31, 1958.

**16-7.** The Wendell Co. uses certain hand tools in manufacturing activities. On December 31, 1955, there are 400 such tools on hand at a cost of $4.65 each. Acquisitions and retirements in the years 1956–1958 follow:

|  | ACQUISITIONS AND COST | RETIREMENTS AND RETIREMENT PROCEEDS |
|---|---|---|
| 1956 | 140 @ $4.80 | 125 @ $.60 |
| 1957 | 165 @ 4.95 | 160 @ .65 |
| 1958 | 150 @ 5.00 | 175 @ .75 |

Retirements may be assumed to be on a first-in, first-out basis.

*Instructions:* Give all of the entries affecting the tools account for 1956, 1957, and 1958, assuming that:

(1) Operations are charged for the cost of tool retirements, less recovery on such units.

(2) Tools on hand at the end of each year are valued at 50% of cost.

(3) Operations are charged for the cost of periodic acquisitions equal to retirements, less recovery on the old units; any tools acquired in excess of retirements are reported as an increase in the asset balance; any deficiency in the acquisitions over retirements calls for an additional charge to operations for the shrinkage in the tools balance on the basis of past costs.

**16-8.** In reviewing the books for the Windsor Co. on December 31, 1958, the end of its first year of operations, you find that a number of errors were made in recording transactions relating to delivery equipment. The delivery equipment account shows the following data:

DELIVERY EQUIPMENT

| 1958 | | | | | 1958 | | |
|---|---|---|---|---|---|---|---|
| Jan. 2 Purchase of Trucks #1 & #2 for cash: | | | | | Mar. 16 Amount recovered on insurance policy for damages to Truck #1 | | 250 |
| | #1 | #2 | Total | | Dec. 31 Depreciation for year, 25% | | 3,122 |
| Contract price | 2,600 | 4,000 | 6,600 | | | | |
| Sales tax | 52 | 80 | 132 | | | | |
| License for 1958 | 45 | 50 | 95 | | | | |
| Mar. 5 Purchase of Truck #3 for cash: | | | | | | | |
| Contract price | | | 3,650 | | | | |
| Sales tax | | | 73 | | | | |
| License for 1958 | | | 50 | | | | |
| Mar. 12 Cost of repairs to Truck #1 resulting from accident | | | 325 | | | | |
| Nov. 6 Additional payment on trade-in of Truck #1 for Truck #4 | | | 1,810 | | | | |

Investigation of the transaction of November 6 discloses the following additional information:

| | |
|---|---|
| Contract price, Truck #4 | $3,600 |
| Sales tax | 72 |
| License for 1958 | 15 |
| | $3,687 |
| Trade-in allowance — Truck #1 | 1,877 |
| Balance paid in cash | $1,810 |

Depreciation had been recorded at 25% of the balance in the delivery equipment account. It is determined that each truck is estimated to have a useful life of 4 years and a trade-in value of approximately 30% of total cost at the end of its useful life.

*Instructions:* Assuming that nominal accounts for 1958 are still open, give all of the entries that are required in correcting the accounts as a result of the data given above.

**16-9.** At the close of each year Grant and Co. determines the total cost of machinery in the assembly department and, without consideration of the acquisition date or life of the individual assets, applies a rate of $16\frac{2}{3}\%$

to the total cost in calculating depreciation for the year. At the end of 1958 it is decided that more satisfactory estimates for depreciation would be obtained by use of the straight-line method as applied to individual machines within the department. Data relative to the machines in the department on this date follow:

| MACHINE | DATE ACQUIRED | COST | ESTIMATED SALVAGE VALUE | ESTIMATED LIFE IN YEARS |
|---------|---------------|------|-------------------------|-------------------------|
| W | April 5, 1956 | $21,900 | $ 900 | 6 |
| X | May 21, 1956 | 12,000 | 2,400 | 4 |
| Y | Nov. 28, 1957 | 4,500 | 300 | 8 |
| Z | Oct. 5, 1958 | 12,500 | 1,500 | 5 |

*Instructions:* (1) Determine (a) the balance in the depreciation allowance account as of January 1, 1958, based upon use of the $16\frac{2}{3}\%$ depreciation rate, and (b) the balance if straight-line depreciation had been recorded. (Show calculations.)

(2) Give the journal entries (a) to adjust the allowance account so it reports depreciation as calculated on individual items and (b) to record the depreciation for 1958 on the revised basis. (Show calculations.)

**16-10.** The Jackson Corp. was organized on January 2, 1958. It was authorized to issue 50,000 shares of common stock, par $20. On the date of organization it sold 20,000 shares at par and gave the remaining shares in exchange for certain land bearing recoverable ore deposits estimated by geologists at 800,000 tons.

During 1958 mine improvements totaled $17,500. Miscellaneous buildings and sheds were constructed at a cost of $22,500. During the year 35,000 tons were mined; 6,500 tons of this amount were on hand unsold on December 31, the balance of the tonnage being sold for cash at $4.50 per ton. Expenses incurred and paid for during the year, exclusive of depletion and depreciation, were as follows:

Mining............................................... $84,000
Delivery.............................................. 9,250
General and administrative............................ 8,800

Cash dividends of $5.00 per share are declared on December 31, payable January 15, 1959.

It is believed that buildings and sheds will be useful only over the life of the mine; hence depreciation is to be recognized in terms of mine output.

*Instructions:* Prepare an income statement and a balance sheet for 1958. Submit working papers showing the development of statement data.

**16-11.** As an independent public accountant, you have been engaged to prepare certain information relating to the comparison of the following three methods of computing depreciation:

(1) Straight-line
(2) Sum of the years'-digits
(3) Declining balance
  a. Explain these three methods.
  b. Assuming the following information, prepare a summary of property and allowance for depreciation, showing beginning balances, additions and retirements and ending balances for the years 1957 and 1958 based on the

three above-described methods. For the purpose of recording depreciation, take one-half year in the year of acquisition and full year in year of retirement. Take maximum depreciation allowed under provisions of the Internal Revenue Code of 1954. (Note: Under the provisions of the tax laws, the taxpayer in applying the declining balance method could use a rate not in excess of double the straight-line rate.) Disregard any salvage value for depreciation purposes.

| YEAR | PROPERTY ACQUIRED | ESTIMATED USEFUL LIFE | SALES OR RETIREMENTS YEAR OF ACQUISITION | AMOUNT |
|------|------|------|------|------|
| 1957 | $50,000 | 10 years | | |
| 1958 | 20,000 | 10 years | 1957 | $7,000 |

(A.I.C.P.A. adapted)

**16-12.** The B. C. Manufacturing Company started in business on January 1, 1954, by acquiring three machines having a cost of $5,240, $4,000, and $4,400 respectively. Since that date the company has computed depreciation at 20% on the balance of the asset account at the end of each year, which amounts have been credited directly to the asset account. All purchases since January 1, 1954, have been debited to the machinery account, and the cash received from the sales has been credited to the account.

The following transactions took place:

(a) On September 30, 1954, a machine was purchased on an installment basis. The list price was $6,000, but 12 payments of $600 each were made by the company. Only the monthly payments were recorded in the machinery account, starting with September 30, 1954. Freight and installation charges of $200 were paid and entered in the machinery account on October 10, 1954.

(b) On June 30, 1955, a machine was purchased for $8,000, 2/10, n/30, and was recorded at $8,000 when paid for on July 7, 1955.

(c) On June 30, 1956, the machine acquired for $5,240 was traded for a larger one having a list price of $9,300. An allowance of $4,300 was received on the old machine, the balance of the list price being paid in cash and charged to the machinery account.

(d) On January 1, 1957, the machine that cost $4,400 was sold for $2,500, but because the cost of removal and crating was $125, the machinery account was credited with only $2,375.

(e) On October 1, 1958, the machine purchased for $4,000 was sold for cash and the cash received was credited to the account.

(f) The balance of the account on January 1, 1958, was $14,505.50, and on December 31, 1958, after adjustment for depreciation, it was $10,644.40.

The company has decided that its method of handling its machinery account has not been satisfactory. Accordingly, after the books were closed in 1958, the management decided to correct the account as of December 31, 1958, in accordance with usual accounting practices, and to provide depreciation on a straight-line basis with a separate allowance account. Straight-line depreciation is estimated to be at the rate of 10% per annum computed on a monthly basis, over one half of a month being considered as a full month for this purpose.

*Instructions:* (1) Give the entries that would have been made for the purchase of assets, the sale of assets, and periodic depreciation for the years

1954 through 1958 if the revised basis of depreciation had been used. Income tax procedures are not to be considered in your solution.

(2) Prepare a schedule showing the balance of the machinery account and of the allowance for depreciation account as of December 31, 1958, on the revised basis.

(3) Prepare a schedule of gain and loss on disposal of assets during the 5-year period on the revised basis. (A.I.C.P.A. adapted)

**16-13.** An income statement and a balance sheet for the Concord Company, showing the results of operations for the year ended December 31, 1958, were prepared for submission to the directors in January, 1959.

Before the statements were approved, a report of an investigation of the accounts of the company for the years 1954, 1955, and 1956 was received from the Internal Revenue Department. This report reduced considerably the large amounts of depreciation written off various assets and made a claim for the difference as additional income taxes.

The claim was subsequently paid, and the directors decided to have the accounts for the years 1957 and 1958 and the balance sheets at the end of those years redrafted in order to bring them into agreement with the figures shown in the internal revenue report. The accounts on the books of the company appeared as follows:

| PROPERTY ACCOUNTS 1957 | VALUATION JAN. 1 | ADDITIONS DURING YEAR | DEPRECIATION DEC. 31 | BALANCE FORWARD |
|---|---|---|---|---|
| Real estate | $200,503.79 | $ 2,249.08* | $10,162.61 | $192,590.26 |
| Machinery & tools | 2,206.95 | 1,799.01 | 1,918.07 | 2,087.89 |
| Auto trucks | 21,521.06 | 31,000.48 | 12,360.08 | 40,161.46 |
| Horse trucks | 132.50 | | 132.50 | |
| Horses | 800.00 | 575.00 | 583.34 | 791.66 |
| Harness | 245.70 | 61.05 | 221.75 | 85.00 |
| Office furniture | 1,774.42 | 2,909.86 | 1,610.59 | 3,073.69 |
| | $227,184.42 | $38,594.48 | $26,988.94 | $238,789.96 |

| PROPERTY ACCOUNTS 1958 | VALUATION JAN. 1 | ADDITIONS DURING YEAR | DEPRECIATION DEC. 31 | BALANCE FORWARD |
|---|---|---|---|---|
| Real estate | $192,590.26 | $ 210.00* | $ 3,300.26 | $189,500.00 |
| Machinery & tools | 2,087.89 | 1,235.38 | 1,755.73 | 1,567.54 |
| Auto trucks | 40,161.46 | 8,782.41 | 17,134.84 | 31,809.03 |
| Horse trucks | | 112.58 | 66.92 | 45.66 |
| Horses | 791.66 | 700.00 | 741.67 | 749.99 |
| Harness | 85.00 | 80.00 | 143.00 | 22.00 |
| Office furniture | 3,073.69 | 3,264.54 | 3,400.86 | 2,937.37 |
| | $238,789.96 | $14,384.91 | $26,543.28 | $226,631.59 |

*The additions to real estate in 1957 and 1958 apply to sheds.

The internal revenue agents traced back the original costs of the assets and all additions. Against these total costs they created depreciation allowances shown in the following table. Note that in the table the item of real estate has been divided by the internal revenue agents into three separate classes to show different rates of depreciation.

SUMMARY OF REPORT OF INTERNAL REVENUE DEPARTMENT AGENTS

|  | TOTAL COST TO JAN. 1, 1957 | DEPRECIATION ALLOWANCE JAN. 1, 1957 | ANNUAL RATE OF DEPRECIATION ALLOWED |
|---|---|---|---|
| Real estate: |  |  |  |
| Land................... | $164,364.60 | (none) | (none) |
| Sheds................. | 9,581.14 | $ 1,578.11 | 10% |
| Brick buildings.......... | 39,596.93 | 2,143.88 | 2% |
| Machinery and tools....... | 8,701.97 | 4,306.77 | 20% |
| Auto trucks.............. | 72,297.42 | 37,429.11 | 20% |
| Horse trucks............. | 1,691.63 | 680.39 | $16\frac{2}{3}$% |
| Horses.................. | 5,788.17 | 2,873.07 | 20% |
| Harness................. | 1,444.59 | 1,116.92 | $33\frac{1}{3}$% |
| Office furniture........... | 5,576.92 | 1,311.03 | 10% |
|  |  | $51,439.28 |  |
| Depreciation allowance (not allocated to specific assets) for period prior to Jan. 1, 1954................... |  | 12,718.36 |  |
|  | $309,043.37 | $64,157.64 |  |

*Instructions:* (1) Take the internal revenue figures as at the date to which the examination was restricted (December 31, 1956) and extend them on the same basis to December 31, 1958. The amounts of additions to assets stated in the books of the company for the years 1957 and 1958 are to be taken as correct.

(2) Bring the amounts of total cost into the accounts of the company, create the necessary allowances for depreciation, and state the adjustments required in the profit and loss accounts, the retained earnings account, and the balance sheet accounts at December 31, 1957 and 1958, in order to show the effect of these changes. (Depreciation at half the annual rate is applicable to acquisitions made during a year.) (A.I.C.P.A. adapted)

**16-14.** The following data are furnished by the Calhoon Copper Company concerning the current year's sales and operations at its mine and smelter:
Inventories at the beginning of the year:
Ore — valued at book cost, which includes depreciation and depletion
100,000 tons at $2.80 per ton.......................... $  280,000
Copper — likewise valued at book cost
30,000,000 pounds at 9.8 cents per pound............... 2,940,000
Production costs, including depreciation but before depletion:
Ore — 2,500,000 tons at $2.052 per ton.................... 5,130,000
Smelting cost — 1.5 cents per pound of copper produced, including cost of transporting ore from mine to smelter
Yield — 30 pounds of copper per ton of ore

Inventories at the end of the year:
Ore..................... 600,000 tons (all at mine)
Copper...................20,000,000 pounds

All sales of copper were made at 11 cents per pound

Ore reserves at the beginning of the year:
Per books — 10,000,000 tons, carried at $8,000,000

No new ore deposits were purchased during the year

Ore reserves at the end of the year:
Per engineer's survey — 13,400,000 tons

*Instructions:* Prepare the following statements showing both quantities and unit costs computed on three alternative bases of valuing inventories consistently applied throughout the problem (beginning inventories are to be corrected in accordance with new estimates):

(a) Cost of ore mined.
(b) Cost of copper sold.
(c) Gross profit on copper sold.  (A.I.C.P.A. adapted)

# Chapter 17

## PLANT AND EQUIPMENT

## REVALUATIONS

**CHANGES IN COST AND DEPRECIATION** It was suggested in the previous chapter that plant and equipment items are recorded at cost, that estimates are made as to the useful lives of the assets, and that schedules are developed for the reasonable and systematic allocation of costs to periodic revenue. These are the normal procedures that are employed in accounting for plant and equipment. But during the course of asset use, certain circumstances may suggest revisions in original cost allotment plans and, in some instances, the actual departure from cost for asset valuation as well as for periodic depreciation charges. These are the problems toward which attention is directed in this chapter.

**CHANGES IN ESTIMATES OF ASSET LIFE OR DEPRECIABLE COST** When an asset is retired, any errors in the estimates of asset life and asset salvage value become evident. Compensation is made for asset overdepreciation or underdepreciation at that time. If depreciation charges have been inadequate, the book value of the asset will exceed its salvage value and a special decrease in proprietorship is recognized; if depreciation charges have been excessive, the book value of the asset will be less than its salvage value and an increase in proprietorship is recognized.

It may become evident during the life of a property item that depreciation is incorrectly estimated and that periodic charges have been inadequate or excessive. Under such circumstances, a choice must be made between the following procedures:

(1) The asset book value may be accepted as it stands, and depreciation charges for the remaining life of the asset may be modified to compensate for errors in charges already made.

(2) The asset book value may be revised by a correcting entry to a depreciated value on the basis of present evidence, and depreciation charges for the remaining life of the asset made in accordance with information now available.

To illustrate the foregoing procedures, assume a property item with an estimated life of 10 years and a depreciation rate of 10%. At the end of 5 years, when the book value of the asset is reduced to 50% of cost, it is determined that the asset still has a useful life of 10 years.  If no correction in prior depreciation is recognized, the remaining asset cost will be distributed over the remaining life or at the rate of 5% a year.  If a correction for past overdepreciation is made, the asset book value will be raised to ⅔ of original cost and depreciation for the remaining life reported in terms of the revised life of the asset or at the rate 6⅔% a year (100% ÷ 15, or 66⅔% ÷ 10).

The first position, which accepts existing book value as a basis for subsequent charges, has received wide support in practice.  Those who support this position insist that cost once assigned to revenue is a permanent disposition of such cost and that it is only cost not yet assigned to revenue that is subject to future allocation.  The correction of accounts for depreciation recognized in prior periods is considered unacceptable, since such revision will result in a series of depreciation charges over the life of the asset whose total will not be the same as original depreciable cost.

The American Accounting Association Committee on Concepts and Standards Underlying Corporate Financial Statements is in general agreement with this position.  The Committee would permit the corrrection of past errors of a mechanical and nonjudgment character, and also the correction of judgment errors when new events of an unusual character and of significant potential effect on future income prove past judgments to have been erroneous.  However, the Committee believes that the reversal, revision, or reaccounting for past depreciation charges or amortizations opens the doors to the possibility of manipulation of the net income calculation.  It recommends:

> . . . . . routine and recurring periodic provisions for depreciation and amortization made in good faith after considered judgment and after competent review should not be reversed, even though such action is seemingly justified by changes in the acts or by later estimates of usefulness or longevity.  The better course is to review these policies from time to time and to make the resultant adjustments by altering the rate of amortization of remaining balances.[1]

Further support for the first position is found in certain practical considerations.  This is the general position that must be taken for income tax purposes; depreciation once allowed for tax purposes is not subject to later revision.  When depreciation on the books is maintained in accordance with income tax requirements, special account analysis and restatement of depreciation data is unnecessary in the preparation of tax returns.

Those taking the second position insist that errors, no matter what their source, call for appropriate correction.  The depreciation to be

---

[1] *Accounting and Reporting Standards for Corporate Financial Statements and Preceding Statements and Supplements,* "Accounting Corrections," 1957 (Columbus: American Accounting Association) p. 35.

recognized each period should be the best estimate that is determinable from the evidence at hand.  Errors in past depreciation, it is maintained, do not warrant compensating errors in subsequent depreciation; such a practice will serve only to distort measurements of the past, present, and future.

The American Institute Committee on Accounting Procedure makes no reference to the matter of restating depreciation charges in its "Restatement and Revision of Accounting Research Bulletins" (Accounting Research Bulletin No. 43) issued in 1953.  However, the Committee did express an opinion on this matter in Accounting Research Bulletin No. 27 issued in 1946.  Here the Committee indicated that the practice of reflecting corrections in estimates by means of revised depreciation charges over the remaining life of the property item was not objectionable when amounts involved were not material or when the alternate course provided no significantly different operating results upon application to all of the property items, some of which involved depreciation overestimates and others underestimates. However, the Committee pointed out:

> In special situations in which material amounts of depreciable assets are determined to have a substantially longer or shorter life than was originally anticipated, a more adequate assignment of cost to future revenues to be derived from such assets during their useful lives may result from an adjustment or restatement of the accumulated depreciation previously recorded.  Such a reallocation of the cost of assets between past and future operations and revenues may be desirable when there have been circumstances which prevented the determination of an ordinary and reasonable approximation of the useful lives of assets and when the amounts of such assets and the annual depreciation charges thereon are large in relation to the total property in use and to the annual net income.  In general, useful financial statements are not achieved by an understatement or an overstatement of asset carrying value which is to be accompanied by an overstatement or understatement of future income because of materially excessive or deficient prior allocations of costs.[1]

There can be little objection on theoretical grounds to the foregoing position.

The nature of the accounting when corrections are made in the accounts for past depreciation is described in the following section.

**RECORDING DEPRECIATION CHANGES IN THE ACCOUNTS**

*Understatement of Depreciation.*  To illustrate the procedure that is followed when depreciation has been inadequate and a correction in such past charges is to be made, assume that machinery costing $15,000 has been depreciated by the

---

[1] *Accounting Research Bulletin No. 27*, "Emergency Facilities," 1946 (New York: American Institute of Certified Public Accountants), p. 225.

straight-line method on an estimated 15-year life. No salvage value on the asset has been anticipated. After the machinery has been used for 5 years, it is determined that the useful life of the asset should have been estimated at only 10 years. The annual depreciation, then, should have been $1,500 instead of $1,000, and the depreciation for the first 5 years has been understated by $2,500. The entry to correct the accounts is:

| | | |
|---|---|---|
| Corrections in Profits of Prior Periods — Understatement of Depreciation (or Retained Earnings)............... | 2,500 | |
| Allowance for Depreciation of Machinery............ | | 2,500 |

The nature of the entry to record the correction depends upon the statement that is to be used in reporting the correction. If corrections in profits of prior periods are to appear on the income statement, a nominal account is opened for such corrections; if corrections are to be reported on the retained earnings statement, retained earnings is charged or credited. This account is subsequently analyzed in developing the detail for the retained earnings statement.

In the example just given, assuming no further revision at a later date, depreciation would be recorded at $1,500 for each of the remaining years of asset life.

For income tax purposes, a taxpayer who has failed to take any depreciation or has taken depreciation that was clearly inadequate, cannot take advantage of such omissions on later tax returns. But it may be possible to prepare amended tax returns for certain prior years, thus permitting the recognition of increased depreciation in accordance with revised estimates for such years. When depreciation charges in past years are considered adequate but current and future conditions will serve to limit the life of the asset to a period that is less than the remaining life according to original estimates, the remaining asset cost may be spread over its estimated remaining life. Under such circumstances, increased charges for depreciation are appropriate for accounting purposes as well as for income tax purposes.

*Overstatement of Depreciation.* When depreciation on an asset has been overstated, a procedure consistent with that for understatements calls for a charge to the asset allowance account and a credit to a nominal account or to retained earnings. The corrected rate is then used in recording subsequent depreciation. To illustrate, assume that machinery costing $15,000 has been depreciated by the straight-line method on an estimated 15-year life. After use of the machinery for 10 years, it is determined that the useful life of the asset should have been estimated at 20 years. The annual depreciation, then, should have been $750 instead of $1,000 and the depreciation for the first

10 years has been overstated by $2,500. The entry to correct the account is:

Allowance for Depreciation of Machinery.............. 2,500
   Corrections in Profits of Prior Periods — Overstatement of Depreciation (or Retained Earnings).......    2,500

In the absence of further revision at some later date, depreciation would be recorded at $750 for each of the remaining years of asset life.

Correction in past depreciation is indicated in the case of a fully depreciated asset that is continued in use, except when continued use involves extraordinary maintenance and repair charges that suggest little or no contribution on the part of the asset itself. For example, a fully depreciated asset may be continued in use during a war period, because of inability to make replacement. Inefficiencies and extraordinary charges may actually make the use of such an asset more costly than a new machine, and under such circumstances no value can be assigned to the property item. Account balances relating to fully depreciated assets should not be offset until the property items are actually retired; financial statements should provide parenthetical or note references to fully depreciated assets still in use and included in the account totals.

For income tax purposes, a taxpayer who has been allowed depreciation at a certain rate in the past is limited to a recovery of no more than the remaining book value over the remaining life of the asset unless amended tax returns are filed for certain prior years. For example, in the preceding illustration, having been allowed deductions of $10,000 during the first 10 years, the taxpayer must regard the remaining book value of the asset as $5,000. Depreciation over the remaining asset life of 10 years is limited to the unrecovered cost, $5,000, or $500 per year.

**DEPRECIATION OF "EMERGENCY FACILITIES"** During World War II and in the post-war period, certain productive facilities essential to war and national defense efforts have been acquired by business units under *certificates of necessity* issued in accordance with provisions of the Internal Revenue Code. The issue of a certificate of necessity by appropriate federal authority certifies the acquisition of certain properties to be in the national interests and designates such properties as *emergency facilities*. Such properties may include land, buildings, machinery, and equipment. Certificates permit the taxpayer to write off part or all of the cost of the facilities over a period of 60 months. When 60 month amortization is allowed for only a part of the asset cost, ordinary depreciation would be recognized on the remaining cost. Depreciation under certificates of necessity takes the place of the depreciation that would otherwise be deductible.

The acquisition of an asset under a certificate of necessity should have no influence upon the plan of cost allocation for book purposes. When facilities are considered of a special-purpose nature and their contribution to revenue is expected to expire over a 60-month period, depreciation for book purposes may properly parallel deductions allowed for tax purposes; when facilities are estimated to have a life materially in excess of the period used for tax purposes, this longer period should be used for book purposes.

Studies undertaken by the American Institute of Certified Public Accountants determined that a great many companies acquiring emergency facilities during the war period used depreciation schedules for accounting purposes that followed those permitted for tax purposes, regardless of the nature and the use of the facilities. As a result, balance sheets for such companies failed to display properties of substantial value. The absence of such property values was accompanied, in turn, by the failure to record depreciation on such assets even though they were in use and contributed to the production of revenue. In 1946, the Committee on Accounting Procedure issued Bulletin No. 27 on "Emergency Facilities" taking issue with the premature allocation of facility costs and recommending the restoration of costs improperly written off and the subsequent recognition of depreciation on properties that continue to serve a useful business purpose.

Subsequent statements were issued by the Institute recommending the recognition of depreciation for accounting purposes in terms of asset usefulness when depreciation calculated in the conventional manner differs materially in amount from that allowed for income tax purposes. In Bulletin No. 43, the Committee on Accounting Procedure commented as follows with respect to the differences between accounting procedures and tax procedures:

> Sound financial accounting procedures do not necessarily coincide with the rules as to what shall be included in "gross income," or allowed as a deduction therefrom, in arriving at taxable net income. It is well recognized that such rules should not be followed for financial accounting purposes if they do not conform to generally accepted accounting principles. However, where the results obtained from following income-tax procedures do not materially differ from those obtained where generally accepted accounting principles are followed, there are practical advantages in keeping the accounts in agreement with the income-tax returns.[1]

---

[1]*Accounting Research Bulletin No. 43*, "Restatement and Revision of Accounting Research Bulletins," 1953 (New York: American Institute of Certified Public Accountants) p. 76.

It should be observed that a material difference between depreciation charges recognized on the books and charges recognized for income tax purposes in accordance with certificates of necessity may suggest the application of income tax allocation procedures as described in Chapter 11. Income taxes that are paid during the 60-month amortization period will be less than the taxes applicable to book income in view of tax deductions for depreciation that exceed book charges; income taxes that are paid after the amortization period will be greater than the taxes applicable to book income in the absence of tax deductions for depreciation and a continuation of book charges. Accordingly, during the 60-month amortization period, an addition would be made to the annual charge for income taxes paid and a tax liability balance credited for the taxes estimated to be paid in the future on the portion of the net income not subject to tax currently; during the life of the facility following the 60-month amortization period, the accrued tax balance would be applied against the annual charges for taxes paid.

**CHANGES IN ASSET COST THROUGH BETTERMENTS**    During the life of plant and equipment items, periodic depreciation charges may require revision as a result of additional expenditures that are made in connection with these properties.

Expenditures that are considered to improve property items are recorded as increases in the asset cost. Such additional costs must be considered in recording depreciation in subsequent periods. For example, assume the acquisition of a machine for $10,000 with an estimated life of 20 years. After the machine is used for 15 years, an expenditure of $2,000 is made that improves the machine but does not prolong its life. The betterment, limited to the remaining life of the asset, has a service life of 5 years. The entry to record the expenditure is:

| | | |
|---|---|---|
| Machinery.................................... | 2,000 | |
| Cash.................................... | | 2,000 |

Annual depreciation is now calculated as follows:

| | | |
|---|---|---|
| Original asset: | $10,000 ÷ 20 | $500 |
| Betterment: | $ 2,000 ÷ 5 | 400 |
| Total annual depreciation | | $900 |

If expenditures serve to rehabilitate certain assets and to increase their service life beyond original estimates, the asset valuation account instead of the asset account is preferably charged with the cost of rehabilitation, and a new depreciation rate is calculated on the property item. To illustrate, assume in the previous example that the expenditure did not represent an enlargement or improvement of the asset but simply prolonged its service life to 8 years. The entry to record the rehabilitation is made as follows:

| | | |
|---|---:|---:|
| Allowance for Depreciation of Machinery............ | 2,000 | |
| Cash........................................ | | 2,000 |

Depreciable cost for the remaining life of the asset is determined as follows:

| | |
|---|---:|
| Asset cost......................................... | $10,000 |
| Less: Allowance for depreciation, $7,500, reduced by a debit of $2,000 as a result of asset rehabilitation................ | 5,500 |
| Asset book value to be written off during the next 8 years | $ 4,500 |

Annual depreciation is now calculated: $4,500÷8, or $562.50.

Expenditures that replace certain asset units call for entries to record the acquisition of the new unit and the retirement of the old. The effect of such asset changes must be considered in calculating subsequent depreciation. For example, assume that a machine that cost $10,000 has an estimated life of 10 years. After six years an important machine part, estimated to represent 25% of the original asset cost, requires replacement. The replacement cost of the new part is $2,800 and the life of the part is expected to terminate with that of the machine; $250 is recovered on the disposal of the old part. The foregoing calls for an entry to retire the old part as follows:

| | | |
|---|---:|---:|
| Cash......................................... | 250 | |
| Allowance for Depreciation of Machinery............ | 1,500 | |
| Loss on Retirement of Machine Parts................ | 750 | |
| Machinery....................................... | | 2,500 |

| Loss on asset retirement: | | |
|---|---:|---:|
| Asset cost estimated at 25% of $10,000, or | $2,500 | |
| Depreciation, 6/10 of cost.............. | 1,500 | |
| Asset book value..................... | $1,000 | |
| Proceeds from sale................... | 250 | |
| Loss............................. | $ 750 | |

The new part is recorded as follows:

| | | |
|---|---:|---:|
| Machinery....................................... | 2,800 | |
| Cash........................................ | | 2,800 |

Annual depreciation is now calculated as follows:

| | |
|---|---:|
| Original asset: ($10,000−$2,500)÷10 | $ 750 |
| New part: $2,800÷4 | 700 |
| Total annual depreciation | $1,450 |

If it had been assumed originally that the machine part would require replacement during the machine lifetime, a higher depreciation rate could have been applied to the machine part; higher periodic depreciation charges would then have been recognized instead of the loss on asset retirement.

**DEPARTURES FROM COST**   In Chapter 1 it was stated that the matching process is fundamental in all accounting activity. It was further stated that this process consists of the measurement of revenue and the matching against revenue of the costs applicable thereto. Costs considered to be related to future revenues were held back from current profit and loss recognition and deferred. Certain exceptions to this practice are generally accepted. Thus current asset items, such as receivables, marketable securities, and inventories, are reported at less than cost when it is felt that realization of these assets may be limited to the lower amounts; long-term investments, such as investments in stocks and bonds, are reported at less than cost when declines in the values of these assets are significant and appear to be permanent; other long-term assets that arise from donation or discovery are reported at their fair market values, valuations that provide a basis for satisfactory asset accountability as well as income measurement. The introduction of appraisal values in the accounts for property items whose replacement values have changed materially since date of acquisition represents a further departure from the cost approach; but this practice is considered acceptable only under exceptional circumstances and then only if full information is made available on the financial statements concerning the nature and the extent of the departures from cost. The problems relating to the use of appraisal values in the accounts are considered in the remaining pages of this chapter.

**REPLACEMENT VALUES FOR ASSETS**   During the early 1930's, companies found that plant values had experienced a severe fall within a relatively short period. In addition, the prices obtained for products sold had fallen to the point where they were insufficient to cover production costs if costs included depreciation charges based on the original asset costs. Then, during the 1940's and 1950's, companies found a steady and significant increase in plant values. This rise was occasioned by a general increase in prices and in many cases by improvements in adjoining areas that increased the value of plant locations. In periods of both falling and rising price levels, proposals have been made that current price levels be recognized in the valuation of property items and in the assignment of depreciation charges for their use.

*Price Level Declines.* When property values decline and recovery to previous levels is not expected, arguments in support of the recognition of such "permanent" declines take the following form: price decline and the ability to replace assets at materially lower prices give rise to a loss that may be compared to that arising from a fire or other casualty; to continue to report property items in the accounts at amounts that exceed the values of the utilities afforded thereby is to permit both financial position and income measurements to be distorted. Recognition of lower replacement values on the records is advocated as being both realistic and conservative.

But those who support the continued use of cost claim that to adjust plant costs for price declines is to engage in normalizing costs and periodic income. This group maintains that the full burden of costs must be assigned to revenues in arriving at net income or loss that measures the sum total of management's activities.

Accountants generally have supported the continued use of cost in periods of price decline. There is agreement that write-downs are appropriate when it is clear that costs will not be recovered through future activities; however, the revision of property items simply in recognition of a declining price level is not encouraged.

*Price Level Advances.* When an increase in the general price level is viewed as permanent, the argument is raised, as in the case of declines, that changes in the accounts must be recognized if financial position and charges to revenue are not to be distorted. Recognition of changed values is supported as a measure for making financial statements more informative and useful.

Here, too, the answer by accountants generally has been that adherence to cost normally provides the most acceptable basis for the development of general purpose statements. Cost, it is maintained, is objective and verifiable, remains unalterable, and is readily understandable; valuation data, on the other hand, are subjective and unverifiable, are continuously changing, and must be defined in terms of the diverse valuation processes and sources. Accountants recognize that there may be occasions when special circumstances, such as the discovery of valuable resources or other special enhancement of values, call for the recognition of higher values as a means of assuring full property accountability and dependable income measurements; but the recognition of increased plant value in the accounts simply in response to an increasing price level is definitely discouraged.

**USE OF APPRAISAL DATA**       Under circumstances where it is considered appropriate for the accounts to report reproduction or replacement values rather than costs, both asset balances and capital accounts require adjustment. The values that are indicated should be supplied by reliable independent appraisal. Furthermore, the published statements should offer full information concerning the source of the values other than cost as well as the authority for the use of such values.

Appraisals by professional engineers or appraisers normally afford information for individual assets concerning:

(1) *Reproduction cost,* which is the present amount required to reproduce the asset new.

(2) *Sound value,* which is the present reproduction cost less depreciation to date based upon such value.

(3) *Condition per cent,* which is the present percentage relationship of sound value to reproduction cost.

Companies may authorize the appraisal of properties for purposes other than use in the accounts. For example, reproduction costs may be sought for special use or reporting in connection with credit, tax, insurance, sale, or consolidation matters. On the other hand, appraisal data may be sought for use in the accounts either: (1) to correct account balances when the relationship of sound values to reproduction costs suggests that there has been past overdepreciation or underdepreciation of cost; or (2) to bring appraisal values into the accounts.

To illustrate the use of appraisal data as a basis for simply correcting the accounts and as a basis for bringing asset and valuation accounts into agreement with current sound values, assume the following: a property item was acquired at a cost of $60,000 and is being depreciated on an 8-year life; after use for 4 years, the property is appraised at a reproduction cost of $100,000 and condition per cent of 60%, or a sound value of $60,000. Cost and appraisal data follow:

|  | PER BOOKS | PER APPRAISAL |
|---|---|---|
| Asset cost | $60,000 | $100,000 |
| Less: Accrued depreciation | 30,000 | 40,000 |
| Depreciated value | $30,000 | $ 60,000 |

The appraisal is regarded as indicating that past depreciation recognized by the company was excessive and that the life of the asset should be considered to be 10 years instead of 8 (the appraisal indicates a 40% asset decline in 4 years or depreciation at the rate of 10% per year). A correcting entry, then, is appropriate to reduce the asset valuation account in bringing cost data up to date.

Disagreement between book and appraisal depreciation would not always suggest a correction in the depreciation reported on the books. Appraisal values may reflect primarily physical deterioration; depreciation for accounting purposes is systematic cost allocation in recognition of physical as well as functional decline. It will be assumed, however, in the examples in this chapter that differences in appraisal and book depreciation indicate errors in prior depreciation.

If higher reproduction costs are to be reflected in the accounts, appropriate correction for overdepreciation in terms of cost would still be made; appraisal increases would then be applied to the corrected cost base in bringing account balances into agreement with appraisal figures.

It should be observed that changes from acquisition costs to reproduction costs as well as any changes in depreciation charges identified with such asset increases or decreases, must be disregarded for income tax purposes. For tax purposes the basis for depreciation continues to be original cost; the basis for computing gain or loss on the disposal of the asset is the asset book value stated in terms of actual cost.

**ASSET DEVALUATION RECORDED IN THE ACCOUNTS**  A write-down of plant and equipment cost reduces both the property item and retained earnings; the asset is credited and a nominal account or retained earnings is debited, depending upon whether the charge is to be reflected on the income statement or on the retained earnings statement. In the case of depreciable assets, devaluation generally affects both asset and related valuation account balances. To illustrate the process of property write-downs, assume that a company reports buildings on its books at cost less depreciation of 30%, as follows:

| | |
|---|---:|
| Buildings........................................................ | $500,000 |
| Allowance for depreciation of buildings.................. | 150,000 |
| Depreciated value............................................. | $350,000 |

An appraisal establishes a present reproduction cost of the buildings of $300,000, and a sound value of $210,000, or 70% of the reproduction cost. Recognition in the accounts of the appraisal calls for a reduction in the buildings account to $300,000 and a reduction in the valuation account to 30% of $300,000, or $90,000. The entry to give effect to the revaluation follows:

| | | |
|---|---:|---:|
| Allowance for Depreciation of Buildings........ .. | 60,000 | |
| Loss on Building Revaluation (or Retained Earnings) | 140,000 | |
| Buildings.................................... | | 200,000 |

However, assume that the appraisal establishes a reproduction cost of $300,000 but a sound value of $180,000, indicating that properties are actually 40% depreciated. Here appraisal suggests both incorrect depreciation in the past as well as a change in the reproduction cost of the assets. This information can be recognized in the accounts by (1) an entry to correct the valuation account to 40% of cost, and (2) an entry to reduce the asset account and the valuation account to a $300,000 reproduction basis. Since the correction in past depreciation and the asset devaluation both affect retained earnings, a single entry may be made as follows:

| | | |
|---|---:|---:|
| Allowance for Depreciation of Buildings........... | 30,000 | |
| Loss on Building Revaluation (or Retained Earnings) | 170,000 | |
|    Buildings..................................... | | 200,000 |

Depreciation after appraisal is based upon the revised value of the asset and the estimated remaining years of its life. If the remaining life is estimated at 30 years, the depreciation rate is 1/30 of 60%, the undepreciated balance of the asset, or 2%. This rate applied to the revised asset value, $300,000, results in annual depreciation of $6,000. The same figure is obtained by computing annual depreciation at 1/30 of $180,000, the asset book value after revaluation.

**CORPORATE READJUSTMENT OR QUASI-REORGANIZATION**     Assume the investment in plant and equipment at a level that does not make possible a profit from operations under current conditions; assume further a deficit from previous operations or a retained earnings balance that is insufficient to absorb a reduction in property items warranted by current conditions and necessary if the company is to be able to report satisfactory operations in future periods. Conditions here call for a restatement of property items and, because of the inability of retained earnings to absorb the asset reduction, for a restatement of paid-in capital. Such a restatement, providing in effect for a "fresh start" accounting-wise on the part of the corporation, is called *corporate readjustment* or *quasi-reorganization*. The corporate readjustment procedure does not require recourse to the courts as would be the case under formal reorganization procedures; there is no change in the legal corporate entity or interruption in business activity.

To illustrate the nature of the corporate readjustment, assume that the Billings Corporation has suffered losses from operations for some time and that revenues both current and anticipated appear to be insufficient to cover costs arising from investments made in an earlier high-price period. With a reduction in plant and equipment items to present reproduction levels and the smaller depreciation charges to follow, it is felt that a profitable operating level may be regained. The elimination of an existing deficit is also desirable. A balance sheet for the company just prior to the corporate readjustment follows:

**BILLINGS CORPORATION**
BALANCE SHEET
JUNE 30, 1958

| | | | | |
|---|---|---|---|---|
| Current assets.......... $ 250,000 | Liabilities.............. $ 400,000 | | | |
| Plant and equipment (net) 1,000,000 | Capital: | | | |
| | Capital stock, | | | |
| | 100,000 shares, | | | |
| | par $10... | $1,000,000 | | |
| | Less: Deficit | 150,000 | 850,000 | |
| Total assets........... $1,250,000 | Total liabilities and capital $1,250,000 | | | |

The readjustment is to be accomplished as follows:

(1) Plant and equipment is to be reduced to a net book value of $750,000.
(2) Capital stock is to be reduced to a par of $5, $500,000 in capital stock thus being converted into paid-in capital.
(3) The deficit of $400,000 ($150,000 as reported on the balance sheet increased by $250,000 arising from the write-down of plant and equipment) is to be applied against the capital from the reduction of the stock par value.

Entries to accomplish the foregoing follow:

| | | | |
|---|---|---|---|
| (1) | Retained Earnings..................... | 250,000 | |
| | Plant and Equipment................. | | 250,000 |
| (2) | Capital Stock (100,000 shares, par $10).... | 1,000,000 | |
| | Capital Stock (100,000 shares, par $5).... | | 500,000 |
| | Paid-In Capital from Reduction in Par of | | |
| | Outstanding Shares................... | | 500,000 |
| (3) | Paid-In Capital from Reduction in Par of | | |
| | Outstanding Shares.................... | 400,000 | |
| | Retained Earnings.................. | | 400,000 |

The balance sheet after corporate readjustment is shown at the top of the opposite page.

Subsequent earnings of the company should be reported in a *dated retained earnings* account; on future balance sheets, retained earnings dated as of the time of the account readjustment will inform readers of the date of corporate readjustment and the fresh start in earnings accumulation.

The American Institute Committee on Accounting Procedure has recommended that a company that elects to bring about a legitimate restatement of its assets, capital stock, and retained earnings through readjustment, thus availing itself of permission to relieve future in-

## BILLINGS CORPORATION
### BALANCE SHEET
#### JUNE 30, 1958

| | | | | |
|---|---|---|---|---|
| Current assets | $ 250,000 | Liabilities | $ 400,000 |
| Plant and equipment (net) | 750,000 | Capital stock, 100,000 shares, par $5 | 500,000 |
| | | Paid-In capital from reduction in par of outstanding shares | 100,000 |
| Total assets | $1,000,000 | Total liabilities and capital | $1,000,000 |

come or retained earnings of charges that should otherwise be made against these, should meet the following conditions:

(1) It should make a clear report to stockholders of the proposed restatements and should obtain their formal consent.

(2) It should present a fair balance sheet with a reasonably complete readjustment of values in order that there will be no continuation of the circumstances that justify charges to invested capital.

(3) Assets should be carried forward as of the date of readjustment at fair and not unduly conservative amounts, determined with due regard for the accounting to be employed thereafter. Excessive write-downs that will result in the overstatement of earnings or retained earnings on the ultimate realization of assets should be avoided.

The Committee recognizes that in some cases the fair value of an asset or the amount of potential losses or charges cannot be measured satisfactorily as of the date of a readjustment. Estimates of such asset and liability balances will have to be made. However, under such circumstances, material differences between book values and ultimate realization or liquidation amounts that cannot be attributed to events or circumstances originating after the date of the readjustment should not be carried to retained earnings but should be recognized as corrections identified with the readjustment.[1]

**ASSET APPRECIATION RECORDED IN THE ACCOUNTS** When an appraisal indicates plant values in excess of cost and this appreciation is to be entered on the books, both the property and the capital balances are increased. The asset increase, while recognized

---

[1] *Accounting Research Bulletin No. 43*, "Restatement and Revision of Accounting Research Bulletins," 1953 (New York: American Institute of Certified Public Accountants), pp. 45-47.

on the books, is still unrealized; the capital increase then, should be designated as appraisal capital.

To illustrate the process of recording asset appreciation, assume that land, cost $50,000, is increased to an appraised value of $80,000. This may be accomplished by the following entry:

Land.......................................... 30,000
    Appraisal Capital—Land ......................       30,000

Land would be shown on the balance sheet at its present appraised value, $80,000. The appraisal capital should not be merged with other capital balances but should be reported separately on the balance sheet so that the reader of the statement may be fully aware of the unrealized nature of such capital.

If the land is sold at a later date for $75,000, $25,000 of the recorded appreciation will have been realized. The gain is recognized and the appraisal capital relating to land is canceled by the following entry:

Cash........................................ 75,000
Appraisal Capital—Land ...................... 30,000
    Land......................................       80,000
    Gain on Sale of Land.......................       25,000

The ultimate result of the recorded appreciation and the subsequent sale is an increase in retained earnings of $25,000. All evidence of the appraisal is canceled, and the account balances are the same as though the asset had been carried at its cost, $50,000, and subsequently sold for $75,000.

When a depreciable asset is to be written up, the effects of the revaluation upon the asset account balance as well as the related valuation account balance must be considered. The appraisal may indicate both a correction in past depreciation and an increased asset reproduction cost. In recording asset devaluation the effects of both the correction and the revaluation are reflected in retained earnings. However, in recording asset appreciation, any correction in depreciation affects retained earnings, but the asset increase gives rise to appraisal capital. Entries, then, are required to record (1) the correction in depreciation on the basis of cost and (2) the appraisal increase in the asset as well as in the allowance for depreciation. Although the appraisal increases may be reported directly in the asset and the valuation accounts, it is normally desirable to report these increases in separate accounts. Cost data are thus preserved and are available in the preparation of income tax returns where the effects of appraisals must be ignored; subsequent depreciation entries that require information concerning both cost and appraisal increases can be more conveniently prepared.

To illustrate the foregoing, assume the following information with respect to a building:

| COST | ESTIMATED LIFE IN YEARS | YEARS USED | ALLOWANCE FOR DEPRECIATION |
|---|---|---|---|
| $200,000 | 50 | 20 | $80,000 |

At this time an appraisal of the asset shows it to have a reproduction cost of $320,000 and a sound value of only $160,000, the asset being 50% depreciated. The appraisal suggests the following changes:

| | COST | TOTAL ESTIMATED LIFE IN YEARS | LIFE IN YEARS TO DATE | ALLOWANCE FOR DEPRECIATION |
|---|---|---|---|---|
| | $200,000 | 50 | 20 | $ 80,000 |
| Correction in depreciation of prior periods........... | | −10 | | +20,000 |
| Cost balances as corrected | $200,000 | 40 | 20 | $100,000 |
| Appraisal increases........ | +120,000 | | | + 60,000 |
| Balances as determined by appraisal.............. | $320,000 | 40 | 20 | $160,000 |

Entries to record the appraisal are required as follows:

| Transaction | Entry | | |
|---|---|---|---|
| (1) To correct allowance for depreciation to 50 % of cost as indicated by appraisal. | Corrections in Profits of Prior Periods — Understatement of Depreciation (or Retained Earnings) ...................... Allowance for Depreciation of Building ................. | 20,000 | 20,000 |
| (2) To increase asset and depreciation allowance to a reproduction cost of $320,000 as indicated by appraisal. | Building—Appraisal Increase... Allowance for Depreciation of Building—Appraisal Increase. Appraisal Capital—Building. | 120,000 | 60,000 60,000 |

The asset book value has changed as follows:

| | BEFORE APPRAISAL | CHANGES | AFTER APPRAISAL |
|---|---|---|---|
| Building ................ | $200,000 | + $120,000 | $320,000 |
| Allowance for depreciation.. | 80,000 | +$20,000 + $60,000 | 160,000 |
| | $120,000 | | $160,000 |

Although the asset was increased from $120,000 to $160,000, it should be noted that the appraisal indicated inadequate depreciation on the basis of cost in past periods of $20,000. Since earnings of past periods were overstated, a reduction in retained earnings was required. The appreciation taken into the accounts was actually $60,000, or asset book value after correction of $100,000 raised to a sound value of $160,000. The latter increase is separately reported as appraisal capital.

**DEPRECIATION ON ASSET APPRECIATION**    When asset appreciation is recorded in the accounts, depreciation may continue to be recognized in terms of original cost, appraisal data finding expression only on the balance sheet. On the other hand, asset appreciation may be recognized in the calculation of periodic depreciation, net income being developed in terms of appraisal values. Both procedures are encountered in practice and arguments are advanced in support of each procedure.

Those who would limit the use of appraisal values to balance sheet presentations insist that costs can arise only from expenditures; it is the past dollar cost that must be matched against dollars earned in arriving at net income. Depreciation accounting, this group maintains, should not be related to the problem of asset replacement; depreciation calls for the allocation of past costs, not for the recognition of future costs. Asset replacement is a separate problem that calls for separate financial planning. Replacement expenditures at a higher level will be made on the assumption that future revenues will recover such outlays; replacement considerations, then, should not be permitted to distort current income measurements.

Practical considerations, too, support the cost approach to depreciation. When depreciation is recorded in terms of cost, charges on the books show the depreciation actually allowable for income tax purposes. When depreciation is recorded on the basis of appraisals, charges must be restated in terms of cost in the preparation of tax returns.

Those who support depreciation on the basis of appraisal values insist that such a procedure must be employed if income measurements are to be meaningful. Comparative evaluations of profit and loss are possible only if current revenues are accompanied by current costs. Replacement value accounting offers management a better guide to sales, dividend, and other operating policies.

Those supporting charges in terms of appraisal values further maintain that a company is obliged to report charges on the income

statement consistent with the representations for depreciable properties made on the balance sheet. The American Institute Committee
on Accounting Procedure takes this position. It states:

> When appreciation has been entered on the books income should
> be charged with depreciation computed on the written-up amounts.
> A company should not at the same time claim larger property valu-
> ations in its statement of assets and provide for the amortization of
> only smaller amounts in its statement of income. When a company
> has made representations as to an increased valuation of plant, depre-
> ciation accounting and periodic income determinations thereafter
> should be based upon such higher amounts.[1]

*Recording Depreciation on Cost.* If depreciation is to be calculated
on original cost, the income statement reports operations on a cost
basis, while only the balance sheet reflects appraisal values. Depreciation is recorded in the usual manner, an expense account being debited
and an allowance account being credited for depreciation on cost.
A second entry is required, however, to recognize the shrinkage that
has taken place in the asset appraisal element. Both the asset increase
arising from the appraisal and the appraisal capital must be reduced.
This is accomplished by a debit to the appraisal capital account and
a credit to the appraisal allowance for depreciation account. The
write-off of asset cost is thus accompanied by a write-off of the appraisal
increase.

To illustrate, assume that at the beginning of 1958, equipment
acquired on January 1, 1955, is shown on the books at cost, $100,000,
less an allowance of $37,500 representing depreciation at $12\frac{1}{2}\%$ a
year, or at a book value of $62,500. An appraisal on January 2, 1958,
sets the reproduction cost of the equipment at $150,000 and its present
sound value at 70% of this amount, or $105,000. Depreciation of
30% in 3 years as indicated by the appraisal suggests correction of
depreciation on the asset to a 10-year basis. The following entries are
required:

| Transaction | Entry | |
|---|---|---|
| JANUARY 2, 1958 | Allowance for Depre- | |
| (1) To decrease allowance for depre- | ciation of Equipment.. | 7,500 |
| ciation to 30% of cost as indi- | Corrections in | |
| cated by appraisal. | Profits of | |
| | Prior Periods— | |
| | Overstate- | |
| | ment of De- | |
| | preciation (or | |
| | Retained Earnings.. | 7,500 |

---

[1] *Accounting Research Bulletin No. 43*, "Restatement and Revision of Accounting
Research Bulletins," 1953 (New York: American Institute of Certified Pulbic Accountants) p. 73.

| Transaction | Entry |
|---|---|
| (2) To increase asset and depreciation allowance to a reproduction cost of $150,000 as indicated by appraisal. | Equipment—Appraisal Increase............ 50,000<br>  Allowance for Depreciation of Equipment Appraisal Increase..     15,000<br>  Appraisal Capital— Equipment........     35,000 |
| DECEMBER 31, 1958<br><br>(1) To record depreciation on cost of $100,000 at corrected rate of 10% as indicated by appraisal. | Depreciation of Equipment............... 10,000<br>  Allowance for Depreciation of Equipment...........     10,000 |
| (2) To reduce appraisal increase of $50,000 at rate of 10% consistent with reduced book value of asset as reported in terms of cost. | Appraisal Capital — Equipment .......... 5,000<br>  Allowance for Depreciation of Equipment—Appraisal Increase............     5,000 |

Assuming that the asset is retired at the end of 1964, the allowance for depreciation on cost is offset against the asset account and the allowance for depreciation on the appraisal increase is applied against the asset appraisal increase account. All of the accounts relating to the property item are thus closed.

The appraisal of an asset may indicate that no revision in the estimate of its service life is needed. No correction then is required in the asset allowance account when the appraisal is recorded, and the original rate is applied in recording depreciation thereafter.

*Recording Depreciation on Appraised Values.* When depreciation is based on appraised values that are higher than cost, operating expenses are overstated and net income is understated from a cost point of view. If depreciation is to be recorded on appraised values, periodic transfers from the appraisal capital account to the retained earnings account may be made in order to correct retained earnings for the understatement in net income.

To illustrate, assume the same facts as in the preceding illustration. The entries to record the revaluation are the same. Periodic entries to record depreciation may be made as follows:

| Transaction | Entry |
|---|---|
| DECEMBER 31, 1958<br>(1) To record depreciation on appraised value of $150,000 at corrected rate of 10% as indicated by appraisal. | Depreciation of Equipment.............. 15,000<br>   Allowance for Depreciation of Equipment.............            10,000<br>   Allowance for Depreciation of Equipment—Appraisal Increase............        5,000 |
| (2) To reduce appraisal capital of $50,000 at rate of 10%, consistent with reduced book value of asset, and to correct retained earnings for understatement of income calculated after depreciation on appraised values. | Appraisal Capital — Equipment.......... 5,000<br>   Retained Earnings..        5,000 |

The first entry records depreciation on the appraised value, the allowance for depreciation on cost being credited for depreciation on cost and the allowance for depreciation on the appraisal increase being credited for depreciation on the appraisal increase. This entry results in an expense overstatement of $5,000 in terms of original cost, with a corresponding understatement of net income. The second entry effects a transfer of the amount of the income understatement from the appraisal capital account to retained earnings. The appraisal capital balance then reflects the actual appraisal increase in the reduced book value of the asset, while retained earnings reports earnings based upon actual costs. When the asset is fully depreciated, the entire balance in the appraisal capital account will have been transferred to retained earnings by the periodic entries. Upon disposal of the asset, allowance for depreciation balances are applied against their respective asset accounts.

Instead of periodic transfers from appraisal capital to retained earnings, transfers may be made to a special income account which is ultimately combined with other profit and loss data and carried to retained earnings. Such special income account is recognized as an adjustment to the summary of operations on the income statement. When such a procedure is followed, operations can be viewed in terms of depreciation calculated on appraisal values, but both final net income and retained earnings balances are developed in accordance with historical cost standards.

Some accountants would raise objection to the transfer of appraisal capital to either income or retained earnings. These persons take the view that appreciation procedures in the accounts should compare with devaluation procedures, both asset and capital changes being regarded as of permanent significance. Asset balances as adjusted would be recognized for all further asset accounting including the determinations of depreciation chargeable to periodic revenue. Appraisal capital would be viewed as permanent capital; neither depreciation nor sale of appraised assets would affect the validity of appraisal capital balances.

**RETAINED EARNINGS APPROPRIATIONS TO PROVIDE FOR ASSET REPLACEMENT AT HIGHER PRICE LEVEL** Regardless of whether cost or appraisal depreciation is reported on the income statement, the practical problem of providing funds to take care of asset replacement at a higher price level still exists. In order to preserve funds for the replacement of assets at a higher price level, the board of directors may authorize the regular appropriation of retained earnings to withhold profits from distribution as dividends. When the cost method for depreciation is used, entries are made for the appropriation of retained earnings following the transfer of net income to the latter account. When the appraisal method of depreciation is used, net income is transferred to retained earnings and this is followed by the transfer from appraisal capital to retained earnings to correct these balances; appropriation of retained earnings can then be recorded as under the cost method. Assuming that funds provided by past profits are actually applied to the replacement of assets at higher costs, appropriated balances may be carried forward indefinitely. On the other hand, appropriations may be returned to retained earnings and retained earnings used as a basis for a stock dividend increasing the permanent capital of the business to match the increased dollar investment in plant and equipment. Appropriations of retained earnings originate with the board of directors; the disposition of such balances is likewise a matter to be resolved by the board of directors. Entries are made in the accounts in accordance with the action taken by the board.

**DISPOSAL OF DEPRECIABLE PROPERTIES ON WHICH APPRECIATION HAS BEEN RECORDED** Disposal of a depreciable asset on which appreciation has been recognized in the accounts calls for cancellation of the cost and appraisal increase balances relating to the property item as well as the appraisal capital balance. To illustrate, assume that books show cost and appraisal increases as follows:

|  | Cost | Appraisal Increase |
|---|---|---|
| Buildings........................ | $100,000 | $50,000 |
| Less: Allowance for Depreciation... | 40,000 | 20,000 |
|  | $ 60,000 | $30,000 |

Sale of the asset for $65,000 is recorded as follows, a gain of $5,000 emerging from the sale of the asset whose depreciated cost was $60,000:

| | | |
|---|---|---|
| Cash....................................... | 65,000 | |
| Allowance for Depreciation of Equipment......... | 40,000 | |
| Allowance for Depreciation of Equipment— | | |
| Appraisal Increase............................ | 20,000 | |
| Appraisal Capital—Equipment.................. | 30,000 | |
| Equipment.................................. | | 100,000 |
| Equipment—Appraisal Increase.............. | | 50,000 |
| Gain on Sale of Equipment.................. | | 5,000 |

Examples in the preceding sections illustrated the procedures that are followed when appraisal increases are reported in separate accounts, cost data thus being preserved in the original account balances. It may be observed that similar accounting procedures could be followed in recording asset devaluation, reductions in asset and asset valuation accounts being reported by means of separate offset or negative account balances, and original asset and valuation accounts continuing to reflect cost.

**DEPRECIATION AND INCREASING REPLACEMENT COSTS**     The sharp increase in the price level since World War II has brought demands that accountants make basic changes in accounting for depreciation on plant and equipment. In general, such demands have called for a departure from cost and the recognition of depreciation on the income statement in terms of current values. This, it is claimed, will provide a "more accurate" statement of a company's real earnings, and will also provide for the retention by the business of resources that will be required to replace productive facilities.

Both the American Institute of Certified Public Accountants and the American Accounting Association have given extensive consideration to this problem and have concluded that changes in the price level that have taken place in recent years do not justify a departure from the cost basis in asset accounting.

In 1947 the American Institute Committee on Accounting Procedure issued Bulletin No. 33 dealing with the specific matter of depreciation and high costs. Here, the Committee suggested that the contemplation of property replacements at a higher price level called for the periodic appropriation of earnings, not for the recognition of higher depreciation charges. In supporting depreciation at cost, the Committee commented as follows:

> . . . accounting and financial reporting for general use will best serve their purposes by adhering to the generally accepted concept of depreciation on cost, at least until the dollar is stabilized at some level. An attempt to recognize current prices in providing depreciation, to be consistent, would require the serious step of formally recording appraised current values for all properties, and continuous and consistent depreciation charges based on the new values. Without such formal steps, there would be no objective standard by which to judge the propriety of the amounts of depreciation charges against current income, and the significance of recorded amounts of profit might be seriously impaired.
>
> It would not increase the usefulness of reported corporate income figures if some companies charged depreciation on appraised values while others adhered to cost. The committee believes, therefore, that consideration of radical changes in accepted accounting procedure should not be undertaken, at least until a stable price level would make it practicable for business as a whole to make the change at the same time.[1]

In the following year the Committee addressed a letter to the members of the Institute in which it stated that a basic change in accounting for plant and equipment to meet the problems created by the decline in the purchasing power of the dollar was neither practicable nor desirable. The Committee indicated that stockholders, employees, and the general public should be afforded a full awareness of the need for a business eventually to replace productive facilities at current prices if it is to stay in business. But in the view of the Committee, this information could best be supplied by financial schedules, explanations, and notes accompanying financial statements prepared in their conventional forms.

The conclusions of the Committee on Accounting Procedures as presented in Bulletin No. 33 and in the special letter to the Institute membership are reaffirmed in Accounting Research Bulletin No. 43 issued in 1953.[2]

The American Accounting Association Committee on Concepts and Standards Underlying Corporate Financial Statements in 1948 issued Supplementary Statement No. 2 dealing specifically with the matter of price level changes and the price level. In taking note of proposals that current or the anticipated replacement costs of assets be used as a means of measuring the cost of capital consumed, the Committee commented that such procedure would serve to destroy

---

[1] *Accounting Research Bulletin No. 33*, "Depreciation and High Costs," 1947 (New York: American Institute of Certified Public Accountants), p. 268.

[2] *Accounting Research Bulletin No. 43*, "Restatement and Revision of Accounting Research Bulletins," 1953 (New York: American Institute of Certified Public Accountants), pp. 67-71.

the objectivity of accounting. The cost of consuming existing properties must be recognized, the Committee maintained, irrespective of the intention to replace in kind, to replace with a different type of property, or not to replace at all.

In its Accounting and Reporting Standards for Corporate Financial Statements issued in 1957, the Committee reaffirms the use of cost for asset accounting in the following recommendation:

> In periodic reports to stockholders, the primary financial statements prepared by management and verified by an independent accountant, should, at the present stage of accounting development, continue to reflect historical dollar costs.[1]

However, the Committee would focus attention on the replacement problem by explanations accompanying the financial statements. It makes the following observation:

> The Committee is not unaware of the importance of replacement costs for many purposes, nor is it insensitive to the fact that comparisons of current revenues with the costs of replacing the capital "consumed" in producing such revenues may be highly significant. Financial management necessarily involves the planning of *future* capital receipts and disbursements; and no valid objection can be raised to any form of explanation which enhances the comprehension of such problems on the part of stockholders and other interests external to corporate management.[2]

The Committee while objecting to a modification of the conventional accounting approach to net income determination, at the same time recognizes that wide fluctuations in the general price level have placed severe limitations upon the validity, and hence the usefulness, of statements based on historical cost. In view of such limitations it suggests that supplementary statements be developed in terms of a general price index to interpret the effects of price level changes. The Committee offers the following conclusions relative to disclosure through supplementary statements:

> Management may properly include in periodic reports to stockholders comprehensive supplementary statements which present the effects of the fluctuation in the value of the dollar upon net income and upon financial position.
>
> Such supplementary statements should be internally consistent; the income statement and the balance sheet should both be adjusted by the same procedures, so that the figures in such complementary statements are coordinate and have the same relative significance.
>
> Such supplementary statements should be reconciled in detail with the primary statements reflecting unadjusted original dollar

[1] *Accounting and Reporting Standards for Corporate Financial Statements and Preceding Statements and Supplements*, "Price Level Changes and Financial Statements," 1957 (Columbus: American Accounting Association), p. 24.
[2] *Ibid.*, p. 26.

costs, and should be regarded as an extension or elaboration of the primary statements rather than as a departure therefrom.

Such supplementary statements should be accompanied by comments and explanations clearly setting forth the implications, uses, and limitations of the adjusted data.[1]

**PLANT AND EQUIPMENT ON THE BALANCE SHEET**      Plant and equipment frequently constitutes a substantial portion of a company's total assets, and a listing on the balance sheet of the principal assets or groups of assets in this classification is normally suggested. Nondepreciable assets should not be combined with those that are subject to reductions for depreciation and depletion allowances; depreciable assets should be reported at their cost or other basis, and allowances shown as subtractions from such values. The basis of an asset, whether cost or a value other than cost, should be disclosed. When an asset is reported at an amount other than cost, the difference between cost and the reported value should be stated, together with an explanation of the source of such value and the authority for such reporting in the accounts. When only summaries of plant and equipment items are provided on the balance sheet, detailed analysis of such summaries may be provided by supporting schedules.

A plant and equipment section may be developed as follows:

| Plant and Equipment: | | |
|---|---|---|
| Tools, patterns, and dies, at inventoried value........................................ | | $ 16,500 |
| Machinery and equipment, at cost........ | $184,000 | |
| Less: Allowance for depreciation.......... | 124,000 | 60,000 |
| Balances include $55,000 of fully depreciated machinery and equipment items still in use | | |
| Buildings, at cost...................... | $320,000 | |
| Less: Allowance for depreciation.......... | 125,000 | 195,000 |
| Land, at cost of acquisition in 1940....... | | 65,000 |
| Land and buildings balances do not include facilities costing $200,000 acquired during World War II under Certificates of Necessity that have been fully amortized but are still in use | | |
| Total plant and equipment............. | | $336,500 |

When appraisal increases have been recorded in the accounts, assets may be stated at appraised balances and cost indicated by

---

[1] *Ibid.*, p. 27.

parenthetical remarks. However, ordinarily it would be preferable to offer full information relating to both asset and asset allowance balances in a form such as follows:

|  | COST | APPRAISAL INCREASE | BOOK VALUE AS APPRAISED |
|---|---|---|---|
| Buildings.............. | $100,000 | $ 75,000 | $175,000 |
| Less: Allowance for Depreciation.............. | 40,000 | 30,000 | 70,000 |
| Balance............... | $ 60,000 | $45,000 | $105,000 |

## QUESTIONS

**1.** What alternative procedures may be followed in the accounts upon determining that depreciation has been incorrectly estimated in past years? Evaluate each position.

**2.** How would you recommend that fully depreciated properties be carried in the accounts when they are still being used by the business?

**3.** What procedures must be followed in reporting income for tax purposes when it is found that: (a) depreciation taken on a property item in past periods was clearly inadequate; (b) the full cost of a property item has been depreciated but the item is continued in use.

**4.** (a) What are "emergency facilities" acquired under "certificates of necessity"? (b) What objections are made to the recognition of depreciation on the books consistent with the charges that are allowed in arriving at taxable income? (c) What positions have been taken by the American Institute of Certified Public Accountants relative to (1) facilities fully written off and still in use and (2) facilities currently acquired?

**5.** Revision of past depreciation and revision of account balances to conform to present appraised values are two aspects of the same problem, the accurate statement of balance sheet data. Do you agree?

**6.** What are the arguments for and against the recognition of changes in plant and equipment values as a result of changes in the price level?

**7.** (a) When, in your opinion, would the recognition of a revision downward in the cost of plant items be appropriate? (b) When would you support a revision upward?

**8.** Distinguish between (a) reproduction cost and sound value, (b) appraisal capital and retained earnings, (c) appreciation and devaluation.

**9.** How will changes from cost to appraisal values affect the charges to be recognized on asset use and disposal for income tax purposes?

**10.** (a) Define quasi-reorganization. (b) Under what circumstances is such a readjustment considered appropriate?

**11.** Officials of the Palmer Corporation insist that the appreciation of plant and equipment should be recorded as an increase in paid-in capital since these assets were acquired originally in exchange for capital stock of the company. Evaluate this argument.

**12.** Assuming that appreciation is recorded in the accounts, what are the arguments in support of (a) depreciation in terms of cost and (b) depreciation in terms of appraised value?

**13.** The management of the Taft Corporation suggests that depreciation on assets that have been written up be recorded on the current higher values in order to assure the availability of funds for the replacement of such assets at a higher price level. Comment on whether, in your opinion, this practice is necessary and sufficient in meeting the problem.

**14.** Officers of the X Corporation feel that prices have reached a permanently higher level and thus insist that depreciation on plant and equipment be recognized in terms of higher reproduction costs if current earnings are to be accurately stated. Officers of the Y Corporation feel that prices are too high and will ultimately decline and thus insist that current revenue be charged with a part of the cost of assets currently acquired if current earnings are to be accurately stated. How would you reply to each of these proposals?

**15.** "Should inflation proceed so far that original dollar costs lose their practical significance, it might become necessary to restate all assets in terms of the depreciated currency, as has been done in some countries." (Committee on Accounting Procedure of the American Institute of Certified Public Accountants in letter to membership of the Institute, October 14, 1948.) (a) Give arguments in support of the foregoing proposal. (b) What practices are suggested in meeting the problems of adequate reporting in a period of advanced inflation short of the restatement of account balances?

## EXERCISES

**1.** Machinery was acquired by the Morrison Co. on July 1, 1955, at a cost of $30,000, and was depreciated on an estimated 8-year life. On December 31, 1958, in reviewing account balances for purposes of making the adjustments for the past fiscal year, it was determined that the machinery will probably have a 10-year life. (a) Assuming that the correction in past period estimates is to be made by revising depreciation charges for the remaining life of the asset, what entry would be made to record depreciation for 1958? (b) Assuming that account balances are to be corrected for past overdepreciation, what entries would be made to correct the accounts and to record depreciation for 1958?

**2.** A concrete mixer costing $5,100 is estimated to have a trade-in value of $600 at the end of 6 years. When it is 4 years old, it is estimated that it will be useful for 4 more years and will have a scrap value as originally estimated at the end of that time. What are the entries at the end of the fourth year if it is decided to correct the allowance account on the basis of revised estimates and to record depreciation on the revised basis?

**3.** The Winston Co. purchased land and an old building for $100,000. The land is estimated to be worth $80,000; the building is estimated to have a remaining life not to exceed 10 years. The building is used for 5 years and is then completely remodeled at a cost of $60,000. It is estimated that the building should have a life of 20 years from the date of such remodeling. What entries are made for (a) purchase of land and building, (b) periodic depreciation, (c) cost of remodeling building, and (d) subsequent depreciation.

**4.** The Brooks Corporation owns office equipment costing $6,000 that has been used for 5 years and that has been reduced to a book value of $1,200, the estimated trade-in value at this time. Because of a shortage of new equipment for replacement, the company spends $1,500 overhauling the old equipment. It is assumed that this overhauling will prolong the life of the equipment by 3 years and that the trade-in value will remain the same. (a) What entry is made to record the expenditure? (b) What is the annual depreciation subsequent to the expenditure?

**5.** The Peroff Co. owns machinery acquired at the beginning of 1950 at a cost of $15,000; the asset is being depreciated on a 15-year basis. At the beginning of 1958, several major worn-out parts are replaced at a cost of $1,800. Worn parts have a cost equal to the new parts; $60 is recovered from their sale as scrap. Give the entries to record (a) depreciation for 1957, (b) the replacement of worn parts at the beginning of 1958, and (c) depreciation for 1958.

**6.** The Gardner Co. has a certain machine acquired at the beginning of 1953 at a cost of $225,000 that is being depreciated on a 15-year life. Three operators are required for the machine, each being paid $4,500 annually. At the beginning of 1958 it is found that a new machine is available that offers the same performance with only two operators required. The new machine sells for $75,000 and would have at least a 10-year life. The old machine can be sold for $7,500. Should the new machine be purchased? Give calculations to support your conclusions.

**7.** The Williams Co. shows property and capital accounts on January 1, 1958, as follows:

| PROPERTY ACCOUNTS | | CAPITAL ACCOUNTS | |
|---|---|---|---|
| Plant and equipment ... | $1,650,000 | Capital stock (par $10) .. | $1,000,000 |
| Allowance for deprecia- | | Additional paid-in capital | 150,000 |
| tion............... | 350,000 | | $1,150,000 |
| | $1,300,000 | Less: Deficit.......... | 200,000 |
| | | | $ 950,000 |

On January 5, stockholders authorize that the property accounts be written down to their present values as indicated by appraisal as follows:

| | |
|---|---|
| Plant and equipment .................................. | $1,210,000 |
| Allowance for depreciation ............................ | 265,000 |
| | $ 945,000 |

They further authorize that both the deficit as reported on the books and the asset write-down be applied against existing paid-in capital, and that any excess be applied against the capital stock account; capital stock outstanding is to be changed from $10 par to no-par. Give the entries that are required in recording the corporate readjustment.

**8.** Machinery, reported on the books at $30,000 with a depreciation allowance of $8,000 and an estimated life of 15 years, was appraised on January 1 and found to have a reproduction cost new of $50,000 and an estimated total life of 20 years. What entries would be made to record the appraisal?

**9.** Machinery acquired on January 1, 1953, at a cost of $300,000 shows a depreciation allowance of $60,000 on January 1, 1958. On this date engineers and appraisers estimate that the machinery should have a remaining useful life of 25 years and a reproduction cost new of $450,000. (a) What entries should be made for the appraisal? (b) What entries should be made to record depreciation on this asset for the year 1958 if operations are (1) charged with cost and (2) charged with appraised values?

**10.** The Anderson Co. acquired buildings at the beginning of 1950 at a cost of $100,000 and is depreciating them on a 50-year basis. At the beginning of 1958 an appraisal indicates that the buildings have a reproduction cost of $200,000 and a sound value of $160,000 based on a 40-year life. The appraisal is recorded in the accounts, and depreciation for 1958 is recorded at cost. On January 3, 1959, the buildings are sold for cash, $175,000. What entries would be made on the books of the Anderson Co. for 1958 and 1959?

## PROBLEMS

**17-1.** The information that follows summarizes transactions of the J.D. Lowry Co. relating to the acquisition of a machine for manufacturing:

| | |
|---|---|
| Jan. 3, 1949. | Purchased machine for $10,000; was allowed a 5% discount for making cash payment. The machine is estimated to have a 5-year life; salvage value is to be disregarded. |
| Dec. 31, 1952. | The estimated life of the machine is revised from 5 years to 8 years, and the effect of such revision is recorded in the accounts. |
| Jan. 3, 1955. | Several major parts of the machine were replaced at a cost of $2,400; cost of such original parts is estimated at $2,000. Additional costs of $1,500 are incurred in overhauling the machine at this point, and it is estimated that replacements |

and overhauling costs will extend the life of the machine to 10 years.

Sept. 7, 1958.   The machine is scrapped, $60 being recovered on the salvage.

*Instructions:* Give all the entries that would be made relative to machinery for the period 1949-1958, including the adjustments that are required at the end of each calendar year to recognize depreciation for the year.

**17-2.** Four machines are found in the machine shop of the Owen Manufacturing Co. at the beginning of 1958 as follows:

| MACHINE | DATE ACQUIRED | COST, INCLUDING INSTALLATION | ESTIMATED USEFUL LIFE | ESTIMATED SALVAGE VALUE |
|---|---|---|---|---|
| A | Mar. 5, 1950 | $ 6,500 | 10 yrs. | $ 500 |
| B | April 1, 1952 | 8,000 | 10 yrs. | 250 |
| C | June 20, 1954 | 9,200 | 10 yrs. | 500 |
| D | Nov. 6, 1955 | 12,400 | 12 yrs. | 1,000 |

During 1958 the following transactions relating to machines in this department are completed:

Jan. 6.   Machine A, which had not been operating satisfactorily, was scrapped, $50 being recovered on salvage.   It was decided that the lives of Machines B and C probably would not exceed 8 years.   In revising the depreciation on these machines, it was agreed that their salvage values would be negligible, and hence are to be disregarded.

Jan. 18.   Machine E was purchased for cash at a cost of $8,000.   The new machine is estimated to have a life of 10 years and no salvage value.

Feb. 11.   Machine D was traded in for a larger machine costing $16,500. Machine D was accepted at a value of $8,500 for purposes of the trade-in, the balance of the purchase price being paid in cash.   The new machine, to be referred to as Machine F, is recorded at $16,500.   It is estimated to have a life of 10 years and a trade-in value of $1,500 at that time.

*Instructions:* (1) Give the journal entries that are required for 1958, including the adjustments at the end of the year (depreciation is calculated to the nearest month).

(2) Prepare a schedule showing the cost, depreciation allowance balance, and book value of each machine on hand as of December 31, 1958.

**17-3.** The Burroughs Co. acquires plant and equipment at a cost of $200,000 at the beginning of 1957 and is permitted to depreciate this asset at 20% per year for income tax purposes under a Certificate of Necessity. For book purposes, however, the company records depreciation at 2½% per year based on the estimated physical life of the asset.   The books showed company earnings for 1957 to be $106,000.   Federal income tax rates for 1957 were 30% on all taxable income plus 22% on taxable income in excess of $25,000.

*Instructions:* (1) Give the entries that would be made in 1957 to recognize the income tax liability and to adjust the income tax charge in recognition of differences in financial and tax reporting.

(2) Give the entry that would be made at the end of 1962 to adjust the income tax charge for that year.   (Assume that the company's profits from 1958 through 1962 continue to exceed $100,000 and income tax rates during this period remain the same.)

**17-4.** The Marge Co. purchased a machine in 1958 by trading in an old machine. The old machine which had been acquired in 1948 had a cost of $77,250. Both the old and new machines have an estimated 20 year life and depreciation for one-half year is taken in years of acquisition and disposal. The terms of the purchase provided for a trade-in allowance of $25,000 and called for a cash payment of $125,000 or 12 monthly payments of $11,000. The latter alternative was chosen. Cash disbursements in connection with the exchange were as follows:

| | |
|---|---:|
| Removal of old machine............................................ | $   800 |
| Repair to factory floor after removal...................... | 700 |
| Installation of new machine............................... | 2,000 |
| Sales engineer who supervised installation 40 hours @ $10 per hour......................................... | 400 |
| Hotel, meals, and travel for sales engineer................. | 200 |
| Freight in — new machine............................... | 1,500 |
| Freight out — old machine............................... | 1,000 |

*Instructions:* Give an entry or entries to record the data relative to the exchange. (Provide supporting calculations for your answer.)

**17-5.** The books of the Atlas Manufacturing Co. are audited for the first time and the following account is found for machinery during the course of the audit in 1959:

MACHINERY

| 1957 | | | | 1957 | | | |
|---|---|---|---:|---|---|---|---:|
| Mar. | 1 | Machine No. 1...... | 6,000 | Dec. | 31 | Depreciation....... | 2,000 |
| | 1 | Machine No. 2...... | 4,200 | 1958 | | | |
| Sept. | 26 | Machine No. 3...... | 12,500 | Mar. | 20 | Machine No. 1...... | 2,500 |
| 1958 | | | | Nov. | 1 | Machine No. 2...... | — |
| Apr. | 21 | Machine No. 4...... | 4,500 | Dec. | 31 | Depreciation....... | 3,000 |
| Nov. | 1 | Machine No. 5...... | 6,000 | | 31 | Balance.......... | 25,700 |
| | | | 33,200 | | | | 33,200 |
| 1959 | | | | | | | |
| Jan. | 1 | Balance........... | 25,700 | | | | |

An examination of the books and records reveals the following additional data concerning machinery: Machines 1, 2, 3, and 4 were purchased for cash. Machines 1 and 2 proved inadequate. Machine 1 was sold for $2,500. Machine 2 was traded for Machine 5. The purchase price of Machine 5 was $8,200; cash of $6,000 was paid for the new machine, an allowance of $2,200 being received on Machine 2 traded in. All machines have an estimated life of 10 years. Depreciation of machinery was recorded on the basis of arbitrary estimates made by company engineers.

*Instructions:* (1) Give the journal entries that should have been made to record properly the above transactions. (Assume that depreciation by the straight-line method is recorded to the nearest month, and an asset acquired by trade-in is reported at its regular purchase price.)

(2) Give the journal entries necessary in 1959 to correct the accounts in view of the entries actually made in prior years.

(3) Show in account form the asset and the allowance for depreciation on the company's books after the corrections have been posted.

**17-6.** The Mathews Co. owns land and buildings that were acquired at a tax auction sale at the beginning of 1950. Account balances for this asset on January 1, 1955, appear as follows:

| | | |
|---|---:|---:|
| Land........................................ | | $20,000 |
| Buildings.................................... | $30,000 | |
| Less: Allowance for depreciation ............... | 7,500 | 22,500 |
| | | $42,500 |

An appraisal of this property on this date indicated that the land was worth $35,000, that buildings had a sound value of $40,000, and that the asset should have a remaining life from this date of 20 years. A correction is made for depreciation of the past, and the appraisal is recorded in the accounts. On July 1, 1958, the company borrows $20,000, issuing a 5-year note secured by a mortgage on the property; interest at 6% is payable annually on July 1. On September 1, 1958, the company sells the land and buildings for $72,500, the purchaser assuming the mortgage note and accrued interest and making payment in cash for the difference.

*Instructions:* (1) Give the entry to record the asset appraisal on January **1,** 1955.

(2) Give the entries to record depreciation in the years 1955-1957. (Operations are charged with depreciation at cost.)

(3) Give the entry to record the sale of property on September 1, 1958.

**17-7.** The following account balances relating to plant and equipment appear on the books of the Briggs Corporation on December 31, 1957:

| | | |
|---|---:|---:|
| Furniture and Fixtures............................ | $ 36,000 | |
| Allowance for Depreciation of Furniture and Fixtures.. | | $ 30,000 |
| Machinery..................................... | 240,000 | |
| Allowance for Depreciation of Machinery............ | | 96,000 |
| Buildings..................................... | 600,000 | |
| Allowance for Depreciation of Buildings............. | | 112,500 |
| Land......................................... | 90,000 | |

These assets have been carried at cost since their acquisition. With the exception of Building B, completed on January 1, 1953, at a cost of $300,000, all of the assets were acquired on January 1, 1948. The company now wishes to show plant and equipment items at their present sound value.

An appraisal firm submitted the following report on January 2, 1958:

|  | REPLACEMENT VALUE (NEW) | PRESENT DEPRECIATED VALUE |
|---|---|---|
| 5 Furniture and Fixtures.............. | $ 45,000 | ⅓ $ 15,000 |
| 10 Machinery........................ | 270,000 | ½ 135,000 |
| 30 Buildings: A Constructed 1/1/48 .... | 360,000 | 270,000 |
| 35 B Constructed 1/1/53 .... | 330,000 | 288,750 |
| Land.......................... | 150,000 | |

*Instructions:* (1) What is the estimated remaining life of the depreciable assets as determined from the appraiser's report?

(2) Prepare journal entries to give effect to appraisal values.

(3) Prepare the plant and equipment section of the balance sheet showing appraisal values.

(4) Give the adjusting entries for depreciation at the end of 1958, assuming that operations are charged with depreciation at cost.

(5) Give the adjusting entries for depreciation at the end of 1958, assuming that operations are charged with depreciation on the appraised values.

**17-8.** Upon its incorporation on July 1, 1954, the Houser Manufacturing Co. purchased plant and equipment for cash as follows:

|  | COST | ESTIMATED USEFUL LIFE |
|---|---|---|
| Land...................................... | $ 60,000 | |
| Buildings................................. | 150,000 | 50 years |
| Machinery and Equipment................ | 240,000 | 20 years |
| Office Furniture and Fixtures.............. | 15,000 | 12 years |

On January 2, 1956, it was decided that the estimated useful lives used in calculating straight-line depreciation on plant items were excessive. Correcting entries and depreciation calculated on the basis of revised estimated lives were authorized as follows:

|  | REVISED ESTIMATE OF USEFUL LIFE |
|---|---|
| Buildings........................................ | 40 years |
| Machinery and Equipment...................... | 12 years |
| Office Furniture and Fixtures................... | 10 years |

On May 4, 1957, additional machinery was acquired at $60,000 less a 5% discount for cash payment. Cost of freight in on the machinery was $2,000. Installation of machinery was completed at the end of June at a cost of $12,500. This machinery is estimated to have a 10-year life.

At the beginning of 1958, an appraisal of plant assets was made by professional appraisers. While no change was indicated in the lives of the assets, it was ascertained that reproduction costs of assets acquired in July, 1954, had increased by the following percentages:

|  |  |
|---|---|
| Land...................................... | 150% |
| Buildings................................. | 80% |
| Machinery and Equipment................. | 80% |
| Office Furniture and Fixtures.............. | 50% |

It was authorized that such appraisal increases be recorded in the accounts and that depreciation be recorded on the basis of appraisal values.

*Instructions:* (1) Give the journal entries relating to plant and equipment accounts for the period July 1, 1954, to December 31, 1958, including the entries for depreciation that are made at the end of each calendar year. (Assume that no changes are made in appraisal capital balances at the end of each year, since dividends are to be limited to net income based on appraisal depreciation.)

(2) Give the information that will appear in the plant and equipment and the appraisal capital sections of the balance sheet prepared as of December 31, 1958.

**17-9.** The Nelson Co. shows account balances as follows as of January 1, 1957:

|  | Cost | Date Acquired | Estimated Useful Life |
|---|---|---|---|
| Machinery and Equipment | $1,200,000 | 1/1/47 | 15 years |
| Machinery and Equipment | 420,000 | 1/1/49 | 15 years |
| Buildings | 2,000,000 | 1/1/47 | 40 years |
| Land | 500,000 | 1/1/45 | |

On this date, January 1, 1957, an independent appraisal company submits the following estimates with respect to asset values and asset lives:

|  | Replacement Value (New) | Estimated Remaining Useful Life |
|---|---|---|
| Machinery and Equipment: | | |
| Acquired 1/1/47 | $1,800,000 | 10 years |
| Acquired 1/1/49 | 500,000 | 12 years |
| Buildings | 3,000,000 | 40 years |
| Land | 800,000 | |

It is authorized that asset appraisal values be recorded in the accounts at this time. However, depreciation for profit and loss purposes is to be calculated on the basis of original costs with useful lives as revised.

On July 1, 1957, a part of the land with an apportioned cost of $100,000 and an appraised value of $160,000 is sold for cash at $185,000.

At the beginning of 1958, machinery and equipment originally acquired on January 1, 1947, with an apportioned cost of $30,000 and appraised at a reproduction cost of $45,000 as of January 1, 1957, is traded in for new equipment costing $100,000. $20,000 is allowed on the old equipment, the balance of the purchase price being paid in cash. The new equipment is recorded at its purchase price and is estimated to have a 20-year life.

*Instructions:* (1) Give the entries relating to plant and equipment for the years 1957 and 1958, including the annual entries for depreciation that are required at the end of 1957 and 1958.

(2) Give the information that will appear in the plant and equipment section and the appraisal capital section of the balance sheet as of December 31, 1958.

**17-10.** The following data were ascertained in reviewing the auto trucks account for the Condon Manufacturing Company as of December 31, 1958:

| | |
|---|---:|
| Truck No. 1, purchased Jan. 1, 1952, cost................. | $2,000 |
| Truck No. 2, purchased July 1, 1952, cost................. | 1,800 |
| Truck No. 3, purchased Jan. 1, 1954, cost................. | 1,200 |
| Truck No. 4, purchased July 1, 1954, cost................. | 1,000 |
| Balance, January 1, 1955.............................. | $6,000 |

The auto trucks depreciation allowance account had a balance on January 1, 1955, of $2,440, being depreciation on the four trucks from the respective dates of purchase based on a 5-year life. No charges had been made against the allowance prior to January 1, 1955.

Transactions between January 1, 1955, and December 31, 1958, and their record in the ledger were as follows:

July 1, 1955. Truck No. 1 was sold for $600 cash; the entry debited Cash and credited Auto Trucks, $600.

Jan. 1, 1956. Truck No. 3 was traded for a larger one (No. 5), the agreed purchase price of which was $1,600. The Condon Manufacturing Company paid the automobile dealer $780 cash on the transaction. The entry was a debit to Auto Trucks and a credit to Cash, $780.

July 1, 1957. Truck No. 4 was damaged in a wreck to such an extent that it was sold as junk for $50 cash. The Condon Manufacturing Company received $300 from the insurance company. The entry made by the bookkeeper was a debit to Cash, $350, and credits to Miscellaneous Income, $50, and Auto Trucks, $300.

July 1, 1957. A new truck (No. 6) was acquired for $1,200 cash and was charged at that amount to the auto trucks account.

Entries for depreciation had been made at the close of each year as follows: 1955, $1,200; 1956, $1,076; 1957, $1,076; 1958, $1,246.

*Instructions:* (1) For each of the four years calculate separately the increase or the decrease in net profits arising from the company's errors in determining or entering depreciation or in recording transactions affecting trucks, ignoring income tax regulations covering gain or loss on trade-ins.

(2) Prove your work by one compound journal entry as of December 31, 1958, to adjust the auto trucks account so that it will reflect the correct balance, assuming that the books have not been closed for 1958.

(A.I.C.P.A. adapted)

**17-11.** An old, established corporation, whose books have never before been audited by a public accountant, requests you to make an examination of its accounts as of December 31, 1958.

As a result of your examination, you find the following items included in the accounts:

Debits:

| | | |
|---|---:|---:|
| Appreciation of land..................................... | $ | 800,000 |
| Appreciation of buildings............................... | | 200,000 |
| Trade-marks........................................... | | 2,000,000 |
| Treasury stock—5,000 shares (at par).................... | | 250,000 |

Credits:

| | |
|---|---:|
| Reserve for depreciation on appreciation of buildings........ | $      15,000 |
| Capital stock, consisting of 200,000 shares of $50 each........ | 10,000,000 |
| Paid-in surplus arising from acquisition of treasury stock at less than par...................................... | 70,000 |
| Surplus balance, including net earnings plus credits arising from book valuations of trade-marks, appreciation, etc., and after deduction for all dividends paid or declared...... | 15,000 |

You have convinced the officers that the values set up for appreciation of land, buildings, and trade-marks should be eliminated and that the treasury stock should be canceled. Since there is insufficient surplus to absorb these adjustments, it has been suggested that they be made against the stockholders' net equity and that new shares of no-par value be exchanged for the present shares outstanding, on the basis of one new share for one old share.

The plan has been duly approved by the stockholders and the change in capital has been properly authorized, effective as of January 1, 1959.

You are now requested to furnish the necessary entries to record the new setup in order to prepare and submit a balance sheet as of March 31, 1959. In the period from December 31, 1958, to March 31, 1959, the net earnings from operations amounted to $40,000. No dividends were paid or declared. All the old shares outstanding have been exchanged for the new ones.

*Instructions:* (1) Submit your adjusting journal entries, giving effect to the reorganization of capital, the elimination of all items of appreciation and intangibles, and the cancellation of treasury stock.

(2) Show the amount of the capital stock account at March 31, 1959, and the manner in which the account would be stated on the balance sheet at that date.

(3) What is the balance in the surplus account at March 31, 1959?

(4) What footnote, if any, would you place on the balance sheet submitted as at March 31, 1959? (A.I.C.P.A. adapted)

**17-12.** The Columbia Corporation had $105,000 of dividends in arrears on its preferred stock as of March 31, 1958. While retained earnings were adequate to meet the accumulated dividends, the company's management did not wish to weaken its working capital position. The management also realized that a portion of the fixed assets were no longer used or useful in their operation. Therefore, the following reorganization was proposed, which was approved by stockholders to be effective as of April 1, 1958:

(1) The preferred stock was to be exchanged for $300,000 of 5% debenture bonds. Dividends in arrears were to be settled by the issuance of $120,000 of $10 par value, 5% noncumulative preferred stock.

(2) Common stock was to be assigned a value of $50 per share.

(3) Goodwill was to be written off.

(4) Property, plant, and equipment were to be written down, based on appraisal and estimates of useful value, by a total of $103,200, consisting of an $85,400 increase in allowance for depreciation and a $17,800 decrease in certain assets.

(5) Current assets were to be written down by $10,460 to reduce certain items to expected realizable values.

The condensed balance sheet as of March 31, 1958 was as follows:

## ASSETS

| | | |
|---|---:|---:|
| Cash............................................. | | $    34,690 |
| Other current assets........................... | | 252,890 |
| Property, plant, and equipment............... | $1,458,731 | |
| Allowance for depreciation.................... | 512,481 | |
| | | 946,250 |
| Goodwill..................................... | | 50,000 |
| | | $1,283,830 |

## LIABILITIES AND CAPITAL

| | |
|---|---:|
| Current liabilities...................................... | $    136,860 |
| 7% Cumulative preferred stock ($100 par)*................. | 300,000 |
| Common stock (9,000 shares, no-par)...................... | 648,430 |
| Premium on preferred stock.............................. | 22,470 |
| Retained earnings...................................... | 176,070 |
| | $1,283,830 |

*$105,000 dividends in arrears.

*Instructions:* (1) Prepare journal entries to give effect to the reorganization as of April 1, 1958. Give complete explanations with each entry and comment on any possible options in recording the reorganization.

(2) Prepare a balance sheet as of April 30, 1958, assuming that net income for April was $10,320 after provision for taxes. The operations resulted in a $5,290 increase in cash, a $10,660 increase in other current assets, a $2,010 increase in current liabilities, and a $3,620 increase in allowance for depreciation.

(3) In making an audit of The Columbia Corporation as of December 31, 1958, you find that the following items had been charged or credited directly to Retained Earnings during the nine months since April 1, 1958:

(a) A debit of $14,496 arising from an income tax assessment applicable to prior years.

(b) A credit of $20,387 resulting from a gain on the sale of equipment that was no longer used in the business. This equipment had been written down by a $10,000 increase in the allowance for depreciation at the time of the reorganization.

(c) A debit of $7,492 resulting from a loss on fixed assets destroyed in a fire on November 2, 1958.

(d) A debit of $13,500 representing dividends declared on common and preferred stock.

For each of these items, state whether you believe it to be correctly charged or credited to Retained Earnings. Give the reasons for your conclusion. If the item is not handled properly, prepare the necessary correcting entry. (A.I.C.P.A. adapted)

# Chapter 18

# INTANGIBLES

**NATURE OF INTANGIBLES** The difference between tangible and intangible assets lies in the physical and nonphysical characteristics of the properties concerned. Tangible assets are physical properties that are used by the business; intangible assets are certain rights, privileges, and competitive advantages that serve the business. From a legal point of view, such assets as shares of stock, bonds, and claims against customers are regarded as intangibles. For the accountant, however, the intangibles classification is limited to certain noncurrent properties that are without physical substance and that are not otherwise classified. Examples of intangibles are patents, copyrights, franchises, trademarks, trade brands, formulas and secret processes, goodwill, organization costs, leaseholds, and similar items.

Intangible assets derive their value from the fact that they contribute to the earnings of the business through the special advantages that they represent or the rights or the privileges that they afford. For example, special advantages contributing to earnings result from the skill of employees, ability of management, desirable location of a business, and good customer relationships—all elements of a company's goodwill. Special rights contributing to earnings result from the ownership of such items as patents and copyrights.

**VALUATION OF INTANGIBLES** In general, valuation for intangible assets should follow the standards employed for the tangible group. Intangibles should be recorded at cost. Cost should include all expenditures identified with the development or the purchase of the assets. When an intangible is acquired in exchange for an asset other than cash, the fair market value of the asset exchanged or that of the intangible, whichever is more clearly determinable, should be used to record the acquisition. When shares of stock or bonds are issued in exchange for an intangible, the market value of the securities issued or of the intangible acquired should be determined in recording the exchange. When several intangibles or a combination of tangible and intangible assets are acquired for one lump sum, this sum must be allocated to the individual units acquired on some equitable basis.

Costs are reported for intangible assets only when certain expenditures can be related to their acquisition. For example, no value should appear on the books for goodwill developed by a company over a period of years or for a franchise acquired without cost. But when an intangible asset without an accountable cost makes significant contribution to the success of the business, reference on the balance sheet to such right or advantage by means of a parenthetical remark or note is appropriate.

The accounting for an intangible subsequent to its acquisition will depend upon its nature. The American Institute Committee on Accounting Procedure classifies intangibles into two general groups as follows:

(a) Those having a term of existence limited by law, regulation, or agreement, or by their nature (such as patents, copyrights, leases, licenses, franchises for a fixed term, and goodwill as to which there is evidence of limited duration);

(b) Those having no such limited term of existence and as to which there is, at the time of acquisition, no indication of limited life (such as goodwill generally, going value, trade names, secret processes, subscription lists, perpetual franchises, and organization costs).[1]

When a limited usefulness is indicated, the asset cost should be assigned to those periods benefiting from its use. When an unlimited life is indicated, it is appropriate to carry the asset at original cost as long as it continues to make a contribution to the profitability of the enterprise. Such procedures parallel those employed for tangible assets: the cost of a building with a limited life is charged to operations over the useful life of the building; land with an unlimited life and continued usefulness is carried forward at original cost.

**INTANGIBLES WITH LIMITED TERM OF EXISTENCE**   The process of assigning the costs of intangibles with a limited life to periodic revenue in some systematic manner is called *amortization*. Amortization of intangible assets, just as cost allocations for plant and equipment items, may be based on time or output factors. Benefits of an intangible cannot be assumed to continue beyond its legal life. When the useful life of an asset is considered to be less than the legal life, the useful life provides the basis for amortization. Cost amortization is recorded by a charge to expense and a credit to the asset or to an asset valuation account.

If it becomes evident during the life of an intangible that the period of its usefulness may differ from the period originally estimated,

---

[1] *Accounting Research Bulletin No. 43*, "Restatement and Revision of Accounting Research Bulletins," 1953 (New York: American Institute of Certified Public Accountants), p. 37.

the original amortization plan may be modified. The Committee on Accounting Procedure has recommended, "If it becomes evident that the period benefited will be longer or shorter than originally estimated, recognition thereof may take the form of an appropriate decrease or increase in the rate of amortization or, if such increased charges would result in distortion of income, a partial write-down may be made to earned surplus."[1]

Intangibles subject to amortization are reported on the balance sheet at unamortized cost or at original cost less a valuation balance summarizing past amortization. If a basis of valuation other than cost is used, full information concerning such valuation should be offered. The periodic amortization charge is reported as a manufacturing expense or an operating expense, depending upon the nature of the contribution made by the intangible.

Federal income tax regulations allow the taxpayer to write off the cost of an intangible by periodic charges when its use in a trade or business or in the production of income is definitely limited in duration. Periodic deductions would be recognized for tax purposes on patents, copyrights, leaseholds, licenses, franchises, and similar properties.

**INTANGIBLES WITHOUT LIMITED TERM OF EXISTENCE**    In the case of intangibles with an unlimited or indefinite existence, partial or complete cost write-offs have been made on the books as a result of: (1) the determination that the usefulness of such intangibles has become limited or has actually come to an end; (2) the adoption of a policy for the arbitrary reduction or elimination of such intangibles.

When it becomes evident that an intangible has lost its usefulness and has become worthless, a write-off of the intangible is justified. When it is reasonable to assume that a part of its usefulness has disappeared and its remaining usefulness is limited to a certain term, a partial write-off would be suggested, followed by amortization of the balance of the cost over the remaining period of usefulness. The Committee on Accounting Procedure suggests the following procedure upon determining that an intangible will serve for only a limited period, "When it becomes reasonably evident that the term of existence of a type (b) intangible has become limited and that it has therefore become a type (a) intangible, its cost should be amortized by systematic charges in the income statement over the estimated remaining period of usefulness. If, however, the period of amortization

---

[1] *Ibid.*, p. 38.

is relatively short so that misleading inferences might be drawn as a result of inclusion of substantial charges in the income statement a partial write-down may be made by a charge to earned surplus, and the rest of the cost may be amortized over the remaining period of usefulness."[1]

The arbitrary write-off of an intangible in the absence of indication of a loss of value is not supportable in theory. The write-off of an intangible that is making a continuing contribution to the success of the business unit is subject to the same criticism that can be made for the write-off of a tangible asset under similar circumstances. Notwithstanding such argument, arbitrary write-offs have been widely applied in practice on the grounds of conservatism. Frequently write-offs have been made immediately after the acquisition of intangibles. It has been argued that the elimination of intangible items is desirable in offering a conservative appraisal of financial condition, since intangibles stand the possibility of losing their usefulness and, furthermore, may prove of little or no value upon the sale or liquidation of a business. It may be observed that the American Institute Committee on Accounting Procedure in a bulletin issued in 1944 discouraged the arbitrary write-off of an intangible whose value remained unimpaired, but did not actually prohibit the practice in view of its wide general acceptance and approval. However, the Committee, in Bulletin No. 43 issued in 1953, takes a positive stand in opposition to such write-offs. The Committee recommends, "Lump-sum write-offs of intangibles should not be made to earned surplus immediately after acquisition. . . . If not amortized systematically, intangibles should be carried at cost until an event has taken place which indicates a loss or limitation on the useful life of the intangibles."[2]

There is general agreement that when a partial or complete write-off of an intangible is made, such a charge should be absorbed by retained earnings and not by a paid-in capital balance. When such a special charge is to be reflected on the income statement, it should not be considered as an operating expense but should be reported as an extraordinary charge. The operating expense section of the income statement, then, shows charges for intangibles only when these can

[1] *Ibid.*, p. 38. It may be observed that the Committee on Accounting Procedure recognizes the existence of a special problem with respect to those intangibles that are not considered to have an unlimited life but that do not indicate a limited life that would call for their reclassification as "class (a) intangibles." Under such circumstances, the Committee would accept amortization over a reasonable period by systematic charges to operations. However, such procedure should be formally approved and the reason for amortization, the rate that is used, and the shareholders' or directors' approval thereof disclosed on the financial statements. It further observes that such amortization is within the discretion of the corporation and is not to be regarded as obligatory.

[2] *Ibid.*, p. 40.

be related to the revenue of the current period; special write-offs are reported in the lower section of the income statement or on the retained earnings statement.

The special accounting problems that arise in connection with specific intangible assets are discussed in the sections that follow.

**PATENTS**                        A patent is an exclusive right issued by the United States Patent Office that enables an inventor to manufacture, sell, or otherwise control his invention for a period of seventeen years from the date of the grant. While patents are not renewable, the life of a patented article is frequently extended by obtaining new patents providing for improvements or changes. The patent may be used by its inventor, or its use may be granted to others under royalty agreements.

When a patent is developed, its cost includes such items as legal fees, patent fees, the cost of models and drawings, and related experimental and developmental expenditures. When a patent is purchased, the patent is recorded at its purchase price. The government gives the owner of the patent an exclusive right to control the use of the invention, but it does not protect him against its infringement. The cost of successfully prosecuting or defending original infringement suits is a cost of establishing the patent right and is properly capitalized. In the event of unsuccessful litigation, both litigation costs and the cost of the patent would be written off as a loss.

The legal life of a patent is used for amortization only when the patent is expected to have usefulness for its full legal life. The useful life of a patent is usually much shorter than its legal life because of factors of obsolescence and supersession. New and more efficient inventions, changes in the demand for certain products, or other conditions frequently result in loss of patent value. Acceptable bases for patent cost amortization may be provided by estimated useful lives expressed in terms of years or in terms of units of product to be produced.

The classification of the charge for patent amortization depends upon the nature and the use of the patent. A charge for patents used in the manufacturing process would be recognized as a manufacturing expense; a charge for patents used in shipping department activities would be recognized as a selling expense.

**COPYRIGHTS**                    Copyrights are exclusive rights granted by the federal government to the author or the artist enabling him to publish, sell, or otherwise control his literary, musical, or artistic works. The right to exclusive control is issued for a period of twenty-eight years, with the privilege of renewal for another twenty-eight years. Copyrights, like patents, may be licensed to others or sold.

The cost assigned to a copyright consists of all of the charges relating to the production of the work, including those required to establish the right. When a copyright is purchased, the copyright is recorded at cost by its new owner.

The useful life of a copyright is generally considerably less than its legal life. It would be appropriate to write off costs of a copyright on the basis of the estimated total sales units relating to such rights; however, as a conservative measure, costs of a copyright are frequently written off against first revenues from this source.

**FRANCHISES**          A franchise is a grant by a governmental unit permitting the use of public properties for certain public benefits. These privileges are ordinarily associated with public utility enterprises and may be granted for a specific number of years, for an indefinite period, or for perpetuity.

The cost of a franchise may be limited to the charges of applying for such franchise. Under these circumstances, only such charges should be assigned to the franchise even though it may have substantially greater value. However, the nature of the rights conferred by the franchise should be fully disclosed on the financial statements. When a sum is paid either to a governmental body for rights that are granted or to another company for rights that are purchased, such sum is recorded as franchise cost. Legal fees and other expenditures incurred in obtaining a franchise are also properly charged to the franchise account.

When the life of a franchise is limited, its cost should be charged to the income of the periods that benefit from its use. When the life of a franchise can be terminated at the option of the granting authority, the cost is best amortized over a relatively short period. Costs of a perpetual franchise may be carried forward indefinitely as long as the franchise is of continuing value. When the cost of a perpetual franchise is arbitrarily reduced or written off, the charge should not be made to operations, since the cost does not relate to current income; instead, the write-off should be treated as an extraordinary charge.

A franchise may call for periodic payments to the governmental unit. Payments may be fixed amounts or they may be variable amounts depending upon revenue, utilization, or other factors. Such payments should be recognized as charges to periodic revenue. When certain improvements are required under terms of the franchise, the costs of the improvements should be capitalized and identified with subsequent revenue in some appropriate manner.

**TRADE-MARKS AND**    Trade-marks, together with trade names,
**TRADE NAMES**    distinctive symbols, labels, and designs are important to all companies that depend upon a public demand for their products. It is by means of such distinctive markings that particular products are differentiated from competing brands. In building up the reputation of a product, relatively large costs may be involved. The federal government offers a person or a business legal protection on trade-marks, through their registry with the United States Patent Office. Prior and continuous use is the important factor in determining the ownership of a particular trade-mark. The right to a trade-mark is retained so long as continuous use is made of it. Protection of trade names, brands, etc., that cannot be registered must be sought in the common law. Distinguishing trade-marks, trade names, and labels, can be assigned or sold.

When a trade-mark is developed, the cost of the trade-mark includes developmental expenditures such as designing expenses, filing and registry fees, and also expenditures for successful litigation in the defense of such right. When a trade-mark is purchased, it is recorded at its purchase price.

Since the life of a trade-mark is not limited, its cost may be carried forward until it is ascertained that there has been a loss in value. However, cost is frequently written off over a relatively short period on the theory that changes in consumer demand may limit its life.

**FORMULAS AND**    Large enterprises engage in continuous re-
**SPECIAL PROCESSES**    search for the improvement of processes and formulas and the development of new and improved products. Expenditures for general research are frequently recorded as a part of regular manufacturing overhead, being regarded as a continuing charge of keeping abreast of current technological advance. When research is directed to certain particular improvements, it is appropriate to capitalize expenditures identified with such projects. When these activities are successful, costs as accumulated can be assigned to future periods that receive the benefits of such outlays. Expenditures on projects that are patentable are summarized and reported as patents; expenditures on projects that are not patentable but that offer exclusive benefits may be summarized and reported as formulas and special or secret processes. When activities directed to certain improvements prove unsuccessful, costs previously capitalized should be

written off as a loss. Formulas and special processes are generally written off over a relatively short period because any advantages offered through their possession may be terminated at any time through their discovery by others.

Some companies follow the practice of charging all costs of research to periodic revenue, even when such research results in the development of valuable rights. However, when such practice is followed, the balance sheet may fail to disclose special processes and improvements of considerable value that will make significant contribution to future business success; the income statement fails to show charges relating to past developments, and in turn may be burdened by charges that are applicable to future periods. It may be observed that for federal income tax purposes the taxpayer may elect to report expenditures for research and development either as (1) expenses that are deductible in the year paid or incurred, or (2) deferred costs to be deducted over a period of 60 months or more.

**GOODWILL**     Goodwill, in a general sense, is considered to arise from all of the special advantages connected with a going concern, such as its good name, capable staff and personnel, high financial standing, reputation for superior products and customer services, and favorable location. From an accounting point of view, goodwill is the ability of a business to realize above-normal profits as a result of these factors. By "above-normal profits" is meant a rate of return on a particular investment that is greater than that ordinarily necessary to attract investors to that type of business.

**CALCULATION OF GOODWILL**     Goodwill is recorded on the books only when it is acquired by purchase or otherwise established through a business transaction. The latter condition includes its recognition on the books in connection with a merger or a reorganization of a corporation, a purchase or a partial purchase of a business, or a change in the membership of a partnership. Recognition only under such circumstances assures an objective approach to the valuation of goodwill. To permit the recognition of goodwill on the basis of judgment and estimates by owners and other interested parties would open the doors to all manner of abuse and misrepresentation. Goodwill reported on the balance sheet arises from a purchase or a contractual arrangement calling for its recognition; above-normal earnings can be pointed to by management and owners as evidence of the existence of additional goodwill that has not found expression in the accounts.

In the purchase of a going business, past earnings ordinarily offer the best basis upon which to develop a specific value for goodwill. It is not these past earnings, however, but similar future earnings that are being purchased. The following points require special attention and analysis in the development of a value for goodwill:

(1) Selection of the earnings periods to be used as a basis for analysis and projection.

(2) Review of past earnings measurement procedures and the restatement of operating data when necessary.

(3) Analysis of the trend and the uniformity of past earnings.

(4) Estimate of the level of future earnings.

(5) Determination of the appropriate rate of return on the investment.

(6) Valuation of business assets other than goodwill.

(7) Use of estimated future earnings and required earnings rates in arriving at a value for goodwill.

In considering past earnings as a basis for projection into the future, reference should be made to earnings most recently experienced. Furthermore, a sufficient number of periods should be included in the analysis so that a fully representative measurement of business performance is available.

Extraordinary and nonrecurring gains and losses that cannot be considered a part of normal activities are usually excluded from past operating results. Examples of such items include gains and losses from the sale of plant and equipment or investments, losses from fire or theft, and gains and losses from other unusual sources.

The ordinary or normal earnings should be analyzed to determine their trend and uniformity. If earnings over a period of years show a tendency to decrease, an explanation should be sought, since this may indicate a continuing shrinkage in future earnings. There may be greater confidence in future possible earnings when earnings of the past have been relatively uniform rather than widely fluctuating.

The past normal earnings are used as a basis for estimating the earnings of the future. Business conditions, the business cycle, sources of supply, demand for the company's products or services, price structures, competition, and other significant factors must be studied in developing data that will make it possible to convert past earnings into estimated future earnings.

The normal earnings rate that is used for the capitalization of income in determining goodwill depends upon such factors as business and economic conditions at the time of purchase, the type of business, competitive factors, risks involved, and entreprenuerial abilities required in assuming control.

Before calculating goodwill, the value of the net assets other than goodwill should be determined. Inventories and securities should be restated in terms of current market values. Receivables should be stated at realizable values. Plant and equipment items may require special appraisals in arriving at their present replacement or reproduction values. Care will be necessary to determine that liabilities are fully recognized. Assets at their current fair market values, less the liabilities that are taken over, provide the net assets total to be acquired, and these data, together with estimated future earnings, are used in arriving at a purchase price for the business.

The actual determination of the price to be paid for goodwill usually results from bargaining and compromises between the parties concerned. The price agreed upon for goodwill is the amount that is recorded on the buyer's books. Such agreement, however, requires some basis from which to start bargaining. Several methods of arriving at a goodwill figure are illustrated below. Assume the following information for Company A:

Net earnings after elimination of extraordinary and nonrecurring items:

| | |
|---|---|
| 1954 | $140,000 |
| 1955 | 90,000 |
| 1956 | 110,000 |
| 1957 | 85,000 |
| 1958 | 115,000 |
| Total | $540,000 |

Average annual earnings ($540,000 ÷ 5), $108,000.

Estimated annual future earnings, $100,000.

Net assets as appraised on January 1, 1959, before recognizing goodwill, $1,000,000. (Land, buildings, equipment, inventories, receivables, $1,200,000; liabilities to be assumed by purchaser, $200,000.)

The average annual earnings figure of $108,000 for the five-year period 1954-58 was used in arriving at an estimate of the probable future annual earnings. It is assumed that an analysis of the assembled information by the prospective purchaser suggests that future earnings may be conservatively estimated at $100,000 a year.

(1) *Capitalization of Average Net Earnings.* The amount to be paid for a business may be determined by capitalizing expected future earnings at a rate that represents the required return on the investment.[1] The difference between the amount to be paid for the properties thus obtained and their appraised value may be considered the price of

---

[1]Capitalization of earnings as used here means the calculation of a principal value that will offer the stated earnings in terms of the required yield.

goodwill. In the example, if a return of 8% is required on the investment and earnings are estimated at $100,000 a year, a valuation of $1,250,000 is obtained ($100,000÷.08). Since net assets, before goodwill, are valued at $1,000,000, the difference between this amount and the price paid, $1,250,000, or $250,000, is the cost assigned to goodwill. If a 10% return were required, the business would be valued at $1,000,000 and there would be no goodwill on the purchase.

(2) *Capitalization of Average Excess Earnings.* The foregoing method considered only earnings in the calculation of the amount to be paid for the business. It would seem more reasonable, however, to consider the net assets to be transferred, as well as the earnings to accompany these assets, in the determination of the price to be paid. To illustrate, assume the following facts:

|  | COMPANY A | COMPANY B |
|---|---|---|
| Estimated annual future earnings | $ 100,000 | $100,000 |
| Net assets as appraised | 1,000,000 | 500,000 |

If the estimated earnings are capitalized at 8%, the value of each company is found to be $1,250,000. The goodwill for Company A is then $250,000, and for Company B, $750,000 as shown:

|  | COMPANY A | COMPANY B |
|---|---|---|
| Total value (earnings capitalized at 8%) | $1,250,000 | $1,250,000 |
| Deduct net assets as appraised | 1,000,000 | 500,000 |
| Goodwill | $ 250,000 | $ 750,000 |

The foregoing calculations ignore the fact that the appraised value of the net assets identified with Company A exceeds that of Company B. Company A, whose earnings of $100,000 are accompanied by properties valued at $1,000,000, would certainly command a higher price than Company B, whose earnings of $100,000 are accompanied by properties valued at only $500,000.

Satisfactory recognition of both earnings and asset contributions is generally effected by requiring a fair return on properties at their appraised values and capitalizing any estimated future earnings in excess of such fair return at a higher rate in support of a goodwill valuation. To illustrate, assume in the foregoing cases that 8% is considered a normal return on net assets acquired and that excess earnings are capitalized at 20% in determining the amount to be paid for goodwill. Use of a higher capitalization rate on the purchase of goodwill is justified on the grounds of the uncertainty and fluctuations in the value of this asset, the inability to divorce this asset from the business as a whole for sales purposes, and the probability of its shrinkage or total loss in the event of subsequent business sale or liquidation. Amounts to be paid for Companies A and B on the above basis are calculated as follows:

|  | COMPANY A | COMPANY B |
|---|---|---|
| Estimated annual earnings: | $ 100,000 | $ 100,000 |
| Co. A—normal return at 8% on net assets of $1,000,000.................. | 80,000 | |
| Co B—normal return at 8% on net assets of $500,000................... | | 40,000 |
| Excess annual earnings............... | $ 20,000 | $ 60,000 |
| Value of net assets offering return of 8% | $1,000,000 | $ 500,000 |
| Value of goodwill: | | |
| Co. A — excess annual earnings of $20,000 capitalized at 20%........... | 100,000 | |
| Co. B — excess annual earnings of $60,000 capitalized at 20%.......... | | 300,000 |
| Total asset valuation including goodwill.. | $1,100,000 | $ 800,000 |

Assuming that Company A is acquired for cash of $1,100,000, individual assets would be recorded on the books of the buyer at the appraised values, goodwill would be recorded at $100,000, liability accounts would be credited for the obligations assumed, and cash would be credited for the amount paid. Goodwill, having been acquired by purchase, is properly reported as an intangible asset on the balance sheet of the purchaser.

One frequently finds that payment for excess earnings is stated in terms of "years' purchase" rather than in terms of capitalization at a certain interest rate. Capitalization of average excess earnings at 20% is the same as payment for five years' excess earnings (1.00 ÷ .20, or 5); capitalization of average excess earnings at 25% is the same as payment for four years' excess earnings (1.00 ÷ .25, or 4); etc.

When a lump sum amount is paid for a business in the absence of an analysis of respective asset acquisitions as illustrated, net assets other than goodwill still require appraisal, and the difference between such net assets and the purchase price is recognized as goodwill. Failure to recognize the payment for goodwill separately and the identification of such cost with depreciable assets will result in the overvaluation of the latter assets and in the misstatement of periodic depreciation and net earnings. Failure to distinguish satisfactorily between costs of intangibles with a limited life and subject to amortization and those with an unlimited life will result in similar misstatements of financial position and earnings.

When capital stock is issued in exchange for a business, the value of the stock determines the consideration that is paid for the assets. Care must be exercised so that what in effect represents a discount on the stock is not reported as goodwill. For example, assume that 10,000 shares of common stock, par $10, but selling on the market at $7\frac{1}{2}$, are exchanged for assets valued at $60,000 before recognition of goodwill. The purchase should be recorded as follows:

| | | |
|---|---|---|
| Assets................................... | 60,000 | |
| Goodwill................................. | 15,000 | |
| Discount on Common Stock.................. | 25,000 | |
| Common Stock, $10 par..................... | | 100,000 |

**GOODWILL ADJUSTMENT AFTER ACQUISITION** It has been maintained that when goodwill is acquired after sound and conservative determination and when its life is not limited, it should continue to be carried at cost indefinitely. This position is supported on the grounds that goodwill has an indeterminate life. Management, in the attempt to continue favorable operations, will maintain the value existing in the acquired goodwill. The intangible values originally obtained are considered to be perpetuated or supplanted by new business advantages.

It would seem that a stronger case can be made for the position of maintaining goodwill at original cost only as long as the advantages supporting its original recognition are continuing. With changes that suggest the impairment or the disappearance of the advantages represented by goodwill, adjustments in this balance are just as appropriate as those made in the case of other assets whose capacities to contribute to the production of future revenue have become limited or have disappeared. In applying the foregoing standard, a reduction in goodwill should be recognized as an extraordinary charge except when such charge is considered to relate to the revenue of the current period.

In some instances goodwill may be considered to have a measurable life. Under such circumstances, the amortization of goodwill is just as appropriate as the amortization of other limited-life intangibles. For example, assume that $100,000 is paid for goodwill on the purchase of a business whose lease expires in ten years. If it is reasonable to assume that the business will not continue beyond the life of the lease, benefits identified with goodwill are limited to a ten-year period, and the cost of the intangible is properly charged to revenues over this period. When goodwill is calculated as the discounted present value of a certain number of years' excess profits on the theory that profits will tend to decline as a result of competition, changes in the business cycle, and the exhaustion of other goodwill factors, an allocation of the cost of goodwill to operations on some systematic basis during its estimated period of usefulness may also be supported.

Although there is theoretical support for maintaining goodwill on the records indefinitely when its value remains unimpaired, the practice of writing off this intangible is widespread. Goodwill is frequently reduced periodically or written off in total upon its acquisition or at some later date. When goodwill, or any other intangible, is arbitrarily written off before the end of its useful life, asset and capital balances are misstated and the ratio of earnings to invested capital is distorted. Earnings thus appear to be more favorable than is actually the case as a result of this "conservative" practice.

A charge for the amortization or the write-off of goodwill is not allowed in calculating income for income tax purposes. Goodwill, for tax purposes, is regarded as an asset of permanent character. However, upon the sale or termination of a business, a deduction would be allowed for the portion of the asset not realized.

Goodwill is frequently listed on published balance sheets at one dollar. The explanation may be either of the following: (1) a company that has built up its own goodwill may have brought it on the books at this value in order to call the reader's attention to its existence without inflating the asset and capital sections of the statement; (2) a company that has purchased goodwill may have arbitrarily written it down to this nominal figure. Similar practices are frequently encountered with respect to patents, trade-marks, copyrights, and other intangibles.

**ORGANIZATION COSTS**     When a corporation is formed, certain expenditures, such as those for legal fees, promotional expenses, stock certificate costs, underwriting fees, taxes, and incorporation fees, are incurred. Such expenditures may be considered to provide benefits that accrue to more than just the first fiscal period. This would support the capitalization of these items. Further, the recognition of such expenditures as expenses at time of organization would commit a corporation to a deficit before it actually began normal activities. This factor, too, encourages the practice of capitalizing initial costs of organization.

Expenditures relating to organization may actually be considered to benefit the corporation during its entire life. Thus, when the life of a company is not limited, there is support for carrying costs as an intangible asset permanently. On the other hand, costs of organization, in the absence of a disposal value, must be applied to revenue before the ultimate net income emerging from business activities is determinable. This approach has led to the widespread practice of writing off the asset, in many instances within a relatively short period such as three to five years from the date of corporate organization. Such cost amortization, when not assignable to current operations, should be reported as an extraordinary charge.

It is sometimes suggested that operating losses of the first few years should be capitalized as organization costs or as goodwill. It is argued that such losses cannot be avoided in the early years when the business is being developed, and hence it is reasonable that later years should absorb these initial losses. Although losses may be inevitable, to report these losses as intangibles will result in the overstatement of assets and capital. Such practice cannot be supported.

Prior to 1954, for income tax purposes organization costs of a corporation could not be written off unless the life of a corporation was limited by its charter or articles of incorporation. Organization costs for a company with an indeterminate life would be recognized as a deductible item, then, only in the last year of the company's life. Under the Revenue Act of 1954, however, all corporations may elect to amortize their organization costs. But such election applies only to organization costs incurred before the end of the taxable year in which the corporation began business. Furthermore, costs must be amortized over a period of not less than 60 months beginning with the month in which the company began business. Amortization is not permitted for costs arising from corporate reorganizations or recapitalizations.

**LEASEHOLDS AND LEASEHOLD IMPROVE-MENTS**    Leaseholds are personal property interests representing rights to the use of land or realty for a specified term. These rights are granted by property owners in consideration of specified rents through terms of a tenure contract called a *lease*. The terms of the lease and the use of the property by the lessee usually determine the accounting procedures to be followed in connection with the lease. If the property is used by the lessee in his regular operations and if rentals under the lease are paid periodically when due, the leasehold need not appear on the lessee's books. Periodic rentals under the lease are charged by the lessee to operating expense for the period covered by each installment.

Recent years have witnessed a sharp growth in *sale and lease-back* arrangements. The following steps are typical under such arrangements: a party acquires land and constructs buildings for his own particular use; the owner then sells the property to a party able to finance its acquisition and simultaneously leases it back from the new owner; occupancy and use of the property are continued without interruption. Such arrangements are entered into when they offer both investor and lessee tax and financial advantages that are not found in alternative arrangements for the construction and use of facilities.

While the possession of a lease with periodic rentals may call for the recognition of neither asset nor liability balances, it nevertheless confers special advantages and creates certain obligations during its lifetime. When such factors are considered of particular significance, whether favorable or unfavorable, they must be brought to the attention of the reader of the financial statements. Disclosure under such circumstances should be made by appropriate note. The American Institute Committee on Accounting Procedure recommends the following disclosures when obligations under long-term leases are material:

(a) disclosure should be made in financial statements or in notes thereto of:
   (1) the amounts of annual rentals to be paid under such leases with some indication of the periods for which they are payable and
   (2) any other important obligation assumed or guarantee made in connection therewith;
(b) the above information should be given not only in the year in which the transaction originates but also as long thereafter as the amounts involved are material; and
(c) in addition, in the year in which the transaction originates, there should be disclosure of the principal details of any important sale-and-lease transaction.[1]

There are certain circumstances under which a leasehold may call for recognition on the books. These situations include the following:

(1) The lessee may be required to pay a certain lump sum amount as advance rental or bonus at the time the lease is first negotiated. Such an amount is properly recognized as an asset that is to be assigned to the periods covered by the advance payment. Such assignment is accomplished on the books by periodic charges to expense and credits to the asset.

(2) The lessee may sublease the property to another party at a rental in excess of that payable under the original lease. If the payment of the rental under the sublease is adequately secured both by the earning power of the sublessee and by improvements made by the sublessee, the original lessee may show the leasehold on his books. The value at which the leasehold may be carried is the discounted value of the excess rentals receivable under the sublease. Under these circumstances the value of the leasehold must be amortized in some reasonable manner over the period covered by the sublease. This procedure may be particularly appropriate when a leasehold is to serve as the basis for the extension of credit.

---

[1] *Accounting Research Bulletin No. 43*, "Restatement and Revision of Accounting Research Bulletins," 1953 (New York: American Institute of Certified Public Accountants), p. 126. It may be observed that the Securities and Exchange Commission requires similar disclosures on statements that are filed with it.

Some authorities have suggested that no more than possession of a lease calls for entries in the accounts. The present value of all future rents, it is suggested, should be calculated, and this value used in setting up both an asset representing the right to use leased property and a liability representing the obligation arising from such right. Present practice, however, shows strong preference for lease disclosure by parenthetical remark and note rather than by account presentation.

Leasehold improvements arise when property has been leased and additions, improvements, or alterations are made by the lessee. Such improvements are usually identified with the original property and accrue to the owner at the expiration of the lease. The lessee, however, enjoys the use of such improvements throughout the period of the lease. Under such circumstances, improvement costs are appropriately recorded by the lessee as leasehold improvements and are regarded as an intangible asset. Improvement costs are written off to operations over the life of the benefits.

Ordinarily, the amortization of leasehold improvements is based on time factors. Since leasehold improvements revert to the lessor upon termination of the lease, the useful life of the improvements to the lessee is limited to that of the lease and hence their costs should be amortized over the lease period. For example, assume that an improvement estimated to have a 25-year life is completed when a lease has only 20 years more to run. Since the property will revert to the lessor, the improvement has only a 20-year useful life to the lessee. If the improvement has a life that is shorter than the lease, both lease and lease improvement costs are spread over their own respective life periods. When leaseholds include renewal options but lease extension is uncertain, improvements should normally be amortized over the life of the original lease period. However, when renewal options carry significant advantages and extension is highly probable, it would be appropriate to spread costs over the extended period. Failure to continue occupancy for the original term of the lease calls for the write-off as a loss of the unamortized leasehold balance.

It is sometimes provided that the lessor, upon the termination of the lease, shall pay a certain amount for leasehold improvements turned over to him. The amount to be paid may be an arbitrary price agreed upon beforehand, the depreciated book value of the property, or the appraised value of the property at time of transfer. When such a payment is involved, the amount to be charged to operations by the lessee is the cost of the improvements less the estimated amount recoverable upon termination of the lease.

In certain instances a lease arrangement may represent, in effect, an installment purchase of property. This would be the case, for example, when property is subject to purchase for a nominal sum upon conclusion of the lease, or when it is provided that periodic rentals may be applied to a purchase price for the leased property. While it may be argued that in the absence of a purchase there is no need to report the property item or an obligation for such property, the American Institute Committee on Accounting Procedure is of the opinion "that the facts relating to all such leases should be carefully considered and that, where it is clearly evident that the transaction involved is in substance a purchase, the 'leased' property should be included among the assets of the lessee with suitable accounting for the corresponding liabilities and for the related charges in the income statement."[1]

**DEFERRED COSTS** Noncurrent assets in the form of investments, plant and equipment, and intangibles have already been described. A fourth subdivision of noncurrent assets is found in the deferred costs group. This group consists of certain other expenditures for services or benefits that are allocable to the income of a number of fiscal periods.

The cost of issuing bonds, including printing, underwriting, and promotion fees, may be capitalized as a deferred cost and written off over the life of the bond issue. When bonds of a corporation are issued at less than face value, the bond discount is frequently combined with the costs of issuing bonds and included among the deferred costs.

Costs of extensive repairs, moving, and rearrangement of existing machinery and equipment are sometimes deferred and charged to the operations of several periods. Such procedure is not objectionable if future periods benefit from the expenditures and full disclosure is made on the balance sheet. When such costs are capitalized, they should be amortized over a reasonably short period in view of the possibility of further improvements and rearrangements.

It is sometimes suggested that expenditures relating to an unusually extensive advertising campaign should be capitalized and written off during subsequent periods, since later periods continue to benefit from such expenditures. However, since the benefits of advertising may prove short-lived and since similar expenditures may be required in following years to perpetuate the benefits acquired through advertising, it is advisable to charge all such expenditures to current revenue.

Expenditures for research, development, and improvement may be recorded as deferred costs when they are related to future revenues

[1] *Ibid.*, p. 127.

but are not considered properly chargeable to plant and equipment or intangibles. In reporting such balances among deferred costs, a full description of the nature of the items should be provided together with explanatory notes in support of the policy of deferral. In the event of any doubt as to future benefit and allocability, such expenditures should be charged to current operations. Exploration and development costs related to the preparation of areas with natural resources for commercial use are also properly recorded as deferred costs. Losses, such as may arise from operations of early years, from catastrophes, or from other extraordinary sources, should not be deferred.

**INTANGIBLES AND DEFERRED COSTS ON THE BALANCE SHEET**    When a single long-term asset classification is given on the balance sheet, tangible and intangible subheadings should be provided and summaries for each group developed. When separate classifications are given for tangible and intangible assets, the intangible classification usually follows the tangible classification. Each intangible should be listed separately. If an intangible has been acquired for a consideration other than cash, special disclosure should be made stating the properties or securities exchanged and the data used in arriving at the original cost assigned to the intangible. Disclosure should also be made of the valuation procedures that are employed for intangibles subsequent to their acquisition.

When a deferred costs classification is provided on the balance sheet, it usually follows the intangibles classification. Deferred costs are normally presented in a manner similar to that employed for intangibles. Each deferred item should be separately reported. Detail should be made available relative to the original valuation of the asset together with the procedure that is followed in assigning this value to periodic revenue when these factors may be of significance.

Intangible and deferred cost classifications as they might appear on the balance sheet follow:

Intangibles:

| | | |
|---|---:|---:|
| Goodwill, at original purchase cost.............. | $221,000 | |
| Licenses, at costs less amortization based on estimated legal or useful lives..................... | 16,300 | |
| Patents, acquired by the issue of 150,000 shares of common stock of the company with a par and market value of $1.00 per share and reported at such value, less amortization based on an estimated useful life of 10 years......................... | 107,500 | $344,800 |

Deferred Costs:

| | | |
|---|---:|---:|
| Bond issue costs............................. | | 5,200 |

## QUESTIONS

**1.** (a) List three intangibles that require no cost amortization under normal conditions. Under what circumstances should such balances be written off, and what accounting procedure should then be followed? (b) List three intangibles that require amortization under normal conditions. Indicate circumstances that might serve to accelerate the amortization process and state the accounting procedures to be followed in such cases.

**2.** State under what circumstances intangible cost is properly charged to (a) operating expense, (b) extraordinary charges, (c) retained earnings.

**3.** Harmon Products, Inc. reports plant, equipment, and intangibles on the balance sheet at $1. The president of the company insists that accounts should be maintained on a conservative basis; hence he has authorized write-downs to the nominal figure. Comment on this practice.

**4.** (a) What items enter into the cost of a patent developed by a business? (b) What factors should be considered in establishing a schedule for amortization of patent costs?

**5.** Master Mechanics, Inc. maintains a shop for experimental work of various kinds. Costs of operating the shop are approximately $100,000 annually. Occasionally valuable patents are developed for factory use as a result of shop operations. What accounting treatment would you recommend for costs within this department?

**6.** (a) Under what conditions may goodwill be reported as an asset? (b) The Barker Company engages in a widespread advertising campaign on behalf of new products, charging above-normal expenditures to goodwill. Do you approve?

**7.** The president of the Baker Company authorizes goodwill of $50,000 to be established on the books in view of very satisfactory profits reported during the past ten years. Comment on this practice.

**8.** What factors would one look for to support the existence of goodwill in making the purchase of a business?

**9.** Describe the procedure to be followed in arriving at a company's excess annual earnings in calculating the amount to be paid for goodwill.

**10.** Give two methods for arriving at a goodwill valuation, using estimated future business earnings as a basis for such calculations.

**11.** Wells, Inc. has valuable patent rights that are being amortized over their legal lives. The president of the company feels that such patents are contributing substantially to company goodwill and recommends that patent amortization be capitalized as company goodwill. What is your reaction to this proposal?

**12.** (a) What are the principal arguments in favor of retaining goodwill on the books at cost? (b) What arguments can be raised in favor of writing off goodwill?

**13.** (a) Define (1) leasehold, (2) leasehold improvements. (b) What factors need to be considered in the amortization of costs identified with these intangibles?

**14.** (a) What items are normally considered to compose the organization costs of a company? (b) Would you approve the inclusion of the following items: (1) common stock discount; (2) first-year advertising costs; (3) first-year loss from operations?

**15.** Would you recommend that organization costs be written off? Give reasons for your answer.

**16.** The Wilson Co. acquires without cost a franchise considered to be of great value. How would you recommend that the intangible be reported on the balance sheet?

**17.** Distinguish between prepaid expenses and deferred costs. Give three examples of each.

**18.** How would you recommend that the cost of machinery rearrangement be treated in the accounts?

## EXERCISES

**1.** The Webb Co. develops patents at a cost of $8,500, and patent rights are granted at the beginning of 1953. It is assumed that the patents will be useful during their full legal life. At the beginning of 1955, the company pays $5,000 in successfully prosecuting an attempted infringement of these patent rights. At the beginning of 1958, $15,000 is paid for the acquisition of patents that could make its own patents worthless; the patents acquired have a remaining life of 15 years but will not be used. How should each of the foregoing costs be recorded? What is the patent cost amortization for the years 1953, 1955, and 1958?

**2.** The Honeywell Mfg. Co. was incorporated on January 1, 1958. In reviewing the accounts in 1959 you find that the account Organization Costs appears as follows:

ORGANIZATION COSTS

| | DEBIT | CREDIT | BALANCE |
|---|---|---|---|
| Discount on common stock issued.......... | 45,500 | | 45,500 |
| Incorporation fees....................... | 1,250 | | 46,750 |
| Legal fees relative to organization......... | 12,000 | | 58,750 |
| Stock certificate cost.................... | 3,750 | | 62,500 |
| Cost of rehabilitating building acquired at beginning of 1958 and estimated to have a remaining life of 10 years............... | 36,000 | | 98,500 |
| Cost of leasing adjoining vacant lot for parking purposes for 10 years .............. | 6,500 | | 105,000 |
| Advertising campaign expenditures to promote company products................. | 24,000 | | 129,000 |
| Amortization of organization costs for 1958 (20% of balance of organization cost, per board of directors' resolution)........... | | 25,800 | 103,200 |
| Net loss for 1958....................... | 28,500 | | 131,700 |

Give the entry or entries required to correct the account.

**3.** In analyzing past profits in an attempt to measure goodwill, net earnings of $200,000 are reported for 1958 after charges and credits for the items listed below. Plant and equipment are appraised at 50% above cost for purposes of the sale.

| | |
|---|---|
| Depreciation of plant and equipment | $20,000 |
| Year-end bonus to president of company | 15,000 |
| Gain on sale of securities | 20,000 |
| Gain from revaluation of marketable securities | 15,000 |
| Write-down of goodwill | 45,000 |
| Amortization of patents and copyrights | 10,000 |

What is the "normal" earnings figure for purposes of your calculations?

**4.** The profits of the Southern Sales Company are stated as follows:

| | | | |
|---|---|---|---|
| 1954 | $40,000 | 1957 | $50,000 |
| 1955 | 45,000 | 1958 | 55,000 |
| 1956 | 30,000 | | |

Tangible net assets of this company are appraised at $500,000. This business is to be acquired by the Universal Sales Corporation. What amount shall be paid for goodwill if:

(a) 8% is assumed to be a normal rate of return on net tangible assets, average excess profits for the last 5 years to be capitalized at 20%?

(b) 6% is assumed to be a normal rate of return on net tangible assets, payment to be made for average excess profits for 4 years?

**5.** The appraised value of net assets of the Melcombe Co. on December 31, 1958, was $60,000. Average profits for the past 5 years after elimination of extraordinary gains and losses were $10,000. Calculate the amount to be paid for goodwill under each of the following assumptions:

(a) Earnings are capitalized at 12½% in arriving at the business worth.

(b) A return of 8% is considered normal on net assets at their appraised value; excess earnings are to be capitalized at 12½% in arriving at the value of goodwill.

(c) A return of 10% is considered normal on net assets at their appraised value; goodwill is to be valued at 4 years' excess earnings.

**6.** The Northlake Development Co. constructs a building at a cost of $150,000, with an estimated life of 50 years, on property leased for a 30-year period at an annual rental of $5,000. (a) What are the entries in connection with the lease and the building depreciation for the first year? (b) What entries would be made at the end of the twentieth year, assuming that the lessee and the lessor agree to cancel the original lease at this time. (c) What entries would be made at the beginning of the twenty-first year, assuming that the lessee and the lessor agree to the extension of the original lease for 10 years beyond its original life? (d) What entries would be made after termination of the original lease, assuming that the lessee and the lessor enter into a new lease for 30 years?

## PROBLEMS

**18-1.** The Steel Product Co. spent $25,500 in developing a patent, the rights being granted January 10, 1950. The patent had an estimated useful life of 10 years. At the beginning of 1954 the Steel Product Co. spent $3,300 in successfully prosecuting an attempted infringement of these rights. At the beginning of 1955, the company purchased for $7,500 a patent which was expected to prolong the life of its original patent by 5 years. On July 1, 1958 a competing company obtained rights to a patent which made the Steel Product Co.'s patent obsolete.

*Instructions:* Give all of the entries that would be made relative to patents for the period 1950–1958, including entries that record patent costs, annual patent amortization, and ultimate patent obsolescence. (Assume that the company's fiscal period is the calendar year.)

**18-2.** In your audit of the books of Chance, Ltd. for the year ending September 30, 1958, you found the following items in connection with the company's patents account.

(a) The company had spent $68,000 during its fiscal year ended September 30, 1957 for research and development costs and charged this amount to its patents account. Your review of the company's special cost records indicated the company had spent a total of $74,800 for the research and development of its patents, of which $6,800 were spent in its fiscal year ended September 30, 1956 and had been charged to expense.

(b) The patents were issued on April 1, 1957. Legal expenses in connection with the issuance of the patents amounting to $13,600 were charged to legal and professional fees.

(c) The company paid a retainer of $6,000 on October 5, 1957, for legal services in connection with an infringement suit against Chance, Ltd. This amount was charged to Deferred Costs.

(d) A letter dated November 15, 1958, from the company's attorneys in reply to your inquiry as to liabilities of the company existing at September 30, 1958, indicated that a settlement of the infringement suit had been arranged. The other party had agreed to drop the suit and to release the company from all future liabilities for $20,000. Additional fees and expenses due to the attorneys amounted to $400 as indicated in their letter.

(e) The balance of the patents account on September 30, 1958, was $64,000. No amortization had been recognized on the patents for the fiscal year ended September 30, 1958.

*Instructions:* (1) From the above information prepare correcting journal entries for the company's books as of September 30, 1958.

(2) Give the entry to record amortization on patents for the year ended September 30, 1958, assuming a life for patents of 17 years from the date of their issuance.

**18-3.** The Belmont Corporation assembles the following data relative to the Foster Co. in determining the amount to be paid for the net assets and goodwill of the latter company:

| | |
|---|---|
| Assets at appraised value (before goodwill).............. | $130,000 |
| Liabilities......................................... | 45,000 |
| Capital............................................ | $ 85,000 |

Net earnings (after elimination of extraordinary items):

| | |
|---|---:|
| 1954........................ | $10,000 |
| 1955........................ | 11,500 |
| 1956........................ | 15,000 |
| 1957........................ | 12,500 |
| 1958........................ | 13,500 |
| | $62,500 |

*Instructions:* Calculate the amount to be paid for goodwill under each of the following assumptions:

(1) Average earnings are capitalized at 12% in arriving at the business worth.

(2) A return of 10% is considered normal on net assets at appraised value; goodwill is valued at 5 years' excess earnings.

(3) A return of 8% is considered normal on net assets at appraised value; excess earnings are to be capitalized at 15%.

(4) Goodwill is valued at the sum of the profits of the last 3 years in excess of a 10% annual yield on net assets. (Assume that net assets are the same for the 3-year period.)

18-4. The Beverly Co. assembles the following information relative to the Drake Corporation in considering the purchase of the assets of the latter company:

### DRAKE CORPORATION
#### BALANCE SHEET
#### DECEMBER 31, 1958

| | Per Corporation's Books | As Adjusted by Appraisal and Audit |
|---|---:|---:|
| **ASSETS** | | |
| Current assets........................ | 105,000 | 97,000 |
| Investments........................ | 60,000 | 35,000 |
| Plant and equipment.................. | 400,000 | 375,000 |
| Goodwill........................... | 100,000 | 100,000 |
| | 665,000 | 607,000 |
| **LIABILITIES AND CAPITAL** | | |
| Current liabilities.................... | 40,000 | 40,000 |
| Long-term debt...................... | 250,000 | 250,000 |
| Capital stock....................... | 200,000 | 200,000 |
| Retained earnings.................... | 175,000 | 117,000 |
| | 665,000 | 607,000 |

ANALYSIS OF RETAINED EARNINGS

| | Per Corporation's Books | As Adjusted by Appraisal and Audit |
|---|---|---|
| Retained earnings, January 1, 1956........ | 122,180 | 73,600 |
| Loss on sale of investments, 1956......... | 4,380 | 6,600 |
| | 117,800 | 67,000 |
| Net income, 1956..................... | 33,000 | 26,000 |
| | 150,800 | 93,000 |
| Dividends, 1956...................... | 12,000 | 12,000 |
| | 138,800 | 81,000 |
| Net income, 1957 ..................... | 27,500 | 29,800 |
| | 166,300 | 110,800 |
| Dividends, 1957...................... | 12,000 | 12,000 |
| | 154,300 | 98,800 |
| Net income, 1958 .................... | 32,700 | 30,200 |
| | 187,000 | 129,000 |
| Dividends, 1958...................... | 12,000 | 12,000 |
| | 175,000 | 117,000 |

*Instructions:* (1) Calculate the amount to be paid for goodwill to the nearest $100, assuming that (a) earnings of the future are expected to be the same as average normal earnings of the past 3 years, and (b) 6% is accepted as a reasonable return on net assets other than goodwill as of December 31, 1958, and average earnings in excess of 6% are capitalized at 15% in determining goodwill.

(2) Give the entry on the books of the Beverly Co., assuming purchase of the assets of the Drake Corporation and assumption of their liabilities on the basis as indicated in (1). Cash is paid for net assets acquired.

**18-5.** The following data are assembled for the Eastern Bakers, Inc. and the Superior Baking Co. as of July 1, 1958, in connection with a proposed merger of the two companies:

| | Eastern Bakers, Inc. | Superior Baking Co. |
|---|---|---|
| Net assets other than goodwill per books as of July 1, 1958............................. | $223,750 | $210,000 |
| Average net earnings per books, July 1, 1953 — June 30, 1958........................... | 33,000 | 21,500 |

It is agreed that the values of the respective assets contributed, including the intangible asset goodwill, are to be determined on the following basis: 10% is to be considered a reasonable return on the net assets other than goodwill; average earnings for the period 1953–1958 in excess of 10% of the assets of July 1, 1958, are to be capitalized at 25% in determining goodwill. However, the following adjustments are to be considered before determining the respective values:

(1) Buildings of the Eastern Bakers, Inc. are estimated to be worth $31,250 more than book value. Buildings have a remaining life of 25 years.

(2) The Superior Baking Co. wrote off organization costs of $13,500 against income in 1955.

(3) The Superior Baking Co. included in earnings a loss of $1,500 resulting from a fire in 1956 and a gain of $3,150 on the acquisition and retirement of bonds in 1957 at less than the book value of the liability.

*Instructions:* Prepare a statement to show for each party to the merger the determination of the amounts to be paid for (1) net assets other than goodwill and (2) goodwill.

**18-6.** Net income and capital balances for a 5-year period for Western Hotels, Inc. follow:

| YEAR | NET INCOME | CAPITAL AT END OF YEAR |
|------|------------|------------------------|
| 1954 | $ 50,000 | $390,000 |
| 1955 | 68,000 | 405,000 |
| 1956 | 85,000 | 444,000 |
| 1957 | 89,000 | 486,000 |
| 1958 | 91,000 | 511,000 |

The Oceanside Resorts Co. agrees to purchase Western Hotels, Inc. and makes cash payment for the net assets on the following basis:

6% is considered a normal return on hotel investments.

Payment for goodwill is to be calculated by capitalizing at 20% the average annual earnings that are in excess of 6% of average annual capitals.

*Instructions:* Give the entry that would be made on the books of the Oceanside Resorts Co. to record the acquisition of the net assets including goodwill of Western Hotels, Inc.

**18-7.** Elbon & Company, lessees, leases a building which has an estimated remaining life of twenty years. The lease runs for fifty years without renewal option. The terms call for $20,000 annual rental and stipulate that taxes, insurance, maintenance, and repairs, as well as the cost of any remodeling, new construction, and so forth, shall be borne by the lessees.

At the end of the eighteenth year Elbon & Company sells the lease to Cassel & Company for $32,000. The building is torn down at the end of the twentieth year as originally estimated, and Cassel & Company erects a new structure at a cost of $210,000. The new structure has an estimated life of forty years.

The rental income from the old building is $30,000 and from the new building $40,000 a year. Taxes, insurance, and repairs aggregate $6,500 a year for the old and $7,500 a year for the new building.

*Instructions:* (1) Compute the aggregate net profit (before deducting federal income taxes) made by Cassel & Company during their ownership of the lease.

(2) Prepare operating statements for the nineteenth and for the twenty-fifth years of the lease.

(A.I.C.P.A. adapted)

**18-8.** As of January 1, 1949, Henry M. Garfield leased for 10 years a building to be used as a retail store. His lease provided that annual rent payment was to be based on gross sales. On sales up to $150,000 per year the rate was to be 3%. On any sales in excess of $150,000 per year, the rate was to be 2%. However, during the first 5 years of the term of the lease, the annual rental was to be a minimum of $4,000 per year, after which the minimum was to be increased by 12½%.

The lease further provided that if, in any one year, the rent based on sales did not equal the minimum annual rental, the minimum would be payable, but the amount paid solely as a result of such minimum could be applied in reduction of the next year's rent to the extent that the next year's rent exceeded the minimum for that year.

Gross sales by years, including 1958, were as follows:

| | | | |
|---|---|---|---|
| 1949.............. | $ 96,000 | 1954.............. | $141,000 |
| 1950.............. | 129,000 | 1955.............. | 165,000 |
| 1951.............. | 148,000 | 1956.............. | 142,000 |
| 1952.............. | 161,000 | 1957.............. | 170,000 |
| 1953.............. | 124,000 | 1958.............. | 197,000 |

*Instructions:* (1) Compute the amount of rent payable each year under the terms of the lease.

(2) Discuss the treatment in the financial statements of any amounts payable under the provision for payment of a minimum amount of rent. (A.I.C.P.A. adapted)

**18-9.** On October 1, 1950, the Peters Publishing Company entered into a special royalty contract for the publication of a book on a religious subject, the royalty of $40 per 100 copies to be paid on or before October 1, 1956, on a minimum publication of 50,000 copies. It was stipulated that in the interval the payments were to be made from time to time as the books were bound and ready for sale. The Peters Publishing Company proceeded to print the minimum number of sheets and included the royalty in the sheet cost, setting up the liability therefor. Up to October 1, 1956, the royalty had been paid as agreed on the basis of 13,500 copies bound, and the balance due on the remaining 36,500 copies became due.

However, because of the slowness of the sale of the book, it was agreed on October 31, 1956, that the original contract was to be modified for the balance of the royalties, and negotiations were commenced to fix the new terms. The Peters Publishing Company, having on hand 2,840 copies of bound stock, then also decided to write off against its retained earnings all the royalty included in its inventories.

During the years 1957 and 1958 there were 1,300 additional copies sold. On December 31, 1958, there remained in the hands of the publisher

1,540 bound copies; but no further sheet stock had been bound. On that date a final arrangement was made whereby the remaining royalty liability was settled and paid at 50¢ on the dollar. Thereupon the Peters Publishing Company, in view of a revived demand for the publication, reinstated as a deferred charge the advance royalty actually paid on the stock in hand.

*Instructions:* (1) Submit a summary of the royalty liability account showing the above transactions and the final settlement.

(2) Submit the journal entry recording the adjustment of October 1, 1956, inventories.

(3) Submit the journal entry setting up the advance royalty at December 31, 1958, as a deferred charge. (A.I.C.P.A. adapted)

**18-10.** The Superior Iron Company leased an iron-ore mine for a term of 15 years on a basic royalty charge of 20¢ per ton of ore mined. A minimum of $10,000 was to be paid to the owners each year, but the Superior Iron Company had the right to recover within the next succeeding 5 years the excess royalties paid in any one year.

At the termination of the lease all the ore had been mined as follows:

| | | | |
|---|---|---|---|
| 1st year | 10,000 tons | Brought forward | 310,000 tons |
| 2nd year | 20,000 tons | 9th year | 50,000 tons |
| 3rd year | 40,000 tons | 10th year | 70,000 tons |
| 4th year | 40,000 tons | 11th year | 150,000 tons |
| 5th year | 60,000 tons | 12th year | 130,000 tons |
| 6th year | 70,000 tons | 13th year | 140,000 tons |
| 7th year | 30,000 tons | 14th year | 110,000 tons |
| 8th year | 40,000 tons | 15th year | 40,000 tons |
| Carried forward | 310,000 tons | Total | 1,000,000 tons |

*Instructions:* (1) Prepare a summary of the royalty payments and charges by means of a statement with the following columnar headings: (1) Year, (2) Number of tons mined, (3) Cash paid, (4) Royalty expense for the year, (5) Royalty prepayment for year (recoverable), (6) Royalty recovery (royalty prepayments of previous years applicable to expense), (7) Royalties lost (prepaid expirations), (8) Royalty prepayment carried forward at end of year, (9) Sum of expense and loss for year.

(2) Give the journal entries that would be made for (a) the first year, (b) the fifth year, (c) the sixth year. (A.I.C.P.A. adapted)

**18-11.** The Cripple Creek Sulphur Company, organized January 1, 1954, was formed to mine, refine, and sell sulphur. To that end it secured a 20-year lease on 500 acres of known sulphur deposits, referred to as Section A, and 500 acres of potential but undiscovered sulphur deposits, referred to as Section B. It was estimated after an engineers' survey that there were 5,000,000 tons of sulphur under Section A at the time of acquisition. Mine reports showed the number of tons taken out by years as follows: 1954, 250,000; 1955, 300,000; 1956, 500,000; 1957, 800,000; 1958, 1,000,000, of which 200,000 tons remained in stock pile.

The following statement is prepared by the company's bookkeeper:

## CRIPPLE CREEK SULPHUR CO.
### BALANCE SHEET
### DECEMBER 31, 1958

| | | | | |
|---|---:|---|---|---:|
| Cash............... | $ 500,000 | Current liabilities, including interest and | | |
| Receivables........... | 300,000 | taxes accrued........ | $ | 150,000 |
| Inventory of crude sulphur at cost of mining and extraction (market value $200,000)... | 180,000 | Bonds payable......... | | 300,000 |
| | | Capital stock......... | | 1,000,000 |
| | | Surplus.............. | | 610,000 |
| Leaseholds—at cost..... | 600,000 | Profit and loss, 1958..... | | 230,000 |
|   Section A $500,000 | | | | |
|   Section B  100,000 | | | | |
| Plant and equipment.... | 460,000 | | | |
| Development—Section A | 200,000 | | | |
| Prospecting—Section B. | 50,000 | | | |
| | $2,290,000 | | | $2,290,000 |

This statement is correct and all accounting requirements have been met, except that the company has never provided for amortization or depletion, since, in the words of the company's president, "it had discovered from prospecting more new deposits than it mined." Nor has provision been made for depreciation or obsolescence of plant and equipment acquired January 1, 1954, which are estimated to have a useful life greater than the 20-year period of the leases and a scrap value of $50,000.

The company had a survey made of Section B by competent engineers. This survey indicated sulphur deposits of 3,200,000 tons on January 1, 1958, which were estimated to have a fair value underground of 11 cents per ton. It was decided to increase the book value of the leasehold, now carried at $100,000, to that value. It was also decided that the company would charge the operations with depletion on the basis of the increased value, although this would not affect the depletion deductible for tax purposes.

Of the total 1958 production of 1,000,000 tons, 400,000 tons were mined from Section B, all of which were sold in 1958. Prior to December 31, 1958, the bookkeeper had written down developmental costs for Section A by $50,000, charging this amount to Surplus.

*Instructions:* (1) Prepare journal entries setting up the proper allowances and making necessary adjustments to other accounts.

(2) Prepare a columnar work sheet showing the changes caused by the adjustments.

(3) Prepare a final balance sheet. (A.I.C.P.A. adapted)

**18-12.** Company A and Company B are engaged in the production and sale of crude oil. On January 1, 1958, Company A acquired from Company B a twenty years' leasehold on a certain undeveloped property on the following terms:

    (a) Of the oil produced, $12\frac{1}{2}$ per cent is to be delivered to Company B as royalty.

(b) On the remaining $87\frac{1}{2}$ per cent, Company A is to pay Company B $0.25 per barrel until the total so paid has aggregated $700,000. The latter sum is understood to be the purchase price of the lease and must be paid unless the geologists' estimate of the total oil underground capable of being produced is less than 3,200,000 barrels. In that event the purchase price will be proportionately reduced.

(c) To insure development of the property, Company A is to keep one string of drilling tools in continuous operation until January 1, 1968, or pay a penalty to Company B for idle periods, calculated on the basis of $50,000 for a whole year's cessation of drilling operations.

(d) Company A is to pay the land rentals, which amount to $75,000 per annum, payable in advance, and which are due on January 1 of each year.

(e) Company A may discontinue development and abandon the leasehold at the end of ten years, at which time any unpaid balance of the purchase price of the lease will become due; and the property, with all its development and equipment, will revert to Company B.

During 1958 Company A drilled continuously and expended $630,000 for drilling, construction of field lines, and other work in the field, and produced 648,000 barrels of oil, which were all sold or delivered within the year. Company A realized an average of $1.00 per barrel on the sales of crude oil, and all costs of producing and handling amounted to $0.40 per barrel on its own share of the oil produced, before depletion and land rentals.

It was agreed by the geologists of both companies that on January 1, 1958, the oil underground capable of being produced from the wells existing on December 31, 1958, aggregated 2,400,000 gross barrels, and that it would require ten years to produce it.

They also estimated that on January 1, 1958, the total oil reserves in the property amounted to 8,000,000 gross barrels and that, with an expenditure of $1,600,000 for additional wells and facilities, this oil could be produced during the life of the lease. The latter sum includes the the estimated cost of keeping one string of drilling tools in continuous operation.

*Instructions:* (1) Give the entries that should be made by Company A on January 1, 1958.

(2) Calculate the gross profit or loss of Company A on the crude oil produced and sold in 1958.  (A.I.C.P.A. adapted)

# Chapter 19

# LONG-TERM DEBT

**NATURE OF LONG-TERM DEBT**     *Long-term* or *fixed liabilities* include all liabilities that are not to be liquidated out of company resources presently classified as current. *Long-term debt* normally comprises the major element of a company's long-term obligations. Long-term debt includes long-term notes and bonds as well as long-term advances from affiliates. Notes and bonds may be unsecured or they may be secured by liens on real estate, equipment, or specific securities owned by a company. Normally, the obligation is designated in terms of the character of the security pledged on it. For example, obligations may be termed first mortgage bonds, equipment notes, collateral trust bonds, etc. Both notes and bonds provide for the payment of interest at regular intervals and the payment of a principal amount at some future date.

**BONDS PAYABLE**     Borrowing through bonds means the issue of a number of certificates of indebtedness, since the total loan cannot normally be obtained from a single source. Bond certificates may represent equal parts of the loan or they may be of varying denominations. Bonds of the business unit are most commonly issued in a denomination of $1,000, referred to as the par, face, or maturity value. Bonds may be subject to call by the corporation under certain conditions. On the other hand, bonds may be convertible into some other class of security at the option of the bondholder. An earlier discussion of long-term investments made reference to the various classes of bonds and their special features.

The group contract between the corporation and the bondholders is known as the *bond* or *trust indenture*. The power of the corporation to create bonded indebtedness is found in the corporation laws of the state and may be specifically granted by its charter. In certain cases action by the board of directors for the issuance of bonds and the pledging of assets as security on such obligations may first require formal authorization by a majority of stockholders. Bonds may be sold by the corporation directly to investors, or they may be underwritten by investment bankers. The underwriters may contract to purchase at a stated price the entire bond issue or only that part of the issue which is not disposed of by the company, or they may agree simply to manage the sale of the security on a commission basis.

Funds to meet short-term needs are normally raised through the issue of short-term notes. Long-term requirements are normally financed through the issue of capital stock or bonds. The issuance of bonds instead of stock may prove attractive to present stockholders for the following reasons: (1) the charge against earnings for bond interest is normally less than the share of earnings that would otherwise be payable as dividends on a new issue of preferred stock or the issue of additional common stock; (2) present owners continue in full control of the corporation; and (3) bond interest is a deductible expense in arriving at taxable income while dividends are not; the net charge to stockholders for the use of capital through bond financing, then, is the interest paid less the resulting income tax reduction.

But certain limitations and disadvantages of bond financing must not be overlooked. Bond financing is possible only when a company is in a satisfactory financial condition and can offer adequate security to a new creditor group. Furthermore, interest on bonds requires payment regardless of earnings and financial position. With operating losses and the inability of a company to raise sufficient cash to meet the periodic interest requirements, bondholders may take legal action to assume control of company properties.

**RECORDING THE BOND ISSUE**     It has already been suggested that the sales price of a bond varies with the interest rate that it offers as compared with the prevailing market rate. Bonds will sell at face value when they offer an interest rate equal to the market rate on the date of issue; they will sell for more than face value when their interest rate is higher than the market rate, and will realize less than face value when their interest rate is lower than the market rate. Although an investment in bonds is normally recorded at cost, it is usually desirable to show the bond liability at its face value — the amount that the company must pay at maturity. Hence, when bonds are issued at an amount other than face value, bonds payable are recorded at their face value and a bond discount or premium balance is established for the difference between cash proceeds and bond face value. The discount or premium balance is written off to Bond Interest Expense over the life of the bond issue, periodic adjustments correcting interest expense to the effective rate on the obligation.

When bonds are issued in exchange for property, the transaction should be recorded in terms of the cash price at which the bonds could be issued. The yield that the bonds would have to provide can be employed in arriving at a cash issue price. When difficulties are encountered in arriving at a fair cash price, the market or appraised value of the property acquired may be used in recording the transaction. A difference between the face value of the bonds and the cash value of the bonds or the value of the property item acquired is recognized as bond discount or bond premium. Satisfactory measurement of future profit and loss is possible only with appropriate recognition of the bond discount or premium related to such an exchange.

When disposal of an entire bond issue does not take place at one time, there are two methods that may be employed in accounting for the sales: (1) only bonds outstanding may be recorded; (2) bonds authorized as well as those unissued may be recorded. To illustrate the two methods, assume that $1,000,000, 5% first mortgage bonds are authorized, bonds to be sold at different times as cash is required. Entries may be made as follows:

| Transaction | (1)<br>If only bonds outstanding<br>are recorded | | (2)<br>If authorized and unissued<br>bonds are recorded | |
|---|---|---|---|---|
| JAN. 15, 1958<br>Received permission to issue $1,000,000 5% first mortgage bonds. Bonds are dated March 1, 1958, and mature in 10 years. | No entry | | Unissued<br>Bonds..... 1,000,000<br>  Authorized Bonds<br>  Payable...........1,000,000 | |
| MAR. 1, 1958<br>Sold bonds of $500,000 at 101½. | Cash........507,500<br>  Bonds Payable.....<br>  Premium on Bonds<br>  Payable.......... | 500,000<br><br>7,500 | Cash........507,500<br>  Unissued Bonds ...<br>  Premium on Bonds<br>  Payable.......... | 500,000<br><br>7,500 |
| SEPT. 1, 1958<br>Sold bonds of $300,000 at 99½. | Cash........298,500<br>Discount on<br>Bonds Payable  1,500<br>  Bonds Payable.... | <br><br><br>300,000 | Cash........298,500<br>Discount on<br>Bonds Payable  1,500<br>  Unissued Bonds... | <br><br><br>300,000 |

Use of the first method above provides for recording the bonds only when they are sold. The second method provides for the recognition of the bonds authorized and that portion still unissued. The sale of bonds is recorded by a credit to the unissued balance; bonds outstanding are determined at any time by subtracting the unissued balance from the authorized balance.

Regardless of the method employed in accounting for the issue, bonds authorized but unissued should be disclosed in reporting bonds payable on the balance sheet. Unissued bonds represent a source of additional cash either through their sale or through their pledge as security on other independent loans without further authorization and mortgaging of properties. Bonds may be reported on the balance sheet in the following manner:

Long-term debt:
5% first mortgage bonds issued, due March 1, 1968. . . .    $800,000
(Bonds authorized but unissued, $200,000)

It would also be possible to report the bonds as follows:

Long-term debt:
Authorized 5% first mortgage bonds, due
March 1, 1968. . . . . . . . . . . . . . . . . . . . . . . .    $1,000,000
Less: Unissued bonds. . . . . . . . . . . . . . . . . .       200,000
                                                          _____
Bonds outstanding. . . . . . . . . . . . . . . . . . . . .      $800,000

Subscriptions may first be obtained for bonds. Upon collection of the full subscription amount, bonds are issued. To illustrate the accounting for subscriptions, assume that a company is authorized to issue 6% debenture bonds of $500,000. Bonds of $300,000 are sold to investment bankers at 98. Subscriptions are received for bonds of $100,000 at the same price from officers of the company who pay 25% of the subscription price. Collections of the remaining 75% of the subscription price are made from officers who have subscribed for bonds of $80,000, and bonds fully paid for are issued. Entries are made as follows:

| Transaction | If only bonds outstanding are recorded | If authorized and unissued bonds are recorded |
|---|---|---|
| Received permission to issue $500,000 6% debenture bonds (500 bonds, $1,000 par). | No entry | Unissued Bonds. . . . . . .500,000<br>  Authorized Bonds Payable. . . . . . . . . . .500,000 |
| Sold 300 bonds to investment bankers at 98. | Cash. . . . . . . .294,000<br>Discount on Bonds Payable 6,000<br>  Bonds Payable. . . . . 300,000 | Cash. . . . . . . .294,000<br>Discount on Bonds Payable 6,000<br>  Unissued Bonds . . . . 300,000 |
| Received subscriptions for 100 bonds at 98 accompanied by 25% down payment.<br>Received: 25% of $98,000, or   $24,500<br>Receivable: 75% of $98,000, or   73,500<br>         $98,000 | Cash. . . . . . . . .24,500<br>Bond Subscriptions Receivable. . . .73,500<br>Discount on Bonds Payable. . . . . . . . . . .2,000<br>  Bonds Payable Subscribed. . . . . . . .100,000 | Cash. . . . . . . . .24,500<br>Bond Subscriptions Receivable. . . .73,500<br>Discount on Bonds Payable. . . . . . . . . . .2,000<br>  Bonds Payable Subscribed. . . . . . . .100,000 |
| Received 75% balance due on bonds of $80,000 subscribed for at 98.<br>Received: 75% of $78,400, or $58,800. | Cash. . . . . . . . . 58,800<br>  Bond Subscriptions Receivable. . . . . . . . .58,800 | Cash. . . . . . . . . 58,800<br>  Bond Subscriptions Receivable. . . . . . . . .58,800 |
| Issued 80 bond certificates to paid-up subscribers. | Bonds Payable Subscribed. . . .80,000<br>  Bonds Payable. . . . . . 80,000 | Bonds Payable Subscribed. . . .80,000<br>  Unissued Bonds . . . . . 80,000 |

Bonds subscribed should be added to bonds issued in reporting bonds on the balance sheet. The result of the bond transactions in the example may be reported as follows:

Long-term debt:

| | | |
|---|---|---|
| 6% debenture bonds issued, due March 1, 1968. | $380,000 | |
| Add: Bonds subscribed.................... | 20,000 | |
| Bonds issued and subscribed............... | | $400,000 |

(Bonds authorized but unissued and unsubscribed, $100,000)

The account Bond Subscriptions Receivable is reported as a current asset when current collection is anticipated and cash is to become available as working capital. In the event that bond proceeds are to be applied to some noncurrent purpose, neither the receivable nor the cash received from the issue of the bonds should be regarded as current. Terms of the bond issue, for example, may require that bond proceeds be applied to the retirement of other debt or the acquisition of plant and equipment. Under such circumstances, claims against subscribers as well as bond proceeds should be reported as noncurrent items with appropriate reference to their ultimate application.

Bond discount is generally reported on the balance sheet as a deferred cost and bond premium as a deferred revenue. Debt discount is viewed as a prepayment of interest by the company that is to be added to charges of future periods and debt premium as an advance of interest by bondholders that is to be subtracted from charges of future periods. While such practice prevails, a bond discount or premium is more logically reported as a valuation account related to bonds payable: a discount is subtracted from bonds reported at par; a premium would be added to bonds at par. Such procedure parallels that used in accounting for investments in bonds, and is fully supportable in theory. The bond sales price determines the balance for the obligation to be reported at the time of the issue. As amortization of discount and premium balances takes place, the obligation approaches its maturity amount. Bonds failing to pay prevailing interest are sold at a discount. Amortization of the discount by charges to the bond interest expense account over the life of the issue raises interest expense to the effective rate and raises the book value of the obligation; periodic interest is viewed as the interest paid plus the accrual of the discount to be paid at bond maturity. Payment of bonds at maturity represents a return of the amount borrowed plus settlement of interest deficiencies of past periods recognized in the bond obligation now increased to par value. Bonds providing for interest payments in excess of the prevailing rate are sold at a premium. Amortization of the premium by credits to the bond interest expense account over the life of the issue reduces expense to the effective rate and reduces the book value of the obligation; periodic interest, here, is viewed as the interest paid less the return of a part of the premium originally advanced by bondholders. Payments of interest in excess of the market rate thus represent settlement of the bond premium; bond payment at maturity cancels the bond obligation now reduced to par value.[1]

The sale of bonds normally involves special costs for printing and engraving, taxes, advertising, and underwriting. When bond premium or discount is regarded as a bond valuation item, issuing costs should be summarized separately as a deferred cost and written off systematically over the life of the bond issue. When bond discount or premium is treated as a deferred cost or deferred revenue item, however, issuing costs are frequently applied as deductions from bond proceeds, thus increasing the discount or reducing the premium.

When coupon bonds are issued, coupons are redeemed by the corporation on regular interest payment dates. Payments on coupons may be made by the corporation directly to bondholders, or payments may be cleared through a bank or a corporate fiscal agent. No subsidiary records with bondholders are maintained, since coupons are redeemable by bearers. In the case of registered bonds, interest checks are mailed either by the corporation or its agent. When bonds are registered, the bonds payable account requires subsidiary ledger support. The subsidiary record shows holdings by individual bond owners and changes in such holdings. Checks are sent to bondholders of record as of the interest payment date.

When an agent is to make interest payments, the corporation normally provides for a transfer of cash for interest to the agent in advance of the payment date. Since the corporation is not freed from its obligation to bondholders until payment has been made by its agent, the cash transfer is recorded by a charge to the account Cash for Bond Interest Deposited with Agent and a credit to Cash. Upon receipt from the agent of paid interest coupons, a certificate of coupon receipt and appropriate disposal, or other required evidence in support of payment, the

---

[1]The American Accounting Association Committee on Concepts and Standards Underlying Corporate Financial Statements states, "Equities should be accorded accounting recognition in the period in which money, goods, or services are received or obligations incurred, and should be measured initially by the agreed cash consideration or its equivalent." (*Accounting and Reporting Standards for Corporate Financial Statements and Preceding Statements and Supplements*, p. 7). Measurement of liabilities by cash received would require that a premium or discount on bonds be identified with the face value of the obligation.

corporation charges the bond interest expense account and credits the interest cash account.

**PREMIUM AND DISCOUNT AMORTIZATION PROCEDURES** When bonds are issued at a premium, this premium is applied as an offset to bond interest payments over the life of the bonds; the premium account is debited and the bond interest expense account is credited periodically for the premium written off. When bonds are issued at a discount, the discount is added to bond interest payments over the life of the issue; the bond interest expense account is debited and the discount account is credited periodically for the discount written off. As in the case of investments, either the straight-line or the compound-interest or scientific method may be used for amortization purposes. The straight-line method calls for writing off an equal amount of premium or discount each period. This procedure results in equal periodic interest charges. Use of the compound-interest method calls for interest charges at the effective interest rate. The effective rate on the bond issue must first be determined. This rate is then applied periodically to the book value of the obligation in arriving at the charge to the bond interest expense account, the difference between the charge to expense and the amount paid being reported as a reduction in the bond premium or discount balance.

To illustrate the application of the straight-line and compound-interest methods of amortization, assume that 5-year bonds of $100,000, interest at 6% payable semiannually, are sold to yield 5%. This price as shown by bond tables is $104,376.03. The following tabulations show the differences in results through the use of the two methods:

### AMORTIZATION OF PREMIUM—STRAIGHT-LINE METHOD
$100,000 5-YEAR BONDS, INTEREST AT 6% PAYABLE SEMIANNUALLY, SOLD AT $104,376.03

| INTEREST PAYMENT | A<br>INTEREST PAID<br>(3% of FACE VALUE) | B<br>PREMIUM AMORTIZATION<br>(1/10×$4,376.03) | C<br>EFFECTIVE INTEREST<br>(A−B) | D<br>BOND PREMIUM<br>(D−B) | E<br>BOND CARRYING VALUE<br>($100,000 + D) |
|---|---|---|---|---|---|
| 1 | $3,000.00 | $437.60 | $2,562.40 | $4,376.03 | $104,376.03 |
| 2 | 3,000.00 | 437.60 | 2,562.40 | 3,938.43 | 103,938.43 |
| 3 | 3,000.00 | 437.60 | 2,562.40 | 3,500.83 | 103,500.83 |
| 4 | 3,000.00 | 437.60 | 2,562.40 | 3,063.23 | 103,063.23 |
| 5 | 3,000.00 | 437.60 | 2,562.40 | 2,625.63 | 102,625.63 |
| 6 | 3,000.00 | 437.60 | 2,562.40 | 2,188.03 | 102,188.03 |
| 7 | 3,000.00 | 437.60 | 2,562.40 | 1,750.43 | 101,750.43 |
| 8 | 3,000.00 | 437.61 | 2,562.39 | 1,312.83 | 101,312.83 |
| 9 | 3,000.00 | 437.61 | 2,562.39 | 875.22 | 100,875.22 |
| 10 | 3,000.00 | 437.61 | 2,562.39 | 437.61 | 100,437.61 |
|  |  |  |  | ——— | 100,000.00 |

## AMORTIZATION OF PREMIUM—COMPOUND-INTEREST METHOD
### $100,000 5-Year Bonds, Interest at 6% Payable Semiannually, Sold at $104,376.03 to Yield 5%

| Inter-est Pay-ment | A Interest Paid (3% of Face Value) | B Effective Interest (2½% of Bond Carrying Value) | C Premium Amortiza-tion (A—B) | D Bond Premium (D—C) | E Bond Carrying Value ($100,000 + D) |
|---|---|---|---|---|---|
| | | | | $4,376.03 | $104,376.03 |
| 1 | $3,000.00 | $2,609.40 (2½% of $104,376.03) | $390.60 | 3,985.43 | 103,985.43 |
| 2 | 3,000.00 | 2,599.64 (2½% of $103,985.43) | 400.36 | 3,585.07 | 103,585.07 |
| 3 | 3,000.00 | 2,589.63 (2½% of $103,585.07) | 410.37 | 3,174.70 | 103,174.70 |
| 4 | 3,000.00 | 2,579.37 (2½% of $103,174.70) | 420.63 | 2,754.07 | 102,754.07 |
| 5 | 3,000.00 | 2,568.85 (2½% of $102,754.07) | 431.15 | 2,322.92 | 102,322.92 |
| 6 | 3,000.00 | 2,558.07 (2½% of $102,322.92) | 441.93 | 1,880.99 | 101,880.99 |
| 7 | 3,000.00 | 2,547.02 (2½% of $101,880.99) | 452.98 | 1,428.01 | 101,428.01 |
| 8 | 3,000.00 | 2,535.70 (2½% of $101,428.01) | 464.30 | 963.71 | 100,963.71 |
| 9 | 3,000.00 | 2,524.09 (2½% of $100,963.71) | 475.91 | 487.80 | 100,487.80 |
| 10 | 3,000.00 | 2,512.20 (2½% of $100,487.80) | 487.80 | ——— | 100,000.00 |

The use of the two methods when bonds are issued at a discount is illustrated below and on the opposite page. Here it is assumed that 5-year bonds of $100,000, interest at 4% payable semiannually, are sold at $95,625, a price that provides a yield of approximately 5%.

Even though bonds may be redeemable or convertible prior to their maturity dates, redemption or conversion cannot ordinarily be anticipated. Amortization schedules, then, are normally developed in terms of the full life of the bond issue. Early bond retirement will call for a cancellation of the bond premium or discount relating to the remaining life of the issue.

The bond investor normally employs straight-line amortization as a matter of practical considerations. With a number of investments, purchases and sales within the bond life, and relatively minor differences in straight-line and scientific procedures, application of the simpler method is justified. But these considerations are not found in the case of the bond issuer. Here, only one or a few issues are

## AMORTIZATION OF DISCOUNT—STRAIGHT-LINE METHOD
### $100,000 5-Year Bonds, Interest at 4% Payable Semiannually, Sold at $95,625

| Interest Payment | A Interest Paid (2% of Face Value) | B Discount Amortization (1/10 × $4,375) | C Effective Interest (A + B) | D Bond Discount (D — B) | E Bond Carrying Value ($100,000 — D) |
|---|---|---|---|---|---|
| | | | | $4,375.00 | $95,625.00 |
| 1 | $2,000.00 | $437.50 | $2,437.50 | 3,937.50 | 96,062.50 |
| 2 | 2,000.00 | 437.50 | 2,437.50 | 3,500.00 | 96,500.00 |
| 3 | 2,000.00 | 437.50 | 2,437.50 | 3,062.50 | 96,937.50 |
| 4 | 2,000.00 | 437.50 | 2,437.50 | 2,625.00 | 97,375.00 |
| 5 | 2,000.00 | 437.50 | 2,437.50 | 2,187.50 | 97,812.50 |
| 6 | 2,000.00 | 437.50 | 2,437.50 | 1,750.00 | 98,250.00 |
| 7 | 2,000.00 | 437.50 | 2,437.50 | 1,312.50 | 98,687.50 |
| 8 | 2,000.00 | 437.50 | 2,437.50 | 875.00 | 99,125.00 |
| 9 | 2,000.00 | 437.50 | 2,437.50 | 437.50 | 99,562.50 |
| 10 | 2,000.00 | 437.50 | 2,437.50 | ——— | 100,000.00 |

## AMORTIZATION OF DISCOUNT—COMPOUND-INTEREST METHOD
### $100,000 5-Year Bonds, Interest at 4% Payable Semiannually, Sold at $95,625 to Yield Approximately 5%

| Interest Payment | A Interest Paid (2% of Face Value) | B Effective Interest (2½% of Bond Carrying Value) | C Discount Amortization (B−A) | D Bond Discount (D−C) | E Bond Carrying Value ($100,000−D) |
|---|---|---|---|---|---|
| 1  | $2,000.00 | $2,390.63 (2½% of $95,625.00) | $390.63 | $4,375.00 | $95,625.00 |
| 2  | 2,000.00 | 2,400.39 (2½% of $96,015.63) | 400.39 | 3,984.37 | 96,015.63 |
| 3  | 2,000.00 | 2,410.40 (2½% of $96,416.02) | 410.40 | 3,583.98 | 96,416.02 |
| 4  | 2,000.00 | 2,420.66 (2½% of $96,826.42) | 420.66 | 3,173.58 | 96,826.42 |
| 5  | 2,000.00 | 2,431.18 (2½% of $97,247.08) | 431.18 | 2,752.92 | 97,247.08 |
| 6  | 2,000.00 | 2,441.96 (2½% of $97,678.26) | 441.96 | 2,321.74 | 97,678.26 |
| 7  | 2,000.00 | 2,453.01 (2½% of $98,120.22) | 453.01 | 1,879.78 | 98,120.22 |
| 8  | 2,000.00 | 2,464.33 (2½% of $98,573.23) | 464.33 | 1,426.77 | 98,573.23 |
| 9  | 2,000.00 | 2,475.94 (2½% of $99,037.56) | 475.94 | 962.44 | 99,037.56 |
| 10 | 2,000.00 | 2,486.50 ($2,000+$486.50)[1] | 486.50 | 486.50 | 99,513.50 |
|    |          |                                |        | —        | 100,000.00 |

[1] 2½% of $99,513.50 is $2,487.84. However, use of 5% when the effective rate was not exactly 5% has resulted in a small discrepancy that requires compensation upon recording the final interest payment. On the final payment the discount balance is closed, interest expense being increased by the balance in the discount account.

involved and amortization schedules can be followed from the time of issuance of the bonds to their retirement. When large issues are involved, the difference between compound-interest amortization and straight-line amortization may be significant. Such circumstances support the use of compound-interest methods that provide for the accurate measure of expense in terms of a changing liability balance. Nevertheless, straight-line amortization is frequently found in practice and is accepted for income tax purposes. Remaining illustrations in this chapter assume the use of straight-line amortization procedures.

**ACCOUNTING FOR BONDS PAYABLE**   When bonds are sold by a corporation between interest dates, the bond price is increased by a charge for accrued interest to the date of sale. Accrued Interest on Bonds Payable is credited for the interest received from the investor; when the company makes payment of interest for the full period, the accrued interest balance is closed and Interest Expense is charged for the excess. The company may prefer to credit Interest Expense for the accrued interest received. The subsequent payment of interest is then charged in full to Interest Expense. The latter procedure is convenient and is used in subsequent illustrations.

It is possible to record the amortization of bond premium or discount (1) at the time of each interest payment or (2) only at the end of the company's annual period. Normally, it is more convenient to record amortization for a full year at the end of the annual period, except for the first and last years when fractional parts of a period may be involved.

The entries for issuance of bonds and the payment of interest are illustrated in the example that follows. Assume that the Crescent Corporation decides to issue bonds of $100,000. Bonds are dated September 1, 1958, pay interest at $4\frac{1}{2}\%$ semiannually on March 1 and September 1, and mature on September 1, 1968. Bonds are sold on December 1, 1958, at $94,150 plus accrued interest. The corporation adjusts and closes its books at the end of each calendar year. In view of the issue of bonds on December 1, bonds will have a life of only $9\frac{3}{4}$ years or 117 months. This is the period that will receive the benefits from the use of borrowed money and hence the period to which the bond discount should be related. A schedule may be prepared by the corporation to summarize discount amortization over the bond life. These data can then be used in making periodic adjustments.[1] The amortization schedule follows:

### AMORTIZATION SCHEDULE—STRAIGHT-LINE METHOD

| PERIOD | A INT. PAYMENT (INCLUD. ADJ. FOR ACCRUALS) | B DISCOUNT AMORTIZATION | | | C EFFECTIVE INTEREST (A+B) | D BOND DISCOUNT (D-B) | E BOND CARRYING VALUE ($100,000 -D) |
|---|---|---|---|---|---|---|---|
| | | No. OF Mos. | FRACTION OF DISC. TO BE AMORTIZED | AMT. OF DISCOUNT AMORTIZATION | | | |
| | | | | | | $5,850 | $94,150 |
| Dec. 1 (sales date)-Dec. 31, 1958 | $ 375 | 1 | 1/117 | $ 50 | $ 425 | 5,800 | 94,200 |
| Year Ended Dec. 31, 1959 | 4,500 | 12 | 12/117 | 600 | 5,100 | 5,200 | 94,800 |
| Year Ended Dec. 31, 1960 | 4,500 | 12 | 12/117 | 600 | 5,100 | 4,600 | 95,400 |
| Year Ended Dec. 31, 1961 | 4,500 | 12 | 12/117 | 600 | 5,100 | 4,000 | 96,000 |
| Year Ended Dec. 31, 1962 | 4,500 | 12 | 12/117 | 600 | 5,100 | 3,400 | 96,600 |
| Year Ended Dec. 31, 1963 | 4,500 | 12 | 12/117 | 600 | 5,100 | 2,800 | 97,200 |
| Year Ended Dec. 31, 1964 | 4,500 | 12 | 12/117 | 600 | 5,100 | 2,200 | 97,800 |
| Year Ended Dec. 31, 1965 | 4,500 | 12 | 12/117 | 600 | 5,100 | 1,600 | 98,400 |
| Year Ended Dec. 31, 1966 | 4,500 | 12 | 12/117 | 600 | 5,100 | 1,000 | 99,000 |
| Year Ended Dec. 31, 1967 | 4,500 | 12 | 12/117 | 600 | 5,100 | 400 | 99,600 |
| Jan. 1-Sept. 1, 1968 (maturity) | 3,000 | 8 | 8/117 | 400 | 3,400 | ——— | 100,000 |
| | | 117 | 117/117 | $5,850 | | | |

Entries that are made on the corporation books in 1958 and 1959 follow:

| Transaction | Entry |
|---|---|
| **DECEMBER 1, 1958** | Cash.................... 95,275 |
| Sold $100,000 of $4\frac{1}{2}\%$ bonds for $94,150, bonds maturing on September 1, 1968, 10 years from date of issue. Interest is payable semiannually on March 1 and September 1. Sales proceeds were as follows: | Discount on Bonds Payable................... 5,850 |
| | Bonds Payable....... 100,000 |
| | Bond Interest Expense. 1,125 |
| Bond sales price................$ 94,150 | |
| Accrued interest, Sept. 1- Dec. 1    1,125 | |
| $ 95,275 | |

[1] Amortization procedures for bond discount are equally applicable to bond issue costs when these are carried separately on the books.

| Transaction | Entry |
|---|---|
| DECEMBER 31, 1958<br>(a) To record accrued interest for 4 months, and (b) to record amortization of bond discount applicable to current year. Amortization: bonds outstanding in current year, one month; total life of bond issue, 9¾ years or 117 months; current amortization, 1/117 of $5,850 = $50 (one month at $50). | (a) Bond Interest Expense................1,500<br>    Accrued Interest<br>    on Bonds Payable...      1,500<br><br>(b) Bond Interest Expense   50<br>    Discount on Bonds<br>    Payable...........      50 |
| JANUARY 1, 1959<br>To reverse 1958 accrued interest. | Accrued Interest on<br>Bonds Payable............1,500<br>    Bond Interest Expense................      1,500 |
| MARCH 1, 1959<br>Paid semiannual interest. | Bond Interest Expense...2,250<br>    Cash..................      2,250 |
| SEPTEMBER 1, 1959<br>Paid semiannual interest. | Bond Interest Expense....2,250<br>    Cash..................      2,250 |
| DECEMBER 31, 1959<br>(a) To record accrued interest for 4 months, and (b) to record amortization of bond discount applicable to current year 12/117 of $5,850, or $600 (or 12 months at $50 a month, $600). | (a) Bond Interest Expense................1,500<br>    Accrued Interest<br>    on Bonds Payable...      1,500<br><br>(b) Bond Interest Expense   600<br>    Discount on Bonds<br>    Payable...........      600 |

Entries similar to those for 1959 would be made each year until 1968. On September 1, 1968, when the last interest payment is made, the following entries are made:

| Transaction | Entry |
|---|---|
| SEPTEMBER 1, 1968<br>(a) To record payment of semiannual interest and principal amount, and (b) to record amortization of bond discount for the last 8-month period, 8/117 of $5,850, or $400 (or 8 months at $50 a month, $400). | (a) Bond Interest Expense.............. 2,250<br>    Bonds Payable.....100,000<br>    Cash............      102,250<br><br>(b) Bond Interest Expense   400<br>    Discount on Bonds<br>    Payable...........      400 |

**BOND REACQUISITION PRIOR TO MATURITY**   Corporations frequently reacquire their own bonds on the market when prices or other conditions make such action favorable. Acquisition in advance of bond maturity calls for the recognition of a gain or a loss based upon the difference between the liability liquidated and the amount paid on such liquidation. When bonds are reacquired at a price that is less than the liability plus the related premium or minus the related discount and issue costs, a gain accrues to the corporation; when bonds are reacquired at a price that is more than the liability plus the related premium or minus the related discount and issue costs, a loss results. The gain or loss should be viewed as an extraordinary item. Payment of accrued interest on bond reacquisition is separately reported as a charge to Bond Interest Expense.

When bonds are reacquired, amortization of bond premium, discount, and issue costs should be brought up to date. Reacquisition calls for the cancellation of the bond face value as reported in the bonds payable account, together with any bond premium, discount, or issue costs as of the reacquisition date. When bonds are purchased and formally canceled, Bonds Payable is debited. When bonds are held for possible future reissue, Treasury Bonds instead of Bonds Payable may be debited. It has already been indicated that treasury bonds cannot be considered an asset. Whether formally retired or kept alive, reacquired bonds are simply the evidence of a liability that has been liquidated. Although treasury bonds may represent a ready source of cash, their sale creates new creditors, a situation that is no different from the debt created by any other type of borrowing. Since treasury bonds represent reductions in a liability, they should be recorded at their face value, a gain or a loss being recognized as in the case of formal bond retirement. Treasury bonds at par are then subtracted from the bonds payable balance in reporting bonds issued and outstanding. If treasury bonds are resold at a price other than face value, Cash is debited, Treasury Bonds is credited, thus reinstating the bond liability, and a premium or a discount on the sale of the bonds is recorded, the latter balance to be amortized over the remaining life of this specific bond group. While held, treasury bonds occupy the same legal status as unissued bonds and can be recorded with the latter. Any balance in a treasury bonds or unissued bonds account at maturity is applied against Bonds Payable.

To illustrate bond reacquisition, assume that in the preceding example for the Crescent Corporation, bonds of $10,000 are reacquired at 98½ by the company on February 1, 1960. Entries in 1960 would be as follows:

| Transaction | Entry |
|---|---|
| January 1, 1960<br>To reverse 1959 accrued interest. | Accrued Interest on<br>Bonds Payable....... 1,500.00<br>  Bond Interest Ex-<br>  pense.................... 1,500.00 |

| Transaction | Entry |
|---|---|
| FEBURARY 1,1960<br>To record reacquisition of own bonds:<br>(a) Amortization of discount on bonds of $10,000 to date of purchase, 1/117 of $585, or $5 (or 1/10 of monthly amortization of $50, $5). | (a) Bond Interest Expense 5.00<br>Discount on Bonds<br>Payable..........     5.00 |
| (b) Payment of accrued interest, Sept. 1-Feb. 1, $10,000 at $4\frac{1}{2}\%$ for 5 months. | (b) Bond Interest<br>Expense.......... 187.50<br>Cash .....................187.50 |
| (c) Loss on bond retirement:<br>Bonds at face value......... $10,000<br>Discount on bonds......$585<br>Less amortization to<br>date of purchase:<br>    1958     $ 5<br>    1959     60<br>    1960     5    70    515<br><br>Book value of bonds........ $9,485<br>Amount paid on reacquisition   9,850<br><br>Loss on retirement........ $ 365 | (c) Bonds Payable<br>(or Treasury<br>Bonds)..........10,000.00<br>Loss on Bond<br>Retirement.......365.00<br>Cash................... 9,850.00<br>Discount on<br>Bonds Payable   515.00 |
| MARCH 1, 1960<br>Paid interest on bonds, face value $90,000 at $4\frac{1}{2}\%$ for 6 months. | Bond Interest Ex-<br>pense.............2,025.00<br>Cash....................2,025.00 |
| SEPTEMBER 1, 1960<br>Paid interest on bonds, face value $90,000, at $4\frac{1}{2}\%$ for 6 months. | Bond Interest Ex-<br>pense............. 2,025.00<br>Cash.................... 2,025.00 |
| DECEMBER 31, 1960<br>(a) To record accrued interest at $4\frac{1}{2}\%$ for 4 months on bonds, face value $90,000, and<br>(b) to record amortization of bond discount applicable to current year, 12/117 of $5,265 ($5,850 — $585), or $540 (or 12 months at $45, monthly amortization on bonds outstanding, $540). | (a) Bond Interest<br>Expense........ 1,350.00<br>Accrued In-<br>terest on Bonds<br>Payable .............. 1,350.00<br><br>(b) Bond Interest<br>Expense..........540.00<br>Discount on<br>Bonds Payable..........540.00 |

For income tax purposes a gain on bond reacquisition is fully taxable and a loss is fully deductible in the period of bond reacquisition.

**BOND RETIREMENT AT MATURITY**   Most bond issues are payable at the end of a specified period. The borrowing corporation may be required to establish a fund for the retirement of bonds. As indicated in an earlier chapter, reacquisition of a company's own bonds through a bond retirement fund calls for the same accounting procedures in cancelling account balances relating to the obligation as those that would be applicable upon direct bond reacquisition.

A borrowing corporation may also agree that during the life of the bond issue it will not use as a basis for dividends a portion or all of the retained earnings at the time of the issue or retained earnings arising from future activities. When retained earnings are restricted, such amount may be transferred to an appropriated retained earnings account. Limitation of dividends until the time bonds are retired reduces the possibility of loss to bondholders.

When bond discount, premium, and issue cost balances have been satisfactorily amortized over the life of the bonds, bond retirement simply calls for a charge to the obligation and a credit to cash. Any bonds not presented for payment at their maturity should be removed from the bonds payable balance and reported separately as *matured bonds;* these are reported as a current liability except where they are to be paid out of a retirement fund. Interest does not accrue on matured bonds that have not been presented for payment.

**SERIAL BONDS**        Foregoing discussions related to *term bonds* or bonds with a single maturity date. *Serial bonds* provide for a series of principal payments on periodic due dates. For example, a $500,000 bond issue may provide that stated bond blocks of $25,000 are to be paid off at the end of each year for 20 years. This plan provides for the gradual amortization of the debt.

The issuance of serial bonds makes unnecessary the use of both the bond retirement fund and the retained earnings appropriations described in the previous section. When a retirement fund cannot produce income at a rate equivalent to that paid on the bond issue, serial bonds are advantageous to the issuing corporation. Here cash that would otherwise be deposited into the retirement fund is applied directly to the retirement of debt, and the interest relating to that portion of the debt is terminated.

**AMORTIZATION PROCEDURES FOR SERIAL BONDS**        When serial bonds are issued, the premium or discount amortization schedule calls for recognition of the declining debt principal. Successive bond years cannot be charged with equal amounts of premium or discount because of a shrinking debt and successively smaller interest charges.

As in the case of term bonds, premium or discount amortization is possible by a straight-line procedure or by a compound-interest procedure. The straight-line method as applied to serial bonds is referred to as the *bonds-outstanding method* and calls for decreases in the amortization schedule proportionate to the decrease in the loan balance. The compound-interest method requires that the effective interest rate at which the bonds were issued first be determined. The charge for interest is then reported at the effective rate applied to the periodic carrying value of the bonds, the difference between the amount reported as expense and the amount of interest paid being reported as a reduction in the premium or discount balance.

*Bonds-Outstanding Method of Amortization.* Amortization by the bonds outstanding method is illustrated in the example that follows. Assume that bonds of $100,000, dated January 1, 1958, are issued on this date for $101,350. Bonds of $20,000 mature at the beginning of each year. The bonds pay interest of 5% annually. The company's fiscal year ends on December 31; the fiscal period and the bond year thus coincide. A table showing the amount of premium to be amortized each year is developed as follows:

AMORTIZATION SCHEDULE—BONDS-OUTSTANDING METHOD

| YEAR | BONDS OUTSTANDING | FRACTION OF PREMIUM TO BE AMORTIZED | PREMIUM ON ISSUE | ANNUAL PREMIUM AMORTIZATION |
|------|------|------|------|------|
| 1958 | $100,000 | 10/30 | $1,350 | $ 450 |
| 1959 | 80,000 | 8/30 | 1,350 | 360 |
| 1960 | 60,000 | 6/30 | 1,350 | 270 |
| 1961 | 40,000 | 4/30 | 1,350 | 180 |
| 1962 | 20,000 | 2/30 | 1,350 | 90 |
| | $300,000 | 30/30 | | $1,350 |

The annual premium amortization is found by multiplying the premium by a fraction whose numerator is the number of bond dollars outstanding in that year and whose denominator is the total number of bond dollars outstanding for the life of the issue. As bonds are retired, the premium amortization is correspondingly reduced. For 1958, for example, amortization is calculated as follows:

$$\frac{\$100,000 \text{ (bond dollars outstanding, 1958)}}{\$300,000 \text{ (total bond dollars outstanding, 1958-1962)}} \text{ or } \frac{10}{30} \times \$1,350 = \underline{\$450}$$

Periodic amortization may be incorporated in a table that summarizes the interest charges and changes in bond carrying values. Such a table follows:

AMORTIZATION OF PREMIUM—SERIAL BONDS
BONDS-OUTSTANDING METHOD

| DATE | A INTEREST PAYMENT (5% OF FACE VALUE) | B PREMIUM AMORTIZATION | C EFFECTIVE INTEREST (A-B) | D PRINCIPAL PAYMENT | E BOND CARRYING VALUE DECREASE (B + D) | F BOND CARRYING VALUE (F-E) |
|------|------|------|------|------|------|------|
| Jan. 1, 1958 | | | | | | $101,350 |
| Dec. 31, 1958 | $5,000 | $450 | $4,550 | $20,000 | $20,450 | 80,900 |
| Dec. 31, 1959 | 4,000 | 360 | 3,640 | 20,000 | 20,360 | 60,540 |
| Dec. 31, 1960 | 3,000 | 270 | 2,730 | 20,000 | 20,270 | 40,270 |
| Dec. 31, 1961 | 2,000 | 180 | 1,820 | 20,000 | 20,180 | 20,090 |
| Dec. 31, 1962 | 1,000 | 90 | 910 | 20,000 | 20,090 | ——— |

*Compound-Interest Method of Amortization.* Tables show that the above bonds were sold to yield approximately 4½%. Use of this rate results in the following interest charges and premium amortization:

AMORTIZATION OF PREMIUM—SERIAL BONDS
COMPOUND-INTEREST METHOD

| DATE | A INTEREST PAYMENT (5% OF FACE VALUE) | B EFFECTIVE INTEREST (4½% OF CARRYING VALUE) | C PREMIUM AMORTI- ZATION (A-B) | D PRINCIPAL PAYMENT | E BOND CAR- RYING VALUE DECREASE (C + D) | F BOND CARRYING VALUE (F-E) |
|---|---|---|---|---|---|---|
| Jan.  1, 1958 | | | | | | $101,350.00 |
| Dec. 31, 1958 | $ 5,000.00 | $4,560.75 | $439.25 | $20,000.00 | $20,439.25 | 80,910.75 |
| Dec. 31, 1959 | 4,000.00 | 3,640.98 | 359.02 | 20,000.00 | 20,359.02 | 60,551.73 |
| Dec. 31, 1960 | 3,000.00 | 2,724.83 | 275.17 | 20,000.00 | 20,275.17 | 40,276.56 |
| Dec. 31, 1961 | 2,000.00 | 1,812.45 | 187.55 | 20,000.00 | 20,187.55 | 20,089.01 |
| Dec. 31, 1962 | 1,000.00 | 910.99* | 89.01 | 20,000.00 | 20,089.01 | ——— |

*4½% of $20,089.01 is $904.01. However, use of 4½% when the effective rate was not exactly 4½% has resulted in a small discrepancy that requires compensation upon the final interest payment. On the final payment the premium balance is closed, interest expense being reduced by the balance in the premium account.

The straight-line method of amortization provides for the recognition of uniform amounts of amortization in terms of the par value of bonds outstanding. The compound-interest method provides for the recognition of interest at a uniform rate on the declining debt balance.

**SERIAL BOND REACQUISITION PRIOR TO MATURITY**  When serial bonds are reacquired prior to their maturity date, it is necessary to cancel the unamortized premium or the discount relating to that part of the bond issue that is liquidated. For example, assume the issuance of serial bonds previously described and amortization of the premium by the bonds-outstanding method as given on page 593. On April 1, 1959, $10,000 of bonds due January 1, 1961, and $10,000 of bonds due January 1, 1962, are reacquired at 100½ plus accrued interest. The premium for the period January 1-April 1, 1959, relating to retired bonds affects bond interest for the current period and will be written off as an adjustment to expense at the end of the period. The balance of the premium from the retirement date to the respective maturity date of the series retired must be canceled. The premium balance relating to retired bonds is calculated as follows:

Premium identified with 1959:    $\frac{20,000}{80,000}$ × $360.00 × 9/12  =  $ 67.50

Premium identified with 1960:    $\frac{20,000}{60,000}$ × $270.00        =   90.00

Premium identified with 1961:    $\frac{10,000}{40,000}$ × $180.00        =   45.00

Total premium identified with retired bonds                     $202.50

Instead of following the procedure illustrated above, it would be possible to calculate the premium cancellation by first determining the premium amortization rate per year on each $1,000 bond. This is determined from the original amortization schedule as follows:

$$\frac{\$1,350 \text{ (total premium—life of bonds)}}{300 \text{ (total \$1,000 bonds outstanding—life of bonds)}} = \begin{array}{l} \$4.50, \quad \text{annual} \quad \text{premium} \\ \text{amortization per \$1,000 bond.} \end{array}$$

The premium cancellation, then, is calculated as follows:

| Year | No. of $1,000 Bonds × | Annual Premium × | Fractional Part of Year = | Total Cancellation |
|------|------|------|------|------|
| 1959 | 20 | $4.50 | $\frac{3}{4}$ | $ 67.50 |
| 1960 | 20 | 4.50 |  | 90.00 |
| 1961 | 10 | 4.50 |  | 45.00 |

Total premium identified with retired bonds................ $202.50

Bonds, carrying value $20,202.50, are retired at a cost of $20,100 resulting in a gain of $102.50. Payment is also made for interest on bonds of $20,000 for a three-month period at 5%, or $250. The entry to record the retirement of bonds and the payment of interest on the series retired follows:

| | | |
|---|---|---|
| Bonds Payable (or Treasury Bonds)......... | 20,000.00 | |
| Premium on Bonds Payable................ | 202.50 | |
| Bond Interest Expense.................... | 250.00 | |
| Cash.................................... | | 20,350.00 |
| Gain on Bond Retirement................ | | 102.50 |

A revised schedule for the amortization of bond premium is prepared as follows:

AMORTIZATION SCHEDULE — BONDS-OUTSTANDING METHOD
REVISED FOR BOND RETIREMENT

| YEAR | ANNUAL PREMIUM AMORTIZATION PER ORIGINAL SCHEDULE | PREMIUM CANCELLATION ON BOND RETIREMENT | ANNUAL PREMIUM AMORTIZATION ADJUSTED FOR BOND RETIREMENT |
|------|------|------|------|
| 1958 | $ 450.00 | | $ 450.00 |
| 1959 | 360.00 | $ 67.50 | 292.50 |
| 1960 | 270.00 | 90.00 | 180.00 |
| 1961 | 180.00 | 45.00 | 135.00 |
| 1962 | 90.00 | | 90.00 |
| | $1,350.00 | $202.50 | $1,147.50 |

**SERIAL BOND AMORTIZATION PROCEDURES WHEN BOND YEAR AND FISCAL YEAR DO NOT COINCIDE**  When serial bond retirement dates do not agree with the company's fiscal year, the amortization schedule must provide for amortization other than for full annual periods. To illustrate, assume $100,000 of 10-year, 5% serial bonds, dated March 1, 1958, are sold on May 1, 1958, at a discount of $3,200. Bonds of $10,000 mature on March 1 of each year. The discount would be amortized over 118 months. An amortization schedule would be prepared as follows:

AMORTIZATION SCHEDULE WHEN BOND YEAR AND FISCAL YEAR DO NOT COINCIDE—BONDS-OUTSTANDING METHOD

| Year | Bonds Out- standing | | Months Out- standing | | Bond Month Dollars | Total Bond Month Dollars | Fraction of Discount to be Amortized | Amount of Discount | Annual Discount Amortization |
|---|---|---|---|---|---|---|---|---|---|
| 1958 | $100,000 | × | 8 | = | $800,000 | $ 800,000 | $\frac{80}{640}$ | $3,200 | $ 400 |
| 1959 | 100,000 | × | 2 | = | 200,000 | 1,100,000 | $\frac{110}{640}$ | 3,200 | 550 |
| | 90,000 | × | 10 | = | 900,000 | | | | |
| 1960 | 90,000 | × | 2 | = | 180,000 | 980,000 | $\frac{98}{640}$ | 3,200 | 490 |
| | 80,000 | × | 10 | = | 800,000 | | | | |
| 1961 | 80,000 | × | 2 | = | 160,000 | 860,000 | $\frac{86}{640}$ | 3,200 | 430 |
| | 70,000 | × | 10 | = | 700,000 | | | | |
| 1962 | 70,000 | × | 2 | = | 140,000 | 740,000 | $\frac{74}{640}$ | 3,200 | 370 |
| | 60,000 | × | 10 | = | 600,000 | | | | |
| 1963 | 60,000 | × | 2 | = | 120,000 | 620,000 | $\frac{62}{640}$ | 3,200 | 310 |
| | 50,000 | × | 10 | = | 500,000 | | | | |
| 1964 | 50,000 | × | 2 | = | 100,000 | 500,000 | $\frac{50}{640}$ | 3,200 | 250 |
| | 40,000 | × | 10 | = | 400,000 | | | | |
| 1965 | 40,000 | × | 2 | = | 80,000 | 380,000 | $\frac{38}{640}$ | 3,200 | 190 |
| | 30,000 | × | 10 | = | 300,000 | | | | |
| 1966 | 30,000 | × | 2 | = | 60,000 | 260,000 | $\frac{26}{640}$ | 3,200 | 130 |
| | 20,000 | × | 10 | = | 200,000 | | | | |
| 1967 | 20,000 | × | 2 | = | 40,000 | 140,000 | $\frac{14}{640}$ | 3,200 | 70 |
| | 10,000 | × | 10 | = | 100,000 | | | | |
| 1968 | 10,000 | × | 2 | = | 20,000 | 20,000 | $\frac{2}{640}$ | 3,200 | 10 |
| | | | 118 | | | $6,400,000 | $\frac{640}{640}$ | | $3,200 |

**BOND REDEMPTION PRIOR TO MATURITY**    Bonds may be issued with provisions making any portion or all of the issue subject to redemption prior to maturity dates as stated on the bonds at the option of the corporation. The inclusion of call provisions in the bond indenture is a feature favoring the issuer. The corporation is in a position to terminate the bond agreement and eliminate future interest charges whenever its financial position makes such action feasible. Furthermore, the corporation is protected in the event of a fall in the market interest rate by being able to retire the old issue from proceeds of a new issue with a lower rate of interest.

Bonds normally provide for payment of a premium in the event of their call before maturity. The bondholder is thus offered special compensation if his investment is terminated and he is faced with the problem of reinvesting his savings. From the corporate point of view, the premium represents the cost of exercising the option of terminating an unfavorable contract. When bonds are called, the difference between the bonds redeemed together with related premium, discount and issue cost balances and the amount paid is reported as a loss or a gain on redemption. For example, assume that bonds of a corporation are callable at a 5% premium or at 105. Bonds of $20,000 are redeemed on this basis. At the time of call, bonds outstanding are shown at $100,000 with an unamortized discount on the issue of $2,500, and unamortized bond issue costs of $1,000. The following entry is made:

| | | |
|---|---:|---:|
| Bonds Payable (or Treasury Bonds) | 20,000 | |
| Loss on Bond Retirement | 1,700 | |
| Cash | | 21,000 |
| Discount on Bonds Payable | | 500 |
| Unamortized Bond Issue Costs | | 200 |

**BOND CONVERSION**     The conversion of bonds into stock at the option of the bondholder is frequently included in the bond agreement to make the bonds more attractive to buyers. Ordinarily such conversion may take place only within a stated period and under certain specified conditions. Conversion terms may provide for the issue of stock equal in par value to the bond value or for the issue of a certain number of shares of stock for each $1,000 bond. In some cases conversion prices for shares of stock increase at stated periods and terminate on a specified date. If corporate activities are successful, the bondholder may participate in this success as an owner of the corporation by exchanging his bonds for stock; if activities are not successful, the bondholder will continue to hold the bonds and to receive payments as a creditor of the corporation.

Alternate procedures can be followed in recording the exchange of bonds for capital stock with a market value that differs from the book value of the obligation:

(1) Invested capital may be increased by an amount equal to the fair market value of the new security issued, a gain or a loss being recognized on the retirement of the obligation.

(2) The amounts identified with the original obligation may simply be assigned to the new equity.

An increase in the corporate capital equal to the market value of the stock issued can be supported on the grounds that bondholders are actually paid an amount equal to the value of the security given in exchange in terminating the bond contract. The exchange of stock for bonds closes the transaction cycle relating to bonds and opens a new cycle relating to stock in which stock is recorded at the value it would bring if sold on the open market. The gain or the loss on conversion represents a correction of charges relating to the bond issue, since it arises from the conversion feature found in the bond contract. Neither advantage nor penalty is assigned to the new stock issue as a result of provisions of the original bond indenture.

The assignment of bond balances to the increase in capital finds support on the theory that the corporation upon issuing the bonds is aware of the fact that the bond sales price may ultimately represent the consideration identified with stock. Thus, when bondholders exercise their conversion privileges, the values identified with the obligation are properly transferred to the security that replaces it.

To illustrate an exchange on the books of the corporation, assume the following facts: a $100,000, 10-year, 5% bond issue dated January 1, 1954, is sold for $94,000 on that date. Interest is payable semiannually on January 1 and July 1. Conditions of conversion provide that for 5 years after issue a $1,000 bond may be exchanged for 40 shares of common stock with a par of $20 per share Any accrued interest is to be paid on the date of conversion. A bondholder who owns ten $1,000 bonds elects to convert these into stock on April 1, 1958, when stock is quoted on the market at 27½.

The entries to record the payment of interest and the conversion if the newly issued stock is to be reported at its sales value follow:

| | | |
|---|---:|---:|
| Bond Interest Expense. | 140 | |
| Cash. | | 125 |
| Discount on Bonds Payable. | | 15 |

To record interest for the period Jan. 1 - April 1 on $10,000 of bonds converted into stocks:

| | |
|---|---:|
| Amount paid, 5% on $10,000 for 3 months. | $125 |
| Discount amortization, ¼ year at $60 per year. | 15 |
| Bond interest expense. | $140 |

| | | |
|---|---:|---:|
| Bonds Payable. | 10,000 | |
| Loss on Bond Conversion. | 1,345 | |
| Discount on Bonds Payable. | | 345 |
| Common Stock (400 shares, par $20). | | 8,000 |
| Premium on Common Stock. | | 3,000 |

Issued 400 shares of common stock in exchange for bonds:
Value of stock, 400 shares quoted at $27\frac{1}{2}$
(par, $20, or $8,000; premium, $7\frac{1}{2}$, or $3,000)......$11,000
Bonds balances on date of conversion:

| | | | |
|---|---|---|---|
| Face value................... | | $10,000 | |
| Less discount: | | | |
| Discount on date of issuance.. | $600 | | |
| Less amortization to date of sale, $4\frac{1}{4}$ years at $60 per year... | 255 | 345 | 9,655 |

Excess of value of stock issued over bond balances — loss on bond conversion........... $1,345

If balances identified with the bonds are to be assigned to capital stock, the entry to record the conversion is made as follows:

| | |
|---|---|
| Bonds Payable...................................... 10,000 | |
| Discount on Bonds Payable........................ | 345 |
| Common Stock (400 shares, par $20)............... | 8,000 |
| Premium on Common Stock....................... | 1,655 |

Issued 400 shares of common stock in exchange for bonds:
Bond balances on date of conversion, assigned to stock:

| | | | |
|---|---|---|---|
| Face value................... | | $10,000 | |
| Less discount: | | | |
| Discount on date of issuance... | $600 | | |
| Less amortization to date of conversion, $4\frac{1}{4}$ years at $60 per year................... | 255 | 345 | $9,655 |

| | |
|---|---|
| Par value of stock, 400 shares at $20 | 8,000 |

Excess of bond balances over par value of stock— premium on common stock............... $1,655

It should be observed that total capital is the same regardless of the value assigned to the stock issued in exchange for bonds. However, when market value was used in the first example, retained earnings of $1,345 were converted into premium on common stock — a part of the corporate invested capital. It appears that modern practice favors the first approach calling for an increase in invested capital by the fair market value of the new security issued.[1]

---

[1]The American Accounting Association Committee on Concepts and Standards Underlying Corporate Financial Statements would take the first approach. The Committee recommends, "Any difference between the amortized amount of a liability as reflected in the accounts and the amount of assets released or equities created should be recognized as a gain or loss in the period of liquidation. When a liability is discharged by conversion to a stock equity, the market value of the liability is ideally the measure of the new equity created. However, if a reliable market price for the liability is not available, the market value of the stock issued may be used. *Accounting and Reporting Standards for Corporate Financial Statements and Preceding Statements and Supplements*, 1957 (Columbus: American Accounting Association), p. 7.

**BOND REFUNDING**   Cash for the retirement of a bond issue is frequently raised through the sale of a new issue. This is referred to as *bond refunding*. Bond refunding may take place at the maturity of a bond issue. Bond refunding may also be effected prior to the maturity of a bond issue when the interest rate has dropped and the interest savings possible on a new issue will more than offset the special costs of retiring the old issue. To illustrate, assume that a corporation has outstanding 6% bonds of $1,000,000 callable at 102 and with 10 years to run, and similar 10-year bonds can be marketed currently at an interest rate of only $4\frac{1}{2}\%$. Under these circumstances it is obvious that it would be advantageous to retire the old issue with the proceeds from a new $4\frac{1}{2}\%$ issue, since the future savings in interest will exceed by a considerable amount the premium to be paid on the call of the old issue.

Frequently, the desirability of refunding an issue will not be as obvious as in the preceding instance. In determining whether refunding is warranted in marginal cases, careful consideration will have to be given to such factors as the different maturity dates of the two issues, possible future changes in interest rates, changed loan requirements, different indenture provisions, and legal fees, taxes, printing costs, and marketing costs involved in refunding.

When refunding takes place before the maturity date of the old issue, the problem arises as to what is to be done with the charges arising from cancellation of the original issue — unamortized discount, unamortized issue costs, and call premium identified with the old issue. Three positions may be taken with respect to disposition of these items:

(1) Such charges are considered an extraordinary loss identified with the bonds being canceled.

(2) Such charges are considered deferrable and to be amortized systematically over the remaining life of the original issue.

(3) Such charges are considered deferrable and to be amortized systematically over the life of the new issue.

The first position views bond retirement on a refunding operation the same as any other debt cancellation. Payment of bonds terminates the old bond contract and any loss on such termination is identified with the original loan period. The new bond issue is considered a new transaction with only its own costs assignable to future periods. Recognition of the charges arising from bond redemption, as a loss, finds support as a conservative measure, and is also the required procedure for income tax purposes.

The second position views the charges arising from bond redemption as the price paid for the option of entering into a new and more attractive borrowing arrangement. Such charges, then, are properly deferred so that they may be identified with the periods receiving the benefits from refunding — the unexpired term of the original issue. The remaining periods covered by the original issue will still realize a savings through reduced interest charges counterbalanced only in part by the amortization of redemption charges.

The third position views the charges from bond redemption as related to new borrowing and hence as distributable over the entire life of the new issue even when this exceeds the life of the original bonds. The decision to refund the issue is made on the basis of the present arrangement as compared with the various alternative borrowing plans that are available. Any charges relating to the changed financing, then, should be absorbed over the full term of the new issue.

It appears that the strongest argument can be made for the treatment of charges related to bond retirement as an extraordinary loss in the period of such retirement. Here redemption charges are viewed as a loss in terminating an agreement that is no longer favorable rather than as costs for entering into more advantageous arrangements for borrowings. The old loan cycle is considered to have ended; a new loan cycle has begun. To capitalize redemption charges would lend support to similar capitalization of the unrecovered book value of assets and removal charges when assets are retired upon the acquisition of new assets. Either instance may be better viewed as an entry into a new situation that occasions a full recognition of losses that have accrued in past periods.

The American Accounting Association Committee on Concepts and Standards Underlying Corporate Financial Statements views the recognition of redemption charges as a loss in the period of redemption as proper.[1] The Committee on Accounting Procedure of the American Institute of Certified Public Accountants also accepts such practice but indicates a preference for deferral of redemption charges and their amortization over the unexpired term of the old bonds. However, it definitely rejects the amortization of such charges over a new issue whose life exceeds that of the issue retired. The Committee views the decision to refund as being made in consideration of the benefits involved, benefits that are limited to the period during which the new issue replaces the previously outstanding issue. Periods beyond the life of the original issue, not a factor in the decision to refund and

---

[1] *Ibid.*, p. 7.

realizing no benefit from such action, should not be required to carry a part of such refunding costs.[1] In accepting two alternatives the Committee has pointed out, "The existence of the two alternatives is not to be construed as a reflection on accounting or accountants. It arises from a difference of opinion as to the relative weight to be attached to different objectives and reflects a conflict between two modes of thought."[2]

Recognition of a loss as compared with the deferral of redemption charges is illustrated in the example that follows. Assume that 6% bonds of $250,000 are retired from the proceeds of a new 4½% $300,000 issue. The original issue has 5 years to run; a discount balance of $3,000 is found on the date of refunding. Bonds are callable at 102. The new bonds have a 10-year life and are sold at 98. Entries are made as follows:

|  | If Redemption Charges are Recognized as a Loss | If Redemption Charges Are Deferred |
|---|---|---|
| JULY 1 Issued bonds of $300,000 at 98. | Cash......... 294,000 Discount on Bonds Payable 6,000 4½% Bonds Payable............300,000 | Cash.........294,000 Discount on Bonds Payable 6,000 4½% Bonds Payable............300,000 |

---

[1] *Accounting Research Bulletin No. 43*, "Restatement and Revision of Accounting Research Bulletins," 1953 (New York: American Institute of Certified Public Accountants), pp. 130–133. It should be observed that differences between taxable income and financial income will result from the deduction of refunding costs in the year of bond refunding in accordance with tax requirements and the deferral of refunding charges and their assignment to a series of future periods. These circumstances may warrant tax allocation procedures whereby an additional charge to income taxes paid is recognized in the period in which bond refunding charges are deducted on the tax return, and a credit to income taxes paid is recognized in subsequent periods in which bond refunding charges do not appear on the tax return. The Institute Committee is aware of the need for applying tax allocation procedures under these circumstances. However, when an item resulting in a material reduction in income taxes is carried forward in a deferred cost balance, the Committee would credit such deferred cost balance instead of an accrued tax balance. The Committee states, "In the period in which the item is taken as a deduction for tax purposes a charge should be made in the income statement of an amount equal to the tax reduction ... with a corresponding credit in the deferred-charge account. Thereafter amortization of the deferred charge should be based on the amount as adjusted by such tax reduction." (*Accounting Research Bulletin No. 43*, "Restatement and Revision of Accounting Research Bulletins," p. 90.) This position has been challenged on the grounds that it suggests an offset of a liability item (accrued taxes resulting from the deduction for tax purposes of an item still recognized as an asset on the books) against an asset item (deferred refunding costs).

[2] *Accounting Research Bulletin No. 2*, "Unamortized Discount and Redemption Premium on Bonds Refunded," 1939 (New York: American Institute of Certified Public Accountants), p. 20.

| | If Redemption Charges are Recognized as a Loss | If Redemption Charges Are Deferred |
|---|---|---|
| ULY 1 Redeemed bonds of $250,000, with unamortized discount of 3,000, at 102. | 6% Bonds Payable......250,000 Loss on Bond Redemption....8,000    Cash...............255,000    Discount on    Bonds Pay-    able..................3,000 | 6% Bonds Payable......250,000 Bond Refunding Costs.........8,000    Cash...............255,000    Discount on    Bonds Pay-    able.................3,000 |
| DECEMBER 31 Paid semiannual interest, ½% of $300,000 for 6 months. | Bond Interest Expense........6,750    Cash................6,750 | Bond Interest Expense........6,750    Cash................6,750 |
| a) To record discount amortization for 6 months on 10-year basis: 1/20 × $6,000 = $300. | Bond Interest Expense..........300    Discount on    Bonds Pay-    able......................300 | Bond Interest Expense..........300    Discount on    Bonds Pay-    able..................300 |
| b) To record deferred refunding costs amortization for 6 months on 5-year basis: 1/10 × $8,000 = $800. | No entry | Amortization of Bond Refunding Costs......800    Bond Refunding    Costs...............800 |

**DEFERRED REVENUES** Deferred revenues arise upon the receipt of cash or the recognition of some other asset in advance of the period in which the asset may be considered to be earned. Cash received or receivables recognized for goods, services, or benefits to be supplied in future periods call for credits to deferred revenue accounts until commitments are fulfilled. Normally, costs are involved before revenues may be considered realized and the net earnings from this source still remain to be determined in the future.

It has already been suggested that when a deferred revenue item is to make significant claim upon the existing current assets in the fulfillment of contract commitments, such an item is properly reported as a current liability. The deferred revenues classification on the balance sheet, then, should be limited to future revenues that will not make significant demands upon current assets. Unearned interest income, for example, may be reported under the deferred revenues heading since it makes no claim on current assets. Leasehold income, when received for a number of years in advance, would also be listed under deferred revenue. Here the deferred revenue balance may be considered to be composed of (1) a claim for periodic expenditures for taxes, insurance, repairs, etc., (2) a claim for use of properties involving depreciation of noncurrent assets, and (3) a residual balance of net earnings to be recognized over the life of the lease. The claim that is made upon current assets presently reported, included in group (1), is relatively small and may be disregarded for all practical purposes. Other items that are usually reported under the noncurrent deferred revenues heading include advances under long-term service contracts, premiums received on long-term insurance contracts, leasehold advances, and deferred profits on installment sales when profits are to be considered as realized only as installment receivables are converted into cash.

**LONG-TERM LIABILITIES ON THE BALANCE SHEET** In reporting long-term obligations on the balance sheet, the nature of the obligations, maturity dates, interest rates, methods of liquidation, conversion privileges, as well as any other significant matters should be indicated. When assets have been pledged to secure an obligation, full particulars of the pledge should be indicated either in the description of the liability or in the description of the specific assets pledged. Creditors, both present and potential, are vitally concerned with such data, since pledged assets must first be applied to the liabilities that they secure in the event of business insolvency. Even though assets and liabilities may be related in some manner, items should not be offset: a mortgage on buildings is reported as a liability, while buildings are reported at their full cost as an asset; the full bond obligation is reported as a liability, while a bond retirement fund is reported as an asset.

Since there is no difference between unissued bonds and treasury bonds, the two may be combined so that potential funds from the bond authorization may be indicated. These may be reported parenthetically after listing bonds outstanding or they may be reported as a subtraction item from bonds payable authorized. Appropriate disclosure should be made when treasury or unissued bonds have been pledged on loans.

Long-term debt maturing within one year should be reported as a current liability only when retirement will claim current assets. If the debt is to be paid from a bond retirement fund or is to be retired through some form of refinancing, it would continue to be reported as noncurrent, with a note as to its maturity date and the method to be used in its liquidation.

Long-term obligations other than long-term debt are generally listed separately or reported under an Other Liability heading after the long-term debt classification. Deferred revenues are normally reported as the last liability classification. Contingent long-term debt, such as accommodation endorsements or guarantees in connection with debt of affiliated companies, should be disclosed by appropriate accompanying remarks.

Long-term liabilities may be reported on a balance sheet as of December 31, 1958, as follows:

Long-term debt:
　20-year, 5% first mortgage bonds
　outstanding, due January 1, 1970　$210,000
　Less: Unamortized bond discount　　4,500　$205,500

　(Authorized and unissued 5% first mortgage bonds, $40,000: pledged as security on short-term loans, $25,000; held in treasury, $15,000)

　Serial 5% debentures, due May 1, 1959 to May 1, 1964, inclusive...　$120,000
　Less: May 1, 1959, maturities reported in current section......　　20,000　100,000

　Purchase money obligations payable 1960 to 1964.............　　　　　　　55,000　$360,500

Estimated employee retirement benefits and pensions payable..........　　　　　　　　　　　120,000

Deferred revenues:
　Leasehold advances............　　　　　　　　　　　　　　50,000

Total long-term liabilities.........　　　　　　　　　　　　　　　　　　$530,500

## QUESTIONS

**1.** What factors would be taken into consideration in determining whether cash should be raised by bond issue or by the sale of additional stock?

**2.** Distinguish between:
　(a) Secured and unsecured bonds.
　(b) Callable and convertible bonds.
　(c) Registered and coupon bonds.
　(d) Term bonds and serial bonds.

**3.** Explain two methods that may be used in recording transactions relating to bond issuance.

**4.** Describe the nature of the following account balances and indicate how each would appear on the balance sheet:

(a) Bond Subscriptions Receivable
(b) Premium on Bonds Payable
(c) Unissued Bonds
(d) Bonds Payable Subscribed

**5.** (a) Distinguish between the straight-line and the scientific methods for premium and discount amortization on bonds payable. (b) What method would you recommend? Why?

**6.** Is it more practical to amortize discount or premium on bonds at each interest date or at the end of the fiscal period? Explain.

**7.** What amortization policy would you recommend that the issuer follow on bonds that are callable prior to maturity?

**8.** How would you suggest that the costs relating to the issuance of bonds be recorded?

**9.** (a) What arguments can you offer for reporting discount on bonds payable and premium on bonds payable as deferred items? (b) What arguments can you offer for reporting these balances as bond valuation accounts?

**10.** The treasurer for the Gardner Co. proposes that treasury bonds be reported as an asset at the amount paid upon their acquisition. What reply would you make to this proposal?

**11.** What values may be assigned to capital stock exchanged for bonds in accordance with bond convertible features? What arguments can be made in support of each of the procedures recommended?

**12.** (a) Describe the bonds-outstanding method for premium or discount amortization. (b) How does this method differ from the compound-interest method of amortization applicable to serial bonds?

**13.** What is meant by refunding a bond issue? Why may refunding be advisable for a corporation?

**14.** Describe three methods for disposing of charges related to bonds retired through refunding. Give arguments pro and con for each method. Which method do you feel has the greatest merit?

**15.** (a) When would it be proper to report bonds as a long-term debt even though they mature currently? (b) What precautions should be exercised in such reporting?

**16.** Comment on the following presentations and indicate what corrections you would make:
(a) Equipment, cost $100,000, on which installment notes of $90,000 are unpaid, is reported on the balance sheet at the company's net equity therein, $10,000.
(b) Treasury bonds, face value $50,000, cost $56,000 are reported as an asset at cost on the balance sheet.
(c) Advances from a subsidiary company are reported as a subtraction from the investment in the stock of the company in reporting the net investment in the subsidiary on the balance sheet.

**17.** The Bingham Corporation combines unissued bonds and treasury bonds and subtracts this total from a bonds authorized total on the balance sheet. Do you support such practice?

## EXERCISES

**1.** The Majestic Co. has issued 10,000 shares of common stock, par $100. The company requires additional working capital and finds that it can sell 2,000 additional shares of common at $100, or it can float a $200,000 bond issue at par with an interest rate of 5%. Earnings of the company before income taxes have been $80,000 annually, and it is expected that these will increase 40% (before additional interest charges) as a result of the additional funds. Assuming that the income tax rate is estimated at 50%, which method of financing would you recommend as an original common stockholder? Why? (Show calculations.)

**2.** The Clark Corporation issues bonds of $100,000 at 98 plus accrued interest on July 1, 1958. Interest at 6% is payable semiannually on March 1 and September 1, and the bonds mature on March 1, 1968. What entries are required to record (a) the issuance of the bonds on July 1, 1958, (b) the interest payment on September 1, 1958, and (c) the accrued interest and amortization on December 31, 1958?

**3.** The Workman Corp. received permission to issue $1,000,000 of 5%, 10-year bonds. The bonds are dated March 1, 1958, and interest is payable at semiannual intervals on March 1 and September 1. Subscriptions for bonds of $80,000 were obtained on April 1, 1958, at 98. Full payment on subscriptions was made on June 1, 1958, including accrued interest to this date, and bonds are issued. The company's fiscal period is the calendar year. Give the entries that are required for 1958, assuming that the company records unissued bonds in the accounts upon bond authorization.

**4.** (a) The Taft Corporation issues $100,000 of 4% debenture bonds on a basis to yield 4.8% receiving $96,480. Interest is payable semiannually and the bonds mature in 5 years. What entries would be made for the first two interest payments, assuming discount amortization on interest dates by (1) the straight-line method and (2) the compound-interest method?

(b) If the sale is made on a 3½% yield, $102,275 being received, what entries would be made for the first two interest payments, assuming premium amortization on interest dates by (1) the straight-line method and (2) the compound-interest method?

**5.** On December 1, 1956, the Miller Company issues 10-year bonds of $100,000 at 102. Interest is payable on December 1 and June 1 at 6%. On April 1, 1958, the Miller Company retires 10 of its own $1,000 bonds at 99 plus accrued interest. What entries are made to record (a) the issuance of the bonds, (b) the interest payments and adjustments relating to the debt in 1957, (c) the retirement of bonds in 1958, and (d) the interest payments and adjustments relating to the debt in 1958?

**6.** The books of the Wesley Co. reported the following on its balance sheet on December 31, 1957:

Bonds payable (interest at 4%, payable January 1 and July 1;
    bonds mature January 1, 1964)..................... $100,000
Bond discount........................................     1,650

On January 1, 1958, bonds of $20,000 were reacquired at 97½. Bonds of $10,000 were resold on October 1, 1958, at 98½ plus accrued interest. Interest checks on bonds outstanding were mailed on December 31, 1958. The company's fiscal period is the calendar year. (a) Give all of the entries relating to the bond issue that would be made on the books of the company in 1958. (Assume that bonds reacquired are recorded as treasury bonds.) (b) What information relating to the bond issue would appear on the financial statements prepared at the end of 1958?

**7.** The Case Corporation issues $1,000,000 of serial bonds on January 1, 1958, bonds of $200,000 to be retired at the end of each year. Interest of 5% is to be paid annually. The issue is sold for $1,013,556, a price that will result in a 4½% yield. (a) Assuming premium amortization by the compound-interest method, prepare a table summarizing interest charges and bond carrying values for the 5-year period similar to that illustrated on page 594. (b) Prepare a similar table assuming premium amortization by the straight-line method.

**8.** On January 1, Palmer and Boyd, Inc. issues $1,000,000 of 5% notes. Notes amounting to $200,000 are to be redeemed annually, the first redemption to be made at the end of the sixth year. The notes are sold at 96. Interest is payable annually. Set up a table showing the amortization of the discount. What entries would be made to record the interest payments (a) at the end of the first year, (b) at the end of the sixth year, (c) at the end of the seventh year?

**9.** On January 1, 1952, Jackson, Inc. sells $100,000 of 6% debenture serial bonds at 90. Bonds of $20,000 are redeemable at annual intervals, the first redemption to be made on January 1, 1958. Interest checks are mailed semiannually on June 30 and December 31. Amortization entries are made at end of each year. Bonds are callable prior to their serial maturity dates at 102.

All outstanding bonds are called in and retired on December 31, 1958. Give the entries to record the interest payment and the bond retirement at the end of 1958.

**10.** Wright, Inc. issues $100,000 of serial bonds on January 1, 1956, bonds of $10,000 being redeemable annually beginning on January 1, 1957. Bonds are sold for $97,250. Interest at 4% is payable semiannually on January 1 and July 1. On May 1, 1958, the bond series due on January 1, 1961, is retired at 99 plus accrued interest. What entry is made to record the bond retirement?

**11.** Alvin Gray is a holder of $10,000 of 10-year convertible bonds of the Clark Corporation that were issued by the company at 101. He has the option of converting each $1,000 bond into 10 shares of common stock, par value $100. The bond rate is 5% payable semiannually. The option is exercised by Gray 2½ years after the issuance of the bonds. (a) What entries are required on Gray's books and on the books of the corporation to record the exchange in the absence of a market value for the stock? (b) If the stock had a market value of $120 per share at the time of exchange, what entries would be made on the books of each party if this value is to be recognized?

**12.** On December 31, 1958, the end of a fiscal year, the ledger for A. P. Jones, Inc. shows the following:

10-Year 4½% Bonds Payable

| | |
|---|---|
| July 1, 1957. . . . . . . . . . . . . 105,000 | Jan. 1, 1956. . . . . . . . . . . 500,000 |

Discount on Bonds Payable

| | |
|---|---|
| Jan. 1, 1956. . . . . . . . . . . . . . 10,000 | |

Interest on bonds is payable semiannually on January 1 and July 1. Discount amortization has never been recorded. Retirement of bonds of $100,000 on July 1, 1957, at a call premium of 5% was recorded by charging the bonds account for the retirement cost. Give whatever correcting entries are necessary on December 31, 1958, as well as the adjustment for accrued interest on this date.

**13.** The Jacobs Corporation maintains a bond retirement fund. The following balances relative to the retirement fund appear in the general ledger at the beginning of 1958:

Bond Retirement Fund:
    Retirement Fund Cash. . . . . . . . . . . . . . . . . . . . . . . . . . . . . . . $140,000
    Bonds of Jacobs Corporation (at par). . . . . . . . . . . . . . . . . . 630,000
    Other Securities. . . . . . . . . . . . . . . . . . . . . . . . . . . . . . . . . . . . 110,000
    Accrued Interest on Other Securities. . . . . . . . . . . . . . . . . . . 1,600

During 1958, the following transactions take place:
  (a)  Other securities, cost $26,000, are sold for $27,500.
  (b)  Jacobs Corporation bonds, par $120,000, are acquired at a cost of $122,500 plus accrued interest of $2,200. (Bonds were originally issued at par.)
  (c)  Cash of $60,000 is transferred to the retirement fund.
  (d)  Collections of income on other securities total $3,500.
  (e)  Bonds in the retirement fund are formally retired.

Give the entries to record the foregoing transactions.

**14.** The Williams Company calls in a $200,000 6% bond issue that is not due for 4 years and on which there is unamortized bond discount of $3,200. The call price is 102. The company then issues 10-year 4¾% bonds of $250,000, which are sold at 99. List the methods available for the disposition of charges relating to the bonds retired and give the entries for refunding that would be made in each case.

**15.** In reviewing the accounts of the Roberts Co. at the beginning of 1958, you find that on January 1, 1954, it had acquired machinery in exchange for its own 6% bonds with a par value of $100,000 maturing on January 1, 1964. You determine that the bonds had a market value on the date of exchange of $92,000; however, the machinery was recorded at par value of the bonds and depreciation was recognized for 1954 through 1957 at the rate of 4% annually. What compound entry would you make to correct the accounts?

## PROBLEMS

**19-1.** The Brown Corporation issued $100,000 4% bonds, interest payable semiannually, bonds maturing 4 years after issue. The bonds were sold at $96,415, a price to yield 5% on the issue.

*Instructions:* (1) Prepare tables to show the periodic adjustments to the discount account and the annual bond interest assuming adjustment by each of the following methods: (a) the straight-line method and (b) the compound-interest method.

(2) Give entries for the interest payment and the discount amortization for the first year of the bond issue assuming use of (a) the straight-line method and (b) the compound-interest method.

**19-2.** Booth and Carl, Inc. was authorized to issue 10-year, 5% bonds of $500,000. The bonds are dated January 1, 1957, and interest is payable semiannually on January 1 and July 1. Checks for interest are mailed on June 30 and December 31. Bond sales were as follows:

April 1, 1957    $300,000 at 98½ plus accrued interest.
July 1, 1958    $100,000 at 102.

On September 1, 1958, remaining unissued bonds were pledged as collateral on the issue of $75,000 of short-term notes.

*Instructions:* (1) Give the journal entries relating to bonds that would appear on the corporation's books in 1957 and 1958. (Straight-line amortization is used; an unissued bonds account is set up.)

(2) Show how information relative to the bond issue will appear on the balance sheet prepared on December 31, 1958. (Give balance sheet section headings and accounts and account balances appearing within such sections.)

**19-3.** The Lowry Corporation received permission as of January 1, 1958, to issue 6% bonds of $3,000,000 maturing on January 1, 1968. The bonds are dated January 1, 1958, and interest is payable semiannually on January 1 and July 1. The bonds are callable at 102 plus accrued interest at any time after January 1, 1963.

On March 1, 1958, the corporation sold bonds of $1,500,000 at 103 plus accrued interest. Checks for interest were placed in the mail on June 30, 1958. The balance of the authorized issue was sold for cash on October 1, 1958, at 99½ plus accrued interest.

The corporation's annual fiscal period ends on November 30. Interest on bonds was accrued to this date, and bond amortization entries for the past fiscal year were recorded.

Interest checks were mailed on December 31, 1958.

*Instructions:* (1) Give the journal entries relating to the bonds that appear on the books for the year 1958. (The straight-line method is used for amortization; an account for bonds unissued is not set up.)

(2) Assuming that the bonds are called in on July 1, 1963, give the journal entries to record the payment of interest and the bond retirement on this date.

**19-4.** The Malloy Co. was authorized to issue $2,000,000 of 6% debentures on April 1, 1953. Interest on the bonds is payable semiannually on April 1 and October 1. Bonds mature on April 1, 1963, but may be called at 101½ on any interest date after 5 years from date of issue.

The entire issue was sold on April 1, 1953, at 96½ less costs of $30,000 involved on the issue. Cash deposits were made periodically to a fund for the purpose of retiring bonds. Bonds were purchased on the open market from the fund and were retired as follows:

| | |
|---|---|
| June 1, 1955 | $200,000 at 98 plus accrued interest. |
| November 1, 1956 | $300,000 at 99¼ plus accrued interest. |

On April 1, 1958, bonds of $500,000 were called in, and the remaining bonds were retired at maturity.

*Instructions:* (1) Give the journal entries, including any adjustments relating to the issuance of bonds and interest on the obligation, that are required for 1953. (The company's fiscal period is the calendar year.)

(2) Prepare a table with columnar headings as shown below. Show for each calendar year over the life of the bond issue the information as listed.

| Year | Bond Interest | | | Bond Retirement | | | | | Balance Sheet Balances | |
|---|---|---|---|---|---|---|---|---|---|---|
| | Expense before Amortization | Discount Amortization | Total Interest Expense | Amount Paid | Reduction in Discount | Reduction in Bonds Payable Account | Loss on Bond Retirement | Balance of Discount Account | Balance of Bonds Payable Account |

**19-5.** The Diamond Company issued 6% bonds of $2,000,000 at 104 plus accrued interest on April 1, 1957. The bond issue is dated January 1, 1957; interest is payable semiannually on January 1 and July 1. On January 1 of each year for 10 years, beginning January 1, 1958, bonds of $200,000 mature and are paid. The company's fiscal period is the calendar year.

*Instructions:* Give the required journal entries relating to the bond issue in 1957 and 1958. Assume that a bonds unissued account is not set up and that checks are issued on December 31 for all payments due January 1.

**19-6.** Jansen, Inc. issued 5% serial bonds of $1,000,000 dated January 1, 1958. The interest is payable semiannually on January 1 and July 1. The bonds provide that four annual redemptions of $100,000 are to be made, the first one on January 1, 1960; three annual redemptions of $200,000 are to be made beginning on January 1, 1964.

*Instructions:* (1) Prepare a table showing the amount of bond discount to be amortized each year by the bonds-outstanding method, assuming bonds are issued on January 1, 1958, at 94. (The company's fiscal period is the calendar year.)

(2) Prepare a table showing the bond discount amortization if the bonds are sold on April 1, 1958, at 94 plus accrued interest.

(3) Assuming the bonds are sold on April 1, 1958, give the journal entries that would be made in 1958 for (a) the issuance of the bonds, (b) the semiannual interest payments, and (c) the amortization of discount.

**19-7.** The Wilson Company sold $1,000,000 of 4% debenture bonds on January 1, 1956, to an investment banking firm at 97½. The bonds have serial maturities; bonds of $200,000 are payable at annual intervals beginning on January 1, 1959. Interest is payable annually on January 1. Checks for principal and interest payments are mailed on December 31 of each year. On July 1, 1958, the company reacquired at 99 plus accrued interest bonds of $100,000 due January 1, 1959, and bonds of $100,000 due January 1, 1960. Bonds were formally retired.

*Instructions:* (1) Assuming discount amortization by the bonds-outstanding method and bond retirements as scheduled, prepare a table summarizing interest charges and bond carrying values for the bond life similar to that illustrated on page 593, supported by a schedule showing the calculation of amortization amounts.

(2) Prepare a similar table summarizing interest charges and bond carrying values for the bond life taking into consideration bond redemptions in advance of maturity dates as indicated.

(3) Record in journal form the retirement of bonds on July 1, 1958.

**19-8.** The Barker Corporation plans to issue 6%, 10-year bonds that are convertible into common stock within 5 years at the option of the bondholders. Each $1,000 bond may be exchanged for 15 shares of stock, par value $50, plus any accrued interest. Interest on bonds is payable on March 1 and September 1. Accrued interest is to be paid when the bonds are converted. The corporation's fiscal period is the calendar year.

Bonds of $1,500,000 are authorized and printed, and are dated March 1, 1956. Bonds unissued are recorded in the accounts. The issue does not take place until May 1, 1956, when bonds are disposed of at 102 plus accrued interest.

On August 1, 1957, holders of bonds of $400,000 elected to convert their holdings into stock; remaining bonds were converted into stock on September 1, 1958. Paid-in capital was credited with the book value of bonds exchanged for stock.

*Instructions:* Give the necessary journal entries relating to the bond issue during the period 1956 to 1958, including any adjusting and reversing entries that may be required. Assume straight-line amortization.

**19-9.** The balance sheet for the Brownson Corp. on December 31, 1957, the close of the fiscal period, shows the following accounts:

Bond discount and expense...................................$18,000
Accrued interest on bonds................................ $22,500
Bonds Payable, due January 1, 1962, interest at 6% payable
  semiannually on January 1 and July 1..................$750,000

On January 1, 1958, the following took place: cash of $975,000 was made available from the sale of $1,000,000 of 10-year, 5½% bonds to West Underwriters. Cash from the new issue was used for retirement of the 6% bonds at a call price of 102 and for payment of accrued interest on this issue; the balance of cash was added to the general funds of the company. Interest on the new issue is payable January 1 and July 1.

*Instructions:* (1) Give the entries that would appear on the books of the corporation relative to bonds and bond interest for the year 1958, assuming that unamortized discount and call premium on the old issue are not to be identified with future fiscal periods.

(2) Give the entries that would appear on the books of the corporation relative to bonds and bond interest for the year 1958, assuming that unamortized discount and call premium on the old issue are to be amortized over the remaining life of the old issue.

**19-10.** In inspecting the records of the Douglas Corporation you find that $4\frac{1}{2}\%$ First Mortgage Serial Bonds were authorized and dated July 1, 1955, with interest payable semiannually. The issue was sold on October 1, 1955, at 99 plus accrued interest of $2,250 and less costs on the issue of $3,250. Bonds of $20,000 mature at annual intervals; the first maturity date is July 1, 1956. Bonds are callable on any interest payment date. On January 1, 1958, the company called in the 1960 maturities at 102. The company maintained a single account for the bond issue, and on December 31, 1958, the close of an annual fiscal period, this account showed a balance of $116,600, and appeared as follows:

$4\frac{1}{2}\%$ First Mortgage Serial Bonds

| | | | | | |
|---|---|---|---|---|---|
| July 1, 1956 | Retirement of 1956 maturities | 20,000 | Oct. 1, 1955 | Proceeds from sale of bonds | 197,000 |
| July 1, 1957 | Retirement of 1957 maturities | 20,000 | | | |
| Jan. 1, 1958 | Retirement of 1960 maturities | 20,400 | | | |
| July 1, 1958 | Retirement of 1958 maturities | 20,000 | | | |

*Instructions:* (1) Give the correcting journal entries as well as any adjusting entries required as of December 31, 1958. (Assume that the books for 1958 have not been closed. Further assume that bond discount and issue costs are combined and carried as a deferred cost. Give any schedules that may be required in developing entry totals.)

(2) What account balances and amounts relating to the bond issue would appear on the balance sheet as of December 31, 1958, and on the income statement for the year ending December 31, 1958?

**19-11.** The Catalina Co. issued $1,000,000 of Convertible 10-year Debentures on July 1, 1957. The debentures provide for 4% interest payable semiannually on January 1 and July 1. Expense and discount in connection with the issue was $19,500 which is being amortized monthly on a straight-line basis.

The debentures are convertible after one year into 7 shares of the Catalina Co.'s $100 par value common stock for each $1,000 of debentures.

On August 1, 1958, $100,000 of debentures were turned in for conversion into common. Interest has been accrued monthly and paid as due. Accrued interest on debentures is paid in cash upon conversion.

*Instructions:* Prepare the journal entries to record the conversion, amortization and interest in connection with the debentures as of: August 1, 1958; August 31, 1958; and December 31, 1958 — including closing entries for end of year. (A.I.C.P.A. adapted)

**19-12.** The board of directors of the Bellview Company authorized a $1,000,000 issue of 5% convertible 20-year bonds dated March 1, 1956. Interest is payable on March 1 and September 1 of each year. The conversion agreement provides that until March 1, 1961, each $1,000 of bonds may be converted into 6 shares of $100 par-value common stock and that interest accrued to date of conversion will be paid in cash. After March 1, 1961, each $1,000 bond is convertible into 5 shares of common.

The company sold the entire bond issue on June 30, 1956, at 98 and accrued interest. Deferrable costs incurred in making the sale amounted to $8,320. The company adjusts its books at the end of each month and closes them on December 31 of each year. Interest is paid as due. On February 1, 1958, a holder of $20,000 of bonds converts them into common stock.

*Instructions:* Prepare entries in journal form to reflect the transactions arising out of the existence of these bonds on each of the following dates:
   (a) June 30, 1956.
   (b) September 1, 1956.
   (c) December 31, 1957 (including closing entries).
   (d) February 1, 1958.
   (e) December 31, 1958 (including closing entries).

In support of the above entries, prepare a summary analysis of the unamortized bond discount and expense account for the period to December 31, 1958. (A.I.C.P.A. adapted)

**19-13.** The Arden Company issued $3,000,000 of 4% first-mortgage bonds on October 1, 1950, at 96 and accrued interest. The bonds were dated July 1, 1950; interest payable semiannually on January 1 and July 1; redeemable after June 30, 1955, and to June 30, 1957, at 104, and thereafter until maturity at 102; and convertible into $100 par value common stock as follows:

   Until June 30, 1955, at the rate of 6 shares for each $1,000 of bonds.
   From July 1, 1955, to June 30, 1958, at the rate of 5 shares for each $1,000 of bonds.
   After June 30, 1958, at the rate of 4 shares for each $1,000 of bonds.

Expenses of issue were $6,360 and are to be combined with the premium or discount, and the total is to be amortized over the life of the bonds from date of issue. The bonds mature in 10 years from their date. The company adjusts its books monthly and closes as of December 31 each year.

The following transactions occur in connection with the bonds:
   (a) July 1, 1956—$500,000 of bonds were converted into stock.
   (b) December 31, 1957—$500,000 face amount of bonds were reacquired at 99¼ and accrued interest. These were immediately retired.
   (c) July 1, 1958—The remaining bonds were called for redemption. For purpose of obtaining funds for redemption and business expansion, a $4,000,000 issue of 2¾% bonds was sold at 98¾. These bonds were dated July 1, 1958 and were due in 20 years.

*Instructions:* Prepare in journal form the entries necessary for the company in connection with the above transactions, including monthly adjustments where appropriate, as of the following dates:
   (1) October 1, 1950.      (3) July 1, 1956.        (5) July 1, 1958.
   (2) December 31, 1950.    (4) December 31, 1957.

(A.I.C.P.A. adapted)

**19-14.** The D Co. issued $800,000 of 4% Serial Bonds on July 1, 1958. These bonds mature at the rate of $100,000 per year starting July 1, 1961. Discount and deferrable expense connected with this issue were $34,600.

*Instructions:* Using the "bonds outstanding" method, compute the amortization of discount and expense for the year ended December 31, 1958, and for the year ended December 31, 1964. (A.I.C.P.A. adapted)

**19-15.** The post-closing trial balance prepared by the accounting department of the Fenwick Company from its records at September 30, 1958, is given at the top of the following page.

It has been determined that the following transactions or circumstances have not been adequately considered by the company's accountants in the preparation of the trial balance:

(1) Discounts receivable represent the uncollected balances of a considerable number of notes receivable, acquired on a discount basis, in the aggregate original amount of $3,750,000. The discount rate was 10% and the deferred income of $375,000 is the full amount of the discount at the dates of acquisition, which were as follows:

| DATE | AGGREGATE AMOUNT |
|------|------------------|
| June 15, 1958...................... | $2,000,000 |
| July 21, 1958...................... | 1,000,000 |
| September 10, 1958................ | 750,000 |

By their terms, the notes are collectible in equal monthly installments over a period of 15 months. The management is of the opinion that the aggregate discount on the notes acquired should be regarded as earned over the life of the notes and has requested that the "sum of months' digits" method* of transferring discount to income be used. It has been agreed that this method is acceptable, but it has further been agreed that no discount will be transferred to income in the month of acquisition.

(2) The company executed a lease agreement in July, 1958, for a 5-year period beginning September 1, 1958, which stipulated an annual rental of $10,000. Under the provisions of the lease, the annual rental is due on the first day of each lease year, but no rent had been paid or accrued at September 30, 1958.

(3) Real estate taxes are payable in two equal installments on March 1 and September 1 of each year. The fiscal year of the assessing body ends on December 31, but taxes are actually assessed on January 15 and become

---

*For example, if notes were collectible in equal installments over a 5-month period the following procedure would be used:

| Month | Sum of Months' Digits | Proportion of Deferred Income to be Considered Realized |
|-------|------------------------|----------------------------------------------------------|
| 1st..................... | 1 | 5/15 |
| 2nd..................... | 2 | 4/15 |
| 3rd..................... | 3 | 3/15 |
| 4th..................... | 4 | 2/15 |
| 5th..................... | 5 | 1/15 |
|  | 15 | 15/15 |

| ACCOUNTS | DEBIT | CREDIT |
|---|---|---|
| Accounts payable and other current liabilities.... | | $ 1,830,000 |
| Accounts receivable......................... | $ 3,800,000 | |
| Bonds payable—4%—1962............. ..... | | 2,000,000 |
| Capital stock (at par)........................ | | 4,000,000 |
| Cash........................................ | 1,983,333 | |
| Deferred income (discounts receivable).......... | | 375,000 |
| Discounts receivable........... ............ | 3,216,667 | |
| Fixed assets..... ....................... | 4,000,000 | |
| Goodwill..................................... | 80,000 | |
| Notes payable............................... | | 1,000,000 |
| Reserve for depreciation..................... | | 1,000,000 |
| Reserve for losses (receivables)................. | | 625,000 |
| | | |
| Surplus: | | |
|     Balance—October 1, 1957................. | | 1,915,000 |
|     Income for the year ended September 30, 1958 | | 435,000 |
| Treasury stock (at par)...................... | 100,000 | |
| | $13,180,000 | $13,180,000 |

a lien against the property on February 1 of the fiscal year to which they are applicable.

The 1958 taxes (due March 1 and September 1, 1958) were billed at $60,000, and were paid when due.

(4) A 2% dividend was declared on September 30, 1958, to holders of record on October 15, 1958. The dividend is payable on November 1, 1958.

(5) Under a contract with an advertising agency, payments of $110,000 were made during the year in connection with a direct-mail campaign. The payments represented a deposit ($25,000) and services and expenses through August 31 ($85,000). A bill for services and expenses for the month of September has been received in the amount of $60,000. All payments have been charged to expense; no accruals are reflected in the records.

The contract was entered into and the program was commenced on June 1, 1958. The campaign is to continue until May 31, 1959, but benefits are expected to accrue over a 3-year period. The deposit is intended to serve as a working fund for the payment of day-to-day expenses by the advertising agency; it will be deducted from the agency's final billing.

Total expenditures under this contract are estimated at $400,000. The company engages in more or less similar campaigns almost continuously.

(6) Cash for the payment of the semiannual bond interest, due October 15, 1958, was deposited in advance with the trustee in September. The transfer of cash was treated as a charge against income.

(7) Notes payable are all due prior to September 30, 1959.

*Instructions:* (1) Prepare a columnar work sheet setting forth the necessary adjustments to the company's accounts.

(2) Prepare a corrected balance sheet as of September 30, 1958.

(A.I.C.P.A. adapted)

# Chapter 20

# PAID-IN CAPITAL

## CAPITAL UPON CORPORATE FORMATION

**FORMING THE CORPORATION**  The corporation is an artificial entity created by law that has an existence separate from  its owners and that may engage in business within prescribed limits just as a natural person. The modern corporation makes it possible for large amounts of property to be assembled under one management. This property is transferred to the corporation by the individual owners because they believe the corporation will make effective use of it. In exchange for this property, the corporation issues an ownership interest in the form of shares of stock to each party making a contribution. Managements, elected by the contributors of the property, supervise the use, operation, and disposition of the property.

Business corporations may be created under the corporation laws of any one of the forty-eight states or of the federal government. Since the states do not follow a uniform incorporating act, many variations are encountered in the conditions under which a corporation may be created and under which it may operate.

In most states at least three individuals must join in applying for a corporate charter. Application is made by submitting to the secretary of state or other appropriate official *articles of incorporation,* which offer detailed information concerning the proposed organization. If such articles conform to the state's laws governing corporate formation, the articles are accepted and a corporate *charter* is issued recognizing the existence of a new corporate entity. Subscriptions to capital stock now become effective. A stockholders' meeting is called at which corporation *by-laws* are adopted, a *board of directors* is elected, and corporate officers are named. Corporate activities may now proceed in conformance with state corporation law and charter authorization. A complete record of the proceedings of both stockholders' and directors' meetings must be maintained in a *minute book.*

Corporations are classified as *public* when they represent governmental subdivisions or government-owned units and as *private* when they are privately owned. The private group includes *nonstock* companies where operations are of a nonprofit nature and stock is not issued, as in the case of hospitals and schools, and *stock* companies where operations are for profit and stock is issued as evidence of an ownership interest. Corporations are also classified as *domestic* and *foreign;* a corporation is termed domestic in the state of its incorporation and foreign in all other states. A corporation whose stock is widely held and is available for purchase is known as an *open corporation;* a corporation whose stock is held by a relatively few individuals and is not available for purchase is called a *close corporation*.

**NATURE OF CAPITAL STOCK**    An ownership interest in corporate assets is evidenced by shares of stock in the form of certificates. When a value is stated for each share of stock, the stock is said to have a *par value;* stock issued without such an assigned value is called *no-par* stock.

When a single class of stock is issued, each stockholder has certain basic rights that are exercised pro rata according to the number of shares represented by his holdings. These include: (1) the right to share in dividends declared by the board of directors out of corporate earnings; (2) the right to vote in the election of directors and in the determination of certain corporate policies; (3) the right to maintain one's fractional interest in the corporation through purchase of additional capital stock issued by the corporation, known as the *preemptive* right; and (4) the right to participate in cash or other property distributions resulting from liquidation.

In assembling property for a corporation, it is frequently found advantageous to make use of more than one kind of stock with varying rights or priorities relating to the different classes. Stock that has certain preferences over the basic issue is known as *preferred stock;* the basic or underlying issue is known as *common stock*. When more than one class of stock is issued, the special rights and limitations relating to each class of stock are stated in the articles of incorporation or in the corporation by-laws and become a part of the stock contract between the corporation and its stockholders. One must be familiar with the over-all capital structure to obtain a full understanding of any single class of stock, including the special rights granted to it as well as any restrictions imposed upon it. Frequently the stock certificate defines the rights and the restrictions relative to the interest it represents, together with those pertaining to other capital interests.

**LEGAL OR STATED CAPITAL**    The owner of stock in a corporation cannot be held personally liable by creditors of the corporation for any claims against the company. Protection is afforded to the creditors, however, through the designation of a portion or all of the stockholders' investment as *legal* or *stated capital*. State incorporation laws provide that such capital cannot be returned to owners in the form of dividends. Modern corporate legislation normally goes beyond these limitations and adds that legal capital cannot be impaired by the reacquisition of capital stock; reductions in legal or stated capital are possible only as a result of corporate losses or of special action as provided for by law. With a portion of the corporate capital restricted as to distribution or withdrawal, creditors can rely on the absorption by the ownership group of losses equal to such restricted capital before their own equity is subject to shrinkage.

When stock has a par value, the legal or stated capital is normally the total par value of all stock issued and subscribed. When stock is no-par, certain states require that the total consideration received on the sale of stock be regarded as legal capital. A number of states, however, permit the corporate directors to assign an arbitrary value to each share regardless of its issuing price, although in some instances the amount assigned to each share cannot be less than a certain minimum required by law. The minimum value required by law or the value fixed by the board of directors is known as the stock's *stated value*.[1] No-par stock whose full proceeds must be regarded as legal capital is frequently referred to as *true no-par stock* to distinguish such issues from no-par with an arbitrary stated value.

The full amount contributed by the stockholder is recognized as *paid-in* or *contributed capital*. The portion of the paid-in capital representing legal or stated capital is reported as *capital stock;* any investment in excess of that portion designated as legal capital is reported as *additional paid-in capital* or *paid-in surplus*. The sale of stock gives rise to legal or stated capital; a stock dividend or other appropriate action on the part of the board of directors providing for the conversion of retained earnings into capital stock increases this capital.

---

[1]Section 1900 of the California Corporation Code (1949) provides, for example, as follows:

"Every stock corporation shall have a stated capital which shall be made up of the sum of the following amounts . . .

(a) The aggregate par value of par value shares . . . except that if par value shares have been issued as fully paid up for a consideration of less than par pursuant to Section 1110, only the amount of the agreed consideration for such shares specified in dollars shall be credited to stated capital.

(b) The aggregate amount specified in dollars of the agreed consideration received or to be received by the corporation for all shares without par value . . . except any portion of the consideration for such shares without liquidation preference which has been expressly designated by the board of directors upon or prior to issue as paid-in surplus. In the absence of such designation by the board of directors, the entire amount of the consideration for shares without par value shall be credited to stated capital.

(c) Such amounts as are transferred from surplus to stated capital upon declaration of a share dividend or by resolution of the board of directors."

Note in (a) that in certain instances a discount on stock with a par value is deductible from par in arriving at stated capital under the California law.

**PAR AND NO-PAR STOCK**     When a corporation is authorized to issue stock with a par value, the incorporation laws of some states permit such issue only for an amount equal to or in excess of par. Sale of the stock for an amount in excess of the par gives rise to a premium; the premium is added to capital stock shown at par in reporting the stockholders' paid-in capital.

In certain states corporations may be permitted to issue stock at an amount less than par, that is, at a discount. Capital stock is still reported at par, but the discount is reported as a subtraction item in presenting paid-in capital. Persons subscribing for stock at a discount fulfill their obligation to the corporation upon payment of the agreed price; however, the laws of the state may provide that creditors of the corporation may hold subscribers liable for the amount of the discount in the event of inability of the corporation to meet its obligations. Creditors are thus protected by the full legal capital as reported by the capital stock account.

Prior to 1912 corporations were permitted to issue only stock with a par value. In 1912, however, New York state changed its corporation laws to permit the issuance of stock without a par value, and since that date all other states have followed with similar statutory provisions. Today many of the common stocks listed on the large securities exchanges have no-par value.

Use of no-par issues was originally encouraged on the grounds that: (1) such stock could be sold as "fully paid" without making the subscriber contingently liable to creditors as in the case of par stock issued at a discount; (2) investors would not be misled by a less-than-par "bargain" price, but would investigate the value of a stock in the absence of a value appearing on stock certificates; and (3) assets would be recorded at their actual value rather than at amounts set by the par of the stock as a means of enabling stockholders to avoid the contingent liability for the discount.

It is questionable whether investors have subjected no-par stock to closer investigation upon its purchase and whether more satisfactory valuations have been applied to properties received in exchange for no-par stock as compared with stock with a par value. Along with these failures, certain undesirable practices have arisen in the treatment of additional paid-in capital arising from the sale of no-par stock in excess of its stated value: (1) this portion of paid-in capital has been reported simply as "surplus" on the balance sheet, suggesting accumulated earnings rather than invested capital to the statement reader; (2) such paid-in capital has been used to absorb operating losses, the balance sheet thus failing to disclose a deficit from operations; and (3) such paid-in capital has been used as a basis for dividends without disclosure to stockholders that dividends under such circumstances represented no more than a return of original investments. A disadvantage in the issue of no-par stock has been the taxes that are normally imposed on stock of this class; transfer fees, stock taxes, and other taxes and fees on no-par stock are frequently based on arbitrary values assigned to the shares that may be grossly in excess of their issuance price or their subsequent market price.

**PREFERRED STOCK**     When a corporation issues both preferred and common stock, the preference attaching to preferred stock over the common stock issue normally consists of a prior claim on earnings distributed as dividends. A dividend preference does not assure the payment of dividends on the preferred issue; it simply means that dividend requirements must be met on preferred stock before anything can be paid on common stock. Dividends do not legally accrue; payment of a dividend on preferred stock, as on common stock, requires the legal ability on the part of the company to make such a distribution, as well as appropriate action by the board of directors.

While a company can make no guarantee for dividends on its own stock, it can undertake to guarantee dividend payments on stock of another company; hence, one may find a company guaranteeing payment of dividends of another company in consideration for certain services or properties.

Preferred stock is ordinarily issued with a par value. When preferred stock has a par value, the dividend preference is stated in terms of a percentage of par value. When preferred stock is no-par, the dividend is stated in terms of dollars and cents. Thus holders of 5%, $50 par, preferred stock are entitled to an annual dividend of $2.50 per share before any distribution is made to common stockholders; holders of $5 no-par preferred stock receive $5 per share annually before distributions to common stockholders.

A corporation may issue more than one kind of preferred stock. Sometimes preferred issues are designated first preferred, second preferred, etc., with the first preferred issue having a first claim on earnings, the second preferred having a second claim, and so on. The common stock would rank after the satisfaction of all prior preferred claims. In other instances the claim to earnings on the part of several preferred issues may have equal priority, but the dividend or asset preferences may vary.

Other characteristics and conditions are frequently added to preferred stock in the extension of certain advantages or in the limitation of certain rights. Such factors may be expressed in adjectives modifying preferred stock, as cumulative preferred stock, participating preferred stock, convertible preferred stock, and redeemable preferred stock. More than one of these characteristics may be applicable to a specific issue of preferred stock. For example, a preferred issue may be described as "$4.50 First Convertible, Cumulative and Participating Preferred."

*Cumulative and Noncumulative Preferred Stock.* *Cumulative* preferred stock provides that, whenever the corporation fails to declare (*passes*) a dividend on this class, such dividends accumulate and require payment in the future before any dividend distributions can be made to common stockholders. For example, assume that a corporation has outstanding 10,000 shares of 6% cumulative preferred stock, par $25, on which the company has passed dividends for the two preceding years. It will be necessary to declare dividends on preferred stock of $30,000 for the two preceding years, together with $15,000 for the current year, or a total of $45,000, before any dividends can be declared on common stock.

If the preferred stock is *noncumulative*, it is not necessary to provide for back dividends. Failure to declare a dividend on preferred stock in any one year means that it is irretrievably lost; a dividend may be declared on common stock as long as the preferred stock receives the preferred rate for the current period. Preferred stock contracts normally provide for cumulative dividends. Courts have generally held that dividend rights on preferred stock are cumulative in the absence of specific conditions to the contrary.

*Participating and Nonparticipating Preferred Stock.* Preferred stock may be *participating,* which means that it shares in dividend declarations with common stock in accordance with certain participation features. If preferred stock is *fully participating,* it receives as high a dividend rate as common stock. If preferred stock is participating up to a certain maximum rate, it shares with common stock only up to such maximum rate. Since it is preferred stock, it still receives its regular dividend before amounts are available for common stock or for distribution on a participating basis. To illustrate, assume that a corporation has outstanding 5% fully participating preferred stock, par $100,000, and common stock, par $200,000. If earnings warrant the payment of $36,000 in dividends, both preferred stock and common stock receive 12%. The amount to be paid as dividends is apportioned as follows:

|                                                                      | PREFERRED       | COMMON         |
|----------------------------------------------------------------------|-----------------|----------------|
| To preferred, 5%...............                                      | $ 5,000         |                |
| To common, up to preferred rate, 5%.......................           |                 | $10,000        |
| To all shares ratably, 7% ($21,000 on stock outstanding of $300,000) | 7,000           | 14,000         |
|                                                                      | $12,000 (12%)   | $24,000 (12%)  |

If the preferred stock were limited in participation to a maximum of 8%, it would then receive $8,000, and common stock would receive the balance of $28,000, or 14%. Participation features of preferred stock may be stated in terms of dollar amounts instead of in terms of a percentage. When preferred stock is no-par, participation would have to be provided in terms of dollar amounts. A variety of participation features are found on preferred stock issues.

When preferred stock is *nonparticipating*, dividends are limited to the preferred rate or amount. Common stockholders may be paid any amount after payment of the preferred dividend for the current year. Preferred issues normally do not include participating features. Courts have generally held that preferred stock is nonparticipating when the stock contract does not specifically provide for participation.

*Convertible Preferred Stock.* Preferred stock is *convertible* when it offers the stockholder the right to exchange such holdings for some other security of the corporation. Conversion rights generally provide for the exchange of preferred stock into common stock. Since preferred stock normally has a prior but limited claim on earnings, large earnings resulting from successful operations accrue to the common stockholders. The privilege of conversion gives the preferred stockholder the opportunity to share with the common stockholders in the successful operations of the corporation. Preferred stock may be convertible into bonds. Under such conditions, the investor has the option of changing his position as an owner to that of a creditor if such a change should appear advantageous.

*Redeemable Preferred Stock.* Preferred stock is *redeemable* when the corporation retains the option of redeeming it. Ordinarily such redemption requires payment by the corporation of an amount in excess of the par value or original issuance price. Payment of any dividends in arrears is also required when stock is redeemed.

*Asset and Dividend Preferences upon Liquidation.* Stock that is preferred as to dividends is generally preferred as to assets; however, such a preference cannot be assumed but must be specifically stated in the preferred stock contract. The preference as to assets may consist of an amount equal to par, to par plus a premium, or to a stated amount in the absence of a par value. Terms of the preferred contract may also provide for the full payment of any dividends in arrears upon liquidation of the business, regardless of the retained earnings balance reported by the company. When this is the case and there are insufficient retained earnings or a deficit, such dividend priorities must be met from paid-in capital; common stockholders receive whatever assets remain after settlement with the preferred group.

**COMMON STOCK**　　　　　Strictly speaking, there should be but one kind of common stock. Common stock represents the residual ownership equity and carries the greatest risk. In return for the risk that it carries, it ordinarily shares in profits to the greatest extent if the corporation is successful. There is no inherent distinction in management rights between preferred and common stocks. Actually, however, the conditions of issue ordinarily give management rights exclusively to common stockholders as long as dividends are paid regularly on preferred stock; upon failure to meet preferred dividend requirements, the preferred contract may provide that special voting rights shall be granted to preferred stockholders in order to afford this group a more prominent role in the management.

Because of certain legal restrictions on preferred stock, a few corporations have issued two types of common stock, known as Class A stock and Class B stock. One of the two types will have special preferences or rights that the other type does not have, such as dividend preferences or voting rights. The distinction between Class A and Class B stock, then, is similar to that normally found between a company's preferred and common issues. The use of such classified common stocks has been so greatly abused that many stock exchanges have refused to list such new issues, and this form of corporate financing has been largely discontinued.

**RECORDING ISSUANCE OF CAPITAL STOCK**　　　　The capital stock of a corporation may be authorized but unissued; it may be subscribed for and held for issuance pending receipt of cash on stock subscriptions; it may be outstanding in the hands of stockholders; it may be reacquired and held by the corporation for subsequent resale or bonus distributions; and it may be canceled with the permission of the proper state authority. An accurate record of the position of the corporation as a result of the exchanges of property between stockholders and the corporation must be maintained in the accounts. Each class of stock requires separate accounting.

*Recording the Stock Authorization.* The authorized capital stock of a corporation is the maximum number of shares that can be issued under the conditions set by the charter. Application to the appropriate state authority is required in obtaining any change in the original authorization. The amount of stock authorized may be recorded by a memorandum entry in the general journal and then reported in memorandum form in the capital stock account.

*Recording the Stock Subscription.* The agreement to purchase stock is known as a *subscription.* This is a legally binding contract on the subscriber and the corporation. By express provisions, however, the contract may be binding only if subscriptions for a stated amount are received. A subscription, while giving the corporation a legal claim for the contract price, also gives the subscriber the status of a stockholder unless certain rights as a stockholder are specifically withheld by law or by terms of the contract. Ordinarily stock certificates are not delivered until the full subscription price has been received.

Upon receiving subscriptions to stock, Capital Stock Subscriptions Receivable is debited for the subscription price, Capital Stock Subscribed is credited for the value to be assigned to the stock, and a paid-in capital account is credited for the amount of the subscription price in excess of par or stated value.[1] Subscriptions for par-value stock and for no-par stock with a stated value are recorded in a similar manner. When no-par stock has no stated value, Capital Stock Subscribed is credited for the full amount of the subscription. If the laws of the state of incorporation permit stock with a par value to be sold at a discount and subscriptions are received on such a basis, Capital Stock Subscriptions Receivable is debited for the subscription price, Discount on Capital Stock is debited for the discount, and Capital Stock Subscribed is credited for the stock par value.

Capital Stock Subscriptions Receivable is a controlling account, individual subscriptions being reported in the subsidiary *subscribers ledger.* Subscriptions receivable is regarded as a current asset only when the corporation expects to collect this balance currently. This is normally the case. When subscription amounts are due or are called for at different intervals, separate receivable or "call" balances may be established for amounts due on each collection date. Balances currently receivable would be recognized as current assets; remaining balances would be regarded as noncurrent. When subscription account balances are to be collected at some future date when cash is required

---

[1]The term "Capital Stock" is used in account titles when there is a single class of stock. When there is more than one class of stock, appropriate class designations are used in the account titles.

and is called for by the company, the total of these balances may be appropriately considered a subtraction from capital stock in the reporting of paid-in capital.

_Recording Payment for Subscriptions._ Payments on subscriptions may be made in cash or in other properties accepted by the corporation. When payment is received, the appropriate asset account is debited and the receivable account is credited. Credits are also made to subscribers' accounts in the subsidiary ledger for individual payments.

_Recording the Issue of Stock._ Stock is normally issued upon the receipt of full payment on subscriptions. The issuance of stock is recorded by a debit to Capital Stock Subscribed and a credit to Capital Stock.

The credit to Capital Stock is accompanied by an entry for the issue of stock in the _stockholders ledger. This ledger is controlled by the capital stock account;_ here separate accounts are maintained with each stockholder showing the number of shares issued to such individual. The issue of stock by the corporation calls for a credit to a stockholder's account for the shares issued. A transfer of stock ownership is recorded by a charge to the account of the person making the transfer and a credit to the account of the person acquiring the stock; since capital stock outstanding remains the same after transfer of individual holdings, general ledger accounts are not affected.

_A stock certificate book also reports stock outstanding._ As certificates are issued, information with respect to the number of shares issued is reported on the certificate stubs; with ownership transfers, the original certificate submitted by the seller is canceled and attached to the original stub and a new certificate is issued to the buyer. Frequently both stockholder and transfer records are maintained by a _transfer agent_ appointed by the corporation.

**ISSUE OF CAPITAL STOCK ILLUSTRATED**    The examples presented on pages 628 and 629 show the entries that are made to record the sale of stock when: (1) stock has a par value, (2) stock is no-par but has a stated value, and (3) stock is no-par and without a stated value. It is assumed that the Globe Corporation is granted permission to issue 10,000 shares of capital stock. Entries are given together with the resulting account balances after transactions have been recorded.

**SUBSCRIPTION DEFAULTS**    If a subscriber defaults on his subscription by failing to make a payment when it is due, the corporation may (1) return to the subscriber the amount paid,

(2) return to the subscriber the amount paid less any loss or expense incurred upon the resale of the stock, (3) declare the full amount that the subscriber has paid as forfeited, or (4) issue to the subscriber shares equal to the number paid for in full. The practice that is followed will depend upon the policy adopted by the corporation within such legal limitations as are set by the state of incorporation. To illustrate the entries under the different circumstances mentioned, assume the subscription of $10 par capital stock at 12½ in the example on page 628. One subscriber for 100 shares defaults after making a 50% down payment. Defaulted shares are subsequently resold at 11.

*(1) Assuming that the corporation returns to the subscriber the amount paid in:*

| | | |
|---|---|---|
| Capital Stock Subscribed.......................... | 1,000 | |
| Premium on Capital Stock......................... | 250 | |
| Capital Stock Subscriptions Receivable............. | | 625 |
| Cash.......................................... | | 625 |
| Cash.......................................... | 1,100 | |
| Capital Stock................................. | | 1,000 |
| Premium on Capital Stock...................... | | 100 |

*(2) Assuming that the corporation returns to the subscriber the amount paid less the loss on the resale:*

| | | |
|---|---|---|
| Capital Stock Subscribed.......................... | 1,000 | |
| Premium on Capital Stock......................... | 250 | |
| Capital Stock Subscriptions Receivable............. | | 625 |
| Payable to Subscriber (payment withheld pending stock resale)................................... | | 625 |
| Cash.......................................... | 1,100 | |
| Payable to Subscriber........................... | 150 | |
| Capital Stock................................. | | 1,000 |
| Premium on Capital Stock...................... | | 250 |
| Payable to Subscriber........................... | 475 | |
| Cash.......................................... | | 475 |

*(3) Assuming that the corporation declares the full amount paid in to be forfeited:*

| | | |
|---|---|---|
| Capital Stock Subscribed.......................... | 1,000 | |
| Premium on Capital Stock......................... | 250 | |
| Capital Stock Subscriptions Receivable............. | | 625 |
| Paid-In Capital from Forfeited Subscriptions........ | | 625 |
| Cash.......................................... | 1,100 | |
| Capital Stock................................. | | 1,000 |
| Premium on Capital Stock...................... | | 100 |

*(4) Assuming that the corporation issues shares to the subscriber equal to the number paid for in full:*

| | | |
|---|---|---|
| Capital Stock Subscribed.......................... | 1,000 | |
| Premium on Capital Stock......................... | 125 | |
| Capital Stock................................. | | 500 |
| Capital Stock Subscriptions Receivable............. | | 625 |

| Transaction | Assuming stock is $10 par value |
|---|---|
| NOVEMBER 1<br>Received cash of $10,000 and equipment valued at $20,000 in exchange for 3,000 shares. | Cash.................... 10,000<br>Equipment............. 20,000<br>   Capital Stock.........     30,000 |
| NOVEMBER 1–30<br>Received subscriptions for 5,000 shares at 12½ with 50% down payment, balance payable in 60 days. | Capital Stock Subscriptions Receivable......... 62,500<br>   Capital Stock Subscribed............... 50,000<br>   Premium on Capital Stock................ 12,500<br><br>Cash.................... 31,250<br>   Capital Stock Subscriptions Receivable....... 31,250 |
| DECEMBER 1–31<br>Received balance due on one half of subscriptions and issued stock to the fully paid subscribers, 2,500 shares. | Cash.................... 15,625<br>   Capital Stock Subscriptions Receivable....... 15,625<br><br>Capital Stock Subscribed. 25,000<br>   Capital Stock......... 25,000 |
| Balance sheet data resulting from above transactions: | ASSETS<br>Cash........................ $56,875<br>Equipment.................. 20,000<br>Capital stock subscriptions receivable................. 15,625<br>                  $92,500<br><br>CAPITAL<br>Paid-In Capital:<br>  Capital stock (par $10), issued and outstanding, 5,500 shares............. $55,000<br>  Capital stock subscribed, 2,500 shares............. 25,000<br>  Premium on capital stock... 12,500<br>                  $92,500 |

Cash............................................... 550
    Capital Stock................................    500
    Premium on Capital Stock.....................     50

Similar procedures are employed in accounting for defaults on no-par stock.

**RECORDING AUTHORIZED STOCK IN THE ACCOUNTS**   If it is desired to maintain in the accounts a record of the stock authorized as well as unissued, an alternate method may be employed in recording stock transactions. Stock authorized, instead of being

| Assuming stock is no-par but has a stated value of $10 | | | Assuming stock is no-par and without a stated value | | |
|---|---|---|---|---|---|
| Cash................ | 10,000 | | Cash................ | 10,000 | |
| Equipment........... | 20,000 | | Equipment........... | 20,000 | |
|   Capital Stock....... | | 30,000 |   Capital Stock....... | | 30,000 |
| | | | | | |
| Capital Stock Subscriptions Receivable....... | 62,500 | | Capital Stock Subscriptions Receivable....... | 62,500 | |
|   Capital Stock Subscribed............ | | 50,000 |   Capital Stock Subscribed............ | | 62,500 |
|   Paid-in Capital from Sale of Stock in Excess of Stated Value | | 12,500 | | | |
| Cash................ | 31,250 | | Cash................ | 31,250 | |
|   Capital Stock Subscriptions Receivable | | 31,250 |   Capital Stock Subscriptions Receivable. | | 31,250 |
| | | | | | |
| Cash................ | 15,625 | | Cash................ | 15,625 | |
|   Capital Stock Subscriptions Receivable | | 15,625 |   Capital Stock Subscriptions Receivable. | | 15,625 |
| | | | | | |
| Capital Stock Subscribed.............. | 25,000 | | Capital Stock Subscribed.............. | 31,250 | |
|   Capital Stock....... | | 25,000 |   Capital Stock....... | | 31,250 |

| ASSETS | | | ASSETS | |
|---|---|---|---|---|
| Cash........................ | $56,875 | | Cash........................ | $56,875 |
| Equipment.................... | 20,000 | | Equipment.................... | 20,000 |
| Capital stock subscriptions receivable.................. | 15,625 | | Capital stock subscriptions receivable.................. | 15,625 |
| | $92,500 | | | $92,500 |

| CAPITAL | | | CAPITAL | |
|---|---|---|---|---|
| Paid-In Capital: | | | Paid-In Capital: | |
|   Capital stock (no-par, stated value $10), issued and outstanding, 5,500 shares.... | $55,000 | |   Capital stock (no-par), issued and outstanding, 5,500 shares..... | $61,250 |
|   Capital stock subscribed, 2,500 shares............ | 25,000 | |   Capital stock subscribed 2,500 shares ................... | 31,250 |
|   Paid-in capital from sale of stock in excess of stated value................. | 12,500 | | | |
| | $92,500 | | | $92,500 |

recognized by a memorandum entry, is recorded by a formal entry debiting Unissued Capital Stock and crediting Authorized Capital Stock. Subscriptions and payments are recorded as in the previous examples. The issue of stock, however, calls for a debit to Capital Stock Subscribed and a credit to Unissued Capital Stock. The amount reported by the account Authorized Capital Stock less the amount of stock unissued as reported by the account Unissued Capital Stock gives the amount of stock issued at any time. The alternate procedure as applied to the sale of $10 par capital stock in the example on page 628 is illustrated on the following page.

| Transaction | Entry | | |
|---|---|---|---|
| NOVEMBER 1<br>Received authorization to issue 10,000 shares of capital stock, par $10. | Unissued Capital Stock. Authorized Capital Stock.............. | 100,000 | 100,000 |
| NOVEMBER 1<br>Received cash of $10,000 and equipment valued at $20,000 in exchange for 3,000 shares. | Cash................<br>Equipment...........<br>Unissued Capital Stock.............. | 10,000<br>20,000 | 30,000 |
| NOVEMBER 1–30<br>Received subscriptions for 5,000 shares at 12½ with 50% down payment, balance payable in 60 days. | Capital Stock Subscriptions Receivable..<br>Capital Stock Subscribed............<br>Premium on Capital Stock.............. | 62,500 | 50,000<br>12,500 |
| | Cash................<br>Capital Stock Subscriptions Receivable. | 31,250 | 31,250 |
| DECEMBER 1–31<br>Received balance due on one half of the subscriptions and issued stock to the fully paid subscribers, 2,500 shares. | Cash................<br>Capital Stock Subscriptions Receivable. | 15,625 | 15,625 |
| | Capital Stock Subscribed..............<br>Unissued Capital Stock.............. | 25,000 | 25,000 |

Balance sheet data are the same as when the first method was used. Paid-in capital may be presented as follows:

Paid-In Capital:
Capital stock issued and outstanding:

| | | |
|---|---|---|
| Authorized capital stock (par $10), 10,000 shares................................. | $100,000 | |
| Less unissued capital stock, 4,500 shares..... | 45,000 | |
| Issued and outstanding, 5,500 shares........ | | $55,000 |
| Capital stock subscribed, 2,500 shares......... | | 25,000 |
| Premium on capital stock.................. | | 12,500 |
| | | $92,500 |

The foregoing method can be used only in the cases of par value stock and no-par value stock with a fixed stated value; in these instances the valuation to be applied to the entire issue is known at the time of stock authorization. Since the first method illustrated on pages 628 and 629 is the simpler one and may be used for all par and no-par issues, its use is assumed in the remaining examples in this chapter.

**SALE OF SECURITY UNITS FOR LUMP-SUM** Corporations sometimes offer for sale for one lump sum *security units* consisting of several classes of securities. In recording sales of this kind, the sales proceeds must be allocated among the different issues. When a sale consists of two different securities and there is a known market value for one of the securities, the sales value of the other may be determined by subtracting the known value from the sales price of the unit. To illustrate, assume that 1 share of common stock, par $100, is offered with each 6%, $1,000 bond at $1,050. If the common stock is selling for $80 per share, the issuance of common stock is recorded at this figure and the sales price applicable to the bonds is calculated as follows:

| | |
|---|---:|
| Unit price of $1,000 bond together with 1 share of common.... | $1,050 |
| Proceeds identified with common share (market value of common share)..... | 80 |
| Proceeds identified with bond........ | $ 970 |

In recording the sale of a unit, discounts are recorded for the common stock and for the bond as determined by the computation above. The entry to record the sale of 100 units would be:

| | | |
|---|---:|---:|
| Cash...... | 105,000 | |
| Discount on Common Stock...... | 2,000 | |
| Discount on Bonds Payable...... | 3,000 | |
| Common Stock, $100 par...... | | 10,000 |
| 6% Bonds Payable...... | | 100,000 |

If two kinds of stock are offered as a unit, the procedure is similar. For example, assume that 2 shares of common, par $50, are offered with 5 shares of preferred, par $100, at $550 per unit. If the preferred stock has a market value of $96 per share, the sales price applicable to common stock is calculated as follows:

| | |
|---|---:|
| Unit price of 5 shares of preferred and 2 shares of common...... | $550 |
| Proceeds identified with 5 shares of preferred (5 shares at 96).... | 480 |
| Proceeds identified with 2 shares of common...... | $ 70 |

The entry to record the sale of 100 units, consisting of 500 shares of preferred and 200 shares of common, at $550 per unit would be:

| | | |
|---|---:|---:|
| Cash...... | 55,000 | |
| Discount on Preferred Stock...... | 2,000 | |
| Discount on Common Stock...... | 3,000 | |
| Preferred Stock, $100 par...... | | 50,000 |
| Common Stock, $50 par...... | | 10,000 |

If, in the previous case, the price charged for each unit had been $500, the common stock might have been designated a "bonus" and offered as an inducement on the purchase of preferred. The market price of the several issues should still be recognized, if determinable. Here the apportionment of proceeds would be made as follows:

| | |
|---|---:|
| Unit price of 5 shares of preferred and 2 shares of common.... | $500 |
| Proceeds identified with 5 shares of preferred (5 shares at 96).... | 480 |
| | |
| Proceeds identified with 2 shares of common................ | $ 20 |

The entry to record the sale follows:

| | | |
|---|---:|---:|
| Cash.......................................... | 50,000 | |
| Discount on Preferred Stock...................... | 2,000 | |
| Discount on Common Stock...................... | 8,000 | |
| Preferred Stock, $100 par...................... | | 50,000 |
| Common Stock, $50 par....................... | | 10,000 |

The use of treasury stock as a bonus on the sale of security units may be favored if the contingent liability for a discount is to be avoided by stockholders.

If neither preferred nor common stock has a market value that can be applied in apportioning the proceeds, it may be necessary to charge the difference between the combined par values and the proceeds from the sale to the account Bonus to Stockholders. This balance would be a subtraction item in presenting corporate invested capital. The bonus account should be closed when an apportionment of sales proceeds to individual issues can be made. If the unit consists of bonds and shares of stock, however, neither of which has a market value, it will be necessary to estimate the amount at which the bonds could be sold, since the sale of bonds at a figure other than face value requires discount or premium amortization in measuring periodic income.

**STOCK ISSUED FOR PROPERTY** Previous examples have dealt primarily with the issue of stock for cash. When assets other than cash are received in exchange for stock, the property items together with the related increase in invested capital should be recorded at the fair market value of the stock or the fair market value of the property acquired, whichever is more clearly determinable. An established market value for the stock may be used in setting a value relating to the exchange. In the absence of such a value, appraisal of the assets is necessary in establishing a basis for recording the investment.

When assets other than cash are contributed for capital stock, the board of directors ordinarily has the right to establish valuations, which will stand for all legal purposes in the absence of proof that fraud was involved in the action. There have been instances where directors, in the exercise of their power to establish values, have assigned excessive values to assets in the attempt to avoid reporting the issue of stock at a discount. When the value of properties received in exchange for stock cannot be clearly established and directors' valuations are used as a basis for reporting assets and invested capital, disclosure should be made on the statements of the basis for assigned valuations.

Stock is said to be *watered* when assets are overvalued and capital items are correspondingly overstated. On the other hand, the balance sheet is said to contain *secret reserves* when there has been a material undervaluation of assets or overstatement of liabilities with a corresponding understatement of capital.

**TREATMENT OF PRE-MIUM AND DISCOUNT ON SALE OF STOCK**   Amounts received on the sale of stock give rise to paid-in or contributed capital. When amounts received on the sale of stock are greater than the value assigned to the stock, such excess is recorded separately and is properly carried on the books as long as the stock to which it relates is outstanding. When stock is retired, cancellation of the capital stock balance, as well as any related paid-in capital element is called for. The retirement of preferred stock originally sold at a premium, for example, calls for cancellation of the preferred stock balance as well as the premium balance relating to that issue. The portion of invested capital designated as capital stock may not be used as a basis for dividends; however, laws of the state of incorporation may not place such limitations upon the use of invested capital in excess of this balance. When paid-in capital is used as a basis for dividends, stockholders should be informed that dividends represent a return of a portion of their investment rather than a distribution of accumulated earnings.[1]

When stock is sold at less than par, a discount balance is recorded that should be subtracted from the capital stock balance with which it is identified in reporting invested capital. As previously stated, such a discount balance indicates a claim that may be made by creditors upon stockholders acquiring stock at a discount in the event the company becomes insolvent; however, from a going-concern point of view, the discount is a valuation balance attached to capital stock.

There have been cases in practice when discounts on stock have been reported as intangible assets or deferred costs and written off against retained earnings balances or periodic revenue. Such practices are objectionable. A discount on stock involves no asset element but

---

[1]Laws of the state of incorporation may provide that the portion of paid-in capital not designated as legal capital can be used for dividend purposes only under certain conditions. The California Corporations Code (1949), for example, permits the declaration of dividends ". . . out of paid-in surplus only upon shares entitled to preferential dividends." The law further states, "The corporation shall give notice to the shareholders receiving such dividends of the source thereof prior to or currently with the payment thereof." (Sec. 1500 [c].)

is an offset to capital stock in measuring the owners' investment in the enterprise. The absorption of a capital stock discount by either a paid-in capital balance or retained earnings serves only to obscure the original stockholders' investment as well as the continuing contingent liability to creditors. Write-off of the discount to current operations is even more objectionable, as such a practice obscures significant capital information and also distorts periodic revenue. The discount is properly carried on the books as long as the stock to which it relates is outstanding; upon stock retirement and cancellation of a capital stock balance, cancellation of a related discount balance would be in order.

**CAPITAL STOCK ASSESSMENTS**    Incorporation laws of some states provide that a corporation by appropriate action may levy assessments upon stockholders when additional invested capital is required. Failure of a stockholder to comply with such special levies by the corporation may result in stock forfeiture. If stock was originally issued at a discount, an additional capital contribution will serve to reduce this discount; if legal capital requirements were fully met by original investments, assessments represent further increases in corporate paid-in capital. A capital stock assessment and its subsequent collection would be recorded as follows:

| | | |
|---|---:|---:|
| Stock Assessments Receivable...................... | 50,000 | |
|     Discount on Capital Stock (or Paid-In Capital from Stock Assessments) ..................... | | 50,000 |
| Cash......................................... | 50,000 | |
|     Stock Assessments Receivable.................. | | 50,000 |

Most states require that stock be issued as nonassessable.

**ISSUANCE OF STOCK IN EXCHANGE FOR A BUSINESS**    A corporation, upon its formation or at some subsequent date, may take over a going business and issue stock to the proprietors in exchange for their properties. In determining the amount of the stock to be issued for business assets, the market value of the stock as well as the values of the properties acquired must be considered. Frequently the value of the stock transferred by the corporation will exceed the value of the tangible assets acquired because of the favorable earnings record of the business acquired. This excess may be considered as the amount paid for goodwill. .

Where a sole proprietorship or partnership is incorporated to secure the advantages of the corporate form of organization, the books of the old organization may be used after the changes that have taken place as a result of the incorporation are recorded, or a new set of records may be opened. The accounting procedure to be followed in each instance will be illustrated. Assume that Martin and Moore, partners who share profits 3:2 respectively, desire to retire from active participation in their business, and they form a corporation to take over firm assets. The partnership balance sheet just before incorporation on March 15, 1959, follows:

MARTIN AND MOORE

BALANCE SHEET

MARCH 15, 1959

| ASSETS | | | LIABILITIES AND CAPITAL | |
|---|---|---|---|---|
| Cash.................. | | $ 8,600 | Accounts payable........ | $12,000 |
| Accounts receivable.... | $15,000 | | Martin, capital.......... | 50,000 |
| Less: Allowance for bad debts......... | 400 | 14,600 | Moore, capital.......... | 16,200 |
| Inventories........... | | 20,000 | | |
| Equipment........... | $50,000 | | | |
| Less: Allowance for depreciation........ | 15,000 | 35,000 | | |
| Total assets. ........ | | $78,200 | Total liabilities and capital | $78,200 |

The corporation is organized as the United Corporation and is authorized to issue 25,000 shares of no-par stock. Fifteen thousand shares are sold at $10. The corporation takes over firm assets other than cash and assumes firm liabilities in exchange for the remaining 10,000 shares. In taking over net assets, the corporation makes the following adjustments:

(1) The allowance for bad debts is increased to $1,000.
(2) Inventories are recorded at their present market value of $23,500.
(3) Equipment is recorded at its appraised reproduction cost of $75,000 less an allowance on this basis of $22,500.
(4) Accrued expenses of $400 are recorded.

The 10,000 shares received by the partners are divided as follows: Martin, 7,500 shares; Moore, 2,500 shares. The firm cash is then withdrawn by partners according to the balances remaining in their respective capital accounts.

*If Original Books Are Retained.* If the firm books are retained, entries are first made to indicate the changes in assets, liabilities, and the partners' interests prior to incorporation. A revaluation account may be charged with losses and credited with gains resulting from revaluation entries, and the balance in this account may subsequently be closed into the capital accounts in the profit and loss ratio. However, with relatively few changes in asset and liability balances, capital accounts may be debited or credited directly in the profit and loss ratio for the net gain or loss resulting from the adjustments. In recording the issuance of stock in exchange for the partners' equities, the partners' capital accounts are charged and Capital Stock is credited. Subsequent corporate transactions are now recorded in the old books that have become the records for the newly formed corporation. The entries to record the incorporation follow:

| Transaction | Entry | | |
|---|---|---|---|
| (a) To record revaluation of assets upon transfer to United Corp., the net gain from revaluation and adjustments of $20,000 being credited to Martin and Moore in the profit and loss ratio of 3:2 respectively. | Inventories............ Equipment............ Allow. for Bad Debts. Allow. for Depreciation................ Accrued Expenses.... Martin, Capital...... Moore, Capital...... | 3,500 25,000 | 600 7,500 400 12,000 8,000 |
| (b) To record goodwill as indicated by excess of value of stock issued to partners over the appraised value of net assets transferred: <br> Value of stock issued (10,000 shares at $10, amount at which stock is currently being sold)...... $100,000 <br> Value of net assets transferred: <br>    Assets......... $90,000 <br>    Less liabilities.. 12,400   77,600 <br> Goodwill credited to partners in profit and loss ratio. $ 22,400 | Goodwill............ Martin, Capital... Moore, Capital.... | 22,400 | 13,440 8,960 |
| (c) To record distribution of capital stock according to agreement: <br> Martin—7,500 shares valued at $10........ $ 75,000 <br> Moore—2,500 shares valued at $10........ $ 25,000 | Martin, Capital..... Moore, Capital...... Capital Stock..... | 75,000 25,000 | 100,000 |
| (d) To record distribution of cash in final settlement of partners' claims according to balances in capital accounts: <br> Martin, capital after adjustment.............. $ 75,440 <br> Less payment in stock... 75,000 <br> Remaining equity paid in cash................. $ 440 <br> Moore, capital after adjustment................ $ 33,160 <br> Less payment in stock... 25,000 <br> Remaining equity paid in cash................. $ 8,160 | Martin, Capital..... Moore, Capital...... Cash............. | 440 8,160 | 8,600 |
| (e) To record sale of 15,000 shares at $10. | Cash.............. Capital Stock..... | 150,000 | 150,000 |

A balance sheet prepared for the corporation after the foregoing transactions is shown below:

UNITED CORPORATION
BALANCE SHEET
MARCH 15, 1959

| ASSETS | | | LIABILITIES AND CAPITAL | |
|---|---|---|---|---|
| Cash................. | | $150,000 | **LIABILITIES** | |
| Accounts receivable... | $15,000 | | Accounts payable............. | $ 12,000 |
| Less allowance for bad debts........ | 1,000 | 14,000 | Accrued expenses............. | 400 |
| Inventories.......... | | 23,500 | | $ 12,400 |
| Equipment.......... | $75,000 | | **CAPITAL** | |
| Less allowance for depreciation....... | 22,500 | 52,500 | Capital stock, no-par, authorized and issued, | |
| Goodwill........... | | 22,400 | 25,000 shares........ | 250,000 |
| Total assets......... | | $262,400 | Total liab. and capital | $262,400 |

*If New Books Are Opened for the Corporation.* If new books are opened for the corporation, all of the accounts on the partnership books are closed and partnership assets and liabilities are recorded on the new records. In closing the partnership books, entries are made to record the transfer of assets and liabilities to the corporation, the receipt of capital stock, and the distribution of stock and cash in payment of partners' respective interests. If desired, it would be possible to record the revaluation of assets and the recognition of goodwill before recording the transfer of assets and liabilities. Entries to close the partnership books for Martin and Moore may be made as follows:

| Transaction | Entry | | |
|---|---|---|---|
| To record the transfer of assets and liabilities to United Corporation, the difference between claim against vendee $100,000 (10,000 shares of stock valued at $10) and book value of net assets transferred, $57,600, representing gain on sale of business of $42,400. This is distributed to partners in the ratio of 3:2 as follows:<br>To Martin: ⅗ of $42,400..... $25,440<br>To Moore: ⅖ of 42,400..... 16,960<br><br>$42,400 | Receivable from United Corporation, Vendee...<br>Accounts Payable.....<br>Allow. for Bad Debts...<br>Allow. for Depreciation.<br>    Accounts Receivable.<br>    Inventories........<br>    Equipment.........<br>    Martin, Capital.....<br>    Moore, Capital...... | 100,000<br>12,000<br>400<br>15,000 | <br><br><br><br>15,000<br>20,000<br>50,000<br>25,440<br>16,960 |
| To record the receipt of capital stock in payment of net assets transferred. | Stock of United Corporation.............<br>    Receivable from United Corporation,.<br>    Vendee............ | 100,000 | <br><br><br>100,000 |

| Transaction | Entry | | |
|---|---|---|---|
| To record distribution of capital stock according to agreement. | Martin, Capital....... | 75,000 | |
| | Moore, Capital........ | 25,000 | |
| | Stock of United Corporation........ | | 100,000 |
| To record distribution of cash in final settlement of partners' claims according to balances in capital accounts. | Martin, Capital....... | 440 | |
| | Moore, Capital........ | 8,160 | |
| | Cash.............. | | 8,600 |

It would be possible to cancel the asset, liability, and capital accounts without recording the gain on the sale of the business and the settlement with the partners. The following entry closes the partnership books, although details of the partnership liquidation are not shown in the accounts.

| | | |
|---|---|---|
| Accounts Payable.................................. | 12,000 | |
| Allowance for Bad Debts............................ | 400 | |
| Allowance for Depreciation.......................... | 15,000 | |
| Martin, Capital................................... | 50,000 | |
| Moore, Capital................................... | 16,200 | |
| Cash......... | | 8,600 |
| Accounts Receivable............................... | | 15,000 |
| Inventories..................................... | | 20,000 |
| Equipment...................................... | | 50,000 |

The entries that would appear on the separate corporation books are given below.

| Transaction | Entry | | |
|---|---|---|---|
| To record acquisition of assets and liabilities from Martin and Moore. | Accounts Receivable... | 15,000 | |
| | Inventories.......... | 23,500 | |
| | Equipment.......... | 75,000 | |
| | Goodwill............ | 22,400 | |
| | Allow. for Bad Debts. | | 1,000 |
| | Allow. for Depreciation............. | | 22,500 |
| | Accounts Payable.... | | 12,000 |
| | Accrued Expenses... | | 400 |
| | Payable to Martin and Moore, Vendors. | | 100,000 |
| To record issuance of stock in payment of net assets acquired. | Payable to Martin and Moore, Vendors....... | 100,000 | |
| | Capital Stock....... | | 100,000 |
| To record sale of stock for cash. | Cash................ | 150,000 | |
| | Capital Stock....... | | 150,000 |

Instead of reporting both cost and allowance balances for plant and equipment transfers, net values may be reported for such properties in view of their ownership by a new business entity.

It may be mentioned that for income tax purposes, when individual owners of a business transfer assets and, immediately after such a transfer, have "control" of the corporation, no gain or loss is recognized on the transfer, and the basis for the property transferred is the same for the corporation as it was for the original owners. Depreciation, then, would continue to be reported in terms of cost to the original owners, and any gain or loss on the disposal of an asset would be calculated on the basis of original cost less depreciation in terms of such cost. Control is defined by the tax law as ownership of stock possessing at least 80% of the total voting power together with at least 80% of the total number of shares of all other classes of stock of the corporation.

## QUESTIONS

**1.** What are the four basic rights of stockholders?

**2.** Distinguish between: (a) a domestic corporation and a foreign corporation, (b) a stock corporation and a nonstock corporation, (c) an open corporation and a close corporation.

**3.** (a) Define legal or stated capital. (b) What limitations are placed upon the corporation by law to safeguard such legal capital?

**4.** (a) Distinguish between par stock and no-par stock. (b) What classes of no-par stock may be found?

**5.** Name the advantages and the disadvantages applying to no-par stock as compared with par-value stock.

**6.** (a) What preferences are usually granted to preferred stock? (b) What is meant by redeemable preferred stock? (c) What is meant by convertible preferred stock? (d) Distinguish between (1) cumulative and noncumulative preferred stock and (2) participating and nonparticipating preferred stock.

**7.** (a) Describe the method of accounting for the issuance of capital stock when authorized and unissued accounts are maintained. (b) Describe the method of accounting when accounts for these items are not maintained.

8. Indicate how the balance of each of the following accounts is reported on the balance sheet:

(a) Capital Stock Subscriptions Receivable
(b) Capital Stock Subscribed
(c) Unissued Capital Stock
(d) Authorized Capital Stock

9. Describe each of the following records: (a) minute book, (b) subscribers ledger, (c) stockholders ledger, (d) stock certificate book.

10. The Wallace Corporation reports subscriptions to capital stock as a subtraction from paid-in capital balances on the balance sheet. What support may there be for such a treatment?

11. The Benson Co. treats proceeds from capital stock subscription defaults as miscellaneous income. Would you approve this practice?

12. (a) How should cash proceeds be assigned to individual securities when two different securities are issued for one lump sum? (b) Would your answer differ if one of the securities is designated a bonus? Give reasons for your answer.

13. (a) What is meant by *watered stock?* (b) What are *secret reserves?*

14. The Gordon Co. has applied a discount on common stock against a premium on preferred stock and reports additional paid-in capital at the net credit balance. What objections, if any, do you have to such a treatment?

15. (a) What is a capital stock assessment? (b) What entry is made upon the collection of such an assessment if (1) shares were originally issued at a discount and (2) shares were originally issued at par?

16. The Cramer Co. gives 5,000 shares of no-par stock valued at $50,000 to promoters of the corporation and incurs expenses of $30,000 in the sale of stock upon the formation of the corporation. How do you recommend that each of these transactions be recorded?

17. (a) Indicate the accounting procedures that are followed when a partnership is incorporated and the partnership books are to be retained as the accounting records for the new unit. (b) What accounting procedures are followed when a new set of records is to be established for the corporation?

18. The Walsh Company acquires the assets of the Goodman Company in exchange for 10,000 shares of its common stock, par value $10. (a) Assuming that the appraised value of the property acquired exceeds the par value of the stock issued, how would you record the acquisition? (b) Assuming that the par value of the stock issued exceeds the appraised value of the property acquired, suggest two methods for recording the acquisition. What factors will determine the method to be used?

## EXERCISES

**1.** The Dayton Co. pays out dividends at the end of each year as indicated: 1956, $50,000; 1957, $150,000; 1958, $240,000. Give the amount payable per share on common and preferred stock each year, assuming capital structures as follows:

(a) 200,000 shares of no-par common; 10,000 shares of $100, 6%, noncumulative, nonparticipating preferred.

(b) 200,000 shares of $10 common; 10,000 shares of $100, 6%, cumulative, fully participating preferred, dividends two years in arrears at the beginning of 1956.

(c) 200,000 shares of $10 common; 10,000 shares of $100, 6%, cumulative nonparticipating preferred.

(d) 200,000 shares of $10 common; 10,000 shares of $100, 6%, noncumulative preferred participating up to $7\frac{1}{2}\%$.

**2.** The Bushnell Corporation was organized on May 15, 1958. It immediately sold its authorized stock of 100,000 shares at 12. What entries are required for the stock issue under each of the following assumptions:

(a) Shares have a par value $10.

(b) Shares are no-par without a stated value.

(c) Shares are no-par with a stated value of $5 as assigned by the board of directors.

**3.** The Davidson Corporation is organized with authorized capital as follows: 20,000 shares of no-par common and 2,000 shares of 6% preferred, par $100. What entries are required for each of the following transactions:

(a) Assets formerly owned by E. Case are accepted as payment for 6,000 shares of common. Assets are recorded at values as follows: land, $15,000; buildings, $25,000; inventories, $80,000.

(b) Remaining common stock is sold at 25.

(c) Subscriptions are received for 2,000 shares of preferred at 105. A 10% down payment is made on preferred.

(d) One subscriber for 100 shares of preferred defaults and his down payment is retained pending sale of this lot. Remaining subscribers pay the balances due and the stock is issued.

(e) Lot of 100 shares of preferred is sold at 102. Loss on resale is charged against the account of the defaulting subscriber, and the down payment less the loss is returned to him.

**4.** Ten shares of Beck, Ltd., with a par value of $100, are subscribed for at par. The subscriber defaults after he has paid $450. This stock is later sold for $950 cash. What entries are required if (a) no refund is made to the defaulting subscriber, (b) a refund is made of the cash paid less the discount allowed when the stock is resold?

**5.** Staley, Inc. receives authorization to issue 5,000 shares of common stock, par $100. Subscriptions are received for 3,000 shares at $105, cash is received in full, and the stock is issued. (a) What entries would be made if the unissued and authorized accounts are used in recording subscriptions? (b) How would the capital section of the balance sheet appear after the foregoing transactions?

**6.** The trial balance of a corporation includes the following items: Unissued Stock, $60,000; Capital Stock Authorized, $100,000; Discount on Stock, $4,000; Subscriptions Receivable, $16,000; Capital Stock Subscribed, $40,000. How much cash has been collected from the sale of stock?

**7.** The Borden Co. issues 10,000 shares of preferred and 100,000 shares of common, each with a par value of $10, in exchange for properties appraised at $1,000,000. What entry would you make to record the exchange on the books of the corporation assuming that:

    (a) No price can be assigned at date of issuance to preferred or common issues.

    (b) Common is selling on the market at $8½ per share; there was no preferred stock prior to this issue.

    (c) Common is selling on the market at $9¼ per share; there was no preferred stock prior to this issue.

**8.** Wells, Inc. sells 1,000 shares of its 5% cumulative preferred stock, par $100, to its bankers at $120 a share, giving 1 share of common stock, par $50, as a bonus with each 2 shares of preferred. The market value of the preferred stock immediately following the sale is $105 per share. What is the entry for the sale?

**9.** Bonds of $1,000,000 are sold at face value, 5 shares of common stock, par $10, being offered as a bonus with each $1,000 bond. At the time the bonds are sold on this basis, stock is selling on the market at $12 per share. What entry would be made to record the sale of the bonds?

**10.** The Gary Corporation has 10,000 shares of 6%, $100 par preferred stock outstanding, dividends being paid semiannually on July 1 and January 1. On May 1, 1958, it sells an additional 2,000 shares of preferred at $105 plus $2 for "accrued dividends to date." On July 1, 1958, it makes a semiannual dividend payment on preferred stock. What entries would you make to record (a) the sale of the shares and (b) the payment of the dividend?

**11.** The ledger of Farris and Simpson shows the following data on December 31: Assets, $53,000; Liabilities, $23,000; Farris, Capital, $12,000; Simpson, Capital, $18,000. The partners decide to sell the business to Distributors, Inc. in exchange for 4,000 shares of that corporation's $10 par common stock. The market value of the stock at this time is $12. What entries are required (a) to record the purchase in the corporation accounts and (b) to close the books of the partnership? (c) How many shares in the new corporation will be distributed to each partner?

**12.** A balance sheet for Miller and Morton, prepared on March 15, appears at the top of the opposite page. Partners share profits in the ratio of 3:1 respectively.

    The Webster Co. issues 4,000 shares of its $1 par stock to the partners in exchange for partnership assets other than cash. The corporation also agrees to assume firm obligations. On this date the corporation stock

## MILLER AND MORTON
### BALANCE SHEET
### MARCH 15, 1958

| ASSETS | | | LIABILITIES AND CAPITAL | |
|---|---|---|---|---|
| Cash.............. | | $ 2,400 | Accounts payable.......... $ 3,400 | |
| Accounts receivable $ 6,200 | | | Miller, capital............. 23,900 | |
| Less: Allowance | | | Morton, capital........... 19,200 | |
| for bad debts.... | 400 | 5,800 | | |
| Inventories........ | | 10,300 | | |
| Equipment........ | $25,000 | | | |
| Less: Allowance | | | | |
| for depreciation of | | | | |
| equipment....... | 7,000 | 18,000 | | |
| Goodwill.......... | | 10,000 | | |
| Total assets...... | | $46,500 | Total liab. and capital .... $46,500 | |

has a market value of $10 per share.  In dissolving the firm, Miller agrees to take 2,200 shares and Morton 1,800 shares.  The firm cash is then appropriately divided between the partners.  What are the entries to record the foregoing on the books of the partnership and on the new books of the corporation, assuming that the corporation retains tangible asset valuations as shown on the firm books?

## PROBLEMS

**20-1.** The Packard Co. was organized on October 10, 1958, with authorized capital stock as follows:

5% Cumulative Preferred, par $100.............. 1,000 shares
Common, no-par................................. 20,000 shares

Statutes of the state of incorporation provide that the board of directors may set a stated value on no-par stock, but that such a stated value shall not be less than $10.  The board of directors sets the stated value at this minimum.

During the remainder of 1958 the following transactions take place:

(a) Assets of Packard and Packard are taken over in exchange for 10,000 shares of common stock.  Assets of the partnership are appraised as follows:

Merchandise Inventory.................. $30,000
Land, Buildings, and Equipment.......... 45,000

The excess of the stated value of the stock issued over the appraised value of tangible assets acquired is regarded as payment for goodwill.

(b) 500 shares of preferred stock were sold at par.

(c) 2,500 shares of common stock were sold at $10.

(d) Subscriptions were received for 5,000 shares of common at 10½; the stock is to be paid for in two equal installments, 50% being paid on the date of subscription and 50% to be paid within 60 days from the date of subscription.

(e) By December 31, $15,750 had been collected from subscribers as second installments on common subscriptions, and fully paid stock was issued.

*Instructions:* (1) Give the journal entries to record the foregoing transactions, assuming the use of unissued and authorized accounts in the ledger.

(2) Give the journal entries to record the foregoing transactions, assuming that unissued and authorized accounts are not used.

(3) Give the capital section of the balance sheet on December 31, 1958.

**20-2.** The Holland Corporation is organized on May 1, 1958, and is authorized to issue stock as follows:

100,000 shares of no-par common stock with a stated value of $10
2,500 shares of 5% preferred stock with a par value of $100

Capital stock transactions were as follows:

May 15. Subscriptions were received for all of the common stock at 15 on the following terms: 10% is paid in cash at the time of subscription, the balance being payable in three equal installments due in 30, 60, and 90 days respectively.

June 1. All of the preferred stock is sold to an investment company for cash at 95 and stock is issued.

June 15. Collected the first installment on subscriptions to 97,600 shares. Terms of the subscription contract provide that defaulting subscribers have 30 days in which to make payment and obtain reinstatement; failure to make payment within the specified period will result in the forfeiture of amounts already paid in.

July 15. Collected the second installment on common subscriptions. Collections include receipt of the first and second installment on 400 shares from subscribers who defaulted on their first installment; however, subscribers to 500 shares default in addition to those already in default.

Aug. 15. Collected the third installment on common subscriptions. Collections include receipt of the second and third installment from subscribers to 400 shares who defaulted on their second installment. Stock certificates are issued to fully paid subscribers.

Sept. 1. Stock in default is sold to an investment company at 12½.

*Instructions:* (1) Give the journal entries to record the transactions listed above.

(2) Prepare a balance sheet summarizing the transactions above.

**20-3.** The Ogden Manufacturing Company is incorporated on February 28 with authorized common stock of $500,000 and 6% cumulative preferred stock of $250,000, each class with a par |value of $50.

Subscriptions are taken for 6,000 shares of common stock at $60 a share, to be paid for in four equal installments on March 1, April 1, May 1, and June 1. The first installment is paid in full. Subscribers for 200 shares default on the second installment, and the amounts already received are returned to the defaulting subscribers. The second, third, and fourth installments are paid in full on their due dates by the remaining subscribers, and the stock is issued.

During March, preferred stock is offered for sale at $60, 1 share of common stock being offered as a bonus with each subscription for 10 shares of preferred. On this basis subscriptions are received for all of the preferred stock. Subscriptions are payable in two equal installments: the first is payable during March at the time of subscription and the second is payable at any time prior to June 15. The first installment is paid in full. By June 1, $120,000 has been received on the second installment, and stock is issued to the fully paid subscribers.

*Instructions:* (1) Journalize the above transactions.

(2) Prepare a balance sheet as of June 1 reflecting the foregoing.

**20-4.** The Wright Corporation was organized on October 1 with an authorized capital stock of 15,000 shares of 5% cumulative preferred with a $25 par value and 200,000 shares of no-par common with a stated value of $20 per share. During the balance of the year the following transactions relating to capital stock were completed:

Oct.   1. Subscriptions were received for 60,000 shares of common stock at 27½, payable $10 down and the balance in two equal installments due November 1 and December 1. On the same date 10,000 shares of common stock were issued to J. H. Wright in exchange for his business. Assets transferred to the corporation were valued as follows: land, $100,000; buildings, $90,000; equipment, $40,000; merchandise, $86,500. Liabilities of the business assumed by the corporation were: mortgage payable, $32,500; accounts payable, $12,500; accrued interest on mortgage, $375. No goodwill is recognized in recording the issuance of the stock for net assets.

Oct.   3. Subscriptions were received for 10,000 shares of preferred stock at 30, payable $12 down and the balance in two equal installments due on November 1 and December 1.

Nov.   1. Amounts due on this date were collected from all common and preferred stock subscribers.

Nov. 12. Subscriptions were received for 40,000 shares of common stock at 28, payable $10 down and the balance in two equal installments due December 1 and January 1.

Dec.   1. Amounts due on this date were collected from all common stock subscribers and fully paid stock was issued. The final installment on preferred stock subscriptions was received from all subscribers except one whose installment due on this date was $13,500. State incorporation laws provide that the company is liable for the return to the subscriber of the amount received minus the loss on the subsequent resale of the stock. Preferred stock fully paid for was issued.

Dec.   6. Preferred stock defaulted on December 1 was sold for cash at 26½. Stock was issued, and settlement was made with the defaulting subscriber.

*Instructions:* (1) Prepare journal entries to record the foregoing transactions.

(2) Prepare the capital section of the balance sheet for the corporation as of December 31.

**20-5.** Archer and Baker, partners, who share profits and losses in a ratio of 3:2 respectively, wish to retire from active participation in their manufacturing business and decide to form a corporation to take over the firm assets. The partnership balance sheet prepared on March 1 appears below:

ARCHER AND BAKER
BALANCE SHEET
MARCH 1, 1959

| ASSETS | | | LIABILITIES AND CAPITAL | |
|---|---|---|---|---|
| Cash.............. | | $ 30,000 | Notes payable.............. | $ 12,000 |
| Notes receivable...... | | 21,000 | Accounts payable........... | 40,000 |
| Accounts receivable... | | 55,000 | Wages payable............. | 1,500 |
| Inventories.......... | | 66,500 | Archer, capital............. | 77,000 |
| Machinery........... | $80,000 | | Baker, capital ............. | 99,000 |
| Less: Allowance for depreciation....... | 56,000 | 24,000 | | |
| Building............. | $45,000 | | | |
| Less: Allowance for depreciation....... | 32,000 | 13,000 | | |
| Land.............. | | 20,000 | | |
| Total assets.......... | | $229,500 | Total liab. and capital........ | $229,500 |

The partners, together with Carlson and Davis who wish to join the new enterprise, agree to the following:

(a) The corporation to be formed shall be known as the Burbank Sales Corporation, and its authorized stock shall consist of 50,000 shares of common stock, par $5, and 2,000 shares of $6\frac{1}{2}\%$ preferred stock, par $100.

(b) Partnership assets other than cash are to be transferred to the corporation and the liabilities are to be assumed by the corporation. The corporation is to issue all of its preferred stock in payment for net assets acquired. (It is assumed that the stock is worth par value.) The stock is to be divided equally between Archer and Baker, and the partnership cash is then to be withdrawn by the partners in settlement of their equities. The corporation records firm properties other than plant and equipment at book value. Plant and equipment are recorded at current sound values as follows:

| | |
|---|---|
| Machinery...................................... | $35,000 |
| Building ....................................... | 19,000 |
| Land........................................... | 42,000 |

(c) Carlson shall take charge of the organization of the corporation and shall be allowed 3,000 shares of common stock in full payment for his services.

(d) Davis, who owns valuable patent rights, shall be given 10,000 shares of common stock upon transfer of these rights to the corporation.

The Burbank Sales Corporation is incorporated on March 1 when the foregoing takes place.

*Instructions:* (1) Prepare the entries to record the transfer of assets and liabilities to the corporation, and the distribution of stock and cash on the partnership books.

(2) Prepare the entries for the separate corporation books.

(3) Prepare a balance sheet for the corporation on March 1 after the foregoing transactions have been recorded.

**20-6.** Kent, Lewis, and Mason, partners sharing profits 2:2:1 respectively, draw up the following partnership balance sheet on March 1:

KENT, LEWIS, AND MASON

BALANCE SHEET

MARCH 1, 19--

| ASSETS | | LIABILITIES AND CAPITAL | |
|---|---|---|---|
| Cash...................... | $ 19,320 | LIABILITIES | |
| Accounts receivable......... | 41,310 | Notes payable.............. | $ 10,000 |
| Merchandise inventory....... | 44,000 | Accounts payable........... | 17,600 |
| Furniture and fixtures. $16,500 | | | |
| Less: Allowance for | | Total liabilities.............. | $ 27,600 |
| depreciation....... 4,950 | 11,550 | | |
| | | CAPITAL | |
| | | Kent, capital ........ $36,600 | |
| | | Lewis, capital........ 27,560 | |
| | | Mason, capital ...... 24,420 | |
| | | Total capital............... | 88,580 |
| Total assets................ | $116,180 | Total liabilities and capital.... | $116,180 |

The partners incorporate on this date as the Budlong Corporation with an authorized capital stock as follows:

Preferred stock, 5,000 shares, par $20
Common stock, 10,000 shares, par $10

The partners agree to the following:

(1) The following adjustments are to be made in asset values:

(a) An allowance for doubtful accounts is to be established at 5% of accounts receivable.

(b) Furniture and fixtures are to be raised to present replacement costs of $19,500 less a depreciation allowance of 30% on such costs.

(c) Expenses of $650 have been prepaid and are to be recognized as an asset.

(2) Each partner is to be paid for his partnership equity as follows, it being assumed that stock has a value equal to its par:

(a) 750 shares of preferred are to be allowed to each partner.

(b) Remaining capital interests are to be paid for with common stock, in even multiples of 100 shares, each partner to be paid cash for any capital balance in excess of the highest 100-share multiple that can be issued.

The above adjustments and transactions are completed and shares not required for the settlement of the partners' interests are immediately sold at par.

*Instructions:* (1) Give journal entries to record the incorporation, assuming that it is to be reflected on the partnership books, no new books being opened by the corporation.

(2) Prepare a balance sheet for the corporation. (Assume that transactions are completed on March 1.)

**20-7.** The Apex Company formed a new corporation — the Vale Company — and on January 1, 1959, paid $100,000 for the entire authorized capital stock, as follows: 10,000 shares of no-par value (stated value, $5 a share).

On the same date the new corporation acquired for $100,000 in cash the business formerly conducted by Baker & Owen. The tangible assets acquired and the liabilities assumed as recorded on the books of Baker & Owen were as follows: accounts receivable, $25,200; inventory, $9,600; 4% bonds, par value, $5,000; land, $15,400; building, less depreciation, $25,000; equipment, less depreciation, $4,300; mortgage payable, $15,000; accounts payable, $25,000.

The building was purchased January 1, 1949; $5,000 of equipment on January 1, 1948, and $6,000 on January 1, 1957. Depreciation is said to have been recorded on a straight-line basis at the following rates: equipment, 10% per annum; building, 5% per annum to December 31, 1953, and 2½% thereafter.

The cash transactions of the Vale Company for the three months ended March 31, 1959, are summarized as follows:

*Receipts*

| | |
|---|---:|
| 10,000 shares of capital stock.......................... | $100,000 |
| Accounts receivable collected........................... | 65,000 |
| $3,000 par value of 4% bonds—sold February 28, 1959.... | 2,800 |
| Accrued interest on bonds sold........................ | 20 |
| $100,000 par value 5% debentures of Vale Company due January 31, 1969 (issued January 31, 1959)............ | 90,000 |
| | $257,820 |

*Disbursements*

| | |
|---|---:|
| Payment to Baker & Owen............................ | $100,000 |
| Merchandise......................................... | 60,000 |
| Mortgage and accounts payable at January 1, 1959......... | 40,000 |
| Selling, general, and administrative expenses.............. | 20,000 |
| Life insurance premium............................... | 2,000 |
| Organization expense ................................ | 1,500 |
| | $223,500 |

On March 31, 1959, accounts receivable amounted to $80,000; accounts payable for merchandise, $35,000; and for expenses, $3,000; the inventory was valued at $40,000; and prepaid expenses were computed at $1,000.

According to the directors' minutes, the building and equipment are to be recorded at cost to Baker & Owen, less depreciation on a straight-line basis at 2½% and 10% per annum respectively, and the other assets at the value shown by the books of Baker & Owen. Organization expense is to be written off in January, 1959, and depreciation is to be provided on the revised basis stated in the minutes.

*Instructions:* Prepare a balance sheet as of March 31, 1959, including provision for federal income tax at 30 per cent, and an income account for the three months ended March 31, 1959. (Assume that the company is the beneficiary on the life insurance policy; hence the premium is nondeductible for income tax purposes.) (A.I.C.P.A. adapted)

**20-8.** Following is the trial balance of the recently organized Dry Ridge Golf Club on December 31, 1958:

|  | DR. | CR. |
|---|---|---|
| Cash in bank.............................. | $ 7,225 | |
| Accounts receivable, members................ | 11,160 | |
| Buildings................................. | 54,500 | |
| Equipment................................ | 8,500 | |
| Golf course construction.................... | 130,000 | |
| Labor..................................... | 26,285 | |
| Golf course supplies and expense............. | 12,446 | |
| General expense........................... | 4,213 | |
| Interest paid.............................. | 5,617 | |
| Rent..................................... | 6,000 | |
| Commissions—soliciting membership.......... | 1,100 | |
| Notes payable—bank....................... | | $ 10,000 |
| Accounts payable.......................... | | 2,341 |
| Entrance fees............................. | | 146,250 |
| Dues..................................... | | 22,950 |
| "Green" fees.............................. | | 5,015 |
| Taxes on dues and entrance fees............. | | 490 |
| Entrance fees underwritten.................. | | 80,000 |
| | $267,046 | $267,046 |

A proprietary membership in the club costs $1,000, plus $100 tax.

An analysis of the entrance fees account shows that it includes $110,000 paid in, fully paying 110 memberships, and $36,250 collected from 60 members. The balance due from these 60 members, plus the tax thereon, is secured by notes for their original unpaid balance. These notes are on hand but not entered.

In September, 1958, a special committee appointed for the purpose handed in a statement with a list of 80 members, each of whom promised to obtain a new member and to advance the entrance fee of this member at once, subject to repayment when the new member paid in his fee; accordingly, the following entry was then made:

Accounts receivable, members..................... 80,000
    To entrance fees underwritten.................. 80,000

Of the above $80,000, $70,000 had been collected from the underwriters at December 31, 1958. Nothing had been repaid to the underwriters on account of new members, although 10 such new members had been elected in December and had paid in $8,800 in cash and signed notes for $2,200 for entrance fees and taxes.

Dues are $200 a year, plus 10% tax, payable quarterly in advance, and have been chargeable and entered on April 1, July 1, and October 1, 1958.

Included in "Accounts receivable, members" are accounts totaling $330 for dues and taxes against two members who have been delinquent for nine months, and accounts aggregating $770 for dues and taxes of eight other members. Collections can be enforced only by deduction from the proceeds of sale of such memberships after the complement of 300 members is attained.

The building account includes:

| | |
|---|---:|
| Caddy and locker house | $10,000 |
| Architect's plans for a club house, discarded as proposal appeared too expensive | 3,000 |
| Architect's fees for new house | 1,500 |
| Payments under a cost-plus contract for the club house (under construction December 31, 1958) with a guaranteed maximum cost of $50,000 | 40,000 |
| | $54,500 |

The golf course was finished and opened on June 30, 1958. At that date, the club being obliged to maintain the course since the original construction contract was completed, the operating accounts stood as follows:

| | |
|---|---:|
| Debits: | |
| Labor | $10,116 |
| Golf-course supplies and expense | 4,539 |
| General expense | 916 |
| Interest paid | 2,890 |
| Rent | 6,000 |
| Credits: | |
| Dues | $ 5,950 |

The club leases its real estate, for which it pays an annual rental of $6,000, payable January 1 in advance.

The estimated life of the equipment is five years from June 30, 1958.

Of the liability on the books for taxes on dues, $390 is now payable to the Director of Internal Revenue, representing collections in December.

*Instructions:* (1) Prepare the journal entries that should be made on the books as of December 31, 1958, and January 1, 1959, disregarding closing entries, as the fiscal year ends June 30.

(2) Submit a statement of assets and liabilities as of the opening of business on January 1, 1959. (A.I.C.P.A. adapted)

**20-9.** The stockholders of the Agricultural Machinery Co., vendors of horse-drawn machinery, resolved at their meeting on June 13, 1958, to liquidate as of August 31, 1958. The May 31, 1958, financial statement on which the stockholders predicated their decision to liquidate is given at the top of the opposite page.

According to the stockholders' resolution of June 13, the liquidation is to be effected by the directors (who, being principal stockholders, serve without compensation) as follows:

"The $15,000 cash bid of a local real estate operator for the equity in the land and building is to be accepted immediately, the purchaser to assume the outstanding mortgage of $10,000 and to pay all expenses of title search, closing, etc. Title is to pass as of June 30, 1958, and Agricultural Machinery Co. is to pay mortgage interest accrued to that date.

## AGRICULTURAL MACHINERY CO.
### BALANCE SHEET
### MAY 31, 1958

#### ASSETS

| | |
|---|---:|
| Cash | $ 36,750 |
| Accounts receivable | 33,500 |
| Inventory of merchandise | 120,250 |
| Furniture, fixtures, trucks, etc., less reserve | 20,500 |
| Land and building, less reserve | 30,000 |
| Total assets | $241,000 |

#### LIABILITIES

| | |
|---|---:|
| Accounts payable, including taxes | $ 15,600 |
| Interest accrued on mortgage | 250 |
| Accrued payroll | 450 |
| 6% Mortgage due January 1, 1960 | 10,000 |
| Total liabilities | $ 26,300 |

#### CAPITAL

| | | |
|---|---:|---:|
| Capital stock, 4,200 shares, par value $50 | | $210,000 |
| Surplus — balance at Jan. 1, 1958 | $ 24,050 | |
| Less loss for 5 mos. to May 31, 1958 | 19,350 | 4,700 |
| Total capital | | 214,700 |
| Total liabilities and capital | | $241,000 |

Insurance and taxes prepaid prior to June 30, 1958, are to be absorbed by vendor.

"All merchandise on hand is to be offered for sale at 80% of regular sales prices; such special sale to be conducted from June 17 to June 26 (both dates inclusive). These sales are to be on a strictly cash basis and to be final—no returns permitted.

"An auction is to be conducted on June 29 on the company's premises and is to include all merchandise not disposed of during the previous 10-day sale. All furniture, fixtures, trucks, and other equipment are also to be auctioned at this time. All sales made at such auction are to be strictly cash and final.

"Any merchandise still remaining unsold after the auction is to be advertised daily in newspapers of neighboring communities and disposed of at best prices obtainable.

"All employees, except the manager-bookkeeper, are to be given immediate notice of their release, at the close of business on June 30, and to be paid up to July 31. The manager-bookkeeper is to be given immediate notice of his release effective August 31, 1958, on which date he will be paid his salary for the four months ending December 31.

"A liquidating dividend (final) is to be paid on September 2, 1958, as of August 31, 1958, to all stockholders of record as at August 31, 1958."

Sales of merchandise to regular customers on credit for the period from June 1 to 16 inclusive amounted to $9,500 and were merged with the liquidation sales. All merchandise unsold after the auction was finally disposed of in August.

Depreciation subsequent to May 31, 1958, may be ignored.

Following is a summary of the cash transactions for the three months ended August 31, 1958:

### CASH TRANSACTIONS

| | DR. | CR. |
|---|---|---|
| June Cash sales—regular.......................... | $ 5,850 | |
| Accounts receivable collections.................. | 23,500 | |
| Cash sale (special 20% discount)................ | 47,350 | |
| Cash received from auction sales— | | |
| Merchandise............................... | 31,500 | |
| Furniture, fixtures, and trucks................. | 8,250 | |
| Auctioneer's commission and expenses............ | | $ 2,850 |
| Interest on mortgage paid to June 30............. | | 300 |
| Proceeds from sale of land and building........... | 15,000 | |
| Officers and office salaries (including separation payments and $450 accrued payroll)................ | | 5,550 |
| Accounts payable.............................. | | 15,600 |
| July Accounts receivable collections.................. | 1,250 | |
| Post-auction sales— | | |
| Merchandise................................ | 3,500 | |
| Furniture, fixtures, and trucks................. | 2,300 | |
| Salary of manager-bookkeeper for July.......... | | 400 |
| Aug. Accounts receivable collections (final)............ | 3,700 | |
| Collection agency fees......................... | | 375 |
| Salary of manager-bookkeeper (including separation payment).................................... | | 2,000 |
| Legal fees and expenses re liquidation............ | | 675 |
| | $142,200 | $27,750 |

*Instructions:* (1) Prepare the necessary adjusting entries.

(2) Prepare a columnar work sheet showing the postings of the cash transactions, the adjustments, and the cash available for final distribution.

(3) Prepare a statement of loss on realization and expenses of liquidation.

(4) Prepare a statement showing the amount of cash to be distributed as a liquidating dividend to each of the following stockholders:

| | |
|---|---|
| A................. | 1,600 shares |
| B................. | 1,200 shares |
| C................. | 900 shares |
| D................. | 360 shares |
| E................. | 140 shares |
| Total............. | 4,200 shares (A.I.C.P.A. adapted) |

# Chapter 21

# PAID-IN CAPITAL

## CHANGES SUBSEQUENT TO FORMATION

**CLASSIFICATION OF CORPORATE CAPITAL BY SOURCE**   Corporate capital originates from different sources. These different sources need to be identified if one is fully to appreciate the character of the stockholders' interest. Capital originates from three primary sources: (1) investments by owners, (2) earnings retained in the business, and (3) recognition in the accounts of appraisal values. Further subdivisions within each of these classes is necessary in completely setting forth the stockholders' equity.

(1) *Investment by owners.* The investment by owners is divided into (a) contributions forming the corporate legal or stated capital, and (b) contributions not classified as legal capital. The amount representing the legal or stated capital is reported as *capital stock*. With more than a single class of stock outstanding the legal capital for each class should be identified. Contributions by owners that are not reported as legal or stated capital are recognized as *additional paid-in capital or paid-in surplus*. Increases in corporate capital as a result of contributions of properties by outsiders are also normally included in the additional paid-in capital grouping, although it would be possible to recognize such increases in a separate *donated capital* category.

(2) *Earnings retained in the business.* Transactions involving the sale of goods and services give rise to profits and losses that are summarized as *retained earnings or earned surplus.* When a portion of retained earnings is unavailable for dividends, it is referred to as *appropriated* or *reserved;* any balance is then regarded as *unappropriated* or *free.* A debit balance in retained earnings resulting from losses is termed a *deficit* and is subtracted from paid-in capital in arriving at the total corporate capital.

(3) *Recognition in the accounts of appraisal values.* The recognition in the accounts of appraisal values, that is, changes in property values that do not emerge from a transaction and hence are unrealized, gives rise to *appraisal capital* or *appraisal surplus.*

Reference has already been made to the objections that have been raised by authorities to the use of the term "surplus" in accounting, and its application to capital emerging from such different sources as investments, earnings, and appraisals. One finds the term *capital surplus* frequently employed to refer to all paid-in capital balances other than capital stock and in other instances to both paid-in and appraisal capital balances. The use of a capital surplus designation is undesirable in view of the varying meanings attached to this term and the fact that the existence of paid-in and appraisal capital elements would warrant separate disclosure and not combined reporting under a catchall heading.

Individual accounts should be maintained in the ledger for each separate capital element within each of the classifications listed. Hence, separate accounts should be provided for a premium on preferred stock and a premium on common stock; for a retained earnings appropriation related to a bond redemption fund and for a retained earnings appropriation required upon the acquisition of treasury stock. In reporting corporate capital on the balance sheet, however, individual paid-in capital and retained earnings balances are frequently combined and presented under class headings.

Whether reported separately or in combined form, neither paid-in capital nor retained earnings balances can be related to specific assets. Paid-in capital balances indicate asset contributions by the owners that gave rise to proprietorship; a retained earnings balance indicates an increase in net assets from profitable operations that gave rise to an increase in proprietorship; a deficit indicates a decrease in net assets from unfavorable operations that resulted in an impairment of invested capital.

Remaining pages of this chapter consider the transactions after corporate formation that affect paid-in capital balances. The two chapters that follow consider those transactions that affect retained earnings and appraisal capital balances.

**STOCK REACQUISITION AND RETIREMENT** The laws of most states permit a corporation to reacquire and retire its own stock when such action will serve some legitimate corporate purpose and can be made without injury or prejudice to creditors and remaining stockholders. Terms of the preferred stock contract frequently provide that such shares may be called for retirement by the issuing company. Shares may be reacquired at the same price at which they were issued. Normally, however, purchase of shares on the market will be made at a price that differs from the original issue price; reacquisition through redemption will call for payment of an amount in excess of the original issuance price as well as accrued dividends to the date of the call.

Whether obtained through purchase on the market or through the exercise of redemption options, retirement of stock at a cost that differs from its original issuance price presents special accounting problems.

Authorities are in full agreement that the <u>reacquisition and retirement of stock cannot be considered to give rise to profit or loss</u>. Sale of a company's shares represents an expansion of corporate paid-in capital and is without profit and loss significance; reacquisition of a company's shares is the contraction of corporate paid-in capital and is viewed similarly as without profit or loss significance. Profit and loss emerges from transactions between the business unit and outsiders, not from capital transactions between the business unit and its owners. Notwithstanding agreement on this matter, there are still certain problems that are raised in recording the stock retirement. These are illustrated in the examples that follow.

Assume that a company has issued 1,000 shares of preferred stock, par $100, at 105. The entry to record the sale is:

| | | |
|---|---:|---:|
| Cash........................................ | 105,000 | |
| Preferred Stock, $100 par...................... | | 100,000 |
| Premium on Preferred Stock.................. | | 5,000 |

If the preferred stock is subsequently redeemed at its original issuance price of $105, preferred stock and premium account balances may simply be debited for their full amounts and Cash credited. All reference to the capital invested by the preferred stockholder group is thus canceled.

Assume redemption of the preferred stock at a price of $102, or for a total of $102,000. Here, capital of $3,000 originally invested by the preferred stockholders is retained by the company. The retirement of an ownership group does not affect the nature of this capital; it is still capital that originated from an investment source. However, instead of being identified with preferred stock, an equity no longer outstanding, the portion of capital retained is more satisfactorily reported in an account that fully explains its source. The reacquisition and retirement of preferred stock under these circumstances may be recorded in the following manner:

| | | |
|---|---:|---:|
| Preferred Stock, $100 par....................... | 100,000 | |
| Premium on Preferred Stock................... | 5,000 | |
| Cash....................................... | | 102,000 |
| Paid-in Capital from Preferred Stock Redemption | | 3,000 |

Now assume the redemption of the same preferred stock at a price of $110, or for a total of $110,000. Authorities are not in agreement as to the procedure that should be followed under circumstances in which payment by the company exceeds the capital originally invested. There are some who would recognize the full payment as shrinkage in the corporate paid-in capital: after exhausting paid-in capital arising from the original sale of the shares, a separate account would be charged for the excess, and this account balance recognized as a negative paid-in capital element in summarizing invested capital. It is the view of this group that all capital stock transactions, whether of an investment or retirement character, must be reflected in corporate paid-in capital.  Others would limit charges to paid-in capital to amounts originally credited on the issuance of the shares, any payment on stock reacquisition that exceeds the original invested amount being charged to retained earnings.  The excess payment, for this group, represents, in effect, retained earnings made available to retiring stockholders; the charge to retained earnings is made, in recognition not of a *loss* but of a *distribution of earnings.* While retained earnings are reduced in the process of stock retirement, remaining stockholders may now view the balance of retained earnings as wholly identified with their equities.  Applying the latter approach to the retirement of preferred stock in the example, the following entry would be made:

| | | |
|---|---|---|
| Preferred stock, $100 par | 100,000 | |
| Premium on Preferred Stock | 5,000 | |
| Retained Earnings | 5,000 | |
| Cash | | 110,000 |

The latter procedure has the support of the American Accounting Association.[1]  Its use is assumed in later illustrations in this chapter.

It should be observed that when stock is retired, there is a reduction in the corporate legal or stated capital.  State law does not bar the reduction of legal or stated capital when stock is issued subject to redemption and redemption is made at a price as provided for by the original terms of the issue.

**TREASURY STOCK**     When a company's own stock once issued is reacquired and held without cancellation, it is known as *treasury stock.*  A company may acquire its own stock by purchase, by acceptance in satisfaction of a claim, or by acceptance as a donation from stockholders.  Such stock, if formally canceled in accordance with requirements of state law, would revert to the status of unissued stock and would be accompanied by a reduction in legal or stated capital.  In the absence of such formal action, the stock is re-

---

[1] *Accounting and Reporting Standards for Corporate Financial Statements and Preceding Statements and Supplements,* 1957 (Columbus: American Accounting Association), p. 7.

garded as treasury stock and the legal or stated capital of the corporation is unaffected by the stock reacquisition.

The preservation of legal or stated capital for protection to the creditor group calls for certain conditions precedent to the reacquisition of stock by purchase. Ordinarily, state statutes provide that treasury stock can be purchased only when the company's retained earnings are equal to or in excess of the amount to be paid for such stock. Treasury stock acquisition serves to restrict retained earnings from use as a basis for dividends; the reissue of the stock removes the retained earnings restriction. To illustrate the effect of such legislation, assume the capital of a corporation as follows:

Capital stock, 10,000 shares, par $10 .................... $100,000
Retained Earnings....................................... 50,000

The company here can declare dividends out of retained earnings of $50,000; net assets of the company will then be $100,000 and creditors will continue to be safeguarded by owners' capital of $100,000 as reported in the capital stock account. But assume the reacquisition by the company of a part of its outstanding stock at a price of $40,000. If dividends of $50,000 were still permitted and dividends of this amount were paid, protection to creditors would shrink to $60,000, capital being impaired by the purchase of stock and the payment of dividends, a total of $90,000. With a reduction in the company's ability to pay dividends to $10,000 upon the purchase of treasury stock for $40,000, the original representation as to protection to the creditor group is assured; the sum of payments for treasury stock purchases and possible dividends will not shrink net assets below the legal capital reported in capital stock, $100,000. Upon sale of the treasury stock and the recovery of the treasury stock outlay, dividends may once more be paid to the extent of the balance in retained earnings.[1]

Despite the fact that the legal capital remains the same after the reacquisition of a company's stock by purchase, treasury stock cannot be viewed as an asset but must be regarded as a reduction in corporate capital. A company cannot have an ownership interest in itself; treasury stock confers upon the corporation no rights as to dividends, voting, liquidation, or pre-emption. Treasury stock, as a matter of fact, may be regarded in exactly the same manner as unissued stock

---

[1] In some states, the purchase of treasury stock results in a permanent reduction in retained earnings by the amount paid for the stock. Purchase of treasury stock is thus treated, in effect, as a dividend. This is the rule in California. A purchase of treasury stock in this state calls for a charge to retained earnings; the capital stock account continues to report the original legal capital at par or stated value even though there has been a decrease in the number of shares outstanding.

except for one matter: having already been issued in accordance with legal requirements governing legal or stated capital, its resale is possible without the conditions that are imposed upon the original issuance of stock.

**ENTRIES FOR TREASURY STOCK**        A number of different methods have been suggested for recording transactions involving treasury stock. These different methods are the products of two general approaches that may be taken to the problem of treasury stock acquisitions:

(1) The acquisition of treasury stock may be viewed as the retirement of a portion of outstanding stock.

(2) The acquisition of treasury stock may be viewed as giving rise to a capital element whose ultimate disposition still remains to be resolved.

The two approaches are described in the following sections. Descriptions are accompanied by illustrations of methods for recording treasury stock that will give effect to the different views that are presented.

*First Approach: Treasury Stock Acquisition Viewed as Capital Retirement.* The acquisition of treasury stock may be regarded as the withdrawal of a group of stockholders calling for the cancellation of capital balances identified with this group. It follows that the resale of treasury stock represents the admittance of a new group of stockholders calling for entries to give effect to the investment by this group. The American Accounting Association Committee on Concepts and Standards Underlying Corporate Financial Statements supports such an approach. The Committee observes:

> The acquisition of its own shares by a corporation represents a contraction of its capital structure. However, statutory requirements are particularly restrictive in this area of corporate activity and, to an important degree, are controlling in the reporting of such transactions. Preferably, the outlay by a corporation for its own shares is reflected as a reduction of the aggregate of contributed capital, and any excess of outlay over the pro-rata portion of contributed capital as a distribution of retained earnings. The issuance of reacquired shares should be accounted for in the same way as the issuance of previously unissued shares, that is, the entire proceeds should be credited to contributed capital.[1]

A special committee of the American Institute of Certified Public Accountants established in 1937 to answer certain questions raised by

---

[1] *Accounting and Reporting Standards for Corporate Financial Statements and Preceding Statements and Supplements,* 1957 (Columbus: American Accounting Association), p. 7.

the New York Stock Exchange relative to the accounting treatment on the purchase and resale by a corporation of its own common stock also viewed the acquisition of treasury stock as stock retirement. It concluded:

> Your committee can see no essential difference between (a) the purchase and retirement of a corporation's own common stock and the subsequent issue of common shares, and (b) the purchase and resale of its own common stock.[1]

When the reacquisition of stock is viewed as stock retirement, alternate methods may be employed in reporting the reduction in the capital stock balance: (1) the capital stock account may be charged directly; (2) a treasury stock account may be charged and this balance treated as a subtraction item from capital stock. The alternate methods are illustrated on pages 660 and 661. The transactions for each case are described below.

*Treasury Stock Reported as a Reduction in Capital Stock:*

Transaction (1): Treasury stock is acquired at a price that exceeds the original issuing price. Original credits to paid-in capital balances are canceled and Retained Earnings is charged for the excess as in the case of formal stock retirement.

Transaction (2): When the stock is resold at more than par, an entry is made as on an original sale at more than par. If the stock were resold at less than par, a discount balance might be established and recognized as a subtraction item in the presentation of paid-in capital; such discount would not be recoverable as a discount on original issue in view of the fact that the stock had once been issued and fully paid for. Instead of establishing a discount balance, the charge may be made to Retained Earnings. Such procedure would preserve capital at the legal or stated balance as reported by the capital stock account.

*Treasury Stock Account Used to Report Reduction in Capital Stock:*

Transaction (1): A treasury stock account instead of capital stock may be charged for the amount of the reduction in the capital stock. The treasury stock account subtracted from the capital stock account reporting the amount issued then gives the capital stock outstanding. Charges to other paid-in capital and retained earnings balances would be made just as described in the preceding section.

Transaction (2): When the treasury stock is sold, the treasury stock account is credited for the amount at which treasury stock is carried, and any difference between the sales price and the carrying amount is treated in exactly the same manner as described in the preceding section.

**Second Approach: Treasury Stock Acquisition Viewed as Giving Rise to Capital Element Awaiting Ultimate Disposition.** The acquisition of treasury stock may be viewed as an application of cash to a capital purpose

---

[1]*Accounting Research Bulletin No. 43*, "Restatement and Revision of Accounting Research Bulletins," 1953 (New York: American Institute of Certified Public Accountants), p. 14.

| Transaction | First Approach: Treasury Stock Acquisition Viewed as Capital Retirement |
|---|---|
| | Treasury Stock Acquisition Reported as Reduction in Capital Stock |
| **1957** Issue of stock, 10,000 shares, $10 par, at 15. | Cash................ 150,000 <br>    Capital Stock.......              100,000 <br>    Premium on Stock...              50,000 |
| Profit for year, $30,000. | Profit and Loss....... 30,000 <br>    Retained Earnings...              30,000 |
| **1958** (1) Reacquisition of 1,000 shares at 16. | Capital Stock......... 10,000 <br> Premium on Stock.....  5,000 <br> Retained Earnings.....  1,000 <br>    Cash..............              16,000 |
| (2) Resale of stock at 20. | Cash................ 20,000 <br>    Capital Stock.......              10,000 <br>    Premium on Stock...              10,000 |
| Capital section after sale of treasury stock: | Capital <br> Capital Stock.......              $100,000 <br> Premium on Stock...              55,000 <br> Retained Earnings...              29,000 <br><br>                        $184,000 |

that has not been finally defined or consummated. Upon the purchase of treasury stock, a treasury stock account is charged for the cost of the purchase. This balance is recognized as a negative capital element that does not call for specific identification with paid-in capital or retained earnings at this time. If treasury stock is retired, the debit balance in the treasury stock account can be allocated to the appropriate capital balances as in preceding analyses; if the treasury stock is resold, the sale is viewed as achievement of the objective originally envisioned, now making possible the recognition of the net effect of treasury stock purchase and sale. It is the retirement or the sale of treasury stock that makes possible a determination of the effect of treasury stock transactions upon corporate capital elements.

The application of this approach is illustrated on page 661. The transactions in the example are described below.

Transaction (1): When treasury stock is purchased, it is recorded at its cost regardless of whether this cost is more or less than the original stock issuance price. In a presentation of corporate capital at this time, treasury

| First Approach: Treasury Stock Acquisition Viewed as Capital Retirement | | Second Approach: Treasury Stock Acquisition Viewed as Giving Rise to Capital Element Awaiting Ultimate Disposition | |
|---|---|---|---|
| Treasury Stock Account Used to Report Reduction in Capital Stock | | | |
| Cash.................. 150,000 | | Cash................. 150,000 | |
| Capital Stock....... | 100,000 | Capital Stock....... | 100,000 |
| Premium on Stock... | 50,000 | Premium on Stock... | 50,000 |
| Profit and Loss........ 30,000 | | Profit and Loss........ 30,000 | |
| Retained Earnings... | 30,000 | Retained Earnings... | 30,000 |
| Treasury Stock........ 10,000 | | Treasury Stock........ 16,000 | |
| Premium on Stock..... 5,000 | | Cash.............. | 16,000 |
| Retained Earnings..... 1,000 | | | |
| Cash.............. | 16,000 | | |
| Cash................. 20,000 | | Cash................. 20,000 | |
| Treasury Stock...... | 10,000 | Treasury Stock...... | 16,000 |
| Premium on Stock... | 10,000 | Paid-In Capital from Sale of Treasury Stock in Excess of Cost.... | 4,000 |
| Capital | | Capital | |
| Capital stock....... | $100,000 | Capital stock....... | $100,000 |
| Premium on stock... | 55,000 | Premium on stock... | 50,000 |
| Retained earnings... | 29,000 | Paid-In capital from sale of treasury stock in excess of cost ............ | 4,000 |
| | | Retained earnings.... | 30,000 |
| | $184,000 | | $184,000 |

stock, consisting of a cost unallocated as to the different capital elements, would be reported as a subtraction item from the sum of paid-in capital and retained earnings.

Transaction (2): When treasury stock is sold at more than its cost, the excess gives rise to paid-in capital arising from treasury stock transactions. If the treasury stock were resold at less than cost, the shrinkage in capital from treasury stock purchase and sale might be summarized in a separate account and the latter recognized as a subtraction item in the presentation of invested capital. Instead of recognizing a shrinkage in paid-in capital for the difference between the purchase and sales price, the charge may be made to Retained Earnings. Such procedure would preserve capital at the legal or stated balance as reported by the capital stock account.

Capital balances arising from the use of each method should be compared. Capital sections after the sale of treasury stock are listed following each set of entries. While total capitals are the same regardless of the method used, there will be differences in paid-in capital and retained earnings balances. Each method can be supported in theory; the nature of the method to be used will depend upon the approach that one feels has the greater merit under the circumstances.

**ACQUISITION OF NO-PAR TREASURY STOCK**      The foregoing illustrations assumed the reacquisition and the resale of stock with a par value. The reacquisition of stock with a stated value provides no new problems; the stated value instead of the par value is used when reductions in the capital stock account are involved or when the treasury stock account is charged with an amount equal to the original credit reported in the capital stock balance. When there is no stated or par value and the capital stock account has been credited with the proceeds from stock issued at different prices, a special problem is faced. Under such circumstances, the capital stock offset is usually considered to be either (1) the original issuing price of the particular lot reacquired, or (2) the average price at which the stock of the company was originally issued. For example, assume the following entries in a capital stock account:

CAPITAL STOCK (NO-PAR)

| | |
|---|---|
| 2,000 shares @ 18............. | 36,000 |
| 2,000 shares @ 20............. | 40,000 |
| 1,000 shares @ 22............. | 22,000 |
| 5,000 shares................. | 98,000 |

Assume that 1,000 shares are reacquired at 16½. The acquisition is identified as the second lot sold, and treasury stock is to be recorded at the original issuing price. The following entry is made:

| | | |
|---|---|---|
| Treasury Stock................................. | 20,000 | |
| Cash......................................... | | 16,500 |
| Paid-In Capital from Stock Reacquisition......... | | 3,500 |

Assume that treasury stock is to be recorded at the average issuing price. The average is calculated as follows:

$$\frac{98,000 \text{ (proceeds from sales)}}{5,000 \text{ (shares issued)}} = \$19.60, \text{ average issuing price per share}$$

The entry in this case would be:

| | | |
|---|---|---|
| Treasury Stock................................. | 19,600 | |
| Cash......................................... | | 16,500 |
| Paid-In Capital from Stock Reacquisition......... | | 3,100 |

**RETAINED EARNINGS APPROPRIATIONS FOR TREASURY STOCK HOLDINGS**      The illustrations on pages 660 and 661 gave the entries for the acquisition and the sale of treasury stock but did not consider the problem of restricting the distribution of retained earnings during the period that the treasury stock was held. When the law provides for retained earnings restrictions upon the acquisition of treasury stock, it will be necessary to give effect to such restrictions regardless of the method employed in recording the treasury stock.

It will be observed that the retained earnings of the company in the example were adequate to permit the purchase of the treasury stock as indicated without reducing the capital below legal capital as reported in the capital stock account.  To assure no impairment in legal capital after the treasury stock is acquired, either of the following procedures may be followed:

(1)_An appropriation may be made for the amount of retained earnings restricted by law.  When the law provides for the cancellation of such a restriction upon the recovery of the price paid for the treasury stock or upon the formal retirement of the stock, the entries recording the sale or the retirement are accompanied by an entry reversing the retained earnings appropriation.

(2) A parenthetical remark may be included in the presentation of the corporate capital on the balance sheet to report the restriction on retained earnings resulting from the treasury stock holdings; this remark must be included on succeeding balance sheets until the stock is sold or formally retired and the restriction is no longer operative.

To illustrate the foregoing, assume the information listed under the second approach on page 661.  With the purchase of treasury stock at $16,000, a second entry may be made as follows:

| | | |
|---|---:|---:|
| Retained Earnings.............................. | 16,000 | |
|    Retained Earnings Appropriated for Purchase of Treasury Stock............................... | | 16,000 |

The capital of the company may be presented as follows:

Paid-in capital:

| | | |
|---|---:|---:|
|   Capital stock — authorized and issued, 10,000 shares, par value $10, which includes 1,000 shares in the treasury (see below)........... | | $100,000 |
|   Premium on stock.......................... | | 50,000 |
|     Total paid-in capital...................... | | $150,000 |
| Retained earnings: | | |
|   Appropriated for purchase of treasury stock.... | $16,000 | |
|   Unappropriated.......................... | 14,000 | 30,000 |
| | | $180,000 |
| Less treasury stock, 1,000 shares at cost......... | | 16,000 |
| Total capital................................ | | $164,000 |

If the retained earnings restriction is to be reported by parenthetical remark, no entry is made and the capital may be presented as follows:

Paid-in capital:
Capital stock — authorized and issued, 10,000 shares, par value $10, which includes 1,000 shares in the treasury (see below)..................................... $100,000
Premium on stock................................. 50,000

Total paid-in capital............................. $150,000
Retained earnings (of which $16,000 cannot be used as a basis for dividends as a result of the purchase of treasury stock)........................................ 30,000
$180,000
Less treasury stock, 1,000 shares at cost................. 16,000
Total capital......................................... $164,000

An alternate procedure such as the following may be used in developing the summary:

Paid-in capital:
Capital stock — authorized and issued, 10,000 shares, par value $10:
Outstanding, 9,000 shares......................... $ 90,000
Held in treasury, 1,000 shares (see below)............ 10,000

Total issued.................................... $100,000
Premium on stock................................. 50,000

Total paid-in capital............................. $150,000
Retained earnings (see note)......................... 30,000
$180,000
Less treasury stock, 1,000 shares at cost................. 16,000
Total capital......................................... $164,000

NOTE: Availability of retained earnings for dividends is limited to $14,000, as a result of restrictions arising from company purchase of treasury stock at a cost of $16,000.

**DONATIONS OF TREASURY STOCK**  Treasury stock may be donated to the company so that it may be resold to provide working capital. Donations of stock with a par value are found where large blocks of stock were originally issued in exchange for properties. Such stock, which is considered fully paid, may be resold at any price to raise working capital without involving the purchaser in a possible liability to the creditors for the difference between par and a lower sales price. Although such a donation may represent a sacrifice on the part of the contributors of the stock, ordinarily it simply represents a return of an overissue of stock for properties transferred. The issuance of an excess number of shares of stock for properties and the subsequent donation of stock that may be sold without a discount liability has been referred to as the "treasury stock subterfuge."

Two methods, similar to those employed in the case of purchase of treasury stock, may be used in recording donations:

(1) Treasury Stock may be debited on a basis consistent with credits to Capital Stock, and Donated Capital, a paid-in capital account, may be credited for an equal amount.

(2) In the absence of any cost, the treasury stock acquisition may be reported by a memorandum entry, recognition of any increase in capital arising from the donation being deferred until the stock is sold.

To illustrate the above procedures, assume that the Lucky Mining Company is formed to take over the mining properties of Adams and Burke, and 10,000 shares of common, par $25, are issued to each party in exchange for properties valued at $250,000. Later Adams and Burke each donate 2,000 shares of stock to the corporation. This stock is subsequently resold at $15 per share. Entries and the effects of transactions upon capital are shown below:

| Transaction | (1) Assuming Treasury Stock Is Reported At Par | | | (2) Assuming Treasury Stock Is Reported At Cost | |
|---|---|---|---|---|---|
| Issued stock in exchange for properties. | Mining Properties..  250,000<br>    Common Stock... | | 250,000 | Mining Properties 250,000<br>    Common Stock | 250,000 |
| Received 4,000 shares as a donation. | Treasury Stock,<br>  Common.........  100,000<br>    Donated Capital.. | | 100,000 | (Memo) Received 4,000 shares of common from stockholders as a donation. | |
| Capital section balance sheet after donation of treasury stock: | Capital<br>Common stock (par $25, authorized and issued 10,000 shares) $250,000<br>Less treasury stock (4,000 shares)...... 100,000<br><br>Outstanding (6,000 shares)... $150,000<br>Donated capital........... 100,000<br><br>Total paid-in capital...... $250,000 | | | Capital<br>Common stock (par $25, authorized and issued, 10,000 shares, less 4,000 shares of treasury stock reacquired by donation).... $250,000 | |
| Sold 4,000 shares of treasury stock at 15. | Cash.............  60,000<br>Donated Capital....  40,000<br>  Treasury Stock,<br>  Common........ | | 100,000 | Cash............. 60,000<br>  Donated Capital.. | 60,000 |
| Capital section balance sheet after sale of treasury stock: | Capital<br>Common stock (par $25, authorized and issued, 10,000 shares).................. $250,000<br>Donated capital .......... 60,000<br><br>Total paid-in capital...... $310,000 | | | Capital<br>Common stock (par $25, authorized and issued, 10,000 shares)............ $250,000<br>Donated capital ........ 60,000<br><br>Total paid-in capital.... $310,000 | |

Similar procedures are employed in recording the donation of no-par stock. When no-par stock is without a stated value and the first method is employed, treasury stock would be reported at its original issuing price or at an average price as in the case of treasury stock purchases.

The second method, recognition of the treasury stock acquisition by a memorandum entry, offers certain advantages over the first method and may be preferred:

(1) Donated capital is recognized only when the treasury stock is sold and the effect of the contribution upon capital is finally measurable. The donation of stock is viewed simply as effecting a reduction in the number of shares outstanding; sale of the stock confirms a donated capital element and establishes its amount.

(2) This method is the simpler one to apply. It avoids the need for entries in the accounts upon donation together with the calculations that may be required in establishing values for the donation that will stand only until the shares are sold and the actual contribution to corporate capital is known.

When assets are overvalued upon the original issuance of stock, the credit emerging from a resale of donated stock is more accurately treated as a reduction in the book value of assets than as an increase in corporate paid-in capital. Assuming, in the illustration just given, that properties were overvalued in the entry recording the original exchange of stock for properties, the proceeds from the resale of the stock may be regarded as a fulfillment of the consideration involved in the original issue of stock. The receipt of properties and cash in exchange for stock of $250,000, then, might be considered to produce the following:

| | | | |
|---|---|---|---|
| Cash.................. | $ 60,000 | Capital stock............ | $250,000 |
| Mining properties........ | 190,000 | | |
| | $250,000 | | $250,000 |

This result is achieved by treating the ultimate proceeds from the treasury stock sale as a reduction in the asset book value. The following rule relative to stock donation has been adopted by the membership of the American Institute of Certified Public Accountants:

> If capital stock is issued nominally for the acquisition of property and it appears that at about the same time, and pursuant to a previous agreement or understanding, some portion of the stock so issued is donated to the corporation, it is not permissible to treat the par value

of the stock nominally issued for the property as the cost of that property. If stock so donated is subsequently sold, it is not permissible to treat the proceeds as a credit to surplus of the corporation.[1]

**STOCK RIGHTS AND STOCK PURCHASE OPTIONS** Corporations may grant stockholders, officers, and employees special rights to subscribe to stock and options to purchase its stock. Such special grants generally arise under the following circumstances:

(1) A company requiring additional capital may offer stockholders special rights to subscribe for stock.

(2) A company may provide rights to subscribe to certain securities with the issue of various classes of securities.

(3) A company may provide rights to subscribe to stock or options to purchase stock to promoters, officers, or employees as compensation or as a bonus for services or other contributions, past, present, or future.

Rights to subscribe to stock are evidenced by certificates called *warrants*. The rights enable their owners to purchase stock at a specified price; the period for exercise may or may not be limited. Such rights have a value because of the difference between the exercise price under the right as compared with a higher market value for the security, either present or potential.

The accounting problems that are faced by the issuing company under each of the conditions listed are described in the following paragraphs:

*Rights Granted to Stockholders as Means of Increasing Invested Capital.* Only a memorandum entry is required on the books of the corporation when rights are issued to stockholders. The memorandum entry should state the number of shares that may be claimed under outstanding rights. This information is required so that the corporation may retain sufficient unissued stock to meet requirements through exercise of the rights. Upon surrender of the rights, stock is issued by the company at the price specified in the rights. The issue of stock acquired with rights calls for a memorandum entry to record the decrease in the number of rights outstanding and an entry to record the stock sale. The entry for the sale depends upon the amount paid for the shares:

(1) When the cash received in the exercise of rights is less than the required credit to Capital Stock at the legal value, the difference

---

[1] *Accounting Research Bulletin No. 43,* "Restatement and Revision of Accounting Research Bulletins," 1953 (New York: American Institute of Certified Public Accountants), p. 12.

must be charged to Retained Earnings; exercise of rights under such conditions results in a permanent capitalization of retained earnings.

(2) When the amount paid is equal to the par or stated value of the stock, Cash is debited and Capital Stock is credited. This would also be the entry for the issue of no-par stock without a stated value.

(3) When the cash received exceeds the par or stated value of the stock, the excess is recorded as paid-in capital from the sale of stock in excess of its par or stated value.

Full information concerning outstanding rights should be reported on the balance sheet so that the effects of the exercise of future rights may be ascertained by those referring to the statements for information concerning corporate capital.

*Rights Issued with the Sale of Bonds or Stock.* When rights are issued with the sale of other securities, recognition of the rights in the entry to record the sale will depend upon whether a value can be related to these rights. When rights have no value on the date of sale, the full sales proceeds may be identified with the sale of the other securities. When the rights are exercised, the stock is recorded as described in the previous section; if the rights are not exercised and lapse, no entry is required since no value was originally assigned to the rights. When rights do have a market value upon issuance, the sales proceeds should be allocated between the rights and the other securities issued. When the rights are exercised, the stock is recorded at the sum of the value assigned to the rights and the amount paid upon their exercise; if the rights are not exercised and lapse, the value assigned to the rights should be transferred to a paid-in capital balance. The sale of securities accompanied by rights is illustrated in the examples that follow:

(1) Assume that the Matson Co. issues 1,000 shares of preferred stock at par, $50, and gives with this issue warrants enabling holders to subscribe to 1,000 shares of no-par common stock at $25 per share during the following year. Common stock has a stated value of $20 and sells at this time at $22 per share. Since rights may be considered to have only minor speculative value at this time, the entry to record the sale of preferred stock and common rights is:

| | | |
|---|--:|--:|
| Cash............................................ | 50,000 | |
|     Preferred Stock................................ | | 50,000 |

In the succeeding year the value of common rises above $25 per share and all of the rights are exercised. Issue of the stock upon exercise of the warrants is recorded as follows:

| | | |
|---|--:|--:|
| Cash............................................ | 25,000 | |
|     Common Stock (stated value $20)................ | | 20,000 |
|     Paid-In Capital from Sale of Common Stock in | | |
|     Excess of Stated Value........................ | | 5,000 |

(2) Assume that the common stock is selling at $28 per share when the preferred shares, together with warrants for the purchase of common, are sold. Under these circumstances, it is reasonable to assume that the $50 sales price represents payment for two assets, a common stock warrant worth $3 and a share of preferred stock worth the balance, $47. The following entry recognizes the sale of preferred stock in this manner:

```
Cash..............................................  50,000
  Discount on Preferred Stock....................   3,000
    Preferred Stock................................          50,000
    Common Stock Warrants Outstanding..........            3,000
```

Subsequent exercise of all of the rights and issue of the common at $25 is recorded as follows:

```
Cash.........................................  25,000
Common Stock Warrants Outstanding.............   3,000
  Common Stock (stated value $20)...............          20,000
  Paid-In Capital from Sale of Common Stock in
    Excess of Stated Value........................           8,000
```

Assume, however, that the market value of the common stock falls below $25 per share and that the rights are not exercised. The following entry cancels the warrants balance:

```
Common Stock Warrants Outstanding.............   3,000
  Paid-In Capital from Receipts on Unexercised
    Warrants.....................................           3,000
```

*Rights or Stock Options Issued as Compensation for Services.* The grant to promoters, officers, and other employees of options to purchase stock or rights to subscribe for stock raises the following questions: (1) What value is to be assigned to the stock issued in compensation for services? (2) What accounts are to be charged for such compensation?

The fair market value of the shares granted under an option may vary considerably over the period of the option. This creates the problem of determining a date that may be used to measure the amount of the compensation. The American Institute Committee on Accounting Procedure suggests six dates that may be considered for this purpose:[1]

(1) The date of the adoption of an option plan.

(2) The date on which an option is granted to a specific individual.

(3) The date on which the grantee has performed any conditions precedent to exercise of the option.

---

[1] *Accounting Research Bulletin No. 43*, "Restatement and Revision of Accounting Research Bulletins," 1953 (New York: American Institute of Certified Public Accountants), p. 121.

(4) The date on which the grantee may first exercise the option.

(5) The date on which the option is exercised by the grantee.

(6) The date on which the grantee disposes of the stock acquired.

The Committee, in reviewing each of these dates, concludes that, in most instances the most appropriate point for measuring the compensation and arriving at a valuation of the option agreement is the date of grant, (2) above. This is the date on which the company acknowledges the claim; this is the date when the company takes action that makes impossible any alternate use of the shares placed in option. Dates prior to this time are not pertinent; plans call for the rendering of services and are no more than proposed courses of action until services are formally recognized and the liability becomes effective. Dates after this time are not pertinent; changes in the values of the compensation award after its accrual are beyond the scope of the plan for compensation and represent matters of concern only to the grantee. Using the date on which the stock option is effectively granted, the value of the rights is calculated as the excess of the fair market value of the stock over the price that must be paid by the grantee in its acquisition.

Although the value of the stock option is set at the date it is granted, the option may represent payment for services over an extended period. In accounting for the option, the period covered by the compensation — whether past, present, or future — must be considered and charges must be assigned in an appropriate manner. For example, if options are granted in recognition of services contributing to the revenues of past periods and there has been no recognition given in the past to the accrual of compensation, an extraordinary charge to profits of prior periods should be recognized or Retained Earnings should be charged; if options are related to services performed currently, the charge is made to current expense; in those instances where options can be considered to result in current and future benefits, the charge for options may be recorded as a deferred cost to be assigned to the periods that will benefit from the services. When options represent payment for services that should be capitalized, charges are made to the appropriate tangible or intangible asset account.

Upon exercise of stock options, the sum of the cash received and the value previously assigned to such options represents the consideration identified with the issuance of the stock.

Accounting for stock options to employees is illustrated in the example that follows: On January 12, 1957, the board of directors of the Miller Co. authorizes the issuance of stock options to certain officers who have been with the company for a ten-year period. The options enable officers to subscribe to a total of 10,000 shares of stock during the next three years at a price of $15. Stock has a par value of $10 and is selling on the market currently at 22½. Options are exercised in 1958.

The value of the stock options at the date of the grant is calculated as follows:

| | |
|---|---|
| Market value of common on January 12, 1957, 10,000 shares at 22 ½........................................... | $225,000 |
| Option price, 10,000 shares at 15...................... | 150,000 |
| Value of stock options................................ | $ 75,000 |

The following entries are made to record (1) the grant of the options in recognition of past services and (2) the exercise of the options by officers in 1958:

(1) Compensation Chargeable to Profits of Prior Periods
    (or Retained Earnings) ........................ 75,000
        Common Stock Options Outstanding...........     75,000

(2) Cash ........................................ 150,000
    Common Stock Options Outstanding............. 75,000
        Common Stock.............................     100,000
        Premium on Common Stock.................     125,000

While option plans are operative, the company balance sheet should reflect full information concerning the number of shares under option, the option price, the number of shares exercised, and the number of shares still exercisable.

The standards and procedures that have been described with respect to stock options offered in compensation for services are equally applicable to transactions in which capital stock of a company is given to an employee. The value of the stock compensation should be established as of the date that the stock is granted to the employee; the charge for compensation should be related to the periods covered by the compensation.

**STOCK CONVERSION**    Stock contracts frequently permit stockholders to exchange their holdings for stock of other classes. In certain instances, the exchanges may affect only paid-in capital balances on the books of the corporation; in other instances the exchanges may affect both paid-in capital and retained earnings.

To illustrate the different conditions, assume that the capital of the Washington Corporation on December 31, 1958, is as follows:

|                                                                          |             |
|--------------------------------------------------------------------------|-------------|
| Preferred Stock, 10,000 shares, $100 par..............                   | $1,000,000  |
| Premium on Preferred Stock.........................                      | 100,000     |
| Common Stock, 100,000 shares, $25 stated value.........                  | 2,500,000   |
| Paid-In Capital from Sale of Common Stock in Excess of                   |             |
| Stated Value........................................                     | 500,000     |
| Retained Earnings..................................                      | 1,000,000   |
| Total Capital......................................                      | $5,100,000  |

Preferred shares are convertible into common shares at any time at the option of the shareholder.

*Case 1:* Assume that conditions of conversion call for the exchange of each share of preferred for 4 shares of common. On December 31, 1958, 1,000 shares of preferred stock are exchanged on the above basis. The amount originally paid for the preferred, $110,000 (1,000 shares at $110 as indicated by the preferred stock and premium balances) now becomes the consideration identified with 4,000 shares of common stock with a total stated value of $100,000. The conversion is recorded as follows:

|                                                      |         |         |
|------------------------------------------------------|---------|---------|
| Preferred Stock (1,000 shares)...................     | 100,000 |         |
| Premium on Preferred Stock...................        | 10,000  |         |
| Common Stock (4,000 shares)................           |         | 100,000 |
| Paid-In Capital from Conversion of Preferred         |         |         |
| Stock into Common Stock...................           |         | 10,000  |

*Case 2:* Assume that conditions of conversion call for the exchange of each share of preferred for 3 shares of common. The conversion of 1,000 shares of preferred stock for common stock calls for the transfer of the preferred stock book value to the common stock; the excess of the book value of preferred holdings over the stated value of the common stock issued in exchange is recognized as paid-in capital relating to the latter issue. The conversion is recorded by the following entry:

|                                                      |         |        |
|------------------------------------------------------|---------|--------|
| Preferred Stock (1,000 shares)...................     | 100,000 |        |
| Premium on Preferred Stock...................        | 10,000  |        |
| Common Stock (3,000 shares)................           |         | 75,000 |
| Paid-In Capital from Conversion of Preferred         |         |        |
| Stock into Common Stock...................           |         | 35,000 |

*Case 3:* Assume that conditions of conversion call for the exchange of each share of preferred for 5 shares of common. Here, an increase in common stock of $125,000 (5,000 shares, stated value per share $25) must be recognized although it is accompanied by a decrease in the preferred stock paid-in capital of only $110,000; the increase in the legal value related to the new issue can be accomplished only by a charge to Retained Earnings. The conversion, then, is recorded as follows:

| | | |
|---|---:|---:|
| Preferred Stock........................... | 100,000 | |
| Premium on Preferred Stock................ | 10,000 | |
| Retained Earnings......................... | 15,000 | |
| Common Stock (5,000 shares)............... | | 125,000 |

The problems relating to the conversion of bonds for capital stock were previously described in Chapter 19. When either stocks or bonds have conversion rights, unissued securities of the class required to meet these rights must be set aside by the corporation in an amount equal to the conversion privileges. Detailed information should be given on the balance sheet relative to security conversion features as well as to the securities set aside to meet conversion requirements.

**RECAPITALIZATION**    Corporate recapitalization occurs when an entire issue of stock is changed by action of the corporation. Such action ordinarily requires approval by the proper state authorities, although some states permit reduction of legal capital by action of the board of directors and the stockholders without permission from state authorities.

A common type of recapitalization is a change from par to no-par stock. If the capital stock balance is to remain the same after the change, the original capital stock account is closed and a new account summarizing the new issue is opened. Any premium relating to the original par-value stock should be transferred to some other paid-in capital account appropriately labeled. If the capital stock balance is to exceed the consideration received on the original sale of the stock, a new capital stock account is credited for the value assigned to the issue, original paid-in capital balances are closed, and Retained Earning is charged for any difference. If the capital stock balance is to be reduced, the original account, as well as any premium account, is closed, a new capital stock account is credited for the value assigned to the new stock, and an appropriately titled account is credited for the difference. The latter balance is part of the corporate paid-in capital, since it has its origin in the investment made by owners.

To illustrate the foregoing, assume a capital for the Signal Corporation as follows:

| | |
|---|---:|
| Capital Stock, 100,000 shares outstanding, par $10 ..... | $1,000,000 |
| Premium on Stock................................ | 100,000 |
| Retained Earnings............................... | 250,000 |
| | $1,350,000 |

Entries for each of the three possibilities are given below:

*Case 1:* Assume that the original stock is exchanged for no-par stock with a stated value of $10:

| Capital Stock (100,000 shares, par $10)....... | 1,000,000 | |
|---|---|---|
| Premium on Stock........................ | 100,000 | |
|    Capital Stock (100,000 shares, stated value $10).................................. | | 1,000,000 |
|    Paid-In Capital from Exchange of Par for No-par Stock........................... | | 100,000 |

*Case 2:* Assume that the original stock is exchanged for no-par stock with a stated value of $12.50:

| Capital Stock (100,000 shares, par $10)....... | 1,000,000 | |
|---|---|---|
| Premium on Stock........................ | 100,000 | |
| Retained Earnings........................ | 150,000 | |
|    Capital Stock (100,000 shares, stated value $12.50)................................ | | 1,250,000 |

*Case 3:* Assume that the original stock is exchanged for no-par stock with a stated value of $5:

| Capital Stock (100,000 shares, par $10)......... | 1,000,000 | |
|---|---|---|
| Premium on Stock........................... | 100,000 | |
|    Capital Stock (100,000 shares, stated value $5) | | 500,000 |
|    Paid-In Capital from Reduction in Value Assigned to Outstanding Stock............. | | 600,000 |

Recapitalizations that involve revisions in the stated values of no-par shares or changes from no-par to a par value call for similar procedures.

Corporate recapitalization that is part of a plan for the elimination of a deficit and possibly the devaluation of assets is referred to as a *corporate readjustment* or *quasi-reorganization.* The procedures involved in achieving a fresh start through corporate readjustment were considered in Chapter 17.

**STOCK SPLIT-UPS**        When the market price for a share of stock is high and it is felt that a lower price will result in a better market and a wider distribution of holdings, the corporation may authorize that the number of shares outstanding be exchanged for a greater number of shares. For example, 100,000 shares of stock, par value per share $100, are called in and exchanged for 500,000 shares of stock, par value $20. Each shareholder receives 5 new shares for each share owned. The increase in shares outstanding in this manner is known as a *split-up.* The reverse procedure, the exchange of the capital stock outstanding for a reduced number of shares, may be desirable when the price of stock is low and it is felt that there will be certain advantages in having a higher price for shares as well as a smaller number of shares outstanding. The reduction of shares outstanding by combining shares is referred to as a *split-down* or *reverse-split.*

After a split-up or a split-down, the capital stock balance remains the same; however, the change in the number of shares of stock outstanding is accompanied by a change in the par or stated value of the stock. The change in the number of shares outstanding, as well as the change in the par or stated value, may be recorded by means of a memorandum entry. However, it would normally be desirable to make an entry transferring the capital stock balance to a new account that reports the full details concerning the nature and the amount of the new issue. In any event, entries will be required in the subsidiary stockholders ledger to report the exchange of stock and the change in the number of shares held by each stockholder.

**PAID-IN CAPITAL NOT DESIGNATED AS LEGAL CAPITAL**    A number of different transactions between the corporation and its stockholders that resulted in paid-in capital balances that are properly added to capital stock in arriving at a company's total paid-in capital have been considered in this and the preceding chapter. Such paid-in capital balances result from a variety of transactions including the sale of shares at amounts in excess of their par or stated value, stock payment forfeitures, stock assessments, stock donations, capital changes resulting from dealings in treasury stock, and recapitalizations. It was suggested that asset contributions by nonownership groups are also generally regarded as giving rise to paid-in capital.

Invested capital that is not designated legal capital has become increasingly important with the introduction of no-par stock with a stated value. When par stock was sold at a premium, the amount paid in excess of par was normally a relatively small percentage of the total price; in the case of no-par stock with a stated value, however, the amount paid in excess of the stated value may be several times the stated value. For example, the sale of 10,000 shares of stock, par $25, sold at $30, results in capital stock of $250,000 and additional paid-in capital of $50,000; the sale of 10,000 shares of no-par stock, stated value $10, sold at $30, produces a capital stock balance of $100,000 and additional paid-in capital of $200,000.

While the prevailing practice is to show a single total for paid-in capital that is to be added to capital stock on the balance sheet, separate accounts should be provided in the ledger to identify the different sources of such additional paid-in capital. Some additional paid-in capital sources and the accounts summarizing these are listed on the following page.

| SOURCE | PAID-IN CAPITAL ACCOUNT |
|---|---|
| Amount received on sale of stock in excess of stock par value | Premium on Stock (or Paid-in Capital from Sale of Stock in Excess of Par Value) |
| Amount received on sale of stock in excess of stock stated value | Paid-in Capital from Sale of Stock in Excess of Stated Value |
| Stock subscription defaults resulting in forfeiture of amounts paid in | Paid-in Capital from Forfeited Subscriptions |
| Receipt of assessments levied on stockholders | Paid-in Capital from Stock Assessments (except where stock was originally sold at a discount and stock assessments are considered to be proper credits to such discount) |
| Retirement of outstanding stock at an amount less than that originally received on the issue of the stock | Paid-in Capital from Stock Redemption |
| Conversion of outstanding stock into a new issue with a smaller total par or stated value | Paid-in Capital from Stock Conversion |
| Reduction in stock par or stated value as a result of recapitalization | Paid-in Capital from Reduction in Value Assigned to Outstanding Stock |
| Sale of treasury stock at more than cost | Paid-in Capital from Sale of Treasury Stock in Excess of Cost |
| Donation of stock or properties or forgiveness of corporate indebtedness by stockholders | Donated (or Paid-in) Capital from Contributions by Stockholders |
| Donation of properties and forgiveness of indebtedness by governmental authorities and other outsiders | Donated (or Paid-in) Capital from Contributions by Governmental Authority (or other party) |

Charges should be made to the paid-in capital balances only when (1) transactions are considered to reduce such paid-in capital balances directly or (2) there is an express authorization for the reduction. To illustrate (1) above, the acquisition and the retirement of a preferred stock issue calls for the cancellation of both the capital stock balance and any premium or other paid-in capital balance relating to the original issue of the preferred stock; all reference to paid-in capital relating to the preferred stock should be canceled with the redemption of this class of stock. However, it would not be appropriate to charge some other paid-in capital balance with any part of the amount paid on the retirement of a preferred issue; to do so would be to obscure the data with respect to capital arising from other sources. To illustrate (2) above, authorization by the board of directors of the capitalization of a portion of a particular paid-in capital element would call for a reduction in the paid-in capital balance and an increase in the capital stock balance.

Additional paid-in capital balances should not be charged with losses whether from normal operations or from extraordinary sources, nor should such paid-in capital be used for the cancellation of a deficit in the absence of formal steps taken to effect a quasi-reorganization as previously described in Chapter 17. Authorities are in general agreement here. The membership of the American Institute of Certified Public Accountants in 1934 adopted the following rule on this matter:

> Capital surplus, however created, should not be used to relieve the income account of the current or future years of charges which would otherwise fall to be made thereagainst. This rule might be subject to the exception that where, upon reorganization, a reorganized company would be relieved of charges which would require to be made against income if the existing corporation were continued, it might be regarded as permissible to accomplish the same result without reorganization provided the facts were as fully revealed to and the action as formally approved by the shareholders as in reorganization.[1]

The Chief Accountant of the Securities and Exchange Commission in a similar vein in Accounting Series Release No. 1 makes the following statement:

> It is my conviction that capital surplus should under no circumstances be used to write off losses which, if currently recognized, would have been chargeable against income. In case a deficit is thereby created, I see no objection to writing off such a deficit against capital surplus, provided appropriate stockholder approval has been obtained. In this event, subsequent statements of earned surplus should designate the point of time from which the new surplus dates.[2]

The availability as a basis for dividends of paid-in capital that is not designated as legal capital depends upon the laws of the state of incorporation. In the absence of legal restrictions, such capital can be used as a basis for dividends. Laws may provide restrictions upon the use of all of the paid-in capital or upon the use of only certain parts of paid-in capital. Separate accounts in the ledger summarizing paid-in elements by source make possible the ready determination of distributable capital. When capital other than retained earnings is used as a basis for dividends, stockholders should be notified by the

---

[1] *Accounting Research Bulletin No. 43*, "Restatement and Revision of Accounting Research Bulletins," 1953 (New York: American Institute of Certified Public Accountants), p. 11.

[2] *Accounting Series Release No. 1*, "Treatment of losses resulting from revaluation of assets," 1937 (Washington, D. C.: United States Securities and Exchange Commission).

corporation concerning the source of such distribution, since this group has the right to assume that dividends represent distributions of earnings in the absence of notice to the contrary.

## QUESTIONS

**1.** The controller for the Scott Co. contends that the redemption of preferred stock at less than its issuance price should be reported as an increase in retained earnings, since redemption at more than issuance price calls for a charge to retained earnings. How would you answer this argument?

**2.** What is the purpose of legislation limiting the reacquisition of a company's own stock to its retained earnings balance?

**3.** The laws of a certain state provide that a company "may purchase . . . shares issued by it . . . out of earned surplus." What criticism can you offer of this expression from an accounting point of view? What changes in the statement would you suggest?

**4.** Distinguish between treasury stock and unissued stock.

**5.** The Waters Co. reports treasury stock as a current asset, explaining that it plans to sell the stock soon to acquire working capital. Do you approve of this reporting?

**6.** In auditing the accounts of the Wooster Co. you find an entry for the payment of dividends on the total shares issued, including treasury stock reacquired, and a second entry recognizing the receipt of dividends on the treasury stock. Would you accept this practice? Give reasons.

**7.** (a) Describe two views that may be taken with respect to accounting for the reacquisition of treasury stock. (b) What are the entries in each case assuming (1) that stock is reacquired at more than the original issuing price, and (2) that stock is reacquired at less than the issuing price?

**8.** Retained earnings of the Saunders Co. equal to the amount paid on the reacquisition of treasury stock cannot be used as a basis for dividends until treasury stock is disposed of or formally retired. What two procedures may be followed by the company in giving effect to this requirement for reporting purposes?

**9.** Explain the "treasury stock subterfuge." What is the effect of this practice on the balance sheet?

**10.** (a) Describe two methods that may be employed in recording the acquisition of treasury stock through donation by stockholders. (b) Which method do you consider preferable? Why?

**11.** The Miller Corporation, with authorized capital stock of 50,000 shares, $100 par value, issues 40,000 shares at par. Later a stockholder donates 5,000 shares to the corporation. A balance sheet issued by the corporation soon after this shows:

| | |
|---|---:|
| Capital stock...................................... | $5,000,000 |
| Less: Treasury stock............................. | 1,500,000 |
| | |
| Capital stock outstanding......................... | $3,500,000 |
| Retained earnings................................ | 500,000 |
| | |
| Capital........................................ | $4,000,000 |

Is this a satisfactory statement? Explain.

**12.** (a) Define a stock option. (b) What are the circumstances that may suggest the issue of stock options?

**13.** (a) What entries should be made on the books when stock rights are issued to stockholders? (b) What entries should be made when stock is issued on rights? (c) What information, if any, should appear on the balance sheet relative to outstanding rights?

**14.** What special accounting problem arises upon the sale of securities accompanied by rights to subscribe to other issues?

**15.** (a) What date should be used for purposes of establishing the value of a stock option and recording it on the books of the issuing corporation? Give reasons for your conclusion. (b) What entries are made upon (1) the issue of such an option and (2) the exercise of such an option?

**16.** How would you recommend that stock options outstanding be reported on the balance sheet of the corporation issuing the options?

**17.** (a) Define a stock split. (b) What are the reasons for effecting a stock split?

**18.** The board of directors of the Parks Co. agrees to the issuance of 1,000 shares of common stock to five retiring officers who have been with the company for a ten-year period. How would you recommend that this action be recorded in the accounts?

**19.** (a) Name the different sources of "additional paid-in capital" and the accounts summarizing such items. (b) Indicate the circumstances that would call for a reduction in each of the accounts named.

**20.** The accountant for the Walter Corporation closes stock discount and deficit balances into paid-in capital from sale of stock in excess of par and reports only the balance of the latter account on the balance sheet. Do you approve?

## EXERCISES

**1.** The Westmore Co. has 10,000 shares of preferred stock and 50,000 shares of common stock, each having been issued at par of $100. On June 1, 1958, the company purchased 1,500 shares of preferred stock at $101\frac{1}{2}$ and formally retired them; on September 15, 1958, the company purchased 1,000 additional shares at 97 and retired them. Give the entries to record the acquisition and the retirement of the preferred shares.

**2.** James, Inc. issued $500,000 of 5% preferred stock, par $100, on January 1, 1958, at 102 with a provision calling for the establishment of a preferred stock redemption fund with annual contributions to the fund equal to 20% of the profits of the preceding year. During 1958 James, Inc. made a profit of $160,000, and on January 2, 1959, created the fund referred to above. On February 3, 1959, it purchased and retired 300 shares of the preferred stock at 104. Give entries for (a) issuance of stock, (b) establishment of the fund, and (c) purchase and retirement of the stock.

**3.** The capital accounts for the Platt Manufacturing Co. show the following balances on June 1, 1958:

| | |
|---|---:|
| Capital Stock, 100,000 shares, par $10................. | $1,000,000 |
| Paid-In Capital from Sale of Stock at 12.............. | 200,000 |
| Retained Earnings................................... | 500,000 |
| | $1,700,000 |

On this date the company reacquires 5,000 shares of stock at 11; and in December of the same year it resells this stock at 14½. (a) What entries are made for the stock acquisition and the resale if the purchase is viewed as a capital retirement with treasury stock being reported at par? (b) What entries are made for the stock acquisition and the resale if the purchase is viewed as giving rise to a capital element awaiting ultimate disposition and treasury stock is reported at cost?

**4.** What are the entries for (a) and (b) in Exercise 3 for the purchase and the resale of the stock at the amounts indicated, assuming the corporate capital on June 1 is as follows:

| | |
|---|---:|
| Capital Stock, 100,000 shares, no par, sold at 12........ | $1,200,000 |
| Retained Earnings................................... | 500,000 |
| | $1,700,000 |

**5.** Assume in Exercise 3 that laws of the state of incorporation for the Platt Manufacturing Co. restrict dividends to the balance of retained earnings less the cost of any treasury stock during the period of such holdings; such restriction on retained earnings is removed upon the resale of treasury stock. If the restriction is to be reported in the accounts, what entries would be made on the date of stock reacquisition and on the date of its resale?

**6.** The Healey Corporation shows the following capital balances: Capital Stock Issued, $200,000; Premium on Capital Stock Issued, $10,000; and Retained Earnings, $50,000. It purchases 3,000 shares of its $10 par-value stock at 10½, recording the acquisition at cost. Retained earnings equal to the purchase price are appropriated so that they will not be used as a basis for dividends during the period of treasury stock ownership in conformance with state laws. Subsequently 2,000 shares of treasury stock are sold at 12 and an adjustment is made in the retained earnings appropriation.

(a) What entries are required to record the above transactions?  (b) Prepare the capital section of the balance sheet (1) after acquisition of the treasury stock and (2) after resale of the treasury stock.

**7.** Stock outstanding of the Webb Co. is no-par with a stated value of $20.  On December 1, a principal stockholder donates 1,000 shares of stock to the corporation.  The stock is subsequently sold at 24.  Record the acquisition and the resale of the treasury stock according to two different methods that might be used.  (Assume that corporation assets are properly valued.)

**8.** The Werner Co. issued 100,000 shares of common stock, par $10, to three partners in exchange for certain undeveloped properties.  The properties were recorded at $1,000,000.  Immediately thereafter, the partners donated to the corporation 25% of the shares to enable the company to raise working capital through the sale of these shares.  The stock was resold at $7.  What entries would you make for the corporation in recording the stock donation and its resale?

**9.** The Crowell Corp. issues $1,000,000 of 5% bonds at 102.  With each subscription for a $1,000 bond it gives transferable warrants permitting the owner to subscribe to 5 shares of common stock at par value, $50, for a one-year period.  (a) What entry should be made by the company for the sale of the bonds assuming that: (1) stock is selling at $45 per share on the date of the bond issue; and (2) stock is selling at $60 per share on the date of the bond issue.  (b) What entries would be made in (1) and (2) above, assuming that all of the rights are ultimately exercised?  (c) What entries would be made in (1) and (2) above, assuming that only 80% of the rights are ultimately exercised?

**10.** The capital for the Baxter Co. on December 31 is as follows:

| | |
|---|---:|
| Preferred stock, 10,000 shares issued and outstanding, par $50..................................................... | $ 500,000 |
| Premium on preferred stock from issue at 55............ | 50,000 |
| Common stock, 100,000 shares issued and outstanding, par $10...................................................... | 1,000,000 |
| Premium on common stock from issue in excess of par... | 126,000 |
| Retained earnings..................................... | 1,600,000 |
| | $3,276,000 |

Preferred stock is convertible into common stock.  Give the entry that is made on the corporation books assuming that 1,000 shares of preferred are converted under each assumption listed:

(a) Preferred shares are convertible into common on a share-for-share basis.
(b) Each preferred share is convertible into $7\frac{1}{2}$ shares of common.
(c) Each preferred share is convertible into 4 shares of common.

**11.** The Burgess Corporation, in order to remove an operating deficit of $35,000, issues 10 shares of no-par-value common stock with a stated value of $5 a share in exchange for each original share of $100 par-value common stock. What entries should be made to record the exchange and the retirement of 1,000 shares of the old stock and to eliminate the deficit?

**12.** The Matson Co. has 10,000 shares of common stock outstanding, each share having a par value of $10. Proceeds from the sale of the stock were $120,000 and this is reflected in the paid-in capital balances. What entry would be made on the company books for each assumption listed below:

(a) A stock split is effected, each shareholder receiving 4 shares of new stock, par $2.50, for each share owned.

(b) A recapitalization is effected, each stockholder receiving 2 shares of new no-par stock with a stated value of $5 for each share owned.

(c) A recapitalization is effected, each shareholder receiving 1 share of new $5 par stock for each share owned.

(d) A recapitalization is effected, each shareholder receiving 3 shares of new $5 par stock for each share owned.

**13.** What entries should be made for the capital transactions of the Eaton Co. that follow. Stock of this company is no-par with a stated value of $25. Assume that treasury stock acquisitions are recorded at cost.

(a) Sold 1,000 shares at $40 a share.

(b) Purchased 100 shares on the market at $34 a share.

(c) Sold 50 shares of treasury stock for $38 a share.

(d) Changed stated value of stock to $10 a share.

**14.** The additional paid-in capital account of the Hardy Corporation shows the following charges and credits. Give whatever entries may be required to correct the account in 1958:

ADDITIONAL PAID-IN CAPITAL

| | | | | |
|---|---|---|---|---|
| Mar. 2 | Discount on issue of preferred stock.... | 15,000 | Jan. 2 Premium on issue of common stock (10,000 shares, par $50, issued at 65)............. | 150,000 |
| Nov. 2 | Loss on retirement of common stock (1,000 shares, par $50, retired at $75). | 25,000 | 3 Donated capital— buildings acquired in governmental grant to company.......... | 50,000 |
| Dec. 31 | Depreciation on buildings acquired through donation.. | 2,000 | | |
| 31 | Transfer to capital stock account pursuant to resolution by board of directors raising common stock par value to $60 per share...... | 90,000 | | |

## PROBLEMS

**21-1.** The capital stock account for the Kurt Sales Co. at the beginning of 1958 shows the following issues of capital stock:

| | |
|---|---|
| 20,000 shares at $12.00..................................... | $240,000 |
| 6,000 shares at $12.50..................................... | 75,000 |
| 4,000 shares at $13.50..................................... | 54,000 |
| | $369,000 |

During 1958 the company reacquires 1,500 shares at $11.50, and these shares are resold at the beginning of 1959 at $14 per share.

*Instructions:* (1) Give the entries to record the acquisition and the resale of treasury stock for each assumption listed below if the treasury stock purchase is viewed as capital retirement and the treasury stock account is charged at par, stated value, or average, whichever is appropriate.

(a) Assume that the stock has a $10 par.

(b) Assume that the stock is no-par with a stated value of $12.

(c) Assume that the stock is no-par and without a stated value.

(2) Give the entries to record the acquisition and the resale of treasury stock for each assumption listed in (1) above if the treasury stock purchase is viewed as a capital element awaiting ultimate disposition and the treasury stock account is charged for the amount paid.

**21-2.** The Johnson Corporation is organized October 1, 1956. It is authorized to issue the following stock:

10,000 shares of 6% cumulative, nonparticipating preferred, $100 par.
200,000 shares of common, $10 par.

On October 1, 8,000 shares of the preferred stock are subscribed for at 108. On October 4, 170,000 shares of common stock are subscribed for at 12¼. Subscriptions on both common and preferred stock are payable 25% upon subscription, the balance in three equal installments due December 1, 1956, and February 1 and April 1, 1957. Defaults on the installment due December 1 are as follows: preferred, 100 shares; common, 800 shares. Subscriptions are received for defaulted stock as follows: preferred at 104; common at 10. Subscriptions on stock that is resold are payable 50% upon subscription, the balance in two equal installments due February 1 and April 1, 1957. Amounts paid in minus losses on the stock resales are returned to defaulting subscribers. The net loss from operations by the corporation for the 3-month period ended December 31, 1956, is $65,000.

In February, 1957, the remaining common stock is sold for cash at 11½. Cash is received in payment of remaining installments from all subscribers with the exception of one subscriber who is unable to pay his final 25% installment on the preferred. He issues to the corporation a note payable in January, 1958, for $13,500, the fourth installment owed. Stock is to be issued upon payment of the note. Stock is issued in April to all fully paid subscribers. The net loss from operations by the corporation for the year ended December 31, 1957, is $95,000.

On January 5, 1958, cash is received in payment of the note for $13,500, and stock is issued. In January, the stockholders agree to the following: each share of common stock is to be exchanged for 2 shares of no-par common with a stated value per share of $4. The paid-in capital in excess of the stock par value created by the recapitalization is to be used in part to cancel the deficit arising from operations of past periods. The exchange is completed in February. The net income after taxes for the year ended December 31, 1958, is $200,000. On December 31 dividends are declared on preferred stock for the past 2¼ years, and a dividend of 10 cents a share is declared on the common stock.

*Instructions:* (1) Prepare journal entries for the transactions given above for the Johnson Corporation. (For annual profit or loss, simply give the entry to close the profit and loss account to the appropriate capital account.)

(2) Construct the capital sections for the corporation balance sheets as of (a) December 31, 1956, (b) December 31, 1957, and (c) December 31, 1958.

**21-3.** The balance sheet for the Bordon Corporation on December 31, 1957, is as follows:

| Assets | $380,500 | Liabilities | | $120,000 |
|---|---|---|---|---|
| | | Capital: | | |
| | | $1.50 Converti- | | |
| | | ble preferred | | |
| | | stock ($25 | | |
| | | par) | $ 60,000 | |
| | | Common stock | | |
| | | ($10 par) | 100,000 | |
| | | Premium from | | |
| | | original sale of | | |
| | | common at 12½ | 25,000 | |
| | | Retained earn- | | |
| | | ings | 80,000 | |
| | | | $265,000 | |
| | | Less: Treasury | | |
| | | stock, com- | | |
| | | mon, 500 | | |
| | | shares at cost | 4,500 | 260,500 |
| | | Total liabilities | | |
| Total assets | $380,500 | and capital | | $380,500 |

During 1958 the following transactions were completed in the order given:

(a) 1,000 shares of common stock were reacquired by purchase at 9¾. (Treasury stock is recorded at cost.)

(b) 200 shares of common stock were reacquired in payment of an account receivable of $2,000.

(c) Semiannual cash dividends of 50 cents on common stock and 75 cents on preferred stock were declared and paid.

(d) Each share of preferred stock is convertible into 3 shares of common stock; 400 shares of preferred stock were turned in for common stock; accrued dividends totaling $120 were paid to preferred stockholders exchanging their holdings.

(e) All of the common treasury stock on hand was sold at 11½.

(f) 2,500 shares of common stock were issued in exchange for unimproved property appraised at $30,000.

(g) Semiannual cash dividends of 50 cents on common stock and 75 cents on preferred stock were declared and paid.

*Instructions:* (1) Give journal entries to record the transactions listed above.

(2) Prepare a balance sheet as of December 31, 1958, assuming that, in addition to the transactions listed, normal operations for the year resulted in a profit of $16,000, and total liabilities at the end of the year remain unchanged at $120,000.

**21-4.** Standard, Inc. was organized on January 2, 1956, and was authorized to issue 60,000 shares of no-par stock. Stock was sold during 1956 as follows, a stated value of $10 being assigned by the board of directors to each share:

| | |
|---|---|
| January 14................................ | 25,000 shares at 30 |
| February 19................................ | 20,000 shares at 35 |
| April 14................................ | 5,000 shares at 40 |

The corporation paid regular quarterly dividends of 50 cents a share, the first quarterly dividend payable to stockholders of record March 15 and the remaining dividends at 3-month intervals thereafter during 1956. Dividends are paid on record date. Earnings for the year were $340,000.

In 1957 the market price of its stock declined and the company reacquired its own stock as follows (treasury stock is recorded at cost):

| | |
|---|---|
| April 12................................ | 2,000 shares at 32½ |
| May 10................................ | 1,000 shares at 28 |
| June 20................................ | 4,000 shares at 24 |

The laws of the state provide that retained earnings must be reduced by an amount equal to the purchase price of treasury stock. The appropriation of retained earnings is canceled when treasury stock is resold and original invested capital restored.

In 1957 the company paid the first and second regular quarterly dividends of 50 cents to stockholders of record March 15 and June 15. For the year the company incurred an operating loss of $3,000.

In 1958 business conditions improved and the company, in order to obtain funds for expansion purposes, resold the 4,000 shares of treasury stock acquired June 20, 1957, as follows:

| | |
|---|---|
| February 5................................ | 3,000 shares at 32 |
| June 1................................ | 1,000 shares at 36 |

During 1958 the corporation paid regular dividends of 40 cents a share to stockholders of record March 15 and at quarterly intervals thereafter.

A 50-cent extra dividend was paid on December 15. The net income for the year was $200,000.

*Instructions:* (1) Prepare journal entries to record the above transactions. (For annual profit or loss figures, simply give the entry to close the profit and loss account to the appropriate capital account.)

(2) Construct the capital section of the balance sheet for the corporation as of December 31, 1956, December 31, 1957, and December 31, 1958.

**21-5.** The Superior Plastic Co. showed a capital balance on December 31, 1956, as follows:

| | |
|---|---:|
| Capital stock, $25 par; 250,000 shares authorized; 100,000 shares issued and outstanding; options to purchase 10,000 shares at $30 per share are held by officers..... | $2,500,000 |
| Premium on stock................................. | 500,000 |
| Retained earnings................................. | 1,850,000 |
| | $4,850,000 |

On May 31, 1957, the company issued bonds of $1,000,000 at par, giving with each $1,000 bond a warrant enabling the holder to obtain 5 shares of stock at $50 for a one-year period. Shares were being sold for 47½ at this time.

By December 31, 1957, 4,000 shares of stock were issued to officers in connection with option agreements and 2,000 shares were issued in connection with rights issued on the sale of bonds. Earnings of the company for 1957 transferred to retained earnings were $280,000.

On January 5, 1958, the corporation issued rights to shareholders (1 right to each share) permitting holders to acquire for a 60-day period 1 share at $52 with every 8 rights submitted. Shares were being sold for $57 at this time. All but 4,000 rights were exercised and the stock was issued.

By December 31, 1958, 1,500 shares of stock were issued to officers in connection with option agreements and 2,500 shares were issued in connection with rights issued on the sale of bonds. Earnings of the company for 1958 transferred to retained earnings were $300,000. A special dividend of $2.50 per share was declared on December 31.

*Instructions:* (1) Give entries to record all of the foregoing transactions affecting corporate capital.

(2) Prepare the capital section as it would appear on the company balance sheet on (a) December 31, 1957, and (b) December 31, 1958.

**21-6.** The trial balance of Walker & Co., Inc., before the closing of its second year on June 30, 1958, and additional data are given on the following pages.

## WALKER & CO., INC.

### TRIAL BALANCE

### JUNE 30, 1958

|  | DR. | CR. |
|---|---:|---:|
| Cash | $ 52,475 |  |
| Accounts receivable | 320,000 |  |
| Allowance for bad debts |  | $ 650 |
| Materials and goods in process — June 30, 1957 | 65,000 |  |
| Finished goods — June 30, 1957 | 158,000 |  |
| Insurance unexpired — June 30, 1957 | 3,000 |  |
| Land | 200,000 |  |
| Buildings | 300,000 |  |
| Allowance for depreciation of buildings |  | 6,000 |
| Machinery and equipment | 148,500 |  |
| Allowance for depreciation of machinery and equipment |  | 11,250 |
| Sinking fund trustee | 25,000 |  |
| Discount on bonds | 25,000 |  |
| Treasury stock | 35,000 |  |
| Accounts payable |  | 40,000 |
| Bond interest accrued |  | 3,125 |
| Taxes accrued |  | 9,000 |
| First mortgage 5% sinking fund bonds |  | 226,250 |
| Capital stock |  | 500,000 |
| Premium on capital stock |  | 50,000 |
| Stock donation |  | 60,000 |
| Reserve for replacements |  | 15,000 |
| Reserve for bond sinking fund |  | 25,000 |
| Surplus — June 30, 1957 |  | 60,000 |
| Sales, less returns and allowances |  | 915,000 |
| Purchases of materials | 305,000 |  |
| Labor | 132,800 |  |
| Operating expenses, repairs, etc. | 121,500 |  |
| General expenses | 17,500 |  |
| Bond interest | 12,500 |  |
|  | $1,921,275 | $1,921,275 |

*Additional data:*

(1) The $500,000 of capital stock had been issued at a 10% premium to the vendors of the property on June 30, 1956, the date on which the company was organized. Stock in the amount of $60,000 par was donated by the vendors and was recorded by a debit of that amount to Treasury Stock and a credit to Stock Donation. It was donated because land and buildings had not been valued accurately when entered on the books and the proceeds were to be considered as an allowance on the purchase price of land and buildings in proportion to their values as first recorded. The stock was sold in the latter part of 1956 for $25,000, which amount was credited to Treasury Stock.

(2) On June 30, 1958, a machine that cost $6,000 when the business was started was removed and replaced by a similar machine costing $10,000, which amount was charged to Operating Expenses, Repairs, etc. The replaced machine had been depreciated at $7\frac{1}{2}\%$ during the first year. The only entry made was one crediting Machinery and Equipment with its sales price of $1,500.

(3) Depreciation of buildings is to be provided at 2% annually and of machinery and equipment at $7\frac{1}{2}\%$.

(4) The inventories at June 30, 1958, were as follows:

| | |
|---|---:|
| Materials...................................... | $ 52,000 |
| Goods in process, cost........................... | 105,000 |
| Finished goods, cost............................. | 137,000 |

(5) The company decided to maintain an allowance for bad debts equal to 1% of the accounts receivable outstanding on June 30. Accordingly, $3,000 had been set aside at June 30, 1957, against which the bad debts of the year ended June 30, 1958, had been written off.

(6) Three years' insurance is carried on buildings, machinery, and equipment, and a premium of $4,500 had been paid on July 1, 1956.

(7) The first mortgage 5% sinking fund bonds mature in 10 years from July 1, 1956, with interest payable on April 1 and October 1. They were sold on July 1, 1956, at 90, and the discount is to be written off over the life of the bonds on the straight-line basis.

(8) A sinking fund and a sinking fund reserve are built up on the straight-line basis with a provision that installments after the first year shall be decreased by the amount of the annual 5% interest accretion to the fund, which interest is to be added both to the fund and to the reserve.

(9) It is learned from the records that the proper installment to the sinking fund was paid by the company on June 30, 1958, but that the amount was charged in error to the first mortgage 5% bond account.

(10) The sinking fund trustee reports that he added $1,250 interest to the fund on June 30, 1958. This had not been recorded by the company.

(11) During the year ended June 30, 1958, taxes were charged at $3,000 monthly to Operating Expenses, Repairs, etc., and Taxes Accrued was credited. The taxes paid during the year amounted to $27,000. The taxes are assessed each time for the year ended March 31.

(12) A dividend of 10% on the outstanding stock was declared June 25, payable July 15, 1958.

*Instructions:* (1) Prepare a columnar work sheet showing in separate columns the adjustments applied to the trial balance and the resulting adjusted balances, the latter segregated into balance sheet and profit and loss columns.

(2) Prepare a balance sheet and an income statement for the year ended June 30, 1958. (A.I.C.P.A. adapted)

**21-7.** On December 31, 1958, the general ledger balances of the Amberley Company are as follows:

| Dr. | | Cr. | |
|---|---|---|---|
| Cash................ | $    500 | Accounts payable... | $ 11,000 |
| National City Bank. | 10,000 | Notes payable...... | 20,000 |
| Accounts receivable. | 15,500 | Mortgage payable... | 25,000 |
| Supplies........... | 30,000 | Preferred stock..... | 25,000 |
| Land.............. | 20,000 | Common stock...... | 50,000 |
| Buildings — cost.... | 40,000 | Surplus............ | 25,000 |
| Equipment — cost.. | 60,000 | Buildings — allowance for depreciation............ | 5,000 |
| Goodwill........... | 10,000 | Equipment — allowance for depreciation............ | 25,000 |
| | $186,000 | | $186,000 |

The common stock of the company (1,000 shares, stated and paid-in value per share $50) is owned by C. M. Dale and A. V. Dale (500 shares each). The preferred stock (250 shares, par $100) is owned as follows: S. S. Dale, 100 shares; W. A. Jones, 100 shares; C. C. Fletcher, 25 shares; B. L. Sweet, 25 shares. This stock is a $6 cumulative issue, and dividends have been declared and paid in full. The mortgage carries a rate of 5% and is held by S. S. Dale. Interest has been paid in full to date. The company notes represent a seasonal borrowing at National City Bank, made December 31, 1957.

Influenced particularly by the high level of corporate taxes, the directors of the company have for some time been giving consideration to the possibility of dissolving the corporation and continuing in business as a partnership. As of January 1, 1959, this plan is carried into effect, and a partnership is formed under the same name as that of the present company by C. M. Dale, A. V. Dale, and S. S. Dale, equal partners.

The reorganization will proceed as follows:

(1) Bad debts are written off in the amount of $4,000, and in addition $1,000 is provided as an allowance against doubtful accounts.

(2) The land is taken over at the estimated fair market value of $22,000.

(3) The corporation borrows $4,000 in cash from each member of the firm for 30 days, giving the company's note in each case at 6%.

(4) The corporation redeems the preferred stockholdings of Jones, Fletcher, and Sweet at the call price of $110 per share.

(5) C. M. Dale and A. V. Dale assigned their stockholdings to the firm; S. S. Dale transfers his holding of preferred stock and the mortgage on corporate real estate to the firm. The firm places a value of $11,000 on the preferred shares and $72,000 on the common shares.

(6) The firm buys all the assets and business of the corporation at the adjusted book values.

(7) The firm pays by assuming all corporate obligations as shown by the company's books and by delivering the outstanding stock certificates, the mortgage, and the partners' notes.

(8) The partners' notes are canceled, their amounts being treated as contributed firm capital.

(9) The corporation is dissolved.

*Instructions:* Prepare a comprehensive work sheet showing in columnar form the partnership's assets and liabilities after all transactions have been completed. Assume that all transactions are carried through as of January 1, 1959. (A.I.C.P.A. adapted)

**21-8.** The Colt Company submits the following balance sheet, dated June 30, 1956:

ASSETS

| | |
|---|---:|
| Current assets....................................... | $2,000,000 |
| Fixed assets, less reserves............................ | 2,500,000 |
| Intangible assets..................................... | 3,000,000 |
| Organization expenses............................... | 500,000 |
| Deferred charges.................................... | 100,000 |
| | $8,100,000 |

LIABILITIES

| | |
|---|---:|
| Current liabilities................................... | $ 500,000 |
| Preferred stock — 8% cumulative — 400,000 shares of $10 each........................................ | 4,000,000 |
| Common stock — 300,000 shares of $10 each.......... | 3,000,000 |
| Earned surplus...................................... | 600,000 |
| | $8,100,000 |

The common stock was issued for the intangible assets acquired at organization.

The company had been in existence for a period of five years but had paid no preferred dividends, so that on June 30, 1956, an amount of $1,600,000 was in arrears. In order to liquidate this obligation and properly restate the accounts, the board of directors had previously submitted a plan of recapitalization, to take effect on June 30, 1956, which was accepted by all the shareholders, as follows:

(1) The company is to amend its articles of incorporation and change its capital structure so that the recapitalization may take effect as of June 30, 1956, as follows:

    (a) The authorized capital will be $5,100,000, consisting of 480,000 shares of 4% preferred of $10 each and 300,000 shares of common of $1 each. The preferred shares may be made either cumulative nonparticipating or noncumulative participating.

    (b) The 8% preferred shareholders are to relinquish all claims for dividends, for which they are to receive 50% of the amount of their claims in new preferred stock at par value.

(c) The 8% preferred shareholders have up to December 31, 1958, the option to exchange their shares and reduced dividend claims par-for-par either for 4% cumulative nonparticipating preferred with dividends cumulative from June 30, 1956, on, or for 4% noncumulative participating preferred shares. The noncumulative shares will participate equally with the common shares in the earnings after June 30, 1956, that are in excess of the preferred dividend requirements, up to 30% of this excess.

(d) The par value of the common shares will be reduced from $10 to $1 a share.

(2) The company is to declare a dividend of 20 cents, payable on July 15, 1956, on the 4% cumulative nonparticipating preferred shares.

On July 1, 1956, holders of 90% of the 8% preferred shares elected to take the 4% cumulative nonparticipating shares and holders of the remaining 10% to postpone their choice.

*Instructions:* (1) Prepare a balance sheet as of June 30, 1956, after giving effect to the recapitalization plan.

(2) Prepare the entries that are to be made on December 31, 1958, in the event that holders of 30,000 shares of 8% preferred elect, between June 30, 1956, and December 31, 1958, to exchange them for 4% cumulative preferred and the holders of the remaining 10,000 shares to take 4% noncumulative shares. Assume that no preferred dividends have been paid or declared since July 15, 1956. (A.I.C.P.A. adapted)

**21-9.** You have been called in by a member of the board of directors of the Fox Corporation for advice in connection with a proposed plan of reorganization. He provides you with the information that follows:

The Fox Corporation is a manufacturer of machine tools. Its business has shown wide fluctuations and there have been corresponding variations in profits. For a number of years prior to 1957 there had not been any significant average earnings; however, for the year 1957 there was a net profit of $942,100. As of December 31, 1957, the following statement was prepared:

| | | |
|---|---:|---:|
| $3 Cumulative preferred stock, $50 par value — outstanding 96,200 shares (dividends in arrears since September 30, 1941) | | $4,810,000 |
| Common stock, no-par — outstanding 120,000 shares at assigned value of | | 3,365,473 |
| Earned deficit 1/1/57 | ($1,174,280) | |
| Profit for 1957 | 942,100 | (232,180) |
| Total | | $7,943,293 |

Parenthesis ( ) denotes red figure.

A plan of capital adjustment had been worked out during 1957, which was ratified by the stockholders and made effective as of January 1, 1958. This plan provided that the $3 preferred was to be reduced from $50 par value to $40 par value; that it continue to be preferred for $3 per share dividends on a cumulative basis and that it be preferred in liquidation at $50 per share and redeemable at the option of the company at $55 per share. In settlement of dividends in arrears, the company paid $360,750 cash and issued 216,450 shares of "B" stock having a par value of $10 per share. The "B" shares are nonvoting and are not entitled to dividends. They are redeemable at $20 per share and entitled to $20 per share after preferred but prior to common in liquidation. The agreement under which they are issued provides that a cash redemption fund shall be set up equal to 50% of the yearly net profits in excess of dividend requirements on preferred stock. The fund is to be used to purchase and retire "B" stock. Tenders are to be obtained from stockholders, the lowest being accepted. If no tenders are received within three months after January 1 of each year, the shares to be retired are to be determined by lot. The provisions of issue also state that as long as any "B" stock is outstanding, no dividends may be paid on common stock. The assigned value of common was also reduced to $600,000.

The surplus created by this restatement of stock was treated in accordance with accepted accounting practice. All stockholders accepted the exchange offer.

The operations for the year 1958 resulted in a net profit, after taxes, of $1,631,316. Dividends for the full year were paid on the preferred stock.

It now appears that operations are going to be profitable for an indefinite period and the board of directors desires to work out a plan whereby common stock can be put on a dividend basis. Preferred is currently selling for $52 per share and "B" stock for $9.50 per share.

Based on these values, a plan is under consideration by the board of directors, which it is hoped will enable them to place common on a dividend basis if good earnings continue. This plan calls for authorizing a 5% debenture issue, which will be offered to the preferred stockholders in exchange for their stock at the rate of $100 of debentures and 2 shares of common for each 2 shares of preferred. It is anticipated that the common will be put on a $1 annual dividend basis after the capital adjustments proposed. Holders of "B" stock are to be offered 1 share of new 6% preferred, which is to be issued having $100 par value, and 5 shares of common for each 10 shares of "B" stock, all before use of the retirement fund.

*Instructions:* (1) Prepare a summary of the capital and the surplus of the company as of December 31, 1958.

(2) Prepare a statement showing the condition that would exist on January 1, 1959, if the reorganization plan were made effective as of that date.

(3) Prepare a statement showing the amount of earnings per share of common stock in 1958 if the proposed plan could have been in effect as of January 1, 1958. (Assume that the corporate income tax rate for 1958 is 40%.) (A.I.C.P.A. adapted)

# Chapter 22

# RETAINED EARNINGS

## EARNINGS AND EARNINGS DISTRIBUTION

**NATURE OF RETAINED EARNINGS** The difference between assets and liabilities is proprietorship or capital, the owners' equity in assets. In a sole proprietorship, the owner's entire interest in assets resulting from investments, withdrawals, and past profit and loss activities is reported in a single capital account. In a partnership, capital balances for the individual partners normally report partners' full equities resulting from investments, withdrawals, and past profits and losses. It has already been indicated that, because of the nature of the corporation form, a portion of corporate capital is designated as paid-in or invested capital. The amount by which the total corporate capital exceeds the invested capital is known as *retained earnings* or *earned surplus*.

In its most elemental form retained earnings is the meeting place of the balance sheet accounts and the income statement accounts. In successive periods the balances of the profit and loss accounts are carried to retained earnings. Distributions in the form of dividends reduce retained earnings. As a result, the retained earnings balance represents the net accumulated reinvested earnings of the corporation. If the nature of retained earnings were as simple as thus indicated, there would be little confusion in its interpretation as well as in its use. But a number of factors tend to complicate the nature of retained earnings, and these must be recognized in the interpretation and the use or disposition of this item. Among these factors are: transactions between the corporation and its stockholders that affect retained earnings; recapitalizations that result in transfers between retained earnings and capital stock; quasi-reorganization and a "fresh-start" retained earnings; legal requirements affecting retained earnings in the protection of owner and creditor groups; contractual limitations upon the use of retained earnings for dividends; and methods of presentation of retained earnings in informing stockholders as to the employment of retained earnings within the enterprise. The retained earnings balance is frequently misunderstood and failure to appreciate the nature of this item may lead to seriously misleading inferences in the interpretation of the balance sheet.

**SOURCE OF RETAINED EARNINGS**

Retained earnings is the terminus of all profit and loss accounting. The retained earnings account is increased by profits from normal operations involving the sale of commodities or services and is reduced by losses from these activities. The retained earnings account is also affected by: (1) extraordinary profit and loss items, including gains and losses arising from the sale of securities or plant assets and the retirement of long-term debt, and charges arising from the write-off of worthless securities or other assets and the arbitrary write-down of goodwill and other intangibles; and (2) corrections in profits of prior periods. As previously indicated, these items may be recorded in separate accounts and reported under appropriate headings following a summary of normally recurring items on the income statement, or they may be recorded directly in retained earnings and reported on the retained earnings statement.

Corporate income increasing retained earnings arises only from transactions with individuals or businesses outside of the company. No earnings are recognized in the construction of machinery or other plant items for a company's own use, even though the cost of such construction is below the price that would have to be paid outsiders for similar assets; self-construction at less than the asset purchase price is simply regarded as a savings in cost. No earnings are recognized on transactions with stockholders involving treasury stock; the purchase and sale of treasury stock are regarded as transactions giving rise to the contraction and expansion of paid-in capital. The receipt of properties through donation and the recognition of changes in asset values in the accounts are not regarded as earnings; donations are regarded as giving rise to additional paid-in capital, while the appraisal increases are recognized as giving rise to a special unrealized capital element.

The earnings of a corporation may be distributed to the stockholders or they may be retained to provide for expanding operations. When earnings are retained, they may be appropriated so as to be reported as unavailable for dividend declaration. Appropriations may be returned to retained earnings after the purpose of the appropriation has been fulfilled. When operating losses or other charges to the retained earnings account produce a debit balance in this account, the debit balance is referred to as a *deficit*.

**DATED RETAINED EARNINGS**

Any profits earned after a corporate readjustment or quasi-reorganization should be separately summarized and reported on the balance sheet as retained earnings dating from the time of such action. _Dated retained earnings_ seek to inform investors and others of the occurrence of a restatement of capital and the financial progress that has been made since that time.

The American Institute Committee on Accounting Procedure in considering the problem of reporting dated retained earnings on the balance sheet originally recommended that a dated balance be disclosed until the time the effective date of readjustment was no longer considered to possess any special significance. In 1956 the Committee in a special bulletin addressed to this matter indicated the belief that dating would rarely, if ever, be of significance after a period of ten years, and under exceptional circumstances might be discontinued upon the conclusion of a lesser period.[1]

The Chief Accountant of the Securities and Exchange Commission has stated that when a deficit is charged to paid-in capital previously existing or arising in the course of a quasi-reorganization, (1) full disclosure of the point of time from which the new retained earnings dates should be made on all subsequent statements of retained earnings, and (2) until such time as the results of operations of the company on the new basis are available for an appropriate period of years (at least three), any statement or showing of retained earnings should, in order to provide additional disclosure of the occurrence and the significance of the quasi-reorganization, indicate the total amount of the deficit and any charges that were made to paid-in capital in the course of the quasi-reorganization which would otherwise have been required to be made against income or retained earnings.[2] Furthermore, when a company is permitted by state law to charge a deficit to paid-in capital pursuant to a resolution by the board of directors and without approval by stockholders, the Commission would require "complete disclosure of all of the attendant facts and circumstances and their effect on the company's financial position in each balance sheet and surplus statement. . . ." A statement indicating the possible effects of such action on the character of future dividends would also be called for, appropriate disclosure being made in a form such as follows:

It should be noted that on ＿＿＿＿＿＿＿ by action of the board of directors, without action by stockholders, the company charged off a $＿＿＿＿＿ deficit in earned surplus against its capital surplus. This procedure will permit the company in the future to reflect undis-

[1] _Accounting Research Bulletin No. 46_, "Discontinuance of Dating Earned Surplus," 1956 (New York: American Institute of Certified Public Accountants).

[2] _Accounting Series Release No. 15_, "Description of surplus accruing subsequent to effective date of quasi-reorganization," 1940 (Washington, D. C.: United States Securities and Exchange Commission).

tributed earnings subsequent to _____ as earned surplus, instead of as a reduction of the deficit charged off to capital surplus. One result of this procedure is to permit the distribution, as ordinary dividends, of earned surplus accruing subsequent to _____, without regard to the deficit charged off to capital surplus. Furthermore, if earnings subsequent to _____ are less than the deficit written off, distributions thereof may in effect represent distributions of capital or capital surplus.[1]

**DIVIDENDS**　　　　　　Dividends are distributions to stockholders of the corporation in proportion to the number of shares that are held by the respective owners. Such distributions may take the form of (1) cash, (2) other properties, (3) evidences of corporate indebtedness, or (4) additional stock issue. All of the foregoing distributions involve a reduction in retained earnings, except dividends in corporate liquidation, which involve a return to stockholders of a portion or all of the corporate legal capital and thus are reductions in capital designated by the capital stock balance.

The term *dividend* is generally used to imply the distribution of a cash dividend, with past accumulated earnings as the source of such a distribution. Dividends in a form other than cash should be designated in terms of the nature of the distribution; dividends that are declared from a capital source other than retained earnings should carry a special description of their special origin. The terms *stock dividend*, *property dividend*, and *scrip dividend* suggest distributions of a special nature; designations such as *liquidating dividend*, *stock dividend of appraisal increment*, and *dividend distribution of paid-in capital* would serve to identify clearly the special origin of the distribution.

"Dividends paid out of retained earnings" is an expression frequently encountered. Accuracy, however, would require the statement that dividends are paid out of cash, which serves to reduce retained earnings. Investment by owners results in an increase in property and in the owners' equity in property. Dividend distribution represents no more than asset withdrawals reducing both the amount of property and the owners' equity in that property.

Dividends require special action as to their declaration by the board of directors. In declaring dividends, the board of directors must observe the legal requirements governing the maintenance of legal or stated capital. These requirements vary with the individual states. In addition to observing legal requirements, the board of directors must consider the financial aspects of dividend distributions — the

---

[1] *Accounting Series Release No. 16*, "Disclosure of charge of deficit to capital surplus without approval of stockholders," 1940 (Washington, D. C.: United States Securities and Exchange Commission).

company asset position, present asset requirements, and future asset requirements. The board of directors, then, must answer two questions: Do we have the legal right to declare a dividend? Is such a distribution financially sound?[1]

When a dividend can legally be declared and the board of directors takes appropriate action and makes announcement of the action to stockholders, revocation of the dividend is not possible. The corporation must now recognize a liability to stockholders. In the event of corporate insolvency prior to the dividend distribution, stockholders have claims as a creditor group to the dividend, and as an ownership group to any residual distributions that may be made after corporate liabilities have been met in full. A dividend that was illegal upon its declaration is revocable; in the event of insolvency, such an action is nullified and stockholders participate in asset distributions only after creditors have been paid in full.

**THE FORMAL DIVIDEND ANNOUNCEMENT**  Three dates are essential in the formal dividend statement: (1) date of declaration, (2) date of payment, and (3) date of stockholders' record. Dividends are made payable to stockholders of record as of a date that follows the date of declaration and precedes the date of payment. The announcement of a formal dividend declaration would read, "The Board of Directors of the Forrest Co. at their meeting on November 5, 1958, declared the regular quarterly dividend on outstanding common stock of 50 cents per share, payable on January 15, 1959, to stockholders of record at the close of business, December 20, 1958." The liability for dividends payable is recorded on the declaration date and is canceled on the payment date. No entry is required on the record date, but a list of the stockholders is made up as of the close of business on December 20. These are the persons who are to receive payment on January 15. A full record of the dividend declaration should be made in the minute book.

**CASH DIVIDENDS**  The most common type of dividend is a *cash dividend*, which provides a cash return to holders of capital stock. For the corporation, such dividends involve

[1] Laws range from those making any part of capital other than that designated legal capital available for dividends to those permitting dividends only from retained earnings and under specified conditions. In most states dividends cannot be declared in the event of a deficit; in a few states, however, dividends, equal to current earnings may be distributed despite a previously accumulated deficit. The availability of capital as a basis for dividends is a determination to be made by the attorney and not by the accountant. The accountant must report accurately the sources of each capital increase; the attorney will investigate the availability of such sources as bases for dividend distributions.

a reduction in retained earnings and in cash. A current liability for dividends payable is recognized on the declaration date; this is canceled when dividend checks are sent out to stockholders. Entries to record the declaration and the payment of a cash dividend follow:

| | | |
|---|---|---|
| Retained Earnings | 100,000 | |
|     Cash Dividends Payable | | 100,000 |
| Cash Dividends Payable | 100,000 | |
|     Cash | | 100,000 |

In declaring a cash dividend, the board of directors must consider the limitations set by the current position and the cash balance. For example, a corporation may have retained earnings of $500,000. If, however, it has cash of only $150,000, it will not be able to pay a $500,000 dividend unless certain other assets can be converted into cash or unless cash is borrowed. If the cash balance required for regular operations is $100,000, the cash immediately available for dividend payment is only $50,000. Although retained earnings may offer a legal basis for the declaration of dividends of $500,000, the amount distributable at this time is limited to one tenth of this figure, since the assets represented by retained earnings are not in a form that makes them available for distribution.

**SCRIP DIVIDENDS**      If a corporation has retained earnings that may be used as a basis for dividend declaration but does not have sufficient funds at the time for a cash dividend, it may declare a *scrip dividend*, which consists of a written promise to pay a certain amount at some future date. The corporation is thus able to take regular dividend action even though it is temporarily short of cash. Stockholders, in turn, are provided currently with an instrument that they may discount for cash if they wish, provided the credit of the corporation is satisfactory. Such dividends are not commonly employed.

Assume that a scrip dividend of $150,000 is declared, payable in six months together with interest at the rate of 6% for the period of payment deferment. The declaration of the dividend is recorded as follows:

| | | |
|---|---|---|
| Retained Earnings | 150,000 | |
|     Scrip Dividend Payable | | 150,000 |

When the scrip matures and scrip and interest payments are made, the entry is:

| | | |
|---|---|---|
| Scrip Dividend Payable | 150,000 | |
| Interest Expense | 4,500 | |
|     Cash | | 154,500 |

**PROPERTY DIVIDENDS**   A distribution to stockholders that is payable in some asset other than cash is generally referred to as a *property dividend*. Frequently, the asset to be distributed is certain securities of other companies that are owned by the corporation. The corporation thus transfers to its stockholders its ownership interest in such securities.

A property dividend avoids the necessity of sale of assets for the payment of dividends. When the value of the property exceeds its cost, no recognition would be made for tax purposes by the corporation of a "gain" on such an asset. However, for tax purposes stockholders will be required to recognize dividend income equal to the fair market value of the asset acquired.

To illustrate the accounting for a property dividend, assume that the State Oil Corporation owns 100,000 shares in the Valley Oil Co., cost $10,000,000, and that it desires to distribute this holding to its stockholders. There are 1,000,000 shares of State Oil Corporation stock outstanding. Accordingly, a dividend of 1/10 of a share of Valley Oil Co. stock is declared on each share of State Oil Corporation stock outstanding. The entries for the declaration and the distribution of the dividend are:

| | | |
|---|---|---|
| Retained Earnings............................ | 10,000,000 | |
|    Dividend Payable in Stock of Valley Oil Co.. | | 10,000,000 |
| Dividend Payable in Stock of Valley Oil Co.... | 10,000,000 | |
|    Investment in Stock of Valley Oil Co........ | | 10,000,000 |

**STOCK DIVIDENDS**   A corporation may issue additional shares of stock in proportion to original share holdings by stockholders. Such a distribution is known as a *stock dividend*. A stock dividend permits the corporation to retain accumulated earnings within the business while at the same time offering stockholders evidence of their respective interests in accumulated corporate earnings.

Reference to a stock dividend usually implies (1) the capitalization of retained earnings and (2) a distribution of common stock to common stockholders. Such distributions are sometimes termed *ordinary stock dividends.* In some states, stock dividends may be effected by transfers of certain paid-in capital or appraisal capital balances to the legal or stated capital accounts. In some instances, common or preferred stock has been issued to holders of preferred stock or preferred stock has been issued to holders of common stock. The latter situations, however, are relatively unusual. Such distributions are sometimes referred to as *special stock dividends.*

The ordinary stock dividend makes a portion of retained earnings no longer available for distribution while raising the legal capital of the corporation. As far as the recipient is concerned, the number of shares that he holds has gone up, but his interest in the corporation remains unchanged; the effects of a stock dividend in terms of his corporate interest are no different from those of a stock split-up.

In recording a stock dividend, a charge is made to retained earnings and paid-in capital balances are credited. The stock dividend is thus viewed in the accounts as constituting, in effect, two transactions: (1) the payment by the corporation of a dividend; and (2) the return of such payment to the corporation in exchange for shares of stock.

In distributing shares of stock as a dividend, the issuing corporation must meet legal requirements as to the amount of retained earnings requiring transfer to the capital stock account. When stock has a par or a stated value, an amount equal to the value of the shares issued normally will have to be transferred from retained earnings to capital stock; when stock is no-par and without a stated value, the laws of the state of incorporation may provide specific requirements as to amounts to be transferred or they may leave such determinations to the corporate directors.

Although laws set requirements as to transfers from retained earnings to legal or stated capital balances upon the issuance of additional shares of stock, the board of directors is not prevented from going beyond legal requirements and taking action to raise capital stock and also additional paid-in capital balances. For example, assume that stock, par $100, was originally issued at 120. Legal requirements may call for the transfer from retained earnings to capital stock of no more than the par value of the stock issued as a dividend. The board of directors, however, in order to preserve the original capital stock and stock premium relationship, may authorize a transfer from retained earnings of $120 per share; capital stock, then, may be increased $100 and the premium balance $20 for every share issued. Or the board of directors may decide that the retained earnings transfer shall be made in terms of the current fair market value of shares, which exceeds the legal value per share. Here, too, the charge to retained earnings exceeds the par or the stated value of the stock issued; the credit to capital stock is accompanied by a credit to a premium or other paid-in capital balance.

The Committee on Accounting Procedure of the American Institute of Certified Public Accountants has indicated that proper corporate policy in certain situations would call for the capitalization of an amount equal to the fair market value of shares issued as a stock dividend. The Committee points out:

... a stock dividend does not, in fact, give rise to any change whatsoever in either the corporation's assets or its respective shareholders' proportionate interests therein. However, it cannot fail to be recognized that, merely as a consequence of the expressed purpose of the transaction and its characterization as a *dividend* in related notices to shareholders and the public at large, many recipients of stock dividends look upon them as distributions of corporate earnings and usually in an amount equivalent to the fair value of the additional shares received. Furthermore, it is to be presumed that such views of recipients are materially strengthened in those instances, which are by far the most numerous, where the issuances are so small in comparison with the shares previously outstanding that they do not have any apparent effect upon the share market price and, consequently, the market value of the shares previously held remains substantially unchanged. The committee therefore believes that where these circumstances exist the corporation should in the public interest account for the transaction by transferring from earned surplus to the category of permanent capitalization (represented by the capital stock and capital surplus accounts) an amount equal to the fair value of the additional shares issued. Unless this is done, the amount of earnings which the shareholder may believe to have been distributed to him will be left, except to the extent otherwise dictated by legal requirements, in earned surplus subject to possible further similar stock issuances or cash distributions.[1]

However, the Committee indicates that certain circumstances would suggest that retained earnings be charged for no more than stock par, stated, or other value as required by law. The Committee points out:

Where the number of additional shares issued as a stock dividend is so great that it has, or may reasonably be expected to have, the effect of materially reducing the share market value, the committee believes that the implications and possible constructions discussed ... are not likely to exist and that the transaction clearly partakes of the nature of a stock split-up. ... Consequently, the committee considers that under such circumstances there is no need to capitalize earned surplus, other than to the extent occasioned by legal requirements. It recommends, however, that in such instances every effort be made to avoid the use of the word *dividend* in related corporate resolutions, notices, and announcements and that, in those cases where because of legal requirements this cannot be done, the transaction be described, for example, as a *split-up effected in the form of a dividend.*[2]

The Committee feels that the majority of stock dividends will probably fall within the first category stated above, suggesting charges to retained earnings of amounts that exceed legal requirements. While the Committee is reluctant to name a dividend percentage that would require adherence to this practice, it does suggest that in stock distri-

---

[1]*Accounting Research Bulletin No. 43*, "Restatement and Revision of Accounting Research Bulletins," 1953 (New York: American Institute of Certified Public Accountants), pp. 51–52.

[2]*Ibid.*, p. 52.

butions of recent years involving the issuance of less than 20% to 25% of the number of shares previously outstanding, there would be but few instances where charges to retained earnings at the fair market value of additional shares issued would not be supportable.

The examples that follow illustrate the entries that are made for the declaration and the issue of a stock dividend. Assume that the capital for the Bradford Co. on July 1 is as follows:

| | |
|---|---:|
| Capital stock, 10,000 shares outstanding, par $10......... | $100,000 |
| Premium on stock.................................... | 10,000 |
| Retained earnings .................................... | 75,000 |

The company declares a 10% stock dividend, or a dividend of 1 share for every 10 held. Shares are selling on the market on this date at $16 per share. The stock dividend is to be recorded at the market value of the shares issued, or $16,000 (1,000 shares at $16). The entries to record the declaration of the dividend and the stock issue follow:

| | | |
|---|---:|---:|
| Retained Earnings............................... | 16,000 | |
|    Stock Dividend Distributable.................. | | 10,000 |
|    Premium on Stock............................ | | 6,000 |
| Stock Dividend Distributable..................... | 10,000 | |
|    Capital Stock, $10 par....................... | | 10,000 |

The effects of the stock dividend upon paid-in capital here are the same as would be the effects of the sale of such additional shares at market price.

Assume, however, that the company declares a 50% stock dividend, or a dividend of 1 share for every 2 held. Legal requirements call for the transfer from retained earnings to capital stock of an amount equal to the par value of the shares issued, and the stock dividend is recorded at this value. Entries for the declaration of the dividend and the dividend issue follow:

| | | |
|---|---:|---:|
| Retained Earnings............................... | 50,000 | |
|    Stock Dividend Distributable.................. | | 50,000 |
| Stock Dividend Distributable..................... | 50,000 | |
|    Capital Stock, $10 par....................... | | 50,000 |

If in the preceding case the board of directors wished to maintain invested capital balances in their original relationship, authorization could be made for capitalization of the issue at $11 per share. Entries to record the dividend declaration and its issue then would be:

| | | |
|---|---:|---:|
| Retained Earnings............................... | 55,000 | |
|    Stock Dividend Distributable.................. | | 50,000 |
|    Premium on Stock............................ | | 5,000 |
| Stock Dividend Distributable..................... | 50,000 | |
|    Capital Stock, $10 par....................... | | 50,000 |

When stock dividends are issued, *fractional share warrants* are given to stockholders whose holdings make them eligible for fractional shares. For example, when a 10% stock dividend is issued, a stockholder owning 25 shares can be given no more than 2 full shares; however, the holdings in excess of an even multiple of 10 shares are recognized by the issue of a fractional share warrant for ½ share. The warrant for ½ share may be sold, or a warrant for an additional ½ share may be purchased so that a full share may be claimed from the company. In some instances the corporation may distribute cash in lieu of fractional warrants or it may issue a full share of stock in exchange for warrants accompanied by cash for the fractional share deficiency.

Assume that the Miller Company in distributing a stock dividend issues fractional share warrants totaling 500 shares, par $50. The entry for the fractional share warrants issued would be as follows:

```
Stock Dividend Distributable ...................  25,000
    Fractional Share Warrants Issued...............        25,000
```

Assuming that 80% of the warrants are ultimately turned in for shares and that the remaining warrants expire, the following entry would be made:

```
Fractional Share Warrants Issued..................  25,000
    Capital Stock, $50 par..........................        20,000
    Paid-in Capital from Forfeitures on Fractional
    Share Warrants.................................         5,000
```

If a balance sheet is prepared after the declaration of a stock dividend but before its payment, Stock Dividend Distributable is reported in the capital section as an addition to Capital Stock Outstanding. By the declaration of the dividend, the corporation has reduced its retained earnings balance and is committed to the increase of capital stock. The difference between capital stock authorized and the sum of (1) capital stock issued, (2) capital stock subscribed, and (3) stock dividends distributable represents the balance of stock that the corporation may still sell.

Although a stock dividend can be compared to a stock split from the investors' point of view, its effects upon corporate capital differ from those of the stock split. A stock dividend results in an increase in the number of shares outstanding and in an increase in the capital stock balance, no change being made in the value assigned to each share of stock on the company records; the increase in capital stock outstanding is effected by a transfer from retained earnings, the retained earnings balance available for dividends being permanently reduced by this transfer. A stock split merely divides the existing capital stock balance into more parts and reduces the par or stated value assigned to each share; there is no change in the retained earnings available for dividends, both capital stock and retained earnings balances remaining unchanged.

There have been suggestions that the restatement of retained income as paid-in capital as a result of stock dividends, recapitalizations, or other appropriate action calls for special disclosure on the balance sheet. Such disclosure will serve to inform the statement reader that a portion of the capital reported as paid-in actually originated from corporate earnings. For example, assume the information for the Bradford Co. on page 702 and the transfer to paid-in capital of $55,000 on the issue of a stock dividend. Corporate capital may be presented in the following manner:

| | | |
|---|---:|---:|
| Paid-in capital: | | |
| Capital stock, $10 par | $150,000 | |
| Premium on stock | 15,000 | $165,000 |
| | | |
| Retained earnings | $ 75,000 | |
| Less amount transferred to paid-in capital by stock dividends | 55,000 | 20,000 |
| | | |
| Total capital | | $185,000 |

**LIQUIDATING DIVIDENDS**    A corporation may declare a *liquidating dividend* when the dividend is to be considered a return to stockholders of a portion of their original investments. Such distributions on the books of the corporation represent a reduction of the invested capital balances. Instead of actually debiting Capital Stock, however, it would be possible to charge a separate account for the impairment in invested capital, this balance to be subtracted from the invested capital balances in the preparation of subsequent statements. Liquidating dividends should be recorded on the books of the investor as recoveries of the cost of the stock.

Corporations owning wasting assets that are not being replaced may regularly declare dividends that are in part a distribution of earnings and in part a distribution of the corporation's invested capital. Entries on the corporation books for such dividend declarations should reflect the decrease in the two capital elements. This analysis should also be reported to stockholders in letters accompanying the dividend checks. The investor will recognize the earnings distribution portion of the dividend as income, the liquidating portion as a reduction in the investment account balance. Accounting for a

ALR

Anna Lee Riggleman
Dorcas,
West Virginia

- 2.5

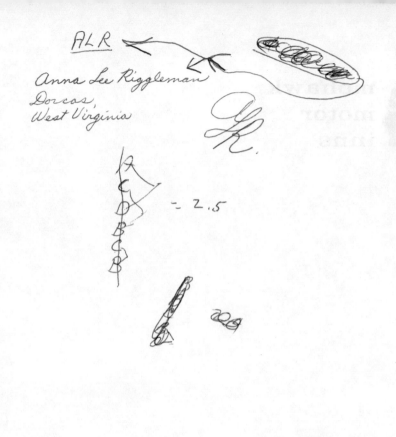

## mohawk
## motor
## inns

BUFF
NEW YC
1640 Main at Michi
TT 6-7

ROCHES
NEW YC
55 Troup at Plymouth
Inner
LOcust 2-9

SYRACU
NEW YC
1060 East Gene
GRanite 6-4

PHILADELPI
PENNSYLVAI
4200 Roosevelt E
U.S. Rou
CUmberland 9-9

BALTIMO
MARYLA
1701 Russel
Wash-Baltimore-Expressv
837-2

INDIANAPO
INDIA
5855 East Washing
U.S. Route
FLeetwood 7-8

CINCINN
O
2880 Central
U.S. 27 &
681-3

company with wasting assets and the entries to record distributions to stockholders representing both earnings and a return of investment were described on pages 498 and 499.

**DIVIDENDS ON PREFERRED STOCK**   When dividends on preferred stock are cumulative, the payment of a definite rate of return on these shares is necessary before any dividends may be paid on common. When the board of directors fails to declare dividends on cumulative preferred stock, information concerning the amount of dividends in arrears should be reported parenthetically or in note form on the balance sheet to provide full disclosure of the status of preferred and common stockholders. A division of retained earnings on the balance sheet into the amount required to meet dividends in arrears and the balance free for other purposes would also serve to inform readers of the dividend arrearages and the implications of such arrearages. Retained earnings would thus be reported on the balance sheet in the following manner:

```
Retained earnings:
  Required to meet dividends in arrears on preferred
    stock....................................   $40,000
  Balance...................................    12,000
                                               _____
    Total retained earnings.....................        $52,000
```

The board of directors may pay a portion of a cumulative preferred dividend or a portion of the total in arrears. For example, 2% may be paid annually on 7% cumulative preferred stock, allowing 5% to accumulate for future payment. Or a payment of $15 may be made on cumulative dividends in arrears of $50, leaving $35 as the balance in arrears.

**DIVIDENDS ON NO-PAR STOCK**   Cash dividends on no-par stock must be expressed as an amount per share, since a par figure upon which a percentage may be applied is lacking. It is also customary to express dividends on par-value stock in the same manner.

When no-par stock is outstanding and the corporation desires to transfer an amount from Retained Earnings to Capital Stock, there is no need actually to declare a stock dividend. The corporation can simply take action to raise the stated value of the no-par stock. An entry such as the following is made on the books:

```
Retained Earnings............................   500,000
  Capital Stock..............................            500,000
      To raise $5 stated value on 100,000 shares of
      no-par stock to $10 in accordance with reso-
      lution by board of directors.
```

**EXTRAORDINARY DIVIDEND DISTRIBUTIONS**    In the case of common stock, a corporation may establish a policy of regular dividends and may provide for greater payments through *extraordinary dividend distributions*, or *extra dividends*, when earnings warrant additional distributions. For example, a corporation may have a regular rate of 50 cents a quarter or $2 a year per share on common stock. In a particular quarter it may wish to declare a dividend of 80 cents a share. Such a dividend may be expressed as a 50-cent regular dividend plus a 30-cent extra dividend.

**SOURCE OF DIVIDENDS**    It is reasonable to assume that dividends have a closer relationship to current earnings than to those of past years. This would suggest that dividends be charged to current profit and loss rather than to Retained Earnings. Dividends Declared may be debited instead of Retained Earnings and the dividends declared account may be closed into the profit and loss account before the latter is closed into Retained Earnings. Dividends would be reported as a subtraction item at the bottom of the income statement, the balance on the statement after subtracting dividends from net income then representing the net change in retained earnings for the period. Such a practice provides a direct comparison between the earnings and the dividends in any one period. A number of corporate reports show dividends as a disposition of current earnings.

**APPRAISAL CAPITAL**    The problems and the procedures involved in recording an increase in plant assets after their valuation by independent appraisers and the authorization for use of this information in the accounts by the board of directors were described in Chapter 17. Charges to assets for increases established by appraisal were accompanied by credits to appraisal capital accounts. Such capital is separately designated in the capital section. Readers of the balance sheet are thus made aware of the fact that property items are stated at amounts in excess of cost and that this action has resulted in an unrealized capital element.

Disposal of an asset that has been increased by appraisal results in cancellation of the asset balance at appraised value, cancellation of the related appraisal capital, and recognition of a gain or loss that is based upon cost.

When a depreciable asset is increased as a result of appraisal and when depreciation is reported on the basis of appraised value, transfers may be made periodically from appraisal capital balances to retained earnings so that the latter account is corrected for the profit understatement and appraisal capital shows no more than the appraisal increase still included in the net asset balance. When the asset is fully depreciated, the full amount of the appraisal capital will have been transferred to retained earnings. Entries that are made periodically to record depreciation on property items at their appraised values and to record the transfer of appraisal capital to retained earnings after the accounts are closed were previously described and illustrated on pages 530 and 531.

When depreciation is recorded at cost, the entry for depreciation is accompanied by an entry reducing the asset increase and the appraisal capital. Here, too, when the asset is fully depreciated, the full amount of the appraisal increase will have been canceled. The entries that are made periodically to record depreciation on appraised property items at cost and to reduce property items and appraisal capital were previously described and illustrated on pages 529 and 530.

Appraisal capital shrinks only as the asset value from which it emerged shrinks. Appraisal capital should never be used to absorb operating losses or the write-down of properties other than those values representing the source of such capital. Appraisal capital representing unrealized earnings is not properly used as a basis for cash dividends; however, its use as a basis for stock dividends is permitted in some states.

## QUESTIONS

1. "Accumulated earnings are in general supported by a cross section of all the assets." "Directors are criticized by stockholders for failure to declare dividends when accumulated earnings are present." Are these two statements related? Explain.

2. (a) What are the sources of retained earnings? (b) What dispositions may be made of retained earnings?

3. What circumstances give rise to a *dated retained earnings?*

4. The Burrows Corporation reports a retained earnings balance of $1,500,000. What reasons may be offered by the company for failure to use such legally available earnings as a basis for dividends?

5. Which of the following transactions are a source of capital? Indicate the class of capital in each case.
   (a) Operating profits.
   (b) Cancellation of a part of a liability upon prompt payment of the balance.
   (c) Reduction of par value of stock outstanding.

(d) Discovery of an understatement of income in a previous period.

(e) Release of Retained Earnings Appropriated for Purchase of Treasury Stock upon the sale of treasury stock.

(f) Issue of bonds at a premium.

(g) Purchase of the corporation's own capital stock at a discount.

(h) Increase in the company's earning capacity, taken to be evidence of considerable goodwill.

(i) Construction of equipment for the company's own use at a cost less than the prevailing market price of identical equipment.

(j) Donation to the corporation of treasury stock.

(k) Sale of plant and equipment at a profit.

(l) Gain on bond retirement.

(m) Revaluation of plant and equipment resulting in

(1) decrease in allowance for depreciation as a result of over-depreciation in past periods, and

(2) increase in asset book value as a result of increase in asset replacement value.

(n) Collection of stock assessments from stockholders.

**6.** What circumstances may call for the declaration of a scrip dividend?

**7.** (a) Define stock dividend. (b) What are the effects of a stock dividend on corporate capital accounts as compared with those of a stock split?

**8.** Summarize the recommendations of the American Institute Committee on Accounting Procedure with respect to the charge to be made to retained earnings in recording a stock dividend.

**9.** It has been recommended that the balance sheet maintain a permanent distinction between paid-in capital and retained earnings. How can such a distinction be maintained when action is taken to convert retained earnings into capital stock?

**10.** Equipment with a book value of $150,000 was sold by the Holmes Corporation for $250,000. The chief accountant believes that the $100,000 profit should be credited to paid-in capital and that it should not be available for dividend declaration. The basis for his reasoning is that the general price level has risen since the asset was originally purchased and, in order to maintain the corporation's assets, a larger amount of fixed capital is now necessary. What is your opinion of this procedure?

**11.** (a) What is a liquidating dividend? (b) Under what circumstances are such distributions made? (c) How would you recommend that liquidating dividends be recorded in the accounts of the corporation?

**12.** The Byron Corporation, acting within the law of the state of incorporation, paid a cash dividend to stockholders for which it debited Paid-In Capital from Sale of Stock at a Premium. A stockholder protested, saying that such a dividend was a partial liquidation of his holdings. Is this true?

**13.** The Arden Co. is permitted by the state within which it is incorporated to distribute as dividends the sum of its net profit plus the amount charged against profits for depletion. How do you recommend that dividends be recorded (a) on the books of the corporation and (b) on the books of the investor?

**14.** The following announcement appeared on the financial page of a newspaper:

"The Board of Directors of the Maxwell Co., at their meeting on June 15, 1958, declared the regular quarterly dividend on outstanding common stock of 50 cents per share and an extra dividend of $1 per share, both payable on July 10, 1958, to the stockholders of record at the close of business June 30, 1958."

(a) What is the purpose of each of the three dates given in the declaration? (b) When would the stock become "ex-dividend"? (c) Why is the $1 designated as an "extra" dividend?

**15.** What methods can be followed in reporting dividends in arrears on preferred stock on the balance sheet?

**16.** Would you recommend reporting dividends on the income statement or on the retained earnings statement? Give reasons for your preference.

**17.** (a) How does revaluation capital arise on the books? (b) What circumstances would call for a reduction in such a balance?

**18.** What objections can you raise for the use of revaluation capital (a) to absorb operating losses, (b) as a basis for cash dividends, and (c) as a basis for stock dividends?

**19.** The J. R. Goodwin Corporation desires to retain its capital from reappraisal of plant and equipment as a part of its permanent capitalization rather than to write it off over the life of the assets. Why may this policy be desirable? How may this be accomplished?

## EXERCISES

**1.** The Foreman Steel Company wished to reduce the carrying value of its intangible assets from $350,000 to $1. To do this, the company decided to reduce the par value of its stock from $10 to $7.50 a share. The intangible assets could then be written off and the resulting deficit applied against the paid-in capital resulting from the recapitalization. On June 30 the corporation capital was as follows:

| | |
|---|---|
| Capital Stock (200,000 shares)...................... | $2,000,000 |
| Additional Paid-In Capital.......................... | 115,000 |
| Retained Earnings.................................. | 60,000 |

(a) What entries would be made to reduce intangible assets to $1 following the plan given above? (b) Assuming that the net income for the company for the balance of the year is $62,500, prepare the capital section as it would be shown on the company balance sheet on December 31.

**2.** The retained earnings account for the Van Horn Company discloses the following charges and credits. Give whatever entries may be required to correct the account.

RETAINED EARNINGS

| | |
|---|---|
| Correction in profit of prior period . . . . . . . . . . . . . . . . . . 1,500 | Jan. 1 Balance . . . . . . . . . . . . . 64,600 |
| Loss from fire . . . . . . . . . . . . . . 850 | Premium on sale of stock . . . . . 18,500 |
| Write-off of goodwill . . . . . . . . 5,000 | Paid-in capital from stock subscription defaults . . . . . . . . . 860 |
| Stock dividend . . . . . . . . . . . . 20,000 | Gain on retirement of preferred at less than issuance price . . . 3,600 |
| Loss on sale of plant items . . . 12,400 | Gain on retirement of bonds at less than book value . . . . . . . 1,250 |
| | Revaluation of buildings: Overdepreciation of past periods . . . . . . . . . . . . . . . 6,000 |
| | Increase from appraisal . . . . 20,000 |
| | Gain on life insurance policy settlement . . . . . . . . . . . . . . . 2,200 |

**3.** The capital accounts for the Burbank Co. on June 30, 1958, follow:

Capital stock, 100,000 shares, par $20 . . . . . . . . . . . . . . . . $2,000,000
Premium on capital stock . . . . . . . . . . . . . . . . . . . . . . . . . . .   800,000
Retained earnings . . . . . . . . . . . . . . . . . . . . . . . . . . . . . . . . 4,500,000

Shares of the company's stock are selling at this time at 36. What entries would you make in each case below:

(a) A stock dividend of 5% is declared and issued.
(b) A stock dividend of 100% is declared and issued.

**4.** The balance sheet of the Brown Corporation shows the following:

Capital stock, 20,000 shares, no par, with $10 stated value . $200,000
Additional paid-in capital . . . . . . . . . . . . . . . . . . . . . . . . . . . 350,000
Retained earnings . . . . . . . . . . . . . . . . . . . . . . . . . . . . . . . . . 250,000

A 25% stock dividend is declared, the board of directors authorizing a transfer from Retained Earnings to Capital Stock at the stock stated value. (a) Give entries to record the declaration and payment of the dividend. (b) What was the book value per share before the dividend declaration and after the issue of the dividend? (c) What was the effect of the issue of the stock dividend on the ownership equity of each stockholder in the corporation?

**5.** The dividend declarations and distributions by the Western Co. over a three-year period are listed below. Give the entry required in each case.

July 1, 1956. Declared a 5% stock dividend on 1,000,000 shares of common stock, par value $10. The stock was originally sold at $12, and retained earnings are to be charged for the stock dividend with an amount equal to the original stock issuance price.

July 15, 1956. Distributed the stock dividend declared on July 1, which included fractional warrants for 1,000 shares.

Sept. 1, 1956. 600 shares were issued for fractional warrants; remaining fractional warrants expired.

July 1, 1957. Declared a scrip dividend of $1 per share, payable on January 1, 1958, with interest at the rate of 6%.

Jan. 1, 1958. Paid scrip dividend.

July 1, 1958. Declared a dividend of 1 share of South-West common stock on every share of Western Company stock owned. South-West common is carried on the books of the Western Company at a cost of $1.50 per share.

July 15, 1958. Distributed South-West common stock to shareholders.

**6.** Variety Chain Stores, Inc., with total assets of $350,000, capital stock outstanding of $175,000, and retained earnings of $65,000, sold five of its stores at their book value, $150,000. This cash is distributed to the present stockholders. What entry should be made?

**7.** The Bell Corporation pays semiannual dividends on $100, 6% preferred stock regularly on July 1 and January 1. On March 1 the corporation sells 5,000 shares of this stock at 105 plus accrued dividends. (a) Give the entries on the books of the corporation for the sale of the stock on March 1 and for the payment of dividends on the stock on July 1. (b) What entries would be made by an investor acquiring 100 shares and receiving the dividend on this lot?

## PROBLEMS

**22-1.** The Morrison Processing Co. reports its capital on the balance sheet prepared on December 31, 1958, as follows:

| | |
|---|---|
| Common stock........................................... | $112,000 |
| Surplus................................................. | 76,500 |
| Total capital......................................... | $188,500 |

The common stock account shows the following debits and credits since date of organization in 1953:

*Credits:*

| | |
|---|---|
| 12,000 shares of common, $10 par.................... | $120,000 |

*Debits:*

| | |
|---|---|
| 1,000 shares of common reacquired at 8.............. | 8,000 |
| | $112,000 |

A preferred stock balance was canceled in 1957 when preferred stock was reacquired and formally retired. The surplus account shows the following credits and debits since date of organization:

*Credits:*

| | |
|---|---|
| Premium on issuance of common | $ 30,000 |
| Gain on sale of unimproved properties | 12,000 |
| Appraisal of land and buildings at the end of 1958: | |
| Adjustment for depreciation overstatement, 1953–1958. | 8,000 |
| Increase in asset book value for appreciation | 50,000 |
| Net income, 1953–1958 | 118,000 |
| | $218,000 |

*Debits:*

| | | |
|---|---|---|
| Loss on bond retirement | $11,500 | |
| Discount on issuance of preferred stock | 10,000 | |
| Payment on retirement of preferred stock issue in excess of stock par value | 5,000 | |
| Fire loss | 25,000 | |
| Cash dividends | 90,000 | 141,500 |
| | | $ 76,500 |

*Instructions:* (1) Give whatever entries are required in correcting the capital accounts. (Assume that treasury stock is to be carried at cost.)

(2) Prepare the capital section of the balance sheet for the corporation reflecting corrections in (1) above.

**22-2.** Capital accounts for the Marshall-Morgan Co. on December 31, 1957, are as follows:

CAPITAL

| | | |
|---|---|---|
| 6% Preferred stock, par $25, 10,000 shares authorized and issued (each share is callable at $26.50 and is convertible into 3 shares of common) | $250,000 | |
| Less discount on preferred stock | 25,000 | |
| | | $ 225,000 |
| Common stock, par value $5, 100,000 shares issued | | 500,000 |
| Premium on common from sale of stock at 8 | | 300,000 |
| Total paid-in capital | | $1,025,000 |
| Retained earnings | | 415,000 |
| Total capital | | $1,440,000 |

During 1958, the following transactions affected capital:

Jan. 2. 2,500 shares of preferred stock were called in for retirement at $26.50 in accordance with call provisions in the preferred contract.

Mar. 2. 5,000 shares of common stock were reacquired at $7.50; treasury stock is reported at cost.

Mar. 30. A 25¢ cash dividend was paid on common stock.

Apr. 20. Common stock reacquired on March 2 was sold at $9.00.

June 30. The semiannual dividend was paid on preferred stock.

July 1. 2,000 shares of preferred stock were converted into common stock on a 3-for-1 basis in accordance with convertible provisions in the preferred contract.

Sept. 30. A 25¢ cash dividend was paid on common stock, together with a 5% stock dividend. Common stock is selling on this date at $9.50, and retained earnings equal to the selling price of the stock issued are transferred to paid-in capital.

Dec. 31. The semiannual dividend was paid on preferred stock and a special dividend of 50¢ was paid on common stock.

Dec. 31. Net income for the year, $215,500, is transferred to retained earnings (debit Profit and Loss).

*Instructions:* (1) Record in journal form the transactions given above.
(2) Prepare the capital section for the company as of December 31, 1958.

**22-3.** Capital balances for the Pacific Co. on June 30, 1958, just prior to a corporate readjustment, were as follows:

| | |
|---|---:|
| 6% Cumulative preferred stock, par $50, 10,000 shares issued, dividends 5 years in arrears.................. | $ 500,000 |
| Common stock, par $10, 100,000 shares issued.......... | 1,000,000 |
| | $1,500,000 |
| Less: Deficit from operations.......................... | 165,000 |
| | $1,335,000 |

On this date the following action was taken:

(a) Common stockholders turned in their stock and received in exchange new common stock, 1 share of the new stock being exchanged for every 5 shares of the old. New stock was given a stated value of $30 per share.

(b) One-half share of the new common stock was issued on each share of preferred stock outstanding in liquidation of dividends in arrears on preferred stock.

(c) The deficit from operations was applied against the paid-in capital arising from the common stock restatement.

Transactions for the remainder of 1958 affecting capital were as follows:

Nov. 10. 20,000 shares of new common stock were sold at 32½.

Nov. 15. 5,000 shares of preferred stock were called in at $52.50 plus dividends for 4½ months at 6%. Stock was formally retired.

Dec. 31. Net income for the six months ended on this date was $46,500. (Debit Profit and Loss.) The semiannual dividend was declared on preferred shares and a 50¢ dividend on common shares, dividends being payable January 20, 1959.

*Instructions:* (1) Record in journal form the transactions given above.
(2) Prepare the capital section of the balance sheet for the company as of December 31, 1958.

22-4. A condensed balance sheet of the Fisher Corporation as of December 31, 1955, appears below:

### FISHER CORPORATION
#### BALANCE SHEET
#### DECEMBER 31, 1955

| Assets................... $248,780 | Liabilities................. $ 29,320 |
|---|---|
| | 5% Preferred stock ($100 par)..................... 50,000 |
| | Common stock ($50 par).... 100,000 |
| | Premium on preferred stock. 5,000 |
| | Retained earnings......... 64,460 |
| $248,780 | $248,780 |

Capital stock authorized: 500 shares of 5% cumulative, nonparticipating preferred stock with a prior claim on assets, and 10,000 shares of common stock.

Information relating to operations of the succeeding three years follows:

| | 1956 | 1957 | 1958 |
|---|---|---|---|
| Dividends declared on Dec. 20, payable on Jan. 10 of following year: | | | |
| Preferred stock.............. | 5% cash | 5% cash | 5% cash |
| Common stock.............. | $1.00 cash / 50% stock* | $1.25 cash | $.50 cash |
| Credit balance in the profit and loss account after recording income tax liability for year..... | $21,000 | $12,000 | $20,000 |

*Retained earnings is reduced by the par value of the stock dividend.

1956: On July 1, land having a book value of $60,000 was appraised at $125,000. The board of directors authorized the recording of the appraisal in the accounts.

1957: On February 12 depreciation allowances were reduced by $36,000 following an income tax investigation. Additional income taxes of $11,000 for prior years were paid. On March 3, 250 shares of common stock were purchased by the corporation at $46 per share. (Treasury stock is recorded at cost.)

1958: On February 28, it was discovered that the merchandise inventory at the end of 1957 had been overstated by $4,800. On August 10 all of the treasury stock was sold at $56 per share. By vote of the stockholders on September 12, each share of the common stock was exchanged by the corporation for 3 shares of no-par, each with a stated value of $20.

*Instructions:* (1) Give the journal entries affecting the capital accounts for the 3-year period ended December 31, 1958. Assume that corrections in profits of prior years are recorded directly in retained earnings.

(2) Prepare the capital section of the balance sheet as it would appear at the end of 1956, 1957, and 1958.

**22-5.** The Bradley Co. was organized on January 2, 1957, with authorized stock consisting of 5,000 shares of 6%, $100 par, nonparticipating preferred and 50,000 shares of no-par common. During the first two years of the company's existence, the following transactions took place:

1957

Jan.  2. Sold 800 shares of common stock at 5¼.
      2. Sold 3,800 shares of preferred stock at 110.

Mar.  2. Sold common stock as follows:
          3,400 shares at 9.
          900 shares at 9½.

July 10. A near-by piece of land, valued at $216,100, was secured for 800 shares of preferred stock and 14,000 shares of common. (Preferred stock was recorded at 110, the balance being assigned to common.)

Dec. 16. The regular preferred and a 50-cent common dividend were declared.
     28. Dividends declared on December 16 were paid.
     31. The profit and loss account showed a credit balance of $70,000, which was transferred to retained earnings.

1958

Feb. 27. The corporation reacquired 4,000 shares of common stock at 8. (State law requires that an appropriation of retained earnings be made for the purchase price of treasury stock. Appropriations may be returned to retained earnings upon resale of the stock.)

June 17. Resold 3,000 shares of treasury stock at 9¾.

July 31. Sold all of the remaining treasury stock at 9.

Sept. 30. The corporation sold 4,000 additional shares of common stock at 9¼.

Dec. 16. The regular preferred dividend and a 30-cent common dividend were declared.
     28. Dividends declared on December 16 were paid.
     31. The profit and loss account showed a credit balance of $50,000, which was transferred to retained earnings.

*Instructions:* (1) Journalize the foregoing transactions.
(2) Prepare the capital section of the balance sheet as of December 31, 1958.

**22-6.** The following trial balance was taken from the books of the Welcome Manufacturing Company as of April 30, 1958:

| ACCOUNT | DEBIT | CREDIT |
|---|---|---|
| Cash | $ 310,000 | |
| Accounts receivable | 800,000 | |
| Raw materials on hand | 750,000 | |
| Finished goods on hand | 500,000 | |
| Finished goods out on consignment | 100,000 | |
| Plant and machinery | 1,460,000 | |
| Prepaid expenses | 5,400 | |
| Sales returns and allowances | 25,000 | |
| Administrative salaries | 65,000 | |
| Cost of sales | 2,350,000 | |
| Traveling expenses | 30,030 | |
| Interest expense | 10,570 | |

| | |
|---|---:|
| Accounts payable........................ | $ 175,000 |
| Notes payable........................... | 100,000 |
| Accrued payroll......................... | 6,000 |
| Accrued interest payable on 6% bonds..... | 10,000 |
| Capital stock — 6% preferred............ | 1,000,000 |
| Capital stock — common................. | 1,416,000 |
| 6% bonds, due June 30, 1966............ | 500,000 |
| Sales................................... | 2,500,000 |
| Surplus, December 31, 1957.............. | 520 |
| Paid-in surplus......................... | 698,480 |
| | $6,406,000  $6,406,000 |

The following transactions had been completed by the company:

(1) The company has purchased various lots of its $100 par value common stock, aggregating 840 shares, at an average price of $65.50 per share, for $55,020. In recording these transactions the company has canceled the stock certificates and charged the common stock account with the par value of $84,000 and credited the paid-in surplus account with the difference of $28,980 between par and the cash paid therefor.

(2) Paid-in surplus was previously credited with (a) a premium at $20 per share on 15,000 shares of common stock issued, and (b) adjustments arising from the appraisal of plant and machinery bought at a receivers' sale, $398,000.

(3) 4½% bonds of the face amount of $250,000 falling due on December 31, 1964, were issued on January 1, 1940, at a 10% discount. To June 30, 1956, $16,500 of this discount had been charged against profits and as of this date the entire issue of these bonds was retired at par and the unamortized discount charged to Paid-in Surplus.

(4) A new issue of $500,000, 6% ten-year bonds was effected as of July 1, 1956, at par. Expenses incurred with respect to this issue in the amount of $20,000 were charged to Paid-in Surplus.

*Instructions:* Prepare a balance sheet as of April 30, 1958, in which effect has been given to such changes as may be necessary in view of the treatment accorded by the company to the transactions described above. (A.I.C.P.A. adapted)

**22-7.** The articles of incorporation of Carlson Manufacturing Company state: "On or before September 1, 1957, and on or before the first day of September in each year thereafter, as long as any shares of preferred stock remain outstanding, the company shall from its profits set aside as a reserve for the retirement of shares of preferred stock an amount equal to not less than 20% of the net earnings of the company for the fiscal year then last expired, after providing for federal income taxes and after deducting the amount of dividends paid on the preferred stock during that fiscal year. The equivalent of the amount so reserved shall be deposited in a special fund to be designated a sinking fund. The amounts so set aside in the sinking fund shall be applied by the company not later than October 31 in the same year to the redemption of outstanding shares of preferred stock called or purchased in the open market at a price not to exceed $12.50 per share. Preferred stock purchased for the sinking fund shall not be reissued and shall be forthwith canceled."

The following ledger balances and notes are submitted:

| | JUNE 30, 1958 | | SEPTEMBER 30, 1958 | |
|---|---|---|---|---|
| | DEBIT | CREDIT | DEBIT | CREDIT |
| Cash........................... | $ 74,000 | | $ 90,000 | |
| Other current assets.............. | 26,000 | | 28,000 | |
| Fixed assets, less depreciation..... | 150,000 | | 140,000 | |
| Deferred charges................ | 6,000 | | 5,000 | |
| Goodwill...................... | 50,000 | | 50,000 | |
| Current liabilities, including all taxes | | $ 10,000 | | $ 15,000 |
| 7% cumulative preferred stock, par value $10 per share (authorized 20,000 shares, issued and outstanding 10,000 shares).......... | | 100,000 | | 100,000 |
| Common stock, no par value, authorized, issued and outstanding 50,000 shares.................. | | 100,000 | | 100,000 |
| Capital surplus.................. | | 30,000 | | 30,000 |
| Earned surplus.................. | | 6,000 | | 66,000 |
| Net profit...................... | | 67,000 | | 11,250 |
| Preferred dividends paid.......... | 7,000 | | 1,750 | |
| Preferred stock purchased........ | | | 7,500 | |
| | $313,000 | $313,000 | $322,250 | $322,250 |

(1) The company had a net loss in its fiscal year ended June 30, 1957.

(2) The company transferred the sinking fund cash to a separate bank account immediately after June 30, 1958, but did not record the transfer on the general books.

(3) The company regularly pays preferred dividends on March 31, June 30, September 30, and December 31 to holders of record three days before these dates.

(4) The net profit for each period is found correct as stated.

(5) The balance in the preferred stock purchased account represents the cost of the following purchases of 7% cumulative preferred stock made for the sinking fund:

| | | |
|---|---|---|
| July   6, 1958 | 200 shares @ $ 9.00 each | $1,800 |
| Aug. 31, 1958 | 520 shares @  10.00 each | 5,200 |
| Sept.  7, 1958 | 40 shares @  12.50 each | 500 |
| | 760 shares | $7,500 |

(6) All the preferred stock purchased, except the last 40 shares acquired, was properly canceled under the laws of the state in which the company was incorporated.

*Instructions:* (1) Prepare a balance sheet as of September 30, 1958, showing the particulars of the capital stock and the sinking fund in accordance with the charter provisions.

(2) Prepare a statement of surplus for the fiscal year ended June 30, 1958, and for the following quarter. (A.I.C.P.A. adapted)

**22-8.** The balance sheet of the Stanley Corporation on December 31, 1958, is shown at the bottom of this and the opposite page.

Through inquiry and investigation the following information is obtained with respect to items in the foregoing balance sheet:

(1) Cash includes $14,000 in an employees' pension fund.

(2) The U. S. Government bonds represent $42,000 face value 2% Treasury bonds valued at cost plus accrued interest. The market value of such bonds on December 31, 1958, was $44,700.

(3) Accounts receivable include $8,400 of advances to employees.

(4) Accounts receivable also include $15,000 advanced to suppliers of raw materials for materials neither received nor in transit. Since

STANLEY

BALANCE

DECEMBER

### ASSETS

| | | |
|---|---:|---:|
| Current assets: | | |
| Cash on hand and in banks. . . . . . . . . . . . . . . . . . . . . . | $137,500 | |
| Notes receivable, less discounted notes of $20,000. . . . | 60,000 | |
| Accounts receivable, less allowance of $8,500. . . . . . . . | 247,800 | |
| U. S. Government bonds, plus accrued interest of $420 | 42,350 | |
| Total current assets. . . . . . . . . . . . . . . . . . . . . . . . . . . | | $ 487,650 |
| Working and trading assets: | | |
| Raw materials and supplies. . . . . . . . . . . . . . . . . . . . . . | $ 92,440 | |
| Work in process. . . . . . . . . . . . . . . . . . . . . . . . . . . . . . . | 110,700 | |
| Finished goods, including consigned merchandise of $21,670. . . . . . . . . . . . . . . . . . . . . . . . . . . . . . . . . . . . | 181,320 | |
| Total working and trading assets. . . . . . . . . . . . . . . . | | 384,460 |
| Investments in the capital stock of other companies. . . . . | | 120,000 |
| Capital assets: | | |
| Land and buildings at cost, less depreciation. . . . . . . . . | $440,000 | |
| Machinery and equipment, less depreciation of $162,800. . . . . . . . . . . . . . . . . . . . . . . . . . . . . . . . . . . . | 332,000 | |
| Furniture and fixtures, less depreciation of $3,200. . . . | 15,900 | |
| Total capital assets. . . . . . . . . . . . . . . . . . . . . . . . . . . | | 787,900 |
| Sinking fund for retirement of first-mortgage bonds. . . . . | | 69,700 |
| Treasury stock. . . . . . . . . . . . . . . . . . . . . . . . . . . . . . . . | | 10,000 |
| Prepaid expenses and deferred charges: | | |
| Unexpired insurance. . . . . . . . . . . . . . . . . . . . . . . . . . . | $ 3,300 | |
| Discount on capital stock. . . . . . . . . . . . . . . . . . . . . . . | 15,000 | |
| Prepaid advertising. . . . . . . . . . . . . . . . . . . . . . . . . . . . | 4,600 | |
| Prepaid interest on notes discounted. . . . . . . . . . . . . . . | 1,800 | |
| Total prepaid expenses and deferred charges. . . . . . . | | 24,700 |
| Total assets. . . . . . . . . . . . . . . . . . . . . . . . . . . . . . . . . . | | $1,884,410 |

the placement of the orders, which are not subject to cancellation, the replacement cost of the materials has declined to 70% of the commitment price.

(5) Raw materials and supplies are stated at amounts lower than market and include invoices received, in the amount of $7,000, for materials shipped f.o.b. point of shipment and in the hands of common carriers on December 31, 1958.  Excluded are $9,000 of raw materials received on December 28, 1958, for which invoices are dated January 15, 1959.

(6) Work in process, which is valued at actual cost of direct materials and direct labor plus a normal charge for manufacturing overhead based upon company experience, is less than market value.

CORPORATION
SHEET
31, 1958

### LIABILITIES

Current liabilities:

| | | |
|---|---|---|
| Accounts payable — trade...................... | $273,000 | |
| Accrued payrolls and interest (exclusive of interest on installment notes payable to bank).............. | 15,620 | |
| Reserve for federal income and excess profits taxes (net of claim for income tax refund of $8,000).... | 72,000 | |
| Reserve for other taxes......................... | 14,300 | |
| Installment notes payable to bank, due $12,000 on first of each month beginning Jan. 1, 1959, and accrued interest of $4,500..................... | 124,500 | |
| Total current liabilities......................... | | $  499,420 |
| Dividends payable January 16, 1959............... | | 6,000 |
| Funded debt: | | |
| 5% First-mortgage bonds due January 1, 1975...... | | 350,000 |

### CAPITAL

Capital stock:

| | | |
|---|---|---|
| Preferred, 2,000 shares authorized; 1,800 shares issued | $180,000 | |
| Common, 3,000 shares authorized; 2,500 shares issued | 250,000 | |
| Subscriptions to common stock, 400 shares........ | 22,000 | |
| Total capital stock.............................. | $452,000 | |
| Earned surplus: | | |
| Reserve for employees' pensions.......... $ 14,000 | | |
| Free and available for dividends......... 159,990 | | |
| Total earned surplus................... | 173,990 | |
| Capital surplus................................. | 403,000 | |
| Total capital stock and surplus..................... | | $1,028,990 |
| Total liabilities and capital........................ | | $1,884,410 |

(7) Finished goods are similarly valued, except for merchandise in the hands of consignees, which is priced and billed on memorandum at 110% of cost. Finished goods valued at $140,000 are pledged against installment notes payable to bank.

(8) Of the capital stock investments in other companies, $95,000 represents investments at cost in 50% or more of the stock of subsidiary companies. The realizable values of such investments exceed cost, and income therefrom is recorded as dividends are received.

(9) The remaining investments represent small stock interests considered necessary for business operations, having an aggregate market value of $21,800 at December 31, 1958.

(10) The land and buildings account, when analyzed, discloses the following:

| | |
|---|---:|
| Cost of land.................................... | $ 75,000 |
| Depreciated cost of buildings as at January 1, 1953, established by revenue agent's report dated July 7, 1954, adjusted for subsequent additions and retirements................................... | 669,500 |
| Accumulated depreciation since January 1, 1953.... | 304,500 |

(11) The sinking fund consists of $19,700 in cash and $50,000 of the company's own first-mortgage 5% bonds.

(12) The treasury stock represents 100 shares of preferred stock valued at par and acquired for resale to employees.

(13) The preferred stock has a $100 par value. It is cumulative at the rate of 6%, and is callable after July 1, 1960, at 105% of par value plus accumulated and unpaid dividends, if any. The 1,800 shares issued include the 100 shares in the treasury.

(14) The common stock also has a $100 par value. The subscriptions to 400 shares of common stock are stated in the balance sheet net of $18,000 representing receivables from subscribers on their stock subscription contracts.

(15) The reserve for employees' pensions of $14,000 offsets the amount of cash in the employees' pension fund. This fund was set up in 1958 as a result of a contract with employees.

(16) The current earned surplus account dates back to July 1, 1949, on which date a voluntary reorganization served to eliminate an operating deficit.

*Instructions:* Prepare in corrected form a revised balance sheet as of December 31, 1958, based upon the preceding information. (A.I.C.P.A. adapted)

# Chapter 23

# RETAINED EARNINGS

## APPROPRIATIONS; THE RETAINED EARNINGS STATEMENT

**USE OF TERM "RESERVE"**     It has already been indicated that the term *reserve* is employed in a variety of different senses in accounting practice. It has been used in the following ways:

(1) *As a valuation account.* The reserve designation is frequently employed to report a valuation account related to a balance sheet item. For example, deductions may be required from the face amount of assets in arriving at the amounts that they are expected to realize, as in the case of marketable securities, receivables, or inventories. When such reductions are related to current revenue, they are recorded by charges to expense accounts and credits to asset valuation accounts. Or, deductions may be required from the face amount of assets in the recognition of cost expirations, as in the case of properties subject to depreciation, depletion, or amortization. When such reductions are related to current revenues, they, too, are recorded by charges to expense balances and credits to asset valuation accounts. In preparing the balance sheet, valuation reserves are subtracted from the related balance sheet items. Such reserves are ultimately applied in the accounts against the items to which they relate. A reserve for bad debts is used to absorb accounts that prove to be uncollectible. A reserve to reduce marketable securities to market value is applied against this item when the asset is sold; a reserve for depreciation is applied against the property item when the latter is disposed of or scrapped. It was suggested earlier that the term *allowance* should be substituted for the term *reserve* in designating balance sheet valuation accounts.

(2) *As an estimate of a liability of uncertain amount.* The reserve title is frequently employed to designate an estimated liability. Estimates may be required in reporting such items as tax obligations, premium claims outstanding, claims under guarantees for services and replacements, and obligations under pension plans. When such claims are related to current revenue, they are recorded by charges to appropriate expense balances and credits to liability accounts. The liabilities are ultimately canceled through payment. Designation of the accounts

in this class as *estimated liabilities* rather than as *reserves* would clarify the nature of the items presented.

(3) *As an appropriation of retained earnings.* The reserve title is used to indicate that a portion of retained earnings has been appropriated in accordance with legal or contractual requirements or as a result of specific authorization on the part of the board of directors. The appropriation of retained earnings does not change the total corporate capital. Amounts are merely transferred from the retained earnings to special retained earnings accounts that are not considered available as a basis for dividends. The appropriation balance is no guarantee that cash or any other specific asset will be available in carrying out the purpose that may be designated by the appropriation. Resources represented by retained earnings may have been applied to the enlargement of plant, to the increase of working capital or perhaps to the increase of cash, or possibly to the retirement of corporate indebtedness. The appropriation of retained earnings merely insures the retention by the business of assets represented by the appropriated earnings; if assets are to be made available for a particular purpose, special action relative to asset use would be called for. When the purpose of the appropriation has been served, the appropriation balance is returned to Retained Earnings. The purposes served by appropriations of retained earnings are considered in detail in the following pages.

It was indicated in an earlier chapter that the American Institute Committee on Terminology holds that the use of the term *reserve* to indicate the retention of assets comes closest to its popular meaning. Accordingly, the Committee recommends that the term *reserve* be limited to appropriations of retained earnings and that any alternate use of the term on the financial statements be discontinued.[1] However, the American Accounting Association Committee on Concepts and Standards Underlying Corporate Financial Statements has gone even farther and has recommended abandonment of the term in financial statements. The Committee holds that although accounting terminology would be improved if the term were limited to balances includible in capital, this would still leave unresolved the conflict between the general and the accounting connotations of the word.[2] There can be little question that greater clarity in financial statement presentation would be promoted through abandonment of the term "reserve" and the adoption of more descriptive terminology.

---

[1] *Accounting Terminology Bulletin No. 1,* "Review and Résumé," 1953 (New York: American Institute of Certified Public Accountants), pp. 26–28.

[2] *Accounting and Reporting Standards for Corporate Financial Statements and Preceding Statements and Supplements,* "Reserves and Retained Income," 1957 (Columbus: American Accounting Association), pp. 19–22.

**RETAINED EARNINGS APPROPRIATIONS**   Appropriations of retained earnings may be classified under the following headings:

(1) _Appropriations to report legal restrictions on the use of retained earnings._ Laws of the state of incorporation may provide for the maintenance of legal capital through restriction in the use of retained earnings as a basis for dividends upon the reacquisition of a company's own stock. The restriction may be given effect in the accounts by the appropriation of retained earnings.

(2) _Appropriations to report contractual restrictions on the use of retained earnings._ An agreement with creditors may provide for the retention of earnings within the company as a means of protecting the creditors and assuring payment of their claims. The restriction on the use of retained earnings as a basis for dividends may be indicated in the accounts by the appropriation of retained earnings.

(3) _Appropriations to report discretionary action by the board of directors in the presentation of retained earnings._ The board of directors may authorize that a portion or all of the retained earnings be presented in a manner that will disclose the actual use in the business at the present time or the planned use in the future of this part of the stockholders' equity. Discretionary action, then, on the part of the board of directors may be the basis for appropriations.

A number of appropriated retained earnings accounts and the purposes for which such balances are established are listed below:

| Account | Purpose |
|---|---|
| (1) _Appropriations to report legal restrictions on the use of retained earnings:_ | |
| Retained Earnings Appropriated for Purchase of Treasury Stock | To retain earnings upon the reacquisition of stock, so that capital may be maintained at original legal or stated balance. |
| (2) _Appropriations to report contractual restrictions on the use of retained earnings:_ | |
| Retained Earnings Appropriated for Bonded Indebtedness<br>Retained Earnings Appropriated for Bond Redemption Fund | To retain earnings so that resources may be available for the retirement of bonds or for transfer to a fund for bond retirement. |
| Retained Earnings Appropriated for Redemption of Preferred Stock<br>Retained Earnings Appropriated for Preferred Stock Redemption Fund | To retain earnings so that resources may be available for the retirement of preferred stock or for transfer to a fund for stock retirement. |

| Account | Purpose |
|---|---|
| *(3) Appropriations to report discretionary action by the board of directors in the presentation of retained earnings:* | |
| Retained Earnings Appropriated for Contingencies<br>Retained Earnings Appropriated for Possible Inventory Decline<br>Retained Earnings Appropriated for Self-Insurance | To retain earnings so that resources may be available for use in meeting possible future losses. |
| Retained Earnings Appropriated for Increased Working Capital<br>Retained Earnings Appropriated for Increased Investment in Plant | To report that net assets from earnings have been applied to some particular business purpose and thus are unavailable for dividends. |

The appropriations that were listed are described in the following paragraphs.

**APPROPRIATIONS RELATING TO STOCK REACQUISITIONS**   The segregation of earnings upon the reacquisition of a company's own stock is recorded by a charge to Retained Earnings and a credit to an appropriately titled appropriations account. When the treasury stock is resold or when it is formally retired in accordance with the law and the restriction on retained earnings is removed, the appropriated balance may be returned to Retained Earnings. To illustrate, assume the acquisition by a corporation of its own stock and the subsequent resale of this stock. Retained earnings of $100,000 are restricted by law from use for dividends during the period of treasury stock holdings. The entries that are made for the appropriation and for its subsequent cancellation follow:

| | | |
|---|---:|---:|
| Retained Earnings.............................. | 100,000 | |
|     Retained Earnings Appropriated for Purchase of Treasury Stock.............................. | | 100,000 |
| Retained Earnings Appropriated for Purchase of Treasury Stock.............................. | 100,000 | |
|     Retained Earnings.............................. | | 100,000 |

**APPROPRIATIONS RELATING TO CORPORATE OBLIGATIONS**   The appropriation of earnings required by an agreement with creditors is recorded by a charge to retained earnings and a credit to an account reporting the appropriation. Upon settlement with the creditor group and the removal of the restriction upon retained earnings, the appropriation is returned to retained earnings. To illustrate, assume that the corporation agrees to restrict retained earnings of $5,000,000 from dividend distribution during the full term of a bond issue. Entries to record the restriction when the loan is made and the ultimate expiration of the restriction when the loan is liquidated follow:

Retained Earnings.......................... 5,000,000
    Retained Earnings Appropriated for Bonded
    Indebtedness...............................              5,000,000
Retained Earnings Appropriated for Bonded In-
debtedness................................. 5,000,000
    Retained Earnings.........................              5,000,000

When the agreement with creditors provides for the periodic appropriation of earnings during the life of the obligation, entries similar to the first entry above would be made each period.

The appropriation of earnings may be accompanied by the segregation of assets in a special fund to be used in the payment of the obligation at maturity. The establishment of the fund may be voluntary or it may be required by contract. A retained earnings appropriation that is accompanied by the establishment of a special fund is said to be *funded.* This practice results not only in the limitation of dividends but also in the accumulation of corporate resources in a fund to meet the requirements that form the basis for dividend limitation. Liquidation of the obligation by means of the redemption fund and the termination of the contract with creditors releases previously existing restrictions, and the appropriated retained earnings may be returned to a free status. It may be observed, however, that when proceeds from a bond issue are used for expansion purposes and when resources from profitable operations have been used to retire the indebtedness, the expansion has in effect been financed by earnings. Under these circumstances, the board of directors may choose to report retained earnings equivalent to the amount applied to expansion as an appropriation under the designation "Retained Earnings Appropriated for Increased Investment in Plant," or it may choose to effect a permanent capitalization of such retained earnings by means of a stock dividend.

**APPROPRIATIONS RELATING TO STOCK REDEMPTION**     Retained earnings may be appropriated at regular intervals as part of a plan for the use of resources arising from earnings to retire shares of stock outstanding, frequently the entire preferred stock issue. The appropriation of earnings in connection with such a plan may be required as a result of an agreement with stockholders or it may be voluntary and established at the discretion of the board of directors. Stock may be reacquired by disbursements out of cash or disbursements out of a redemption fund established by regular transfers from the cash account. In either case, upon the ultimate retirement of outstanding stock, the board of directors may authorize the return of the appropriation balance to retained earnings. However, it should be observed that retained earnings now take the place of the capital stock equity previously reported. In recognition of this factor, the board of directors may choose to designate these earnings as applied to the retirement of a previously existing stockholders' equity; on the other hand, it may choose to effect a permanent capitalization of such retained earnings by means of a stock dividend.

**APPROPRIATIONS FOR POSSIBLE FUTURE LOSSES** Appropriations of retained earnings may be authorized by the board of directors in anticipation of possible future losses. Three examples of such appropriations are described in the following paragraphs: (1) the general purpose contingency appropriation, (2) the appropriation for possible inventory decline, and (3) the appropriation for self-insurance.

(1) *Appropriation for General Contingencies.* Company managements frequently authorize that provision be made in the accounts for possible future losses of a contingent nature. Such authorization calls for the appropriation of retained earnings to assure the availability of resources to absorb the losses if they should materialize. The establishment of neither an asset valuation balance nor a liability balance is appropriate under these circumstances; the provision for contingencies is related to losses that may or may not emerge in the future, not to losses related to the past or present. In the event that the contingencies fail to materialize, the board of directors may authorize cancellation of the provision for contingencies; the appropriated balance would then be returned to retained earnings. If the contingencies do materialize, the appropriated balance would still be returned to retained earnings; the losses would be assigned to the period in which they materialized by charges to revenue or by direct charges to retained earnings.

The procedure that was described is illustrated in the example that follows. Assume that the management of a company, in reviewing business conditions at the end of 1956 and feeling that there may be a general business decline in the next year or two, authorizes that provision be made in the accounts for possible losses of $500,000. In 1958 the company sells its marketable securities at a loss of $115,000. At the end of 1958, with prospects for business good, management decides that the provision for possible losses is no longer required and may be canceled. The following entries record the appropriation of retained earnings in anticipation of the possible losses, the sale of the securities, and the return of the appropriation to retained earnings.

1956: Retained Earnings.......................... 500,000
      Retained Earnings Appropriated for Contin-
      gencies................................. 500,000
1958: Cash...................................... 265,000
      Loss on Sale of Marketable Securities (or Retained
      Earnings)................................ 115,000
        Marketable Securities...................... 380,000
      Retained Earnings Appropriated for Contin-
      gencies................................. 500,000
        Retained Earnings......................... 500,000

It should be observed that the provision for contingencies established at the end of 1956 can be viewed only as a part of retained earnings; neither asset shrinkage nor a liability has been established at this
date. Since such provision is part of retained earnings, it must be established not by a charge to current revenue but by a charge to retained
earnings. If revenue for 1956 is charged for such provision, earnings
for the year would be understated; income of $500,000 would by-pass
recognition on the income statement. Having established the provision
for contingencies by a charge to retained earnings, it would be improper
to charge it for the losses resulting from the sale of securities in 1958.
Such a practice would serve to overstate the earnings for 1958; losses
would by-pass recognition on the income statement or the retained
earnings statement. The appropriation for contingencies is returned to
retained earnings when the losses have been incurred or when they are
no longer in prospect. The return is made directly to retained earnings
and not through a revenue account since no revenue is involved in
transfers between retained earnings balances. The appropriation procedure has served to withhold resources from possible distribution in
the form of dividends until the contingency has been resolved.

(2) *Appropriation for Possible Inventory Decline.* When inventories
are acquired in a high-price period, managements have frequently
authorized that provision be made in the accounts for inventory losses
anticipated in future periods. It will be recalled that valuation accounts
reducing inventory costs to a lower market were established by charges
to current revenue; valuation accounts providing for inventory
obsolescence, deterioration, and similar losses already incurred would
be established by similar entries. A provision for possible future inventory decline, however, cannot be viewed as an inventory valuation
account; such a provision would have to be considered a part of retained earnings. Accordingly, the procedure that is followed here should
be similar to that for the general purpose contingency in the preceding
section. An appropriation for possible inventory decline is established
by a charge to Retained Earnings, and the appropriated balance is
ultimately returned to Retained Earnings; no costs or losses should be

charged to the appropriation, nor should any part of such balance be transferred to income. The emergence of a loss on inventories requires separate recognition in the period in which it is measurable.

The American Institute Committee on Accounting Procedure has considered the problems that arise in anticipating possible future losses from general contingencies and from inventory declines. The Committee cautions against improper accounting treatment in these matters that may serve to arbitrarily reduce income or shift income from one period to another. The Committee states:

> If a provision for a reserve, made against income, is not properly chargeable to current revenues, net income for the period is understated by the amount of the provision. If a reserve so created is used to relieve the income of subsequent periods of charges that would otherwise be made against it, the income of such subsequent periods is thereby overstated. By use of the reserve in this manner, profit for a given period may be significantly increased or decreased by mere whim. As a result of this practice the integrity of financial statements is impaired, and the statements tend to be misleading.

> The committee recognizes the character of the income statement as a tentative instalment in the record of long-time financial results, and is aware of the tendency to exaggerate the significance of the net income for a single year. Nevertheless, there still exist the responsibility for determining net income as fairly as possible by sound methods consistently applied and the duty to show it clearly. In accomplishing these objectives, it is deemed desirable to provide, by charges in the current income statement, properly classified, for all forseeable costs and losses applicable against current revenues, to the extent that they can be measured and allocated to fiscal periods with reasonable approximation. . . .

> The committee is . . . of the opinion that reserves such as those created:
>     (a) for general undetermined contingencies, or
>     (b) for any indefinite possible future losses, such as, for example, losses on inventories not on hand or contracted for, or
>     (c) for the purpose of reducing inventories other than to a basis which is in accordance with generally accepted accounting principles, or
>     (d) without regard to any specific loss reasonably related to the operations of the current period, or
>     (e) in amounts not determined on the basis of any reasonable estimates of costs or losses
> are of such a nature that charges or credits relating to such reserves should not enter into the determination of net income.

> Accordingly, it is the opinion of the committee that if a reserve of the type described . . . is set up:
>     (a) it should be created by a segregation or appropriation of earned surplus,
>     (b) no costs or losses should be charged to it and no part of it should be transferred to income or in any way used to affect the determination of net income for any year,
>     (c) it should be restored to earned surplus directly when such a reserve or any part thereof is no longer considered necessary, and

(d) it should preferably be classified in the balance sheet as a part of shareholders' equity.[1]

(3) *Appropriation for Self-Insurance.* A company may face certain risks but may not obtain insurance on the theory that the self-absorption of losses will prove less expensive in the long run than the cost of insurance protection from an insurance company. When a course of self-insurance is followed, the company may authorize that provision be made in the accounts in anticipation of charges or losses that may have to be absorbed.

When self-insurance is considered to involve definitely accruing obligations, the accounting for such a course of action would call for the recognition of liabilities through charges to periodic revenues; liability balances would absorb losses as they emerge. However, a self-insurance plan related to losses or casualties that cannot be considered to accrue would call for retained earnings appropriations; this procedure would require recognition of the loss as a charge to revenue at the time it emerges.

To illustrate, assume that a construction company decides to assume the risks for workmen's compensation and wishes to make provision in the accounts for costs emerging from this policy. The company is satisfied that it can make reliable estimates of the amounts payable under compensation claims arising from employee accidents which had occurred. Under these circumstances, it is appropriate to recognize the estimated amounts payable at the end of each period by a charge to an expense account and a credit to an estimated liability account; when payments are made in subsequent periods, the liability balance is debited and cash is credited. If the claims estimate proves to be inadequate or excessive, appropriate correcting entries would be required. A fund may be established in connection with a self-insured workmen's compensation plan for payments to be made under the plan.

On the other hand, assume that a company with a number of branches throughout the country decides to act as self-insurer for any fire losses and authorizes that provision be made in the accounts for fire losses that may have to be absorbed as a result of this policy. Fire damage cannot be considered to accrue; it is a contingency that may or may not occur. Until a fire occurs no loss has been incurred; the absence of a fire loss in one period does not increase the vulnerability to such a loss in the next. Under these circumstances, there is no support for the recognition in the accounts either of an asset valuation

---

[1]*Accounting Research Bulletin No. 43*, "Restatement and Revision of Accounting Research Bulletins," 1953 (New York: American Institute of Certified Public Accountants), pp. 41–43.

account or a liability balance; any provision in the accounts for possible future fire losses would have to be regarded as an appropriation of retained earnings. Accounting for possible fire losses, then, would be similar to that employed for other contingencies. Appropriations arising from a policy of self-insurance must be established by a charge to retained earnings. Fire losses would be recorded in the periods in which they are incurred by charges to appropriate loss accounts or to retained earnings and credits to the property balances. At the same time amounts in the appropriation account may be returned to retained earnings to absorb the losses that will be summarized in the latter account. When the appropriation account is credited for insurance premiums that would otherwise be paid and is charged for transfers to retained earnings based upon fire losses sustained, the balance in the account will measure the savings accruing to the company as a result of the self-insurance plan. The appropriation may be funded so that cash will be available for asset replacement.

The two procedures described are illustrated below. It is assumed that a cash fund is maintained in each case to meet losses that may emerge under the self-insurance plans.

| Transaction | Self-Insurance Considered to Involve Accruable Losses | Self-Insurance Considered to Involve Nonaccruable Losses |
|---|---|---|
| (a) Estimated liability under workmen's compensation self-insurance plan.<br><br>(b) Retained earnings appropriation under fire loss self-insurance plan. | (a)<br>Workmen's Compensation...... 20,000<br>   Estimated Claims under Workmen's Compensation Plan......... 20,000 | (b)<br>Retained Earnings........... 20,000<br>   Retained Earnings Appropriated for Self-Insurance — Fire Loss.. 20,000 |
| Establishment of cash fund to meet self-insurance plans. | Workmen's Compensation Cash Fund.......... 20,000<br>   Cash........ 20,000 | Fire Loss Cash Fund.......... 20,000<br>   Cash........ 20,000 |
| (a) Workmen's compensation paid, $15,000.<br><br>(b) Fire loss, asset book value, $15,000 building replacement cost, $23,500, paid $15,000 from cash fund and $8,500 from regular cash balance. | (a)<br>Estimated Claims under Workmen's Compensation Plan............15,000<br>   Workmen's Compensation Cash Fund... 15,000 | (b)<br>Fire Loss...... 15,000<br>Allowance for Dep. of Buildings 6,500<br>   Buildings.... 21,500<br><br>Retained Earnings Appropriated for Self-Insurance — Fire Loss...... 15,000<br>   Retained Earnings 15,000<br><br>Buildings...... 23,500<br>   Fire Loss Cash Fund 15,000<br>   Cash........ 8,500 |

**APPROPRIATIONS TO DESCRIBE BUSINESS PURPOSES SERVED BY RETAINED EARNINGS**
Corporate officials may authorize appropriations to show the use of retained earnings within the business. For example, assume that profitable operations over a period of years have enabled a company to make significant expansion in its plant and equipment. Instead of continuing to report undistributed profits in retained earnings, which may be interpreted by stockholders as amounts available for distribution as dividends, the company may authorize transfers from retained earnings to a special account that describes the utilization of past earnings for plant and equipment expansion purposes. A permanent increase in a company's working capital position may likewise suggest an appropriation of earnings. Such appropriations may be carried forward indefinitely. On the other hand, the company may wish to effect a permanent capitalization of such retained earnings. Accordingly, appropriations may be returned to retained earnings; transfer of retained earnings to paid-in capital can then be effected by means of a stock dividend.

**OBJECTIONS TO APPROPRIATION PROCEDURES**
The American Accounting Association Committee on Concepts and Standards Underlying Corporate Financial Statements has taken issue with the general practice of earmarking retained earnings through the appropriation procedure. It feels that such a practice may serve to confuse and mislead readers of the statement. When earnings have been retained as a matter of managerial policy for purposes of prospective or accomplished reinvestment of earnings or to provide for possible future losses, the Committee feels that such objectives can best be explained by properly descriptive narrative material accompanying the statements. The Committee points out that managerial policy arises from a number of complex factors; the equity section of the balance sheet is hardly the most practical vehicle for the description of such policy. When earnings are retained as a result of legal or contractual requirement, the facts would best be displayed in footnote or narrative form where permissible. In those instances where a formal appropriation is required by law or contract, the Committee would employ terminology that adequately describes the restrictions upon the use of retained earnings.

In considering the problems presented by "reserves" and retained earnings, the Committee has made the following recommendations:

1. The term "reserve" should not be employed in published financial statements of business corporations.

2. The "reserve section" in corporate balance sheets should be eliminated and its elements exhibited as deduction-from-asset, or liability, or retained income amounts.

3. Appropriations of retained income should not be made or displayed in such a manner as to create misleading inferences.

(a) Appropriations of retained income which purport to reflect managerial policies relative to earnings retention are ineffective, and frequently misleading, unless all retained income which has in fact been committed to operating capital is earmarked. Partial appropriation fosters the implication that retained earnings not earmarked are available for distribution as dividends.

(b) Appropriations of retained income required by law or contract preferably should be disclosed by footnote. If required to be displayed as balance sheet amounts, such appropriations should be included in the proprietary section.

(c) Appropriations of retained income reflecting anticipated future losses, or conjectural past or present losses (when it is not established by reasonably objective evidence that any loss has been incurred) preferably should be disclosed by footnote. If displayed as balance sheet amounts, such appropriations should be included in the proprietary section.

(d) In any event, whenever appropriations are exhibited in a balance sheet, the retained income (excluding amounts formally capitalized) should be summarized in one total.

4. The determination of periodic earnings is not affected by the appropriation of retained income or the restoration of such appropriated amounts to unappropriated retained income.[1]

There can be little objection to the position taken by the American Accounting Association Committee.

**THE RETAINED EARNINGS STATEMENT** All persons who desire to be completely informed on the financial position and the financial progress of a corporation will require full information accounting for the change in retained earnings balances on successive balance sheets. When the change in retained earnings for the period can be explained by simply considering profits and dividends, a reconciliation of this balance can be provided on the balance sheet. Ordinarily, however, there are a number of factors to be recognized in accounting for the change. When this is the case, a separate retained earnings statement is prepared.

The nature and form of the retained earnings statement depends upon the method of treating extraordinary items and corrections. When extraordinary items and corrections are not reported on the income statement but are considered to affect retained earnings directly, these

---

[1] *Accounting and Reporting Standards for Corporate Financial Statements and Preceding Statements and Supplements*, "Reserves and Retained Income,"1957 (Columbus: American Accounting Association), p. 19.

## GENERAL MANUFACTURING COMPANY
### INCOME STATEMENT
### FOR YEAR ENDED DECEMBER 31, 1958

| | |
|---|---:|
| Sales................................................. | $1,500,000 |
| Net income before income taxes.......................... | $ 225,000 |
| Less: Income taxes applicable to net income (total tax provision, $112,500 less $7,500 applicable to extraordinary items).... | 105,000 |
| Net income after income taxes........................... | $ 120,000 |

**Income Statement Prepared in Current Operating Performance Form**

## GENERAL MANUFACTURING COMPANY
### RETAINED EARNINGS STATEMENT
### FOR YEAR ENDED DECEMBER 31, 1958

| | | | |
|---|---:|---:|---:|
| Retained earnings appropriated: | | | |
| Appropriated for purchase of treasury stock, balance, January 1, 1958.................. | $60,000 | | |
| Deduct return to retained earnings of earnings previously restricted, upon sale of treasury stock in 1958 (see below)........ | 20,000 | $ 40,000 | |
| Appropriated for contingencies, balance, January 1, 1958............................ | $50,000 | | |
| Add appropriation in 1958 (see below).... | 35,000 | 85,000 | |
| Total appropriated balance, December 31, 1958.............. | | | $125,000 |
| Retained earnings unappropriated: | | | |
| Balance, January 1, 1958........................ | | $200,000 | |
| Add: Net income after income taxes for year per income statement.......................... | | 120,000 | |
| Gain on sale of securities.................. | | 35,000 | |
| Transfer from appropriation for purchase of treasury stock (see above)................. | | 20,000 | |
| | | $375,000 | |
| Deduct: Loss on sale of equipment....... | $ 5,000 | | |
| Organization costs written off... | 32,500 | | |
| Income taxes applicable to extraordinary items............. | 7,500 | | |
| Corrections in profits of prior periods — understatements of depreciation charges, 1955–1957.... | 20,000 | | |
| Cash dividends................ | 50,000 | | |
| Transfer to appropriation for contingencies (see above)......... | 35,000 | 150,000 | |
| Total unappropriated balance, December 31, 1958.............. | | | 225,000 |
| Total retained earnings, December 31, 1958, per balance sheet.... | | | $350,000 |

**Retained Earnings Statement to Accompany Income Statement in
Current Operating Performance Form**

## GENERAL MANUFACTURING COMPANY
### PAID-IN CAPITAL STATEMENT
#### FOR YEAR ENDED DECEMBER 31, 1958

| | PREFERRED STOCK | COMMON STOCK | ADDITIONAL PAID-IN CAPITAL | TOTAL |
|---|---|---|---|---|
| Paid-in capital, January 1, 1958.......... | $500,000 | $230,000 | $205,000 | $ 935,000 |
| Add: Increase from sale of 10,000 shares of common stock, stated value $5 for $10.50 per share........... | | 50,000 | 55,000 | 105,000 |
| Increase from sale of treasury stock, cost $20,000 for $36,000.. | | 20,000 | 16,000 | 36,000 |
| Paid-in capital, December 31, 1958....... | $500,000 | $300,000 | $276,000 | $1,076,000 |

**Paid-In Capital Statement**

are reported on the retained earnings statement. The retained earnings statement is relieved of considerable detail when the income statement includes extraordinary items and corrections. When changes have taken place in the corporate paid-in capital on successive balance sheets, a separate statement should be prepared to explain fully the changes in capital stock and additional paid-in capital balances. Appraisal capital balances and changes in these balances would call for a statement summarizing changes in appraisal capital.

Although the forms of the statements reconciling capital balances vary greatly, the following rules should be observed in statement construction:

(1) Paid-in capital, retained earnings, and appraisal capital changes should be summarized separately.
(2) The beginning balances should agree with the balance sheet figures at the beginning of the period; the ending balances should agree with the balance sheet figures at the end of the period.
(3) Items should be classified and listed in some consistent order.

An income statement prepared in current operating performance form, and accompanying paid-in capital and retained earnings statements for the General Manufacturing Company for the year ended December 31, 1958, are illustrated on this and the preceding page. The balance sheet for this company as of December 31, 1958, appears on pages 738 and 739.

Assume that the General Manufacturing Company prepares its income statement in all-inclusive form as shown below. The change in retained earnings, then, is affected only by the increase as reported by the income statement, by dividends, and by appropriations. In the illustration on page 736 the analysis of changes in appropriated and unappropriated retained earnings balances is prepared in columnar form.

### GENERAL MANUFACTURING COMPANY
#### INCOME STATEMENT
#### FOR YEAR ENDED DECEMBER 31, 1958

| | | | |
|---|---:|---:|---:|
| Sales............................................................ | | | $1,500,000 |
| Net income before income taxes............................ | | | $ 225,000 |
| Less: Income taxes applicable to net income (total tax provision, $112,500 less $7,500 applicable to extraordinary items).... | | | 105,000 |
| Net income after income taxes.............................. | | | $ 120,000 |
| Extraordinary items: | | | |
| Gains, other increases: | | | |
| Gain on sale of securities............... | | $35,000 | |
| Losses, other decreases: | | | |
| Loss on sale of equipment.............. | $ 5,000 | | |
| Organization costs written off.......... | 32,500 | | |
| Income taxes applicable to extraordinary items.................................. | 7,500 | | |
| Corrections in profits of prior periods — understatement of depreciation charges, 1955–1957........................... | 20,000 | 65,000 | |
| Excess of losses and other decreases over gains and other increases........................................................ | | | 30,000 |
| Net income and extraordinary items......................... | | | $ 90,000 |

**Income Statement Prepared in All-Inclusive Form**

**CAPITAL ON THE BALANCE SHEET**  The principles of balance sheet form and content discussed in preceding chapters are illustrated in the balance sheet for the General Manufacturing Company on pages 738 and 739. Special attention is directed to the balance sheet capital section, which is related to the income and capital statements just illustrated.

The following points in the capital section of the balance sheet deserve special attention:

## GENERAL MANUFACTURING COMPANY
### RETAINED EARNINGS STATEMENT
#### FOR YEAR ENDED DECEMBER 31, 1958

| | RETAINED EARNINGS | | |
| --- | --- | --- | --- |
| | Appropriated for Purchase of Treasury Stock | Appropriated for Contingencies | Unappropriated |
| Balances, January 1, 1958.. | $60,000 | $50,000 | $200,000 |
| Net income and extraordinary items for year per income statement........ | | | 90,000 |
| Cash dividends............ | | | (50,000) |
| Earnings appropriated for contingencies........... | | 35,000 | (35,000) |
| Return to retained earnings of earnings previously restricted through ownership of reasury stock........ | (20,000) | | 20,000 |
| Balances, December 31, 1958, per balance sheet........ | $40,000 | $85,000 | $225,000 |

**Retained Earnings Statement to Accompany Income Statement in All-Inclusive Form**

(1) The various classes of capital stock are reported separately and are described in detail, and information is offered concerning amounts authorized, issued, and held in the treasury.

(2) The first preferred stock is convertible into common at the option of the stockholders on the basis of three shares of common for each share of first preferred. Shares of unissued common stock have been set aside to provide for such conversions.

(3) The items making up additional paid-in capital and appropriated retained earnings are reported individually, although one frequently finds related balances combined and totals reported for these classes of capital on the balance sheet.

(4) In complying with legal requirements, the corporation has reported retained earnings equivalent to the cost of common stock reacquired and still held as an appropriation identified with the reacquisition.

A reference to the notes accompanying financial statements would appear at the bottom of each statement.

**SPECIAL MEASUREMENTS BASED ON CORPORATE STATEMENTS** Reference is frequently made to two measurements that are based upon corporate statement data: (1) *book value per share*, as indicated by the balance sheet and (2) *earnings per share*, as indicated by the income statement. These measurements are of particular interest to stockholders, both present and prospective. The nature of these measurements and the problems involved in their calculation are described in the remaining pages of this chapter.

**BOOK VALUE
PER SHARE**  Share book value is the dollar equity of each share in corporate capital. It is the amount that would be paid to each shareholder assuming corporate liquidation and the realization of assets in amounts equal to values reported on the books.

When only one class of stock is outstanding, the calculation of book value is a simple matter: total corporate capital is divided by the number of shares of stock in the hands of stockholders. When stock has been reacquired and a treasury stock account reports a debit balance, this balance should be recognized as a subtraction item in arriving at corporate capital, and the number of shares represented by the treasury stock should be subtracted from the number of shares issued in arriving at the number of shares outstanding. When shares of stock have been subscribed for but are unissued, capital stock subscribed should be included in summarizing total capital and the number of shares subscribed should be added to the number of shares issued and outstanding for purposes of the book value calculation.

To illustrate the computation of book value when there is only one class of stock, assume capital accounts for the Mosich Corporation as shown below.

| | | |
|---|---:|---:|
| Capital stock, 100,000 shares issued, par $10 (5,000 shares reacquired and held in treasury — see below)............... | | $1,000,000 |
| Capital stock subscribed, 20,000 shares..................... | | 200,000 |
| Additional paid-in capital................................ | | 350,000 |
| Retained earnings: | | |
|   Appropriated.................................... | $200,000 | |
|   Unappropriated................................. | 450,000 | 650,000 |
| | | $2,200,000 |
| Less stock reacquired and held in treasury, 5,000 shares, reported at cost................................. | | 75,000 |
| Total capital......................................... | | $2,125,000 |

The book value per share of stock is calculated as follows:

$2,125,000 (total capital) ÷ 115,000 (shares issued, 100,000, plus shares subscribed, 20,000, minus treasury shares, 5,000) = $18.48.

When there are both preferred and common shares, it is first necessary to determine the portion of the capital identified with the pre-

| ASSETS | | | |
|---|---|---|---|

Current assets:

| Cash on hand and on deposit.................... | | | $   54,000 |
| U. S. Government securities at cost (market, $87,500) | | | 86,000 |
| Trade notes and accounts receivable — less allowance for bad debts, $2,600.................... | | | 180,000 |

Inventories (valuation at cost or market, whichever is lower, cost being calculated by the first-in, first-out method):

| Raw materials and supplies.................. | | $  185,000 | |
| Goods in process............................ | | 201,000 | |
| Finished goods............................. | | 190,000 | 576,000 |

| Loans, advances, and accrued income items........ | | | 20,000 |
| Prepayments including taxes, insurance, and sundry items................................... | | | 14,500 |

| Total current assets.......................... | | | $  930,500 |

Investments:

| Fund consisting of U. S. Government securities to be used for property additions................. | | $  250,000 | |
| Investment in land not currently in use.......... | | 110,000 | 360,000 |

Plant and equipment:

| Property, plant, and equipment, at cost.......... | | $1,235,000 | |
| Less: Allowances for depreciation............... | | 580,000 | 655,000 |

Intangible assets:

| Patents, copyrights, and goodwill — less amortization (See Note A)........................... | | | 120,000 |

Deferred costs:

| Unamortized bond issue costs................... | | $   15,000 | |
| Deferred developmental costs (See Note B)....... | | 40,000 | 55,000 |

Other assets:

| Advance payments on equipment purchase contracts | | $   25,000 | |
| Long-term receivables....................... | | 22,500 | 47,500 |

The accompanying notes A through F are an integral part of this financial statement.

| Total assets.................................. | | | $2,168,000 |

# TURING COMPANY

SHEET

31, 1958

## LIABILITIES AND CAPITAL

### LIABILITIES

Current liabilities:

| | | |
|---|---|---|
| Notes and accounts payable.............................. | $ | 52,500 |
| Estimated income taxes payable for current and prior years..... | | 62,000 |
| Accrued payrolls, interest, social security, and general taxes.... | | 23,500 |
| Serial debenture bonds due May 1, 1959..................... | | 20,000 |
| Customers' deposits and credit balances, and sundry items.... | | 24,000 |
| Total current liabilities................................... | $ | 182,000 |

Contingent liabilities (See Note C)

Long-term debt:

| | | | |
|---|---|---|---|
| Twenty-year 5 ½% first mortgage bonds......... | $ | 260,000 | |
| Less: Unamortized discount on first mortgage bonds | | 10,000 | |
| | $ | 250,000 | |
| Serial 5¾% debenture bonds due May 1, 1960, to May 1, 1968, inclusive........................ | | 180,000 | 430,000 |
| Estimated employee pensions payable (See Note D)............ | | | 60,000 |

Deferred revenues:

| | | |
|---|---|---|
| Deferred leasehold income extending to Jan. 1, 1970 (See Note E) | | 110,000 |
| Total liabilities......................................... | $ | 782,000 |

### CAPITAL

Paid-in capital:

| | | |
|---|---|---|
| First preferred 5% stock, cumulative and convertible into common, par $25, 10,000 shares authorized, 8,000 issued................................ | $ | 200,000 |
| Second preferred 6% stock, cumulative and redeemable, par $10, 50,000 shares authorized, 30,000 issued (See Note F)........................... | | 300,000 |
| No-par common stock, stated value $5, 100,000 shares authorized, 24,000 shares reserved for conversion of first preferred, 60,000 shares issued (treasury stock reacquired, 5,000 shares — deducted below)............................. | | 300,000 |
| | $ | 800,000 |

Additional paid-in capital:

| | | | |
|---|---|---|---|
| From sale of common stock in excess of stated value..................... | $260,000 | | |
| From sale of treasury stock in excess of cost........................... | 16,000 | 276,000 | |
| Total paid-in capital......................... | | $1,076,000 | |

Retained earnings:

Appropriated:

| | | | |
|---|---|---|---|
| For purchase of treasury stock.. | $40,000 | | |
| For contingencies............ | 85,000 | $125,000 | |
| Unappropriated........................ | 225,000 | | |
| Total retained earnings........................ | | 350,000 | |
| | | $1,426,000 | |
| Less common treasury stock, at cost (5,000 shares acquired at $8)............................. | | 40,000 | |
| Total capital...................................... | | | 1,386,000 |
| Total liabilities and capital....................... | | | $2,168,000 |

**739**

## GENERAL MANUFACTURING COMPANY
### NOTES TO FINANCIAL STATEMENTS — YEAR ENDED DECEMBER 31, 1958

Note A: Intangible assets are being written off over the period of their estimated useful life, with the exception of goodwill, which is carried at its original cost, $75,000. The balance of organization costs, $32,500, was written off during the year.

Note B: Certain research and developmental costs in 1957 and 1958 relating to new products that will be marketed beginning in 1959 have been deferred and will be charged to subsequent operations.

Note C: The Company is contingently liable on guaranteed notes and accounts totaling $40,000. Also, various suits are pending on which the ultimate legal responsibility cannot be determined. In the opinion of counsel and management, such liability, if any, will not be material. Retained earnings have been appropriated for contingencies in anticipation of possible losses.

Note D: The liability under the Company pension plan has been calculated on the basis of actuarial studies.

Note E: The Company leased Market Street properties for a fifteen-year period ending January 1, 1970. Leasehold payment received in advance is being recognized as income over the lifetime of the lease.

Note F: Second preferred stock may be redeemed at the option of the board of directors at $12\frac{1}{2}$ plus accrued dividends on or before December 31, 1960, and at gradually reduced amounts but at not less than $10\frac{1}{2}$ plus accrued dividends after January 1, 1966.

ferred shares. The portion of capital related to preferred shares when subtracted from total capital gives the portion of capital related to the common shares. The capital related to preferred shares divided by the number of preferred shares gives the book value of a preferred share. The capital related to common shares divided by the number of common shares gives the book value of a common share.

The portion of capital related to preferred shares would be that portion distributable to preferred stockholders in the event of corporate liquidation. The capital relating to preferred shares calls for consideration of the following items:

*Liquidation value.* Preferred shares may have a liquidating value equal to par, to par plus a premium, or to an arbitrary dollar amount. Capital equal to this liquidating value for the number of preferred shares outstanding should be assigned to preferred. A preferred call price, when this differs from the amount to be paid to preferred stockholders upon liquidation, would not be applicable for purposes of the book value computations; the call of preferred stock is not obligatory, hence call prices are not operative in liquidation and in the apportionment of values between preferred and common stockholders.

*Dividend rights.*   (a) Preferred stock may have certain rights in retained earnings as a result of special dividend privileges.  For example, preferred shares may be entitled to dividends not yet declared for a portion of the current year, assuming liquidation; here a portion of retained earnings equal to the requirements would be related to preferred shares.  (b) Preferred stock may be cumulative with dividends in arrears.  When, in the event of liquidation, preferred stockholders are entitled to dividends in arrears regardless of any retained earnings or deficit balance reported on the books, capital equivalent to the dividends in arrears is assigned to preferred shares even though this means the impairment or the elimination of the invested capital equity relating to common stockholders.  When preferred stockholders are entitled to dividends in arrears only in the event of accumulated earnings, as much retained earnings as are available but not in excess of such dividend requirements are related to preferred stock.  (c) Preferred stock may be participating.  When a retained earnings balance is subject to distribution on a participating basis, the basis of participation should be applied to retained earnings and the portion distributable to preferred stock should be assigned to this equity.

The computation of book values for preferred and common shares is illustrated in the series of examples that follow.  Examples are based upon the capital of the Maxwell Corporation on December 31, 1958, which follows:

| | |
|---|---:|
| 6% Preferred Stock, 10,000 shares, par $50 | $ 500,000 |
| Common Stock, 100,000 shares, par $10 | 1,000,000 |
| Retained Earnings | 250,000 |
| Total Capital | $1,750,000 |

*Example 1.*  Assume that preferred dividends have been paid to July 1, 1958.  Preferred stock has a liquidating value of $52 and is entitled to current unpaid dividends.  Book values on December 31, 1958, are developed as follows:

| | | |
|---|---:|---:|
| Total capital | | $1,750,000 |
| Capital identified with preferred: | | |
| Liquidation value, 10,000 shares @ 52 | $520,000 | |
| Current dividends, 3% of $500,000 | 15,000 | 535,000 |
| Balance — capital identified with common | | $1,215,000 |
| Book values per share: | | |
| Preferred: $ 535,000 ÷ 10,000 | | $53.50 |
| Common: $1,215,000 ÷ 100,000 | | $12.15 |

*Example 2.* Assume that preferred stock has a liquidating value of $52. Preferred is cumulative, with dividends 5 years in arrears on December 31, 1958, that must be paid in the event of liquidation. Book values for common and preferred shares would be developed as follows:

| | | |
|---|---:|---:|
| Total capital.......................................... | | $1,750,000 |
| Capital identified with preferred: | | |
|   Liquidation value, 10,000 shares @ 52 ......... | $520,000 | |
|   Dividends in arrears, 30% of $500,000......... | 150,000 | 670,000 |
| Balance — capital identified with common................ | | $1,080,000 |
| Book values per share: | | |
|   Preferred: $ 670,000 ÷ 10,000...................... | | $67.00 |
|   Common: $1,080,000 ÷ 100,000...................... | | $10.80 |

*Example 3.* Assume that preferred stock has a liquidating value of par. Preferred is cumulative with dividends 10 years in arrears on December 31, 1958, that are fully payable in the event of liquidation even though impairing the invested capital of the common share-holders. Book values for common and preferred shares are developed as follows:

| | | |
|---|---:|---:|
| Total capital.......................................... | | $1,750,000 |
| Capital identified with preferred: | | |
|   Liquidation value, 10,000 shares @ 50.......... | $500,000 | |
|   Dividends in arrears, 60% of $500,000......... | 300,000 | 800,000 |
| Balance — capital identified with common................ | | $ 950,000 |
| Book values per share: | | |
|   Preferred: $800,000 ÷ 10,000....................... | | $80.00 |
|   Common:  950,000 ÷ 100,000....................... | | $ 9.50 |

*Example 4.* Assume that preferred stock has a liquidating value of par. A preferred dividend of $1.50 has been paid for the first half of 1958, but no common dividends have been declared or paid. Preferred stock is entitled to full participation ratably with the common stock after the common stock has received the preferred rate for the current year.

The portions of the retained earnings relating to the preferred and common issues on December 31, 1958, are calculated at the top of the next page:

| | | | To PREFERRED | To COMMON |
|---|---|---|---|---|
| Balance of retained earnings | | $250,000 | | |
| Less current dividend requirements on preferred, 3% of $500,000 | | 15,000 | $15,000 | |
| | | $235,000 | | |
| Less current dividend requirements on common, 6% of $1,000,000 | | 60,000 | | $60,000 |
| | | $175,000 | | |
| Balance of retained earnings, distributable ratably to preferred and common, 11.6667% ($175,000, earnings available to both classes ÷ $1,500,000, par value of stock of both classes). Distributable to preferred, 11.6667% of $500,000 | | 58,333 | 58,333 | |
| Distributable to common, 11.6667% of $1,000,000 | | $116,667 | | 116,667 |
| Totals to common and preferred | | | $73,333 | $176,667 |

Book values may now be developed as follows:

| | | | |
|---|---|---|---|
| Total capital | | | $1,750,000 |
| Capital identified with preferred: | | | |
| Liquidation value, 10,000 shares @ 50 | | $500,000 | |
| Current dividends and retained earnings in participation with common | | 73,333 | 573,333 |
| Balance — capital identified with common | | | $1,176,667 |

Book values per share:

| | | |
|---|---|---|
| Preferred: $ 573,333 ÷ 10,000 | | $57.33 |
| Common: $1,176,667 ÷ 100,000 | | $11.77 |

The nature and the limitations of the share book value measurements should be fully appreciated in the use of these data. Share book values are developed from the values as reported on the books. Furthermore, calculations require the assumption of liquidation in the allocation of amounts to the several classes of stock. Book values of property items on the accounting records may vary materially from the present worth of such properties. Moreover, book values of property items are stated in terms of the "going concern"; the full implications of a "quitting concern" approach would call for many significant changes in property values as reported by the books. Share book values simply offer a measurement of the net assets related to each share in terms of the valuation employed on the financial statements.

**EARNINGS PER SHARE**      The *earnings per share* measurement is the amount earned during the course of the period on each share of the capital stock outstanding. This measurement is frequently sought as an index of stock worth. It is also used in judging the dividend policies of the company, the earnings per share being compared with the dividends paid per share during a period in obtaining the company's *payout percentage.*

When only one class of stock is outstanding, the entire net income is identified with these shares; net income, then, divided by the number of shares of stock outstanding gives the earnings relating to each share. When preferred and common shares are outstanding, the claim that preferred shares make on net earnings should be deducted from net income in arriving at the earnings related to common. In the event of a net loss, a *loss per share* figure would be calculated. With cumulative preferred shares outstanding, cumulative preferred dividend requirements would be added to a net loss in arriving at the loss per share on common.

To illustrate per-share earnings calculations, assume net income of $1,500,000 and stock of a single class outstanding consisting of 1,000,000 shares. Per-share earnings are calculated as follows:

$$\frac{\$1,500,000}{1,000,000} = \$1.50 \text{ per share}$$

However, assume the same earnings but two classes of stock outstanding as follows: 6% preferred stock, par $100, 80,000 shares; and common stock, 1,000,000 shares. Preferred is cumulative and non-participating. Earnings per share are calculated as follows:

| | |
|---|---:|
| Net income.......................................... | $1,500,000 |
| Dividend requirements on preferred shares, 6% of $8,000,000........................................ | 480,000 |
| Net income identified with common shares............ | $1,020,000 |

Per-share earnings on common: $\dfrac{\$1,020,000}{1,000,000} = \$1.02$ per share

Periodic net earnings are frequently related to the number of shares of preferred stock outstanding. For example, in the preceding illustration, the relationship of earnings to preferred shares may be calculated as follows: $1,500,000 (net income) ÷ 80,000 (number of preferred shares) = $18.75. This value is commonly referred to as the "earnings per share on preferred." It should be observed that the connotation to be drawn from this calculation differs from that which is found in the common share calculation. Division of residual earnings by the number of shares of common outstanding offers a measurement of the earnings that actually accrue on each common share; such earnings, if not made available to the common stockholders in dividends, will actually increase their equity in the corporation. Division of the total earnings by the number of shares of preferred outstanding, however, offers no more than the earnings protection that is available in meeting the dividend requirements on the preferred equity. In view of this difference, the American Institute Committee on Accounting Procedure in Accounting Research Bulletin No. 49 issued in 1958 recommends that use of the term *earnings per share* be limited to earnings applicable to each share of common stock or other residual equity. Although the committee agrees that it may be helpful to show the number of times or the extent to which the requirements of preferred dividends have been earned, it feels that the term earnings per share is not properly applicable under conditions that involve only limited dividend rights for senior securities.[1]

In calculating per-share earnings the question arises as to whether earnings should include extraordinary items and corrections in profits of prior periods or whether the earnings amount should be limited to the result of normally recurring items. It would seem that when financial statements develop a net income balance in terms of normally recurring items and report special and nonrecurring items separately either on the income statement or as changes in retained earnings on the retained earnings statement, two per-share measurements would be called for: (1) per-share earnings before special charges and credits for the period, and (2) per-share effects of special charges and credits recognized during the period. Such practice is recommended by the American Institute Committee on Accounting Procedure. The Committee comments:

> In its deliberations concerning the nature and purpose of the income statement, the committee has been mindful of the disposition of even well-informed persons to attach undue importance to a single net income figure and to *earnings per share* shown for a particular year. The committee directs attention to the undesirability in many cases of the dissemination of information in which major prominence is given to a single figure of *net income* or *net income per share*. However, if such income data are reported (as in newspapers, investors' services, and annual corporate reports), the committee strongly urges that any determination of *income per share* be related to the amount designated in the income statement as net income and that where material extraordinary charges or credits have been excluded from the determination of net income, the corresponding total or per-share amount of such charges and credits also be reported separately and simultaneously.[2]

---

[1] *Accounting Research Bulletin No. 49*, "Earnings per Share," 1958 (New York: American Institute of Certified Public Accountants), p. 34.

[2] *Accounting Research Bulletin No. 43*, "Restatement and Revision of Accounting Research Bulletins," 1953 (New York: American Institute of Certified Public Accountants), p. 65.

## QUESTIONS

**1.** Describe each of the following: (a) valuation reserve, (b) liability reserve, (c) surplus reserve.

**2.** (a) What criticisms have been made of the term "reserve"? (b) What position has been taken by the American Institute of Certified Public Accountants and by the American Accounting Association with respect to the use of the term? (c) What position would you take with respect to use of the term? What substitute terms would you employ?

**3.** Appropriations limiting the use of retained earnings may arise from (a) legal requirements, (b) contractual requirements, and (c) managerial policy. Give an example of each of the above.

**4.** What is meant by a funded appropriation?

**5.** A stockholder of Michel, Inc. does not understand the purpose of the Appropriation for Bond Redemption Fund that has been set up by periodic charges to Retained Earnings. He is told that this balance will not be used to redeem the bonds at their maturity. (a) What account will be reduced by the payment of the bonds? (b) What purpose is accomplished by Appropriation for Bond Redemption Fund? (c) What possible dispositions may be made of the appropriation?

**6.** (a) Describe a general purpose contingency appropriation. (b) How should it be established? (c) Assuming that certain contingencies materialize and that significant losses are incurred, how would you recommend that these be recorded, and what ultimate disposition should be made of the appropriation balance?

**7.** Management of the Rossmore Co., considering the possibility of a strike by employees, authorized the establishment of an appropriation for contingencies at the end of 1957 by a charge to revenue. The strike was called in 1958, and company losses incurred to the date of the strike settlement were charged against the appropriation. The company management points out that it exercised good judgment in anticipating strike losses and providing a cushion for such costs. What criticism, if any, can you offer of the accounting procedures that were followed by the company?

**8.** (a) What is meant by self-insurance? (b) Describe the accounting procedures in considering possible future charges and in recognizing such charges when they occur assuming that (1) self-insurance is considered to involve accruable losses and (2) self-insurance is considered to involve nonaccruable losses.

**9.** What objections are made by the American Accounting Association to the appropriation of retained income to reflect managerial policies relative to earnings?

**10.** The Carrabino Co. reports appropriations as a subtraction from net income at the bottom of the income statement. When an appropriation is returned to retained income, it is reported as an addition to net income on the income statement. What objections, if any, would you raise to such a practice?

**11.** State where each of the following accounts will appear on the balance sheet:

(a) Reserve for Contingencies
(b) Reserve for Doubtful Accounts
(c) Reserve for Possible Inventory Decline
(d) Reserve for Self-Insurance— Fire Loss
(e) Reserve for Bond Retirement
(f) Reserve for Income Taxes
(g) Reserve for Plant Expansion
(h) Reserve for Increased Investment in Plant Assets
(i) Reserve for Depletion
(j) Reserve for Redeemable Coupons Outstanding
(k) Reserve for Repairs and Replacements
(l) Reserve for Purchase of Treasury Stock
(m) Reserve for Personal Injury Claims Pending
(n) Reserve for Unrealized Plant Appreciation

**12.** Define share book value. What problems arise in the calculation of share book value when stock outstanding consists of both preferred and common shares?

**13.** Define per-share earnings. What problems arise in the calculation of per-share earnings when stock outstanding consists of both preferred and common shares?

**14.** How would you recommend that per-share earnings be reported when the increase in retained earnings accrues from both normally recurring items and extraordinary items that are material in amount?

**15.** Which of the following transactions change total capital? What is the nature of the change?

(a) Declaration of a cash dividend on capital stock.
(b) Payment of a cash dividend on capital stock.
(c) Retirement of bonds payable for which both a redemption fund and an appropriation had been established.
(d) Declaration of a stock dividend.
(e) Payment of a stock dividend.
(f) Conversion of bonds payable into preferred stock.
(g) The passing of a dividend on cumulative preferred stock.
(h) Donation by the officers of shares of stock.
(i) Operating loss for the period.

**16.** How would you report the following items on the balance sheet: (a) dividends in arrears on cumulative preferred stock, (b) unclaimed bond interest and unclaimed dividends, (c) stock purchase rights issued but not exercised as of the balance sheet date, (d) stock that is callable at the option of the corporation at a premium?

## EXERCISES

**1.** As a result of an agreement with bondholders, the Barney Co. is required to appropriate earnings of $200,000 at the end of each calendar year for the years 1953–1957. At the beginning of 1958, upon liquidation of the bonded indebtedness, the retained earnings appropriation is canceled. This is followed by the declaration and the issue of a 50% common stock dividend on 250,000 shares of $10 par common stock outstanding. Retained earnings are charged for the stock dividend at par. What entries are required for (a) periodic appropriations, (b) cancellation of the appropriation in 1958, and (c) capitalization of retained earnings by means of the stock dividend?

**2.** Suits for damages totaling $100,000 are pending against the Swift Co. on December 31, 1958. Counsel for the company advises that losses on such suits, if any, should not be material. However, company management authorizes that provision be made in the accounts for any possible loss up to $100,000. All of the suits are settled in 1959, payments of $14,500 being made. Give entries to record (a) the provision for losses authorized by management, in 1958, (b) payments made in 1959, (c) cancellation of the provision for losses in 1959.

**3.** A physical inventory taken by the Bernard Co. on December 31, 1958, discloses goods on hand with a cost of $315,000; the inventory is recorded at this figure less a reserve of $12,500 to reduce it to the lower of cost or market. At the same time, the company authorizes that a reserve for possible future inventory decline of $100,000 be established. (a) Give the entries to be made at the end of 1958 in recording the inventory and establishing the reserves as indicated. (b) Give the entries in 1958 to close the beginning inventory and reserve balances established at the end of 1958, assuming that the estimated inventory decline does not materialize and that the inventory at the end of 1959 is properly reported at cost, which is lower than market. (c) Give the entries in 1959 to close the inventory and reserve balances established at the end of 1958 if a decline in the value of the December 31, 1958, inventory of $125,000 is to be recognized; the inventory at the end of 1959 is properly reported at cost, which is lower than its market at this date.

**4.** State for each of the following accounts whether it is a valuation balance, liability balance, or retained earnings appropriation and give the entry whereby the account balance is established.

    (a) Reserve for Amortization of Patents
    (b) Reserve for Federal Income Taxes
    (c) Reserve for Possible Inventory Decline
    (d) Reserve for Obsolete Merchandise
    (e) Reserve for Self-Insurance — Fire Loss
    (f) Reserve for Payments under Employee Retirement Plan
    (g) Reserve for Sales Discounts
    (h) Reserve for Plant Expansion
    (i) Reserve to Meet Claims on Product Guarantees
    (j) Reserve for Purchase of Treasury Stock
    (k) Reserve for Premium Claims Outstanding
    (l) Reserve for Redeemable Purchase Orders Outstanding
    (m) Reserve for Depreciation — Appraisal Increase
    (n) Reserve for Repairs and Replacements
    (o) Reserve for Contingencies
    (p) Reserve for Claims Arising from Company Defaults on Contracts
    (q) Reserve for Vacation Payments to Employees

**5.** The Weisfield Co. reports appropriated retained earnings on its balance sheet at the end of 1958 at $480,000. Analysis of the account balances in support of this total discloses the following:

Reserve for contingencies — to meet estimated claims arising
from accidents in 1958 for which the company is liable. . . .     $ 22,500
Reserve for self-insurance — fire loss — to meet possible
future fire losses as a result of self-insurance on this con-
tingency. . . . . . . . . . . . . . . . . . . . . . . . . . . . . . . . . . . . . . . . . . . . . . . . . . . . . .     30,000
Reserve for pensions — to meet estimated pension costs
arising from contracts with employees. . . . . . . . . . . . . . . . . . .     310,000
Reserve for revaluation of plant properties — arising from
asset appraisal increases. . . . . . . . . . . . . . . . . . . . . . . . . . . . . . .     85,000
Reserve for possible declines on marketable securities — to
meet possible future losses on marketable securities held. .     20,000
Reserve for plant rehabilitation costs — to meet costs of rehabilitating plant at termination of lease in accordance
with contractual requirements. . . . . . . . . . . . . . . . . . . . . . . .     12,500

$480,000

Which of the above items, if any, would you exclude from the appropriated retained earnings classification? State how you would classify such
items.

**6.** Name the errors in the entries shown below:

### RETAINED EARNINGS

| | |
|---|---|
| (a) Dividends declared to common stockholders. | (d) Appraisal of plant and equipment. |
| (b) Transfer to reserve for bond redemption fund. | (e) Net income for year. |
| (c) Sale of stock at a discount. | (f) Gain from sale of treasury stock. |

### ADDITIONAL PAID-IN CAPITAL

| | |
|---|---|
| (g) Dividends declared to preferred stockholders. | (i) Profit from sale of building. |
| (h) Correction reducing profit of previous fiscal period. | (j) Reserve for bond redemption fund. |
| | (k) Premium from sale of bonds. |

**7.** Capital accounts of the Palmerville Co. report the following balances:
Authorized Capital Stock, 100,000 shares, par value $25. . .     $2,500,000
Unissued Capital Stock (20,000 shares). . . . . . . . . . . . . . . .     500,000
Treasury Stock (2,000 shares, at cost). . . . . . . . . . . . . . . .     60,000
Additional Paid-in Capital. . . . . . . . . . . . . . . . . . . . . . . . . .     185,000
Deficit. . . . . . . . . . . . . . . . . . . . . . . . . . . . . . . . . . . . . . . . . .     280,000
Calculate the amount of the book value per share of stock outstanding.

**8.** Capital balances of Hall, Inc., on December 31, 1958, follow:
Common stock, 50,000 shares, par $10. . . . . . . . . . . . . . . . . .     $500,000
6% preferred stock, 5,000 shares, par $25. . . . . . . . . . . . . . .     125,000
Additional paid-in capital. . . . . . . . . . . . . . . . . . . . . . . . . . . .     75,000
Retained earnings. . . . . . . . . . . . . . . . . . . . . . . . . . . . . . . . . .     50,000

$750,000

Calculate the book values per share of preferred stock and common
stock under each of the following assumptions:

(a) Preferred stock is noncumulative and nonparticipating, callable at $30, and preferred as to assets at $27.50 upon corporate liquidation.

(b) Preferred stock is cumulative, nonparticipating, with dividends in arrears for 6 years; upon corporate liquidation, shares are preferred as to assets up to par, and must be paid any dividends in arrears before distributions may be made to common shares.

(c) Preferred stock is fully participating with common stock; upon corporate liquidation any distributions beyond stock par values are to be made ratably on preferred and common shares.

**9.** The income statement for the Samson Co. for the year ended December 31, 1958, shows:

| | |
|---|---|
| Net income before income taxes | $310,000 |
| Income taxes | 75,000 |
| | $235,000 |
| Add extraordinary gain from sale of Springfield branch store. | 205,000 |
| Net income and extraordinary gain | $440,000 |

Calculate per-share earnings for 1958 under each of the following assumptions:

(a) The company has only one class of stock, the number of shares outstanding totaling 200,000.

(b) The company has shares outstanding as follows:

5% cumulative, nonparticipating preferred, par $100, 10,000 shares
Common, par $25, 200,000 shares

## PROBLEMS

**23-1.** Accounts of the Hewitt Co. after closing on December 31, 1958, show the balances listed below. From this data prepare a balance sheet capital section for the corporation as it would appear on December 31.

| ACCOUNT | DR. | CR. |
|---|---|---|
| Authorized Capital Stock ($10 par) | | 500,000 |
| Bonds Payable | | 250,000 |
| Bond Retirement Fund | 140,000 | |
| Capital Stock Subscribed | | 40,000 |
| Current Assets | 502,000 | |
| Current Liabilities | | 80,000 |
| Dividends Payable — Cash | | 12,000 |
| Dividends Payable — Stock | | 70,000 |
| Plant | 800,000 | |
| Plant — Appraisal Increase | 340,000 | |
| Premium on Stock | | 35,000 |
| Reserve for Bond Retirement Fund | | 140,000 |

| | | |
|---|---:|---:|
| Reserve for Contingencies............................ | | 115,000 |
| Reserve for Customers' Deposits.................. | | 15,000 |
| Reserve for Depreciation of Plant................ | | 210,000 |
| Reserve for Depreciation of Plant — Appraisal Increase...................................... | | 85,000 |
| Reserve for Federal Income Taxes............... | | 40,000 |
| Reserve for Purchase of Treasury Stock.......... | | 60,000 |
| Appraisal Capital................................. | | 255,000 |
| Treasury Stock (at par).......................... | 60,000 | |
| Treasury Stock Capital.......................... | | 45,000 |
| Unappropriated Retained Earnings............... | | 50,000 |
| Unissued Capital Stock......................... | 160,000 | |
| | 2,002,000 | 2,002,000 |

**23-2.** The balance sheet for Pan American, Inc. showed the following capital balances on December 31, 1957:

CAPITAL

Paid-in capital:

| | | | |
|---|---:|---:|---:|
| Preferred stock, 10,000 shares, par $25............... | | $ 250,000 | |
| Common stock, 60,000 shares, stated value $15........ | | 900,000 | |
| | | $1,150,000 | |
| Additional paid-in capital: | | | |
| From sale of no-par common............. | $ 40,000 | | |
| From sale of treasury stock............. | 11,000 | 51,000 | |
| Total paid-in capital......................... | | $1,201,000 | |
| Retained earnings: | | | |
| Appropriated — | | | |
| For bond redemption fund............... | $ 95,000 | | |
| For plant expansion................... | 30,000 | | |
| | $125,000 | | |
| Unappropriated........................ | 65,000 | | |
| Total retained earnings....................... | | 190,000 | |
| Total capital....................................... | | $1,391,000 | |

An audit of the corporation's books one month later disclosed the following errors and omissions:

(1) Machinery purchased July 1, 1956, for $20,000 has not been depreciated. It is expected to have a life of 10 years and no salvage value.

(2) Merchandise received in 1957, but not entered in the purchase journal until January 5, 1958, was included in the inventory at the end of 1957, $5,000.

(3) Premium of $700 on the resale of forfeited common stock was recorded as an operating profit.

Transactions during 1958 that affected the capital accounts were as follows:

(1) 20,000 shares of no-par common stock, stated value $15 a share, were sold for $16 a share.

(2) The first mortgage bonds were retired, releasing the appropriation for bond redemption fund.

(3) Machinery purchased January 1, 1955, for $16,000 and depreciated on the basis of a 15-year life with a $1,000 salvage value was sold on July 1, 1958, for $9,500, retained earnings being charged for the loss.

(4) An appraisal of land by an appraisal company showed this property to be worth $45,000 in excess of original cost. A revaluation on the books was approved by the board of directors.

(5) The board of directors declared a cash dividend of 5% on the preferred stock.

(6) Organization costs of $6,500 and goodwill of $10,000 were written off against retained earnings.

(7) The credit balance in the profit and loss account at the end of 1958, after income taxes, was $56,000.

(8) A new $500,000 bond issue was floated at the beginning of 1958. Bonds mature in 20 years. Terms of the bond issue call for equal annual appropriations of retained earnings, the sum of such appropriations at the end of 20 years to equal the full amount of the obligation. An appropriate entry was made at the end of 1958.

(9) Retained earnings appropriations were authorized by management as follows: for plant expansion, $30,000; for possible inventory decline, $50,000.

*Instructions:* (1) Give the journal entries to record the foregoing data. (The corporation records corrections in profits of prior periods directly in retained earnings.)

(2) Prepare the balance sheet capital section as of December 31, 1958, and a paid-in capital statement, retained earnings statement, and appraisal capital statement to support the ending capital balances.

**23-3.** The balance sheet of the Holmby Corporation on December 31, 1957, is shown on the opposite page.

The following transactions affecting capital were completed in 1958:

Jan. 10. 2,000 shares of 5% preferred stock were sold for cash at 13.

31. The following errors were discovered as of the end of 1957:

Merchandise inventory was understated by $1,750.

Depreciation had not been recorded on store furniture and fixtures. These had been purchased on April 1, 1957. The depreciation rate is 20%.

Building repairs of $500 were improperly capitalized. (Disregard effect upon depreciation.)

Feb. 2. 2,100 shares of no-par common stock were sold for cash at 23.

Mar. 31. A semiannual dividend of 25 cents was declared and paid on common stock.

May 16. 2,000 shares of no-par common stock were issued to P. Lynn in exchange for his going business. Assets taken over were recorded at the following values: land, $10,000; building, $20,000; merchandise inventory, $8,000; accounts receivable, $5,000. Accounts payable of $5,000 were assumed. No goodwill was recognized on the purchase.

## HOLMBY CORPORATION
### BALANCE SHEET
### DECEMBER 31, 1957

| ASSETS | | LIABILITIES AND CAPITAL | | |
|---|---|---|---|---|
| | | **Liabilities** | | |
| Cash........................ | $11,500 | Notes payable......... | $10,000 | |
| Notes receivable.............. | 10,000 | Accounts payable....... | 17,000 | |
| Accounts receivable (net)....... | 15,000 | Preferred dividends pay- | | |
| Merchandise inventory......... | 20,000 | able............... | 750 | |
| Store furniture and fixtures...... | 7,500 | Mortgage payable...... | 5,000 | $32,750 |
| Building.............. $12,500 | | | | |
| Less allow. for depr.... 1,000 | 11,500 | **Capital** | | |
| | | 5% Preferred stock — | | |
| Land...................... | 10,000 | 1,500 shares, $10 par.. | $15,000 | |
| Organization costs............ | 5,000 | Common stock — 1,900 | | |
| | | shares no-par, $10 | | |
| | | stated value......... | 19,000 | |
| | | Additional paid-in capital* | 14,000 | |
| | | Retained earnings...... | 9,750 | 57,750 |
| Total assets.................. | $90,500 | Total liabilities and capital | | $90,500 |

*Additional paid-in capital on the balance sheet consists of premium on preferred stock $4,000 and paid-in capital from sale of common stock in excess of stated value, $10,000.

Aug. 15. 500 shares of the company's own common stock were reacquired on the market for cash at 17. Stock was recorded at cost.

Sept. 30. A semiannual dividend of 25 cents and an extra dividend of 10 cents were declared and paid on common stock.

Oct. 3. 400 shares of treasury stock were sold for cash at $20 per share.

Nov. 10. Merchandise, cost $2,300, was destroyed by fire. The loss was charged to retained earnings, no insurance having been carried.

Dec. 21. The 5% annual dividend was declared on preferred stock, payable January 12, 1959. The board of directors authorized an appropriation of retained earnings for plant expansion of $5,000.

31. The credit balance of the profit and loss account after income taxes was $8,650; this was transferred to the proper capital account.

*Instructions:* (1) Record the information above in journal entry form. (The corporation records corrections in profits of prior periods directly in retained earnings.)

(2) Prepare the capital section of the balance sheet and statements of paid-in capital and retained earnings to support capital balances for the year ended December 31, 1958.

**23-4.** The following accounts are taken from the ledger of Wallace, Inc.:

### RETAINED EARNINGS APPROPRIATED FOR PLANT EXPANSION

| | | |
|---|---|---|
| 1958 | | |
| Jan. 1 Balance | | 60,000 |
| Dec. 31 | | 30,000 |

## RETAINED EARNINGS APPROPRIATED FOR TREASURY STOCK ACQUISITION

| | | | |
|---|---|---|---|
| 1958 | | 1958 | |
| July 1 | 66,000 | Jan. 1 Balance | 45,000 |
| | | Apr. 1 | 42,000 |

## UNAPPROPRIATED RETAINED EARNINGS

| | | | |
|---|---|---|---|
| 1958 | | 1958 | |
| Jan. 10 Correction for understatement of depreciation charges, 1952–1957. | 35,000 | Jan. 1 Balance............. | 600,000 |
| Mar. 12 Additional federal income taxes for 1957.... | 3,000 | 10 Correction for inventory understatement on Dec. 31, 1957............. | 15,000 |
| April 1 Appropriated for treasury stock............. | 42,000 | 10 Correction for capital expenditures recorded as expenses in 1957....... | 9,000 |
| Oct. 31 Preferred dividends.... | 50,000 | July 1 Appropriated for treasury stock acquisitions.. | 66,000 |
| 31 Stock dividend on common stock........... | 200,000 | Oct. 12 Gain on sale of plant and equipment items...... | 20,000 |
| Dec. 31 Organization costs written off........... | 10,000 | Dec. 31 Net income after income taxes, 1958........... | 120,000 |
| 31 Appropriated for plant expansion............. | 30,000 | | |

*Instructions:* (1) Assuming that the income statement reports only net income from regularly recurring items, prepare a retained earnings statement for 1958 in support of the capital balance to be reported on the company's balance sheet at the end of the year.

(2) Assuming that the income statement reports extraordinary items and corrections, prepare a statement of retained earnings for 1958 in support of the balance to be reported on the company's balance sheet at the end of the year.

**23-5.** Capital balances of the Riverside Corporation on December 31, 1958, follow:

| | |
|---|---|
| 5% Preferred Stock, 20,000 shares, par $50............... | $1,000,000 |
| Common Stock, 100,000 shares, par $20................ | 2,000,000 |
| Additional Paid-In Capital............................ | 40,000 |
| Retained Earnings.................................... | 160,000 |
| | $3,200,000 |

*Instructions:* Calculate the book values of preferred shares and common shares as of December 31, 1958, under each of the following assumptions:

(1) Preferred dividends have been paid to October 1, 1958; preferred shares have a call value of $55, a liquidating value of $52.50, and are entitled to current unpaid dividends.

(2) Preferred shares have a liquidating value of par; shares are cumulative, with dividends 3 years in arrears and fully payable in the event of liquidation.

(3) Preferred shares have a liquidating value of par; shares are cumulative, with dividends 5 years in arrears and fully payable in the event of liquidation.

(4) Preferred shares have been paid 5% in 1958 but nothing has been paid on common; preferred is entitled to full participation ratably with common after common has been paid the preferred rate.

**23-6.** The balance sheet of the Sterns Company on September 30, 1958, has the following items on the credit side of the statement:

| | |
|---|---:|
| Current liabilities.................................. | $103,732 |
| Bonds payable..................................... | 300,000 |
| Reserve for bond retirement......................... | 160,000 |
| 6% Cumulative preferred stock, $100 par value (entitled to $110 and accumulated dividends per share in voluntary liquidation and to $100 per share in involuntary liquidation). Authorized — 3,000 shares, issued — 2,000 shares, in treasury — 150 shares ........................... | 185,000 |
| Common stock, $100 par value, authorized — 10,000 shares, issued and outstanding — 4,000 shares................ | 400,000 |
| Premium on preferred stock.......................... | 10,000 |
| Premium on common stock........................... | 67,300 |
| Retained earnings.................................. | 131,260 |

The company proposes to finance a plant expansion program by issuing an additional 2,000 shares of common stock. Common stockholders of record October 1, 1958, were notified that they will be permitted to subscribe to the new issue at $150 per share up to 50% of their holdings. The market value of the stock on October 1, 1958, was $172.50 per share. The stock goes ex-rights in the market on October 3, 1958.

Peter Singer owns 100 shares of the Sterns Company common stock that he purchased in 1956 for $16,431.20. He does not want to exercise his rights but wishes to sell them.

*Instructions:* (1) Compute the book value of a share of common stock as of September 30, 1958. Preferred dividends have been paid or set up as payable through September 30, 1958.

(2) Compute the theoretical value of Peter Singer's rights as of October 1, 1958.

(3) State the federal income tax rule as to stock rights and show the computation and the treatment of the transaction if Singer sells his rights for $800. Indicate any further assumed facts on which your computation is based. (A.I.C.P.A. adapted)

**23-7.** A corporation presents the following condensed balance sheet as of the close of the year:

| | | | | |
|---|---:|---|---|---:|
| Cash.................. | $ 90,000 | | Liabilities.............. | $ 500,000 |
| Other assets........... | 1,510,000 | | Common stock......... | 500,000 |
| | | | 6% preferred stock...... | 300,000 |
| | | | 8% preferred stock...... | 200,000 |
| | | | Surplus............... | 100,000 |
| | $1,600,000 | | | $1,600,000 |

The 6% stock is cumulative, the 8% stock is noncumulative, and both participate equally in the remaining surplus profits by being entitled to an extra dividend equal to the excess of any common dividend rate over and above 6% per annum. Par value of all stock outstanding is $100.

*Instructions:* (1) Compute the book value per share for eacn class of stock in the following cases:

(a) Current year's dividends unpaid.

(b) Dividends unpaid for 2 years.

(c) Dividends unpaid for 3 years.

(2) What dividends could legally be declared to the various classes of stockholders, assuming that the 6% stock is nonparticipating, the 8% stock is participating on the basis stated, and no dividends are in arrears? (A.I.C.P.A. adapted)

**23-8.** The Duncan Company has outstanding on January 1, 1957, 1,500 shares of common stock, par value $100, owned as follows:

| | |
|---|---|
| John Dean | 600 shares |
| Mary Green | 200 shares |
| Frank Burke | 300 shares |
| James Riley | 400 shares |

The surplus and reserves on the above date were: Earned Surplus, $50,000; and Reserve for Bond Sinking Fund, $25,000.

During the year the company declared and paid a 4% dividend in June and declared a 4% dividend on December 20, 1957, payable January 10, 1958. The profits were $20,000 after depreciation, and $6,000 was charged to Earned Surplus as an addition to the sinking fund reserve.

On January 1, 1958, the company purchased one half of Riley's stock at book value and sold it on January 10 to Ruby Feltz for $190 per share.

During 1958 the company declared and paid a dividend of 9%. Its operating profits were $25,000 after depreciation. The accountant set up a reserve for contingencies of $2,000, and the directors ask that the following amounts be added to the reserves: $4,000 for possible declines in market value of inventories, $10,000 for expansion of plant, and $3,000 for sinking fund.

*Instructions:* (1) Prepare journal entries to record the purchase and the sale of the stock in January, 1958.

(2) Prepare a statement showing how the book values of the stock on December 31, 1957, and December 31, 1958, should be calculated. (A.I.C.P.A. adapted)

**23-9.** You are a senior accountant responsible for the annual audit of Desco, Inc., for the year ended 12/31/58. The information available to you is presented below. You may assume that any pertinent information not presented below has already been checked and found satisfactory.

(1) Excerpts from Trial Balance 12/31/58.

|  | Debit | Credit |
|---|---|---|
| Surplus..................... |  | 40,000 |
| Inventory reserve.............. |  | 7,500 |
| Capital stock (600 shares)........ |  | 60,000 |

(2) The books have not been closed but all adjusting entries which the company expects to make have been posted. Their trial balance shows a $15,000 net profit for the year.

(3) Selected Ledger Accounts.

*Surplus*

| 8/ 6/58 | CD62 | 160 | 12/31/57 | Balance | 52,960 |
|---|---|---|---|---|---|
| 10/10/58 | J34 | 10,000 | 4/29/58 | CR8 | 200 |
| 12/31/58 | J40 | 3,000 |  |  |  |

(*Note: The balance at 12/31/57 agrees with last year's working papers and represents the net difference over the years between credits from the profit and loss account and debits for dividends.*)

*Inventory reserve*

| 9/26/58 | CD78 | 500 | 6/30/58 | J19 | 5,000 |
|---|---|---|---|---|---|
|  |  |  | 12/31/58 | J40 | 3,000 |

(4) Analysis of Selected Cash Receipts.

| Date | Page | Account Credited | Explanation | Amount |
|---|---|---|---|---|
| 4/29/58 | 8 | {Capital stock<br>{Surplus | Sold $100 par stock @ $102 | 10,000<br>200 |
| 10/10/58 | 20 | Building | See J34 | 20,000 |

(5) Analysis of Selected Cash Disbursements.

| Date | Page | Account debited | Explanation | Amount |
|---|---|---|---|---|
| 8/ 6/58 | 62 | Surplus | Freak accident to company truck not covered by insurance; repair by Doe & Co. | 160 |
| 9/26/58 | 78 | {Inventory<br>  reserve<br>{Purchases | Purchase of materials (X Co.) to be used on orders taken prior to 6/30/58. $500 is price increase since 6/30/58. | 500<br>6,300 |

(6) Selected Entries in General Journal.

| Date | Page | Entry and Explanation | Debit | Credit |
|---|---|---|---|---|
| 6/30/58 | 19 | Inventory loss (P & L)<br>    Inventory reserve<br>Provision voted by Board of Directors for estimated future price increases in materials needed to complete orders on hand. (*Note: Orders do not represent contractual obligations.*) | 5,000 | 5,000 |
| 10/10/58 | 34 | Reserve for depreciation<br>Surplus<br>    Building<br>Sale of main office bldg., moved to rental quarters downtown. (See CR20) | 50,000<br>10,000 | 60,000 |

| Date | Page | Entry and Explanation | Debit | Credit |
|------|------|----------------------|-------|--------|
| 12/31/58 | 40 | Surplus | 3,000 | |
| | |    Inventory reserve | | 3,000 |
| | | Provision to value materials inventory at lower of cost or market in accordance with company pricing policy. | | |

|  |  |
|---|---|
| Cost.............$30,000 | |
| Market........ 28,000 | |
| $ 3,000 | |

*Instructions:* Prepare in good form:

(1) Schedule of recommended adjusting entries to be placed on the books to state the stockholders' equity accounts in accordance with accepted accounting principles.

(2) Statement of retained earnings for 1958.

(3) Stockholders' equity section of balance sheet. (A.I.C.P.A. adapted)

**23-10.** The following are some of the accounts appearing in a trial balance of the Westwood Corporation at December 31, 1958:

| | Debit | Credit |
|---|-------|--------|
| Capital stock, no par common issued at $5................... | | $ 5,000 |
| Capital stock, no par common issued at $7................... | | 3,500 |
| Capital stock, no par common issued at $4................... | | 152,000 |
| Treasury stock, no par common acquired at $5............... | $ 15,000 | |
| Capital stock, $100 preferred A, 500 shares............... | | 55,000 |
| Capital stock, $100 preferred B, 500 shares............... | | 47,000 |
| Capital stock, no par common authorized 50,000 shares....... | — | |
| Class A preferred authorized, $100 par value............... | | 100,000 |
| Class A preferred unissued, 500 shares............... | 100,000 | |
| Class B preferred authorized, 500 shares................... | | 3,000 |
| Class B preferred unissued................... | 3,000 | |
| Reserve for 1958 federal income taxes (set up in 1958)........ | | 46,400 |
| Reserve for loss on accounts ($6,000 added in 1958).......... | | 7,200 |
| Reserve for bond sinking fund ($2,000 added in 1958)........ | | 8,000 |
| Reserve for reduction of 1958 inventory to market (set up in 1958)...... | | 9,100 |
| Reserve for possible 1959 inventory declines (set up in 1958)... | | 10,000 |
| Reserve for preferred dividends declared (set up in 1958)...... | | 2,750 |
| Reserve for revaluation of fixed assets.................... | | 24,000 |
| Reserve for depreciation of fixed assets — cost ($4,600 from 1958)...... | | 33,000 |
| Reserve for depreciation of fixed assets — revaluation ($900 from 1958)...... | | 6,300 |
| Reserve for general contingencies (set up in 1955)........... | | 10,000 |
| Reserve for common stock dividends to be declared (set up in 1958)...... | | 7,300 |
| Common stock dividend of 7,300 shares declared on common of record 1/1/59 (set up in 1958)..................... | | 7,300 |
| Suspense — amount books were out of balance.............. | 3,160 | |
| Suspense — Cash over and short...................... | 480 | |
| Loss on sale of fixed assets (1958)........................ | 3,620 | |
| Organization expense unamortized........................ | 2,500 | |
| Bond discount amortized................................ | | 825 |
| Bond discount....................................... | 3,400 | |
| Loss on inventory decline in 1958........................ | 9,100 | |
| Retained earnings 1/1/58............................... | 22,070 | |
| 1958 profit........................................... | | 125,000 |
| The remaining accounts comprised the following:............ | | |
| Cash, receivables, inventories, prepaid expenses and fixed assets | 803,600 | |
| Accounts, notes and expenses payable, and bonds payable..... | | 303,255 |
| | $965,930 | $965,930 |

*Instructions:* (1) Prepare the capital section of the December 31, 1958 balance sheet in acceptable form for a report.

(2) Prepare a schedule (or schedules) showing the changes which you make in profit to arrive at the corrected net income for the year, and an analysis of changes in surplus accounts. (You may ignore the need for revision of the amount of the *Reserve for 1958 federal income taxes* arising from your correction of 1958 profit.)

(3) For each balance-sheet account which you do not include in (1) above, give a brief, *one-sentence* explanation of its proper disposition. (You need not give consideration to recommended changes in descriptive titles.) (A.I.C.P.A. adapted)

**23-11.** You have been asked by the president of the Holden Corporation, manufacturer of home appliances, to review the company's capital, surplus, and reserve accounts and to make such proposals for their revision and balance sheet presentation as good accounting may suggest.

On April 30, 1957, the liability section of the company's published balance sheet appeared as follows:

Capital:

| | | |
|---|---:|---:|
| Capital stock, preferred, $10 par, 10,000 shares authorized and issued — | | |
| 9,000 shares in hands of public............... | $    90,000 | |
| 1,000 shares held in treasury at cost of $15,000, per contra.................................. | 10,000 | $  100,000 |
| Capital stock, common, no par value — | | |
| 100,000 shares authorized, 56,000 shares issued and in hands of public..................... | $  224,000 | |
| Paid-in surplus (50% on preferred shares in 1940)... | 50,000 | 274,000 |
| Current liabilities (detail omitted)................. | | 388,000 |
| Reserves for: | | |
| Doubtful accounts............................. | $     2,000 | |
| Postwar rehabilitation......................... | 1,000,000 | |
| Depreciation................................. | 384,000 | |
| Fire and accident insurance.................... | 60,000 | 1,446,000 |
| Surplus......................................... | | 2,671,000 |
| Total liabilities................................ | | $4,879,000 |

(1) On April 30, 1958, half of the shares of the treasury preferred stock, which had been purchased in 1954 at $15 per share, were sold at $19 per share, the proceeds being credited to the treasury stock account.

(2) The preferred capital stock carries an annual dividend of $1 per share, and the dividend is cumulative. On April 30, 1957, unpaid dividends attaching to each share amounted to $5, which were liquidated on January 1, 1958, by issuing to preferred stockholders 9,000 shares of no-par-value common stock on which a value of $5 per share had been declared.

(3) A cash dividend of $1 per share was declared to preferred stockholders of record April 1, 1958, payable May 1, 1958.

(4) Balances in the reserves for doubtful accounts and depreciation at April 30, 1958, were $2,200 and $401,000, respectively.

(5) The reserve for postwar rehabilitation was created in the preceding year by a provision out of income for a like amount. The intent was to set aside profits for possible but unknown future contingencies. During the current year, the sum of $500,000, also charged to income, was added to the reserve.

(6) Plant expansion costs, amounting to $285,000, for the manufacture of a postwar product unlike anything the company had previously put out, were charged against the rehabilitation reserve during the year 1957–58.

(7) The fire insurance reserve was increased during the year by a further provision of $10,000 charged to profit and loss.

(8) The fire insurance reserve was decreased by $2,000 — the cost, less $400 depreciation, of a building destroyed by fire on April 15, 1958. Additional costs arising out of the fire, and not yet appearing on the books, for injuries to persons are expected to aggregate $1,500.

(9) Surplus, as shown on last year's balance sheet, consisted of the value, ten years ago, of a donated plant site, amounting to $134,000; gains of $6,300 from the purchase and the sale in 1953 of 2,000 shares of treasury preferred stock; and undistributed earnings of $2,530,700.

(10) During the past year, charges for the dividend in no-par common stock, for the cash dividend, and for an adjustment of $4,100 in the previous year's tax liability reduced the account to $2,612,900.

(11) Book net income tor the year, after deducting reserve provisions, amounted to $222,500.

*Instructions:* (1) Prepare a work sheet and brief notes or adjusting entries that will indicate and explain the changes that you would recommend.

(2) Prepare the capital stock, surplus, and reserve sections of the balance sheet as of April 30, 1958, as they should be presented. (A.I.C.P.A. adapted)

**23-12.** The balance sheet of a corporation shows $200,000 capital stock, consisting of 2,000 shares of $100 each, and a surplus of $150,000. An audit of the accounts reveals that the treasurer is $40,000 short in his accounts and has concealed this by adding the amount to the inventory. He owns 400 shares of the company's stock and in settlement of the shortage offers this stock at its book value. The offer is accepted; the company pays him the excess value and distributes the 400 shares thus acquired to the other shareholders.

*Instructions:* (1) What amount should the company pay him?

(2) By what journal entries should the foregoing transactions be recorded?

(3) What is the company's capital and surplus after the above distribution?

(4) What would be done if the company had had a deficit of $50,000 and the 400 shares had been accepted at par? (A.I.C.P.A. adapted)

**23-13.** You have been engaged to audit the books of The Keystone Company as of December 31, 1958. A summary of the general ledger accounts is presented on page 762. Transactions summarized in the accounts are listed below and on pages 763 and 764.

SUMMARY OF TRANSACTIONS RECORDED DURING THE YEAR

(a) Accounts Receivable.................................... 190,000
 Sales.................................................... 
  Sales on account.           190,000

(b) Cash.................................................... 181,000
 Accounts Receivable.................................... 
 Recoveries of Accounts Charged Off in Prior Years......   180,000
  Cash collections from accounts.      1,000

(c) Purchases............................................. 140,000
 Accounts Payable....................................... 12,000
 Cash................................................... 
  Purchases for the year and payment of the opening balance of accounts payable.   152,000

(d) Prepaid Expenses...................................... 2,000
 Expenses............................................... 
  Net change in prepaid expenses during the year.   2,000

(e) Expenses.............................................. 24,000
 Interest on Bonds...................................... 6,000
 Life Insurance — Company President.................... 1,000
 Cash...................................................
  Disbursement for operating expenses, bond interest (including interest deposited with trustee) and life insurance premium.   31,000

(f) Investment in Lacker Co.............................. 30,000
 U. S. Tax Notes........................................ 2,000
 Marketable Securities.................................. 10,000
 Cash...................................................
  Disbursement on January 1, 1958 for stock of Lacker Company, tax notes and marketable securities.   42,000

(g) Cash.................................................. 205,000
 Bonds Payable.......................................... 
 Unamortized Bond Discount..............................   200,000
  Issuance for cash on January 1, 1958 of $200,000 of 3% twenty-year bonds at $102.50.   5,000

(h) Bonds Payable......................................... 100,000
 Unamortized Bond Discount.............................. 2,000
 Cash...................................................
  Redemption at $102 on January 1, 1958 of the outstanding issue of 5% bonds which were due January 1, 1963.   102,000

(i) Accounts Receivable................................... 5,000
 Cash...................................................
  Cash advance to the company president.   5,000

(j) Cash.................................................. 40,000
 Common Stock........................................... 
 Surplus................................................   10,000
  Issue for cash on June 30, 1958 of 10,000 shares of no-par common stock at $4 per share. (See comment under "Additional Information, Item 3.")   30,000

(k) Treasury Stock........................................ 7,000
 Cash...................................................
  Purchase on July 31, 1958 of 2,000 shares of the company's own common stock at $3.50 per share.   7,000

(l) Cash.................................................. 4,000
 Treasury Stock.........................................
  Sale at $4 per share on August 31, 1958 of 1,000 shares of the stock reacquired on July 31, 1958. (See Item k above.)   4,000

| Account | Ledger Balances 12/31/57 Debit | Credit | Summary of Transactions Debit | | Credit | | Ledger Balances 12/31/58 Debit | Credit |
|---|---|---|---|---|---|---|---|---|
| Cash............... | $ 8,000 | | (b) $ 181,000 | (c) | $ 152,000 | | | |
| | | | (g) 205,000 | (e) | 31,000 | | | |
| | | | (j) 40,000 | (f) | 42,000 | | | |
| | | | (l) 4,000 | (h) | 102,000 | | | |
| | | | (r) 10,000 | (i) | 5,000 | | | |
| | | | | (k) | 7,000 | | | |
| | | | | (m) | 9,000 | | | |
| | | | | (n) | 10,000 | | | |
| | | | | (t) | 30,000 | | | |
| | | | | (w) | 3,000 | | $ 57,000 | |
| Accounts receivable.... | 17,000 | | (a) 190,000 | (b) | 180,000 | | | |
| | | | (i) 5,000 | | | | | |
| | | | (t) 15,000 | | | | 47,000 | |
| Inventory............. | 20,000 | | (q) 30,000 | | | | 50,000 | |
| U. S. tax notes......... | | | (f) 2,000 | | | | 2,000 | |
| Marketable securities... | 3,000 | | (f) 10,000 | | | | 13,000 | |
| Life insurance — company president....... | 7,000 | | (e) 1,000 | | | | 8,000 | |
| Investment in Lacker Co. (90% owned)..... | | | (f) 30,000 | | | | 30,000 | |
| Land................. | 10,000 | | | | | | 10,000 | |
| Buildings............. | 200,000 | | | | | | 200,000 | |
| Accumulated depreciation — buildings..... | | $ 50,000 | | (o) | 4,000 | | | $ 54,000 |
| Machinery............ | 100,000 | | (n) 10,000 | | | | 110,000 | |
| Accumulated depreciation — machinery.... | | 50,000 | | (o) | 11,000 | | | 61,000 |
| Goodwill............. | | | (t) 14,000 | (u) | 14,000 | | | |
| Unamortized bond discount............... | 3,000 | | (h) 2,000 | (g) | 5,000 | | | |
| Prepaid expenses....... | 1,000 | | (d) 2,000 | | | | 3,000 | |
| Accounts payable....... | | 12,000 | (c) 12,000 | (p) | 20,000 | | | 20,000 |
| Reserve for 1957 and 1958 income taxes.... | | 15,000 | (m) 9,000 | | | | | 2,200 |
| | | | (z) 3,800 | | | | | |
| Reserve for possible inventory price declines. | | 5,000 | | (v) | 5,000 | | | 10,000 |
| Bonds payable ......... | | 100,000 | (h) 100,000 | (g) | 200,000 | | | 200,000 |
| Reserve for losses....... | | 10,000 | (u) 14,000 | (v) | 15,000 | | | 17,300 |
| | | | (w) 3,000 | (y) | 5,500 | | | |
| | | | | (z) | 3,800 | | | |
| | | | | (s) | 475 | | | 2,475 |
| Reserve for bad accounts | | 2,000 | | (j) | 10,000 | | | |
| Common stock......... | | 30,000 | | (x) | 4,000 | | | 44,000 |
| | | | | (j) | 30,000 | | | 121,000 |
| Surplus.............. | | 95,000 | (x) 4,000 | (l) | 4,000 | | | |
| Treasury stock......... | | | (k) 7,000 | | | | 3,100 | |
| | | | (x) 100 | | | | | |
| Sales................ | | | | (a) | 190,000 | | | 190,000 |
| Purchases............ | | | (c) 140,000 | (q) | 30,000 | | | |
| | | | (p) 20,000 | | | | | |
| | | | (t) 1,000 | | | | | |
| | | | (v) 5,000 | | | | 136,000 | |
| Expenses............. | | | (e) 24,000 | (d) | 2,000 | | | |
| | | | (v) 15,000 | | | | 37,000 | |
| Depreciation expense... | | | (o) 15,000 | | | | | |
| | | | (y) 5,500 | | | | 20,500 | |
| Bad debt expense....... | | | (s) 475 | | | | 475 | |
| Recoveries of accounts charged off in prior years............... | | | | (b) | 1,000 | | | 1,000 |
| Dividend and interest income............. | | | | (r) | 10,000 | | | |
| | | | | (x) | 100 | | | 10,100 |
| Interest on bonds....... | | | (e) 6,000 | | | | 6,000 | |
| | $369,000 | $369,000 | $1,135,875 | | $1,135,875 | | $733,075 | $733,075 |

(m) Reserve for 1957 Income Taxes.........................   9,000
    Cash.................................................        9,000
      Payment of 1957 income taxes in full.

(n) Machinery..........................................  10,000
    Cash.................................................       10,000
      Payment for machinery purchased on January 2, 1958
      together with $200 freight and $800 installation cost.

(o) Depreciation Expense................................  15,000
    Accumulated Depreciation — Buildings ...............        4,000
    Accumulated Depreciation — Machinery...............       11,000
      Depreciation expense for the year at the rate of 10% on
      machinery and 2% on buildings.

(p) Purchases..........................................  20,000
    Accounts Payable....................................       20,000
      Set up the unrecorded purchases and accounts payable at
      December 31, 1958.

(q) Inventory..........................................  30,000
    Purchases...........................................       30,000
      To adjust the inventory balance as of December 31, 1957
      to the correct balance as of December 31, 1958.

(r) Cash...............................................  10,000
    Dividend and Interest Income........................       10,000
      Interest and dividend collected. The dividend of $9,000
      was from Lacker Company. It was declared on Janu-
      ary 10, 1958. The surplus accounts of Lacker Company
      decreased $10,000 during the year 1958.

(s) Bad Debt Expense...................................     475
    Reserve for Bad Accounts............................          475
      Provision for estimated loss on accounts receivable. The
      company bases its provision on ¼ of 1% of sales under
      the theory that the net uncollectible receivables (charge-
      offs less recoveries) arising in each year will approximate
      that amount.

(t) Accounts Receivable.................................  15,000
    Purchases...........................................   1,000
    Goodwill............................................  14,000
    Cash.................................................       30,000
      On July 1, 1958, the company purchased the inventory
      and receivables of the Cole Sales Co. at a cost of $30,000.
      The purchase was made primarily to obtain an exclusive
      agency having seven years of remaining life. The
      inventory obtained in the purchase was valued at
      $1,000 and the receivables, all of which were collectible,
      amounted to $15,000. (Also see the following item.)

(u) Reserve for Losses..................................  14,000
    Goodwill............................................       14,000
      The $14,000 set up as goodwill as a result of the purchase
      of the business of the Cole Sales Co. was written off to
      reserve for losses "in order to avoid showing goodwill on
      the balance sheet."

(v) Expenses...........................................  15,000
    Purchases...........................................   5,000
    Reserve for Possible Inventory Price Declines..........        5,000
    Reserve for Losses..................................       15,000
      The directors decided that, in view of the general business
      uncertainty, the reserve for losses and the reserve for
      possible inventory price decline should be increased.
      These provisions were charged to expense of the year, the
      inventory provision being charged to purchases and the
      loss provision to expenses.

(w) Reserve for Losses..................................   3,000
    Cash.................................................        3,000
      Payment to B. Walter, an employee, in settlement of his
      claim for personal injury as a result of an accident on
      March 2, 1958. The charge was to reserve for losses.

(x) Surplus................................................. 4,000
Treasury Stock....................................... 100
    Common Stock....................................... 4,000
    Dividend and Interest Income........................ 100
      A stock dividend of 10% was declared and paid on September 1, 1958. The stock was credited to capital stock account at $1 per share.

(y) Depreciation Expense.................................. 5,500
Reserve for Losses................................... 5,500
      The board of directors approved the following action applicable to 1958 accounts: "In view of the 50% rise in machinery prices over average prices at which the company acquired its machinery now in use, it is suggested that depreciation on machinery should be increased 50%, with the credit made to reserve for losses rather than to the depreciation reserve in order to keep the latter account on a cost basis"

(z) Reserve for 1957 and 1958 Income Taxes.................. 3,800
Reserve for Losses................................... 3,800
      The reserve for income taxes was debited $3,800 with a corresponding credit to reserve for losses in order to reduce the reserve for income taxes down to the estimated liability as of the close of 1958. (The amount of $2,200 liability may be assumed to be the correct liability for the purpose of this solution even though you may adjust net profit.)

Additional information was developed during the course of your audit (which is the first audit that the company has ever had) as follows:

(1) The cash surrender value of life insurance was $2,000 on December 31, 1957, and $2,500 on December 31, 1958.

(2) On December 31, 1958, the "bid" price of the bonds included under marketable securities was $13,500 and the "ask" price was $14,000.

(3) Common stock has no par value. The original issue of 30,000 shares was at $2 per share. The company set up each share at $1 per share in the stock account in order to have the account show the number of shares outstanding. The board of directors approved this practice.

(4) The analysis of surplus shows the following summary of transactions since inception of the company:

Amount received from issuance of 30,000 shares of common stock at $2 per share above the amount credited to the capital stock account......................... $ 30,000
Net operating profits................................ 90,000

Total......................................... $120,000
Dividends paid....................................... 25,000

Balance December 31, 1957..................... $ 95,000

*Instructions:* Prepare working papers that show in detail "Ledger Balance 12/31/58," "Audit Adjustments," "Profit and Loss for Year," and "Balance Sheet 12/31/58." Columns for "Surplus Changes" may be included, or entries to "Surplus" may be shown in the other columns provided such entries are clearly identified as applicable to "Surplus." Key all audit adjustments and in journal form present the adjusting entry together with a brief explanation of the purpose of or the reason for the entry. *There are no posting errors or mathematical errors in the trial balances or in the transactions for the year.* (A.I.C.P.A. adapted)

# Chapter 24

# STATEMENTS
# FROM INCOMPLETE RECORDS

**SINGLE-ENTRY BOOKKEEPING** The procedures leading to the preparation of financial statements as illustrated in the preceding chapters are those required in the adoption of a *double-entry system*. This is the characteristic system employed in practice and requires the analysis of each transaction in terms of changes in the fundamental accounting equation, Assets = Liabilities + Proprietorship.

Double-entry records may not be found in relatively small organizations, particularly sole proprietorships, where the volume of business does not warrant employment of a bookkeeper. For such small units the owner of the business usually maintains informal records and employs an accountant to prepare financial statements and income tax returns. When transactions are not analyzed and recorded in terms of debits and credits, the system employed is known as *single entry*. Single-entry procedures may vary from a narrative of transactions recorded in a single journal, called a *daybook*, to a relatively complete set of journals, and a ledger providing accounts for all significant items. All of the variations of single-entry bookkeeping encountered in practice cannot be described here. Differences in procedures depend upon the needs of the organization and the originality and fancy of the person establishing or maintaining the system.

**RECORDS IN SINGLE-ENTRY BOOKKEEPING** A characteristic single-entry system consists of the following bookkeeping records: (1) a daybook or general journal, (2) a cashbook, and (3) ledger accounts showing debtor and creditor balances. The simplest form of single-entry bookkeeping consists of the daybook in which transactions are described in chronological order. No accounts are kept. At the other extreme of single-entry procedures, a number of journals may be maintained, such as cash journals, sales and purchases journals, returns and allowances journals, and a general journal. Ledger accounts may be kept for debtors, creditors, and the proprietor, as well as for certain other significant items such as sales, purchases, and expenses. The practice, however, falls short of standard double-entry bookkeeping unless each transaction is analyzed and recorded in terms of debit and credit and a trial balance can be drawn up at the end of the period.

Single-entry procedures commonly take the following form. A cashbook is maintained that shows all transactions affecting cash. Instead of naming accounts to be debited or credited as a result of cash receipts and disbursements, a description of the transaction is offered. Transactions not shown in the cashbook are recorded in a daybook in descriptive form. Whenever the account of a debtor, a creditor, or the proprietor is affected, attention is directed to the need for posting by indicating "dr" or "cr" before the amount. Offsetting debits or credits are not shown, since accounts in the ledger are maintained only for customers, creditors, and the owner. No summary of nominal items or of asset and liability balances is prepared other than those with debtors and creditors.

In the absence of records offering a complete summary of transactions, the preparation of accurate statements at the end of an operating period raises certain problems. These are discussed in the sections that follow.

**BALANCE SHEET PREPARATION**        Since the ledger normally fails to show assets and liabilities other than receivables and payables, it is necessary to refer to other sources of information in the determination of the remaining balance sheet items. Cash is reported at the balance shown in the cashbook after this figure has been reconciled with the totals of cash on hand and on deposit with the bank. Receivables and payables are summarized from the accounts maintained with debtors and creditors. Merchandise and supplies balances are found by taking inventories. Past statements, cash records, and other documents are reviewed in determining the book values of depreciable assets. Other assets and liabilities, including accrued and prepaid items, are determined by a review of the records, including invoices, documents, and other available sources offering evidence or information concerning transactions of the past, present, and future. Proprietorship in double-entry bookkeeping represents a balance arrived at by combining beginning capital, additional investments and withdrawals, and income and expense account balances; in single-entry bookkeeping, it is simply a residual amount, or the total of the values assigned to assets less the total of the liability items.

**DETERMINATION OF NET INCOME OR LOSS FROM COMPARATIVE BALANCE SHEETS**        In the absence of income and expense accounts, the net income or loss for a fiscal period may be determined by finding the difference between beginning and ending capitals and adjusting this difference by proprietary investments or withdrawals for the period.

Beginning and ending capital balances are taken from the balance sheets prepared at the end of the previous period and at the end of the current period. Investments and withdrawals are ascertained from capital and drawing accounts maintained in the ledger, or in the absence of these, from the cashbook and other memorandum records.

To illustrate the calculation of the net income or loss, assume that comparative balance sheets show capitals as follows: on January 1, $7,500; on December 31, $10,000. In the absence of investments or withdrawals by the proprietor, it must be concluded that the net income for the year was $2,500. However, assume that the proprietor has invested $1,000 and withdrawn $3,000 during the year; the net income would then be calculated as follows:

| | | |
|---|---:|---:|
| Capital, December 31 | | $10,000 |
| Capital, January 1 | | 7,500 |
| Net increase in capital | | $ 2,500 |
| Add excess of proprietor's withdrawals over investments: | | |
| Withdrawals | $3,000 | |
| Investments | 1,000 | 2,000 |
| Net income for year | | $ 4,500 |

An excess of investments over withdrawals would be subtracted from the net increase in capital in arriving at the net income.

**PREPARATION OF INCOME STATEMENT**   A summary showing the net income or loss calculated from comparative capital balances is generally inadequate for the business unit. The owner needs a detailed statement of operations in viewing past success or failure and in planning future activities. Creditors may insist upon a detailed statement of operations. In addition, governmental agencies require a listing of income and expense items for income tax purposes.

An itemized income statement can be prepared by (1) rewriting transactions in double-entry form or (2) analyzing cash receipts and disbursements together with asset and liability changes. Obviously, little or nothing is saved by the adoption of a single-entry as compared with a double-entry system if transactions are to be rewritten in double-entry form and posted to accounts in the development of income and expense data. When the second procedure is followed, an analysis and summary of all cash receipts and disbursements is required, unless such a summary is already available from cash journals with special analysis columns. Cash receipts must be classified as: (1) proceeds from cash sales, (2) receipts of other income items, (3) collections on customers' accounts, (4) proceeds from the sale of assets other than merchandise,

(5) amounts borrowed, and (6) investments by owners. Disbursements are classified as (1) payments on cash purchases of merchandise, (2) payments of other expense items, (3) payments on trade creditors' accounts, (4) payments for assets other than merchandise, (5) payments of loans, and (6) withdrawals by owners. This information, together with balance sheet data, is used in the preparation of the income statement. The procedures that are employed in determining the various income and expense balances are explained in the section that follows.

*Sales.* The figure to be reported for sales consists of the total of cash sales and sales on account. Sales are calculated from the cash receipts analysis and comparative balance sheet data as follows:

SALES

| | | |
|---|---:|---:|
| Cash sales............................................ | | $ 7,500 |
| Sales on account: | | |
| Notes and accounts receivable on hand at the end of the period.................................... | $1,500 | |
| Collections on notes and accounts receivable during the period.................................... | 3,000 | |
| | $4,500 | |
| Deduct notes and accounts receivable on hand at the beginning of the period.................... | 2,000 | 2,500 |
| Sales for the period ................................ | | $10,000 |

Notes and accounts receivable in the foregoing tabulation would be limited to those arising from sales of merchandise.

*Cost of Goods Sold.* The inventory shown on the balance sheet prepared at the end of the preceding fiscal period is reported on the income statement as the beginning inventory.

Purchases consist of cash purchases and purchases on account. Purchases are calculated from the cash payments analysis and comparative balance sheet data as follows:

PURCHASES

| | | |
|---|---:|---:|
| Cash purchases...................................... | | $1,500 |
| Purchases on account: | | |
| Notes and accounts payable at the end of the period................................................ | $2,000 | |
| Payments on notes and accounts payable during the period........................................ | 5,000 | |
| | $7,000 | |
| Deduct notes and accounts payable at the beginning of the period.................................... | 3,000 | 4,000 |
| Purchases for the period............................ | | $5,500 |

Notes and accounts payable in the foregoing tabulation would be limited to those arising from purchases of merchandise.

The ending inventory is reported on the income statement at the figure shown on the balance sheet prepared at the close of the current period. Beginning and ending inventories and purchases provide the data for calculating the cost of goods sold for the period.

*Expense Items.* An expense balance is computed from the analysis of cash payments and comparative balance sheet data. The calculation of an expense item may be made as follows:

EXPENSE ITEM (Sales Salaries, Interest Expense, etc.)

| | | |
|---|---:|---:|
| Cash payments during the period representing expense | | $1,000 |
| Add amounts not included in payments but chargeable to current period: | | |
|     Amount prepaid at the beginning of the period.... | $250 | |
|     Amount accrued at the end of the period......... | 150 | 400 |
| | | $1,400 |
| Deduct amounts included in payments but not chargeable to current period: | | |
|     Amount prepaid at the end of the period....... | $200 | |
|     Amount accrued at the beginning of the period.. | 100 | 300 |
| Expense for the period.......................... | | $1,100 |

*Income Items.* An income balance is calculated from the cash receipts analysis and comparative balance sheet data. The calculation of an income item may be made as follows:

INCOME ITEM (Rental Income, Interest Income, etc.)

| | | |
|---|---:|---:|
| Cash receipts during the period representing income..... | | $800 |
| Add amounts not included in receipts but to be credited to current period: | | |
|     Amount prepaid at the beginning of the period...... | $100 | |
|     Amount accrued at the end of the period......... | 50 | 150 |
| | | $950 |
| Deduct amounts included in receipts but not to be credited to current period: | | |
|     Amount prepaid at the end of the period......... | $200 | |
|     Amount accrued at the beginning of the period.... | 150 | 350 |
| Income for the period............................ | | $600 |

*Profit and Loss Items Requiring Special Analysis.* The determination of certain profit and loss items, such as losses from bad debts, sales discounts, and purchases discounts, requires special data in addition to the information offered by cash records and comparative balance sheets. For example, assume sales data as follows:

Data from cash records:

| | |
|---|---:|
| Cash sales......................................... | $10,000 |
| Collections on accounts receivable arising from sales...... | 42,000 |

Data from balance sheets:

| | |
|---|---:|
| Accounts receivable at the beginning of the period....... | 14,300 |
| Accounts receivable at the end of the period............ | 12,500 |

Supplementary data from special analysis of records:

| | |
|---|---:|
| Accounts written off during the period.................. | 600 |
| Sales discounts allowed customers during the period...... | 850 |
| Sales returns and allowances.......................... | 300 |

The supplementary data indicate that a loss from bad debts of $600, sales discounts of $850, and sales returns and allowances of $300 are to be recognized. These three amounts must be added to cash collections in arriving at gross sales, since there must have been sales equivalent to the reductions in accounts receivable from these sources. The gross sales for the period are calculated as follows:

SALES

| | | |
|---|---:|---:|
| Cash sales.................................... | | $10,000 |
| Sales on account: | | |
| Accounts receivable on hand at the end of the period..................................... | $12,500 | |
| Collections on accounts receivable during the period.................................... | 42,000 | |
| Accounts receivable written off during the period.................................... | 600 | |
| Accounts receivable reduced by discounts during the period............................. | 850 | |
| Accounts receivable reduced by sales returns and allowances during the period.............. | 300 | |
| | $56,250 | |
| Deduct accounts receivable on hand at the beginning of the period.................... | 14,300 | 41,950 |
| Gross sales for the period .................... | | $51,950 |

It should be noted that failure to recognize data relating to bad debts, sales discounts, and sales returns and allowances, will have no effect upon the net income figure. Failure to recognize these balances would be counterbalanced by an understatement in gross sales.

When purchases discounts and purchases returns and allowances have been applied on the payment of purchases invoices, the treatment is similar to that illustrated for sales discounts and sales returns and allowances. The purchases balance is increased by the total of purchases discounts and purchases returns and allowances since there must have been purchases equivalent to the reduction in the accounts payable resulting from discounts and returns and allowances.

The charge for depreciation or amortization to be recognized on the income statement requires special analysis of balance sheet as well as cash payments data. For example, assume no acquisition or disposal of property during the period and beginning and ending store furniture balances of $30,000 and $28,500. Depreciation is reported at $1,500, the net decrease in the store furniture account. Assume, however, that the following information is assembled at the end of a fiscal period:

Data from cash records:

| | |
|---|---:|
| Payments for store furniture, including payments on notes arising from acquisition of store furniture........... | $ 2,500 |

Data from balance sheets:

| | |
|---|---:|
| Store furniture at the beginning of the period........... | 32,000 |
| Store furniture at the end of the period................ | 34,200 |
| Installment notes payable arising from acquisition of store furniture........................................ | 4,000 |

Depreciation is calculated as follows:

DEPRECIATION

| | | |
|---|---:|---:|
| Balance of store furniture at the beginning of the period..................................... | | $32,000 |
| Add acquisitions of store furniture: | | |
| Cash paid on acquisition of store furniture....... | $2,500 | |
| Amount owed at the end of the period on acquisition of store furniture..................... | 4,000 | 6,500 |
| Balance of store furniture before depreciation...... | | $38,500 |
| Deduct balance of store furniture at the end of the period..................................... | | 34,200 |
| Depreciation of store furniture for period......... | | $ 4,300 |

**PREPARATION OF STATEMENTS FROM SINGLE-ENTRY RECORDS ILLUSTRATED**    The preparation from single-entry records of (1) a balance sheet, (2) a summary of profit or loss by analysis of capital changes, and (3) an income statement reporting income and expense detail is illustrated in the example that follows. Assume that Edwin C. Hall does not maintain double-entry records. Balance sheet data, analyses of cash receipts and disbursements, and supplementary data required in the development of financial statements from the single-entry data are assembled at the end of 1958 as shown below and on the next page.

Supplementary data developed from an analysis of business papers include the following:

(1) Purchases discounts of $600 were received on the payment of creditors invoices during the year. Sales returns and allowances amounted to $480.

| ASSETS | JANUARY 1 1958 | DECEMBER 31 1958 |
|---|---|---|
| Cash...................................... | $ 4,000 | $ 8,500 |
| Notes Receivable ...................... | 1,000 | 1,500 |
| Accounts Receivable.................... | 5,000 | 3,500 |
| Accrued Interest Income................ | 60 | 80 |
| Merchandise Inventory.................. | 14,000 | 15,000 |
| Supplies on Hand ...................... | 400 | 150 |
| Prepaid Interest Expense............... | — | 30 |
| Furniture and Fixtures, cost less depreciation............................... | 3,600 | 5,650 |

| LIABILITIES | | |
|---|---|---|
| Notes Payable.......................... | — | 4,000 |
| Accounts Payable....................... | 5,000 | 6,500 |
| Accrued Salaries....................... | 100 | 50 |
| Rentals Received in Advance............ | 100 | 150 |

An analysis of the cash records discloses the following:

| Balance, January 1, 1958...................... | | $ 4,000 |
|---|---|---|

Receipts:

| | | |
|---|---|---|
| Cash sales................................ | $ 9,200 | |
| On accounts and notes receivable arising from sales..................................... | 48,000 | |
| From rental of store space................... | 1,550 | |
| From interest on balance of cash on deposit..... | 50 | |
| From sale of furniture...................... | 350 | |
| From discounting of own notes at bank........ | 9,850 | 69,000 |
| | | $73,000 |

Disbursements:

| | | |
|---|---|---|
| On accounts payable arising from purchases..... | $40,000 | |
| For salaries............................... | 4,200 | |
| For rent.................................. | 4,400 | |
| For supplies.............................. | 200 | |
| On acquisition of furniture and fixtures......... | 3,500 | |
| For miscellaneous expense................... | 1,200 | |
| To bank on notes payable................... | 6,000 | |
| Proprietor's withdrawals.................... | 5,000 | 64,500 |
| Balance, December 31, 1958.................. | | $ 8,500 |

(2) Proceeds from the sale of furniture and fixtures at the beginning of the year were $350 as reported in cash receipts. The furniture and fixtures that were sold had an original cost of $1,600 and were 50 per cent depreciated.

(3) Proceeds from bank loans during the year on which notes were issued were $9,850 as reported under cash receipts. The face values of the notes were $10,000, $150 being deducted by the bank for interest. Notes of $6,000 were paid during the year.

A balance sheet prepared from the foregoing data on December 31, 1958, appears below:

EDWIN C. HALL
BALANCE SHEET
DECEMBER 31, 1958

| ASSETS | | | LIABILITIES AND PROPRIETORSHIP | | |
|---|---|---|---|---|---|
| Current assets: | | | Current liabilities: | | |
| Cash............. | $ 8,500 | | Notes payable...... | $ 4,000 | |
| Notes receivable.... | 1,500 | | Accounts payable... | 6,500 | |
| Accounts receivable. | 3,500 | | Accrued salaries.... | 50 | $10,550 |
| Accrued interest income........... | 80 | | | | |
| | | | Deferred revenues: | | |
| Merchandise inventory............ | 15,000 | | Rentals received in advance........ | | 150 |
| Supplies on hand... | 150 | | | | |
| Prepaid interest expense........ | 30 | $28,760 | Total liabilities....... | | $10,700 |
| | | | Proprietorship: | | |
| | | | E. C. Hall, Capital.. | | 23,710 |
| Furniture and fixtures (net)............. | | 5,650 | | | |
| Total assets.......... | | $34,410 | Total liabilities and proprietorship...... | | $34,410 |

The results from operations can be determined by the preparation of a summary of changes in capital as follows:

EDWIN C. HALL
SUMMARY OF CHANGES IN CAPITAL
FOR YEAR ENDED DECEMBER 31, 1958

| | |
|---|---|
| Edwin C. Hall, Capital, December 31, 1958.............. | $23,710 |
| Edwin C. Hall, Capital, January 1, 1958*............... | 22,860 |
| Net increase in capital................................ | $   850 |
| Add proprietor's withdrawals during year............... | 5,000 |
| Net income for year................................... | $ 5,850 |

| | |
|---|---|
| *Capital, January 1, is calculated as follows: | |
| Assets, January 1.......................... | $28,060 |
| Less liabilities, January 1.................... | 5,200 |
| Capital, January 1........................ | $22,860 |

An income statement with income and expense detail is shown on page 774. This is followed by schedules in support of the balances reported on the income statement.

## EDWIN C. HALL
### INCOME STATEMENT
### FOR YEAR ENDED DECEMBER 31, 1958

| | | | | |
|---|---|---|---:|---:|
| Gross sales | (A) | | $56,680 | |
| Less: Sales return and allowances | (A-1) | | 480 | $56,200 |
| Cost of goods sold: | | | | |
| Merchandise inventory, January 1 | | | $14,000 | |
| Purchases | (B) | $42,100 | | |
| Less: Purchases discounts | (B-1) | 600 | 41,500 | |
| Goods available for sale | | | $55,500 | |
| Less: Merchandise inventory, December 31 | | | 15,000 | |
| Cost of goods sold | | | | 40,500 |
| Gross profit on sales | | | | $15,700 |
| Operating expenses: | | | | |
| Salaries | (C) | $ 4,150 | | |
| Rent | (D) | 4,400 | | |
| Supplies used | (E) | 450 | | |
| Depreciation of furniture and fixtures | (F) | 650 | | |
| Miscellaneous expense | (G) | 1,200 | | |
| Total operating expenses | | | | 10,850 |
| Net profit from operations | | | | $ 4,850 |
| Other income and expense: | | | | |
| Other income: | | | | |
| Interest income | (H) | $ 70 | | |
| Rental income | (I) | 1,500 | | |
| | | $ 1,570 | | |
| Other expense: | | | | |
| Interest expense | (J) | 120 | | |
| Add excess of other income over other expense | | | | 1,450 |
| Net income | | | | $ 6,300 |
| Extraordinary loss: | | | | |
| Loss on sale of furniture and fixtures | (K) | | | 450 |
| Net income and extraordinary items | | | | $ 5,850 |

| | | |
|---|---:|---:|
| (A) Calculation of sales: | | |
| Cash sales | | $ 9,200 |
| Sales on account: | | |
| Notes and accounts receivable balances, December 31 | $ 5,000 | |
| Collections on notes and accounts during the year | 48,000 | |
| (A-1) Sales returns and allowances during the year | 480 | |
| | $53,480 | |
| Deduct notes and accounts receivable balances, January 1 | 6,000 | 47,480 |
| Gross sales for the year | | $56,680 |

(B)  Calculation of purchases:

Purchases on account:

| | |
|---|---:|
| Accounts payable balance, December 31....... | $ 6,500 |
| Payments on account during the year......... | 40,000 |

(B-1) Discounts allowed on accounts payable
during the year.......................... | 600

| | |
|---|---:|
| | $47,100 |
| Deduct accounts payable balance, January 1... | 5,000 |
| Gross purchases for the year ............... | $42,100 |

Calculation of operating expenses:

(C)  Salaries:

| | |
|---|---:|
| Payments for salaries during the year.............. | $4,200 |
| Add accrued salaries, December 31................ | 50 |
| | $4,250 |
| Deduct accrued salaries, January 1................ | 100 |
| Salaries for the year........................... | $4,150 |

(D)  Rent:

| | |
|---|---:|
| Payments for rent during the year............... | 4,400 |

(E)  Supplies used:

| | |
|---|---:|
| Payments for supplies during the year................ | $200 |
| Add supplies on hand, January 1.................... | 400 |
| | $600 |
| Deduct supplies on hand, December 31............... | 150 |
| Supplies used during the year..................... | 450 |

(F)  Depreciation of furniture and fixtures:

Balance of furniture and fixtures on hand, January 1... $3,600
Add net increase in furniture and fixtures during the
year:

| | | |
|---|---:|---:|
| Furniture and fixture acquisition........ | $3,500 | |
| Furniture and fixture disposal (depreciated value) ...................... | 800 | $2,700 |
| | | $6,300 |
| Deduct balance of furniture and fixtures on hand, December 31..................................... | | 5,650 |
| Depreciation of furniture and fixtures for the year.. | | 650 |

(G)  Miscellaneous expense:

| | |
|---|---:|
| Payments for miscellaneous expense during the year..... | 1,200 |
| Total operating expenses for the year.............. | $10,850 |

(H) Calculation of interest income:

| | | |
|---|---:|---:|
| Interest received during the year..................... | $ 50 | |
| Add accrued interest income, December 31........... | 80 | |
| | $130 | |
| Deduct accrued interest income, January 1........... | 60 | |
| Total interest income for the year.................. | | $ 70 |

(I) Calculation of rental income:

| | | |
|---|---:|---:|
| Rentals received during the year..................... | $1,550 | |
| Add rentals received in advance, January 1........... | 100 | |
| | $1,650 | |
| Deduct rentals received in advance, December 31...... | 150 | |
| Total rental income for the year.................. | | $1,500 |

(J) Calculation of interest expense:

Interest charges on notes discounted:

| | | | |
|---|---:|---:|---:|
| Face value of notes payable discounted... | $10,000 | | |
| Proceeds from notes.................. | 9,850 | | |
| Interest charges for the year .................... | | $150 | |
| Deduct prepaid interest expense, December 31.......... | | 30 | |
| Total interest expense for the year ................ | | | $120 |

(K) Calculation of loss on sale of furniture and fixtures:

| | | |
|---|---:|---:|
| Depreciated value of furniture and fixtures sold......... | $800 | |
| Proceeds from sale................................ | 350 | |
| Loss on sale of furniture and fixtures.............. | | $450 |

**CHANGE FROM SINGLE ENTRY TO DOUBLE ENTRY**     With the need for adequate accounting records as a result of an increase in the number as well as the complexity of transactions, it often becomes necessary to convert single-entry bookkeeping records into a double-entry system. Such a change may be effected by first drawing up a balance sheet as of the date of change. This statement is used as the basis for a journal entry in compound form with debits to all of the asset accounts and credits to asset allowances, liability, and proprietorship accounts. If additional accounts are to be added to an incomplete ledger already in use, folio check marks are made opposite balances that already appear in the ledger; accounts are opened and balances recorded for those items not checked. If new books are to be used, accounts are opened and balances are recorded for all of the items listed in the opening journal entry.

**USE OF SINGLE-ENTRY BOOKKEEPING** Single entry is discussed here because it represents a system that the accountant frequently encounters when he is called upon to prepare financial statements, to audit books and records, and to prepare government informational reports and income tax returns. Single-entry systems are employed because of their simplicity and economy by relatively small businesses, nonprofit organizations, and persons acting in a fiduciary capacity such as estate executors and trust custodians. A great many individuals maintain records of personal transactions so that financial statements and income tax returns may be prepared satisfactorily, but they seldom maintain these records on a double-entry basis. In all such instances the type of analysis suggested in this chapter is required in developing financial statements.

The adoption of single-entry bookkeeping cannot be recommended for any but the very simplest types of organization. Among the intrinsic shortcomings of single-entry bookkeeping are the following:

(1) In the absence of a record of transactions in terms of debit and credit, preparation of a trial balance that offers a check on the mathematical accuracy of posting is not available.

(2) In the absence of accounts for most of the assets and liabilities, preparation of the balance sheet from miscellaneous sources and memoranda may result in omissions and misstatements.

(3) Without nominal accounts, detailed analysis of transactions is necessary in obtaining operating data. Misstatement of assets and liabilities, particularly the failure to report assets at properly depreciated or amortized balances, affects income and expense balances and may result in the material misstatement of profit and loss.

(4) There is failure to provide a centralized and co-ordinated accounting system subject to internal check and available for satisfactory and convenient audit by public and governmental auditors.

## QUESTIONS

**1.** Distinguish between single-entry and double-entry bookkeeping.

**2.** Describe the records and the nature of recording under typical single-entry bookkeeping.

**3.** What are the sources of information for balance sheet items when the single-entry plan is followed?

**4.** John Day has his assets appraised at the end of each year and draws up a balance sheet using such appraisal values. He then calculates the change in capital for the year and adjusts this for investments and withdrawals in arriving at the profit or the loss for the year. In your opinion, does this procedure provide a satisfactory measurement of profit and loss?

**5.** State how each of the following items is calculated in the preparation of an income statement when single-entry bookkeeping and the accrual basis are followed:

    (a) Merchandise sales.
    (b) Merchandise purchases.
    (c) Depreciation on equipment.
    (d) Sales salaries.

    (e) Insurance expense.
    (f) Interest income.
    (g) Rental income.
    (h) Taxes.

**6.** "Single-entry bookkeeping is obsolete and has no place in modern business." Do you agree? Explain.

**7.** Give the disadvantages of single-entry bookkeeping as compared with double-entry bookkeeping.

**8.** Describe the procedure to be followed in changing from a single-entry system to double entry.

## EXERCISES

**1.** From the following data calculate the interest income balance to be reported on the income statement for the month of December:

|  | DECEMBER 1 | DECEMBER 31 |
|---|---|---|
| Unearned Interest Income.............. | $20 | $200 |
| Accrued Interest Income................ | 40 | 60 |

Interest collections during December were $300.

**2.** From the following data, calculate the interest expense balance to be reported on the income statement for the month of December:

|  | DECEMBER 1 | DECEMBER 31 |
|---|---|---|
| Prepaid Interest Expense................ | $20 | $15 |
| Accrued Interest Expense................ | 30 | 10 |

Disbursements for interest during December were $80.

**3.** Interest Income is reported on the income statement for 1958 at $750. Balance sheet data relating to interest income are as follows:

|  | JAN. 1, 1958 | DEC. 31, 1958 |
|---|---|---|
| Unearned Interest Income........... | $ 25 | $ 10 |
| Accrued Interest Income............ | 260 | 220 |

How much cash was collected during 1958 representing interest income?

**4.** Interest Expense is reported on the income statement for 1958 at $1,850. Balance sheet data relating to interest expense are as follows:

|  | JAN. 1, 1958 | DEC. 31, 1958 |
|---|---|---|
| Prepaid Interest Expense............ | $ 45 | $ 60 |
| Accrued Interest Expense............ | 250 | 325 |

How much cash was paid out during 1958 representing interest expense?

**5.** On January 1 the capital of J. E. Clay was $4,800 and on January 31 his capital was $5,450. During the month Clay withdrew merchandise costing $150, and on January 25 he paid a $1,200 note payable of the business with interest at 6% for 3 months with a check drawn on his personal checking account. What was Clay's net income or loss for the month of January?

**6.** The Bates Manufacturing Company showed on its balance sheet on December 31, 1958, total capital of $119,800. During the year 1958 capital was affected by: (1) an adjustment to retained earnings for a $200 understatement of net income in 1957, (2) a dividend declared but not paid of $8,000, and (3) a net income for 1958 of $7,600. A capital stock figure of $100,000 remained unchanged during the year. What was the retained earnings balance on January 1, 1958?

**7.** Total accounts receivable for the Star Sales Company were as follows: on January 1, $5,000; on January 31, $4,700. In January $8,000 was collected on accounts, $600 was received for cash sales, accounts receivable of $400 were written off as uncollectible, and allowances on sales of $150 were made. What were the sales to be reported on the income statement for January?

**8.** The accounts payable balance for A. M. Jones on November 1 was $2,200; on November 30 the balance was $2,800. During the month $300 was paid for cash purchases, $450 was allowed on purchases returned, $5,600 was paid on accounts payable, and $200 was paid representing freight in. The inventory on November 1 was $1,000 and on November 30 was $1,200. What cost of sales information would be reported on the income statement for November?

**9.** The balance sheet for Kenneth Rhoads on December 31, 1958, is as follows:

KENNETH RHOADS
BALANCE SHEET
DECEMBER 31, 1958

| | | | |
|---|---|---|---|
| Cash................ | $ 2,500 | Accounts Payable..... | $ 5,000 |
| Accounts Receivable..... | 6,000 | K. Rhoads, Capital.... | 11,500 |
| Merchandise Inventory.. | 8,000 | | |
| | $16,500 | | $16,500 |

During 1958 Rhoads withdrew cash of $6,000 and merchandise costing $2,500 for his personal use. He paid out $26,000 to merchandise creditors during the year and paid $8,000 for operating expenses. Rhoads' balance sheet at the beginning of the year showed only two assets: cash, $1,500, and merchandise inventory, $8,500. Prepare an income statement for the year, together with supporting schedules for income and expense items from the data above.

**10.** The following data are obtained from a single-entry set of books kept by H. C. Turner:

| | JAN. 1 | DEC. 31 | | JAN. 1 | DEC. 31 |
|---|---|---|---|---|---|
| Accounts Receivable... | $4,000 | $6,000 | Notes Payable........ | — | $1,000 |
| Inventories.......... | 3,500 | 4,000 | Accounts Payable..... | $2,000 | 1,200 |
| Prepaid Expenses..... | 300 | 280 | Accrued Expenses..... | 200 | 250 |
| Store Equipment...... | 3,000 | 2,700 | | | |

The cashbook shows the following information:

| | | |
|---|---:|---:|
| Balance, January 1.............................. | | $1,500 |
| Receipts: | | |
|   Collections on accounts receivable............... | $3,000 | |
|   Amount borrowed on issuance of note............ | 1,000 | 4,000 |
| | | $5,500 |
| Disbursements: | | |
|   Withdrawals by owner......................... | $ 500 | |
|   Purchase of store equipment.................... | 800 | |
|   Payment of accounts payable.................. | 3,400 | |
|   Payment of expenses.......................... | 1,000 | 5,700 |
|     Cash overdraft................................ | | $(200) |

(a) Prepare an income statement for 1958.

(b) Prepare a schedule to prove the accuracy of the net income or loss figure reported on the income statement.

## PROBLEMS

**24-1.** The following data are obtained from a single-entry set of books kept by J. R. Casey, proprietor of a marine supply store:

| | JAN. 1 | MARCH 31 |
|---|---:|---:|
| Notes receivable............................. | $ 500 | $ 800 |
| Accounts receivable........................... | 4,000 | 5,000 |
| Accrued interest on notes receivable............. | 85 | 60 |
| Merchandise inventories....................... | 4,000 | 2,400 |
| Store equipment.............................. | 3,000 | 2,850 |
| Notes payable................................ | 1,600 | 1,800 |
| Accounts payable............................. | 2,500 | 2,000 |
| Accrued interest on notes payable............. | 60 | 45 |

The cashbook shows the following information:

| | | |
|---|---:|---:|
| Balance, January 1........................... | | $ 2,500 |
| Receipts: Accounts receivable.................. | $7,500 | |
|       Notes receivable..................... | 2,400 | |
|       Interest on notes.................... | 100 | 10,000 |
| | | $12,500 |
| Payments: Accounts payable.................. | $3,800 | |
|       Notes payable...................... | 3,200 | |
|       Interest on notes................... | 120 | |
|       Operating expenses................. | 2,000 | |
|       Withdrawals...................... | 1,000 | 10,120 |
| Balance, March 31............................ | | $ 2,380 |

The following supplementary information is available:

Accounts receivable of $250 were written off as uncollectible.

Purchases allowances of $140 were received on merchandise purchases.

*Instructions:* (1) Prepare an income statement for the three-month period accompanied by schedules in support of income and expense totals.

(2) Prove the net income or loss by reconciling beginning and ending capital balances.

**24-2.** The following information is obtained from the single-entry records of James Sparks:

|  | JAN. 1 | JUNE 30 |
|---|---|---|
| Notes receivable.............................. | $1,700 | $1,300 |
| Accounts receivable........................... | 4,500 | 8,500 |
| Accrued interest on notes receivable.............. | 120 | 100 |
| Merchandise inventories....................... | 3,800 | 1,000 |
| Prepaid operating expenses.................... | 50 | 10 |
| Store equipment.............................. | 3,250 | 3,000 |
| Notes payable................................ | 1,000 | 1,200 |
| Accounts payable............................. | 3,500 | 2,500 |
| Accrued interest on notes payable............... | 40 | 50 |
| Accrued operating expenses..................... | 270 | 300 |
| Unearned interest income...................... | 20 | 10 |

A cashbook shows the following:

| | | |
|---|---|---|
| Balance, January 1............................ | | $1,850 |
| Receipts: Accounts receivable................... | $4,850 | |
| Notes receivable...................... | 1,500 | |
| Interest income...................... | 150 | 6,500 |
| | | $8,350 |
| Payments: Accounts payable................... | $5,250 | |
| Notes payable...................... | 800 | |
| Interest expense..................... | 155 | |
| Operating expenses.................. | 1,650 | |
| Withdrawals by James Sparks......... | 600 | 8,455 |
| Balance, June 30.............................. | | $ 105* |

*Credit

*Instructions:* (1) Prepare an income statement accompanied by schedules in support of income and expense totals.

(2) Prove the net income or loss by reconciling beginning and ending capital balances.

**24-3.** Statements of condition and an analysis of cash from C. H. Stacy's incomplete records are prepared as follows:

BALANCE SHEET OF C. H. STACY AS OF JANUARY 1, 1958

| | | | |
|---|---|---|---|
| Cash........................ | $ 400 | Notes payable............... | $ 1,000 |
| Notes receivable............. | 1,450 | Accounts payable............. | 1,300 |
| Accounts receivable.......... | 3,710 | Accrued interest on notes pay- | |
| Accrued interest on notes receiv- | | able..................... | 3 |
| able..................... | 18 | Accrued wages and salaries.... | 70 |
| Merchandise inventory........ | 1,500 | Unearned interest income...... | 7 |
| Unexpired insurance.......... | 40 | C. H. Stacy, Capital.......... | 11,348 |
| Prepaid interest expense....... | 10 | | |
| Delivery equipment........... | 1,200 | | |
| Buildings.................... | 2,400 | | |
| Land....................... | 3,000 | | |
| | $13,728 | | $13,728 |

BALANCE SHEET OF C. H. STACY AS OF JANUARY 31, 1958

| | | | | |
|---|---|---|---|---|
| Cash........................ | | $ 463 | Notes payable............... | $ 1,000 |
| Notes receivable............. | | 1,600 | Accounts payable............. | 1,580 |
| Accounts receivable.......... | | 3,080 | Accrued interest on notes pay- | |
| Accrued interest on notes receiv- | | | able..................... | 6 |
| able..................... | | 9 | Accrued wages and salaries..... | 45 |
| Merchandise inventory........ | | 1,700 | Accrued taxes................ | 15 |
| Unexpired insurance.......... | | 65 | Unearned interest income...... | 2 |
| Prepaid interest expense....... | | 8 | C. H. Stacy, Capital.......... | 11,212 |
| Delivery equipment.... | $1,200 | | | |
| Less allow. for depr... | 25 | 1,175 | | |
| Buildings............. | $2,800 | | | |
| Less allow. for depr... | 40 | 2,760 | | |
| Land....................... | | 3,000 | | |
| | | $13,860 | | $13,860 |

CASH

| | | | | | |
|---|---|---|---|---|---|
| Jan. 1 | Balance................. | 400 | Jan. | Withdrawal by Stacy..... | 500 |
| | Accounts receivable...... | 7,800 | | Building................ | 400 |
| | Sales................... | 1,200 | | Purchases............... | 340 |
| | Interest income.......... | 12 | | Accounts payable........ | 6,000 |
| | | | | Wages and salaries....... | 300 |
| | | | | Insurance............... | 44 |
| | | | | Miscellaneous operating | |
| | | | | expense.............. | 900 |
| | | | | Freight in............... | 450 |
| | | | | Interest expense......... | 15 |
| | | | Feb. 1 | Balance................. | 463 |
| | | 9,412 | | | 9,412 |
| Feb. 1 | Balance................. | 463 | | | |

*Instructions:* (1) Calculate the net income or loss for January by considering the changes in the owner's capital balance.

(2) **Prepare an income statement with income and expense detail, supported** by schedules showing determination of amounts reported.

**24-4.** A balance sheet for H. L. Lincoln on January 1, 1958, showed the following:

**H. L. LINCOLN**
BALANCE SHEET
JANUARY 1, 1958

| | | | |
|---|---:|---|---:|
| Cash............................ | $ 1,100 | Notes payable............... | $ 1,200 |
| Notes receivable.............. | 1,400 | Accounts payable............ | 1,510 |
| Accounts receivable.......... | 3,060 | Accrued interest on notes payable..................... | 5 |
| Accrued interest on notes receivable..................... | 15 | Accrued wages and salaries.... | 80 |
| Merchandise inventory........ | 1,600 | Unearned interest income...... | 8 |
| Unexpired insurance.......... | 120 | H. L. Lincoln, capital......... | 12,504 |
| Prepaid interest expense....... | 12 | | |
| Delivery equipment........... | 1,500 | | |
| Building..................... | 4,800 | | |
| Land........................ | 1,700 | | |
| | $15,307 | | $15,307 |

On January 31, 1958, the asset and liability balances are:

| ASSETS | | LIABILITIES | |
|---|---:|---|---:|
| Cash........................ | $ 1,940 | Notes payable............... | $   880 |
| Notes receivable.............. | 1,500 | Accounts payable............ | 1,500 |
| Accounts receivable.......... | 3,500 | Accrued interest on notes payable..................... | 7 |
| Accrued interest on notes receivable..................... | 12 | Accrued wages and salaries..... | 50 |
| Merchandise inventory........ | 1,650 | Accrued taxes............... | 60 |
| Unexpired insurance.......... | 45 | Unearned interest income...... | 6 |
| Prepaid interest expense....... | 9 | | $ 2,503 |
| Delivery equipment........... | 1,455 | | |
| Building..................... | 4,776 | | |
| Land........................ | 2,700 | | |
| | $17,587 | | |

Uncollectible accounts receivable of $225 were written off during the month. All notes receivable and notes payable arose from merchandise transactions.

Cash receipts and disbursements for the month were:

| RECEIPTS | | DISBURSEMENTS | |
|---|---:|---|---:|
| Accounts and notes receivable.. | $ 8,500 | Land........................ | $ 1,000 |
| Investment by Lincoln........ | 800 | Purchases................... | 150 |
| Sales....................... | 720 | Accounts and notes payable.... | 6,200 |
| Interest income............. | 30 | Wages and salaries.......... | 350 |
| | $10,050 | Insurance................... | 50 |
| | | Miscellaneous operating expense | 1,050 |
| | | Freight in.................. | 400 |
| | | Interest expense............. | 10 |
| | | | $ 9,210 |

*Instructions:* (1) Calculate the net income or loss for January by considering the changes in capital.

(2) Prepare an income statement with income and expense detail, supported by schedules showing determination of amounts reported.

**24-5.** A balance sheet prepared for Ashby and Bailey on January 1, 1958, had the following balances:

ASHBY AND BAILEY
BALANCE SHEET
JANUARY 1, 1958

| | | | |
|---|---|---|---|
| Cash......................... | $ 750 | Accounts payable............. | $ 5,875 |
| Notes receivable.............. | 1,500 | Accrued expenses............. | 275 |
| Accounts receivable........... | 6,500 | | |
| Interest receivable........... | 40 | | |
| Merchandise inventory........ | 7,000 | | |
| Prepaid expenses............. | 260 | Ashby, capital............... | 6,375 |
| Furniture and fixtures........ | 3,200 | Bailey, capital............... | 6,725 |
| | $19,250 | | $19,250 |

On December 31, 1958, asset and liability balances are:

| ASSETS | | LIABILITIES | |
|---|---|---|---|
| Notes receivable.............. | $ 2,100 | Cash overdraft............... | $ 250 |
| Accounts receivable........... | 7,150 | Notes payable............... | 2,500 |
| Interest receivable........... | 50 | Accounts payable............. | 7,270 |
| Merchandise inventory........ | 7,500 | Accrued expenses............. | 140 |
| Prepaid expenses............. | 280 | | $10,160 |
| Furniture and fixtures........ | 4,020 | | |
| | $21,100 | | |

Cash receipts and disbursements for the year were:

| RECEIPTS | | | DISBURSEMENTS | | |
|---|---|---|---|---|---|
| Investment by Ashby......... | | $ 1,200 | Withdrawals by Ashby ($225 monthly)................... | | $ 2,700 |
| Cash sales.................. | | 4,200 | Withdrawals by Bailey ($225 monthly)................... | | 2,700 |
| Receipts on accounts and notes.......... | $30,000 | | On accounts payable.. | $22,300 | |
| Less discount allowed.......... | 400 | 29,600 | Less discounts allowed .......... | 500 | 21,800 |
| Interest on notes............. | | 80 | | | |
| Proceeds from own 6-month, $2,500 note discounted at the bank at 6% on September 1, 1958..................... | | 2,425 | Purchases of store fixtures on July 1, 1958............... | | 1,200 |
| | | | Operating expenses.......... | | 10,105 |
| | | $37,505 | | | $38,505 |

Prepaid interest on the note payable of $25 is included in the prepaid expenses total of $280 on the balance sheet as of December 31.

Bad accounts written off during the year totaled $370.

Sales returns and allowances were $690.

*Instructions:* (1) Prepare a balance sheet as of December 31, 1958, supported by a schedule summarizing changes in capital accounts.

(2) Prepare an income statement showing the income and expense detail, supported by schedules to show determination of reported amounts.

**24-6.** Balance sheets for the Craft Company on January 1 and June 30, 1958, have the following balances:

| ASSETS | JANUARY 1 | JUNE 30 |
|---|---|---|
| Cash.......................................... | $ 15,000 | $ 76,000 |
| Notes receivable............................. | 20,000 | 15,000 |
| Accounts receivable.......................... | 75,000 | 95,000 |
| Merchandise inventories...................... | 210,000 | 200,000 |
| Prepaid expenses............................. | 12,000 | 10,000 |
| Investments (at cost)........................ | 30,000 | 10,000 |
| Buildings and equipment...................... | 300,000 | 320,000 |
| | $662,000 | $726,000 |

| LIABILITIES AND CAPITAL | | |
|---|---|---|
| Notes payable................................ | $ 47,000 | $ 57,000 |
| Accounts payable............................. | 60,000 | 75,000 |
| Accrued expenses............................. | 3,000 | 2,500 |
| Bonds payable................................ | 50,000 | — — |
| Capital stock, $100 par...................... | 300,000 | 350,000 |
| Paid-in capital from sale of common stock........ | 100,000 | 125,000 |
| Retained earnings............................ | 102,000 | 116,500 |
| | $662,000 | $726,000 |

An analysis of cash receipts and disbursements discloses the following:

| RECEIPTS | | DISBURSEMENTS | |
|---|---|---|---|
| Capital stock............... | $ 75,000 | Trade creditors.............. | $210,000 |
| Trade debtors............... | 230,000 | Expenses (operating and other) | 70,000 |
| Cash sales.................. | 80,000 | Dividends................... | 40,000 |
| Notes receivable discounted: | | Equipment.................. | 28,000 |
| face value, $20,000, proceeds | 19,500 | Bonds...................... | 50,000 |
| Notes payable discounted: | | | |
| face value, $30,000, proceeds | 28,500 | | |
| Sale of investments.......... | 26,000 | | |

*Instructions:* (1) **Prepare an income statement supported by schedules** showing calculation of income and expense balances for the six-month period ended June 30, 1958.

(2) Prove the net income or loss determined in part (1) by the preparation of a retained earnings statement.

**24-7.** R. A. Ward, an attorney, prepared the operating statement on page 786 from the information shown in his cash account.

The following facts are ascertained upon inspection of additional informal records that are available:

(1) On January 1, 1958, clients owed Ward $2,800; on December 31, 1958, the amounts owed by clients totaled $2,550.

(2) Ward collected $2,100 as a retainer for the period March 1, 1958, to February 28, 1959.

## R. A. WARD
### OPERATING STATEMENT
### FOR YEAR ENDED DECEMBER 31, 1958

| | | |
|---|---:|---:|
| Cash receipts: | | |
| Collection of fees and retainers.................. | | $20,000 |
| Cash disbursements: | | |
| Office salaries............................... | $4,740 | |
| Rent......................................... | 1,200 | |
| Utilities...................................... | 120 | |
| Office supplies................................ | 100 | |
| Miscellaneous expense......................... | 400 | |
| Total expenses............................... | | 6,560 |
| Net income for year............................ | | $13,440 |

(3) Rent was paid in advance on the fifteenth of each month. On November 15 rent was increased from $96 to $120 per month.

(4) Office supplies on hand on January 1 were $25; on December 31, $40.

(5) On December 1, Ward received a $2,400, 90-day note, interest at 5% payable at maturity, in payment for services rendered.

(6) Salaries are paid on the fifteenth of each month. A secretary was employed throughout the year at $320 a month. An office clerk was continuously employed since September 16 at $300 a month.

(7) Miscellaneous expense includes taxes of $60 that were paid on September 1 for the taxable year July 1, 1958, to June 30, 1959. At the beginning of the year the amount of prepaid taxes was $25.

(8) Furniture and fixtures, cost $3,200, were acquired on March 1, 1956. Assets are estimated to have a 10-year life.

*Instructions:* Prepare an operating statement on the accrual basis, supported by schedules showing how income and expense balances are determined.

**24-8.** Dr. Robert J. Perry, a credit dentist, keeps a record of cash receipts and disbursements that shows the following information for 1958:

| Receipts: | | Payments (continued): | |
|---|---:|---|---:|
| Collections of fees....... | $18,100 | Laboratory tools......... | $ 440 |
| Loan from bank........ | 2,000 | Dental supplies.......... | 1,370 |
| | | Repairs to dental | |
| Payments: | | equipment............. | 25 |
| Salaries............... | 7,320 | Advertising............. | 2,000 |
| Office supplies.......... | 246 | Rent.................... | 1,620 |
| Office furniture and | | Utilities................. | 150 |
| fixtures............. | 800 | Miscellaneous expense.... | 304 |
| Insurance for 1958...... | 250 | Personal drawings........ | 5,600 |

The following information is obtained from additional informal vouchers and records found in the office:

(1) Amounts receivable from clients on January 1, 1958, totaled $2,150. On December 31, 1958, amounts receivable are $3,900.

(2) The dental supplies inventory on January 1 was $320; on December 31 the inventory is $440.

(3) The office supplies inventory on January 1 was $35; on December 31 the inventory is $95.

(4) On December 30, Dr. Perry sold doubtful accounts of $450 to Commercial Factors for $200. Cash has not yet been received on the sale. All of the remaining accounts are expected to be fully collectible.

(5) The loan from the bank was made on October 31 and is due at the end of 3 months with interest at 6%.

(6) Office furniture and fixtures were purchased on March 31, 1958, and are estimated to last 8 years with no salvage value.

(7) Estimated depreciation of dental equipment for 1958 was $360.

(8) Dental tools were inventoried at $700 at the beginning of the year; the inventory on December 31 is $620.

(9) The office secretary was paid $310 a month at the end of each month; a laboratory assistant was hired on March 16 and was paid $400 on the fifteenth of each month.

(10) Rent was paid in advance on the tenth of each month. Rent was increased on July 10 from $120 to $150 monthly.

(11) Prepaid advertising on December 31 is $125 and accrued charges for advertising are $375. No advertising was done in 1957.

(12) Miscellaneous expense includes personal and property taxes of $100, paid on August 1, for the taxable year ended June 30, 1959. Prepaid taxes on January 1, 1958, were $25.

*Instructions:* Prepare an income statement for 1958 on the accrual basis, supported by schedules showing how income and expense balances are determined.

**24-9.** Buxby and Landon are partners in the operation of a retail store. They are concerned about the apparent discrepancy between their income and their volume of sales. Although they maintain incomplete accounting records, their experience in the business suggests to them that there is possible theft or larceny on the part of their staff.

The partners have asked you, in connection with your initial audit (covering the calendar year 1958), to apply such tests as you can to determine whether there is any indication of shortage. In the course of your investigation you obtain the following facts having a bearing on the problem:

(a) The physical inventory taken December 31, 1958, under your observation, amounted to $4,442 cost, $4,171 market. The inventory of December 31, 1957 was $6,256 cost, $6,013 market. It has been the firm's practice to value inventory at lower of cost or market, treating any loss or decline in market value as "other expense."

(b) Using the treatment of "loss or decline in market value" of inventory as mentioned in (a) above, the average gross profit in recent periods has been 35% of net sales. The partners inform you that this per cent seems reasonable and that they expected the same result for 1958, since their mark-up per cent was approximately the same as in the past.

(c) The December 31, 1957 balance sheet shows accounts receivable of $2,057. Notes payable to banks and trade accounts payable were combined on the December 31, 1957 balance sheet. They totaled $9,622. The firm records accounts payable at the net figure, as cash discounts are seldom missed. Purchases have been shown net in past income statements. Sales discounts have been treated as deductions from sales in the past.

(d) During 1958 accounts were written off in the amount of $216, and an account for $148 written off in 1957 was collected and recorded as a regular collection on account.

(e) Unpaid sales slips show that customers owed $3,246 on December 31, 1958.

(f) Unpaid invoices indicate that the firm owed trade creditors $5,027 at the end of 1958. Record of notes outstanding indicates that $3,000 was owed to banks on December 31, 1958.

(g) Sales returns amounted to $95 and purchase returns amounted to $272.

(h) Of the items in the cash records, the following are pertinent:

Receipts:

| | |
|---|---:|
| From customers (after $272 discounts) | $49,851 |
| From bank loan (net of 60-day, 6% discount) | 2,970 |

Disbursements:

| | |
|---|---:|
| To trade creditors (after $916 cash discounts) | 38,970 |
| To banks on loans | 4,000 |
| To customers for returned goods | 72 |

*Instructions:* Compute the amount by which the physical inventory is short, assuming the gross profit rate of 35% is reasonable. (A.I.C.P.A. adapted)

**24-10.** Paul Canby, a merchant, kept very limited records. Purchases of merchandise were paid for by check, but most other items of cost were paid out of cash receipts. Weekly the amount of cash on hand was deposited in a bank account. No record was kept of cash in the bank, nor was a record kept of sales. Accounts receivable were recorded only by keeping a copy of the sales ticket, and this copy was given to the customer when he paid his account.

Canby had started in business on January 1, 1958, with $20,000 cash and a building that had cost $15,000, of which one third was the value of the building site. The building depreciated 4% a year. An analysis of the bank statements showed total deposits, including the original cash investment, of $130,500. The balance in the bank per bank statement on December 31, 1958, was $5,300, but there were checks amounting to $2,150 dated in December but not paid by the bank until January. Cash on hand on December 31 was $334.

An inventory of merchandise taken on December 31, 1958, showed $16,710 of merchandise on a cost basis. Tickets for accounts receivable totaled $1,270, but $123 of that amount is probably not collectible. Unpaid suppliers' invoices for merchandise amount to $3,780. During the year Canby had borrowed $10,000 from his bank, but he repaid by check $5,000 principal and $100 interest. He has taken for personal expense $4,800 from the cash collections. Expenses paid in cash were as follows:

| | |
|---|---:|
| Utilities.......................................... | $554 |
| Advertising...................................... | 50 |
| Sales help (part time)............................ | 590 |
| Supplies, stationery, etc.......................... | 100 |
| Insurance........................................ | 234 |
| Real estate taxes................................. | 350 |

Store fixtures with a list price of $7,000 were purchased early in January on a one-year installment basis. During the year, checks for the down payment and all maturing installments totaled $5,600. At December 31, the final installment of $1,525 remains unpaid. The fixtures have an estimated useful life of 10 years.

*Instructions:* Based on the above information, prepare an income statement for 1958, supported by all computations necessary to determine the sales and the purchases for the year. (A.I.C.P.A. adapted)

**24-11.** The Hardin Furniture Store (a sole proprietorship) did not have complete records on a double-entry basis. However, from an investigation of its records you have established the information shown below:

(1) The assets and the liabilities as of December 31, 1957, were:

| | DEBIT | CREDIT |
|---|---:|---:|
| Cash...................................... | $ 5,175 | |
| Accounts receivable......................... | 10,556 | |
| Allowance for loss on accounts............... | | $ 740 |
| Fixtures................................... | 3,130 | |
| Accumulated depreciation ................... | | 1,110 |
| Prepaid insurance........................... | 158 | |
| Prepaid supplies............................ | 79 | |
| Accounts payable........................... | | 4,244 |
| Accrued miscellaneous expenses............... | | 206 |
| Accrued taxes.............................. | | 202 |
| Merchandise inventory...................... | 19,243 | |
| Note payable.............................. | | 5,000 |
| Hardin, capital............................ | | 26,839 |

(2) A summary of the transactions for 1958 as recorded in the checkbook shows:

| | |
|---|---:|
| Deposits for the year (including the redeposit of $304 of checks charged back by the bank)...................... | $83,187 |
| Checks drawn during the year......................... | 84,070 |
| Customers' checks charged back by the bank............ | 304 |
| Bank service charges................................ | 22 |

(3) The following information is available as to accounts payable:

| | |
|---|---:|
| Purchases on account during year...................... | $57,789 |
| Returns of merchandise allowed as credits against accounts by vendors.......................................... | 1,418 |
| Payments of accounts by check........................ | 55,461 |

(4) Information as to accounts receivable shows the following:

| | |
|---|---:|
| Accounts written off................................ | $ 812 |
| Accounts collected.................................. | 43,083 |
| Balance of accounts December 31, 1958 (of this balance $700 is estimated to be uncollectible)...................... | 11,921 |

(5) Checks drawn during the year include checks for the following items:

| | |
|---|---:|
| Salaries. | $10,988 |
| Rent. | 3,600 |
| Heat, light, and telephone. | 394 |
| Supplies. | 280 |
| Insurance. | 341 |
| Taxes and licenses. | 1,017 |
| Drawings of proprietor. | 6,140 |
| Miscellaneous expense. | 769 |
| Merchandise purchases. | 2,080 |
| Note payable. | 3,000 |
| | $28,609 |

(6) Merchandise inventory December 31, 1958, was $17,807. Prepaid insurance amounted to $122 and supplies on hand amounted to $105 as of December 31, 1958. Accrued taxes were $216 and miscellaneous accrued expenses were $73 at the year end.

(7) Cash sales for the year are assumed to account for all cash received other than that collected on accounts. Fixtures are to be depreciated at the rate of 10% per annum.

*Instructions:* (1) Prepare a balance sheet as of December 31, 1958.

(2) Prepare an income statement for the year 1958. (A.I.C.P.A. adapted)

**24-12.** As of December 31, 1957, the Clyde Manufacturing Company, with outstanding capital stock of $30,000, had the following assets and liabilities:

| | |
|---|---:|
| Cash. | $ 5,000 |
| Accounts receivable. | 10,000 |
| Raw material inventory. | 4,000 |
| Work-in-process inventory. | 2,000 |
| Finished goods inventory. | 6,000 |
| Prepaid expenses. | 500 |
| Fixed assets (net). | 30,000 |
| Current liabilities. | 17,500 |

During the year 1958 the surplus account increased 50% as a result of the year's business. No dividends were paid during the year. Balances of accounts receivable, prepaid expenses, current liabilities, and capital stock were the same on December 31, 1958, as they had been on December 31, 1957. Inventories were reduced by exactly 50%, except for the finished goods inventory which was reduced by one third. Fixed assets (net) were reduced by depreciation of $4,000, charged three fourths to manufacturing expense and one fourth to general expense. Sales were made at 50% above their cost of $40,000. Direct labor cost was $9,000 and manufacturing expense amounted to $11,000. Total general expense and selling expense amounted to 15% and 10% respectively of the gross sales.

*Instructions:* Prepare a balance sheet as of December 31, 1958, and an income statement for the year 1958 including therein or in a separate schedule the details of cost of goods manufactured and sold. Support the formal statements with working papers. (A.I.C.P.A. adapted)

# Chapter 25

## ERRORS AND THEIR CORRECTION

**PREVENTING MISSTATEMENTS**      A number of special practices are usually adopted by a business unit to insure accuracy in recording and summarizing business transactions. A prime requisite, of course, in achieving accuracy is the establishment of an accounting system with procedures that provide safeguards against both carelessness and dishonesty. Such a system should provide for regular and integrated routines. Personnel should have well-defined responsibilities. Procedures should provide for checks and controls that offer means for the continuous reconciliation and proof of recorded data. An internal auditing staff whose function it is to verify recorded data may be established as a part of the accounting system. Independent public accountants may be engaged for the verification of recorded data and as a further means of insuring accounting accuracy in the accumulation, summary, and presentation of financial data.

Despite the accounting system that is established and the verification procedures that are employed, some misstatements will enter into the financial statements. Misstatements may be minor ones whose effects on the presentations are immaterial; others may be of a major nature, resulting in the serious misrepresentation of financial position and the results of operations. Misstatements on the financial statements may arise from intentional acts on the part of employees or officers to misrepresent the facts or from unintentional acts on the part of employees resulting in inaccuracies or omissions in recorded data.

*Intentional Misstatements.* When incorrect statements result from intentional falsification of entries or records, the motive or motives may be: (1) to evade taxation; (2) to develop statements that will affect the market price of securities issued by the company in a desired manner; (3) to obtain certain favorable decisions of regulatory bodies; (4) to conceal the theft of cash, securities, merchandise, or other assets; (5) to conceal facts that may embarrass management; (6) to make possible more favorable statements for credit purposes; or (7) to develop statements that will provide for higher bonus accruals to key employees. The best possible accounting system will not prevent misstatements that are made under the direction of managing officials.

*Unintentional Misstatements.* It would be impossible to offer a complete list of the misstatements that might arise unintentionally. Unintentional misstatements arise from clerical errors in recording or from failures in the application of accounting principles. Among the most common errors are postings to the wrong customer or creditor accounts, the recording of activities in the wrong profit or loss account, the failure to state inventories accurately, the omission of depreciation, the failure to distinguish properly between capital and revenue expenditures, and the failure to recognize all adjustments for accrued and prepaid items. These and other unintentional errors can be kept to a reasonable minimum through adequate systems of internal check and satisfactory procedures for the audit and review of accounting data.

The discussion in this chapter is devoted to the misstatements that arise from failures in recording or properly summarizing activities and to the accounting procedures that are required upon the discovery of such misstatements.

**TYPES OF ERRORS** Certain errors affect balance sheet data only. For example, Cash is debited instead of Accounts Receivable. Discovery of the error calls for the correction of the real account balances. Other errors affect income statement data only. For example, Sales Salaries is debited instead of Office Salaries. The discovery of this error before the accounts are closed calls for a correction in the nominal accounts; discovery after the accounts are closed would require no action since the real accounts carried into the new period are accurately stated.

Certain errors affect both balance sheet and income statement accounts. Such errors fall into two classes:

(1) Errors which, when not detected, are counterbalanced in the regular course of bookkeeping in the succeeding fiscal period. The income statements for two successive periods are incorrect; the balance sheet at the end of the first period is incorrect, but the balance sheet at the end of the succeeding period is correctly stated. Examples of such errors are: the misstatement of inventories, the omission of adjustments for accrued income and expense items, and the omission of adjustments for prepaid income and expense items.

(2) Errors that affect both the income statement and the balance sheet but that are not counterbalanced in the regular course of bookkeeping during the subsequent period. Balance sheets prepared after the error is made are incorrect until entries are

made to compensate for or to correct such errors. In this class are such errors as the misstatement of depreciation and the recognition of a capital expenditure as a revenue expenditure or *vice versa*.

When errors affecting both balance sheet and income statement accounts are discovered, they must be carefully analyzed to determine the action that is required in correcting the accounts.

Errors are generally discovered when the periodic adjusting entries are being made, when an audit is being undertaken, when a business is to be sold, when a change of ownership is made in a partnership, when questions of taxation are to be decided, when heirs of an estate are to be satisfied, or when a merger or a consolidation of two or more concerns is contemplated or accomplished.

**CORRECTING ENTRIES**     It has been observed in earlier chapters that two procedures are available in correcting accounts for errors in profits of prior periods: (1) If the "clean surplus approach" is to be followed and modification of past profits is to be reported in a special section on the income statement, corrections are summarized in nominal accounts that are ultimately transferred to Retained Earnings. (2) If the income statement is to be limited to transactions of the current period and if errors in past profits are viewed as requiring correction in the accounts that now include such errors, corrections are recorded directly in retained earnings. When the latter practice is followed, the retained earnings statement will display changes in retained earnings resulting from recognition of errors in past profit measurements. Analysis of the retained earnings account is required in providing the detail for the development of this statement. To simplify presentations it will be assumed in the examples in this chapter that corrections are recorded directly in the retained earnings account.

It may be observed that, in practice, no action is generally taken in the accounts upon the discovery of errors that do not involve material amounts and that will be counterbalanced in the normal course of accounting. Justification for such a procedure is made on the grounds of expediency. In the illustrations in this chapter, however, it is assumed that corrections are to be made in the accounts for all errors that are discovered.

The entries that are required in correcting errors are illustrated in the example that follows. The errors to be considered are representative of those that are frequently found.

Assume that the books of the Monarch Wholesale Co. are reviewed in 1959 before the accounts for 1959 have been adjusted and closed. During the course of review, the errors that are listed below and on the following pages are discovered.

(1) *Misstatement of Merchandise Inventory.* It is discovered that the merchandise inventory as of December 31, 1957, was understated by $1,000. The effects of the misstatement were as follows:

| INCOME STATEMENT | BALANCE SHEET |
|---|---|
| For 1957: Cost of Goods Sold Overstated (Ending Inventory too low) Net Income Understated | Assets Understated (Inventory too low) Retained Earnings Understated |
| For 1958: Cost of Goods Sold Understated (Beginning Inventory too low) Net Income Overstated | Balance sheet items not affected, retained earnings understatement for 1957 being corrected by net income overstatement for 1958. |

Since the balance sheet items at the end of 1958 were correctly stated, no entry to correct the accounts is required in 1959, the error made in 1957 having been counterbalanced by the misstatement in 1958.

If the error had been discovered in 1958 instead of 1959, an entry would have been made to correct the account balances in order that the operations for 1958 might be reported accurately notwithstanding past errors. The correcting entry to increase the inventory and Retained Earnings would have been made as follows in 1958:

Merchandise Inventory............................ 1,000
    Retained Earnings............................... 1,000

(2) *Misstatement of Merchandise Purchases.* It is discovered that a purchase invoice as of December 28, 1957, for $500 was not recorded until 1958. The goods were included in the inventory at the end of 1957. The effects of the failure to record the purchase were as follows:

| INCOME STATEMENT | BALANCE SHEET |
|---|---|
| For 1957: Cost of Goods Sold Understated (Purchases too low) Net Income Overstated | Liabilities Understated (Accounts Payable too low) Retained Earnings Overstated |
| For 1958: Cost of Goods Sold Overstated (Purchases too high) Net Income Understated | Balance sheet items not affected, retained earnings overstatement for 1957 being corrected by net income understatement for 1958. |

Since the balance sheet items at the end of 1958 were correctly stated, no entry to correct the accounts is required in 1959.

If the error had been discovered in 1958 instead of 1959, a correcting entry would have been necessary. In 1958 Purchases was debited and Accounts Payable credited for $500 for merchandise acquired in 1957 and included in the ending inventory for 1957. Retained Earnings would have to be reduced by $500, representing the net income overstatement for 1957, and Purchases would have to be credited for a similar amount to reduce Purchases to the cost of merchandise acquired in 1958. The correcting entry in 1958 would have been:

| | | |
|---|---|---|
| Retained Earnings............................... | 500 | |
| Purchases...................................... | | 500 |

(3) *Failure to Record Prepaid Expense.* It is discovered that interest expense for 1957 included $50 that should have been deferred in adjusting the accounts on December 31, 1957. The effects of the failure to record the prepaid expense were as follows:

| INCOME STATEMENT | BALANCE SHEET |
|---|---|
| For 1957: Expenses Overstated (Interest Expense too high) | Assets Understated (Prepaid Interest Expense not reported) |
| Net Income Understated | Retained Earnings Understated |
| For 1958: Expenses Understated (Interest Expense too low) | Balance sheet items not affected, retained earnings understatement for 1957 being corrected by net income overstatement for 1958. |
| Net Income Overstated | |

Since the balance sheet items at the end of 1958 were correctly stated, no entry to correct the accounts is required in 1959.

If the error had been discovered in 1958 instead of 1959, a correcting entry would have been necessary. If the prepaid interest expense had been properly recorded at the end of 1957, the balance in this account would have been transferred to the debit side of the interest expense account by means of a reversing entry at the beginning of 1958. This would have to be recognized in preparing the correcting entry. Interest Expense, then, would have to be debited for $50, the expense relating to operations of 1958, and Retained Earnings would have to be credited for a similar amount representing the net income understatement for 1957. The correcting entry in 1958 would have been:

| | | |
|---|---|---|
| Interest Expense................................. | 50 | |
| Retained Earnings............................. | | 50 |

(4) *Failure to Record Accrued Income.* Accrued interest on notes receivable of $20 was overlooked in adjusting the accounts on December 31, 1957. The income was recognized when the interest was collected in 1958. The effects of the failure to record the accrued income were as follows:

| INCOME STATEMENT | BALANCE SHEET |
|---|---|
| For 1957: Income Understated (Interest Income too low) | Assets Understated (Accrued Interest on Notes Receivable not reported) |
| Net Income Understated | Retained Earnings Understated |
| For 1958: Income Overstated (Interest Income too high) | Balance sheet items not affected, retained earnings understatement for 1957 being corrected by net income overstatement for 1958. |
| Net Income Overstated | |

Since the balance sheet items at the end of 1958 were correctly stated, no entry to correct the accounts is required in 1959.

If the error had been discovered in 1958 instead of 1959, an entry would have been necessary to correct the account balances. If the accrued interest on notes receivable had been properly recorded at the end of 1957, the balance in the asset account would have been transferred to the debit side of the interest income account by means of a reversing entry at the beginning of 1958. The debit in Interest Income would have been offset against interest collections reported on the credit side of the account in determining the amount actually earned in 1958. The effect of the reversing entry would have to be recognized in preparing the correcting entry. Interest Income would have to be debited for $20, the income accrued in 1957 and to be subtracted from receipts of 1958, and Retained Earnings would be credited for a similar amount representing the net income understatement for 1957. The correcting entry in 1958 would have been:

| | | |
|---|---|---|
| Interest Income............................... | 20 | |
| Retained Earnings.............................. | | 20 |

(5) *Overstatement of Prepaid Expense*. On January 2, 1957, $180 representing insurance for a three-year period was paid. The charge was made to the asset account Unexpired Insurance. No adjustment was made at the end of 1957. At the end of 1958, the unexpired insurance account was reduced to the unexpired balance on that date, $60, insurance for two years or $120 being charged to operations of 1958. The effects of the misstatements were as follows:

| INCOME STATEMENT | BALANCE SHEET |
|---|---|
| For 1957: Expenses Understated (Insurance Expense not reported) | Assets Overstated (Unexpired Insurance too high) |
| Net Income Overstated | Retained Earnings Overstated |
| For 1958: Expenses Overstated (Insurance Expense too high) | Balance sheet items not affected, retained earnings overstatement for 1957 being corrected by net income understatement for 1958. |
| Net Income Understated | |

Since the balance sheet items at the end of 1958 were correctly stated, no entry to correct the accounts is required in 1959.

If the error had been discovered in 1958 instead of 1959, an entry would have been necessary to correct the account balances. Retained Earnings and Unexpired Insurance would have been decreased for the expired insurance of $60 relating to 1957 by the following entry in 1958:

| | | |
|---|---:|---:|
| Retained Earnings............................... | 60 | |
| Unexpired Insurance.............................. | | 60 |

The expired insurance of $60 for 1958 would have been recorded at the end of that year by an appropriate adjustment.

(6) *Failure to Record Prepaid Income.* Unearned interest on notes receivable of $75 as of December 31, 1957, and $125 as of December 31, 1958, were overlooked in adjusting the accounts on each of these dates. Interest Income had been credited for interest receipts. The effects of the failure to recognize the income of $75 that was to be deferred at the end of 1957 were as follows:

| INCOME STATEMENT | BALANCE SHEET |
|---|---|
| For 1957: Income Overstated (Interest Income too high) Net Income Overstated | Liabilities Understated (Unearned Interest Income not reported) Retained Earnings Overstated |
| For 1958: Income Understated (Interest Income too low) Net Income Understated | Balance sheet items not affected, retained earnings overstatement for 1957 being corrected by net income understatement for 1958. |

The effects of the failure to recognize the prepaid income of $125 at the end of 1958 were as follows:

| INCOME STATEMENT | BALANCE SHEET |
|---|---|
| For 1958: Income Overstated (Interest Income too high) Net Income Overstated | Liabilities Understated (Unearned Interest Income not reported) Retained Earnings Overstated |

No entry is required in 1959 to correct the accounts for the failure to record the prepaid income at the end of 1957, the misstatement in 1957 having been counterbalanced by the misstatement in 1958. An entry is required, however, to correct the accounts for the failure to record the prepaid income at the end of 1958 if the net income for 1959 is not to be misstated. If the prepaid income had been recorded at the end of 1958, the balance in Unearned Interest Income would have been transferred to the credit side of the interest income account by means of a reversing entry at the beginning of 1959. This must be recognized in recording the correcting entry. Retained Earnings must be debited for $125, representing the net income overstatement for 1958, and Interest Income must be credited for the same amount, representing the income that is to be identified with 1959. The correcting entry is:

Retained Earnings.................................. 125
    Interest Income................................. 125

If the failure to adjust the accounts for the prepaid income of 1957 had been recognized in 1958 instead of 1959, an entry similar to the one above would have been required in 1958 to correct the account balances. The entry at that time would have been:

Retained Earnings.................................. 75
    Interest Income................................. 75

(7) *Failure to Record Accrued Expense.* Accrued sales salaries of $240 as of December 31, 1957, and $210 as of December 31, 1958, were overlooked in adjusting the accounts on each of these dates. Sales Salaries is debited for salary payments. The effects of the failure to record the accrued expense of $240 as of December 31, 1957, were as follows:

| INCOME STATEMENT | BALANCE SHEET |
|---|---|
| For 1957: Expenses Understated (Sales Salaries too low) Net Income Overstated | Liabilities Understated (Accrued Salaries not reported) Retained Earnings Overstated |
| For 1958: Expenses Overstated (Sales Salaries too high) Net Income Understated | Balance sheet items not affected, retained earnings overstatement for 1957 being corrected by net income understatement for 1958. |

The effects of the failure to recognize the accrued expense of $210 on December 31, 1958, were as follows:

| INCOME STATEMENT | BALANCE SHEET |
|---|---|
| For 1958: Expenses Understated (Sales Salaries too low) Net Income Overstated | Liabilities Understated (Accrued Salaries not reported) Retained Earnings Overstated |

No entry is required in 1959 to correct the accounts for the failure to record the accrued expense at the end of 1957, the misstatement in 1957 having been counterbalanced by the misstatement in 1958. An entry is required, however, to correct the accounts for the failure to record the accrued expense at the end of 1958 if the net income for 1959 is not to be misstated. If the accrued expense had been recorded at the end of 1958, the balance in Accrued Salaries would have been transferred to the credit side of the sales salaries account by means of a reversing entry at the beginning of 1959. This must be recognized in recording the correcting entry. Retained Earnings must be debited for $210, representing the net income overstatement for 1958, and Sales Salaries must be credited for a similar amount, representing the expense accruing in 1958 and to be subtracted from salary payments in 1959. The correcting entry is:

| | | |
|---|---|---|
| Retained Earnings............................... | 210 | |
| Sales Salaries.................................. | | 210 |

If the failure to adjust the accounts for the accrued expense of 1957 had been recognized in 1958, an entry similar to the one above would have been required in 1958 to correct the account balances. The entry in 1958 would have been:

| | | |
|---|---|---|
| Retained Earnings............................... | 240 | |
| Sales Salaries.................................. | | 240 |

(8) *Failure to Record Depreciation.* Depreciation of delivery equipment costing $500 was overlooked at the end of 1957 and 1958. The equipment has an estimated five-year life. The effects of the failure to record depreciation for 1957 were as follows:

| INCOME STATEMENT | BALANCE SHEET |
|---|---|
| For 1957: Expenses Understated (Depreciation of Delivery Equipment too low) | Assets Overstated (Allowance for Depreciation of Delivery Equipment too low) |
| Net Income Overstated | Retained Earnings Overstated |
| For 1958: Expenses Not Affected | Assets Overstated (Allowance for Depreciation of Delivery Equipment too low) |
| Net Income Not Affected | Retained Earnings Overstated |

It should be observed that misstatement of net income as a result of failure to record depreciation is not counterbalanced in the succeeding year. As a result, asset and retained earnings balances require correction when the failure is discovered.

Failure to record depreciation for 1958 affected the statements as shown below:

| INCOME STATEMENT | BALANCE SHEET |
|---|---|
| For 1958: Expenses Understated (Depreciation of Delivery Equipment too low) | Assets Overstated (Allowance for Depreciation of Delivery Equipment Understated) |
| Net Income Overstated | Retained Earnings Overstated |

When the omission is recognized, Retained Earnings must be reduced and the allowance for depreciation must be increased by the total amount of depreciation that should have been recorded. The correcting entry in 1959 for depreciation that should have been recognized for 1957 and 1958 is as follows:

Retained Earnings................................... 200
   Allowance for Depreciation of Delivery Equipment..        200

(9) *Overstatement of Prepaid Income.* Unearned Rental Income was credited for $240 representing income for December, 1958, and for January and February, 1959. No adjustment was made on December 31, 1958. The effects of the failure to adjust the accounts to show income of $80 for 1958 were as follows:

| INCOME STATEMENT | BALANCE SHEET |
|---|---|
| For 1958: Income Understated (Rental Income too low)<br>Net Income Understated | Liabilities Overstated (Unearned Rental Income too high)<br>Retained Earnings Understated |

When the error is discovered in 1959, Unearned Rental Income is reduced by the income that should have been recognized in 1958 and Retained Earnings is increased by the following entry:

Unearned Rental Income.......................... 80
   Retained Earnings................................        80

(10) *Failure to Provide an Allowance for Bad Debts.* The company has recognized losses on accounts receivable in the period in which accounts were determined to be uncollectible, as follows:

|  | IN 1957 | IN 1958 |
|---|---|---|
| Accounts originating from: |  |  |
| Sales of 1957 | $100 | $260 |
| Sales of 1958 |  | 150 |
|  | $100 | $410 |

In addition to the losses recognized in 1957 and 1958, it is estimated that additional losses will be incurred as follows: on 1957 accounts, $120; on 1958 accounts, $250.

The effects of the failure to recognize the full amount of uncollectibles relating to 1957 income were as follows:

| INCOME STATEMENT | BALANCE SHEET |
|---|---|
| For 1957: Expenses Understated (Bad Debts too small)<br>Net Income Overstated | Assets Overstated (Allowance for Bad Debts not reported)<br>Retained Earnings Overstated |
| For 1958: Expenses Overstated (Bad Debts of previous year recognized currently)<br>Net Income Understated | Assets Overstated (Allowance for Bad Debts not reported)<br>Retained Earnings Overstated (overstatement of net income for previous year counterbalanced only in part by understatement of net income currently) |

It should be observed that the misstatement of net income as a result of the failure to relate bad debt losses to the period in which the account receivable arose may not be counterbalanced in the succeeding year. As a result, special analysis is necessary in determining the correction that is required in asset and retained earnings account balances. Failure to recognize uncollectibles relating to 1958 had the following effects:

| INCOME STATEMENT | BALANCE SHEET |
|---|---|
| For 1958: Expenses Understated (Bad Debts too small) | Assets Overstated (Allowance for Bad Debts not reported) |
| Net Income Overstated | Retained Earnings Overstated |

The correcting entry in 1959 requires analysis of the extent to which past failures to recognize uncollectibles were counterbalanced by charges in later periods; Retained Earnings is debited and Allowance for Bad Debts is credited for charges that have not been made to prior periods and that are expected to emerge in the course of realization of receivables. Required charges and actual charges are summarized as follows:

|  | 1957 | 1958 | TOTAL |
|---|---|---|---|
| Required charges: |  |  |  |
| Losses already recognized | $360 | $150 | $510 |
| Losses still anticipated | 120 | 250 | 370 |
| Amounts chargeable to each year | $480 | $400 | $880 |
| Amounts charged to each year | 100 | 410 | 510 |
| Charge understatement (overstatement) | $380 | $(10) | $370 |

The correcting entry in 1959 is:

| Retained Earnings. . . . . . . . . . . . . . . . . . . . . . . . . . . . . . . . . . . | 370 | |
| Allowance for Bad Debts. . . . . . . . . . . . . . . . . . . . . . . . . | | 370 |

If the failures to provide for uncollectibles were recognized in 1958, the entry to correct account balances would be as follows:

| Retained Earnings. . . . . . . . . . . . . . . . . . . . . . . . . . . . . . . . . . . | 380 | |
| Allowance for Bad Debts. . . . . . . . . . . . . . . . . . . . . . . . . | | 380 |

The allowance would then have been raised at the end of 1958 by the provision for bad debts relating to 1958 receivables, $250, and reduced by the accounts receivable of 1957 written off, $260, thus producing a balance in the allowance account of $370 at the beginning of 1959.

The analysis sheet on pages 802 and 803 summarizes the effects of the errors that are listed on pages 794 to 800. Effects on the financial statements are listed on the assumption that the errors were not discovered in 1957, 1958, or 1959. A plus sign (+) indicates an overstatement in the statement section; a minus sign (−) indicates an understatement in the statement section.

| | AT END OF 1957 | | | |
| --- | --- | --- | --- | --- |
| | INCOME STATEMENT | | BALANCE SHEET | |
| | SECTION | NET INCOME | SECTION | RETAINED EARNINGS |
| (1) Understatement of Merchandise Inventory of $1,000 on December 31, 1957. | Cost of Goods Sold + | − | Current Assets − | − |
| (2) Failure to record merchandise of $500 purchased on account in 1957; purchase was recorded in 1958. | Cost of Goods Sold − | + | Current Liabilities − | + |
| (3) Failure to record Prepaid Interest Expense of $50 on December 31, 1957; amount was included as Interest Expense. | Other Exp. + | − | Current Assets − | − |
| (4) Failure to record Accrued Interest on Notes Receivable of $20 on December 31, 1957; income was recognized on collection in 1958. | Other Income − | − | Current Assets − | − |
| (5) Failure to record Insurance Expense of $60 in 1957, insurance for 1957 and 1958 of $120 being charged to 1958. | General Exp. − | + | Current Assets + | + |
| (6) Failure to record Unearned Interest Income, amounts received being shown as income. On December 31, 1957, $75. | Other Income + | + | Deferred Revenues − | + |
| On December 31, 1958, $125. | | | | |
| (7) Failure to record Accrued Sales Salaries; expense was recognized when payment was made. On December 31, 1957, $240. | Selling Exp. − | + | Current Liabilities − | + |
| On December 31, 1958, $210. | | | | |
| (8) Failure to record Depreciation of Delivery Equipment. On December 31, 1957, $100. | Selling Exp. − | + | Fixed Assets + | + |
| On December 31, 1958, $100. | | | | |
| (9) Failure to record Rental Income of $80 for 1958; Unearned Rental Income was credited for amount received. (It is assumed that $240 is recognized as income in 1959.) | | | | |
| (10) Failure to recognize additional bad debt loss of $380 relating to 1957 and emerging in 1958 and thereafter. | General Exp. − | + | Current Assets + | + |
| Failure to recognize additional bad debt loss of $250 relating to 1958 and emerging in 1959 and thereafter. | | | | |

| At End of 1958 | | | | At End of 1959 | | | |
| Income Statement | | Balance Sheet | | Income Statement | | Balance Sheet | |
| Section | Net Income | Section | Retained Earnings | Section | Net Income | Section | Retained Earnings |
|---|---|---|---|---|---|---|---|
| Cost of Goods Sold − | + | | No Effect | | | | |
| Cost of Goods Sold + | − | | No Effect | | | | |
| Other Exp. − | + | | No Effect | | | | |
| Other Income + | + | | No Effect | | | | |
| General Exp. + | − | | No Effect | | | | |
| Other Income − | − | | No Effect | | | | |
| Other Income + | + | Deferred Revenues − | + | Other Income − | − | | No Effect |
| Selling Exp. + | − | | No Effect | | | | |
| Selling Exp. − | + | Current Liab. − | + | Selling Exp. + | − | | No Effect |
| | No Effect | Fixed Assets + | + | | No Effect | Fixed Assets + | + |
| Selling Exp. − | + | Fixed Assets + | + | | No Effect | Fixed Assets + | + |
| Other Income − | − | Deferred Revenues + | − | Other Income + | + | | No Effect |
| General Exp. + | − | Current Assets + | + | General Exp. + | − | | No Effect* |
| General Exp. − | + | Current Assets + | + | General Exp. + | − | Current Assets + | + |

*It is assumed that all of the 1957 accounts are collected or written off prior to the end of 1959.

**CORRECTION OF RETAINED EARNINGS** It is assumed in the following sections that the errors previously listed are discovered in 1959 before the accounts for the year are adjusted and closed. Accounts must be corrected so that the asset, liability, and capital accounts may be stated accurately and so that income and expense balances may report only balances identified with the current period. Instead of preparing a separate entry for each correction, a single compound entry is generally made for all of the errors that are discovered. The corrected retained earnings and profit or loss balances of past years, as well as the data to correct the books at the time the errors are discovered, may be obtained by the preparation of working papers. Assume the following retained earnings account for the Monarch Wholesale Co.:

Retained Earnings

| | | | | | |
|---|---|---|---|---|---|
| Dec. 20, 1958 | Div. Declared.... | 2,000 | Dec. 31, 1957 | Balance......... | 3,000 |
| Dec. 31, 1958 | Balance......... | 3,500 | Dec. 31, 1958 | Net Income...... | 2,500 |
| | | 5,500 | | | 5,500 |
| | | | Jan. 1, 1959 | Balance......... | 3,500 |

The working papers to determine the corrected retained earnings balance on December 31, 1957, and the actual net income for 1958 are shown on page 805.

The working papers indicate that Retained Earnings is to be reduced by $825 as of January 1, 1959. The reduction arises from the following:

Retained Earnings overstatement as of Dec. 31, 1957:
    Retained Earnings as of the date as originally reported.................................... $3,000
    Retained Earnings as of this date as corrected.......  2,715    $285

Retained Earnings overstatement in 1958:
    Net income as originally reported................ $2,500
    Net income as corrected.........................  1,960    540

Retained Earnings overstatement as of January 1, 1959.    $825

The following entry is made from the working papers in correcting the account balances in 1959:

Retained Earnings.....................................  825
Unearned Rental Income............................   80
    Interest Income...................................    125
    Sales Salaries....................................    210
    Allowance for Depreciation of Delivery Equipment....    200
    Allowance for Bad Debts..........................    370

The debit to Retained Earnings corrects this balance for overstatement of profits in past periods. The debit to Unearned Rental

## MONARCH WHOLESALE CO.

### Working Papers for Correction of Account Balances

### December, 1959

| Explanation | Retained Earnings Dec. 31, 1957 | | Profit and Loss Year Ended Dec. 31, 1958 | | Accounts Requiring Correction in 1959 | | |
|---|---|---|---|---|---|---|---|
| | Dr. | Cr. | Dr. | Cr. | Dr. | Cr. | Account |
| Reported Retained Earnings Balance, Dec. 31, 1957 | | 3,000 | | | | | |
| Reported Net Income for Year Ended Dec. 31, 1958 | | | | 2,500 | | | |
| Corrections[1]: | | | | | | | |
| (1) Understatement of inventory on Dec. 31, 1957, $1,000 | | 1,000 | 1,000 | | | | |
| (2) Failure to record merchandise purchases in 1957, $500 | 500 | | | 500 | | | |
| (3) Failure to record Prepaid Interest Expense on Dec. 31, 1957, $50 | | 50 | 50 | | | | |
| (4) Failure to record Accrued Interest on Notes Receivable on Dec. 31, 1957, $20 | | 20 | 20 | | | | |
| (5) Failure to record Insurance Expense on Dec. 31, 1957, $60, insurance of $120 for 1957 and 1958 being charged to 1958 | 60 | | | 60 | | | |
| (6) Failure to record Unearned Interest on Notes Receivable: | | | | | | | |
|     (a) On Dec. 31, 1957, $75 | 75 | | | 75 | | | |
|     (b) On Dec. 31, 1958, $125 | | | 125 | | | 125 | Interest Income |
| (7) Failure to record Accrued Sales Salaries: | | | | | | | |
|     (a) On Dec. 31, 1957, $240 | 240 | | | 240 | | | |
|     (b) On Dec. 31, 1958, $210 | | | 210 | | | 210 | Sales Salaries |
| (8) Failure to record Depreciation of Delivery Equipment: | | | | | | | |
|     (a) On Dec. 31, 1957, $100 | 100 | | | | | 100 | Allowance for Depr. of |
|     (b) On Dec. 31, 1958, $100 | | | 100 | | | 100 | Delivery Equip. |
| (9) Failure to record Rental Income on Dec. 31, 1958, $80 | | | | 80 | 80 | | Unearned Rental Income |
| (10) (a) Allowance requirement, 1957 | 380 | | | | | 380 | |
|     (b) 1957 losses charged to 1958 | | | | 260 | 260 | | Allowance for Bad Debts |
|     (c) Allowance requirement, 1958 | | | 250 | | | 250 | |
| | 1,355 | 4,070 | 1,755 | 3,715 | 340 | 1,165 | |
| Corrected Retained Earning Balance, Dec. 31, 1957 | 2,715 | | | | | | |
| | 4,070 | 4,070 | | | | | |
| Corrected Net Income for 1958 | | | 1,960 | | | | |
| | | | 3,715 | 3,715 | | | |
| Net Correction to Retained Earnings as of January 1, 1959 | | | | | 825 | | Retained Earnings |
| | | | | | 1,165 | 1,165 | |

[1]For more detailed description of errors and their corrections, refer to pages 794 to 801.

Income reduces this balance to the rentals unearned at the beginning of 1959. Interest Income is credited for the amount received in 1958 but applicable to 1959. Sales Salaries is credited for the salaries that had accrued at the end of 1958 but that are not to be paid until 1959. Allowance for Depreciation of Delivery Equipment is credited for depreciation that should have been recorded in 1957 and 1958. Allowance for Bad Debts is credited for receivables estimated to be uncollectible.

After recording the correcting entry, Retained Earnings will appear with a balance of $2,675 as follows:

RETAINED EARNINGS

| | | | | | |
|---|---|---|---|---|---|
| 1959 | Corrections in net incomes of prior periods discovered during the course of audit. | 825 | Jan. 1, 1959 | Balance......... | 3,500 |

By reconstructing the retained earnings account from the detail shown on the working papers, this balance may be proved to be correct. If the retained earnings balance as of December 31, 1957, and the net income of 1958 had been reported properly, Retained Earnings would have appeared as follows:

RETAINED EARNINGS

| | | | | | |
|---|---|---|---|---|---|
| Dec. 20, 1958 | Div. declared .... | 2,000 | Dec. 31, 1957 | Corrected balance per working papers ........ | 2,715 |
| Dec. 31, 1958 | Balance......... | 2,675 | Dec. 31, 1958 | Corrected net income for 1958 per working papers.......... | 1,960 |
| | | 4,675 | | | 4,675 |
| | | | Jan. 1, 1959 | Balance......... | 2,675 |

In the foregoing example, a corrected net income figure for only the preceding year, 1958, was required; hence any corrections in years prior to this date were shown as affecting the retained earnings balance as of December 31, 1957. Working papers on page 805 were constructed to summarize this information by providing a pair of columns for retained earnings as of December 31, 1957, and a pair of columns for profit and loss data for 1958. It may be desirable to determine corrected operating results for a number of years. When this is to be done, a pair of columns must be provided for retained earnings as of the beginning of the period under review and a separate pair of profit and loss columns for each year for which a corrected profit or loss balance is to be determined. For example, assume that an analysis of errors is to be made and that corrected profit and loss figures for the years 1956, 1957, and 1958 are to be determined. Working papers for the correction of account balances would be constructed with headings as shown below. The omission of accrued salaries for a four-year period is listed below to illustrate the process of correction.

| EXPLANATION | RETAINED EARNINGS DEC. 31, 1955 | | PROFIT AND LOSS YR. ENDED DEC. 31, 1956 | | PROFIT AND LOSS YR. ENDED DEC. 31, 1957 | | PROFIT AND LOSS YR. ENDED DEC. 31, 1958 | | ACCOUNTS REQUIRING CORRECTION IN 1959 | | |
|---|---|---|---|---|---|---|---|---|---|---|---|
| | DR. | CR. | DR. | CR. | DR. | CR. | DR. | CR. | DR. | CR. | ACCOUNT |
| Failure to record accrued sales salaries: | | | | | | | | | | | |
| End of: | | | | | | | | | | | |
| 1955, $150 | 150 | | | 150 | | | | | | | |
| 1956, $160 | | | 160 | | | 160 | | | | | |
| 1957, $180 | | | | | 180 | | | 180 | | | |
| 1958, $125 | | | | | | | 125 | | | 125 | Sales Salaries |

**CORRECTION OF FINAN-CIAL STATEMENTS OF PRIOR PERIODS** It is frequently desirable to prepare corrected financial statements for prior periods, particularly when comparisons and analyses of balance sheets and income statements for several years are to be made. In preparing corrected statements, working papers for each statement for each year are prepared.

The preparation of corrected financial statements for the Monarch Wholesale Co. for 1958 is illustrated in the remaining pages of this chapter. The data affecting statements of 1958 and to be recognized in correcting the balance sheet and the income statement are:

(1) Understatement of inventory on December 31, 1957 $1,000.

(2) Failure to record purchases in 1957, $500.

(3) Failure to record prepaid interest expense on December 31, 1957, $50.

(4) Failure to record accrued interest on notes receivable on December 31, 1957, $20.

(5) Failure to record insurance expense on December 31, 1957, $60, insurance of $120 for 1957 and 1958 being charged to 1958.

(6) Failure to record unearned interest on notes receivable:

    (a) On December 31, 1957, $75.

    (b) On December 31, 1958, $125.

(7) Failure to record accrued sales salaries:

    (a) On December 31, 1957, $240.

    (b) On December 31, 1958, $210.

(8) Failure to record depreciation of delivery equipment:

    (a) On December 31, 1957, $100.

    (b) On December 31, 1958, $100.

(9) Failure to record rental income on December 31, 1958, $80.

(10) Failure to provide allowance for bad debts:

    (a) Estimated loss from bad debts relating to 1957 accounts, $380, bad debts of $260 for 1957 being charged to 1958.

    (b) Estimated loss from bad debts relating to 1958 accounts, $250.

Working papers for the preparation of a corrected income statement for 1958 are shown below:

MONARCH WHOLESALE CO.

WORKING PAPERS FOR CORRECTED INCOME STATEMENT

FOR YEAR ENDED DECEMBER 31, 1958

| ACCOUNT | BALANCES BEFORE CORRECTION DR. | CR. | CORRECTIONS DR. | CR. | CORRECTED BALANCES DR. | CR. |
|---|---|---|---|---|---|---|
| Sales................. | | 65,000 | | | | 65,000 |
| Sales Discounts..... | 1,400 | | | | 1,400 | |
| Mdse. Inv., Jan. 1, 1958.............. | 15,000 | | (1) 1,000 | | 16,000 | |
| Purchases........... | 40,000 | | | (2) 500 | 39,500 | |
| Mdse. Inv., Dec. 31, 1958.............. | | 12,000 | | | | 12,000 |
| Sales Salaries....... | 5,000 | | (7b) 210 | (7a) 240 | 4,970 | |
| Delivery Expense.... | 3,000 | | (8b) 100 | | 3,100 | |
| Adm. and Office Salaries.......... | 5,590 | | | | 5,590 | |
| Loss from Bad Debts | 410 | | (10b) 250 | 10a) 260 | 400 | |
| Other General Expense ......... | 4,000 | | | (5) 60 | 3,940 | |
| Interest Income..... | | 500 | {(4) 20 / 6b) 125 | (6a) 75 | | 430 |
| Rental Income...... | | 1,000 | | (9) 80 | | 1,080 |
| Interest Expense.... | 1,600 | | (3) 50 | | 1,650 | |
| Net Income......... | 2,500 | | {(2) 500 / (5) 60 / (6a) 75 / (7a) 240 / (9) 80 / (10a) 260 | (1) 1,000 / (3) 50 / (4) 20 / (6b) 125 / (7b) 210 / (8b) 100 / (10b) 250 } 1,960 | | |
| | 78,500 | 78,500 | 2,970 | 2,970 | 78,510 | 78,510 |

The corrected income statement prepared from the working papers would appear as follows:

MONARCH WHOLESALE CO.

CORRECTED INCOME STATEMENT

FOR YEAR ENDED DECEMBER 31, 1958

| | | |
|---|---:|---:|
| Gross sales....................................................... | $65,000 | |
| Less: Sales discounts..................................... | 1,400 | $63,600 |
| | | |
| Cost of goods sold: | | |
| Merchandise inventory, January 1, 1958..................... | $16,000 | |
| Add: Merchandise purchases............................. | 39,500 | |
| | | |
| Merchandise available for sale............................. | $55,500 | |
| Deduct: Merchandise inventory, December 31, 1958.......... | 12,000 | |
| | | |
| Cost of goods sold........................................ | | 43,500 |
| | | |
| Gross profit on sales....................................... | | $20,100 |
| | | |
| Operating expenses: | | |
| | | |
| Selling expenses: | | |
| Sales salaries.................................... | $4,970 | |
| Delivery expense................................. | 3,100 | |
| | | |
| Total selling expenses................................. | $ 8,070 | |
| | | |
| General expenses: | | |
| Administrative and office salaries................... | $5,590 | |
| Loss from bad debts............................. | 400 | |
| Other general expense........................... | 3,940 | |
| | | |
| Total general expenses................................. | 9,930 | |
| | | |
| Total operating expenses................................ | | 18,000 |
| | | |
| Net profit from operations................................... | | $ 2,100 |
| | | |
| Other income and expenses: | | |
| | | |
| Other income: | | |
| Interest income................................. | $ 430 | |
| Rental income.................................. | 1,080 | |
| | | |
| Total other income................................. | $ 1,510 | |
| | | |
| Other expenses: | | |
| Interest expense..................................... | 1,650 | |
| | | |
| Deduct excess of other expenses over other income............ | | 140 |
| | | |
| Net income................................................ | | $ 1,960 |

Working papers from which a corrected balance sheet as of December 31, 1958, may be prepared are shown below:

MONARCH WHOLESALE CO.
WORKING PAPERS FOR CORRECTED BALANCE SHEET
DECEMBER 31, 1958

| ACCOUNT | BALANCES BEFORE CORRECTION | | CORRECTIONS | | CORRECTED BALANCES | |
|---|---|---|---|---|---|---|
| | DR. | CR. | DR. | CR. | DR. | CR. |
| Cash.............. | 14,230 | | | | 14,230 | |
| Notes Receivable.... | 15,000 | | | | 15,000 | |
| Accounts Receivable. | 24,000 | | | | 24,000 | |
| Allowance for Bad Debts........... | | | | (10a) 120<br>(10b) 250 | | 370 |
| Merchandise Inventory, Dec. 31...... | 12,000 | | | | 12,000 | |
| Unexpired Insurance. | 60 | | | | 60 | |
| Delivery Equipment........... | 8,000 | | | | 8,000 | |
| Allowance for Depreciation of Delivery Equipment....... | | 3,500 | | (8a) 100<br>(8b) 100 | | 3,700 |
| Notes Payable...... | | 6,500 | | | | 6,500 |
| Accounts Payable.... | | 9,500 | | | | 9,500 |
| Accrued Interest on Notes Payable..... | | 50 | | | | 50 |
| Unearned Rental Income.......... | | 240 | (9) 80 | | | 160 |
| Capital Stock, $10 par | | 40,000 | | | | 40,000 |
| Premium on Stock ... | | 10,000 | | | | 10,000 |
| Retained Earnings... | | 3,500 | (6b) 125<br>(7b) 210<br>(8a) 100<br>(8b) 100<br>(10a) 120<br>(10b) 250 | (9) 80 | | 2,675 |
| Unearned Interest Income ........... | | | | (6b) 125 | | 125 |
| Accrued Salaries..... | | | | (7b) 210 | | 210 |
| | 73,290 | 73,290 | 985 | 985 | 73,290 | 73,290 |

The corrected balance sheet prepared from the working papers appears on the opposite page.

## QUESTIONS

**1.** Name three errors that are counterbalanced in a succeeding period and that do not require corrections if discovered after such time.

**2.** Name three errors that will not be counterbalanced in a subsequent period and that require corrections upon their discovery.

## MONARCH WHOLESALE CO.
### CORRECTED BALANCE SHEET
### DECEMBER 31, 1958

### ASSETS

| | | | |
|---|---|---|---|
| Current assets: | | | |
| Cash | | $14,230 | |
| Notes receivable | | 15,000 | |
| Accounts receivable | $24,000 | | |
| Less: Allowance for bad debts | 370 | 23,630 | |
| Merchandise inventory | | 12,000 | |
| Unexpired insurance | | 60 | $64,920 |
| Delivery equipment: | | $ 8,000 | |
| Less: Allowance for depreciation | | 3,700 | 4,300 |
| Total assets | | | $69,220 |

### LIABILITIES

| | | | |
|---|---|---|---|
| Current liabilities: | | | |
| Notes payable | | $ 6,500 | |
| Accounts payable | | 9,500 | |
| Accrued interest on notes payable | | 50 | |
| Accrued salaries | | 210 | $16,260 |
| Deferred revenues: | | | |
| Unearned rental income | | $ 160 | |
| Unearned interest income | | 125 | 285 |
| Total liabilities | | | $16,545 |

### CAPITAL

| | | | |
|---|---|---|---|
| Paid-in capital: | | | |
| Capital stock, $10 par | $40,000 | | |
| Premium on stock | 10,000 | $50,000 | |
| Retained earnings | | 2,675 | |
| Total capital | | | 52,675 |
| Total liabilities and capital | | | $69,220 |

**3.** Name three errors that result in misstatements on the income statement but that do not affect the balance sheet at the end of the current period.

**4.** Name three errors that result in misstatements on the balance sheet but that do not affect the income statement at the end of the current period.

**5.** (a) What two methods of recording corrections in profit or loss of prior periods may be employed? (b) Which method do you prefer? Why?

**6.** The controller for the Wellman Co. states: "The understatement of an expense in one year calls for an overstatement of the same expense in the following year even when the error is discovered; if this is not done, expense will by-pass the income statement." Comment on this opinion.

7. State the effect upon net income in 1957 and 1958 of each of the following errors that are made at the end of 1957:

(a) Accrued salaries are understated.

(b) Accrued interest on notes receivable is understated.

(c) Prepaid interest on notes payable is understated.

(d) Unearned rental income is understated.

(e) Depreciation on a plant and equipment item is overlooked.

8. State the effect of each of the following errors made at the end of 1957 upon the balance sheets and the income statements prepared for 1957 and 1958:

(a) The ending inventory is understated as a result of an error in the count of goods on hand.

(b) The ending inventory is overstated as a result of the inclusion of goods acquired and held on a consignment basis.

(c) A purchase of merchandise at the end of 1957 is not recorded as such until payment is made for the goods in 1958; the goods purchased were included in the inventory at the end of 1957.

(d) A sale of merchandise at the end of 1957 is not recorded as such until cash is received for the goods in 1958; the goods sold were excluded from the inventory at the end of 1957.

(e) Goods shipped to consignees in 1957 were reported as sales; goods in the hands of consignees at the end of 1957 were ignored for inventory purposes; sale of such goods in 1958 and collections on such sales were recorded as credits to the receivables established with consignees in 1957.

## EXERCISES

*In solving the following exercises, assume that corrections in profits of prior periods are recorded in Retained Earnings.*

1. In reviewing the books and records of the Kane Co. at the beginning of 1959, it is found that the adjustments for accrued and prepaid interest as stated below were ignored in preparing statements in 1956, 1957, and 1958. (a) Give the entries to correct the accounts in 1959. (b) Assuming that the omissions were discovered before the books were closed at the end of 1958, what correcting entries and adjustments for year-end balances are required?

|  | END OF 1956 | END OF 1957 | END OF 1958 |
|---|---|---|---|
| (1) Accrued interest expense | $350 | $600 | $750 |
| (2) Prepaid interest expense | 110 | 130 | 125 |
| (3) Accrued interest income | 600 | 750 | 800 |
| (4) Unearned interest income | 15 | 45 | 40 |

2. The following errors were discovered in auditing the records for the Baylor Co. at the beginning of 1959 after the accounts were closed. What correcting entries are required?

(a) A sale for $250 had been recorded at the end of 1958; goods, cost $185, were set aside for shipment but were erroneously included in the ending inventory.

(b) Goods of $4,000 shipped to consignees were included in the ending inventory; however goods, cost $1,500, had been sold by consignees on December 31, but the company did not record the sales until January 15 when remittances of $1,850 were received from consignees relating to 1958 sales.

(c) A purchase of $350 was recorded in 1958, but the goods were not included in the ending inventory since they were not delivered by the transportation agency until January 2.

(d) Errors in extensions on inventory sheets were found that resulted in 1958 inventory overstatements of $650 and understatements of $310.

**3.** State the effect, if any, that each of the following errors of 1958 had on the statements prepared on December 31, 1958. Indicate the sections of the statements that are affected.

(a) The adjustment for interest accrued on notes receivable was omitted.

(b) The adjustment for interest collected but not earned was omitted. Income was originally credited for collections.

(c) No adjustment was made for rental income that was earned during 1958. Unearned Rental Income was originally credited for collections.

(d) Depreciation of office furniture was omitted.

(e) Merchandise received and on hand on December 31, 1958, was not included in the inventory figure, and no entry was made for the purchase until January 3, 1959.

(f) In December, 1958, an entry was made for a purchase of merchandise; the merchandise had not been received and was not included in the inventory of December 31, 1958, although the company had title to the goods.

(g) No adjustment was made for interest expense that should have been deferred.

**4.** Give the correcting entry that should be made in 1959 when each of the following errors is discovered:

(a) On December 20, 1958, $15 was deducted as interest on a note receivable for the period December 20 to January 19. Interest Income was credited. No adjustment was made on December 31.

(b) No adjustment was made on December 31, 1958, for the interest on a 60-day, 6%, $2,400 note receivable that is due on January 12.

(c) Accrued sales salaries of $300 were overlooked in adjusting the accounts at the end of 1958.

(d) During December, 1958, merchandise of $500 was received; this merchandise was included in the inventory, but no entry was made for the purchase until the invoice was received in January. At that time Purchases was debited.

(e) Prepaid Insurance was debited for $360, representing the premium for three years from October 1, 1958. No adjustment was made on December 31, 1958.

**5.** An auditor in examining a company's books and records on December 31, 1958, before the accounts are closed, discovers the following errors. What correcting entries are required?

(a) Office Equipment, cost $5,000, acquired on July 1, 1955, depreciated on a 5-year basis, was destroyed by fire on May 1, 1958. Cash was debited and Office Equipment was credited for $2,000, the proceeds from an insurance policy.

(b) Safety guards were installed on plant machinery at a cost of $2,000 at the beginning of July, 1957. Manufacturing Expense was charged for the betterment. The machinery had been acquired originally on July 1, 1955, and was being depreciated on a 10-year basis.

**6.** In auditing the accounts of Dudley and Bearman, Inc., on December 31, 1958, before accounts have been closed for the annual fiscal period, you find the following account:

MACHINERY

| 1956 | | | 1958 | | |
|---|---|---|---|---|---|
| Jan. 2 Machine 1 | 12,000 | | Apr. 1 Proceeds from sale | | |
| July 1 Machine 2 | 8,000 | | of Machine #2 | 4,600 | |

You find that, while each machine had an estimated life of 10 years, no depreciation has ever been recorded. Machine #2 was sold when it was found that the volume of production did not warrant its continued use. Give the correcting and adjusting entries required on December 31, 1958.

**7.** A condensed income statement for the Palmer Corporation for 1958 shows the following:

| | |
|---|---:|
| Net sales | $120,000 |
| Cost of goods sold | 85,000 |
| Gross profit on sales | $ 35,000 |
| Expenses | 37,500 |
| Net loss | $ 2,500 |

An investigation of the records made in 1959 discloses the following errors in summarizing transactions for 1958:

(a) The ending inventory was overstated $2,600.

(b) Purchases of $6,000 made at the end of the year were not recorded although the goods were received and were included in the physical inventory.

(c) Miscellaneous maintenance and repair items totaling $700 were recorded as additions to machinery in 1958, and depreciation at 5% was recognized as depreciation on such additions.

(d) Accrued expenses of $750 were ignored.

Prepare a corrected income statement for 1958 and entries to correct the accounts in 1959.

**8.** The Jarvis Co. reports net incomes for a three-year period as follows:

| | |
|---|---|
| 1956 | $16,500 |
| 1957 | 7,500 |
| 1958 | 12,000 |

In reviewing the accounts in 1959 after the books have been closed, you find that the following errors have been made in summarizing activities:

|                                                                 | 1956    | 1957    | 1958    |
| --------------------------------------------------------------- | ------- | ------- | ------- |
| Overstatement of inventories as a result of errors in count     | $1,500  | $4,000  | $1,800  |
| Understatement of accrued advertising                           | 250     | 600     | 350     |
| Overstatement of accrued interest income                        | 100     |         | 150     |
| Understatement of depreciation on property items still in use   | 600     | 600     | 750     |

(a) Prepare working papers summarizing corrections and reporting corrected net incomes for 1956, 1957, and 1958. (b) Give the entry to bring the books of the company up to date in 1959.

**9.** The Bayshore Corporation has recognized losses on accounts receivable in the periods in which accounts were determined to be bad, as follows:

|                | In 1956 | In 1957 | In 1958 |
| -------------- | ------- | ------- | ------- |
| 1954 Accounts  | $150    | $ 50    | ——      |
| 1955 Accounts  | 300     | 700     | $  250  |
| 1956 Accounts  | ——      | 450     | 1,200   |
| 1957 Accounts  | ——      | ——      | 200     |

In addition to the losses recognized to date, it is estimated that additional losses will be incurred as follows:

|                   |        |
| ----------------- | ------ |
| On 1957 accounts  | $  100 |
| On 1958 accounts  | 1,250  |

Reported net income for the Bayshore Co. was as follows:

| 1956 | $17,600 |
| ---- | ------- |
| 1957 | 20,000  |
| 1958 | 24,200  |

(a) Calculate corrected net income figures for 1956, 1957, and 1958. (b) What entry is required in 1959 in correcting the net income of prior periods?

## PROBLEMS

**25-1.** Before the accounts of the M. J. Thams Corp. are adjusted and closed for the annual fiscal period ended December 31, 1958, an examination of the company records by the auditor discloses the following facts. Give any correcting and adjusting entries called for by the information given. (Assume that corrections in profits and losses of past periods are recorded directly in Retained Earnings.)

(a) Accrued sales commissions had been overlooked in adjusting the accounts at the end of 1956 and 1957. Accrued amounts were: 1956, $475; 1957, $450. Accrued commissions at the end of 1958 are $570.

(b) Checks totaling $300 issued to former employees in 1956 are still outstanding. Present whereabouts of such employees are unknown, and it is doubtful whether the checks will ever be presented for payment.

(c) Raw materials, cost $600, received on December 31, 1957, had been included in the physical inventory taken on that date; however, the purchase was recorded when the invoice was received on January 4, 1958.

(d) Ten-year, 5% bonds of $1,000,000 were issued on January 1, 1955, bonds of $100,000 to be redeemed annually. Interest is payable annually on January 1. The bonds were sold at 89. One tenth of the discount had been amortized at the end of 1955, 1956, and 1957.

(e) In March, 1957, the company had received a 25% common stock dividend on 100 shares of Wilshire Farms common acquired in 1956 at 54. The shares received as a stock dividend had been sold for cash in April, 1957, at 60 and an income account had been credited for the full proceeds.

(f) Store Equipment, cost $70,000, book value $30,000, had been traded for new equipment priced at $100,000 on January 2, 1957. An allowance of $20,000 was received on equipment traded in; in recording the transaction, the entry was made in accordance with income tax requirements, the asset account showing the basis for tax purposes. Depreciation on a 10-year estimated life had also been recorded on the tax basis. It is decided to correct accounts so that the asset is reported at a cost of $100,000 with depreciation on this basis.

**25-2.** An auditor is engaged by the Marty-Lou Co. in March, 1959, to examine their books and records and to make whatever corrections are necessary. The retained earnings account on the date of the audit is as follows:

RETAINED EARNINGS

| | | | | | |
|---|---|---|---|---|---|
| Jan. 10, 1957 | Dividends paid | 6,000 | Jan. 1, 1956 | Balance | 30,600 |
| Dec. 31, 1957 | Net loss for year | 3,600 | Dec. 31, 1956 | Net income | |
| Jan. 10, 1958 | Dividends paid | 6,000 | | for year | 7,050 |
| Dec. 31, 1958 | Net loss for year | 8,000 | Mar. 6, 1957 | Premium on | |
| | | | | sale of capital | |
| | | | | stock | 14,750 |

An examination of the accounts discloses the following:

(1) Dividends had been declared on December 15 in 1956 and 1957 but had not been entered in the books until paid.

(2) Betterments in plant and equipment of $3,600 had been charged to expense at the end of April, 1955. Such improvements are estimated to have an 8-year life.

(3) The physical inventory of merchandise taken at the end of 1956 had been overstated by $1,200.

(4) The merchandise inventories at the end of 1957 and 1958 did not include merchandise that was then in transit and to which the company had title. These shipments of $1,600 and $3,000 respectively were recorded as purchases in January of 1958 and 1959 respectively.

(5) The company had failed to record accrued sales commissions of $600 and $850 at the end of 1957 and 1958 respectively.

*Instructions:* (1) Prepare working papers for the correction of account balances similar to those illustrated on pages 805 and 807, using the following columns:

| EXPLANATION | RETAINED EARNINGS JAN. 1, 1956 | | PROFIT AND LOSS YR. ENDED DEC. 31, 1956 | | PROFIT AND LOSS YR. ENDED DEC. 31, 1957 | | PROFIT AND LOSS YR. ENDED DEC. 31, 1958 | | ACCOUNTS REQUIRING CORRECTION IN 1959 | | |
|---|---|---|---|---|---|---|---|---|---|---|---|
|  | DR. | CR. | DR. | CR. | DR. | CR. | DR. | CR. | DR. | CR. | ACCOUNT |
|  |  |  |  |  |  |  |  |  |  |  |  |

(2) Journalize corrections required in March, 1959, in compound form.

(3) Prepare a statement of retained earnings covering the 3-year period beginning January 1, 1956. This statement should report the corrected retained earnings balance on January 1, 1956, the annual changes in the account, and the corrected retained earnings balances as of December 31, 1956, 1957, and 1958.

(4) Set up an account for retained earnings before correction, and post correcting data to this account from part (2) above. Balance the account, showing the corrected retained earnings as of December 31, 1958.

**25-3.** The retained earnings account for the Searles Company at the end of 1958 appears below:

RETAINED EARNINGS

| | | | |
|---|---|---|---|
| Dec. 31, 1957 Net loss for year | 1,200 | December 31, 1956 Balance | 20,000 |
| Dec. 31, 1958 Net loss for year | 3,200 | | |

An audit of the books of the company in February, 1959, disclosed the following errors in recording activities for 1956, 1957, and 1958:

(1) No adjustment was made on December 31, 1957, for accrued wages of $500.

(2) On December 10, 1957, a 60-day, $12,000, non-interest-bearing note was received from a customer and the customer was given credit for $12,000 less 6% discount for the 60 days. The discount was entered in a nominal account. No adjustment was made on December 31, 1957.

(3) At the end of 1957 an adjustment for $300 representing depreciation on a delivery truck was omitted. (The correct depreciation for 1958 was recorded on December 31, 1958.)

(4) Because of errors in counting, the physical inventory of merchandise taken on December 31, 1956, was overstated by $600; the inventory taken on December 31, 1957, was understated by $1,000.

(5) In March, 1958, a $700 balance of 1957 accounts receivable was written off to Loss from Bad Debts. The loss should have been identified with operations of 1957.

(6) Merchandise of $600 was received on December 31, 1957, and was included in the physical inventory taken on that date. The purchase was not recorded until the invoice was received January 6, 1958.

(7) On May 1, 1957, $360 was charged to Unexpired Insurance for a 3-year fire insurance policy on a building. No adjustments for the premium were made at the end of 1957 and 1958.

(8) On December 20, 1957, the company borrowed $2,400 on a non-interest-bearing note payable. The bank deducted 6% for 60 days,

the company charging Interest Expense for the discount. No adjustment was made on December 31, 1957.

(9) No adjustment was made on December 31, 1958, for accrued interest on a $1,200, 6%, 60-day note receivable that was dated December 17, 1958.

(10) The Unearned Rental Income account was credited on December 1, 1958, for $300 representing rent received for a 3-month period from that date. No adjustment was made on December 31, 1958.

(11) The company gave a $900, 6%, 60-day note payable to the First State Bank on December 8, 1958. No adjustment for accrued interest was made on December 31, 1958.

(12) Merchandise ordered at a cost of $100 during December, 1958, was received on December 31, 1958, but was not included in the inventory. The purchase was recorded when payment for the purchase was made on January 5, 1959.

*Instructions:* (1) Prepare working papers for the correction of account balances similar to those illustrated on pages 805 and 807, with the following columns:

| EXPLANATION | RETAINED EARNINGS DEC. 31, 1956 | | PROFIT AND LOSS YR. ENDED DEC. 31, 1957 | | PROFIT AND LOSS YR. ENDED DEC. 31, 1958 | | ACCOUNTS REQUIRING CORRECTION IN 1959 | | |
|---|---|---|---|---|---|---|---|---|---|
| | DR. | CR. | DR. | CR. | DR. | CR. | DR. | CR. | ACCOUNT |
| | | | | | | | | | |

(2) Prepare a compound journal entry to correct the accounts in February, 1959.

(3) Prepare the retained earnings account as it would have appeared if no errors had been made to prove the correction to Retained Earnings in part (2) above.

**25-4.** The statements at the top of the opposite page were prepared for the Nashton Company at the end of 1958.

During February, 1959, the following information is disclosed in connection with an audit of the books of the company:

(1) Store equipment that cost $4,500 and that had an estimated life of 6 years when purchased on January 2, 1956, is estimated at this time to have a life of 10 years.

(2) The merchandise inventory as of December 31, 1958, was overstated by $720.

(3) Merchandise in transit amounting to $1,320 was not included in the inventory of December 31, 1958, but the invoice had been entered in the purchases journal in 1958.

(4) A loss of $2,000 resulting from fire, the loss not being covered by insurance, was charged to General Expenses in 1958.

(5) On January 3, 1958, store equipment costing $5,000, with an allowance for depreciation of $4,000, was sold for $600. Cash was debited and Store Equipment was credited for this amount.

| INCOME STATEMENT FOR YEAR ENDED DEC. 31, 1958 | | |
|---|---|---|
| Sales | | 87,000 |
| Cost of Goods Sold: | | |
| Mdse. Inv., Jan. 1 | 24,000 | |
| Purchases | 48,000 | |
| Mdse. Available for Sale | 72,000 | |
| Less: | | |
| Mdse. Inv., Dec. 31 | 23,000 | 49,000 |
| Gross Profit on Sales | | 38,000 |
| Operating Expenses: | | |
| Selling Expenses | 16,000 | |
| General Expenses | 10,000 | |
| Total Operating Expenses | | 26,000 |
| Net Profit from Operations | | 12,000 |
| Other Income and Expenses: | | |
| Other Income: | | |
| Royalty Income | 900 | |
| Rental Income | 3,000 | |
| | 3,900 | |
| Other Expense: | | |
| Interest Expense | 1,400 | |
| Add excess of other income over other expenses | | 2,500 |
| Net Income | | 14,500 |

| BALANCE SHEET DECEMBER 31, 1958 | | |
|---|---|---|
| Assets: | | |
| Cash | | 16,200 |
| Accounts Receivable | 14,000 | |
| Less: | | |
| All. for Bad Debts | 560 | 13,440 |
| Mdse. Inventory | | 23,000 |
| Delivery Equipment | | 800 |
| Store Equipment | 12,000 | |
| Less: | | |
| All. for Depr. | 7,000 | 5,000 |
| Building | 40,000 | |
| Less: | | |
| All. for Depr. | 20,000 | 20,000 |
| Land | | 18,000 |
| Total Assets | | 96,440 |
| Liabilities: | | |
| Accounts Payable | | 13,600 |
| Capital: | | |
| Capital Stock, $1 par | 50,000 | |
| Retained Earnings | 32,840 | |
| Total Capital | | 82,840 |
| Total Liabilities and Capital | | 96,440 |

(6) A truck was purchased on a conditional sales contract on December 30, 1958. The total purchase price was $2,500, but the purchase was recorded by a debit to Delivery Equipment and a credit to Cash for $800, the amount of the down payment.

(7) A check for $64 received from Joseph Voss on account had been deposited and then returned in December, 1958, by the bank. No entry was made when the bank returned the check. The cash was collected from Voss on January 20, 1959.

(8) A part of the building was leased for $3,000 for 12 months ending April 30, 1959. The cash received was reported as income for 1958.

*Instructions:* (1) Prepare working papers for the correction of account balances in 1959 similar to those illustrated on pages 805 and 807, with the following columns:

| EXPLANATION | RETAINED EARNINGS DECEMBER 31, 1957 | | PROFIT AND LOSS YEAR ENDED DEC. 31, 1958 | | ACCOUNTS REQUIRING CORRECTION IN 1959 | | |
|---|---|---|---|---|---|---|---|
| | DR. | CR. | DR. | CR. | DR. | CR. | ACCOUNT |
| | | | | | | | |

(2) Prepare a compound entry to correct the accounts in February, 1959.

(3) Prepare working papers for a corrected income statement and for a corrected balance sheet for 1958.

(4) Prepare a corrected income statement and a balance sheet.

**25-5.** The statements that follow were prepared for Gerry, Inc. at the end of 1958:

| INCOME STATEMENT FOR YEAR ENDED DEC. 31, 1958 | | | BALANCE SHEET DECEMBER 31, 1958 | | |
|---|---|---|---|---|---|
| Sales | 204,000 | | Assets: | | |
| Less: Sales Discounts | 3,000 | 201,000 | Cash | 73,000 | |
| | | | Petty Cash | 200 | |
| Cost of Goods Sold: | | | Accounts Receivable | 52,000 | |
| Mdse. Inv., Jan. 1 | 66,000 | | Mdse. Inventory | 70,000 | |
| Purchases | 140,000 | | Investment in Bonds | 50,000 | |
| Mdse. Available for Sale | 206,000 | | Total Assets | | 245,200 |
| Less Mdse. Inv., Dec. 31 | 70,000 | 136,000 | | | |
| | | | Liabilities: | | |
| Gross Profit on Sales | | 65,000 | Accounts Payable | 34,800 | |
| Operating Expenses: | | | Bonds Payable | 96,000 | |
| Selling Expense | 27,000 | | Total Liabilities | | 130,800 |
| General Expense | 32,000 | | | | |
| Total Operating Expenses | | 59,000 | Capital: | | |
| Net Profit from Operations | | 6,000 | Capital Stock, $5 par | 80,000 | |
| | | | Retained Earnings | 34,400 | |
| Other Income: | | | Total Capital | | 114,400 |
| Interest Income | | 1,500 | | | |
| Net Income | | 7,500 | Total Liabilities and Capital | | 245,200 |

During January, 1959, the following facts were discovered:

(a) On January 2, 1958, a 3-year fire insurance policy was purchased for $480 and charged to General Expense. No adjustment was made at the end of 1958 for the unexpired insurance.

(b) Ten-year, 5% bonds of $100,000 par were issued at 96 on June 30, 1958. The bonds payable account was credited for the amount of cash received. The interest is payable annually on June 30. No adjustments were made at the end of 1958.

(c) A 25% stock dividend, payable on February 1, 1959, was declared on December 15, 1958. No entry had been made.

(d) The petty cash fund, kept under the imprest system, had not been replenished at the end of the fiscal period. Payments had been made out of the fund as follows: $70 for General Expense and $60 for Selling Expense.

(e) 5% bonds, face value $50,000, had been purchased at face value on January 2, 1958. Interest is collected semiannually on January 1 and July 1. No adjustment for accrued interest was made at the end of 1958.

(f) Accrued expenses of $55 for utilities had not been included in the adjustments at the end of 1958.

(g) The board of directors had authorized an appropriation of retained earnings of $10,000 for possible losses on damage suits at the end of 1958. No entry had been made.

(h) Accounts receivable have been written off when discovered to be uncollectible as follows:

|                      | In 1957 | In 1958 |
| -------------------- | ------- | ------- |
| 1956 accounts.       | $350    | $150    |
| 1957 accounts.       | 250     | 300     |
| 1958 accounts.       | —       | 100     |

In addition to the losses recognized to date, it is estimated that additional losses will be incurred as follows: on 1957 accounts, $100; on 1958 accounts, $500.

*Instructions:* (1) Prepare working papers for the correction of account balances in 1959 similar to those illustrated on pages 805 and 807, with the following columns:

| EXPLANATION | RETAINED EARNINGS DECEMBER 31, 1958 | | ACCOUNTS REQUIRING CORRECTION IN 1959 | | |
| --- | --- | --- | --- | --- | --- |
| | DR. | CR. | DR. | CR. | ACCOUNT |
| | | | | | |

(2) Prepare a compound entry to correct the accounts in January, 1959.

(3) Prepare working papers for corrected statements and prepare a corrected income statement and a corrected balance sheet for 1958.

**25-6.** The White-Knoll Axle Co. was organized January 2, 1956. Before the accounts of the company are adjusted and closed at the end of the annual fiscal period, December 31, 1958, an auditor is engaged for the first time to inspect the books and records of the corporation and to prepare the necessary correcting, adjusting, and closing entries and the accounting statements. Examination of the books and records by the auditor discloses the following:

(a) The cash balance includes: (1) A check for $799 signed by Fred Hyde and returned to the company by the bank marked "Not Sufficient Funds." (2) I.O.U.'s for $600 representing advances to employees. (3) $10,000 that is on deposit in the bank as a fund to provide for the retirement of bonds on their maturity.

(b) The notes receivable balance includes: (1) Notes past due of $6,000 (all of the notes were obtained by the corporation in 1956), of which notes of $2,000 are known to be uncollectible. No allowance for doubtful notes had been provided. It is decided that an allowance of $500 should be set up for possible losses on the remaining overdue notes. (2) Notes from officers of the corporation, $15,000.

(c) The accounts receivable balance includes accounts of $2,800 that are known to be uncollectible. The allowance for doubtful accounts is to be increased by 1% of net sales. Net sales during 1958 were $415,000.

(d) The auditor is given the following physical inventory figures for use in making inventory adjustments:

Finished Goods........................................ $27,000
Raw Materials........................................ 14,300
Goods in Process..................................... 18,300

However, it is found that the finished goods figure includes: (1) merchandise costing $2,000 that has been set aside for shipment, the entry for the sale already having been made; (2) merchandise that has been returned by a customer included in the inventory at the selling price, $3,000. The company sells merchandise at a gross profit of 25% of the sales price.

It is also found that the raw materials figure reports raw materials at market price, which is 10% above the cost to the company.

Raw materials included in the goods in process balance are estimated at $8,250, which is also 10% above cost.

(e) The machinery and equipment account has a balance of $60,000 that includes: (1) the cost of additional machinery purchased at the end of July, 1958, $6,000; (2) the cost of repairs to machinery during 1958, $500, which was improperly capitalized. Machinery and equipment is depreciated at 5% per year.

(f) The store furniture and fixtures account has a balance of $15,000 that includes a purchase of furniture at the end of March, 1957, $400, upon which no depreciation has been recorded. Store furniture and fixtures is depreciated on an estimated 5-year life.

(g) Delivery equipment is shown at a cost of $10,000. Equipment costing $8,000 was purchased on January 2, 1956, and the remainder was purchased January 2, 1957. The equipment has been depreciated on a 5-year life with an estimated salvage value of 10% of cost. It is now believed, however, that all of the equipment will have to be replaced at the end of 1959; the salvage value at that time is estimated to be 15% of cost for equipment purchased in 1956 and 25% of cost for equipment purchased in 1957.

(h) The shipping equipment account is shown at a cost of $5,000 on January 2, 1958, representing equipment purchased January 2, 1956. No additional purchases have been made. On December 1, 1958, equipment costing $600 was destroyed by fire. It is estimated that insurance of $400 may be recovered on this loss. No entries have been made with regard to the loss and probable recovery. The depreciation rate on the shipping equipment is 10%.

(i) Prepaid items are to be reduced as follows: (1) Prepaid Insurance by $1,750, the amount of insurance expired; (2) Office Supplies by $370, the cost of office supplies consumed.

(j) Prepaid interest on notes payable is $180. The company has failed to record prepaid interest on notes payable at the end of the past two years as follows: 1956, $150; 1957, $300.

(k) Accrued interest on notes receivable is $410. The company has failed to record accrued interest at the end of the past two years as follows: 1956, $350; 1957, $340.

(l) Ten-year, 5% bonds of $100,000 were issued at 90 on July 1, 1957. The company has failed to amortize any of the discount.

(m) Accrued office salaries are $450. The company has failed to record accrued office salaries at the end of the past two years as follows: 1956, $350; 1957, $540.

(n) Accrued interest on notes payable at the end of 1958 is $200.

(o) It is determined that the company failed to record unearned interest on notes receivable of $150 at the end of 1957.

*Instructions:* Prepare the correcting and adjusting entries required at the end of 1958 as a result of the foregoing data. (Assume that corrections in net income of prior periods are recorded directly in Retained Earnings. No closing entries or financial statements are required.)

**25-7.** After the various nominal accounts are closed into the profit and loss summary account for the year ended December 31, 1958, but *before* the profit and loss summary account is closed into earned surplus, the books of Clay, Incorporated show a profit of $200,000. In arriving at this profit, the company's bookkeeper took into account the actual cash receipts and disbursements during the year with regard to the following:

| | |
|---|---:|
| Interest received...................................... | $ 9,000 |
| Interest paid......................................... | 1,250 |
| Taxes paid........................................... | 12,000 |
| Insurance paid....................................... | 7,000 |
| Cash discounts allowed customers..................... | 12,500 |

The accruals that were not taken into consideration at the end of the previous year and the accruals at the end of the current year are as follows:

| | DECEMBER 31 | |
|---|---|---|
| | 1957 | 1958 |
| Interest receivable accrued.............. | $2,500 | $3,000 |
| Interest payable accrued................ | 200 | 180 |
| Taxes prepaid......................... | 2,500 | 3,000 |
| Insurance prepaid..................... | 3,250 | 2,000 |
| Res. for cash discounts on accts. rec....... | 3,750 | 2,500 |
| Depreciation omitted................... | 1,500 | 2,000 |
| | overstated | understated |
| Inventory at close.................... | $2,000 | $ 500 |

*Instructions:* Prepare the journal entries, with explanations, that will serve to correct the profit and loss account for 1958 and to bring into the balance sheet the proper accounts and amounts as of December 31, 1958. (A.I.C.P.A. adapted)

**25-8.** The surplus account of the Walker Manufacturing Company appears as follows:

SURPLUS

| | | | |
|---|---:|---|---:|
| Dividends, 1956 | 40,000.00 | Balance, Dec. 31, 1955 | 235,000.00 |
| Dividends, 1957 | 35,000.00 | Profits, 1956 | 65,000.00 |
| Dividends, 1958 | 20,000.00 | Profits, 1957 | 78,300.00 |
| Balance, Dec. 31, 1958 | 331,300.00 | Profits, 1958 | 48,000.00 |
| | 426,300.00 | | 426,300.00 |

The company has not provided for accruals and deferred items in closing its books and has ignored the following items at the various dates of closing:

| | DEFERRED CHARGES | DEFERRED INCOME | ACCRUED EXPENSES | ACCRUED INCOME |
|---|---|---|---|---|
| December 31, 1955 | $2,125.00 | ........ | $5,200.00 | $475.00 |
| December 31, 1956 | 2,640.00 | ........ | 3,135.00 | ....... |
| December 31, 1957 | 3,100.00 | $1,250.00 | 6,120.00 | 290.00 |
| December 31, 1958 | 1,950.00 | 700.00 | 4,200.00 | ....... |

In closing the books the inventory was priced at cost or market, whichever was lower, and, in addition, reserves for possible future declines in market value were set up as follows:

At December 31, 1956.................................... $ 8,000.00
At December 31, 1957.................................... 12,600.00
At December 31, 1958.................................... 9,250.00

Each reserve was set up by a charge to Profit and Loss and remained on the books until the next closing, when it was credited to the account with the opening inventory. The reserve set up at the end of 1958 is still on the books.

Consigned goods have been included in the inventories at billed price. The company has billed all goods sent to consignees at 130% of the cost. The following consigned goods inventories have been included:

At December 31, 1956.................................... $15,600.00
At December 31, 1957.................................... 10,400.00
At December 31, 1958.................................... 18,200.00

*Instructions:* Prepare a corrected statement of surplus from December 31, 1955, to December 31, 1958. (A.I.C.P.A. adapted)

**25-9.** The Mills Company has paid no dividends in recent years. The books show a surplus at December 31, 1958, of $421,000 made up as follows:

Balance at December 31, 1956........................... $189,000
Profit, 1957........................................... 92,000
Profit, 1958........................................... 140,000

$421,000

The following matters call for consideration at the close of the respective years:

DECEMBER 31, 1956:

(1) Bad debts amount to $12,000 and are to be written off Accounts Receivable.

(2) Consigned goods (own) are included in the inventory at $120,000 and are priced at 20% in excess of cost.

(3) The following liabilities are omitted from the books:

New construction....................................... $25,000
Material included in inventory......................... 3,000
Wages.................................................. 2,400
Accrued taxes.......................................... 1,700

DECEMBER 31, 1957:

(4) Bad debts amount to $9,000 and are to be written off Accounts Receivable.

(5) Consigned goods (own) amount to $180,000, which is 20% in excess of cost.

(6) Liabilities omitted from the books are:

| | |
|---|---:|
| Goods on hand (also omitted from inventory) | $ 8,000 |
| Accrued taxes | 2,100 |

(7) Plant additions, amounting to $9,000, have been erroneously charged to Profit and Loss.

(8) The inventory is found to be overstated by $14,300 because of an error in recapitulation.

(9) No provision for depreciation was made on the books; your calculations show that $5,000 should be provided.

DECEMBER 31, 1958:

(10) Bad debts amounting to $11,000 are to be written off Accounts Receivable.

(11) Consigned goods (own) amount to $156,000, being valued at 30% in excess of cost.

(12) Liabilities omitted from the books are:

| | |
|---|---:|
| For purchases of new machinery | $12,000 |
| Accrued wages | 3,200 |
| Accrued taxes | 2,700 |

(13) No provision was made in the books for depreciation; your calculations show that $7,000 should be provided.

(14) The profits for the year include a credit of $8,000 in settlement of a lawsuit arising from transactions of the year 1955.

*Instructions:* Prepare a reconciliation of the surplus at December 31, 1956, and of the profits in 1957 and 1958, as shown by the books, with the adjusted figures as shown by the audited statement. (A.I.C.P.A. adapted)

**25-10.** The trial balance of the Albers Company on December 31, 1958, is given at the top of the following page.

An examination of the company books discloses the following facts:

(1) Checks totaling $10,000 in settlement of accounts payable were dated and issued in December, 1958, but were not entered in the cashbook until January, 1959.

(2) Accounts Receivable includes an amount of $400,000 representing capital advances to subsidiary companies. The balance is receivable from customers.

(3) It is estimated that 10% of the customers' accounts receivable and 10% of the notes receivable are doubtful of collection. All accounts and notes were considered collectible at the beginning of the year.

(4) The inventory at January 1, 1958, includes the following:

| | |
|---|---:|
| Machinery and equipment | $200,000 |
| Less — Allowance for depreciation | 100,000 |
| | $100,000 |

(5) The inventory at December 31, 1958 (excluding Machinery and Equipment and its related allowance), is as follows:

| | | |
|---|---:|---:|
| Inventory on hand | $500,000 | |
| Inventory in transit for which the liability has not been recorded | 10,000 | $510,000 |

## ALBERS COMPANY
### TRIAL BALANCE
### DECEMBER 31, 1958

| | | |
|---|---:|---:|
| Cash in banks......................................... | $ 180,000 | |
| Petty cash funds...................................... | 5,000 | |
| Customers' notes receivable............................ | 80,000 | |
| Accounts receivable.................................... | 900,000 | |
| Current advances to subsidiary companies................ | 25,000 | |
| Investment in subsidiary companies..................... | 500,000 | |
| Land.................................................. | 5,000 | |
| Buildings............................................. | 20,000 | |
| Machinery and equipment.............................. | 50,000 | |
| Furniture and fixtures................................. | 40,000 | |
| Allowance for depreciation, Jan. 1, 1958................ | | $ 35,000 |
| Life insurance........................................ | 200,000 | |
| Inventory at Jan. 1, 1958............................. | 500,000 | |
| Trade creditors....................................... | | 220,000 |
| Common stock ($100 par) authorized and issued.......... | | 500,000 |
| Surplus at Jan. 1, 1958............................... | | 960,000 |
| Net sales............................................. | | 5,800,000 |
| Purchases............................................. | 3,500,000 | |
| Manufacturing expenses................................ | 400,000 | |
| Selling, administrative, and general expense............. | 1,150,000 | |
| Other income......................................... | | 40,000 |
| | $7,555,000 | $7,555,000 |

(6) The balance of the life insurance account represents the accumulated premiums that were charged to this account. The premiums paid to December 31, 1957, amounted to $160,000, and the premiums paid in 1958 amounted to $40,000. An examination of the policies shows that the cash surrender value at December 31, 1957, amounted to $85,000, and the cash surrender value at December 31, 1958, amounted to $100,000.

(7) There has been no change in the various property accounts during 1958. Depreciation should be provided at the following rates:

| | |
|---|---:|
| Buildings...................................... | 5% per year |
| Machinery and equipment...................... | 10% per year |
| General office furniture and fixtures............. | 10% per year |

(8) Insurance premiums, charged to General Expense:

| | |
|---|---:|
| Prepaid at December 31, 1957...................... | $3,000 |
| Prepaid at December 31, 1958...................... | 2,000 |

(9) Taxes, charged to General Expense:

| | |
|---|---:|
| Prepaid at December 31, 1957...................... | $5,000 |
| Prepaid at December 31, 1958...................... | 8,000 |

(10) Commissions, charged to selling expenses:

| | |
|---|---:|
| Accrued at December 31, 1957...................... | $4,000 |
| Accrued at December 31, 1958...................., | 5,000 |

Inventories, fixed assets, and investments are shown throughout at cost. Income taxes are not to be considered.

*Instructions:* Prepare working papers showing the necessary adjustments and the segregation of balance sheet and profit and loss items. (A.I.C.P.A. adapted)

# Chapter 26

# FINANCIAL STATEMENT ANALYSIS

## USE OF COMPARATIVE DATA

**STATEMENT ANALYSIS**  The financial statements give vital information concerning the position of the enterprise and the results of its operation.  This information is important to the many groups that are interested in the business, including:

1. The owners — sole proprietor, partners, or stockholders.
2. The management.
3. The creditors.
4. Prospective owners and prospective creditors.
5. Government — local, state, and federal, including regulatory, taxing, and analysis units.
6. Employees of the business and their labor unions.
7. The general public.

Analysis of the data reported on the financial statements is necessary in reaching conclusions regarding financial position and operations.  The nature of the analysis will depend upon the type of questions that are raised.  For example, inquiry concerning the current condition of a company may be answered by comparing current assets as reported on the balance sheet with current liabilities.  Questions concerning growth of a company or the trend of dollar sales can be answered only by reference to income statements for a number of periods.  Questions concerning the relationship of earnings to investment are answered by a comparison of income statement and proprietorship data.  The process of analysis involves the development of comparisons and the measurement of relationships.  The results of analysis will form the bases for conclusions that are made and the policies that are adopted with respect to the business.

When the financial position and the progress of a business are being considered, three general factors are normally of primary interest: (1) its solvency, (2) its stability, and (3) its profitability.

To be solvent, a business must be able to meet its liabilities as they mature.  Statements are analyzed to determine whether the business is and will continue to be solvent.  Such analysis includes studies of the relationship of current assets to current liabilities, the security afforded the various groups through the soundness of asset values, the size and the nature of the various creditor and ownership equities, and the amounts and the trend of periodic earnings.

Stability is judged by (a) the company's ability currently to meet interest requirements on its debt and ultimately to repay principal amounts owed, and (b) the company's ability to pay dividends regularly to its stockholders. In judging stability, data concerning both operations and financial position require study. There must be a regular demand for the goods or services sold, and the margin on sales must be sufficient to provide for dividends after operating expenses and interest charges have been fully met. There should be a satisfactory turnover of current assets. Plant and equipment must be productively employed.

Profitability is measured by the company's success in maintaining and increasing the owners' equity as indicated by its income statements. The nature and the amount of earnings as well as their regularity and trend are all significant in an appraisal of profitability.

Although attention is normally directed to an evaluation of each of the foregoing factors, analysis must also serve the various groups that have certain special questions of individual interest. For example, management seeks guides to better control, to more satisfactory selling, purchasing, and financing policies, and to more efficient utilization of plant and equipment. Creditors are interested not only in a company's position as a "going concern," but also in its position should it be forced to liquidate and become a "quitting concern." Owners may be interested in the question of expansion and whether this should be effected through the retention of earnings, through additional borrowing, or through increased investment by owners.

The various groups interested in the facts of business have looked to the accountant, not only for general purpose financial statements concerning position and the results of operations, but also for the special analyses of financial data that they may require for their own individual purposes. They have looked to the accountant as best qualified to develop analytical data in view of his full appreciation of the conventions and processes that are applied in developing statements that form the basis for analysis. It is not uncommon now for the accountant to submit, along with the regular financial statements, comprehensive analyses of significant financial information that will assist individuals in reaching intelligent conclusions with respect to the business.

**PRIMARY INSPECTION OF FINANCIAL STATEMENTS**    Obviously, if analytical data are to be reliable, they must be developed from financial statements that properly exhibit the facts of business. As a first step, statements to be used as a basis for analysis should be carefully reviewed to determine whether they display any shortcomings or discrepancies.  In the course of the examination, the following questions should be asked: Is there full disclosure of all relevant financial data?  Have proper accounting standards and procedures been employed?  Have appropriate and consistent bases for valuation been used?  Are the data properly classified?  Where necessary, statements should be corrected so that they report the full financial story in conformance with accepted accounting standards.

**ANALYTICAL PROCEDURES**     Analytical procedures fall into two main categories: (1) comparisons and measurements based upon financial data for two or more periods, and (2) comparisons and measurements based upon the financial data of only the current fiscal period.  The first category includes the preparation of comparative statements, the determination of ratios and trends for data on successive balance sheets and income statements, and special analyses of changes in balance sheet items and operating data.  The second category includes the determination of current balance sheet and profit and loss relationships and special analyses of earnings and earning power.  Normally, an adequate review of financial data requires analyses based upon both current data and data covering a number of periods.

The analytical procedures that are commonly employed are illustrated in this and the next two chapters.  While individual analyses will be presented in report and tabular forms, such data are frequently reported in graphic form for more effective presentation of significant financial relationships.  It should be emphasized that the various analyses are simply guides to the evaluation of financial data.  Sound conclusions are reached only through intelligent use and interpretation.

**COMPARATIVE STATEMENTS**     Financial data become more meaningful when compared with similar data for a previous period or a number of prior periods.  Statements prepared in a form that reflects financial data for two or more periods are known as *comparative statements*.  Annual data can be compared with similar data for prior years.  Monthly or quarterly data can be compared with similar data for the previous months or quarters or similar data for the same months or quarters of previous years. Accounting authorities have strongly encouraged the preparation of statements in comparative form.  The Committee on Accounting Procedure of the American Institute recommends that the use of comparative statements be extended.  In taking this position, it comments:

The presentation of comparative financial statements in annual and other reports enhances the usefulness of such reports and brings out more clearly the nature and trends of current changes affecting the enterprise. Such presentation emphasizes the fact that statements for a series of periods are far more significant than those for a single period and that the accounts for one period are but an instalment of what is essentially a continuous history.

In any one year it is ordinarily desirable that the balance sheet, the income statement, and the surplus statement be given for one or more preceding years as well as for the current year. Footnotes, explanations, and accountants' qualifications which appeared on the statements for the preceding years should be repeated, or at least referred to, in the comparative statements to the extent that they continue to be of significance. If, because of reclassifications or for other reasons, changes have occurred in the manner of or basis for presenting corresponding items for two or more periods, information should be furnished which will explain the change. This procedure is in conformity with the well recognized principle that any change in practice which affects comparability should be disclosed.[1]

Companies in increasing number each year are issuing statements prepared in comparative form.

**COMPARATIVE STATE-MENTS—HORIZONTAL ANALYSIS** Regardless of its financial strength at a given point, a company must operate successfully if it hopes to continue as a going concern. The income statement measures the effects of operations. The progress of these operations may be viewed over a number of periods by preparing the income statement in comparative form. The comparative report may go beyond a simple listing of comparative values by offering analytical information in the form of the dollar changes and the percentage changes in profit and loss data for several periods under review. The absolute changes, together with the relative changes, are thus shown. The development of data summarizing changes taking place over a number of periods is known as *horizontal analysis*. A comparative income statement for the Marshall Company reporting both dollar and percentage changes for a three-year period is illustrated on the following page.

It would be possible to show the detail concerning cost of goods sold, expenses, other income, and other expense by expanding this statement or by providing this detail by means of separate comparative schedules. A comparative schedule reporting the cost of goods sold data, for example, is also illustrated on the next page.

The effects of operations on financial position and the progress of a business in terms of financial position can be presented by means

[1] *Accounting Research Bulletin No. 43*, "Restatement and Revision of Accounting Research Bulletins," 1953 (New York: American Institute of Certified Public Accountants), p. 15.

MARSHALL COMPANY
CONDENSED COMPARATIVE INCOME STATEMENT
FOR THE YEARS ENDED DECEMBER 31, 1956, 1957, AND 1958

| | 1956 | 1957 | 1958 | INCREASE OR DECREASE* | | | |
| --- | --- | --- | --- | --- | --- | --- | --- |
| | | | | 1956-1957 | | 1957-1958 | |
| | | | | AMOUNT | PER CENT | AMOUNT | PER CENT |
| Gross sales................ | 1,000,000 | 1,750,000 | 1,500,000 | 750,000 | 75% | 250,000* | 14%* |
| Sales returns............. | 50,000 | 100,000 | 75,000 | 50,000 | 100% | 25,000* | 25%* |
| Net sales................. | 950,000 | 1,650,000 | 1,425,000 | 700,000 | 74% | 225,000* | 14%* |
| Cost of goods sold......... | 630,000 | 1,200,000 | 1,000,000 | 570,000 | 90% | 200,000* | 17%* |
| Gross profit on sales........ | 320,000 | 450,000 | 425,000 | 130,000 | 41% | 25,000* | 6%* |
| Selling expenses........... | 240,000 | 300,000 | 280,000 | 60,000 | 25% | 20,000* | 7%* |
| General expenses.......... | 100,000 | 110,000 | 100,000 | 10,000 | 10% | 10,000* | 9%* |
| Total expenses............ | 340,000 | 410,000 | 380,000 | 70,000 | 21% | 30,000* | 7%* |
| Net profit or loss* from operations................... | 20,000* | 40,000 | 45,000 | 60,000 | — | 5,000 | 13% |
| Other income ............ | 50,000 | 65,000 | 75,000 | 15,000 | 30% | 10,000 | 15% |
| | 30,000 | 105,000 | 120,000 | 75,000 | 250% | 15,000 | 14% |
| Other expenses ........... | 10,000 | 20,000 | 20,000 | 10,000 | 100% | — | — |
| Net income before income tax | 20,000 | 85,000 | 100,000 | 65,000 | 325% | 15,000 | 18% |
| Income taxes ............. | 5,000 | 25,000 | 30,000 | 20,000 | 400% | 5,000 | 20% |
| Net income after income taxes. | 15,000 | 60,000 | 70,000 | 45,000 | 300% | 10,000 | 17% |

MARSHALL COMPANY
COMPARATIVE SCHEDULE OF COST OF GOODS SOLD
FOR THE YEARS ENDED DECEMBER 31, 1956, 1957, 1958

| | 1956 | 1957 | 1958 | INCREASE OR DECREASE* | | | |
| --- | --- | --- | --- | --- | --- | --- | --- |
| | | | | 1956-1957 | | 1957-1958 | |
| | | | | AMOUNT | PER CENT | AMOUNT | PER CENT |
| Merchandise inventory, Jan. 1................. | 105,000 | 125,000 | 330,000 | 20,000 | 19% | 205,000 | 164% |
| Purchases............... | 650,000 | 1,405,000 | 895,000 | 755,000 | 116% | 510,000* | 36%* |
| Goods available for sale..... | 755,000 | 1,530,000 | 1,225,000 | 775,000 | 103% | 305,000* | 20%* |
| Less: Merchandise inventory, Dec. 31................ | 125,000 | 330,000 | 225,000 | 205,000 | 164% | 105,000* | 32%* |
| Cost of goods sold......... | 630,000 | 1,200,000 | 1,000,000 | 570,000 | 90% | 200,000* | 17%* |

of a comparative balance sheet. Here, too, both dollar changes and percentage changes may be presented to show the absolute as well as the relative changes that have taken place over a period of years. Such a comparative balance sheet for the Marshall Company for the three-year period, 1956–1958 inclusive, is illustrated on the following page.

MARSHALL COMPANY
CONDENSED COMPARATIVE BALANCE SHEET
DECEMBER 31, 1956, 1957, 1958

| | 1956 | 1957 | 1958 | INCREASE OR DECREASE* | | | |
| | | | | 1956-1957 | | 1957-1958 | |
| | | | | AMOUNT | PER CENT | AMOUNT | PER CENT |
|---|---|---|---|---|---|---|---|
| **ASSETS** | | | | | | | |
| Current assets............ | 673,500 | 955,500 | 855,000 | 282,000 | 42% | 100,500* | 11%* |
| Investments ............. | 250,000 | 400,000 | 500,000 | 150,000 | 60% | 100,000 | 25% |
| Plant and equipment (net).. | 675,000 | 875,000 | 775,000 | 200,000 | 30% | 100,000* | 11%* |
| Intangibles.............. | 100,000 | 100,000 | 100,000 | | | | |
| Deferred costs .......... | 61,500 | 60,500 | 48,000 | 1,000* | 2%* | 12,500* | 21%* |
| Total assets.............. | 1,760,000 | 2,391,000 | 2,278,000 | 631,000 | 36% | 113,000* | 5%* |
| **LIABILITIES** | | | | | | | |
| Current liabilities......... | 130,000 | 546,000 | 410,000 | 416,000 | 320% | 136,000* | 25%* |
| Long-term debt........... | 300,000 | 400,000 | 400,000 | 100,000 | 33% | | |
| Total liabilities........... | 430,000 | 946,000 | 810,000 | 516,000 | 120% | 136,000* | 14%* |
| **CAPITAL** | | | | | | | |
| 6% Preferred stock........ | 250,000 | 350,000 | 350,000 | 100,000 | 40% | | |
| Common stock ........... | 750,000 | 750,000 | 750,000 | | | | |
| Additional paid-in capital ... | 100,000 | 100,000 | 100,000 | | | | |
| Retained earnings ........ | 230,000 | 245,000 | 268,000 | 15,000 | 7% | 23,000 | 9% |
| Total capital............. | 1,330,000 | 1,445,000 | 1,468,000 | 115,000 | 9% | 23,000 | 2% |
| Total liabilities and capital... | 1,760,000 | 2,391,000 | 2,278,000 | 631,000 | 36% | 113,000* | 5%* |

Here, too, it is possible to expand the statement to show asset, liability, and capital group detail, or the detail may be presented in the form of separate supporting schedules. A comparative schedule of current assets in support of the balance sheet summary and a comparative retained earnings statement are given on the opposite page.

Information concerning percentage changes on the comparative statements serves to point out certain relationships that require further investigation and possible action. For example, the comparative schedule of current assets shows an increase in notes receivable of $30,000 at the end of 1957. The indication that this is a 300% increase serves to emphasize the significance of the change. Investigation may disclose that collections on account are slow and customers are postponing payments by the issuance of notes. The comparative income statement reports an increase in sales returns of $50,000 for 1957. The significance of this amount is fully appreciated only when it is seen that this represents a 100% increase in sales returns as compared with only a 75% increase in sales for the period. An investigation of causes for the disproportionate increase appears warranted.

MARSHALL COMPANY
COMPARATIVE SCHEDULE OF CURRENT ASSETS
DECEMBER 31, 1956, 1957, 1958

| | 1956 | 1957 | 1958 | INCREASE OR DECREASE* | | | |
| | | | | 1956-1957 | | 1957-1958 | |
| | | | | AMOUNT | PER CENT | AMOUNT | PER CENT |
|---|---|---|---|---|---|---|---|
| Cash..................... | 115,000 | 100,500 | 60,000 | 14,500* | 13%* | 40,500* | 40%* |
| Marketable securities....... | 100,000 | 150,000 | 150,000 | 50,000 | 50% | — | — |
| Notes receivable........... | 10,000 | 40,000 | 50,000 | 30,000 | 300% | 10,000 | 25% |
| Accounts receivable........ | 328,500 | 350,000 | 380,000 | 21,500 | 7% | 30,000 | 9% |
| Total receivables......... | 338,500 | 390,000 | 430,000 | 51,500 | 15% | 40,000 | 10% |
| Less: Allowance for bad debts................ | 5,000 | 15,000 | 10,000 | 10,000 | 200% | 5,000* | 33%* |
| Net receivables.......... | 333,500 | 375,000 | 420,000 | 41,500 | 12% | 45,000 | 12% |
| Merchandise inventory...... | 125,000 | 330,000 | 225,000 | 205,000 | 164% | 105,000* | 32%* |
| Total current assets......... | 673,500 | 955,500 | 855,000 | 282,000 | 42% | 100,500* | 11%* |

MARSHALL COMPANY
COMPARATIVE RETAINED EARNINGS STATEMENT
FOR THE YEARS ENDED DECEMBER 31, 1956 1957, 1958

| | 1956 | 1957 | 1958 | INCREASE OR DECREASE* | | | |
| | | | | 1956-1957 | | 1957-1958 | |
| | | | | AMOUNT | PER CENT | AMOUNT | PER CENT |
|---|---|---|---|---|---|---|---|
| Retained earnings at beginning of year............. | 240,000 | 230,000 | 245,000 | 10,000* | 4%* | 15,000 | 7% |
| Net income per income statement.............. | 15,000 | 60,000 | 70,000 | 45,000 | 300% | 10,000 | 17% |
| Total.................... | 255,000 | 290,000 | 315,000 | 35,000 | 14% | 25,000 | 9% |
| Dividends: | | | | | | | |
| Preferred stock.......... | 15,000 | 21,000 | 21,000 | 6,000 | 40% | — | — |
| Common stock.......... | 10,000 | 24,000 | 26,000 | 14,000 | 140% | 2,000 | 8% |
| Total................. | 25,000 | 45,000 | 47,000 | 20,000 | 80% | 2,000 | 4% |
| Retained earnings at end of year ................. | 230,000 | 245,000 | 268,000 | 15,000 | 7% | 23,000 | 9% |

When absolute amounts or relative amounts appear out of line, conclusions, favorable or unfavorable, are not justified until investigation has disclosed the full story of the factors responsible for the change.

Percentage changes in the previous examples have been given in terms of the data for the year immediately preceding. With data covering more than two years, this procedure results in a changing base that makes the comparison of relative changes over the years difficult. When comparisons of data for two or more years are involved, it is frequently desirable to develop all comparisons in terms of the earliest years given. Each amount on the statement representing the base year is considered 100%. On succeeding statements the amount of each item is represented as a percentage of the base amount. The set of percentages for several years may thus be interpreted as trend values or as a series of index numbers relating to the particular item. If 1956 is used as the base year, comparative income statement data for the Marshall Company may be presented in the manner shown below.

When relationships for a certain base period can be considered as "normal," a statement such as the one below serves as a clearer medium for interpretation than those previously illustrated. For example, the comparative income statement on page 831 shows that sales increased 75%, then dropped 14%; sales returns increased 100%, then decreased 25%. Analyses were based on data for the year immedi-

MARSHALL COMPANY
CONDENSED COMPARATIVE INCOME STATEMENT
FOR THE YEARS ENDED DECEMBER 31, 1956, 1957, AND 1958

| | 1956 | 1957 | 1958 | INCREASE OR DECREASE* | | | |
| | | | | 1956-1957 | | 1956-1958 | |
| | | | | AMOUNT | PER CENT | AMOUNT | PER CENT |
|---|---|---|---|---|---|---|---|
| Gross sales............... | 1,000,000 | 1,750,000 | 1,500,000 | 750,000 | 75% | 500,000 | 50% |
| Sales returns............. | 50,000 | 100,000 | 75,000 | 50,000 | 100% | 25,000 | 50% |
| Net sales................. | 950,000 | 1,650,000 | 1,425,000 | 700,000 | 74% | 475,000 | 50% |
| Cost of goods sold......... | 630,000 | 1,200,000 | 1,000,000 | 570,000 | 90% | 370,000 | 59% |
| Gross profit on sales ....... | 320,000 | 450,000 | 425,000 | 130,000 | 41% | 105,000 | 33% |
| Selling expenses........... | 240,000 | 300,000 | 280,000 | 60,000 | 25% | 40,000 | 17% |
| General expenses.......... | 100,000 | 110,000 | 100,000 | 10,000 | 10% | ——— | ——— |
| Total expenses............ | 340,000 | 410,000 | 380,000 | 70,000 | 21% | 40,000 | 12% |
| Net profit or loss* from operations............. | 20,000* | 40,000 | 45,000 | 60,000 | — | 65,000 | — |
| Other income............. | 50,000 | 65,000 | 75,000 | 15,000 | 30% | 25,000 | 50% |
| | 30,000 | 105,000 | 120,000 | 75,000 | 250% | 90,000 | 300% |
| Other expenses............ | 10,000 | 20,000 | 20,000 | 10,000 | 100% | 10,000 | 100% |
| Net income before income taxes ................. | 20,000 | 85,000 | 100,000 | 65,000 | 325% | 80,000 | 400% |
| Income taxes ............. | 5,000 | 25,000 | 30,000 | 20,000 | 400% | 25,000 | 500% |
| Net income after income taxes ................ | 15,000 | 60,000 | 70,000 | 45,000 | 300% | 55,000 | 367% |

ately preceding.  The illustration on page 834 shows that sales increased 75% and 50% in terms of 1956 results.  It also shows that sales returns increased 100% and 50% as compared with 1956 figures.  Here it is shown that, while sales returns increased disproportionately as compared with sales in 1957, the increase was proportionate in 1958, both sales and returns increasing 50% in terms of 1956 data.

Analysis in terms of a base year is a desirable practice, not only for the comparison of entire statements but also for the comparison of various related single items, ratios, and other pertinent data.  Data expressed in terms of a base year are well adapted for graphic presentation.

The changes in comparative statement balances may be reported in terms of percentages, as was illustrated in previous examples, or the changes may be reported in terms of ratios.  A 50% increase in an item results in the designation of a ratio to the base figure of 1.50; a 25% decrease in an item results in a ratio to the base figure of .75.  Plus and minus designations are thus avoided.  Use of ratios instead of percentages is illustrated in the statement below.

MARSHALL COMPANY
CONDENSED COMPARATIVE INCOME STATEMENT
FOR THE YEARS ENDED DECEMBER 31, 1956, 1957, AND 1958

| | 1956 | 1957 | 1958 | INCREASE OR DECREASE* | | | |
| | | | | 1956-1957 | | 1956-1958 | |
| | | | | AMOUNT | RATIO | AMOUNT | RATIO |
|---|---|---|---|---|---|---|---|
| Gross sales | 1,000,000 | 1,750,000 | 1,500,000 | 750,000 | 1.75 | 500,000 | 1.50 |
| Sales returns | 50,000 | 100,000 | 75,000 | 50,000 | 2.00 | 25,000 | 1.50 |
| Net sales | 950,000 | 1,650,000 | 1,425,000 | 700,000 | 1.74 | 475,000 | 1.50 |
| Cost of goods sold | 630,000 | 1,200,000 | 1,000,000 | 570,000 | 1.90 | 370,000 | 1.59 |
| Gross profit on sales | 320,000 | 450,000 | 425,000 | 130,000 | 1.41 | 105,000 | 1.33 |
| Selling expenses | 240,000 | 300,000 | 280,000 | 60,000 | 1.25 | 40,000 | 1.17 |
| General expenses | 100,000 | 110,000 | 100,000 | 10,000 | 1.10 | ——— | 1.00 |
| Total expenses | 340,000 | 410,000 | 380,000 | 70,000 | 1.21 | 40,000 | 1.12 |
| Net profit or loss* from operations | 20,000* | 40,000 | 45,000 | 60,000 | ——— | 65,000 | ——— |
| Other income | 50,000 | 65,000 | 75,000 | 15,000 | 1.30 | 25,000 | 1.50 |
| | 30,000 | 105,000 | 120,000 | 75,000 | 3.50 | 90,000 | 4.00 |
| Other expenses | 10,000 | 20,000 | 20,000 | 10,000 | 2.00 | 10,000 | 2.00 |
| Net income before income taxes | 20,000 | 85,000 | 100,000 | 65,000 | 4.25 | 80,000 | 5.00 |
| Income taxes | 5,000 | 25,000 | 30,000 | 20,000 | 5.00 | 25,000 | 6.00 |
| Net income after income taxes | 15,000 | 60,000 | 70,000 | 45,000 | 4.00 | 55,000 | 4.67 |

When a base figure is zero or a minus value, it is possible to report a dollar change but the change cannot be expressed in terms of a percentage. When there is a positive base figure, however, both absolute values and relative percentage values can be calculated. When ratio analysis is employed, ratios can be reported only when two positive values are given. The foregoing practices are illustrated in the examples below:

| | Year Ended December 31 | | Increase or Decrease* | | |
| | 1957 | 1958 | Amount | Per Cent | Ratio |
| --- | --- | --- | --- | --- | --- |
| Net income or loss* ........ | 0 | 20,000 | 20,000 | ——— | ——— |
| | 0 | 2,000* | 2,000* | ——— | ——— |
| | 5,000* | 2,000 | 7,000 | ——— | ——— |
| | 5,000* | 10,000* | 5,000* | ——— | ——— |
| | 10,000 | 0 | 10,000* | 100%* | ——— |
| | 10,000 | 2,000* | 12,000* | 120%* | ——— |
| | 10,000 | 35,000 | 25,000 | 250% | 3.50 |
| | 10,000 | 8,000 | 2,000* | 20%* | .80 |
| | 10,000 | 10,000 | ——— | ——— | 1.00 |

Although the illustrations show comparisons in terms of annual data, it is frequently desirable to develop comparative data for shorter periods. It would be possible, for example, to prepare comparative statements for monthly or quarterly intervals. Furthermore, in the case of profit and loss data, it may be desirable to compare a current month with the same month of preceding years, or cumulative data for the current year to date with data for the equivalent period of preceding years.

A number of companies have adopted the thirteen-month year, dividing the calendar year into thirteen equal periods of four weeks. Variations for the total number of days and number of Saturdays and Sundays found in the calendar months are thus eliminated in the development of comparative "monthly" statements. More reliable conclusions can be drawn from analyses developed from data for periods of comparable length.

**COMPARATIVE STATE-MENTS—VERTICAL ANALYSIS**  Comparative data may include analyses in terms of percentages or ratios based upon the related data of each individual period. For example, in presenting comparative operating data, it may be desirable to show the relationship of the component profit and loss elements to sales for each period. This procedure is known as *vertical*

*analysis.* Vertical analysis as applied to the comparative profit and loss data for the Marshall Company is illustrated below. Net sales is used as the base figure, or 100%. If analysis were to be made by means of ratios, net sales would be considered 1.00 and component items would be expressed in terms of this base.

### MARSHALL COMPANY
#### CONDENSED COMPARATIVE INCOME STATEMENT
#### FOR THE YEARS ENDED DECEMBER 31, 1956, 1957, AND 1958

| | 1956 | | 1957 | | 1958 | |
|---|---|---|---|---|---|---|
| | AMOUNT | PER CENT | AMOUNT | PER CENT | AMOUNT | PER CENT |
| Gross sales................. | 1,000,000 | 105.3% | 1,750,000 | 106.1% | 1,500,000 | 105.3% |
| Sales returns.............. | 50,000 | 5.3 | 100,000 | 6.1 | 75,000 | 5.3 |
| Net sales.................. | 950,000 | 100.0% | 1,650,000 | 100.0% | 1,425,000 | 100.0% |
| Cost of goods sold.......... | 630,000 | 66.3 | 1,200,000 | 72.7 | 1,000,000 | 70.2 |
| Gross profit on sales......... | 320,000 | 33.7% | 450,000 | 27.3% | 425,000 | 29.8% |
| Selling expenses............. | 240,000 | 25.3% | 300,000 | 18.2% | 280,000 | 19.7% |
| General expenses............ | 100,000 | 10.5 | 110,000 | 6.7 | 100,000 | 7.0 |
| Total expenses.............. | 340,000 | 35.8% | 410,000 | 24.9% | 380,000 | 26.7% |
| Net profit or loss* from opera- tions.................... | 20,000* | 2.1%* | 40,000 | 2.4% | 45,000 | 3.1% |
| Other income.............. | 50,000 | 5.3 | 65,000 | 3.9 | 75,000 | 5.3 |
| | 30,000 | 3.2% | 105,000 | 6.3% | 120,000 | 8.4% |
| Other expenses............. | 10,000 | 1.1 | 20,000 | 1.2 | 20,000 | 1.4 |
| Net income before income taxes ................... | 20,000 | 2.1% | 85,000 | 5.1% | 100,000 | 7.0% |
| Income taxes ............. | 5,000 | .5 | 25,000 | 1.5 | 30,000 | 2.1 |
| Net income after income taxes . | 15,000 | 1.6% | 60,000 | 3.6% | 70,000 | 4.9% |

Although it may not be possible to specify a normal gross profit rate, it can be determined from the statement that a severe decline in the gross profit percentage took place in 1957 with a partial recovery in 1958. This would suggest that an analysis be made of the causes responsible for the increase in the cost of goods sold percentage. Notwithstanding the gross profit shrinkage, the net profit percentage on each dollar of sales increased in 1957 and again in 1958. This resulted from a reduced expense percentage per dollar of sales that more than compensated for the increased cost of goods sold. The comparative statement points to certain relationships and trends that merit further study for a full appreciation of the changes and the interpretation that may be placed on these.

When supporting schedules are prepared for the detail relating to totals on the condensed statement illustrated, individual items may be expressed percentage-wise in terms of net sales or in terms of the total reported on the schedule. Sales salaries, for example, may be reported as a certain percentage of sales, with the selling expense schedule accounting for expenses totaling 25.3%; or the salaries may be reported as a percentage of total selling expenses, with the individual items on the schedule adding up to 100%.

Vertical analysis may be employed in the case of comparative balance sheets and retained earnings statements. On the balance sheet related items are expressed in percentages or ratios based upon total assets or total liabilities plus capital. A comparative balance sheet with percentage analysis for the Marshall Company is given below:

MARSHALL COMPANY
CONDENSED COMPARATIVE BALANCE SHEET
DECEMBER 31, 1956, 1957, 1958

|  | 1956 | | 1957 | | 1958 | |
|---|---|---|---|---|---|---|
|  | AMOUNT | PER CENT | AMOUNT | PER CENT | AMOUNT | PER CENT |
| **ASSETS** | | | | | | |
| Current assets.............. | 673,500 | 38% | 955,500 | 40% | 855,000 | 38% |
| Investments ............... | 250,000 | 14 | 400,000 | 17 | 500,000 | 22 |
| Plant and equipment (net).... | 675,000 | 38 | 875,000 | 37 | 775,000 | 34 |
| Intangibles................. | 100,000 | 6 | 100,000 | 4 | 100,000 | 4 |
| Deferred costs ............. | 61,500 | 4 | 60,500 | 2 | 48,000 | 2 |
| Total assets................ | 1,760,000 | 100% | 2,391,000 | 100% | 2,278,000 | 100% |
| **LIABILITIES** | | | | | | |
| Current liabilities........... | 130,000 | 7% | 546,000 | 23% | 410,000 | 18% |
| Long-term debt............. | 300,000 | 17 | 400,000 | 17 | 400,000 | 18 |
| Total liabilities............. | 430,000 | 24% | 946,000 | 40% | 810,000 | 36% |
| **CAPITAL** | | | | | | |
| 6% Preferred stock.......... | 250,000 | 14% | 350,000 | 15% | 350,000 | 15% |
| Common stock.............. | 750,000 | 43 | 750,000 | 31 | 750,000 | 33 |
| Additional paid-in capital .... | 100,000 | 6 | 100,000 | 4 | 100,000 | 4 |
| Retained Earnings .......... | 230,000 | 13 | 245,000 | 10 | 268,000 | 12 |
| Total capital................ | 1,330,000 | 76% | 1,445,000 | 60% | 1,468,000 | 64% |
| Total liabilities and capital..... | 1,760,000 | 100% | 2,391,000 | 100% | 2,278,000 | 100% |

As in the case of profit and loss schedules, when supporting schedules are prepared to show the detail for group totals, individual items may be expressed as a percentage of balance sheet base figures or as a percentage of the schedule total.

In preparing a comparative retained earnings statement, either the beginning or the ending retained earnings balance may be used as the base for analysis. Use of the beginning retained earnings balance as a percentage base is illustrated on the following page.

MARSHALL COMPANY
COMPARATIVE RETAINED EARNINGS STATEMENT
FOR THE YEARS ENDED DECEMBER 31, 1956, 1957, AND 1958

| | 1956 | | 1957 | | 1958 | |
|---|---|---|---|---|---|---|
| | AMOUNT | PER CENT | AMOUNT | PER CENT | AMOUNT | PER CENT |
| Retained earnings at beginning of year.................. | 240,000 | 100% | 230,000 | 100% | 245,000 | 100% |
| Net income per income statement.................... | 15,000 | 6 | 60,000 | 26 | 70,000 | 29 |
| Total...................... | 255,000 | 106% | 290,000 | 126% | 315,000 | 129% |
| Dividends: | | | | | | |
| Preferred stock............ | 15,000 | 6% | 21,000 | 9% | 21,000 | 9% |
| Common stock............. | 10,000 | 4 | 24,000 | 10 | 26,000 | 11 |
| Total...................... | 25,000 | 10% | 45,000 | 19% | 47,000 | 20% |
| Retained earnings at end of year ..................... | 230,000 | 96% | 245,000 | 107% | 268,000 | 109% |

It should be observed that both horizontal and vertical analyses are required for a full understanding of business trends and financial and operating relationships.

**COMMON-SIZE STATEMENTS**    Comparative statements that give only the vertical percentages or ratios for financial data without giving dollar values are known as *common-size statements* or *100% statements* since the comparative reports are expressed in terms of a common size or 100%. Common-size statements may be prepared for (1) the same business as of different dates or periods or (2) two or more business units as of the same date or period. For example, a common-size income statement for the Marshall Company comparing operations for 1956, 1957, and 1958, is illustrated at the top of the following page.

The example that is given at the bottom of page 840 illustrates the preparation of a common-size statement comparing balance sheet data for two different companies as of the same date. Here the relationships of the various items on the balance sheet for the Marshall Company are compared with those for the Norris Corporation as of December 31, 1958. This summary provides a clear display of comparative relationships of balance sheet items for the two companies. It is readily seen, for example, that the proportion of the owners' equity for each company is approximately the same. Although the Norris Corporation has a larger proportion of current obligations than the Marshall Company, its ratio of current assets to current liabilities far exceeds that of the Marshall Company, resulting in a much stronger current position.

## MARSHALL COMPANY
### CONDENSED COMMON-SIZE INCOME STATEMENT
### FOR THE YEARS ENDED DECEMBER 31, 1956, 1957, AND 1958

|  | 1956 | 1957 | 1958 |
|---|---|---|---|
| Gross sales.......................... | 105.3% | 106.1% | 105.3% |
| Sales returns...................... | 5.3 | 6.1 | 5.3 |
| Net sales........................ | 100.0% | 100.0% | 100.0% |
| Cost of goods sold................. | 66.3 | 72.7 | 70.2 |
| Gross profit on sales .............. | 33.7% | 27.3% | 29.8% |
| Selling expenses................... | 25.3% | 18.2% | 19.7% |
| General expenses.................. | 10.5 | 6.7 | 7.0 |
| Total expenses.................... | 35.8% | 24.9% | 26.7% |
| Net profit or loss* from operations.... | 2.1%* | 2.4% | 3.1% |
| Other income..................... | 5.3 | 3.9 | 5.3 |
|  | 3.2% | 6.3% | 8.4% |
| Other expenses.................... | 1.1 | 1.2 | 1.4 |
| Net income before income taxes..... | 2.1% | 5.1% | 7.0% |
| Income taxes ..................... | .5 | 1.5 | 2.1 |
| Net income after income taxes...... | 1.6% | 3.6% | 4.9% |

## MARSHALL COMPANY AND NORRIS CORPORATION
### CONDENSED COMMON-SIZE BALANCE SHEET
### DECEMBER 31, 1958

|  | MARSHALL COMPANY | NORRIS CORPORATION |
|---|---|---|
| **ASSETS** | | |
| Current assets....................... | 38% | 64% |
| Investments ....................... | 22 | — |
| Plant and equipment (net)............... | 34 | 35 |
| Intangibles........................ | 4 | — |
| Deferred costs..................... | 2 | 1 |
| Total assets....................... | 100% | 100% |
| **LIABILITIES** | | |
| Current liabilities...................... | 18% | 20% |
| Long-term debt..................... | 18 | 12 |
| Deferred revenues ................... | — | 2 |
| Total liabilities...................... | 36% | 34% |
| **CAPITAL** | | |
| Preferred stock..................... | 15% | — |
| Common stock...................... | 33 | 46% |
| Additional paid-in capital............... | 4 | 5 |
| Retained earnings................... | 12 | 15 |
| Total capital....................... | 64% | 66% |
| Total liabilities and capital.............. | 100% | 100% |

In preparing common-size balance sheets and income statements for two companies, one should be certain that the financial data for each company were developed in terms of comparable accounting methods, classification procedures, and valuation bases. Comparative data are valid only under such circumstances.

**STATEMENT ACCOUNT-ING FOR VARIATION IN NET INCOME** As previously illustrated, the comparative income statement shows comparative balances, changes in individual profit and loss items, and also changes in the net income. Comparative income statement data may be used in the preparation of a statement accounting for the variation in net income. Here comparative data are assembled and presented in a manner that directs attention to those elements responsible for the change in net income. To illustrate, comparative operating data for the Marshall Company for the years 1957 and 1958 may be presented as follows in accounting for the increased net income in 1958:

MARSHALL COMPANY

STATEMENT ACCOUNTING FOR VARIATION IN NET INCOME

1958 AS COMPARED WITH 1957

| | | | | | |
|---|---:|---:|---:|---:|---:|
| Net income after income taxes for year ended December 31, 1957 | | | | | $60,000 |
| Net income was increased as a result of: | | | | | |
| Decrease in selling expenses | | | | | |
| 1957.......................... | | $300,000 | | | |
| 1958.......................... | | 280,000 | $20,000 | | |
| Decrease in general expenses | | | | | |
| 1957.......................... | | $110,000 | | | |
| 1958.......................... | | 100,000 | 10,000 | | |
| Increase in other income | | | | | |
| 1958.......................... | | $ 75,000 | | | |
| 1957.......................... | | 65,000 | 10,000 | $40,000 | |
| Net income was decreased as a result of: | | | | | |
| Decrease in gross profit on sales: | | | | | |
| Decrease in net sales | | | | | |
| 1957...................... | $1,650,000 | | | | |
| 1958...................... | 1,425,000 | $225,000 | | | |
| Less decrease in cost of goods sold | | | | | |
| 1957...................... | $1,200,000 | | | | |
| 1958...................... | 1,000,000 | 200,000 | $25,000 | | |
| Increase in provision for income taxes | | | | | |
| 1958.......................... | | $30,000 | | | |
| 1957.......................... | | 25,000 | 5,000 | 30,000 | 10,000 |
| Net income after income taxes for year ended December 31, 1958 | | | | | $70,000 |

The statement shows that while a decrease in income resulted from a decrease in the gross profit on sales and an increase in income taxes, decreased operating expenses and an increase in other income more than compensated for the gross profit shrinkage. Thus it would appear that increased operating efficiency has been a significant factor in increasing profits.

It may be desirable to go further and analyze the change in the reported gross profit to determine what part is due to a change in sales volume and what part is due to a change in the sales price-cost relationship or the gross profit rate. To illustrate the analytical procedure involved, assume that sales prices of the Marshall Company in 1958 are 10% above those of 1957. A schedule summarizing the change in gross profit can be prepared as follows:

MARSHALL COMPANY

SCHEDULE OF ANALYSIS OF VARIATION IN GROSS PROFIT

TO ACCOMPANY STATEMENT ACCOUNTING FOR VARIATION IN NET INCOME

1958 AS COMPARED WITH 1957

Decrease in gross profit caused by:
Decrease in volume of sales:
Actual net sales, 1957 . . . . . . . . . . . . . . . . . . . . . . . . . . . . . . . . . . . . . . . . . $1,650,000
Net sales, 1958, at 1957 prices ($1,425,000 ÷ 1.10) . . . . . . . . . . . . 1,295,455

Volume decrease at 1957 prices . . . . . . . . . . . . . . . . . . . . . . . . . . . . . . $ 354,545

Gross profit rate, 1957, applied to volume decrease
$\left(\frac{450,000}{1,650,000} \times \$354,545\right)$ equals decrease in gross profit
resulting from decreased sales volume . . . . . . . . . . . . . . . . . . . . . . .   $96,694

Increase in gross profit rate:
Increased sales price:
Actual net sales, 1958 . . . . . . . . . . . . . . . . . . . . . . . . . . $1,425,000
Net sales, 1958, at 1957 prices . . . . . . . . . . . . . . . . . . . . 1,295,455 $ 129,545

Less increase in cost of goods sold:
Actual cost of goods sold, 1958 . . . . . . . . . . . . . . . . . . . . $1,000,000
Cost of goods sold, 1958, on basis of 1957 cost
percentage $\left(\frac{1,200,000}{1,650,000} \times \$1,295,455\right)$ . . . . . . . . . . . . 942,149     57,851     71,694

Total decrease in gross profit . . . . . . . . . . . . . . . . . . . . . . . . . . . . . . . . . . . . $25,000

The foregoing schedule shows that, while sales decreased from $1,650,000 to $1,425,000, a decrease in sales volume of $354,545 actually took place in terms of 1957 sales prices. This would have resulted in a decrease in the gross profit of $96,694, were it not for an increase in the gross profit of $71,694 arising from sales price increases of $129,545 accompanied by cost increases of only $57,851 in terms of 1957 prices and costs. Increased prices, then, offer the explanation for there being only a minor change in the business gross profit in spite of a relatively significant decrease in sales volume.

With information relating to the number of units sold, one can determine the effects upon gross profit of:

(a) The change in sales as a result of the change in the number of units sold.

(b) The change in sales as a result of the change in sales prices.

(c) The change in cost of goods sold as a result of the change in the number of units sold.

(d) The change in cost of goods sold as a result of the change in the unit cost prices.

To illustrate, assume that, instead of a sales price increase of 10% for the Marshall Company in 1958, records show that the number of units sold by the company in 1958 was only 80% of those sold in 1957. A schedule can be prepared to analyze the change in gross profit as follows:

MARSHALL COMPANY

SCHEDULE OF ANALYSIS OF VARIATION IN GROSS PROFIT

TO ACCOMPANY STATEMENT ACCOUNTING FOR VARIATION IN NET INCOME

1958 AS COMPARED WITH 1957

| | | | |
|---|---:|---:|---:|
| Decrease in gross profit caused by: | | | |
| Decrease in net sales: | | | |
| Decrease in sales due to change in number of units sold: | | | |
| Actual net sales, 1957 | $1,650,000 | | |
| Net sales, 1958, in the absence of price change, would have been 80% of $1,650,000, or | 1,320,000 | $330,000 | |
| Less increase in sales due to change in sales price: | | | |
| Actual net sales, 1958 | $1,425,000 | | |
| Net sales, 1958, at 1957 prices | 1,320,000 | 105,000 | |
| Decrease in net sales | | | $225,000 |
| Decrease in cost of goods sold: | | | |
| Decrease in cost of goods sold due to change in number of units sold: | | | |
| Actual cost of goods sold, 1957 | $1,200,000 | | |
| Cost of goods sold, 1958, in the absence of cost changes would have been 80% of $1,200,000, or | 960,000 | $240,000 | |
| Less increase in cost of goods sold due to change in cost prices: | | | |
| Actual cost of goods sold, 1958 | $1,000,000 | | |
| Cost of goods sold, 1958, at 1957 costs | 960,000 | 40,000 | |
| Decrease in cost of goods sold | | | 200,000 |
| Total decrease in gross profit | | | $ 25,000 |

The above analysis suggests that, while sales went down $225,000, the drop would have been even greater as a result of the shrinkage in the number of units sold were it not for increases that were made in sales prices. The decreases in selling and general expenses for the year had previously been interpreted as evidence of increased operating efficiency. It would now appear that this conclusion needs to be questioned, in view of the analysis showing a significant reduction in the number of units sold. The gross profit analysis also shows that increases in sales prices exceeded the increased cost of goods sold, thus helping to maintain the gross profit at close to the total for the previous year in spite of the sales volume shrinkage. It would appear from an over-all view that the increased profit for the Marshall Company for 1958 is due to the rising prices rather than to greater managerial efficiency.

The schedule illustrated on page 843 can be prepared for a business that sells only a single uniform commodity. If several different commodities are sold, information would have to be assembled and separate schedules developed concerning unit sales, costs, and sales prices for each. The gross profit variations relating to each class of sales would thus be analyzed.

**BREAK-EVEN POINT ANALYSIS**    Financial statements are frequently analyzed to determine the business unit's _break-even point_, that level of sales which will just cover all expenses. At the break-even point the business would neither make a profit nor incur a loss, but would merely "break even."

Analysis of comparative profit and loss data will reveal those expenses that fluctuate with the volume of sales, known as _variable expenses_, and those expenses that remain constant in spite of such changing conditions, known as _fixed expenses_. Variable items include cost of sales arising from purchases or production, sales commissions, shipping expenses, supplies, and similar items affected by the volume of sales. Fixed items include depreciation, taxes, insurance, heat and light, administrative salaries, and similar items that do not fluctuate with the volume of sales.

If all expenses vary in direct proportion to sales and sales are made at a price in excess of such expenses, there is no break-even point, for profit is recognized from the first sale; here profit varies directly with the sales total. Whenever fixed expenses exist, however, the sales price must cover both variable and fixed expenses in reaching the break-even point. Stated differently, the sales price after covering variable expenses serves to absorb fixed expenses; the break-even point is achieved when the fixed expenses are fully absorbed. A profit is realized only when the sales figure exceeds both the variable and fixed expenses related to sales. The ratio of variable expense to the sales dollar is commonly referred to as the _variable expense ratio_. The part of the sales dollar after variable expenses that becomes available to cover fixed expenses and provide profit is referred to as the *marginal income ratio*, or *the profit-volume ratio* commonly designated P/V. Recovery through the latter source of an amount in excess of the fixed expenses results in a profit. The difference between the total sales and the sales at the break-even point is referred to as the *margin of safety*, commonly designated M/S.

The break-even point can be developed by means of a graph or it can be arrived at mathematically. In either case two amounts must be known: (1) the total fixed expenses of all categories — production, selling, general, and administrative; and (2) the relationship of variable expenses of all categories to the sales figure. The break-even point can be determined graphically by plotting fixed and variable expenses and sales information on a chart. When the maximum sales that can be achieved at full capacity or production are known, a full analysis of profit and loss at any sales level can be developed. To illustrate, assume the following facts for the Eastern Manufacturing Corporation:

(a) Variable expenses are 40% of sales.
(b) Total fixed expenses are $180,000.
(c) The sale price of units, assuming full production, is $500,000.

These data may be plotted as follows:

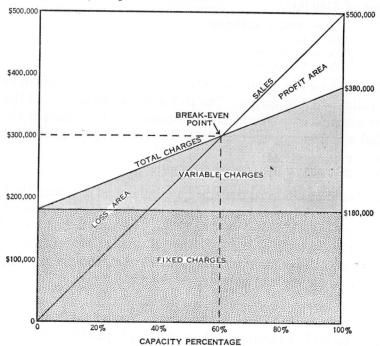

Graph Showing Break-Even Point

A number of observations can be made from the graph. To break even, sales of $300,000 must be reached; stated differently, 60% of full capacity must be achieved. This is the point where the total expenses line and the sales line intersect. At this point variable expenses are $120,000 (40% of $300,000) and fixed expenses are $180,000.

The profit or loss, assuming any volume of sales, can be determined from the graph. The smaller the sales figure below the break-even point, the greater the loss; the larger the sales figure above the break-even point, the greater the profit. Sales of $250,000, for example, will result in a loss of $30,000 ($250,000 − [(40% of $250,000) + $180,000]); sales of $400,000 will produce a profit of $60,000 ($400,000 − [(40% of $400,000) + $180,000]). Maximum sales will result in a profit of $120,000 ($500,000 − [(40% of $500,000) + $180,000]). With sales at $400,000, a margin of safety of 25% (sales in excess of sales at break-even point, $100,000 ÷ sales, $400,000) would be achieved; stated differently, sales would have to decrease 25% before the company will suffer a loss.

The break-even point may be calculated in the following manner. Let X equal sales at the break-even point. Then X is equal to the sum of the variable expenses, which are 40% of sales, plus the fixed charges of $180,000:

$$X = .40X + $180,000$$
$$X - .40X = $180,000$$
$$.60X = $180,000$$
$$X = $300,000$$

The break-even point can also be calculated by employing the P/V ratio described earlier. The P/V ratio or the portion of the sales dollar available for meeting fixed expenses in the example above is .60 (sales 1.00 − variable costs .40). The following calculation is made:

$$X = $180,000 ÷ .60$$
$$X = $300,000$$

It should be observed that the higher the fixed expenses, the higher will be the break-even point. Assuming that fixed expenses in the preceding example were $240,000, the break-even point would be $400,000 [(X = .40 X + $240,000) or (X = $240,000 ÷ .60)]. With a sales figure at maximum capacity of $500,000, 80% of the full sales potential would have to be achieved in breaking even.

In developing the preceding measurements, it is first necessary to classify expenses as fixed or variable. Semivariable expenses will have to be broken down into their fixed and variable components for this purpose. Break-even point analysis assumes that the fixed expenses will not vary regardless of the level of sales and that variable items will vary in direct proportion to sales. Obviously, however, such conditions will seldom be found in this precise manner in practice. Fixed items may vary to some degree depending upon sales; on the other hand, variable items may not vary in direct proportion to sales as assumed. For example, economies of purchasing and production may serve to lower certain variable expenses; many expenses, both variable and fixed, may rise sharply upon reaching a certain point and may contract markedly below a certain level. When actual conditions vary from the assumptions that are required in developing the break-even analysis, the limitations that are found in such measurement should be recognized.

Many practical applications may be made of break-even analysis. Break-even point information is useful in predicting the effect of an increase or a decrease in business. For example, if it is predicted for the Eastern Manufacturing Company on page 845 that operations of the following year will reach 90% of capacity, profits would be estimated at $90,000 ($450,000 − [$180,000 + 40% of $450,000]). This information may be used in the determination of policy with respect to property acquisitions, borrowings, and dividend payments.

Break-even point analysis may be particularly valuable in making decisions concerning the expansion of plant facilities. For example, assume that the Eastern Manufacturing Company, in view of operations at 90% capacity or sales at $450,000, considers an increase in plant facilities that will raise maximum sales possibilities to $800,000 but will raise fixed expenses to $240,000. Assume variable expenses are 40% of sales in either case. The following observations may be made:

|  | UNDER PRESENT CONDITIONS | UNDER PROPOSED CONDITIONS |
|---|---|---|
| Break-even point: | $X = .40X + \$180,000,$ or $300,000 | $X = .40X + \$240,000,$ or $400,000 |
| Profit assuming sales at 90% of present capacity, or $450,000: | $450,000 − [(40% of $450,000) + $180,000], or $ 90,000 | $450,000 − [(40% of $450,000) + $240,000], or $ 30,000 |
| Sales necessary to reach profit of $90,000: | $S(Sales) = [(.40S + \$180,000 + \$90,000$ or $450,000 | $S = .40S + \$240,000 + \$90,000$ or $550,000 |
| Maximum profit at capacity: | $500,000 − [40% of $500,000) + $180,000] or $120,000 | $800,000 − [(40% of $800,000) + $240,000] or $240,000 |

In deciding whether expansion is warranted at this stage, the increased break-even point, the decreased profit if sales remain $450,000, and the increased sales required to produce the same profit would be weighed against the increased sales and profit potentials.

**STATEMENT OF APPLI-CATION OF FUNDS** Comparative balance sheet data show the change that has taken place in a company's working capital position. However, it may be of interest to determine the reasons for the change. To what extent did such factors as profits, property acquisitions, retirement of long-term debt, and the issuance of additional capital stock affect the company's working capital during the period? Analysis of comparative balance sheet data together with a review of activities of the period will reveal the sources and the dispositions of working capital. Information with respect to working capital is presented in the form of a special exhibit known as the statement of application of funds. Because of the importance of this statement, it is considered separately in Chapter 28.

## QUESTIONS

**1.** Explain how an understanding of accounting assists in the analysis and interpretation of financial statements.

**2.** What are the factors that one would look for in judging a company's (1) solvency, (2) stability, (3) profitability?

**3.** What are the advantages of statements prepared in comparative form?

**4.** Distinguish between horizontal and vertical analytical procedures. What special purpose does each serve?

**5.** Distinguish between a cumulative income statement and a comparative income statement. What purpose does each serve?

**6.** When data for more than two years are involved, what are the advantages of developing comparisons in terms of the earliest year given? What are the advantages of developing comparisons in terms of the preceding year?

**7.** What are the relative advantages of changes reported as percentages as compared with changes reported as ratios?

**8.** What is meant by a *thirteen-month year*. What advantages and disadvantages can you name in the use of such a year for accounting purposes?

**9.** What is meant by a *common-size* statement?

**10.** What are the factors that are responsible for a change in a company's gross profit?

**11.** (a) The Marsh Co. reports an increase in gross profit in 1958 over 1957 of $60,000. What other information would be useful in the evaluation of this increase? (b) Give possible unfavorable circumstances that might accompany such a change.

**12.** The Atlas Co. develops the following measurements for 1958 as compared with the year 1957. What additional information would you require before arriving at favorable or unfavorable conclusions for each item?

(a) Net income has increased $50,000.
(b) Sales returns and allowances have increased by $30,000.
(c) The gross profit rate has increased by 5%.
(d) Purchases discounts have increased by $5,000.
(e) Cash has increased by $85,000.
(f) Inventories have decreased by $100,000.
(g) Retained earnings have decreased by $300,000.

**13.** (a) Distinguish between fixed expenses and variable expenses. (b) What is meant by the P/V ratio?

**14.** (a) What is meant by a company's *break-even point?* (b) How is it calculated? (c) Suggest certain practical applications that can be made of break-even point analysis.

**15.** Assuming the same total expenses and income figures at full production for two companies, what will cause a lower break-even point for one company than for the other?

## EXERCISES

**1.** Indicate the dollar change, the percentage change, and also the ratio that would be reported for each case below, assuming horizontal analysis:

Gain or loss* on sale of securities:

| | 1957 | 1958 | | | 1957 | 1958 |
|---|---|---|---|---|---|---|
| (a) | $20,000 | $45,000 | | (f) | $    0 | $20,000* |
| (b) | 50,000 | 20,000 | | (g) | 5,000* | 5,000 |
| (c) | 0 | 30,000 | | (h) | 5,000 | 20,000* |
| (d) | 40,000 | 0 | | (i) | 10,000* | 10,000* |
| (e) | 20,000 | 30,000* | | (j) | 10,000 | 10,000 |

**2.** The following comparative data are developed for the Moore Company:

|  | 1957 | 1958 |
|---|---|---|
| Gross sales. | $510,000 | $760,000 |
| Sales returns. | 10,000 | 10,000 |
| Net sales. | $500,000 | $750,000 |
| Cost of goods sold. | 300,000 | 465,000 |
| Gross profit on sales | $200,000 | $285,000 |
| Operating expenses. | 220,000 | 240,000 |
| Net profit or loss* from operations. | $ 20,000* | $ 45,000 |
| Other income. | 5,000 | 5,000 |
|  | $ 15,000* | $ 50,000 |
| Other expenses. | 10,000 | 10,000 |
| Net income or loss* before income taxes | $ 25,000* | $ 40,000 |
| Income taxes. |  | 10,000 |
| Net income or loss*. | $ 25,000* | $ 30,000 |

(a) What was the net sales percentage increase for 1958?
(b) What was the gross profit percentage increase for 1958?
(c) What was the mark-up percentage on cost for 1957 and 1958?
(d) What is the percentage of net income or loss to net sales?
(e) What is the net profit dollar increase for 1958?
(f) What are the factors accounting for the variation in net operating results?

**3.** From the following data for the Foster Co., explain the causes for the reduced profit supported by a detailed analysis of the causes for the change in gross profit.

|  | 1957 | | 1958 | |
|---|---|---|---|---|
| Sales | 20,000 units @ $4 | $80,000 | 25,000 units @ $4.20 | $105,000 |
| Cost of goods sold | | 50,000 | | 80,000 |
| Gross profit on sales | | $30,000 | | $ 25,000 |
| Operating expenses | | 10,000 | | 15,000 |
| Net income | | $20,000 | | $ 10,000 |

**4.** Comparative data for the Winston Co. appear below:

|  | 1957 | 1958 |
|---|---|---|
| Sales. | $5,000,000 | $6,875,000 |
| Cost of goods sold. | 3,000,000 | 4,262,500 |
| Gross profit on sales. | $2,000,000 | $2,612,500 |

(a) If it is assumed that sales prices in 1958 average 25% above those for 1957, what part of the change in gross profit is due to a change in the sales volume and what part is due to a change in the gross profit rate?

(b) Assume, instead, that a single commodity is sold, and that the sales price of this commodity was $2.50 in 1957 and $2.75 in 1958. Prepare a statement analyzing the change in gross profit in terms of volume and price changes for both sales and costs.

**5.** It is determined that the variable expenses for the Forrester Company are 40% of sales. Sales at capacity operations are $1,000,000. What are the break-even points, assuming that total fixed expenses are (a) $150,000, and (b) $450,000?

**6.** The total fixed expenses for the Williams Manufacturing Co. are $120,000; variable expenses are 25% of the product sales price. Units sell for $5 each. (a) How many units must be sold for the company to break even? (b) How many units must be sold for the company to realize a net income of $10,000?

**7.** The Westholme Corporation shows the following results for 1958:

| | | |
|---|---:|---:|
| Sales. . . . . . . . . . . . . . . . . . . . . . . . . . . . . . . . . . . . . . . . . | | $500,000 |
| Fixed expenses. . . . . . . . . . . . . . . . . . . . . . . . . . . . | $350,000 | |
| Variable expenses. . . . . . . . . . . . . . . . . . . . . . . . . . | 100,000 | 450,000 |
| Net income. . . . . . . . . . . . . . . . . . . . . . . . . . . . . . . . | | $ 50,000 |

Operations during 1958 were at 80% of capacity. Management assumes that capacity can be increased by 50% by plant remodeling and enlargement, which will increase fixed expenses by $200,000 annually. Variable expenses are expected to remain at 20% of sales.

(a) Compute the break-even point under both current and proposed conditions.

(b) Compute the profits at capacity under both current and proposed conditions.

(c) Compute the sales necessary under the proposed plan to reach the equivalent of maximum profits under current conditions.

**8.** The DR Co. has sales of $600,000, a margin of safety of 40%, and a P/V ratio of .30.

(a) What is the company's break-even point?
(b) What is the total for the fixed expenses?
(c) What is the net income?

## PROBLEMS

**26-1.** The following tabulations summarize operations of the Little Corporation for 1957 and 1958:

|  | 1957 | 1958 |
|---|---|---|
| Sales.......................................... | $205,000 | $260,000 |
| Sales returns................................. | 5,000 | 10,000 |
| Net sales...................................... | $200,000 | $250,000 |
| Cost of goods sold............................. | 120,000 | 170,000 |
| Gross profit on sales.......................... | $ 80,000 | $ 80,000 |
| Selling and general expenses................... | 50,000 | 65,000 |
| Net profit from operations..................... | $ 30,000 | $ 15,000 |
| Other expenses................................ | 10,000 | 20,000 |
| Net income or loss* before income taxes........ | $ 20,000 | $ 5,000* |
| Income taxes.................................. | 5,000 | |
| Net income or loss* .......................... | $ 15,000 | $ 5,000* |

*Instructions:* (1) Prepare a comparative income statement showing dollar changes and percentage changes for 1958 as compared with 1957.

(2) Prepare a comparative income statement offering a percentage analysis of component profit and loss items in terms of net sales for each year.

(3) Prepare a statement accounting for the variation in net income for 1958 as compared with 1957.

**26-2.** The financial condition of Dot, Inc. is summarized below:

| ASSETS | 1957 | 1958 |
|---|---|---|
| **Current assets:** | | |
| Cash on hand and on deposit.................. | $ 60,000 | $ 40,000 |
| U. S. Government securities at cost............. | 85,000 | 65,000 |
| Notes and accounts receivable, less allowance.... | 240,000 | 280,000 |
| Raw materials and supplies.................... | 210,000 | 300,000 |
| Goods in process............................. | 160,000 | 210,000 |
| Finished goods............................... | 300,000 | 450,000 |
| Miscellaneous prepaid items.................. | 20,000 | 20,000 |
| Total current assets ......................... | $1,075,000 | $1,365,000 |
| **Investments:** | | |
| Bond redemption fund ....................... | $ 300,000 | $ 350,000 |
| Investment in properties not in current use....... | 250,000 | 250,000 |
| Total investments ........................... | $ 550,000 | $ 600,000 |

|  | 1957 | 1958 |
|---|---|---|
| Plant and equipment at cost, less allowance........ | $ 800,000 | $ 750,000 |
| Intangible assets, less amortization............... | $ 150,000 | $ 125,000 |
| Deferred costs: | | |
| Unamortized bond issue costs................. | $ 30,000 | $ 25,000 |
| Miscellaneous deferred costs................. | 20,000 | 15,000 |
| Total deferred costs........................ | $ 50,000 | $ 40,000 |
| Total assets.................................. | $2,625,000 | $2,880,000 |

### LIABILITIES

| | 1957 | 1958 |
|---|---|---|
| Current liabilities: | | |
| Notes and accounts payable.................. | $ 140,000 | $ 260,000 |
| Income taxes payable........................ | 20,000 | 40,000 |
| Accrued payrolls, interest, and taxes............ | 25,000 | 40,000 |
| Cash dividends payable ...................... | 15,000 | 20,000 |
| Miscellaneous payables...................... | 5,000 | 5,000 |
| Total current liabilities...................... | $ 205,000 | $ 365,000 |
| Long-term debt—10-year first mortgage bonds..... | $ 250,000 | $ 250,000 |
| Estimated employee pensions payable............ | $ 130,000 | $ 150,000 |
| Deferred revenues............................. | $ 30,000 | $ 25,000 |
| Total liabilities.............................. | $ 615,000 | $ 790,000 |

### CAPITAL

| | 1957 | 1958 |
|---|---|---|
| Paid-in capital: | | |
| $4\frac{1}{2}\%$ preferred stock, par $25................... | $ 500,000 | $ 500,000 |
| No-par common stock, stated value $10......... | 500,000 | 500,000 |
| Additional paid-in capital.................... | 650,000 | 650,000 |
| Total paid-in capital........................ | $1,650,000 | $1,650,000 |
| Retained earnings: | | |
| Appropriated............................... | $ 160,000 | $ 200,000 |
| Free....................................... | 200,000 | 240,000 |
| Total retained earnings...................... | $ 360,000 | $ 440,000 |
| Total capital................................. | $2,010,000 | $2,090,000 |
| Total liabilities and capital..................... | $2,625,000 | $2,880,000 |

*Instructions:* (1) Prepare a comparative balance sheet showing dollar changes and changes in terms of ratios for 1958 as compared with 1957.

(2) Prepare a common-size balance sheet comparing financial structure ratios for 1958 with those for 1957.

**26-3.** Statements for the Clason Manufacturing Co. are given below and on pages 855 and 856.

## CLASON MANUFACTURING CO.

### BALANCE SHEETS

### DECEMBER 31, 1956, 1957, 1958

| ASSETS | 1956 | 1957 | 1958 |
|---|---|---|---|
| Current assets...................... | $ 760,000 | $ 990,000 | $1,215,000 |
| Investments ....................... | 300,000 | 250,000 | 300,000 |
| Plant and equipment (net)........... | 1,050,000 | 980,000 | 1,350,000 |
| Intangibles......................... | 150,000 | 140,000 | 180,000 |
| Total assets....................... | $2,260,000 | $2,360,000 | $3,045,000 |
| **LIABILITIES** | | | |
| Current liabilities.................. | $ 310,000 | $ 370,000 | $ 320,000 |
| Long-term debt (5%)................ | 200,000 | 200,000 | 300,000 |
| Deferred revenues................... | 20,000 | 30,000 | 25,000 |
| Total liabilities.................... | $ 530,000 | $ 600,000 | $ 645,000 |
| **CAPITAL** | | | |
| 6% Cumulative, non participating preferred stock, par $50............ | $ 500,000 | $ 500,000 | $ 500,000 |
| Common stock, par $50.............. | 1,000,000 | 1,000,000 | 1,500,000 |
| Additional paid-in capital............ | 250,000 | 250,000 | 350,000 |
| Retained earnings (Deficit*)......... | 20,000* | 10,000 | 50,000 |
| Total capital...................... | $1,730,000 | $1,760,000 | $2,400,000 |
| Total liabilities and capital........... | $2,260,000 | $2,360,000 | $3,045,000 |

## CLASON MANUFACTURING CO.

### INCOME STATEMENTS

### FOR THE YEARS ENDED DECEMBER 31, 1956, 1957, 1958

| | 1956 | 1957 | 1958 |
|---|---|---|---|
| Gross sales.......................... | $1,800,000 | $2,400,000 | $2,800,000 |
| Sales returns....................... | 40,000 | 80,000 | 100,000 |
| Net sales........................... | $1,760,000 | $2,320,000 | $2,700,000 |

|  | 1956 | 1957 | 1958 |
|---|---|---|---|
| Beginning finished goods inventory.... | $ 230,000 | $ 220,000 | $ 330,000 |
| Cost of goods manufactured.......... | 1,230,000 | 1,630,000 | 1,840,000 |
| Goods available for sale............. | $1,460,000 | $1,850,000 | $2,170,000 |
| Ending finished goods inventory...... | 220,000 | 330,000 | 350,000 |
| Cost of goods sold.................. | $1,240,000 | $1,520,000 | $1,820,000 |
| Gross profit on sales................ | $ 520,000 | $ 800,000 | $ 880,000 |
| Selling expenses.................... | $ 400,000 | $ 480,000 | $ 560,000 |
| General and administrative expenses... | 160,000 | 170,000 | 180,000 |
| Total operating expenses............. | $ 560,000 | $ 650,000 | $ 740,000 |
| Net profit or loss* from operations..... | $ 40,000* | $ 150,000 | $ 140,000 |
| Other income...................... | 30,000 | 30,000 | 40,000 |
|  | $ 10,000* | $ 180,000 | $ 180,000 |
| Other expenses..................... | 20,000 | 20,000 | 40,000 |
| Net income or loss* before income taxes. | $ 30,000* | $ 160,000 | $ 140,000 |
| Income taxes...................... |  | 60,000 | 50,000 |
| Net income or loss*................. | $ 30,000* | $ 100,000 | $ 90,000 |

### CLASON MANUFACTURING CO.
#### Schedules of Cost of Goods Manufactured
#### For the Years Ended December 31, 1956, 1957, 1958

|  | 1956 | 1957 | 1958 |
|---|---|---|---|
| Beginning raw materials inventory.... | $ 180,000 | $ 160,000 | $ 210,000 |
| Raw materials purchases............. | 600,000 | 920,000 | 1,080,000 |
|  | $ 780,000 | $1,080,000 | $1,290,000 |
| Deduct: Ending raw materials inventory | 160,000 | 210,000 | 300,000 |
| Cost of raw materials............... | $ 620,000 | $ 870,000 | $ 990,000 |
| Direct labor...................... | 360,000 | 440,000 | 510,000 |
| Manufacturing expenses............. | 300,000 | 360,000 | 380,000 |
|  | $1,280,000 | $1,670,000 | $1,880,000 |
| Add: Beginning goods in process inventory...................... | 150,000 | 200,000 | 240,000 |
|  | $1,430,000 | $1,870,000 | $2,120,000 |
| Deduct: Ending goods in process inventory...................... | 200,000 | 240,000 | 280,000 |
| Cost of goods manufactured.......... | $1,230,000 | $1,630,000 | $1,840,000 |

## CLASON MANUFACTURING CO.
### RETAINED EARNINGS STATEMENTS
#### FOR THE YEARS ENDED DECEMBER 31, 1956, 1957, 1958

| | 1956 | 1957 | 1958 |
|---|---|---|---|
| Retained earnings or deficit* at the beginning of the year................... | $ 10,000 | $ 20,000* | $ 10,000 |
| Net income or loss* per income statement | 30,000* | 100,000 | 90,000 |
| | | $ 80,000 | $100,000 |
| Cash dividends: | | | |
| Preferred stock.................... | | $ 60,000 | $ 30,000 |
| Common stock.................... | | 10,000 | 20,000 |
| Total ............................ | | $ 70,000 | $ 50,000 |
| Retained earnings or deficit* at the end of the year............................ | $ 20,000* | $ 10,000 | $ 50,000 |

*Instructions:* Prepare comparative statements for the three-year period showing dollar and percentage changes in terms of 1956, which is to be considered the base period.

**26-4.** (a) From the data for the Clason Manufacturing Co. given in Problem 26-3, develop a comparative income statement for the three-year period, offering percentage analysis of component profit and loss items in terms of net sales for each period.

(b) Prepare a comparative schedule of cost of goods manufactured for the three-year period in support of the comparative income statement, offering percentage analysis of component cost of goods manufactured items in terms of the total cost of goods manufactured for each year.

**26-5.** From the data for the Clason Manufacturing Co. given in Problem 26-3, prepare a condensed common-size balance sheet comparing financial structure percentages for the three-year period.

**26-6.** From the data for the Clason Manufacturing Co. given in Problem 26-3, prepare statements accounting for the variation in net income (1) for 1958 as compared with 1956, and (2) for 1958 as compared with 1957.

**26-7.** The Bayley Company, which sells a single commodity, shows the following operating results for a three-year period:

| | 1956 | 1957 | 1958 |
|---|---|---|---|
| Sales.............................. | $4,500,000 | $6,000,000 | $6,200,000 |
| Cost of goods sold................. | 2,925,000 | 4,080,000 | 4,216,000 |
| Gross profit on sales................ | $1,575,000 | $1,920,000 | $1,984,000 |
| Expenses......................... | 1,200,000 | 1,400,000 | 1,500,000 |
| Net income....................... | $ 375,000 | $ 520,000 | $484,000 |

Sales prices of the commodity sold were as follows: in 1956, $2.25; in 1957, $2.40; in 1958, $2.50.

*Instructions:* Prepare statements for 1957 and 1958 analyzing the change in gross profit as compared with the year immediately preceding in terms of volume changes and price changes for both sales and costs.

**26-8.** Comparative profit and loss data for the Morrison Company for 1957 and 1958 follow:

|  | 1957 | 1958 |
|---|---|---|
| Sales.................................... | $2,688,000 | $3,450,000 |
| Cost of goods sold....................... | 1,920,000 | 2,760,000 |
| Gross profit on sales.................... | $ 768,000 | $ 690,000 |
| Expenses................................ | 500,000 | 550,000 |
| Net income.............................. | $ 268,000 | $ 140,000 |

*Instructions:* Prepare a statement analyzing the variation in gross profit, giving as much information as can be determined concerning factors responsible for the change, under each of the following assumptions:

(1) No data are available concerning price and volume changes.

(2) Sales prices in 1958 are 20% above those in 1957.

(3) Total units sold in 1958 are 25% above those sold in 1957.

**26-9.** The total of all fixed expenses of Williams Products, Inc. is estimated to be $50,000; the variable expenses, $20,000 at full capacity. The estimated sales price of goods sold at full capacity is $80,000. Assume that fixed expenses are constant at all rates of business activity and that variable expenses vary in direct proportion to sales.

*Instructions:* (1) Draw a chart showing the above assumptions and also calculate the break-even point.

(2) Calculate the break-even point, assuming estimates to be the same except that the total expenses of $70,000 at full capacity are composed of only $25,000 fixed and $45,000 variable.

**26-10.** The following data are determined for the Harris Manufacturing Co.: up to 40% activity or sales, the fixed expenses are $500,000; above 40%, the fixed expenses are $600,000. The variable expenses are estimated as follows:

| RATE OF ACTIVITY OR SALES | ESTIMATED VARIABLE EXPENSES | RATE OF ACTIVITY OR SALES | ESTIMATED VARIABLE EXPENSES |
|---|---|---|---|
| 10%............ | $300,000 | 60%............ | $620,000 |
| 20%............ | 400,000 | 70%............ | 740,000 |
| 30%............ | 460,000 | 80%............ | 775,000 |
| 40%............ | 500,000 | 90%............ | 790,000 |
| 50%............ | 600,000 | 100%............ | 800,000 |

The sales at 100% capacity are assumed to be $2,000,000.

*Instructions:* Construct a chart and determine the approximate break-even point from the chart.

**26-11.** The Rose-Ann Co. has prepared the following summary relating to current activities at capacity and estimated activities at capacity with proposed enlarged facilities:

|  | WITH PRESENT FACILITIES | | WITH ENLARGED FACILITIES | |
|---|---|---|---|---|
| Sales.................... |  | $1,000,000 |  | $1,500,000 |
| Fixed expenses.......... | $600,000 |  | $850,000 |  |
| Variable expenses........ | 250,000 | 850,000 | 300,000 | 1,150,000 |
| Net income............ |  | $ 150,000 |  | $ 350,000 |

*Instructions:* (1) Calculate the break-even point under present and under proposed conditions.

(2) Calculate the sales necessary under proposed conditions in reaching current income at capacity operations.

(3) Calculate the result from operations if sales do not exceed the present total under proposed conditions.

**26-12.** The Helms Corporation, which has been operating at capacity, shows the following results for 1958:

|  |  |  |
|---|---|---|
| Sales..................................... |  | $500,000 |
| Fixed expenses........................... | $300,000 |  |
| Variable expenses......................... | 125,000 | 425,000 |
| Net income............................... |  | $ 75,000 |

Management assumes that sales can be increased 50% by improving and enlarging the plant. It is estimated that such a program will increase fixed expenses by 40%; however, variable expenses are expected to decrease about 5% in terms of sales as a result of the improved plant facilities, thus resulting in a P/V ratio of .80.

*Instructions:* (1) Calculate the break-even point under present conditions and under proposed conditions.

(2) Calculate the sales necessary under proposed conditions if the current income is to be maintained.

(3) Calculate the income if operations under proposed conditions reach 80% of capacity.

(4) Calculate the maximum income that can be realized under proposed conditions.

**26-13.** The president of the Redbrick Tile Company is concerned because his gross profit has decreased from $130,000 in 1957 to $87,960 in 1958. He asks you to prepare an analysis of the causes of change.

You find that the company operates two plants, each as a separate unit. Investigation reveals the following information:

PLANT NO. 1 (Makes a variety of products)

|  | 1958 | 1957 |
|---|---|---|
| Sales..................................... | $200,000 | $300,000 |
| Cost of sales............................. | 160,000 | 210,000 |
| Gross profit............................. | $ 40,000 | $ 90,000 |

PLANT NO. 2 (Makes only one product)

|  | 1958 | | 1957 | |
|---|---|---|---|---|
|  | AMOUNT | PER UNIT | AMOUNT | PER UNIT |
| Sales................. | $112,200 | $10.20 | $100,000 | $10.00 |
| Cost of sales.......... | 64,240 | 5.84 | 60,000 | 6.00 |
| Gross profit......... | $ 47,960 | $ 4.36 | $ 40,000 | $ 4.00 |

Prepare a detailed analysis of the causes for the change in gross profit for each of the plants to the extent that the above data permit such an analysis. Critical comment on the analysis is *not* required. (A.I.C.P.A. adapted)

**26-14.** A client has recently leased manufacturing facilities for production of a new product. Based on studies made by his staff, the following data have been made available to you:

| Estimated annual sales.................... | 24,000 units | |
|---|---|---|

|  | AMOUNT | PER UNIT |
|---|---|---|
| Estimated costs: | | |
| Material............................... | $ 96,000 | $4.00 |
| Direct labor........................... | 14,400 | .60 |
| Overhead.............................. | 24,000 | 1.00 |
| Administrative expense.................. | 28,800 | 1.20 |
| Total............................... | $163,200 | $6.80 |

Selling expenses are expected to be 15% of sales and profit is to amount to $1.02 per unit.

*Instructions:* (a) Compute the selling price per unit.

(b) Project a profit and loss statement for the year.

(c) Compute a break-even point expressed in dollars and in units assuming that overhead and administrative expenses are fixed but that other costs are fully variable. (A.I.C.P.A. adapted)

**26-15.** The Clark Metals Co. manufactures three different models of a single product. The following data are available:

| Model Number | Annual Sales Budget (Units) | Budgeted Unit Sales Price | Budgeted Sales Allowances for a Year |
|---|---|---|---|
| 100 | 30,000 | $15.00 | $1,260 |
| 200 | 16,000 | 18.00 | 480 |
| 300 | 10,000 | 25.00 | 410 |

### 1958 ESTIMATES

| Model Number | Quantity Budgeted For Production | Over-all Estimated Cost per Unit Total | Variable Cost | Non-Variable Cost |
|---|---|---|---|---|
| 100 | 30,500 | $15.072 | $ 9.871 | $5.201 |
| 200 | 15,000 | 17.335 | 10.250 | 7.085 |
| 300 | 10,000 | 23.756 | 15.436 | 8.320 |

*Instructions:* Prepare a schedule, supported by computations, showing the sales quantity and the sales dollar figure for each model necessary to enable the company to cover its costs. (A.I.C.P.A. adapted)

# Chapter 27

# FINANCIAL STATEMENT ANALYSIS

## SPECIAL RATIOS AND MEASUREMENTS

**EXTENSIONS OF HORIZONTAL AND VERTICAL PROCEDURES** The importance of comparative reports, as well as the special analyses that may be developed from such data, was discussed in the preceding chapter. However, it has already been suggested that of equal importance is the development of appropriate ratios and measurements based upon the data of the single period. For example, it is important to show how the net income figure for the current period compares with net incomes of prior periods. But it is also important to determine the relationship of the net income for the current year to owner's equity as well as to the total resources used in the business. Furthermore, if the relationships developed from data of the current period are to have the widest interpretative value, they should be compared with similar relationships for previous periods. Comparative data, relationships as of a certain date, and trends for such relationships are thus given expression.

The measurement of changes in financial data from one period to another was called horizontal analysis. The measurement of individual items in terms of other items as of the same date or period was called vertical analysis. A number of special measurements developed from financial data for a single period will be illustrated in this chapter. These represent an extension of the vertical analysis procedure. The presentation of such measurements in comparative form represents the further application of the horizontal procedure.

There are a great many special measurements that may be developed from balance sheet, income statement, and supplementary financial data as of a certain date or period. Such measurements may be divided into two classes: (1) those that analyze balance sheet position, and (2) those that analyze operating results. A number of representative measurements of both classes will be suggested. Some of these have special significance to particular groups. Other measurements may be of general interest to all groups. Creditors, both present and potential, for example, are concerned with the ability of a company to pay current obligations and require information concerning the ratio of current assets to current liabilities. Stockholders, both present and potential, are concerned with dividends and are interested in the earnings per share that will form the basis for dividend declarations.

Management is concerned with the liquidity of the merchandise stock and requires information concerning the number of times the stock has turned over during the past period. All parties are vitally interested in the profitability of operations and desire information concerning the relationship of earnings to both creditor and ownership equities.

The analyses that are described and illustrated in this chapter should not be considered all-inclusive; other special ratios and measurements may be suggested to the various groups, depending upon their particular needs. It should be emphasized once again that arbitrary conclusions cannot be reached from an individual ratio or measurement; but this information, together with adequate investigation and study, may lead to a satisfactory interpretation and evaluation of financial data. The analyses to be developed are based upon the financial statements for the Marshall Company for 1956, 1957, and 1958 as presented in the preceding chapter.

**CURRENT RATIO**    A fundamental measurement in the analysis of balance sheet position involves the comparison of current assets with current liabilities as of a certain date. Total current assets divided by total current liabilities gives the ratio of current assets to current liabilities, variously referred to as the *current ratio*, the *working capital ratio*, or the *banker's ratio*.

The current ratio is a valuable measure of the ability of a business unit to meet its current obligations. Since it is a measure of liquidity, care must be taken to determine that the proper items have been included in the current asset and current liability categories. Ordinarily a ratio of less than 2 to 1 for an industrial enterprise is regarded as unsatisfactory. A comfortable margin of current assets over current liabilities is assurance that the business will be able to meet maturing obligations even in the event of an unfavorable turn in business conditions and a shrinkage of values in the realization of such items as marketable securities, receivables, and inventories. Bond indentures frequently require that a current ratio of 3 to 1 or higher be maintained during the life of the bond issue.

In considering current condition, reference is frequently made to a company's *working capital*. This term may be used to indicate total current assets or simply the excess of current assets over current liabilities. When the term "working capital" is used to indicate total current assets, the term "net working capital" is used to represent the excess of current assets over current liabilities. Because of the differences in use, care must be exercised to interpret the term working capital in accordance with the definition that is placed on it. Here working capital is used to denote the excess of current assets over current liabilities.

The amount of working capital and the current ratio for the Marshall Company for 1957 and 1958 are developed as follows:[1]

|  | 1957 | 1958 |
|---|---|---|
| Current assets.......................... | $955,500 | $855,000 |
| Current liabilities....................... | 546,000 | 410,000 |
| Working capital......................... | $409,500 | $445,000 |
| Current ratio........................... | 1.8 : 1 | 2.1 : 1 |

Ratio calculations are sometimes carried out to two or more decimal places; however, ratios do not need to be carried out beyond one decimal place unless some particularly significant interpretative value is afforded by the more refined measurement. The current ratio just given, as well as the other ratios to be described in this chapter, can be expressed in terms of percentages. The current ratio above, expressed as a percentage, would appear:

|  | 1957 | 1958 |
|---|---|---|
| Current ratio........................ | 175% | 209% |

From the standpoint of solvency it is more important to consider the ratio of current assets to current liabilities than the amount of working capital. For example, assume balance sheet data for Companies A and B as follows:

Company A: Total current assets, $400,000; total current liabilities, $50,000.

Company B: Total current assets, $1,050,000; total current liabilities, $700,000.

Both Company A and Company B have a working capital of $350,000, but Company A has a current ratio of 8:1 while Company B has a current ratio of 1.5:1. The short-term creditors of Company A are more certain of receiving prompt and full payment than those of Company B. Bankers would normally be more favorable to Company A on a request for a short-term loan than to Company B.

It is possible, however, to overemphasize the importance of a high current ratio. Assume that a company is normally able to carry on its operations with current assets of $200,000 and current liabilities of

---

[1]Frequently, comparative data for more than two years are required in judging the trend of relationships. Analyses for only two years are given in the examples in this chapter, since these are sufficient to illustrate the comparative procedures involved.

$100,000. If the company finds itself with current assets of $500,000, current liabilities remaining at $100,000, its current ratio has increased from 2:1 to 5:1. The company here has considerably more working capital than it actually requires. It should also be observed that certain unfavorable conditions may be accompanied by an improving ratio. For example, with a slowdown in business a company may postpone programs for plant and equipment replacement, improvement, and repairs. At the same time slower collections and slower sales may serve to raise receivable and inventory balances.

The amount of working capital required by a particular enterprise depends upon both its size and the character of its business. A company doing business for cash and enjoying a rapid inventory turnover does not require as much working capital as a company selling goods on a credit basis and maintaining a large inventory with a relatively · slow turnover, assuming the same volume of business for each. However, the current ratio for individual businesses of similar character may vary depending upon the nature of their activities and their particular requirements.

**ACID-TEST RATIO**　　　A test of immediate solvency is made by comparing the sum of cash, readily marketable securities, notes receivable, and accounts receivable, known as the *quick assets*, with current liabilities. The total of the quick assets when divided by current liabilities gives the ratio of quick assets to current liabilities, known as the *acid-test ratio* or *quick ratio*. Some time may be required in the conversion of raw materials, goods in process, and finished goods into receivables and then receivables into cash. A company with a satisfactory current ratio may be in an unsatisfactory condition in terms of immediate solvency when inventories form a significant part of the current asset total. This is revealed by the acid-test ratio. In developing the ratio, close inspection must be given to receivables and the securities included in the quick asset total. There may be instances where such items are actually less liquid than inventories.

Normally one looks for a ratio of quick assets to current liabilities of not less than 1 to 1. Again, however, special conditions applicable to the particular business unit must be evaluated. Questions such as the following should be considered: What is the composition of the quick assets? What special requirements are made by current activities upon these assets? How soon are the current payables due?

The acid-test ratio for the Marshall Company is shown at the top of the opposite page.

|                              | 1957      | 1958      |
| ---------------------------- | --------- | --------- |
| Quick assets:                |           |           |
| Cash.......................  | $100,500  | $ 60,000  |
| Marketable securities......  | 150,000   | 150,000   |
| Receivables (net)..........  | 375,000   | 420,000   |
| Total quick assets.........  | $625,500  | $630,000  |
| Total current liabilities... | $546,000  | $410,000  |
| Acid-test ratio............  | 1.1 : 1   | 1.5 : 1   |

**OTHER MEASURES OF WORKING CAPITAL POSITION**  It may be desirable to develop other ratios analyzing the working capital position of the company. For example, it may be of interest to show the relationship of total current assets to total assets, of individual current assets such as receivables and inventories to total current assets, and of individual current assets to total assets. In the case of liabilities, relationships may be developed for current liabilities and total liabilities, individual current liabilities and total current liabilities, and individual current liabilities and total liabilities. Vertical analysis as applied to comparative statements in the previous chapter made available such data and also reported the changes and the trends in such relationships over a period of years. Individual current assets may also be compared with individual current liabilities or with the current liabilities total. For example, the relationships of cash to accounts payable and of cash to total current liabilities may be developed for analysis purposes.

The foregoing comparisons make available information concerning the relative liquidity of total assets and the maturity of total obligations, as well as the structure of working capital and shifts within the current group. The latter data are significant, since all the items within the current classification are not equally current. What may be considered reasonable relationships in the analysis of the working capital position again depends upon the particular enterprise.

**ANALYSIS OF RECEIVABLES**  There are special tests that may be applied in considering the liquidity of two significant working capital elements, receivables and inventories. In the case of receivables, analysis is directed to evaluation of both the size of the receivables carried and the quality of the receivables.

*Accounts Receivable Turnover.* The amount of receivables carried normally bears a close relationship to the volume of sales on a credit basis. The receivable position and approximate collection time may be evaluated by calculation of the *turnover of accounts receivable.* This rate is determined by <u>dividing net credit sales for the period by the average accounts and notes receivable from trade debtors.</u> In developing a representative average figure, monthly balances should be used if available. The average receivables figure is calculated from thirteen monthly balances, those of January 1, January 31, February 28, etc.

Assume that all of the sales of the Marshall Company are made on a credit basis, that all of the receivables arose from sales, and that only balances of receivables at the beginning and the end of the year are available in determining the average receivables. Receivable turnover figures are calculated as follows:

|  | 1957 | 1958 |
|---|---|---|
| Net credit sales..................... | $1,650,000 | $1,425,000 |
| Net receivables: |  |  |
| Beginning of year................... | $ 333,500 | $ 375,000 |
| End of year....................... | $ 375,000 | $ 420,000 |
| Average receivables................. | $ 354,250 | $ 397,500 |
| Receivables turnover within year........ | 4.7 | 3.6 |

*Number of Days' Sales in Receivables.* Average receivables are sometimes expressed in terms of average days' credit sales uncollected. The average time required to collect receivables is thus shown.

To illustrate this calculation, assume 300 business or sales days for the Marshall Company. Annual dollar sales may be divided by 300 to find average daily sales. <u>Average receivables divided by average daily sales then gives the number of days' sales in average receivables.</u> This procedure is applied to the data for the Marshall Company below:

|  | 1957 | 1958 |
|---|---|---|
| Average receivables.................. | $ 354,250 | $ 397,500 |
| Net credit sales..................... | $1,650,000 | $1,425,000 |
| Average daily credit sales (net credit sales ÷ 300)...................... | $ 5,500 | $ 4,750 |
| Number of days' sales in average receivables | 64 | 84 |

The same measurements can be obtained by simply dividing the number of days representing the year by the turnover rates of 4.7 and 3.6 for 1957 and 1958 respectively, as developed earlier. A comparable number of days should be used in developing comparisons. Computations are normally based on the calendar year consisting of 365 days or a business year consisting of 300 days (365 days less Sundays and holidays).

Instead of developing the number of days' sales in average receivables, it is possible to report the number of days' credit sales in receivables at the end of the period. Data in this form would be of special significance when an evaluation of current position and particularly of the receivable position as of a given date is sought. This information for the Marshall Company is presented on the following page.

|  | 1957 | 1958 |
|---|---|---|
| Receivables at end of period................ | $375,000 | $420,000 |
| Average daily credit sales.................. | $ 5,500 | $ 4,750 |
| Number of days' sales in receivables at the end of the period........................... | 68 | 88 |

What constitutes a reasonable number of days in receivables varies with the individual business. For example, if merchandise is sold on terms of net 60 days, 40 days' sales in receivables would not be unreasonable; if terms are net 30 days, however, a receivable balance equal to 40 days' sales would indicate an unfavorable situation.

Sales activity just before the close of the period should be considered in interpreting the relationships that are developed. If sales are unusually light or heavy just before the end of the period, receivables are affected and the measurements in turn distorted. When such unevenness prevails, it may be better to analyze accounts according to their due dates, as was illustrated in Chapter 7.

The problem of keeping accounts receivable at a minimum without losing desirable business is important. Every company must pay interest to lenders for the use of money, and it is expected to pay dividends to its stockholders. The company's investment in receivables usually does not provide income. The cost of carrying these accounts must be covered by the margin of profit made on sales. The longer the account is carried, the smaller will be the percentage return realized on invested capital. In addition, heavier collection charges and increased bad debt losses must be considered.

In the attempt to gain new and continued business, credit is frequently granted for relatively long periods. The element of cost involved in granting long-term credit should be recognized. Assume that a business has an average daily credit sales volume of $5,000 and the average amount of accounts receivable is $250,000. The latter figure represents the average daily business done for 50 days. If collections and the credit period can be improved so that outstanding accounts receivable represent only 30 days' sales, then accounts receivable will be reduced to $150,000. Assuming a cost of 6% to carry the accounts, the decrease of $100,000 in accounts would represent a savings of $6,000 annually. Assuming that the company has 10,000 shares of stock outstanding, the reduction in average receivables will increase the per-share earnings by 60 cents.

**MERCHANDISE INVEN-**      In evaluating inventory position, procedures
**TORY ANALYSIS**      similar to those for evaluating receivables may be employed. Both the number of times the average inventory

has been replenished during a fiscal period, known as the *merchandise turnover*, and the number of days' sales in average inventories may be computed from inventory and profit and loss data.

_Merchandise Turnover._ The amount of merchandise carried in stock normally bears a close relationship to the sales volume. The inventory position and the approximate disposal time may be evaluated by calculation of the merchandise turnover. The merchandise turnover is determined by dividing the cost of goods sold by the average inventory for the period. Again, when available, monthly figures should be used in developing a representative average.

Assume that only the inventories at the beginning and the end of the year are available for the Marshall Company. Merchandise turnover figures are calculated as follows:

|                                            | 1957 | 1958 |
|--------------------------------------------|------|------|
| Cost of goods sold                         | $1,200,000 | $1,000,000 |
| Merchandise inventory:                     |      |      |
|   Beginning of year              | $ 125,000 | $ 330,000 |
|   End of year                    | $ 330,000 | $ 225,000 |
| Average merchandise inventory              | $ 227,500 | $ 277,500 |
| Merchandise turnover for the year          | 5.3  | 3.6  |

_Number of Days' Sales in Inventories._ Average inventories are sometimes expressed in terms of average days' sales. Information is thus afforded concerning the average time it takes to dispose of the inventory. The number of days' sales in inventories is calculated by dividing the average inventory by the average daily cost of goods sold. When a turnover figure has been calculated, the same measurement can be obtained by simply dividing the days in the year by the turnover figure for the year. The latter procedure is illustrated for the Marshall Company:

|                                            | 1957 | 1958 |
|--------------------------------------------|------|------|
| Merchandise turnover for the year          | 5.3  | 3.6  |
| Number of days' sales in average inventory (assuming a business year of 300 days) | 57 | 83 |

Instead of developing the number of days' sales in average inventories, the number of days' sales in inventories at the end of the period may be determined by dividing the ending inventory by the average daily cost of goods sold. An expression in this form would be especially helpful for purposes of evaluating current position and particularly the inventory position as of a given date.

A company with departmental classifications for merchandise will find it desirable to support the inventory measurements for the company as a whole with individual measurements for each department, since there may be considerable variation among departments. A company manufacturing its product may compute turnovers for finished goods, goods in process, and raw materials. The finished goods turnover is computed by dividing the cost of goods sold by the average finished goods inventory; the goods in process turnover is computed by dividing the cost of goods manufactured by the average goods in process inventory; and the raw materials turnover is computed by dividing the cost of raw materials used by the average raw materials inventory.

Equivalent valuation bases must be employed if measurements that are developed from inventory figures are to be comparable. Maximum accuracy in developing measurements is possible if information relating to cost of goods sold and inventories is available in terms of number of units rather than sales dollars.

The effect of seasonal factors on the size of inventories at the end of the period should be considered in the inventory analyses. Inventories may be abnormally high or low at the end of the period. Many companies adopt a fiscal year that ends when operations are at their lowest point. This is referred to as the adoption of the *natural business year*. When such a plan is adopted, stocks will normally be at their lowest point at the end of the period. The organization is able to take inventory and complete year-end closing most conveniently with inventories at minimum levels and selling activities at their low point. Under such circumstances, monthly inventory balances should be developed by the gross profit method as illustrated in Chapter 10 in arriving at a representative average inventory value.

The greater the rate of turnover of the stock of merchandise, the smaller is the amount of investment necessary for a given volume of business and consequently the higher is the rate of return on invested capital. This conclusion is based on the assumption that the enterprise is able to purchase goods in smaller quantities sufficiently often at no disadvantage in price. If merchandise must be bought in very large quantities in order to get a favorable price, then the savings on quantity purchases must be weighed against the additional investment and increased costs of storage.

The financial advantage of an increased turnover figure may be illustrated as follows: Assume that the cost of sales figure for a year has been $1,000,000, and the average inventory at cost, $250,000; the rate of turnover, then, is 4. Assume that through careful buying the same volume of business can be maintained with an increased turnover of 5, or an average inventory of only $200,000. If the cost of money for carrying the inventory is 6%, the savings on $50,000 will be $3,000 annually. The above does not include possible advantages gained from a decrease in merchandise spoilage and obsolescence losses; the saving in costs of storage space, insurance, and taxes on the excess inventory; and the reduction in the risk of losses from price declines.

Inventory investments and turnover rates vary between different enterprises. The facts of each business unit must be judged in terms of the financial structure and the activities of the particular unit. Each business must plan an inventory policy that will avoid the extremes of a dangerously low stock that may impair sales volume and an overstocking of goods with a heavy capital investment attended by dangers of shrinking prices and possible difficulties in meeting the obligations arising from the purchases.

**RATIO OF OWNERS'**    The relationship of the equities of the owner-
**CAPITAL TO LIABILITIES**  ship group and the creditor group in total
business assets may be measured in terms of ratios. The statements employing vertical analysis as given in the preceding chapter illustrated the development of such measurements. Instead of expression in terms of assets, owners' and creditors' equities may be expressed in terms of each other. For example, owners may have a 60% interest in total assets and creditors a 40% interest. Here one can say that the ratio of the ownership interest to the creditors' interest is 1.5 to 1, or that the owners' interest is 150% of the liabilities of the business.

Comparative data summarizing ownership and creditor equities in assets or the relationship of the equities to each other show the changes taking place in equities. As the ownership equity rises in relation to the creditors' equity, the margin of protection to the creditor group goes up. From the point of view of the owners, an increase in the ownership equity makes the organization less vulnerable to a decline in the business cycle and possible inability to meet obligations, and also serves to reduce the expenses of carrying the debt.

However, it should not be overlooked that it is normally advantageous to supplement funds contributed by the owners with a certain amount contributed by a creditor group. The employment of funds contributed by creditors is known as *trading on the equity*. It is assumed that the additional earnings accruing to the business through use of borrowed capital will exceed the interest charged for the use of such funds. When the rate earned on borrowed funds exceeds the rate paid on borrowings, a gain by trading on the equity is said to have accrued to the stockholders; when the rate earned is less than that paid, a loss is incurred.

The ratio of owners' capital to total liabilities is considered in judging whether trading on the equity has been carried to an excess with possible danger to business solvency from a long-term approach. The relationship of capital to liabilities for the Marshall Company follows:

|  | 1957 | 1958 |
|---|---|---|
| Total capital............................ | $1,445,000 | $1,468,000 |
| Total liabilities.......................... | $ 946,000 | $ 810,000 |
| Ratio of capital to liabilities............. | 1.5:1 | 1.8:1 |

**RATIO OF PLANT AND EQUIPMENT TO LONG-TERM DEBT**    Comparisons may be made between plant and equipment and the total long-term debt. When plant and equipment are pledged on the long-term obligations, this ratio indicates the protection afforded to the long-term creditor group, as well as the possibility for the expansion of long-term indebtedness on the basis of available security.

In the development of this ratio, present sound values of plant and equipment instead of book values should be used if available, since the protection to creditors as well as the ability of the business to borrow is based on the market values of the assets representing the security. If a bond retirement fund is maintained consisting of a company's own obligations that have been reacquired but not retired, this fund should be subtracted from the long-term debt in developing the ratio; a bond retirement fund consisting of other investments, however, would represent additional security on the indebtedness rather than a reduction in debt and should be added to plant and equipment for purposes of this ratio. Normally, long-term creditors limit their loans to 50 to 60% of the value of properties pledged, so that there may be an adequate margin of safety in the event of business failure and the need to apply the security to the payment of the indebtedness.

The ratio of plant and equipment to long-term debt for the Marshall Company follows:

|  | 1957 | 1958 |
|---|---|---|
| Total plant and equipment (net)............. | $875,000 | $775,000 |
| Total long-term debt...................... | $400,000 | $400,000 |
| Ratio of plant and equipment to long-term debt. | 2.2:1 | 1.9:1 |

**RATIO OF OWNERS' CAPITAL TO PLANT AND EQUIPMENT**    The changes in the relationship of owners' capital to plant and equipment need to be considered in judging whether expansion is taking place through an increased ownership equity or through borrowing. An increasing ratio indicates that plant and equipment are being increasingly financed through funds supplied by the sale of stock or the retention of earnings within the business, and normally this would be looked upon favorably. A declining ratio indicates that the increase of plant properties has exceeded the expansion in capital. This may suggest possible overexpansion, the excessive use of credit supplied by the creditor group, and greater vulnerability to financial difficulties in the event of a decline in business activities.

The ratio of capital to plant and equipment for the Marshall Company follows:

|  | 1957 | 1958 |
|---|---|---|
| Total capital............................ | $1,445,000 | $1,468,000 |
| Total plant and equipment (net)........... | $ 875,000 | $ 775,000 |
| Ratio of capital to plant and equipment .... | 1.7:1 | 1.9:1 |

**BOOK VALUES PER SHARE OF STOCK**    An important measurement of the owners' interest in the business is afforded by a determination of the *book value per share*. This is the dollar equity related to each share. The calculation of share book value was described earlier in Chapter 23. It was indicated there that, when there is only one class of stock, book value per share is calculated by dividing the total capital by the number of shares outstanding. When both common and preferred stock have been issued, it becomes necessary to allocate capital to the two classes. Redemption or liquidation values and cumulative and participating features of the preferred issue must be considered in determining the portion of capital relating to preferred stock and the balance relating to the residual or common stock equity.

Both common and preferred stock of the Marshall Company are $10 par. The preferred stock is cumulative and nonparticipating, and no dividends are in arrears. The preferred stock has a liquidation value equal to its par value. The book values per share for common and preferred stock are calculated as follows:

|  | 1957 | 1958 |
|---|---|---|
| 6% preferred stock........................ | $350,000 | $350,000 |
| Common stock............................ | $750,000 | $750,000 |
| Additional paid-in capital................. | $100,000 | $100,000 |
| Retained earnings........................ | $245,000 | $268,000 |

|  | 1957 | 1958 |
|---|---|---|
| Book value per share of preferred: | $\dfrac{\$350,000}{35,000\ \text{shares}} = \$10.00$ | $\dfrac{\$350,000}{35,000\ \text{shares}} = \$10.00$ |
| Book value per share of common: | $\dfrac{\$750,000 + \$345,000}{75,000\ \text{shares}} = \$14.60$ | $\dfrac{\$750,000 + \$368,000}{75,000\ \text{shares}} = \$14.91$ |

Frequently, for analysis purposes, the book value of stock is calculated after retained earnings are reduced by the amount of intangible assets reported on the balance sheet. Book value of the stock thus reported offers a more conservative appraisal of the ownership equity.

**OTHER MEASUREMENTS OF BALANCE SHEET STRUCTURE** A number of measurements of balance sheet structure other than those already described are developed in specific instances. Among these might be mentioned the ratio of individual noncurrent assets to total assets of the business or to total assets of the group, and individual noncurrent liabilities to total liabilities of the business or to total liabilities of the group. Relationships such as the foregoing may be presented directly on comparative statements by means of vertical analysis procedures.

**RATIO OF SALES TO ASSETS** Among the measurements that are developed from balance sheet and income statement data may be mentioned the _ratio of sales to assets_, sometimes called the _assets turnover rate_, which measures the contribution of assets to the sales total. This ratio is calculated by dividing the net sales figure by the business assets that produced the sales. Comparative data reporting the ratio of sales dollars to the asset dollar investment indicates the relative effectiveness of asset utilization. A ratio increase may suggest the better utilization of assets, although a point may be reached where it is concluded that there is a strain on assets and that the capital may be insufficient for the company to reach its full sales potential. A ratio decrease may indicate that sales are not keeping pace with asset changes, thus suggesting the possibility of overinvestment in assets or their inefficient use.

In developing the ratio, long-term investments should be excluded from the asset total when these are considered to make no contribution to the sales total. If monthly figures for assets are available, they may be used in developing a representative average for assets employed during the year. Sometimes the assets at the end of the year are used as a basis for the computation. When sales can be expressed in terms of units sold, ratios in terms of sales units per dollar invested offer more reliable guides to interpretation than sales dollars, since unit results are not affected by price level fluctuations.

Assume that only asset totals for the beginning and end of the year are available for the Marshall Company and that sales cannot be expressed in terms of units. Ratios are computed as follows:

|                                                | 1957        | 1958        |
| ---------------------------------------------- | ----------- | ----------- |
| Net sales                                      | $1,650,000  | $1,425,000  |
| Assets (excluding long-term investments):      |             |             |
| Beginning of year                              | $1,510,000  | $1,991,000  |
| End of year                                    | $1,991,000  | $1,778,000  |
| Average assets for the year                    | $1,750,500  | $1,884,500  |
| Ratio of sales to average assets               | .9:1        | .8:1        |

**RATIO OF SALES TO PLANT AND EQUIPMENT** Related to the ratio just described is the *ratio of sales to plant and equipment,* sometimes referred to as the *plant and equipment turnover* or the *fixed asset turnover.* The sales total, here, is divided by the investment in plant and equipment, and the resulting figure indicates how effectively plant and equipment are utilized in terms of sales. With comparative data, judgments may be made concerning the relative efficiency of utilization of these assets and the effects on sales of increases or decreases in property totals. An increase in plant and equipment when accompanied by a ratio decrease may suggest overexpansion in plant facilities.

Assume that beginning and ending plant and equipment balances are used in measuring the average investment for the Marshall Company. Ratios are computed as follows:

|                                                   | 1957        | 1958        |
| ------------------------------------------------- | ----------- | ----------- |
| Net sales                                         | $1,650,000  | $1,425,000  |
| Plant and equipment:                              |             |             |
| Beginning of year                                 | $ 675,000   | $ 875,000   |
| End of year                                       | $ 875,000   | $ 775,000   |
| Average investment in plant and equipment         | $ 775,000   | $ 825,000   |
| Ratio of sales to average plant and equipment     | 2.1:1       | 1.7:1       |

In certain instances it may be desirable to combine intangible assets with plant and equipment in establishing the base for this measurement.

**RATE EARNED ON TOTAL ASSETS** The adequacy of net income may be measured in terms of (1) the return on sales, (2) the return on assets producing the income, and (3) the return on the owners' equity. There should be an adequate return in terms of each of the three standards if operating results are to be viewed as satisfactory. The return on sales was measured in the previous chapter where vertical analysis was applied to income statement data. The return on total assets, frequently referred to as the *asset productivity rate,* is found by dividing the net income after income taxes by the total assets employed in the production of such income.

If the assets by months are available, they should be used in developing the average assets for the year. Frequently, however, the assets at the beginning of the year or the assets at the end of the year are used for the calculation. In some instances it may be desirable to exclude certain income items relating to investments, such as interest, dividends, and rents, so that net income is limited to that resulting from trading operations. When this is the case, assets should be reduced by the investments in developing the rate of return. Sometimes the rate of net operating income to total assets, or, perhaps, the rate of net income before income taxes to total assets, is developed in comparative form so that rates of return may not be affected by financial management items or by fluctuations in income tax rates.

The rate of net income after income taxes on total assets for the Marshall Company is determined below:

|                                          | 1957        | 1958        |
|------------------------------------------|-------------|-------------|
| Net income after income taxes........... | $    60,000 | $    70,000 |
| Total assets:                            |             |             |
|   Beginning of year...................... | $1,760,000  | $2,391,000  |
|   End of year......................... | $2,391,000  | $2,278,000  |
| Average assets........................   | $2,075,500  | $2,334,500  |
| Rate earned on average total assets....... | 2.89%     | 3.00%       |

**RATE EARNED ON OWNERS' EQUITY**  The return on the owners' equity in the business is found by dividing the net income after income taxes by the total capital. In the development of this rate, it is preferable to use the average capital for a year calculated from monthly data, particularly when significant changes in capital have occurred during the year as a result of the sale of additional stock, the retirement of stock, the payment of dividends, and the retention of earnings. Sometimes the beginning or the ending capital is used for the measurement.

The rate of net income after income taxes on total capital for the Marshall Company is calculated as follows:

|                                          | 1957        | 1958        |
|------------------------------------------|-------------|-------------|
| Net income after income taxes........... | $    60,000 | $    70,000 |
| Capital:                                 |             |             |
|   Beginning of year...................... | $1,330,000  | $1,445,000  |
|   End of year......................... | $1,445,000  | $1,468,000  |
| Average capital ......................   | $1,387,500  | $1,456,500  |
| Rate earned on average capital.......... | 4.32%     | 4.81%       |

**TIMES BOND INTEREST REQUIREMENTS WERE EARNED** Earnings also may be measured in terms of (1) their relationship to bond interest requirements, (2) their relationship to preferred dividend requirements, and (3) their availability to common stockholders.

Calculation of the number of times earnings cover the bond interest is made by dividing net income before any charge for interest by the bond interest requirements for the period. The ability of the company to meet interest payments and the degree of safety afforded the bondholders is thus reported. The number of times interest charges were earned by the Marshall Company follows:

|  | 1957 | 1958 |
|---|---|---|
| Net income after income taxes . . . . . . . . . . . . . . | $ 60,000 | $ 70,000 |
| Add bond interest ($4\frac{1}{2}\%$ on long-term debt) . . . . | 18,000 | 18,000 |
| Amount available in meeting bond interest requirements. . . . . . . . . . . . . . . . . . . . . . . . . . . . . | $ 78,000 | $ 88,000 |
| Number of times bond interest requirements were earned. . . . . . . . . . . . . . . . . . . . . . . . . . . | 4.3 | 4.9 |

**TIMES PREFERRED DIVIDEND REQUIRE-MENTS WERE EARNED** Calculation of the number of times earnings cover the preferred dividends is made by dividing the net income after income taxes by the preferred dividend requirements for the period. The ability of the company to meet dividend requirements on preferred is thus indicated. For the Marshall Company calculations are as follows:

|  | 1957 | 1958 |
|---|---|---|
| Net income after income taxes. . . . . . . . . . . . . . | $ 60,000 | $ 70,000 |
| Preferred dividend requirements. . . . . . . . . . . . . | $ 21,000 | $ 21,000 |
| Number of times preferred dividend requirements were earned. . . . . . . . . . . . . . . . . . . . . . | 2.9 | 3.3 |

The relationship of earnings to preferred dividend requirements may be indicated by means of an alternate calculation. Net income after income taxes may be divided by the number of shares of preferred stock outstanding. It should be recognized that this calculation does not offer the amount of earnings to which preferred shares are entitled, but simply the amount of earnings that are available in meeting preferred dividend requirements.

Earnings available in meeting preferred share requirements of the Marshall Company are calculated as follows:

|                                                          | 1957    | 1958    |
|----------------------------------------------------------|---------|---------|
| Net income after income taxes................            | $60,000 | $70,000 |
| Number of shares of preferred outstanding.......          | 35,000  | 35,000  |
| Earnings available in meeting preferred share requirements................................ | $1.71 | $2.00 |

Since preferred stock is 6%, $10 par, earnings required to cover preferred dividends would be 60 cents per share.

**RATE EARNED ON COMMON STOCKHOLDERS' EQUITY** The rate of earnings on the common stockholders' equity, sometimes referred to as the *financial ratio,* is calculated by dividing the net income after income taxes and after preferred dividend requirements by the equity of the common stockholders. The average equity for common stockholders should be determined, although the rate is frequently calculated on the basis of the beginning or ending common equity.

In the case of the Marshall Company, whose preferred stock is non-participating, preferred requirements are limited to 6%. The rate earned on the common equity, then, is calculated as follows:

|                                                          | 1957        | 1958        |
|----------------------------------------------------------|-------------|-------------|
| Net income after income taxes ...........               | $  60,000   | $  70,000   |
| Less dividend requirements on preferred stock            | 21,000      | 21,000      |
| Income identified with common stockholders' equity....................... | $  39,000 | $  49,000 |
| Common stockholders' equity:                             |             |             |
| Beginning of year....................                    | $1,080,000  | $1,095,000  |
| End of year.........................                     | $1,095,000  | $1,118,000  |
| Average common equity................                    | $1,087,500  | $1,106,500  |
| Rate earned on average common stockholders' equity....................... | 3.6% | 4.4% |

**EARNINGS PER SHARE ON COMMON STOCK** Earnings on common stock may be expressed in terms of the dollar amount relating to each share. In computing common share earnings, net income after income taxes and after the prior claim on earnings of preferred stock is divided by the number of shares of common stock outstanding. In the case of the Marshall Company, earnings per share on common stock are computed as follows:

|                                                          | 1957    | 1958    |
|----------------------------------------------------------|---------|---------|
| Net income after income taxes................            | $60,000 | $70,000 |
| Less dividend requirements on preferred stock....         | 21,000  | 21,000  |
| Income identified with common stock equity.....           | $39,000 | $49,000 |
| Number of shares of common stock outstanding..            | 75,000  | 75,000  |
| Earnings per share on common stock..........              | $ .52   | $ .65   |

**DISTRIBUTION OF EARNINGS TO CREDITOR AND OWNERSHIP EQUITIES** Inasmuch as earnings are the ultimate source upon which the creditors and the owners of an enterprise must rely for a return of both principal and income, and because the different classes of security holders normally obtain different rates of return, a percentage analysis of the disposition of the earnings of a company is frequently of interest to all groups. In the case of the Marshall Company it is possible to prepare a summary of the distribution of earnings as follows:

| | Equity Totals[1] | | Equity Percentage | | Amount of Earnings Paid and Accruing* to Equities | | Percentage Distribution of Total Earnings Paid or Accruing* | | Percentage Paid or Accruing* to Equities | |
| | 1957 | 1958 | 1957 | 1958 | 1957 | 1958 | 1957 | 1958 | 1957 | 1958 |
|---|---|---|---|---|---|---|---|---|---|---|
| Bondholders (4½% long-term debt) | $ 400,000 | $ 400,000 | 22% | 22% | $18,000 | $18,000 | 23% | 20% | 4.5% | 4.5% |
| Preferred stockholders... | 350,000 | 350,000 | 19% | 19% | 21,000 | 21,000 | 27% | 24% | 6.0% | 6.0% |
| Common stockholders... | 1,087,500 | 1,106,500 | 59% | 59% | {24,000 {15,000* | 26,000 23,000* | 31% 19%* | 30% 26%* | 2.2%[2] 1.4%* | 2.3% 2.1%* |
| Total................. | $1,837,500 | $1,856,500 | 100% | 100% | $78,000 | $88,000 | 100% | 100% | 4.2% | 4.7% |

**OTHER MEASUREMENTS OF OPERATIONS** A number of other measurements of operations and operating results that are significant in various instances can be developed. Among these may be mentioned such ratios as gross profit to sales, net operating income to sales, net income to sales, individual manufacturing expenses to cost of goods manufactured, individual selling expenses and individual general and administrative expenses to the totals for these respective groups. These relationships are generally presented by means of comparative statements offering horizontal and vertical analyses of profit and loss data.

**INTERPRETATION OF ANALYSES** Analyses introduced in Chapter 26 and in this chapter are developed to help the analyst arrive at certain conclusions with regard to the business. It has already been suggested that these are merely guides to the intelligent interpretation of financial data.

All of the ratios and measurements need not be used, but rather only those that will actually assist in the development of opinions with respect to the questions that have been raised by the analyst. Such measurements as are developed need to be interpreted in terms of the conditions relating to the particular enterprise, the conditions relating to the particular industry to which the enterprise is related, and the conditions relating to general business and the economic

---

[1]Average equities for the year are indicated in this illustration. It would be possible to base analyses on equities as of the beginning of the year or equities as of the end of the year.

[2]This percentage, while stated in terms of the common stockholders' equity, could be stated in terms of the par or stated value of the common stock or in terms of market value of the stock.

environment within which the enterprise operates.  If measurements are to be of maximum value, they need to be compared with similar data developed for the particular enterprise for past periods, with similar measurements that may be available for the industry as a whole and that may be regarded as standard or normal, and with pertinent data relating to general business conditions and the business cycle as these affect the individual enterprise.  Only by intelligent use and integration of the foregoing sources of data can financial maladjustments be recognized and reliable opinions be developed concerning operation, progress, and financial structure of the business unit.

## QUESTIONS

**1.** (a) Define working capital.  (b) What is the importance of working capital?

**2.** Distinguish between the current ratio and the acid-test ratio.  What are usually considered minimums for each ratio?

**3.** The working capital for the Wright Company has increased in amount as follows.  Comment on the change:

|  | 1957 | 1958 |
|---|---|---|
| Current assets: | | |
| Cash...................................... | $15,000 | $ 20,000 |
| Receivables............................... | 32,000 | 40,000 |
| Inventories............................... | 39,500 | 86,000 |
| | $86,500 | $146,000 |
| Current liabilities ....................... | 32,000 | 83,500 |
| Working capital .......................... | $54,500 | $ 62,500 |

**4.** Balance sheets for the Blake Corporation and the Carlson Corporation each show a working capital total of $500,000.  Does this indicate that the short-term solvencies of the two companies are approximately equal?  Explain.

**5.** The current ratio for the Decker Co. is 4 to 1; the working capital ratio for the Evarts Co. is 9 to 1.  The current position of the Evarts Co. may thus be considered the sounder of the two.  Evaluate this argument.

**6.** Define each of the following:  (a) banker's ratio, (b) quick assets, (c) financial ratio.

**7.** (a) How is the accounts receivable turnover calculated?  (b) How would you interpret a rising accounts receivable turnover rate?

**8.** (a) How is the merchandise turnover calculated?  (b) What precautions are necessary in arriving at the basis for the turnover calculation? (c) How would you interpret a rising merchandise turnover?

**9.** (a) What is meant by *trading on the equity?* (b) Give figures to illustrate a gain accruing to owners through this practice.

**10.** "The ratio of owners' capital to total liabilities offers information concerning the long-term solvency of the business unit." Explain.

**11.** Give rules for calculating share book values when a company has both common and preferred shares outstanding.

**12.** State the significance of each of the following measurements: (a) ratio of plant and equipment to long-term debt, (b) ratio of owners' capital to plant and equipment, (c) ratio of sales to total assets, and (d) ratio of sales to plant and equipment.

**13.** (a) What is meant by the *asset productivity rate?* (b) How is it calculated?

**14.** Indicate how each of the following measurements is calculated and appraise its significance:
  (a) The number of times bond interest requirements were earned.
  (b) The number of times preferred dividend requirements were earned.
  (c) The rate of earnings on the common stockholders' equity.
  (d) The earnings per share on common stock.

**15.** (a) Distinguish between the *natural business year* and the *thirteen-month year.* (b) What advantages are found in the adoption of each for accounting purposes?

## EXERCISES

**1.** The data that follow are taken from comparative balance sheets prepared for the Stanford Company:

|  | 1957 | 1958 |
|---|---|---|
| Cash. | $ 16,000 | $ 30,000 |
| Marketable securities. | 20,000 | 10,000 |
| Trade receivables (net). | 45,000 | 55,000 |
| Inventories. | 60,000 | 75,000 |
| Prepaid expenses. | 1,500 | 2,500 |
| Plant and equipment. | 80,000 | 85,000 |
| Intangibles. | 25,000 | 22,500 |
| Deferred costs. | 5,000 | 6,000 |
|  | $252,500 | $286,000 |
| Current liabilities. | $ 60,000 | $100,000 |

  (a) From the above data calculate for both 1957 and 1958: (1) the working capital, (2) the current ratio, (3) the acid-test ratio, (4) the ratio of current assets to total assets, (5) the ratio of cash to current liabilities.

  (b) Evaluate each of the above changes.

**2.** Statements for the Hancock Co. show the following balances:

|  | 1956 | 1957 | 1958 |
|---|---|---|---|
| Average receivables (net).......... | $ 30,000 | $ 40,000 | $ 60,000 |
| Net sales....................... | 345,000 | 390,000 | 480,000 |

Give any significant measurements that may be developed in analyzing the foregoing, assuming a 300-day business year and assuming that approximately one third of the sales are for cash the balance being on account. What conclusions may be made concerning the receivables if sales on account are made on a 2/30, n/60 basis?

**3.** The average inventory for the ABC Company at cost price is $40,000; sales for 1958 were made at 20% above cost and totaled $300,000. (a) What was the merchandise turnover rate? (b) What is the average age of the inventory on hand, assuming a 300-day year?

**4.** Operating statements for the Merriman Sales Co. show the following:

|  | 1956 | 1957 | 1958 |
|---|---|---|---|
| Sales............................. | $75,000 | $96,000 | $105,000 |
| Cost of goods sold: |  |  |  |
| Beginning inventory.............. | $16,000 | $15,000 | $ 29,000 |
| Purchases....................... | 50,000 | 80,000 | 86,000 |
|  | $66,000 | $95,000 | $115,000 |
| Ending inventory................ | 15,000 | 29,000 | 41,000 |
|  | $51,000 | $66,000 | $ 74,000 |
| Gross profit on sales............... | $24,000 | $30,000 | $ 31,000 |

Give whatever measurements may be developed in analyzing the inventory positions at the end of each year. What conclusions would you make concerning the inventory trend?

**5.** The following data are taken from the Mason Corporation records for years ending December 31, 1956, 1957, and 1958:

|  | 1956 | 1957 | 1958 |
|---|---|---|---|
| Finished goods inventory................. | $ 15,000 | $ 30,000 | $ 60,000 |
| Goods in process inventory............... | 40,000 | 40,000 | 40,000 |
| Raw materials inventory................. | 25,000 | 40,000 | 50,000 |
| Sales...................................... | 360,000 | 340,000 | 400,000 |
| Cost of goods sold....................... | 210,000 | 235,000 | 230,000 |
| Cost of goods manufactured.............. | 200,000 | 250,000 | 260,000 |
| Cost of materials used................... | 120,000 | 130,000 | 150,000 |

Calculate turnover figures for 1957 and 1958 for (a) finished goods, (b) goods in process, and (c) raw material.

**6.** The total purchases of goods by the Bailey Wholesale Company during 1958 were $360,000. All purchases were on a 2/10, n/30 basis. The average balance in the vouchers payable account was $45,000. Was the company prompt, slow, or average in paying for goods? How many days' average purchases were there in accounts payable, assuming a 300-day year?

**7.** The capital for the Mathews Corporation on December 31, 1958, is as follows:

| | |
|---|---:|
| 6% Preferred stock, $50 par | $ 500,000 |
| Common stock, $10 par | 1,000,000 |
| Additional paid-in capital | 200,000 |
| Retained earnings | 100,000 |
| | $1,800,000 |

What is the book value per share for both preferred and common stock, assuming each of the following conditions:

(a) Preferred stock is cumulative and nonparticipating, with no dividends in arrears.

(b) Preferred stock is cumulative and nonparticipating, and dividends are in arrears since January 1, 1957.

(c) Preferred stock is cumulative and fully participating, with no dividend arrearages.

(d) Preferred stock is cumulative and fully participating, and dividends are in arrears since January 1, 1957.

**8.** The balance sheets for the Keller Company showed the following equities at the end of each year:

| | 1957 | 1958 |
|---|---:|---:|
| 4% Bonds payable | $ 500,000 | $ 500,000 |
| 6% Nonparticipating preferred stock, $100 par | 500,000 | 600,000 |
| Common stock, $25 par | 1,000,000 | 1,200,000 |
| Additional paid-in capital | 100,000 | 100,000 |
| Retained earnings | 200,000 | 300,000 |

Net income after income taxes was: 1957, $60,000; 1958, $105,000. Using the foregoing data, calculate for each year:

(a) The rate of earnings on total capital at the end of the year.

(b) The number of times bond interest requirements were earned.

(c) The number of times preferred dividend requirements were earned.

(d) The rate earned on the common stockholders' equity.

(e) The dollar earnings per share of common stock.

## PROBLEMS

**27-1.** The balance sheet data for the Mantle Sales Co. on December 31, 1958, appear below:

### MANTLE SALES CO.
#### BALANCE SHEET
#### DECEMBER 31, 1958

| ASSETS | | LIABILITIES AND CAPITAL | |
|---|---:|---|---:|
| Cash...................... | $ 45,000 | Notes and accounts payable.. | $ 70,000 |
| Marketable securities ....... | 175,000 | Income taxes payable........ | 15,000 |
| Notes and accounts receivable | | Accrued wages, interest..... | 10,000 |
| (net).................... | 180,000 | Dividends payable (cash).... | 5,000 |
| Inventories ................ | 300,000 | Bonds payable............. | 400,000 |
| Prepaid expenses........... | 15,000 | Deferred revenues.......... | 10,000 |
| Bond redemption fund (secur- | | Common stock, $20 par..... | 1,000,000 |
| ities of other companies).. | 150,000 | Preferred stock, $10 par (non- | |
| Plant and equipment........ | 930,000 | participating, noncumula- | |
| Intangible assets........... | 200,000 | tive).................... | 200,000 |
| Unamortized bond discount | | Retained earnings.......... | 140,000 |
| and costs................ | 5,000 | Retained earnings appropri- | |
| | | ated for contingencies..... | 150,000 |
| | $2,000,000 | | $2,000,000 |

*Instructions:* From the foregoing, calculate the following:

(a) The amount of working capital.

(b) The current ratio.

(c) The acid-test ratio.

(d) The ratio of current assets to total assets.

(e) The ratio of total capital to liabilities.

(f) The ratio of plant and equipment to bonds payable.

(g) The book value per share of preferred stock.

(h) The book value per share of common stock.

**27-2.** Comparative data for the Mays Heating Co. for the three-year period 1956–1958 are presented below and on the following page.

### INCOME STATEMENT DATA

| | 1956 | 1957 | 1958 |
|---|---:|---:|---:|
| Net sales................................ | $ 800,000 | $1,000,000 | $1,200,000 |
| Cost of goods sold...................... | 500,000 | 660,000 | 760,000 |
| Gross profit on sales.................... | $ 300,000 | $ 340,000 | $ 440,000 |
| Selling, general, and other expenses...... | 280,000 | 300,000 | 350,000 |
| Net income from operations............ | $ 20,000 | $ 40,000 | $ 90,000 |
| Income taxes.......................... | 5,000 | 15,000 | 35,000 |
| Net income after income taxes.......... | $ 15,000 | $ 25,000 | $ 55,000 |
| Dividends paid........................ | 15,000 | 30,000 | 40,000 |
| Net increase or decrease* in retained earnings................................ | — | $ 5,000* | $ 15,000 |

BALANCE SHEET DATA

|  | 1956 | 1957 | 1958 |
|---|---|---|---|
| ASSETS |  |  |  |
| Cash.................................... | $ 50,000 | $ 35,000 | $ 55,000 |
| Trade notes and accounts receivables (net). | 245,000 | 320,000 | 400,000 |
| Merchandise inventory (at cost)......... | 320,000 | 380,000 | 420,000 |
| Prepaid expenses...................... | 20,000 | 10,000 | 30,000 |
| Plant and equipment (net)............. | 650,000 | 600,000 | 680,000 |
| Intangibles........................... | 100,000 | 100,000 | 100,000 |
| Miscellaneous long-term deferrals....... | 5,000 | 5,000 | 15,000 |
|  | $1,390,000 | $1,450,000 | $1,700,000 |

LIABILITIES AND CAPITAL

|  | 1956 | 1957 | 1958 |
|---|---|---|---|
| Trade notes and accounts payable....... | $ 130,000 | $ 165,000 | $ 205,000 |
| Wages, interest, dividends payable....... | 15,000 | 25,000 | 45,000 |
| Income taxes payable................... | 5,000 | 15,000 | 35,000 |
| Miscellaneous current liabilities......... | 10,000 | 15,000 | 10,000 |
| 5% bonds payable..................... | 300,000 | 300,000 | 300,000 |
| Deferred revenues..................... | 5,000 | 10,000 | 10,000 |
| 6% preferred stock, nonparticipating, $100 par................................ | 200,000 | 200,000 | 200,000 |
| No-par common stock, $10 stated value.... | 400,000 | 400,000 | 500,000 |
| Additional paid-in capital............... | 200,000 | 200,000 | 260,000 |
| Retained earnings — free............... | 65,000 | 60,000 | 55,000 |
| Retained earnings — appropriated....... | 60,000 | 60,000 | 80,000 |
|  | $1,390,000 | $1,450,000 | $1,700,000 |

*Instructions:* From the foregoing data, calculate the following comparative structural measurements for 1957 and 1958 as follows:

(a) The amount of working capital.

(b) The current ratio.

(c) The acid-test ratio.

(d) The trade receivables turnover rate.

(e) The average days' sales in receivables at the end of the period (assume a 300-day business year and all sales on a credit basis).

(f) The trade payables turnover rate.

(g) The average days' purchases in payables at the end of the period.

(h) The merchandise turnover rate.

(i) The number of days' sales in the inventory at the end of the period.

(j) The ratio of total capital to total liabilities.

(k) The ratio of plant and equipment to bonds payable.

(l) The ratio of capital to plant and equipment.

(m) The book value per share of preferred stock.

(n) The book value per share of common stock.

**27-3.** Using the comparative data for the Mays Heating Co. (Problem 27-2), calculate the comparative operating measurements for 1957 and 1958 as follows:

    (a) The ratio of sales to average assets.
    (b) The ratio of sales to average plant and equipment.
    (c) The rate earned on net sales.
    (d) The gross profit rate on net sales.
    (e) The rate earned on average total assets.
    (f) The rate earned on average total capital.
    (g) The number of times bond interest requirements were earned.
    (h) The number of times preferred dividend requirements were earned.
    (i) The rate earned on average common stockholders' equity.
    (j) The earnings per share on common stock.

**27-4.** Using the comparative data for the Mays Heating Co. as given in Problem 27-2, prepare a summary of the distribution of earnings for the three-year period similar to that illustrated on page 878. Measurements are to be based on equity totals as of the end of each year.

**27-5.** Using the data for the Clason Manufacturing Co. as given in Problem 26-3 on pages 854–856, calculate comparative structural measurements for 1957 and 1958 as follows:

    (a) The amount of working capital.
    (b) The current ratio.
    (c) The acid-test ratio.
    (d) The current asset turnover rate.
    (e) The finished goods inventory turnover rate.
    (f) The raw materials inventory turnover rate.
    (g) The number of days' sales in the average finished goods inventory (assume a 300-day business year).
    (h) The number of days' raw materials requirements in the average raw materials inventory.
    (i) The ratio of capital to liabilities.
    (j) The ratio of plant and equipment to the long-term debt.
    (k) The book value per share of the preferred stock.
    (l) The book value per share of the common stock.

**27-6.** Using the data for the Clason Manufacturing Co. as given in Problem 26-3 on pages 854–856, calculate comparative operating measurements for 1957 and 1958 as follows:

    (a) The ratio of sales to average assets (excluding long-term investments).
    (b) The ratio of sales to average plant and equipment.
    (c) The rate earned on net sales.
    (d) The gross profit rate on net sales.
    (e) The rate earned on average total assets.
    (f) The rate earned on average total capital.
    (g) The number of times long-term debt interest requirements were earned.
    (h) The number of times preferred dividend requirements were earned.
    (i) The rate earned on average common stockholders' equity.
    (j) The earnings per share on common stock.

**27-7.** Using the comparative data for the Clason Manufacturing Co. as given in Problem 26-3, pages 854–856, prepare a summary of the distribution of earnings for 1957 and 1958 similar to that illustrated on page 878. Measurements are to be based on equity totals as of the end of each year.

**27-8.** Inventory and receivable balances and also gross profit data for the Harris Company appear below:

| BALANCE SHEET DATA: | 1956 | 1957 | 1958 |
|---|---|---|---|
| Merchandise inventory, December 31.... | $ 40,000 | $ 50,000 | $80,000 |
| Trade receivables, December 31......... | 30,000 | 35,000 | 50,000 |
| | | | |
| PROFIT AND LOSS DATA: | | | |
| Net sales............................ | $210,000 | $270,000 | $300,000 |
| Cost of sales....................... | 150,000 | 200,000 | 230,000 |
| | | | |
| Gross profit on sales................ | $ 60,000 | $ 70,000 | $ 70,000 |

*Instructions:* Assuming a 300-day business year and all sales on a credit basis, calculate the following measurements for 1957 and 1958:
   (a) The trade receivables turnover rate.
   (b) The average days' sales in receivables at the end of the period.
   (c) The merchandise turnover rate.
   (d) The number of days' sales in the inventory at the end of the period.

**27-9.** Capital accounts for Aaron Corporation at the end of 1957 and 1958 follow:

| | 1957 | 1958 |
|---|---|---|
| 6% Pref. stock, par and liquidating value $50.. | $100,000 | $100,000 |
| Common stock, $10 par..................... | 250,000 | 350,000 |
| Additional paid-in capital.................. | 400,000 | 500,000 |
| Retained earnings ........................ | 20,000 | 60,000 |

What is the book value of both common and preferred stock at the end of 1957 and at the end of 1958, assuming each of the conditions below:
   (a) Preferred is cumulative and nonparticipating; dividend requirements have been met on preferred annually.
   (b) Preferred is cumulative and nonparticipating; the last dividend on preferred stock was paid for the year 1955.
   (c) Preferred is cumulative and fully participating; dividend requirements have been met on preferred annually.
   (d) Preferred is cumulative and fully participating; the last dividend on preferred stock was paid for the year 1955.

**27-10. (a)** For each of the following numbered items you are to select the letter item(s) which indicate(s) its effect(s) on the corporation's statements. Indicate your choice by giving the letter(s) identifying the effect(s) which you select. If there is no appropriate response among the effects listed, leave the item blank. If more than one effect is applicable to a particular item, be sure to list *all* applicable letters. (Assume that the state statutes do not permit declaration of nonliquidating dividends except from earnings.)

| ITEM | EFFECT |
|---|---|
| (1) Declaration of a cash dividend due in one month on non-cumulative preferred stock. | A. Reduces working capital. |
| | B. Increases working capital. |
| | C. Reduces current ratio. |
| (2) Declaration and payment of an ordinary stock dividend. | D. Increases current ratio. |
| | E. Reduces the dollar amount of total capital stock. |
| (3) Receipt of a cash dividend, not previously recorded, on stock of another corporation. | F. Increases the dollar amount of total capital stock. |
| (4) Passing of a dividend on cumulative preferred stocks. | G. Reduces total retained earnings. |
| | H. Increases total retained earnings. |
| (5) Receipt of preferred shares as a dividend on stock held as a temporary investment. This was not a regularly-recurring dividend. | S. Reduces equity per share of common stock. |
| | T. Reduces equity of each common stockholder. |
| (6) Payment of dividend mentioned in (1). | |
| (7) Issue of new common shares in a five for one stock split. | |

**(b)** The following are partially condensed financial statements of the X Corporation.

## X Corporation — Balance Sheet
### DECEMBER 31, 1958

| | |
|---|---:|
| Cash.............................................................. | $ 63,000 |
| Trade receivables, less estimated uncollectibles of $12,000........ | 238,000 |
| Inventories...................................................... | 170,000 |
| Prepaid expenses................................................. | 7,000 |
| Property and equipment, cost less $182,000 charged to operations | 390,000 |
| Other assets..................................................... | 13,000 |
| | $881,000 |
| | |
| Accounts and notes payable — trade........................ | $ 98,000 |
| Accrued liabilities.............................................. | 17,000 |
| Estimated federal income tax liability....................... | 18,000 |
| First mortgage, 4% bonds, due in 1968....................... | 150,000 |
| $7 Preferred stock — no par value (entitled to $110 per share in liquidation); authorized 1,000 shares; in treasury 400 shares; outstanding 600 shares.................................... | 108,000 |
| Common stock — no par; authorized 100,000 shares, issued and outstanding 10,000 shares stated at a nominal value of $10 per share...................................................... | 100,000 |
| Excess of amounts paid in for common stock over stated values.. | 242,000 |
| Reserve for plant expansion.................................... | 50,000 |
| Reserve for cost of treasury stock............................ | 47,000 |
| Retained earnings............................................... | 98,000 |
| Cost of 400 shares of treasury stock.......................... | (47,000) |
| | $881,000 |

NOTES: (1) Working capital — 12/31/57 was $205,000. (2) Trade receivables — 12/31/57 were $220,000 gross, $206,000 net. (3) Dividends for 1958 have been declared and paid. (4) There has been no change in amount of bonds outstanding during 1958.

## X Corporation—Income Statement

### YEAR ENDED DECEMBER 31, 1958

|  | CASH | CHARGE | TOTAL |
|---|---|---|---|
| Gross sales......................... | $116,000 | $876,000 | $992,000 |
|  |  |  |  |
| Less — Discounts..................... | $   3,000 | $ 12,000 | $ 15,000 |
| Returns and allowances......... | 1,000 | 6,000 | 7,000 |
|  |  |  |  |
|  | $   4,000 | $ 18,000 | $ 22,000 |
|  |  |  |  |
| Net sales........................... | $112,000 | $858,000 | $970,000 |

| Cost of sales: |  |  |
|---|---|---|
| Inventory of finished goods — January 1 | $ 92,000 |  |
| Cost of goods manufactured........... | 680,000 |  |
| Inventory of finished goods — December 31..................... | (100,000) | 672,000 |
|  |  |  |
| Gross profit on sales.................... |  | $298,000 |
| Selling expenses........................ | $173,000 |  |
| General expenses....................... | 70,000 | 243,000 |
|  |  |  |
| Net profit on operations............... |  | $ 55,000 |
| Other additions and deductions (net)..... |  | 3,000 |
|  |  |  |
| Net income before federal income tax..... |  | $ 58,000 |
| Federal income tax (estimated)......... |  | 18,000 |
|  |  |  |
| Net income........................... |  | $ 40,000 |

*Instructions:* For each item listed below select the best answer from the approximate answers. Indicate your choice by giving the appropriate letter for each. Give the calculations in support of each choice.

| ITEMS TO BE COMPUTED | APPROXIMATE ANSWERS | | | | |
|---|---|---|---|---|---|
|  | (a) | (b) | (c) | (d) | (e) |
| (1) Acid test ratio........... | 3.2:1 | 2.3:1 | 2.9:1 | 2.4:1 | 3.07:1 |
| (2) Average number of days' charge sales uncollected.. | 89 | 94 | 35 | 100 | 105 |
| (3) Average finished goods turnover................... | 7 | 10.1 | 10.3 | 9.7 | 6.7 |
| (4) Number of times bond interest was earned (before taxes)................ | 6⅔ | 10⅔ | 7⅔ | 9⅔ | 20⅓ |
| (5) Number of times preferred dividend was earned..... | 5.71 | 8.3 | 13.8 | 9.52 | 8.52 |
| (6) Earnings per share of common stock............. | $4.00 | $3.30 | $3.58 | $5.10 | $5.38 |
| (7) Book value per share of common stock......... | $33.80 | $35.00 | $49.80 | $48.80 | $53.20 |
| (8) Current ratio............ | 3.6:1 | 1:2.7 | 2.7:1 | 4.2:1 | 1:3.6 |

(A.I.C.P.A. adapted)

# Chapter 28

# STATEMENT OF
# APPLICATION OF FUNDS

**NATURE AND PURPOSE OF THE STATEMENT OF APPLICATION OF FUNDS** The periodic statements and analytical summaries illustrated in the previous chapters may be supplemented by a special report that summarizes the flow of working capital through the business during the fiscal period. This report is known as the *statement of application of funds*, also variously called the *funds statement*, the *source and application of funds statement*, the *statement of financial benefits earned and employed*, the *statement of financial changes*, and the *where-got, where-gone statement*.

Changes in working capital position of a business unit are significant considerations in the analysis of operating results and financial condition. The sources of working capital, the dispositions of working capital, and the composition of the working capital at the end of the period, are all important factors in appraising past activities and in judging a company's ability to prosper in the future.

Although comparative balance sheets offer important data concerning net changes in working capital items, together with other asset, liability, and capital items, the comparative data fail to show what resources were made available to the business during the period and how such resources were employed. For example, assume that an increased working capital has resulted from profitable operations. This will not be apparent from an inspection of comparative retained earnings figures where the ending balance results from such various factors as profits, dividends, corrections in profits of prior periods, and appropriations of retained earnings. Or assume that working capital has been applied to the purchase of plant and equipment. This cannot be determined from an inspection of comparative plant and equipment balances where the ending balance may result from a combination of factors such as plant and equipment purchases, sales, trade-ins, write-offs against depreciation allowances, and revaluations.

The statement of application of funds adopts a broader scope than the statement of cash receipts and disbursements. The latter statement shows the movement of cash, summarizing the sources of cash receipts and the nature of cash disbursements. Organizations whose activities

center around cash, such as charitable organizations, professional socie-
ties, fraternal organizations, and governmental units, require statements summarizing the movement of cash. The statement of cash
receipts and disbursements occupies a significant position in reporting
past activities; cash forecasts and budgets are important instruments
in the control and utilization of cash.

The business unit is vitally concerned with the movement of cash
and cash planning. But the business unit is also concerned with the
movement of current resources as a whole — cash and marketable
securities, receivables, and inventories, less those items making a claim
against current assets. Although similar in nature and function to the
statement of cash receipts and disbursements, the statement of application of funds summarizes the flow of current resources; working
capital and not cash occupies the focal position. This statement offers
an understanding of the factors affecting working capital in the past;
it may be used as an instrument for the control of working capital in
the future.

The statement of application of funds summarizes both the sources
of working capital and the uses made of working capital during the
period. This information is presented as support for the change that
took place in working capital from its balance at the beginning of the
period to the amount reported at the end of the period. The flow of
working capital and the effects of this flow on the working capital
balance are illustrated in the summary below:

Working Capital, January 1                    $500,000

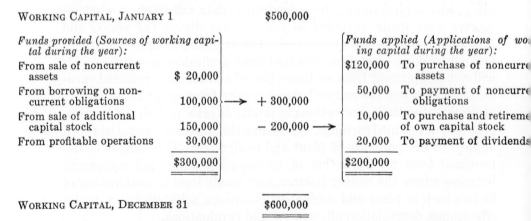

Working Capital, December 31                  $600,000

The summary shows $300,000 in working capital made available
and $200,000 in working capital consumed during the year, resulting
in an increase in the business unit's working capital position from
$500,000 to $600,000.

The funds statement is normally prepared in two parts. In the first part the net change in working capital for the period is summarized. Here individual sources of working capital are listed under the heading "Funds Provided" and individual dispositions of working capital are listed under the heading "Funds Applied." The difference between funds provided and funds applied is reported as the net increase or decrease in working capital for the period. The second part of the statement, which may be prepared as a second section on the statement or as a separate supporting schedule, offers a listing of the individual working capital items both at the beginning of the period and the end of the period, together with the net change in each item. Thus the net increase or decrease that has taken place in the business unit's working capital as summarized in the first part of the statement is supported here in terms of the separate working capital items and their individual changes.

The statement of application of funds offers the answers to questions asked by management and owners, such as: "What is responsible for the change in our working capital position?" "How have our profits been employed?" "How have we used funds raised through long-term borrowing and the sale of stock?" "What did we get from the sale of securities?" "How much did we invest in plant and equipment?" These are important questions that receive their full answer only through this statement.

**PREPARATION OF THE STATEMENT OF APPLICATION OF FUNDS** The statement of application of funds is prepared from comparative balance sheet data supplemented by an explanation of the account changes for all noncurrent and capital items. This information is analyzed in developing the explanations for the sources and applications of working capital. To illustrate the process of analysis and the development of the statement, assume the following balance sheet information at the beginning and the end of the fiscal year for the Austin Manufacturing Company.

| ASSETS | DEC. 31 1957 | DEC. 31 1958 | LIABILITIES AND CAPITAL | DEC. 31 1957 | DEC. 31 1958 |
|---|---|---|---|---|---|
| Cash................ | $ 90,000 | $ 60,000 | Notes Payable...... | $ 20,000 | $ 30,000 |
| Accounts Receivable | 110,000 | 120,000 | Accounts Payable.. | 140,000 | 120,000 |
| Inventories........ | 180,000 | 220,000 | Bonds Payable..... | 50,000 | |
| Buildings and | | | Capital Stock...... | 200,000 | 350,000 |
| Equipment...... | | 120,000 | Retained Earnings.. | 20,000 | 70,000 |
| Land............. | 50,000 | 50,000 | | | |
| | $430,000 | $570,000 | | $430,000 | $570,000 |

An investigation of balance sheet changes reveals that expenditures of $120,000 were made for buildings and equipment during the year, and $50,000 was applied to the retirement of bonds. Working capital was made available in part by the issuance of capital stock of $150,000. Retained earnings were affected only by net income for the year. When operations are profitable, sales that produce cash and receivables exceed cost of sales and expenses that involve reductions in cash and inventories and the increase in payables; hence, profitable operations are a source of working capital. In the example, profitable operations reflected in the increased retained earnings balance made available additional working capital of $50,000. Funds from profitable operations together with funds from the sale of capital stock exceeded funds applied to buildings and equipment and to the retirement of bonds. Such excess resulted in an improvement of the working capital position of the business. A statement reporting the sources and applications of funds together with the nature of the changes in working capital is given below:

### AUSTIN MANUFACTURING COMPANY
#### STATEMENT OF APPLICATION OF FUNDS
#### FOR YEAR ENDED DECEMBER 31, 1958

| | | |
|---|---|---|
| Funds were provided by: | | |
| Profitable operations. . . . . . . . . . . . . . . . . . . . . . | $ 50,000 | |
| Issuance of capital stock. . . . . . . . . . . . . . . . . . | 150,000 | $200,000 |
| Funds were applied to: | | |
| Purchases of buildings and equipment. . . . . . . . | $120,000 | |
| Retirement of bonds. . . . . . . . . . . . . . . . . . . . . . | 50,000 | 170,000 |
| Increase in working capital. . . . . . . . . . . . . . . . . | | $ 30,000 |

The increase in working capital is accounted for as follows:

| | | | WORKING CAPITAL | |
|---|---|---|---|---|
| WORKING CAPITAL ITEMS | DEC. 31 1957 | DEC. 31 1958 | INCREASE | DECREASE |
| Current assets: | | | | |
| Cash. . . . . . . . . . . . . . . . . . . . . . . . . . | 90,000 | 60,000 | | 30,000 |
| Accounts receivable. . . . . . . . . . . | 110,000 | 120,000 | 10,000 | |
| Inventories. . . . . . . . . . . . . . . . . . | 180,000 | 220,000 | 40,000 | |
| Current liabilities: | | | | |
| Notes payable. . . . . . . . . . . . . . . . | 20,000 | 30,000 | | 10,000 |
| Accounts payable. . . . . . . . . . . . . | 140,000 | 120,000 | 20,000 | |
| | | | 70,000 | 40,000 |
| Increases in working capital items. . | | | | 70,000 |
| Decreases in working capital items. . | | | | 40,000 |
| Increase in working capital. . . . . . . . | | | | 30,000 |

In the example, no difficulty was found in the analysis of changes of balance sheet items and in the preparation of the statement directly from comparative balance sheets; in most instances, however, the use of working papers will facilitate the preparation of the statement. If working papers were to be prepared in the foregoing example, these would appear as shown on page 894.

In preparing working papers, balance sheet items are listed in the first pair of columns just as they appear on the comparative balance sheet. The net change in each account for the year appears in the second pair of columns. Increases in assets, decreases in liabilities, and decreases in capital balances are shown in the debit column, since the debits must have exceeded the credits to the accounts during the year; decreases in assets, increases in liabilities, and increases in capital balances are reported in the credit column, since in these instances the credits must have exceeded the debits. Change balances are now carried across to the last two pairs of columns. Debit excesses in non-current asset, noncurrent liability, or capital accounts are reported in the funds applied column; credit excesses in noncurrent asset, non-current liability, or capital accounts are reported in the funds provided column. Debit excesses in current asset and current liability items are reported in the working capital increase column; credit excesses in these are shown as working capital decreases. If funds provided by changes in noncurrent and capital items exceed the funds applied to such items, then working capital has gone up by the difference; if funds applied to noncurrent and capital items exceed funds provided through these sources, then working capital has gone down by the difference. The last two pairs of columns are brought into balance with a summary of the net effect of activities upon working capital.

**ANALYSIS OF ACCOUNT CHANGES IN PREPARATION OF FUNDS STATEMENT**     As previously explained, the preparation of the funds statement requires comparative balance sheet information supplemented by data explaining changes in noncurrent and capital balances. The net change in an account balance cannot be relied upon to offer a full explanation of the effect of that item on working capital. To illustrate, assume that comparative balance sheets report a $50,000 increase in bonds payable. Without further investigation, this might be interpreted as a source of funds of $50,000; but reference to the bonds account may disclose that bonds of $150,000 were issued while bonds of $100,000 were retired during the period. A further analysis of the transactions affecting the bonds account may reveal that the bonds were issued at a discount of $7,500, only $142,500

## AUSTIN MANUFACTURING COMPANY
### Working Papers for Statement of Application of Funds
### For Year Ended December 31, 1958

| Accounts | Balances | | Net Changes | | Funds | | Working Capital | |
|---|---|---|---|---|---|---|---|---|
| | Dec. 31 1957 | Dec. 31 1958 | Dr. | Cr. | Applied | Provided | Increase | Decrease |
| Cash | 90,000 | 60,000 | | 30,000 | | | | 30,000 |
| Accounts receivable | 110,000 | 120,000 | 10,000 | | | | 10,000 | |
| Inventories | 180,000 | 220,000 | 40,000 | | | | 40,000 | |
| Buildings and equipment | | 120,000 | 120,000 | | 120,000 | | | |
| Land | 50,000 | 50,000 | | | | | | |
| | 430,000 | 570,000 | | | | | | |
| Notes payable | 20,000 | 30,000 | | 10,000 | | | | 10,000 |
| Accounts payable | 140,000 | 120,000 | 20,000 | | | | 20,000 | |
| Bonds payable | 50,000 | | 50,000 | | 50,000 | | | |
| Capital stock | 200,000 | 350,000 | | 150,000 | | 150,000 | | |
| Retained earnings | 20,000 | 70,000 | | 50,000 | | 50,000 | | |
| | 430,000 | 570,000 | 240,000 | 240,000 | 170,000 | 200,000 | 70,000 | 40,000 |
| Increase in working capital | | | | | 30,000 | | | 30,000 |
| | | | | | 200,000 | 200,000 | 70,000 | 70,000 |

being received on the issue, while a call premium of $2,000 was paid on bonds retired, $102,000 thus being expended; in this instance, the statement should report funds provided by the issuance of bonds, $142,500, and funds applied to bond retirement, $102,000.

**SOURCES OF FUNDS**    Decreases in noncurrent assets and increases in noncurrent liabilities and in capital items require analysis in determining and calculating funds provided; increases in noncurrent assets and decreases in noncurrent liabilities and in capital items require analysis in calculating funds applied. The following examples indicate sources of working capital and suggest the nature of the analysis that is necessary in determining the actual amount of funds provided.

(1) *Decreases in noncurrent asset accounts.* Balances in land, equipment, investment, and other noncurrent asset accounts may show decreases in amount as a result of sales of such items, thus representing sources of funds. An analysis of the transactions giving rise to account change is necessary, however, in calculating the amounts provided; disposal of investments at a profit, for example, provides funds that exceed the decrease in the asset account.

(2) *Increases in noncurrent liabilities.* Balances in long-term note, bond, and other noncurrent liability accounts may show increases as a result of amounts borrowed, thus representing fund sources. An analysis of the transactions giving rise to the account change is necessary; issuance of bonds at a discount, for example, provides funds that are less than the increase in the bond account.

(3) *Increases in capital.* The balance in the capital stock account may increase as a result of the issuance of stock, thus representing a source of funds. In reporting funds provided, however, the amount received for the stock must be determined because this may differ from the increase in the capital stock account. When the change in retained earnings has not resulted solely from net income for the period, an analysis of the retained earnings account is necessary. The increase in retained earnings as a result of net income represents a source of funds. A decrease in retained earnings resulting from cash dividends should be separately recognized as an application of funds.

**APPLICATIONS OF FUNDS**    The following examples indicate applications of working capital and suggest the nature of the analysis necessary in determining the actual amount of funds applied.

(1) *Increases in noncurrent assets.* Balances in land, buildings, patents, and other noncurrent asset accounts may show increases in amount as a result of the acquisitions of such items, thus representing fund applications. An analysis of transactions giving rise to the account change is necessary; the amount paid for patents, for example, may be greater than the increase in the patents account because of credits made to the account during the course of the period for patents cost amortization.

(2) *Decreases in noncurrent liabilities.* The balances in mortgage, bond, and other noncurrent liability accounts may show decreases resulting from retirement of obligations, thus representing fund applications. An analysis of transactions giving rise to the account change is necessary; the amount paid bondholders, for example, may exceed the decrease in the bonds account as a result of a call premium paid upon bond retirement.

(3) *Decreases in capital.* Capital stock outstanding may go down as a result of the acquisition of capital stock previously issued, thus representing fund applications. The amount paid for the stock reacquired must be determined, for this amount may differ from the decrease in the capital stock balance. When the change in retained earnings has not resulted solely from a loss from operations reported for a period, an analysis of the retained earnings account is necessary. The decrease in retained earnings resulting from a net loss represents an application of funds. An additional decrease resulting from cash dividends should be separately recognized as an application of funds.

**ADJUSTMENTS IN DE-VELOPING SOURCE AND APPLICATION AMOUNTS** In the working papers illustrated on page 894 adjustments were not required in the account changes in reporting fund sources and applications, and changes were carried to the appropriate funds columns just as reported. The preceding discussion has indicated that the net change balances require adjustment when they do not report the actual amounts of funds provided or applied.

When adjustments are required, working papers should provide a pair of columns in which adjusting data may be recorded. Changes in account balances as revised by data in the adjustment columns are carried to the appropriate funds columns.

The adjustments that are made on the working papers may be classified under three headings:

(1) *Adjustments to cancel account changes that had no effect upon working capital.* Certain account changes may arise from entries that

are not related to fund movements. For example, properties may have been appraised and the appraisal changes may have been recorded in the accounts. Intangible assets may have been written off against retained earnings. An asset may have been improperly charged to expense in a previous period and, upon discovery of the error, the asset may have been charged and retained earnings credited. A stock dividend may have been issued, retained earnings being transferred to the capital stock account. The foregoing items, although resulting in changes in account balances, actually had no effect on working capital. The changes in account balances are canceled on the working papers by adjustments that reverse the entries originally made, leaving only change balances that do represent fund sources or applications.

(2) *Adjustments to report the individual sources and applications of working capital when several transactions are summarized in a single account.* The change in the balance of an account may be the result of several separate fund sources or applications or a combination of fund sources and applications. For example, the plant and equipment balance may reflect both the purchase of land and buildings and the trade of equipment. An investment account balance may reflect the effects of both investment acquisitions and disposals. Adjustments are made on the working papers to make possible separate reporting of the different fund sources and applications.

(3) *Adjustments to report a single source or application of working capital when this information is reported in two or more accounts.* The amount of funds provided or funds applied as a result of a certain transaction may be reflected in two or more accounts. For example, certain investments may have been sold for more than cost; the decrease in the investment balance and the related increase in retained earnings must be combined in arriving at funds provided from the sale. Bonds may have been issued at a discount; the discount balance must be applied against the bond account increase in arriving at the actual funds provided from the issue. Stock may have been retired at a premium; the decreases in the paid-in capital and retained earnings balances must be combined in arriving at the funds applied to stock retirement. Adjustments are made on the working papers so that related change balances may be summarized and expressed satisfactorily as fund sources and applications.

Retained earnings is an example of an account that may be affected by all three types of adjustments mentioned above. To illustrate, assume that a retained earnings balance shows an increase for a year of $10,000. Inspection of the account discloses the following:

RETAINED EARNINGS

| | | | | |
|---|---|---|---|---|
| Mar. 1 Goodwill written off.... | 20,000 | Dec. 1 Balance............. | 200,000 |
| July 10 Cash dividends........ | 30,000 | Dec. 31 Net income for year... | 60,000 |

Goodwill was written off against Retained Earnings, both asset and retained earnings balances reporting reductions of $20,000. Since the write-off had no effect upon funds, reductions in the account balances should be restored on the working papers; the account changes from this action are thus canceled and receive no further consideration in the development of the funds statement. Cash dividends of $30,000 will have to be reported separately as an application of funds. This leaves $60,000 in the retained earnings account to be reported as a source of funds resulting from profitable operations.

The net income figure offers only a part of the story of funds made available if charges or credits in the calculation of net income arose from book entries that had no effect upon funds. For example, assume that depreciation of $15,000 was recorded in calculating net income. The entry for depreciation, while increasing the allowance for depreciation account and representing a charge in the calculation of the net income, had no effect upon funds in the current period; its effects should therefore be canceled. The funds resulting from profitable operations, then, consist of $60,000, as reported, plus $15,000, the charge against income that required no current fund outlay. The purpose of this adjustment may be illustrated by the simple case that follows. Assume that comparative balance sheets for an attorney show the following:

| | JANUARY 1 | | DECEMBER 31 | |
|---|---|---|---|---|
| Working capital.................. | | $2,000 | | $12,000 |
| Furniture and fixtures............. | $2,500 | | $2,500 | |
| Less: Allowance for depreciation.. | 1,000 | 1,500 | 1,500 | 1,000 |
| Capital....................... | | $3,500 | | $13,000 |

The income statement for the year reports the following:

| | | |
|---|---|---|
| Income from fees (received in cash or currently receivable)..................................... | | $14,000 |
| Less: Expenses (paid in cash or currently payable)... | $4,000 | |
| Depreciation............................ | 500 | 4,500 |
| Net income................................... | | $ 9,500 |

Observe that, while the net income for the period was $9,500, working capital produced by operations was actually $10,000 ($14,000 less

$4,000). A statement of application of funds, in this instance, would report funds of $10,000 provided by operations and applied to the increase of working capital. Services produced working capital of $14,000; this meant net earnings of $9,500 after the recapture of charges in the form of working capital outlays of $4,000 and furniture and fixture depreciation of $500. However, the working capital increase for the period was $10,000, that is, the net income for the period, $9,500, increased by a recovery of the charge made for asset depreciation, $500.

In calculating the funds provided by operations, adjustments that raise the net income figure are required for all items that were charged against income but that did not involve an application of working capital in the current period. Net income would be raised for such items as depreciation of plant and equipment items, depletion, and the amortization of patents, leaseholds, bond payable discounts, and bond investment premiums. Adjustments that reduce the net income figure are required for all items that raised net income but that did not provide working capital in the current period. Net income would be reduced for such items as the amortization of bond payable premiums and the accumulation of bond investment discounts. When extraordinary gains and losses are included in profit and loss accounting, these are identified with their particular sources; funds provided by operations are thus limited to funds produced by activities summarized as the business net income.

**ADJUSTMENTS ON WORKING PAPERS** The nature of the adjustments required on the working papers is illustrated in the example that follows. Comparative balance sheet data for the Kelly Trading Co. are reported on page 900.

The retained earnings account appears as follows:

RETAINED EARNINGS

| | | | | | | |
|---|---|---|---|---|---|---|
| Mar. | 1 | Cash dividends...... | 5,000 | Jan. | 1 | Balance............... 7,500 |
| July | 1 | Goodwill written off.... | 10,000 | Dec. 31 | | Net income and extraordinary items........ 20,000 |

The income statement shows depreciation of $6,000 on plant and equipment for the year and summarizes operations as follows:

| | |
|---|---|
| Net income......................................... | $21,500 |
| Less: Loss on sale of 100 shares of Smith Co. stock........ | 1,500 |
| Net income and extraordinary items.................... | $20,000 |

Analysis of accounts and records reveals that $60,000 was realized on the issue of additional stock with a par value of $50,000. Land,

| | DEC. 31, 1957 | | DEC. 31, 1958 | |
|---|---|---|---|---|
| Cash........................... | | $ 20,000 | | $ 15,000 |
| Notes receivable................. | | 5,000 | | 5,000 |
| Accounts receivable.............. | $25,000 | | $ 45,000 | |
|    Less: Allowance for bad debts.... | 1,500 | 23,500 | 2,000 | 43,000 |
| Inventories...................... | | 20,000 | | 51,500 |
| Investment in Smith Co. stock...... | (300 shares) | 15,000 | (200 shares) | 10,000 |
| Buildings and equipment .......... | $60,000 | | $105,000 | |
|    Less: Allowance for depreciation.. | 16,000 | 44,000 | 22,000 | 83,000 |
| Land............................ | | 10,000 | | 25,000 |
| Goodwill........................ | | 10,000 | | |
| | | $147,500 | | $232,500 |
| Notes payable................... | | $ 10,000 | | $ 5,000 |
| Accounts payable................. | | 15,000 | | 25,000 |
| Capital stock.................... | | 100,000 | | 150,000 |
| Premium on stock................. | | 15,000 | | 25,000 |
| Retained earnings................ | | 7,500 | | 12,500 |
| Appraisal capital................. | | | | 15,000 |
| | | $147,500 | | $232,500 |

cost $10,000, was appraised at $25,000 and the appraisal increase was recorded in the accounts. One hundred shares of Smith Co. stock, cost $5,000, had been sold for $3,500, which accounted for the loss of $1,500 reported on the income statement.

Working papers for the statement of application of funds for the year ended December 31, 1958, are prepared as shown on page 901. It should be observed that the allowance for bad debts is subtracted from accounts receivable and the accounts are shown net on the working papers. Depreciation allowances are shown separately since these accounts require adjustment; instead of being reported as negative or credit balances in the debit section, however, it is more convenient to report these together with liability and capital items in the credit section. Similarly, negative liability or proprietorship items may be more conveniently reported with assets in the debit section.

After reporting account changes, adjustments are entered in the adjustment columns. Each adjustment is explained below:

(a) Analysis of the retained earnings account shows an increase as reported by the income statement of $20,000. The adjustment to remove this balance from Retained Earnings to a section that summarizes funds provided by operations is:

Retained Earnings. .............................. 20,000
    Funds Provided by Operations: Net Income and
    Extraordinary Items per Income Statement.......        20,000

## KELLY TRADING COMPANY
### Working Papers for Statement of Application of Funds
### For Year Ended December 31, 1958

| Accounts | Balances Dec. 31 1957 | Balances Dec. 31 1958 | Net Changes Dr. | Net Changes Cr. | Adjustments Dr. | Adjustments Cr. | Funds Applied | Funds Provided | Working Capital Increase | Working Capital Decrease |
|---|---|---|---|---|---|---|---|---|---|---|
| Cash | 20,000 | 15,000 | | 5,000 | | | | | | 5,000 |
| Notes Receivable | 5,000 | 5,000 | | | | | | | | |
| Accounts Receivable (net) | 23,500 | 43,000 | 19,500 | | | | | | 19,500 | |
| Inventories | 20,000 | 51,500 | 31,500 | | | | | | 31,500 | |
| Investment in Smith Co. Stock | 15,000 | 10,000 | | 5,000 | (g) 5,000 | | | | | |
| Buildings and Equipment | 60,000 | 105,000 | 45,000 | | | | 45,000 | | | |
| Land | 10,000 | 25,000 | 15,000 | | | (f) 15,000 | | | | |
| Goodwill | 10,000 | | | 10,000 | (c) 10,000 | | | | | |
| | 163,500 | 254,500 | | | | | | | | |
| Allowance for Depreciation—Plant and Equipment | 16,000 | 22,000 | | 6,000 | | (d) 6,000 | | | | |
| Notes Payable | 10,000 | 5,000 | 5,000 | | | | | | 5,000 | |
| Accounts Payable | 15,000 | 25,000 | | 10,000 | | | | | | 10,000 |
| Capital Stock | 100,000 | 150,000 | | 50,000 | (e) 50,000 | | | | | |
| Premium on Stock | 15,000 | 25,000 | | 10,000 | (e) 10,000 | | | | | |
| Retained Earnings | 7,500 | 12,500 | | 5,000 | (a) 20,000 | (b) 5,000 (c) 10,000 | | | | |
| Appraisal Capital | | 15,000 | | 15,000 | (f) 15,000 | | | | | |
| | 163,500 | 254,500 | 116,000 | 116,000 | | | | | | |
| Funds Provided by Operations: | | | | | | | | | | |
| Net Income and Extraordinary Items per Income Statement | | | | | | (a) 20,000 | | | | |
| Add: Depreciation | | | | | | (d) 6,000 | | | | |
| Loss on Sale of Smith Co. Stock | | | | | | (g) 1,500 | | 27,500 | | |
| Funds Applied to Payment of Dividends | | | | | (b) 5,000 | | 5,000 | | | |
| Funds Provided by Issuance of Capital Stock | | | | | | (e) 60,000 | | 60,000 | | |
| Funds Provided by Sale of Smith Co. Stock | | | | | | (g) 3,500 | | 3,500 | | |
| | | | | | 121,000 | 121,000 | 50,000 | 91,000 | 56,000 | 15,000 |
| Increase in Working Capital | | | | | | | 41,000 | | | 41,000 |
| | | | | | | | 91,000 | 91,000 | 56,000 | 56,000 |

"Funds Provided by Operations" is reported on a separate line below the comparative balance sheet detail. Since a number of adjustments to this balance may be required in arriving at the funds provided by operations, adequate space should be allowed after this line for such adjustments. Other adjustments not related to this section but requiring entries in the lower section of the working papers are reported below the space alloted for this summary.

(b) Analysis of the retained earnings account shows a charge for dividends. This information is to be reported separately as an application of funds. The charge is removed from Retained Earnings and is reported on a separate line below the space alloted for the adjustments to funds provided by operations. The entry for dividends on the work sheet is:

Funds Applied to Payment of Dividends............. 5,000
    Retained Earnings............................... 5,000

(c) The retained earnings account shows that goodwill of $10,000 was written off. Since this action had no effect upon funds, changes in the accounts affected by the write-off are canceled by the following adjustment:

Goodwill....................................... 10,000
    Retained Earnings............................. 10,000

Debits to Retained Earnings of $20,000 and credits of $15,000, or net debit adjustments of $5,000, cancel the increase of $5,000 reported in the net changes credit column; all of the changes in retained earnings have been analyzed and fund information has been reported under appropriate headings.

(d) The change in the depreciation allowance account is canceled and Funds Provided by Operations is increased by the following adjustment:

Allowance for Depreciation — Plant and Equipment... 6,000
    Funds Provided by Operations: Depreciation....... 6,000

(e) Capital Stock was increased $50,000 and Premium on Stock was increased $10,000 upon the sale of additional stock. In reporting a single source of funds through sale of stock, the following adjustment is made:

Capital Stock................................... 50,000
Premium on Stock............................... 10,000
    Funds Provided by Issuance of Capital Stock..... 60,000

Instead of transferring both balances to a new line in the lower section of the working papers, it would be possible to transfer the increase in premium on stock to the capital stock account. The capital stock account would then show a credit change of $50,000 increased by an adjustment credit of $10,000. The sum of the credits, $60,000, would be carried to the funds provided column. While such a procedure may be followed in each instance where two or more balances account for a single source or application of funds, it is generally more satisfactory to transfer related balances to a separate line as illustrated so that adequate detail and explanation concerning the nature of the transaction can be offered.

(f) The revaluation of land had no effect upon funds, hence changes in the accounts resulting from the book entry are canceled by the following adjustment:

| | | |
|---|---|---|
| Appraisal Capital...................................... | 15,000 | |
| Land................................................ | | 15,000 |

(g) The account Investment in Smith Co. Stock shows a decrease of $5,000, and an extraordinary loss of $1,500 has been subtracted from net income in summarizing activities of the period as a result of the sale of the asset for $3,500. Since the net effect of the transaction was to provide funds of $3,500, this is reported separately, and both the change in the investment account and the extraordinary loss are canceled. This is accomplished by the following adjustment:

| | | |
|---|---|---|
| Investment in Smith Co. Stock.................... | 5,000 | |
| Funds Provided by Operations: Loss on Smith Co. Stock........................................ | | 1,500 |
| Funds Provided by Sale of Smith Co. Stock....... | | 3,500 |

The foregoing procedure results in the following:

(1) Funds relating to the noncurrent items are separately stated at the actual amount provided or applied.

(2) Funds Provided by Operations, after adjustment, summarizes only those funds made available through regular activities giving rise to the net income of the period.

If the loss on the sale of the stock in the preceding example had originally been charged to Retained Earnings, this account instead of to Funds Provided by Operations would be credited in adjusting the accounts.

Balances shown in the net changes columns as adjusted together with the supplementary data established by adjustments are extended to the funds and working capital columns and the working capital change is calculated. Working papers may now be used as a basis for the preparation of the statement of application of funds. A statement prepared from the working papers illustrated on page 901 follows:

## KELLY TRADING CO.
### Statement of Application of Funds
#### For Year Ended December 31, 1958

Funds were provided by:

Operations:

| | | | |
|---|---|---|---|
| Net income and extraordinary items per income statement................... | | $20,000 | |
| Add: Depreciation..................... | $6,000 | | |
| Loss on sale of stock (proceeds from sale reported separately)............... | 1,500 | 7,500 | $27,500 |
| Issuance of capital stock.................. | | | 60,000 |
| Sale of Smith Co. stock.................. | | | 3,500 |
| | | | $91,000 |

Funds were applied to:

| | | |
|---|---|---|
| Purchase of plant and equipment............ | $45,000 | |
| Payment of dividends.................... | 5,000 | 50,000 |
| Increase in working capital.................. | | $41,000 |

The increase in working capital is accounted for as follows:

| WORKING CAPITAL ITEMS | DEC. 31 1957 | DEC. 31 1958 | WORKING CAPITAL | |
|---|---|---|---|---|
| | | | INCREASE | DECREASE |
| Current assets: | | | | |
| Cash...................... | 20,000 | 15,000 | | 5,000 |
| Notes receivable............. | 5,000 | 5,000 | | |
| Accounts receivable (net)....... | 23,500 | 43,000 | 19,500 | |
| Inventories .................. | 20,000 | 51,500 | 31,500 | |
| Current liabilities: | | | | |
| Notes payable............... | 10,000 | 5,000 | 5,000 | |
| Accounts payable............. | 15,000 | 25,000 | | 10,000 |
| | | | 56,000 | 15,000 |
| Increases in working capital items.. | | | | 56,000 |
| Decreases in working capital items | | | | 15,000 |
| Increase in working capital....... | | | | 41,000 |

**PREPARATION OF WORKING PAPERS AND STATEMENT ILLUSTRATED**

The following pages illustrate the preparation of working papers and a statement of application of funds where adjustments are more numerous and more complex than those offered in the previous example.

Comparative account balances for Richard and Rodger, Inc. are listed on the working papers on pages 906 and 907. The information that follows is assembled in obtaining explanations for changes as reported by account balances. The necessary adjustments resulting from the analysis of the accounts are listed and also appear in the adjustment columns of the working papers.

The retained earnings account for 1958 shows the following information:

RETAINED EARNINGS

| 1958 | | | 1958 | | |
|---|---|---|---|---|---|
| Mar. 1 Cash Dividends....... | 5,000 | | Jan. 1 Balance............. | | 20,000 |
| Aug. 10 Correction for Understatement of Depreciation on Office Equipment in 1957........ | 400 | | Dec. 31 Return of Balance Appropriated for Plant Extension.......... | | 65,000 |
| Sept. 1 50% Stock Dividend... | 50,000 | | | | |
| Dec. 31 Net Loss and Extraordinary Items per Income Statement .... | 6,800 | | | | |
| 31 Balance............. | 22,800 | | | | |
| | 85,000 | | | | 85,000 |
| | | | 1959 | | |
| | | | Jan. 1 Balance............. | | 22,800 |

The adjustments required on the working papers to cancel the changes in the retained earnings account and to report separately the individual items are as follows:

(a) Funds Provided by Operations: Net Loss and Extraordinary Items per Income Statement................. 6,800

    Retained Earnings................................ 6,800

        To transfer net loss and extraordinary items closed into Retained Earnings at end of year to separate section reporting funds provided by operations.

(b) Funds Applied to Payment of Dividends.............. 5,000

    Retained Earnings................................ 5,000

        To transfer charge to Retained Earnings to separate line reporting funds applied to dividends.

(c) Allowance for Depreciation of Office Equipment........ 400

    Retained Earnings................................ 400

        To cancel effects of entry correcting accounts for understatement of depreciation of prior year since funds were not affected.

(d) Capital Stock..................................... 50,000

    Retained Earnings................................ 50,000

        To cancel effects of entry recording distribution of stock dividend since funds were not affected.

(e) Retained Earnings................................. 65,000

    Retained Earnings Appropriated for Plant Extension.. 65,000

        To cancel effects of entry returning appropriation balance to Retained Earnings since funds were not affected.

The income statement summarizes activities for the year as follows:

| | | |
|---|---|---|
| Net loss........................................... | | $12,000 |
| Extraordinary items: | | |
| Gain on sale of Bruin Co. stock................... | $6,000 | |
| Less: Loss on trade of delivery equipment......... | 800 | 5,200 |
| Net loss and extraordinary items.................... | | $ 6,800 |

RICHARD AND

WORKING PAPERS FOR STATEMENT

FOR YEAR ENDED

| ACCOUNTS | BALANCES | |
|---|---|---|
| | DEC. 31 1957 | DEC. 31 1958 |
| Cash............................................................. | 14,400 | 8,200 |
| Accounts Receivable (net)......................................... | 25,000 | 25,000 |
| Inventories...................................................... | 60,000 | 75,000 |
| Prepaid Expenses................................................. | 2,000 | 2,600 |
| Investment in Bruin Co. Stock.................................... | 10,000 | |
| Machinery and Equipment......................................... | 60,000 | 100,000 |
| Office Equipment................................................. | 6,000 | 7,200 |
| Delivery Equipment............................................... | 5,000 | 5,300 |
| Buildings........................................................ | 80,000 | 140,000 |
| Land............................................................. | 25,000 | 25,000 |
| Patents.......................................................... | 12,000 | 10,500 |
| Discount on Bonds Payable........................................ | | 2,700 |
| Treasury Stock, at par............................................ | | 10,000 |
| | 299,400 | 411,500 |
| Allowance for Depreciation of Buildings........................... | 16,000 | 31,500 |
| Allowance for Depreciation of Machinery and Equipment.................. | 25,000 | 24,000 |
| Allowance for Depreciation of Office Equipment.......................... | 2,400 | 3,800 |
| Allowance for Depreciation of Delivery Equipment........................ | 2,000 | 2,100 |
| Accounts Payable................................................. | 36,000 | 50,000 |
| Accrued Salaries................................................. | 1,000 | 800 |
| Bonds Payable.................................................... | | 50,000 |
| Capital Stock.................................................... | 100,000 | 150,000 |
| Additional Paid-in Capital........................................ | 32,000 | 30,000 |
| Retained Earnings................................................ | 20,000 | 22,800 |
| Retained Earnings Appropriated for Plant Extension..................... | 65,000 | |
| Appraisal Capital................................................. | | 46,500 |
| | 299,400 | 411,500 |

Funds Provided by Operations:
  Net Loss and Extraordinary Items per Income Statement.....................................
  Deduct: Gain on Sale of Bruin Co. Stock....................................................
  Add: Loss on Trade of Delivery Equipment...................................................
      Depreciation and Patent Cost Amortization .............................................
      Bond Discount Amortization.............................................................

Funds Applied to Payment of Dividends.........................................................
Funds Provided by Sale of Bruin Co. Stock.....................................................
Funds Applied to Purchase of Delivery Equipment...............................................
Funds Applied to Overhauling of Machinery.....................................................
Funds Applied to Purchase of Machinery........................................................

Funds Provided by Issuance of Bonds...........................................................
Funds Applied to Purchase of Treasury Stock...................................................

**Decrease in Working Capital.................................................................**

RODGER, INC.

OF APPLICATION OF FUNDS

DECEMBER 31, 1958

| NET CHANGES | | ADJUSTMENTS | | | | FUNDS | | WORKING CAPITAL | |
|---|---|---|---|---|---|---|---|---|---|
| DR. | CR. | DR. | | CR. | | APPLIED | PROVIDED | INCREASE | DECREASE |
| | 6,200 | | | | | | | | 6,200 |
| 15,000 | | | | | | | | 15,000 | |
| 600 | | | | | | | | 600 | |
| | 10,000 | (f) | 10,000 | | | | | | |
| 40,000 | | (k) | 5,000 | (m) | 45,000 | | | | |
| 1,200 | | | | | | 1,200 | | | |
| 300 | | (g) | 2,400 | (g) | 2,700 | | | | |
| 60,000 | | | | (i) | 60,000 | | | | |
| | 1,500 | (h) | 1,500 | | | | | | |
| 2,700 | | (o) | 300 | (n) | 3,000 | | | | |
| 10,000 | | | | (p) | 10,000 | | | | |
| | 15,500 | (h) | 2,000 | | | | | | |
| | | (i) | 12,000 | | | | | | |
| | | (j) | 1,500 | | | | | | |
| 1,000 | | (h) | 12,000 | (k) | 5,000 | | | | |
| | | | | (l) | 8,000 | | | | |
| | 1,400 | (c) | 400 | | | | | | |
| | | (h) | 1,000 | | | | | | |
| | 100 | (h) | 1,100 | (g) | 1,000 | | | | |
| | 14,000 | | | | | | | | 14,000 |
| 200 | | | | | | | | 200 | |
| | 50,000 | (n) | 50,000 | | | | | | |
| | 50,000 | (d) | 50,000 | | | | | | |
| 2,000 | | | | (p) | 2,000 | | | | |
| | 2,800 | (e) | 65,000 | (a) | 6,800 | | | | |
| | | | | (b) | 5,000 | | | | |
| | | | | (c) | 400 | | | | |
| | | | | (d) | 50,000 | | | | |
| 65,000 | | | | (e) | 65,000 | | | | |
| | 46,500 | (i) | 48,000 | (j) | 1,500 | | | | |
| 198,000 | 198,000 | | | | | | | | |
| .................... | | (a) | 6,800 | | | | | | |
| .................... | | (f) | 6,000 | | | | | | |
| .................... | | | | (g) | 800 | | 5,900 | | |
| .................... | | | | (h) | 17,600 | | | | |
| .................... | | | | (o) | 300 | | | | |
| .................... | | (b) | 5,000 | | | 5,000 | | | |
| .................... | | | | (f) | 16,000 | | 16,000 | | |
| .................... | | (g) | 2,100 | | | 2,100 | | | |
| .................... | | (l) | 8,000 | | | 8,000 | | | |
| .................... | | (m) | 45,000 | | | 45,000 | | | |
| .................... | | | | (n) | 47,000 | | 47,000 | | |
| .................... | | (p) | 12,000 | | | 12,000 | | | |
| | | 347,100 | | 347,100 | | 73,300 | 68,900 | 15,800 | 20,200 |
| .................... | | | | | | | 4,400 | 4,400 | |
| | | | | | | 73,300 | 73,300 | 20,200 | 20,200 |

An analysis of extraordinary items reveals that Bruin Co. stock cost $10,000 and was sold for $16,000. A delivery truck, cost $2,400, book value $1,400, was traded in on a new truck costing $2,700, an allowance of $600 being received on the old truck. The following entry was made at the time of the trade.

| | | |
|---|---:|---:|
| Delivery Equipment.................................. | 2,700 | |
| Allowance for Depreciation of Delivery Equipment..... | 1,000 | |
| Loss on Trade of Delivery Equipment................ | 800 | |
| Delivery Equipment............................. | | 2,400 |
| Cash.......................................... | | 2,100 |

Depreciation charges reported on the income statement are: buildings, $2,000; machinery and equipment, $12,000; office equipment, $1,000; delivery equipment, $1,100. Operations were charged with $1,500 representing patent cost amortization.

The foregoing information results in the following adjustments:

| | | | |
|---|---|---:|---:|
| (f) | Investment in Bruin Co. Stock...................... | 10,000 | |
| | Funds Provided by Operations: Deduct Gain on Sale of Bruin Co. Stock...................................... | 6,000 | |
| | Funds Provided by Sale of Bruin Co. Stock.......... | | 16,000 |
| | To cancel changes in account balances affected by sale of investment, funds provided by sale of stock being reported separately. | | |

| | | | |
|---|---|---:|---:|
| (g) | Funds Applied to Purchase of Delivery Equipment...... | 2,100 | |
| | Delivery Equipment................................ | 2,400 | |
| | Delivery Equipment............................. | | 2,700 |
| | Allowance for Depreciation of Delivery Equipment.. | | 1,000 |
| | Funds Provided by Operations: Add Loss on Trade of Delivery Equipment............................. | | 800 |
| | To cancel changes in account balances affected by trade-in of delivery equipment, funds applied to acquisition of equipment being reported separately. | | |

| | | | |
|---|---|---:|---:|
| (h) | Allowance for Depreciation of Buildings.............. | 2,000 | |
| | Allowance for Depreciation of Machinery and Equipment. | 12,000 | |
| | Allowance for Depreciation of Office Equipment........ | 1,000 | |
| | Allowance for Depreciation of Delivery Equipment..... | 1,100 | |
| | Patents........................................ | 1,500 | |
| | Funds Provided by Operations: Add Depreciation and Patent Cost Amortization....................... | | 17,600 |
| | To cancel changes in depreciation allowances and patents accounts and to increase funds provided by operations for charges to profit and loss that did not require funds. | | |

After adjusting data as supplied by the retained earnings statement and income statement have been recorded on the working papers, further analysis of all noncurrent asset, noncurrent liability, and capital accounts showing changes not fully explained or canceled is in order. Changes in the following accounts have already been fully accounted for and require no further attention:

Investment in Bruin Co. Stock
Delivery Equipment
Allowance for Depreciation of Delivery Equipment
Patents
Retained Earnings
Retained Earnings Appropriated for Plant Extension

The following changes, however, require further analysis and explanation:

Buildings, $60,000 dr.; Allowance for Depreciation of Buildings, $13,500 cr. ($15,500 cr. less $2,000 dr. adjustment)
Machinery and Equipment, $40,000 dr.; Allowance for Depreciation of Machinery and Equipment, $13,000 dr. ($1,000 dr. plus $12,000 dr. adjustment)
Office Equipment, $1,200 dr. (Allowance for Depreciation of Office Equipment, $1,400 cr., has already been canceled by $1,400 dr.)
Discount on Bonds Payable, $2,700 dr.
Treasury Stock, $10,000 dr.
Bonds Payable, $50,000 cr.
Additional Paid-in Capital, $2,000 dr.
Appraisal Capital, $46,500 cr.

The information that follows is disclosed upon reference to transactions that support the account balance changes:

Buildings, cost $80,000, were appraised at a replacement cost of $140,000, the revaluation entry being:

| | | |
|---|---|---|
| Buildings (appraisal increase) | 60,000 | |
| Allowance for Depreciation of Buildings (appraisal increase) | | 12,000 |
| Appraisal Capital | | 48,000 |

Depreciation was recorded in terms of asset cost. Depreciation of the appraisal increase was recorded by the following entry:

| | | |
|---|---|---|
| Appraisal Capital | 1,500 | |
| Allowance for Depreciation of Buildings (appraisal increase) | | 1,500 |

Adjustments on the working papers that cancel change balances in the buildings, allowance, and appraisal capital accounts are:

(i) 
| | | |
|---|---|---|
| Allowance for Depreciation of Buildings | 12,000 | |
| Appraisal Capital | 48,000 | |
| Buildings | | 60,000 |

To cancel effects of entry recording appraisal since funds were not affected.

(j) Allowance for Depreciation of Buildings .............. 1,500
    Appraisal Capital................................... 1,500
        To cancel effects of entry recording depreciation on
        building appraisal increase since funds were not
        affected.

Fully depreciated machinery, cost $5,000, was scrapped, the asset balance being charged against the allowance for depreciation as follows:

Allowance for Depreciation of Machinery and Equipment 5,000
    Machinery and Equipment......................... 5,000

The life of remaining machinery was extended by overhauling and parts replacement at a cost of $8,000, which was recorded in the following manner:

Allowance for Depreciation of Machinery and Equipment 8,000
    Cash............................................. 8,000

Machinery was acquired during the year at a cost of $45,000.

Adjustments as a result of the foregoing are:

(k) Machinery and Equipment............................ 5,000
    Allowance for Depreciation of Machinery and Equipment......................................... 5,000
        To cancel effects of applying machinery and equipment against depreciation allowance on scrapping machinery since funds were not affected.

(l) Funds Applied to Overhauling of Machinery........... 8,000
    Allowance for Depreciation of Machinery and Equipment......................................... 8,000
        To transfer charge against allowance to separate line reporting funds applied to overhauling of machinery.

(m) Funds Applied to Purchase of Machinery.............. 45,000
    Machinery and Equipment....................... 45,000
        To transfer charges to machinery to separate line reporting funds applied to purchase of machinery.

Adjustment (m) could be omitted, $45,000, the result of a $40,000 debit in the net change column and a $5,000 debit in the adjustment column being carried to the funds applied column. However, the adjustment is made in the interest of clarity; the change balance is cleared and a full explanation is offered in the lower section of the working papers.

Office equipment of $1,200 was acquired. An adjustment is not made here, since there was a single change of $1,200 in the account. The $1,200 debit change is simply carried to the funds applied column in completion of the working papers. The account Allowance for Depreciation of Office Equipment was cleared by previous adjustments.

Ten-year bonds of $50,000 were issued at 94 at the beginning of the year. Bond discount of $300 was charged to operations during the year. The following adjustments are made:

(n)  Bonds Payable.....................................  50,000
    Discount on Bonds Payable.......................              3,000
    Funds Provided by Issuance of Bonds................             47,000
        To cancel changes in account balances affected by bond issue, funds provided by sale of bonds being reported separately.

(o)  Discount on Bonds Payable.........................     300
    Funds Provided by Operations: Add Bond Discount
    Amortization...................................                300
        To cancel change in bond discount account and increase funds provided by operations for charge to profit and loss that did not require funds.

Treasury stock, par $10,000, was acquired for $12,000, additional paid-in capital being charged for the premium on the purchase. The following adjustment is made:

(p)  Funds Applied to Purchase of Treasury Stock...........  12,000
    Treasury Stock.................................             10,000
    Additional Paid-in Capital......................              2,000
        To cancel changes in account balances affected by acquisition of treasury stock, funds applied to the acquisition being reported separately.

Working papers can now be completed by transferring fund sources and applications to the Funds columns and calculating the change in working capital. The statement of application of funds prepared from the working papers illustrated on pages 906 and 907 is given on the following page.

**SPECIAL PROBLEMS**    The analyses that are required in the development of the funds statement may be simple or complex as already illustrated. In each instance where a noncurrent or a capital account balance has changed, the question is asked: "Does this indicate a change in working capital?" Frequently the answer to this question is obvious; but in some cases careful analysis is required. The following items require special mention:

(1) Assume that retained earnings are reduced upon the declaration of a cash dividend that is to be paid in the following period. Declaration of the dividend has raised current liabilities and thus reduced working capital. Subsequent payment of the dividend will have no further

RICHARD AND RODGER, INC.

STATEMENT OF APPLICATION OF FUNDS

FOR YEAR ENDED DECEMBER 31, 1958

Funds were provided by:

Operations:

| | | | |
|---|---|---|---|
| Depreciation and patent cost amortization.. | $17,600 | | |
| Bond discount amortization............... | 300 | | |
| Loss on trade of delivery equipment (net funds applied to purchase of asset reported separately below)...................... | 800 | $18,700 | |
| Deduct: Net loss and extraordinary items per income statement.......... | $ 6,800 | | |
| Gain on sale of investment in stock (total sales proceeds reported separately below).............. | 6,000 | 12,800 | $ 5,900 |
| Sale of Bruin Co. stock..................... | | 16,000 | |
| Issuance of bonds......................... | | 47,000 | |
| | | | $68,900 |

Funds were applied to:

Purchase of plant and equipment items:

| | | | |
|---|---|---|---|
| Office equipment...................... | $ 1,200 | | |
| Delivery equipment..................... | 2,100 | | |
| Machinery............................. | 45,000 | $48,300 | |
| Overhauling of machinery.................. | | 8,000 | |
| Purchase of treasury stock................ | | 12,000 | |
| Payment of dividends..................... | | 5,000 | 73,300 |
| Decrease in working capital.................. | | | $ 4,400 |

The decrease in working capital is accounted for as follows:

| WORKING CAPITAL ITEMS | DEC. 31 1957 | DEC. 31 1958 | WORKING CAPITAL | |
|---|---|---|---|---|
| | | | INCREASE | DECREASE |
| Current assets: | | | | |
| Cash........................ | 14,400 | 8,200 | | 6,200 |
| Accounts receivable (net)...... | 25,000 | 25,000 | | |
| Inventories.................. | 60,000 | 75,000 | 15,000 | |
| Prepaid expenses.............. | 2,000 | 2,600 | 600 | |
| Current liabilities: | | | | |
| Accounts payable.............. | 36,000 | 50,000 | | 14,000 |
| Accrued salaries.............. | 1,000 | 800 | 200 | |
| | | | 15,800 | 20,200 |
| Decreases in working capital items | | | | 20,200 |
| Increases in working capital items.. | | | | 15,800 |
| Decrease in working capital....... | | | | 4,400 |

effect upon the amount of working capital, simply serving to shrink Cash and Dividends Payable by equal amounts. Declaration of a dividend thus should be reported as funds applied; confirmation of the reduction in working capital is offered in the working capital schedule supporting the statement.

(2) Assume that a long-term obligation becomes payable within a year, and hence requires change to the current classification. Such a change calls for recognition as funds applied. It is not the payment of this item but the change in classification that has operated to impair working capital; payment will have no effect on working capital, since Cash and the payable will shrink by equal amounts. The reduction in the noncurrent liability item provides the basis for the application of funds analysis. The nature of the application would be described as "Funds applied to long-term obligations maturing currently"; the schedule of working capital will confirm such working capital reduction.

(3) Assume the acquisition of a parcel of real estate. The property is bought for cash, part of the cash being acquired through the issue of long-term notes. Here, the increase in long-term notes would be recognized as a source of funds; the increase in real estate would be represented as an application of funds; the two transactions would result in an excess of funds applied, which is confirmed by a decreased working capital position. However, assume the acquisition of such real estate with the issue to the seller of a first-mortgage note for a part of the purchase price and payment of cash for the balance. Under such circumstances, instead of treating the increase in the long-term obligation as a source of funds and the increase in the property item as an application of funds, it would be better to show the net reduction in working capital arising from the acquisition of the property subject to mortgaged indebtedness as follows:

Funds applied:
  To purchase of real estate:
    Purchase price.......................... $100,000
    Less obligation assumed in connection with
      purchase..............................   40,000  $60,000

(4) In the previous illustrations, prepaid expenses were classified on the balance sheet as current and therefore were treated as working capital items in the analysis of the change in working capital. It was indicated in previous chapters that prepaid expenses are sometimes classified with long-term deferred items. Such treatment calls for the special analysis of the prepaid expenses just as for other items classified as noncurrent, since their exclusion from the current group makes them

part of the explanation for the change that took place in the current classification.

**ALTERNATE FORM OF WORKING PAPERS**  It should be noted that, in previous illustrations, adjustments were required only to noncurrent asset and liability balances and to capital balances. Since adjustments do not affect the working capital items, it is possible in developing working papers to substitute working capital totals for the individual current assets and current liabilities for each year. This reduces the amount of detail listed on the working papers. With the working capital change already calculated and reported, there is no need for a pair of columns to summarize the working capital change; the difference between funds provided and funds applied is ultimately reconciled with the working capital change originally reported and is shown as a balancing figure in the funds columns. Further removal of detail on the working papers is possible by eliminating the first two columns listing comparative balance sheet amounts and simply beginning with a listing of account change balances. Working papers incorporating the modifications indicated above would appear as follows:

| ACCOUNTS | NET CHANGES | | ADJUSTMENTS | | FUNDS | |
| --- | --- | --- | --- | --- | --- | --- |
| | DR. | CR. | DR. | CR. | APPLIED | PROVIDED |
| Working Capital........ (followed by noncurrent asset, noncurrent liability, and capital accounts. | 30,000 | | | | | |
| | | | | | 170,000 | 200,000 |
| Increase in Working Capital................. | | | | | 30,000 | |
| | | | | | 200,000 | 200,000 |

## QUESTIONS

**1.** Describe the statement of application of funds. What information does it offer that is not provided by the income statement? by the comparative balance sheet? by the statement of cash receipts and disbursements?

**2.** Define the term "funds" as used in relation to the statement of application of funds.

**3.** From what sources is the necessary information obtained in preparing a statement of application of funds?

**4.** Name a source of funds originating from a transaction involving (a) noncurrent assets, (b) noncurrent liabilities, (c) capital stock, (d) retained earnings. Name an application of funds identified with each group.

**5.** What three classes of adjustments are usually necessary in the preparation of working papers for a statement of application of funds?

**6.** Give five adjustments to cancel book entries that have no effect upon funds.

**7.** Give five adjustments that summarize changes in two or more accounts in stating a source or application of funds.

**8.** Give five examples where a single account change may provide a basis for recognizing both a source and an application of funds.

**9.** Explain why depreciation is added back to the net income balance in arriving at funds provided by operations.

**10.** The management of the Mason Co. is surprised to find that the funds statement reports "Funds provided from operations, $60,000," after the income statement had shown a net loss of $15,000. What may be a possible explanation of this difference?

**11.** (a) In the preparation of the funds statement, what adjustment is made for an increase in a bond discount balance arising from the issuance of bonds? (b) What adjustment is made for a decrease in a bond discount balance arising from bond discount amortization?

**12.** (a) Give five adjustments that raise the net income figure in calculating funds provided by operations. (b) Give five adjustments that reduce the net income figure in calculating funds provided by operations.

**13.** The Palace Corporation had no transactions for the year 1958. However, on December 10 the board of directors of the company met and declared a cash dividend of $50,000 payable on January 15, 1959. Does such action give rise to information that is properly reflected on a statement of application of funds?

**14.** Notes of $50,000 due on July 1, 1959, were reported by the Webb Co. as a long-term obligation on the balance sheet prepared on December 31, 1957, but as a short-term obligation on the balance sheet prepared on December 31, 1958. What effect, if any, will such a change in classification have on the funds statement prepared for the year 1958?

**15.** Companies A and B each show an increase in working capital for 1958 of $30,000. Funds statements for the year for the two companies are as follows:

|  | COMPANY A | | COMPANY B | |
|---|---|---|---|---|
| Funds provided: | | | | |
| By operations (as adjusted)...... | $ 15,000 | | $15,000 | |
| By issue of long-term notes....... | 60,000 | | | |
| By sale of capital stock......... | | $ 75,000 | 60,000 | $75,000 |
| Funds applied: | | | | |
| To acquisition of additional plant | $ 20,000 | | $40,000 | |
| To payment of dividends........ | 25,000 | 45,000 | 5,000 | 45,000 |
| Increase in working capital........ | | $ 30,000 | | $30,000 |

The increase in working capital is accounted for as follows:

|  | INCREASE | DECREASE | INCREASE | DECREASE |
|---|---|---|---|---|
| Current assets: |  |  |  |  |
| Cash........................ |  | $ 10,000 | $15,000 |  |
| Accounts receivable........... | $ 40,000 |  | 10,000 |  |
| Inventories.................. | 60,000 |  | 25,000 |  |
| Current liabilities: |  |  |  |  |
| Notes payable............... |  | 20,000 |  | $ 5,000 |
| Accounts payable............ |  | 40,000 |  | 15,000 |
|  | $100,000 | $ 70,000 | $50,000 | $20,000 |
| Increase in working capital ...... |  | 30,000 |  | 30,000 |
|  | $100,000 | $100,000 | $50,000 | $50,000 |

Evaluate and compare the financial policies followed by Companies A and B for 1958 as revealed by the funds statements above.

# EXERCISES

1. The balance sheets of the Rex Company at the end of 1957 and 1958 are:

|  | 1957 | 1958 |
|---|---|---|
| Cash.......................................... | $ 20,000 | $ 15,000 |
| Accounts receivable (net)..................... | 34,000 | 32,000 |
| Merchandise inventory........................ | 50,000 | 64,000 |
| Investment in branch......................... | — | 14,000 |
| Plant and equipment.......................... | 75,000 | 85,000 |
| Delivery equipment........................... | 16,000 | 21,000 |
| Real estate................................... | 51,000 | 53,000 |
| Patents....................................... | 20,000 | 19,000 |
|  | $266,000 | $303,000 |
| Allowance for depreciation of plant and equipment | $ 7,500 | $ 16,000 |
| Allowance for depreciation of delivery equipment. | 3,200 | 7,600 |
| Accounts payable............................. | 7,300 | 4,400 |
| Notes payable................................ | 28,000 | — |
| Mortgage payable............................. | — | 30,000 |
| Capital stock................................. | 200,000 | 220,000 |
| Retained earnings............................. | 20,000 | 25,000 |
|  | $266,000 | $303,000 |

Assuming no trade or sale of property items during the year and that the only change in retained earnings arose from net income, prepare a statement of application of funds without the use of working papers.

**2.** State how each of the following transactions will be reflected on the statement of application of funds:

(a) Marketable securities are purchased for $12,000.

(b) Equipment, book value $6,000, is traded for new equipment costing $15,000; a trade-in value of $5,000 is allowed on the old equipment, the balance of the purchase price to be paid in twelve monthly installments.

(c) Buildings are acquired for $60,000, the company paying $25,000 cash and signing a mortgage note payable in 5 years for the balance of the purchase price.

(d) Uncollectible accounts of $650 are written off against the allowance for bad debts.

(e) As part of a quasi-reorganization, Capital from Reduction in Stock Stated Value of $210,000 is established by a reduction in the capital stock balance, and plant and equipment items of $185,000 are then written off against this account.

(f) 5% bonds of $150,000 are issued at 99, part of the proceeds being applied to the retirement of 6% bonds of $50,000 at 102.

(g) Cash of $100,000 was paid on the purchase of business assets consisting of: merchandise, $40,000; fixtures, $15,000; land and buildings, $25,000; and goodwill, $20,000.

(h) A cash dividend of $5,000 is declared, payable at the beginning of the following year.

**3.** Give the adjustments needed for working papers for the statement of application of funds upon analysis of the following account:

RETAINED EARNINGS

| 1958 | | | 1958 | | |
|---|---|---|---|---|---|
| June | 1 Stock dividend...... | 200,000 | Jan. 1 | Balance............. | 760,000 |
| | 1 Goodwill written off... | 100,000 | Mar. 20 | Correction for understatement of inventory at end of 1957.. | 12,000 |
| Aug. | 5 Discount on sale of treasury stock, par $150,000, for $125,000 | 25,000 | Mar. 25 | Gain on sale of X Co. stock (cost, $60,000) | 20,000 |
| Dec. | 5 Cash dividends...... | 50,000 | July 1 | Gain on redemption of bonds of $200,000 at 96.............. | 8,000 |
| | 31 Appropriated for contingencies......... | 100,000 | | | |
| | 31 Balance............. | 325,000 | | | |
| | | 800,000 | | | 800,000 |
| | | | 1959 | | |
| | | | Jan. 1 | Balance............. | 325,000 |

**4.** The retained earnings account for the Meadows Co. at the end of 1958 shows the following:

RETAINED EARNINGS

| 1958 | | | 1958 | | |
|---|---|---|---|---|---|
| Jan. 30 | Call premium paid on retirement of bonds of $400,000............ | 12,000 | Jan. 1 | Balance............. | 160,000 |
| Mar. 1 | Goodwill written off..... | 50,000 | Mar. 20 | Gain on sale of land (cost $50,000)...... | 15,000 |
| Mar. 15 | Correction for understatement of depreciation in prior periods......... | 40,500 | Dec. 31 | Net income per income statement........ | 42,500 |

(a) What adjustments would be made for the changes in retained earnings on working papers for a statement of application of funds?

(b) Assume that extraordinary items including corrections are reported in nominal accounts, the income statement reporting income and extraordinary items resulting in a net decrease in retained earnings of $45,000 for the year. What adjustments would be made on the working papers under such circumstances for each of the above items?

5. From the information that follows, give the necessary adjustments to clear the change balances for the accounts listed in the preparation of working papers for an application of funds statement for the year 1958.

|  | 1957 | 1958 |
|---|---|---|
| Tools............................................ | $ 12,000 | $ 14,000 |
| Machinery....................................... | 45,000 | 39,000 |
| Allowance for Depreciation of Machinery........ | 16,000 | 15,500 |
| Delivery Equipment............................. | 15,000 | 18,000 |
| Allowance for Depreciation of Delivery Equipment | 6,000 | 6,500 |
| Buildings....................................... | 100,000 | 100,000 |
| Allowance for Depreciation of Buildings......... | 62,500 | 68,500 |
| Land............................................ | 40,000 | 25,000 |
| Patents......................................... | 4,500 | 3,500 |
| Goodwill........................................ | 50,000 | — |
| Discount on Bonds Payable...................... | 6,000 | — |
| Bonds Payable.................................. | 100,000 | — |
| Capital Stock................................... | 250,000 | 350,000 |
| Treasury Stock.................................. | — | 22,000 |
| Retained Earnings ............................. | 180,000 | 147,700 |
| Retained Earnings Appropriated for Bond Retirement Fund .......................................... | 100,000 | — |

### RETAINED EARNINGS

| | | | |
|---|---|---|---|
| Stock dividend................ | 100,000 | Balance...................... | 180,000 |
| Loss on scrapping of machinery, cost $6,000, for which an allowance of $4,500 had been provided.................. | 1,500 | Gain on sale of land, cost $15,000, sold for $18,000..... | 3,000 |
| Premium on purchase of treasury stock, par $22,000....... | 8,000 | Gain on trade of delivery equipment, cost $4,000, book value, $2,500, allowance of $3,200 being received on new equipment costing $7,000......... | 700 |
| Goodwill.................... | 50,000 | | |
| Discount, $4,000, call premium, $2,500, on bond retirement... | 6,500 | Retained earnings appropriated for bond retirement fund.... | 100,000 |
| Cash dividends.............. | 10,000 | Net income for year......... | 40,000 |
| Balance.................... | 147,700 | | |
| | 323,700 | | 323,700 |
| | | Balance...................... | 147,700 |

The income statement reports depreciation of buildings, $6,000; depreciation of machinery, $4,000; depreciation of delivery equipment, $2,000; tools amortization, $4,000; patents amortization, $1,000; and bond discount amortization, $2,000.

## PROBLEMS

**28-1.** The following data were obtained from the books and records of the Wallace Co.:

|  | DECEMBER 31 | |
|---|---|---|
|  | 1957 | 1958 |
| Current assets | $250,000 | $301,500 |
| Plant and equipment (net) | 140,000 | 165,000 |
| Goodwill | 20,000 | — |
|  | $410,000 | $466,500 |
| Current liabilities | $110,000 | $155,000 |
| Bonds payable | — | 100,000 |
| Bond discount | — | (3,800) |
| Preferred stock | 100,000 | — |
| Common stock | 100,000 | 150,000 |
| Additional paid-in capital | 20,000 | 20,000 |
| Retained earnings | 55,000 | 45,300 |
| Appraisal capital | 25,000 | — |
|  | $410,000 | $466,500 |

RETAINED EARNINGS

| | | | |
|---|---|---|---|
| Premium on retirement of preferred stock | 5,000 | Balance, Jan. 1 | 55,000 |
| Stock dividend on common stock | 50,000 | Gain on sale of land | 35,000 |
| Cash dividends paid during year | 13,500 | Net income after income taxes | 43,800 |
| Goodwill written off | 20,000 | | |

Ten-year bonds of $100,000 were issued on July 1, 1958, at 96, proceeds being used in the retirement of preferred stock. Land, cost $30,000 and recorded on the books at an appraised value of $55,000, was sold for $65,000. The cash proceeds from the sale were applied to the construction of new buildings costing $88,000. Depreciation recorded for the year was $8,000.

*Instructions:* Prepare working papers and a statement of application of funds.

**28-2.** The following data were taken from the books and records of the Thompson Company:

RETAINED EARNINGS

| | | | |
|---|---|---|---|
| Goodwill Written Off | 24,999 | Balance | 24,750 |
| Premium on Retirement of Preferred Stock | 1,000 | Net Income and Extraordinary Items per Income Statement | 36,150 |
| Cash Dividends | 15,000 | | |

### INCOME STATEMENT DATA

| | | |
|---|---:|---:|
| Net Income after Income Taxes.................. | | $40,650 |
| Add: Gain on Trade of Equipment................ | | 1,500 |
| | | $42,150 |
| Deduct: | | |
| Loss on Sale of Securities...................... | $2,500 | |
| Loss on Retirement of Bonds................... | 3,500 | 6,000 |
| Net Income and Extraordinary Items............ | | $36,150 |

### BALANCE SHEET DATA

DECEMBER 31

| | 1957 | | 1958 | |
|---|---:|---:|---:|---:|
| Current Assets (net) ................ | | $128,500 | | $145,400 |
| Plant and Equipment................ | $96,000 | | $100,500 | |
| Less Allowance for Depreciation .... | 30,000 | 66,000 | 34,000 | 66,500 |
| Investments in Stocks and Bonds..... | | 30,000 | | 27,000 |
| Goodwill......................... | | 25,000 | | 1 |
| | | $249,500 | | $238,901 |
| Current Liabilities................... | | $ 26,000 | | $ 39,000 |
| Bonds Payable...................... | | 50,000 | | — |
| Unamortized Bond Discount ......... | | (1,250) | | — |
| Preferred Stock ($100 par)........... | | 50,000 | | — |
| Common Stock ($10 par)............ | | 100,000 | | 150,000 |
| Additional Paid-in Capital........... | | — | | 30,000 |
| Retained Earnings................... | | 24,750 | | 19,901 |
| | | $249,500 | | $238,901 |

Fully depreciated equipment, original cost $10,500, was traded in on new equipment costing $15,000, $1,500 being allowed by the vendor on the trade-in. One hundred shares of Bliss Co. preferred stock, cost $15,000, held as a long-term investment, were sold at the beginning of the year. Additional changes in the investments account resulted from the purchase of Bell Co. bonds. The company issued common stock in April, and part of the proceeds was used to retire preferred stock at 102 shortly thereafter. On July 1 the company called in its bonds outstanding, paying a premium of 5% on the call. Discount amortization on the bonds to the date of call was $250. Depreciation for the year taken on plant and equipment was $14,500.

*Instructions:* Prepare working papers and a statement of application of funds.

28-3. The following information is assembled in the preparation of a statement of application of funds for the Bowman Corporation:

BALANCE SHEET DATA

DECEMBER 31

| | 1957 | | 1958 | |
|---|---|---|---|---|
| Cash............................... | | $ 3,125* | | $ 35,875 |
| Accounts Receivable................ | | 66,125 | | 50,000 |
| Inventories........................ | | 72,000 | | 90,000 |
| Plant and Equipment................ | $95,000 | | $130,000 | |
| Less: Allowance for Depreciation.... | 20,000 | 75,000 | 21,500 | 108,500 |
| Investments....................... | | 20,000 | | 8,000 |
| Patents........................... | | 30,000 | | — |
| | | $260,000 | | $292,375 |
| Accounts Payable................... | | $ 50,000 | | $ 55,000 |
| Bonds Payable..................... | | 20,000 | | 50,000 |
| Premium on Bonds Payable.......... | | — | | 2,375 |
| Preferred Stock ($100 par)........... | | 50,000 | | — |
| Common Stock ($10 par)............ | | 100,000 | | 150,000 |
| Premium on Common Stock......... | | | | 20,000 |
| Retained Earnings.................. | | 40,000 | | 15,000 |
| | | $260,000 | | $292,375 |

*Credit Balance

INCOME STATEMENT DATA FOR YEAR ENDED DECEMBER 31, 1958:

| | | |
|---|---|---|
| Net Income after Income Taxes.................. | | $24,000 |
| Add: Gain on Sale of Investments............... | | 3,000 |
| | | $27,000 |
| Deduct: | | |
| Premium on Retirement of Bonds.............. | $ 1,000 | |
| Loss on Disposal of Equipment............... | 3,500 | |
| Patents Written Off........................ | 30,000 | 34,500 |
| Net Income and Extraordinary Items (decrease in retained earnings)........................... | | ($ 7,500) |

RETAINED EARNINGS

| 1958 | | | 1958 | | |
|---|---|---|---|---|---|
| Oct. 15 | Cash Dividends....... | 12,500 | Jan. 1 Balance............. | | 40,000 |
| Dec. 12 | Premium on Retirement of Preferred Stock... | 5,000 | | | |
| Dec. 31 | Net Income and Extraordinary Items per Income Statement....... | 7,500 | | | |

Equipment, cost $10,000, book value, $4,000, was scrapped, salvage of $500 being recovered on the disposal. Additional equipment, cost $45,000, was acquired during the year. Securities, cost $12,000, were sold for $15,000. Patents of $30,000 were written off against profits. 7% bonds, face value $20,000, were called in at 105, and new 10-year, 5% bonds of $50,000 were issued at 105 on July 1. Preferred stock was retired at a cost of 110 while $50,000 in common stock was issued at 14. Depreciation on plant and equipment for the year was $7,500.

*Instructions:* Prepare working papers and a statement of application of funds.

**28-4.** Financial data for the Riviera Manufacturing Co. are presented on this and the following page.

## RIVIERA MANUFACTURING CO.
### COMPARATIVE BALANCE SHEET
### DECEMBER 31, 1957 AND 1958

| | | 1957 | | 1958 |
|---|---|---|---|---|
| **ASSETS** | | | | |
| Cash...................................... | | $ 23,000 | | $ 74,050 |
| Notes receivable.......................... | | 1,000 | | |
| Accounts receivable...................... | $ 26,625 | | $ 53,000 | |
| Less: Allowance for bad debts.......... | 2,125 | 24,500 | 2,500 | 50,500 |
| Inventories.............................. | | 40,000 | | 54,000 |
| Supplies................................. | | 1,500 | | 1,000 |
| Miscellaneous prepaid expenses........... | | 3,000 | | 3,500 |
| Investments in outside companies......... | | 16,000 | | 27,000 |
| Machinery............................... | $ 75,000 | | $ 95,000 | |
| Less: Allowance for depreciation........ | 40,000 | 35,000 | 44,000 | 51,000 |
| Buildings................................ | $ 90,000 | | $125,000 | |
| Less: Allowance for depreciation........ | 36,000 | 54,000 | 40,500 | 84,500 |
| Land..................................... | | 40,000 | | 80,000 |
| Goodwill................................. | | 50,000 | | |
| | | $288,000 | | $425,550 |
| **LIABILITIES AND CAPITAL** | | | | |
| Notes payable............................ | | $ 11,000 | | $ 20,000 |
| Accounts payable........................ | | 23,000 | | 17,500 |
| Miscellaneous accrued expenses........... | | 4,000 | | 6,500 |
| Estimated income taxes payable........... | | 10,000 | | 15,000 |
| Bonds payable........................... | $ 50,000 | | $175,000 | |
| Less: Bond discount.................... | 4,250 | 45,750 | 10,875 | 164,125 |
| Capital stock (Par $10)................. | | 100,000 | | 125,000 |
| Additional paid-in capital............... | | 30,000 | | 35,000 |
| Retained earnings........................ | | 64,250 | | 42,425 |
| | | $288,000 | | $425,550 |

Ten-year bonds of $50,000 had been issued on July 1, 1956, at 90. Additional ten-year bonds of $125,000 had been issued on July 1, 1958, at 94.

The following entry was made in 1958 upon the sale of obsolete machinery:

| | | |
|---|---|---|
| Cash........................................................ | 6,000 | |
| Allowance for Depreciation of Machinery........... | 3,500 | |
| Loss on Disposal of Machinery..................... | 1,500 | |
| Machinery........................................... | | 11,000 |

Fully depreciated storage quarters were dismantled during the year, and buildings, cost $1,500, were written off against the allowance for depreciation of buildings account. Investments in outside companies that

## RIVIERA MANUFACTURING CO.

CONDENSED STATEMENT OF INCOME AND RETAINED EARNINGS

FOR YEAR ENDED DECEMBER 31, 1958

| | | | |
|---|---:|---:|---:|
| Gross income.............................. | | | $215,400 |
| Deduct: Cost of goods sold................. | $104,500 | | |
| Selling, general, administrative, and other expenses .................. | 40,225 | | |
| Depreciation of buildings.... $6,000 | | | |
| Depreciation of machinery... 7,500 | 13,500 | | |
| Income taxes.................... | 18,000 | 176,225 | |
| Net income after income taxes ............... | | | $ 39,175 |
| Balance of retained earnings at beginning of 1958 | | | 64,250 |
| | | | $103,425 |
| Add: Gain on sale of outside securities........ | | | 6,500 |
| | | | $109,925 |
| Deduct: Loss on disposal of machinery......... | $ 1,500 | | |
| Cash dividends..................... | 16,000 | | |
| Goodwill written off................. | 50,000 | 67,500 | |
| Balance of retained earnings at end of 1958 .... | | | $ 42,425 |

cost $12,000 were sold at the beginning of the year for $18,500, and additional securities were subsequently acquired during the year. Additional capital stock was issued by the company during the year at 12 in order to raise working capital.

*Instructions:* Prepare working papers and a statement of application of funds.

**28-5.** The following data are assembled in the preparation of a statement of application of funds for Kraft Inc.:

RETAINED EARNINGS

| | | | |
|---|---:|---|---:|
| Stock Dividend.............. | 42,500 | Balance...................... | 57,250 |
| Cash Dividends.............. | 10,000 | Net Income and Extraordinary | |
| Retained Earnings Appropriated for Contingencies........... | 25,000 | Items..................... | 42,500 |

INCOME STATEMENT DATA FOR YEAR ENDED DECEMBER 31, 1958

| | | |
|---|---:|---:|
| Net Income.......................................... | | $40,000 |
| Add: Gain on sale of outside investments................ | | 7,500 |
| | | $47,500 |
| Deduct: | | |
| Loss on bond retirement........................... | $4,000 | |
| Loss on trade of machinery........................ | 1,000 | 5,000 |
| Net income and extraordinary items.................. | | $42,500 |

BALANCE SHEET DATA

| | DECEMBER 31, 1957 | | DECEMBER 31, 1958 | |
|---|---|---|---|---|
| Cash............................. | | $ 13,250 | | $ 16,750 |
| Accounts Receivable.............. | $29,900 | | $24,575 | |
| Less Allowance for Bad Debts.... | 900 | 29,000 | 875 | 23,700 |
| Inventories....................... | | 52,000 | | 40,000 |
| Supplies.......................... | | 750 | | 1,000 |
| Prepaid Expenses................. | | 1,250 | | 1,600 |
| Outside Investments.............. | | 25,000 | | — |
| Office Equipment................. | $ 7,500 | | $ 8,000 | |
| Less Allowance for Depreciation... | 1,800 | 5,700 | 1,200 | 6,800 |
| Machinery........................ | $55,000 | | $60,000 | |
| Less Allowance for Depreciation... | 12,500 | 42,500 | 14,000 | 46,000 |
| Buildings......................... | $80,000 | | $86,000 | |
| Less Allowance for Depreciation... | 22,000 | 58,000 | 22,500 | 63,500 |
| Land............................. | | 30,000 | | 30,000 |
| | | $257,450 | | $229,350 |
| Notes Payable.................... | | $ 8,000 | | $ 5,000 |
| Accounts Payable................. | | 17,500 | | 20,400 |
| Accrued Expenses and Taxes....... | | 700 | | 6,200 |
| Bonds Payable................... | $50,000 | | | — |
| Less: Discount on Bonds Payable. | 2,000 | 48,000 | | — |
| Capital Stock (Par $10)........... | | 100,000 | | 127,500 |
| Additional Paid-in Capital......... | | 26,000 | | 23,000 |
| Retained Earnings................. | | 57,250 | | 22,250 |
| Retained Earnings Appropriated for Contingencies.................. | | — | | 25,000 |
| | | $257,450 | | $229,350 |

Explanations of account balance changes follow:

Outside investments were sold during the year. A part of the buildings was rebuilt and enlarged, the following entry being made:

| | | |
|---|---|---|
| Buildings......................................... | 6,000 | |
| Allowance for Depreciation of Buildings............ | 4,000 | |
| Cash......................................... | | 10,000 |

Depreciation of buildings for the year was reported at $4,500. Machinery was traded in for new machinery, the following entry being made:

| | | |
|---|---|---|
| Machinery....................................... | 12,000 | |
| Depreciation of Machinery........................ | 500 | |
| Allowance for Depreciation of Machinery........... | 4,500 | |
| Loss on Trade of Machinery...................... | 1,000 | |
| Machinery..................................... | | 7,000 |
| Cash......................................... | | 11,000 |

Depreciation of machinery for the year was reported at $6,500 which includes depreciation of $500 recognized on machinery traded. Fully depreciated office equipment of $1,500 was written off against the allowance. Additional office equipment was acquired during the year. Depreciation of office equipment for the year was $900. Bond discount amortization of $500 was recorded before bonds were called in at 105. Fifteen hundred shares of stock were acquired at 12 and canceled; a stock dividend of one share for two was subsequently issued. Retained earnings were appropriated for contingencies during the year as a result of pending lawsuits.

*Instructions:* Prepare working papers and a statement of application of funds.

**28-6.** A comparative balance sheet for the Stanford Corporation appears as follows:

|  | DECEMBER 31 | |
|---|---|---|
|  | 1957 | 1958 |
| Cash........................................ | $ 135,000 | $ 204,000 |
| Marketable securities...................... | 120,000 | 116,000 |
| Accounts and notes receivable, less allowances for bad debts.................... | 220,000 | 250,000 |
| Inventories................................ | 300,000 | 360,000 |
| Investments in stock of subsidiary companies (at cost).............................. | 335,000 | 240,000 |
| Plant and equipment, less allowance......... | 800,000 | 1,040,000 |
| Patents and goodwill...................... | 140,000 | 36,000 |
| Unamortized bond discount and issuance costs................................. | 30,000 | 21,600 |
|  | $2,080,000 | $2,267,600 |
| Accounts and notes payable................ | $ 145,000 | $ 180,000 |
| Miscellaneous accrued liabilities including taxes................................... | 65,000 | 88,200 |
| 4% Mortgage bonds....................... | 500,000 | 400,000 |
| Preferred stock (par $25, each share convertible into two shares of common)....... | 250,000 | 210,000 |
| Common stock (par value $10)............. | 300,000 | 432,000 |
| Additional paid-in capital................. | 200,000 | 288,000 |
| Retained earnings........................ | 620,000 | 669,400 |
|  | $2,080,000 | $2,267,600 |

An analysis of balance sheet changes discloses the following:

(a) Stock owned in the Taylor Co., a partially owned subsidiary, was sold for $200,000. Stock had originally cost $95,000.

(b) The entire goodwill of $100,000 was written off the books in 1958.

(c) The patents had a remaining life of ten years on December 31, 1957, and are being written off over this period.

(d) Mortgage bonds mature on January 1, 1968. On July 1, 1958, bonds of $100,000 were purchased on the market at $103\frac{1}{2}$ and formally canceled.

(e) The decrease in preferred stock outstanding resulted from the exercise of the conversion privilege by preferred stockholders.

(f) 10,000 shares of common stock were sold during the year at $18.

(g) During the year equipment that cost $60,000 and that had a book value of $12,000 was sold for $8,600. Depreciation of $64,000 was taken during the year on buildings and equipment. Additional changes in the plant and equipment balance resulted from the purchase of equipment.

(h) The net income for the year transferred to retained earnings was $107,000.

(i) Dividends paid during the year totaled $50,000.

*Instructions:* Prepare working papers and a statement of application of funds.

**28-7.** A comparative balance sheet for The Morgan Corporation appears as follows:

| | December 31 1957 | December 31 1958 | Increase (or decrease) of working capital, etc. |
|---|---|---|---|
| Current and working assets: | | | |
| Cash.............................. | $ 40,000 | $ 102,800 | $ 62,800 |
| Bid deposits...................... | — | 100,000 | 100,000 |
| Estimated receivables.............. | 380,000 | 450,600 | 70,600 |
| Miscellaneous receivables.......... | 45,650 | 65,800 | 20,150 |
| U. S. Treasury tax anticipation notes... | 100,000 | 10,000 | (90,000) |
| Supplies.......................... | 20,100 | 22,800 | 2,700 |
| Insurance policy cash-surrender values (less loans)....................... | 10,000 | 25,050 | 15,050 |
| Postwar excess-profit refund.......... | 18,000 | 40,000 | 22,000 |
| | $ 613,750 | $ 817,050 | $203,300 |
| Less: Current liabilities: | | | |
| Notes payable..................... | $ 150,000 | $ 50,000 | $100,000 |
| Accounts payable.................. | 190,000 | 215,000 | (25,000) |
| Accrued liabilities................ | 18,400 | 30,900 | (12,500) |
| Federal income tax accrued.......... | 150,000 | 240,000 | (90,000) |
| | $ 508,400 | $ 535,900 | $(27,500) |
| Working capital.................... | $ 105,350 | $ 281,150 | $175,800 |
| Plant and equipment................ | $1,050,200 | $ 806,050 | |
| Less: Allowance for depreciation....... | 660,300 | 303,800 | |
| | $ 389,900 | $ 502,250 | 112,350 |
| Other assets: | | | |
| Investment in stock of Blake Co.—90% owned............................ | $ 170,000 | $ 177,200 | 7,200 |
| Treasury stock—bought for $90,000.... | — | 40,000 | 40,000 |
| Organization expenses................ | 12,000 | 6,000 | (6,000) |
| Unamortized discount on bonds payable. | 9,000 | 8,000 | (1,000) |
| | $ 686,250 | $1,014,600 | $328,350 |
| Reserves and capital: | | | |
| Reserve for contingencies............. | $ — | $ 100,000 | $100,000 |
| Deferred profit on contract........... | | 65,000 | 65,000 |
| Bonds payable...................... | 100,000 | 100,000 | — |
| Capital stock...................... | 200,000 | 200,000 | — |
| Earned surplus..................... | 386,250 | 549,600 | 163,350 |
| | $ 686,250 | $1,014,600 | $328,350 |

A summary of earned surplus for the year 1958 follows:

| | | |
|---|---:|---:|
| Balance, December 31, 1957........................................ | | $386,250 |
| Add: Net profit (before federal taxes) for the year 1958........ | $275,000 | |
| Restatement of property and allowance accounts to agree with depreciated cost values established by Treasury Department as at January 1, 1958................... | 172,350 | 447,350 |
| Total.............................................. | | $833,600 |
| Deduct: Dividends declared.............................. | $ 25,000 | |
| Provision for federal income taxes after refund credit.. | 203,000 | |
| Purchase price of treasury stock, | | |
| $90,000 in excess of par value, $40,000............. | 50,000 | |
| Organization expense amortized..................... | 6,000 | 284,000 |
| Balance, December 31, 1958................................ | | $549,600 |

As of January 1, 1958, the plant and equipment account was reduced $110,150 and the related allowance account was reduced $282,500 to agree with adjusted depreciated cost values as of that date as determined by the U. S. Treasury Department. During 1958 equipment having a gross book value of $354,000 and a net book value of $235,000 on the revalued basis was sold at a profit of $42,500. Additions and depreciation constitute the remaining changes in the respective accounts.

The investment in stock of Blake Co. account was adjusted during the year to give effect to subsidiary company earnings of $20,000 and dividends declared of $12,000.

*Instructions:* Prepare working papers and a statement of application of funds. (A.I.C.P.A. adapted)

**28-8.** The following information is assembled in the preparation of a statement of application of funds for the Silver Star Company:

BALANCE SHEET DATA

| | DECEMBER 31 | |
|---|---:|---:|
| | 1957 | 1958 |
| Cash......................................... | $ 40,409 | $ 30,337 |
| Accounts receivable.......................... | 67,186 | 65,638 |
| Temporary investments....................... | 112,500 | 85,000 |
| Prepaid insurance............................ | 710 | 755 |
| Inventories................................. | 82,164 | 94,438 |
| Cash surrender value of life insurance policies... | 8,315 | 9,061 |
| Unamortized bond discount.................... | 4,305 | 2,867 |
| Land, buildings, machinery and equipment..... | 172,778 | 207,782 |
| | $488,367 | $495,878 |

| | DECEMBER 31 | |
| --- | --- | --- |
| | 1957 | 1958 |
| Accounts payable.......................... | $ 34,081 | $ 31,314 |
| Notes payable to banks..................... | 40,000 | 45,000 |
| Accrued interest, taxes, etc................. | 12,307 | 21,263 |
| First-mortgage 4% serial bonds............... | 82,000 | 68,500 |
| Allowance for loss on accounts............... | 4,630 | 3,815 |
| Allowance for depreciation................... | 96,618 | 81,633 |
| Allowance for inventory loss................. | 1,000 | 7,500 |
| Reserve for contingencies.................... | 37,500 | 63,600 |
| Common stock, $100 par value............... | 100,000 | 92,500 |
| Paid-in surplus............................. | 11,000 | 10,175 |
| Retained earnings.......................... | 69,231 | 70,578 |
| | $488,367 | $495,878 |

The following information concerning the transactions is available:

(1) Net profit for 1958 was shown by the profit and loss statement as $48,097.

(2) During the year 75 shares of the capital stock were repurchased at $111 and were being held in the treasury. Subsequent to the stock reacquisition a 10% cash dividend was paid.

(3) The 1958 premium on life insurance policies was $1,673. Expense was charged with $927 of this payment.

(4) Machinery was purchased for $31,365 and machinery costing $32,625 was retired. The retired machinery had accumulated depreciation of $29,105 at date of retirement. It was sold as scrap for $1,000, which was credited against the profit and loss on retirement of asset account. The remaining increase in fixed assets resulted from construction of a building.

(5) The serial bonds mature at the rate of $5,000 per year. In addition to the retirement of the $5,000 of bonds due in 1958, the company purchased and retired $8,500 of the bonds at $103. Both the premium on retirement and the applicable discount were charged to expense.

(6) The allowance for inventory loss was created by a charge to expense in each year. It is set up to reduce the inventory value of obsolete items to estimated market value. Bad accounts of $3,702 were written off against the allowance for loss on accounts.

(7) The reserve for contingencies was provided by charges against retained earnings. A debit to the reserve of $11,400 was made during the year. This represented the final settlement of a part of 1955 income tax liability which had been the subject of controversy.

*Instructions:* Prepare working papers and a statement of application of funds. (A.I.C.P.A. adapted)

**28-9.** The Cold River Corporation finds that it is unable to pay a year-end cash dividend without borrowing. However, its profits for the year 1958, shown by its books as $83,485, were the largest in its history of operations. Some of the directors are puzzled as to the reason for the small cash balance and weak current position. The accounts have not been audited, but the company management engages you to assist them in preparing an explanation of the situation for the directors. As a part of your engagement you are to prepare a formal statement showing source and application of funds, accepting their profit figure of $83,485 as a starting point. The following information is available:

### TRIAL BALANCES

| | POST-CLOSING 12/31/57 | | PRE-CLOSING 12/31/58 | |
|---|---|---|---|---|
| ACCOUNTS | DEBIT | CREDIT | DEBIT | CREDIT |
| Cash.................................. | $ 25,000 | | $ 5,000 | |
| Accounts receivable..................... | 18,000 | | 20,000 | |
| Allowance for loss on accounts............. | | $ 1,500 | | $ 1,800 |
| Installment notes receivable.............. | | | 25,000 | |
| Inventory of materials................... | 30,000 | | 22,000 | |
| Inventory of finished goods.............. | 19,000 | | 13,000 | |
| Inventory of supplies.................... | 2,000 | | 2,500 | |
| Investment in Blake Co. (50% of stock).... | 42,500 | | 47,275 | |
| Land used in business................... | 10,000 | | 25,000 | |
| Land not used in business............... | 20,000 | | | |
| Buildings.............................. | 90,000 | | 90,000 | |
| Allowance for depreciation of buildings...... | | 60,000 | | 36,100 |
| Machinery............................. | 170,000 | | 191,000 | |
| Allowance for depreciation of machinery.... | | 80,000 | | 72,050 |
| Goodwill and patents.................... | 14,000 | | 17,000 | |
| Bond discount unamortized............... | 3,000 | | 2,160 | |
| Prepaid insurance...................... | 1,000 | | 1,500 | |
| Accounts payable....................... | | 48,000 | | 47,500 |
| Notes payable.......................... | | 10,000 | | 15,000 |
| Accrued liabilities...................... | | 15,000 | | 18,000 |
| Bonds payable — 4%.................... | | 50,000 | | 40,000 |
| Reserve for future inventory price declines... | | 10,000 | | 2,000 |
| Reserve for contingencies................ | | 10,000 | | 5,000 |
| Reserve for preferred stock retirement...... | | 15,000 | | 5,000 |
| Preferred stock — 6%, $100 par.......... | | 25,000 | | 25,000 |
| Common stock — $100 par.............. | | 100,000 | | 100,000 |
| Treasury stock — common — 100 shares.... | | | 10,000 | |
| Surplus............................... | | 20,000 | | 20,500 |
| Sales (net)............................ | | | | 188,000 |
| Cost of goods manufactured and sold....... | | | 142,000 | |
| Selling and general expense.............. | | | 28,075 | |
| Bond interest and discount............... | | | 2,040 | |
| Federal income tax expense.............. | | | 5,600 | |
| Loss on disposal of assets................ | | | 3,000 | |
| Gain in value of assets.................. | | | | 25,000 |
| Reduction of depreciation allowance....... | | | | 45,000 |
| Dividends and profits of Blake Co......... | | | | 6,900 |
| Miscellaneous income and expense........ | | | 700 | |
| | $444,500 | $444,500 | $652,850 | $652,850 |

Explanations of changes in certain of the accounts have been obtained. They show:

(1) Provision for loss on accounts was ½ of 1% of net sales, which was charged to selling expense and credited to the allowance. Recoveries amounted to $500, which were netted against the expense.

(2) Investment in Blake Co. has been debited with 50% of the profit of Blake Co. and credited with a cash dividend of $2,125 received. The contra entries have been to Dividends and Profits of Blake Co. and to Cash.

(3) An appraisal was made of fixed assets as of January 1, 1958. It was as follows:

| | Undepreciated Value | Depreciation | Net Value |
|---|---|---|---|
| Land used in business.......... | $ 25,000 | | $ 25,000 |
| Land not used in business...... | 30,000 | | 30,000 |
| Buildings..................... | 140,000 | $ 85,000 | 55,000 |
| Machinery and equipment...... | 210,000 | 100,000 | 110,000 |
| Total..................... | $405,000 | $185,000 | $220,000 |

This appraisal was recorded by the following entry:

| | | |
|---|---|---|
| Land Used in Business................. | 15,000 | |
| Land Not Used in Business............. | 10,000 | |
| Allowance for Depreciation of Buildings... | 25,000 | |
| Allowance for Depreciation of Machinery.. | 20,000 | |
| Gain in Value of Assets............................ | | 25,000 |
| Reduction of Depreciation Allowance................. | | 45,000 |

The land not used in the business was subsequently sold for $27,000, payable $2,000 in cash and the remainder in notes due in equal annual payments over a five-year period starting 7/1/59. The $3,000 difference between the sale price and the $30,000 undepreciated value was debited to Loss on Disposal of Assets. Depreciation, computed on an acceptable basis, was charged to expense of the year in the amount of $13,150. Purchase of new machinery in the amount of $21,000 was made for cash.

(4) The company charged $5,000 of research and patent expenditures to the goodwill and patents account and amortized against manufacturing cost the amount of $2,000 of the previous balance.

(5) The company wrote off to Bond Interest and Discount one fifth of the bond discount upon retirement of $10,000 of the bonds at 94 on July 1, 1958. The regular amortization and the result of the bond retirement, including profit, have been included in the bond interest expense.

(6) The company had $9,000 liability for income taxes included in the accrued liabilities as of 12/31/57. However, only $4,000 was paid; therefore $5,000 was credited to Surplus and current expense was charged with the estimated expense for 1958.

(7) Because of price declines during the year, $8,000 of the Reserve for Future Inventory Price Declines was utilized by a credit to Cost of Goods Sold.

(8) During the year the company paid a $5,000 award rendered against them in a suit. The charge was to the Reserve for Contingencies that had been created in 1957 because of this and other pending suits.

(9) During the year the company purchased 100 shares of its own preferred stock for $11,000. It charged $10,000 to the preferred stock retirement reserve account and $1,000 to Surplus. It has charged Surplus with $1,500 of preferred dividends paid and credited Miscellaneous Income with the $300 that it kept because it owned 100 shares of the stock.

(10) During the year the company reacquired 100 shares of its own common stock for $12,000. It charged the $2,000 excess over par to Surplus.

*Instructions:* Prepare working papers and a statement of application of funds. (A.I.C.P.A. adapted)

**28-10.** You have completed the field work in connection with your audit of The Delmar Corporation for the year ended December 31, 1958. You have decided to include a Statement of Source and Application of Funds in your long-form report. The following schedule shows the balance sheet accounts at the beginning and end of the year:

| | Dec. 31, 1958 | Dec. 31, 1957 | Increase or (Decrease) |
|---|---|---|---|
| Cash............................................. | $  282,400 | $  320,000 | $  (37,600) |
| Accounts receivable....................... | 490,000 | 410,000 | 80,000 |
| Inventory............................... | 695,000 | 660,000 | 35,000 |
| Prepaid expenses....................... | 10,000 | 8,000 | 2,000 |
| Investment in Subsidiary Co.............. | 106,000 | — | 106,000 |
| Cash surrender value of life insurance...... | 2,100 | 1,800 | 300 |
| Machinery.............................. | 186,600 | 190,000 | (3,400) |
| Buildings............................... | 566,500 | 507,500 | 59,000 |
| Land.................................... | 52,500 | 52,500 | — |
| Patents................................. | 71,000 | 60,000 | 11,000 |
| Goodwill................................ | 40,000 | 50,000 | (10,000) |
| Bond discount and expense.............. | 4,680 | — | 4,680 |
| | $2,506,780 | $2,259,800 | $ 246,980 |
| | | | |
| Accrued taxes payable.................. | $  92,000 | $  80,000 | $  12,000 |
| Accounts payable....................... | 301,280 | 280,000 | 21,280 |
| Dividends payable....................... | 60,000 | — | 60,000 |
| Bonds payable — 4%.................. | 125,000 | — | 125,000 |
| Bonds payable — 6%.................. | — | 100,000 | (100,000) |
| Allowance for bad debts................. | 45,300 | 40,000 | 5,300 |
| Accumulated depreciation — building...... | 407,000 | 400,000 | 7,000 |
| Accumulated depreciation — machinery.... | 141,000 | 130,000 | 11,000 |
| Premium on bonds payable.............. | — | 1,600 | (1,600) |
| Capital stock — no par................. | 1,301,200 | 1,453,200 | (152,000) |
| Paid-in capital......................... | 14,000 | — | 14,000 |
| Reserve for plant expansion............. | 10,000 | — | 10,000 |
| Retained earnings...................... | 10,000 | (225,000) | 235,000 |
| | $2,506,780 | $2,259,800 | $ 246,980 |

#### STATEMENT OF RETAINED EARNINGS

| December 31, 1957 | Balance (deficit)............................. | $(225,000) |
|---|---|---|
| March 31, 1958 | Profit for first quarter of 1958................. | 25,000 |
| April 1, 1958 | Transfer from capital surplus................. | 200,000 |
| | Balance.................................... | $  —0— |
| December 31, 1958 | Profit for last three quarters of 1958............ | 80,000 |
| | Dividend declared — payable January 20, 1959.... | (60,000) |
| | Reserve for plant expansion.................... | (10,000) |
| | Balance.................................... | $  10,000 |

Your working papers contain the following information:

(1) On April 1, 1958 the existing deficit was written off against capital surplus created by reducing the stated value of the no-par stock.

(2) On November 1, 1958, 8,000 shares of no-par stock were sold for $62,000. The board of directors voted to regard $6 per share as stated capital.

(3) A patent was purchased for $16,000.

(4) Machinery was purchased for $4,600 and installed in December 1958. A check for this amount was sent to the vendor in January 1959.

(5) During the year machinery which had a cost basis of $8,000 and on which there was accumulated depreciation of $5,000 was sold for $1,000. No other fixed assets were sold during the year.

(6) The 6%, 20-year bonds were dated and issued on January 2, 1946. Interest was payable on June 30 and December 31. They were sold originally at 104. These bonds were retired at 101 and accrued interest on March 31, 1958.

(7) The 4%, 40-year bonds were dated January 1, 1958 and were sold on March 31, at 97 and accrued interest. Interest is payable semiannually on June 30 and December 31. Expense of issuance was $1,020.

(8) The Delmar Corporation acquired 80% control in Subsidiary Co. on January 2, 1958 for $100,000. The income statement of Subsidiary Co. for 1958 shows a net income of $7,500.

(9) Extraordinary repairs to buildings of $7,000 were charged to accumulated depreciation — building.

*Instructions:* From the above information prepare a statement accounting for the decrease in net working capital (Statement of Source and Application of Funds) and a schedule of working capital changes. A worksheet is not necessary, but the principal computations should be supported by schedules or skeleton ledger accounts. (A.I.C.P.A. adapted)

**28-11.** The Reynold Corporation's condensed statements of income for the fiscal year 1958 and of financial position at the beginning and end of the fiscal year, together with other pertinent data, are reproduced on this and the following page.

The board of directors of the corporation recognizes that the readers of the corporation's report to stockholders may be puzzled by the fact

### THE REYNOLD CORPORATION
#### INCOME STATEMENT
#### YEAR ENDED DECEMBER 31, 1958

| | | |
|---|---:|---:|
| Income: | | |
| Gross operating income............................ | | $2,410,655 |
| Nonoperating income, including dividends and interest.... | | 21,708 |
| Total income.................................. | | $2,432,363 |
| Deductions: | | |
| Operating charges: | | |
| Materials and supplies used.......................... | $870,531 | |
| Wages and salaries................................ | 906,387 | |
| Provision for depreciation charged to operations.......... | 114,079 | |
| Taxes, other than federal income..................... | 26,221 | |
| Other operating charges............................ | 33,762 | |
| Interest charges.................................... | 1,297 | |
| Loss on investments................................ | 6,016 | |
| Estimated federal income tax........................ | 284,442 | 2,242,735 |
| Net income (after taxes)............................... | | $ 189,628 |

## THE REYNOLD CORPORATION
### COMPARATIVE STATEMENT OF FINANCIAL POSITION
### DECEMBER 31, 1957 AND 1958

| | 1958 | 1957 | INCREASE OR DECREASE* |
|---|---|---|---|
| **Current assets:** | | | |
| Cash.................................... | $ 215,221 | $ 225,351 | $ 10,130* |
| Marketable securities, at cost.............. | 180,767 | 251,388 | 70,621* |
| Receivables — trade, less estimated uncollectibles................................. | 266,559 | 195,991 | 70,568 |
| Inventories (at cost)...................... | 322,438 | 359,175 | 36,737* |
| Prepaid operating expenses............... | 15,209 | 17,894 | 2,685* |
| Total current assets...................... | $1,000,194 | $1,049,799 | |
| | | | |
| **Less: Current liabilities:** | | | |
| Accounts and notes payable — trade........ | $ 108,623 | $ 254,181 | 145,558* |
| Accrued wages and salaries............... | 12,602 | 11,495 | 1,107 |
| Accrued estimated taxes.................. | 295,580 | 299,466 | 3,886* |
| Dividends payable....................... | 23,726 | 25,591 | 1,865* |
| Accrued interest payable................. | 750 | 296 | 454 |
| Other accrued operating expenses.......... | 12,622 | 14,942 | 2,320* |
| Total current liabilities................... | $ 453,903 | $ 605,971 | |
| | | | |
| Working capital.......................... | $ 546,291 | $ 443,828 | |
| Property, plant, and equipment — less amount of cost charged to operations to date........ | 1,356,132 | 1,200,816 | 155,316 |
| | | | |
| Total assets, less current liabilities........... | $1,902,423 | $1,644,644 | |
| Deduct: Long-term bank loans.............. | 50,000 | — | 50,000 |
| Net assets............................... | $1,852,423 | $1,644,644 | $207,779 |
| | | | |
| **Stockholders' Equity:** | | | |
| Preferred stock, 6% cumulative, par value $100 (2,602 shares).................... | $ 260,200 | $ 265,200 | $ 5,000* |
| Common stock — par value $100 (12,724 shares)............................... | 1,272,400 | 1,092,300 | 180,100 |
| Amount paid in — in excess of par value.... | 61,524 | 42,043 | 19,481 |
| Retained earnings....................... | 258,299 | 245,101 | 13,198 |
| Total................................. | $1,852,423 | $1,644,644 | $207,779 |

that, despite a substantial "net income after taxes," the cash balance decreased and the corporation resorted to some long-term borrowing. Accordingly, the directors have requested that you prepare a statement that will reveal clearly the flow of cash into and out of The Reynold Corporation during the past fiscal year and that will indicate why operations alone did not provide sufficient cash for the corporation's needs.

You have decided that the statement should be constructed to show the cash disbursements other than for operations, the net cash provided by operations, the amount by which operations failed to provide sufficient cash, and the manner in which this deficiency was met.

The following additional information is available:

(1) During the year, marketable securities were purchased at a cost of $24,692.

(2) The "estimated uncollectible receivables" increased $11,448, despite the write-off of $2,605 of bad accounts. During the year, an account of $2,000, written off in a prior year, was recovered; the credit was made to Recovery of Bad Debts, which was netted against "other operating charges" in the income statement.

(3) During the year, 50 shares of preferred stock were reacquired by purchase at a 9% premium. These shares were canceled, at which time the excess of the purchase price over the average amount originally contributed for these shares ($105 per share) was debited to Retained Earnings.

(4) The only entries in the retained earnings account for the year were for net income, dividend declaration, and cancellation of preferred stock.

(5) There were no sales or retirements of fixed assets during the year.

*Instructions:* Prepare the "Cash Flow" statement (statement of source and application of cash) supported by a schedule showing the conversion of the income statement to a cash basis, item by item. This schedule should show the amount of cash produced or used as a result of each item on the statement. Use the following column headings in this schedule:

| Per Income Statement | Adjustments to Cash Basis | | Cash Result |
|---|---|---|---|
| | Add | Deduct | |

(A.I.C.P.A. adapted)

# APPENDIX

Statements for several well-known representative corporations are found on the pages that follow. Company statements of financial condition and operations together with accompanying statement notes as presented in the corporate annual reports are reproduced. These statements illustrate practical applications of contemporary accounting standards and concepts.

A summary is presented preceding each set of statements pointing out matters of particular interest in viewing the statements. The forms, procedures, and items that are pointed out are not necessarily examples of good reporting or unsatisfactory reporting; rather, these are matters of interest that call for evaluation in terms of the accounting framework as a whole as developed in the text.

Reference to the statements and statement items may be made throughout the course as various phases of statement structure, form, and content are considered.

Statements are included for the following companies:

(1) Douglas Aircraft Company, Inc.
(2) The Flintkote Company
(3) Armco Steel Corporation
(4) American Telephone and Telegraph Company
(5) The Oliver Corporation
(6) Chrysler Corporation
(7) Royal McBee Corporation

## DOUGLAS AIRCRAFT COMPANY, INC.

The following features are of interest in viewing the financial statements and the accompanying notes taken from the annual report of Douglas Aircraft Company, Inc.

Two financial statements are presented under the headings Statement of Income and Retained Earnings and Statement of Financial Position. Statements are presented in comparative form. The annual report also includes a summary headed Ten Year Comparative Financial Data in which income statement and balance sheet data for the years 1948 through 1957 are presented in condensed form together with ratios and measurements that are significant in the interpretation of such data. This summary has been reproduced and follows the financial statements for the current period.

**Statement of Income and Retained Earnings.** Income data are presented in single-step form except for income taxes, which are recognized as a special subtraction item. The retained earnings balance as of the beginning of the year is added to net income for the year and the resulting total is reduced by the dividends for the year in arriving at retained earnings at the end of the year.

**Statement of Financial Position.** The balance sheet is prepared in the conventional account form. A footnote on the balance sheet indicates that a change in the classification of prepaid items was made in 1957 in recognition of the present-day accounting concept of working capital, such items now being recognized as current assets. Observe the presentation of long-term debt and the reference there to convertible features of the debenture issue, and the presentation of capital stock and the reference there to shares reserved for the exercise of debenture conversion privileges. Note at the bottom of the statement the prominent reference to contingent liabilities and commitments.

**Notes to Financial Statements.** The following matters are described in the notes accompanying financial statements: inventories, their composition and valuation; income taxes, including reference to possible deficiencies that may be asserted by the government and the effect of such possible deficiencies upon financial position; restrictions on the use of retained earnings resulting from the indenture under which bonds were issued; renegotiation proceedings and the position of the government and the company on these matters, including the effects of possible refunds upon financial position; commitments made by the company for improvements to its properties and facilities; future costs to emerge from the company's pension plans including the cost to fund the past service cost. The auditors' report is not reproduced (Ernst & Ernst, Certified Public Accountants).

## STATEMENT OF INCOME AND RETAINED EARNINGS

| | Years ended November 30th | |
| --- | --- | --- |
| | **1957** | **1956** |
| Net sales, including fees accrued and amounts reimbursable under cost-plus-a-fixed-fee contracts .............. | $1,091,366,415 | $1,073,515,406 |
| Other income ........................................ | 1,273,672 | 1,166,151 |
| | $1,092,640,087 | $1,074,681,557 |
| Costs and expenses (1): | | |
| Manufacturing costs (2) ......................... | $ 918,895,804 | $ 938,974,543 |
| Selling, administrative, and general expenses ........ | 26,882,371 | 20,084,696 |
| California franchise tax ......................... | 2,300,000 | 2,044,000 |
| Property taxes on inventories .................... | 5,406,881 | 3,573,868 |
| Contribution to employes' pension trusts ........... | 14,500,000 | 13,300,000 |
| Experimental costs .............................. | 54,669,390 | 24,377,479 |
| Interest on long-term debt ...................... | 889,700 | — |
| Other interest expense .......................... | 1,439,693 | 443,523 |
| Renegotiation refund, net—Note D ................ | 1,320,066 | — |
| Other deductions ............................... | 105,130 | 158,442 |
| | $1,026,409,035 | $1,002,956,551 |
| INCOME BEFORE TAXES THEREON.............. | $ 66,231,052 | $ 71,725,006 |
| Taxes on income—estimated: | | |
| Federal (3) ..................................... | $ 35,450,000 | $ 38,350,000 |
| State and other ................................. | 115,800 | 172,702 |
| | $ 35,565,800 | $ 38,522,702 |
| NET INCOME FOR THE YEAR................... | $ 30,665,252 | $ 33,202,304 |
| Retained earnings at beginning of year ................ | 121,167,776 | 102,787,332 |
| | $ 151,833,028 | $ 135,989,636 |
| Cash dividends paid ($4 a share in each year) .......... | 14,822,760 | 14,821,860 |
| Retained earnings at end of year ..................... | $ 137,010,268 | $ 121,167,776 |

(1) Provision for depreciation and amortization of property, plant, and equipment amounted to $10,041,415 for 1957; $7,759,591 for 1956.

(2) Manufacturing costs for 1957 includes $6,422,059 inventory write-down representing costs incurred on DC-8 jet transports in process of manufacture at November 30, 1957, in excess of proportionate amount of proceeds to be realized under related sales contracts.

(3) The amount for federal taxes on income for fiscal year 1956 includes $1,000,000 provision for additional taxes on income of prior years.

*See notes to financial statements*

1957

## STATEMENT OF FINANCIAL POSITION

As of November 30th

| ASSETS | 1957 | 1956 |
|---|---|---|
| **CURRENT ASSETS** | | |
| Cash . . . . . . . . . . . . . . . . . . . . . . . . . . . . . . . . . . . . . . . . . . | $ 32,577,447 | $ 57,797,320 |
| U. S. Treasury Bills . . . . . . . . . . . . . . . . . . . . . . . . . . . . | – | 14,960,792 |
| Trade accounts receivable from U. S. Government . . | 25,737,239 | 19,569,920 |
| Other trade accounts receivable . . . . . . . . . . . . . . . . | 15,017,858 | 15,047,788 |
| Unreimbursed costs and fees under cost-plus-a-fixed-fee contracts, less $50,000 allowance for adjustments . . . . . . . . . . . . . . . . . . . . . . . . . . | 82,870,135 | 77,044,697 |
| Inventories of fixed-price contracts in process, materials, etc., less advance and progress payments received—Note A . . . . . . . . . . . . . . . . . . . . . . . | 160,132,917 | 106,481,029 |
| Taxes, insurance, and other prepaid expenses . . . . . . | 15,275,608 | 10,814,188 |
| **TOTAL CURRENT ASSETS** . . . . . . . . . . . . . . . . . . . . | **$331,611,204** | **$301,715,734*** |
| | | |
| **PROPERTY, PLANT, AND EQUIPMENT** | | |
| Land (1957—$2,813,216; 1956—$1,439,102) and buildings, equipment, etc.—at cost less accumulated allowances (1957—$40,275,177; 1956—$33,043,105) for depreciation and amortization | 71,028,937 | 52,787,240 |
| | | |
| **OTHER ASSETS** | | |
| Sundry accounts receivable, deposits, etc. . . . . . . . . . . | 4,572,737 | 2,003,376* |
| | **$407,212,878** | **$356,506,350** |

*Prepaid expenses ($10,814,188) and miscellaneous items ($103,085) shown as deferred charges in the 1956 Annual Report are included as current assets and other assets, respectively. This change has been made in recognition of present-day accounting concept of working capital.

As of November 30th

| LIABILITIES AND STOCKHOLDERS' EQUITY | 1957 | 1956 |
|---|---|---|
| **CURRENT LIABILITIES** | | |
| Notes payable to banks — unsecured .............. | $ 55,000,000 | $ — |
| Accounts payable and accrued interest ........... | 56,716,646 | 55,634,871 |
| Estimated costs to be incurred on delivered products | 162,464 | 577,578 |
| Contribution to employes' pension trusts .......... | 14,500,000 | 10,299,000 |
| Wages and salaries payable ..................... | 17,324,600 | 17,246,262 |
| Pay roll deductions for bond purchases and taxes... | 5,780,196 | 6,060,686 |
| Taxes, other than federal taxes on income ........ | 10,681,769 | 8,219,658 |
| Estimated refunds under target-price contracts .... | 1,588,487 | 9,051,801 |
| Advance payments received in excess of expenditures on related fixed-price contracts .............. | 19,607,714 | 61,562,077 |
| Federal taxes on income — estimated — Note B ..... | 29,114,774 | 34,860,681 |
| **TOTAL CURRENT LIABILITIES** ................ | **$210,476,650** | **$203,512,614** |
| **LONG-TERM DEBT** | | |
| 4% Convertible Subordinated Debentures, due February 1, 1977 (annual sinking fund requirement beginning February 1, 1967 — $2,100,000 less credit for Debentures repurchased) convertible into Capital Stock at $95 a share............. | $ 27,900,000 | $ — |
| **STOCKHOLDERS' EQUITY** | | |
| Capital Stock — no par value; 4,000,000 shares authorized; 3,705,690 shares outstanding; 293,684 shares reserved for conversion of 4% Convertible Subordinated Debentures......... | $ 30,880,750 | $ 30,880,750 |
| Additional capital paid in ...................... | 945,210 | 945,210 |
| Retained earnings — Note C .................... | 137,010,268 | 121,167,776 |
| **TOTAL STOCKHOLDERS' EQUITY**............. | **$168,836,228** | **$152,993,736** |
| **CONTINGENT LIABILITIES AND COMMITMENTS** See Notes D, E, and F | | |
| | **$407,212,878** | **$356,506,350** |

*See notes to financial statements*

# 1957  TEN YEAR COMPARATIVE FINANCIAL DATA

| | 1957 | 1956 | 1955 | 1954 |
|---|---|---|---|---|
| **Net Sales** | $1,091,366,415 | $1,073,515,406 | $ 867,504,228 | $ 915,216,705 |
| Other Income | 1,273,672 | 1,166,151 | 447,709 | 191,435 |
| **Total Income** | $1,092,640,087 | $1,074,681,557 | $ 867,951,937 | $ 915,408,140 |
| Costs and Expenses | 1,026,409,035 | 1,002,956,551 | 809,529,631 | 835,416,898 |
| **Earnings Before Taxes on Income** | $ 66,231,052 | $ 71,725,006 | $ 58,422,306 | $ 79,991,242 |
| Provision for Taxes | 35,565,800 | 38,522,702 | 30,207,044 | 43,834,381 |
| **Net Earnings** | $ 30,665,252 | $ 33,202,304 | $ 28,215,262 | $ 36,156,861 |
| **Percent of Net Sales** | | | | |
| Earnings before Taxes | 6.07% | 6.68% | 6.73% | 8.74% |
| Earnings after Taxes | 2.81 | 3.09 | 3.25 | 3.95 |
| **Earnings per Share*** | $8.28 | $8.96 | $7.65 | $9.80 |
| **Dividends per Share*** | 4.00 | 4.00 | 4.00 | 4.33 |
| **Cash and U. S. Government Securities** | $ 32,577,447 | $ 72,758,112 | $ 81,619,452 | $ 57,631,141 |
| **Receivables and Other Current Assets†** | 138,900,840 | 122,476,593 | 86,592,879 | 86,892,881 |
| **Inventories—Net** | 160,132,917 | 106,481,029 | 75,859,931 | 73,130,697 |
| **Total Current Assets†** | $ 331,611,204 | $ 301,715,734 | $ 244,072,262 | $ 217,654,719 |
| Deduct: Notes Payable to Banks | 55,000,000 | –– | –– | –– |
| Other Current Liabilities | 155,476,650 | 203,512,614 | 151,003,755 | 137,605,622 |
| **Working Capital†** | $ 121,134,554 | $ 98,203,120 | $ 93,068,507 | $ 80,049,097 |
| **Properties—Land** | $ 2,813,216 | $ 1,689,852 | $ 1,243,099 | $ 822,291 |
| Buildings | 39,368,088 | 32,728,897 | 21,409,142 | 18,630,072 |
| Equipment | 69,122,810 | 51,411,596 | 44,613,331 | 42,052,284 |
| Total | $ 111,304,114 | $ 85,830,345 | $ 67,265,572 | $ 61,504,647 |
| Less: Depreciation and Amortization | 40,275,177 | 33,043,105 | 27,979,687 | 23,018,703 |
| **Net Properties** | $ 71,028,937 | $ 52,787,240 | $ 39,285,885 | $ 38,485,944 |
| Other Assets | 4,572,737 | 2,003,376 | 1,992,875 | 2,356,124 |
| **Total** | $ 196,736,228 | $ 152,993,736 | $ 134,347,267 | $ 120,891,165 |
| Less: Long-Term Debt | 27,900,000 | –– | –– | –– |
| **Net Assets** | $ 168,836,228 | $ 152,993,736 | $ 134,347,267 | $ 120,891,165 |
| Number of Shares of Stock* | 3,705,690 | 3,705,690 | 3,689,790 | 3,689,790 |
| Book Value per Share* | $45.56 | $41.29 | $36.41 | $32.76 |
| Number of Stockholders of Record | 17,167 | 15,602 | 14,126 | 10,673 |
| Backlog at year end | $1,803,620,000 | $2,209,049,000 | $2,065,000,000 | $2,035,000,000 |
| Payrolls | 463,228,000 | 442,192,000 | 393,329,000 | 339,973,000 |
| Employes at year end | 76,400 | 80,400 | 77,600 | 71,900 |

† Amounts heretofore shown for 1948 to 1956, inclusive, were revised to include

* Adjusted for stock-splits in 1951, 1954, and 1955.

| 1953 | 1952 | 1951 | 1950 | 1949 | 1948 |
|---|---|---|---|---|---|
| $ 874,515,463<br>352,451 | $ 522,619,409<br>1,077,388 | $ 225,173,226<br>1,002,187 | $ 129,892,551<br>1,632,358 | $ 117,421,954<br>2,001,264 | $ 118,581,847<br>1,506,009 |
| $ 874,867,914<br>813,333,547 | $ 523,696,797<br>490,165,915 | $ 226,175,413<br>207,578,231 | $ 131,524,909<br>118,310,469 | $ 119,423,218<br>108,735,518 | $ 120,087,856<br>108,995,418 |
| $ 61,534,367<br>42,948,062 | $ 33,530,882<br>22,738,597 | $ 18,597,182<br>11,684,353 | $ 13,214,440<br>6,000,000 | $ 10,687,700<br>5,171,000 | $ 11,092,438<br>5,263,232 |
| $ 18,586,305 | $ 10,792,285 | $ 6,912,829 | $ 7,214,440 | $ 5,516,700 | $ 5,829,206 |
| 7.04%<br>·2.13<br>$5.15<br>2.17 | 6.42%<br>2.07<br>$3.00<br>1.25 | 8.26%<br>3.07<br>$1.92<br>1.17 | 10.17%<br>5.55<br>$2.00<br>1.04 | 9.10%<br>4.70<br>$1.53<br>1.54 | 9.35%<br>4.92<br>$1.62<br>.83 |
| $ 55,688,411<br>105,570,482<br>78,344,518 | $ 35,355,803<br>81,981,945<br>98,951,503 | $ 22,924,409<br>44,216,027<br>77,528,212 | $ 20,515,628<br>25,673,983<br>40,167,976 | $ 37,503,578<br>22,362,148<br>23,339,019 | $ 35,499,150<br>28,587,141<br>20,835,083 |
| $ 239,603,411<br>35,000,000<br>139,912,091 | $ 216,289,251<br>52,500,000<br>108,254,449 | $ 144,668,648<br>30,000,000<br>60,427,137 | $ 86,357,587<br><br>25,543,923 | $ 83,204,745<br><br>23,156,645 | $ 84,921,374<br><br>24,089,931 |
| $ 64,691,320<br>$ 797,037<br>16,409,650<br>34,580,946 | $ 55,534,802<br>$ 771,000<br>15,660,743<br>30,791,430 | $ 54,241,511<br>$ 770,383<br>14,525,330<br>24,642,794 | $ 60,813,664<br>$ 730,711<br>12,170,247<br>16,736,788 | $ 60,048,100<br>$ 728,220<br>12,110,020<br>15,017,710 | $ 60,831,443<br>$ 739,720<br>12,052,987<br>14,663,031 |
| $ 51,787,633<br>19,443,742 | $ 47,223,173<br>16,193,634 | $ 39,938,507<br>13,594,170 | $ 29,637,746<br>12,261,753 | $ 27,855,950<br>10,989,312 | $ 27,455,738<br>10,774,783 |
| $ 32,343,891<br>1,568,425 | $ 31,029,539<br>1,135,465 | $ 26,344,337<br>821,673 | $ 17,375,993<br>505,035 | $ 16,866,638<br>799,082 | $ 16,680,955<br>875,408 |
| $ 98,603,636<br>— | $ 87,699,806<br>— | $ 81,407,521<br>— | $ 78,694,692<br>— | $ 77,713,820<br>3,333,568 | $ 78,387,806<br>4,049,254 |
| $ 98,603,636 | $ 87,699,806 | $ 81,407,521 | $ 78,694,692 | $ 74,380,252 | $ 74,338,552 |
| 3,607,656<br>$27.33<br>8,659 | 3,600,000<br>$24.36<br>8,486 | 3,600,000<br>$22.61<br>8,608 | 3,600,000<br>$21.86<br>8,466 | 3,600,000<br>$20.66<br>8,434 | 3,600,000<br>$20.65<br>8,478 |
| $2,214,000,000<br>292,443,000<br>66,500 | $1,840,000,000<br>244,120,000<br>62,200 | $1,635,000,000<br>142,100,000<br>44,000 | $ 656,300,000<br>81,800,000<br>25,500 | $ 275,500,000<br>66,200,000<br>18,900 | $ 233,000,000<br>52,900,000<br>15,400 |

taxes, insurance, and other prepaid expenses to conform with treatment accorded such items in 1957.

# NOTES TO FINANCIAL STATEMENTS

## NOTE A-INVENTORIES

Inventories included items to which the U. S. Government held title by reason of contract provisions. Amounts were determined on the basis of lower of cost (generally first-in, first-out method) or market, and comprised the following classifications:

|  | 1957 | 1956 |
|---|---|---|
| Fixed-price contracts, orders, etc. in process............... | $291,348,611 | $238,712,545 |
| Materials, spare parts, etc................................. | 58,596,173 | 50,218,154 |
| Advances under material purchase agreements............. | 8,421,326 | 10,471,205 |
|  | $358,366,110 | $299,401,904 |
| Less advance and progress payments received............... | 198,233,193 | 192,920,875 |
|  | $160,132,917 | $106,481,029 |

## NOTE B-INCOME TAXES

Federal tax returns of the Company for fiscal years 1951, 1952, and 1953 have been under examination by the Internal Revenue Service. The revenue agent's report covering those years has not been received; however, preliminary discussions indicate that a deficiency will be asserted. The Company contends that there is no deficiency. If, however, one is asserted and sustained, there would be certain offsetting adjustments in tax liabilities for subsequent years not yet examined by the Internal Revenue Service. The Company believes that the net effect on its reported financial position which would result from such a deficiency would not be material.

## NOTE C-RESTRICTION ON USE OF RETAINED EARNINGS

The Indenture under which the Debentures were issued prohibits the payments of cash dividends on Capital Stock or the purchase of such stock by the Company, if upon giving effect thereto the aggregate amount expended for such purposes subsequent to November 30, 1956, shall exceed the sum of (a) the accumulated earnings of the Company earned subsequent to November 30, 1956, (b) the net proceeds of the sale after November 30, 1956, of stock of the Company, (c) the net proceeds of the sale after November 30, 1956, of any indebtedness (including the Debentures) which has been converted into shares of stock of the Company subsequent to that date, and (d) the sum of $15,000,000. At November 30, 1957, $106,167,776 of retained earnings were so restricted.

## NOTE D-RENEGOTIATION

Renegotiation proceedings for the fiscal year 1953 were concluded in 1957 by payment, under protest, of a unilateral net assessment of $1,320,066 shown as a charge against income for the fiscal year 1957. The Company contends that it realized no excessive profits and has filed a petition in the Tax Court of the United States for refund of the payment together with interest thereon.

The Company was recently notified by the Regional Renegotiation Board in Los Angeles that it proposes to recommend to the Renegotiation Board in Washington that the Company's profits for the fiscal year 1954, be considered excessive in the gross amount of $6,000,000. If the Renegotiation Board in Washington were to adopt this recommendation, it would require a net refund to the Government by the Company, after giving effect to adjustments for applicable state and federal income and excess profits taxes, of approximately $2,027,000. The Company is of the opinion that it has not earned excessive profits for the year ended November 30, 1954, or for any following year. Accordingly, no provision for renegotiation refunds for the fiscal year 1954 and subsequent has been made in the financial statements. There is no assurance, however, that such refunds will not ultimately be required by the Government, but it is believed that such refunds, if any, would not materially affect the accompanying financial statements.

## NOTE E-COMMITMENTS

The Company has authorized expenditures of approximately $12,500,000 (a substantial portion of which was committed for at November 30, 1957) in connection with additions and improvements to its properties and facilities.

## NOTE F-PENSION PLANS

The future annual costs of the Company's pension plans are indeterminate because they will be dependent upon future pay rolls. On the basis of present employment and pay levels the annual charge against income for the continuance of the plans would be approximately $9,915,600 with respect to current services and $4,584,400 (for 10 years after November 30, 1957) with respect to the past service cost of the plans.

It is estimated that approximately $39,330,000 would be required to fund the past service cost of the plans at November 30, 1957.

## THE FLINTKOTE COMPANY

The following features are of interest in viewing the financial statements and the accompanying notes taken from the 1957 annual report of the Flintkote Company.

Three financial statements for the year are presented under the headings Comparative Consolidated Balance Sheet, Comparative Statement of Consolidated Income, and Comparative Statement of Consolidated Earned Surplus. Statements are prepared in comparative form. Financial statements are accompanied by condensed consolidated statements for a ten-year period that have not been reproduced here.

**Comparative Consolidated Balance Sheet.** The balance sheet is prepared in the conventional account form. Valuation procedures are explained in reporting assets. Full data are provided relative to liability and capital items either by means of remarks on the statement or special accompanying notes. The cost of preferred stock purchased for retirement is reported as a subtraction from the sum of capital stock and earned surplus.

**Comparative Statement of Consolidated Income.** The income statement is prepared in multiple-step form with designations for (1) gross profit on sales, (2) income before federal and foreign taxes on income, (3) net income for the year before special credit, and (4) net income and special credit.

**Comparative Statement of Consolidated Earned Surplus.** The comparative earned surplus balances that are reported on the balance sheet are reconciled on the statement of earned surplus. Earned surplus increases are reported as a result of (1) net income (and special credits) and (2) the retirement of stock at less than the amount originally paid in; earned surplus decreases are reported as a result of (1) cash dividends, (2) stock dividends, and (3) an exchange of stock upon the absorption of another company through merger.

**Notes to Financial Statements.** Notes to financial statements offer a full reporting and analysis of a number of significant aspects of company position and progress: (1), details of a merger completed in 1957 are explained; (2) and (3), terms of the debenture and promissory note obligations are stated together with limitations on stock repurchase and earnings distributions that are provided in these contracts; (4) and (5), liquidation, redemption, and retirement provisions found in preferred issues are stated; (6), full data concerning stock option plans for officers and employees are provided; (7), commitments in the form of authorized additions to plant and property are described.

# The Flintkote Company and its Consolidated Subsidiaries

At December 31,

| | 1957 | 1956 | Increases Decreases* |
|---|---|---|---|
| **Assets** Cash in banks and on hand . . . . . . . . . . . . | $ 7,210,164.45 | $ 6,981,881.30 | $ 228,283.15 |
| United States and British Government securities at cost . . . | 2,174,748.60 | 2,640,825.42 | 466,076.82* |
| Short-term commercial paper at cost . . . . . . . . . | 299,945.01 | — | 299,945.01 |
| | 2,474,693.61 | 2,640,825.42 | 166,131.81* |
| Accounts and notes receivable: | | | |
| Customers, less allowance for doubtful items, 1957, $566,784; | | | |
| 1956, $527,650 . . . . . . . . . . . . . . | 10,494,325.54 | 10,716,306.04 | 221,980.50* |
| Other . . . . . . . . . . . . . . . . . . | 415,246.78 | 453,409.88 | 38,163.10* |
| | 10,909,572.32 | 11,169,715.92 | 260,143.60* |
| Inventories, at the lower of average cost or market: | | | |
| Finished goods . . . . . . . . . . . . . . | 8,001,465.81 | 6,796,857.03 | 1,204,608.78 |
| Raw materials, felt and operating supplies . . . . . . . | 6,927,009.80 | 6,867,186.67 | 59,823.13 |
| | 14,928,475.61 | 13,664,043.70 | 1,264,431.91 |
| Total current assets . . . . . . . . . . . . | 35,522,905.99 | 34,456,466.34 | 1,066,439.65 |
| | | | |
| Property, plant and equipment, at cost, less allowance for depreciation and depletion, 1957, $37,658,994; 1956, $34,777,645 | 58,415,378.56 | 50,069,724.49 | 8,345,654.07 |
| Amount receivable on claims for refund of federal income taxes (Note 1) . . . . . . . . . . . . . . . . . . | 1,000,000.00 | — | 1,000,000.00 |
| Receivable under stock option agreements, not current (Note 6) . | 216,958.35 | — | 216,958.35 |
| Investments at cost . . . . . . . . . . . . . . | 24,818.97 | 266,754.87 | 241,935.90* |
| Patents, other rights and good will, at December 31, 1932 ($1), plus cost of good will subsequently acquired . . . . . | 2,878,108.19 | 2,878,108.19 | — |
| Prepaid and deferred expenses . . . . . . . . . . . | 1,998,892.54 | 1,837,983.01 | 160,909.53 |
| | $100,057,062.60 | $89,509,036.90 | $10,548,025.70 |

The notes on page 14 are an integral part of the

# Comparative Consolidated Balance Sheet

1957 and 1956

| | 1957 | 1956 | Increases Decreases* | |
|---|---|---|---|---|
| Accounts payable and accrued expenses . . . . . . . . | $ 5,997,177.72 | $ 5,664,245.00 | $ 332,932.72 | **Liabilities** |
| Promissory note, 3%, prepayment due March 15 (Note 3) . . | 300,000.00 | 300,000.00 | — | |
| Promissory notes of subsidiary companies . . . . . . . . | 482,856.35 | 643,612.35 | 160,756.00* | |
| Accrued federal, state and other taxes . . . . . . . . | 3,444,354.91 | 5,432,473.60 | 1,988,118.69* | |
| Reserves for self-insurance and product guarantees . . . . | 532,377.19 | 627,090.45 | 94,713.26* | |
| Total current liabilities . . . . . . . . . | 10,756,766.17 | 12,667,421.40 | 1,910,655.23* | |
| | | | | |
| Sinking fund debentures, 4⅜%, due April 1, 1977 (Note 2) . . | 10,000,000.00 | — | 10,000,000.00 | |
| Promissory note, 3%, maturing March 15, 1968 (Note 3) . . . | 2,850,000.00 | 3,150,000.00 | 300,000.00* | |
| Total liabilities . . . . . . . . . . | $ 23,606,766.17 | $15,817,421.40 | $ 7,789,344.77 | |

| | 1957 | 1956 | Increases Decreases* | |
|---|---|---|---|---|
| Capital stock: | | | | **Capital** |
| $4 cumulative preferred stock without par value (Note 4): | | | | |
| Authorized and issued: 1957, 68,060 shares; 1956, 75,870 | | | | |
| shares . . . . . . . . . . . . . . . . . . | $ 7,218,613.75 | $ 8,046,961.87 | $ 828,348.12* | |
| 4½% convertible second preferred stock, par value $100 per | | | | |
| share (Note 5): | | | | |
| Authorized and issued: 1957, 73,000 shares . . . . . | 7,300,000.00 | 7,300,000.00 | — | |
| Common stock, $5 par value (Note 6): | | | | |
| Authorized 5,000,000 shares; of which 153,300 shares are | | | | |
| reserved for exchange for second convertible preferred | | | | |
| stock; issued and outstanding: 1957, 1,775,672 shares; | | | | |
| 1956, 1,679,158 shares; stated at . . . . . . . | 33,343,474.72 | 29,836,764.66 | 3,506,710.06 | |
| Issuable under stock option plan purchase contracts, 5,912 | | | | |
| shares . . . . . . . . . . . . . . . . . . | 222,591.35 | — | 222,591.35 | |
| | 48,084,679.82 | 45,183,726.53 | 2,900,953.29 | |
| | | | | |
| Earned surplus, statement annexed (Notes 2 and 3) . . . . . | 29,080,887.65 | 29,369,213.97 | 288,326.32* | |
| | 77,165,567.47 | 74,552,940.50 | 2,612,626.97 | |
| | | | | |
| Less: | | | | |
| Cost of $4 cumulative preferred stock purchased for retire- | | | | |
| ment (1957, 7,505 shares; 1956, 7,660 shares)(Note 4) | 715,271.04 | 749,726.86 | 34,455.82* | |
| Cost of 2,800 shares of common stock reacquired and held | | | | |
| in treasury . . . . . . . . . . . . . . . . | — | 111,598.14 | 111,598.14* | |
| | 715,271.04 | 861,325.00 | 146,053.96* | |
| | $ 76,450,296.43 | $73,691,615.50 | $ 2,758,680.93 | |
| | $100,057,062.60 | $89,509,036.90 | $10,548,025.70 | |

above comparative consolidated balance sheet.

# The Flintkote Company

## Comparative Statement of Consolidated Income

### For the Years Ended December 31, 1957 and 1956

| | 1957 | 1956 | Increases Decreases* |
|---|---|---|---|
| Net sales . . . . . . . . . . . . . . . . . . | $116,249,877.60 | $113,655,116.42 | $2,594,761.18 |
| Cost of goods sold . . . . . . . . . . . . . . | 89,026,467.05 | 86,156,251.15 | 2,870,215.90 |
| Gross profit on sales . . . . . . . . . . . | 27,223,410.55 | 27,498,865.27 | 275,454.72* |
| Selling, administrative and general expenses . . . . . . | 15,555,298.30 | 14,198,613.37 | 1,356,684.93 |
| | 11,668,112.25 | 13,300,251.90 | 1,632,139.65* |
| Other income: | | | |
| Profit on sales of investments . . . . . . . . . . | 85,000.00 | 547,462.05 | 462,462.05* |
| Cash discounts on purchases . . . . . . . . . . . | 261,004.47 | 263,284.09 | 2,279.62* |
| Commissions . . . . . . . . . . . . . . . | 186,272.32 | 203,477.72 | 17,205.40* |
| Interest and dividends . . . . . . . . . . . . . | 100,601.92 | 142,455.89 | 41,853.97* |
| Miscellaneous . . . . . . . . . . . . . . . . | 559,908.09 | 396,533.53 | 163,374.56 |
| | 1,192,786.80 | 1,553,213.28 | 360,426.48* |
| | 12,860,899.05 | 14,853,465.18 | 1,992,566.13* |
| Other charges: | | | |
| Cash discounts on sales . . . . . . . . . . . . . | 1,731,111.17 | 1,765,807.75 | 34,696.58* |
| Interest . . . . . . . . . . . . . . . . . . | 482,431.43 | 171,289.91 | 311,141.52 |
| Past service premium under Group Retirement Pension Plan | 253,815.48 | 145,341.30 | 108,474.18 |
| Loss or gain† from fluctuation in foreign exchange rates . | 28,172.53 | 98,222.13† | 126,394.66 |
| Miscellaneous . . . . . . . . . . . . . . . . | 470,725.90 | 300,870.43 | 169,855.47 |
| | 2,966,256.51 | 2,285,087.26 | 681,169.25 |
| Income before federal and foreign taxes on income . . | 9,894,642.54 | 12,568,377.92 | 2,673,735.38* |
| Federal and foreign taxes on income: | | | |
| United States . . . . . . . . . . . . . . . | 3,300,000.00 | 4,668,685.59 | 1,368,685.59* |
| Canada and United Kingdom . . . . . . . . . . . | 544,794.92 | 765,580.13 | 220,785.21* |
| | 3,844,794.92 | 5,434,265.72 | 1,589,470.80* |
| Net income for the year before special credit below . . | 6,049,847.62 | 7,134,112.20 | 1,084,264.58* |
| Refund of federal income taxes—years 1956-1952 (Note 1). . | 1,000,000.00 | | 1,000,000.00 |
| Net income and special credit . . . . . . . . . | $ 7,049,847.62 | $ 7,134,112.20 | $ 84,264.58* |
| Provision for depreciation and depletion included above . . . | $ 3,987,139.54 | $ 3,628,138.42 | $ 359,001.12 |

The notes on page 14 are an integral part of the above comparative statement of consolidated income.

## and its Consolidated Subsidiaries

## Comparative Statement of Consolidated Earned Surplus

For the Years Ended December 31, 1957 and 1956

|  | 1957 | 1956 | Increases Decreases* |
|---|---|---|---|
| Balance, January 1: |  |  |  |
| The Flintkote Company and subsidiaries consolidated . . . | $29,369,213.97 | $29,711,445.89 | $ 342,231.92* |
| Kosmos Portland Cement Company (Note 1) . . . . . . | — | 4,579,338.25 | 4,579,338.25* |
|  | 29,369,213.97 | 34,290,784.14 | 4,921,570.17* |
| Add: |  |  |  |
| Net income (and in 1957 special credit), as annexed . . | 7,049,847.62 | 7,134,112.20 | 84,264.58* |
| Excess of paid-in amount over cost of $4 cumulative |  |  |  |
| preferred stock retired . . . . . . . . . . | 64,770.86 | 6,002.83 | 58,768.03 |
|  | 36,483,832.45 | 41,430,899.17 | 4,947,066.72* |
| Deduct: |  |  |  |
| Cash dividends on: |  |  |  |
| $4 cumulative preferred stock ($4.00 per share) . . | 249,955.00 | 296,670.00 | 46,715.00* |
| 4½% convertible second preferred ($1.425 per share) | 104,025.00 | — | 104,025.00 |
| Common stock ($2.40 per share) . . . . . . | 3,821,392.80 | 3,318,070.20 | 503,322.60 |
| Kosmos Portland Cement Company—dividends on common stock paid prior to date of pooling of interests |  |  |  |
| (Note 1) . . . . . . . . . . . . . . . | 99,000.00 | 198,000.00 | 99,000.00* |
| Stock dividend on: |  |  |  |
| Common stock, 5% paid in common stock (84,556 shares, 1957; 70,827 shares, 1956) . . . . . . | 3,128,572.00 | 2,478,945.00 | 649,627.00 |
| Excess of par value of convertible second preferred stock and common stock of The Flintkote Company over par value of common stock of Kosmos Portland Cement Company received in exchange therefor |  |  |  |
| (Note 1) . . . . . . . . . . . . . . . | — | 5,770,000.00 | 5,770,000.00* |
|  | 7,402,944.80 | 12,061,685.20 | 4,658,740.40* |
| Balance, December 31 . . . . . . . . . . . . | $29,080,887.65 | $29,369,213.97 | $ 288,326.32* |

The notes on page 14 are an integral part of the above comparative statement of consolidated surplus.

## AUDITORS' REPORT

# NOTES TO FINANCIAL STATEMENTS

1. On August 22, 1957, the company acquired all of the outstanding shares of common stock of Kosmos Portland Cement Company in exchange for 73,000 shares of 4½% Convertible Second Preferred Stock and 189,000 shares of common stock of The Flintkote Company. For accounting purposes, this acquisition has been treated as a "pooling of interests" and, accordingly, the consolidated financial statements for the years 1957 and 1956 include the financial position and the results of operations of Kosmos Portland Cement Company for each of those years, as if such pooling had taken place as of January 1, 1956.

As a result of the recent U. S. Treasury Department Technical Information Release No. 62, involving depletion of brick, clay and cement rock deposits, Kosmos has filed claims for refund of federal income taxes for the years 1952-1956 which are reflected in the accompanying financial statements in 1957. The portion of such claims relating to 1956 amounts to $235,000.

2. The terms of the 4⅜% Sinking Fund Debentures provide that they may be redeemed at the option of the company, in whole or in part, at any time at premiums ranging from 6½% to no premium, depending on the year of redemption. Beginning with March 31, 1962, and each year, annually thereafter, to and including March 31, 1976, the company will pay to the trustee as a sinking fund a sum in cash sufficient to retire by redemption not less than $500,000, or if the company so elects, not to exceed $1,000,000 principal amount of the debentures at premiums ranging from .82% to no premium, depending on the year of redemption. The terms also restrict the purchase, redemption or retirement of shares of capital stock, and dividends or other distributions (other than dividends payable in shares of stock of the company). At December 31, 1957, approximately $22,800,000 of the consolidated earned surplus was free of such restriction.

3. The terms of the 3% promissory note maturing March 15, 1968 provide that on March 15 of each year through 1967 the company shall prepay $300,000 and may prepay without premium, an additional amount not to exceed $300,000. The company also may at any time prepay the balance of the note in whole or in part at premiums ranging from 2% to ⅛% depending on the period in which prepaid.

The terms also restrict the purchase, redemption or retirement of shares of the capital stock and dividends or other distributions other than in stock of the company, which terms are less restrictive than those described in Note 2.

4. The $4 cumulative preferred stock is entitled upon involuntary liquidation to $100 per share, and upon voluntary liquidation or redemption to $107 per share, plus in each case an amount equal to accrued dividends.

For each year the company must purchase for retirement or redeem 2,000 shares of the $4 cumulative preferred stock. At December 31, 1957 this requirement had been satisfied.

5. The 4½% convertible second preferred stock is redeemable after September 15, 1962, at $105 per share plus an amount equal to accrued dividends; each share is convertible at the option of the holder thereof into 2¹⁄₁₀ shares of common stock.

To the Board of Directors and Stockholders,
The Flintkote Company,
New York, N. Y.

We have examined the consolidated balance sheets of THE FLINTKOTE COMPANY and its CONSOLIDATED SUBSIDIARIES as of December 31, 1957 and 1956 and the related statements of income and surplus for the years then ended. Our examinations were made in accordance with generally accepted auditing standards, and accordingly included such tests of the accounting records and such other auditing procedures as we considered necessary in the circumstances.

In our opinion, the accompanying balance sheets (pages 10 & 11) and statements of income (page 12) and earned surplus (page 13) present fairly the consolidated financial position of The Flintkote Company and its Consolidated Subsidiaries at December 31, 1957 and 1956, and the results of their operations for the years then ended, in conformity with generally accepted accounting principles, applied on a consistent basis.

*Lybrand Ross Bros. & Montgomery*

New York, January 31, 1958

6. Under a stock option plan adopted in 1951 and amended in March, 1957, certain officers and employees were granted options to purchase common stock of the company. The changes in the number of shares issuable under outstanding options during the year were:

|  | Number of Shares of Common Stock |
|---|---|
| Issuable under outstanding options December 31, 1956 | 41,843 |
| Issuable under options granted during 1957 | 39,325 |
| Adjustments resulting from stock dividend paid December 16, 1957 | 3,439 |
|  | 84,607 |
| Less, Options exercised (at prices ranging from $26.28 to $42.39 per share): |  |
| Shares issued | 11,958 |
| Shares to be issued (options exercised under Section 6b of the plan) on completion of payments therefor, within ten years from the date on which the option was granted | 5,912 |
|  | 17,870 |
| Issuable under outstanding options December 31, 1957 | 66,737 |

The unoptioned shares available at the beginning and end of the year were 13 and 11,244, respectively.

The option prices are not less than 95% of the fair value of the stock at the time the option is granted. Such exercise prices of options granted under the plan have not changed, except as affected by normal operations of antidilution provisions.

7. The company and its subsidiaries at December 31, 1957 had authorized future additions to plant and property of which the estimated cost to complete is $5,000,000.

# ARMCO STEEL CORPORATION

The following features are of interest in viewing the financial statements and accompanying notes taken from the 1957 report of the Armco Steel Corporation.

Three financial statements for the year are presented under the headings Statement of Consolidated Income, Statement of Consolidated Financial Condition, and Statement of Shareholders' Equity. Statements are prepared in comparative form. Statements are accompanied by a summary of changes in working capital, which is reproduced here, and comparative consolidated income and financial condition statements for a ten-year period, which are not reproduced.

**Statement of Consolidated Income.** The statement of income lists revenues followed by costs and expenses including income taxes in arriving at "Net Income Before Extraordinary Credit." This balance is followed by the special gain on sale of investments less the income taxes related thereto in arriving at the "Net Income for the Year." Dividends are then subtracted from the net income balance in developing a "Net Income for the Year Retained in the Business."

**Statement of Consolidated Financial Condition.** The statement of financial condition is prepared in report form. Assets, liabilities and reserves, and share-holders' equity items are listed. An equity total is reported equal to the difference between the total assets and the total liabilities and reserves. Detailed support of inventories, investments, property, plant and equipment, long-term debt, and reserves is offered in the form of supplementary schedules which have not been reproduced.

**Statement of Shareholders' Equity.** The statement of shareholders' equity offers a full accounting of the changes for the year in capital balances composed of common stock, capital contributed in excess of par value of common stock, and income retained in the business. The statement summarizes the effects upon capital balances of net income as reported on the income statement, cash dividends, the sale of stock, the issue of stock under stock option plans, and the reacquisition and retirement of stock.

**Notes to Financial Statements.** Notes make reference to such matters as a merger consummated after the balance sheet date, another merger plan awaiting approval by stockholders, stock option plans, credit agreements with banks, restrictions upon earnings distributions under agreements with creditor groups, terms of agreements entered into with creditors of affiliated companies, and commitments for the purchase of property, plant, and equipment.

**Summary of Changes in Working Capital.** Sources and applications of funds are listed in detailed form in the Summary of Changes in Working Capital in accounting for the change in working capital for the year.

# ARMCO STEEL CORPORATION

## STATEMENT OF CONSOLIDATED INCOME

*For the years ended December 31, 1957 and 1956*

|  | 1957 | 1956 |
|---|---|---|
| **Revenues** | | |
| Sales, less discounts, returns and allowances | $776,736,401 | $761,800,102 |
| Dividends, royalties, interest, etc. | 14,568,598 | 12,285,524 |
| Total | $791,304,999 | $774,085,626 |
| **Costs and Expenses** | | |
| Employment costs | | |
| Wages and salaries | $206,663,267 | $195,440,677 |
| Social security taxes | 3,844,571 | 3,557,385 |
| Pensions, group insurance, and supplemental unemployment benefits (page 6) | 16,647,539 | 13,758,156 |
| Total | $227,155,377 | $212,756,218 |
| Materials and services (1957 includes $9,431,835 writedown of scrap in inventories to market prices) | 408,402,894 | 394,007,817 |
| Depreciation | 34,620,270 | 33,328,458 |
| Loss on assets retired | 1,581,012 | 321,454 |
| Interest and expense on long-term debt | 2,141,407 | 1,989,083 |
| Other charges | 319,002 | 241,447 |
| State, local, and miscellaneous taxes | 8,191,634 | 6,530,139 |
| Federal income taxes | 54,353,188 | 62,297,199 |
| Total | $736,764,784 | $711,471,815 |
| **Net Income Before Extraordinary Credit** | $ 54,540,215 | $ 62,613,811 |
| **Gain on Sale of Investments in Ore Companies** | | |
| *less Federal Income Tax of $168,098 in 1957 and $993,123 in 1956* | 504,294 | 2,979,371 |
| **Net Income for the Year** | $ 55,044,509 | $ 65,593,182 |
| **Cash Dividends** | 35,957,901 | 27,709,798 |
| **Net Income for the Year Retained in the Business** | $ 19,086,608 | $ 37,883,384 |

*See notes to financial statements on page 21.*

# ARMCO STEEL CORPORATION

## STATEMENT OF CONSOLIDATED FINANCIAL CONDITION

*December 31, 1957 and 1956*

|  | 1957 | 1956 |
|---|---|---|
| **Assets** | | |
| Current Assets | | |
| Cash | $ 67,389,256 | $ 38,727,395 |
| Marketable securities—at cost (quoted market value, $20,618,665 for 1957) | 20,580,221 | 15,065,350 |
| Receivables, less allowance for doubtful accounts, $839,858 for 1957 and $827,172 for 1956 | 54,236,134 | 66,375,223 |
| Inventories (page 22) | 177,547,577 | 187,857,647 |
| Total Current Assets | $319,753,188 | $308,025,615 |
| Cash Set Aside for Use in the Modernization and Expansion Program | 50,000,000 | |
| Investments—at cost (page 23) | 37,844,352 | 36,415,989 |
| Property, Plant, and Equipment—at cost, less accumulated depreciation (page 24) | 310,974,941 | 263,551,281 |
| Prepaid Expenses Applicable to Future Periods | 4,790,110 | 4,835,604 |
| Total Assets | $723,362,591 | $612,828,489 |
| **Liabilities and Reserves** | | |
| Current Liabilities | | |
| Accounts payable | $ 30,494,690 | $ 43,877,679 |
| Accrued taxes | 40,616,004 | 46,245,176 |
| Accrued salaries, wages, commissions, etc. | 22,687,527 | 20,707,473 |
| Long-term debt due within one year | 5,870,000 | 5,870,000 |
| Total Current Liabilities | $ 99,668,221 | $116,700,328 |
| Long-Term Debt, less current portion (page 24) | 95,460,000 | 51,330,000 |
| Deferred Credits Applicable to Future Periods (Note 5) | 14,121,873 | 9,800,497 |
| Reserves (page 23) | 6,421,696 | 6,017,865 |
| Total Liabilities and Reserves | $215,671,790 | $183,848,690 |
| **Shareholders' Equity** | | |
| Common Stock, $10 par value a share. For 1957—authorized 24,000,000 shares; issued 11,996,038³⁰⁄₁₀₀ shares, less 2,567²⁰⁄₁₀₀ shares in treasury; outstanding 11,993,471¹⁰⁄₁₀₀ shares (Note 2) | $119,934,711 | $108,798,267 |
| Capital Contributed in Excess of Par Value of Common Stock | 96,602,515 | 48,114,565 |
| Income Retained in the Business (Note 4) | 291,153,575 | 272,066,967 |
| Total Shareholders' Equity | $507,690,801 | $428,979,799 |

*See notes to financial statements on page 21.*

# ARMCO STEEL CORPORATION

## STATEMENT OF SHAREHOLDERS' EQUITY

*For the Year Ended December 31, 1957*

| | Total | Common Stock | Capital Contributed in Excess of Par Value of Common Stock | Income Retained in the Business |
|---|---|---|---|---|
| Balance, January 1, 1957 ........ | $428,979,799 | $108,798,267 | $48,114,565 | $272,066,967 |
| Net income for the year ......... | 55,044,509 | | | 55,044,509 |
| Cash dividends ($3.00* a share) ... | (35,957,901) | | | (35,957,901) |
| Net proceeds from sale of 1,088,179 shares of common stock .............. | 59,146,849 | 10,881,790 | 48,265,059 | |
| Stock issued for cash under the stock option plans (Note 2) ..... | 477,158 | 254,770 | 222,388 | |
| Treasury stock transactions ....... | 387 | (116) | 503 | |
| Balance, December 31, 1957 ....... | $507,690,801 | $119,934,711 | $96,602,515 | $291,153,575 |

*Cash dividends of $2.55 a share were paid in 1956.
*Amounts in parentheses represent deductions.*

## ACCOUNTANTS' CERTIFICATE

### HASKINS & SELLS
CERTIFIED PUBLIC ACCOUNTANTS

*The First National Bank Building*

*Cincinnati 2*

*Armco Steel Corporation:*

We have examined the statement of consolidated financial condition of Armco Steel Corporation and consolidated subsidiaries as of December 31, 1957 and the related statements of consolidated income and shareholders' equity for the year then ended. Our examination was made in accordance with generally accepted auditing standards, and accordingly included such tests of the accounting records and such other auditing procedures as we considered necessary in the circumstances.

In our opinion, the accompanying statements of consolidated financial condition, consolidated income, and shareholders' equity present fairly the financial condition of the companies at December 31, 1957 and the results of their operations for the year then ended, in conformity with generally accepted accounting principles applied on a basis consistent with that of the preceding year.

February 8, 1958

# ARMCO STEEL CORPORATION
## NOTES TO FINANCIAL STATEMENTS

**1.** It is the practice to consolidate all domestic operating subsidiaries functionally significant in the business; foreign subsidiaries, except Canadian, are not consolidated.

**2.** Preferred stock, 150,000 shares of $100 par value each, was authorized but unissued.

In January 1958, the Company issued 264,000 shares of its common stock for the acquisition of the net assets and business of Union Wire Rope Corporation.

Under the terms of a Joint Plan and Agreement of Merger dated February 14, 1958, The National Supply Company would be merged with and into Armco Steel Corporation. This agreement is subject to adoption by the shareholders of each company at meetings to be held in April 1958. If the said agreement becomes effective, each share of common stock of The National Supply Company outstanding on the effective date of the agreement would be converted into eighty-five one-hundredths of a share of common stock of Armco Steel Corporation, the surviving corporation. It is expected that approximately 2,500,500 shares of common stock would be issued in connection with the conversion.

At December 31, 1957 and 1956, there were 249,530 shares and 261,230 shares, respectively, of common stock reserved under the Stock Option Plan (for key employees), and 373,724 shares and 387,501 shares, respectively, of common stock reserved under the Employee Stock Option Plan (other than key employees). Option prices and other information with respect to these plans are set forth below:

|  | Stock Option Plan | | Employee Stock Option Plan |
|---|---|---|---|
| Option Price | $20.75 | $17.625 | $17.625 |
| Options granted but not exercised at December 31 (shares): |  |  |  |
| 1956 | 20,300 | 15,330 | 13,787 |
| 1957 | 11,300 | 12,630 | 10 |
| Options exercised during 1957 (shares) | 9,000 | 2,700 | 13,777 |

Option prices are the market quotation values of the shares on dates of grants (Stock Option Plan) or 95% thereof on date of grants (Employee Stock Option Plan). The $477,158 received from optionees for options exercised during the year was $222,388 more than the par value of shares issued to them; this latter amount was credited to capital contributed in excess of par value of common stock.

**3.** Under the terms of a credit agreement with a group of banks, the Company may borrow on or before December 31, 1958, on a revolving credit basis, an aggregate principal amount not to exceed $50,000,000 at any one time outstanding. Under the said agreement, the banks have agreed to convert the loans to term loans on December 31, 1958, up to the same maximum amount, to mature in five equal instalments on each December 31 from 1959 to 1963. There were no borrowings under the agreement at the end of the year.

**4.** At December 31, 1957, under restrictive provisions of the indenture covering the sinking fund debentures and the credit agreements with a group of banks, the unrestricted balance of consolidated income retained in the business out of which dividends could be declared was approximately $75,700,000.

Income retained in the business is exclusive of $16,519,646 transferred in prior years to other capital accounts in connection with stock dividends.

**5.** The Company owns 50% of the capital stock of Reserve Mining Company, the other 50% being owned by Republic Steel Corporation. The two shareholders are obligated (until the outstanding $132,998,000 principal amount of 4¼% First Mortgage bonds due June 1, 1980 of Reserve is paid in full) to take the entire production of Reserve, and as to each half-owner, to pay 50% of Reserve's operating costs and interest charges. If and to the extent that Reserve shall not have made the necessary payments, each shareholder is also obligated to pay one-half of amounts needed by Reserve for (a) fixed sinking fund requirements on the said bonds, and (b) certain future capital replacements.

A substantial portion of Reserve's facilities has been certified as being eligible for amortization over a 5-year period for Federal income tax purposes. The excess of such amortization over depreciation based upon normal rates has not been included in Reserve's operating costs but is deductible by the two shareholders for purposes of determining their Federal income taxes. The Company has followed the practice of deferring (through a charge to provision for Federal income taxes) the resulting reduction in such taxes attributable to this deduction. The accumulated amount at December 31, 1957, $12,393,786, is included in deferred credits applicable to future periods in the statement of consolidated financial condition.

**6.** Commitments for the purchase of property, plant, and equipment amounted to approximately $34,000,000 at December 31, 1957.

# ARMCO STEEL CORPORATION

## SUMMARY OF CHANGES IN WORKING CAPITAL

*For the Year Ended December 31, 1957*

Additions to Working Capital

| | | |
|---|---|---|
| Net income for the year | | $ 55,044,509 |
| Net proceeds from sale of 1,088,179 shares of common stock | | 59,146,849 |
| Cash received for shares issued to optionees under stock option plans | | 477,158 |
| Increase in long-term debt (bank loans of $50,000,000 in December, less $5,870,000 sinking fund payments on debentures) | | 44,130,000 |
| Treasury stock transactions | | 387 |
| Non-cash charges to income | | |
| Provision for depreciation | | 34,620,270 |
| Net book value of assets retired | | 875,736 |
| Increase in deferred credits | | 4,321,376 |
| Increase in reserves | | 403,831 |
| Decrease in prepaid expenses | | 45,494 |
| Total | | $199,065,610 |

Deductions from Working Capital

| | | |
|---|---|---|
| Expenditures for property, plant, and equipment | $ 82,919,666 | |
| Cash set aside for use in the modernization and expansion program | 50,000,000 | |
| Cash dividends on common stock | 35,957,901 | |
| Increase in investments | 1,428,363 | |
| Total | | 170,305,930 |
| Increase in Working Capital | | $ 28,759,680 |

Working Capital Per Statement of Consolidated Financial Condition

| | | |
|---|---|---|
| December 31, 1957 | | |
| Current assets | $319,753,188 | |
| Current liabilities | 99,668,221 | $220,084,967 |
| December 31, 1956 | | |
| Current assets | $308,025,615 | |
| Current liabilities | 116,700,328 | 191,325,287 |
| Increase in Working Capital | | $ 28,759,680 |

## AMERICAN TELEPHONE AND TELEGRAPH COMPANY

The following features are of particular interest in viewing the financial statements and the accompanying notes taken from the 1957 annual report of American Telephone and Telegraph Company.

Three financial statements for the year are presented under the headings Balance Sheets, Income Statements, and Statements of Retained Earnings. Statements are presented in comparative form.

**Balance Sheets.** Plant and long-term investments are listed first in presenting assets, and owners' capital and funded debt are listed first in presenting equities. Emphasis is thus placed upon long-term assets and the means for their financing rather than upon the working capital data, an order of presentation that is typical for balance sheets of public utility enterprises. It should be observed that current assets and current liabilities form only a small fraction of the respective asset and equity totals.

**Income Statements.** The earnings data are presented in multiple-step form with a series of revenue and income designations referred to as (1) total operating revenues, (2) net operating revenues, (3) net operating income, (4) income available for fixed charges, and (5) net income. The earnings per share are presented following the net income determination, such calculation being based on the average number of shares outstanding.

**Statements of Retained Earnings.** Special charges and credits are recognized as adjustments to retained earnings and are presented on the statement of retained earnings. These include profit on the sale of securities, organization and capital stock expense write-offs, as well as other special items. The change in retained earnings for the year is reconciled here.

**Notes to Financial Statements.** A full description is offered of debenture conversion privileges and the reservation of shares to meet such future conversions. Further data are offered relative to employee stock purchase plans (notes b and c). Notes are followed by a statement of the company's pension plan and the administration of this plan. The "Certificate of Audit" has not been reproduced here (Lybrand, Ross Bros. & Montgomery, auditors).

**Additional Statements and Summaries.** It should be observed that investments in subsidiary companies account for nearly ten billion dollars of the asset total. In order to present the full economic implications of such investments and subsidiary control, the company prepares consolidated statements summarizing position and operations as though the related units were one entity. The consolidated statements referred to as the "Bell System Consolidated Financial Statements" are included in the annual report for the American Telephone and Telegraph Company but have not been reproduced here.

## American Telephon

### balanc

**ASSETS**

|  | December 31, 1957 | December 31, 1956 |
|---|---|---|
| PLANT AND OTHER INVESTMENTS | | |
| Telephone Plant (a) | | |
| Telephone Plant in Service......................... | $ 1,568,321,883 | $ 1,390,490,149 |
| Telephone Plant under Construction................. | 119,051,189 | 96,022,969 |
| Property Held for Future Telephone Use............ | 544,667 | 625,190 |
| | $ 1,687,917,739 | $ 1,487,138,308 |
| Less: Depreciation Reserve......................... | 560,541,371 | 523,237,088 |
| *Portion of cost of telephone plant which has been charged against operations.* | | |
| | $ 1,127,376,368 | $ 963,901,220 |
| Investments in Subsidiaries—at cost (see page 34)....... | 9,692,545,928 | 8,764,632,993 |
| Stocks ......................... $9,340,064,083 | | |
| Advances ........................ 352,481,845 | | |
| Other Investments—at cost (see page 34).............. | 100,105,189 | 89,252,298 |
| Stocks .......................... $ 77,072,282 | | |
| Advances ........................ 22,480,000 | | |
| Miscellaneous ..................... 552,907 | | |
| **Total** ..................................... | $10.920,027.485 | $ 9.817,786.511 |
| CURRENT ASSETS | | |
| Cash and Demand Deposits........................... $ | 16,004,162 | $ 16,110,331 |
| Temporary Cash Investments........................... | 791,541,392 | 1,207,773,504 |
| *Principally U. S. short-term obligations.* | | |
| Special Cash Deposits............................... | 2,109,061 | 1,954,786 |
| Receivables ....................................... | 57,593,039 | 63,145,526 |
| *Amounts due for service (less reserve for uncollectibles), working advances, interest and dividends receivable, etc.* | | |
| Material and Supplies (b)........................... | 15,383,268 | 18,975,253 |
| *Principally for construction and maintenance purposes.* | | |
| **Total Current Assets** ...................... $ | 882,630,922 | $ 1,307,959,400 |
| DEFERRED CHARGES ............................... $ | 13,677,393 | $ 10,911,397 |
| **Total Assets** ........................... | $11,816,335,800 | $11,136,657,308 |

For notes, see page 33.

nd Telegraph Company

heets

## LIABILITIES

| | December 31, 1957 | December 31, 1956 |
|---|---|---|
| CAPITAL STOCK EQUITY | | |
| Common Stock—Par Value ($100 per share)............ | $ 6,464,817,800 | $ 6,289,388,900 |
| *At December 31, 1957, authorized 100,000,000 shares; outstanding, 64,648,178 shares. (c)* | | |
| Common Stock Subscribed............................ | .......... | 11,964,600 |
| Common Stock Installments (d)...................... | .......... | 156,909,315 |
| Premium on Common Stock.......................... | 1,860,757,911 | 1,780,815,328 |
| *Amount received in excess of par value.* | | |
| Retained Earnings (see page 33)..................... | 771,357,363 | 659,201,434 |
| **Total Capital Stock Equity**................. | $ 9,096,933,074 | $ 8,898,279,577 |
| | | |
| FUNDED DEBT | | |
| Convertible Debentures (c)........................... | $ .......... | $ 29,986,400 |
| Other Debentures (e).............................. | 2,440,000,000 | 1,940,000,000 |
| **Total Funded Debt** ........................ | $ 2,440,000,000 | $ 1,969,986,400 |
| | | |
| CURRENT AND ACCRUED LIABILITIES | | |
| Accounts Payable ................................. | $ 44,822,014 | $ 47,383,408 |
| Dividend Payable ................................. | 145,458,401 | 141,503,155 |
| Taxes Accrued ................................... | 53,180,968 | 50,427,113 |
| Interest Accrued ................................. | 22,283,962 | 17,742,188 |
| **Total Current and Accrued Liabilities** ...... | $ 265,745,345 | $ 257,055,864 |
| | | |
| DEFERRED CREDITS | | |
| Unextinguished Premium on Funded Debt—net......... | $ 13,268,950 | $ 11,062,029 |
| Other Deferred Credits........ ..................... | 388,431 | 273,438 |
| **Total Deferred Credits** .................... | $ 13,657,381 | $ 11,335,467 |
| **Total Liabilities** ....................... | $11,816,335,800 | $11,136,657,308 |

American Telephon

## income statements

| OPERATING REVENUES | Year 1957 | Year 1956 |
|---|---|---|
| Toll Service Revenues (f)........................... | $385,278,512 | $354,000,865 |
| License Contract Revenues.......................... | 59,720,464 | 54,972,525 |
| *Received for services furnished telephone companies.* | | |
| Miscellaneous Revenues ........................... | 21,870,278 | 20,567,877 |
| Less: Uncollectible Operating Revenues................ | 1,941,955 | 1,403,439 |
| **Total Operating Revenues** ................ | **$464,927,299** | **$428,137,828** |

| OPERATING EXPENSES (g) | | |
|---|---|---|
| Current Maintenance .............................. | $ 94,907,448 | $ 86,649,114 |
| Depreciation Expense ............................. | 56,095,924 | 49,335,208 |
| *Represented approximately 3.9% in 1957 and 3.8% in 1956 of average investment in depreciable plant.* | | |
| Traffic Expenses .................................. | 36,540,685 | 35,952,670 |
| Commercial Expenses .............................. | 18,440,995 | 17,148,795 |
| Operating Rents .................................. | 7,451,936 | 5,636,177 |
| General Administration ............................ | 19,746,607 | 18,301,747 |
| Accounting and Treasury Expenses................... | 18,211,077 | 18,841,220 |
| Development and Research (h)...................... | 34,504,458 | 32,503,410 |
| Provision for Employees' Service Pensions............. | 9,717,536 | 9,642,463 |
| Employees' Sickness, Accident, Death and Other Benefits.. | 4,454,169 | 3,045,985 |
| Other General Expenses............................ | 15,004,834 | 14,275,322 |
| Less: Expenses Charged Construction.................. | 2,575,188 | 2,172,324 |
| **Total Operating Expenses** ................ | **$312,500,481** | **$289,159,787** |
| **Net Operating Revenues** ................... | **$152,426,818** | **$138,978,041** |

| OPERATING TAXES | | |
|---|---|---|
| Federal Taxes on Income............................ | $ 53,778,000 | $ 49,033,000 |
| Other Taxes—principally State, local and Social Security.. | 27,077,643 | 24,030,000 |
| **Total Operating Taxes** .................... | **$ 80,855,643** | **$ 73,063,000** |
| **Net Operating Income** .................... | **$ 71,571,175** | **$ 65,915,041** |

| OTHER INCOME | | |
|---|---|---|
| Dividend Income—principally from subsidiaries.......... | $637,730,122 | $574,199,411 |
| Interest Income .................................. | 48,038,027 | 38,068,726 |
| Miscellaneous Income ............................. | 669,963 | 1,410,880 |
| Less: Miscellaneous Deductions from Income........... | 645,976 | 1,753,358 |
| **Income Available for Fixed Charges** ....... | **$757,363,311** | **$677,840,700** |

| FIXED CHARGES | | |
|---|---|---|
| Interest on Funded Debt............................ | $ 69,153,779 | $ 59,108,671 |
| Other Interest ................................... | 2,525,052 | 2,496,917 |
| Less: Release of Premium on Funded Debt—net......... | 373,476 | 255,095 |
| **Net Income** ............................. | **$686,057,956** | **$616,490,207** |
| Earnings per share (i)................................ | $10.75 | $10.74 |

## Statements of Retained Earnings

| | Year 1957 | Year 1956 |
|---|---|---|
| BALANCE AT BEGINNING OF PERIOD.................... | $659,201,434 | $561,729,110 |
| Net Income ....................................... | $686,057,956 | $616,490,207 |
| Profit on sales of securities......................... | 884,095 | 836,146 |
| Miscellaneous additions ............................ | 8,088 | 558 |
| TOTAL ADDITIONS ..................... | $686,950,139 | $617,326,911 |
| Dividends declared ............................... | $574,302,856 | $516,803,616 |
| Organization and Capital Stock Expense charged off.... | 344,181 | 2,854,361 |
| Miscellaneous deductions ........................... | 147,173 | 196,610 |
| TOTAL DEDUCTIONS .................... | $574,794,210 | $519,854,587 |
| BALANCE AT CLOSE OF PERIOD....................... | $771,357,363 | $659,201,434 |

## Notes to Financial Statements

(a) Telephone Plant, with minor exceptions, is stated at cost to the Company.

(b) Effective January 1, 1957 in connection with a revised practice of accounting for station equipment an amount of $4,975,455 was transferred from Material and Supplies to Telephone Plant.

(c) On January 15, 1958 the Board of Directors reserved 7,183,130 shares of capital stock for issuance upon conversion of $718,313,000 principal amount of Fifteen Year 4¼% Convertible Debentures, due March 12, 1973 which were offered to stockholders of record on January 24, 1958. These debentures will be convertible into stock of the Company beginning May 12, 1958 at $142 per share. On January 15, 1958 the stockholders authorized the Company to place in effect an Employees' Stock Plan under which not to exceed 7,000,000 shares may be issued and sold on an installment basis to employees of the Company and of its subsidiaries.

(d) At December 31, 1956 represents installment payments and interest thereon applicable to shares of Capital Stock under elections to purchase pursuant to the Employees' Stock Plan approved by the stockholders in 1950. Such elections to purchase provided for completion of installment payments by July 1957.

(e) Of these debentures, $140,000,000 mature in 1970, $775,000,000 from 1971 to 1980, and $1,525,000,000 thereafter.

(f) Represents the Company's share of toll revenues of $1,334,598,000 in 1957 and $1,205,497,000 in 1956 from toll business handled jointly with subsidiary and other telephone companies.

(g) Operating expenses are incurred principally in providing the Company's long distance communication services and in performing License Contract services furnished telephone companies.

(h) Cost of work carried on for the Company by Bell Telephone Laboratories.

(i) Based on average shares outstanding—63,811,428 in 1957 and 57,422,624 in 1956.

---

The Company has established a fund with Bankers Trust Company, New York, N. Y., as Trustee, which is irrevocably devoted to service pension purposes. Regular payments are made to the fund pursuant to an accrual program. At December 31, 1957 the pension fund amounted to $136,809,597. Future service pension payments to those now on the pension rolls and those now entitled to retire on pensions at their own request are fully provided for by the amount in the fund. The fund is not a part of the assets of the Company and is therefore not reflected in the balance sheets.

## THE OLIVER CORPORATION

The following features are of particular interest in viewing the financial statements and the accompanying notes taken from the 1957 annual report of the Oliver Corporation.

Three financial statements for the year are presented under the headings Consolidated Statement of Financial Position, Consolidated Statement of Income, and Consolidated Statement of Earnings Retained in the Business. Statements are prepared in comparative form. The annual report also includes a Statement of Application of Funds and a 20 Year Historical Summary listing data concerning sales, earnings, dividends, and net worth; these have not been reproduced.

**Consolidated Statement of Financial Position.** The statement of financial position develops a Net Current Assets (working capital) balance, and then develops a Net Assets total by adding noncurrent assets and subtracting noncurrent liabilities. The statement then summarizes the ownership interest consisting of preferred and common stock, and earnings retained in the business, less the amount paid on the reacquisition of shares of stock.

**Consolidated Statement of Income.** Income data are presented in single-step form except for income taxes which are recognized as a separate subtraction item. It should be observed that straight-line depreciation was recognized on the books but accelerated depreciation was allowed for tax purposes; as a result of this difference, the provision for taxes was adjusted to reflect taxes applicable to book income and a future tax liability was recognized.

**Consolidated Statement of Earnings Retained in the Business.** Comparative balances for Earnings Retained in the Business as reported on the balance sheet are reconciled by reporting the balance at the beginning of the year, the increase from net earnings for the year as summarized on the statement of income, and decreases from dividends together with estimated losses and costs of a special nature arising from the suspension and the consolidation of certain activities.

**Notes to Consolidated Financial Statements.** Notes to financial statements provide detail relating to: loan agreements including limitations on dividends and stock reacquisition as a result of the terms of the loans; features of preferred and common issues including stock option arrangements; company retirement and pension plans; renegotiation proceedings both completed and in prospect; and differences in financial accounting and tax accounting procedures. The "Auditors' Opinion" has not been reproduced here (Arthur Andersen & Co., auditors).

# NOTES TO CONSOLIDATED
# FINANCIAL STATEMENTS

**1** Term loans outstanding at October 31, 1957, consist of: (1) $8,040,000 for $3\frac{1}{2}\%$ loan due 1969, subject to required prepayments of (a) $300,000 semiannually and (b) annually the lesser of $200,000 or 20% of net income, as defined, in excess of $1,200,000 for the preceding fiscal year; and (2) $5,092,000 for $4\frac{1}{8}\%$ loan due 1972, subject to required prepayments of $134,000 semiannually. The prepayments due in the next fiscal year, aggregating $868,000 for these loans, are included in current liabilities.

Under the loan agreements, $30,527,000 of earnings retained at October 31, 1957, were restricted against payments for cash dividends on common stock or acquisition of common or preferred stock of the company.

**2** The authorized preferred stock is 118,006 shares, par value $100 per share, cumulative as to dividends, and issuable in series. The 75,006 shares outstanding at October 31, 1957, are designated as $4\frac{1}{2}\%$ cumulative convertible preferred stock, redeemable at $104 per share plus accrued dividends. The preferred stock is convertible at its par value at the option of the holder into common stock at the conversion price of $16.40 per share of common stock.

The authorized common stock is 4,000,000 shares. Of the unissued common stock, 457,537 shares are reserved for conversion of preferred stock, and 73,649 shares are reserved for sale to officers and employees or for other corporate purposes under terms and conditions to be approved by the shareholders. At October 31, 1957, there were 2,096,527 shares of common stock outstanding, after deducting 36,152 shares in the treasury.

Options are held by certain officers and employees for the purchase of 25,749 shares of common stock at $15.125 per share. The options expire in 1962, and may be exercised in whole or in part while the optionee is employed by the company, or within three months after employment ceases. An option, expiring in 1960, is held by an officer for the purchase of 9,300 shares of common stock in the treasury, at $10.75 per share. At October 31, 1957, the quoted market price was lower than the option prices.

**3** Retirement or pension plans are in effect for substantially all employees. The amounts charged to costs and expenses under the plans were $841,000 in 1957 and $438,000 in 1956. The company's consulting actuary estimates that as of October 31, 1957, the amount required to fund the past-service costs would be $14,654,000, of which $10,528,000 is applicable to plans under union contracts.

**4** Renegotiation of sales under defense contracts through 1953 has been completed, and no refunds were required. The effect, if any, of renegotiation proceedings for subsequent years is not now determinable, but in the opinion of the company, the profits on defense contracts were not excessive; accordingly no provision for renegotiation refunds has been made.

**5** The company uses straight-line depreciation in its accounts and accelerated depreciation for income tax purposes. The provision and accrual for future income taxes are equivalent to the tax reductions resulting from use of accelerated depreciation.

# THE OLIVER CORPORATIO

## CONSOLIDATED STATEMENT OF FINANCIAL POSITION

|  | October 31, 1957 | October 31, 1956 |
|---|---|---|
| **CURRENT ASSETS:** | | |
| Cash .............................................. | $ 5,930,466 | $ 4,694,736 |
| Trade receivables (including $5,484,834 in 1957 and $4,166,866 in 1956, due after one year), less allowance for losses and discounts (1957, $1,724,423; 1956, $1,615,650).......... | 37,184,459 | 31,291,437 |
| Inventories (except defense inventories), at cost principally on last-in, first-out basis, less allowance for obsolescence and other losses (1957, $884,404; 1956, $1,226,913).......... | 44,535,265 | 41,009,691 |
| Receivables, inventories, etc., relating to defense contracts.... | 2,770,074 | 2,157,072 |
| Total current assets....................... | $90,420,264 | $79,152,936 |
| **CURRENT LIABILITIES:** | | |
| Bank loans—short-term .............................. | $15,500,000 | $ 5,000,000 |
| Term loans—current portion (Note 1)..................... | 868,000 | 928,000 |
| Accounts payable and accrued expenses................... | 11,933,344 | 8,370,201 |
| Dividend declared on common stock..................... | 314,478 | 314,478 |
| Accrued income taxes................................ | 483,901 | 1,145,774 |
| Total current liabilities..................... | $29,099,723 | $15,758,453 |
| **NET CURRENT ASSETS** (working capital).................. | $61,320,541 | $63,394,483 |
| **OTHER ASSETS:** | | |
| Prepaid expenses ...................................... | 847,469 | 579,323 |
| Common stock of Waukesha Motor Co., at cost (represents 13% of shares outstanding in 1957, quoted market $2,094,400)... | 1,602,187 | 1,357,231 |
| Other investments .................................... | 195,808 | 213,617 |

|  | 1957 | 1956 |  |  |
|---|---|---|---|---|
| **PLANT AND EQUIPMENT,** at cost | $62,022,323 | $61,220,050 | | |
| Less reserves for— | | | | |
| Depreciation .............. | 35,474,856 | 34,158,244 | | |
| Reduction to estimated realizable value of plant and equipment which may be retired (net of estimated tax effect) ................ | 1,074,253 | 474,253 | 25,473,214 | 26,587,553 |
| **DEDUCT:** | | | | |
| Term loans—noncurrent portion (Note 1)................. | | | 13,132,000 | 14,000,000 |
| Accrual for future income taxes (Note 5)................. | | | 815,000 | 453,000 |
| **NET ASSETS** ......................................... | | | $75,492,219 | $77,679,207 |
| **THE NET ASSETS WERE DERIVED FROM:** | | | | |
| 4½% convertible preferred stock, $100 par value (Note 2)... | | | $ 7,500,600 | $ 7,500,600 |
| Common stock, $1.00 par value (Note 2).................. | | | 30,934,888 | 30,934,888 |
| Earnings retained in the business (Note 1)................. | | | 37,474,131 | 39,661,119 |
| Deduct—Treasury common stock, at cost (Note 2).......... | | | 417,400 | 417,400 |
| **SHAREHOLDERS' INVESTMENT** ........................... | | | $75,492,219 | $77,679,207 |

Reference is made to the notes on page 8 which are an integral part of this statement.

# *nd Subsidiaries*

## CONSOLIDATED STATEMENT OF INCOME

| | For Years Ended October 31 | |
| --- | --- | --- |
| | 1957 | 1956 |
| **NET SALES** (including sales under defense contracts: 1957, $6,380,954; 1956, $10,908,021) .................... | $101,678,450 | $107,857,381 |
| **COSTS AND EXPENSES:** | | |
| Cost of goods sold...................................... | $ 84,274,566 | $ 87,721,407 |
| Selling, administrative and general expenses................ | 9,993,706 | 9,932,411 |
| Charge to operations as cost of wear and tear on buildings, machinery and equipment (depreciation) (Note 5)....... | 3,637,679 | 3,748,064 |
| Social security, state, local and general taxes.............. | 2,458,230 | 2,161,263 |
| Interest expense ...................................... | 1,204,537 | 1,360,805 |
| Less—Other income, net............................... | 1,111,722 | 792,950 |
| Total costs and expenses.................... | $100,456,996 | $104,131,000 |
| **NET EARNINGS BEFORE INCOME TAXES** ................... | $  1,221,454 | $  3,726,381 |
| **PROVISION FOR INCOME TAXES,** including $362,000 in 1957 and $453,000 in 1956 for future income taxes (Note 5)...... | 613,000 | 1,805,000 |
| **NET EARNINGS FOR THE YEAR**........................... | $   608,454 | $  1,921,381 |

## CONSOLIDATED STATEMENT OF EARNINGS RETAINED IN THE BUSINESS

| | | |
| --- | --- | --- |
| **BALANCE** at October 31, 1956............................ | | $ 39,661,119 |
| **NET EARNINGS** for the year ended October 31, 1957, as shown above ................................................ | | 608,454 |
| | | $ 40,269,573 |
| **DEDUCT—** | | |
| Cash Dividends on— | | |
| Preferred stock ($4.50 per share)....................... | $    337,527 | |
| Common stock ($ .60 per share)....................... | 1,257,915 | |
| | $  1,595,442 | |
| Provision for estimated losses and costs (1) of suspending operations of South Bend foundries and reduction of these foundries to estimated realizable value, and (2) for possible consolidation of other manufacturing activities (net of estimated tax effect).................................... | 1,200,000 | 2,795,442 |
| **BALANCE** at October 31, 1957 (see Note 1 for restrictions)..... | | $ 37,474,131 |

Reference is made to the notes on page 8 which are an integral part of these statements.

## CHRYSLER CORPORATION

The following features are of particular interest in viewing the financial statements taken from the 1957 annual report for the Chrysler Corporation.

Four financial statements for the year are presented under the headings Consolidated Balance Sheets, Consolidated Statement of Net Earnings, Consolidated Statement of Additional Paid-In Capital, and Consolidated Statement of Net Earnings Retained for Use in the Business. A supplementary statement offering financial statistics relative to operating results and year-end financial position for a six-year period is not reproduced.

**Consolidated Balance Sheets.** The balance sheet is prepared in conventional account form. Full information is offered relative to valuation procedures employed for assets. Note particularly the footnote describing the change in inventory valuation and the effects of such change on position and profit and loss measurements. Full data are offered relative to maturity dates and convertible privileges on long-term debt. Descriptions are also afforded of thrift-stock ownership programs and stock option plans together with reference to the numbers of shares of stock reserved for such purposes.

**Consolidated Statement of Net Earnings.** The statement of net earnings is prepared in single-step form, a summary of revenue items being followed by a summary of charges against such revenue.

**Consolidated Statement of Additional Paid-In Capital.** The statement of additional paid-in capital reconciles beginning and ending additional paid-in capital balances as reported on the balance sheet. Sale of shares at an amount in excess of par under terms of the stock option plan was responsible for the increase in capital stock as reported on the balance sheet and the increase in additional paid-in capital as summarized on the statement of additional paid-in capital.

**Consolidated Statement of Net Earnings Retained for Use in the Business.** The statement of net earnings retained for use in the business reconciles beginning and ending retained earnings balances as reported on the comparative balance sheets. Net earnings retained for use in the business at the beginning of the year are increased by net earnings for the year as summarized on the statement of net income and are reduced by dividends for the year.

Explanatory data relative to statement items are provided by means of remarks or footnotes rather than by separate presentation as notes accompanying the formal exhibits. The "Accountants Report" has not been reproduced here (Touche, Niven, Bailey & Smart, Certified Public Accountants).

**CHRYSLER CORPORATION AND ALL WHOLLY-OWNED SUBSIDIARIES**

## Consolidated Statement of Net Earnings

*Years ended December 31, 1957, and December 31, 1956*

|  | 1957 | 1956 |
|---|---|---|
| Net sales...................................................... | $3,564,982,510 | $2,676,334,431 |
| Interest and miscellaneous revenues................................ | 14,392,132 | 5,963,817 |
|  | $3,579,374,642 | $2,682,298,248 |
| Cost of products sold, other than items below....................... | $2,909,552,012 | $2,318,549,649 |
| Depreciation of plant and equipment............................. | 87,825,298 | 67,994,525 |
| Administrative, engineering, selling, advertising, service and general expenses...................................................... | 276,038,681 | 217,387,981 |
| Pension and retirement plans.................................... | 35,302,260 | 30,060,259 |
| Provision for incentive compensation plan.......................... | 10,500,860 | —0— |
| Interest on long-term debt....................................... | 8,203,125 | 5,852,865 |
| Taxes on income (including foreign of $3,300,000 in 1957 and $6,900,000 in 1956)................................................... | 132,000,000 | 22,500,000 |
|  | $3,459,422,236 | $2,662,345,279 |
| Net earnings......................................... | $ 119,952,406 | $ 19,952,969 |

# Consolidated Balance Sheets—Chrysler

### December 31, 1957, and December 31, 1956

|  | DECEMBER 31 | |
| --- | ---: | ---: |
|  | 1957 | 1956 |
| **CURRENT ASSETS:** | | |
| Cash.......................................................... | $ 62,712,576 | $ 80,540,424 |
| Short-term marketable securities—at cost and accrued interest........ | 469,505,866 | 124,158,784 |
| Trade accounts receivable, including defense, less allowance for doubtful accounts ($1,500,000 at December 31, 1957)..................... | 76,543,992 | 120,277,001 |
| Other accounts receivable, including account with partially-owned Australian subsidiary ($2,064,158 at December 31, 1957)........... | 4,637,405 | 4,368,950 |
| Unbilled costs under defense contracts............................. | 10,175,483 | 14,999,849 |
| Inventories—at lower of cost or market (see note)................... | 300,389,316 | 312,243,949 |
| Prepaid insurance, taxes and other expenses........................ | 16,077,759 | 12,715,950 |
| TOTAL CURRENT ASSETS............................. | $ 940,042,397 | $ 669,304,907 |
| | | |
| **INVESTMENTS AND OTHER ASSETS:** | | |
| Investment in partially-owned Australian subsidiary................. | $ 3,318,457 | $ 3,101,397 |
| Investments in Dealer Enterprise dealerships........................ | 4,168,986 | 4,363,624 |
| Common Stock of Chrysler Corporation acquired for distribution under incentive compensation plan (10,524 shares at December 31, 1957)— at cost.................................................... | 788,347 | 171,417 |
| Sundry advances and investments................................. | 2,259,615 | 4,276,653 |
| | $ 10,535,405 | $ 11,913,091 |
| | | |
| **PROPERTY, PLANT AND EQUIPMENT:** | | |
| Land ($24,699,568 at December 31, 1957), buildings, machinery, equipment and tools—at cost...................................... | $ 967,905,011 | $ 959,293,436 |
| Less accumulated depreciation..................................... | 421,877,434 | 345,751,054 |
| | $ 546,027,577 | $ 613,542,382 |
| | $1,496,605,379 | $1,294,760,380 |

*At December 31, 1957, the last-in, first-out cost method was used for stating substantially all United States inventories (except defense) which comprise approximately 90% of the consolidated inventories. At December 31, 1956, the first-in, first-out cost method was used. Because of this change, inventories at December 31, 1957, are stated approximately $10,000,000 lower than they would have been under the former method, and net earnings for 1957 are reduced approximately $5,000,000.*

# Corporation and all wholly-owned subsidiaries

|  | DECEMBER 31 | |
|  | 1957 | 1956 |
| --- | --- | --- |
| CURRENT LIABILITIES: | | |
| Accounts payable and pay rolls.................................. | $ 261,763,920 | $ 338,166,346 |
| Accrued expenses................................................ | 87,981,815 | 75,074,556 |
| United States and foreign taxes on income........................ | 164,551,757 | 47,847,143 |
| TOTAL CURRENT LIABILITIES........................ | $ 514,297,492 | $ 461,088,045 |
| 3¾% PROMISSORY NOTES, due July 1, 2054; convertible by either party after January 1, 1962, into 3½% notes due in equal installments over twenty years........................................... | 250,000,000 | 187,500,000 |
| SHAREHOLDERS' INVESTMENT: | | |
| Represented by | | |
| Common Stock—par value $25.00 a share: | | |
| Authorized 20,000,000 shares (at December 31, 1957, 150,000 shares were reserved for the Thrift-Stock Ownership Program and 376,500 shares were reserved for the Stock Option Plan for Salaried Officers and Key Employees; of the latter, options for 347,000 shares were outstanding at prices ranging from $61.52 to $77.07 a share, the average being $71.51; these prices representing 95% of fair market values on the dates the options were granted; of these, options for 240,063 shares were exercisable) | | |
| Issued 8,992,250 shares at December 31, 1957, of which 266,486 shares were in treasury and 8,725,764 shares were outstanding... | $ 218,144,100 | $ 217,767,600 |
| Additional paid-in capital..................................... | 1,050,612 | 383,171 |
| Net earnings retained for use in the business.................... | 513,113,175 | 428,021,564 |
|  | $ 732,307,887 | $ 646,172,335 |
|  | $1,496,605,379 | $1,294,760,380 |

*Net assets in foreign countries which have been included in this statement were $73,797,724 at December 31, 1957, and $60,318,798 at December 31, 1956, including net current assets at those dates of $30,404,214 and $14,670,395, respectively. Net earnings in these countries amounted to $3,163,312 in 1957 and $6,838,527 in 1956.*

*The Corporation's share ($5,885,325 at December 31, 1957) of accumulated net earnings retained for use in the business since acquisition of an unconsolidated partially-owned Australian subsidiary has not been included in this statement. The Corporation's share of net earnings of this subsidiary in 1957 was $194,940.*

**CHRYSLER CORPORATION AND ALL WHOLLY-OWNED SUBSIDIARIES**

## Consolidated Statement of Additional Paid-In Capital

*Years ended December 31, 1957, and December 31, 1956*

|  | 1957 | 1956 |
|---|---|---|
| Balance at beginning of year.......................................... | $ 383,171 | $ 213,795 |
| Excess of option price over par value of shares of Common Stock issued under the Stock Option Plan during the year (15,060 shares in 1957)............ | 667,441 | 169,376 |
| Balance at end of year............................................ | $ 1,050,612 | $ 383,171 |

## Consolidated Statement of Net Earnings Retained for Use in the Business

*Years ended December 31, 1957, and December 31, 1956*

|  | 1957 | 1956 |
|---|---|---|
| Balance at beginning of year.......................................... | $428,021,564 | $434,187,357 |
| Net earnings for the year............................................ | 119,952,406 | 19,952,969 |
|  | $547,973,970 | $454,140,326 |
| Dividends paid ($4.00 a share in 1957, $3.00 a share in 1956)............. | 34,860,795 | 26,118,762 |
| Balance at end of year............................................ | $513,113,175 | $428,021,564 |

# ROYAL McBEE CORPORATION

The following features are of particular interest in viewing the financial statements and the accompanying notes taken from the 1957 annual report of Royal McBee Corporation.

Three financial statements for the year are presented under the headings Consolidated Statement of Income, Consolidated Statement of Earnings Retained in the Business, and Consolidated Statement of Financial Position. Statements are presented in comparative form. The annual report also includes two special summaries entitled Five Year Summary of Operations, and Sources and Use of Working Capital that are not reproduced here.

**Consolidated Statement of Income.** The income statement is prepared in multiple-step form with designations for (1) gross profit on sales, (2) income from operations, (3) income before provision for taxes on income, and (4) net earnings for the year.

**Consolidated Statement of Earnings Retained in the Business.** Changes in earnings retained in the business are summarized in support of the ending balances for this account as reported on the balance sheet. The beginning balance is increased by net earnings for the year as summarized on the statement of income and decreased by dividends in developing the ending balance.

**Consolidated Statement of Financial Position.** The statement of financial position lists current assets followed by current liabilities in developing a working capital balance. Noncurrent assets are added to working capital and noncurrent liabilities subtracted in arriving at the company's net assets. A listing of balances for capital stock, capital surplus, and earnings retained in the business follows.

**Notes to Financial Statements.** Notes to financial statements provide detail relating to such matters as procedures underlying statement consolidation, inventory valuation, terms of long-term debt contracts, classes of preferred stock including redemption features and liquidation preferences, stock option and savings plans for officers and other key employees, source of the change in capital surplus for year, restrictions on payment of dividends as provided by long-term notes, payments on pension plans, and proposed change in authorized common shares. The "Auditors' Report" has not been reproduced here (Lybrand, Ross Bros. & Montgomery, auditors).

*Royal McBee Corporation and its Consolidated Subsidiaries*

| Consolidated Statement of Income | For the fiscal years ended | July 31, 1957 | July 31, 1956 |
|---|---|---|---|
| | Net sales of products and services . . | $107,648,268 | $95,876,277 |
| | Cost of sales . . . . . . . . | 61,065,706 | 52,955,045 |
| | Gross profit on sales . . . . | 46,582,562 | 42,921,232 |
| | Selling and administrative expenses . | 37,483,292 | 32,019,723 |
| | Income from operations . . . | 9,099,270 | 10,901,509 |
| | Other income . . . . . . . | 612,569 | 884,983 |
| | | 9,711,839 | 11,786,492 |
| | Other deductions . . . . . . | 565,735 | 447,689 |
| | Income before provision for United States and Canadian taxes on income | 9,146,104 | 11,338,803 |
| | Provision for United States and Canadian taxes on income . . | 4,690,000 | 5,673,000 |
| | Net earnings for the year | $ 4,456,104 | $ 5,665,803 |

| Consolidated Statement of Earnings Retained in the Business | For the fiscal years ended | July 31, 1957 | July 31, 1956 |
|---|---|---|---|
| | Balance at beginning of year . . . | $ 26,943,145 | $ 23,630,288 |
| | Net earnings for the year . . . . | 4,456,104 | 5,665,803 |
| | | 31,399,249 | 29,296,091 |
| | Dividends paid: | | |
| | On preferred stock at required rates . . . . . | 338,161 | 338,161 |
| | On common stock at $1.40 per share . . . . | 2,149,104 | 2,014,785 |
| | Balance at end of year (Note 7) | $ 28,911,984 | $ 26,943,145 |

*The appended notes are an integral part of these financial statements.*

*Royal McBee Corporation and its Consolidated Subsidiaries*

## Consolidated Statement of Financial Position

| Current Assets: | July 31, 1957 | July 31, 1956 |
|---|---|---|
| Cash . . . . . . . . . . . . . . | $ 2,920,213 | $ 5,189,186 |
| Governmental securities, at cost (approximately market) . . . . . . . | | 4,171,312 |
| Accounts receivable, less allowance for doubtful accounts . . . . . . . . . | 21,422,542 | 18,635,045 |
| Inventories, at the lower of cost or market (Note 2) . . . . . . . . . . | 18,999,071 | 16,371,322 |
| Total Current Assets . . . . . . | 43,341,826 | 44,366,865 |

| Current Liabilities: | | |
|---|---|---|
| Notes payable . . . . . . . . . | 2,470,000 | |
| Accounts payable . . . . . . . . | 3,650,803 | 2,609,843 |
| Accrued expenses: | | |
| Taxes . . . . . . . . . . . | 1,117,845 | 998,771 |
| Salaries, wages, commissions, etc. . . . . . | 3,028,091 | 1,993,676 |
| Unredeemed merchandise coupons . . . . | 926,000 | 811,000 |
| Provision for United States and Canadian taxes on income . . . . . . . . . | 3,687,500 | 5,270,796 |
| Total Current Liabilities . . . . . . | 14,880,239 | 11,684,086 |

| Working Capital: | 28,461,587 | 32,682,779 |
|---|---|---|
| Investments in unconsolidated subsidiaries, at cost or less (see page 3) . . . . . . | 3,497,887 | 1,537,137 |
| Investments in other affiliates at cost . . . . | 1,564,916 | 684,000 |
| Property, plant and equipment at cost, less accumulated depreciation and amortization: 1957, $8,880,432; 1956, $8,290,834 . . | 17,510,018 | 14,825,312 |
| Deferred expense and other assets . . . . | 1,877,720 | 1,684,061 |
| | 52,912,128 | 51,413,289 |
| Less, long-term notes payable (Note 3) . . . | 9,530,000 | 10,000,000 |

| Stockholders' Equity: | $43,382,128 | $41,413,289 |
|---|---|---|
| Represented by: | | |
| Preferred cumulative stock (Note 4) . . . | $ 7,181,300 | $ 7,181,300 |
| Common stock, authorized 2,000,000 shares of $1 par value each; issued and outstanding 1,535,074 shares (Notes 5 and 10) . | 1,535,074 | 1,535,074 |
| Capital surplus (Note 6) . . . . . . | 5,753,770 | 5,753,770 |
| Earnings retained in the business (Note 7) | 28,911,984 | 26,943,145 |
| | $43,382,128 | $41,413,289 |

*The appended notes are an integral part of these financial statements.*

# Notes to financial statements

1. The consolidated financial statements include the accounts of the Company and all wholly-owned domestic and Canadian subsidiaries except RMB Corporation, a domestic finance subsidiary, which was formed in May 1957. At July 31, 1957, RMB Corporation had assets of $5,222,000, including $5,204,000 of installment receivables sold to it by the Company, and liabilities of $4,228,000 including $3,950,000 of short-term bank loans.
2. The last-in, first-out method was used in determining cost for approximately 70 per cent of the inventories of each year.
3. The long-term notes payable (interest at $3\frac{1}{2}$ per cent per annum) mature November 1, 1974. Beginning November 1, 1957 principal payments are required annually in the amount of $470,000. The principal payment due November 1, 1957 is included among the current liabilities shown in the balance sheet. While the notes are outstanding, the Company and all of its wholly-owned domestic and Canadian subsidiaries must maintain consolidated net current assets at 150 per cent of consolidated long-term borrowing.
4. Preferred stock (authorized 100,000 shares of $100 par value each) is issued and outstanding as follows:

|  | Shares | Amount |
|---|---|---|
| Series A, $4\frac{1}{2}\%$ | 56,813 | $5,681,300 |
| Series B, 5% | 5,000 | 500,000 |
| Series C, $5\frac{1}{4}\%$ | 5,000 | 500,000 |
| Series D, 6% | 5,000 | 500,000 |
|  | 71,813 | $7,181,300 |

The Series A preferred stock is redeemable at and entitled in voluntary liquidation to $103 per share. The other series of preferred stock are redeemable at $102 per share and entitled in voluntary liquidation to $100 per share. All series of preferred stock are entitled to $100 per share in involuntary liquidation.

5. An incentive stock option plan, approved by the stockholders in November 1956, authorized the granting, prior to October 31, 1961, of options to officers and other key employees of the Company or of any subsidiary, to purchase a maximum of 75,000 shares of the Company's common stock at not less than 95% of the fair market value at date granted. The options are exercisable generally at any time during the period from three to ten years subsequent to the date of grant. Options were granted in January 1957 for 46,250 shares at $32 per share, of which options for 2,000 shares were later cancelled, and in June 1957 for 3,250 shares at $38 per share. At July 31, 1957 options for 47,500 shares were outstanding.

The Board of Directors on September 19, 1957, voted to submit for stockholders' approval a stock option and savings plan for employees (including officers) who have not been granted options under the plan described above, and who have completed at least two years of service with the Company. Such plan proposes the granting of options for not in excess of 100,000 shares of unissued common stock at option prices not less than 95% of fair market value (as defined) on date of granting the option.

6. Capital surplus was increased during the year ended July 31, 1956 by $4,363,601, representing the net proceeds in excess of par from the sale of 191,884 common shares. There was no change during the year ended July 31, 1957.
7. The long-term notes payable (and the provisions relating to preferred stock to a lesser degree) contain restrictions on the payment of common stock dividends. The notes provide that the Company may not pay dividends on common stock (except in common stock of the Company) if, since July 31, 1954, the aggregate thereof, plus dividends paid on preferred stock and net expenditures for the reacquisition of common stock, will exceed consolidated net income (as defined) since that date plus $2,000,000. Approximately $9,050,000 of consolidated earnings retained in the business at July 31, 1957 is free of this restriction.
8. The allowances for depreciation and amortization of property, plant and equipment are shown on page 3.
9. In the current year, the Company elected to pay only current service costs of the noncontributory pension plan. In the previous year the Company paid $467,000 of past service costs.
10. The Board of Directors, on September 19, 1957 voted to submit for stockholders' approval a proposal to increase the authorized common stock of the Company from 2,000,000 to 3,000,000 shares.

# INDEX